DATE			

PHARMACOLOGICAL AND CHEMICAL SYNONYMS

Pharmacological and Chemical Synonyms

A collection of names of drugs, pesticides and other
compounds drawn from the medical literature of the world

Compiled by

E.E.J. MARLER, M.D., M.Sc., Ph.D.

EIGHTH EDITION

1985
ELSEVIER
Amsterdam - New York - Oxford

ISBN 0 444 90359 3

Published by:
Elsevier Science Publishers B.V.
P.O. Box 1126
1000 BC Amsterdam

Sole distributors for the USA and Canada:
Elsevier Science Publishing Co. Inc.
52 Vanderbilt Avenue
New York, NY 10017

Printed in the Netherlands by Casparie, Amsterdam

INTRODUCTION

This alphabetical compilation of names used for drugs, pesticides and other substances of pharmacological or biochemical interest has now reached its eighth edition.

The process of maintaining the information present in 'Marler's PCS' in electronic form, begun with the seventh edition, has been continued. Indeed, the techniques used have been developed to enable an ordering of synonyms within the main entries by the type of name, as well as alphabetically.

We remain confident that the special features of previous editions of this compilation – comprehensiveness, international scope and extensive cross referencing – have been preserved in this new edition. The practice of using consistent chemical nomenclature, giving full stereochemical information, has been continued, and, for many entries, several alternative chemical names, derived from different systems of nomenclature, have been included.

TYPES OF NAMES

The types of names used are: 1. Nonproprietary (common) names; 2. Research code numbers; 3. Proprietary names.

Nonproprietary names

1. Chemical names.
2. Abbreviated chemical names.
3. Source names, i.e. names referring to the (biological) origin of compounds such as hormones and plant alkaloids.
4. Pharmacological names (also termed approved, official, or generic names). Lists of such nonproprietary names are issued periodically for general use by
   a. the WHO, under the designation recINN or pINN = recommended or proposed International Nonproprietary Names.
   b. national bodies in various countries, including Great Britain (BAN), the United States (USAN), France (DCF) and the Scandinavian countries (NFN). The names in categories (a) and (b) are often identical or differ only slightly in spelling.
5. Pesticide names. These are common names assigned by international (ISO) and/or national (BSI, ANSI etc.) standardization organizations to compounds used as pesticides. Some of these compounds also have a pharmacological (INN) name, in which case the latter is used as preferred term.
6. Other nonproprietary (trivial) names not classifiable in any of the above categories, e.g. those derived from names of places, plants or persons.

Proprietary names

These are in fact not names of chemical compounds as such and their use in this way
is improper. They are registered trademarks. Such a name is the property of the regis-
tering manufacturer and is applicable only to the product (with or without additives)
produced and/or marketed by him. Its use as if it were a common name is unjustifia-
ble, being
a. unintentional advertising,
b. infringement of a legal right,
c. confusing (resulting in the indexing of a single substance under separate headings).
Unfortunately this misuse of trade names is still very common and it is for that rea-
son that a number of such names have been included in this list.

ARRANGEMENT OF THE ALPHABETICAL LIST

The substances are presented in an alphabetical list under a nonproprietary name,
while the alphabetical list also gives the synonyms in the form of cross-references to
these nonproprietary names.

Main entries

The main entries consist of a heading (printed in capital letters), always a nonproprietary name, followed by a list of synonyms. Each synonym is separated from the next
by a semicolon (;). The synonyms are presented in the following order: first as a systematic chemical name or the source name, followed by other systematic chemical
names, then pharmacological names, then abbreviated chemical names, trivial and
transliterated names, then salt names (e.g. hydrochlorides), followed by research code
numbers and finally trade names, which are encased in inverted comma's. Within
each of these groups the synonyms are sorted alphabetically.
    Trade names of certain well established drugs may not be listed in the main entry
but remain as cross-references. As in the previous edition, this was necessary to allow
space for new material.

Cross-references

Each of the synonyms given after a heading has its own entry referring to the
heading, in the form X... *see* Y... This means that the user who looks first under X...
(a synonym) is directed immediately to Y... (the main entry) in the *same* alphabetical
list.

Status of name (see also under *Nonproprietary names*)

This is indicated in the following way:
*** = recINN
  ** = pINN
    * = (a) BAN, USAN, CDF or NFN name, or (b) pesticide name
(tr) = name transliterated from the Russian (or other Cyrillic) alphabet

no marking = chemical name; common name without official status; research code number

inverted commas = names known or believed to be trademarks.

CHOICE OF ENTRIES

As a general rule the INN name (if any) is used as heading (for pesticides the ISO name), but sometimes one of the national names or the chemical name has been used. The choice is then purely arbitrary and has usually been based on the practical consideration of which name arrived first in our index. The alternatives are given as references.

Multiple products: It is obviously impossible to include all the trade names that refer to products containing more than one active substance. The few which have been included refer to drugs commonly used in the form of mixtures of 2 agents (e.g. the 'pill'). Only the active components are mentioned, not the proportions in which they are present.

Vitamins: For the well-known vitamins only the chemical and other nonproprietary names are listed; the trade names (which are usually self-evident and seldom used in medical literature) are not included. Synthetic derivatives with vitaminic action are given with all their synonyms (including the trade names).

Biological products: Substances of incompletely defined chemical composition are included only if they have been given a pharmacological (approved, generic, official) name.

SPELLING

The spelling of all names (including official and trademarks) has been 'translated' into American spelling. We apologise for this liberty but experience has shown that where some names are spelt, for instance, Sulf... and others Sulph..., the result is highly confusing for the reader. Where necessary a note to this effect has been placed at the appropriate point in the alphabetical list.

REMARKS

Proprietary names

Trade names have been included in this list for the convenience of readers because they are so often given in the literature without statement of the chemical composition or approved name, or are *misused* as though they were common names. It is obviously impossible to trace all the trade names in use in different countries. The inclusion of such a name is purely a matter of the chance of its having come to our notice and inclusion or noninclusion *does not imply any recommendation or the reverse.*

The reference 'X...' *see* Y where 'X' is a trade name and Y a heading, means simply that the drug Y is the *active component* of the proprietary product 'X...'. This list does not provide any information as to additives or excipients which may be included under the trademark, nor does it give any statement about concentration or form (tablet, solution for injection, etc.).

A name which is in some countries a nonproprietary name may be a registered trademark in others. This is a difficulty for us in view of our attempt at international scope. We have endeavoured to avoid it as best we can, and where we have failed we must ask for the indulgence of the persons or bodies concerned, pointing out once more that this is a *compilation without official status*.

Soviet names

Some of these are trademarks elsewhere. Such names have not been used as headings. Soviet names for products described only in literature from the USSR have been regarded as nonproprietary and used as headings. They are marked (tr).

Use of inverted commas

While we have attempted to distinguish proprietary (or possibly proprietary) from nonproprietary names in this way, we cannot guarantee that no mistakes have been made in this respect:

a. The fact that a name is printed *without* inverted commas *does not exclude the possibility that it may have been registered as a trademark in some part of the world.* We are confident, however, that such cases are not numerous.

b. The fact that a name is printed in inverted commas does not *necessarily* mean that it is a registered trademark. To be on the safe side, however, our rule has been 'when in doubt use inverted commas'.

A

A-1 *see* Ethymidine.
A-2 *see* Pyrophos.
A-3 *see* Terofenamate.
A/8 327 *see* Teicoplanin.
A-15 *see* Schradan.
A-16 *see* Ambucetamide.
A-21 *see* Isoprenaline *and* Ketobemidone.
A-66 *see* Phenmetrazine.
A-82 *see* Nitroxoline.
A-101 *see* Nordazepam.
A-102 *see* Temazepam.
A-118 *see* Sultroponium.
A-124 *see under* Phenytoin.
A-145 *see* Promazine.
A-163 *see* Triaziquone.
A-272 *see* Rutamycin.
A-301 *see* Norgestrienone.
A-350 *see* Aminochlorthenoxazine
A-377 *see* Chlortetracycline.
A-1981-12 *see* Prodilidine.
A-2205 *see* Profadol.
A-2358 *see* Ketocaine.
A-2371 *see* Plicamycin.
A-2655 *see* Dioxamate.
A-2701 *see* Candicidin.
A-4020 **Linz** *see* Midodrine.
A-4180 *see* Isometamidium chloride.
A-4696 *see* Actaplanin.
A-4828 *see* Trofosfamide.
A-5283 *see* Natamycin.
A-5610 *see* Azelastine.
A-7283 *see* Guanoctine.
A-8103 *see* Pipobroman.
A-8999 *see* Aspartocin.
A-12253A *see* Nebramycin.
A-16612 *see* Teroxalene.
A-16900 *see* Teflurane.
A-17624 *see* Ditolamide.
A-19120 *see* Pargyline.
A-19757 *see* Encyprate.
A-20968 *see* Piposulfan.
A-22370 *see* Trimetozine.
A-23187 *see* Calcimycin.
A-27053 *see* Carbocromen.
A-30400 *see under* Pemoline.
A-31528 *see under* Pemoline.
A-32686 *see* Proscillaridin.
A-35957 *see* Altrenogest.
A-41300 *see* Altrenogest.
A-41304 *see* Desoximetasone.
A-46745 *see* Gestrinone.

A-732179 *see* Intermedin.
AA-149 *see* Trepibutone.
'Aafac' *see* Prothoate.
AAFC *see* Flurocitabine.
'Aarane' *see under* Cromoglicate disodium.
'Aasevin' *see* Carbaril.
'Aasystem' *see* Thiometon.
'Aat' *see* Parathion.
'Aatrex' *see* Atrazine.
AB-01 *see* Bemegride.
AB-42 *see* Cyacetacide.
AB-100 *see* Uredepa.
AB-103 *see* Benzodepa.
AB-132 *see* Meturedepa.
AB-35616 *see* Clorazepate dipotassium.
'Abacin' *see* Co-trimoxazole.
'Abactrim' *see* Co-trimoxazole.
'Abadole' *see* Aminothiazole.
'Abalgin' *see* Dextropropoxyphene.
'Abar' *see* Leptophos.
'Abate' *see* Temefos.
'Abathion' *see* Temefos.
'Abbokinase' *see* Urokinase.
Abbott 16900 *see* Teflurane.
Abbott 19957 *see* Lorbamate.
Abbott 24091 *see* Berythromycin.
Abbott-34842 *see* Butylcaine picrate.
Abbott 35616 *see* Clorazepate dipotassium.
Abbott 36581 *see* Butamirate citrate.
Abbott 38414 *see* Ancrod.
Abbott 38579 *see* Protirelin.
Abbott-38642 *see* Fosfonet sodium.
Abbott-40728 *see* Cetocycline.
Abbott 41070 *see* Gonadorelin acetate.
Abbott 43326 *see* Carteolol.
Abbott 44089 *see* Valproic acid.
Abbott 44090 *see* Valproic acid.
Abbott 46811 *see* Cefsulodin.
Abbott 48999 *see* Cefotiam.
Abbott-50912 *see* Cefmenoxime.
'Abbotticine' *see* Erythromycin ethylsuccin-
ate.
ABC 8/3 *see* Oxametacin.
'Abdoman' *see* Dropempine.
'Abequito' *see* Nimidane.
'Aberel' *see* Tretinoin.
'Abicol' *see under* Reserpine.
'Abimasten' *see* Nifuroquine.
'Abirol' *see* Metandienone.
Abitylguanide *see* Moroxydine.
'Abminthic' *see* Dithiazanine iodide.

1

ABOB *see* Moroxydine.

'Abrastol' *see* Calcinaphthol.

Abrine *see* *N*-Methyltryptophan.

ABSINTHOL (taneceton; 3-thujanone; thujone; thuyon).

'Abstem' *see* Calcium carbimide citrate.

'Abstinyl' *see* Disulfiram.

'Abten' *see* Alseroxylon.

'Abuphenine' *see* Butetamate.

AC-17 *see* Carbazochrome sodium sulfonate.

AC-32 *see* Clinolamide.

AC-223 *see* Melinamide.

AC-485 *see* Moctamide.

AC-528 *see* Dioxation.

AC-601 *see* Buramate.

AC-695 *see* Ethotoin.

AC-1075 *see* Cytarabine.

AC-1198 *see* Dimethadione.

AC-1802 *see* Aprindine.

AC-2770 *see* Gitoformate.

AC-3810 *see* Bamifylline.

AC-12402 *see* Chlorbicyclen.

'Acabel' *see* Bevonium metilsulfate.

ACACETIN (5,7-dihydroxy-4'-methoxyflavone).

Acamylophenine *see* Camylofin.

ACAPRAZINE** (1-(3-acetamidopropyl)-4-(2,5-dichlorophenyl)piperazine; *N*-[3-[4-(2,5-dichlorophenyl)piperazin-1-yl]propyl]acetamide).

'Acaprin' *see* Quinuronium sulfate.

'Acapron' *see* Quinuronium sulfate.

'Acaralate' *see* Chloropropylate.

ACARBOSE** (*O*-4,6-dideoxy-4-[[4,5,6-trihydroxy-3-(hydroxymethyl)-2-cyclohexen-2-yl]amino]-α-D-glucopyranosyl(1→4)-*O*-α-D-glucopyranosyl)(1→4)-D-glucopyranoside; α-GHI; BAY g-5421).

'Acarol' *see* Bromopropylate.

'Accelerase' *see* Pancrelipase.

'Accent' *see* Sodium glutamate.

'Accothion' *see* Fenitrothion.

'Accutane' *see* Isotretinoin.

ACEBROCHOL** (5,6β-dibromo-5α-cholestan-3β-ol acetate).

ACEBURIC ACID** (4-acetoxybutyric acid; 4-hydroxybutyric acid acetate).

ACEBUTOLOL** ((±)-3'-acetyl-4'-[2-hydroxy-3-(isopropylamino)propoxy]butyranilide; (±)-*N*-[3-acetyl-4-[2-hydroxy-3-(1-methylethyl)-amino]propoxy]butanamide; acebutolol hydrochloride; IL-17803; M & B-17803; 'neptall'; 'prent'; 'sectral').

ACEBUTOLOL plus MEFRUSIDE ('sali-prent').

ACECAINIDE** (4-acetamido-*N*-(2-diethylaminoethyl)benzamide; 4-(acetylamino)-*N*-[2-(diethylamino)ethyl]benzamide; 4'-[[2-(diethylamino)ethyl]carbamoyl]acetanilide; acecainide hydrochloride; ASL-601; 'NAPA').

ACECARBROMAL** (1-acetyl-3-(2-bromo-2-ethylbutyryl)urea; acetylcarbromal; acetylbromdiethylacetylurea).

ACECARBROMAL plus PARACETAMOL ('apromal').

ACECLIDINE** (3-acetoxyquinuclidine; 3-quinuclidinyl acetate; glaucostat).

ACECLIDINE plus EPINEPHRINE ('glaucadrin').

ACEDAPSONE** (4',4'''-sulfonylbis(acetanilide); 4,4'-diacetamidodiphenyl sulfone; *p*,*p*'-sulfonyldiacetanilide; acetyldiphenasone; diacetyldapsone; diacetyldiaphenylsulfone; sulfadiamine; sulfodiamine; BF-103; CI-556; CN-1883; DADDS; F-1399; PAM-MR-1165; 'atilon'; 'hansolar'; 'rodilone').
See also under Cycloguanil embonate.

ACEDIASULFONE MORPHOLINE SALT ('bentrofene').

ACEDIASULFONE SODIUM** (*N*-[*p*-(*p*-aminophenylsulfonyl)phenyl]glycine; 4-amino-4'-(carboxymethylamino)diphenyl sulfone sodium salt; *N*-(*p*-sulfanilylphenyl)glycine).

'Acedicon' *see* Thebacon.

'Acedist' *see* Bromofenofos.

ACEDOBEN** (*p*-acetamidobenzoic acid).
See also Inosine pranobex.

'Acedoxin' *see* Acetyldigitoxin.

ACEFLURANOL** (4,4'-[(1*RS*,2*SR*)-1-ethyl-2-methylethylene]bis[6-fluoropyrocatechol] tetraacetate; (1*RS*,2*SR*)-4,4'-diacetoxy-5,5'-difluoro-(1-ethyl-2-methylethylene)di-*m*-phenylene, diacetate; (α*RS*,α'*SR*)-α-ethyl-5,5'-difluoro-α'-methylbibenzyl 3,3',4,4'-tetrayl tetraacetate; BX-591).

ACEFURTIAMINE** (*N*-(4-amino-2-methylpyrimidin-5-ylmethyl)-*N*-(4-hydroxy-2-mercapto-1-methyl-1-butenyl)formamide *O*-glycolate acetate *S*-ester with thio-2-furoic acid).

ACEFYLLINE CLOFIBROL** (2-(*p*-chlorophenyl)-2-methylpropyl 1,2,3,6-tetrahydro-1,3-dimethyl-2,6-dioxopurine-7-acetate; 2-(*p*-chlorophenyl)-2-methylpropyl theophyllin-7-ylacetate; fibrafylline).

ACEFYLLINE PIPERAZINE** (piperazine theophyllin-7-ylacetate; piperazine bis(theophyllin-7-ylacetate); theophylline-piperazine ethanoate; acepiphylline).

ACEGLATONE** (saccharic acid 1,4:6,3-dilactone acetate; 'glucaron').

ACEGLUTAMIDE** (L-2-acetamido-4-carbamoylbutyric acid; *N*²-acetyl-L-glutamine).

ACEGLUTAMIDE ALUMINIUM (aceglutamide aluminium hydroxide complex; aluminium aceglutamide; pentakis(*N*²-acetyl-L-glutamine)-tetrahydroxytrialuminium; KW-110; 'glumal'; 'glumol').

'Acelat' *see* Spironolactone.

ACEMETACIN** (*O*-[[1-(*p*-chlorobenzoyl)-5-methoxy-2-methylindol-3-yl]acetyl]glycolic acid; BAY f-4975; TVX-1322; 'rantudil').

Acemethadone *see* Acetylmethadol.

Acenocoumarin* *see* Acenocoumarol.

ACENOCOUMAROL** (3-[2-acetyl-1-(*p*-nitrophenyl)ethyl]-4-hydroxycoumarin; 3-(α-acetonyl-*p*-nitrobenzyl)-4-hydroxycoumarin; acenocoumarin; nicoumalone; G-23350).

ACEPERONE** (4-(4-acetamidomethyl-4-phenylpiperid-1-yl)-4'-fluorobutyrophenone; 4-

(acetamidomethyl)-1-[3-(*p*-fluorobenzoyl)prop-yl]-4-phenylpiperidine; acetobutone; R-3248).

ACEPHATE* (*O*,*S*-dimethyl acetylphosphor-amidothioate; 'orthene').

Acephenazine* *see* Acetophenazine.

Acepiphylline* *see* Acefylline piperazine.

'Acepril' *see* Captopril.

ACEPROMAZINE*** (2-acetyl-10-(3-dimethyl-aminopropyl)phenothiazine; 10-[3-(dimethyl-amino)propyl]phenothiazin-2-yl methyl ketone; acetazine; acepromazine maleate; acetylpromaz-ine).
See also under Etorphine.

ACEPROMETAZINE*** (2-acetyl-10-(2-dimeth-ylaminopropyl)phenothiazine; CB-1664).

ACEPROMETAZINE plus MEPROBAMATE ('mepronizine').

ACEQUINOLINE*** (3-acetyl-7-methoxy-2,4-di-methylquinoline; 7-methoxy-2,4-dimethyl-3-qui-nolyl methyl ketone; CB-4984).

Acesal *see* Acetylsalicylic acid.

ACESULFAME*** (6-methyl-1,2,3-oxathiazin-4(3*H*)-one 2,2-dioxide; acetosulfam; acesulfame potassium; HE-733293; HOE-095K).

ACETAL (1,1-diethoxyethane; acetaldehyde di-ethylacetal; diethylacetal; ethylidene diethyl ether; acetol).

ACETALDEHYDE (ethanal; ethanone).

Acetaldehyde diethylacetal *see* Acetal.

Acetaldol *see* Aldol.

5-Acetamido-3-acetamidomethyl-2,4,6-triiodobenzo-ic acid *see* Iodamide.

Acetamidoacetic acid *see* Aceturic acid.

4-Acetamido-4′-aminodiphenyl sulfone *see* Acetyl-dapsone.

ACETAMIDOAZOTOLUENE (4-acetamido-2′,3-dimethylazobenzene; *N*-acetyl-4-(*o*-tolyl-azo)-*o*-toluidine; azodermin).

***p*-Acetamidobenzaldehyde thiosemicarbazone** *see* Thioacetazone.

***p*-Acetamidobenzoic acid** *see* Acedoben.

Acetamidocaproic acid *see* Acexamic acid.

2-Acetamido-4-carbamoylbutyric acid *see* Aceglut-amide.

2-Acetamido-3-*O*-[[1-[[1-(3-carbamoyl-1-carboxy-propyl)carbamoyl]ethyl]carbamoyl]ethyl]-2-de-oxy-D-glucopyranose, butyl ester *see* Murabut-ide.

1-Acetamido-5-cyanopyrimidin-4-one *see* Ciapil-ome.

1-[(2-Acetamido-3,5-dibromobenzyl)methylamino]-adamantane *see* Adamexine.

4-Acetamido-*N*-(2-diethylaminoethyl)benzamide *see* Acecainide.

7-Acetamido-6,7-dihydro-1,2,3,10-tetramethoxy-benzo[*a*]heptalen-9(5*H*)-one *see* Colchicine.

4-Acetamido-2′,3-dimethylazobenzene *see* Acet-amidoazotoluene.

***N*⁴-(7-Acetamido-3,6-disulfo-1-hydroxy-2-naphthal-eneazo)sulfanilamide** *see* Azosulfamide.

4-Acetamido-2-ethoxybenzoic acid methyl ester *see* Ethopabate.

2-Acetamidoethyl 2-(4-chlorophenyl)-2-(3-trifluoro-methylphenoxy)acetate *see* Halofenate.

S-2-ACETAMIDOETHYL *O*,*O*-DIMETHYL PHOSPHORODITHIOATE (DAEP; 'ami-phos').

2-Acetamidofluorene *see* Fluorenylacetamide.

4-Acetamido-15-glucopyranosyloxy-13,14-dimeth-oxy-8-methylthio-7-oxotricyclo-[10.4.0.0⁵,¹¹]-hexadeca-1(12),5,8,10,13,15-hexaene *see* Thio-colchicoside.

3-Acetamido-5-glycolamido-2,4,6-triiodobenzoic acid *see* Ioxotrizoic acid.

6-Acetamidohexanoic acid *see* Acexamic acid.

3-Acetamido-4-hydroxybenzenearsonic acid *see* Acetarsol.

5-Acetamido-*N*-(2-hydroxyethyl)-2,4,6-triiodoisoph-thalamic acid *see* Ioxitalamic acid.

2-(3-Acetamido-4-hydroxyphenyl)-1,3-dithia-2-arsa-cyclopentane-4-methanol *see* Arsthinol.

2-Acetamido-4-mercaptobutyric acid *see* Acetylho-mocysteine.

2-Acetamido-4-mercaptobutyric acid clofibrate ester *see* Serfibrate.

2-Acetamido-4-mercaptobutyric acid γ-thiolactone *see* Citiolone.

***p*-Acetamido-*m*-methoxybenzaldehyde thiosemicarb-azone** *see* Amithizone.

4-(Acetamidomethyl)-1-[3-(*p*-fluorobenzoyl)propyl]-4-phenylpiperidine *see* Aceperone.

4-(4-Acetamidomethyl-4-phenylpiperid-1-yl)-4′-fluorobutyrophenone *see* Aceperone.

2-Acetamido-5-nitrothiazole *see* Aminitrozole.

***m*-Acetamidophenol** *see* Metacetamol.

***p*-Acetamidophenol** *see* Paracetamol.

2-(*p*-Acetamidophenoxy)ethyl acetylsalicylate *see* Etersalate.

2-(*p*-Acetamidophenoxy)ethyl salicylate acetate *see* Etersalate.

1-(*p*-Acetamidophenoxy)-3-isopropylamino-2-pro-panol *see* Practolol.

1-(*p*-Acetamidophenoxy)-2,2,2-trichloroethanol *see* Cloracetadol.

***p*-Acetamidophenyl acetate** *see* Diacetamate.

***p*-Acetamidophenyl acetylsalicylate** *see* Benorilate.

1-Acetamidophenyl-4-(3-dimethylaminopropyl)pip-erazine *see* Piperamide.

4-Acetamidophenyl salicylate *see* Acetaminosalol.

4-Acetamidophenyl salicylate acetate *see* Benoril-ate.

1-(3-Acetamidopropyl)-4-(2,5-dichlorophenyl)pip-erazine *see* Acaprazine.

5-Acetamido-2-sulfamoyl-1,3,4-thiadiazole *see* Acetazolamide.

α-Acetamido-γ-thiobutyrolactone *see* Citiolone.

3-Acetamido-2,4,6-triiodobenzoic acid *see* Acetrizo-ic acid.

2-[3-Acetamido-2,4,6-triiodo-5-(*N*-methylacet-amido)benzamido]-2-deoxy-D-glucose *see* Metriz-amide.

3-Acetamido-2,4,6-triiodo-5-(*N*-methylacetamido)-benzoic acid *see* Metrizoic acid.

5-Acetamido-2,4,6-triiodo-*N*-[(methylcarbamoyl)-methyl]isophthalamic acid *see* Ioglicic acid.

5-Acetamido-2,4,6-triiodo-*N*-methylisophthalamic

acid *see* Iotalamic acid.

2-[2-(3-Acetamido-2,4,6-triiodophenoxy)ethoxymethyl]butyric acid *see* Iopronic acid.

Acetaminophen* *see* Paracetamol.

ACETAMINOSALOL* (4'-hydroxyacetanilide salicylate; 4-acetamidophenyl salicylate; acetyl *p*-aminosalol).

ACETANILIDE (*N*-phenylacetamide; *N*-acetylaniline; antifebrin).

Acetarsenic acid *see* Arsonoacetic acid.

ACETARSOL* (*N*-acetyl-4-hydroxy-*m*-arsanilic acid; 3-acetamido-4-hydroxybenzenearsonic acid; acetarsone; acetphenarsine; osarsol; Ehrlich 594).

Acetarsone *see* Acetarsol.

Acetarsonic acid *see* Arsonoacetic acid.

'Acetasal' *see* Choline salicylate.

Acetate-replacing factor *see* Thioctic acid.

'Acetazide' *see* Acetazolamide.

Acetazine *see* Acepromazine.

ACETAZOLAMIDE* (5-acetamido-2-sulfamoyl-1,3,4-thiadiazole; diacarb).

ACETERGAMINE* ((+)-*N*-acetyl-9,10-dihydrolysergamine; (+)-*N*-acetyl-8β-aminomethyl-6-methyl-10a-ergoline; (+)-*N*-(6-methylergolin-8β-ylmethyl)acetamide; acetergamine tartrate; VUFB-6683).

'Acetexa' *see* Nortriptyline.

ACETIAMINE* (*N*-((4-amino-2-methylpyrimidin-5-yl)methyl)-*N*-(4-hydroxy-2-mercapto-1-methyl-1-butenyl)formamide *O,S*-diacetate; DAT; diacetylthiamine).

ACETIC ACID (ethanoic acid).

Acetic acid 5-nitrofurfurylidenehydrazide *see* Nihydrazone.

'Acetidone' *see* Sodium acetrizoate.

ACETIROMATE** (4-(4-acetoxy-3-iodophenoxy-3,5-diiodobenzoic acid; 4-(4-hydroxy-3-iodophenoxy)-3,5-diiodobenzoic acid acetate; TBF-43; 'adecol').

Acetoarsinic acid *see* Arsonoacetic acid.

Acetobutone *see* Aceperone.

'Acetochlorone' *see* Chlorbutol.

Acetocinnamone *see* Benzylideneacetone.

ACETOHEXAMIDE* (4-acetyl-*N*-[(cyclohexylamino)carbonyl]benzenesulfonamide; 1-[(*p*-acetylphenyl)sulfonyl]-3-cyclohexylurea).

ACETOHYDROXAMIC ACID** (*N*-hydroxyacetamide).

ACETOIN (3-hydroxy-2-butanone; acetyl methyl carbinol).

Acetol salicylate *see* Salicyl acetol.

Acetomenadione *see* Acetomenaphthone.

ACETOMENAPHTHONE* (2-methyl-1,4-naphthalenediol diacetate; vitamin K₄; acetomenadione; menadiol diacetate).

Acetomenophen *see* Paracetamol.

ACETOMEROCTOL* (2-acetoxymercuri-4-(1,1,3,3-tetramethylbutyl)phenol).

ACETOMESIDIDE (2',4',6'-trimethylacetanilide; acetylmesidine).

Acetomorphine *see* Diamorphine.

ACETONE (2-propanone).

Acetone bis(3,5-di-*tert*-butyl-4-hydroxyphenyl)mercaptole *see* Probucol.

Acetone-chloroform *see* Chlorbutol.

ACETONITRILE (ethane nitrile; methyl cyanide).

3-(α-Acetonylbenzyl)-4-hydroxycoumarin *see* Warfarin.

[3-(α-Acetonylbenzyl)-4-hydroxycoumarin]dimethylaminoethanol *see* Warfarin-deanol.

3-(α-Acetonyl-*p*-chlorobenzyl)-4-hydroxycoumarin *see* Coumachlor.

3-(α-Acetonylfurfuryl)-4-hydroxycoumarin *see* Coumafuryl.

3-(α-Acetonyl-*p*-nitrobenzyl)-4-hydroxycoumarin *see* Acenocoumarol.

8-Acetonyloxy-5-[3-[(3,4-dimethoxyphenethyl)-amino]-2-hydroxypropoxy]-3,4-dihydrocarbostyril *see* Bometolol.

2-Acetonylpiperidine *see* Pelletierine.

ACETOPHENAZINE* (2-acetyl-10-[3-[4-(2-hydroxyethyl)piperazin-1-yl]propyl]phenothiazine; acephenazine; acetophenazine maleate; NSC-70600; Sch-6673).

***p*-Acetophenetidide** *see* Phenacetin.

Acetophenetidin* *see* Phenacetin.

'Acetophenidin' *see* Phenacetin.

Acetophenomethane *see* Bisacodyl.

ACETOPHENONE (methyl phenyl ketone; hypnone).

Acetopherane* *see* Levofacetoperane.

ACETORPHINE* (6,7,8,14-tetrahydro-7a-(1-hydroxy-1-methylbutyl)-6,14-*endo*-ethenooripavine 3-acetate; 3-*O*-acetyl-19-propylnorvinol; etorphine acetate; M-183).

Acetosal *see* Acetylsalicylic acid.

Acetosulfam *see* Acesulfame.

Acetosulfaminum *see* Sulfacetamide.

Acetosulfone *see* Sulfadiasulfone sodium.

ACETOTOLUIDIDE(S) (*N*-acetyltoluidine(s); *ar*-methylacetanilide(s)).

Acetovanillone *see* Apocynin.

Acetoxatrine *see* Acoxatrine.

5-Acetoxy-3-(2-aminoethyl)-1-(*p*-methoxybenzyl)-2-methylindole *see* Hydroxindasate.

1-Acetoxy-6-aminooctahydroindolizine *see* Slaframine.

2-Acetoxybenzoic acid *see* Acetylsalicylic acid.

α-Acetoxy-α-benzylhydrocinnamic acid 2-piperid-1-ylethyl ester *see* Fenperate.

17α-Acetoxy-6-bromo-6-dehydro-16-methyleneprogesterone *see* Bromo-MDAP.

4-Acetoxybutyric acid *see* Aceburic acid.

17α-Acetoxy-6-chloro-6-dehydro-16-methyleneprogesterone *see* Chloro-MDAP.

17α-Acetoxy-6-chloro-6-dehydroprogesterone *see* Chlormadinone acetate.

2-Acetoxy-4'-chloro-3,5-diiodobenzanilide *see* Clioxanide.

21-Acetoxy-3-(2-chloroethoxy)-9α-fluoro-6-formyl-11β-hydroxy-16α,17α-isopropylidenedioxy-pregna-3,5-dien-20-one *see* Formocortal.

17α-Acetoxy-6-chloro-16-methylenepregna-4,6-diene-3,20-dione *see* Chloro-MDAP.

8-Acetoxy-5-chloroquinoline *see* Cloxiquine acetate.

(11β,16α)-21-Acetoxy-16,17-[cyclopentylidenebis-(oxy)]-9-fluoro-11-hydroxypregna-1,4-diene-3,20-dione *see* Amcinonide.

17α-Acetoxy-6-dehydro-16-methyleneprogesterone *see* MDAP.

4-Acetoxy-2′,4′-dibromo-6′-[[(cyclohexyl)(methyl)-amino]methyl]-3-methoxybenzanilide *see* Brovanexine.

2-Acetoxy-3-(diethylcarbamoyl)hexahydro-9,10-dimethoxybenzo[a]quinolizine *see* Benzquinamide.

10-Acetoxy-9,10-dihydro-8,8-dimethyl-9-(α-methyl-butyryloxy)benzodipyran-2-one *see* Visnadine.

4′-Acetoxy-3′,4′-dihydro-3′-(2-methylbutyryloxy)se-selin *see* Visnadine.

3-Acetoxy-6-(dimethylamino)-4,4′-diphenylheptane *see* Acetylmethadol; Alphaacetylmethadol.

6-Acetoxy-4,5-epoxy-3-methoxy-N-methylmorphi-nan-6-ene *see* Thebacon.

17β-Acetoxy-8,13-epoxy-1α,6β,9α-trihydroxylabd-14-en-11-one *see* Forskolin.

(2-Acetoxyethyl)(2-chloroethyl)methylamine *see* Acetylcholine mustard.

17-Acetoxy-3,3-ethylenedioxy-6-methylpregn-5-en-20-one *see* Edogestrone.

10-[3-[4-(2-Acetoxyethyl)piperazin-1-yl]propyl]-2-chlorophenothiazine *see* Thiopropazate.

(2-Acetoxyethyl)trimethylammonium chloride *see* Acetylcholine chloride.

4-Acetoxy-4′-fluorobiphenyl-3-carboxylic acid *see* Flufenisal.

3-Acetoxy-4-hydroxy-2-(p-methoxybenzyl)pyrrolid-ine *see* Anisomycin.

21-Acetoxy-3α-hydroxy-5α-pregnane-11,20-dione *see* Alfadolone acetate.

4-(4-Acetoxy-3-iodophenoxy-3,5-diiodobenzoic acid *see* Acetiromate.

'Acetoxyl' *see* Benzoyl peroxide.

ACETOXYLIDIDE(S) (N-acetylxylidine(s); ar,ar-dimethylacetanilide(s)).

2-Acetoxymercuri-4-(1,1,3,3-tetramethylbutyl)phen-ol *see* Acetomeroctol.

3-Acetoxymethyl-7-(5-amino-5-carboxy-valer-amido)-2-cephem-2-carboxylic acid *see* Cephalosporin C.

α-3-Acetoxy-6-(methylamino)-4,4-diphenylheptane *see* Noracymethadol.

2-Acetoxy-5-methylbenzoic acid *see* Acetylcresotic acid.

3-Acetoxymethyl-2-cephem-2-carboxylic acid *see* Cephalosporanic acid.

Acetoxymethyl 4-(2-chloro-m-toluidino)thiophene-3-carboxylate *see* Aclantate.

3-Acetoxymethyl-7-(2-cyanoacetamido)-2-cephem-2-carboxylic acid *see* Cefacetrile.

17-Acetoxy-11β-methyl-19-norpregn-4-ene-3,20-di-one *see* Norgestomet.

17-Acetoxy-11β-methyl-19-norprogesterone *see* Norgestomet.

3-Acetoxymethyl-7-(2-phenylacetamido)-2-cephem-2-carboxylic acid *see* Cefaloram.

Acetoxymethyl 6-phenylacetamidopenicillanate *see* Penamecillin.

17α-Acetoxy-6α-methylprogesterone *see* Medroxy-progesterone acetate.

3-Acetoxymethyl-7-[2-(pyrid-4-ylthio)acetamido]-2-cephem-2-carboxylic acid *see* Cefapirin.

3-Acetoxymethyl-7-(2-thien-2-ylacetamido)-2-cephem-2-carboxylic acid *see* Cefalotin.

3β-Acetoxy-11-oxoolean-12-en-30-oic acid cinnamyl ester *see* Cinoxolone.

Acetoxypregnenolone *see* Pregnenolone acetate.

3-Acetoxyquinuclidine *see* Aceclidine.

Acetoxythymoxamine *see* Moxisylyte.

2-Acetoxy-4-(trifluoromethyl)benzoic acid *see* Triflusal.

Acetoxytriphenylstannane *see* Fentin acetate.

Acetparaphenalide *see* Phenacetin.

Acetphenarsine *see* Acetarsol.

ACETPHENOLISATIN* (3,3-bis(p-acetoxyphen-yl)isatin; 3,3-bis-(p-acetoxyphenyl)oxindole; di-phesatine; oxyphenisatine acetate; bisatin; di-acetoxydiphenylisatin; diacetyldihydroxyphenyl-isatin; diacetyldiphenolisatin; diasatin; endo-phenolphthalein; isaphenin; NSC-59687).

ACETPYROGALL* (pyrogallol triacetate; 1,2,3-triacetoxybenzene).

ACETRIZOIC ACID* (3-acetamido-2,4,6-triiodo-benzoic acid; 'triumbren'; 'urokolin'). *See also* Ethyl acetrizoate; Sodium acetrizoate; Meglumine acetrizoate.

ACETRYPTINE*** (5-acetyl-3-(2-aminoethyl)-indole; 2-(5-acetylindol-3-yl)ethylamine; 5-acet-yltryptamine; 3-(2-aminoethyl)indol-5-yl methyl ketone).

Acetsulfanilamide *see* Sulfacetamide.

ACETURIC ACID (acetamidoacetic acid; N-acet-ylglycine; ethanoylaminoethanoic acid). *See also* Closiramine aceturate.

ACETYLACETONE (2,4-pentanedione).

Acetylaminocaproic acid *see* Acexamic acid.

4-(Acetylamino)-N-[2-(diethylamino)ethyl]benz-amide *see* Acecainide.

2-Acetyl-4α-amino-4aβ,12a-dihydro-3,10,11,12aβ-tetrahydroxy-6,9-dimethyl-1,12(4H,5H)-naph-thacenedione *see* Cetocycline.

2-Acetylaminofluorene *see* Fluorenylacetamide.

(+)-N-Acetyl-8β-aminomethyl-6-methyl-10a-ergol-ine *see* Acetergamine.

N-Acetyl-m-aminophenol *see* Metacetamol.

N-Acetyl-p-aminophenol *see* Paracetamol.

Acetyl p-aminosalol *see* Acetaminosalol.

8-Acetyl-10-[(3-amino-2,3,6-trideoxy-α-L-lyxo-hexopyranosyl)oxy]-7,8,9,10-tetrahydro-1,6,8,11-tetrahydroxy-5,12-naphthacenedione *see* Carubicin.

9-Acetyl-7-[(3-amino-2,3,6-trideoxy-α-L-lyxo-hexo-pyranosyl)oxy]-7,8,9,10-tetrahydro-6,9,11-tri-hydroxy-5,12-naphthacenedione *see* Idarubicin.

3-(Acetylamino)-2,4,6-triiodo-5-[[[[(methylamino)-carbonyl]methyl]amino]carbonyl]benzoic acid *see* Ioglicic acid.

N-Acetyl-N-(3-amino-2,4,6-triiodophenyl)-2-methyl-β-alanine *see* Iocetamic acid.

17-Acetylandrostane *see* Pregnan-20-one.

N-Acetylaniline *see* Acetanilide.

N-(*N*-Acetyl-L-β-aspartyl)-L-glutamic acid *see* Spaglumic acid.

α-[[(8-Acetyl-1,4-benzodioxan-5-yl)oxy]methyl]-4-(3,4,5-trimethyloxycinnamoyl)-1-piperazineethanol *see* Cinepaxadil.

1-(2-Acetylbenzofuran-7-yloxy)-3-(isopropylamino)-2-propanol *see* Befunolol.

N-Acetyl-*S*-(2-benzoylpropyl)cysteine *see* Bencisteine.

N-Acetyl-3-[(2-benzoylpropyl)thio]alanine *see* Bencisteine.

N-Acetyl-*p*-[bis(2-chloroethyl)amino]phenylalanine ethyl ester *see* Phenaphan.

N-[*N*-Acetyl-3-[*p*-[bis(2-chloroethyl)amino]phenyl]-alanyl]-L-leucine ethyl ester *see* Asaley.

N-[*N*-Acetyl-3-[*p*-[bis(2-chloroethyl)amino]phenyl]-alanyl]-DL-valine ethyl ester *see* Asaline.

N-Acetyl-*N*,*O*-bis(methylcarbamoyl)hydroxylamine *see* Caracemide.

Acetylbromdiethylacetylurea *see* Acecarbromal.

Acetylbromdiethylurea *see* Carbromal.

1-Acetyl-3-(2-bromo-2-ethylbutyryl)urea *see* Acecarbromal.

3-[3-Acetyl-4-[3-(*tert*-butylamino)-2-hydroxypropoxy]phenyl]-1,1-diethylurea *see* Celiprolol.

3-Acetyl-5-*sec*-butyl-4-hydroxy-3-pyrrolin-2-one *see* Tenuazonic acid.

α-Acetyl-5-*sec*-butyltetramic acid *see* Tenuazonic acid.

Acetyl carbinol *see* Hydroxyacetone.

Acetylcarbocholine *see* 3,3-Dimethylbutyl acetate.

N-Acetyl-*N*-(2-carboxypropyl)-2,4,6-triiodo-*m*-phenylenediamine *see* Iocetamic acid.

Acetylcarbromal *see* Acecarbromal.

(3-Acetyl-5-chloro-2-hydroxybenzyl)-diethyl(2-phenoxyethyl)ammonium 3-hydroxy-2-naphthoate *see* Difezil.

3-[2-Acetyl-1-(*p*-chlorophenyl)ethyl]-4-hydroxycoumarin *see* Coumachlor.

17β-Acetyl-6-chloro-1β,1a,2β,8β,9α,10,11,12,13,14α,15,16β,16a,17-tetradecahydro-10β,13β-dimethyl-3*H*-dicyclopropa(1,2:16,17)cyclopenta[*a*]phenanthren-3-one *see* Gestaclone.

ACETYLCHOLINE CHLORIDE*** ((2-acetoxyethyl)trimethylammonium chloride; choline acetate).

ACETYLCHOLINE MUSTARD ((2-acetoxyethyl)(2-chloroethyl)methylamine; 2-[(2-chloroethyl)methylamino]ethyl acetate).

'Acetylcodone' *see* Thebacon.

ACETYLCRESOTIC ACID (2-acetoxy-5-methylbenzoic acid; 'cresopyrine'; 'ervasin').

4-Acetyl-*N*-[(cyclohexylamino)carbonyl]benzenesulfonamide *see* Acetohexamide.

ACETYLCYSTEINE*** (*N*-acetyl-L-cysteine; NSC-111180).

ACETYLCYSTEINE plus HYPROMELLOSE ('ilube').

Acetylcysteine acetate *see* Dacisteine.

ACETYLDAPSONE (4-acetamido-4'-aminodiphenyl sulfone; acetyldiaphenylsulfone; sulfone *N*-acetate).

Acetyldiaphenylsulfone *see* Acetyldapsone.

1-Acetyl-4-[4-[[2-(2,4-dichlorophenyl)-2-(1*H*-imidazol-1-ylmethyl)-1,3-dioxolan-4-yl]methoxy]phenyl]piperazine *see* Ketoconazole.

1-[2-Acetyl-4-[(diethylcarbamoyl)amino]phenoxy]-3-(*tert*-butylamino)-2-propanol *see* Celiprolol.

1-Acetyl-*N*,*N*-diethyllysergamide *see* Acetyllysergide.

ACETYLDIGITOXIN*** (3β,14β-dihydroxy-5β-card-20(22)-enolide 3-(4'''-acetyltridigitoxoside); α-acetyldigitoxin; 4'''-acetyldigitoxin).

β-ACETYLDIGOXIN (3β,12,14-trihydroxy-5β-card-20(22)-enolide 3-(4'''-acetyltridigitoxoside); acetyl-12-hydroxydigitoxin; desglucolanatoside C).

β-ACETYLDIGOXIN plus DILAZEP ('cormelian digotab').

Acetyldihydrocodeinone *see* Thebacon.

(+)-*N*-Acetyl-9,10-dihydrolysergamine *see* Acetergamine.

Acetyldimepheptanol *see* Acetylmethadol.

2-Acetyl-10-(2-dimethylaminopropyl)phenothiazine *see* Aceprometazine.

2-Acetyl-10-(3-dimethylaminopropyl)phenothiazine *see* Acepromazine.

*N*¹-Acetyl-*N*¹-(3,4-dimethylisoxazol-5-yl)sulfanilamide *see* Acetylsulfafurazole.

Acetyldiphenasone *see* Acedapsone.

ACETYLENE (ethine; ethyne; 'narcylene').

Acetylenecarboxylic acid *see* Propiolic acid.

Acetylene tetrachloride *see* Tetrachloroethane.

17-Acetylestratriene *see* 19-Norpregnatrien-20-one.

4-(2-Acetylethyl)-1,2-diphenyl-3,5-pyrazolidinedione *see* Kebuzone.

Acetylformaldehyde *see* Methylglyoxal.

Acetylformic acid *see* Pyruvic acid.

3-(2-Acetyl-1-furan-2-ylethyl)-4-hydroxycoumarin *see* Coumafuryl.

ACETYLGITALOXIN (16-formylacetylgitoxin).

16-ACETYLGITOXIN ('resorptol').

Acetylglutamine *see* Aceglutamide.

N-Acetylglycine *see* Aceturic acid.

3-Acetyl-1,2,3,4,6,11-hexahydro-3,5,10,12-tetrahydroxy-6,11-dioxo-1-naphthacenyl 3-amino-2,3,6-trideoxy-α-L-*lyxo*-hexopyranoside *see* Carubicin.

3-Acetyl-1,2,3,4,6,11-hexahydro-3,5,12-trihydroxy-6,11-dioxo-1-naphthacenyl 3-amino-2,3,6-trideoxy-α-L-*lyxo*-hexopyranoside *see* Idarubicin.

(1*S*,3*S*)-3-Acetyl-1,2,3,4,6,11-hexahydro-3,5,12-trihydroxy-10-methoxy-6,11-dioxo-1-naphthacenyl 3-amino-2,3,6-trideoxy-α-L-*lyxo*-hexopyranoside *see* Daunorubicin.

ACETYLHOMOCYSTEINE (*N*-acetylhomocysteine; 2-acetamido-4-mercaptobutyric acid).

N-Acetylhomocysteine clofibrate *see* Serfibrate.

Acetylhomocysteine thiolactone *see* Citiolone.

N-Acetyl-4-hydroxy-*m*-arsanilic acid *see* Acetarsol.

Acetyl-12-hydroxydigitoxin *see* β-Acetyldigoxin.

1-Acetyl-2-(3-hydroxy-3,3-diphenylpropionyl)hydrazine *see* Diphoxazide.

N-[3-(Acetyl(2-hydroxyethyl)amino]-2,4,6-triiodo-5-[(methylamino)carbonyl]phenyl]-D-gluconamide *see* Ioglucol.

2-Acetyl-10-[3-[4-(2-hydroxyethyl)piperazin-1-yl]-propyl]phenothiazine *see* Acetophenazine.

2-Acetyl-10-[3-[4-(2-hydroxyethyl)piperid-1-yl]prop-yl]phenothiazine *see* Piperacetazine.

N-[p-Acetyl-β-hydroxy-α-(hydroxymethyl)phen-ethyl]-2,2-dichloroacetamide *see* Cetofenicol.

3′-Acetyl-4′-[2-hydroxy-3-(isopropylamino)prop-oxy]acetanilide *see* Diacetolol.

2-Acetyl-7-(2-hydroxy-3-isopropylaminopropoxy)-benzofuran *see* Befunolol.

(±)-3′-Acetyl-4′-[2-hydroxy-3-(isopropylamino)-propoxy]butyranilide *see* Acebutolol.

3-O-Acetyl-7α-(1(R)-hydroxy-1-methylbutyl)tetra-hydro-6,14-*endo*-ethenooripavine *see* Acetorph-ine.

(±)-N-[3-Acetyl-4-[2-hydroxy-3-(1-methylethyl)-amino]propoxy]butanamide *see* Acebutolol.

N-[3-Acetyl-4-[2-hydroxy-3-[(1-methylethyl)amino]-propoxy]phenyl]acetamide *see* Diacetolol.

2-Acetyl-5-hydroxy-3-oxo-4-hexenoic acid δ-lactone *see* Dehydroacetic acid.

N-Acetylhydroxyproline *see* Oxaceprol.

1-Acetyl-4-hydroxy-L-proline *see* Oxaceprol.

2-Acetylimino-3-(2-hydroxy-2-thien-2-ylethyl)thiaz-oline *see* Antazonite.

5-Acetylimino-4-methyl-2-sulfamoyl-1,3,4-thiadi-azoline *see* Methazolamide.

2-(5-Acetylindol-3-yl)ethylamine *see* Acetryptine.

ACETYLLEUCINE*** (N-acetyl-DL-leucine).

Acetylleucine monoethanolamine salt *see* Ethanol-amine acetylleucinate.

1-Acetyllysergic acid diethylamide *see* Acetyllyserg-ide.

ACETYLLYSERGIDE (1-acetyl-N,N-diethyllys-ergamide; 1-acetyllysergic acid diethylamide).

N-Acetylmerphalan leucine peptide ethyl ester *see* Asaley.

N-Acetylmerphalan valine peptide ethyl ester *see* Asaline.

Acetylmetacresol *see* m-Cresyl acetate.

ACETYLMETHADOL*** (3-acetoxy-6-dimethyl-amino-4,4-diphenylheptane; methadyl acetate; acemethadone; acetyldimepheptanol; dimephep-tanol acetate).
See also Alphacetylmethadol; Betacetylmethad-ol; Levacetylmethadol.

N-ACETYLMETHIONINE (methionine acetate; 'methionamine'; 'thiomedon').

ACETYLMETHIONINE CHOLINE SALT ('hepsan').

3-Acetyl-7-methoxy-2,4-dimethylquinoline *see* Ace-quinoline.

N¹-Acetyl-N¹-(3-methoxypyrazin-2-yl)-sulfanil-amide *see* Acetylsulfalene.

N-Acetyl-5-methoxytryptamine *see* Melatonin.

N-Acetyl-N-methyl-L-alanine 11-chloro-21-hydr-oxy-12,20-dimethoxy-2,5,9,16-tetramethyl-8,23-dioxo-4,24-dioxa-9,22-diazatetracyclohexacosa-10,12,14(26),16,18-pentaen-6-yl ester *see* Mai-tansine.

Acetyl methyl carbinol *see* Acetoin.

Acetyl-β-methylcholine *see* Methacholine chloride.

N¹-Acetyl-N¹-(5-methylisoxazol-3-yl)sulfanilamide

see Acetylsulfamethoxazole.

trans-α-Acetyl-1-methyl-5-nitroimidazole-2-acrylic acid ethyl ester *see* Propenidazole.

3-Acetyl-6-methyl-2H-pyran-2,4(3H)-dione *see* De-hydroacetic acid.

N-Acetyl-O-methylserotonin *see* Melatonin.

N¹-Acetyl-N¹-(p-nitrophenyl)sulfanilamide *see* Sul-fanitran.

Acetyloleandomycin* *see* Troleandomycin.

4-(Acetyloxy)-6-[[3,6-dideoxy-4-O-[2,6-dideoxy-3-C-methyl-4-O-3-methyl-1-oxobutyl]-α-L-*ribo*-hexopyranosyl]-3-(dimethylamino)-β-D-glucopyr-anosyl]oxy]-10-hydroxy-5-methoxy-9,16-dimeth-yl-2-oxooxacyclohexadeca-11,13-diene-7-acet-aldehyde *see* Josamycin.

4-[(p-Acetylphenoxy)acetyl]morpholine p-oxime *see* Mofoxime.

1-[(p-Acetylphenoxy)acetyl]piperidine p-oxime *see* Pifoxime.

N-[N-(N-Acetyl-3-phenyl-L-alanyl)-3-phenyl-L-alanyl]-L-histidine methyl ester *see* Triletide.

1-(p-Acetylphenyl)-2-(dichloroacetamido)-1,3-pro-panediol *see* Cetofenicol.

Acetylphenylsalicylate *see* Acetylsalol.

1-[(p-Acetylphenyl)sulfonyl]-3-cyclohexylurea *see* Acetohexamide.

Acetylphosphoramidothioic acid dimethyl ester *see* Acephate.

4-(4-Acetylpiperazin-1-yl)-α-[2-(2,4-dichlorophen-yl)-r-2-imidazol-1-ylmethyl-1,3-dioxolan-c-4-yl]-anisole *see* Ketoconazole.

3-Acetylpropionic acid *see* Levulinic acid.

3-O-Acetyl-19-propylnorvinol *see* Acetorphine.

Acetylpropylorvinol *see* Acetorphine.

4-Acetylpyrogallol *see* Gallacetophenone.

N-Acetylsalicylamide *see* Salacetamide.

ACETYLSALICYLIC ACID (2-acetoxybenzoic acid; salicylic acid acetate; acesal; acetosal; acet-ysal; 'aspirin').

ACETYLSALICYLIC ACID plus ASCORBIC ACID ('boxacin').

ACETYLSALICYLIC ACID plus GLYCINE ('go-damed').

ACETYLSALICYLIC ACID plus PARACETAM-OL ('safapryn'; 'safprin').
See also Acetopyrine; Acetylsalol; Aloxiprin; Be-norilate; Carbasalate calcium; Guacetisal; Talo-salate; *and under* Calcium; Chlormezanone; Dextropropoxyphene; Dipyridamole; Lysine; Magnesium.

ACETYLSALICYLSALICYLIC ACID (salsalate acetate; 'diplosal acetate').

ACETYLSALOL (acetylphenylsalicylate; phenyl acetylsalicylate; 'spiroform'; 'vesipin'; 'vesipyr-in').

Acetylsarcolysylleucine ethyl ester *see* Asaley.

Acetylsarcolysylvaline ethyl ester *see* Asaline.

N-Acetylserotonin methyl ether *see* Melatonin.

ACETYLSULFAFURAZOLE (N¹-acetyl-N¹-(3,4-dimethylisoxazol-5-yl)sulfanilamide; acetylsulf-isoxazole; 'lipogantrisin').

ACETYLSULFALENE (N¹-acetyl-N¹-(3-meth-oxypyrazin-2-yl)-sulfanilamide; acetylsulfameth-

7

oxypyrazine; RP 11589).

ACETYLSULFAMETHOXAZOLE (N^1-acetyl-N^1-(5-methylisoxazol-3-yl)sulfanilamide; acetyl-sulfisomezole).

Acetylsulfamethoxypyrazine see Acetylsulfalene.

4'-(Acetylsulfamoyl)phthalanilic acid see Phthalyl-sulfacetamide.

N^1-**Acetylsulfanilamide** see Sulfacetamide.

Acetylsulfisomezole see Acetylsulfamethoxazole.

Acetylsulfisoxazole see Acetylsulfafurazole.

3-O-Acetyltetrahydro-7α-(1-hydroxy-1-methylbutyl-6,14-endo-ethenooripavine see Acetorphine.

ACETYLTHIOCHOLINE ((2-mercaptoethyl)tri-methylammonium hydroxide acetate; thiochol-ine acetate; ACS).

7α-(Acetylthio)-4',5'-dihydrospiro[androst-4-ene-17,2'(3'H)-furan]-3-one see Spiroxasone.

3-[7α-(Acetylthio)-17β-hydroxy-3-oxoandrost-4-en-17α-yl]propionic acid γ-lactone see Spironolact-one.

3-(3-Acetylthio-7-methoxycarbonylheptyldithio)-4-[N-(4-amino-2-methylpyrimid-5-ylmethyl)form-amido]pent-3-en-1-ol see Octotiamine.

7α-Acetylthio-20-spirox-4-en-3-one see Spiroxas-one.

N-Acetyl-4-(o-tolylazo)-o-toluidine see Acetamido-azotoluene.

5-Acetyltryptamine see Acetryptine.

Acetysal see Acetylsalicylic acid.

ACEVALTRATE*** (1,7a-dihydro-1,6-dihydroxy-spiro[cyclopenta[c]pyran-7(6H),2'-oxirane]-4-methanol 4-acetate 1(or 6)-isovalerate 6(or 1)-(3-hydroxy-3-methylbutyrate) acetate).
See also Valepotriate.

ACEXAMIC ACID*** (6-acetamidohexanoic acid; acetamidocaproic acid; acetylaminocaproic acid; CY-153).
See also Prednisolone acexamate; Sodium acex-amate.

ACG see Aciclovir.

'**Achromin**' see Hydroquinone.

'**Achromycin**' see Tetracycline.

'**Aciban**' see Calcium caseinate.

ACICLOVIR*** (9-[(2-hydroxyethoxy)methyl]-guanine; 2-amino-9-[(2-hydroxyethoxy)methyl]-6H-purin-6-one; acyclovir; acycloguanosine; aciclovir sodium; ACG; Wellcome 248U; 'zovi-rax').

Acid blue CI-92 see Anazolene sodium.

Acid fuchsine see Fuchsine sulfonate.

'**Acidol**' see Betaine.

'**Acidoride**' see Glutamic acid.

'**Acidulin**' see Glutamic acid.

ACIFRAN** ((±)-4,5-dihydro-5-methyl-4-oxo-5-phenyl-2-furoic acid).

'**Acillin**' see Ampicillin.

'**Acimetion**' see Methionine.

'**Acinidazil**' see under Benzoyl peroxide.

Acinitrazole* see Aminitrozole.

Aciphenochinolinum see Cinchophen.

ACIPIMOX*** (5-methylpyrazinecarboxylic acid 4-oxide).

'**Aciquel**' see Potassium glucaldrate.

ACIVICIN*** (α-amino-3-chloro-2-isoxazoline-5-acetic acid; α-amino-5-chloro-4,5-dihydro-5-isoxazoleacetic acid; AT-125; NSC-163501; U-42126).

'**Acket**' see Salicylamide.

ACL-59 see Troclosene potassium.

ACL-60 see Troclosene sodium.

ACL-85 see Symclosene.

'**Aclan**' see under Aklomide.

ACLANTATE*** (acetoxymethyl 4-(2-chloro-m-toluidino)thiophene-3-carboxylate; N-(3-carb-oxythien-4-yl)-2-chloro-m-toluidine acetoxyme-thyl ester; 4-(2-chloro-m-toluidino)thiophene-3-carboxylic acid hydroxymethyl ester acetate; Hoe-473).

ACLARUBICIN*** ((1R,2R,4S)-2-ethyl-1,2,3,4,6,11-hexahydro-2,5,7-trihydroxy-6,11-di-oxo-4-[[2,3,6-trideoxy-4-O-[2,6-dideoxy-4-O-(tetrahydro-6-methyl-5-oxo-2N-pyran-2-yl)-α-L-lyxo-hexopyranosyl]-3-(dimethylamino)-α-L-lyxo-hexopyranosyl]oxy]-1-naphthacenecarbo-xylic acid methyl ester).

ACLATONIUM NAPADISILATE*** (choline 1,5-naphthalenedisulfonate (2:1), dilactate, di-acetate; bis[[2-(O-acetyllactyloxy)ethyl]trimeth-ylammonium] naphthalene-1,5-disulfonate; acla-tonium napadisylate; SK&F-100916J).

'**Acnegel**' see Benzoyl peroxide.

ACNU see Nimustine.

Acoantherin see Ouabain.

ACODAZOLE*** (N-methyl-4'-[(7-methyl-1H-imidazo[4,5-f]quinolin-9-yl)amino]acetanilide; acodazole hydrochloride; acodazole monohy-drochloride; NSC-305884).

'**Acodeen**' see Butamirate citrate.

'**Acoin**' see Guanicaine.

ACONIAZIDE*** (o-carboxymethoxybenzalde-hyde isonicotinoylhydrazone; o-formylphenoxy-acetic acid isonicotinoylhydrazone; isonico-phen).

ACOXATRINE*** ((±)-4-(N-acetylaminometh-yl)-1-(1,4-benzodioxan-2'-ylmethyl)-4-phenylpiperidine; (±)-N-[1-(1,4-benzodioxan-2-ylmethyl)-4-phenylpiperid-4-ylmethyl]acet-amide; acetoxatrine; R-5385).

'**Acramidine**' see Aminoacridine.

'**Acramine**' see Aminoacridine.

'**Acrex**' see Dinobuton.

Acrichine (tr) see Mepacrine.

'**Acricid**' see Binapacryl.

ACRIDAN (9,10-dihydroacridine).

ACRIDINE (10-azaanthracene; dibenzo[b,e]pyrid-ine).

ACRIDINE ORANGE (3,6-bis(dimethylamino)ac-ridine).

ACRIDINIC ACID (2,3-quinolinedicarboxylic acid).

4'-(Acridin-9-ylamino)methanesulfon-m-anisidide see Amsacrine.

4'-(Acridin-9-ylamino)-3'-methoxymethanesulfon-anilide see Amsacrine.

N-(2-Acridin-9-ylethyl)-α-methylphenethylamine see Acridorex.

ACRIDOREX* (9-[2-(α-methylphenethyl-amino)ethyl]acridine; *N*-(2-acridin-9-ylethyl)-α-methylphenethylamine; BS-7573-a).

Acriflavine* *see* Acriflavinium chloride.

ACRIFLAVINIUM CHLORIDE* (mixture of 3,6-diamino-10-methylacridinium chloride and 3,6-diaminoacridine (proflavine) as hydrochlorides; acriflavine; euflavine; xanthacridine).

'**Acriflex**' *see* Aminoacridine.

ACRIHELLIN* (3β,5,14-trihydroxy-19-oxo-5β-bufa-20,22-dienolide 3-(3-methylcrotonate)).

'**Acrinol**' *see* Ethacridine lactate.

'**Acrinolin**' *see* Ethacridine lactate.

Acriquine (tr) *see* Mepacrine.

'**Acrisan**' *see* Aminoacridine.

ACRISORCIN* (aminoacridine 4-hexylresorcinolate; Sch-7056).

'**Acrisuxin**' *see under* Ethosuximide.

ACRIVASTINE* ((*E*)-6-[(*E*)-3-pyrrolidin-1-yl-1-*p*-tolylpropenyl]-2-pyridineacrylic acid; BW-825C).

'**Acrizane**' *see* Phenacridan chloride.

ACROCINONIDE* (triamcinolone cyclic 16,17-acetal with acrolein; SD-2101-18).

'**Acrol**' *see* 2,4-Diaminophenol.

'**Acrolactine**' *see* Ethacridine lactate.

ACROLEIN (acrylyl aldehyde; propenal).

ACRONINE* (3,12-dihydro-6-methoxy-3,3,12-trimethyl-7*H*-pyrano[2,3-*c*]acridin-7-one; acronycine).

'**Acronize**' *see* Chlortetracycline.

Acronycine *see* Acronine.

Acrosoxacin* *see* Rosoxacin.

ACRYLIC ACID (propenoic acid; vinylformic acid).

Acrylic acid polymer cross-linked with allyl sucrose *see* Carbomer.

ACRYLONITRILE (cyanoethylene; propene nitrile; vinyl cyanide; 'fumigrain'; 'ventox').

ACRYLOPHENONE (phenyl vinyl ketone).

Acrylyl aldehyde *see* Acrolein.

ACS *see* Acetylthiocholine.

ACTAGARDIN* (polypeptide antibiotic from *Actinoplanes garbadinensis* or *A. liguriae*).

'**Actagen**' *see under* Pseudoephedrine.

'**Actal**' *see* Alexitol sodium.

'**Actamer**' *see* Bithionol.

'**Actamol**' *see* Mebanazine.

ACTAPLANIN* (glycopeptide antibiotic from *Actinoplanes str.*; ATCC 23342; A-4696; 'kamoran').

'**Actasal**' *see* Choline salicylate.

'**Actase**' *see* Fibrinolysin (human).

'**Actebral**' *see* Cyprodenate.

'**Actellic**' *see* Pirimiphos methyl.

'**Actemil**' *see* Etofylline nicotinate.

'**Acterol**' *see* Nimorazole.

ACTH *see* Corticotrophin.

'**Actidil**' *see* Triprolidine.

'**Actidione**' *see* Cicloheximide.

'**Actifed**' *see under* Pseudoephedrine.

'**Actilin**' *see* Framycetin.

ACTINOBOLIN (antibiotic from *Str. griseoviridus*

var. *atrofaciens*; NSC-31083).

Actinochinol* *see* Actinoquinol.

'**Actinochrysin**' *see* Cactinomycin.

Actinomycin C* *see* Cactinomycin.

Actinomycin D* *see* Dactinomycin.

Actinoplanes teichomyceticus, antibiotic *see* Teicoplanin.

ACTINOQUINOL* (8-ethoxy-5-quinolinesulfonic acid; actinochinol; actinoquinol sodium; aktinokinol; etoquinol; tequinol).

Actinospectinomycin *see* Spectinomycin.

'**Actocortin**' *see* Hydrocortisone sodium phosphate.

ACTODIGIN* (3β-(β-D-glucopyranosyloxy)-14,23-dihydroxy-24-nor-5β,14β-chol-20(22)-en-21-oic acid γ-lactone; AY-22241).

'**Actomol**' *see* Mebanazine.

'**Actosin**' *see* Warfarin.

'**Actospar**' *see* Sparteine.

'**Actozine**' *see* Phenprobamate.

'**Actrapid**' *see* Neutral insulin injection.

'**Actril**' *see* Ioxynil.

'**Actril-D**' *see under* Ioxynil.

'**Actriol**' *see* Epiestriol.

'**Acupan**' *see* Nefopam.

'**Acutran**' *see* Amfecloral.

Acycloguanosine *see* Aciclovir.

Acyclovir* *see* Aciclovir.

'**Acygoxin**' *see* β-Acetyldigoxin.

'**Acylanid**' *see* Acetyldigitoxin.

AD-106 *see* Cicrotoic acid.

AD-122 *see* Atropine octyl bromide.

'**Ada**' *see* Aluminium glycinate.

ADAFENOXATE* (2-(1-adamantylamino)ethyl *p*-chlorophenoxyacetate).

'**Adalate**' *see* Nifedipine.

'**Adalin**' *see* Carbromal.

1-Adamantanamine *see* Amantadine.

ADAMANTANE (tricyclo[3.3.1.1³,⁷]decane; diamantane).

N-**(1-Adamantanecarbonyl-3,4-dihydroxyphenethyl-amine** *see* Dopamantine.

Adamantane-1-carboxylic acid esters *see* Amantanium bromide; Bolmantalate.

ADAMANTOYLCYTARABINE (cytarabine 5'-(1-adamantanecarboxylate); AdOCA).

1-Adamantylamine *see* Amantadine.

2-(1-Adamantylamino)ethyl *p*-chlorophenoxyacetate *see* Adafenoxate.

1-Adamant-1-ylazetidine-2-carboxylic acid *see* Carmantadine.

N-**Adamant-1-yl-2-(2-dimethylaminoethoxy)acet-amide** *see* Tromantadine.

α-(1-Adamantylmethylamino)-4',6'-dibromo-*o*-acetotoluidide *see* Adamexine.

ADAMEXINE* (α-(1-adamantylmethylamino)-4',6'-dibromo-*o*-acetotoluidide; 1-[(2-acetamido-3,5-dibromobenzyl)methylamino]adamantane).

Adamon *see* Bornyl dibromodihydrocinnamate.

'**Adamon**' *see* Ciclonium bromide.

Adamsite *see* Phenarsazine chloride.

'**Adanon**' *see* Methadone.

'**Adapin**' *see* Doxepin.

'**Adaptinol**' *see* Xantofyl palmitate.
'**Adazine**' *see* Triflupromazine.
'**Adbiol**' *see* Bufetolol.
'**Adchnon**' *see* Adrenochrome guanylhydrazone.
'**Adcortyl**' *see* Triamcinolone.
ADD-3878 *see* Ciglitazone.
'**Adebit**' *see* Buformin.
'**Adecol**' *see* Acetiromate.
ADEMETIONINE** ((*S*)-5'-[(3-amino-3-carboxy-propyl)methylsulfonio]-5'-deoxyadenosine hydroxide inner salt).
'**Ademil**' *see* Flumethiazide.
'**Ademol**' *see* Hydroflumethiazide.
ADENINE (6-aminopurine; vitamin B_4).
Adenine arabinofuranoside *see* Vidarabine.
Adenine 3-deoxyriboside *see* Cordycepin.
Adenine psicofuranoside *see* Angustmycin C.
Adenine riboside *see* Adenosine.
ADENOSINE (adenine riboside).
ADENOSINE DIPHOSPHATE (ADP).
Adenosine monophosphate *see* Adenosine phosphate.
ADENOSINE PHOSPHATE (5'-adenylic acid; adenosine 5-phosphate; adenosine monophosphate; ergadenylic acid; 5-AMP; A5MP; MAP; NSC-20264).
ADENOSINE 3',5'-PHOSPHATE (adenyl cyclate; CAMP; cyclic adenylate; cyclic AMP).
ADENOSINE PHOSPHATES ('fosfostimol').
Adenosine 5'-pyrophosphate inner salt 5'-ester with 3-carbamoyl-1-β-D-ribofuranosylpyridinium hydroxide *see* Nadide.
ADENOSINE TRIPHOSPHATE (adenylpyrophosphoric acid; ATP; triphosadenine).
Adenosylcobamide *see* Cobamamide.
ADENOSYLMETHIONINE (*S*-adenosyl-L-methionine; SAM; 'samyr').
'**Adenovite**' *see* Adenosine phosphate.
Adenyl cyclate *see* Adenosine 3',5'-phosphate.
4-Aden-9-yl-2,3-dihydroxybutyric acid *see* Eritadenine.
5'-Adenylic acid *see* Adenosine phosphate.
Adenylic acid sparteine salt *see* Sparteine adenylate.
Adenylpyrophosphoric acid *see* Adenosine triphosphate.
'**Adepril**' *see* Amitriptyline.
'**Adergon**' *see* Crystal violet.
'**Aderman**' *see* Phenylmercuric borate.
Adermine *see* Pyridoxine.
'**Adermykon**' *see* Chlorphenesin.
'**Adeturon**' *see under* AET.
ADICILLIN*** (6-D-(5-amino-5-carboxyvaleramido)penicillanic acid; 4-amino-4-carboxybutylpenicillin; α-aminoadipic penicillin; cephalosporin N; penicillin N; synnematin B).
(−)-**ADICILLIN** (6-L-(5-amino-5-carboxyvaleramido)penicillanic acid; isopenicillin N).
'**Adigal**' *see* Lanatoside A.
ADIMOLOL** ((±)-1-[3-[[2-hydroxy-3-(1-naphthyloxy)propyl]amino]-3-methylbutyl]-2-benzimidazolinone; imidolol).
ADINAZOLAM*** (8-chloro-1-[(dimethylamino)methyl]-6-phenyl-4*H*-s-triazolo[4,3-*a*]-[1,4]benzodiazepine).
'**Adipan**' *see* Amphetamine.
'**Adipex**' *see* Methamphetamine.
'**Adipex-neu**' *see* Phentermine resin.
ADIPHENINE*** (2-(diethylamino)ethyl diphenylacetate; adiphenine hydrochloride; difacil; spasmolytin; NSC-129224).
ADIPIC ACID (1,4-butanedicarboxylic acid; hexanedioic acid).
Adipic acid bis(3-carboxy-2,4,6-triiodoanilide) *see* Adipiodone.
Adipic acid bis[3-carboxy-2,4,6-triiodo-5-(*N*-methylcarboxamido)anilide] *see* Iocarmic acid.
ADIPIODONE*** (adipic acid bis(3-carboxy-2,4,6-triiodoanilide); *N*,*N*'-adipoylbis(3-amino-2,4,6-triiodobenzoic acid); 3,3'-(adipoyldiimino)bis(2,4,6-triiodobenzoic acid); iodipamide; bilignost).
ADIPIODONE MEGLUMINE (adipiodone methylglucamine; methylglucamine iodipamide). *See also under* Meglumine diatrizoate.
Adipiodone methylglucamine *see* Adipiodone meglumine.
ADIPIODONE SODIUM (adipiodone disodium salt; sodium iodipamide; BE-426).
'**Adiposettin**' *see* Cathine.
Adipoylbis(aminotriiodobenzoic acid) *see* Adipiodone.
N,*N*'-**Adipoylbis(3-amino-2,4,6-triiodobenzoic acid)** *see* Adipiodone.
3,3'-(Adipoyldiimino)bis(2,4,6-triiodobenzoic acid) *see* Adipiodone.
5,5'-(Adipoyldiimino)bis(2,4,6-triiodo-*N*-methylisophthalamic acid) *see* Iocarmic acid.
'**Adiprazine**' *see* Piperazine.
ADITEREN*** (5-(4-amino-3,5-dimethoxybenzyl)-2,4-pyrimidinediamine; 2,4-diamino-5-(4-amino-3,5-dimethoxybenzyl)pyrimidine).
ADITOPRIM*** (2,4-diamino-5-[4-(dimethylamino)-3,5-dimethoxybenzyl]pyrimidine; 5-[4-(dimethylamino)-3,5-dimethoxybenzyl]pyrimidine-2,4-diamine).
'**Adiuretin**' *see* Desmopressin.
ADNAMINE (2,3,7,8-tetrahydroxy-5-methylaminomethyldibenzo[*a*,*e*]cycloheptatriene).
'**Adobiol**' *see* Bufetolol.
AdOCA *see* Adamantoylcytarabine.
'**Adoisine**' *see* Warfarin-deanol.
'**Adona**' *see* Carbazochrome sodium sulfonate.
'**Adopon**' *see* Camylofin.
ADRAFINIL*** (2-[(diphenylmethyl)sulfinyl] acetohydroxamic acid; CRL-40028).
'**Adrenalin**' *see* Epinephrine.
Adrenaline* *see* Epinephrine.
ADRENALONE** (3',4'-dihydroxy-2-(methylamino)acetophenone; adrenone).
ADRENOCHROME (3-hydroxy-1-methyl-5,6-indolinedione).
ADRENOCHROME GUANYLHYDRAZONE (adrenochrome monoguanylhydrazone).
ADRENOCHROME GUANYLHYDRAZONE MESILATE (adrenochrome guanylhydrazone methanesulfonate).

Adrenochrome semicarbazone *see* Carbazochrome.
Adrenocorticotrophin *see* Corticotrophin.
ADRENOLUTIN (5,6-dihydroxy-1-methylindoxyl; 3,5,6-trihydroxy-1-methylindole).
Adrenone* *see* Adrenalone.
'Adrenoscan' *see* Iodocholesterol ^{131}I.
'Adrenosem' *see* Carbazochrome salicylate.
'Adrenoxyl' *see* Carbazochrome.
'Adreson' *see* Cortisone.
'Adrestat' *see* Carbazochrome salicylate.
'Adrevil' *see* Butalamine.
Adriamycin *see* Doxorubicin.
'Adriblastina' *see* Doxorubicin.
'Adroyd' *see* Oxymetholone.
ADS-3 *see under* Aminophenazone.
'Adsorbon' *see* Magnesium trisilicate.
'Aducin' *see* Sodium dibunate.
'Adumbran' *see* Oxazepam.
'Adurix' *see* Clopamide.
'Adversuten' *see* Prazosin.
'Adynol' *see* Adenosine triphosphate.
'Adyston' *see under* Norfenefrine.
AE-9 *see* Feclobuzone.
AE-705-W *see* Neutramycin.
Aecachinum *see* Quinine ethyl carbonate.
'Aequamen' *see* Betahistine.
'Aerbron' *see* Proxazole.
'Aerial grammoxone' *see* Paraquat metilsulfate.
'Aerogastol' *see* Diphenylpyraline.
'Aero-ped' *see* Phenylmercuric nitrate.
'Aerosol OT' *see* Docusate sodium.
'Aerosporin' *see* Polymyxin B.
'Aerugipen' *see* Ticarcillin.
Aesculetin *see* Esculetin.
Aesculin *see* Esculin.
AESCULUS HIPPOCASTANUM (horse chestnut).
See also Escin.
AET (2-(2-aminoethyl)-2-pseudothiourea hydrobromide; *S*-(2-aminoethyl)isothiuronium bromide hydrobromide; carbamimidothioic acid 2-aminoethyl ester dihydrobromide; ethiron; ethyrone; etiron; NSC-22877).
AET plus ADENOSINE TRIPHOSPHATE ('adeturon').
Aetaphen *see* Oxedrine.
Aeth... *see* Eth...
Aetio...see Etio...
'Aethoxysklerol' *see* Polidocanol.
Aetian *see* 5β-Androstane.
'Aetoxisclerol' *see* Polidocanol.
AF-2 *see* Furylfuramide.
AF-438 *see* Oxolamine citrate.
AF-634 *see* Proxazole.
AF-864 *see* Benzydamine.
AF-983 *see* Bendazac.
AF-1161 *see* Trazodone.
AF-1980 *see* Lonidamine.
AF-2071 *see* Bendacort.
AF-2259 *see* Ibuprofen guaiacol ester.
'Afalon' *see* Linuron.
AFLOQUALONE*** (6-amino-2-(fluoromethyl)-3-*o*-tolyl-4(3*H*)-quinazolinone).

'Afonilum' *see* Theophylline.
'Afos' *see* Mecarbam.
Afoxanide *see* Rafoxanide.
'Afragil' *see under* Mobecarb.
'Afrazine' *see* Oxymetazoline.
'Afrin' *see* Oxymetazoline.
'Afugan' *see* Pyrazophos.
'Afungin' *see* Sulbentine.
AFUROLOL** (7-[3-(*tert*-butylamino)-2-hydroxypropoxy]phthalide; 1-(*tert*-butylamino)-3-(phthalid-7-yloxy)-2-propanol).
AG-3 *see* Carbocromen.
AG-58107 *see* Ioxitalamic acid.
AGANODINE** ((4,7-dichloro-2-isoindolinyl)guanidine).
AGARIC ACID (2-hydroxynonadecane-1,2,3-tricarboxylic acid; α-hexadecylcitric acid; agaricin; laricic acid).
Agarin *see* Muscimol.
'Agasten' *see* Clemastine.
'Agedal' *see* Noxiptiline.
'Agena' *see* Benzalkonium chloride.
'Agene' *see* Nitrogen trichloride.
'Ageroplas' *see* Ditazole.
'Agerpen' *see* Amoxicillin.
'Agiocur' *see* Psyllium.
'Agit' *see* Dihydroergotamine.
Agkistrodon rhodostoma venom *see* Ancrod.
'Agliral' *see* Glycyclamide.
'Agluco' *see* Carbutamide.
'Aglunat' *see* Lanatoside A.
AGMATINE (1-(4-aminobutyl)guanidine).
AGN-20 *see* Metamfazone.
AGN-197 *see* Pifenate.
AGN-511 *see* Prazitone.
AGN-616 *see* Fantridone.
AGN-1414 *see* Mitotenamine.
'Agofell' *see* Diisopromine.
'Agofollin' *see* Estradiol dipropionate.
'Agolene' *see* Menbutone.
'Agontan' *see* Diiodotyrosine.
Agr-1240 *see* Minaprine.
'Agreal' *see* Veralipride.
'Agrisil' *see* Trichloronat.
'Agroxyl' *see* 2-(4-Chloro-2-methylphenoxy)acetic acid.
AH-2 *see* Methapyrilene.
'AH3' *see* Etoloxamine.
AH-289 *see* Chlorcyclizine.
AH-853 *see* *p*-Methyldiphenhydramine.
AH-3232 *see* Clorazepate dipotassium.
AH-3365 *see* Salbutamol.
AH-3923 *see* Salmefamol.
AH-5158A *see* Labetalol.
AH-8165D *see* Fazadinium bromide.
AH-19065 *see* Ranitidine.
AH-22216 *see* Lamtidine.
AH-23844 *see* Loxtidine.
AHR-85 *see* Methocarbamol.
AHR-224 *see* Pyroxamine.
AHR-233 *see* Mephenoxalone.
AHR-438 *see* Metaxalone.
AHR-483 *see* Hexopyrronium bromide.

11

AHR-504 *see* Glycopyrronium bromide.
AHR-619 *see* Doxapram.
AHR-712 *see* Butaperazine.
AHR-857 *see* Sulfametoxydiazine.
AHR-965 *see* Fenfluramine.
AHR-1118 *see* Pridefine.
AHR-1680 *see* Fenpipalone.
AHR-2277 *see* Lenperone.
AHR-2438B *see* Polignate sodium.
AHR-3000 *see* Butaperazine.
AHR-3002 *see* Fenfluramine.
AHR-3015 *see* Cinnopentazone.
AHR-3018 *see* Azapropazone.
AHR-3053 *see* Carbocisteine.
AHR-3070-C *see* Metoclopramide.
AHR-3096 *see* Salinomycin.
AHR-3260B *see* Polycarbophil.
AHR-5850D *see* Amfenac.
AHR-6134 *see* Cloroperone.
AHR-8559 *see* Fluzinamide.
'Ahypnon' *see* Bemegride.
AI-306 *see* Broxyquinoline.
AI-307 *see under* Broxyquinoline.
AI-27303 *see* Cetamolol.
AICA *see* Orazamide.
'Aicamine' *see* Orazamide.
'Aimax' *see* Metallibure.
'Airbron' *see* Acetylcysteine.
'Airol' *see* Tretinoin.
'Ajan' *see* Nefopam.
(17*R*)-Ajmalan-17,21α-diol *see* Ajmaline.
AJMALICINE (16,17-didehydro-19α-methyl-
   oxayohimban-16-carboxylic acid methyl ester;
   raubasine; tetrahydroserpentine; δ-yohimbine;
   'hydrosarpan'; 'lamuran').
AJMALICINE plus ALMITRINE (SE-5023; 'du-
   xil').
AJMALICINE plus DIHYDROERGOCRISTINE
   (DF-69; 'defluina'; 'iskedyl').
AJMALICINE plus PIPRATECOL ('hydrosarpan
   711').
AJMALINE ((17*R*)-ajmalan-17,21α-diol; neo-
   ajmaline; pseudobrucine; rauwolfine; 'cardio-
   rhythmine'; 'gilurytmal'; 'tachmalin').
Ajmaline 17-(chloroacetate) *see* Lorajmine.
AK-123 *see* Flavoxate.
'Akaritox' *see* Tetradifon.
'Akatinol' *see* Memantine.
'Akineton' *see* Biperiden.
'Akinophyl' *see* Biperiden.
AKLOMIDE* (2-chloro-4-nitrobenzamide;
   clomide; 'novastat').
AKLOMIDE plus SULFANITRAN ('aclan'; 'no-
   vostat').
'Akne-mycin' *see under* Erythromycin.
'Akneroxid' *see* Benzoyl peroxide.
Akrichin (tr) *see* Mepacrine.
'Akrinol' *see* Acrisorcin.
'Akrinor' *see under* Cafedrine.
'Aktiferrin' *see* Iron-serine complex.
Aktinokinol *see* Actinoquinol.
AL-20 *see* Clemizole.
AL-0361 *see* Oxyfenamate.

AL-0559 *see* Fenamole.
AL-842 *see* Deterenol.
AL-1021 *see* Carperone.
ALACEPRIL** (*N*-[1-[(*S*)-3-mercapto-2-methyl-
   propionyl]-L-prolyl]-3-phenyl-L-alanine acetate
   (ester)).
ALACHLOR* (2-chloro-*N*-(2,6-diethylphenyl)-*N*-
   (methoxymethyl)acetamide; *N*-(2-chloroacetyl)-
   2,6-diethyl-*N*-(methoxymethyl)aniline; 'alo-
   chlor'; 'lasso').
'Alacortril' *see* Fluperolone.
'Aladione' *see* Diftalone.
ALAFOSFALIN* ([(1*R*)-1-[(2*S*)-2-aminopro-
   pionamido]ethyl]phosphonic acid; 1-(alanylamino)ethylphosphonic acid; alaphosphin; Ro
   3-7008).
Ala²⁶-gly²⁷-ser³¹-α¹⁻³⁹-corticotrophin *see* Seractide.
'Alamine' *see* Aluminium glycinate.
'Alanap' *see* Naptalam.
ALANINE* (2-aminopropionic acid; α-alanine).
β-ALANINE (3-aminopropionic acid).
DL-Alanine *p*-chloro-α,α-dimethylphenethyl ester
   see Alaproclate.
**1-β-Alanine-17-[L-2,6-diamino-*N*-(4-aminobutyl)-
   hexanamide]-α¹,¹⁷-corticotrophin** *see* Alsactide.
Alanine nitrogen mustard *see* Melphalan.
Alanino-2′,6′-xylidide *see* Tocainide.
ALANOSINE* ((−)-(*S*)-2-amino-3-(hydroxynitrosoamino)propionic acid; L(−)-2-amino-3-(*N*-
   nitrosohydroxylamino)propionic acid; NSC-
   143647).
Alant camphor *see* Alantolactone.
Alantidanhydride *see* Alantolactone.
Alantin *see* Inulin.
ALANTOLACTONE ((3α*R*)-3aα,5,6,7,8,8a,9,9aα-
   octahydro-5β,8aβ-dimethyl-3-methylenenaph-
   tho[2,3-*b*]furan-2(3*H*)-one; 8β-hydroxy-4α*H*-eu-
   desm-5-en-12-oic acid γ-lactone; alant camphor;
   alantidanhydride; elecamphane camphor; helenin; inula camphor; 'eupatal').
Alant starch *see* Inulin.
1-(Alanylamino)ethylphosphonic acid *see* Alafosfal-
   in.
**L-Alanylglycyl-L-cysteinyl-L-lysyl-L-asparaginyl-
   L-phenylalanyl-L-phenylalanyl-L-tryptophyl-L-
   lysyl-L-threonyl-L-phenylalanyl-L-threonyl-L-
   seryl-L-cysteine cyclic (3→14) disulfide** *see* Somatostatin.
Alanylglycylisoleucinylvalylserine *see* Peptide 67-
   82.
***N*-(β-Alanyl)histidine** *see* Carnosine.
***N*-(β-Alanyl)-1-methylhistidine** *see* Anserine.
***N*-(β-Alanyl)-2-methylhistidine** *see* Ophidine.
Alaphosphin *see* Alafosfalin.
ALAPROCLATE* (DL-alanine *p*-chloro-α,α-
   dimethylphenethyl ester).
'Alar' *see* Daminozide.
'Alaxa' *see* Bisacodyl.
ALAZANINE TRICLOFENATE* (mixture of 1
   mol. 3-ethyl-2-[3-(3-ethyl-2-benzothiazolinylid-
   ene)propenyl]benzothiazolium 2,4,5-trichloro-
   phenate and 2 mol. 2,4,5-trichlorophenol).
'Alba' *see* Monobenzone.

'Albacon' *see* Naphazoline.
'Albalon' *see* Naphazoline.
'Albamycin' *see* Novobiocin.
'Albego' *see* Camazepam.
ALBENDAZOLE*** (methyl 5-(propylthio)benz-imidazole-2-carbamate; SK&F-62979; 'valba-zan'; 'zentel').
'Albicort' *see* Triamcinolone acetonide.
'Albiotic' *see* Lincomycin.
'Albocresil' *see* Methylenedi(*m*-cresolsulfonic acid) polymer.
ALBOMYCIN (tr) (an antibiotic from *Actinomyces subtropicus*, identical with grisein).
'Albon' *see* Sulfadimethoxine.
'Albone' *see* Hydrogen peroxide.
'Albothyl' *see* Methylenedi(*m*-cresolsulfonic acid) polymer.
ALBUMIN TANNATE (albutannin; tannalbumin; 'entero-norm'; 'tannalbin').
'Albumotope' *see* Macrosälb (¹³¹I).
Albutannin *see* Albumin tannate.
Albuterol* *see* Salbutamol.
ALBUTOIN*** (5-allyl-5-isobutyl-2-thiohydanto-in; Bax-422-Z).
ALCA *see* Alcloxa.
'Alcaine' *see* Proxymetacaine.
Alcanfor *see* Camphor.
Alcapton *see* Homogentisic acid.
Alcaptonic acid *see* Homogentisic acid.
'Alchloquin' *see* Clioquinol.
ALCLOFENAC*** (2-(4-allyloxy-3-chlorophen-yl)acetic acid; W-7320; 'mervan'; 'mirvan'; 'neo-ston'; 'prinalgin').
ALCLOMETASONE*** (7α-chloro-11β,17,21-trihydroxy-16α-methylpregna-1,4-diene-3,20-di-one).
ALCLOMETASONE DIPROPIONATE* (7α-chloro-11β-hydroxy-16α-methyl-17,21-bis(1-oxopropoxy)pregna-1,4-diene-3,20-dione; Sch-22219).
ALCLOXA*** (chlorotetrahydroxy[(2-hydroxy-5-oxo-2-imidazolin-4-yl)ureato]dialuminium; aluminium chlorohydroxy allantoinate; ALCA; RC-173).
'Alcobon' *see* Flucytosine.
Alcohol *see* Ethanol.
'Alcopar' *see* Bephenium hydroxynaphthoate.
ALCURONIUM CHLORIDE*** (*N*,*N*'-dial-lylnortoxiferinium dichloride; *N*,*N*'-diallylbis-nortoxiferine dichloride; allnortoxiferin; DANT; Ro 4-3816).
ALDA *see* Aldioxa.
'Aldace' *see* Spironolactone.
'Aldactazine' *see under* Altizide.
'Aldactide' *see under* Hydroflumethiazide.
'Aldactone' *see* Spironolactone.
Aldadiene *see* Canrenoate potassium.
'Aldarsone' *see* Phenarsone sulfoxylate.
'Aldecin' *see* Beclometasone dipropionate.
'Aldefur' *see* Nifuraldezone.
'Alderlin' *see* Pronetalol.
ALDESULFONE SODIUM*** (4,4'-diaminodi-phenyl sulfone formaldehyde sulfoxylate sodium salt; sodium sulfonylbis(*p*-phenyleneimino)di-methanesulfinate; sulfoxone).
ALDICARB* (2-methyl-2-(methylthio)propanal *O*-[(methylamino)carbonyl]oxime; 2-methyl-2-(methylthio)propionaldehyde *O*-(methylcarba-moyl)oxime; 'temick'; 'temik').
'Aldinamide' *see* Pyrazinamide.
ALDIOXA*** (dihydroxy-[(2-hydroxy-5-oxo-2-imidazolin-4-yl)ureato]aluminium; aluminium dihydroxyallantoinate; ALDA; RC-172).
'Aldoclor' *see under* Methyldopa.
'Aldocorten' *see* Aldosterone.
ALDOL (acetaldol; β-hydroxybutyraldehyde).
'Aldomet' *see* Methyldopa.
'Aldomet ester' *see* Methyldopate.
'Aldometil' *see* Methyldopa.
'Aldoril' *see under* Methyldopa.
'Aldosone' *see under* Butizide.
ALDOSTERONE*** (11β,21-dihydroxy-3,20-di-oxo-4-pregnen-18-al; 11β,21-dihydroxypregn-4-ene-3,18,20-trione; 18-formyl-11β,21-dihydroxy-pregn-4-ene-3,20-dione; 18-oxocorticosterone; 'aldocorten'; 'electrocortin').
ALDRIN (1,2,3,4,10,10-hexachloro-1,4,4a,5,8,8a-hexahydro-1,4:5,8-dimethanonaphthalene *endo-exo* form; HHDN; 'octalene'; 'seedrin').
Aldrin *endo-endo* isomer *see* Isodrin.
'Aldrisone' *see* Endrisone.
'Alentin' *see* Carbutamide.
ALEPRIDE*** (2-(allyloxy)-4-amino-5-chloro-*N*-[1-(3-cyclohexen-1-ylmethyl)piperid-4-yl]benz-amide).
'Alergosan' *see* Chloropyramine.
'Alermine' *see* Chlorpheniramine.
'Alertol' *see* Pipradrol.
Aletamine* *see* Alfetamine.
'Aleudrine' *see* Isoprenaline.
'Aleukon' *see* Chlornaphazine.
'Alevaire' *see* Tyloxapol.
'Alexan' *see* Cytarabine.
ALEXIDINE*** (1,1'-hexamethylenebis[5-(2-eth-ylhexyl)biguanide]; WIN-21904; 'bisguadine').
ALEXITOL SODIUM*** (sodium polyhydroxy-aluminium monocarbonate hexitol complex; 'ac-tal').
ALFACALCIDOL** ((5*Z*,7*E*)-9,10-secocholesta-5,7,10(19)-triene-1α,3β-diol; 1α-hydroxychole-calciferol; 1α-hydroxycolecalciferol; 'one-al-pha').
'Alfaciclina' *see* Tetracycline phosphate complex.
ALFADOLONE*** (3α,21-dihydroxy-5α-pregn-ane-11,20-dione; alphadolone; GR2/1574).
ALFADOLONE ACETATE (21-acetoxy-3α-hydr-oxy-5α-pregnane-11,20-dione).
ALFADOLONE ACETATE plus ALFAXALONE (CT-1341; 'alfatesin'; 'althesin'; 'aurantex'; 'saf-fan').
'Alfadryl' *see* Moxastine.
ALFAPROSTOL*** (methyl 7-[2-(5-cyclohexyl-3-hydroxy-1-pentynyl)-3,5-dihydroxycyclopentyl]-5-heptenoate).
'Alfasol' *see* Algestone acetonide.
Alfasone *see* Algestone.

13

'Alfatesin' *see under* Alfadolone acetate.
'Alfatil' *see* Cefaclor.
ALFAXALONE*** (3α-hydroxy-5α-pregnane-11,20-dione; alphaxalone; GR2/234).
See also under Alfadolone acetate.
'Alfenamin' *see* Aluminium flufenamate.
ALFENTANIL*** (*N*-[1-[2-(4-ethyl-5-oxo-2-tetrazolin-1-yl)ethyl]-4-(methoxymethyl)piperid-4-yl]-propionanilide; alfentanil hydrochloride; R-39209; 'rapifen').
'Alferin' *see* Warfarin.
Alfetadrin* *see* Alfetamine.
ALFETAMINE** (α-allylphenethylamine; aletamine; alfetadrin; NDR-5061A).
'Alfuran' *see* Nitrofurantoin.
'Alflorone' *see* Fludrocortisone.
ALFUZOSIN*** ((±)-*N*-[3-[(4-amino-6,7-dimethoxyquinazolin-2-yl)methylamino]propyl]tetrahydro-2-furamide; alfuzosin hydrochloride; SL-77499).
'Algaphan' *see* Dextropropoxyphene.
ALGELDRATE** (aluminium hydroxide, colloidal; hydrated aluminium hydroxide; W-4600).
ALGELDRATE plus CALCIUM CARBONATE ('solugastril').
ALGELDRATE plus DIMETICONE ('paractol').
See also Glucalox; Sucralox.
'Algeril' *see* Propiram fumarate.
'Algesal suractive' *see* Myrtecaine.
ALGESTONE*** (16α,17-dihydroxypregn-4-ene-3,20-dione; 16α,17-dihydroxyprogesterone; alfasone).
ALGESTONE ACETOFENIDE** (algestone cyclic acetyl with acetophenone; algestone acetophenide; alphasone acetophenide; DPA; SQ-15010; 'deladroxone'; 'droxone'; 'neo-alfasol').
ALGESTONE ACETOFENIDE plus ESTRADIOL ENANTATE ('deladroxate').
ALGESTONE ACETONIDE* (16α,17α-isopropylidenedioxypregn-4-ene-3,20-dione; algestone cyclic acetal with acetone; alphasone acetonide; W-3395; 'alfasol').
'Algin' *see* Sodium alginate.
ALGINIC ACID (norgine; polymannuronic acid).
See also Calcium alginate; Sodium alginate.
'Alglyn' *see* Aluminium glycinate.
'Algobaz' *see* Mecobalamin.
'Algopriv' *see under* Diproqualone camsilate.
'Alhydex' *see* Glutaral.
ALIBENDOL*** (5-allyl-*N*-(2-hydroxyethyl)-3-methoxysalicylamide; H-3774).
'Alicap' *see under* Chlorbufam.
ALICONAZOLE*** ((*Z*)-1-[2,4-dichloro-β-(*p*-chlorophenyl)cinnamyl]imidazole).
'Alidase' *see* Hyaluronidase.
'Alidine' *see* Anileridine.
ALIFEDRINE** (1-cyclohexyl-3-[[(α*S*,β*R*)-β-hydroxy-α-methylphenethyl]amino]-1-propanone).
ALIFLURANE*** (2-chloro-1,2,3,3-tetrafluorocyclopropyl methyl ether; 1-chloro-1,2,3,4-tetrafluoro-3-methoxycyclopropane; P-26).
ALIMADOL*** (*N*-(3-methoxy-3,3-diphenylpropyl)allylamine).
'Alimax' *see* Metallibure.
ALIMEMAZINE*** (10-[3-(dimethylamino)-2-methylpropyl]phenothiazine; methylpromazine; trimeprazine; RP 6549).
Alimemazine *S*,*S*-dioxide *see* Oxomemazine.
'Alinam' *see* Chlormezanone.
'Alinamin' *see* Prosultiamine.
ALINIDINE*** (2-(*N*-allyl-2,6-dichloroanilino)-2-imidazoline; *N*-allylclonidine; alinidine hydrobromide; ST 567-BR).
'Alinur' *see under* Chlorbufam.
ALIPAMIDE*** (4-chloro-3-sulfamoylbenzoic acid 2,2-dimethylhydrazide; CI-546; CN-38474; D-1721).
'Alipur' *see under* Chlorbufam.
Alisactide *see* Alsactide.
Alisobumal* *see* Butalbital.
'Alival' *see* Nomifensine maleate.
'Alivin' *see* Penethamate hydriodide.
ALIZAPRIDE*** (*N*-[(1-allylpyrrolidin-2-yl)-methyl]-6-methoxy-1*H*-benzotriazole-5-carboxamide; alizapride hydrochloride; 'plitican'; 'vergentan').
ALIZARIN (1,2-dihydroxyanthraquinone).
Alizarin yellow *see* Gallacetophenone.
'Alkacitron' *see* Disodium hydrogen citrate.
'Alkalovert' *see* Phytic acid.
'Alkam' *see* Aluminium glycinate.
ALKAVERVIR* (standardized preparation of *Veratrum viride* alkaloids; 'veriloid').
'Alkeran' *see* Melphalan.
'Alkron' *see* Parathion.
Alkylbenzyldimethylammonium chloride *see* Benzalkonium chloride.
Alkyl(3,4-dichlorobenzyl)dimethylammonium chloride *see* Aralkonium chloride.
Allacyl (tr) *see* Aminometradine.
ALLANTOIN* (5-ureidohydantoin; (2,5-dioxoimidazolin-4-yl)urea; cordianin; glyoxyldiureide; 'alphosyl').
'Allardorm' *see* Butethal.
Allatsil (tr) *see* Aminometradine.
'Allegron' *see* Nortriptyline.
ALLENOIC ACID (6-hydroxy-2-naphthalenepropionic acid).
Allergan-211 *see* Idoxuridine.
'Allergisan' *see* Chlorpheniramine.
'Allergosil' *see* Ethane-1,2-disulfonic acid.
'Allergospasmin' *see under* Cromoglicate disodium.
ALLETHRIN* (3-allyl-2-methyl-4-oxo-2-cyclopenten-1-yl chrysanthemate; 2-methyl-4-oxo-3-(2-propenyl)-2-cyclopenten-1-yl 2,2-dimethyl-3-(2-methyl-1-propenyl)cyclopropanecarboxylate; allyl cinerin; pallethrine; 'presyn').
See also Bioallethrin.
ALLETORPHINE*** (*N*-allyl-7,8-dihydro-7α-(1(*R*)-hydroxy-1-methylbutyl)-*O*⁶-methyl-6,14-*endo*-ethenonormorphine; 17-allyl-17-demethyl-7α-((*R*)-1-hydroxy-1-methylbutyl)-6,14-*endo*-ethenotetrahydrooripavine; N-allylnoretorphine; R&S 218-M).
ALLICIN (allylthiosulfinic acid allyl ester).

14

ALLIDOCHLOR* (2-chloro-*N*,*N*-dipropenylacet-amide; *N*-(2-chloroacetyl)diallylamine; *N*,*N*-di-allyl-2-chloroacetamide; CDAA; 'randox').
ALLIN (*S*-allyl-L-cysteine sulfoxide).
'Allisan' *see* Dicloran.
Allisat (tr) *see* Allium sativum.
ALLITHIAMINE (*N*-[2-(allyldithio)-4-hydroxy-1-methyl-1-butenyl]-*N*-(4-amino-2-methylpyrimid-in-5-ylmethyl)formamide; thiamine allyl disulf-ide).
ALLIUM SATIVUM (allisat; garlic).
Allnortoxiferin *see* Alcuronium chloride.
ALLOBARBITAL* (5,5-diallylbarbituric acid; allobarbitone; diallylbarbital; diallymal; NSC-9324).
See also under Aminophenazone.
Allobarbitone* *see* Allobarbital.
ALLOCLAMIDE* (2-allyloxy-4-chloro-*N*-(2-di-ethylaminoethyl)benzamide; CE-264).
ALLOCUPREIDE SODIUM* (*m*-[1-(3-allyl-*S*-cupropseudothioureido)]benzoic acid sodium salt; *m*-[[(allylimino)mercaptomethyl]amino]-benzoic acid *S*-copper derivative sodium salt; sodium cuproallylthioureidobenzoate; cupradyl; cupralyl).
'Alloferine' *see* Alcuronium chloride.
Allomaleic acid *see* Fumaric acid.
'Allomaron' *see under* Allopurinol.
ALLOMETHADIONE* (3-allyl-5-methyl-2,4-oxazolidinedione; aloxidone).
Allophanamide *see* Biuret.
ALLOPHANIC ACID (carbamoylcarbamic acid).
Allopregnane *see* 5α-Pregnane.
Allopropylbarbital *see* Aprobarbital.
'Allopur' *see* Allopurinol.
ALLOPURINOL* (1*H*-pyrazolo[3,4-*d*]pyrimid-in-4-ol; 4-hydroxypyrazolopyrimidine; HPP; BW-56-158; NSC-1390).
ALLOPURINOL plus BENZBROMARONE ('al-lomaron').
Allorphine *see* Nalorphine.
ALLOXAN (2,4,5,6(1*H*,3*H*)-pyrimidinetetrone; mesoxalylurea; ENT-7169).
ALLOXANTIN (5,5′-dihydroxy-5,5′-bibarbituric acid; 5,5′-dihydroxyhydurilic acid; uroxin).
Alloxazine mononucleotide *see* Flavin mononucleo-tide.
'Alltox' *see* Campheclor.
'Allural' *see* Allopurinol.
'Allydione' *see* Allomethadione.
ALLYL ALCOHOL (2-propen-1-ol).
ALLYLAMINE (2-propenylamine).
1-Allyl-6-amino-3-ethyluracil *see* Aminometradine.
2-(Allylamino)-4-thiazolecarboxylic acid 3-(5-nitro-2-furyl)allylidene)hydrazide *see* Nifuralide.
1-(2-Allylamino-1,3-thiazol-4-yl)-6-(5-nitro-2-furyl)-1-oxo-2,3-diaza-3,5-hexadiene *see* Nifuralide.
_m_-[1-(3-Allyl-_S_-auropseudothioureido)]benzoic acid sodium salt *see* Sodium auroallylthioureidobenz-oate.
Allylbarbital* *see* Butalbital.
Allylbarbituric acid* *see* Butalbital.
5-Allyl-5-(2-bromoallyl)barbituric acid *see* Brallo-barbital.
5-Allyl-5-_sec_-butylbarbituric acid *see* Talbutal.
Allylcatechol methylene ether *see* Safrole.
_N_¹-Allyl-4-chloro-6-(3-hydroxy-2-butenylidene-amino)-1,3-benzenedisulfonamide *see* Ambuside.
Allyl cinerin *see* Allethrin.
_N_-Allylclonidine *see* Alinidine.
_m_-[1-(3-Allyl-_S_-cupropseudothioureido)]benzoic acid sodium salt *see* Allocupreide sodium.
5-Allyl-5-(2-cyclohexen-1-yl)-2-thiobarbituric acid *see* Thialbarbital.
5-Allyl-5-cyclopenten-1-ylbarbituric acid *see* Cyclo-pentobarbital.
17-Allyl-17-demethyl-7α-((_R_)-1-hydroxy-1-methyl-butyl)-6,14-_endo_-ethenotetrahydrooripavine *see* Alletorphine.
2-(_N_-Allyl-2,6-dichloroanilino)-2-imidazoline *see* Alinidine.
Allyldiethylacetamide *see* Valdetamide.
6-Allyl-6,7-dihydro-5_H_-dibenz[_c_,_e_]azepine *see* Aza-petine.
_N_-Allyl-7,8-dihydro-7α-(1(_R_)-hydroxy-1-methylbut-yl)-_O_⁶-methyl-6,14-_endo_-ethenonormorphine *see* Alletorphine.
5-Allyl-5-(2,2-dimethylpropyl)barbituric acid *see* Nealbarbital.
_N_-[2-(Allyldithio)-4-hydroxy-1-methyl-1-butenyl]-_N_-(4-amino-2-methylpyrimidin-5-ylmethyl)form-amide *see* Allithiamine.
17-Allyl-4,5α-epoxy-3,14-dihydroxymorphinan-6-one *see* Naloxone.
9a-Allyl-4,5-epoxymorphin-7-ene-3,6-diyl diacetate *see* Diacetylnalorphine.
ALLYLESTRENOL* (17α-allyl-4-estren-17β-ol; 3-desoxy-19-nortestosterone; allyloestrenol; allylestrenol tartrate).
17α-Allyl-4-estren-17β-ol *see* Allylestrenol.
5-Allyl-3-ethylbarbituric acid *see* Ethallymal.
ALLYLGLYCINE (2-amino-4-pentenoic acid).
17α-Allyl-17-hydroxyestra-4,9,11-trien-3-one *see* Altrenogest.
5-Allyl-_N_-(2-hydroxyethyl)-3-methoxysalicylamide *see* Alibendol.
1-Allyl-2-[2-hydroxy-3-(isopropylamino)propoxy]-benzene *see* Alprenolol.
_N_-Allyl-3-hydroxymorphinan *see* Levallorphan.
_N_-Allyl-14-hydroxynordihydromorphinone *see* Nal-oxone.
5-Allyl-5-(2-hydroxypropyl)barbituric acid *see* Pro-xibarbal.
_m_-[[(Allylimino)mercaptomethyl]amino]benzoic acid _S_-copper derivative sodium salt *see* Allocupreide sodium.
_m_-[[(Allylimino)mercaptomethyl]amino]benzoic acid _S_-gold derivative sodium salt *see* Sodium auro-allylthioureidobenzoate.
5-Allyl-5-isoamyl-2-thiobarbituric acid *see* Thiamyl-al.
5-Allyl-5-isobutylbarbituric acid *see* Butalbital.
5-Allyl-5-isobutyl-2-thiobarbituric acid *see* Buthali-tal sodium.
5-Allyl-5-isobutyl-2-thiohydantoin *see* Albutoin.
Allylisopropylacetylurea *see* Apronal.

5-Allyl-5-isopropylbarbituric acid *see* Aprobarbital.
5-Allyl-5-isopropyl-1-methylbarbituric acid *see* En-allylpropymal.
ALLYL ISOTHIOCYANATE (mustard oil).
·Allylmercaptomethylpenicillin *see* Almecillin.
1-Allyl-3-methoxy-4,5-methylenedioxybenzene *see* Myristicin.
4-Allyl-2-methoxyphenol *see* Eugenol.
2-(4-Allyl-2-methoxyphenoxy)-*N*,*N*-diethylacet-amide *see* Estil.
5-Allyl-5-(1-methylbutyl)barbituric acid *see* Seco-barbital.
5-Allyl-5-(1-methylbutyl)-2-thiobarbituric acid *see* Thiamylal.
4-Allyl-1,4-methylenedioxybenzene *see* Safrole.
5-Allyl-1-methyl-5-(1-methyl-2-pentynyl)barbituric acid *see* Methohexital.
3-Allyl-5-methyl-2,4-oxazolidinedione *see* Allo-methadione.
3-Allyl-2-methyl-4-oxo-2-cyclopenten-2-yl chrysan-themate *see* Allethrin; Bioallethrin.
3-Allyl-1-methyl-4-phenyl-4-propionoxypiperidine *see* Allylprodine.
5-Allyl-5-(2-methylpropyl)barbituric acid *see* But-albital.
5-Allyl-5-(1-methylpropyl)barbituric acid *see* Tal-butal.
5-Allyl-5-(2-methylpropyl)-2-thiobarbituric acid *see* Buthalital sodium.
5-Allyl-5-neopentylbarbituric acid *see* Nealbarbital.
N-Allylnoratropine *see* Naltropine.
N-Allylnoretorphine *see* Alletorphine.
N-Allylnormorphine *see* Nalorphine.
N-Allylnoroxymorphone *see* Naloxone.
Allyloestrenol* *see* Allylestrenol.
2-(Allyloxyamino)-7-chloro-5-(*o*-chlorophenyl)-3*H*-1,4-benzodiazepine *see* Uldazepam.
2-(Allyloxy)-4-amino-5-chloro-*N*-[1-(3-cyclohexen-1-ylmethyl)piperid-4-yl]benzamide *see* Alepride.
2-Allyloxy-4-chloro-*N*-(2-diethylaminoethyl)benz-amide *see* Alloclamide.
2-(4-Allyloxy-3-chlorophenyl)acetic acid *see* Alclo-fenac.
1-(β-(Allyloxy)-2,4-dichlorophenethyl)imidazole *see* Enilconazole.
2-Allyloxy-*N*-(2-diethylaminoethyl)-4-trifluoro-methylbenzamide *see* Flualamide.
2-Allyloxy-*N*-(2-diethylaminoethyl)-α,α,α-trifluoro-*p*-toluamide *see* Flualamide.
1-(*o*-Allyloxyphenoxy)-3-isopropylaminopropan-2-ol *see* Oxprenolol.
2-ALLYL-4-PENTENOIC ACID (diallylacetic acid).
See also Bismuth 2-allyl-4-pentenoate.
α-Allylphenethylamine *see* Alfetamine.
1-(*o*-Allylphenoxy)-3-(isopropylamino)propan-2-ol *see* Alprenolol.
5-ALLYL-5-PHENYLBARBITURIC ACID ('al-phasem'; 'alpheba'; 'alphenal'; 'alphenate'; 'lub-ergal'; 'phenyral'; 'prophenal').
2-ALLYL-2-PHENYL-4-PENTENOIC ACID (2-phenyl-2-prop-2-enyl-4-pentenoic acid; phenyl-diallylacetic acid).

2-(4-Allylpiperazin-1-yl)-4-amino-6,7-dimethoxyqui-nazoline *see* Quinazosin.
ALLYLPRODINE* (3-allyl-1-methyl-4-phenyl-4-propionoxypiperidine; Ro 2-7113).
Allylpyrocatechol methylene ether *see* Safrole.
N-[(1-Allylpyrrolidin-2-yl)methyl]-4-amino-5-(meth-ylsulfamoyl)-*o*-anisamide *see* Alpiropride.
N-[(1-Allylpyrrolidin-2-yl)methyl]-2,3-dimethoxy-5-sulfamoylbenzamide *see* Veralipride.
N-[(1-Allylpyrrolidin-2-yl)methyl]-6-methoxy-1*H*-benzotriazole-5-carboxamide *see* Alizapride.
N-[(1-Allylpyrrolidin-2-yl)methyl]-5-sulfamoyl-*o*-veratramide *see* Veralipride.
2-Allylsulfamoyl-5-chloro-4-sulfamoyl-*N*-(3-hydr-oxy-2-butenylidene)aniline *see* Ambuside.
12-Allyl-7,7a,8,9-tetrahydro-3,7a-dihydroxy-[4a*H*][8,9-*c*]iminoethanophenanthro[4,5-*bcd*]fu-ran-5(6*H*)-one *see* Naloxone.
3-(Allyltetrahydro-5-methyl-2-oxo-3-furoyl)urea *see* Valofane.
6-[2-(Allylthio)acetamido]penicillanic acid *see* Al-mecillin.
3-[(Allylthio)methyl]-6-chloro-3,4-dihydro-2*H*-1,2,4-benzothiadiazine-7-sulfonamide 1,1-dioxide *see* Altizide.
3-[(Allylthio)methyl]-6-chloro-3,4-dihydro-2-methyl-2*H*-1,2,4-benzothiadiazine-7-sulfonamide 1,1-di-oxide *see* Methalthiazide.
Allylthiomethylpenicillin *see* Almecillin.
Allylthiosulfinic acid allyl ester *see* Allicin.
ALLYLTHIOUREA** (1-allyl-2-thiourea; rho-dallin; thiosinamine; tiosinamine).
1-Allyl-2-thiourea *see* Allylthiourea.
α-Allyl-3,4,5-trimethoxy-*N*-methylphenethylamine *see* Trimoxamine.
Allypropymal* *see* Aprobarbital.
ALMADRATE SULFATE** (aluminium magne-sium hydroxide oxide sulfate hydrate; dimagne-sium tetraaluminium hydroxide oxide sulfate hydrate; W-4425).
ALMAGATE* (aluminium magnesium carbon-ate hydroxide $(Al_2Mg_6(CO_3)_2(OH)_{14})$ tetrahydr-ate).
ALMASILATE* (magnesium aluminosilicate $(MgAl_2Si_2O_8)$ hydrate).
See also Simaldrate.
ALMECILLIN** (6-[2-(allylthio)acetamido]peni-cillanic acid; allylmercaptomethylpenicillin; al-lylthiomethylpenicillin; penicillin O).
'Almederm' *see* Hexachlorophene.
ALMESTRONE* (3-hydroxy-17α-methylestra-1,3,5(10)-trien-17-one).
'Alminate' *see* Aluminium glycinate.
ALMINOPROFEN* (*p*-[(2-methylallyl)amino]-hydratropic acid; 2-[*p*-[(2-methylallyl)amino]-phenyl]propionic acid).
ALMITRINE* (2,4-bis(allylamino)-6-[4-[bis(*p*-fluorophenyl)methyl]piperazin-1-yl]-*s*-triazine; 'vectarion').
See also under Ajmalicine.
ALMITRINE DIMESILATE (almitrine di(meth-anesulfonate); S-2620; SE-2620).
'Almocarpine' *see* Pilocarpine.

'**Almora**' *see* Magnesium gluconate.
ALMOXATONE* ((+)-(*R*)-3-[*p*-[(*m*-chlorobenz-yl)oxy]phenyl]-5-[(methylamino)methyl]-2-ox-azolidinone).
'**Alnovin**' *see* Fendosal.
ALO-1401-02 *see* Betaxolol.
'**Alochlor**' *see* Alachlor.
'**Alodan**' *see* Chlorbicyclen *and* Pethidine.
ALOE-EMODIN (1,8-dihydroxy-3-(hydroxymeth-yl)anthraquinone; 3-(hydroxymethyl)chrysazin; rhabarberone).
'**Alofen**' *see* Promazine.
ALOGLUTAMOL (tris(hydroxymethyl)amino-methane gluconate aluminate; trometamol glu-conate aluminate; 'tasto').
ALONIMID* (2,3-dihydrospiro[naphthalene-1(4*H*),3'-piperidine]-2',4,6'-trione).
'**Alotec**' *see* Orciprenaline.
Aloxidone* *see* Allomethadione.
ALOXIPRIN* (polymeric condensation product of aluminium oxide and acetylsalicylic acid).
'**Aloxyn**' *see* 8-Quinolinol sulfate aluminium.
ALOZAFONE* (4'-chloro-2-[(2-cyano-1-meth-ylethyl)methylamino]-2-(*o*-fluorobenzoyl)-*N*-methylacetanilide; 5-chloro-2-[[[[(2-cyano-1-methylethyl)methylamino]methyl]carbonyl]-methylamino]-2'-fluorobenzophenone).
'**Alpen**' *see* Ampicillin.
ALPERTINE* (1-[2-[2-(ethoxycarbonyl)-5,6-di-methoxyindol-3-yl]ethyl]-4-phenylpiperazine; ethyl 5,6-dimethoxy-3-[2-(4-phenylpiperazin-1-yl)ethyl]indole 2-carboxylate; WIN-31665).
Alpha amylase* *see* α-Amylase.
ALPHACETYLMETHADOL* (α-3-acetoxy-6-dimethylamino-4,4-diphenylheptane).
See also Acetylmethadol.
'**Alphacortisone**' *see* Hydrocortisone.
'**Alphaderm**' *see* Hydrocortisone.
Alphadolone* *see* Alfadolone.
'**Alphadryl**' *see* Moxastine.
Alphahypophamine *see* Oxytocin.
ALPHAMEPRODINE* (α-3-ethyl-1-methyl-4-phenyl-4-propionoxypiperidine).
ALPHAMETHADOL* (α-6-dimethylamino-4,4-diphenyl-3-heptanol).
See also Dimepheptanol.
Alpha methyl dopa *see* Methyldopa.
'**Alphamine**' *see* Midodrine.
'**Alphamucase**' *see under* Chymotrypsin.
ALPHAPRODINE* (α-1,3-dimethyl-4-phenyl-4-propionoxypiperidine; anadol; Nu-1196).
'**Alpharesidol**' *see* Hydroxocobalamin.
'**Alphasem**' *see* 5-Allyl-5-phenylbarbituric acid.
'**Alphasol MA**' *see* Sodium dihexyl sulfosuccinate.
'**Alphasol OT**' *see* Docusate sodium.
Alphasone acetonide* *see* Algestone acetonide.
Alphasone acetophenide* *see* Algestone acetofen-ide.
'**Alphatron**' *see* Radon.
Alphaxalone* *see* Alfaxalone.
'**Alphazurine 2G**' *see* Patent blue.
'**Alpheba**' *see* 5-Allyl-5-phenylbarbituric acid.
'**Alphenal**' *see* 5-Allyl-5-phenylbarbituric acid.

'**Alphenate**' *see* 5-Allyl-5-phenylbarbituric acid.
'**Alphintren**' *see* Chymotrypsin.
Alphol *see* 1-Naphthyl salicylate.
'**Alphosyl**' *see* Allantoin.
ALPIROPRIDE* ((±)-*N*-[(1-allylpyrrolidin-2-yl)methyl]-4-amino-5-(methylsulfamoyl)-*o*-anis-amide).
ALPRAZOLAM* (8-chloro-1-methyl-6-phenyl-4*H*-*s*-triazolo[4,3-*a*][1,4]benzodiazepine; U-31889; 'xanax').
ALPRENOLOL* (1-(*o*-allylphenoxy)-3-(isopropylamino)propan-2-ol; 1-allyl-2-[2-hydr-oxy-3-(isopropylamino)propoxy]benzene; alpre-nolol hydrochloride; H-56/28).
ALPROSTADIL* ((11α,13*E*,15*S*)-11,15-dihydr-oxy-9-oxoprost-13-en-1-oic acid; (1*R*,2*R*,3*R*)-3-hydroxy-2[(*E*)-(3*S*)-3-hydroxy-1-octenyl]-5-oxo-cyclopentaneheptanoic acid; PGE₁; prostagland-in E₁; U-10136; 'prostin VR').
ALRESTATIN* (1,3-dioxo-1*H*-benz[*de*]isoqui-noline-2(3*H*)-acetic acid; sodium 1,3-dioxo-1*H*-benz[*de*]isoquinoline-2(3*H*)-acetate; alrestatin sodium; AY-22284A).
'**Alrheumat**' *see* Ketoprofen.
'**Alrheumun**' *see* Ketoprofen.
ALSACTIDE* (1-β-alanine-17-[L-2,6-diamino-*N*-(4-aminobutyl)hexanamide]-α¹,¹⁷-cortico-trophin; alisactide).
'**Alsadorm**' *see* Doxylamine.
ALSEROXYLON* (fractionally purified extract of *Rauwolfia serpentina*; 'abten'; 'koglucoid'; 'rautensin'; 'rauwiloid').
'**Altacite**' *see* Hydrotalcite.
'**Altafur**' *see* Furaltadone.
'**Altan**' *see* Dantron.
ALTANSERIN* (3-[2-[4-(*p*-fluorobenzoyl)pip-erid-1-yl]ethyl]-2-thio-2,4(1*H*,3*H*)-quinazolinedi-one).
'**Altest**' *see* Sulfosalicylic acid.
'**Althesin**' *see under* Alfadolone acetate.
Althiazide* *see* Altizide.
'**Althose**' *see* Methadone.
'**Altilev**' *see* Nortriptyline.
'**Altimol**' *see* Nitrefazole.
'**Altinil**' *see* Tiazesim.
ALTIZIDE* (3-[(allylthio)methyl]-6-chloro-3,4-dihydro-2*H*-1,2,4-benzothiadiazine-7-sulfon-amide 1,1-dioxide; althiazide; P-1779).
ALTIZIDE plus SPIRONOLACTONE ('aldactaz-ine').
'**Altodel**' *see* Kinoprene.
'**Altodor**' *see* Etamsylate.
'**Altorick**' *see* Triprene.
'**Altosid**' *see* Methoprene.
ALTRENOGEST* (17α-allyl-17-hydroxyestra-4,9,11-trien-3-one; 17α-hydroxy-19,21,24-trinor-chola-4,9,11,22-tetraen-3-one; A-41300; A-35957).
ALTRETAMINE* (hexamethylmelamine; 2,4,6-tris(dimethylamino)-*s*-triazine; NSC-13875; 'hexastat').
'**Alubasine**' *see* Aluminium glycinate.
'**Aludrine**' *see* Isoprenaline.

Alufibrate see Aluminium clofibrate.
'Alugan' see Bromociclen.
'Aluglycin' see Aluminium glycinate.
Aluminium aceglutamide see Aceglutamide aluminium.
Aluminium aminoacetate see Aluminium glycinate.
Aluminium chlorohydroxy allantoinate see Alcloxa.
ALUMINIUM CLOFIBRATE** (bis[2-(*p*-chlorophenoxy)-2-methylpropionato]hydroxyaluminium; alufibrate).
ALUMINIUM CLOFIBRATE plus NICOTINIC ACID ('vasoatherolip').
Aluminium dextran sulfate complex see Detralfate.
Aluminium dihydroxyallantoinate see Aldioxa.
ALUMINIUM FLUFENAMATE (aluminium (α,α,α-trifluoro-*m*-tolyl)anthranilate; 'alfenamin').
ALUMINIUM GLYCINATE (basic aluminium aminoacetate; dihydroxy aluminium aminoacetate; aluminium aminoacetate).
Aluminium hydroxide, colloidal see Algeldrate.
Aluminium magnesium carbonate hydroxide tetrahydrate see Almagate.
Aluminium magnesium hydroxide carbonate hydrate see Hydrotalcite.
Aluminium magnesium hydroxide oxide sulfate hydrate see Almadrate sulfate.
Aluminium magnesium hydroxide sulfate hydrate see Magaldrate.
Aluminium magnesium silicate see Attapulgite.
Aluminium sucrose hydrogen sulfate basic salt see Sucralfate.
Aluminium (α,α,α-trifluoro-*m*-tolyl)anthranilate see Aluminium flufenamate.
'Alupent' see Orciprenaline.
'Alurene' see Chlorothiazide.
ALUSULF*** (heptaaluminium heptadecahydroxide bis(sulfate)).
ALVERINE** (*N*-ethyl-3,3'-diphenyldipropylamine; *N,N*-bis(3-phenylpropyl)ethylamine; phenpropamine; alverine citrate; alverine tartrate; dipropyline; gamatran).
'Alvinine' see Xenysalate.
'Alvit-55' see Dieldrin.
'Alvodine' see Piminodine.
'Alvonal' see Strophanthin.
'Alvora' see Naled.
'Alvothane' see Hexachloroethane.
'Alvyl' see Polyvinyl alcohol.
'Alzinox' see Aluminium glycinate.
AM-109 see Methitural.
AM-684-beta see Relomycin.
AM-715 see Norfloxacin.
'Amabevan' see Carbarsone.
'Amadil' see Paracetamol.
AMADINONE*** (6-chloro-17-hydroxy-19-norpregna-4,6-diene-3,20-dione).
AMADINONE ACETATE* (RS-2208).
AMAFOLONE*** (3α-amino-2β-hydroxy-5α-androstan-17-one; Org-6001).
'Amandacide' see Calcium mandelate.
AMANOZINE*** (2-amino-4-anilino-*s*-triazine; *N*-phenylformoguanamine; amanozine hydro-

chloride; W-1191-2).
AMANTADINE** (1-adamantanamine; 1-adamantylamine; 1-aminoadamantane; EXP-105-1; NSC-83653).
'Amantan' see Amantadine.
AMANTANIUM BROMIDE*** (decyl(2-hydroxyethyl)dimethylammonium bromide 1-adamantanecarboxylate).
AMANTOCILLIN*** (6-(3-amino-1-adamantanecarboxamido)penicillanic acid; 3-aminoadamantyl-1-penicillin).
AMARANTH* (chiefly the tri-Na salt of 2-hydroxy-1-(4-sulfonaphth-1-ylazo)naphthalene-3,6-disulfonic acid; Bordeaux *S*).
AMARINE (2,4,5-triphenyl-2-imidazoline).
'Ambacamp' see Bacampicillin.
'Ambathizon' see Thioacetazone.
'Ambaxin' see Bacampicillin.
AMBAZONE*** (*p*-benzoquinone guanylhydrazone thiosemicarbazone; 'iversal').
Ambegon* see Ambenonium chloride.
AMBENONIUM CHLORIDE*** (*N,N'*-bis(2-diethylaminoethyl)oxamide bis(2-chlorobenzyl chloride); [oxalylbis(iminoethylene)]bis[(*o*-chlorobenzyl)diethylammonium chloride]; ambegon; ambestigmin; WIN-8077).
AMBENOXAN*** (*N*-[2-(2-methoxyethoxy)-ethyl]-1,4-benzodioxan-2-methylamine; 2-[[2-(2-methoxyethoxy)ethyl]aminomethyl]-1,4-benzodioxan).
Amber acid see Succinic acid.
'Amberlite IRP-88' see Polacrilin.
Ambestigmin* see Ambenonium chloride.
AMBICROMIL** (4,6-dioxo-10-propyl-4*H*,6*H*-benzo[1,2-*b*:5,4-*b'*]dipyran-2,8-dicarboxylic acid; probicromil).
'Ambilhar' see Niridazole.
'Amblosin' see Ampicillin.
'Ambocillin' see under Dihydrostreptomycin.
'Amboclorin' see Chlorambucil.
'Ambodryl' see Bromazine.
AMBOMYCIN** (antibiotic from *Str. ambofaciens*; duazomycin C; NSC-10270; NSC-53397).
'Ambramycin' see Tetracycline.
'Ambravein' see Pipacycline.
AMBROXOL*** (*trans*-[(2-amino-3,5-dibromobenzyl)amino]cyclohexanol; 3,5-dibromo-*N*^α-(*trans*-4-hydroxycyclohexyl)toluene-α,2-diamine; NA-872; 'fluibron'; 'mucosolvan').
AMBRUTICIN*** (6-[2-[2-[5-(6-ethyl-3,6-dihydro-5-methyl-2*H*-pyran-2-yl)-3-methyl-1,4-hexadienyl]-3-methylcyclopropyl]vinyl]tetrahydro-4,5-dihydroxy-2*H*-pyran-2-acetic acid; SMP-78 acid S; W-7783).
AMBUCAINE*** (2-(diethylamino)ethyl 4-amino-2-butoxybenzoate; ambutoxate; WIN-3706; 'sympocaine').
AMBUCETAMIDE*** (2-dibutylamino-4'-methoxyacetanilide; dibutamide; A-16).
Ambuphylline* see Bufylline.
'Ambush' see Permethrin.
AMBUSIDE*** (*N*^1-allyl-4-chloro-6-(3-hydroxy-2-butenylideneamino)-1,3-benzenedisulfon-

18

amide; 2-allylsulfamoyl-5-chloro-4-sulfamoyl-*N*-(3-hydroxy-2-butenylidene)aniline; EX-4810).

AMBUTONIUM BROMIDE* ((3-carbamoyl-3,3-diphenylpropyl)ethyldimethylammonium bromide; ethyl(3-hydroxy-3,3-diphenylpropyl)dimethylammonium bromide carbamate; R-100).

Ambutoxate *see* Ambucaine.

Ambutyrosin *see* Butirosin.

'Ambylan' *see* Apramycin.

AMCA *see* Tranexamic acid.

AMCHA *see* Tranexamic acid.

'Amchafibrin' *see* Tranexamic acid.

'Amcill' *see* Ampicillin.

AMCINAFAL* (triamcinolone cyclic 16,17-acetal with 3-pentanone; SQ-15102).

AMCINAFIDE* (triamcinolone cyclic 16,17-acetal with acetophenone; SQ-15112).

AMCINONIDE* ((11β,16α)-21-acetoxy-16,17-[cyclopentylidenebis(oxy)]-9-fluoro-11-hydroxy-pregna-1,4-diene-3,20-dione; triamcinolone cyclic 16,17-acetal with cyclopentanone, 21-acetate; CL-34699; 'penticort').

'Amdelate' *see* Ammonium mandelate.

Amdinocillin *see* Mecillinam.

'Amebacilin' *see* Fumagillin.

'Amebacillin' *see* Fumagillin.

'Amebarsin' *see* Difetarsone.

'Amebil' *see* Clioquinol.

'Amecytine' *see* Mitomycin.

AMEDALIN* (3-methyl-3-[3-(methylamino)propyl]-1-phenyl-2-indolinone; amedalin hydrochloride; UK-3540).

'Amenyl' *see under* Chlormadinone acetate.

'Americaine' *see* Benzocaine.

'Amerscan' *see* Medronate disodium.

'Amertan' *see* Thiomersal tannate.

AMETANTRONE* (1,4-bis[[2-[(2-hydroxyethyl)amino]ethyl]amino]anthraquinone).

AMETANTRONE DIACETATE (HAQ; NSC-287513).

Ametazole* *see* Betazole.

Amethocaine* *see* Tetracaine.

'Amethone' *see* Amolanone.

'Amethopterin' *see* Methotrexate.

'Ametox' *see* Sodium thiosulfate.

'Ametrint' *see* Ametryn.

AMETRYN* (*N*-ethyl-*N'*-(1-methylethyl)-6-(methylthio)-1,3,5-triazine-2,4-diamine; 2-(ethylamino)-4-isopropylamino-6-(methylthio)-*s*-triazine; G-34162; 'ametrint'; 'gesapax').

'Ametycin' *see* Mitomycin.

AMEZEPINE* (5-methyl-10-[2-(methylamino)ethyl]-5*H*-dibenz[*b,f*]azepine).

AMEZINIUM METILSULFATE* (4-amino-6-methoxy-1-phenylpyridazinium methyl sulfate; LU-1631; 'regulton').

AMFEBUTAMONE* ((±)-2-*tert*-butylamino-3'-chloropropiophenone; (±)-1-(*m*-chlorophenyl)-2-[(1,1-dimethylethyl)amino]-1-propanone; bupropin; bupropion; bupropion hydrochloride; BW-323; 'wellbutrin').

AMFECLORAL* (α-methyl-*N*-(2,2,2-trichloroethylidene)phenethylamine; 1-phenyl-2-(2,2,2-trichloroethylidene-amino)propane; amphechloral).

AMFENAC* ((2-amino-3-benzoylphenyl)acetic acid; amfenac sodium; AHR-5850D).

AMFEPENTOREX* (*N*,α-dimethyl-*p*-pentyl-phenethylamine; *p*-pentylmethamphetamine; CB-2201).

AMFEPRAMONE* (1-benzoyltriethylamine; 2-(diethylamino)propiophenone; diethylpropion; diethylopropion hydrochloride; T-712).

AMFETAMINIL* (*N*-(α-cyanobenzyl)amphetamine; 2-[(1-methyl-2-phenylethyl)amino]-2-phenylacetonitrile; 2-(α-methylphenethylamino)-2-phenylacetonitrile; 2-phenyl-2-(phenylisopropylamino)acetonitrile; amphetaminil; AN-1; 'apo-neuron').

Amfetyline *see* Fenetylline.

'Amfipen' *see* Ampicillin.

AMFLUTIZOLE* (4-amino-3-(α,α,α-trifluoro-*m*-tolyl)-5-isothiazolecarboxylic acid).

'Amfodyne' *see* Imidecyl iodine.

AMFOMYCIN* (antibiotic from *Str. canus*; amphomycin; 'ecomytrin').

AMFONELIC ACID* (7-benzyl-1-ethyl-1,4-di-hydro-4-oxo-1,8-naphthyridine-3-carboxylic acid; NSC-100638; WIN-25978).

'Amiben' *see* Chloramben.

'Amicar' *see* Aminocaproic acid.

AMICARBALIDE* (1,3-bis(*m*-amidinophenyl)-urea; 3,3'-diamidinocarbanilide; amicarbalide di(ethanol-2-sulfonate); amicarbalide diisethionate; amicarbalide isetionate; M & B-5062A).

AMICIBONE* (1-(2-hexahydroazepin-1-yl-ethyl)-2-oxocyclohexanecarboxylic acid benzyl ester).

AMICLORAL* (6-*O*-(2,2,2-trichloro-1-hydroxy-ethyl)-α,D-glucopyranose 1→4 polymer with α-D-glucopyranose; SK&F-39186).

AMICYCLINE* (9-amino-4-dimethylamino-1,4,4a,5,5a,6,11,12a-octahydroxy-3,10,12,12a-tetrahydroxy-1,11-dioxonaphthacene-2-carbox-amide).

AMIDANTEL* (4'-[[1-(dimethylamino)ethylid-ene]amino]-2-methoxyacetanilide; amidantel hydrochloride; BAY d-8815).

AMIDAPSONE* (*p*-amino-*p'*-ureidodiphenyl-sulfone; (*p*-sulfanilylphenyl)urea; carbamoyl-dapsone; NSC-28120).

'Amidazophen' *see* Aminophenazone.

Amidazotoluene *see* Aminoazotoluene.

AMIDEFRINE MESILATE* (3'-(1-hydroxy-2-methylaminoethyl)methanesulfonanilide meth-anesulfonate; amidephrine mesylate; MJ-5190).

Amidephrine mesylate* *see* Amidefrine mesilate.

Amide PP *see* Nicotinamide.

***N*-(4-(Amidinoamidino)piperazin-1-yl-methyl)tetra-cycline** *see* Guamecycline.

9-(*p*-Amidinobenzylidene)fluorene *see* Renytoline.

1-Amidino-3-(3-chloro-4-cyanophenyl)urea *see* Cloguanamil.

***N*-Amidino-3,5-diamino-6-chloropyrazinamide** *see* Amiloride.

***N*-Amidino-2-(2,6-dichlorophenyl)acetamide** *see*

19

Guanfacine.

N''-(2-Amidinoethyl)-4-formamido-1,1',1''-trimethyl-*N*,4':*N*',4''-ter(pyrrole-2-carboxamide) *see* Stallimycin.

N-Amidinoglycine *see* Glycocyamine.

1-Amidino-3-(*p*-nitrophenyl)urea *see* Nitroguanil.

*N*⁵-Amidinoornithine *see* Arginine.

Amidinopenicillin HX *see* Mecillinam.

3-[3-(*m*-Amidinophenyl)-2-triazeno]-3-amino-5-ethyl-6-phenylphenanthridinium chloride *see* Isometamidium chloride.

*N*¹-Amidinosulfanilamide *see* Sulfaguanidine.

2-Amidino-1,2,3,4-tetrahydroisoquinoline *see* Debrisoquine.

AMIDITHION* (*S*-[2-[(2-methoxyethyl)amino]-1-oxoethyl] *O*,*O*-dimethyl phosphorodithioate; 'thiocron').

Amidoazotoluene diacetate *see* Diacetazotol.

Amidofebrin *see* Aminophenazone.

Amidofen (tr) *see* Aminophenazone.

'Amidofos' *see* Dimethoate.

'Amidol' *see* 2,4-Diaminophenol.

Amidoline *see* Etomidoline.

'Amidonal' *see* Aprindine.

Amidone* *see* Methadone.

Amidophen (tr) *see* Aminophenazone.

Amidopyrazoline *see* Aminophenazone.

Amidopyrine *see* Aminophenazone.

Amidotrizoate *see* Sodium diatrizoate.

Amidotrizoic acid *see* Diatrizoic acid.

'Amidozol' *see* Sulfasomizole.

Amidozone *see* Aminophenazone.

AMIFLAMINE** ((+)-4-(diethylamino)-α,2-dimethylphenethylamine).

AMIFLOVERINE*** (2-(3,5-diethoxyphenoxy)-triethylamine; 5-[2-(diethylamino)ethoxy]-1,3-diethoxybenzene).

AMIFLOXACIN** (6-fluoro-1,4-dihydro-1-(methylamino)-7-(4-methylpiperazin-1-yl)-4-oxo-3-quinolinecarboxylic acid).

AMIFOSTINE*** (2-[(3-aminopropyl)amino]ethanethiol dihydrogen phosphate (ester); *S*-[2-[(3-aminopropyl)amino]ethyl] dihydrogen phosphorothioate monohydrate; ethiophos; gammaphos; APAETF; NSC-296961; WR-2721).

AMIKACIN** (*O*-3-amino-3-deoxy-α-D-glucopyranosyl-(1→4)-*O*-[6-amino-6-deoxy-α-D-glucopyranosyl-(1→6)]-*N*³-(4-amino-L-2-hydroxybutyryl)-2-deoxy-L-streptamine; BBK-8; 'amikin'; 'amukin'; 'biklin'; 'briclin').

'Amikapron' *see* Tranexamic acid.

AMIKHELLINE*** (8-(2-diethylaminoethoxy)-5-hydroxy-2-methylfurano-6,7-chromone; 9-[2-(diethylamino)ethoxy]-4-hydroxy-7-methyl-5*H*-furo[3,2-*g*][1]benzopyran-5-one; F-19; 'nokhel').

'Amikin' *see* Amikacin.

AMILOMER** (starch epichlorohydrin reaction product).

AMILORIDE*** (*N*-amidino-3,5-diamino-6-chloropyrazinamide; desmethylpipazuroylguanidine; 2,6-diamino-3-carboguanidino-5-chloropyrazine; (3,5-diamino-6-chloropyrazinoyl)guanidine; amipramidine; amipramizide; guanam-

prazine; DCP; MK-870).

AMILORIDE plus HYDROCHLOROTHIAZIDE ('moduretic').

'Amilyt' *see* Benzoquinonium chloride.

Amimethyline *see* Protriptyline.

'Amimycin' *see* Oleandomycin.

Aminacrin *see* Aminoacriquine.

Aminacrine* *see* Aminoacridine.

Aminarsone *see* Carbarsone.

Aminarsonic acid *see* Arsanilic acid.

Aminazin (tr) *see* Chlorpromazine.

'Amindan' *see* Sulfanilamide sulfosalicylate.

AMINDOCATE** (deanol ester with 1-(2-dimethylaminoethyl)-2,3-dimethylindole-5-carboxylic acid).

Amine oxidase *see* Monoamine oxidase.

AMINEPTINE*** (7-[(10,11-dihydro-5*H*-dibenzo[*a*,*d*]cyclohepten-5-yl)amino]heptanoic acid; S-1694; 'survector').

Aminic acid *see* Formic acid.

AMINITROZOLE*** (2-acetamido-5-nitrothiazole; *N*-(5-nitrothiazol-2-yl)acetamide; acinitrazole; nithiamide; CL-5279).

2-(2-Aminoacetamido)-4'-chloro-2'-(*o*-chlorobenzoyl)-*N*-methylacetanilide *see* Lorzafone.

Aminoacetic acid *see* Glycine.

N-(Aminoacetyl)-*p*-phenetidine *see* Phenocoll.

AMINOACRIDINE*** (5-aminoacridine; 9-aminoacridine; aminacrine; NSC-7571).

Aminoacridine 4-hexylresorcinolate *see* Acrisorcin.

AMINOACRIQUINE (tr) (2-amino-3-chloro-9-(4-diethylamino-1-methylbutylamino)-7-methoxyacridine; aminacrin).

1-Aminoadamantane *see* Amantadine.

6-(3-Amino-1-adamantanecarboxamido)penicillanic acid *see* Amantocillin.

3-Aminoadamantyl-1-penicillin *see* Amantocillin.

α-Aminoadipic cephalosporin *see* Cephalosporin C.

α-Aminoadipic penicillin *see* Adicillin.

*N*¹-[4-Amino-5-[(3-[(4-aminobutyl)amino]propyl)-carbamoyl]pentyl]-13-[(4-amino-4,6-dideoxy-α-L-talopyranosyl)oxy]-19-demethyl-12-hydroxybleomycinamide *see* Talisomycin.

2-Amino-4-(2-amino-2-carboxyethylthio)butyric acid *see* Cystathionine.

4-*O*-[3α-Amino-6α-[(4-amino-4-deoxy-α-D-glucopyranosyl)oxy]-2,3,4,4aβ,6,7,8,8aα-octahydro-8β-hydroxy-7β-(methylamino)pyrano[3,2-*b*]pyran-2α-yl]-2-deoxy-D-streptamine *see* Apramycin.

5-Amino-6-(7-amino-5,8-dihydro-6-methoxy-5,8-dioxoquinolin-2-yl)-4-(2-hydroxy-3,4-dimethoxyphenyl)-3-methylpicolinic acid *see* Rufocromomycin.

4-Amino-6-[(2-amino-1,6-dimethylpyrimid-4-yl)-amino]-1,2-dimethylquinolinium dichloride *see* Quinapyramine.

4-Amino-1-(2-amino-*N*-methylacetamido) 1,4-dideoxy-3-*O*-(2,6-diamino-2,3,4,6,7-pentadeoxy-β-L-*lyxo*-heptopyranosyl)-6-*O*-methyl-L-*chiro*-inositol *see* Astromicin.

3-Amino-8-[(2-amino-6-methylpyrimidin-4-yl)-amino]-6-(*p*-aminophenyl)-5-methylphenanthridinium bromide 1'-methobromide *see* Pyritidium bromide.

8-Amino-6-(*p*-aminophenyl)-5-methylphenanthridi-nium chloride *see* Phenidium chloride.

2-Amino-4-anilino-*s*-triazine *see* Amanozine.

4-AMINOANTIPYRINE (4-amino-2,3-dimethyl-1-phenyl-3-pyrazolin-5-one; 4-aminophenaz-one).

4-Aminoantipyrine sodium *N*⁴-methanesulfonate *see* Sulfamidopyrine sodium.

4-Amino-1-arabinofuranosyl-1,2-dihydro-2-pyrimi-dinone *see* Cytarabine.

2-Amino-4-arsenosophenol *see* Oxophenarsine.

p-**AMINOAZOBENZENE** (*p*-phenylazoaniline).

AMINOAZOTOLUENE (amidazotoluene; 4-amino-2',3-dimethylazobenzene; non-staining scarlet).

5-Aminobarbituric acid *see* Uramil.

'Aminobenz' *see* Orthocaine.

p-**Aminobenzenearsonic acid** *see* Arsanilic acid.

p-**Aminobenzenephosphonic acid** *see* Phosphanilic acid.

p-**AMINOBENZENESTIBONIC ACID** ('penta-stib').
See also Ethylstibamine; Stibamine.

p-**Aminobenzenesulfocyanamide** *see* Sulcymide.

m-**Aminobenzenesulfonamide** *see* Metanilamide.

o-**Aminobenzenesulfonamide** *see* Orthanilamide.

p-**Aminobenzenesulfonamide** *see* Sulfanilamide.

p-**Aminobenzenesulfonic acid** *see* Sulfanilic acid.

o-**Aminobenzoic acid** *see* Anthranilic acid.

p-**AMINOBENZOIC ACID** (vitamin B$_x$; vitamin H$_1$; PAB; PABA; pabacidum).
See also Amoxecaine; Benzocaine; Butacaine; Butamin; Butethamine; Butylcaine; Dimethoca-ine; Isobutamben; Leucinocaine; Naepaine; Pro-caine; Risocaine; Sodium *p*-aminobenzoate; Pot-assium *p*-aminobenzoate.

N-(*p*-**Aminobenzoylglycine** *see* *p*-Aminohippuric acid.

(2-Amino-3-benzoylphenyl)acetic acid *see* Amfenac.

2-Amino-6-benzyl-3-ethoxycarbonyl-4,5,6,7-tetra-hydrothieno[2,3-*c*]pyridine *see* Tinoridine.

α-**Aminobenzylpenicillin** *see* Ampicillin.

p-**Aminobenzylpenicillin** *see* Penicillin T.

4-Amino-*N*-(1-benzylpiperid-4-yl)-5-chloro-*o*-anis-amide *see* Clebopride.

2-Amino-6-benzyl-4,5,6,7-tetrahydrothieno[2,3-*c*]-pyridine-3-carboxylic acid ethyl ester *see* Tinorid-ine.

Aminobiphenyl *see* Biphenylamine.

5-Amino[3,4'-bipyridin]-6(1*H*)-one *see* Amrinone.

5-Amino-1-(bisdimethylaminophosphoryl)-3-phenyl-1,2,4-triazole *see* Triamiphos.

5-Amino-1,3-bis(2-ethylhexyl)hexahydro-5-methyl-pyrimidine *see* Hexetidine.

4-Amino-bromo-*N*-[1-(*p*-chlorobenzyl)piperid-4-yl]-*o*-anisamide *see* Broclepride.

4-Amino-5-bromo-*N*-(2-diethylaminoethyl)-*o*-anis-amide *see* Bromopride.

4-Amino-5-bromo-*N*-(2-diethylaminoethyl)-2-meth-oxybenzamide *see* Bromopride.

5-Amino-4-bromo-2-phenylpyridazin-3(2*H*)-one *see* Brompyrazon.

3-Amino-4-butoxybenzoic acid 2-(2-diethylamino-ethoxy)ethyl ester *see* Betoxycaine.

3-Amino-2-butoxybenzoic acid diethylaminoethyl ester *see* Metabutoxycaine.

4-Amino-2-butoxybenzoic acid diethylaminoethyl ester *see* Ambucaine.

4-Amino-3-butoxybenzoic acid diethylaminoethyl ester *see* Oxybuprocaine.

p-**Amino-α-(*sec*-butylaminomethyl)benzyl alcohol** *see* Amiterol.

4-Amino-α-[(*tert*-butylamino)methyl]-3-chloro-5-(trifluoromethyl)benzyl alcohol *see* Mabuterol.

4-Amino-α-[(*tert*-butylamino)methyl]-3,5-dichloro-benzyl alcohol *see* Clenbuterol.

1-(4-Aminobutyl)guanidine *see* Agmatine.

3-(2-Aminobutyl)indole *see* Etryptamine.

4-Amino-6-*tert*-butyl-3-(methylthio)-*as*-triazin-5(4*H*)-one *see* Metribuzin.

5-Amino-*N*-butyl-2-prop-2-ynyloxybenzamide *see* Parsalmide.

4-AMINOBUTYRIC ACID (γ-aminobutyric acid; GABA).

4-Aminobutyric acid lactam *see* 2-Pyrrolidinone.

4-Amino-2-(4-butyrylhexahydro-1,4-diazepin-1-yl)-6,7-dimethoxyquinazoline *see* Bunazosin.

N-(4-**Aminobutyryl)histidine** *see* Homocarnosine.

N-(4-**Aminobutyryl)-1-methylhistidine** *see* Homo-anserine.

AMINOCAPROIC ACID*** (6-aminohexanoic acid; ε-aminocaproic acid; EACA; CL-10304; CY-116; JD-177; NSC-26154).

α-**Aminocaproic acid** *see* Norleucine.

Aminocaproic lactam *see* Caprolactam.

AMINOCARB* (4-(dimethylamino)-3-methyl-phenyl methylcarbamate; 4-(dimethylamino)-*m*-tolyl methylcarbamate; arprocarb; 'matacil').

3-(Aminocarbonyl)-4-[4,4-bis(4-fluorophenyl)butyl]-*N*-(2,6-dichlorophenyl)-1-piperazineacetamide *see* Mioflazine.

4-Amino-4-carboxybutylpenicillin *see* Adicillin.

2-(2-Amino-2-carboxyethyl)-*N*,*N*-bis(2-chloro-ethyl)-4-nitrophenethylamine *see* Nitrocaphane.

2-(2-Amino-2-carboxyethyl)-*N*,*N*-bis(2-chloro-ethyl)phenethylamine *see* Ocaphane.

2-Amino-3-*O*-(1-carboxyethyl)-2-deoxy-D-glucose *see* Muramic acid.

2-[2-(2-Amino-4-carboxyethyl)-4-nitrophenyl]-2',2''-dichlorotriethylamine *see* Nitrocaphane.

2-[2-(2-Amino-2-carboxyethyl)phenyl]-2',2'''-di-chlorotriethylamine *see* Ocaphane.

7-[(2-Amino-2-carboxyethyl)thio]-2-(2,2-dimethyl-cyclopropanecarboxamido)-2-heptenoic acid *see* Cilastatin.

*N*²-[(+)-**5-Amino-5-carboxypentylaminomethyl]-tetracycline** *see* Lymecycline.

3-Amino-*N*-(α-carboxyphenethyl)succinamic acid *N*-methyl ester *see* Aspartame.

(3-Amino-3-carboxypropyl)dimethylsulfonium salt *see* Vitamin U.

5'-[(3-Amino-3-carboxypropyl)methylsulfonio]-5'-deoxyadenosine hydroxide inner salt *see* Ademe-tionine.

7-(5-Amino-5-carboxyvaleramido)cephalosporanic

21

acid *see* Cephalosporin C.

6-D-(5-Amino-5-carboxyvaleramido)penicillanic acid *see* Adicillin.

6-L-(5-Amino-5-carboxyvaleramido)penicillanic acid *see* (−)-Adicillin.

Aminochinuride *see* Aminoquinuride.

2-Amino-4-(*p*-chloroanilino-*s*-triazine) *see* Chlorazanil.

1-(4-Amino-5-chloro-*o*-anisoyl)-4-piperonylpiperazine *see* Peralopride.

4-Amino-2-chlorobenzoic acid 2-diethylaminoethyl ester *see* Chloroprocaine.

3-Amino-4-chlorobenzoic acid 2-dimethylaminoethyl ester *see* Clormecaine.

2-Amino-5-chlorobenzoxazole *see* Zoxazolamine.

4-Amino-5-chloro-*N*-(2-diethylaminoethyl)-*o*-anisamide *see* Metoclopramide.

4-Amino-5-chloro-*N*-(2-diethylaminoethyl)-2-methoxybenzamide *see* Metoclopramide.

2-Amino-3-chloro-9-(4-diethylamino-1-methylbutylamino)-7-methoxyacridine *see* Aminoacriquine.

4-Amino-5-chloro-*N*-(1,2-diethylpyrazolidin-4-yl)-*o*-anisamide *see* Dazopride.

α-Amino-5-chloro-4,5-dihydro-5-isoxazoleacetic acid *see* Acivicin.

6-Amino-2-(2-chloroethyl)-2,3-dihydro-1,3-benzoxazin-4-one *see* Aminochlorthenoxazine.

6-Amino-9-(2-chloro-6-fluorobenzyl)purine *see* Arprinocid.

***cis*-4-Amino-5-chloro-*N*-[1-[3-(*p*-fluorophenoxy)-propyl]-3-methoxypiperid-4-yl]-*o*-anisamide** *see* Cisapride.

4a-Amino-8-chloro-1,2,3,4,4a,10a-hexahydro-2-methyl-10*H*-benzopyrano[3,2-*c*]pyridin-10-ylacetic acid lactam *see* Lortalamine.

α-Amino-3-chloro-2-isoxazoline-5-acetic acid *see* Acivicin.

4-(4-Amino-5-chloro-2-methoxybenzamido)-1-benzylpiperidine *see* Clebopride.

1-(4-Amino-5-chloro-2-methoxybenzoyl)-4-[3,4-(methylenedioxy)benzyl]piperazine *see* Peralopride.

4-Amino-3-(*p*-chlorophenyl)butyric acid *see* Baclofen.

2-Amino-5-(*p*-chlorophenyl)-2-oxazoline *see* Clominorex.

5-Amino-4-chloro-2-phenylpyridazin-3(2*H*)-one *see* Chloridazon.

AMINOCHLORTHENOXAZINE (6-amino-2-(2-chloroethyl)-2,3-dihydro-1,3-benzoxazin-4-one; A-350; AP-350; ICI-350).
See also under Aminophenazone.

4-Amino-5-cyano-7-(β-D-ribofuranosyl)pyrrolo[2,3-*d*]pyrimidine *see* Toyocamycin.

7-[2-Amino-2-(1,4-cyclohexadien-1-yl)acetamido]-3-methoxy-2-cephem-2-carboxylic acid *see* Cefroxadine.

7-[2-Amino-2-(1,4-cyclohexadien-1-yl)acetamido]-3-methyl-2-cephem-2-carboxylic acid *see* Cefradine.

6-(2-Amino-2-(1,4-cyclohexadien-1-yl)acetamido)-penicillanic acid *see* Epicillin.

6-(1-Aminocyclohexanecarboxamido)penicillanic acid *see* Ciclacillin.

4-Amino-*N*-[1-(3-cyclohexen-1-ylmethyl)piperid-4-yl]-2-ethoxy-5-nitrobenzamide *see* Cinitapride.

(1-Aminocyclohexyl)penicillin *see* Ciclacillin.

1-Aminocyclopentanecarboxylic acid *see* Cycloleucine.

'Aminodal' *see* Sodium theophyllin-7-ylacetate.

1-Amino-3-(decyloxy)-2-propanol *see* Decominol.

4-Amino-4-deoxyfolic acid sodium salt *see* Aminopterin sodium.

1-Amino-1-deoxy-D-glucitol *see* Glucamine.

2-Amino-2-deoxy-β-D-glucopyranose *see* Glucosamine.

***O*-3-Amino-3-deoxy-α-D-glucopyranosyl(1→6)-*O*-[(6-amino-6-deoxy-α-D-glucopyranosyl(1→4)-*N*¹-[(*S*)-4-amino-2-hydroxybutyl]-2-deoxy-D-streptamine** *see* Butikacin.

***O*-3-Amino-3-deoxy-α-D-glucopyranosyl(1→4)-*O*-[6-amino-6-deoxy-α-D-glucopyranosyl(1→6)]-*N*³-(4-amino-L-2-hydroxybutyryl)-2-deoxy-L-streptamine** *see* Amikacin.

***O*-6-Amino-6-deoxy-α-D-glucopyranosyl(1→4)-*O*-[3-deoxy-4-*C*-methyl-3-(methylamino)-β-L-arabinopyranosyl(1→6)]-2-deoxy-D-streptamine** *see* Betamicin.

***O*-3-Amino-3-deoxy-α-D-glucopyranosyl(1→4)-*O*-[2,6-diamino-2,6-dideoxy-α-D-glucopyranosyl(1→6)]-2-deoxy-*N*³-[2-hydroxy-1-(hydroxymethyl)ethyl]-L-streptamine** *see* Propikacin.

L-*O*-(3-Amino-3-deoxy-α-D-glucopyranosyl)-(1→4)-*O*-[2,6-diamino-2,6-dideoxy-α-D-glucopyranosyl(1→6)]-2-deoxystreptamine *see* Bekanamycin.

***O*-3-Amino-3-deoxy-α-D-glucopyranosyl-(1→4)-*O*-[2,6-diamino-2,3,4,6-tetradeoxy-α-D-*erythro*-hexopyranosyl(1→6)]-2-deoxy-L-streptamine** *see* Dibekacin.

***O*-3-Amino-3-deoxy-α-D-glucopyranosyl(1→4)-*O*-[2,6-diamino-2,3,6-trideoxy-α-D-*ribo*-hexopyranosyl(1→6)]-2-deoxystreptamine** *see* Tobramycin.

2-Amino-2-deoxy-3-*O*-β-D-glucopyranosyl-D-glucose *see* Hyalobiuronic acid.

2-Amino-2-deoxy-D-glucose *see* Glucosamine.

2′-Amino-2′-deoxykanamycin *see* Bekanamycin.

4-Amino-4-deoxy-*N*¹⁰-methylfolic acid *see* Methotrexate.

9-(3-Amino-3-deoxy-β-D-ribofuranosyl)-6-dimethylaminopurine *see* Puromycin aminonucleoside.

[1-Amino-3-[[[2-[(diaminomethylene)amino]thiazol-4-yl]methyl]thio]propylidene]sulfamide *see* Famotidine.

***trans*-[(2-Amino-3,5-dibromobenzyl)amino]cyclohexanol** *see* Ambroxol.

***N*-(2-Amino-3,5-dibromobenzyl)-*N*-cyclohexylmethylamine** *see* Bromhexine.

***N*-(2-Amino-3,5-dibromobenzyl)-*N*-methylcyclohexylamine** *see* Bromhexine.

2-Amino-3,5-dibromo-*N*-cyclohexyl-*N*-methylbenzylamine *see* Bromhexine.

2-Amino-4-(dichloroarsino)phenol *see* Dichlorophenarsine.

3-Amino-2,5-dichlorobenzoic acid *see* Chloramben.

4-Amino-3-(2,6-dichlorobenzylidenehydrazino)-1,2,4-triazine *see* Nebidrazine.

3-Amino-1-(3,4-dichloro-α-methylbenzyl)-2-pyrazolin-5-one *see* Muzolimine.

1-(4-Amino-3,5-dichlorophenyl)-2-*tert*-butylaminoethanol *see* Clenbuterol.

3-Amino-1-[1-(3,4-dichlorophenyl)ethyl]-2-pyrazolin-5-one *see* Muzolimine.

4-Amino-3-[2-[(2,6-dichlorophenyl)methylene]hydrazino]-4*H*-1,2,4-triazole *see* Nebidrazine.

22-[(3-Amino-3,6-dideoxy-β-D-mannopyranosyl)oxy]-1,3,26-trihydroxy-12-methyl-10-oxo-6,11,28-trioxatricyclo[2.2.3.1.0^{5,7}]octacosa-8,14,16,18,20-pentaene-25-carboxylic acid *see* Natamycin.

O-2-Amino-2,3-dideoxy-α-D-ribohexopyranosyl(1→4)-*O*-[*O*-α-D-mannopyranosyl(1→4)-*O*-2,6-diamino-2,6-dideoxy-β-L-idopyranosyl(1→3)-β-D-ribofuranosyl(1→5)]-2-deoxy-D-streptamine *see* Lividomycin.

o-Amino-*N*-(2-diethylaminoethyl)benzamide *see* Orthoprocainamide.

p-Amino-*N*-[2-(diethylamino)ethyl]benzamide *see* Procainamide.

2-Amino-4′-diethylaminoethyl-*o*-benzotoluidide *see* Atolide.

2-Amino-1,9-dihydro-9-[(2-hydroxyethoxy)methyl]-6*H*-purin-6-one *see* Aciclovir.

6-Amino-1,5-dihydro-4*H*-imidazo[4,5-*c*]pyridin-4-one *see* Dezaguanine.

α-Amino-2,5-dihydro-5-methyl-2-furanacetic acid *see* Furanomycin.

3-Amino-1,5-dihydro-5-methyl-1-β-D-ribofuranosyl-1,4,5,6,8-pentaazaacenaphthylene *see* Triciribine.

N-[4-[[2-(2-Amino-1,4-dihydro-4-oxo-pteridin-6-yl)ethyl]amino]benzoyl]-L-glutamic acid *see* Homofolic acid.

2-Amino-3′,4′-dihydroxyacetophenone *see* Noradrenalone.

2-Amino-3-(3,4-dihydroxyphenyl)-2-methylpropionic acid *see* Methyldopa.

2-Amino-6-(1,2-dihydroxypropyl)-4(3*H*)-pteridinone *see* Biopterin.

2-Amino-4,6-dihydroxypteridine *see* Xanthopterin.

3-(3-Amino-4,6-diiodophenyl)-β-alanine *see* Betamine.

5-(4-Amino-3,5-dimethoxybenzyl)-2,4-pyrimidinediamine *see* Aditeren.

2-Amino-1-(2,5-dimethoxy-4-methylphenyl)butane *see* Dimoxamine.

2-Amino-1-(2,5-dimethoxy-4-methylphenyl)propane *see* 2,5-Dimethoxy-4-methylamphetamine.

(±)-2-Amino-*N*-[2-(2,5-dimethoxyphenyl)-2-hydroxyethyl]acetamide *see* Midodrine.

2-Amino-1-(2,5-dimethoxyphenyl)-1-propanol *see* Methoxamine.

1-(4-Amino-6,7-dimethoxyquinazolin-2-yl)-4-(1,4-benzodioxan-2-ylcarbonyl)piperazine *see* Doxazosin.

1-(4-Amino-6,7-dimethoxyquinazolin-2-yl)-4-butyrylhexahydro-1*H*-1,4-diazepine *see* Bunazosin.

1-(4-Amino-6,7-dimethoxyquinazolin-2-yl)-4-(2-furoyl)piperazine *see* Prazosin.

(±)-*N*-[3-[(4-Amino-6,7-dimethoxyquinazolin-2-yl)methylamino]propyl]tetrahydro-2-furamide *see* Alfuzosin.

1-(4-Amino-6,7-dimethoxyquinazolin-2-yl)-4-[[(5-methylthio)-1,3,4-oxadiazol-2-yl]carbonyl]piperazine *see* Tiodazosin.

1-(4-Amino-6,7-dimethoxyquinazolin-2-yl)-4-(tetrahydro-2-furoyl)piperazine *see* Terazosin.

4-Amino-6,7-dimethoxyquinoline *see* Amiquinsin.

3-Amino-7-(dimethylamino)-2-methylphenazthionium chloride *see* Tolonium chloride.

3-Amino-7-(dimethylamino)phenazthionium chloride *see* Azure A.

4-Amino-2′,3-dimethylazobenzene *see* Aminoazotoluene.

4-Amino-6-(1,1-dimethylethyl)-3-(methylthio)-1,2,4-triazin-5(4*H*)-one *see* Metribuzin.

2-Amino-4,4-dimethyl-2-oxazoline *see* Xinomiline.

2-Amino-*N*-(2,6-dimethylphenyl)propanamide *see* Tocainide.

4-Amino-2,3-dimethyl-1-phenyl-3-pyrazolin-5-one *see* 4-Aminoantipyrine.

2-Amino-2′,6′-dimethylpropionanilide *see* Tocainide.

Aminodiphenyl *see* Biphenylamine.

α-Aminodiphenylethane *see* Stilbylamine.

3-Amino-1,1-dithien-2-ylbut-1-ene *see* Thiambutene.

4-Amino-1-dodecylquinaldinium acetate *see* Laurolinium acetate.

'Aminodur' *see* Aminophylline.

2-Aminoethaneselenol *see* Selenomercaptamine.

2-Aminoethanesulfinic acid *see* Hypotaurine.

2-Aminoethanesulfonic acid *see* Taurine.

2-Aminoethanethiol *see* Mercaptamine.

2-Aminoethanol *see* Ethanolamine.

Aminoethanol nitrate *see* Itramin.

5-(2-Aminoethyl)-1,2,4-benzenetriol *see* Oxidopamine.

(±)-α-(1-Aminoethyl)benzyl alcohol *see* Phenylpropanolamine.

(+)-*threo*-α-(1-Aminoethyl)benzyl alcohol *see* Cathine.

3-(2-Aminoethyl)-1-benzyl-5-methoxy-2-methylindole *see* Benanserin.

α-(1-Aminoethyl)-2,5-dimethoxybenzyl alcohol *see* Methoxamine.

α-(1-Aminoethyl)-*m*-hydroxybenzyl alcohol *see* Metaraminol.

3-(2-Aminoethyl)-5-hydroxy-1-(*p*-methoxybenzyl)-2-methylindole *see* Hydroxindasol.

2-(2-Aminoethyl)imidazole *see* 2-Imidazoleethylamine.

4-(2-Aminoethyl)imidazole *see* Histamine.

3-(2-Aminoethyl)indole *see* Tryptamine.

3-(2-Aminoethyl)indol-5-yl methyl ketone *see* Acetryptine.

S-(2-Aminoethyl)isothiuronium bromide hydrobromide *see* AET.

3-(2-Aminoethyl)-1-(*p*-methoxybenzyl)-2-methylindol-5-ol *see* Hydroxindasol.

2-Aminoethyl nitrate *see* Itramin.

p-(2-Aminoethyl)phenol *see* Tyramine.

α-(1-Aminoethyl)protocatechuyl alcohol *see* Corbadrine.

3-(2-Aminoethyl)pyrazole *see* Betazole.

4-(2-Aminoethyl)pyrocatechol *see* Dopamine.

4-Amino-*N*-[(1-ethylpyrrolidin-2-yl)methyl]-5-(ethylsulfonyl)-2-methoxybenzamide *see* Amisulpride.

2-Aminoethyl sodium thiophosphate *see* Cystafos.

2-Amino-6-ethyl-5,6,7,8-tetrahydro-4*H*-oxazolo[4,5-*d*]azepine *see* Azepexole.

2-Amino-4-(ethylthio)butyric acid *see* Ethionine.

3-[(2-Aminoethyl)thio]-6-(1-hydroxyethyl)-7-oxo-1-azabicyclo[3.2.0]hept-2-ene-2-carboxylic acid *see* Thienamycin.

2-(2-Aminoethyl)-2-thiopseudourea hydrobromide *see* AET.

2-Amino-6-[(*p*-fluorobenzyl)amino]-3-pyridinecarbamic acid ethyl ester *see* Flupirtine.

4-Amino-5-fluoro-1,2-dihydropyrimidin-2-one *see* Flucytosine.

6-Amino-2-(fluoromethyl)-3-*o*-tolyl-4(3*H*)-quinazolinone *see* Afloqualone.

Aminoform *see* Methenamine.

Aminoformamidine *see* Guanidine.

6-Amino-9-(L-1,2-furopyranosenyl)purine *see* Angustmycin A.

4-Amino-2-[4-(2-furoyl)piperazin-1-yl]-6,7-dimethoxyquinazoline *see* Prazosin.

Aminoglutaramic acids *see* Glutamine; Isoglutamine.

2-Aminoglutaric acid *see* Glutamic acid.

AMINOGLUTETHIMIDE*** (α-*p*-aminophenyl-α-ethylglutarimide; BA-16038; ND-1966).

Aminoglyoxylic acid *see* Oxamic acid.

AMINOGUANIDINE (guanylhydrazine).

2-Amino-5-guanidovaleric acid *see* Arginine.

2-Aminoheptane *see* Tuaminoheptane.

6-Amino-1,1a,2,8,8a,8b-hexahydro-8-(hydroxymethyl)-8a-methoxy-1,5-dimethylazirino-[2′,3′:3,4]pyrrolo[1,2-*a*]indole-4,7-dione carbamate *see* Porfiromycin.

6-Amino-1,1a,2,8,8a,8b-hexahydro-8-hydroxymethyl-8a-methoxy-5-methylazirino[2′,3′:3,4]pyrrolo[1,2-*a*]indole-4,7-dione carbamate *see* Mitomycin.

N-[*p*-[[2-(2-Amino-1,4,5,6,7,8-hexahydro-5-methyl-4-oxopteridin-6-yl)ethyl]amino]benzoyl]-L-glutamic acid *see* Ketotrexate.

2-Aminohexanoic acid *see* Norleucine.

6-Aminohexanoic acid *see* Aminocaproic acid.

α-(1-Aminohexyl)benzhydrol *see* Hexapradol.

p-Aminohippurate *see* Sodium *p*-aminohippurate.

p-AMINOHIPPURIC ACID (*N*-(*p*-aminobenzoyl)glycine; PAH).
See also Sodium *p*-aminohippurate.

2-Aminohydracrylic acid *see* Serine.

α-Aminohydrocinnamic acid *see* Phenylalanine.

3α-Amino-2β-hydroxy-5α-androstan-17-one *see* Amafolone.

3-Amino-4-hydroxybenzenearsonic acid *N*-methanal sulfoxylate *see* Phenarsone sulfoxylate.

4-Amino-2-hydroxybenzoic acid *see* Aminosalicylic acid.

4-Amino-3-hydroxybenzoic acid methyl ester *see* Orthocaine.

α-Amino-*p*-hydroxybenzylpenicillin *see* Amoxicillin.

2-Amino-3-hydroxybutyric acid *see* Threonine.

2-Amino-4-hydroxybutyric acid *see* Homoserine.

3-AMINO-4-HYDROXYBUTYRIC ACID (β-amino-γ-hydroxybutyric acid; GOBAB).

4-AMINO-3-HYDROXYBUTYRIC ACID (γ-amino-β-hydroxybutyric acid; 3-hydroxyGABA; GABOB; 'gamibetol'; 'ganibetol').

4-Amino-3-hydroxybutyric acid trimethylbetaine *see* Carnitine.

Aminohydroxycaproic acid *see* Hexahomoserine.

2-Amino-3-(4-hydroxy-3,5-diiodophenyl)propionic acid *see* 3,5-Diiodotyrosine.

(±)-2-Amino-*N*-(β-hydroxy-2,5-dimethoxyphenethyl)acetamide *see* Midodrine.

2-Amino-4-hydroxy-3,3-dimethylbutyric acid *see* Pantonine.

2-Amino-6-hydroxy-7,7-dimethylpurine *see* Herbipolin.

2-Amino-6-hydroxyhexanoic acid *see* Hexahomoserine.

α-Amino-*p*-hydroxyhydrocinnamic acid *see* Tyrosine.

β-Amino-*p*-hydroxyhydrocinnamic acid *see* β-Tyrosine.

1-[4-Amino-2-hydroxy-4-(hydroxyimino)butoxy]-naphthalene *see* Nadoxolol.

α-Amino-3-hydroxy-5-isoxazoleacetic acid *see* Ibotenic acid.

4-Amino-5-hydroxymethyl-2-methylpyrimidine *see* Toxopyrimidine.

2-Amino-2-(hydroxymethyl)-1,3-propanediol *see* Trometamol.

2-Amino-3-(hydroxynitrosoamino)propionic acid *see* Alanosine.

2-Amino-3-(3-hydroxy-4-oxopyrid-1-yl)propionic acid *see* Leucenol.

(6*R*,7*R*)-7-(*R*)-2-Amino-2-[*p*-hydroxyphenyl)acetamido]-3-methyl-2-cephem-2-carboxylic acid *see* Cefadroxil.

7-[2-Amino-2-(*p*-hydroxyphenyl)acetamido]-3-[[(5-methyl-1,3,4-thiadiazol-2-yl)thio]methyl]-2-cephem-2-carboxylic acid *see* Cefaparole.

6-[D(−)-2-Amino-2-(*p*-hydroxyphenyl)acetamido]-penicillanic acid *see* Amoxicillin.

7-[2-Amino-2-(*p*-hydroxyphenylacetamido)-3-(*v*-triazol-4-ylthio)methyl]-2-cephem-2-carboxylic acid *see* Cefatrizine.

[6*R*-[6α,7β(*R*)]]-7-[[Amino-(4-hydroxyphenyl)acetyl]amino]-3-methyl-2-cephem-2-carboxylic acid *see* Cefadroxil.

m-Amino-*p*-hydroxyphenylarsenoxide *see* Oxophenarsine.

2-Amino-1-(3-hydroxyphenyl)ethanol *see* Norfenefrine.

2-Amino-3-hydroxypropionic acid *see* Serine.

3-Amino-2-hydroxypropionic acid *see* Isoserine.

p-[(2-Amino-4-hydroxy-6-pteridylmethyl)amino]-benzoic acid *see* Pteroic acid.

2-Amino-6-hydroxypurine *see* Guanine.

6-Amino-2-hydroxypurine *see* Isoguanine.

α-Amino-(3-hydroxy-4-pyridinone)propionic acid
see Leucenol.

5-Amino-7-hydroxy-1*H*-*v*-triazolo[4,5-*d*]pyrimidine
see Azaguanine.

2-Amino-3-hydroxy-2'-(2,3,4-trihydroxybenzyl)pro-
pionohydrazide see Benserazide.

2-Amino-4-hydroxy-6-(1,2,3-trihydroxypropyl)pte-
ridine see Neopterin.

2-Aminohypoxanthine see Guanine.

5-Aminoimidazole-4-carboxamide orotate see Orazamide.

2-Amino-3-imidazolylpropionic acid see Histidine.

N-(Aminoiminomethyl)-2,6-dichlorobenzeneacet-
amide see Guanfacine.

7-Amino-3-imino(3*H*)phenothiazine see Thionine.

2-Amino-3-indolepropionic acid see Tryptophan.

α-Aminoisocaproic acid see Leucine.

Aminoisometradine see Amisometradine.

2-Amino-1-(isopropylsulfonyl)-6-benzimidazole
phenyl ketone oxime see Enviroxime; Viroxime;
Zinviroxime.

2-Amino-1-(isopropylsulfonyl)-6-(1-phenylpropen-
yl)benzimidazole see Enviradene.

α-Aminoisovaleric acid see Valine.

4-Amino-3-isoxazolidinone see Cycloserine.

3-Aminolactic acid see Isoserine.

2-Amino-4-mercaptobutyric acid see Homocysteine.

2-Amino-3-mercaptopropionic acid see Cysteine.

2-Amino-6-mercaptopurine see Tioguanine.

7-[2-Amino-2-(*m*-methanesulfonamidophenyl)acet-
amido]-3-methyl-2-cephem-2-carboxylic acid see
Cefsumide.

2-Amino-4-methoxybutyric acid see Methoxinine.

3-Amino-*N*-(α-methoxycarbonylphenethyl)succin-
amic acid see Aspartame.

3'-(L-α-Amino-*p*-methoxyhydrocinnamido)-3'-
deoxy-*N*,*N*-dimethyladenosine see Puromycin.

4-Amino-6-methoxy-1-phenylpyridazinium methyl
sulfate see Amezinium metilsulfate.

4-Amino-2-methoxy-5-pyrimidinemethanol see Bacimethrin.

9-Amino-4-methylacridine see Methylaminacrin.

3-Amino-7-(methylamino)phenazthionium chloride
see Azure C.

p-Aminomethylbenzenesulfonamide see Mafenide.

1-(3-Amino-4-methylbenzenesulfonyl)-3-cyclohexyl-
urea see Metahexamide.

p-AMINOMETHYLBENZOIC ACID (α-amino-
p-toluic acid; PAMBA; 'gumbix'; 'styptopur').

α-(Aminomethyl)benzyl alcohol see Phenylethanolamine.

8-(4-Amino-1-methylbutylamino)-6-methoxyquinol-
ine see Primaquine.

2-Amino-3-methylbutyric acid see Valine.

6-[2-[2-Amino-3-(methylcarbamoyl)propionamido]-
2-(*p*-hydroxyphenyl)acetamido]penicillanic acid
see Aspoxicillin.

β-Aminomethyl-*p*-chlorohydrocinnamic acid see
Baclofen.

1-(Aminomethyl)cyclohexaneacetic acid see Gabapentin.

4-Aminomethylcyclohexanecarboxylic acid see
Tranexamic acid.

(−)-α-(Aminomethyl)-3,4-dihydroxybenzyl alcohol
see Norepinephrine.

L-2-Amino-3-(2-methylenecyclopropyl)propionic
acid see Hypoglycin A.

2-(Aminomethylene)indan-1-one see Drinidene.

3-Aminomethyl-7-fluoro-1-phenylisochroman see
Fenisorex.

2-Amino-6-methylheptane see Octodrine.

6-Amino-2-methyl-2-heptanol see Heptaminol.

3'-Amino-4'-methylhexanophenone *O*-(2-amino-
ethyl)oxime see Caproxamine.

α-Aminomethyl-*m*-hydroxybenzyl alcohol see Norfenefrine.

α-Aminomethyl-*p*-hydroxybenzyl alcohol see Octopamine.

α-Aminomethyl-4-hydroxy-3-methoxybenzyl alcohol
see Normetanephrine.

4-(Aminomethyl)-5-hydroxy-6-methyl-3-pyridine-
methanol see Pyridoxamine.

5-Aminomethyl-3-isoxazolol see Muscimol.

α-(Aminomethyl)-5-methoxyindole-3-acetic acid
methyl ester see Indorenate.

6-Amino-3-methyl-1-(2-methylallyl)uracil see Amisometradine.

8β-Aminomethyl-6-methyl-10a-ergoline see Dihydrolysergamine.

2-Amino-6-(1-methyl-4-nitroimidazol-5-ylthio)pur-
ine see Tiamiprine.

2-Amino-4-[2-(1-methyl-5-nitroimidazol-2-yl)vinyl]-
pyrimidine see Azanidazole.

2-Amino-4-methyl-1-pentanol see Leucinol.

7-[*o*-(Aminomethyl)phenylacetamido]-3-[[[1-(carboxymethyl)-1*H*-tetrazol-5-yl]thio]methyl]-2-
cephem-2-carboxylic acid see Ceforanide.

p-Amino-*N*-(1-methyl-2-phenylethyl)phenylacet-
amide see Fepracet.

4-Amino-6-methyl-2-phenyl-3-pyridazinone see Metamfazone.

1-(4-Amino-2-methyl-5-phenylpyrrol-3-yl)-2-methyl-
1-propanone see Isoprazone.

p-Amino-α-[(1-methylpropyl)aminomethyl]benzyl alcohol see Amiterol.

3-(Aminomethyl)pyridine see Picolamine.

N-(2-Amino-6-methylpyrid-3-ylmethyl)-3,4,5-tri-
methoxybenzamide see Trimetamide.

4-Amino-2-methyl-5-pyrimidinemethanol see Toxopyrimidine.

3-(4-Amino-2-methylpyrimidin-5-ylmethyl)-5-(2-
chloroethyl)-4-methylthiazolium chloride see Beclotiamine.

3-[(4-Amino-2-methylpyrimidin-5-yl)methyl]-1-(2-
chloroethyl)-1-nitrosourea see Nimustine.

4-*N*-(4-Amino-2-methylpyrimidin-5-ylmethyl)form-
amido-3-(benzoylthio)pent-3-enyl benzoate see
Bentiamine.

4-*N*-(4-Amino-2-methylpyrimidin-5-ylmethyl)form-
amido-3-(benzoylthio)pent-3-enyl phosphate see
Benfotiamine.

8-[2-[*N*-(4-Amino-2-methylpyrimidin-5-ylmethyl-
formamido)-1-(2-hydroxyethyl)propenyl]dithio]-6-
mercaptooctanoic acid methyl ester acetate see
Octotiamine.

1-(4-Amino-2-methylpyrimidin-5-ylmethyl)-3-(2-

hydroxyethyl)-2-methylpyridinium bromide *see* Pyrithiamine.

N-(4-Amino-2-methylpyrimidin-5-ylmethyl)-N-(4-hydroxy-2-mercapto-1-methyl-1-butenyl)formamide *S*-benzoate *O*-phosphate *see* Benfotiamine.

N-((4-Amino-2-methylpyrimidin-5-yl)methyl)-N-(4-hydroxy-2-mercapto-1-methyl-1-butenyl)formamide *O*,*S*-diacetate *see* Acetiamine.

N-(4-Amino-2-methylpyrimidin-5-ylmethyl)-N-(4-hydroxy-2-mercapto-1-methyl-1-butenyl)formamide *O*,*S*-dibenzoate *see* Bentiamine.

N-(4-Amino-2-methylpyrimidin-5-ylmethyl)-N-(4-hydroxy-2-mercapto-1-methyl-1-butenyl)formamide ethyl carbonate *S*-ester with ethyl thiocarbonate *see* Cetotiamine.

N-(4-Amino-2-methylpyrimidin-5-ylmethyl)-N-(4-hydroxy-2-mercapto-1-methyl-1-butenyl)formamide *O*-glycolate acetate *S*-ester with thio-2-furoic acid *see* Acefurtiamine.

N-(4-Amino-2-methylpyrimidin-5-ylmethyl)-N-[4-hydroxy-1-methyl-2-(propyldithio)-1-butenyl]formamide *see* Prosultiamine.

N-(4-Amino-2-methylpyrimidin-5-ylmethyl)-N-[4-hydroxy-1-methyl-2-(tetrahydrofurfuryldithio)-1-butenyl]formamide *see* Fursultiamine.

N-(4-Amino-2-methylpyrimidin-5-ylmethyl)-N-[1-(2-oxo-1,3-oxathian-4-ylidene)ethyl]formamide *see* Cycotiamine.

N-(4-Amino-2-methylpyrimid-5-ylmethyl)-N-[2-(2-benzoylvinylthio)-4-hydroxy-1-methyl-1-butenyl]formamide *see* Vintiamol.

3-[(4-Amino-2-methyl-5-pyrimidyl)methyl]-5-(2-hydroxyethyl)-4-methylthiazolium chloride *see* Thiamine.

2-Amino-4-(methylselenyl)butyric acid *see* Selenomethionine.

2-Amino-4-(methylsulfinyl)butyric acid *see* Methionine sulfoxide.

5-(Aminomethyl)-2,3,7,8-tetrahydroxydibenzo[*a,e*]cycloheptatriene *see* Noradnamine.

2-Amino-4-(methylthio)butyric acid *see* Methionine.

2-Amino-2-(methylthio)-5-pyrimidinemethanol *see* Methioprim.

1-[*m*-[3-[(3-Amino-1-methyl-1*H*-1,2,4-triazol-5-yl)amino]propoxy]benzyl]piperidine *see* Lamtidine.

3-Amino-1-methyl-1*H*-1,2,4-triazol-5-yl[3-[(α-piperid-1-yl)-*m*-tolyloxy]propyl]amine *see* Lamtidine.

2-Amino-3-methylvaleric acid *see* Isoleucine.

2-Amino-4-methylvaleric acid *see* Leucine.

AMINOMETRADINE*** (1-allyl-6-amino-3-ethyl-1,2,3,4-tetrahydro-2,4-pyrimidinedione; 1-allyl-6-amino-3-ethyluracil; aminometramide; allacyl; allatsil).

Aminometramide* *see* Aminometradine.

4-Amino-1-naphthalenesulfonic acid *see* Naphthionic acid.

4-Amino-1-naphthoic acid diethylaminoethyl ester *see* Naphthocaine.

3-Amino-6-(5-nitrofurfurylidenemethyl)-1,2,4-triazine *see* Furalazine.

3-Amino-6-[2-(5-nitrofuryl)vinyl]pyridazine *see* Nifurprazine.

3-Amino-6-[2-(5-nitro-2-furyl)vinyl]-*as*-triazine *see* Furalazine.

L(−)-2-Amino-3-(*N*-nitrosohydroxylamino)propionic acid *see* Alanosine.

2-Amino-1-octadecanol *see* Sphingine.

2-Amino-4-octadecene-1,3-diol *see* Sphingosine.

6-Aminooctahydro-1-hydroxyindolizine acetate *see* Slaframine.

(−)-13β-Amino-5,6,7,8,9,10,11α,12-octahydro-5α-methyl-5,11-methanobenzocyclodecen-3-ol *see* Dezocine.

Amino oxidase *see* Monoamine oxidase.

Aminooxoacetic acid *see* Oxamic acid.

α-Aminooxy-6-bromo-*m*-cresol *see* Brocresine.

5-(Aminooxymethyl)-2-bromophenol *see* Brocresine.

Aminopentamide *see* Dimevamide.

2-Aminopentanedioic acid *see* Glutamic acid.

2-Amino-4-pentenoic acid *see* Allylglycine.

8-(4-Aminopentylamino)-6-methoxyquinoline *see* Quinocide.

N-[5-[3-[(5-Aminopentyl)hydroxycarbamoyl]propionamido]pentyl]-3-[[5-(*N*-hydroxyacetamido)pentyl]carbamoyl]propionylhydroxamic acid *see* Deferoxamine.

Aminophan *see* Cinchophen.

AMINOPHENAZONE*** (4-(dimethylamino)-2,3-dimethyl-1-phenyl-3-pyrazolin-5-one; 4-(dimethylamino)antipyrine; 4-dimethylaminophenazone; aminopyrine; amidofebrin; amidofen; amidophen; amidopyrazoline; amidopyrine; amidozone).

AMINOPHENAZONE plus ALLOBARBITAL ('cibalgin'; 'pabialgin').

AMINOPHENAZONE plus AMINOCHLOR-THENOXAZINE ('dereuma').

AMINOPHENAZONE plus BAMETHAN (ADS-3; 'prontylin').

AMINOPHENAZONE plus 1,2-DIPHENYL-3,5-PYRAZOLIDINEDIONE ('osadrin').

AMINOPHENAZONE plus PHENYLBUTAZONE ('butapyrine'; 'irgapyrin'; 'pyra-elmedal').

AMINOPHENAZONE ASCORBATE ('vaditon').

Aminophenazone butyl iodide *see* Butopyrammonium iodide.

AMINOPHENAZONE CYCLAMATE** (aminophenazone cyclohexylsulfamate).

AMINOPHENAZONE ETHYL SALICYLATE ('latepyrine').

AMINOPHENAZONE GENTISATE ('gentamidon'; 'pirissal').

4-Aminophenazone *see* 4-Aminoantipyrine.

1-(*p*-Aminophenethyl)-4-phenylisonipecotic acid ethyl ester *see* Anileridine.

3-(4-Aminophenethyl)-2,3,4,5-tetrahydro-7,8-dimethoxy-1*H*-3-benzazepine *see* Verilopam.

2-(*p*-Aminophenethyl)-1,2,3,4-tetrahydro-6,7-dimethoxy-1-methylisoquinoline *see* Veradoline.

(−)-3-(*p*-Aminophenethyl)-2,3,4,5-tetrahydro-8-methoxy-2-methyl-1*H*-3-benzazepine *see* Anilopam.

N-(5-*p*-Aminophenoxypentyl)phthalimide *see* Amphotalide.

26

Aminophenurobutane* see Carbutamide.
7-(α-Aminophenylacetamido)cephalosporanic acid see Cefaloglycin.
7-(2-Amino-2-phenylacetamido)-3-chloro-2-cephem-2-carboxylic acid see Cefaclor.
7-((+)-2-Amino-2-phenylacetamido)-3-methyl-2-cephem-2-carboxylic acid see Cefalexin.
6-(2-Amino-2-phenylacetamido)penicillanic acid see Ampicillin.
p-Aminophenylacetic acid phenylisopropylamide see Fepracet.
2-Amino-2-phenylacetophenone see Desylamine.
N-(p-Aminophenylacetyl)amphetamine see Fepracet.
p-Aminophenyl 2-aminothiazol-5-yl sulfone see Thiazosulfone.
4-Aminophenylarsonic acid see Arsanilic acid.
1-(p-Aminophenyl)-2-sec-butylaminoethanol see Amiterol.
4-AMINO-3-PHENYLBUTYRIC ACID (fenigama; phenigama; phenygam; phGABA).
α-p-Aminophenyl-α-ethylglutarimide see Aminoglutethimide.
2-Amino-5-phenyl-2-oxazoline see Aminorex.
2-Amino-5-phenyl-2-oxazolin-4-one see Pemoline.
(±)-2-Amino-1-phenylpropane see Amphetamine.
2-Amino-1-phenyl-1-propanol see Phenylpropanolamine.
2-Amino-3-phenylpropionic acid see Phenylalanine.
1-(m-Aminophenyl)-2(1H)-pyridinone see Amphenidone.
N-[p-(p-Aminophenylsulfonyl)phenyl]glycine see Acediasulfone sodium.
5-Amino-1-phenyl-1H-tetrazole see Fenamole.
P-(5-Amino-3-phenyl-1,2,4-triazol-1-yl)-N,N,N',N'-phosphonic diamide see Triamiphos.
AMINOPHON (dibutyl 1-(butylamino)cyclohexylphosphonate).
AMINOPHYLLINE** (theophyllamine; theophylline-ethylenediamine).
See also under Quinine sulfate.
3α-Amino-5α-pregnan-2-ol see Funtumidine.
AMINOPROMAZINE*** (10-[2,3-bis(dimethylamino)propyl]phenothiazine; iminopromazine; proquamezine; tetrameprozine; Bayer-A 124; RP 3828).
AMINOPROMAZINE FUMARATE ('myspamol').
3-Aminopropanesulfonic acid see Homotaurine.
[1-(2-Aminopropionamido)ethyl]phosphonic acid see Alafosfalin.
3-AMINOPROPIONITRILE (β-aminopropionitrile; BAPN; lathyrus factor).
2-Amino-2',6'-propionoxylidide see Tocainide.
2-Aminopropiophenone see Cathinone.
3-Amino-4-propoxybenzoic acid diethylaminoethyl ester see Proxymetacaine.
4-Amino-2-propoxybenzoic acid diethylaminoethyl ester see Propoxycaine.
1-(2-Aminopropoxy)-2,6-xylene see Mexiletine.
2-(2-Aminopropoxy)-m-xylene see Mexiletine.
2-[(3-Aminopropyl)amino]ethanethiol dihydrogen phosphate (ester) see Amifostine.

S-[2-[(3-Aminopropyl)amino]ethyl] dihydrogen phosphorothioate monohydrate see Amifostine.
N-(3-Aminopropyl)-1,4-butanediamine see Spermidine.
1-(3-Aminopropyl)-1,3-dihydro-N,3,3-trimethyl-1-phenylbenzo[c]thiophene see Talsupram.
3-Amino-3-propylheptane see Diprobutine.
2-(1-Aminopropyl)-2-indanol see Indanorex.
m-(2-Aminopropyl)phenol see Gepefrine.
p-(2-Aminopropyl)phenol see Hydroxyamphetamine.
N-(3-Aminopropyl)putrescine see Spermidine.
1-(4-Amino-2-propylpyrimidin-5-ylmethyl)-2-picolinium chloride see Amprolium.
6-Amino-9-(β-D-psicofuranosyl)purine see Angustmycin C.
AMINOPTERIN SODIUM*** (N-[p-[(2,4-diaminopterid-6-ylmethyl)amino]benzoyl]glutamic acid sodium salt; 4-amino-4-deoxyfolic acid sodium salt; antifolic acid; APGA; NSC-739).
6-Aminopurine see Adenine.
2-Aminopurine-6-thiol see Tioguanine.
4-(6-Aminopurin-9-yl)-4-deoxy-D-erythronic acid see Eritadenine.
4-(6-Aminopurin-9-yl)-2,3-dihydroxybutyric acid see Eritadenine.
'Aminopyrazolin' see Aminophenazone.
4-Amino-2-(1H)-pyrimidinone see Cytosine.
2-[2-(2-Aminopyrimidin-4-yl)vinyl]-1-methyl-5-nitroimidazole see Azanidazole.
Aminopyrine* see Aminophenazone.
'Aminoquin' see Pamaquine.
AMINOQUINOL*** (7-chloro-2-(o-chlorostyryl)-4-[(4-diethylamino-1-methylbutyl)amino]quinoline).
AMINOQUINURIDE*** (1,3-bis(4-amino-2-methylquinolin-6-yl)urea; 6,6'-carbonylbis(2-methyl-4-aminoquinoline); aminochinuride; 'revasa'; 'surfen').
AMINOREX*** (2-amino-5-phenyl-2-oxazoline; aminorex fumarate; aminoxaphen; McN-742; NSC-66952).
2-Amino-9-β-D-ribofuranosylpurine-6-thiol see Thioguanosine.
7-Amino-3-(β-D-ribofuranosyl)pyrazolo[4,3-d]pyrimidine see Formycin A.
4-Amino-7-β-D-ribofuranosyl-7H-pyrrolo[2,3-d]pyrimidine see Tubercidin.
4-Amino-7-β-D-ribofuranosyl-7H-pyrrolo[2,3-d]pyrimidine-5-carbonitrile see Toyocamycin.
4-Amino-1-β-D-ribofuranosyl-1,3,5-triazin-2(1H)-one see Azacitidine.
AMINOSALICYLIC ACID* (4-amino-2-hydroxybenzoic acid; p-aminosalicylic acid; aminosalylum; PAS; PASA; PASK).
See also Calcium aminosalicylate; Fenamisal; Hydroxyprocaine; Pasiniazid; Pheniramine p-aminosalicylate; Potassium 4-aminosalicylate.
AMINOSALICYLIC ACID plus ASCORBIC ACID ('pascorbic').
AMINOSALICYLIC ACID HYDRAZIDE ('pasdrazide').
p-Aminosalol see Fenamisal.

Aminosalylum *see* Aminosalicylic acid.

Aminosidin *see* Paromomycin.

Aminosine *see* Chlorpromazine.

2-Aminosuccinamic acid *see* Asparagine.

2-Aminosuccinamide *see* Aspartamide.

2-Aminosuccinic acid *see* Aspartic acid.

4-Amino-4′-succinylaminodiphenyl sulfone *see* Succisulfone.

3-(Aminosulfonyl)-4-chloro-*N*-(2,3-dihydro-2-methyl-1*H*-indol-1-yl)benzamide *see* Indapamide.

5-(Aminosulfonyl)-4-chloro-*N*-(2,6-dimethylphenyl)-2-hydroxybenzamide *see* Xipamide.

3-(Aminosulfonyl)-4-phenoxy-5-(1-pyrrolidinyl)-benzoic acid *see* Piretanide.

O-[2-Amino-2,3,4,6-tetradeoxy-6-(methylamino)-α-D-*erythro*-hexopyranosyl (1→4)]-*O*-[3-deoxy-4-*C*-methyl-3-(methylamino)-β-L-arabinopyranosyl(1→6)]-2-deoxy-D-streptamine *see* Micronomicin.

9-Amino-1,2,3,4-tetrahydroacridine *see* Tacrine.

6-Amino-1,2,3,4-tetrahydro-3-methyl-1-(2-methylallyl)-2,4-pyrimidinedione *see* Amisometradine.

8-Amino-1,2,3,4-tetrahydro-2-methyl-4-phenylisoquinoline *see* Nomifensine.

10-[(4-Aminotetrahydro-6-methyl-2*H*-pyran-2-yl)-oxy]-8-glycoloyl-7,8,9,10-tetrahydro-6,8,11-trihydroxy-1-methoxy-5,12-naphthacenedione *see* Esorubicin.

4-Amino-2,2,5,5-tetrakis(trifluoromethyl)-3-imidazoline *see* Midaflur.

2-Aminotetralin *see* 1,2,3,4-Tetrahydro-2-naphthylamine.

AMINOTHIAZOLE*** (2-aminothiazole; 2-thiazylamine; aminothiazole hydrogen succinate; aminothiazole maleate; RP 2921).

2-Amino-2-thiazoline phenylbutazone salt *see* Thiazolinobutazone.

7-[2-(2-Aminothiazol-4-yl)acetamido]-3-[[[1-[2-(dimethylamino)ethyl]-1*H*-tetrazol-5-yl]thio]methyl]-2-cephem-2-carboxylic acid *see* Cefotiam.

7-[2-(2-Aminothiazol-4-yl)-1-(1-carboxy-1-methylethyoxyimino)acetamido]-3-(1-pyridinomethyl)-3-cephem-4-carboxylate *see* Ceftazidime.

7-[2-(2-Aminothiazol-4-yl)glyoxylamido]-3-[[(5-(carboxymethyl)-4-methylthiazol-2-yl)thio]methyl]-2-cephem-2-carboxylic acid 7²-(*Z*)-(*O*-methyloxime) *see* Cefodizime.

1-[7-[2-(2-Aminothiazol-4-yl)glyoxylamido]-2-carboxy-8-oxo-5-thia-1-azabicyclo[4.2.0]oct-2-en-3-yl]methyl]-6,7-dihydro-5*H*-1-pyrindinium hydroxide inner salt 7²-(*Z*)-(*O*-methyloxime) *see* Cefpirome.

1-[[7-[2-(2-Aminothiazol-4-yl)glyoxylamido]-2-carboxy-8-oxo-5-thia-1-azabicyclo[4.2.0]oct-2-en-3-yl]methyl]pyridinium hydroxide inner salt 7²-(*Z*)-[*O*-(1-carboxy-1-methylethyl)oxime] *see* Ceftazidime.

7-[2-(2-Aminothiazol-4-yl)glyoxylamido]-2-cephem-2-carboxylic acid 7-(*O*-methyloxime) *see* Ceftizoxime.

7-[2-(2-Aminothiazol-4-yl)glyoxylamido]-2-cephem-2-carboxylic acid 7²-(*O*-methyloxime) *see* Cefetamet.

7-[2-(2-Aminothiazol-4-yl)glyoxylamido]-3-[[(2,5-dihydro-6-hydroxy-2-methyl-5-oxo-*s*-triazin-3-yl)-thio]methyl]-2-cephem-2-carboxylic acid 7²-(*Z*)-(*O*-methyloxime) *see* Ceftriaxone.

7-[2-(2-Aminothiazol-4-yl)glyoxylamido]-3-[(6,7-dihydro-5*H*-pyrindin-1-yl)methyl]-2-cephem-2-carboxylic acid inner salt 7²-(*O*-methyloxime) *see* Cefpirome.

7-[2-(2-Aminothiazol-4-yl)glyoxylamido]-3-[2-[[4-(formylmethyl)-1,4,5,6-tetrahydro-5,6-dioxo-*as*-triazin-3-yl]thio]vinyl]-2-cephem-2-carboxylic acid 7²-(*O*-methyloxime) *see* Ceftiolene.

7-[2-(2-Aminothiazol-4-yl)glyoxylamido]-3-(hydroxymethyl)-2-cephem-2-carboxylic acid α-(*O*-methyloxime) acetate *see* Cefotaxime.

7-[2-(2-Amino-4-thiazolyl)glyoxylamido]-3-(hydroxymethyl)-2-cephem-2-carboxylic acid 7²-(*O*-methyloxime) acetate 5-oxide *see* Ceftioxide.

7-[2-(2-Aminothiazol-4-yl)glyoxylamido]-3-[[(1-methyl-1*H*-tetrazol-5-yl)thio]methyl]-2-cephem-2-carboxylic acid 7²-(*Z*)-(*O*-methyloxime *see* Cefmenoxime.

7-[2-(2-Aminothiazol-4-yl)glyoxylamido]-3-(pyrid-1-ylmethyl)-2-cephem-2-carboxylic acid betaine 7²-(*Z*)-[*O*-(1-carboxy-1-methylethyl)oxime] *see* Ceftazidime.

[[[(2-Aminothiazol-4-yl)][2-(hydroxymethyl)-4-oxo-1-sulfoazetidin-3-yl]carbamoyl]methylene]amino]-oxy]acetic acid carbamate *see* Carumonam.

7-[2-(2-Aminothiazol-4-yl)-2-(methoxyimino)acetamido]-3-cephem-4-carboxylic acid *see* Ceftizoxime.

7-[2-(2-Aminothiazol-4-yl)-2-(methoxyimino)acetamido]-3-[[2,5-dihydro-6-hydroxy-2-methyl-5-oxo-1,2,4-triazin-3-yl)thio]methyl]-3-cephem-4-carboxylic acid *see* Ceftriaxone.

2-[[[(2-Aminothiazol-4-yl)-[(2-methyl-4-oxo-1-sulfoazetidin-3-yl)carbamoyl]methylene]amino]oxy]-2-methylpropionic acid *see* Aztreonam.

p-Aminothiolobenzoic acid diethylaminoethyl ester *see* Thiocaine.

α-Amino-*p*-toluic acid *see* *p*-Aminomethylbenzoic acid.

7-[2-(α-Amino-*o*-tolyl)acetamido]-3-[[[1-(carboxy-methyl)-1*H*-tetrazol-5-yl]thio]methyl]-2-cephem-2-carboxylic acid *see* Ceforanide.

Aminotrate phosphate *see* Trolnitrate.

4-Amino-*s*-triazin-2-one riboside *see* Azacitidine.

3-Amino-1*H*-1,2,4-triazole *see* Amitrole.

4-Amino-6-(trichloroethenyl)benzene-1,3-disulfonamide *see* Clorsulon.

4-Amino-3,5,6-trichloropicolinic acid *see* Picloram.

4-Amino-3,5,6-trichloropyridine-2-carboxylic acid *see* Picloram.

4-Amino-6-(trichlorovinyl)-*m*-benzenedisulfonamide *see* Clorsulon.

(8*S*,10*S*)-10-[(3-Amino-2,3,6-trideoxy-α-L-*arabino*-hexopyranosyl)oxy]-8-glycoloyl-7,8,9,10-tetrahydro-6,8,11-trihydroxy-1-methoxy-5,12-naphthacenedione *see* Epirubicin.

7-[(3-Amino-2,3,6-trideoxy-α-L-*lyxo*-hexopyranosyl)oxy]-9-glycoloyl-7,8,9,10-tetrahydro-6,9,11-trihydroxy-5,12-naphthacenedione *see* Medorubic-

28

in.

(8S,10S)-10[3-Amino-2,3,6-trideoxy-α-L-*lyxo*-hexo-pyranosyl)oxy]-8-glycolyl-7,8,9,10-tetrahydro-6,8,11-trihydroxy-1-methoxy-5,12-naphthacenedi-one *see* Doxorubicin.

1-(3-Amino-4,5,6-triethoxyphthalid-3-yl)-1,2,3,4-tetrahydro-8-methoxy-2-methyl-6,7-methylenedi-oxyisoquinoline *see* Tritoqualine.

7-Amino-4,5,6-triethoxy-(5,6,7,8-tetrahydro-4-methoxy-6-methyl-1,3-dioxolo[4,5-*g*]isoquinolin-5-yl)phthalide *see* Tritoqualine.

4-Amino-3-(α,α,α-trifluoro-*m*-tolyl)-5-isothiazole-carboxylic acid *see* Amflutizole.

2-Amino-5-(α,α,α-trifluoro-*p*-tolyl)-2-oxazoline *see* Fluminorex.

30-Amino-3,14,25-trihydroxy-3,9,14,20,25-penta-azatriacontane-2,10,13,21,24-pentaone *see* Defe-roxamine.

N-(3-Amino-2,4,6-triiodobenzoyl)-N-phenyl-β-alan-ine *see* Iobenzamic acid.

3-[(3-Amino-2,4,6-triiodobenzoyl)phenylamino]pro-pionic acid *see* Iobenzamic acid.

2-(3-Amino-2,4,6-triiodobenzyl)butyric acid *see* Io-panoic acid.

3'-Amino-2',4',6'-triiodo-N-methylglutaranilic acid *see* Iomeglamic acid.

3-[N-(3-Amino-2,4,6-triiodophenyl)acetamido]-2-methylpropionic acid *see* Iocetamic acid.

3-(3-Amino-2,4,6-triiodophenyl)-2-ethylpropionic acid *see* Iopanoic acid.

4-[N-(3-Amino-2,4,6-triiodophenyl)-N-methylcarba-moyl)butyric acid *see* Iomeglamic acid.

N-(3-Amino-2,4,6-triiodophenyl)-N-methylgluta-ramic acid *see* Iomeglamic acid.

α-[[4-Amino-5-(3,4,5-trimethoxybenzyl)pyrimidin-2-yl]amino]-3-ethoxy-4-hydroxy-α-toluenesulfonic acid *see* Vaneprim.

N-[4-Amino-5-(3,4,5-trimethoxybenzyl)pyrimidin-2-yl]phthalimide *see* Talmetoprim.

4-(4-Amino-6,7,8-trimethoxyquinazolin-2-yl)piper-azine-1-carboxylic acid 2-hydroxy-2-methylprop-yl ester *see* Trimazosin.

Aminourea *see* Semicarbazide.

p-**Amino-*p*'-ureidodiphenylsulfone** *see* Amidapsone.

2-Amino-4-ureidovaleric acid *see* Citrulline.

2-Aminovaleric acid *see* Norvaline.

'Aminoweidnerit' *see* Methenamine thiocyanate.

Aminoxaphen *see* Aminorex.

'Aminoxidin' *see* Paromomycin.

AMINOXYTRIPHENE* (2,3,3-tris(*p*-methoxy-phenyl)-N,N-dimethylallylamine; 3-(dimethyl-amino)-1,1,2-tris(*p*-methoxyphenyl)-1-propene; amotriphene; WIN-5494-1).

Aminoxytropine tropate *see* Atropine oxide.

AMIODARONE* (2-butyl-3-[4-(2-diethyl-aminoethoxy)-3,3-diiodobenzoyl]benzofuran; 2-butyl-3-benzofuranyl 4-(2-diethylaminoethoxy)-3,5-diiodophenyl ketone; amiodarone hydro-chloride; L-3428; SK&F-33134-A).

AMIODOXYL BENZOATE* (ammonium *o*-iod-oxybenzoate; 'arthrytin'; 'oxo-ate').

'Amipaque' *see* Metrizamide.

AMIPERONE* (4-(*p*-chlorophenyl)-1-[3-(*p*-fluorobenzoyl)propyl]-N,N-dimethylisonipecot-amide; 4-[4-(*p*-chlorophenyl)-4-dimethylcarba-moylpiperid-1-yl]-4'-fluorobutyrophenone; R-2962).

AMIPHENAZOLE* (2,4-diamino-5-phenyl-thiazole; daftazol; phenamizole; DAPT; DHA 245).

'Amiphos' *see* S-2-Acetamidoethyl O,O-dimethyl phosphorodithioate.

AMIPIZONE* (2-chloro-4'-(1,4,5,6-tetrahydro-4-methyl-6-oxopyridazin-3-yl)propionanilide).

Amipramidine *see* Amiloride.

Amipramizide *see* Amiloride.

AMIPROFOS-METHYL* (O-methyl O-(4-methyl-2-nitrophenyl N-isopropylphosphor-amidothioate; 'tokunol M').

AMIQUINSIN* (4-amino-6,7-dimethoxyqui-noline; U-935).

AMISOMETRADINE* (6-amino-1,2,3,4-tetra-hydro-3-methyl-1-(2-methylallyl)-2,4-pyrimidinedione; 6-amino-3-methyl-1-(2-methyl-allyl)uracil; aminoisometradine).

AMISULPRIDE* (4-amino-N-[(1-ethylpyrrolid-in-2-yl)methyl]-5-(ethylsulfonyl)-2-methoxy-benzamide).

AMITEROL* ((±)-*p*-amino-α-[(1-methylprop-yl)aminomethyl]benzyl alcohol; (±)-*p*-amino-α-(*sec*-butylaminomethyl)benzyl alcohol; (±)-1-(*p*-aminophenyl)-2-*sec*-butylamino)ethanol).

Amithiozone *see* Thioacetazone.

AMITHIZONE (tr) (*p*-acetamido-*m*-methoxy-benzaldehyde thiosemicarbazone; amitizon; SHCH-85).

Amitizon (tr) *see* Amithizone.

AMITON* ([[2-(diethoxyphosphinyl)thio]ethyl]di-methylamine; S-[2-(diethylamino)ethyl] O,O-di-ethyl phosphorothioate; DSDP; 'inferno'; 'me-tramas'; 'tetram').

AMITRAZ (N-methyl-N'-2,4-xylyl-N-(N-2,4-xylylformimidoyl)formamidine; N'-(2,4-dimeth-ylphenyl)-N-[N-(2,4-dimethylphenyl)formimido-yl]-N-methylformamidine; N'-(2,4-dimethyl-phenyl)-N-[[(2,4-dimethylphenyl)imino]methyl]-N-methylmethanimidamide; methylbis(2,4-xylyl-iminomethyl)amine; U-36059; 'ectodex'; 'mita-ban'; 'mitac'; 'taktic').

'Amitrene' *see* Dexamphetamine.

'Amitril' *see* Amitriptyline.

AMITRIPTYLINE* (10,11-dihydro-N,N-di-methyl-5H-dibenzo[a,d]cycloheptene-Δ⁵,γ-prop-ylamine; 5-[3-(dimethylamino)propylidene]-10,11-dihydrodibenzo[a,d]cycloheptene; amitri-ptyline hydrochloride; proheptadiene; N-750; Ro 4-1575).

AMITRIPTYLINE plus CHLORDIAZEPOXIDE ('limbitrol'; 'pantrop').

AMITRIPTYLINE plus PERPHENAZINE ('etra-fon'; 'mutabon'; 'mutanxion'; 'mutaspline'; 'tri-avil'; 'triptafen').

Amitriptyline N-oxide *see* Amitriptylinoxide.

AMITRIPTYLINOXIDE* (amitriptyline N-oxide; 'dano'; 'equilibrin').

Amitrol *see* Amitrole.

29

AMITROLE* (3-amino-1*H*-1,2,4-triazole; 1*H*-1,2,4-triazol-3-amine; amitrol; ATA; 3A-T; 'amizol'; 'cytrol'; 'ustinex PA'; 'weedazol').

AMIXETRINE* (1-(2-isoamyloxy-2-phenylethyl)pyrrolidine; 1-(β-isopentyloxyphenethyl)-pyrrolidine; 1-[2-(3-methylbutoxy)-2-phenylethyl]pyrrolidine; CERM-898; 'somagest').

'Amizepin' see Carbamazepine.

Amizil see Benactyzine.

'Amizine' see Simazine.

'Amizol' see Amitrole.

Amizole see Sulfamidopyrine sodium.

Ammicardin see Khellin.

Ammidin see Pentosalen.

Amminosidine see Paromomycin.

'Ammivin' see Khellin.

'Ammocycline' see under Prazosin.

Ammoidin see Methoxsalen.

'Ammoket' see Ammonium mandelate.

Ammonium bithiolicum see Ammonium sulfobituminate.

Ammonium camphocarbonate see Camphoramine.

Ammonium camphocarboxylate see Camphoramine.

Ammonium ichthosulfonate see Ammonium sulfobituminate.

Ammonium *o*-iodoxybenzoate see Amiodoxyl benzoate.

AMMONIUM MANDELATE ('amdelate'; 'ammoket'; 'mandicid'; 'manduryl').

Ammonium 2-oxobornane-3-carboxylate see Camphoramine.

AMMONIUM PHTHALAMATE (ammonium *o*-carbamoylbenzoate; 'spirogen').

AMMONIUM SULFOBITUMINATE (ammonium bithiolicum; ammonium ichthosulfonate; ammonium sulfobituminosum; ammonium sulfoichthyolate; bithyolum; ichthammol; ichthammonium; ichthium; ichthosulfol).

Ammonium sulfobituminosum see Ammonium sulfobituminate.

Ammonium sulfoichthyolate see Ammonium sulfobituminate.

'Ammophylline' see Aminophylline.

'A.M.N' see Flavin mononucleotide.

AMOBARBITAL* (5-ethyl-5-(3-methylbutyl)-barbituric acid; 5-ethyl-5-isoamylbarbituric acid; 5-ethyl-5-isopentylbarbituric acid; amylobarbitone; pentymal; barbamyl).

AMOBARBITAL plus SCOPOLAMINE METHYL NITRATE ('veryl').

Amocaine* see Amolanone.

AMODIAQUINE* (4-(7-chloro-4-quinolylamino)-α-diethylamino-*o*-cresol; 7-chloro-4-(3-diethylaminoethyl-4-hydroxyanilino)quinoline; SN-10751).

AMODIAQUINE plus PRIMAQUINE ('camoprim').

'Amoebal' see Arsthinol.

'Amoebin' see Ethacridine lactate.

'Amoenol' see Clioquinol.

AMOGASTRIN (*N*-carboxy-L-tryptophyl-L-methionyl-L-α-aspartyl-3-phenyl-L-alaninamide

N-tert-pentyl ester).

AMOLANONE (4-(diethylamino)-2-(*o*-hydroxyphenyl)-2-phenylbutyric acid lactone; amocaine; AP-43).

AMOPROXAN* (4-(2-hydroxy-3-isopentyloxypropyl)morpholine 3,4,5-trimethoxybenzoate; *N*-[3-isoamyloxy-2-(3,4,5-trimethoxybenzoyloxy)propyl]morpholine; α-isopentyloxymethyl-4-morpholineethanol 3,4,5-trimethoxybenzoate; CERM-370; 'mederal').

AMOPYROQUINE* (7-chloro-4-(4-hydroxy-3-pyrrolidin-1-yl-methylanilino)quinoline; 4-(7-chloroquinolin-4-ylamino)-α-pyrrolidin-1-yl-*o*-cresol; PAM-780).

'Amorphan' see Cathine.

AMOSCANATE* (4-isothiocyanato-4'-nitrodiphenylamine; *p*-(*p*-nitroanilino)phenyl isothiocyanate; C-9333; Go/CGP-4540).

AMOSULALOL ((±)-5-[1-hydroxy-2-[[2-(*o*-methoxyphenoxy)ethyl]amino]ethyl]-*o*-toluenesulfonamide; amosulalol hydrochloride; YM-09583).

Amotriphene see Aminoxytriphene.

AMOXAPINE* (2-chloro-11-piperazin-1-yldibenz[*b,f*][1,4]oxazepine; CL-67772; 'asendin'; 'moxadil').

AMOXECAINE (1-[2-[2-(diethylamino)ethyl]ethylamino]ethyl *p*-aminobenzoate; *N,N',N'*-triethyl-*N*-(2-hydroxyethyl)ethylenediamine *p*-aminobenzoate; RP 2856).

AMOXICILLIN* (6-[D(−)-2-amino-2-(*p*-hydroxyphenyl)acetamido]penicillanic acid; (6*R*)-6-[α-D-(*p*-hydroxyphenyl)glycylamino]penicillanic acid; α-amino-*p*-hydroxybenzylpenicillin; BRL-2333).
See also under Metronidazole.

AMOXICILLIN plus CLAVULANIC ACID ('augmentan'; 'augmentin').

AMOXICILLIN plus FLUCLOXACILLIN (FI-7302; 'flumoxil').

'Amoxid' see Amoxicillin.

'Amoxil' see Amoxicillin.

AMOXYDRAMINE CAMSILATE* (*N,N*-dimethyl-2-(diphenylmethoxy)ethylamine-*N*-oxide 2-oxo-10-bornanesulfonate; amyoxydramine camphorsulfonate; diphenhydramine aminoxide camsylate).

AMOXYDRAMINE UNDECENATE ('mykestron').

AMP see Rifampicin.

5-AMP see Adenosine phosphate.

A5MP see Adenosine phosphate.

'Ampazine' see Promazine.

'Ampecyclal' see Heptaminol adenosine phosphate.

AMPEROZIDE* (4-[4,4-bis(*p*-fluorophenyl)-butyl]-*N*-ethyl-1-piperazinecarboxamide).

Amphaethamine see Amphetamine.

Amphechloral* see Amfecloral.

AMPHENIDONE* (1-(*m*-aminophenyl)-2(1*H*)-pyridinone; 'dornwal').

AMPHETAMINE* (α-methylphenethylamine; (±)-2-amino-1-phenylpropane; (±)-β-phenylisopropylamine; amphaethamine; desoxynorephedrine; fenamin; phenamine).

(+)-**Amphetamine** *see* Dexamphetamine.

(−)-**Amphetamine** *see* Levamfetamine.

Amphetamine *p*-aminophenylacetate *see* Fepracet.

(±)-**AMPHETAMINE *p*-CHLOROPHENOXY-ACETATE** ('satietyl').

Amphetamine-pyridoxine condensation product *see* Pyridoxiphen.

Amphetaminil *see* Amfetaminil.

Amphetyline *see* Fenetylline.

'**Amphodyne**' *see* Imidecyl iodine.

Amphomycin* *see* Amfomycin.

AMPHOTALIDE*** (*N*-(5-*p*-aminophenoxypentyl)phthalimide; M & B-1948-A).

AMPHOTERICIN B*** (antibiotic from *Str. nodosus*).
See also under Tetracycline.

'**Amphotropine**' *see* Hexacamphamine.

'**Amphozone**' *see* Amphotericin B.

'**Ampibel**' *see* Ampicillin.

AMPICILLIN*** (D(−)-6-(2-amino-2-phenylacetamido)penicillanic acid; (6*R*)-6-(α-D-phenylglycylamino)penicillanic acid; α-aminobenzylpenicillin; ampicillin sodium; ampicillin trihydrate; AY-6108; BRL-1341; NSC-528986; P-50; Wy-5103).
See also Azidocillin; Bacampicillin; Lenampicillin; Pivampicillin; Sultamicillin; Talampicillin.

AMPICILLIN plus CLOXACILLIN ('ampiclox'; 'ampiox'; 'amplium'; 'cloxamp'; 'electopen'; 'lactaclox'; 'summopenil'; 'tupen').

AMPICILLIN plus DICLOXACILLIN (HI-56; 'ampiplus'; 'ampliclox-D'; 'cervantal'; 'diamplicil'; 'duplexcillin'; 'totocillin').

AMPICILLIN plus FLUCLOXACILLIN ('magnapen').

AMPICILLIN plus OXACILLIN ('cervantal parenteral'; 'lucipen'; 'totocillin').

AMPICILLIN plus OXYPHENBUTAZONE ('ampifenil').

AMPICILLIN plus PROBENECID ('prototapen').

Ampicillin 2,3-dihydroxy-2-butenyl ester cyclic carbonate *see* Lenampicillin.

AMPICILLIN GUAIACOLSULFONATE ('broncopen'; 'guaiacillin'; 'tauglicolcillin').

AMPICILLIN GUAIACYLDIETHYLAMINO-ACETATE ('diampicicol').

'**Ampiclox**' *see under* Ampicillin.

'**Ampifenil**' *see under* Ampicillin.

'**Ampiox**' *see under* Ampicillin.

'**Ampiplus**' *see under* Ampicillin.

'**Amplicaine**' *see* Octacaine.

'**Ampliclox-D**' *see under* Ampicillin.

'**Amplidione**' *see* Oxazidione.

'**Amplital**' *see* Ampicillin.

'**Amplium**' *see under* Ampicillin.

'**Ampliuril**' *see* Benziodarone.

'**Amplivix**' *see* Benziodarone.

Amprocidum* *see* Amprolium.

'**Amprol**' *see* Amprolium.

AMPROLIUM*** (1-(4-amino-2-propylpyrimidin-5-ylmethyl)-2-picolinium chloride; amproci-

dum; amprolium hydrochloride).

'**Amprolmix**' *see* Amprolium.

AMPROTROPINE* (3-(diethylamino)-2,2-dimethylpropyl tropate; AP-407; 'syntropan').

AMPYRIMINE*** (1,4,7-triamino-5-phenylpyrimido[4,5-*d*]pyrimidine; 5-phenylpyrimido[4,5-*d*]pyrimidine-2,4,7-triamine; SK&F-13338).

'**Ampyrone**' *see* 4-Aminoantipyrine.

'**Ampyrox**' *see* Scopolamine methyl bromide.

AMPYZINE*** (2-(dimethylamino)pyrazine; ampyzine sulfate; W-3580B).

AMQUINATE*** (methyl 7-diethylamino-4-hydroxy-6-propyl-3-quinolinecarboxylate).

AMR-69 *see* Pirfenidone.

AMRINONE*** (5-amino[3,4′-bipyridin]-6(1*H*)-one; WIN-40680).

m-**AMSA** *see* Amsacrine.

AMSACRINE** (4′-(acridin-9-ylamino)-3′-methoxymethanesulfonanilide; 4′-(acridin-9-ylamino)methanesulfon-*m*-anisidide; *m*-AMSA; CI-880; NSC-156303; NSC-249992; SN-11841).

AMSONIC ACID* (4,4′-diaminostilbene-2,2′-disulfonic acid).

'**Amstat**' *see* Tranexamic acid.

'**Amukin**' *see* Amikacin.

'**Amuno**' *see* Indometacin.

'**Amycycline**' *see under* Chlortetracycline.

'**Amyderm**' *see* Povidone-iodine.

Amygdalic acid *see* Mandelic acid.

AMYGDALIN (mandelonitrile gentiobioside; NSC-15780; 'aprikern'; 'bee-17'; 'laetrile'; 'vitamin B-17').

tert-**Amyl alcohol** *see* 2-Methyl-2-butanol.

2-(Amylamino)ethyl *p*-aminobenzoate *see* Naepaine.

α-**AMYLASE** (alpha amylase; diastase; 'buclamase'; 'fortizyme'; 'maxilase'; 'oramyl').
See also under Chlortetracycline.

5-*sec*-Amyl-5-(bromoallyl)barbituric acid *see* 5-(2-Bromoallyl)-5-(1-methylbutyl)barbituric acid.

'**Amylcaine**' *see* Naepaine.

Amyleine* *see* Amylocaine.

Amylene hydrate *see* 2-Methyl-2-butanol.

AMYLMETACRESOL* (6-pentyl-*m*-cresol).

AMYL NITRITE (isoamyl nitrite).

Amylobarbitone* *see* Amobarbital.

AMYLOCAINE* (1-[(dimethylamino)methyl]-1-methylpropyl benzoate; amyleine; 'stovaine').

Amylopectin sodium sulfate *see* Sodium amylosulfate.

Amylosulfate *see* Sodium amylosulfate.

Amylpenicillin *see* Penicillin F.

'**Amylsine**' *see* Naepaine.

'**Amytal**' *see* Amobarbital.

AN-1 *see* Amfetaminil.

AN-148 *see* Methadone.

AN-448 *see* Mazindol.

AN-1317 *see* Perimetazine.

AN-1320 *see* Fumaria officinalis extract.

AN-1324 *see* Glybuzole.

'**Anabactyl**' *see* Carbenicillin.

ANABASEINE (3,4,5,6-tetrahydro-2,3′-bipyridine; 3,4,5,6-tetrahydro-2-pyrid-3-ylpyridine).

ANABASINE (1,2,3,4,5,6-hexahydro-2,3′-bipyridine; 2-pyrid-3-ylpiperidine; neonicotine).

'Anabile' *see* Ox bile.

'Anabolex' *see* Androstanolone.

ANACAROL*** ((±)-2'-[3-(*tert*-butylamino)-2-hydroxypropoxy]-2-furananilide).

Anadol (tr) *see* Alphaprodine.

'Anadrol' *see* Oxymetholone.

'Anadur' *see* Nandrolone (*p*-hexyloxy)hydrocinnamate.

'Anaestheform' *see* Benzocaine.

'Anaesthesin' *see* Benzocaine.

'Anafebrina' *see* Aminophenazone.

'Anaflex' *see* Polynoxylin.

'Anafranil' *see* Clomipramine.

ANAGESTONE*** (3-deoxy-17α-hydroxy-6α-methylprogesterone; 17α-hydroxy-6α-methyl-pregn-4-en-20-one).

ANAGESTONE ACETATE* ('anatropin').

ANAGESTONE ACETATE plus MESTRANOL (MI-860; 'preventa').

ANAGRELIDE*** (6,7-dichloro-1,5-dihydroimidazo[2,1-*b*]quinazolin-2(3*H*)-one; anagrelide hydrochloride; BL-4162A).

'Analeptan' *see* Endomide.

'Analeptin' *see* Oxedrine.

'Analexin' *see* Fenyramidol.

Analgesine *see* Phenazone.

Analgin (tr) *see* Dipyrone.

'Analutos' *see* Calcium acetylsalicylate.

'Ananase' *see* Bromelains.

'Anapolon' *see* Oxymetholone.

'Anaprel' *see* Rescinnamine.

Anaprilin (tr) *see* Propranolol.

'Anaprox' *see* Naproxen.

'Anarcon' *see* Nalorphine.

'Anarel' *see* Guanadrel.

'Anasclerol' *see* Vincamine.

'Anastil' *see* Guaiacol.

'Anasyth' *see* Stanozolol.

'Anatensol' *see* Fluphenazine decanoate.

'Anathrombase' *see* Dicoumarol.

'Anatran' *see* Acepromazine.

'Anatropin' *see* Anagestone acetate.

Anautine* *see* Diphenhydramine.

'Anavar' *see* Oxandrolone.

ANAZOCINE** (9-*syn*-methoxy-3-methyl-9-phenyl-3-azabicyclo[3.3.1]nonane; 4β-methoxy-1-methyl-4α-phenyl-3α,5α-propanopiperidine; 9-methoxy-3-methyl-9-phenylisogranatanine; azabicyclane).

ANAZOLENE SODIUM** (4-(4-anilino-5-sulfonaphth-1-ylazo)-5-hydroxy-2,7-naphthalenedisulfonic acid trisodium salt; trisodium 4-anilino-8-hydroxy-1,1'-azonaphthalene-3,5',6-trisulfonate; sodium anazolene; sodium anoxynaphthonate; acid blue CI-92; CI-92; 'coomassie blue'; 'wofazurin').

'Ancaris' *see* Thenium closilate.

'Ancef' *see* Cefazolin.

Anchoic acid *see* Azelaic acid.

ANCITABINE*** ((2*R*,3*R*,3a*S*,9a*R*)-2,3,3a,9a-tetrahydro-3-hydroxy-6-imino-6*H*-furo-[2',3':4,5]oxazolo[3,2-*a*]pyrimidine-2-methanol;

2,2'-anhydro-1-β-D-arabinofuranosylcytosine; 2,2'-cyclo-1β-D-arabinofuranosylcytosine; 2,2'-anhydrocytarabine; 2,2'-cyclocytarabine; cyclocytidine; anhydro-ara-C; 2,2'-c-ara-C; 2,2'-cyclo-ara-C; NSC-145668).

ANCITABINE ACETATE (NSC-129220).

'Ancobon' *see* Flucytosine.

'Ancolan' *see* Meclozine.

'Anconcen' *see under* Chlormadinone acetate.

'Ancotil' *see* Flucytosine.

ANCROD*** (anticoagulant (defibrinating) fraction from *Agkistrodon rhodostoma* venom; Abbott 38414; 'arvin'; 'venacil').

'Ancylol' *see* Disophenol.

ANCYMIDOL* (α-(*p*-anisyl)-α-cyclopropyl-5-pyrimidinemethanol; α-cyclopropyl-α-(*p*-methoxyphenyl)-5-pyrimidinemethanol; EL-531).

'Ancyte' *see* Piposulfan.

'Andantol' *see* Isothipendyl.

'Andradurin' *see* Testosterone 3-*p*-(hexyloxy)-hydrocinnamate.

'Andramine' *see* Hexobendine.

'Andriol' *see* Testosterone undecanoate.

'Androcur' *see* Cyproterone acetate.

'Androdurin' *see* Testosterone ketolaurate.

Androfurazanol *see* Furazabol.

'Androlone' *see* Androstanolone.

'Androstalone' *see* Mestanolone.

Androstanazole *see* Stanozolol.

5α-ANDROSTANE (etioallocholane; NSC-49000).

5β-ANDROSTANE (aetian; etian; etiocholane).

ANDROSTANOLONE*** (17β-hydroxy-5α-androstan-3-one; dihydrotestosterone; 5α-dihydrotestosterone; stanolone).

ANDROSTERONE (3α-hydroxy-5α-androstan-17-one).

'Anelmid' *see* Dithiazanine iodide.

ANEMONIN (1,2-dihydroxy-1,2-cyclobutanediacrylic acid dilactone).

'Ane-pad' *see* Ketocaine.

'Anergan' *see* Acepromazine.

'Anergex' *see* Poisonoak extract.

'Anesthesin' *see* Benzocaine.

'Anesthone' *see* Benzocaine.

ANETHOLE (1-methoxy-4-propenylbenzene; *p*-propenylanisole; anise camphor).

ANETHOLE TRITHIONE (3-(*p*-anisyl)trithione; 5-(*p*-methoxyphenyl)-1,2-dithiole-3-thione; 1-(*p*-methoxyphenyl)-4,5-dithia-1-cyclopentene-3-thione; *p*-methoxyphenylpropenetrithione; *p*-methoxyphenyltrithiopropene; trithio-(*p*-methoxyphenyl)propene; SK&F-1717).

Aneurine *see* Thiamine.

'Aneuxol' *see* Aminophenazone.

'Anexate' *see* Mefenorex.

'Anfix' *see* Formothion.

ANGELIC ACID (*cis*-α,β-dimethylacrylic acid).

'Anghirol' *see* Cynarine.

'Angicid' *see* Sulfanilamide.

'Angicone' *see* Bismuth valproate.

'Anginin' *see* Pyricarbate.

'Anginyl' *see* Diltiazem.

'Angiocapsul' *see* Clofibrate.

'**Angiociclan**' *see* Bencyclane.
'**Angio-conray**' *see* Sodium iotalamate.
'**Angiografin**' *see* Meglumine diatrizoate.
'**Angiokapsul**' *see under* Clofibrate.
'**Angiombrine**' *see* Meglumine acetrizoate.
'**Angiopac**' *see* Vincamine.
ANGIOTENSIN(S) (angiotonin; hypertensin).
See also Arfalasin; Saralasin.
β-ANGIOTENSIN-II (Ba-33902).
ANGIOTENSINAMIDE* (*N*-[1-[*N*-[*N*-(*N*-(*N*²-asparaginylarginyl)valyl)tyrosyl]valyl]histidyl]propyl]-3-phenylalanine; val₅-hypertensin II-asp-β-amide; angiotensin amide; NSC-107678; 'hypertensin-Ciba').
Angiotonin *see* Angiotensin(s).
'**Angioxin**' *see* Pyricarbate.
'**Angioxyl**' *see* Kallidinogenase.
'**Angitrit**' *see* Trolnitrate.
'**Angium**' *see* Bufuralol.
'**Angolon**' *see* Imolamine.
'**Angopril**' *see* Bepridil.
ANGUSTMYCIN A (6-amino-9-(L-1,2-furopyranosenyl)purine).
ANGUSTMYCIN C (adenine psicofuranoside; 6-amino-9-(β-D-psicofuranosyl)purine; 'psicofuranine').
Anhaline *see* Hordenine.
2,2′-Anhydro-1-β-D-arabinofuranosylcytosine *see* Ancitabine.
Anhydro-ara-C *see* Ancitabine.
Anhydro-4,4′-bis(diethylamino)-5′′-hydroxytriphenylmethanol-2′′,4′′-disulfonic acid sodium salt *see* Patent blue.
Anhydro-4,4′-bis(diethylamino)triphenylmethanol-2′′,4′′-disulfonic acid sodium salt *see* Isosulfan blue.
N¹,N¹-Anhydrobis(2-hydroxyethyl)biguanide *see* Moroxydine.
2,2′-Anhydrocytarabine *see* Ancitabine.
3,6-Anhydro-4-O-β-D-galactopyranosyl-α-D-galactopyranose 2,4′-bis(potassium/sodium sulfate)-(1→3′)polysaccharide *see* Poligeenan.
Anhydrogitalin *see* Gitoxin.
Anhydroglucochloral *see* Chloralose.
Anhydrohydroxynorprogesterone *see* Norethisterone.
ANHYDROMETHYLENECITRIC ACID (β-(hydroxymethoxy)tricarballylic acid γ-lactone).
See also Sodium anhydromethylenecitrate.
'**Anhydron**' *see* Cyclothiazide.
ANICAINE (tr) (2-piperid-1-ylethyl 2,2-diphenylacetate).
ANIDOXIME** (3-(diethylamino)propiophenone *O*-[(*p*-methoxyphenyl)carbamoyl] oxime; 3-(diethylamino)-1-phenyl-1-propanone *O*-[[(4-methoxyphenyl)amino]carbonyl]oxime; bamoxine; BRL-11870; E-142).
ANILAMATE** (salicylanilide methylcarbamate).
ANILAZINE* (4,6-dichloro-2-(*o*-chloroanilino)-*s*-triazine; 4,6-dichloro-*N*-(2-chlorophenyl)-1,3,5-triazin-2-amine; 'dyrene'; 'kemate').
ANILERIDINE** (ethyl 1-(*p*-aminophenethyl)-4-

phenylisonipecotate; MK-89).
ANILINE (benzenamine; phenylamine).
Aniline violet *see* Crystal violet.
2-[(Anilinocarbonyl)oxy]-*N*-ethylpropionamide *see* Carbetamide.
1-(2-Anilinoethyl)-4-[4,4-bis(*p*-fluorophenyl)butyl]-piperazine *see* Difluanazine.
1-(2-Anilinoethyl)-4-(2-diethylaminoethoxy)-4-phenylpiperidine *see* Diamocaine.
4′-Anilino-8-hydroxy-1,1′-azonaphthalene-3,5′,6-trisulfonic acid trisodium salt *see* Anazolene sodium.
2-Anilinomethyl-2-imidazoline *see* Phenamazoline.
1-(3-Anilinopropyl)-4-phenylisonipecotic acid ethyl ester *see* Piminodine.
4-(4-Anilino-5-sulfonaphth-1-ylazo)-5-hydroxy-2,7-naphthalenedisulfonic acid trisodium salt *see* Anazolene sodium.
ANILOPAM* ((−)-3-(*p*-aminophenethyl)-2,3,4,5-tetrahydro-8-methoxy-2-methyl-1*H*-3-benzazepine; anilopam hydrochloride).
ANILPYRINE (acetanilide-phenazone condensation product).
Animal galactose factor *see* Orotic acid.
'**Animert**' *see* Tetrasul.
ANIPAMIL** (2-[3-[(*m*-methoxyphenethyl)methylamino]propyl]-2-(*m*-methoxyphenyl)tetradecanenitrile).
ANIRACETAM** (1-*p*-anisoyl-2-pyrrolidinone; 1-(*p*-methoxybenzoyl)pyrrolidin-2-one; Ro 13-5057).
ANISACRIL** (2-(*o*-methoxyphenyl)-3,3-diphenylacrylic acid; SK&F-16046).
ANISALDEHYDE (*p*-methoxybenzaldehyde).
m-**Anisaldehyde** *O*-[2-hydroxy-3-[4-(*o*-methoxyphenyl)piperazin-1-yl]propyl]oxime *see* Peradoxime.
ANISAMIDE(S) (methoxybenzamide(s)).
1-[*p*-[2-(*o*-Anisamido)ethyl]benzenesulfonyl]-3-cyclopentylurea *see* Glipentide.
Anise camphor *see* Anethole.
ANISIC ACID (*p*-methoxybenzoic acid).
m-**Anisic acid 3-piperid-1-ylpropyl ester** *see* Pribecaine.
ANISIDINE(S) (*ar*-methoxyaniline(s)).
ANISINDIONE** (2-(*p*-anisyl)-1,3-indandione; 2-(*p*-methoxyphenyl)-1,3-indandione).
ANISOLE (methoxybenzene; methyl phenyl ether).
ANISOMYCIN* (3-acetoxy-4-hydroxy-2-(*p*-methoxybenzyl)pyrrolidine; PA-106).
ANISOPERIDONE* (4′-methoxy-4-(4-phenylpiperid-1-yl)butyrophenone; 1-[3-(*p*-methoxybenzoyl)propyl]-4-phenylpiperidine; R-1647).
ANISOPIROL** ((+)-α-(*p*-fluorophenyl)-4-(*o*-methoxyphenyl)-1-piperazinebutanol; R-2159).
Anisotropine methylbromide* *see* Octatropine methylbromide.
3-(*p*-Anisoyl)-3-bromoacrylic acid *see* Bromebric acid.
1-(*p*-Anisoyl)-1-(3,4-dichlorophenyl)-3,3-dimethylurea *see* Anisuron.
3-(*p*-Anisoyl)-6-methoxy-2-methylindole-1-acetic

acid *see* Duometacin.

1-*p*-Anisoyl-2-pyrrolidinone *see* Aniracetam.

ANISURON* (1-(*p*-anisoyl)-1-(3,4-dichlorophen-yl)-3,3-dimethylurea; 1-(3,4-dichlorophenyl)-1-(*p*-methoxybenzoyl)-3,3-dimethylurea; methoxymarc; metoxymarc).

α-(*p*-Anisyl)-α-cyclopropyl-5-pyrimidinemethanol *see* Ancymidol.

2-(*p*-Anisyl)-1-[*p*-(2-diethylaminoethoxy)phenyl]-1-phenylethanol *see* Ethamoxytriphetol.

***trans*-1-(*m*-Anisyl)-2-[(dimethylamino)methyl]cyclo-hexanol** *see* Tramadol.

2-(*p*-Anisyl)-1,3-indandione *see* Anisindione.

3-(*o*-Anisyloxy)-1-(isopropylamino)-2-propanol *see* Moprolol.

3-(*p*-Anisyl)trithione *see* Anethole trithione.

'Aniten' *see* Flurenol-butyl.

ANITRAZAFEN*** (5,6-bis(*p*-methoxyphenyl)-3-methyl-*as*-triazine; LY-122512).

'Ankilostin' *see* Tetrachloroethylene.

'Anobesina' *see* Dinex sodium.

'Anodynon' *see* Chloroethane.

'Anoestrulin' *see* Medroxyprogesterone acetate.

ANOL (*p*-(1-propenyl)phenol).

'Anovan' *see* Phendimetrazine.

'Anovlar' *see under* Norethisterone acetate.

ANOXOMER* (*tert*-butylhydroquinone polymer with divinylbenzene, *p-tert*-butylphenol, *p*-methoxyphenol, 4,4'-isopropylidenediphenol and *p*-cresol; D-00079).

ANP-146 *see* Clofexamide.

ANP-235 *see* Meclofenoxate.

ANP-297 *see* Mefexamide.

ANP-3260 *see* Clofezone.

ANP-3401 *see* Cinametic acid.

ANP-3548 *see* Fenoxedil.

ANP-3624 *see* Tienilic acid.

ANP-4364 *see* Diclofurime mesilate.

'Anquil' *see* Benperidol *and* Reserpine.

'Ansadol' *see* Salicylanilide.

ANSERINE (*N*-(β-alanyl)-1-methylhistidine).

'Ansolysen' *see* Pentolonium tartrate.

'Ansopal' *see* Chloral hydrate acetylglycinamide.

'Anspor' *see* Cefradine.

'Antabus' *see* Disulfiram.

'Antabuse' *see* Disulfiram.

'Antacidin' *see* Calcium saccharate.

ANTAFENITE*** ((+)-5,6-dihydro-6-phenylimidazo[2,1-*b*]thiazole; 2-(*N*-benzylanilinomethyl)-imidazole; R-8193).

'Antagosan' *see* Aprotinin.

'Antagothyroil' *see* Thiouracil.

'Antalby' *see* Theophylline piperazine *p*-aminobenzoate.

'Antallin' *see* Sodium calcium edetate.

'Antalon' *see* Pimozide.

'Antalvic' *see* Dextropropoxyphene.

'Antamin' *see* Diphenhydramine ascorbate.

'Antapentan' *see* Phendimetrazine.

'Antarox A' *see* Octoxinol.

'Antasol' *see* Fluphenazine.

ANTAZOLINE*** (2-(*N*-benzylanilinomethyl)-2-imidazoline; imidamin; phenazoline; M-5512;

PM-265).

ANTAZONITE** (2-acetylimino-3-(2-hydroxy-2-thien-2-ylethyl)thiazoline; *N*-[3-(2-hydroxy-2-thien-2-ylethyl)-4-thiazolin-2-ylidene]acetamide; thiazothienol; R-6348).

ANTELMYCIN*** (antibiotic from *Str. longissimus*; anthelmycin).

'Antemovis' *see* Serotonin creatinine sulfate.

'Antepan' *see* Protirelin.

'Antepar' *see* Piperazine.

'Antepsin' *see* Sucralfate.

'Antergan' *see* Phenbenzamine.

'Anthalazine' *see* Piperazine.

Anthelmycin* *see* Antelmycin.

'Anthelvet' *see* Tetramisole.

'Anthio' *see* Formothion.

ANTHIOLIMINE*** (antimony lithium thiomalate; LAT; lithium antimony thiomalate; mercaptosuccinic acid triester with thioantimonic acid (H_3SbS_3), hexalithium salt; 'anthiomaline').

'Anthiomaline' *see* Anthiolimine.

'Anthiphen' *see* Dichlorophen.

9,10-Anthracenedicarboxaldehyde bis[(4,5-dihydro-1*H*-imidazol-2-yl)hydrazone] *see* Bisantrene.

9,10-Anthracenedicarboxaldehyde bis(2-imidazolin-2-ylhydrazone) *see* Bisantrene.

9,10-Anthracenedione *see* Anthraquinone.

'Anthra-derm' *see* Dithranol.

Anthralin* *see* Dithranol.

2-ANTHRAMINE (aminoanthracene).

Anthramycin* *see* Antramycin.

ANTHRANILIC ACID (*o*-aminobenzoic acid).

Anthranol *see* 9-Anthrol.

β-Anthranoylalanine *see* Kynurenine.

Anthrapurol *see* Dantron.

ANTHRAQUINONE (9,10-anthracenedione).

ANTHRAROBIN (1,2,10-anthratriol; 3,4,9-an-thratriol; desoxyalizarin; dihydroxyanthranol; leucoalizarin).

1,2,10-Anthratriol *see* Anthrarobin.

1,8,9-Anthratriol *see* Dithranol.

3,4,9-Anthratriol *see* Anthrarobin.

Anthridonium chloride* *see* Isometamidium chloride.

9-ANTHROL (anthranol; 9-hydroxyanthracene).

ANTHRONE (9,10-dihydro-9-oxoanthracene; carbothrone).

Anthropodeoxycholic acid *see* Chenodeoxycholic acid.

Antialopecia factor *see* Inositol.

Antibiotic 452-7 *see* Violarin.

Antibiotic 1037 *see* Toyocamycin.

Antibiotic 1719 *see* Azotomycin.

Antibiotic A-23187 *see* Calcimycin.

Antibiotic BM-123-γ *see* Cinodine.

Antibiotic FI-1163 *see* Lucimycin.

Antibiotic PAA 155 *see* Indolmycin.

'Anticarie' *see* Hexachlorobenzene.

'Antichlor' *see* Sodium thiosulfate.

'Anticoccid' *see* Amprolium.

'Antideprin' *see* Imipramine.

Antidiuretic hormone *see* Vasopressin.

'Antidol' *see* Etosalamide.

'Antidrase' see Diclofenamide.
ANTIENITE*** ((+)-5,6-dihydro-6-thien-2-ylimidazo[2,1-b]thiazole; thiazothielite; R-8025; R-8141).
Antierythrite see Erythritol.
Antifebrin see Acetanilide.
'Antiformin' see Sodium hypochlorite.
'Antigest' see under MDAP.
Antihemorrhagic vitamin see Phytomenadione.
'Antihydral' see Methenamine.
Antiinflammatory hormone see Hydrocortisone.
'Antilon' see Eterobarb.
ANTILYMPHOCYTE IMMUNOGLOBULIN (HORSE)* ('pressimune').
'Antilysin' see Aprotinin.
'Antimalarine' see Plasmocid.
'Antiminth' see Pyrantel embonate.
Antimony compounds see Meglumine antimonate; Sodium antimonyl gluconate; Sodium stibocaptate; Sodium stibogluconate; and under Stib....
Antimony 2,3-dimercaptosuccinate see Stibocaptic acid.
Antimony lithium thiomalate see Anthiolimine.
ANTIMONYL POTASSIUM TARTRATE (potassium antimony tartrate; tartar emetic; APT; PAT).
ANTIMONY TRISULFIDE COLLOID* (Sb$_2$S$_3$; 'lymphoscan').
'Antimosan' see Stibophen.
'Antin' see Phenyltoloxamine.
'Antio' see Formothion.
Antipernicious anemia factor see Cyanocobalamin.
'Antiphen' see Dichlorophen.
'Anti-pica' see Fluanisone.
Antipyrine see Phenazone.
(Antipyrinylisobutylamino)methane sulfonate see Dibupyrone.
N-[(Antipyrinylisopropylamino)methyl]nicotinamide see Niprofazone.
N-Antipyrinylnicotinamide see Nifenazone.
N-Antipyrinylstearamide see Stampyrine.
'Antiradon' see AET.
Antispectacled eye factor see Inositol.
Anti-sprout see Propham.
Antisterility vitamin see α-Tocopherol.
Antistiffness factor see Stigmasterol.
'Antistina' see Antazoline.
'Antisukrin' see Carbutamide.
'Antitanil' see Dihydrotachysterol.
ANTITHEINE (tr) (N,N-diethyl-1-methylimidazole-4,5-dicarboxamide).
'Antithermin' see Levulinic acid phenylhydrazone.
'Antitrem' see Trihexyphenidyl.
Antiulcer vitamin see Vitamin U.
'Antivert' see Meclozine.
Antivitamin K$_3$ see 2-Chloro-1,4-naphthoquinone.
'Antivom' see Diphenylpyraline.
Antorfin (tr) see Nalorphine.
Antorphine (tr) see Nalorphine.
'Antracol' see Propineb.
ANTRAFENINE*** (2-[4-(α,α,α-trifluoro-m-tolyl)piperazin-1-yl]ethyl N-[7-(trifluoromethyl)-4-quinolyl]anthranilate; SL-73033; 'stakane').

ANTRAMYCIN** (5,10,11,11a-tetrahydro-9,11-dihydroxy-8-methyl-5-oxo-1H-pyrrolo[2,1-c]-[1,4]benzodiazepine-trans-2-acrylamide; anthramycin).
Antrapurol see Dantron.
'Antrenyl' see Oxyphenonium bromide.
Antridonium see Isometamidium chloride.
'Antroidin' see Chorionic gonadotrophin.
'Antrycide' see Quinapyramine.
'Antrypol' see Suramin sodium.
ANTU* (1-naphth-1-yl-2-thiourea; α-naphthyl-thiourea; 'anturat'; 'bantu'; 'krysid'; 'milogard'; 'rattrack').
'Antuitrin-T' see Growth hormone.
'Antupex' see Tipepidine.
'Anturan' see Sulfinpyrazone.
'Anturat' see Antu.
'Anucaine' see Procaine.
'Anugesic' see Pramocaine.
'Anumedin' see under Prednisolone acetate.
'Anvene' see Mytatrienediol.
'Anvitoff' see Tranexamic acid.
'Anxiolit' see Oxazepam.
'Anxitol' see Medazepam.
'Anxon' see Ketazolam.
'Aolept' see Periciazine.
'Aolet' see Periciazine.
AOMA see Surfomer.
'Aovin' see Troleandomycin.
AP-14 see Difenamizole.
AP-43 see Amolanone.
AP-67 see Chlorthenoxazine.
AP-350 see Aminochlorthenoxazine.
AP-407 see Amprotròpine.
'Apacarb' see Propoxur.
APAETF see Amifostine.
APALCILLIN** ((2S,5R,6R-6-(R)-2-(4-hydroxy-1,5-naphthyridine-3-carboxamido)-2-phenyl-acetamido]penicillanic acid; PC-904; 'lumota').
'Apamide' see Paracetamol.
'Apap' see Paracetamol.
'Apaurin' see Diazepam.
Apazone* see Azapropazone.
'Apegmone' see Tioclomarol.
'Apesan' see Carisoprodol.
APGA see Aminopterin sodium.
'Aphamite' see Parathion.
'Aphlozyme' see Chymotrypsin.
APHOLATE (2,2,4,4,6,6-hexakis(1-aziridinyl)-2,2,4,4,6,6-hexahydro-1,3,5,2,4,6-triazatriphosphorine; hexakis(1-aziridinyl) phosphonitrilate; ENT-26316; NSC-26812).
Aphoxide see Tepa.
Aphrodine see Yohimbine.
'Aphthiria' see Lindane.
'Apicosan' see Bee venom.
APICYCLINE** (4-(2-hydroxyethyl)-α-tetracyclinyl-1-piperazineacetic acid; N-[[4-(2-hydroxyethyl)piperazin-1-yl]carboxymethyl]tetracycline; RIT-1140; 'traserit').
APIGENIN (5,7-dihydroxy-2-(4-hydroxyphenyl)-chromone; 4',5,7-trihydroxyflavone; 'versulin').
Apilit (tr) see Bee venom.

'**Apiquel**' see Aminorex.
'**Apisate**' see Amfepramone.
'**Apliobal**' see Alprenolol.
'**Aplodan**' see Creatinolfosfate.
APOATROPINE (atropamine; atropyltropeine).
15-Apo-β-caroten-15-al see Retinal.
APOCYNIN (4'-hydroxy-3'-methoxyacetophen-one; acetovanillone).
'**Apodrine**' see Phenylpropanolamine.
Apoephedrine see Phenylpropanolamine.
Apolate see Sodium apolate.
APOMORPHINE (6aβ-aporphine-10,11-diol; (*R*)-5,6,6a,7-tetrahydro-6-methyl-4*H*-dibenzo[*de*,*g*]-quinoline-10,11-diol).
APOMORPHINE METHYL BROMIDE ('bromophin'; 'euporphin').
Apomorphine 10-methyl ether see Morphothebaine.
'**Aponal**' see Doxepin.
'**Aponeuron**' see Amfetaminil.
'**Apophedrine**' see Phenylpropanolamine.
APOPINENE (6,6-dimethylbicyclo[3.1.1]hept-2-ene; 6,6-dimethyl-2-norpinene).
'**Aporex**' see Dextropropoxyphene.
APORPHINE (5,6,6a,7-tetrahydo-6-methyl-4*H*-dibenzo[*de*,*g*]quinoline).
6aβ-Aporphine-10,11-diol see Apomorphine.
'**Apothesine**' see Cinnacaine.
APOVINCAMINE* (methyl (13a*S*,13b*S*)-13a-ethyl-2,3,5,6,13a,13b-hexahydro-1*H*-indolo-[3,2,1-*de*]pyrido[3,2,1-*ij*][1,5]naphthyridine-12-carboxylate; methyl (3α,16α)-eburnamenine-14-carboxylate).
Apovincamin-22-oic acid ethyl ester see Vinpocetine.
'**A-poxide**' see Chlordiazepoxide.
'**Apozepam**' see Diazepam.
'**Apralan**' see Apramycin.
APRAMYCIN* (4-*O*-[3α-amino-6α-[(4-amino-4-deoxy-α-D-glucopyranosyl)oxy]-2,3,4,4aβ,6,7,8,8aα-octahydro-8β-hydroxy-7β-(methyl-amino)pyrano[3,2-*b*]pyran-2α-yl]-2-deoxy-D-streptamine; apramycin sulfate; EL-857; 'ambyl-an'; 'apralan').
'**Apranax**' see Naproxen.
'**Apresoline**' see Hydralazine.
Apressin (tr) see Hydralazine.
'**Aprikern**' see Amygdalin.
APRINDINE* (*N*-[3-(diethylamino)propyl]-*N*-phenyl-2-indanamine; *N*-(2,3-dihydro-1*H*-inden-2-yl)-*N*',*N*'-diethyl-*N*-phenyl-1,3-propanedi-amine; AC-1802; compound 99170; 'amidonal'; 'fibocil'; 'fiboran').
'**Aprinox**' see Bendroflumethiazide.
'**Apritox**' see Trichloronat.
APROBARBITAL* (5-allyl-5-isopropylbarbi-turic acid; allypropymal; allopropylbarbital).
'**Aprobit**' see Promethazine hydroxyethyl chloride.
Aprocarb see Propoxur.
APROFENE* (2-(diethylamino)ethyl 2,2-di-phenylpropionate; aprophen).
'**Apromal**' see under Acecarbromal.
APRONAL (1-(2-isopropyl-3-pentenoyl)urea; al-lylisopropylacetylurea; apronalid; 'sedormid').

Apronalid see Apronal.
Aprophen (tr) see Aprofene.
'**Aprosone**' see 2-(4-Chloro-2-methylphenoxy)acetic acid.
APROTININ** (kallikrein-trypsin inhibitor; Frey inhibitor; Bayer A-128; Riker 52G; RP 9921).
APT see Antimonyl potassium tartrate.
APTAZAPINE** ((±)-1,3,4,14b-tetrahydro-2-methyl-2*H*,10*H*-pyrazino[1,2-*a*]pyrrolo[2,1-*c*]-[1,4]benzodiazepine).
'**Aptine**' see Alprenolol.
APTOCAINE* (2-methyl-2-pyrrolidin-1-yl-*o*-acetotoluidide; 2'-methyl-2-pyrrolidin-1-ylpro-pionanilide; *N*-(2-pyrrolidin-1-ylpropionyl)-*o*-toluidine; 'pirothesin').
'**Aptrol**' see *p*-Methylamphetamine.
'**Apurin**' see Allopurinol.
'**Apurone**' see Flumequine.
APY-606 see Spiclomazine.
'**Apyron**' see Magnesium acetylsalicylate.
AQ-110 see Tretoquinol.
AQ-A39 see Falipamil.
AQL-208 see Tretoquinol.
'**Aquachloral**' see Chloral hydrate.
'**Aquacide**' see Diquat.
'**Aquacillin**' see Procaine-penicillin.
'**Aqualose**' see Poloxyl lanolin.
'**Aquamephyton**' see Phytomenadione.
'**Aquamollin**' see Tetrasodium edetate.
'**Aquamox**' see Quinethazone.
'**Aquamycetin**' see Chloramphenicol hemisuccinate sodium.
'**Aquaphor**' see Xipamide.
'**Aquareduct**' see Spironolactone.
'**Aquatag**' see Benzthiazide.
'**Aquatensen**' see Methyclothiazide.
'**Aquedux**' see Clofenamide.
'**Aquex**' see Clopamide.
AQUOCOBALAMIN (vitamin B$_{12b}$).
    See also Hydroxocobalamin.
Aquocobinamide cyanide see Cyanocobalamin.
AR-12008 see Trapidil.
Ara-A see Vidarabine.
9-β-D-Arabinofuranosyladenine see Vidarabine.
1-β-D-Arabinofuranosylcytosine see Cytarabine.
N-**(1-β-D-Arabinofuranosyl-1,2-dihydro-2-oxopyr-imidin-4-yl)docosanamide** see Enocitabine.
9-β-D-Arabinofuranosyl-2-fluoroadenine see Fluda-rabine.
Arabinofuranosyl-5-fluorocytosine see Flucytosine arabinoside.
Arabinofuranosylguanine see Guanine arabinoside.
[5-[19-(α-D-Arabinofuranosyloxy)-35-butyl-10,12,14,16,18,22,26,30,34-nonahydroxy-3,5,21,33-tetramethyl-36-oxooxacyclohexatria-conta-4,20-dien-2-yl]-4-hydroxyhexyl]guanidine see Primycin.
9-β-D-Arabinofuranosyl(9*H*)purine-6-thiol see Mer-captopurine arabinoside.
Araboascorbic acid see Isoascorbic acid.
Ara-C see Cytarabine.
Arachic acid see Arachidic acid.
ARACHIDIC ACID (arachic acid; eicosanoic

36

acid).

ARACHIDONIC ACID (5,8,11,14-eicosatetraenoic acid).

Ara-CMP *see* Cytarabine 5'-phosphate.

Ara-cytidine *see* Cytarabine.

'Aracytine' *see* Cytarabine.

Ara-FC *see* Flucytosine arabinoside.

Ara-G *see* Guanine arabinoside.

'Aralen' *see* Chloroquine.

ARALKONIUM CHLORIDE* (alkyl(3,4-dichlorobenzyl)dimethylammonium chloride).

'Aramine' *see* Metaraminol.

'Aramite' *see* 2-(*p-tert*-Butylphenoxy)isopropyl 2-chloroethyl sulfite.

ARANOTIN*** (5,5a,13,13a-tetrahydro-5,13-dihydroxy-8*H*,16*H*-7a,15a-epidithio-7*H*,15*H*-bis-oxepino[3',4':4,5]pyrrolo[1,2-*a*:1',2'-*d*]pyrazine-7,15-dione 5-acetate).

'Arasan' *see* Thiram.

'Arathane' *see* Dinocap.

ARBAPROSTIL*** ((*E,Z*)-(1*R*,2*R*,3*R*)-7-[3-hydroxy-2-[(3*R*)-(3-hydroxy-3-methyl-1-octenyl)]-5-oxocyclopentyl]-5-heptenoic acid; 15-methyldinoprostone; 15-methylprostaglandin E$_2$; U-42842).

Arbutin *see* Hydroquinone β-D-glucopyranoside.

'Arcalion' *see* Sulbutiamine.

'Arcanax' *see* Hydroxyzine.

Archin *see* Emodin.

ARC-I-K-1 *see* Metofoline.

'Arcobutine' *see* Mofebutazone.

'Arcolax' *see* Psyllium.

'Arcomonol' *see* Mofebutazone.

'Arcosal' *see* Tolbutamide.

'Arcton 6' *see* Dichlorodifluoromethane.

'Arcton 33' *see* Cryofluorane.

'Arcton-63' *see* 1,1,2-Trichloro-1,2,2-trifluoroethane.

'Arcylate' *see* Sodium sulfosalicylate.

'Ardesyl' *see* Vitamin U.

ARDF-26 *see* Gliquidone.

ARDMA *see* Puromycin aminonucleoside.

'Arduan' *see* Pipecuronium bromide.

ARECAIDINE (1,2,5,6-tetrahydro-1-methylnicotinic acid; arecaine).

Arecaidine methyl ester *see* Arecoline.

Arecaine *see* Arecaidine.

Arecaline *see* Arecoline.

ARECOLINE (methyl 1,2,5,6-tetrahydro-1-methylnicotinate; arecaidine methyl ester; arecaline).

ARECOLINE-ACETARSOL (molecular compound of arecoline with acetarsol).

'Arelix' *see* Piretanide.

'Aremyxin' *see* Polymyxin methylenesulfonic acid.

'Arentyl' *see* Nortriptyline.

'Aresin' *see* Monolinuron.

'Aretit' *see* Dinoseb acetate.

'Arezine' *see* Monolinuron.

ARFALASIN*** (L-2-phenyl-*N*-[*N*-[*N*-[*N*-[*N*-[*N*-(*N*²-succinamoyl-L-arginyl)-L-valyl]-L-tyrosyl]-L-valyl]-L-histidyl]-L-prolyl]glycine; 1-succinamic acid-5-L-valine-8-(L-2-phenylglycine)angiotensin II).

ARFENDAZAM*** (ethyl 7-chloro-2,3,4,5-tetrahydro-4-oxo-5-phenyl-1*H*-1,5-benzodiazepine-1-carboxylate).

'Arfonad' *see* Trimetaphan camsilate.

'Argicillin' *see* Methocidin.

ARGININE*** (*N*⁵-amidinoornithine; 2-amino-5-guanidovaleric acid; L(+)-arginine).

ARGININE ASPARTATE ('sargenor').

ARGININE GLUTAMATE* (L(+)-glutamic acid compound with L(+)-arginine (1:1); 'modumate').

ARGININE MALATE ('rocmaline').

ARGININE OXOGLURATE (arginine 2-oxoglutarate; 'eucol').

8-Arginineoxytocin *see* Argiprestocin.

ARGININE PIDOLATE (arginine pyroglutamate; pirglutargine; G-728).

Arginine thiazolidinecarboxylate *see* Timonacic arginine.

Arginine 2,4-thiazolidinedicarboxylate *see* Tidiacic arginine.

8-Argininevasopressin *see* Argipressin.

Arginine vasotocin *see* Argiprestocin.

***N*-[*N*-[*N*-(*N*²-L-Arginyl-L-lysyl)-L-α-aspartyl]-L-valyl]-L-tyrosine** *see* Thymopentin.

ARGIPRESSIN*** (8-argininevasopressin; AVP).

ARGIPRESSIN TANNATE* (CI-107; 'pitressin tannate').

ARGIPRESTOCIN*** (8-arginineoxytocin; arginine vasotocin; vasotocin).

'Arg-vasopressin' *see* Argipressin.

Aribine *see* Harman.

'Arichin' *see* Mepacrine.

ARILDONE** (4-[6-(2-chloro-4-methoxyphenoxy)hexyl]-3,5-heptanedione; WIN-38020).

'Arilin' *see* Metronidazole.

'Aristocort' *see* Triamcinolone diacetate.

'Aristodan' *see* Triamcinolone.

'Aristoderm' *see* Triamcinolone acetonide.

ARISTOLOCHIC ACID (8-methoxy-3,4-methylenedioxy-10-nitrophenanthrene-1-carboxylic acid; 'descresept'; 'tardolyt').

'Aristosol' *see* Triamcinolone acetonide sodium phosphate.

'Aristospan' *see* Triamcinolone hexacetonide.

'Arkitropin' *see* Homatropine methyl bromide.

AR-L 115-BS *see* Sulmazole.

'Arlamol E' *see* PPG-15 stearyl ether.

'Arlef' *see* Flufenamic acid.

'Arlevert' *see under* Cinnarizine.

'Arlidin' *see* Buphenine.

'Arlytene' *see* Moxisylyte.

'Armazal' *see* Cyacetacide.

'Armazide' *see* Isoniazid.

'Armidexan' *see* Iron dextran injection.

ARMIN (tr) (ethyl *p*-nitrophenyl ethylphosphonate; ethylethoxyphosphoryl *p*-nitrophenolate).

'Arocan' *see* Hexacamphamine.

'Aroclor' *see* Polychlorinated biphenyl; Polychlorinated terphenyl.

AROTINOLOL*** ((±)-5-[2-[[3-(*tert*-butylamino)-2-hydroxypropyl]thio]thiazol-4-yl]-2-thiophenecarboxamide; S-596).

'Aroxine' *see* Forminitrazole.

ARPENAL (tr) (3-(diethylamino)propyl 2,2-diphenylacetate).

Arpenal methyl methosulfate *see* Mesfenal.

'Arpezine' *see* Piperazine.

'Arphoral' *see* Mofoxime.

'Arpocox' *see* Arprinocid.

ARPRINOCID*** (6-amino-9-(2-chloro-6-fluorobenzyl)purine; 9-(2-chloro-6-fluorobenzyl)-adenine; 9-[(2-chloro-6-fluorophenyl)methyl]-9H-purin-6-amine; 'arpocox').

Arprocarb *see* Aminocarb *and* Propoxur.

'Arquel' *see* Meclofenamic acid.

'Arrhenal' *see* Disodium methanearsonate.

ARSANILIC ACID*** (*p*-aminobenzenearsonic acid; 4-aminophenylarsonic acid; aminarsonic acid; arsanilate sodium; AS-101; 'kilscour'; 'progen').

'Arsenamide' *see* Thiacetarsamide sodium.

ARSENIC TRIOXIDE (arsenious acid; arsenious anhydride; arsenious oxide).

Arsenious acid *see* Arsenic trioxide.

Arsenious anhydride *see* Arsenic trioxide.

Arsenious oxide *see* Arsenic trioxide.

ARSENOBENZENE (arsenodibenzene).

Arsenodibenzene *see* Arsenobenzene.

Arsenophenolamine *see* Arsphenamine.

ARSENOSOBENZENE (oxophenylarsine; phenylarsenoxide; 'arzene').

'Arsenyl' *see* Disodium methanearsonate.

'Arsinyl' *see* Disodium methanearsonate.

'Arsobal' *see* Melarsoprol.

ARSONOACETIC ACID (acetarsenic acid; acetarsonic acid; acetoarsinic acid).

ARSPHENAMINE* (3,3'-diamino-4,4'-dihydroxyarsenobenzene; arsenophenolamine; arsphenolamine; salvarsan; Ehrlich 606; NSC-3097).

Arsphendichloride *see* Dichlorophenarsine.

Arsphenolamine *see* Arsphenamine.

Arsphenoxide *see* Oxophenarsine.

ARSTHINOL** (2-(3-acetamido-4-hydroxyphenyl)-1,3-dithia-2-arsacyclopentane-4-methanol; mercaptoarsenol).

'Arsynal' *see* Disodium methanearsonate.

'Artalan' *see* Thiopropazate.

'Artamin' *see* Penicillamine.

'Artane' *see* Trihexyphenidyl.

'Artegodan' *see* Papaverine.

Artemisia ketone *see* Artemisin.

ARTEMISIN (3a,5,5a,9b-tetrahydro-4-hydroxy-3,5a,9-trimethylnaphtho[1,2-*b*]furan-2,8(3H,4H)-dione; 6α,8α-dihydroxy-3-oxoeudesma-1,4-dien-12-oic acid 12,6-lactone; 8-hydroxysantonin; artemisia ketone; qinghaosu).

'Arteparon' *see* Glycosaminoglycan polysulfate(s).

Arterenol *see* Norepinephrine.

'Arthriticin' *see* Piperazine.

'Arthrocine' *see* Sulindac.

'Arthropan' *see* Choline salicylate.

'Arthrytin' *see* Amiodoxyl benzoate.

ARTICAINE*** (methyl 4-methyl-3-[2-(propylamino)propionamido]-2-thiophenecarboxylate; carticaine; HOE-045; HOE-40045; 'ultracain').

'Artosin' *see* Tolbutamide.

'Artracin' *see* Indometacin.

'Artricid' *see* Niflumic acid.

'Artrochin' *see* Chloroquine.

'Arvin' *see* Ancrod.

'Arvynol' *see* Ethchlorvynol.

'Arzene' *see* Arsenosobenzene.

AS-101 *see* Arsanilic acid.

AS-716 *see* Thenalidine.

AS-17665 *see* Nifurthiazole.

5-ASA *see* Fisalamine.

ASA-158/5 *see* Benproperine.

ASA-226 *see* Chlorazanil.

'Asacol' *see* Fisalamine.

Asahina *see* Naringenin.

Asalea *see* Asaley.

ASALEY (tr) (*N*-[*N*-acetyl-3-[*p*-[bis(2-chloroethyl)-amino]phenyl]alanyl]-L-leucine ethyl ester; *N*-acetylmerphalan leucine peptide ethyl ester; acetylsarcolysylleucine ethyl ester; asalea).

ASALINE (tr) (*N*-[*N*-acetyl-3-[*p*-[bis(2-chloroethyl)amino]phenyl]alanyl]-DL-valine ethyl ester; *N*-acetylmerphalan valine peptide ethyl ester; acetylsarcolysylvaline ethyl ester).

'Asaprol' *see* Calcinaphthol.

Asarabacca camphor *see* Asarone.

ASARONE (*trans*-2,4,5-trimethoxy-1-propenylbenzene; asarabacca camphor).

β-ASARONE (*cis*-2,4,5-trimethoxy-1-propenylbenzene).

'Asasantin' *see under* Dipyridamole.

'ASC-4' *see under* Dibromsalan.

'Ascabin' *see* Benzyl benzoate.

'Ascabiol' *see* Benzyl benzoate.

'Ascal' *see* Calcium acetylsalicylate.

'Ascarex' *see* Piperazine.

'Ascaricum' *see* Ascaridole.

ASCARIDOLE (2*p*-menthene 1,4-peroxide; askaridol; 'ascaricum'; 'ascarisin'; 'vermi-drageletten').

'Ascarisin' *see* Ascaridole.

ASCARYLOSE (3,6-bisdeoxy-L-mannose).

'Asciatine' *see* Butylchloralamidopyrine.

ASCORBIC ACID*** (3-oxo-L-gulofuranolactone; vitamin C; avitamic acid; xyloascorbic acid).
See also Galascorbin; Isoascorbic acid; Sodium ascorbate; *and under* Acetylsalicylic acid; Clioquinol; Paracetamol; Tetracycline.

ASCORBIC ACID plus DISODIUM FRUCTOSE 1,6-DIPHOSPHATE ('fructergyl').

ASCORBIC ACID HYDROGEN PEROXIDE CUPRIC COMPLEX ('ascoxal').

ASCORBIC ACID NICOTINAMIDE COMPLEX ('nicascorbin'; 'nicastubin').

ASCORBIC ACID PYRIDOXINE COMPLEX ('pyridoscorbine').

'Ascorphylline' *see* Choline theophyllinate *and* Etofylline.

'Ascoxal' *see* Ascorbic acid hydrogen peroxide cupric complex.

Asebogenol *see* Phloretin.

Asebotin *see* Phlorizin.

'**Asellacrin**' *see* Human growth hormone.
'**Asendin**' *see* Amoxapine.
'**Aseptanide**' *see* Triclocarban.
'**Aseptol**' *see* 2-Phenolsulfonic acid.
'**Aseptorid**' *see* Sulfatolamide.
'**Asevin**' *see* Carbaril.
ASIATIC ACID (2α,3β,23-trihydroxyurs-12-en-28-oic acid).
ASIATICOSIDE (asiatic acid glycoside; 'madecassol').
ASIATICOSIDE plus ASIATIC, MADASIATIC & MADECASSIC ACIDS* ('emdecassol').
'**Asipol**' *see* Fenpiprane.
Askaridol *see* Ascaridole.
ASL-279 *see* Dopamine.
ASL-601 *see* Acecainide.
ASL-603 *see* Bretylium tosilate.
ASL-8052 *see* Esmolol.
'**Aslavital**' *see under* Procaine.
Asnase *see* Asparaginase.
ASOCAINOL* ((±)-6,7,8,9-tetrahydro-2,12-dimethoxy-7-methyl-6-phenethyl-5*H*-dibenz[*d,f*]-azonin-1-ol).
L-Asparagineaminohydrolase *see* Asparaginase; Crisantaspase
ASPARAGINASE* (L-asparagine aminohydrolase; asnase; colaspase; ATCC-9376; FB b-6366; NSC-109229; 'crasnitin'; 'elspar'; 'kidrolase'; 'krasnitin').
See also Crisantaspase.
ASPARAGINE (2-aminosuccinamic acid; aspartamic acid).
4-L-Asparagine oxytocin *see* Aspartocin.
Asparaginic acid *see* Aspartic acid.
'**Aspardoxine**' *see* Pyridoxine aspartate.
ASPARTAME* (3-amino-*N*-(α-carboxyphenethyl)succinamic acid *N*-methyl ester; 3-amino-*N*-(α-methoxycarbonylphenethyl)succinamic acid; L-aspartyl-L-phenylalanine methyl ester; SC-18862; 'canderel'; 'equa'; 'trisweet').
Aspartamic acid *see* Asparagine.
ASPARTAMIDE (2-aminosuccinamide).
ASPARTIC ACID* (2-aminosuccinic acid; asparaginic acid).
See also Arginine aspartate; Magnesium aspartate; Ornithine aspartate; Potassium aspartate; Pyridoxine aspartate.
25-L-Aspartic acid-26-L-alanine-27-glycine-30-L-glutamine-30-L-serine α¹⁻³⁹-corticotrophin (pig) *see* Seractide.
ASPARTOCIN* (antibiotic from *Str. griseus* var. *spiralis*; 4-L-asparagine oxytocin; A-8999).
L-Aspartyl-L-phenylalanine methyl ester *see* Aspartame.
L-Aspartyl-L-tyrosyl-L-methionylglycyl-L-tryptophyl-L-methionyl-L-aspartylphenyl-L-alaninamide hydrogen sulfate (ester) *see* Sincalide.
'**Aspegic**' *see* Lysine acetylsalicylate.
Aspergillin O *see* Brinase.
Aspergillus melleus, alkaline proteinase *see* Promelase.
Aspergillus ochraceus, enzyme *see* Ocrase.
Aspergillus oryzae, enzyme *see* Brinase.

ASPERLIN* (6,7-epoxy-4,5-dihydroxy-2-octenoic acid δ-lactone acetate; 6-(1,2-epoxypropyl)-5,6-dihydro-5-hydroxy-2*H*-pyran-2-one acetate; NSC-93158; U-13933).
ASPIDINOL (4-butyryl-2-methylphloroglucinol-1-methyl ether; 2',6'-dihydroxy-4'-methoxy-3'-methylbutyrophenone).
'**Aspiral**' *see* Amyl nitrite.
'**Aspirin**' *see* Acetylsalicylic acid.
'**Aspogen**' *see* Aluminium glycinate.
ASPOXICILLIN* ((2*S*,5*R*,6*R*)-6-[(2*R*)-2-[(2*R*)-2-amino-3-(methylcarbamoyl)propionamido]-2-(*p*-hydroxyphenyl)acetamido]penicillanic acid).
Asta-3746 *see* Ciclonium bromide.
Asta-4828 *see* Trofosfamide.
Asta-4942 *see* Ifosfamide.
Asta 5122 *see* Sufosfamide.
Asta C-4898 *see* Dilazep.
ASTEMIZOLE* (1-(*p*-fluorobenzyl)-2-[[1-(4-methoxyphenethyl)piperid-4-yl]amino]benzimidazole; 1-[(4-fluorophenyl)methyl]-*N*-[2-(4-methoxyphenyl)ethyl]-4-piperidinyl]benzimidazol-2-amine; R-43512; 'hismanal').
'**Asterit**' *see* Chloroxylenol.
'**Asterol**' *see* Dimazole.
'**Asthmalitan**' *see* Isoetarine.
'**Asthmolysin**' *see* Diprophylline.
'**Astiban**' *see* Sodium stibocaptate.
'**Astinon**' *see* Fludrocortisone.
'**Astomin**' *see* Dimemorfan.
'**Astomol**' *see* Mebanazine.
'**Astonin**' *see* Fludrocortisone.
Astra-1512 *see* Prilocaine.
Astra-1572 *see* Iron sorbitex.
Astra-4241 *see* Imiclopazine.
'**Astrafer**' *see* Dextriferron.
'**Astrobain**' *see* Ouabain.
ASTROMICIN* (4-amino-1-(2-amino-*N*-methyl-acetamido) 1,4-dideoxy-3-*O*-(2,6-diamino-2,3,4,6,7-pentadeoxy-β-L-*lyxo*-heptopyranosyl)-6-*O*-methyl-L-*chiro*-inositol).
'**Astrumal**' *see* Potassium perchlorate.
'**Asturidon**' *see* Secbutabarbital.
'**Astyryl**' *see* Glycarsamide.
'**Asuccin**' *see* Succinic acid.
ASULAM* (methyl [(*p*-aminophenyl)sulfonyl]-carbamate; methyl sulfanilylcarbamate; 'asulox').
'**Asulox**' *see* Asulam.
'**Asuntol**' *see* Coumafos.
'**Asverin**' *see* Tipepidine.
AS XVII *see* Trospium chloride.
3A-T *see* Amitrole.
AT-7 *see* Hexachlorophene.
'**AT-10**' *see* Dihydrotachysterol.
AT-17 *see* Dimemorfan.
AT-101 *see* Isosorbide.
AT-125 *see* Acivicin.
AT-327 *see* Tipepidine.
AT-581 *see* Ocaphane.
AT-1258 *see* Nitrocaphane.
AT-2266 *see* Enoxacin.
ATA *see* Amitrole.

'Atabrine' *see* Mepacrine.
'Atamine' *see* Mepyramine.
'Ataractan' *see* Azacyclonol.
'Atarax' *see* Hydroxyzine.
ATC *see* Timonacic arginine.
ATCC-9376 *see* Asparaginase.
'Atelor' *see* Dimazole.
'Atelora' *see* Dimazole.
'Atempol' *see* Nitrazepam.
ATENOLOL** (1-(*p*-carbamoylmethylphenoxy)-3-isopropylamino-2-propanol; *p*-[2-hydroxy-3-(isopropylamino)propoxy]phenylacetamide; ICI-66082; 'tenormine').
ATENOLOL plus CHLORTALIDONE ('diube'; 'teneretic'; 'tenoretic').
ATENOLOL plus INDAPAMIDE (SF-979).
'Atensine' *see* Diazepam.
'Aterofal' *see* Pyricarbate.
'Ateroid' *see* Glycosaminoglycan polysulfate(s).
'Aterosol' *see* Clofibrate.
'Atgard' *see* Dichlorvos.
'Atheroitin' *see* Chondroitin 4-sulfate.
'Atherolip' *see* Clofibrate.
'Atheropront' *see* Clofibrate.
'Athrombin' *see* Warfarin.
'Athymil' *see* Mianserin.
'Athyromazole' *see* Carbimazole.
'Atilon' *see* Acedapsone.
'Ativan' *see* Lorazepam.
'Atlachlor' *see* Chlorpheniramine.
'Atladiol' *see* Estradiol valerate.
'Atlasetox' *see under* Demephion-O.
'Atlatest' *see* Testosterone enantate.
ATOLIDE*** (2-amino-4'-diethylaminoethyl-*o*-benzotoluidide; Go-1213; Wy-5733).
'Atonyl' *see* Carbachol.
'Atorel' *see* Inosine.
ATP *see* Adenosine triphosphate.
ATRACURIUM BESILATE*** (2-(2-carboxyethyl)-1,2,3,4-tetrahydro-6,7-dimethoxy-2-methyl-1-veratrylisoquinolinium benzenesulfonate pentamethylene ester; 2,2'-(3,11-dioxo-4,10-dioxatridecylenebis[6,7-dimethoxy-1-(3,4-dimethoxybenzyl)-1,2,3,4-tetrahydro-2-methylisoquinolinium] dibenzenesulfonate; 'tracrium').
'Atratan' *see* Atropine tannate.
'Atratol' *see* Atrazine.
ATRATON* (*N*-ethyl-6-methoxy-*N'*-(1-methylethyl)-1,3,5-triazine-2,4-diamine; 2-(ethylamino)-4-isopropylamino-6-methoxy-*s*-triazine; atratone; 'gestamin').
Atratone *see* Atraton.
'Atravet' *see* Acepromazine.
'Atraxin' *see* Meprobamate.
ATRAZINE* (2-chloro-4-ethylamino-6-isopropylamino-*s*-triazine; 6-chloro-*N*-ethyl-*N'*-(1-methylethyl)-1,3,5-triazine-2,4-diamine; G-30027; W-6693; 'aatrex'; 'atratol'; 'gesaprim'; 'hungazin'; 'zeazint').
Atremon (tr) *see* Chromocarb.
'Atrilon 5' *see* Propatylnitrate.
'Atrinal' *see* Atropine sulfate ester.
'Atriphos' *see* Adenosine triphosphate.

'Atrium 300' *see under* Febarbamate.
Atrochin *see* Scopolamine.
'Atrol' *see* Deanol tartrate.
ATROLACTAMIDE (2-hydroxy-2-phenylpropionamide; α-methylmandelamide; M-144; 'themisone').
ATROLACTIC ACID (2-hydroxy-2-phenylpropionic acid; α-methylmandelic acid; α-phenyllactic acid).
Atrolactic acid tropine ester *see* Pseudoatropine.
ATROMENTIN (2,5-dihydroxy-3,6-bis(*p*-hydroxyphenyl)-*p*-benzoquinone).
ATROMEPINE*** ((−)-3α-tropanyl 2-methyl-2-phenylhydracrylate; (−)-atromepine; levomepate).
(+)-ATROMEPINE (TMT).
(−)-Atromepine *see* Atromepine.
'Atromid' *see under* Clofibrate.
'Atromidin' *see* Clofibrate.
'Atromid-S' *see* Clofibrate.
Atropamine *see* Apoatropine.
ATROPINE (DL-tropanyl 2-hydroxy-1-phenylpropionate; D-hyoscyamine).
See also under Diphenoxylate; Metrifonate.
Atropine *p*-biphenylylmethyl bromide *see* Xenytropium bromide.
Atropine L-isomer *see* Hyoscyamine.
ATROPINE METHOBROMIDE (8-methylatropinium bromide; methylatropine bromide; tropin).
ATROPINE METHONITRATE*** (8-methylatropinium nitrate; methylatropine nitrate).
ATROPINE OCTYL BROMIDE (octylatropinium bromide; AD-122).
ATROPINE OXIDE*** (atropine oxide hydrochloride; aminoxytropine tropate; genatropine).
Atropine propionate ester *see* Prampine.
ATROPINE SULFATE ESTER ('atrinal').
ATROPINE TANNATE ('atratan').
'Atroplex' *see under* Magnesium clofibrate.
Atropyltropeine *see* Apoatropine.
Atroquin *see* Scopolamine.
DL-Atroscine *see* Hyoscine.
L-Atroscine *see* Scopolamine.
'Atrovent' *see* Ipratropium bromide.
ATTAPULGITE (aluminium magnesium silicate; 'gastropulgit').
ATTAPULGITE plus GUAR GUM ('mucipulgite').
'Atumin' *see* Dicycloverine.
'Aturbal' *see* Phenglutarimide.
'Aturbane' *see* Phenglutarimide.
'Audax' *see* Choline salicylate.
'Augmentan' *see under* Amoxicillin.
'Augmentin' *see under* Amoxicillin.
'Auraloin' *see* Barbaloin.
AURAMINE (bis[*p*-(dimethylamino)phenyl]methyleneiminium chloride).
AURANOFIN*** ((1-thio-β-D-glucopyranosato)-(triethylphosphine)gold 2,3,4,6-tetraacetate; *S*-(triethylphosphoranediylaurio)-1-thio-β-D-glucopyranose 2,3,4,6-tetraacetate; SK&F-39162; SK&F D-39162; 'ridaura').

'**Aurantex**' *see under* Alfadolone acetate.
AURANTIIN (naringenin 7-rhamnoglucoside; naringenin 7-rutoside; isohesperidin; naringin; naringoside).
'**Aurcoloid-198**' *see* Gold (^{198}Au) colloidal.
'**Aureocina**' *see* Chlortetracycline.
'**Aureomycin**' *see* Chlortetracycline.
'**Aureoquin**' *see* Quinetalate.
'**Aureotan**' *see* Aurothioglucose.
'**Aureoton**' *see* Aurothioglucose.
'**Aureotope**' *see* Gold (^{198}Au) colloidal.
'**Aurex**' *see* Carbaril.
'**Auricidin**' *see* Sodium aurotiosulfate.
Auroallylthioureidobenzoate *see* Sodium auroallyl-thioureidobenzoate.
'**Aurolin**' *see* Sodium aurotiosulfate.
α-**Auromercaptoacetanilide** *see* Aurothioglycanide.
'**Auromyose**' *see* Aurothioglucose.
'**Auropex**' *see* Sodium aurotiosulfate.
'**Auropin**' *see* Sodium aurotiosulfate.
'**Aurosan**' *see* Sodium aurotiosulfate.
AUROTHIOGLUCOSE* ((1-thio-D-glucopyra-nosato)gold; thioglucose *S*-gold derivative).
AUROTHIOGLYCANIDE*** (2-mercaptoacet-anilide *S*-gold derivative; α-auromercaptoacet-anilide; gold mercaptoacetanilide).
Aurothiomalate *see* Sodium aurothiomalate.
'**Aurothion**' *see* Sodium aurotiosulfate.
Aurothiosinamine-*m***-benzoic acid** *see* Sodium auro-allylthioureidobenzoate.
Aurothiosulfate *see* Sodium aurotiosulfate.
'**Aurumine**' *see* Aurothioglucose.
'**Ausomina**' *see* Vincamine.
'**Autan**' *see* Diethyltoluamide.
'**Auxiloson**' *see* Dexamethasone isonicotinate.
'**Auxisone**' *see* Dexamethasone isonicotinate.
'**Auxit**' *see* Bromhexine.
'**Avacan**' *see* Camylofin.
'**Avadex**' *see* Diallate.
'**Avadex BW**' *see* Triallate.
'**Avafortan**' *see under* Camylofin.
'**Avatec**' *see* Lasalocid.
'**Avazyme**' *see* Chymotrypsin.
'**Avenge**' *see* Difenzoquat.
'**Aventol**' *see* Aceglutamide.
'**Aventyl**' *see* Nortriptyline.
'**Aversan**' *see* Disulfiram.
'**Aviamide-6**' *see* Policapram.
'**Avicalm**' *see* Metoserpate.
'**Avicol**' *see* Chlorphentermine.
'**Avicol SL**' *see* Cloforex.
'**Aviester**' *see* Pegoterate.
'**Avil**' *see* Pheniramine *p*-aminosalicylate.
AVILAMYCIN*** (antibiotic from *Str. virido-chromogenes*).
'**Avinar**' *see* Uredepa.
'**Avipron**' *see* Chlorphentermine.
Avitamic acid *see* Ascorbic acid.
'**Avlocardyl**' *see* Propranolol.
'**Avloclor**' *see* Chloroquine.
'**Avlosulfon**' *see* Dapsone.
'**Avlosulfone-EOS**' *see* Dapsonedisulfonic acid disodium salt.

'**Avolin**' *see* Dimethyl phthalate.
'**Avomine**' *see* Promethazine teoclate.
AVOPARCIN*** (glycopeptide antibiotic from *Str. candidus*; 'avotan').
Avornin *see* Frangulin.
'**Avotan**' *see* Avoparcin.
AVP *see* Argipressin.
AVRIDINE** (2,2′-[[3-(dioctadecylamino)propyl]-imino]diethanol).
AW-10 *see* Sitogluside.
AW-142333 *see* Perlapine.
AW-142446 *see* Clodazon.
AW-1151129 *see* Desipramine.
'**Awelysin**' *see* Streptokinase.
'**Axeen**' *see* Proxibarbal.
Axerophthal *see* Retinal.
Axerophthol *see* Retinol.
'**Axiquel**' *see* Valnoctamide.
'**Axuris**' *see* Crystal violet.
AY-5312 *see* Chlorhexidine.
AY-5406-1 *see* Benactyzine.
AY-5710 *see* Magaldrate.
AY-5810 *see* Pentapiperium metilsulfate.
AY-6108 *see* Ampicillin.
AY-6204 *see* Pronetalol.
AY-6608 *see* Pentagastrin.
AY-8682 *see* Cyheptamide.
AY-11440 *see* Clogestone acetate.
AY-11483 *see* Estrofurate.
AY-15613 *see* Citenamide.
AY-17611 *see* Digitoxigenin hemisuccinate.
AY-20385 *see* Nequinate.
AY-20694 *see* Dexpropranolol.
AY-21011 *see* Practolol.
AY-21367 *see* Furobufen.
AY-21554 *see* Talopram.
AY-22124 *see* Intriptyline.
AY-22214 *see* Taclamine.
AY-22241 *see* Actodigin.
AY-22284A *see* Alrestatin.
AY-22469 *see* Deprostil.
AY-23028 *see* Butaclamol.
AY-23289 *see* Prodolic acid.
AY-23713 *see* Pirandamine.
AY-23946 *see* Tandamine.
AY-24031 *see* Gonadorelin.
AY-24169 *see* Dexclamol.
AY-24236 *see* Etodolac.
AY-24269 *see* Proroxan.
AY-24559 *see* Doxaprost.
AY-24856 *see* Pareptide.
AY-24873 *see* Somatostatin.
AY-24910 *see* Somatostatin.
AY-25392 *see* Azaclorzine.
AY-61122 *see* Metallibure.
AY-61123 *see* Clofibrate.
AY-62013 *see* Etoglucid.
AY-62014 *see* Butriptyline.
AY-62021 *see* Clopenthixol.
AY-62022 *see* Medrogestone.
AY-64043 *see* Propranolol.
'**Ayphylline**' *see* Diprophylline.
AZ-8 *see* Guaiazulene.

10-Azaanthracene see Acridine.

5-Aza-10-arsenaanthracene chloride see Phenarsazine chloride.

Azabicyclane see Anazocine.

3-AZABICYCLO[3.3.1]NONANE (3,5-propanopiperidine; isogranatanine).

9-Azabicyclo[3.3.1]nonane see Granatanine.

9-Azabicyclo[3.3.1]nonan-3-ol see Granatoline.

4-(3-Azabicyclo[3.2.2]non-3-yl)-4'-fluorobutyrophenone see Nonaperone.

1-Azabicyclo[2.2.2]octane see Quinuclidine.

8-Azabicyclo[3.2.1]octane see Nortropane.

1-(3-Azabicyclo[3.3.0]oct-3-yl)-3-(p-toluenesulfonyl)urea see Gliclazide.

AZABON** (3-sulfanilyl-3-azabicyclo[3.2.2]nonane).

AZABUPERONE*** (4'-fluoro-4-(hexahydropyrrolo[1,2-a]pyrazin-2(1H)yl)-butyrophenone; 2-[3-(p-fluorobenzoyl)propyl]hexahydropyrrolo[1,2-a]pyrazine).

AZACITIDINE*** (4-amino-1-β-D-ribofuranosyl-1,3,5-triazin-2(1H)-one; 4-amino-s-triazin-2-one riboside; 5-azacytidine; ladakamycin; NSC-102816; U-18496).

AZACLORZINE** (2-chloro-10-[3-(1,4-diazabicyclo[4.2.0]nonan-4-yl)propionyl]phenothiazine; 2-chloro-10-[3-(hexahydropyrrolo[1,2-a]-pyrazin-2(1H)-yl)propionyl]phenothiazine; 2(1H)-[2-[(2-chlorophenothiazin-10-yl)carbonyl]ethyl]-hexahydropyrrolo[1,2-a]pyrazine; 2-chlorophenothiazin-10-yl 2-(hexahydropyrrolo[1,2-a]-pyrazin-2(1H)-ylethyl ketone; azaclorzine hydrochloride; nonachlazine; AY-25392).

'**Azacon**' see Prothipendyl.

AZACONAZOLE*** (1-[[2-(2,4-dichlorophenyl)-1,3-dioxolan-2-yl]methyl]-1H-1,2,4-triazole).

Azacort see Deflazacort.

'**Azacortid**' see Fluazacort.

AZACOSTEROL*** (20,25-diazacholesterol; 17β-[[3-(dimethylamino)propyl]methylamino]androst-4-en-3β-ol; azacosterol hydrochloride; SC-12937).

Azacycloheptane see Hexamethylenimine.

Azacycloheptatriene see Azepine.

2-(Azacycloheptyl)ethyl m-nitrophenyl ketone see Fenitron.

AZACYCLONOL*** (α,α-diphenyl-4-piperidinemethanol; Mer-17).

Azacyclooctane see Heptamethylenimine.

1-[2-(1-Azacyclooctyl)ethyl]guanidine see Guanethidine.

Azacyclopropane see Aziridine.

5-Azacytidine see Azacitidine.

Azafen (tr) see Pipofezine.

2-Azafluorene see 2-Pyridindene.

AZAFTOZINE** (10-(3-(hexahydropyrrolo[1,2-a]pyrazin-2-(1H)-yl)propionyl)-2-trifluoromethylphenothiazine).

AZAGUANINE (5-amino-7-hydroxy-1H-v-triazolo[4,5-d]pyrimidine; 8-azaguanine; guanazolo; NSC-749).

'**Azak**' see Terbucarb.

AZALOMYCIN*** (antibiotic from *Str. hygros-*

copicus var. *azalomyceticus*; azalomycin F).

Azalomycin F* see Azalomycin.

Azamethone see Azamethonium bromide.

AZAMETHONIUM BROMIDE*** ([(methylimino)diethylene]bis(ethyldimethylammonium bromide); 3-methyl-3-azapentane-1,5-bis(dimethylethylammonium bromide); azamethone; azapenthyleneammonium; pentamethazene; pentamine; C-9295; P-9295).

Azamin see Melamine.

AZANATOR*** (5-(1-methyl-4-piperidylidene)-5H-[1]-benzopyrano[2,3-b]pyridine).

AZANATOR MALEATE* (Sch-15280).

AZANIDAZOLE*** (2-amino-4-[2-(1-methyl-5-nitroimidazol-2-yl)vinyl]pyrimidine; 2-[2-(2-aminopyrimidin-4-yl)vinyl]-1-methyl-5-nitroimidazole; 4-[2-(1-methyl-5-nitroimidazol-2-yl)vinyl]pyrimidin-2-ylamine; 'triclose').

5-AZAOROTIC ACID (s-triazine-2,4-dione-6-carboxylic acid).

Azapenthyleneammonium see Azamethonium bromide.

AZAPERONE*** (4'-fluoro-4-(4-pyrid-2-ylpiperazin-1-yl)butyrophenone; 1-[3-(p-fluorobenzoyl)propyl]-4-pyrid-2-ylpiperazine; R-1929).

AZAPETINE* (6-allyl-6,7-dihydro-5H-dibenz[c,e]azepine; azapetine phosphate; Ro 2-3248; 'azephine'; 'ilidar').

Azaphen (tr) see Pipofezine.

AZAPROCIN*** (3-cinnamyl-8-propionyl-3,8-diazabicyclo[3.2.1]octane).

AZAPROPAZONE*** (3-(dimethylamino)-1,2-dihydro-7-methyl-1,2-(propylmalonyl)-1,2,4-benzotriazine; 5-(dimethylamino)-9-methyl-2-propyl-1H-pyrazolo[1,2-a][1,2,4]benzotriazine-1,3(2H)-dione; apazone; cinnopropazone; AHR-3018; Mi-85; NSC-102824).

AZAPROPAZONE plus DEXTROPROPOXYPHENE ('dolo-prolixan').

8-AZAPURINE (v-triazolo[3,4-d]pyrimidine).

AZAQUINZOLE*** (1,3,4,6,7,11b-hexahydro-2H-pyrazino[2,1-a]isoquinoline).

AZARIBINE*** (2-β-D-ribofuranosyl-as-triazine-3,5-(2H,4H)dione 2',3',5'-triacetate; 2',3',5'-tri-O-acetyl-6-azauridine; azauridine triacetate; riboazauracil; CB-304; NSC-67239; 'triazure').

AZAROLE* (1,1'-(2,5-cyclohexadiene-1,4-diylidenedinitrilo)dipyrrole; N,N'-2,5-cyclohexadiene-1,4-diylidenebis[1H-pyrrol-1-amine; WIN-38770).

AZASERINE*** (L-serine diazoacetate; O-diazoacetyl-L-serine; AZS; CI-337; CN-15757; NSC-742; P-165).

AZASPIRIUM CHLORIDE** (8,9-dihydro-4,11-dimethoxy-9-methylene-5-oxospiro[5H-furo-[3',2':6,7][1]benzopyrano[3,2-c]pyridine-7(6H),1'-piperidinium] chloride).

[2-(6-Azaspiro[2.5]oct-6-yl)ethyl]guanidine see Spirgetine.

AZASTENE** (4,4,17-trimethylandrosta-2,5-dieno[2,3-d]isoxazol-17β-ol; WIN-17625).

AZATADINE*** (6,11-dihydro-11-(1-methylpiperid-4-ylidene)-5H-benzo[5,6]cyclohepta[1,2-b]-

pyridine; azatadine maleate; Sch-10649).

AZATADINE plus PSEUDOEPHEDRINE ('congestan').

AZATEPA*** (bis(1-aziridinyl)-*N*-ethyl-*N*-(1,3,4-thiadiazol-2-yl)phosphinic amide; azetepa; CL-25477; NSC-64826).

1-Aza-4-thia-2,3,5,6-dibenzocycloheptadiene *see* 10,11-Dihydrodibenzo[*b*,*f*][1,4]thiazepine.

AZATHIOPRINE*** (6-(1-methyl-4-nitroimidazol-5-ylthio)purine; BW-57-322; NSC-39084; 'imuran'; 'imurel').

AZATHYMIDINE (6-azathymine desoxyriboside).

AZATHYMINE (6-methyl-1,4,6-triazine-3,5-dione; NSC-3426).

N-**(4-Aza-*endo*-tricyclo[5.2.1.0²·⁶]decan-4-yl)-4-chloro-3-sulfamoylbenzamide** *see* Tripamide.

AZAURACIL (2,3,4,5-tetrahydro-1,2,4-triazine-3,5-dione; *as*-triazine-3,5-dione; NSC-3425).

AZAURIDINE (2-β-D-ribofuranosyl-*as*-triazine-3,5-(2*H*,4*H*)dione; 6-azauracil riboside; NSC-32074).

Azauridine triacetate *see* Azaribine.

AZELAIC ACID (1,7-heptanedicarboxylic acid; nonanedioic acid; anchoic acid; lepargylic acid).

AZELASTINE*** (4-(*p*-chlorobenzyl)-2-(hexahydro-1-methyl-1*H*-azepin-4-yl)-1(2*H*)-phthalazinone; A-5610).

'Azene' *see* Clorazepate monopotassium.

AZEPEXOLE*** (2-amino-6-ethyl-5,6,7,8-tetrahydro-4*H*-oxazolo[4,5-*d*]azepine; B-HT933).

'Azephine' *see* Azapetine.

Azepinamide *see* Glypinamide.

AZEPINDOLE*** (2,3,4,5-tetrahydro-1*H*-(1,4)diazepino[1,2-*a*]indole; McN-2453).

AZEPINE (azacycloheptatriene; homopiperidine).

Azetepa* *see* Azatepa.

AZIDAMFENICOL*** (D(−)-*threo*-2-azido-*N*-[β-hydroxy-α-(hydroxymethyl)-*p*-nitrophenethyl]acetamide; 2-azidoacetamido-1-(*p*-nitrophenyl)-1,3-propanediol; azido-amphenicol).

AZIDAMFENICOL plus CLOTRIMAZOLE & DEXAMETHASONE* ('baycuten').

Azidithion *see* Menazon.

2-Azidoacetamido-1-(*p*-nitrophenyl)-1,3-propanediol *see* Azidamfenicol.

Azido-amphenicol *see* Azidamfenicol.

1-(*p*-Azidobenzoyl)-5-methoxy-2-methylindole-3-acetic acid *see* Zidometacin.

D-(−)-(α-Azidobenzyl)penicillin *see* Azidocillin.

AZIDOCILLIN*** (6-(2-azido-2-phenylacetamido)penicillanic acid; D-(−)-(α-azidobenzyl)penicillin; BRL-2534; DAN-10510; SPC-297D).

2-Azido-*N*-[β-hydroxy-α-(hydroxymethyl)-*p*-nitrophenethyl]acetamide *see* Azidamfenicol.

2-Azido-4-isopropylamino-6-(methylthio)-*s*-triazine *see* Aziprotryne.

4-Azido-*N*-(1-methylethyl)-6-(methylthio)-1,3,5-triazin-2-amine *see* Aziprotryne.

6-(2-Azido-2-phenylacetamido)penicillanic acid *see* Azidocillin.

Azidophosphonic bisdimethylamide *see* Mazidox.

AZIMEXON*** (2-(2-carbamoyl-1-aziridinyl)-2-(2-cyano-1-aziridinyl)propane; 1-[1-(2-cyanoaziridin-1-yl)-1-methylethyl]-2-aziridinecarboxamide; BM-12531).

Azindole *see* Benzimidazole.

Azinepurine *see* Pteridine.

AZINPHOS-ETHYL* (*O*,*O*-diethyl phosphorodithioate *S*-ester with 3-(mercaptomethyl)-1,2,3-benzotriazin-4(3*H*)-one; benzotriazinylmethyldithiophosphoric acid diethyl ester; *O*,*O*-diethyl *S*-(4-oxobenzotriazin-3-ylmethyl) phosphorodithioate; triazotion; 'ethyl-gusathion'; 'ethyl guthion').

AZINPHOS-METHYL* (benzotriazinylmethyldithiophosphoric acid dimethyl ester; *O*,*O*-dimethyl *S*-(4-oxobenzotriazin-3-ylmethyl) phosphorodithioate; *O*,*O*-dimethyl phosphorodithioate *S*-ester with 3-(mercaptomethyl)-1,2,3-benzotriazine-4(3*H*)-one; methylthiazothion; metiltriazotion; Bayer 17147; 'gusathion'; 'guthion'; 'methyl guthion').

AZINPHOS-METHYL plus DEMETON-S-METHYLSULFON ('gusathion-MS').

AZINTAMIDE*** (6-chloro-3-[[(diethylcarbamoyl)methyl]thio]pyridazine; 2-(6-chloropyridazin-3-ylthio)-*N*,*N*-diethylacetamide; ST-9067; X-23).

AZIPRAMINE*** (1-[2-(benzylmethylamino)-ethyl]-6,7-dihydroindolo[1,7-*ab*][1]benzazepine; azipramine hydrochloride; Pierrel-TQ 86; TQ-86).

AZIPROTRYNE* (2-azido-4-isopropylamino-6-(methylthio)-*s*-triazine; 4-azido-*N*-(1-methylethyl)-6-(methylthio)-1,3,5-triazin-2-amine; C-7019; 'brassoran'; 'mesoranil').

AZIRIDINE (azacyclopropane; dimethylenimine; ethylene imine; ethylenimine).

1-AZIRIDINECARBOXYLIC ACID (*N*,*N*-ethylenecarbamic acid).

1-AZIRIDINEETHANOL (2-aziridin-1-ylethanol; 1-(2-hydroxyethyl)aziridine; hydroxyimine).

Aziridine polymer with diepoxybutane *see* Polyetadene.

2-Aziridin-1-ylethanol *see* 1-Aziridineethanol.

AZLOCILLIN*** (6-[D-2-(2-oxoimidazolidine-1-carboxamido)-2-phenylacetamido]penicillanic acid; azlocillin sodium; BAY e-6905; 'securopen').

'Azoangin' *see* Chrysoidine-citrate complex.

AZOBENZENE (azodibenzene; phenylazobenzene).

1,1′-Azobis(chloroformamidine) *see* Chlorazodin.

1,1′-Azobis(*N*,*N*-dimethylformamide) *see* Diamide.

1,1′-Azobisformamide *see* Azoformamide.

1,1′-Azobis(3-methyl-2-phenyl-1*H*-imidazo[1,2-*a*]pyridinium bromide) *see* Fazadinium bromide.

'Azochloramide' *see* Chlorazodin.

Azodermin *see* Acetamidoazotoluene.

Azodibenzene *see* Azobenzene.

p,*p*′-**Azodibenzoic acid bis(diethylaminoethyl) ester** *see* Azoprocaine.

Azodicarbonamide *see* Azoformamide.

Azodipyridine *see* Azopyridine.

AZODISALICYLIC ACID (5,5′-azodisalicylic acid; disodium 5,5′-azodisalicylate; di-5-aminosalicylic acid; di-5-ASA).

5,5′-Azodisalicylic acid *see* Azodisalicylic acid.

'Azodrin' *see* Monocrotophos.

'Azodyne' *see* Phenazopyridine.

AZOFORMAMIDE (1,1′-azobisformamide; azodicarbonamide; dicarbamoyldiimide).

'Azohel' *see* Chrysoidine-citrate complex.

'Azoiodine' *see* Chrysoidine dihydroiodide.

'Azojod' *see* Chrysoidine dihydroiodide.

'Azolid' *see* Phenylbutazone.

AZOLIMINE* (2-imino-3-methyl-1-phenyl-4-imidazolidinone; CL-90748).

Azolinic acid *see* Cinoxacin.

'Azone' *see* Laurocapram.

Azoniaspiro(3α-benziloyloxynortropane-8,1′-pyrrolidine) chloride *see* Trospium chloride.

Azophen *see* Phenazone.

Azophenylene *see* Phenazine.

AZOPROCAINE (*p,p′*-azodibenzoic acid bis(diethylaminoethyl) ester).

AZOPYRIDINE (azodipyridine; pyridylazopyridine).

'Azopyrine' *see* Salazosulfapyridine.

'Azorhodan' *see* Chrysoidine monothiocyanate.

Azorubrum *see* Bordeaux B.

AZOSEMIDE* (2-[[3-chloro-4-sulfamoyl-6-(1*H*-tetrazol-5-yl)anilino]methyl]thiophene; 2-chloro-5-(1*H*-tetrazol-5-yl)-*N*⁴-2-thenylsulfanilamide; 5-[4-chloro-5-sulfamoyl-2-(2-thenylamino)phenyl]-1*H*-tetrazole).

AZOSULFAMIDE (*N*⁴-(7-acetamido-3,6-disulfo-1-hydroxy-2-naphthaleneazo)sulfanilamide;

'drometil'; 'neoprontosil'; 'prontosil soluble').

AZOTHOATE* (4-chloro-4′-[(dimethoxyphosphinothioyl)oxy]azobenzene; *O*-[4-[(4-chlorophenyl)azo]phenyl] *O,O*-dimethyl phosphorothioate; 'slam').

AZOTOMYCIN* (antibiotic from *Str. ambofaciens*; duazomycin B; antibiotic 1719; NSC-56654).

Azotoyperite *see* Chlormethine.

Azovan blue* *see* Evans blue.

Azoxodone (tr) *see* Pemoline.

AZS *see* Azaserine.

AZTREONAM* ((*Z*)-2-[[[(2-aminothiazol-4-yl)-[[(2*S*,3*S*)-2-methyl-4-oxo-1-sulfoazetidin-3-yl]-carbamoyl]methylene]amino]oxy]-2-methylpropionic acid; SQ-26776).

'Azubromaron' *see* Benzbromarone.

'Azudimidine' *see* Salazosulfadimidine.

AZULENE (cyclopentacycloheptene).

'Azulfidine' *see* Salazosulfapyridine.

'Azulon' *see* Guaiazulene.

AZURE A (3-amino-7-(dimethylamino)phenazthionium chloride; *asym*-dimethylthionine chloride).

AZURE B (7-(dimethylamino)-3-(methylamino)-phenazthionium chloride; trimethylthionine chloride).

AZURE C (3-amino-7-(methylamino)phenazthionium chloride; methylthionine chloride).

AZURESIN* (complex of azure A with a carbacrylamine cation-exchange resin; 'diagnex blue').

B

B1 Q16 *see* Hedaquinium chloride.
B-22 *see* Propham.
B-23 *see* Tifenamil.
B-44-P *see* Streptovarycin.
B-80 *see* Ibuprofen.
B-100 *see* Methaqualone.
B-194 *see* Zolamine.
B-306 *see* Flufenamic acid.
B-360 *see* Paroxypropione.
B-436 *see* Prenylamine.
B-518 *see* Cyclophosphamide.
B-557 *see* Colfenamate.
B-577 *see* Etofenamate.
B-663 *see* Clofazimine.
B-712 *see* Disopyramide.
B-862 *see* Dibusadol.
B-907 *see* Pyrithione sodium.
B-1312 *see* Bupranolol.
B-1420 *see* Propanidid.
B-1464 *see* Guanacline.
B-2311 *see* Morinamide.
B-4130 *see* Iodamide.
B-5833 *see* Camazepam.
B-6518 *see* Clanobutin.
B-10610 *see* Meglumine iodoxamate.
B-11420 *see* Iopronic acid.
B-14030 *see* Suncillin.
B-15000 *see* Iopamidol.
B-35251 *see* Mitocromin.
B-64114 *see* Bumadizone.
B-66256 *see* Urapidil.
Ba-168 *see* Lofexidine.
BA-253 *see* Oxitropium bromide.
BA-4164-8 *see* Diflumidone.
BA-4197 *see* Flucrilate.
BA-4223 *see* Triflumidate.
Ba-5473 *see* Oxyphenonium bromide.
Ba-5968 *see* Hydralazine.
BA-7602-06 *see* Talniflumate.
BA-7604-02 *see* Talosalate.
Ba-10370 *see* Sulfachlorpyridazine.
Ba-11391 *see* Xylometazoline.
Ba-13155 *see* Meladrazine.
BA-16038 *see* Aminoglutethimide.
Ba-18605 *see* Sulfapyrazole.
Ba-20684 *see* Etonitazene.
Ba-21401 *see* Tribenoside.
Ba-29038 *see* Boldenone undecenoate.
Ba-29837 *see* Deferoxamine.
Ba-30803 *see* Benzoctamine.
Ba-30920 *see* Tetracosactide.

Ba-31458 *see* Gestadienol acetate.
Ba-32644 *see* Niridazole.
Ba-32968 *see* Delfantrine.
Ba-33122 *see* Deferoxamine mesilate.
Ba-33902 *see* β-Angiotensin-II.
Ba-34276 *see* Maprotiline.
Ba-34647 *see* Baclofen.
Ba-36278A *see* Cefacetrile.
Ba-39089 *see* Oxprenolol.
Ba-40088 *see* Proxibutene.
Ba-41166/E *see* Rifampicin.
Ba-41795 *see* Codactide.
Ba-42915 *see* Tetracosactide zinc phosphate complex.
Ba-49802B *see* Oxaprotiline.
'Babesan' *see* Quinuronium sulfate.
'Baburon' *see* Quinuronium sulfate.
BACAMPICILLIN*** (ampicillin ester with ethyl 1-hydroxyethyl carbonate; bacampicillin hydrochloride; 'ambacamp'; 'ambaxin'; 'bacocil'; 'penglobe').
'Bacarate' *see* Phendimetrazine.
'Bacdip' *see* Quintiofos.
'Bacillosporin' *see* Polymyxin B.
Bacillus cereus, enzyme *see* Penicillinase.
Bacillus cereus sphaericus, enzyme *see* Sfericase.
Bacillus cereus subtilis, enzymes *see* Sutilains.
BACIMETHRIN (4-amino-2-methoxy-5-pyrimidinemethanol).
BACITRACIN*** (basic polypeptide from *B. subtilis*; bacitracin zinc).
See also Neomycin.
BACLOFEN*** (β-aminomethyl-*p*-chlorohydrocinnamic acid; 4-amino-3-(*p*-chlorophenyl)butyric acid; β-(4-chlorophenyl)GABA; Ba-34647; 'lioresal').
BACMECILLINAM** ((2*S*,5*R*,6*R*)-6-[[(hexahydro-1*H*-azepin-1-yl)methylene]amino]penicillanic acid ester with ethyl 1-hydroxyethyl carbonate; mecillinam ester with ethyl 1-hydroxyethyl carbonate).
'Bacocil' *see* Bacampicillin.
'Bactine' *see* Methylbenzethonium chloride.
'Bactocill' *see* Oxacillin.
'Bactol' *see* Clioquinol.
'Bactrim' *see* Co-trimoxazole.
'Bactrimel' *see* Co-trimoxazole.
'Badil' *see* Crystal violet.
'Badional' *see* Sulfathiourea.
Baksacor (tr) *see* Etafenone.
'Baktolan' *see* Chlorocresol.

BAL *see* Dimercaprol.
'Balan' *see* Benfluralin.
'Balarsen' *see* Arsthinol.
'Baldon' *see* Dimethylthiambutene.
Balipramine* *see* Depramine.
'Balkis' *see* Xylometazoline.
BALSALAZIDE** ((*E*)-5-[[*p*-[(2-carboxyethyl)-carbamoyl]phenyl]azo]salicylic acid; balsalazide sodium; BX-661A).
'Baltix' *see* Clofedanol.
'Balusil' *see* Proguanil.
BAMBERMYCIN** (antibiotic from *Str. bambergiensis*; bambermycins; moenomycin; 'flavomycin').
Bambermycins* *see* Bambermycin.
BAMBUTEROL** ((±)-5-[2-(*tert*-butylamino)-1-hydroxyethyl]-*m*-phenylene bis(dimethylcarbamate)).
BAMETHAN** (2-butylamino-1-(*p*-hydroxyphenyl)ethanol; α-[(butylamino)methyl]-*p*-hydroxybenzyl alcohol).
BAMETHAN plus ENDOMIDE ('euvasculin').
BAMETHAN plus INOSITOL NICOTINATE ('vascunicol').
See also under Aminophenazone.
BAMIFYLLINE** (8-benzyl-7-[2-[ethyl(2-hydroxyethyl)amino]ethyl]theophylline; benzetamophylline; AC-3810; BAX-2739-Z; CB-8102).
BAMIPINE** (4-(*N*-benzylanilino)-1-methylpiperidine; *N*-(1-methylpiperid-4-yl)-*N*-phenylbenzylamine; piperamine).
BAMNIDAZOLE** (1-(2-carbamoyloxyethyl)-2-methyl-5-nitroimidazole; 2-methyl-5-nitroimidazole-1-ethanol carbamate ester; RP-20578).
Bamoxine* *see* Anidoxime.
'Banamine' *see* Flunixin meglumine.
'Bancaris' *see* Thenium closilate.
'Bandol' *see* Carbifene.
'Bangina' *see* Clonitrate.
Banisterine *see* Harmine.
'Banistyl' *see* Dimetotiazine mesilate.
'Banminth' *see* Pyrantel.
'Banminth II' *see* Morantel tartrate.
'Banocide' *see* Diethylcarbamazine.
'Banol' *see* Carbanolate.
'Bantu' *see* Antu.
'Banvel' *see* Dicamba.
'Banvel T' *see* Tricamba.
BAPN *see* 3-Aminopropionitrile.
Baptitoxine *see* Cytisine.
BAQD-10 *see* Dequalinium chloride.
'Baratol' *see* Indoramin.
BARBALOIN (*Aloe vera* glycoside; curacaolin; 'auraloin').
Barbamate *see* Barban.
'Barbamon' *see* Barbipyrine.
Barbamyl (tr) *see* Amobarbital.
BARBAN* (4-chlorobut-2-yn-1-yl (*m*-chlorophenyl)carbamate; 4-chlorobut-2-yn-1-yl *m*-chloro-carbanilate; barbamate; chlorinat; klorinat; 'carbyne').
BARBEXACLONE** (compound of phenobarbital with *N*,α-dimethylcyclohexaneethylamine;

1-cyclohexyl-2-methylaminopropyl 5-ethyl-5-phenylbarbiturate; phenobarbital-propylhexedrine; phenomitur; propylhexedrine-phenobarbital; P-841).
BARBITAL** (5,5-diethylbarbituric acid; barbitone; diemal).
Barbitone* *see* Barbital.
BARBITURIC ACID (hexahydro-2,4,6-pyrimidinetrione; malonylurea; 2,4,6(1*H*,3*H*,5*H*)-pyrimidinetrione).
'Barbonin' *see* Ethaverine.
'Barbosec' *see* Secobarbital.
'Barnetil' *see* Sultopride.
'Baron' *see* Erbon.
BAROTAL (5-(2-butenyl)-5-ethylbarbituric acid; crotylethylbarbituric acid).
'Barquinol' *see* Clioquinol.
'Barricade' *see* Cypermethrin.
'BAS' *see* Benanserin.
BAS-3179F *see* Diethyltoluamide.
BAS 3510H *see* Bentazon.
'Basamid' *see* Dazomet.
'Basanor' *see under* Brompyrazon.
'Basedol' *see* Aminothiazole.
'Basergin' *see* Ergometrine.
'Basfitox' *see under* Buturon.
'Basodexan' *see* Urea.
'Basofortina' *see* Methylergometrine.
'Basolest' *see* Carbimazole.
'Basudin' *see* Dimpylate.
BATILOL** (3-octadecyloxy-1,2-propanediol; batyl alcohol).
'Batrafen' *see* Ciclopirox olamine.
BATROXOBIN** (thrombin-like enzyme from venom of *Bothrops atrox*; S-25; ST-25; 'defibrase'; 'reptilase').
BATROXOBIN plus HEPARIN ('darkinal'; 'diabtyl').
'Batticol' *see* Povidone-iodine.
Batyl alcohol *see* Batilol.
Bax-422-Z *see* Albutoin.
Bax-1400-Z *see* Dimethadione.
BAX-1515 *see* Sutilains.
BAX-1526 *see* Chymopapain.
BAX-2739-Z *see* Bamifylline.
'Baxacor' *see* Etafenone.
'Baxan' *see* Cefadroxil.
'Baxarytmon' *see* Propafenone.
BAY-1470 *see* Xylazine.
BAY-1500 *see* Mefruside.
BAY-1521 *see* Noxiptiline.
BAY-4503 *see* Propiram fumarate.
BAY-41831 *see* Fenitrothion.
BAY-79770 *see* Chloraniformethan.
BAY-94337 *see* Metribuzin.
BAY a-1040 *see* Nifedipine.
BAY a-7168 *see* Niludipine.
BAY b-4231 *see* Glisoxepide.
BAY b-5097 *see* Clotrimazole.
BAY b-5369 *see* Carbenicillin.
'Baycaine' *see* Tolycaine.
'Baycaron' *see* Mefruside.
'Baycid' *see* Fenthion.

'Baycillin' *see* Propicillin.
'Baycuten' *see under* Azidamfenicol.
BAY d-8815 *see* Amidantel.
BAY e-5009 *see* Nitrendipine.
BAY e-6905 *see* Azlocillin.
BAY e-6975 *see* Climbazole.
BAY e-9736 *see* Nimodipine.
Bayer-73 *see* Clonitralide.
Bayer-186 *see* Clofedanol.
Bayer-205 *see* Suramin sodium.
Bayer-693 *see* Ethylstibamine.
Bayer-1213 *see* Levomepromazine.
Bayer-1355 *see* Fencarbamide.
Bayer-1362 *see* Butaperazine.
Bayer 1420 *see* Propanidid.
Bayer-1470 *see* Xylazine.
Bayer-2349 *see* Metrifonate.
Bayer-2353 *see* Niclosamide.
Bayer 2502 *see* Nifurtimox.
Bayer-3231 *see* Triaziquone.
Bayer-3504 *see* Polyvinylpyridine *N*-oxide.
Bayer-5360 *see* Metronidazole.
Bayer-5400 *see* Sulfametoxydiazine.
Bayer-8196 *see under* Demeton-O.
Bayer-9002 *see* Naftalofos.
Bayer 9015 *see* Niclofolan.
Bayer 9053 *see* Phoxim.
Bayer 17147 *see* Azinphos-methyl.
Bayer 21199 *see* Coumafos.
Bayer-25141 *see* Fensulfothion.
Bayer-29493 *see* Fenthion.
Bayer-37344 *see* Methiocarb.
Bayer-38819 *see* O,O-Bis(p-chlorophenyl) *N*-acet-
   imidoylphosphoramidothioate.
Bayer-39007 *see* Propoxur.
Bayer-41831 *see* Fenitrothion.
Bayer-45515 *see* Parathion-methyl.
Bayer-A 124 *see* Aminopromazine.
Bayer A-128 *see* Aprotinin.
'Bayercillin' *see* Propicillin.
Bayer L-1359 *see* Metrifonate.
Bayer S-1752 *see* Fenthion.
BAY f-1353 *see* Mezlocillin.
BAY f-4975 *see* Acemetacin.
BAY f-8751 *see* Valconazole.
'Bayfidan' *see* Triadimenol.
BAY g-2821 *see* Muzolimine.
BAY g-5421 *see* Acarbose.
BAY g-6575 *see* Nafazatrom.
'Baygon' *see* Propoxur.
BAY h-4502 *see* Bifonazole.
BAY h-5757 *see* Febantel.
BAY h-6020 *see* Lombazole.
BAY i-7433 *see* Copovithane.
BAY k-5552 *see* Nisoldipine.
'Bayleton' *see* Triadimefon.
'Bayluscide' *see* Clonitralide.
'Baymicin' *see* Sisomicin.
'Baymix' *see* Coumafos.
BAY o-6893 *see* Rioprostil.
BAY o-9867 *see* Ciprofloxacin.
'Baypen' *see* Mezlocillin.
BAY q-3939 *see* Ciprofloxacin.

'Bayrena' *see* Sulfametoxydiazine.
'Bayrusil' *see* Quinalphos.
'Baytan' *see* Triadimenol.
'Bayten' *see* Fenthion.
'Baytex' *see* Fenthion.
'Baythion' *see* Phoxim.
'Baytroid' *see* Cyfluthrin.
BAY Va-1470 *see* Xylazine.
BAY Va-4059 *see* Brotianide.
BAY Va-9387 *see* Etisazole.
BAY Va-9391 *see* Olaquindox.
'Bayverm' *see* Febantel.
BAY Vh-5757 *see* Febantel.
BAY vk-4999 *see* Fuzlocillin.
BAY vl-4718 *see* Etisomicin.
BAY vl-6045 *see* Flumethrin.
BBA *see* 3-Benzylidenebutyric acid.
BBK-8 *see* Amikacin.
'B-b-S' *see* Benzyl benzoate.
BC-17 *see* Iodoxamic acid.
BC-40 *see* Hexadistigmine.
BC-48 *see* Demecarium bromide.
BC-51 *see* Distigmine bromide.
BC-105 *see* Pizotifen.
(−)-BC-2627 *see* Butorphanol.
BCM *see* Mannomustine.
BCME *see* Bis(chloromethyl) ether.
BCNU *see* Carmustine.
BCP *see* Bucolome.
BCX-2600 *see* Stiripentol.
BDH-312 *see* Mephenesin.
BDH-1298 *see* Megestrol acetate.
BDH-1921 *see* Melengestrol acetate.
BE-419 *see* Ioglycamic acid.
BE-426 *see* Adipiodone sodium.
Be-724-A *see* Bendroflumethiazide.
'Beaprine' *see* Carsalam.
'Beatiline' *see* Benactyzine.
'Beatol' *see* Amobarbital.
'Bebate' *see* Betamethasone benzoate.
'Becantal' *see* Sodium dibunate.
'Becantex' *see* Sodium dibunate.
Becanthone* *see* Becantone.
BECANTONE** (1-[[2-ethyl-(2-hydroxy-2-meth-
   ylpropyl)amino]ethylamino]-4-methylthioxan-
   then-9-one; becanthone; NSC-15796; WIN-
   13820).
'Becantyl' *see* Sodium dibunate.
BECLAMIDE** (*N*-benzyl-3-chloropropion-
   amide; benzchlorpropamide; chloracon; chloroethylphenamide).
BECLOBRATE*** (2-[4-(p-chlorobenzyl)phen-
   oxy]-2-methylbutyric acid ethyl ester; ethyl (±)-
   2-[[α-(p-chlorophenyl)-p-tolyl]oxy]-2-methylbu-
   tyrate; Sgd-24774).
BECLOMETASONE*** (9-chloro-11β,17,21-tri-
   hydroxy-16β-methylpregna-1,4-diene-3,20-di-
   one; 9α-chloro-16β-methylprednisolone; beclomethasone).
BECLOMETASONE DIPROPIONATE* (9-
   chloro-11β-hydroxy-16β-methyl-17,21-bis(1-
   oxopropoxy)pregna-1,4-diene-3,20-dione; Sch-
   18020W).

Beclomethasone* *see* Beclometasone.
'Beclomycin' *see* Colistin.
BECLOTIAMINE* (3-(4-amino-2-methylpyr-imidin-5-ylmethyl)-5-(2-chloroethyl)-4-methyl-thiazolium chloride; chloroethylthiamine).
'Beconase' *see* Beclometasone dipropionate.
'Becotide' *see* Beclometasone dipropionate.
'Bee-17' *see* Amygdalin.
BEE VENOM (apilit; melittin; 'apicosan'; 'forap-in').
'Befeniol' *see* Bephenium hydroxynaphthoate.
BEFUNOLOL* (2-acetyl-7-(2-hydroxy-3-isopropylaminopropoxy)benzofuran; 1-(2-acet-ylbenzofuran-7-yloxy)-3-(isopropylamino)-2-propanol; 7-[2-hydroxy-3-(isopropylamino)-propoxy]-2-benzofuranyl methyl ketone; BFE-60).
BEFURALINE* (1-(2-benzofuranylcarbonyl)-4-benzylpiperazine; 2-[(4-benzylpiperazin-1-yl)-carbonyl]benzofuran).
BEHENIC ACID (docosanoic acid).
Bei-1293 *see* Xipamide.
BEIH *see* Nialamide.
'Bekadid' *see* Hydrocodone.
BEKANAMYCIN* (L-*O*-(3-amino-3-deoxy-α-D-glucopyranosyl)-(1→4)-*O*-[2,6-diamino-2,6-dideoxy-α-D-glucopyranosyl-(1→6)]-2-deoxy-streptamine; 2'-amino-2'-deoxykanamycin; ka-namycin B; kanendomycin; bekanamycin sulf-ate; NK-1006; 'stereocidin').
BELARIZINE* (1-(diphenylmethyl)-4-(*p*-hydr-oxybenzyl)piperazine; α-[4-(diphenylmethyl)pip-erazin-1-yl]-*p*-cresol).
'Belcomycin' *see* Colistin.
'Belfacillin' *see* Meticillin.
'Belfene' *see* Diphenylpyraline.
'Belganyl' *see* Suramin sodium.
'Bellacristin' *see* Belladonnin.
BELLADONNIN (isatropic acid ditropine ester; ditropyl isatropate; isatropyldytropeine; tropyl isatropate; C-45).
'Belmark' *see* Fenvalerate.
'Beloc' *see* Metoprolol.
'Belosin' *see* Camylofin.
BELOXAMIDE* (*N*-benzyloxy-*N*-(3-phenyl-propyl)acetamide; W-1372).
'Bemaphate' *see* Chloroquine.
'Bemarsal' *see* Difetarsone.
BEMEGRIDE* (β-ethyl-β-methylglutarimide; 4-ethyl-4-methyl-2,6-piperidinedione; methethar-imide; AB-01; NP-13).
BEMETIZIDE* (6-chloro-3,4-dihydro-3-(α-methylbenzyl)-2*H*-1,2,4-benzothiadiazine-7-sul-fonamide 1,1-dioxide; Diu-60).
BEMETIZIDE plus BUPRANOLOL & TRIAM-TERENE ('cardiotensin').
BEMETIZIDE plus TRIAMTERENE ('di-ucomb').
See also under Guabenxan.
Bemidone *see* Hydroxypethidine.
BENACTYZINE* (2-(diethylamino)ethyl benz-ilate; amizil; diazil; AY-5406-1; WIN-5606).
See also under Meprobamate.

Benactyzine methobromide *see* Methylbenactyzium bromide.
'Benadryl' *see* Diphenhydramine.
BENAFENTRINE (*cis*-4'-(1,2,3,4,4a,10b-hexa-hydro-8,9-dimethoxy-2-methylbenzo[*c*]-[1,6]naphthyridin-6-yl)acetanilide).
'Benalgin' *see* Benzydamine.
BENANSERIN* (3-(2-aminoethyl)-1-benzyl-5-methoxy-2-methylindole; 1-benzyl-2,5-dimethyl-serotonin; benzyl antiserotonin; serotonin benz-yl analogue; Woolley's antiserotonin; 'BAS').
BENAPRIZINE* (2-(ethylpropylamino)ethyl benzilate; benapryzine; benaprizine hydrochlor-ide; BRL-1288; 'brizin').
Benapryzine* *see* Benaprizine.
BENAXIBINE (*p*-(D-xylosylamino)benzoic acid).
BENAZOLIN* (3-(carboxymethyl)-4-chloroben-zothiazol-3(2*H*)-one; 4-chloro-2-oxo-3(2*H*)-benzothiazoleacetic acid; 'cornox CWK'; 'legu-mex extra'; 'ley cornox'; 'tricornox').
Benazoline* *see* Metizoline.
Bencaine (tr) *see* 2-(Diethylamino)ethyl benzoate.
Benchinox *see* Benquinox.
BENCIANOL ((2*R*,3*S*)-3',4'-[(diphenylmethyl-ene)dioxy]-3,5,7-flavantriol).
Bencifurolin *see* Resmethrin.
BENCISTEINE (*N*-acetyl-3-[(2-benzoylpropyl)-thio]alanine; *N*-acetyl-*S*-(2-benzoylpropyl)cyste-ine).
BENCLONIDINE* (1-benzoyl-2-(2,6-dichloro-anilino)-2-imidazoline).
Bencurine iodide *see* Gallamine triethiodide.
BENCYCLANE* (3-(1-benzylcycloheptyloxy)-*N*,*N*-dimethylpropylamine; 1-benzyl-1-(3-di-methylaminopropoxy)cycloheptane; benzcyclan; bencyclane fumarate; Egyt-201).
BENDACORT (hydrocortisone 1-[(1-benzyl-1*H*-indazol-3-yloxy)acetate]; bendazac hydrocorti-sone ester; AF-2071; 'versacort').
BENDAMUSTINE* (5-[bis(2-chloroethyl)-amino]-1-methyl-2-benzimidazolebutyric acid; IMET-3993; 'cytostasan').
BENDAZAC* (2-(1-benzyl-1*H*-indazol-3-yl-oxy)acetic acid; bindazac; bendazac sodium; AF-983; 'bendazolic acid'; 'versus').
Bendazac hydrocortisone ester *see* Bendacort.
BENDAZOL (2-benzylbenzimidazole; dibaz-ole; 'tromasedan').
BENDERIZINE (2-(3,4-dimethoxybenzyl)-4-(diphenylmethyl)-1,2-dimethylpiperazine; (*R*)-4-(diphenylmethyl)-1,2-dimethyl-2-veratrylpiper-azine).
BENDIOCARB* (2,2-dimethyl-1,3-benzodioxol-4-yl methylcarbamate; NC-6897; OMS-1394; 'fi-cam').
'Bendopa' *see* Levodopa.
'Bendralan' *see* Pheneticillin.
Bendrofluazide* *see* Bendroflumethiazide.
BENDROFLUMETHIAZIDE* (3-benzyl-3,4-dihydro-6(trifluoromethyl)-2*H*-1,2,4-benzothia-diazine-7-sulfonamide 1,1-dioxide; bendrofluaz-ide; benzydroflumethiazide; benzylhydroflu-

methiazide; Be-724-A; FT-81).

BENDROFLUMETHIAZIDE plus MEPRO-BAMATE ('tenavoid').

BENDROFLUMETHIAZIDE plus NADOLOL ('solgeretic').

BENDROFLUMETHIAZIDE plus PROPRA-NOLOL ('dociretic'; 'inderetic'; 'inderex'). *See also under* Reserpine; Timolol maleate.

'Benedorm' *see* Pyrithyldione.

Benefin *see* Benfluralin.

'Benemid' *see* Probenecid.

'Benetazone' *see* Tribuzone.

BENETHAMINE PENICILLIN*** (*N*-benzyl-phenethylamine 6-(phenylacetamido)penicillanate; *N*-benzyl-2-phenylethylamine salt of penicillin G).

BENEXTRAMINE (*N,N'*-bis[6-[(*o*-methoxybenzyl)amino]hexyl]cystamine; BHC).

BENFLUOREX** (2-[[α-methyl-*m*-(trifluoromethyl)phenethyl]amino]ethanol benzoate; *N*-(2-benzoyloxyethyl)-*m*-(trifluoromethyl)amphetamine; *N*-(2-benzoyloxyethyl)norfenfluramine; benzoyloxyfenfluramine; S-780; S-992; SE-780; 'mediator').

BENFLUOREX MESILATE (benfluorex methanesulfonate; SE-1513).

BENFLURALIN* (*N*-butyl-*N*-ethyl-2,6-dinitro-4-(trifluoromethyl)aniline; *N*-butyl-*N*-ethyl-α,α,α-trifluoro-2,6-dinitro-*p*-toluidine; benefin; bethrodine; 'balan'; 'binnell'; 'quilan').

BENFOSFORMIN*** ([(benzylamidino)amidino]phosphoramidic acid disodium salt; 5-benzyl-1-phosphorylbiguanide disodium salt; JAV-852).

BENFOTIAMINE*** (*N*-(4-amino-2-methylpyrimidin-5-ylmethyl)-*N*-(4-hydroxy-2-mercapto-1-methyl-1-butenyl)formamide *S*-benzoate *O*-phosphate; 4-*N*-(4-amino-2-methylpyrimidin-5-ylmethyl)formamido-3-(benzoylthio)pent-3-enyl phosphate; *S*-benzoylthiamine *O*-phosphate; CB-8088).

BENFURODIL HEMISUCCINATE*** (2-(1-hydroxyethyl)-β-hydroxymethyl-3-methyl-5-benzofuranacrylic γ-lactone hydrogen succinate; CB-4091; 'eucilat').

BENHEPAZONE*** (1-benzyl-2(1*H*)-cyclohept-imidazolinone; RCH-314).

'Ben-hex' *see* Lindane.

Benhexol *see* Orphenadrine.

'Benisone' *see* Betamethasone benzoate.

'Benlate' *see* Benomyl.

'Benlo' *see* Benzyl benzoate.

'Benlotex' *see* Benzyl benzoate.

BENMOXIN*** (benzoic acid 2-(α-methylbenzyl)hydrazide; 1-benzoyl-2-(α-methylbenzyl)hydrazine).

'Benodaine' *see* Piperoxan.

BENOLIZIME*** (1,2,3,4,4a,6,7,11b,12,13a-decahydro-9,10-dimethoxy-13*H*-dibenzo[*a,f*]quinolizin-13-one oxime).

BENOMYL* (methyl 1-(butylcarbamoyl)benzimidazole-2-carbamate; MBC; IPO-1250; 'benlate').

BENOMYL plus THIRAM ('benlate-T').

'Benoquin' *see* Monobenzone.

'Benoral' *see* Benorilate.

BENORILATE*** (4-acetamidophenyl salicylate acetate; *p*-acetamidophenyl 2-acetoxybenzoate; *p*-acetamidophenyl acetylsalicylate; benorylate; fenasprate; WIN-11450; 'benoral'; 'benortan'; 'salipran').

'Benortan' *see* Benorilate.

BENORTERONE*** (17β-hydroxy-17-methyl-*B*-norandrost-4-en-3-one; 17α-methyl-*B*-nortestosterone; SK&F-7690).

Benorylate* *see* Benorilate.

BENOXAFOS*** (*S*-(5,7-dichlorobenzoxazol-2-ylmethyl) *O,O*-diethyl phosphorodithioate).

BENOXAPROFEN*** (5-(1-carboxyethyl)-2-(*p*-chlorophenyl)benzoxazole; 2-(*p*-chlorophenyl)-α-methyl-5-benzoxazoleacetic acid; 2-[2-(*p*-chlorophenyl)benzoxazol-5-yl]propionic acid; compound 90459; LRCL-3794; 'coxigon'; 'opren').

Benoxinate *see* Oxybuprocaine.

Benoxiquine *see* Benzoxiquine.

'Benoxyl' *see* Benzoyl peroxide.

BENPENOLISIN*** (*N*[6]-[D-2-(4-carboxy-5,5-dimethylthiazolidin-2-yl)-*N*-(phenylacetyl)glycyl]-L-lysine monopotassium salt decapeptide).

BENPERIDOL** (4'-fluoro-4-[4-(2-oxobenzimidazolin-1-yl)piperid-1-yl]butyrophenone; 1-[1-[3-(*p*-fluorobenzoyl)propyl]piperid-4-yl]-2-benzimidazolinone; benzoperidol; benzperidol; CB-8089; McN-JR-4584; R-4584).

BENPROPERINE*** (1-[2-(2-benzylphenoxy)-1-methylethyl]piperidine; 1-(2-benzylphenoxy)-2-piperid-1-ylpropane; ASA-158/5; 'pirexyl').

BENPROPERINE EMBONATE ('tussafug').

BENQUINOX* (benzoic acid [(4-hydroxyimino)-2,5-cyclohexadien-1-ylidene]hydrazide; benchinox; COBH; QBH; 'ceredon'; 'cerenox').

BENQUINOX plus METHYLTHIOXOARSINE ('rhizoctol').

BENRIXATE*** (2-(diethylamino)ethyl 4-benzyl-1-piperidinecarboxylate).

BENSALAN*** (3,5-dibromo-*N*-(*p*-bromobenzyl)salicylamide).

BENSERAZIDE*** (DL-serine 2-(2,3,4-trihydroxybenzyl)hydrazide; 2-amino-3-hydroxy-2'-(2,3,4-trihydroxybenzyl)propionohydrazide; 1-seryl-2-(2,3,4-trihydroxybenzyl)hydrazine; serazide; benserazide hydrochloride; Ro 4-4602). *See also under* Levodopa.

BENSULDAZIC ACID*** (5-benzyldihydro-6-thioxo-2*H*-1,3,5-thiadiazine-3(4*H*)-acetic acid; benuldazate sodium; 'defungit').

Bensulfamide *see* Mafenide.

BENSULFENE (benzoyl disulfide; dibenzoyl disulfide; 'septiolan').

BENSULIDE* (*S*-[2-(benzenesulfonamido)ethyl] *O,O*-diisopropyl phosphorodithioate; *O,O*-bis(1-methylethyl) *S*-[2-[(phenylsulfonyl)amino]ethyl] phosphorodithioate; *N*-[2-[(diisopropoxyphosphinothioyl)thio]ethyl]benzenesulfonamide; 'beta-san'; 'prefar').

Bensylyt* *see* Phenoxybenzamine.

BENTAZEPAM*** (1,2-dihydro-5-phenyl-6,7-

tetramethylene-3*H*-thieno[2,3-*e*][1,4]diazepin-2-one; 1,3,6,7,8,9-hexahydro-5-phenyl-2*H*-(1)-benzothieno[2,3-*e*]-1,4-diazepin-2-one; CI-718; QM-6008; 'thiadipon').

BENTAZON* (3-isopropyl-1*H*-2,1,3-benzothiadiazin-4(3*H*)-one 2,2-dioxide; 3-(1-methylethyl)-1*H*-2,1,3-benzothiadiazin-4(3*H*)-one 2,2-dioxide; BAS 3510H).

BENTEMAZOLE*** (1-benzyl-2-(1*H*-tetrazol-5-yl)imidazole; 5-(1-benzylimidazol-2-yl)-1*H*-tetrazole).

BENTHIOCARB (*S*-(*p*-chlorophenyl) diethylcarbamothioate; 'saturn').

BENTIAMINE*** (*N*-(4-amino-2-methylpyrimidin-5-ylmethyl)-*N*-(4-hydroxy-2-mercapto-1-methyl-1-butenyl)formamide *O,S*-dibenzoate; 4-*N*-(4-amino-2-methylpyrimidin-5-ylmethyl)-formamido-3-(benzoylthio)pent-3-enyl benzoate; dibenthiamine; dibenzoylthiamin; 'nevriton').

BENTIPIMINE*** (1-[2-(*o*-chloro-α-phenylbenzylthio)ethyl]-4-(*o*-methylbenzyl)piperazine).

BENTIROMIDE*** ((*S*)-4-[2-benzamido-3-(4-hydroxyphenyl)propionamido]benzoic acid; (*S*)-*p*-(α-benzamido-*p*-hydroxyhydrocinnamido)-benzoic acid; 4-[(*N*-benzoyl-L-tyrosyl)amino]-benzoic acid; (*S*)-4-[[2-(benzoylamino)-3-(4-hydroxyphenyl)-1-oxopropyl]amino]benzoic acid; BTPABA; E-2663; PFT; Ro 11-7891; 'chymex').

'Bentonyl' *see* Trolnitrate.

'Bentrofene' *see* Acediasulfone morpholine salt.

'Bentyl' *see* Dicycloverine.

'Bentylol' *see* Dicycloverine.

BENURESTAT** (4-chloro-*N*-[2-(hydroxy-amino)-2-oxoethyl]benzamide; 2-(*p*-chlorobenzamido)acetohydroxamic acid; EU-2826).

'Benuride' *see* Pheneturide.

'Ben-u-ron 500' *see* Paracetamol.

'Benvil' *see* Tybamate.

'Benylate' *see* Benzyl benzoate.

'Benzabor' *see* Dimethylamine trichlorobenzoate.

'Benzac' *see* Dimethylamine trichlorobenzoate.

Benzacine (tr) *see* Deanol benzilate.

'Benzaknen' *see* Benzoyl peroxide.

Benzalacetone *see* Benzylideneacetone.

β-Benzalbutyric acid *see* 3-Benzylidenebutyric acid.

Benzaldehyde-2-carboxylic acid *see* Phthalaldehydic acid.

BENZALDEHYDE-4-CARBOXYLIC ACID (*p*-formylbenzoic acid).

'Benzalin' *see* Nitrazepam.

BENZALKONIUM CHLORIDE*** (mixture of alkylbenzyldimethylammonium chlorides; BTC).

'Benzamelid' *see* Isobutamben.

BENZAMIDE (benzoic acid amide).

N-[2-[6-Benzamido-2-chlorobenzyl)methylamino]-acetyl]morpholine *see* Fominoben.

α-Benzamido-*p*-[2-(diethylamino)ethoxy]-*N*,*N*-dipropylhydrocinnamamide *see* Tiropramide.

4-Benzamido-*N*,*N*-dipropylglutaramic acid *see* Proglumide.

p-(α-Benzamido-*p*-hydroxyhydrocinnamamido)benz-

oic acid *see* Bentiromide.

4-[2-Benzamido-3-(4-hydroxyphenyl)propionamido]-benzoic acid *see* Bentiromide.

4-Benzamido-1-(2-indol-3-ylethyl)-piperidine *see* Indoramin.

p-Benzamidophenyl 11,15-dihydroxy-15-methyl-9-oxo-13-thiaprostanoate *see* Tiprostanide.

p-Benzamidophenyl 7-[3-hydroxy-2-[(2-hydroxy-2-methylheptyl)thio]-5-oxocyclopentyl]heptanoate *see* Tiprostanide.

3-[2-(4-Benzamidopiperid-1-yl)ethyl]-indole *see* Indoramin.

BENZAMIDOSALICYLIC ACID (4-benzoyl-aminosalicylic acid).

See also Calcium benzamidosalicylate.

Benzamine blue *see* Trypan blue.

Benzamon (tr) *see* Furtrethonium besilate.

BENZAMYL (tr) (*N*-benzoylamobarbital; *N*-benzoylbarbamyl; 1-benzoyl-5-ethyl-5-isoamylbarbituric acid).

Benzanidine *see* Betanidine.

BENZANILIDE (benzoic acid anilide; *N*-benzoyl-aniline; *N*-phenylbenzamide).

BENZAPRINOXIDE*** (1-chloro-5-(3-(dimethylamino)propylidene)-5*H*-dibenzo[*a*,*d*]cycloheptene *N*-oxide; 1-chloro-*N*,*N*-dimethyl-5*H*-dibenzo[*a*,*d*]cycloheptene-Δ$^{5,\gamma}$-propylamine *N*-oxide).

BENZARONE*** (2-ethyl-3-(4-hydroxybenzoyl)-benzofuran; 2-ethylbenzofuran-3-yl 4-hydroxyphenyl ketone; L-2197).

Benzarone diethylaminoethyl ether *see* Etabenzarone.

BENZATHINE (*N*,*N*′-dibenzylethylenediamine; DBED).

Benzathine benzylpenicillin*** *see* Benzathine penicillin.

BENZATHINE PENICILLIN* (benzathine benzylpenicillin; benzethacil; pendepon; penicillin benzatin).

BENZATHINE TENUAZONATE (*N*,*N*′-dibenzylethylenediamine derivative of 3-acetyl-5-*sec*-butyl-4-hydroxy-3-pyrrolin-2-one; NSC-82260).

BENZATROPINE*** (3-(diphenylmethoxy)tropane; tropine benzhydryl ether; benztropine; benzotropine; benzotropine mesilate; MK-02).

2-Benzazine *see* Isoquinoline.

1-Benzazole *see* Indole.

Benzazolin *see* Tolazoline.

BENZBROMARONE*** (3,5-dibromo-4-hydroxyphenyl 2-ethylbenzofuran-3-yl ketone; L-2214; MJ-10061).

See also under Allopurinol.

Benzcarbimine *see* Benzodepa.

Benzchinamide* *see* Benzquinamide.

Benzchlorpropamide *see* Beclamide.

Benzcurine iodide *see* Gallamine triethiodide.

Benzcyclan *see* Bencyclane.

'Benzedrex' *see* Propylhexedrine.

'Benzedrine' *see* Amphetamine.

'Benzelia' *see* Benzyl benzoate.

Benzenamine *see* Aniline.

Benzene carbonitrile *see* Benzonitrile.

Benzenedicarboxylic acids *see* Isophthalic acid; Phthalic acid; Terephthalic acid.

Benzeneethanamine *see* Phenethylamine.

Benzenehexachlor *see* Lindane.

Benzene hexachloride *see* Lindane.

Benzenemethanol *see* Benzyl alcohol.

Benzenepropanoic acid *see* Hydrocinnamic acid.

S-[2-(Benzenesulfonamido)ethyl] *O,O*-diisopropyl phosphorodithioate *see* Bensulide.

2-Benzenesulfonamido-1,3,4-thiadiazole-5-sulfonamide *see* Benzolamide.

Benzenesulfonic acid esters and salts *see* Besilate(s).

'Benzerial' *see* Guanoxabenz.

Benzestrofol *see* Estradiol benzoate.

BENZESTROL*** (1,2-diethyl-1,3-bis(*p*-hydroxyphenyl)-3-methylpropane; 4,4'-(1,2-diethyl-3-methyltrimethylene)diphenol; 3-ethyl-2,4-bis(*p*-hydroxyphenyl)hexane; benzoestrol; octestrol; octoestrol; 'ocestrol').

Benzetamophylline *see* Bamifylline.

Benzethacil* *see* Benzathine penicillin.

BENZETHIDINE*** (ethyl 1-(2-benzyloxyethyl)-4-phenylisonipecotate; NIH-7574).

BENZETHONIUM CHLORIDE*** (benzyldimethyl(tetramethylbutylphenoxyethoxyethyl)-ammonium chloride).

BENZETIMIDE** (1-benzyl-4-(2,6-dioxo-3-phenylpiperid-3-yl)piperidine; 2-(1-benzylpiperid-4-yl)-2-phenylglutarimide; benzetimide hydrochloride; McN-JR-4929; R-4929). *See also* Dexetimide.

'Benzevan' *see* Benzyl benzoate.

Benzhexachlor *see* Lachesine.

Benzhexol* *see* Trihexyphenidyl.

Benzhydramine *see* Diphenhydramine.

Benzhydrate(s) *see* Hibenzate(s).

Benzhydrazide *see* Benzohydrazide.

BENZHYDROL (diphenylmethanol; diphenylcarbinol).

BENZHYDRYLAMINE (α-phenylbenzylamine).

BENZHYDRYLAMINE PENICILLINATE ('orencil'; 'penidryl').

BENZIDINE (4,4'-diaminobiphenyl).

BENZIL (dibenzoyl; diphenyl diketone; diphenylglyoxal).

BENZILAMIDE (benzilic acid amide).

BENZILIC ACID (diphenylglycolic acid; α-phenylmandelic acid).

BENZILONIUM BROMIDE*** (1,1-diethyl-3-hydroxypyrrolidinium bromide benzilate;benzilone bromide; CI-379; CN-20172-3; PU-239).

8α-Benziloyloxy-6,10-ethano-5-azoniaspiro[4,5]decane chloride *see* Trospium chloride.

(2-Benzilyloxyethyl)ethyldimethylammonium chloride *see* Lachesine.

2-Benzilyloxymethyl-1,1-dimethylpyrrolidinium methosulfate *see* Poldine metilsulfate.

BENZIMIDAZOLE (1,3-benzodiazole; *N,N'*-methenyl-*o*-phenylenediamine; azindole; benziminazole; benzoglyoxaline).

Benzimidazole-2-carbamic acid ethyl ester *see* Lobendazole.

Benzimidazole-1,3-dimethanol-2-thione *see* Thi-benzazoline.

2-Benzimidazolepropionic acid *see* Procodazole.

Benziminazole *see* Benzimidazole.

Benzindamine* *see* Benzydamine.

BENZINDOPYRINE*** (1-benzyl-3-(2-pyrid-4-ylethyl)indole; pyrbenzindole; IN-461; NSC-17789).

'Benzinoform' *see* Carbon tetrachloride.

BENZIODARONE*** (2-ethylbenzofuran-3-yl 4-hydroxy-3,5-diiodophenyl ketone; 2-ethyl-3-(4-hydroxy-3,5-diiodobenzoyl)benzofuran; 2-ethyl-3-(4-hydroxy-3,5-diiodobenzoyl)coumarone; L-2329).

1,2-Benzisothiazol-3(2*H*)-one 1,1-dioxide *see* Saccharin.

Benzmalacene *see* Benzmalecene.

BENZMALECENE*** (*N*-[2,3-bis(*p*-chlorophenyl)-1-methylpropyl]maleamic acid; benzmalacene; MK-135).

Benzmethoxazone *see* Chlorthenoxazine.

BENZNIDAZOLE** (*N*-benzyl-2-nitroimidazole-1-acetamide; 1-[(*N*-benzylcarbamoyl)methyl]-2-nitroimidazole; Ro 7-1051; 'radanil').

Benzoaric acid *see* Ellagic acid.

BENZOBARBITAL*** (1-benzoyl-5-ethyl-5-phenylbarbituric acid; *N*-benzoylphenobarbital; benzonal).

'Benzo blue' *see* Trypan blue.

BENZOCAINE*** (ethyl *p*-aminobenzoate; ethoform; norcaine).

'Benzocal' *see* Polybenzarsol.

'Benzochloryl' *see* DDT.

BENZO[*b*]CHRYSENE (3,4-benzotetraphene; 3,4-benzotetraphine).

BENZOCLIDINE** (3-benzoyloxyquinuclidine; 3-quinuclidinyl benzoate; oxylidine).

Benzoctametamina *see* Benzoctamine.

BENZOCTAMINE*** (*N*-methyl-9,10-ethanoanthracene-9(10*H*)-methylamine; benzoctametamina; Ba-30803).

Benzoctarpomine *see* Maprotiline.

3α-[5*H*-Benzo[4,5]cyclohepta[1,2-*b*]-pyridyl)-5-oxy]-tropane *see* Tropirine.

BENZODEPA*** (benzyl bis(1-aziridinyl)phosphinylcarbamate; bis(1-aziridinyl)benzyloxycarbonylaminophosphine oxide; benzcarbimine; AB-103; NSC-37096).

1,2-Benzodiazine *see* Cinnoline.

1,4-Benzodiazine *see* Quinoxaline.

1,3-Benzodiazole *see* Benzimidazole.

1,4-BENZODIOXAN (benzodioxane; 1,2-ethylenedioxybenzene).

Benzodioxane *see* Benzodioxan *and* Piperoxan.

2-(1,4-Benzodioxan-2-yl)-2-imidazoline *see* Idazoxan.

1-(1,4-Benzodioxan-2-ylmethyl)-1-benzylhydrazine *see* Domoxin.

(1,4-Benzodioxan-2-ylmethyl)guanidine *see* Guanoxan.

(1,4-Benzodioxan-6-ylmethyl)guanidine *see* Guabenxan.

N-[1-[(1,4-Benzodioxan-2-ylmethyl)-4-phenylpiperid-4-yl]methyl]acetamide *see* Acoxatrine.

8-(1,4-Benzodioxan-2-ylmethyl)-1-phenyl-1,3,8-tri-azaspiro[4.5]decan-4-one *see* Spiroxatrine.

1-(1,4-Benzodioxan-6-yl)-3-(3-phenylpyrrolidin-1-yl)-1-propanone *see* Proroxan.

1,3-BENZODIOXOLE (1,2-methylenedioxybenzene).

1-(1,3-Benzodioxol-5-yl)-4,4-dimethyl-1-penten-3-ol *see* Stiripentol.

5-[2-[[3-(1,3-Benzodioxol-5-yl)-1-methylpropyl]amino]-1-hydroxyethyl]-2-hydroxybenzamide *see* Medroxalol.

1-[(1,3-Benzodioxol-5-yl)methyl]-4-(3,7,11-trimethyl-2,6,10-dodecatrienyl)piperazine *see* Pifarnine.

BENZODODECINIUM CHLORIDE* (benzyldodecyldimethylammonium chloride; benzyllauryldimethylammonium chloride).

Benzoestrol *see* Benzestrol.

BENZOFURAN (coumarone).

2-Benzofurancarboxylic acid *see* Coumarilic acid.

1-(2-Benzofuranylcarbonyl)-4-benzylpiperazine *see* Befuraline.

α-Benzofuran-2-yl-*p*-chlorobenzyl alcohol *see* Cloridarol.

4-(Benzofuran-2-yl)-2-(dimethylamino)-1-pyrroline *see* Prifuroline.

N-Benzofuran-2-ylmethyl-*N',N'*-dimethyl-*N*-pyrid-2-ylethylenediamine *see* Etofuradine.

BENZOFURAZAN (2,1,3-benzoxadiazole).

BENZOFURAZAN *N*-OXIDE (benzofuroxan).

4-(4-Benzofurazanyl)-1,4-dihydro-2,6-dimethyl-3,5-pyridinedicarboxylic acid diethyl ester *see* Darodipine.

Benzofuroxan *see* Benzofurazan *N*-oxide.

2-Benzofuryl *p*-chlorophenyl carbinol *see* Cloridarol.

Benzoglyoxaline *see* Benzimidazole.

BENZOHYDRAZIDE (benzhydrazide; benzoic acid hydrazide; benzoylhydrazine).

Benzohydrazide daunorubicin hydrazone *see* Zorubicin.

BENZOHYDROXAMIC ACID (*N*-benzoylhydroxylamine).

BENZOIC ACID (dracylic acid; phenylformic acid).

Benzoic acid amide *see* Benzamide.

Benzoic acid anilide *see* Benzanilide.

Benzoic acid hydrazide *see* Benzohydrazide.

Benzoic acid hydrazide 3-hydrazone with daunorubicin *see* Zorubicin.

Benzoic acid [(4-hydroxyimino)-2,5-cyclohexadien-1-ylidene]hydrazide *see* Benquinox.

Benzoic acid 2-(α-methylbenzyl)hydrazide *see* Benmoxin.

***o*-Benzoic sulfimide** *see* Saccharin.

BENZOIN (2-hydroxy-1,2-diphenylethanone; α-hydroxy-α-phenylacetophenone; benzoyl phenyl carbinol).

BENZOLAMIDE (2-benzenesulfonamido-1,3,4-thiadiazole-5-sulfonamide; CL-11366; W-1803).

Benzolin (tr) *see* Tolazoline.

Benzomate *see* Benzoximate.

6,7-BENZOMORPHAN (1,2,3,4,5,6-hexahydro-2,6-methano-3-benzazocine).

Benzonal (tr) *see* Benzobarbital.

Benzonaphthol *see* 2-Naphthyl benzoate.

BENZONATATE* (2,5,8,11,14,17,20,23,26-nonoxaoctacosan-28-ol *p*-butylaminobenzoate; 2-methoxyoctaethyleneoxyethyl *p*-butylaminobenzoate; nonaethylene glycol methyl *p*-butylaminobenzoate; benzonatinum; benzononatine; Egyt-13; KM-65).

Benzonatinum *see* Benzonatate.

BENZONITRILE (benzene carbonitrile; cyanobenzene; phenyl cyanide).

Benzononatine *see* Benzonatate.

Benzoparadiazine *see* Quinoxaline.

Benzoperidol *see* Benperidol.

BENZOPHENONE (diphenyl ketone).

Benzo[*g*]pteridine-2,4(3*H*,10*H*)-dione *see* Isoalloxazine.

4*H*-1-BENZOPYRAN (chromene).

2*H*-1-Benzopyran-2-one *see* Coumarin.

4*H*-1-Benzopyran-4-one *see* Chromone.

Benzo[*a*]pyrazine *see* Quinoxaline.

BENZOPYRAZONE (4-(2-benzoylethyl)-1,2-diphenyl-3,5-pyrazolidinedione; 4-(3-oxo-3-phenylpropyl)-1,2-diphenyl-3,5-pyrazolidinedione).

BENZO[*a*]PYRENE (3,4-benzpyrene).

BENZO[*e*]PYRENE (1,2-benzpyrene).

Benzo[*d*]pyridazine *see* Phthalazine.

Benzo[*b*]pyridine *see* Quinoline.

Benzo[*a*]pyrimidine *see* Quinazoline.

Benzopyrinium *see* Benzpyrinium bromide.

Benzo-α-pyrone *see* Coumarin.

γ-Benzopyrone *see* Chromone.

2,3-Benzopyrrole *see* Indole.

BENZOPYRRONIUM BROMIDE* (3-hydroxy-1,1-dimethylpyrrolidinium bromide benzilate).

Benzoquinamide *see* Benzquinamide.

Benzo[*c*]quinoline *see* Phenanthridine.

***o*-BENZOQUINONE** (1,2-benzoquinone).

***p*-BENZOQUINONE** (1,4-benzoquinone; 2,5-cyclohexadiene-1,4-dione; quinone).

***p*-Benzoquinone guanylhydrazone thiosemicarbazone** *see* Ambazone.

BENZOQUINONIUM CHLORIDE* (bis(benzylchloride) of 2,5-bis(3-diethylaminopropylamino)-*p*-benzoquinone; WIN-2747; 'amilyt'; 'mytolon').

Benzorphanol *see* Levophenacylmorphan.

Benzosalicin *see* Salicin benzoate.

Benzostigmin *see* Benzpyrinium bromide.

***o*-Benzosulfimide** *see* Saccharin.

3,4-Benzotetraphene *see* Benzo[*b*]chrysene.

3,4-Benzotetraphine *see* Benzo[*b*]chrysene.

Benzotetrazine *see* Pteridine.

(*p*-Benzothiazol-2-ylbenzyl)phosphonic acid diethyl ester *see* Fostedil.

1-Benzothiazol-2-yl-1,3-dimethylurea *see* Methabenzthiazuron.

1-Benzothiazol-2-yl-3-methylurea *see* Benzthiazuron.

BENZO[*b*]THIEN-4-YL METHYLCARBAM-

ATE (Mc-A-600; OMS-708; 'mobam').

Benzotriazinylmethyldithiophosphoric acid diethyl ester see Azinphos-ethyl.

2-(2*H*-Benzotriazol-2-yl)-4-methylphenol see Drometrizole.

2-(2*H*-Benzotriazol-2-yl)-4-(1,1,3,3-tetramethylbutyl)phenol see Octrizole.

BENZOTRIPT** (2-(*p*-chlorobenzamido)-3-indolepropionic acid; *N*-(*p*-chlorobenzoyl)-L-tryptophan).

Benzotropine see Benzatropine.

2,1,3-Benzoxadiazole see Benzofurazan.

N-**Benzoxazol-2-yl-***N***-benzyl-***N′***,***N′***-dimethylethylethylenediamine** see Oxadimedine.

2-Benzoxazolyl *N*-**methyldithio-1-naphthalenecarbamate** see Naftoxate.

Benzoxazone see Caroxazone.

BENZOXIMATE* (ethyl *O*-benzoyl-3-chloro-2,6-dimethoxybenzohydroxamate; 3-chloro-*N*-ethoxy-2,6-dimethoxybenzenecarboximidic acid anhydride with benzoic acid; benzomate; 'citrazon').

BENZOXIQUINE*** (8-benzoyloxyquinoline; benoxiquine; NSC-3951).

BENZOXONIUM CHLORIDE*** (benzyldodecylbis(2-hydroxyethyl)ammonium chloride; D-301).

4-[[2-(Benzoylamino)-3-(4-hydroxyphenyl)-1-oxopropyl]amino]benzoic acid see Bentiromide.

4-Benzoylaminosalicylic acid see Benzamidosalicylic acid.

N-**Benzoylamobarbital** see Benzamyl.

N-**Benzoylaniline** see Benzanilide.

N-**Benzoylbarbamyl** see Benzamyl.

5-Benzoyl-2-benzimidazolecarbamic acid methyl ester see Mebendazole.

Benzoyl carbinol see 2-Hydroxyacetophenone.

O-**Benzoyl-3-chloro-2,6-dimethoxybenzohydroxamic acid ethyl ester** see Benzoximate.

2′-Benzoyl-4′-chloro-2-[(2-hydroxyethyl)methylamino]-*N***-methylacetanilide** see Oxazafone.

2′-Benzoyl-4′-chloro-*N***-methyl-2-[(2-methylallyl)amino]acetanilide** see Dinazafone.

1-Benzoyl-2-(2,6-dichloroanilino)-2-imidazoline see Benclonidine.

1-Benzoyl-1-(3,4-dichlorophenyl)-3,3-dimethylurea see Phenobenzuron.

3′-Benzoyl-1,1-difluoromethanesulfonanilide see Diflumidone.

5-Benzoyl-2,3-dihydro-1*H***-pyrrolizine-1-carboxylic acid** see Ketorolac.

Benzoyl disulfide see Bensulfene.

1-[[1-(2-Benzoylethyl)benzimidazol-2-yl]methyl]-4-cinnamylpiperazine see Cinprazole.

4-[[1-(2-Benzoylethyl)benzimidazol-2-yl]methyl]-*N***-isopropyl-1-piperazineacetamide** see Nilprazole.

1-(2-Benzoylethyl)-2-[(4-cinnamylpiperazin-1-yl)methyl]benzimidazole see Cinprazole.

4-(2-Benzoylethyl)-1,2-diphenyl-3,5-pyrazolidinedione see Benzopyrazone.

1-Benzoyl-5-ethyl-5-isoamylbarbituric acid see Benzamyl.

1-(2-Benzoylethyl)-2-[[4-[(isopropylcarbamoyl)meth-

yl]piperazin-1-yl]methyl]benzimidazole see Nilprazole.

1-Benzoyl-5-ethyl-5-phenylbarbituric acid see Benzobarbital.

'Benzoyl-flagyl' see Metronidazole benzoate.

5-Benzoylhexahydro-1*H***-furo[3,4-*c*]pyrrole** see Octazamide.

m-**Benzoylhydratropic acid** see Ketoprofen.

Benzoylhydrazine see Benzohydrazide.

6-Benzoyl-3-hydrazino-5,6,7,8-tetrahydropyrido[4,3-*c*]pyridazine see Endralazine.

N-**Benzoylhydroxylamine** see Benzohydroxamic acid.

5-Benzoyl-4-hydroxy-2-methoxybenzenesulfonic acid see Sulisobenzone.

Benzoylindolizine see Butoprozine.

1-Benzoyl-2-(α-methylbenzyl)hydrazine see Benmoxin.

1-Benzoylmethyl-3-(*m*-hydroxyphenyl)-2,3-dimethylpiperidine see Myfadol.

1-Benzoyl-2-methylindole-3-acetic acid see Delmetacin.

m-**Benzoyl-***N***-(4-methylpyrid-2-yl)hydratropamide** see Piketoprofen.

5-Benzoyl-α-methyl-2-thiopheneacetic acid see Tiaprofenic acid.

1-Benzoyl-3-[1-(2-naphthylmethyl)piperid-4-yl]urea see Panuramine.

N-**(2-Benzoyloxyethyl)norfenfluramine** see Benfluorex.

N-**(2-Benzoyloxyethyl)-***m***-trifluoromethylamphetamine** see Benfluorex.

Benzoyloxyfenfluramine see Benfluorex.

8-Benzoyloxyquinoline see Benzoxiquine.

3-Benzoyloxyquinuclidine see Benzoclidine.

Benzoylpas calcium* see Calcium benzamidosalicylate.

BENZOYL PEROXIDE* (dibenzoyl peroxide; NSC-676).

See also under 8-Quinolinol.

BENZOYL PEROXIDE plus MICONAZOLE ('acinidazil').

N-**Benzoylphenobarbital** see Benzobarbital.

Benzoyl phenyl carbinol see Benzoin.

2-(3-Benzoylphenyl)propionic acid see Ketoprofen.

BENZOYLPROP-ETHYL* (*N*-(3,4-dichlorophenyl)-*N*-[1-(ethoxycarbonyl)ethyl]benzamide; ethyl *N*-benzoyl-*N*-(3,4-dichlorophenyl)-L-alanine; WL-17731; 'shellsol A').

N[1]-**Benzoylsulfanilamide** see Sulfabenzamide.

9-Benzoyl-1,2,3,4-tetrahydro-6-methoxycarbazole-3-carboxylic acid see Oxarbazole.

Benzoylthiamine disulfide see Bisbentiamine.

S-**Benzoylthiamine** *O*-**phosphate** see Benfotiamine.

2-(5-Benzoylthien-2-yl)propionic acid see Tiaprofenic acid.

1-Benzoyltriethylamine see Amfepramone.

m-**Benzoyl-***N***-trifluoromethylsulfonylcarbanilic acid ethyl ester** see Triflumidate.

4-[(*N*-Benzoyl-L-tyrosyl)amino]benzoic acid see Bentiromide.

'Benzperidine' see Perastine.

Benzperidol see Benperidol.

53

BENZPHETAMINE* (*N*-benzyl-*N*,α-dimethyl-phenethylamine; *N*-benzyl-*N*-methylamphet-amine; *N*-benzylmethamphetamine).

Benzphetamine oxide *see* Oxifentorex.

BENZPIPERYLONE* (4-benzyl-1-(1-methyl-piperid-4-yl)-3-phenyl-3-pyrazolin-5-one; KB-95).

1,2-Benzpyrene *see* Benzo[*e*]pyrene.

3,4-Benzpyrene *see* Benzo[*a*]pyrene.

BENZPYRINIUM BROMIDE* (1-benzyl-3-hydroxypridinium bromide dimethylcarbamate; benzopyrinium; benzostigmin; benzstigmine).

BENZQUERCIN* (3,3′,4′,5,7-pentakis(benzyloxy)flavone; quercetin pentabenzyl ether).

BENZQUINAMIDE* (2-acetoxy-3-(diethylcarbamoyl)hexahydro-9,10-dimethoxybenzo[*a*]quinolizine; *N*,*N*-diethylhexahydro-2-hydroxy-9,10-dimethoxybenzo[*a*]quinolizine-3-carboxamide acetate; benzchinamide; benzoquinamide; NSC-64375; P-2647).

Benzstigmine *see* Benzpyrinium bromide.

BENZTHIAZIDE* (3-[(benzylthio)methyl]-6-chloro-2*H*-1,2,4-benzothiadiazine-7-sulfonamide 1,1-dioxide; benzylthiomethylchlorothiazide; P-1393).

BENZTHIAZIDE plus TRIAMTERENE ('diteriam'; 'dytide').

See also under Methoserpidine.

BENZTHIAZURON* (1-benzothiazol-2-yl-3-methylurea; 2-(methylcarbamido)benzothiazole; 'gatnon').

'Benzthiozone' *see* Thioacetazone.

Benztropine* *see* Benzatropine.

BENZYDAMINE* (1-benzyl-3-(3-dimethyl-aminopropoxy)indazole; benzindamine; benzydamine hydrochloride; AF-864; C-1523).

BENZYDAMINE plus ERYTHROMYCIN (ER-72; 'etriflogin').

BENZYDAMINE plus HEXAMIDINE ISETIONATE (C-1605; 'hexo-imotryl').

BENZYDAMINE plus TETRACYCLINE ('tantum biotic').

BENZYDAMINE PHENYLBUTAZONE ENOLATE (LS-701; 'butazidamina').

Benzydroflumethiazide* *see* Bendroflumethiazide.

2-Benzylacetic acid *see* Hydrocinnamic acid.

o-(*N*-Benzylacetimidoyl)phenol *see* Oletimol.

BENZYL ALCOHOL* (benzenemethanol; phenmethylol; phenyl carbinol).

[(Benzylamidino)amidino]phosphoramidic acid disodium salt *see* Benfosformin.

4-Benzylaminobenzenesulfonamide *see* Benzylsulfamide.

4-(Benzylamino)-2-methyl-7*H*-pyrrolo[2,3-*d*]pyrimidine *see* Rolodine.

2-(*N*-Benzylanilino)acetamidoxime *see* Cetoxime.

[2-(*N*-Benzylanilino)ethyl]ethyldimethylammonium bromide *see* Phenbenzamine ethobromide.

2-(*N*-Benzylanilinomethyl)-2-imidazoline *see* Antazoline.

4-(*N*-Benzylanilino)-1-methylpiperidine *see* Bamipine.

Benzyl antiserotonin *see* Benanserin.

2-Benzylbenzimidazole *see* Bendazol.

BENZYL BENZOATE (benzoic acid phenylmethyl ester; peruscabin).

Benzyl bis(1-aziridinyl)phosphinylcarbamate *see* Benzodepa.

2-Benzyl-3-butylamino-5-carboxybenzenesulfonamide *see* Besunide.

4-Benzyl-3-butylamino-5-sulfamoylbenzoic acid *see* Besunide.

Benzylcarbamoylethanol *see* Buramate.

N′-(2-Benzylcarbamoylethyl)isoniazid *see* Nialamide.

1-[(*N*-Benzylcarbamoyl)methyl]-2-nitroimidazole *see* Benznidazole.

Benzyl carbinol *see* Phenethyl alcohol.

2-Benzyl-4-chlorophenol *see* Clorofene.

N-Benzyl-3-chloropropionamide *see* Beclamide.

Benzyl cinnamate *see* Cinnamein.

1-Benzyl-2(1*H*)-cycloheptimidazolinone *see* Benhepazone.

3-(1-Benzylcycloheptyloxy)-*N*,*N*-dimethylpropylamine *see* Bencyclane.

N-Benzylcyclopropanecarbamic acid ethyl ester *see* Encyprate.

Benzyl(2-diethylaminoethyl)malonic acid diethyl ester *see* Diethyl benzyl(2-diethylaminoethyl)malonate.

Benzyldiethyl[2-[4-(1,1,3,3-tetramethylbutyl)phenoxy]ethyl]ammonium chloride *see* Octafonium chloride.

Benzyldiethyl(2,6-xylylcarbamoylmethyl)ammonium benzoate *see* Denatonium benzoate.

Benzyl 9,10-dihydro-1-methyl-(+)-lysergamine-*N*-carboxylate *see* Metergoline.

5-Benzyl-4,5-dihydro-4-oxo-1*H*-1,2,5-benzotriazepine-3-carboxamidoxime *see* Trizoxime.

5-Benzyldihydro-6-thioxo-2*H*-1,3,5-thiadiazine-3(4*H*)-acetic acid *see* Bensuldazic acid.

3-Benzyl-3,4-dihydro-6(trifluoromethyl)-2*H*-1,2,4-benzothiadiazine-7-sulfonamide 1,1-dioxide *see* Bendroflumethiazide.

S-**BENZYL** *O*,*O*-**DIISOPROPYL PHOSPHOROTHIOATE** ('kitazin P').

2-[Benzyl(2-dimethylaminoethyl)amino]benzoxazole *see* Oxadimedine.

4-Benzyl-2-(2-dimethylaminoethyl)-1(2*H*)-phthalazinone *see* Talastine.

4-Benzyl-1-(2-dimethylaminoethyl)piperidine *see* Pimetine.

1-Benzyl-3-(dimethylamino)-2-methyl-1-phenylpropyl propionate *see* Dextropropoxyphene; Levopropoxyphene.

1-Benzyl-3-(3-dimethylaminopropoxy)indazole *see* Benzydamine.

2-Benzyl-3-[[3-(dimethylamino)propyl]thio]-2*H*-indazole *see* Dazidamine.

1-Benzyl-2,3-dimethylguanidine *see* Betanidine.

1-Benzyl-2,3-dimethylindole-5-carboxylic acid dimethylaminoethyl ester *see* Indocate.

Benzyldimethyl(octylcresoxyethoxyethyl)ammonium chloride *see* Methylbenzethonium chloride.

N-Benzyl-*N*,α-dimethylphenethylamine *see* Benzphetamine.

N-Benzyl-*N*,α-dimethylphenethylamine *N*-oxide *see* Oxifentorex.

Benzyldimethyl(phenoxyethyl)ammonium ion *see* Bephenium embonate.

N-Benzyl-*N'*,*N'*-dimethyl-*N*-phenylethylenediamine *see* Phenbenzamine.

N-Benzyl-*N'*,*N'*-dimethyl-*N*-pyrid-2-ylethylenediamine *see* Tripelennamine.

1-Benzyl-2,5-dimethylserotonin *see* Benanserin.

Benzyldimethyltetradecylammonium chloride *see* Miristalkonium chloride.

Benzyldimethyl(tetramethylbutylphenoxyethoxyethyl)ammonium chloride *see* Benzethonium chloride.

Benzyldimethyl(tetramethylbutyltoloxyethoxyethyl)ammonium chloride *see* Methylbenzethonium chloride.

1-Benzyl-4-(2,6-dioxo-3-phenylpiperid-3-yl)piperidine *see* Benzetimide.

Benzyl[2-(*p*-dodecoylphenoxy)ethyl]-dimethylammonium chloride *see* Lauralkonium chloride.

Benzyldodecylbis(2-hydroxyethyl)ammonium chloride *see* Benzoxonium chloride.

Benzyl[(dodecylcarbamoyl)methyl]dimethylammonium chloride *see* Dodecarbonium chloride.

Benzyldodecyldimethylammonium chloride *see* Benzododecinium chloride.

7-Benzyl-1-ethyl-1,4-dihydro-4-oxo-1,8-naphthyridine-3-carboxylic acid *see* Amfonelic acid.

1-Benzyl-3-ethyl-6,7-dimethoxyisoquinoline *see* Moxaverine.

8-Benzyl-7-[2-[ethyl(2-hydroxyethyl)amino]ethyl]-theophylline *see* Bamifylline.

S-BENZYL *O*-ETHYL PHENYLPHOSPHONOTHIOATE ('inezin').

α-Benzyl-*N*-ethyltetrahydrofurylamine *see* Zylofuramine.

o-(*N*-Benzylformimidoyl)phenol *see* Norletimol.

cis-(+)-5-Benzylfuran-3-ylmethyl 2,2-dimethyl-3-(2-methyl-1-propenyl)cyclopropanecarboxylate *see* Cismethrin.

cis,*trans*-(±)-5-Benzylfuran-3-ylmethyl 2,2-dimethyl-3-(2-methyl-1-propenyl)cyclopropanecarboxylate *see* Resmethrin.

trans-(±)-5-Benzylfuran-3-ylmethyl 2,2-dimethyl-3-(2-methyl-1-propenyl)cyclopropanecarboxylate *see* Bioresmethrin.

trans-(±)-5-Benzylfuran-3-ylmethyl 3-(3-methoxy-2-methyl-3-oxo-1-propenyl)-2,2-dimethylcyclopropanecarboxylate *see* Pyresmethrin.

Benzylfuroline *see* Resmethrin.

cis-(+)-5-Benzyl-3-furylmethyl chrysanthemate *see* Cismethrin.

cis,*trans*-(±)-5-Benzyl-3-furylmethyl chrysanthemate *see* Resmethrin.

trans-(±)-5-Benzyl-3-furylmethyl chrysanthemate *see* Bioresmethrin.

(5-Benzyl-3-furyl)methyl (+)-*trans*-2,2-dimethyl-3-(2-methylpropenyl)cyclopropanecarboxylate *see* Bioresmethrin.

Benzylglucofuranoside *see* Tribenoside.

Benzylhexadecyldimethylammonium chloride *see* Cetalkonium chloride.

Benzylhydroflumethiazide *see* Bendroflumethiazide.

Benzyl *p*-hydroxybenzoate *see* Benzyl paraben.

4-Benzyl-1-[3-hydroxy-3-(*p*-hydroxyphenyl)prop-2-yl]piperidine *see* Ifenprodil.

O-Benzylhydroxylamine *see* Benzyloxyamine.

4-Benzyl-α-(*p*-hydroxyphenyl)-β-methyl-1-piperidineethanol *see* Ifenprodil.

1-Benzyl-3-hydroxypridinium bromide dimethylcarbamate *see* Benzpyrinium bromide.

BENZYLIDENEACETONE (4-phenyl-3-buten-2-one; acetocinnamone; benzalacetone; cinnamyl methyl ketone; methyl styryl ketone).

3-BENZYLIDENEBUTYRIC ACID (3-methyl-4-phenyl-3-butenoic acid; β-benzalbutyric acid; BBA).

2-Benzylidenecycloheptanone *O*-[2-(diisopropylamino)ethyl]oxime *see* Stirocainide.

2-Benzylidene-1-[[2-(diisopropylamino)ethoxy]imino]cycloheptane *see* Stirocainide.

N[1]-BENZYLIDENEISONIAZID (benzaldehyde isonicotinoylhydrazone; 'isoteben').

4-Benzylidene-5,6,7,8-tetrahydro-1,3(2*H*,4*H*)-isoquinolinedione *see* Tesimide.

2-Benzyl-2-imidazoline *see* Tolazoline.

5-(1-Benzylimidazol-2-yl)-1*H*-tetrazole *see* Bentemazole.

α-(Benzylimino)-*o*-cresol *see* Norletimol.

2-[1-(Benzylimino)ethyl]phenol *see* Oletimol.

2-(Benzyliminomethyl)phenol *see* Norletimol.

2-(1-Benzyl-1*H*-indazol-3-yloxy)acetic acid *see* Bendazac.

N-Benzyl-β-(isobutoxymethyl)-*N*-phenyl-1-pyrrolidineethylamine *see* Bepridil.

Benzyllauryldimethylammonium chloride *see* Benzododecinium chloride.

N-Benzylmethamphetamine *see* Benzphetamine.

1-[2-(Benzylmethylamino)ethyl]-6,7-dihydroindolo[1,7-*ab*][1]benzazepine *see* Azipramine.

2-(Benzylmethylamino)ethyl methyl 1,4-dihydro-2,6-dimethyl-4-(3-nitrophenyl)-3,5-pyridinedicarboxylate *see* Nicardipine.

N-Benzyl-*N*-methylamphetamine *see* Benzphetamine.

1-Benzyl-2-(5-methylisoxazol-3-ylcarbonyl)hydrazine *see* Isocarboxazid.

α-Benzyl-β-methyl-α-phenyl-1-pyrrolidinepropanol acetate *see* Pyrrolifene.

4-Benzyl-1-(1-methylpiperid-4-yl)-3-phenyl-3-pyrazolin-5-one *see* Benzpiperylone.

N-Benzyl-*N*-methyl-2-propynylamine *see* Pargyline.

BENZYLMORPHINE (morphine benzyl ether; 'peronine').

Benzylmorphine myristyl ester *see* Myrophine.

BENZYL NICOTINATE ('pycaril').

See also under Dexamethasone.

N-Benzyl-2-nitroimidazole-1-acetamide *see* Benznidazole.

N-(8-Benzyl-1α*H*,5α*H*-nortropan-3β-yl)-2,3-dimethoxybenzamide *see* Tropapride.

N-(8-Benzyl-1α*H*,5α*H*-nortropan-3β-yl)-*o*-veratramide *see* Tropapride.

1-Benzyl-2-oxocyclohexanepropionic acid *see* Hexacyprone.

BENZYLOXYAMINE (*O*-benzylhydroxylamine).
7-Benzyloxy-6-butyl-1,4-dihydro-4-oxoquinoline-3-carboxylic acid methyl ester *see* Nequinate.
7-Benzyloxy-6-butyl-4-hydroxy-3-quinolinecarboxylic acid methyl ester *see* Nequinate.
8β-(Benzyloxycarbonylaminomethyl)-1-methyl-10α-ergoline *see* Metergoline.
3-Benzyloxy-6-hydroxy-*N*-methyl-4,5-epoxymorphin-7-ene tetradecanoate ester *see* Myrophine.
3-Benzyloxy-*N*-methyl-6-myristyloxy-4,5-epoxy-morphin-7-ene *see* Myrophine.
p-**Benzyloxyphenol** *see* Monobenzone.
N-**Benzyloxy-*N*-(3-phenylpropyl)acetamide** *see* Beloxamide.
BENZYL PARABEN (benzyl *p*-hydroxybenzoate; 'nipabenzyl').
Benzylpenicillin *see* Penicillin G.
N-**Benzylphenethylamine 6-(phenylacetamido)penicillanate** *see* Benethamine penicillin.
o-**BENZYLPHENOL** (α-phenyl-*o*-cresol; 'delegol').
1-[2-(2-Benzylphenoxy)-1-methylethyl]piperidine *see* Benproperine.
1-(2-Benzylphenoxy)-2-piperid-1-ylpropane *see* Benproperine.
Benzylphenyl carbamate *see* Diphenan.
Benzylphenylurethan *see* Diphenan.
5-Benzyl-1-phosphorylbiguanide disodium salt *see* Benfosformin.
1-Benzyl-4-picolinylpiperazine *see* Piberaline.
4-Benzylpipecolinic acid 2-diethylaminoethyl ester *see* Benrixate.
2-[(4-Benzylpiperazin-1-yl)carbonyl]benzofuran *see* Befuraline.
4-Benzyl-1-piperidinecarboxylic acid 2-diethylaminoethyl ester *see* Benrixate.
α-[1-(4-Benzylpiperid-1-yl)ethyl]-*p*-hydroxybenzyl alcohol *see* Ifenprodil.
2-(4-Benzylpiperid-1-yl)-1-(*p*-hydroxyphenyl)-1-propanol *see* Ifenprodil.
N-**(1-Benzylpiperid-4-yl)-6-methoxy-1*H*-benzotriazole-5-carboxamide** *see* Trazolopride.
2-(1-Benzylpiperid-4-yl)-2-phenylglutarimide *see* Benzetimide.
Benzylpivaloylhydrazine *see* Pivhydrazine.
2-Benzyl-2-propylamine *see* Phentermine.
3-Benzylpyrido[3,4-*e*]-1,2,4-triazine *see* Triafungin.
1-Benzyl-4-(pyrid-2-ylcarbonyl)piperazine *see* Piberaline.
1-Benzyl-3-(2-pyrid-4-ylethyl)indole *see* Benzindopyrine.
Benzylrhodanide *see* Benzyl thiocyanate.
BENZYLSULFAMIDE*** (4-benzylaminobenzenesulfonamide; *N*⁴-benzylsulfanilamide; M & B-125; RP 46).
*N*⁴-**Benzylsulfanilamide** *see* Benzylsulfamide.
p-**Benzylsulfonamidobenzoic acid** *see* Carinamide.
5-Benzyl-1,3,4,5-tetrahydro-2-methyl-2*H*-pyrid[4,3-*b*]indole *see* Mebhydrolin.
1-Benzyl-2,3,4,9-tetrahydro-1*H*-pyrid[3,4-*b*]indole *see* Fenharmane.
1-Benzyl-2-(1*H*-tetrazol-5-yl)imidazole *see* Bentemazole.

S-**Benzyl thiobenzoate** *see* Tibenzate.
BENZYL THIOCYANATE (benzylrhodanide).
3-[(Benzylthio)methyl]-6-chloro-2*H*-1,2,4-benzothiadiazine-7-sulfonamide 1,1-dioxide *see* Benzthiazide.
3-[(Benzylthio)methyl]-6-chloro-3,4-dihydro-2*H*-1,2,4-benzothiadiazine-7-sulfonamide 1,1-dioxide *see* Hydrobentizide.
Benzylthiomethylchlorothiazide *see* Benzthiazide.
Benzyl(trimethylacetyl)hydrazine *see* Pivhydrazine.
'Beosit' *see* Endosulfan.
'Bepanthen' *see* Dexpanthenol.
'Beparin' *see* Dermatan sulfate.
Beperiden *see* Biperiden.
BEPHENIUM EMBONATE (benzyldimethyl-(phenoxyethyl)ammonium ion; bephenium pamoate).
BEPHENIUM HYDROXYNAPHTHOATE*** (3-hydroxy-2-naphthoic acid benzyldimethyl(2-phenoxyethyl)ammonium salt; naftamon).
BEPIASTINE*** (6-[2-(dimethylamino)ethyl]pyrido[2,3-*b*][1,5]benzothiazepin-5(6*H*)-one; UP-107).
BEPRIDIL*** (*N*-benzyl-β-(isobutoxymethyl)-*N*-phenyl-1-pyrrolidineethylamine; β-[(2-methylpropoxy)methyl]-*N*-phenyl-*N*-(phenylmethyl)-1-pyrrolidineethanamine; CERM-1978; 'angopril'; 'cordium').
'Beprochin' *see* Pamaquine.
'Beracillin' *see* Penicillamine.
BERBINE (5,6,13,13a-tetrahydro-8*H*-dibenzo-[*a,g*]quinolizine; tetrahydroprotoberberine).
'Berenil' *see* Diminazene.
BERGAPTEN (6-hydroxy-4-methoxy-5-benzofuranacrylic acid δ-lactone; 4-methoxy-7*H*-furo-[3,2-*g*][1]benzopyran-7-one; 5-methoxypsoralen).
'Berkazon' *see* Thioacetazone.
'Berkdopa' *see* Levodopa.
'Berkfurin' *see* Nitrofurantoin.
'Berkmycen' *see* Oxytetracycline.
'Berkolol' *see* Propranolol.
'Berkomin' *see* Imipramine.
'Berkozide' *see* Bendroflumethiazide.
'Berlicetin' *see* Chloramphenicol.
'Berlocombin' *see under* Trimethoprim.
'Berocillin' *see* Pivampicillin.
'Berodual' *see under* Fenoterol.
'Berolase' *see* Cocarboxylase.
BEROMYCIN (tr) (antibiotic (anthracycline derivative) from *Actinomyces griseoruber* var. *beromycini*).
'Berotec' *see* Fenoterol.
BERYTHROMYCIN*** (12-deoxyerythromycin; erythromycin B; Abbott 24091).
'Beserol' *see under* Chlormezanone.
BESILATE(S)** (benzenesulfonic acid esters and salts; besylate(s)).
'Beston' *see* Bisbentiamine.
BESUNIDE** (2-benzyl-3-butylamino-5-carboxybenzenesulfonamide; 4-benzyl-3-butylamino-5-sulfamoylbenzoic acid; 3-(butylamino)-α-phenyl-5-sulfamoyl-*p*-toluic acid).
Besylate(s)* *see* Besilate(s).

'**Betabloc**' *see* Metoprolol.
'**Beta-cardone**' *see* Sotalol.
BETACAROTENE* (*(all-E)*-3,7,12,16-tetra-methyl-1,18-bis(2,6,6-trimethyl-1-cyclohexen-1-yl)-1,3,5,7,9,11,13,15,17-octadecanonaene; β,β-carotene; Ro 1-8300; 'carotaben'; 'solatene').
BETACETYLMETHADOL* (β-3-acetoxy-6-di-methylamino-4,4-diphenylheptane).
See also Acetylmethadol.
'**Beta-chlor**' *see* Chloral betaine.
'**Betacor**' *see* Cetamolol.
'**Beta-corlan**' *see* Betamethasone sodium phosphate.
'**Betadine**' *see* Povidone-iodine.
'**Betadorm**' *see under* Carbromal.
'**Betadorm A**' *see under* Chlorotheophylline.
'**Betadorm N**' *see under* Valdetamide.
'**Betadran**' *see* Bupranolol.
'**Betadrenol**' *see* Bupranolol.
'**Betafluorene**' *see* Dexamethasone succinate.
BETAHISTINE* (2-[2-(methylamino)ethyl]pyr-idine; PT-9).
BETAHISTINE DIMESILATE ('extovyl'; 'melo-pat'; 'ribrain').
Beta-hypophamine *see* Vasopressin.
Betain chloralum* *see* Chloral betaine.
BETAINE ((carboxymethyl)trimethylammonium hydroxide inner salt; trimethylglycine hydroxide inner salt; trimethylglycocoll anhydride; lycine; oxyneurine; betaine hydrochloride).
BETAINE ASPARTATE ('somatyl').
'**Betaisodona**' *see* Povidone-iodine.
'**Betajel**' *see* Psyllium.
'**Betaloc**' *see* Metoprolol.
'**Betalone**' *see* Meprednisone.
BETAMEPRODINE* (3-ethyl-1-methyl-4-phenyl-4-propionoxypiperidine; NU-1932).
BETAMETHADOL* (β-6-dimethylamino-4,4-diphenyl-3-heptanol).
See also Dimepheptanol.
BETAMETHASONE* (9α-fluoro-11β,17,21-tri-hydroxy-16β-methylpregna-1,4-diene-3,20-di-one; 9α-fluoro-16β-methylprednisolone; fluben-isolone; NSC-39470; RG-833; Sch-4831).
BETAMETHASONE plus ACETYLSALICYLIC ACID ('glido').
BETAMETHASONE plus DEXCHLORPHEN-IRAMINE MALEATE ('celestamine').
BETAMETHASONE ACETATE (betamethasone 21-acetate).
BETAMETHASONE ACETATE plus BETA-METHASONE SODIUM PHOSPHATE ('ce-lestene-chronodose'; 'celestone-soluspan').
BETAMETHASONE ACIBUTATE* (beta-methasone 21-acetate 17-isobutyrate; betameth-asone 21-acetate 17-(2-methylpropionate); GR2/541).
BETAMETHASONE ADAMANTOATE ('betso-vet').
BETAMETHASONE BENZOATE* (betamethas-one 17-benzoate; MS-1112; 'bebate'; 'benisone'; 'euvaderm'; 'flurobate'; 'uticort').
BETAMETHASONE DIPROPIONATE (S-8440;

Sch-11460; 'diproderm'; 'diprosone').
BETAMETHASONE DIPROPIONATE plus GENTAMICIN ('diprogenta').
BETAMETHASONE DIPROPIONATE plus SA-LICYLIC ACID ('diprosalic').
BETAMETHASONE SODIUM PHOSPHATE*
(betamethasone disodium phosphate; 'beta-cor-lan'; 'celestan soluble').
BETAMETHASONE VALERATE (betamethas-one-17-valerate).
BETAMETHASONE VALERATE plus DEX-TRAN SULFATE ('stranoval').
Betamezid (tr) *see* Pivhydrazine.
BETAMICIN* (*O*-6-amino-6-deoxy-α-D-gluco-pyranosyl-(1→4)-*O*-[3-deoxy-4-*C*-methyl-3-(methylamino)-β-L-arabinopyranosyl-(1→6)]-2-deoxy-D-streptamine; betamicin sulfate; Sch-14342).
BETAMINE (tr) (3-(3-amino-4,6-diiodophenyl)-β-alanine).
'**Betanal**' *see* Phenmedipham.
'**Beta-neg**' *see* Propranolol.
BETANIDINE* (1-benzyl-2,3-dimethylguanid-ine; benzanidine; bethanidine; BW-467C60; NSC-106563).
'**Betapar**' *see* Meprednisone.
'**Betapred**' *see* Meprednisone.
'**Betapressin**' *see* Penbutolol.
BETAPRODINE* (β-1,3-dimethyl-4-phenyl-4-propionoxypiperidine; NU-1779).
See also Alphaprodine.
'**Betaprone**' *see* Propiolactone.
Betapyrimidum *see* Nikethamide.
'**Betares**' *see* Propranolol.
'**Betasan**' *see* Bensulide.
'**Betasemid**' *see under* Furosemide.
'**Betaserc**' *see* Betahistine.
Betasin (tr) *see* Betazine.
'**Betathiazid**' *see under* Hydrochlorothiazide.
BETAXOLOL* (1-[4-[2-(cyclopropylmethoxy)-ethyl]phenoxy]-3-(isopropylamino)-2-propanol; betoxolol; betaxolol hydrochloride; ALO-1401-02; SL-75212; 'kerlone').
BETAZINE (tr) (diiodo-β-tyrosine; 3-(4-hydroxy-3,5-diiodophenyl)-β-alanine; betasin).
BETAZOLE (3-(2-aminoethyl)pyrazole; amet-azole).
BETHANECHOL* ((2-hydroxypropyl)trimethyl-ammonium chloride carbamate; carbamoyl-β-methylcholine; β-methylcholine carbamate).
Bethanidine* *see* Betanidine.
Bethrodine *see* Benfluralin.
'**Betim**' *see* Timolol maleate.
Betitol *see* Inositol.
'**Betnelan**' *see* Betamethasone.
'**Betnesol**' *see* Betamethasone.
'**Betneval**' *see* Betamethasone valerate.
'**Betnovate**' *see* Betamethasone valerate.
Betol *see* 2-Naphthyl salicylate.
Betometine *see* Meobentine.
Betoxicaine* *see* Betoxycaine.
Betoxolol *see* Betaxolol.
BETOXYCAINE* (2-[2-(diethylamino)ethoxy]-

ethyl 3-amino-4-butoxybenzoate; betoxicaine).
'Betsovet' *see* Betamethasone adamantoate.
Betula oil *see* Methyl salicylate.
BEVANTOLOL*** (1-[3,4-dimethoxyphenethyl)-amino]-3-(*m*-tolyloxy)-2-propanol; 1-homoveratrylamino-3-*m*-toloxy-2-propanol; *N*-[2-hydroxy-3-(*m*-toloxy)propyl]-3,4-dimethoxyphenethylamine; *N*-(2-hydroxy-3-*m*-toloxypropyl)homoveratrylamine; bevantolol hydrochloride; CI-775).
'Beveno' *see* Cyclovalone.
'Bevidine' *see* Povidone-iodine.
Bevonium methylsulfate* *see* Bevonium metilsulfate.
BEVONIUM METILSULFATE*** (2-hydroxymethyl-1,1-dimethylpiperidinium methyl sulfate benzilate; bevonium methylsulfate; piribenzil; CG-201; 'acabel').
'Bextasol' *see* Betamethasone valerate.
BEZAFIBRATE*** (2-[*p*-[2-(*p*-chlorobenzamido)-ethyl]phenoxy]-2-methylpropionic acid; BM-15075; LO-44; 'bezalip'; 'cedur').
'Bezalip' *see* Bezafibrate.
BEZITRAMIDE*** (1-(3-cyano-3,3-diphenylpropyl)-4-(2-oxo-3-propionylbenzimidazolin-1-yl)piperidine; 1-[1-(3-cyano-3,3-diphenylpropyl)-piperid-4-yl]-3-propionyl-2-benzimidazolinone; R-4845).
BF-103 *see* Acedapsone.
BFE-60 *see* Befunolol.
BFP *see* Dimefox.
BFPO *see* Dimefox.
BH-135 *see* Tolpentamide.
BHA *see* Butylated hydroxyanisole.
BHC *see* Benextramine.
γ-BHC *see* Lindane.
BHT *see* Butylated hydroxytoluene.
B-HT933 *see* Azepexole.
Bi-58 *see* Dimethoate.
4',4''-Biacetophenone-2',2''-bis[(2-hydroxyethyl)dimethylammonium] *see* Hemicholinium.
Biacetyl *see* 2,3-Butanedione.
BIALAMICOL*** (5,5'-diallyl-α,α'-bis(diethylamino)-*m*,*m*'-bitolyl-4,4'-diol; 6,6'-diallyl-2,2'-bis(diethylaminomethyl)-4,4'-biphenol; biallylamicol; biethylamicol; CAM-807; CI-301; CT-871; NSC-6386; PAA-701; SN-6771).
Biallylamicol *see* Bialamicol.
'Biarison' *see* Proquazone.
5,5'-Bibarbituric acid *see* Hydurilic acid.
Bibenzone *see* Bibenzonium bromide.
BIBENZONIUM BROMIDE*** ([2-(1,2-diphenylethoxy)ethyl]trimethylammonium bromide; bibenzone; diphenetholine).
BIBENZYL (1,2-diphenylethane).
BIBROCATHOL*** (bismuth tetrabromopyrocatechuate).
Bibrophen *see* Bismuth tribromophenate.
'Bica-penicillin' *see* Benzathine penicillin.
'Bicarnesine' *see* Bicarnitine.
BICARNITINE (carnitine carnitinate; dicarnitine; 'bicarnesine').
BICIFADINE** ((±)-1-*p*-tolyl-3-azabicyclo-

[3.1.0]hexane; bicifadine hydrochloride; CL-220075).
'Bicillin' *see* Benzathine penicillin.
'Bicine' *see* *N*,*N*-Bis(2-hydroxyethyl)glycine.
'Biciron' *see* Tramazoline.
BICLOFIBRATE*** (1-methylpyrrolidin-2-ylmethyl bis(*p*-chlorophenoxy)acetate).
BICLOTYMOL*** (2,2'-methylenebis(6-chlorothymol)).
'Bicnu' *see* Carmustine.
'Bicor' *see* Terodiline.
'Bicordin' *see* Gapicomine citrate.
'Bicortone' *see* Prednisone.
BICOZAMYCIN*** ((1*R*,6*S*)-6-hydroxy-5-methylene-1-(1,2,3-trihydroxy-2-methylpropyl)-2-oxa-7,9-diazabicyclo[4.2.2]decane-8,10-dione; bicyclomycin).
BICP *see* Chlorbufam.
BICUCULLINE (6-(5,6,7,8-tetrahydro-6-methyl-1,3-dioxolo[4,5-*g*]isoquinolin-5-yl)furo[3,4-*e*]-1,3-benzodioxol-8(6*H*)-one).
Bicyclo[2.2.1]heptane *see* Norbornane.
Bicyclo[2.2.1]hept-2-ene *see* Norbornene.
[BICYCLOHEXYL]-1-CARBOXYLIC ACID (1-cyclohexylcyclohexanecarboxylic acid). *See also* Dicycloverine; Dihexyverine.
Bicyclomycin *see* Bicozamycin.
***p*-BIDA** *see* Butilfenin.
'Bidex' *see* Chlorhexidine.
BIDIMAZIUM IODIDE*** (4-biphenyl-4-yl-2-(4-dimethylaminostyryl)-3-methylthiazolium iodide).
'Bidisin' *see* Chlorfenprop-methyl.
'Bidizole' *see* Sulfasomizole.
'Bidocef' *see* Cefadroxil.
'Bidrin' *see* Dicrotophos.
Biebrich scarlet R medicinal *see* Scarlet red.
'Bietamine' *see* Benfotiamine.
BIETAMIVERINE*** (2-(diethylamino)ethyl α-phenyl-1-piperidineacetate).
BIETASERPINE** (1-[2-(diethylamino)ethyl]reserpine; DL-152; S-1210).
BIETASERPINE plus HYDROCHLOROTHIAZIDE ('pleiatensin').
Biethylamicol *see* Bialamicol.
'Bi-euglucon' *see under* Glibenclamide.
BIFEPRAMIDE*** ((±)-*N*-[2-(diethylamino)-ethyl]-α-methyl-4-biphenylacetamide; biprofenide).
BIFLURANOL*** (*erythro*-2,3-bis(3-fluoro-4-hydroxyphenyl)pentane; *erythro*-4,4'-(1-ethyl-2-methylethylene)di(2-fluorophenol); BX-341).
BIFONAZOLE*** (1-(α-biphenyl-4-ylbenzyl)imidazole; 1-(*p*,α-diphenylbenzyl)imidazole; BAY h-4502; 'mycospor').
Biformylchlorazin *see* Triforine.
'Bifteral' *see* Lactulose.
Bigitalin *see* Gitoxin.
Biguamor (tr) *see* Moroxydine.
BIGUANIDE (amidinoguanidine; diguanide; formamidinylimiourea; guanylguanidine).
Bigumal *see* Proguanil.
'Bihypnal' *see* Dichloralphenazone.

Biioquinol *see* Quinine iodobismuthate.
'Biklin' *see* Amikacin.
'Bilagol' *see* Diisopromine.
'Bilarcil' *see* Metrifonate.
'Bilevon' *see* Niclofolan.
'Bilharcid' *see* Piperazine diantimonyl tartrate.
'Biligen' *see* Fencibutirol.
Bilignost (tr) *see* Adipiodone.
'Biligrafin' *see* Adipiodone sodium.
'Biligram' *see* Meglumine ioglycamate.
'Bilijodon' *see* Iopanoic acid.
'Bilimiron' *see* Iopronic acid.
'Biliodyl' *see* Phenobutiodil.
'Bilipolin' *see* Meglumine ioglycamate.
'Biliscopin' *see* Meglumine iotroxate.
'Biliton' *see* Dehydrocholic acid.
'Bilitox' *see* Cupric chloride.
Bilitrast (tr) *see* Pheniodol sodium.
'Bilivison' *see* Meglumine ioglycamate.
'Bilivistan' *see under* Meglumine ioglycamate.
'Bilobran' *see* Dodine.
'Bilopaque' *see* Sodium tyropanoate.
'Biloptin' *see* Sodium iopodate.
'Biltricide' *see* Praziquantel.
BIMETOPYROL (4,5-bis(p-methoxyphenyl)-2-methylpyrrole).
'Bimixin' *see under* Neomycin.
2,2′-Bimorphine *see* Pseudomorphine.
BIN-7 *see* Usnic acid sodium salt.
Binan (tr) *see* Usnic acid sodium salt.
BINAPACRYL* (2-*sec*-butyl-4,6-dinitrophenyl 3,3-dimethylacrylate; 2-*sec*-butyl-4,6-dinitrophenyl 3-methylcrotonate; 2-*sec*-butyl-4,6-dinitrophenyl senecioate; 2-(1-methylpropyl)-4,6-dinitrophenyl 3-methyl-2-butenoate; dinoseb 3-methyl-2-butenoate; dinoseb senecioate; 'acricid'; 'endosan'; 'morocide').
'Binartrina' *see under* Oxyphenbutazone.
'Binasol' *see* Bismuth sodium neutral tartrate.
'Binazin' *see* Todralazine.
Bindazac* *see* Bendazac.
BINEDALINE* (1-[[2-(dimethylamino)ethyl]methylamino]-3-phenylindole; binedaline hydrochloride; binodaline; Sgd-Scha-1059).
BINIFIBRATE* (clofibric acid ester with 1,3-dinicotinoyloxy-2-propanol).
BINIRAMYCIN* (antibiotic from *Str. bikiniensis*).
'Binnell' *see* Benfluralin.
Binodaline *see* Binedaline.
'Binotal' *see* Ampicillin.
Bio-66 *see* 4-Pregnene-3,11,20-trione.
BIOALLETHRIN* (3-allyl-2-methyl-4-oxo-2-cyclopenten-2-yl *trans*-chrysanthemate; *trans*-(+)-2-methyl-4-oxo-3-(2-propenyl)-2-cyclopenten-1-yl 2,2-dimethyl-3-(2-methyl-1-propenyl)-cyclopropanecarboxylate; EA-3054; ENT-16275).
See also Allethrin.
'Biobasal AG' *see* Histaglobin.
BIOCHANIN A (5,7-dihydroxy-4′-methylisoflavone; genistein 4-methyl ether).
'Biocholine' *see* Choline.

'Biocidan' *see* Cethexonium chloride.
'Biocodone' *see* Hydrocodone.
'Biocolina' *see* Choline.
Biocolorin *see* Esculin.
BIOCYTIN (N^6-[5-(hexahydro-2-oxo-1H-thieno[3,4-*d*]imidazolin-4-yl)-1-oxopentyl]lysine; biotinyllysine).
'Biodramine' *see* Dimenhydrinate.
'Bioepiderm' *see* Biotin.
'Biogastrone' *see* Carbenoxolone.
'Biogest' *see under* Chloro-MDAP.
'Bio-met' *see* Bis(tributyltin) oxide.
'Biomioran' *see* Chlorzoxazone.
Biomitsin (tr) *see* Chlortetracycline.
'Biomorphyl' *see* Hydromorphone.
Biomycin *see* Chlortetracycline.
'Bional' *see* Carbenoxolone.
BIOPROPAZEPAN (tetrahydro-1H-1,4-diazepine-1,4(5H)-dipropanol; homopiperazine-1,4-dipropanol).
Biopropazepan bis(3,4,5-trimethoxybenzoate) *see* Dilazep.
BIOPTERIN (2-amino-6-(1,2-dihydroxypropyl)-4(3H)-pteridinone).
'Bioquin' *see* 8-Quinolinol.
BIORESMETHRIN* ((5-benzyl-3-furyl)methyl (+)-*trans*-2,2-dimethyl-3-(2-methylpropenyl)-cyclopropanecarboxylate; *trans*-(±)-5-benzylfuran-3-ylmethyl 2,2-dimethyl-3-(2-methyl-1-propenyl)cyclopropanecarboxylate; *trans*-(±)-5-benzyl-3-furylmethyl chrysanthemate; NRDC-107).
Bios-I *see* Biotin.
'Biosept' *see* Cetylpyridinium bromide.
Bios-II *see* Inositol.
'Biosone' *see* Enoxolone.
'Biostat' *see* Oxytetracycline.
Biosterol *see* Retinol.
'Biosupressin' *see* Hydroxycarbamide.
'Biotexin' *see* Novobiocin.
BIOTIN* (*cis*-tetrahydro-2-oxothieno[3,4-*d*]imidazoline-4-valeric acid; vitamin B$_w$; vitamin H; bios-I; coenzyme R; 'bioepiderm').
'Biotinin' *see* Thiamine disulfide phosphate.
Biotinyllysine *see* Biocytin.
'Biotirmone' *see* Dextrothyroxine.
Biovetin (tr) *see* Chlortetracycline.
Biovit-40 (tr) *see* Chlortetracycline.
Bioxone *see* Chlormethazole.
BiPC *see* Chlorbufam.
'Bipenicillin' *see* Procaine-penicillin.
BIPERIDEN* (α-(5-norbornen-2-yl)-α-phenyl-1-piperidinepropanol; beperiden; LM-203A).
BIPHASIC INSULIN INJECTION* (suspended insulin crystals in solution of insulin buffered at pH 7; 'insulin novo rapitard').
'Biphecillin' *see* Benzathine penicillin v.
'Biphenabid' *see* Probucol.
'Biphenal' *see* Hydroxypethidine.
Biphenamine *see* Xenysalate.
BIPHENYL (diphenyl (the compound); phenylbenzene).
[1,1′-Biphenyl]-4-acetic acid *see* Biphenylylacetic

59

acid.

BIPHENYLAMINE (aminobiphenyl; aminodiphenyl).

Biphenylenebis(diphenyltetrazolium chloride) *see* Neotetrazolium.

p,p′-**Biphenylenebisglyoxal** *see* Xenygloxal.

Biphenylene oxide *see* Dibenzofuran.

[4-Biphenyl]thiobutyric acid *S*-**[2-(diethylamino)ethyl] ester** *see* Xenthiorate.

BIPHENYLYLACETIC ACID (2-(*p*-biphenylyl)acetic acid; [1,1′-biphenyl]-4-acetic acid; xenylacetic acid).

Biphenylylacetic acid 2-fluoroethyl ester *see* Fluenetil.

1-(α-Biphenyl-4-ylbenzyl)imidazole *see* Bifonazole.

4,4′-Biphenylylbisazo(1-naphthylamine-4-sulfonic acid) *see* Congo red.

2-(*p*-Biphenylyl)butyric acid *see* Xenbucin.

3-(4-Biphenylylcarbonyl)-2-methylpropionic acid *see* Metbufen.

3-(4-Biphenylylcarbonyl)propionic acid *see* Fenbufen.

1-(α-4-Biphenylyl-2-chlorobenzyl)imidazole *see* Lombazole.

(±)-**1-[(Biphenyl-4-yl)(2-chlorophenyl)methyl]imidazole** *see* Lombazole.

4,4′-Biphenylyldiglyoxyl aldehyde *see* Xenygloxal.

4-Biphenyl-4-yl-2-(4-dimethylaminostyryl)-3-methylthiazolium iodide *see* Bidimazium iodide.

4-Biphenylylethylacetic acid *see* Xenbucin.

4-(4-Biphenylyl)-3-ethyl-2-(*p*-pyrrolidin-1-ylstyryl)thiazolium iodide *see* Pretamazium iodide.

2-(*p*-Biphenylyl)-4-hexenoic acid *see* Xenyhexenic acid.

8-(*p*-Biphenylylmethyl)atropinium bromide *see* Xenytropium bromide.

4-Biphenylyl methylcarbamate *see* Paxamate.

cis-**1-[[4-[(4-Biphenylyloxy)methyl]-2-(2,4-dichlorophenyl)-1,3-dioxolan-2-yl]methyl]imidazole** *see* Doconazole.

4-Biphenyl-4-yl-3-penten-2-one *see* Xenipentone.

2-Biphenyl-4-yl-*N*-pyrid-2-ylacetamide *see* Diphenpyramide.

BIPIPERIDINE (dipiperidyl).

2,2′-([4,4′-Bipiperidine]-1,1′-diyldiethylene)bis[10-methoxy-7*H*-pyrido[4,3-*c*]carbazolium]dichloride *see* Ditercalinium chloride.

Biprofenide *see* Bifepramide.

2,2′-Bipseudoindoxyl *see* Indigotin.

BIPYRIDINE (dipyridyl (the compound); pyridylpyridine).

BIRIPERONE** ((±)-4′-fluoro-(3,4,6,7,12,12a-hexahydropyrazino[1′,2′:1,6]pyrido[3,4-*b*]indol-2(1*H*)-yl)butyrophenone).

'**Birlane**' *see* Clofenvinfos.

(−)-α-**Bisabolol** *see* Levomenol.

2,2′-Bis(4-acetamidophenoxy)ethyl ether *see* Diamfenetide.

Bis(4-acetamidophenyl)sulfone *see* Acedapsone.

3,3-Bis(*p*-acetoxyphenyl)-1-acetyloxindole *see* Phenisatin.

2,2-Bis(4-acetoxyphenyl)-2*H*-1,4-benzoxazin-3(4*H*)-one *see* Bisoxatin diacetate.

Bis(*p*-acetoxyphenyl)cyclohexylidenemethane *see* Cyclofenil.

3,3-Bis(*p*-acetoxyphenyl)isatin *see* Acetphenolisatin.

2-[Bis(*p*-acetoxyphenyl)methyl]pyridine *see* Bisacodyl.

1-[3,17-Bis(acetoxy)-2-piperidin-1-yl-5α-androstan-16-yl]-1-methylpiperidinium bromide *see* Vecuronium bromide.

Bis[[2-(*O*-acetyllactyloxy)ethyl]trimethylammonium] naphthalene-1,5-disulfonate *see* Aclatonium napadisilate.

1α,7α-Bis(acetylthio)-17β-hydroxy-17-methylandrost-4-en-3-one *see* Tiomesterone.

BISACODYL** (2-[bis(*p*-acetoxyphenyl)methyl]pyridine; 4,4′-pyrid-2-ylmethylenediphenol diacetate; acetophenomethane).

BISACODYL plus DIMETICONE ('laxbene').

BISACODYL TANNEX* (complex of bisacodyl with tannins; 'clysodrast').

Bis[2-(*N*-adamant-1-yl-*N*-methylamino)ethyl] succinate dimethiodide *see* Diadonium iodide.

2,4-Bis(allylamino)-6-[4-[bis(*p*-fluorophenyl)methyl]piperazin-1-yl]-*s*-triazine *see* Almitrine.

1,3-Bis(4-amidino-2-bromophenoxy)propane *see* Dibrompropamidine.

Bis(*p*-amidinophenyl)ether *see* Phenamidine.

1,3-Bis(*p*-amidinophenyl)triazene *see* Diminazene.

1,3-Bis(*m*-amidinophenyl)urea *see* Amicarbalide.

Bis(2-amino-2-carboxyethyl)sulfide *see* Lanthionine.

1,3-Bis(4-amino-2-methylquinolin-6-yl)urea *see* Aminoquinuride.

Bis(*p*-aminophenyl) sulfone *see* Dapsone.

N,N′-**Bis(3-aminopropyl)-1,4-butanediamine** *see* Spermine.

N,N′-**Bis(3-aminopropyl)putrescine** *see* Spermine.

4,4′-Bis(1-amino-4-sulfonaphth-2-ylazo)biphenyl *see* Congo red.

BISANTRENE*** (9,10-anthracenedicarboxaldehyde bis(2-imidazolin-2-ylhydrazone); 9,10-anthracenedicarboxaldehyde bis[(4,5-dihydro-1*H*-imidazol-2-yl)hydrazone]; bisantrene hydrochloride; CL-216942; NSC-337766).

N,N′-**Bis(*p*-arsonophenyl)ethylenediamine** *see* Difetarsone.

Bisatin *see* Acetphenolisatin.

2,5-Bis(1-aziridinyl)-*p*-benzoquinone-3,6-dicarbamic acid diethyl ester *see* Diaziquone.

Bis(1-aziridinyl)benzyloxycarbonylaminophosphine oxide *see* Benzodepa.

2,4-Bis(1-aziridinyl)-6-chloropyrimidine *see* Ethymidine.

Bis(1-aziridinyl)(cyclohexylamino)phosphine sulfide *see* Hexaphosphamide.

P,P-**Bis(1-aziridinyl)-*N*-[2-(dimethylamino)-7-methylpurin-6-yl]phosphinic amide** *see* Pumitepa.

2,5-Bis(1-aziridinyl)-3,6-dipropoxy-*p*-benzoquinone *see* Inproquone.

Bis(1-aziridinyl)ethoxycarbonylaminophosphine oxide *see* Uredepa.

Bis(1-aziridinyl)-*N*-ethyl-*N*-(1,3,4-thiadiazol-2-yl)phosphinic amide *see* Azatepa.

2,5-Bis(1-aziridinyl)-3-(2-hydroxy-1-methoxyethyl)-6-methyl-*p*-benzoquinone carbamate *see* Carboquone.

Bis(1-aziridinyl)phosphinylcarbamic acid esters *see* Benzodepa; Meturedepa; Uredepa.

BISBENDAZOLE* (bis[1-(1-methylbenzimidazol-2-yl)ethyl] tetrathio-*p*-benzenedicarbamate; HOE-193).

BISBENTIAMINE* (*N,N'*-[dithiobis[2-(2-benzoyloxyethyl)-1-methylvinylene]]bis[*N*-(4-amino-2-methylpyrimidin-5-ylmethyl)formamide]; *N,N'*-[dithiobis[2-(2-hydroxyethyl)-1-methylvinylene]]bis[*N*-[(4-amino-2-methylpyrimidin-5-yl)methyl]formamide]benzoate; benzoylthiamine disulfide; thiamine disulfide benzoate).

***N,N*-Bis[2-[bis(carboxymethyl)amino]ethyl]glycine** *see* Pentetic acid.

2',7'-Bis[[bis(carboxymethyl)amino]methyl]fluorescein *see* Oftasceine.

1,4-Bis[*N,N'*-bisethylene)diamidothiophosphoryl]piperazine *see* Thiodipin.

2,6-Bis[bis(2-hydroxyethyl)amino]-4,8-bis(1-piperidyl)pyrimido[5,4-*d*]pyrimidine *see* Dipyridamole.

2,6-Bis[bis(2-hydroxyethyl)amino]-4-piperid-1-yl-pyrimido[5,4-*d*]pyrimidine *see* Mopidamol.

2,2-Bis(*p*-bromophenyl)glycolic acid isopropyl ester *see* Bromopropylate.

3,12-Bis(3-bromopropionyl)-3,12-diaza-6,9-diazoniadispiro[5.2.5.2]hexadecane dichloride *see* Dibrospidium chloride.

1,4-Bis(3-bromopropionyl)piperazine *see* Pipobroman.

Bisbutiamine *see* Sulbutiamine.

5-[Bis[2-(2-butoxyethoxy)ethoxy]methyl]-1,3-benzodioxole *see* Piperonal bis[2-(2-butoxyethoxy)ethyl]acetal.

1,3-Bis(3-butoxy-2-hydroxypropyl)phenobarbital dicarbamate *see* Difebarbamate.

2,2-Bis(carbamoyloxymethyl)-3-methylpentane *see* Mebutamate.

1,3-Bis(carbamoylthio)-*N,N*-dimethyl-2-propylamine *see* Cartap.

5,7-Bis(carboxymethoxy)flavone *see* Flavodic acid.

3,12-Bis(carboxymethyl)-6,9-dioxa-3,12-diazatetradecanedioic acid *see* Egtazic acid.

***N,N*-Bis(carboxymethyl)glycine** *see* Nitrilotriacetic acid.

1,3-Bis(2-carboxy-4-oxobenzopyran-5-yloxy)-2-propanol *see* Cromoglicic acid.

1,3-Bis(2-carboxy-4-oxochromen-5-yloxy)propan-2-ol *see* Cromoglicic acid.

Bis(*o*-carboxyphenyl) salicylate *see* Succinylsalicylic acid.

1,3-Bis(*p*-chlorobenzylideneamino)guanidine *see* Robenidine.

1,6-Bis(2-chloroethylamino)-1,6-dideoxy-D-mannitol *see* Mannomustine.

3-[2-[Bis(2-chloroethyl)amino]ethyl]-1,3-diazaspiro[4.5]decane-2,4-dione *see* Spiromustine.

3-[2-[2-[Bis(2-chloroethyl)amino]ethyl]-4-nitrophenyl]alanine *see* Nitrocaphane.

3-[*o*-[2-[Bis(2-chloroethyl)amino]ethyl]phenyl]alanine *see* Ocaphane.

5-[Bis(2-chloroethyl)amino]-1-methyl-2-benzimidazolebutyric acid *see* Bendamustine.

5-[Bis(2-chloroethyl)amino]-6-methyluracil *see* Dopan.

***p*-[Bis(2-chloroethyl)amino]-*N*-nicotinoylphenylalanine ethyl ester** *see* Nicosin.

***p*-[Bis(2-chloroethyl)amino]phenylacetamidobenzoic acid ethyl ester** *see* Phenastezin.

2-[*p*-[Bis(2-chloroethyl)amino]phenylacetamido]-3-imidazol-4-ylpropionic acid methyl ester *see* Hisphen.

2-[*p*-[Bis(2-chloroethyl)amino]phenylacetamido]-4-(methylthio)butyric acid ethyl ester *see* Phenamet.

2-[*p*-[Bis(2-chloroethyl)amino]phenylacetamido]-3-phenylpropionic acid *see* Lofenal.

***p*-[Bis(2-chloroethyl)amino]phenylacetic acid** *see* Chlorphenacyl.

***p*-[Bis(2-chloroethyl)amino]phenylacetic acid cholesteryl ester** *see* Phenesterin.

***N*-[*p*-[Bis(2-chloroethyl)amino]phenylacetyl]-L-histidine methyl ester** *see* Hisphen.

***N*-[*p*-[Bis(2-chloroethyl)amino]phenylacetyl]methionine ethyl ester** *see* Phenamet.

***N*-[*p*-[Bis(2-chloroethyl)amino]phenylacetyl]-DL-phenylalanine** *see* Lofenal.

D-3-[*p*-[Bis(2-chloroethyl)amino]phenyl]alanine *see* Medphalan.

L-3-[*m*-[Bis(2-chloroethyl)amino]phenyl]alanine *see* Metamelfalan.

L-3-[*p*-[Bis(2-chloroethyl)amino]phenyl]alanine *see* Melphalan.

DL-3-[*m*-[Bis(2-chloroethyl)amino]phenyl]alanine *see* m-Sarcolysin.

DL-3-[*o*-[Bis(2-chloroethyl)amino]phenyl]alanine *see* *o*-Sarcolysin.

DL-3-[*p*-[Bis(2-chloroethyl)amino]phenyl]alanine *see* Sarcolysin.

4-[*p*-[Bis(2-chloroethyl)amino]phenyl]butyric acid *see* Chlorambucil.

4-[*p*-[Bis(2-chloroethyl)amino]phenyl]butyric acid prednisolone 21-ester *see* Prednimustine.

2-[*p*-(Bis(2-chloroethyl)amino]phenyl)ethyl acetate *see* Phenester.

DL-3-[*p*-[Bis(2-chloroethyl)amino]phenyl]-*N*-formylalanine *see* Formylsarcolysin.

2-[Bis(2-chloroethyl)amino]tetrahydro-2*H*-1,3,2-oxazaphosphorine 2-oxide *see* Cyclophosphamide.

2-[[2-[Bis(2-chloroethyl)amino]tetrahydro-2*H*-1,3,2-oxazaphosphorin-4-yl]thio]ethanesulfonic acid *P*-oxide *see* Mafosfamide.

5-[Bis(2-chloroethyl)amino]uracil *see* Uramustine.

Bis(2-chloroethyl)carbamic acid 3-ester with estradiol *see* Estramustine.

Bis(2-chloroethyl) (3-chloro-4-methylcoumarin-7-yl) phosphate *see* Haloxon.

***N,N*-Bis(2-chloroethyl)-*N'*-(3-hydroxypropyl)phosphorodiamidic acid intramolecular ester** *see* Cyclophosphamide.

***N,N*-Bis(2-chloroethyl)-4-methoxy-3-methyl-1-naphthylamine** *see* Mitoclomine.

61

N,*N*-**Bis(2-chloroethyl)methylamine** *see* Chlormethine.

Bis(2-chloroethyl)-2-naphthylamine *see* Chlornaphazine.

1,3-Bis(2-chloroethyl)-1-nitrosourea *see* Carmustine.

N,*N*-**Bis(2-chloroethyl)phosphorodiamidic acid esters** *see* Cyclophosphamide; Defosfamide.

Bis(2-chloroethyl)sulfide *see* Mustard gas.

N,3-**Bis(2-chloroethyl)tetrahydro-2***H***-1,3,2-oxazaphosphorin-2-amine 2-oxide** *see* Ifosfamide.

3,12-Bis(2-chloroethyl)-3,6,9,12-tetrazadispiro-[5.5.5]hexadecane *see* Spirazidine.

Bis(5-chloro-2-hydroxyphenyl) sulfide *see* Fenticlor.

3,12-Bis(3-chloro-2-hydroxypropyl)-3,12-diaza-6,9-diazoniadispiro[5.2.5.2]hexadecane dichloride *see* Prospidium chloride.

N,*N*³-**Bis(3-chloro-2-hydroxypropyl)-***N*,*N*²-**dispirotripiperazine dichloride** *see* Prospidium chloride.

BIS(CHLOROMETHYL) ETHER (dichlorodimethyl ether; BCME).

2,2-Bis(chloromethyl)-1,3-propanediol *see* Loprodiol.

2,2-Bis(*p*-chlorophenoxy)acetic acid, esters *see* Biclofibrate; Lifibrate.

Bis[2-(*p*-chlorophenoxy)-2-methylpropionato]hydroxyaluminium *see* Aluminium clofibrate.

Bis[2-(*p*-chlorophenoxy)-2-methylpropionato]magnesium *see* Magnesium clofibrate.

O,*O*-**BIS(*p*-CHLOROPHENYL) *N*-ACETIMIDOYLPHOSPHORAMIDOTHIOATE** (Bayer-38819; 'gophicide').

1,4-Bis[*N*¹-[*N*¹-(*p*-chlorophenyl)amidino]amidino]piperazine *see* Picloxydine.

α,α-**Bis(*p*-chlorophenyl)cyclopropanemethanol** *see* Proclonol.

2,2-Bis(*p*-chlorophenyl)glycolic acid ethyl ester *see* Chlorobenzilate.

2,2-Bis(*p*-chlorophenyl)glycolic acid isopropyl ester *see* Chloropropylate.

O,*O*-**Bis(*p*-chlorophenyl)(1-iminoethyl)phosphoramidothioate** *see* Phosacetim.

Bis(*p*-chlorophenyl) methyl carbinol *see* Chlorfenethol.

N-**[2,3-Bis(*p*-chlorophenyl)-1-methylpropyl]maleamic acid** *see* Benzmalecene.

2-[[4,5-Bis(*p*-chlorophenyl)-2-oxazolyl]thio]propionic acid *see* Tioxaprofen.

α,α-**Bis(*p*-chlorophenyl)-3-pyridinemethanol** *see* Parinol.

Biscumarol *see* Dicoumarol.

4,4′-Bis[*p*-(13-cyclopentyltridecanamido)phenyl] sulfone *see* Chaulmosulfone.

6,7-Bis(cyclopropylmethoxy)-4-hydroxyquinoline-3-carboxylic acid ethyl ester *see* Ciproquinate.

Bis(DEAE)fluorenone *see* Tilorone.

3,6-Bisdeoxy-L-mannose *see* Ascarylose.

1,4-Bis(diaziridinylphosphinylidyne)piperazine *see* Dipin.

2,2-Bis(3,5-di-*tert*-butyl-4-hydroxyphenyl)acetic acid *see* Terbuficin.

Bisdichlorohydroxyphenyl sulfide *see* Bithionol.

Bis(2,4-dichlorophenyl)iodonium chloride *see* Feniodium chloride.

Bis[*S*-(diethoxyphosphinothioyl)mercapto]methane *see* Ethion.

2,7-Bis(2-diethylaminoethoxy)fluoren-9-one *see* Tilorone.

6,7-Bis(2-diethylaminoethoxy)-4-methylcoumarin *see* Oxamarin.

N,*N*′-**Bis(2-diethylaminoethyl)oxamide bis(2-chlorobenzyl chloride)** *see* Ambenonium chloride.

2,4-Bis(diethylamino)-6-hydrazino-*s*-triazine *see* Meladrazine.

4-[3,5-Bis(diethylaminomethyl)-4-hydroxyanilino]-7-chloroquinoline *see* Cycloquine.

Bis(diethylthiocarbamyl) disulfide *see* Disulfiram.

Bis(diethylthiocarbamyl) sulfide *see* Sulfiram.

Bis(dihydrogen 8-hydroxy-5,7-quinolinedisulfinato)-copper compound with diethylamine (1:4) *see* Cuproxoline.

2,3-Bis(3,4-dihydroxybenzyl)butane *see* Nordihydroguaiaretic acid.

1,4-Bis(3,4-dihydroxyphenyl)-2,3-dimethylbutane *see* Nordihydroguaiaretic acid.

N,*N*′-**Bis[2-(3,4-dihydroxyphenyl)-2-hydroxyethyl]hexamethylenediamine** *see* Hexoprenaline.

N,*N*′-**Bis(2,3-dihydroxypropyl)-5-[*N*-(2,3-dihydroxypropyl)acetamido]-2,4,6-triiodoisophthalamide** *see* Iohexol.

N,*N*′-**Bis(2,3-dihydroxypropyl)-2,4,6-triiodo-5-(2-methoxyacetamido)-*N*-methylisophthalamide** *see* Iopromide.

Bis(dimethylamido)fluorophosphate *see* Dimefox.

3,6-Bis(dimethylamino)acridine *see* Acridine orange.

Bis(dimethylamino)fluorophosphine oxide *see* Dimefox.

3,7-Bis(dimethylamino)phenazathionium chloride *see* Methylene blue.

[4-[Bis[*p*-(dimethylamino)phenyl]methylene]-2,5-cyclohexadien-1-ylidene]-*N*-methylmethanaminium chloride *see* Crystal violet.

Bis[*p*-(dimethylamino)phenyl]methyleneiminium chloride *see* Auramine.

5,6-Bis[*p*-(dimethylamino)phenyl]-2-methyl-*as*-triazin-3(2*H*)-one *see* Metrazifone.

1,3-Bis(dimethylamino)-2-propanol dimethiodide *see* Prolonium iodide.

10-[2,3-Bis(dimethylamino)propyl]phenothiazine *see* Aminopromazine.

Bis(2,2-dimethyl-1-aziridinyl)phosphinylcarbamic acid ethyl ester *see* Meturedepa.

S,*S*′-**Bis(dimethylcarbamodithioato)zinc** *see* Ziram.

Bis(dimethylcarbamoyl)diimide *see* Diamide.

2,6-Bis(1,1-dimethylethyl)-4-methylphenyl methylcarbamate *see* Terbucarb.

1,1′-Bis[3,5-dimethylmorpholinocarbonylmethyl)-4,4′-bipyridinium dichloride *see* Morfamquat.

1,1′-Bis[2-(3,5-dimethylmorpholino)-2-oxoethyl]-4,4′-bipyridinium dichloride *see* Morfamquat.

2-[2-[(Bis(2,6-dimethylphenyl)methoxy]ethoxy]-*N*,*N*-dimethylethylamine *see* Xyloxemine.

1-[Bis(2,6-dimethylphenyl)methoxy]-3-(isopropylamino)-2-propanol *see* Xipranolol.

2β,16β-Bis(4,4-dimethyl-1-piperazino)-3α,17β-di-

acetoxyandrostane dibromide *see* Pipecuronium bromide.

Bis[3-(2,5-dimethylpyrrolidin-1-yl)propyl]hexadecylmethylammonium bromide *see* Pirralkonium bromide.

Bis(dimethylthiocarbamoyl) disulfide *see* Thiram.

1,2-Bis(3,5-dioxopiperazin-1-yl)propane *see* Razoxane.

'Bisecurin' *see under* Etynodiol diacetate.

1,1'-Bis(2,3-epoxypropyl)-4,4'-bipiperidine *see* Epipropidine.

1,4-Bis(2,3-epoxypropyl)piperazine *see* Epoxypropylpiperazine.

'Biseptol' *see* Co-trimoxazole.

S-[1,2-Bis(ethoxycarbonyl)ethyl] *O,O*-dimethyl phosphorodithioate *see* Malathion.

S-[1,2-Bis(ethoxycarbonyl)ethyl] *O,O*-dimethyl phosphorothioate *see* Malaoxon.

1,2-Bis(3-ethoxycarbonyl-2-thioureido)benzene *see* Thiophanate.

N,N'-**Bis(*p*-ethoxyphenyl)acetamidine** *see* Phenacaine.

4,6-Bis(ethylamino)-2-(methylthio)-*s*-triazine *see* Simetryne.

2,6-Bis(2-ethylhexyl)hexahydro-7α-methyl-1*H*-imidazo[1,5-*c*]imidazole *see* Hexedine.

N¹,N³-**Bis(2-ethylhexyl)-2-methyl-1,2,3-propanetriamine** *see* Propoctamine.

Bis(*N*-ethylidenethreoninato) hydrogen diaquoferrate (II) *see* Ferrotrenine.

2,2-Bis(ethylsulfonyl)butane *see* Methylsulfonal.

Bis(ethylxanthogen) *see* Dixanthogen.

BISFENAZONE* (3-[[(2,3-dimethyl-5-oxo-1-phenyl-3-pyrazolin-4-yl)amino]methyl]-4-isopropyl-2-methyl-1-phenyl-3-pyrazolin-5-one).

erythro-**2,3-Bis(3-fluoro-4-hydroxyphenyl)pentane** *see* Bifluranol.

4-[4,4-Bis(*p*-fluorophenyl)butyl]-3-carbamoyl-2',6'-dichloro-1-piperazineacetanilide *see* Mioflazine.

1-[4,4-Bis(*p*-fluorophenyl)butyl]-4-(5-chloro-2-oxobenzimidazolin-1-yl)piperidine *see* Clopimozide.

1-[4,4-Bis(*p*-fluorophenyl)butyl]-4-(4-chloro-α,α,α-trifluoro-*m*-tolyl)-4-piperidinol *see* Penfluridol.

4-[4,4-Bis(*p*-fluorophenyl)butyl]-*N*-ethyl-1-piperazinecarboxamide *see* Amperozide.

1-[4,4-Bis(*p*-fluorophenyl)butyl]-4-(2-oxobenzimidazolin-1-yl)piperidine *see* Pimozide.

8-[4,4-Bis(*p*-fluorophenyl)butyl]-1-phenyl-1,3,8-triazaspiro[4.5]-decan-4-one *see* Fluspirilene.

[4-[4,4-Bis(*p*-fluorophenyl)butyl]piperazin-1-yl]-2',6'-acetoxylidide *see* Lidoflazine.

1-[1-[4,4-Bis(*p*-fluorophenyl)butyl]piperid-4-yl]-2-benzimidazolinone *see* Pimozide.

1-[1-[4,4-Bis(*p*-fluorophenyl)butyl]piperid-4-yl]-5-chlorobenzimidazolin-2-one *see* Clopimozide.

2-[Bis(*p*-fluorophenyl)methoxy]ethylamine *see* Flunamine.

4-[Bis(*p*-fluorophenyl)methyl]-α-(*p-tert*-butylphenyl)-1-piperazinebutanol *see* Flotrenizine.

1-[Bis(*p*-fluorophenyl)methyl]-4-cinnamylpiperazine *see* Flunarizine.

6-[2-[4-[Bis(*p*-fluorophenyl)methylene]piperid-1-yl]ethyl]-7-methyl-5*H*-thiazolo[3,2-*a*]pyrimidin-5-one *see* Ritanserin.

4,5-Bis(*p*-fluorophenyl)-2-[(1,1,2,2-tetrafluoroethyl)sulfonyl]imidazole *see* Tiflamizole.

1,3-Bis(4-formylpyridinium)propane dibromide dioxime *see* Trimedoxime bromide.

trans-**3,4-Bis[4-(2-furoyloxy)phenyl]hex-3-ene** *see* Furostilbestrol.

'Bisguadine' *see* Alexidine.

Bishydroxycoumarin *see* Dicoumarol.

2-[Bis(2-hydroxyethyl)amino]-4,5-diphenyloxazole *see* Ditazole.

1,4-Bis[[2-[(2-hydroxyethyl)amino]ethyl]amino]anthraquinone *see* Ametantrone.

3-[Bis(2-hydroxyethyl)amino]-6-hydrazinopyridazine *see* Oxdralazine.

8-[Bis(2-hydroxyethyl)aminomethyl]-6,7-dihydroxy-4-methylcoumarin *see* Esculamine.

4-[Bis(2-hydroxyethyl)amino]-2-(5-nitrofur-2-yl)quinazoline *see* Nifurquinazol.

N,N-**BIS(2-HYDROXYETHYL)GLYCINE** (diethylolthioglycine; 'bicine'; 'fe-3-specific').

1,4-Bis(2-hydroxyethyl)piperazine bis(2-phenylbutyrate) *see* Febuverine.

6-[2-[6-[*p*-[Bis(2-hydroxyethyl)sulfamoyl]phenyl]-1,2-dihydro-2-oxonicotinamido)-2-(*p*-hydroxyphenyl)acetamido]penicillanic acid *see* Piridicillin.

Bis(2-hydroxyethyl) sulfide *see* Thiodiglycol.

2,4-Bis(1-hydroxyethyl)-1,3,5,8-tetramethylporphine-6,7-dipropionic acid *see* Hematoporphyrin.

1,10-Bis(2-hydroxyethylthio)decane *see* Tiadenol.

N,N'-**Bis[2-hydroxy-1-(hydroxymethyl)ethyl]-2,4,6-triiodo-5-lactamidoisophthalamide** *see* Iopamidol.

Bis(3-hydroxy-4-(hydroxymethyl)-2-methylpyrid-5-ylmethyl) disulfide *see* Pyritinol.

Bis[(4-hydroxyiminomethyl)pyridinium-1-methyl] ether dichloride *see* Obidoxime chloride.

1,3-Bis(4-hydroxyiminomethylpyridinium)propane dibromide *see* Trimedoxime bromide.

1,3-Bis(hydroxymethyl)benzimidazole-2-thione *see* Thibenzazoline.

[4,5-Bis(hydroxymethyl)-2-methylpyrid-3-yloxy]glycolic acid compound with 2-[(5-hydroxy-4-hydroxymethylpyrid-3-yl)methoxy]glycolic acid *see* Piridoxilate.

3,4-Bis(*p*-hydroxy-*m*-methylphenyl)hexane *see* Methestrol.

2,2-Bis(hydroxymethyl)-1,3-propanediol *see* Pentaerythritol.

N,N'-**Bis(1-hydroxymethylpropyl)ethylenediamine** *see* Ethambutol.

2,6-Bis(hydroxymethyl)pyridyl bis(methylcarbamate) *see* Pyricarbate.

(5,5-Bis(hydroxymethyl)-2-(trichloromethyl)-1,3-dioxane *see* Penthrichloral.

1,3-BIS(HYDROXYMETHYL)UREA (dimethylolurea; 'methural').

3,3-Bis(*p*-hydroxyphenyl)-2,1-benzoxathiole 1,1-dioxide *see* Phenolsulfonphthalein.

2,2-Bis(*p*-hydroxyphenyl)-1,4-benzoxazin-3-one *see* Bisoxatin.

Bis(*p*-hydroxyphenyl)cyclohexylidenemethane diacetate *see* Cyclofenil.

1,4-Bis(*p*-hydroxyphenyl)-2,3-diisocyanato-1,3-

butadiene *see* Xantocillin.

3,4-Bis(*p*-hydroxyphenyl)-2,4-hexadiene *see* Dienestrol.

3,4-BIS(*p*-HYDROXYPHENYL)-2-HEXENE (pseudostilbestrol).

trans-**3,4-Bis(*p*-hydroxyphenyl)-3-hexene** *see* Diethylstilbestrol.

3,3-Bis(*p*-hydroxyphenyl)-2-indolinone *see* Oxyphenisatine.

o-**[Bis(*p*-hydroxyphenyl)methyl]benzyl alcohol** *see* Phenolphthalol.

4-(Bis(*p*-hydroxyphenyl)methylene)-2,5-cyclohexadien-1-one *see* Roseolic acid.

3,3-Bis(*p*-hydroxyphenyl)-7-methyl-2-indolinone bis-(hydrogen sulfate) *see* Sulisatin.

2,3-Bis(*p*-hydroxyphenyl)oxindole *see* Oxyphenisatine.

3,3-Bis(*p*-hydroxyphenyl)phthalide *see* Phenolphthalein.

1,4-Bis(3-hydroxypropionyl)piperazine dimesylate *see* Piposulfan.

Bis(1-hydroxy-2(1*H*)-pyridinethionato) zinc *see* Pyrithione zinc.

3,3′-Bis(2-imidazolin-2-yl)carbanilide *see* Imidocarb.

4,4′-Bis(isopentyloxy)thiocarbanilide *see* Tiocarlide.

Bis(isopropylamino)fluorophosphine oxide *see* Mipafox.

4,6-Bis(isopropylamino)-2-methoxy-*s*-triazine *see* Prometon.

4,6-Bis(isopropylamino)-2-(methylthio)-*s*-triazine *see* Prometryn.

1,6-Bis(methanesulfonyl)mannitol *see* Mannityl dimesilate.

1,4-Bis(methanesulfonyloxy)butane *see* Busulfan.

N,N′-**Bis[6-[(*o*-methoxybenzyl)amino]hexyl]cystamine** *see* Benextramine.

2′-(2,3-Bismethoxycarbonylguanidino)-2-methoxy-5′-(phenylthio)-2-methoxyacetanilide *see* Febantel.

1,2-Bis(3-methoxycarbonyl-2-thioureido)benzene *see* Thiophanate-methyl.

Bis(6-methoxy-1-phenazinol-5,10-dioxidato-*O*^{1},*O*^{10})copper *see* Cuprimyxin.

1,1-Bis(*p*-methoxyphenyl)-2,2-dimethylpropane *see* Dianisylneopentane.

2,3-Bis(*p*-methoxyphenyl)indole *see* Indoxole.

4,5-Bis(*p*-methoxyphenyl)-2-methylpyrrole *see* Bimetopyrol.

5,6-Bis(*p*-methoxyphenyl)-3-methyl-*as*-triazine *see* Anitrazafen.

4,5-Bis(*p*-methoxyphenyl)-2-trifluoromethylimidazole *see* Flumizole.

1,4-Bis(2-methoxy-4-propylphenoxyacetyl)piperazine *see* Simetride.

Bis(1-methylamyl) sodium sulfosuccinate *see* Sodium dihexyl sulfosuccinate.

Bis[1-(1-methylbenzimidazol-2-yl)ethyl] tetrathio-*p*-benzenedicarbamate *see* Bisbendazole.

2,6-Bis(3,4-methylenedioxyphenyl)-3,7-dioxabicyclo[3.3.0]octane *see* Sesamin.

α-**[2-[Bis(1-methylethyl)amino]ethyl]-α-(2-chlorophenyl)-1-piperidinebutanamide** *see* Disobutamide.

N,N′-**Bis(1-methylethyl)-6-(methylthio)-1,3,5-triazine-2,4-diamine** *see* Prometryn.

N-**[2-[[2,6-Bis(1-methylethyl)phenyl]amino]-2-oxoethyl]-*N*-(carboxymethyl)glycine** *see* Disofenin.

O,O-**Bis(1-methylethyl) *S*-[2-[(phenylsulfonyl)-amino]ethyl] phosphorodithioate** *see* Bensulide.

N,N′-**Bis(1-methylethyl)phosphorodiamidic fluoride** *see* Mipafox.

1,4-Bis(α-methylphenethyl)piperazine *see* Diphenazine.

N,N-**Bis[*N*-methyl-*N*-(phenyl-*tert*-butyl)acetamido]-2-hydroxyethylamine** *see* Oxetacaine.

Bis(4-methylphenyl)iodonium chloride *see* Toliodium chloride.

3,4-Bis(*m*-methyl-*p*-propionoxyphenyl)hexane *see* Methestrol dipropionate.

Bis(2-methylpropyl)carbamothioic acid *S*-ethyl ester *see* Butylate.

Bis[2-(1-methylpyrrolidinium)ethyl]methylamine *see* Azapyrrolidinium.

5,7-Bis(2-morpholinoethoxy)-4-methylcoumarin *see* Moxicoumone.

BISMUTH 2-ALLYL-4-PENTENOATE (bismuth diallylacetate; 'medobis').

BISMUTH CARBONATE (basic bismuth carbonate; $2Bi_2O_3.2CO_2.H_2O$; bismuth oxycarbonate; bismuth subcarbonate).

BISMUTH CHLORIDE (basic bismuth chloride; bismuth oxychloride; bismuth subchloride).

BISMUTH CHRYSOPHANATE (basic bismuth chrysophanate; 4,5-dihydroxy-2-methylanthraquinone Bi salt; 'dermol').

Bismuth diallylacetate *see* Bismuth 2-allyl-4-pentenoate.

Bismuth dipropylacetate *see* Bismuth valproate.

BISMUTH GALLATE* (basic bismuth gallate; bismuth oxygallate; bismuth subgallate; 'dermatol'; 'gallabis'; 'helcosol').

Bismuth glycolylarsanilate *see* Glycobiarsol.

BISMUTH HYDROXIDE (hydrated Bi oxide; bismuth oxide).

Bismuth hydroxide 6-methyl-8-quinolinol compound *see* Mebiquine.

BISMUTH NITRATE (basic bismuth nitrate; bismuth oxynitrate; bismuth subnitrate).
See also under Camylofin.

Bismuth oxide *see* Bismuth hydroxide.

Bismuth oxycarbonate *see* Bismuth carbonate.

Bismuth oxychloride *see* Bismuth chloride.

Bismuth oxygallate *see* Bismuth gallate.

Bismuthoxy *p*-*N*-glycolylarsanilate *see* Glycobiarsol.

Bismuth oxynitrate *see* Bismuth nitrate.

Bismuth oxysalicylate *see* Bismuth salicylate.

Bismuth 2-propylvalerate *see* Bismuth valproate.

BISMUTH SALICYLATE (basic bismuth salicylate; bismuth oxysalicylate; bismuth subsalicylate).

BISMUTH SODIUM NEUTRAL TARTRATE (bismuthyl tartrate; sodium tartrobismuthate).

Bismuth subcarbonate *see* Bismuth carbonate.

Bismuth subchloride *see* Bismuth chloride.

BISMUTH SUBCITRATE (tripotassium dicitrato-bismuthate; 'de-nol').

Bismuth subgallate *see* Bismuth gallate.

Bismuth subnitrate *see* Bismuth nitrate.

Bismuth subsalicylate *see* Bismuth salicylate.

Bismuth tetrabromopyrocatechuate *see* Bibrocathol.

BISMUTH TRIBROMOPHENATE (bibrophen; bromphenol bismuth; 'bromphenobis'; 'sigmaform'; 'xeroform').

BISMUTH VALPROATE (bismuth 2-propylvalerate; bismuth dipropylacetate; 'angicone'; 'suppangin').

Bismuthyl *N*-glycolylarsanilate *see* Glycobiarsol.

Bismuthyl tartrate *see* Bismuth sodium neutral tartrate.

1,4-Bis[2-(2-naphth-1-ylpropionyloxy)ethyl]piperazine *see* Nafiverine.

1,5-Bis(5-nitro-2-furyl)-1,4-pentadien-3-one amidinohydrazone *see* Nitrovin.

BISOBRIN*** (1,1'-tetramethylenebis(1,2,3,4-tetrahydro-6,7-dimethoxyisoquinoline)).

BISOBRIN LACTATE* (*meso*-1,1'-tetramethylenebis(1,2,3,4-tetrahydro-6,7-dimethoxyisoquinoline) dilactate; EN-1661L).

'Bisolpent' *see under* Bromhexine.

'Bisolvomycin' *see under* Bromhexine.

'Bisolvon' *see* Bromhexine.

'Bisolvonamide' *see under* Bromhexine.

BISOPROLOL*** ((±)-1-[[α-(2-isopropoxyethoxy)-*p*-tolyl]oxy]-3-(isopropylamino)-2-propanol).

BISOPROLOL FUMARATE (EMD-33512).

BISORCIC*** (2,5-diacetamidovaleric acid; N^2,N^5-diacetyl-L-ornithine).

BISOXATIN*** (2,2-bis(*p*-hydroxyphenyl)-1,4-benzoxazin-3-one; La-271).

Bisoxatin acetate* *see* Bisoxatin diacetate.

BISOXATIN DIACETATE* (2,2-bis(4-acetoxyphenyl)-2*H*-1,4-benzoxazin-3(4*H*)-one; bisoxatin acetate; La-271a; Wy-8138).

1,2-Bis[(2-oxo-1-pyrrolidinyl)acetyl]hydrazine *see* Dupracetam.

1,3-Bis[(2-oxopyrrolidin-1-yl)methyl]urea *see* Imuracetam.

Bis[2-(pantothenylamino)ethyl] disulfide *see* Pantethine.

Bis(1,2,2,6,6-pentamethylpiperid-4-yl) succinate *see* Suxemerid.

1,4-Bis(2-phenylbutyryloxyethyl)piperazine *see* Febuverine.

1,4-Bis(phenylisopropyl)piperazine *see* Diphenazine.

N,N-Bis(3-phenylpropyl)ethylamine *see* Alverine.

1,4-Bis(3-phenylprop-2-yl)piperazine *see* Diphenazine.

1,3-Bis(2-platineciumethoxy)benzene *see* Diplacin.

Bis(2-propoxyethyl) 1,4-dihydro-2,6-dimethyl-4-(3-nitrophenyl)pyridine-3,5-dicarboxylate *see* Niludipine.

Bis(8-quinolinato-N^2,O^8)copper *see* Oxine-copper.

3,3'-Bis(sulfomethylamino)-*p*-arsenophenol disodium salt *see* Sulfarsphenamine.

'Bisteril' *see* Phenazopyridine.

Bis(*N,N,N',N'*-tetramethylphosphorodiamidic) anhydride *see* Schradan.

2,6-Bis(2-thenylidene)cyclohexanone *see* Tenylidone.

Bis(thymol iodide) *see* Dithymol diiodide.

'Bistreptase' *see under* Streptodornase.

BIS(TRIBUTYLTIN) OXIDE ('bio-met'; 'fungiban'; 'hollicide'; 'lastanox'; 'sun-nitt'; 'T.B.T.O'; 'tin anti-slime').

Bis(2,2,2-trichloroethyl) carbonate *see* Cloretate.

1,3-Bis(2,2,2-trichloro-1-hydroxyethoxy)-3-*o*-toloxypropane *see* Toloxychlorinol.

1,3-Bis(2,2,2-trichloro-1-hydroxyethyl)urea *see* Dicloralurea.

1,4-BIS(TRICHLOROMETHYL)BENZENE (hexachloro-*p*-xylene; 'chloxyl').

Bis(2,2,2-trifluoroethyl) ether *see* Flurotyl.

5,5'-Bis(trimethylammonium)dipentyl ether dichloride *see* Oxydipentonium chloride.

'Bistrimin' *see* Phenyltoloxamine.

Bis[tris(*p*-aminophenyl)methylium] 4,4'-methylenebis(3-hydroxy-2-naphthoate) *see* Pararosaniline embonate.

Bistropamide *see* Tropicamide.

Bithiodine *see* Tipepidine.

'Bithion' *see* Temefos.

BITHIONOL*** (2,2-thiobis(4,6-dichlorophenoxide); tetrachlorodihydroxydiphenyl sulfide; bisdichlorohydroxyphenyl sulfide; D-26; TBP; TPB; XL-7).

Bithionolate sodium* *see* Sodium bitionolate.

BITHIONOLOXIDE*** (2,2'-sulfinylbis[4,6-dichlorophenol]; bithionol sulfoxide; 'bitin-S'; 'disto-5'; 'neodistol').

Bithionol sulfoxide *see* Bithionoloxide.

Bithymoldiiodide *see* Dithymol diiodide.

Bithyolum *see* Ammonium sulfobituminate.

'Bitin-S' *see* Bithionoloxide.

BITIPAZONE*** (2,3-butanedione bis(4-(2-piperid-1-yl-ethyl)thiosemicarbazone)).

BITOLTEROL*** (4-(2-(*tert*-butylamino)-1-hydroxyethyl)-*o*-phenylene di-*p*-toluate; α-[(*tert*-butylamino)methyl]-3,4-dihydroxybenzyl alcohol 3,4-di-*p*-toluate; 4-[2-[(1,1-dimethylethyl)amino]-1-hydroxyethyl]-1,2-phenylene bis(4-methylbenzoate); colterol 3,4-di-*p*-toluate; S-1540).

BITOLTEROL MESILATE (bitolterol mesylate; bitolterol methanesulfonate; WIN-32784; 'effectin'; 'tornalate').

BITOSCANATE*** (*p*-phenylene bis(isothiocyanate); phenylene diisothiocyanate; Ho-16842; HOE-16842).

'Bitrex' *see* Denatonium benzoate.

BIURET (allophanamide; allophanic acid amide; carbamylurea; ureidoformamide).

'Bi-vaspit' *see under* Fluocortin butyl.

'Bivelin' *see under* Co-dergocrine.

BL-5 *see* Cyclocoumarol.

BL-139 *see* Dimevamide.

BL-191 *see* Pentoxifylline.

BL-3912A *see* Dimoxamine.

BL-4162A *see* Anagrelide.

BL-4566 *see* Moxazocine.

BL-5111 *see* Tiodazosin.
BL-5572M *see* Proxorphan tartrate.
BL-5641 *see* Etintidine.
'Bladafum' *see* Sulfotep.
'Bladan' *see* Parathion.
'Bladan 393'' *see* Sulfotep.
'Bladex' *see* Cyanazine.
'Blattanex' *see* Propoxur.
'Bledocaine' *see* Prilocaine.
'Bleminol' *see* Allopurinol.
'Blenoxane' *see* Bleomycin.
BLEOMYCIN** (antibiotic from *Str. verticillus*; bleomycin A; bleomycin sulfate; NSC-125066; 'blenoxane').
Bleomycin A* *see* Bleomycin.
'Blitex' *see* Fenclofos.
'Blitol' *see* Metrifonate.
'Bloat guard' *see* Poloxalene.
'Blocadren' *see* Timolol maleate.
'Blockaine' *see* Propoxycaine.
BL-P152 *see* Pheneticillin.
BL-P804 *see* Hetacillin.
BL-P1322 *see* Cefapirin.
BL-P1462 *see* Suncillin.
BL-P1761 *see* Sarpicillin.
BL-P1780 *see* Sarmoxicillin.
BL-R743 *see* Intrazole.
BL-S578 *see* Cefadroxil.
BL-S640 *see* Cefatrizine.
BL-S786 *see* Ceforanide.
BLUENSOMYCIN*** (antibiotic from *Str. bluensis*; U-12898).
Blue tetrazolium *see* Tetrazolium blue.
'Blue VRS' *see* Sulfan blue.
Blue VRS *see* Isosulfan blue.
'Blutene' *see* Tolonium chloride.
BM-123-γ *see* Cinodine.
BM-10188 *see* Doxaminol.
BM-12531 *see* Azimexon.
BM-15075 *see* Bezafibrate.
BM-15100 *see* Picumast.
BMIH *see* Isocarboxazid.
'B-nine' *see* Daminozide.
'Bocasan' *see* Sodium perborate.
BOEA *see* Ethyl biscoumacetate.
Boforsin *see* Colforsin.
BOFUMUSTINE*** (1-(2-chloroethyl)-3-(2,3-*O*-isopropylidene-D-ribofuranosyl)-1-nitrosourea 5'-*p*-nitrobenzoate).
'Bogadin-TM' *see* Ibogaine.
'Bol' *see* Bamethan.
Bol-148 *see* Bromolysergide.
BOLANDIOL*** (estr-4-ene-3β,17-diol; bolandiol dipropionate; SC-7525).
BOLASTERONE*** (7α,17-dimethyltestosterone; 17β-hydroxy-7α,17-dimethylandrost-4-en-3-one; NSC-66233; U-19763; 'myagen').
BOLAZINE** (17β-hydroxy-2α-methyl-5α-androstan-3-one azine).
'Boldane' *see* Boldenone undecanoate.
BOLDENONE*** (17β-hydroxyandrosta-1,4-dien-3-one).
BOLDENONE UNDECANOATE* ('boldane';

BOLDENONE UNDECENOATE (boldenone undec-10-enoate; boldenone undecylenate; Ba-29038; 'parenabol').
Boldenone undecylenate* *see* Boldenone undecenoate.
BOLDINE (1,10-dimethoxy-6aα-aporphine-2,9-diol; 5,6,6a,7-tetrahydro-1,10-dimethoxy-6-methyl-4*H*-dibenzo[*de,g*]quinoline-2,9-diol).
Boldine dimethyl ether *see* Glaucine.
BOLENOL** (17α-ethyl-5-estren-17-ol; 17α-ethyl-17β-hydroxyestr-5-ene; 19-nor-17α-pregn-5-en-17-ol).
Boletic acid *see* Fumaric acid.
'Bolfo' *see* Propoxur.
'Bolfortan' *see* Testosterone nicotinate.
BOLMANTALATE*** (17β-hydroxyestr-4-en-3-one 1-adamantanecarboxylate; nandrolone adamantane-1-carboxylate).
'Bolvidon' *see* Mianserin.
BOMETOLOL*** ((±)-8-acetonyloxy-5-[3-[(3,4-dimethoxyphenethyl)amino]-2-hydroxypropoxy]-3,4-dihydrocarbostyril; OPC-1427).
'Bona' *see* 3-Hydroxy-2-naphthoic acid.
'Bonadoxin' *see* Meclozine.
Bonafton (tr) *see* Bonaphthone.
'Bonaid' *see* Buquinolate.
'Bonamine' *see* Meclozine.
'Bonapar' *see* Fenyramidol.
BONAPHTHONE (tr) (6-bromo-1,2-naphthoquinone; bonafton).
'Bonifen' *see* Pyritinol.
'Bonine' *see* Meclozine.
'Bonjela' *see under* Choline salicylate.
'Bonoform' *see* Tetrachloroethane.
'Bonomol' *see* Dimethyl phthalate.
'Bonomycin' *see* Sancycline.
'Bontourist' *see* Dimenhydrinate.
BOP *see* 9α-Bromo-4-pregnene-3,11,20-trione.
BOPINDOLOL*** ((±)-1-(*tert*-butylamino)-3-[(2-methylindol-4-yl)oxy]-2-propanol benzoate).
Boracic acid *see* Boric acid.
BORAX ($Na_2B_4O_7 \cdot 10H_2O$; sodium biborate; sodium borate; sodium tetraborate).
BORDEAUX B (chiefly the di-Na salt of 2-hydroxy-1-(naphth-1-ylazo)-3,6-naphthalenedisulphonic acid; 1-(naphth-1-ylazo)-2-naphthol-3,6-disulfonic acid; azorubrum).
Bordeaux S *see* Amaranth.
'Borgal' *see under* Trimethoprim.
BORIC ACID (boracic acid; H_3BO_3; orthoboric acid).
See also Borax; Boroglyceride; Methenamine borate.
2-BORNANAMINE (isobornylamine).
BORNANE (1,7,7-trimethylbicyclo[2.2.1]heptane; 1,7,7-trimethylnorbornane; camphane).
2-Bornanol *see* Borneol.
2-Bornanone *see* Camphor.
BORNAPRINE*** (3-(diethylamino)propyl 2-phenylbicyclo[2.2.1]heptane-2-carboxylate; 'sormodren').
BORNAPROLOL*** (1-(isopropylamino)-3-[*o*-

66

(2-*exo*-norbornyl)phenoxy]-2-propanol; FM-24).
BORNELONE** (5-(3,3-dimethyl-2-norbornylid-
ene)-3-penten-2-one; 'prosalol S-9').
BORNENE (3,3-dimethyl-2-methylenebicyclo-
[2.2.1]heptane; 3,3-dimethyl-2-methylenenor-
bornane; camphene).
Bornene chlorination product *see* Campheclor.
BORNEOL (2-bornanol; 2-hydroxybornane;
bornyl alcohol; 2-camphanol; camphol).
Bornyl alcohol *see* Borneol.
BORNYL DIBROMODIHYDROCINNAMATE
(adamon).
'**Borocarpine**' *see* Pilocarpine.
BOROGLYCERIDE (boric acid-glycerol paste;
boroglycerin; boroglycerol).
Borohexamine *see* Methenamine borate.
'**Borovertine**' *see* Methenamine borate.
Bothrops atrox venom, enzyme *see* Batroxobin.
BOTIACRINE*** (deanol ester of 9,9-dimethyl-
10-acridancarbothioic acid; 9,9-dimethylacri-
dan-10-carbothioic acid 2-dimethylaminoethyl
thioester; *S*-[2-(dimethylamino)ethyl] 9,9-di-
methyl-10-acridancarbothioate).
'**Botran**' *see* Dicloran.
'**Botrilex**' *see* Quintozene.
'**Bourbonal**' *see* Homovanillin.
'**Bourbonal-inh**' *see* Homovanillideneisoniazid.
'**Bovicam**' *see* Cambendazole.
'**Bovisynchron**' *see* Chlormadinone.
'**Boxacin**' *see under* Acetylsalicylic acid.
'**Boxazin**' *see* Acetylsalicylic acid.
BOXIDINE** (1-[2-[4'-(trifluoromethyl)biphenyl-
4-yloxy]ethyl]pyrrolidine; CL-65205).
BP-400 *see* Pimethixene.
BP-1184 *see* Guanoctine.
BQ-22-708 *see* Endralazine mesilate.
BR-18 *see* Pipoxolan.
BR-700 *see* Fentiazac.
BR-750 *see* Guanabenz acetate.
BR-931 *see* Pirinixil.
'**Bradilan**' *see* Nicofuranose.
'**Bradosol**' *see* Domiphen bromide.
BRADYKININ (kallidin II; BRS-640).
Bradykinyl-isoleucyl-tyrosine *O*-**sulfate** *see* Phyllo-
kinin.
'**Bradyl 250**' *see* Nadoxolol.
BRALLOBARBITAL*** (5-allyl-5-(2-bromo-
allyl)barbituric acid; UCB-5033).
**BRALLOBARBITAL plus HYDROXYZINE &
SECOBARBITAL** ('vesparax').
'**Brassel**' *see* Citicoline.
'**Brassicol**' *see* Quintozene.
BRASSIDIC ACID (*trans*-13-docosenoic acid).
'**Brassoran**' *see* Aziprotryne.
'**Braunol**' *see* Povidone-iodine.
'**Bravo**' *see* Chlorothalonil.
'**Braxoron**' *see* 9α-Bromo-4-pregnene-3,11,20-tri-
one.
BRAZERGOLINE*** (2-bromo-6-methylergol-
ine-8β-methanol hexahydro-1*H*-azepine-1-carb-
oxylate ester).
'**Bredon**' *see* Oxolamine citrate.
BREMAZOCINE*** (6-ethyl-1,2,3,4,5,6-hexa-

hydro-3-[(1-hydroxycyclopropyl)methyl]-11,11-
dimethyl-2,6-methano-3-benzazocin-8-ol; 5-
ethyl-2-[(1-hydroxycyclopropyl)methyl]-2'-hydr-
oxy-9,9-dimethyl-6,7-benzomorphan).
Brenzschleimsaure *see* 2-Furoic acid.
Brenztraubensaure *see* Pyruvic acid.
'**Brestan**' *see* Fentin acetate.
'**Brethine**' *see* Terbutaline.
'**Bretylate**' *see* Bretylium tosilate.
BRETYLIUM TOSILATE*** ((*o*-bromobenzyl)-
ethyldimethylammonium *p*-toluenesulfonate;
bretylium tosylate; ornid; ASL-603; BW-
373C57; NSC-62164).
Bretylium tosylate* *see* Bretylium tosilate.
'**Bretylol**' *see* Bretylium tosilate.
'**Brevatonal**' *see* Oxydipentonium chloride.
'**Brevidil E**' *see* Suxamethonium.
'**Brevidil M**' *see* Suxamethonium.
'**Brevinor**' *see under* Norethisterone.
'**Brevital**' *see* Methohexital.
'**Bricanyl**' *see* Terbutaline.
'**Briclin**' *see* Amikacin.
'**Bridal**' *see* Phenbenzamine.
'**Brietal**' *see* Methohexital.
BRILLIANT GREEN* (*N*-[4-[[4-(diethylamino)-
phenyl]phenylmethylene]-2,5-cyclohexadien-1-
ylidene]-*N*-ethylethanaminium sulfate; diamond
green G; emerald green; ethyl green; fast green J;
malachite green G; solid green; viride nitens; CI-
662).
'**Brinaldix**' *see* Clopamide.
BRINASE*** (fibrinolytic enzyme from *Asp. oryzae*; brinolase; aspergillin O; mould fibrinolysin;
CA-7).
'**Brinastase**' *see under* Chymotrypsin.
BRINDOXIME*** (2-[[(6,8-dibromo-9*H*-inde-
no[2,1-*d*]pyrimidin-9-ylidene)amino]oxy]-*N*-(2-
dimethylaminoethyl)propionamide; *N*-[2-[[(6,8-
dibromo-9*H*-indeno[2,1-*d*]pyrimidin-9-ylidene)-
amino]oxy]propionyl]-*N'*,*N'*-dimethylethylenedi-
amine; 6,8-dibromo-9-oxo-9*H*-indeno[2,1-*d*]pyr-
imidine *O*-[1-[[(2-dimethylaminoethyl)amino]-
carbonyl]ethyl]oxime).
'**Brinerdine**' *see under* Reserpine.
Brinolase* *see* Brinase.
'**Bripadon**' *see* Fluoresone.
'**Briserin**' *see under* Reserpine.
'**Bristab**' *see* Hydroflumethiazide.
'**Bristaciclina A**' *see* Tetracycline phosphate com-
plex.
'**Bristacin**' *see* Rolitetracycline.
'**Bristacycline**' *see* Tetracycline.
'**Bristain**' *see* Phenyltoloxamine.
'**Bristamine**' *see* Phenyltoloxamine.
'**Bristamycin**' *see* Erythromycin stearate.
'**Bristocef**' *see* Cefapirin.
'**Bristopen**' *see* Oxacillin.
'**Britacil**' *see* Ampicillin.
British antilewisite *see* Dimercaprol.
'**Brizin**' *see* Benaprizine.
BRL-152 *see* Pheneticillin.
BRL-284 *see* Levopropicillin.
BRL-556 *see* Oxypyrronium bromide.

BRL-804 *see* Hetacillin.
BRL-1241 *see* Meticillin.
BRL-1288 *see* Benaprizine.
BRL-1341 *see* Ampicillin.
BRL-1621 *see* Cloxacillin.
BRL-1702 *see* Dicloxacillin.
BRL-2039 *see* Flucloxacillin.
BRL-2064 *see* Carbenicillin.
BRL-2288 *see* Ticarcillin.
BRL-2333 *see* Amoxicillin.
BRL-2534 *see* Azidocillin.
BRL-3000 *see* Penicillin G, purified.
BRL-3475 *see* Carfecillin.
BRL-4664 *see* Nonabine.
BRL-4910A *see* Pseudomonic acid.
BRL-8988 *see* Talampicillin.
BRL-10833 *see* Nivimedone sodium.
BRL-11870 *see* Anidoxime.
BRL-12594 *see* Ticarcillin cresyl sodium.
BRL-13856 *see* Clopirac.
BRL-14151 *see* Clavulanic acid.
BRL-14342 *see* Clemeprol.
BRL-14777 *see* Nabumetone.
BRL-17421 *see* Temocillin.
BRL-29060A *see* Paroxetine.
BRL-50216 *see* Clociguanil.
Brobenzoxaldine* *see* Broxaldine.
'Brocadisipal' *see* Orphenadrine.
'Brocadopa' *see* Levodopa.
'Brocalcin' *see* Calcium bromide-lactobionate.
'Brocasipal' *see* Orphenadrine.
'Brocide' *see* 1,2-Dichloroethylene.
'Brocillin' *see* Propicillin.
BROCLEPRIDE*** (4-amino-5-bromo-*N*-[1-(*p*-chlorobenzyl)piperid-4-yl]-*o*-anisamide; 4-amino-5-bromo-*N*-[1-(4-chlorobenzyl)piperid-4-yl]-2-methoxybenzamide).
BROCRESINE*** (α-aminooxy-6-bromo-*m*-cresol; 5-(aminooxymethyl)-2-bromophenol; 4-bromo-3-hydroxybenzyloxyamine; *O*-(*p*-bromo-*m*-hydroxybenzyl)hydroxylamine; CL-54998; NSD-1055; 'contramine').
BROCRINAT** ([[7-bromo-3-(*o*-fluorophenyl)-1,2-benzisoxazol-6-yl]oxy]acetic acid; halocrinic acid).
BRODIMOPRIM*** (2,4-diamino-5-(4-bromo-3,5-dimethoxybenzyl)pyrimidine).
'Brofene' *see* Bromofos.
BROFEZIL** (4-(*p*-bromophenyl)-α-methyl-2-thiazoleacetic acid; 2-[4-(*p*-bromophenyl)thiazol-2-yl]-propionic acid; brofezil sodium; ICI-54594).
BROFOXINE** (6-bromo-1,4-dihydro-4,4-dimethyl-2*H*-3,1-benzoxazin-2-one; FI-6820; 'dimetabrone').
'Brolene' *see* Dibrompropamidine.
'Brolitene' *see* Idrocilamide.
'Brolon' *see* 9α-Bromo-4-pregnene-3,11,20-trione.
BROMACIL* (5-bromo-3-*sec*-butyl-6-methyluracil; 5-bromo-6-methyl-3-(1-methylpropyl)-2,4-(1*H*,3*H*)-pyrimidinedione; 'hyvar X').
BROMACRYLIDE*** (*N*-(3-bromopropionamidomethyl)acrylamide).

Bromadal *see* Carbromal.
BROMADOLINE*** (*trans-p*-bromo-*N*-[2-(dimethylamino)cyclohexyl]benzamide).
BROMADOLINE MALEATE* (U-47931E).
'Bromadryl' *see* Embramine.
'Bromalin' *see* Methenamine ethobromide.
BROMAMIDE*** (3-(*p*-bromoanilino)-*N*,*N*-dimethylpropionamide; bromanylpromide; NA-119).
Bromanautine *see* Diphenhydramine 8-bromotheophyllinate.
Bromanylpromide *see* Bromamide.
'Bromat' *see* Cetrimonium bromide.
BROMAZEPAM*** (7-bromo-1,3-dihydro-5-pyrid-2-yl-2*H*-1,4-benzodiazepin-2-one; Ro 5-3350; 'lectopam'; 'lexatin'; 'lexomil'; 'lexotan'; 'lexotanil'; 'normoc').
BROMAZEPAM plus CLIDINIUM BROMIDE (Ro 10-7453).
BROMAZINE*** (2-(*p*-bromo-α-phenylbenzyloxy)-*N*,*N*-dimethylethylamine; bromodiphenhydramine).
Brombenzonium *see* Bromhexine.
Bromchlophos *see* Naled.
BROMCHLORENONE*** (6-bromo-5-chloro-2-benzoxazolinone; NSC-24970; 'vinyzene').
Bromdiethylacetylurea *see* Carbromal.
Bromdylamine *see* Brompheniramine.
BROMEBRIC ACID*** ((*E*)-3-(*p*-anisoyl)-3-bromoacrylic acid; *cis*-3-bromo-3-(*p*-methoxybenzoyl)acrylic acid; bromebrate sodium; MBBA; 'cytembena'; 'cytoval').
BROMELAINS*** (mixture of proteolytic enzymes from *Ananas comosus*; bromelins). *See also under* Tetracycline.
Bromelin *see* Bromelains.
BROMERGURIDE** (3-(2-bromo-9,10-didehydro-6-methylergolin-8α-yl)-1,1-diethylurea).
Brometazepam *see* Metaclazepam.
BROMETENAMINE*** (equimolecular complex of bromoform and hexamethylenetetramine; methenamine bromoform complex).
BROMETHOL* (2,2,2-tribromoethanol; ethobrome; 'narkolan').
Bromethylformin *see* Methenamine ethobromide.
Bromeval *see* Bromisoval.
'Bromex' *see* Naled.
Bromfenoxim *see* Bromofenoxim.
BROMFENVINFOS (2-bromo-1-(2,4-dichlorophenyl)vinyl diethyl phosphate; IPO-62).
BROMFENVINFOS-METHYL (2-bromo-1-(2,4-dichlorophenyl)vinyl dimethyl phosphate; IPO-63; 'polfos').
BROMHEXINE*** (2-amino-3,5-dibromo-*N*-cyclohexyl-*N*-methylbenzylamine; *N*-(2-amino-3,5-dibromobenzyl)-*N*-cyclohexylmethylamine; *N*-(2-amino-3,5-dibromobenzyl)-*N*-methylcyclohexylamine; 3,5-dibromo-*N*α-cyclohexyl-*N*α-methyltoluene-α,2-diamine; bromhexine hydrochloride; brombenzonium; NA-274; 'auxit'; 'bisolvon'; 'quat').
BROMHEXINE plus CEFACLOR ('muco-panoral').

BROMHEXINE plus FEPRAZONE ('sovelin').
BROMHEXINE plus FOMINOBEN ('Pq-tus').
BROMHEXINE plus ORCIPRENALINE ('bisol-pent').
BROMHEXINE plus OXYTETRACYCLINE ('bisolvomycin').
BROMHEXINE plus SULFADIAZINE ('bisolvonamide').
See also under Erythromycin.
'Brominal' see Bromoxynil.
BROMINDIONE*** (2-(p-bromophenyl)-1,3-indandione; bromophenindione; brophenadion; Mg-2555).
'Brominil' see Bromoxynil.
BROMISOVAL*** (1-(2-bromo-3-methylbutyr-yl)urea; α-bromoisovalerylurea; bromoisopropylacetylurea; bromvaletone; bromeval; bromurea; bromvalerylurea; bromvalurea; BVU).
See also under Carbromal.
5-(2-Bromoallyl)-5-sec-butylbarbituric acid see Butallylonal.
5-(2-Bromoallyl)-5-isopropylbarbituric acid see Propallylonal.
5-(2-Bromoallyl)-5-isopropyl-1-methylbarbituric acid see Enibomal.
5-(2-BROMOALLYL)-5-(1-METHYLBUTYL)-BARBITURIC ACID (5-sec-amyl-5-(bromo-allyl)barbituric acid; R-239; 'rectidon'; 'recton'; 'sigmodal').
5-(2-Bromoallyl)-5-(1-methylpropyl)barbituric acid see Butallylonal.
3-(p-Bromoanilino)-N,N-dimethylpropionamide see Bromamide.
Bromoaprobarbital see Propallylonal.
'Bromo-benadryl' see Bromazine.
p-Bromobenzothiohydroxamic acid S-(2-diethyl-aminoethyl)ester see Dietixim.
(Bromobenzyl) (chloroisopropylmethylphenoxyprop-yl)dimethylammonium chloride see Halopenium chloride.
(o-Bromobenzyl)ethyldimethylammonium p-toluene-sulfonate see Bretylium tosilate.
4-Bromo-α-(4-bromophenyl)-α-hydroxybenzeneacet-ic acid 1-methylethyl ester see Bromopropylate.
2-Bromo-6-[(4-bromophenyl)thiocarbamoyl]-4-chlorophenyl acetate see Brotianide.
3-Bromo-α-[(tert-butylamino)methyl]-5-isoxazole-methanol see Broxaterol.
4'-Bromo-3-tert-butyl-2-hydroxy-6-methyl-5-nitro-2'-(trifluoromethyl)benzanilide see Bromoxanide.
5-Bromo-3-sec-butyl-6-methyluracil see Bromacil.
4'-Bromo-3-tert-butyl-α',α',α'-trifluoro-5-nitro-2-cresoto-o-toluidide see Bromoxanide.
6-Bromo-5-chloro-2-benzoxazolinone see Bromchlorenone.
5-Bromo-N-(2-chloroethyl)-N-ethylbenzo[b]thio-phene-3-methylamine see Mitotenamine.
7-Bromo-6-chlorofebrifugine see Halofuginone.
7-Bromo-6-chloro[3-(3-hydroxypiperid-2-yl)aceton-yl]-4(3H)-quinazolinone see Halofuginone.
2-Bromo-4-(o-chlorophenyl)-9-cyclohexyl-6H-thie-no[3,2-f]-s-triazolo[4,3-a][1,4]diazepine see Ciclotizolam.

7-Bromo-5-(o-chlorophenyl)-2,3-dihydro-2-(meth-oxymethyl)-1-methyl-1H-1,4-benzodiazepine see Metaclazepam.
1-(4-Bromo-3-chlorophenyl)-3-methoxy-3-methyl-urea see Chlorbromuron.
2-Bromo-4-(o-chlorophenyl)-9-methyl-6H-thie-no[3,2-f]-s-triazolo[4,3-a][1,4]diazepine see Brotizolam.
5-BROMO-4'-CHLOROSALICYLAMIDE (5-bromosalicyl-4-chloroanilide; 'multifungin'; 'salifungin').
2-Bromo-2-chloro-1,1,1-trifluoroethane see Halothane.
Bromochromium see Merbromin.
BROMOCICLEN*** (5-bromomethyl-1,2,3,4,7,7-hexachloro-2-norbornene; bromocyclen; 'alugan'; 'bromodan').
'Bromocoll' see Gelatin bromotannate.
5-Bromo-2,3-cresotamide see Brosotamide.
BROMOCRIPTINE*** ((5'α)-2-bromo-12'-hydr-oxy-2'-(1-methylethyl)-5'-(2-methylpropyl)ergo-taman-3',6',18-trione; 2-bromo-α-ergocryptine; CB-154; NSC-169774).
BROMOCRIPTINE MESILATE (bromocriptine methanesulfonate; 'parlodel'; 'pravidel').
Bromociclen* see Bromociclen.
'Bromodan' see Bromociclen.
5-Bromo-2'-deoxyuridine see Broxuridine.
4-Bromo-2,5-dichlorophenyl dimethyl phosphoro-thioate see Bromofos.
O-(4-Bromo-2,5-dichlorophenyl) O-methyl phenyl-phosphonothioate see Leptophos.
2-Bromo-1-(2,4-dichlorophenyl)vinyl diethyl phos-phate see Bromfenvinfos.
2-Bromo-1-(2,4-dichlorophenyl)vinyl dimethyl phos-phate see Bromfenvinfos-methyl.
3-(2-Bromo-9,10-didehydro-6-methylergolin-8α-yl)-1,1-diethylurea see Bromerguride.
Bromodiethylacetylurea see Carbromal.
D-2-Bromo-N,N-diethyllysergamide see Bromolys-ergide.
2-Bromo-6β,9-difluoroprednisolone see Halopred-one.
6-Bromo-1,4-dihydro-4,4-dimethyl-2H-3,1-benz-oxazin-2-one see Brofoxine.
7-Bromo-3,4-dihydro-2(1H)-isoquinolinecarboxa-midine sulfate see Guanisoquine.
7-Bromo-1,3-dihydro-5-pyrid-2-yl-2H-1,4-benzodia-zepin-2-one see Bromazepam.
4'-Bromo-2,6-dihydroxybenzanilide see Resorantel.
4-(2-Bromo-4,5-dimethoxybenzyl)-4-[2-[2-(6,6-di-methylbicyclo[3.1.1]hept-2-yl)ethoxy]ethyl]mor-pholinium bromide see Pinaverium bromide.
trans-p-Bromo-N-[2-(dimethylamino)cyclohexyl]-benzamide see Bromadoline.
2-[p-Bromo-α-(2-dimethylaminoethyl)benzyl]pyrid-ine see Brompheniramine.
Bromodiphenhydramine* see Bromazine.
2-Bromo-α-ergocryptine see Bromocriptine.
1-(2-Bromo-2-ethylbutyryl)urea see Carbromal.
m-Bromo-N-ethylcinnamamide see Cinromide.
2-Bromo-N-ethyl-N-isopropylacetamide see Ibrot-amide.

69

1-Bromo-2-(*p*-ethylphenyl)-1,2-diphenylethylene *see* Broparestrol.

3-Bromo-*N*-[(1-ethylpyrrolidin-2-yl)methyl]-2,6-dimethoxybenzamide *see* Remoxipride.

BROMOFENOFOS* (3,3′,5,5′-tetrabromo-2,2′-biphenyldiol mono(dihydrogen phosphate); bromophenophos; 'acedist').

BROMOFENOXIM* (3,5-dibromo-4-hydroxybenzaldehyde *O*-(2,4-dinitrophenyl)oxime; bromfenoxim; 'faneron').

[[7-Bromo-3-(*o*-fluorophenyl)-1,2-benzisoxazol-6-yl]oxy]acetic acid *see* Brocrinat.

10-Bromo-11b-(*o*-fluorophenyl)-2,3,7,11b-tetrahydrooxazolo[3,2-*d*][1,4]benzodiazepin-6(5*H*)-one *see* Haloxazolam.

17α-Bromo-6α-fluoroprogesterone *see* Haloprogesterone.

BROMOFORM (tribromomethane).
See also Brometenamine.

'Bromoformin' *see* Methenamine ethobromide.

BROMOFOS* (*O*-(4-bromo-2,5-dichlorophenyl) *O*,*O*-dimethyl phosphorothioate; bromophos; bromphos; CELA S-1942; 'brofene'; 'brophene'; 'nexion').

BROMOFOS-ETHYL (*O*-(4-bromo-2,4-dichlorophenyl) *O*,*O*-diethyl phosphorothioate; 'filariol'; 'nexagan').

[3-(5-Bromo-2-furoyloxy)butyl]diethylmethylammonium iodide *see* Fubrogonium iodide.

BROMOHYDRIN (3-bromo-1,2-propanediol; α-bromohydrin; glycerol α-monobromohydrin).

3-Bromo-6-hydroxybenz-*p*-bromanilide *see* Dibromsalan.

O-(*p*-Bromo-*m*-hydroxybenzyl)hydroxylamine *see* Brocresine.

4-Bromo-3-hydroxybenzyloxyamine *see* Brocresine.

5-Bromo-2-hydroxy-3-methylbenzamide *see* Brosotamide.

6-Bromo-17α-hydroxy-16-methylenepregna-4,6-diene-3,20-dione acetate *see* Bromo-MDAP.

(5′α)-2-Bromo-12′-hydroxy-2′-(1-methylethyl)-5′-(2-methylpropyl)ergotaman-3′,6′,18-trione *see* Bromocriptine.

Bromoisopropylacetylurea *see* Bromisoval.

5-Bromo-3-isopropyl-6-methyluracil *see* Isocil.

α-Bromoisovalerylurea *see* Bromisoval.

BROMOLYSERGIDE (D-2-bromo-*N*,*N*-diethyllysergamide; Bol-148).

BROMO-MDAP (17α-acetoxy-6-bromo-6-dehydro-16-methyleneprogesterone; 6-bromo-17α-hydroxy-16-methylenepregna-4,6-diene-3,20-dione acetate; 'bromsuperlutin').

[[[(3-Bromomesityl)carbamoyl]methyl]imino]diacetic acid *see* Mebrofenin.

3-Bromo-3-(*p*-methoxybenzoyl)acrylic acid *see* Bromebric acid.

1-(2-Bromo-3-methylbutyryl)urea *see* Bromisoval.

2-Bromo-6-methylergoline-8β-methanol hexahydro-1*H*-azepine-1-carboxylate *see* Brazergoline.

5-Bromomethyl-1,2,3,4,7,7-hexachloro-2-norbornene *see* Bromociclen.

5-Bromo-6-methyl-3-(1-methylethyl)-2,4-(1*H*,3*H*)-pyrimidinedione *see* Isocil.

5-Bromo-6-methyl-3-(1-methylpropyl)-2,4-(1*H*,3*H*)-pyrimidinedione *see* Bromacil.

5-Bromo-2-methyl-5-nitro-*m*-dioxane *see* Nibroxane.

2-(*p*-Bromo-α-methyl-α-phenylbenzyloxy)-*N*,*N*-dimethylethylamine *see* Embramine.

7-Bromo-5-methyl-8-quinolinol *see* Tilbroquinol.

1-BROMO-2-NAPHTHOL ('wormin').

6-Bromo-1,2-naphthoquinone *see* Bonaphthone.

5-Bromonicotinic acid ester with 10-methoxy-1,6-dimethylergoline-8β-methanol *see* Nicergoline.

8β-(5-Bromonicotinoyloxymethyl)-10-methoxy-1,6-dimethylergoline *see* Nicergoline.

2-Bromo-2-nitro-1,3-propanediol *see* Bronopol.

9α-Bromo-11-oxoprogesterone *see* 9α-Bromo-4-pregnene-3,11,20-trione.

Bromoperidol *see* Bromperidol.

Bromophenindione *see* Bromindione.

Bromophenophos *see* Bromofenofos.

2-(*p*-Bromo-α-phenylbenzyloxy)-*N*,*N*-dimethylethylamine *see* Bromazine.

3-[1-(*p*-Bromophenyl)-3-(dimethylamino)propenyl]pyridine *see* Zimeldine.

3-(4-Bromophenyl)-*N*,*N*-dimethyl-3-pyrid-3-ylallylamine *see* Zimeldine.

3-(*m*-Bromophenyl)-*N*-ethyl-2-propenamide *see* Cinromide.

4-(*p*-Bromophenyl)-1-[3-(*p*-fluorobenzoyl)propyl]-4-piperidinol *see* Bromperidol.

4-[4-(*p*-Bromophenyl)-4-hydroxypiperid-1-yl]-4′-fluorobutyrophenone *see* Bromperidol.

2-(*p*-Bromophenyl)-1,3-indandione *see* Bromindione.

5-BROMO-2-PHENYL-1,3-INDANDIONE ('uridione').

1-(*p*-Bromophenyl)-3-methoxy-3-methylurea *see* Metobromuron.

3-[1-(*p*-Bromophenyl)-3-(methylamino)propenyl]pyridine *see* Nomelidine.

4-(*p*-Bromophenyl)-α-methyl-2-thiazoleacetic acid *see* Brofezil.

2-[1-(*p*-Bromophenyl)-1-phenylethoxy]-*N*,*N*-dimethylethylamine *see* Embramine.

2-(*m*-Bromophenyl)succinimide *see* Brosuximide.

1-[3-[5-(3-Bromophenyl)-2*H*-tetrazol-2-yl]propionyl]piperidine *see* Broperamole.

2-[4-(*p*-Bromophenyl)thiazol-2-yl]propionic acid *see* Brofezil.

'Bromophin' *See* Apomorphine methyl bromide.

Bromophos* *see* Bromofos.

9α-BROMO-4-PREGNENE-3,11,20-TRIONE (9α-bromo-11-oxoprogesterone; BOP; 'braxoron'; 'brolon'; 'broxoron').

BROMOPRIDE* (4-amino-5-bromo-*N*-(2-diethylaminoethyl)-2-methoxybenzamide; 4-amino-5-bromo-*N*-(2-diethylaminoethyl)-*o*-anisamide; 'cascapride'; 'viaben').

3-Bromo-1,2-propanediol *see* Bromohydrin.

Bromoprophenpyridamine *see* Brompheniramine.

N-(3-Bromopropionamidomethyl)acrylamide *see* Bromacrylide.

BROMOPROPYLATE* (isopropyl 2,2-bis(*p*-bromophenyl)glycolate; isopropyl 4,4′-dibromobenzilate; 1-methylethyl 4-bromo-α-(4-bromo-phenyl)-α-hydroxybenzeneacetate; phen-isobromolate; 'acarol'; 'neoron').

(4-Bromo-γ-pyrid-3-ylcinnamyl)dimethylamine *see* Zimeldine.

4'-Bromo-γ-resorcylanilide *see* Resorantel.

5-Bromosalicyl-4-chloroanilide *see* 5-Bromo-4'-chlorosalicylamide.

Bromosulfonphthalein *see* Sulfobromphthalein.

2-Bromo-1,1,1,2-tetrafluoroethane *see* Teflurane.

3-Bromo-1,1,2,2-tetrafluoropropane *see* Haloprop-ane.

Bromotrifluoroethyl methyl ether *see* Roflurane.

Bromotriphenylethylene *see* Broparestrol.

4-(6-Bromoveratryl)-4-[2-[2-(6,6-dimethyl-2-norpin-yl)ethoxy]ethyl]morpholinium bromide *see* Pina-verium bromide.

11-Bromovincamine *see* Brovincamine.

BROMOXANIDE** (4'-bromo-3-*tert*-butyl-2-hydroxy-6-methyl-5-nitro-2'-(trifluoromethyl)-benzanilide; 4'-bromo-3-*tert*-butyl-α',α',α'-tri-fluoro-5-nitro-2-cresoto-*o*-toluidide; SK&F-61636).

Bromoxine *see* Broxyquinoline.

BROMOXYNIL* (3,5-dibromo-4-hydroxybenzo-nitrile; 'brominal'; 'brominil'; 'buctril').

BROMPERIDOL*** (4-(*p*-bromophenyl)-1-[3-(*p*-fluorobenzoyl)propyl]-4-piperidinol; 4-[4-(*p*-bromophenyl)-4-hydroxypiperid-1-yl]-4'-fluoro-butyrophenone; bromoperidol; R-11333; 'im-promen').

BROMPERIDOL DECANOATE (R 46541).

BROMPHENIRAMINE*** (2-[*p*-bromo-α-(2-di-methylaminoethyl)benzyl]pyridine; parabrom-dylamine; bromdylamine; bromoprophenpyrid-amine; brompheniramine maleate; brompro-phenpyridamine).
See also Dexbrompheniramine.

'Bromphenobis' *see* Bismuth tribromophenate.

Bromphenol bismuth *see* Bismuth tribromophenate.

Bromphos *see* Bromofos.

Bromphthalein *see* Sulfobromphthalein.

Bromprophenpyridamine *see* Brompheniramine.

BROMPYRAZON* (5-amino-4-bromo-2-phenyl-pyridazin-3(2*H*)-one; brompyrazone).

BROMPYRAZON plus ISONORURON ('basa-nor').

'Bromsulfalein' *see* Sulfobromphthalein.

Bromsulfophthalein *see* Sulfobromphthalein.

'Bromsulfphthalein' *see* Sulfobromphthalein.

'Bromsuperlutin' *see* Bromo-MDAP.

Bromtannigel *see* Gelatin bromotannate.

'Brom-tetragnost' *see* Sulfobromphthalein.

'Bromthalein' *see* Sulfobromphthalein.

'Bromural' *see* Bromisoval.

Bromurea *see* Bromisoval.

Bromvalerylurea *see* Bromisoval.

Bromvaletone* *see* Bromisoval.

Bromvalurea *see* Bromisoval.

'Bronchiol' *see* Ethyl acetrizoate.

'Bronchocillin' *see* Penethamate hydriodide.

'Bronchodil' *see* Reproterol.

Bronchodilator-1313 *see* Phenisonone.

'Bronchodine' *see* Codeine.

'Broncholysin' *see* Acetylcysteine.

'Bronchopen' *see* Penethamate hydriodide.

'Bronchoretard' *see* Theophylline.

'Bronchoselectan' *see* Sodium acetrizoate.

'Bronchospasmin' *see* Reproterol.

'Broncopen' *see* Ampicillin guaiacolsulfonate.

'Broncoplus' *see* Stepronin.

'Broncovaleas' *see* Salbutamol.

BRONOPOL*** (2-bromo-2-nitro-1,3-propanedi-ol).

'Bronsecur' *see* Carbuterol.

Brontine *see* Deptropine.

'Brontyl' *see* Proxyphylline.

BROPARESTROL*** (1-bromo-2-(*p*-ethylphen-yl)-1,2-diphenylethylene; bromotriphenylethyl-ene; LN-107).

BROPERAMOLE*** (1-[3-[5-(3-bromophenyl)-2*H*-tetrazol-2-yl]propionyl]piperidine; TR-2378).

Brophenadion *see* Bromindione.

'Brophene' *see* Bromofos.

BROQUINALDOL*** (5,7-dibromo-2-methyl-8-quinolinol).

BROSOTAMIDE*** (5-bromo-2,3-cresotamide; 5-bromo-2-hydroxy-3-methylbenzamide).

BROSUXIMIDE*** (2-(*m*-bromophenyl)succin-imide).

BROTIANIDE** (3,4'-dibromo-5-chlorothiosalic-ylanilide acetate; 2-bromo-6-[(4-bromophenyl)-thiocarbamoyl]-4-chlorophenyl acetate; BAY Va-4059; FBA-4059; 'dirian').

BROTIZOLAM*** (2-bromo-4-(*o*-chlorophenyl)-9-methyl-6*H*-thieno[3,2-*f*]-*s*-triazolo[4,3-*a*]-[1,4]diazepine; WE-941; 'lendorm').

BROVANEXINE** (4-acetoxy-2',4'-dibromo-6'-[[(cyclohexyl)(methyl)amino]methyl]-3-methoxy-benzanilide; 2',4'-dibromo-α-(cyclohexylmethyl-amino)-*o*-vanillotoluidide acetate; UR-389).

BROVINCAMINE*** (11-bromovincamine).

'Brovon' *see* Atropine methonitrate.

BROXALDINE** (5,7-dibromomethyldihydroxy-quinoline; 5,7-dibromo-2-methyl-8-quinolinol benzoate; brobenzoxaldine).
See also under Broxyquinoline.

BROXATEROL** ((±)-3-bromo-α-[(*tert*-butyl-amino)methyl]-5-isoxazolemethanol).

'Broxil' *see* Phenethicillin.

'Broxoron' *see* 9α-Bromo-4-pregnene-3,11,20-tri-one.

BROXURIDINE** (5-bromo-2'-deoxyuridine; BUDR; NSC-38297).

BROXYQUINOLINE*** (5,7-dibromo-8-quino-linol; dibromohydroxyquinoline; bromoxine; AI-306; 'dibromoquin').

BROXYQUINOLINE plus BROXALDINE (AI-307; 'fenilor'; 'intestopan'; 'phenipan').

BROXYQUINOLINE plus BROXALDINE & CHLOROQUINE DIPHOSPHATE ('intesto-pan-Q').

BROXYQUINOLINE plus BROXALDINE & TETRACYCLINE ('sandocycline').

BRS-640 *see* Bradykinin.

'Brufacaine' *see* Guafecainol.

'**Brufaneuxol**' *see* Aminophenazone.
'**Brufen**' *see* Ibuprofen.
'**Brulidine**' *see* Dibrompropamidine.
Bruneomycin (tr) *see* Rufocromomycin.
BS-100-141 *see* Guanfacine.
BS-272 *see under* Proscillaridin.
BS-556 *see* Medrylamine.
BS-572 *see* Cyclandelate.
BS-749 *see* Metacetamol.
BS-4231 *see* Glisoxepide.
BS-5892 *see* Buformin.
BS-5930 *see* Orphenadrine.
BS-6534 *see* Bufenadrine.
BS-6748 *see* Xyloxemine.
BS-6987 *see* Deptropine.
BS-7029 *see* Cyheptamide.
BS-7051 *see* Hepzidine.
BS-7161-D *see* Pytamine.
BS-7173-D *see* Xylocoumarol.
BS-7561 *see* Tixadil.
BS-7573-a *see* Acridorex.
BS-7723 *see* Tropirine.
BS-7977D *see* Xipranolol.
BSA *see* Sulisobenzone.
BSP *see* Sulfobromphthalein.
BSSG *see* Sitogluside.
BT *see* Tetrazolium blue.
BT-325 *see* Sulfaperin.
BT-436 *see* Dehydroemetine.
BT-621 *see* Todralazine.
BTC *see* Benzalkonium chloride.
BTPABA *see* Bentiromide.
BTS-13622 *see* Hexaprofen.
BTS-17345 *see* Fluprofen.
BTS-18322 *see* Flurbiprofen.
BTS-40542 *see* Prochloraz.
BU-2231A *see* Talisomycin.
'**Bubulin**' *see under* Metrifonate.
BUCAINIDE*** (1-hexyl-4-[*N*-(2-methylpropyl)-benzimidoyl]piperazine; 1-hexyl-4-(*N*-isobutyl-benzimidoyl)piperazine).
BUCAINIDE MALEATE (RHC-G233).
'**Bucarban**' *see* Carbutamide.
BUCARPOLATE (2-(2-butoxyethoxy)ethyl 3,4-methylenedioxybenzoate; 2-(2-butoxyethoxy)-ethyl piperonylate).
'**Buccalsone**' *see* Hydrocortisone sodium succinate.
BUCETIN*** (4'-ethoxy-3'-hydroxybutyranilide; 3-hydroxy-*p*-butyrophenetidide).
BUCINDOLOL*** (1-(2-cyanophenoxy)-3-[(2-indol-3-yl-1,1-dimethylethyl)amino]-2-propanol; *o*-[2-hydroxy-3-[(2-indol-3-yl-1,1-dimethylethyl)-amino]propoxy]benzonitrile; bucindolol hydrochloride; MJ-13105).
BUCLADESINE*** (*N*-(9-β-D-ribofuranosyl-9*H*-purin-6-yl)butyramide cyclic 3',5'-(hydrogen phosphate) 2'-butyrate).
'**Buclamase**' *see* α-Amylase.
BUCLIZINE*** (1-(*p-tert*-butylbenzyl)-4-(*p*-chloro-α-phenylbenzyl)piperazine; NSC-25141; UCB-4445).
BUCLOSAMIDE*** (*N*-butyl-4-chlorosalicyl-amide; 'demycin').

BUCLOSAMIDE plus SALICYCLIC ACID ('ja-dit').
BUCLOXIC ACID*** (3-(3-chloro-4-cyclohexyl-benzoyl)propionic acid; 4-(3-chloro-4-cyclohex-ylphenyl)-4-oxobutyric acid; 'esfar').
See also Calcium bucloxate.
BUCOLOME*** (5-butyl-1-cyclohexylbarbituric acid; BCP; 'paramidine').
BUCRICAINE** (9-(butylamino)-1,2,3,4-tetra-hydroacridine).
BUCRILATE*** (isobutyl 2-cyanoacrylate; bucr-ylate; IBC).
'**Bucrol**' *see* Carbutamide.
BUCROMARONE*** (2-[4-[3-(dibutylamino)-propoxy]-3,5-dimethylbenzoyl]chromone).
Bucrylate *see* Bucrilate.
'**Buctril**' *see* Bromoxynil.
BUCUMOLOL*** (1-*tert*-butylamino-3-(5-meth-ylcoumarin-8-yloxy)-2-propanol; 8-[3-(*tert*-but-ylamino)-2-hydroxypropoxy]-5-methylcoumar-in; bucumolol hydrochloride; C-3 Sankyo; CS-359).
'**Budale**' *see* Paracetamol.
BUDESONIDE*** ((*RS*)-11β,16α,17,21-tetra-hydroxypregna-1,4-diene-3,20-dione cyclic 16,17-acetal with butyraldehyde; 16α,17α-butyl-idenedioxy-11β,21-dihydroxypregna-1,4-diene-3,20-dione; S-1320; 'pulmicort').
BUDIPINE*** (1-*tert*-butyl-4,4-diphenylpiperid-ine).
BUDR *see* Broxuridine.
BUDRALAZINE*** (1-[2-(1,3-dimethyl-but-2-en-ylidene)hydrazino]phthalazine; 4-methyl-3-pen-ten-2-one (1-phthalazinyl)hydrazone).
'**Bufedil**' *see* Buflomedil.
'**Bufedon**' *see* Buphenine.
Bufenadine* *see* Bufenadrine.
BUFENADRINE*** (2-(*o-tert*-butyl-α-phenyl-benzyloxy)-*N,N*-dimethylethylamine; *o-tert*-but-yldiphenhydramine; bufenadine; BS-6534).
BUFENIODE*** (4-hydroxy-3,5-diiodo-α-[1-(1-methyl-3-phenylpropylamino)ethyl]benzyl alco-hol; diiodobuphenine; HF-241; 'proclival').
BUFETOLOL** (2-[[*o*-(3-*tert*-butylamino-2-hydr-oxypropoxy)phenoxy]methyl]tetrahydrofuran; 1-(*tert*-butylamino)-3-(*o*-(tetrahydrofurfuryl-oxy)phenoxy)-2-propanol; bufuronol; bufetolol hydrochloride; Y-6124; 'adbiol'; 'adobiol').
BUFEXAMAC*** (2-(*p*-butoxyphenyl)aceto-hydroxamic acid; CP-1044-J3; 'droxaryl'; 'fexi-mac'; 'malipuran'; 'norfemac'; 'parfenac').
BUFEZOLAC*** (1-isobutyl-3,4-diphenylpyraz-ole-4-acetic acid; 1-(2-methylpropyl)-3,4-diphen-ylpyrazole-4-acetic acid).
BUFLOMEDIL*** (3-pyrrolidin-1-ylpropyl 2,4,6-trimethoxyphenyl ketone; 2',4',6'-trimethoxy-4-pyrrolidin-1-ylbutyrophenone; 1-[3-(2,4,6-tri-methoxybenzoyl)propyl]pyrrolidine; buflomedil hydrochloride; LL-1656; 'bufedil'; 'fonzylane'; 'loftyl').
BUFOGENIN*** (14,15β-epoxy-3β-hydroxy-5β-bufa-10,22-dienolide; 'respigon').
BUFORMIN** (1-butylbiguanide; *N*[1]-butylbi-

guanide; BS-5892; DBV; H-224; W-37).

'Buformin' *see* Chlormebuform.

BUFOTENINE (*N*,*N*-dimethylserotonin; 5-hydr-oxy-*N*,*N*-dimethyltryptamine; mappine).

BUFROLIN** (6-butyl-1,4,7,10-tetrahydro-4,10-dioxo-1,7-phenanthroline-2,8-dicarboxylic acid; bufrolin disodium; bufrolin sodium; ICI-74917).

BUFURALOL** (2-(2-*tert*-butylamino-1-hydr-oxyethyl)-7-ethylbenzofuran; 2-(*tert*-butyl-amino)-1-(7-ethylbenzofuran-2-yl)ethanol; α-[(*tert*-butylamino)methyl]-7-ethyl-2-benzofuran-methanol; Ro 3-4787; 'angium').

Bufuronol *see* Bufetolol.

BUFYLLINE* (theophylline-aminoisobutanol; theophylline-isobutanolamine; ambuphylline).

BULBOCAPNINE ((*S*)-6,7,7a,8-tetrahydro-11-methoxy-7-methyl-5*H*-benzo[*g*]-1,3-benzodioxol-o[6,4,5-*de*]quinolin-12-ol; 10-methoxy-1,2-(methylenedioxy)-6aα-aporphin-11-ol).

BUMADIZONE*** (butylmalonic acid mono(1,2-diphenylhydrazide); B-64114).

BUMADIZONE CALCIUM ('eumotol').

BUMECAINE** (1-butyl-2′,4′,6′-trimethyl-2-pyr-rolidinecarboxanilide; 1-butyl-*N*-(2,4,6-trimeth-ylphenyl)-2-pyrrolidinecarboxamide; CS-611).

BUMEPIDIL*** (8-*tert*-butyl-7,8-dihydro-5-methyl-6*H*-pyrrolo[3,2-*e*]-*s*-triazolo[1,5-*a*]pyr-imidine).

BUMETANIDE*** (3-(butylamino)-4-phenoxy-5-sulfamoylbenzoic acid; Ro 10-6338; 'bumex'; 'burinex'; 'fordiuran').

BUMETRIZOLE*** (2-*tert*-butyl-6-(5-chloro-2*H*-benzotriazol-2-yl)-*p*-cresol; 2-(5-chloro-2*H*-benzotriazol-2-yl)-6-(1,1-dimethylethyl)-4-meth-ylphenol; 'tinuvin 326').

'Bumex' *see* Bumetanide.

Bunaftide *see* Bunaftine.

BUNAFTINE*** (*N*-butyl-*N*-(2-diethylamino-ethyl)-1-naphthamide; *N*-butyl-*N'*,*N'*-diethyl-*N*-naphth-1-oyl-ethylenediamine; bunaftide; EU-16738).

BUNAFTINE CITRATE ('meregon').

BUNAMIDINE*** (*N*,*N*-dibutyl-4-hexyloxy-1-naphthamidine; bunamidine hydrochloride; BW-62-415; NSC-106571).

BUNAMIODYL*** (3-(3-butyramido-2,4,6-triio-dophenyl)-2-ethylacrylic acid; 2-(3-butyramido-3,4,6-triiodophenylmethylene)butyric acid; bu-niodyl; bunamiodyl sodium).

BUNAPSILATE(S)** (3,7-di-*tert*-butylnaphthal-ene-1,5-disulfonic acid, esters and salts).

BUNAZOSIN** (1-(4-amino-6,7-dimethoxyquin-azolin-2-yl)-4-butyrylhexahydro-1*H*-1,4-diazep-ine; 4-amino-2-(4-butyrylhexahydro-1,4-diazep-in-1-yl)-6,7-dimethoxyquinazoline; E-643).

Buniodyl* *see* Bunamiodyl.

BUNITROLOL*** (*o*-(3-*tert*-butylamino-2-hydr-oxypropoxy)benzonitrile; 1-*tert*-butylamino-3-(*o*-cyanophenoxy)-2-propanol; 2-nitrilo-*N*-*tert*-butylphenoxypropanolamine; Ko-1366; 'stres-son').

BUNOLOL*** ((±)-5-[3-(*tert*-butylamino)-2-hydroxypropoxy]-3,4-dihydro-1(2*H*)-naphtha-lenone; bunolol hydrochloride; W-6412A).

See also Levobunolol.

'Bunt-cure' *see* Hexachlorobenzene.

'Bunt-no-more' *see* Hexachlorobenzene.

BUPARVAQUONE** (2-[(4-*tert*-butylcyclohex-yl)methyl]-3-hydroxy-1,4-naphthoquinone; BW-720C).

'Bupatol' *see* Bamethan.

BUPHENINE*** (*p*-hydroxy-α-[1-(1-methyl-3-phenylpropylamino)ethyl]benzyl alcohol; 1-(*p*-hydroxyphenyl)-2-(1-methyl-3-phenylpropyl-amino)-1-propanol; nylidrin; buphenine hydro-chloride; phenyl-sec-butylnorsuprifen; SK&F-1700-A).

BUPICOMIDE** (5-butyl-2-pyridinecarbox-amide; 5-butylpicolinamide; fusaric acid amide; Sch-10595).

BUPIVACAINE*** (1-butyl-2-(2,6-xylylcarbamo-yl)piperidine; 1-butyl-2′,6′-pipecoloxylidide; *N*-butylpipecolic acid 2,6-dimethylanilide; bupiva-caine hydrochloride; LAC-43; WIN-11318).

BUPRANOLOL*** (3-*tert*-butylamino-1-(2-chloro-5-methylphenoxy)-2-propanol; 1-*tert*-butylamino-3-(6-chloro-*m*-toloxy)-2-propanol; B-1312; KL-255; 'betadran'; 'betadrenol'; 'oph-torenin'; 'panimit').

See also under Bemetizide.

BUPRENORPHINE*** (21-cyclopropyl-7α-((*S*)-1-hydroxy-1,2,2-trimethylpropyl)-6,14-*endo*-eth-ano-6,7,8,14-tetrahydrooripavine; buprenor-phine hydrochloride; CL-112302; NIH-8805; RX-6029-M; UM-952; 'temgesic').

Bupropin* *see* Amfebutamone.

Bupropion* *see* Amfebutamone.

BUQUINERAN*** (1-butyl-3-[1-(6,7-dimethoxy-quinazolin-4-yl)piperid-4-yl]urea; 4-[4-[[(butyl-amino)carbonyl]amino]piperid-1-yl]-6,7-dimeth-oxyquinazoline; UK-14275).

BUQUINOLATE*** (ethyl 4-hydroxy-6,7-di-isobutoxyquinoline-3-carboxylate; EU-1093; U-1093; 'bonaid').

BURAMATE** (2-hydroxyethyl benzylcarbamate; benzylcarbamoylethanol; AC-601; NSC-30223).

'Burgodin' *see* Bezitramide.

BURIMAMIDE (1-(4-imidazol-4(5)-ylbutyl)-3-methylthiourea; 4(5)-[4-(3-methylthioureido)-butyl]imidazole).

'Burinex' *see* Bumetanide.

BURODILINE** (2-pyrrolidin-1-ylethyl 4-butoxy-3,5-dimethoxybenzoate; 1-pyrrolidineethan-ol 4-butoxy-3,5-dimethoxybenzoate; 'vasopent-ol').

'Buronil' *see* Melperone.

'Bursoline' *see* Diglycocoll hydriodide iodine.

'Buscalide' *see under* Proglumide.

'Buscapine' *see* Scopolamine butyl bromide.

'Buscolysin' *see* Scopolamine butyl bromide.

'Buscopan' *see* Scopolamine butyl bromide.

'Buscopax' *see under* Scopolamine butyl bromide.

BUSERELIN*** (6-[*O*-(1,1-dimethylethyl)-D-ser-ine]-9-(*N*-ethyl-L-prolinamide)-10-deglycin-amidoluteinizing hormone releasing factor (pig); 5-oxo-L-prolyl-L-histidyl-L-tryptophyl-L-seryl-

L-tyrosyl-(*O-tert*-butyl-D-seryl)-L-leucyl-L-arginyl-*N*-ethyl-L-prolinamide).

BUSERELIN ACETATE* (buserelin monoacetate (salt); HOE-766).

BUSPIRONE** (4-[4-(7,9-dioxo-8-azaspiro-[4.5]dec-7-yl)butyl]-1-pyrimidin-2-ylpiperazine; 2-[4-[4-(7,9-dioxo-8-azaspiro[4.5]dec-8-yl)butyl]-piperazin-1-yl]pyrimidine; 8-[4-[4-(pyrimidin-2-yl)piperazin-1-yl]butyl]-8-azaspiro[4.5]decane-7,9-dione; buspirone hydrochloride; MJ-9022).

BUSULFAN*** (1,4-bis(methanesulfonyloxy)butane; dimethylsulfonyloxybutane; tetramethylene dimesilate; busulphan; myelosan; sulfabutin; CB-2041; GT 41; NSC-750).

Busulphan* *see* Busulfan.

Butabarbital* *see* Secbutabarbital.

'Butabarpal' *see* Secbutabarbital.

BUTACAINE*** (3-dibutylaminopropyl *p*-aminobenzoate; butaprobenz; butocaine; butacaine sulfate).

BUTACETIN* (4'-*tert*-butoxyacetanilide; BW-63-90; NSC-106564; 'tromal').

Butachlor* *see* Butoclor.

BUTACID (*p*-dibutylsulfamoylbenzoic acid; 'long-acid').

'Butacide' *see* Piperonyl butoxide.

BUTACLAMOL** (3α-*tert*-butyl-2,3,4,4aβ,8,9,13bα,14-octahydro-1*H*-benzo[6,7]cyclohepta-[1,2,3-*de*]pyrido[2,1-*a*]isoquinolin-3-ol; AY-23028).

'Butacote' *see* Phenylbutazone.

BUTADIAZAMIDE*** (*N*-(5-butyl-1,3,4-thiadiazol-2-yl)-*p*-chlorobenzenesulfonamide; 5-butyl-2-(*p*-chlorobenzenesulfonamido)-1,3,4-thiadiazole).

Butadion (tr) *see* Phenylbutazone.

BUTAFOSFAN*** ([1-(butylamino)-1-methylethyl]phosphinic acid; 'coforta').

BUTALAMINE*** (5-(2-dibutylaminoethylamino)-3-phenyl-1,2,4-oxadiazole; butalamine hydrochloride; LA-1221; 'adrevil'; 'surheme').

BUTALAMINE plus PAPAVERINE ('oxadilene').

BUTALBITAL*** (5-allyl-5-(2-methylpropyl)barbituric acid; 5-allyl-5-isobutylbarbituric acid; alisobumal; allylbarbital; allylbarbituric acid; itobarbital; tetrallobarbital; 'sandoptal').

'Butalidon' *see* Phenylbutazone.

BUTALLYLONAL* (5-(2-bromoallyl)-5-*sec*-butylbarbituric acid; 5-(2-bromoallyl)-5-(1-methylpropyl)barbituric acid; butylallonal sodium).

Butamben* *see* Butylcaine.

Butamid (tr) *see* Tolbutamide.

BUTAMIN (3-(dimethylamino)-1,2-dimethylpropyl *p*-aminobenzoate; butamin hydrochloride).

BUTAMIRATE*** (2-[2-(diethylamino)ethoxy]-ethyl 2-phenylbutyrate; 2-[2-(diethylamino)eth-oxy]ethyl phenylethylacetate; butamyrate).

BUTAMIRATE CITRATE (Abbott 36581; HH-197; 'acodeen'; 'sinecod').

BUTAMISOLE*** ((−)-2-methyl-3'-(2,3,5,6-tetrahydroimidazo[2,1-*b*]thiazol-6-yl)propionanilide; (−)-2,3,5,6-tetrahydro-6-[3-[(2-methylpropionyl)amino]phenyl]imidazo[2,1-*b*]thiazole;

butamisole hydrochloride; CL-206214).

Butamiverine* *see* Butaverine.

BUTAMOXANE*** (2-butylaminomethyl-1,4-benzodioxan; F-1052).

Butamyrate* *see* Butamirate.

Butanamide *see* Butyramide.

1-Butanecarboxylic acid *see* Valeric acid.

1,4-Butanediamine *see* Putrescine.

Butanedinitrile *see* Succinonitrile.

Butanedioic acid *see* Succinic acid.

2,3-BUTANEDIONE (biacetyl; diacetyl).

2,3-Butanedione bis(4-(2-piperid-1-yl-ethyl)thiosemicarbazone) *see* Bitipazone.

2,3-Butanedione monoxime *see* Diacetyl monoxime.

erythro-**1,2,3,4-Butanetetrol** *see* Erythritol.

threo-**1,2,3,4-Butanetetrol** *see* Threitol.

BUTANILICAINE*** (2-butylamino-6'-chloro-*o*-acetotoluidide; *N*-butylaminoacetyl-6-chloro-*o*-toluidine; 'hostacaine').

Butanimide *see* Succinimide.

BUTANIXIN** (2-(*p*-butylanilino)nicotinic acid).

Butanoic acid *see* Butyric acid.

1-BUTANOL (butyl alcohol).

2-BUTANOL (*sec*-butyl alcohol).

BUTANSERIN** (3-[4-[4-(*p*-fluorobenzoyl)piperid-1-yl]butyl]-2,4(1*H*,3*H*)-quinazolinedione).

BUTANTRONE*** (10-butyryl-1,8-dihydroxy-anthrone).

BUTAPERAZINE** (1-[10-[3-(4-methylpiperazin-1-yl)propyl]phenothiazin-2-yl]-1-butanone; butaperazine maleate; butyrylperazine; AHR-712; AHR-3000; Bayer-1362; Riker-595).

'Butaphyllamine' *see* Bufylline.

Butaprobenz *see* Butacaine.

'Butapyrine' *see under* Aminophenazone.

BUTAVERINE*** (butyl 3-phenyl-3-piperid-1-yl-propionate; butamiverine).

BUTAXAMINE*** (2-(*tert*-butylamino)-1-(2,5-dimethoxyphenyl)-1-propanol; α-[1-(*tert*-butyl-amino)ethyl]-2,5-dimethoxybenzyl alcohol; *N*-*tert*-butylmethoxamine; butoxamine; butoxamine hydrochloride; BW-64-9; NSC-106565).

'Butazidamina' *see* Benzydamine phenylbutazone enolate.

'Butazolidine' *see* Phenylbutazone.

'Butellin' *see* Butacaine.

2-Butenamide *see* Crotonamide.

Butenedioic acids *see* Fumaric acid; Maleic acid.

Butenemal* *see* Vinbarbital.

'Butenil' *see* Butethal.

cis-**2-Butenoic acid** *see* Isocrotonic acid.

trans-**2-Butenoic acid** *see* Crotonic acid.

5-(2-Butenyl)-5-ethylbarbituric acid *see* Barotal.

2-(2-Butenyl)-4-hydroxy-3-methyl-2-cyclopenten-1-one *see* Cinerolone.

2-(2-Butenyl)-4-hydroxy-3-methyl-2-cyclopenten-1-one esters *see* Cinerin I; Cinerin II.

Butenylideneisoniazid *see* Crotoniazide.

3-(2-butenyl)-2-methyl-4-oxo-2-cyclopenten-1-yl esters *see* Cinerin I; Cinerin II.

p-**(2-Buten-2-yl)phenyl acetate** *see* Fenabutene.

BUTERIZINE** (2-butyl-5-[[4-(diphenylmethyl)-

piperazin-1-yl]methyl]-1-ethylbenzimidazole; R-38198).

'Butesamid' *see* Ethyl butylethylmalonamate.

'Butesin' *see* Butylcaine.

BUTETAMATE*** (2-(diethylamino)ethyl 2-phenylbutyrate; 2-(diethylamino)ethyl phenylethylacetate; butethamate; butetamate citrate).

BUTETAMATE plus SULFOGAIACOL ('latuss').

BUTETHAL* (5-butyl-2-ethylbarbituric acid; butobarbitone; butobarbital).

Butethamate* *see* Butetamate.

BUTETHAMINE* (2-(isobutylamino)ethyl *p*-aminobenzoate; ibylcaine; 'monocaine').

'Butex' *see* Parabens.

BUTHALITAL SODIUM*** (5-allyl-5-isobutyl-2-thiobarbituric acid; 5-allyl-5-(2-methylpropyl)-2-thiobarbituric acid sodium derivative; buthalitone; thialbutone; thialisobumal; thiobutone).

Buthalitone* *see* Buthalital sodium.

Buthiazide* *see* Butizide.

BUTHIOPURINE (6-(4-carboxybutylthio)purine; 5-(purin-6-ylthio)valeric acid; NSC-130678).

'Buthoid' *see* Bufylline.

BUTIBUFEN*** (2-(*p*-isobutylphenyl)butyric acid).

'Butidrate' *see under* Butidrine.

BUTIDRINE*** (α-[(*sec*-butylamino)methyl]-5,6,7,8-tetrahydro-2-naphthalenemethanol; 2-(*sec*-butylamino)-1-(5,6,7,8-tetrahydro-2-naphthyl)ethanol; 2-(1-methylpropylamino)-1-(5,6,7,8-tetrahydronaphth-2-yl)ethanol; 5,6,7,8-tetrahydro-α-[(1-methylpropylamino)methyl]-2-naphthalenemethanol; butydrine; hydrobutamine; idrobutamina; CO-405).

BUTIDRINE plus PENTAERYTHRITYL TETRANITRATE ('butidrate').

BUTIKACIN*** (*O*-3-amino-3-deoxy-α-D-glucopyranosyl(1→6)-*O*-[(6-amino-6-deoxy-α-D-glucopyranosyl(1→4)-*N*¹-[(*S*)-4-amino-2-hydroxybutyl]-2-deoxy-D-streptamine; UK-18892).

Butilchlorofos (tr) *see* Butonate.

BUTILFENIN*** (*N*-[2-[(4-butylphenyl)amino]-2-oxoethyl]-*N*-(carboxymethyl)glycine; [[[(*p*-butylphenyl)carbamoyl]methyl]imino]diacetic acid; *p*-BIDA; 'hepatolite').

Butilklorophos (tr) *see* Butonate.

BUTIN (3',4',7-trihydroxyflavanone).

BUTINOLINE*** (1,1-diphenyl-4-pyrrolidin-1-yl-but-2-yn-1-ol).

'Butipyrine' *see* Butylchloralamidopyrine.

Butirao *see* Buturon.

BUTIROSIN*** (mixture of A and B forms of *O*-[2,6-diamino-2,6-dideoxy-α-D-glucopyranosyl-(1→4)]-*O*-[β-D-xylofuranosyl-(1→5)]-*N*¹-(4-amino-2-hydroxybutyryl)-2-deoxystreptamine; ambutyrosin; butirosin sulfate; CI-642).

'Butisol' *see* Secbutabarbital.

'Butisulfina' *see* Carbutamide.

BUTIXIRATE*** (α-ethyl-4-biphenylacetic acid compound with *trans*-4-phenylcyclohexylamine (1:1); xenbucin salt with *trans*-4-phenylcyclohexylamine; xenbucin salt with *trans*-4-phenylcyclo-

hexylamine; *trans*-4-phenylcyclohexylamine 2-(*p*-biphenylyl)butyrate; Mg-5771; 'flectar').

BUTIZIDE*** (6-chloro-3,4-dihydro-3-isobutyl-2*H*-1,2,4-benzothiadiazine-7-sulfonamide 1,1-dioxide; buthiazide; isobutylhydrochlorothiazide; thiabutizide; thiobutazine).

BUTIZIDE plus METIPRANOLOL ('torrat').

BUTIZIDE plus SPIRONOLACTONE ('aldosone').

Butobarbital *see* Butethal.

Butobarbitone* *see* Butethal.

'Butoben' *see* Butyl paraben.

BUTOBENDINE*** (ethylenebis[(methylimino)-(2-ethylethylene)] bis(3,4,5-trimethoxybenzoate)).

Butocaine *see* Butacaine.

BUTOCIN (ethyl *N*-[5-(purin-6-ylthio)valeryl]glycinate; *N*-[1-oxo-5(1*H*)-(purin-6-ylthio)pentyl]-glycine ethyl ester; NSC-172755).

BUTOCLOR* (*N*-(butoxymethyl)-2-chloro-2',6'-diethylacetanilide; *N*-(butoxymethyl)-2-chloro-*N*-(2,6-diethylphenyl)acetamide; *N*-(butoxymethyl)-*N*-(2-chloroacetyl)-2,6-diethylaniline; butachlor; 'machete').

BUTOCONAZOLE*** ((±)-1-[4-(4-chlorophenyl)-2-[(2,6-dichlorophenyl)thio]butyl]imidazole; butoconazole nitrate; RS-35887).

BUTOCROLOL*** (9-[3-(*tert*-butylamino)-2-hydroxypropoxy]-4-hydroxy-7-methyl-5*H*-furo[3,2-*g*]benzopyran-5-one; 1-(*tert*-butylamino)-3-(4-hydroxy-7-methyl-5-oxofuro[3,2-*g*]-benzopyran-9-yloxy)-2-propanol).

BUTOCTAMIDE*** (*N*-(2-ethylhexyl)-3-hydroxybutyramide).

BUTOCTAMIDE HEMISUCCINATE (L-2; M-2H).

BUTOFILOLOL*** ((±)-2'-[3-(*tert*-butylamino)-2-hydroxypropoxy]-5'-fluorobutyrophenone; 1-(*tert*-butylamino)-3-(4-fluoro-2-propionylphenoxy)-2-propanol).

BUTOFILOLOL MALEATE ('cafide').

Butoforme* *see* Butylcaine.

BUTOMELIDE (tr) (4-butoxy-4'-(4-methylpiperazin-1-yl)thiocarbanilide; 1-[*p*-[3-(*p*-butoxyphenyl)thioureido]phenyl]-4-methylpiperazine).

BUTONATE** (dimethyl (2,2,2-trichloro-1-hydroxyethyl)phosphonate butyrate; butilchlorofos; butilklorophos; butylchlorophos; metrifonate butyrate; ENT-20852; F-139; T-113).

BUTOPAMINE*** ((*R*)-*p*-hydroxy-α-[[[3-(*p*-hydroxyphenyl)-1-methylpropyl]amino]methyl]benzyl alcohol; LY-131126).

BUTOPIPRINE*** (2-butoxyethyl α-phenyl-1-piperidineacetate; LD-2351).

BUTOPROZINE*** (*p*-[3-(dibutylamino)propoxy]phenyl) 2-ethyl-3-indolizinyl ketone; 3-[*p*-(3-dibutylaminopropoxy)benzoyl]-2-ethylindolizine; benzoylindolizine; butoprozine hydrochloride; L-9394).

BUTOPYRAMMONIUM IODIDE*** (butyl(2,3-dimethyl-5-oxo-1-phenyl-3-pyrazolin-4-yl)dimethylammonium iodide; aminophenazone quaternary butyl iodide).

BUTOPYRONOXYL* (butyl 4,5-dihydro-6,6-dimethyl-4-oxopyran-2-carboxylate; butyl mesityl oxide; indalone).

BUTORPHANOL** ((−)-17-(cyclobutylmethyl)-morphinan-3,14-diol; butorphanol tartrate; (−)-BC-2627; levo-BC-2627; 'stadol').

Butoxamine* *see* Butaxamine.

4′-*tert*-Butoxyacetanilide *see* Butacetin.

p-**Butoxybenzoic acid 3-diethylamino-1,2-dimethylpropyl ester ethiodide** *see* Quateron.

[3-[(*p*-Butoxybenzoyl)oxy]-2,3-dimethylpropyl]triethylammonium iodide *see* Quateron.

8-(*p*-Butoxybenzyl)-3α-hydroxy-1α*H*,5α*H*-tropanium bromide (−)-tropate *see* Butropium bromide.

6-Butoxy-3-(2,6-diaminopyrid-3-ylazo)pyridine *see* Neotropin.

2-Butoxy-*N*-(2-diethylaminoethyl)cinchoninamide *see* Cinchocaine.

4-Butoxy-3,5-dimethoxybenzoic acid 2-pyrrolidin-1-ylethyl ester *see* Burodiline.

4-Butoxy-4′-dimethylamino-2-thiocarbanilide *see* Thiambutosine.

α-[2-(2-Butoxyethoxy)ethoxy]-4,5-methylenedioxy-2-propyltoluene *see* Piperonyl butoxide.

5-[[2-(2-Butoxyethoxy)ethoxy]methyl]-6-propyl-1,3-benzodioxole *see* Piperonyl butoxide.

2-(2-Butoxyethoxy)ethyl 3,4-methylenedioxybenzoate *see* Bucarpolate.

2-(2-Butoxyethoxy)ethyl piperonylate *see* Bucarpolate.

2-Butoxyethyl nicotinate *see* Nicoboxil.

2-Butoxyethyl α-phenyl-1-piperidineacetate *see* Butopiprine.

1-(2-Butoxy-2-hydroxypropyl)-5-ethyl-5-phenylbarbituric acid carbamate ester *see* Febarbamate.

BUTOXYLATE** (butyl 1-(3-cyano-3,3-diphenylpropyl)-4-phenylpiperidine-4-carboxylate; butyl difenoxilate).

1-*tert*-Butoxy-3-methoxy-2-propanol *see* Terbuprol.

N-**(Butoxymethyl)-*N*-(2-chloroacetyl)-2,6-diethylaniline** *see* Butoclor.

N-**(Butoxymethyl)-2-chloro-2′,6′-diethylacetanilide** *see* Butoclor.

N-**(Butoxymethyl)-2-chloro-*N*-(2,6-diethylphenyl)-acetamide** *see* Butoclor.

4-Butoxy-4′-(4-methylpiperazin-1-yl)thiocarbanilide *see* Butomelide.

N-**[2-(*p*-Butoxyphenoxy)acetyl]-*N*-(2,5-diethoxyphenyl)-*N′*,*N′*-diethylethylenediamine** *see* Fenoxedil.

1-[2-[[2-(*p*-Butoxyphenoxy)acetyl]-(*o*-methoxyphenyl)amino]ethyl]pyrrolidine *see* Fexicaine.

N-**(2-(*p*-Butoxyphenoxy)acetyl)-*N*-(2-pyrrolidin-1-ylethyl)-*o*-anisidine** *see* Fexicaine.

2-(*p*-Butoxyphenoxy)-*N*-(2,5-diethoxyphenyl)-*N*-(2-diethylaminoethyl)acetamide *see* Fenoxedil.

6-[[2-[[3-(*p*-Butoxyphenoxy)-2-hydroxypropyl]amino]ethyl]amino]-1,3-dimethyluracil *see* Pirepolol.

2-(*p*-Butoxyphenoxy)-*N*-(*o*-methoxyphenyl)-*N*-(2-pyrrolidin-1-ylethyl)acetamide *see* Fexicaine.

1-Butoxy-3-phenoxy-2-propanol *see* Febuprol.

2-(*p*-Butoxyphenyl)acetohydroxamic acid *see* Bufexamac.

1-(*p*-Butoxyphenyl)-3-(*p*-dimethylaminophenyl)-2-thiourea *see* Thiambutosine.

p-**Butoxyphenyl 3-morpholinopropyl ether** *see* Pramocaine.

1-[*p*-[3-(*p*-Butoxyphenyl)thioureido]phenyl]-4-methylpiperazine *see* Butomelide.

4′-Butoxy-3-piperid-1-ylpropiophenone *see* Dyclonine.

BUTRIPTYLINE** (10,11-dihydro-*N*,*N*,β-trimethyl-5*H*-dibenzo[*a*,*d*]cycloheptene-5-propylamine; 5-[3-(dimethylamino)-1-methylpropyl]-10,11-dihydro-5*H*-dibenzo[*a*,*d*]cycloheptene; 5-[4-(dimethylamino)isobutyl]-10,11-dihydro-5*H*-dibenzo[*a*,*d*]cycloheptene; DL-butriptyline; butriptyline hydrochloride; AY-62014).

BUTROPIUM BROMIDE** (8-(*p*-butoxybenzyl)-3α-hydroxy-1α*H*,5α*H*-tropanium bromide (−)-tropate; 'choliopan').

Butter yellow *see* *p*-(Dimethylamino)azobenzene.

BUTURON* (1-(*p*-chlorophenyl)-3-methyl-3-(1-methyl-2-propynyl)urea; butirao; 'butyron'; 'eptapur').

BUTURON plus ISONORURON ('basfitox').

Butydrine *see* Butidrine.

Butylacetic acid *see* Hexanoic acid.

tert-**Butylacetic acid esters and salts** *see* Tebutate(s).

Butyl alcohols *see* 1-Butanol; 2-Butanol; 2-Methyl-2-propanol.

N-**Butylaminoacetyl-6-chloro-*o*-toluidine** *see* Butanilicaine.

Butyl *p*-aminobenzoate *see* Butylcaine.

p-**Butylaminobenzoic acid esters** *see* Benzonatate; Paridocaine; Tetracaine.

4-[4-[[(Butylamino)carbonyl]amino]piperid-1-yl]-6,7-dimethoxyquinazoline *see* Buquineran.

[1-[(Butylamino)carbonyl]-1*H*-benzimidazol-2-yl]-carbamic acid methyl ester *see* Benomyl.

2-Butylamino-6′-chloro-*o*-acetotoluidide *see* Butanilicaine.

2-(*tert*-Butylamino)-6-chloro-4-(ethylamino)-*s*-triazine *see* Terbuthylazine.

3-*tert*-Butylamino-1-(2-chloro-5-methylphenoxy)-2-propanol *see* Bupranolol.

(±)-2-*tert*-Butylamino-3′-chloropropiophenone *see* Amfebutamone.

1-*tert*-Butylamino-3-(6-chloro-*m*-toloxy)-2-propanol *see* Bupranolol.

1-*tert*-Butylamino-3-(*o*-cyanophenoxy)-2-propanol *see* Bunitrolol.

1-(Butylamino)cyclohexylphosphonic acid dibutyl ester *see* Aminophon.

1-*tert*-Butylamino-3-[*p*-(3-cyclohexylureido)phenoxy]-2-propanol *see* Talinolol.

1-*tert*-Butylamino-3-(*o*-cyclopentylphenoxy)-2-propanol *see* Penbutolol.

1-(*tert*-Butylamino-3-(2,5-dichlorophenoxy)-2-propanol *see* Cloranolol.

1-(*tert*-Butylamino-3-(3,4-dihydro-2(1*H*)-oxoquinolin-5-yl)-2-propanol *see* Carteolol.

2-(*tert*-Butylamino)-1-(3,5-dihydroxyphenyl)ethanol

see Terbutaline.

2-(*tert*-Butylamino)-1-(2,5-dimethoxyphenyl)-1-propanol *see* Butaxamine.

1-(*tert*-Butylamino)-3-(2,3-dimethylphenoxy)-2-propanol *see* Xibenolol.

2-(*sec*-Butylamino)-4-ethylamino-6-methoxy-*s*-triazine *see* Secbumeton.

2-(*tert*-Butylamino)-4-ethylamino-6-methoxy-*s*-triazine *see* Terbumeton.

2-*tert*-Butylamino-4-ethylamino-6-(methylthio)-*s*-triazine *see* Terbutryn.

2-(*tert*-Butylamino)-1-(7-ethylbenzofuran-2-yl)ethanol *see* Bufuralol.

α-[1-(*tert*-Butylamino)ethyl]-2,5-dimethoxybenzyl alcohol *see* Butaxamine.

4-(Butylamino)-1-ethyl-6-methyl-1*H*-pyrazolo[3,4-*b*]pyridine-5-carboxylic acid ethyl ester *see* Tracazolate.

4-(Butylamino)-1-ethyl-1*H*-pyrazolo[3,4-*b*]pyridine-5-carboxylic acid ethyl ester *see* Cartazolate.

1-(*tert*-Butylamino)-3-(4-fluoro-2-propionylphenoxy)-2-propanol *see* Butofilolol.

1-(*tert*-Butylamino)-3-[*o*-(6-hydrazinopyridazin-3-yl)phenoxy]-2-propanol *see* Prizidilol.

5-(2-*tert*-Butylamino-1-hydroxyethyl)-*N*-carbamoyl-2-hydroxyaniline *see* Carbuterol.

2-(2-*tert*-Butylamino-1-hydroxyethyl)-7-ethylbenzofuran *see* Bufuralol.

1-[5-(2-*tert*-Butylamino-1-hydroxyethyl)-2-hydroxyphenyl]urea *see* Carbuterol.

5-[2-(*tert*-Butylamino)-1-hydroxyethyl]-*m*-phenylene bis(dimethylcarbamate) *see* Bambuterol.

5-(2-*tert*-Butylamino-1-hydroxyethyl-*m*-phenylene diisobutyrate *see* Ibuterol.

5-[2-(*tert*-Butylamino)-1-hydroxyethyl]-*m*-phenylene dipivalate *see* Divabuterol.

4-(2-(*tert*-Butylamino)-1-hydroxyethyl)-*o*-phenylene di-*p*-toluate *see* Bitolterol.

5-[2-(*tert*-Butylamino)-1-hydroxyethyl]-*m*-phenylene di-*p*-toluate *see* Tobuterol.

5-[2-(*tert*-Butylamino)-1-hydroxyethyl]resorcinol diester with *p*-toluic acid *see* Tobuterol.

5-(2-(*tert*-Butylamino)-1-hydroxyethyl)resorcinol diisobutyrate *see* Ibuterol.

2-*tert*-Butylamino-1-(5-hydroxy-6-hydroxymethylpyrid-2-yl)ethanol *see* Pirbuterol.

1-(*tert*-Butylamino)-3-(4-hydroxy-7-methyl-5-oxofuro[3,2-*g*]benzopyran-9-yloxy)-2-propanol *see* Butocrolol.

2-Butylamino-1-(*p*-hydroxyphenyl)ethanol *see* Bamethan.

o-(3-*tert*-Butylamino-2-hydroxypropoxy)benzonitrile *see* Bunitrolol.

3-[2-[3-(*tert*-Butylamino)-2-hydroxypropoxy]-4-chlorophenyl]-2-cyclopenten-1-one *see* Ericolol.

5-[3-(*tert*-Butylamino)-2-hydroxypropoxy]-3,4-dihydrocarbostyril *see* Carteolol.

5-[3-(*tert*-Butylamino)-2-hydroxypropoxy]-3,4-dihydro-2(1*H*)-isoquinolinecarboxaldehyde *see* Soquinolol.

5-[3-(*tert*-Butylamino)-2-hydroxypropoxy]-3,4-dihydro-1(2*H*)-naphthalenone *see* Bunolol.

2′-[3-(*tert*-Butylamino)-2-hydroxypropoxy]-5′-fluorobutyrophenone *see* Butofilolol.

2′-[3-(*tert*-Butylamino)-2-hydroxypropoxy]-2-furananilide *see* Anacarol.

9-[3-(*tert*-Butylamino)-2-hydroxypropoxy]-4-hydroxy-7-methyl-5*H*-furo[3,2-*g*]benzopyran-5-one *see* Butocrolol.

4-[3-(*tert*-Butylamino)-2-hydroxypropoxy]indole-2-carboxylic acid isopropyl ester *see* Carpindolol.

8-[3-(*tert*-Butylamino)-2-hydroxypropoxy]-5-methylcoumarin *see* Bucumolol.

3-(3-*tert*-Butylamino-2-hydroxypropoxy)-4-morpholino-1,2,5-thiadiazole *see* Timolol.

2-[*o*-[3-(*tert*-Butylamino)-2-hydroxypropoxy]phenoxy]-*N*-methylacetamide *see* Cetamolol.

2-[[*o*-(3-*tert*-Butylamino-2-hydroxypropoxy)phenoxy]methyl]tetrahydrofuran *see* Bufetolol.

1-[*p*-(3-*tert*-Butylamino-2-hydroxypropoxy)phenyl]-3-cyclohexylurea *see* Talinolol.

7-[3-(*tert*-Butylamino)-2-hydroxypropoxy]phthalide *see* Afurolol.

4′-[3-(*tert*-Butylamino)-2-hydroxypropoxy]spiro-[cyclohexane-1,2′-indan]-1′-one *see* Spirendolol.

5-[3-(*tert*-Butylamino)-2-hydroxypropoxy]-1,2,3,4-tetrahydro-8-hydroxy-1,4-ethanonaphthalene *see* Nafetolol.

1-[3-(*tert*-Butylamino)-2-hydroxypropoxy]-5,6,7,8-tetrahydro-*cis*-6,7-naphthalenediol *see* Nadolol.

8-[3-(*tert*-Butylamino)-2-hydroxypropoxy]thiochroman *see* Tertatolol.

(±)-5-[2-[[3-(*tert*-Butylamino)-2-hydroxypropyl]thio]thiazol-4-yl]-2-thiophenecarboxamide *see* Arotinolol.

Butylaminomethylbenzodioxan *see* Butamoxane.

α-[(*tert*-Butylamino)methyl]-*o*-chlorobenzyl alcohol *see* Tulobuterol.

3-[(*tert*-Butylamino)methyl]-4′-chloro-5-[(7-chloro-4-quinolyl)amino]-2-biphenylol *see* Tebuquine.

2-Butylaminomethyl-8-(2-chloroethoxy)-1,4-benzodioxan *see* Chlorethoxybutamoxane.

1-*tert*-Butylamino-3-(5-methylcoumarin-8-yloxy)-2-propanol *see* Bucumolol.

α-[(*tert*-Butylamino)methyl]-3,4-dihydroxybenzyl alcohol *see* Colterol.

α-[(*tert*-Butylamino)methyl]-3,5-dihydroxybenzyl alcohol *see* Terbutaline.

α-[(*tert*-Butylamino)methyl]-3,4-dihydroxybenzyl alcohol 3-acetate 4-*p*-anisate *see* Nisbuterol.

2-[(Butylamino)methyl]-8-ethoxy-1,4-benzodioxan *see* Ethomoxane.

α-[(*tert*-Butylamino)methyl]-7-ethyl-2-benzofuranmethanol *see* Bufuralol.

[1-(Butylamino)-1-methylethyl]phosphinic acid *see* Butafosfan.

α-[(Butylamino)methyl]-*p*-hydroxybenzyl alcohol *see* Bamethan.

α-[(*tert*-Butylamino)methyl]-4-hydroxy-3-(hydroxymethyl)benzyl alcohol *see* Salbutamol.

α-[(*tert*-Butylamino)methyl]-4-hydroxy-3-(methylsulfonylmethyl)benzyl alcohol *see* Sulfonterol.

α⁶-[(*tert*-Butylamino)methyl]-3-hydroxy-2,6-pyridinedimethanol *see* Pirbuterol.

α-[(*tert*-Butylamino)methyl]-4-hydroxy-3-ureidobenzyl alcohol *see* Carbuterol.

α¹-[(*tert*-Butylamino)methyl]-4-hydroxy-*m*-xylene-α,α′-diol *see* Salbutamol.

1-(*tert*-Butylamino)-3-[(2-methylindol-4-yl)oxy]-2-propanol benzoate *see* Bopindolol.

1-(*tert*-Butylamino)-3-[*o*-[2-(3-methylisoxazol-5-yl)vinyl]phenoxy]-2-propanol *see* Isoxaprolol.

α-[(*sec*-Butylamino)methyl]-5,6,7,8-tetrahydro-2-naphthalenemethanol *see* Butidrine.

1-(*tert*-Butylamino)-3-(4-morpholino-1,2,5-thiadiazol-3-yloxy)-2-propanol *see* Timolol.

3-(Butylamino)-4-phenoxy-5-sulfamoylbenzoic acid *see* Bumetanide.

3-(Butylamino)-α-phenyl-5-sulfamoyl-*p*-toluic acid *see* Besunide.

1-(*tert*-Butylamino)-3-(phthalid-7-yloxy)-2-propanol *see* Afurolol.

1-(*tert*-Butylamino)-3-[*o*-(2-propynyloxy)phenoxy]-2-propanol *see* Pargolol.

4-(Butylamino)salicylic acid dimethylaminoethyl ester *see* Hydroxytetracaine.

9-(Butylamino)-1,2,3,4-tetrahydroacridine *see* Bucricaine.

1-(*tert*-Butylamino)-3-[(5,6,7,8-tetrahydro-*cis*-6,7-dihydroxynaphth-1-yl)oxy]-2-propanol *see* Nadolol.

1-(*tert*-Butylamino)-3-(*o*-(tetrahydrofurfuryloxy)phenoxy)-2-propanol *see* Bufetolol.

1-(*tert*-Butylamino)-3-[(1,2,3,4-tetrahydro-8-hydroxy-1,4-ethanonaphthalen-5-yl)oxy]-2-propanol *see* Nafetolol.

2-(*sec*-Butylamino)-1-(5,6,7,8-tetrahydro-2-naphthyl)ethanol *see* Butidrine.

1-(*tert*-Butylamino)-3-(thiochroman-8-yloxy)-2-propanol *see* Tertatolol.

1-(*tert*-Butylamino)-3-(2,3-xyloxy)-2-propanol *see* Xibenolol.

2-(*p*-Butylanilino)nicotinic acid *see* Butanixin.

BUTYLATE (*S*-ethyl bis(2-methylpropyl)carbamothioate; 'sutan').

BUTYLATED HYDROXYANISOLE* (mixture of 2-*tert*-butyl-4-methoxyphenol and 3-*tert*-butyl-4-methoxyphenol; BHA; 'embanox'; 'nipantiox 1-F'; 'tenox-BHA').

BUTYLATED HYDROXYTOLUENE (3,5-di-*tert*-butyl-4-hydroxytoluene; 2,6-di-*tert*-butyl-*p*-cresol; di-*tert*-butylmethylphenol; BHT; DBPC; 'impruvol'; 'ionol'; 'vianol').

BUTYLATED HYDROXYTOLUENE plus TOLNAFTATE ('tinaderm').

5-Butyl-2-benzimidazolecarbamic acid methyl ester *see* Parbendazole.

2-Butyl-3-benzofuranyl 4-(2-diethylaminoethoxy)-3,5-diiodophenyl ketone *see* Amiodarone.

α-Butylbenzyl alcohol *see* Fenipentol.

1-(*p*-*tert*-Butylbenzyl)-4-(*p*-chloro-α-phenylbenzyl)piperazine *see* Buclizine.

1-Butylbiguanide *see* Buformin.

N-*tert*-Butyl-1,4-butanediamine *see* Dibutadiamin.

'Butyl butex' *see* Butyl paraben.

BUTYLCAINE* (butyl *p*-aminobenzoate; butamben; butoforme).

BUTYLCAINE PICRATE (Abbott-34842).

tert-Butylcarbamic acid *m*-(dimethylcarbamoyl-amino)phenyl ester *see* Karbutilate.

1-(Butylcarbamoyl)benzimidazole-2-carbamic acid methyl ester *see* Benomyl.

5-Butyl-5-(2-carbamoyloxyethyl)barbituric acid carbamate ester *see* Carbubarb.

1-[*m*-(*tert*-Butylcarbamoyloxy)phenyl]-3,3-dimethylurea *see* Karbutilate.

*N*¹-(Butylcarbamoyl)sulfanilamide *see* Carbutamide.

α-Butyl-5-carboxy-2-hydroxybenzyl alcohol *see* Fepentolic acid.

BUTYLCHLORAL HYDRATE* (2,2,3-trichloro-1,1-butanediol; croton-chloral hydrate; trichlorobutylidene glycol).

5-Butyl-2-(*p*-chlorobenzenesulfonamido)-1,3,4-thiadiazole *see* Butadiazamide.

2-*tert*-Butyl-6-(5-chloro-2*H*-benzotriazol-2-yl)-*p*-cresol *see* Bumetrizole.

4-*tert*-Butyl-2-(chloromercuri)phenol *see* Mercurobutol.

N-Butyl-*N*′-(4-chloro-2-methylphenyl)-*N*-methylformamidine *see* Chlormebuform.

3-*tert*-Butyl-5-chloro-6-methyluracil *see* Terbacil.

1-[2-*tert*-Butyl-1-(*p*-chlorophenoxy)-2-hydroxyethyl]-1*H*-1,2,4-triazole *see* Triadimenol.

1-[2-*tert*-Butyl-1-(*p*-chlorophenoxy)-2-oxoethyl]-1*H*-1,2,4-triazole *see* Triadimefon.

4-*tert*-Butyl-2-chlorophenyl methyl *N*-methylphosphoramidate *see* Crufomate.

Butylchlorophos *see* Butonate.

N-Butyl-4-chlorosalicylamide *see* Buclosamide.

Butyl 2-cyanoacrylate *see* Enbucrilate.

Butyl 1-(3-cyano-3,3-diphenylpropyl)-4-phenylpiperidine-4-carboxylate *see* Butoxylate.

5-Butyl-1-cyclohexylbarbituric acid *see* Bucolome.

2-[(4-*tert*-Butylcyclohexyl)methyl]-3-hydroxy-1,4-naphthoquinone *see* Buparvaquone.

BUTYL 2,4-DICHLOROPHENOXYACETATE ('lironox'; 'weedone aero concentrate').

1-Butyl-2-(3,4-dichlorophenylimino)pyrrolidine *see* Clenpirin.

1-Butyl-3-(3,4-dichlorophenyl)-1-methylurea *see* Neburon.

1-*sec*-Butyl-4-[*p*-[4-[*p*-[[2-(2,4-dichlorophenyl)-2-(1*H*-1,2,4-triazol-1-ylmethyl)-1,3-dioxolan-4-yl]methoxy]phenyl]piperazin-1-yl]phenyl]-Δ²-1,2,4-triazolin-5-one *see* Itraconazole.

2-Butyl-3-[4-(2-diethylaminoethoxy)-3,3-diiodobenzoyl]benzofuran *see* Amiodarone.

N-Butyl-*N*-(2-diethylaminoethyl)-1-naphthamide *see* Bunaftine.

N-Butyl-*N*′,*N*′-diethyl-*N*-naphth-1-oyl-ethylenediamine *see* Bunaftine.

Butyl difenoxilate *see* Butoxylate.

Butyl 4,5-dihydro-6,6-dimethyl-4-oxopyran-2-carboxylate *see* Butopyronoxyl.

4-Butyl-1,2-dihydro-5-hydroxy-1,2-diphenyl-3,6-pyridazinedione *see* Denpidazone.

8-*tert*-Butyl-7,8-dihydro-5-methyl-6*H*-pyrrolo[3,2-*e*]-*s*-triazolo[1,5-*a*]pyrimidine *see* Bumepidil.

1-Butyl-3-[1-(6,7-dimethoxyquinazolin-4-yl)piperid-4-yl]urea *see* Buquineran.

2-Butyl-1-(2-dimethylaminoethoxy)isoquinoline *see*

Quinisocaine.

5-Butyl-2-(dimethylamino)-4-hydroxy-6-methylpyrimidine *see* Dimethirimol.

2-(4-*tert*-Butyl-2,6-dimethylbenzyl)-2-imidazoline *see* Xylometazoline.

Butyl(2,3-dimethyl-5-oxo-1-phenyl-3-pyrazolin-4-yl)dimethylammonium iodide *see* Butopyrammonium iodide.

2-*tert*-Butyl-4,6-dinitrophenol *see* Dinoterb.

6-*sec*-Butyl-2,4-dinitrophenol *see* Dinoseb.

2-*sec*-Butyl-4,6-dinitrophenyl 3,3-dimethylacrylate *see* Binapacryl.

2-*sec*-Butyl-4,6-dinitrophenyl isopropyl carbonate *see* Dinobuton.

2-*sec*-Butyl-4,6-dinitrophenyl 3-methylcrotonate *see* Binapacryl.

2-*sec*-Butyl-4,6-dinitrophenyl senecioate *see* Binapacryl.

o-*tert*-Butyldiphenhydramine *see* Bufenadrine.

2-Butyl-5-[[4-(diphenylmethyl)piperazin-1-yl]methyl]-1-ethylbenzimidazole *see* Buterizine.

1-*tert*-Butyl-4,4-diphenylpiperidine *see* Budipine.

4-Butyl-1,2-diphenyl-3,5-pyrazolidinedione *see* Phenylbutazone.

5-Butyl-2-(ethylamino)-6-methyl-4-pyrimidinol *see* Ethirimol.

5-Butyl-2-ethylbarbituric acid *see* Butethal.

5-*sec*-Butyl-5-ethylbarbituric acid *see* Secbutabarbital.

1-Butyl-2-ethylbiguanide *see* Etoformin.

Butylethylcarbamothioic acid *S*-propyl ester *see* Pebulate.

N-Butyl-N-ethyl-2,6-dinitro-4-(trifluoromethyl)aniline *see* Benfluralin.

2-But-2-yl-2-ethylmalonamic acid ethyl ester *see* Ethyl butylethylmalonamate.

5-*sec*-Butyl-5-ethyl-2-thiobarbituric acid *see* Thiobutabarbital.

N-Butyl-N-ethyl-α,α,α-trifluoro-2,6-dinitro-p-toluidine *see* Benfluralin.

Butyl flufenamate *see* Ufenamate.

Butyl 6α-fluoro-11β-hydroxy-16α-methyl-3,20-dioxopregna-1,4-dien-21-oate *see* Fluocortin butyl.

***tert*-Butylhydroquinone polymer with divinylbenzene etc.** *see* Anoxomer.

Butyl p-hydroxybenzoate *see* Butyl paraben.

α-Butyl-α-hydroxy-4,3-cresotic acid *see* Fepentolic acid.

2-(4-*tert*-Butyl-3-hydroxy-2,6-dimethylbenzyl)-2-imidazoline *see* Oxymetazoline.

p-*tert*-Butyl-α-[3-[4-(hydroxydiphenylmethyl)piperid-1-yl]propyl]benzyl alcohol *see* Terfenadine.

4-Butyl-3-hydroxy-1,2-diphenyl-3-pyrazolin-5-one sodium salt compound with glycerol *see* Phenbutazone sodium glycerate.

Butyl 9-hydroxy-9H-fluorene-9-carboxylate *see* Flurenol-butyl.

4-Butyl-4-hydroxymethyl-1,2-diphenyl-3,5-pyrazolidinedione p-chlorobenzoate ester *see* Feclobuzone.

4-Butyl-4-(hydroxymethyl)-1,2-diphenyl-3,5-pyrazolidinedione hydrogen succinate *see* Suxibuzone.

4-Butyl-1-(p-hydroxyphenyl)-2-phenyl-3,5-pyrazolidinedione *see* Oxyphenbutazone.

16α,17α-Butylidenedioxy-11β,21-dihydroxypregna-1,4-diene-3,20-dione *see* Budesonide.

6-*tert*-Butyl-3-(2-imidazolin-2-ylmethyl)-2,4-dimethylphenol *see* Oxymetazoline.

6-*tert*-Butyl-4-(isobutylideneamino)-3-(methylthio)-1,2,4-triazine-5(4H)-one *see* Isomethiozine.

Butylmalonic acid mono(1,2-diphenylhydrazide) *see* Bumadizone.

Butyl mesityl oxide *see* Butopyronoxyl.

N-*tert*-Butylmethoxamine *see* Butaxamine.

***tert*-Butyl-4-methoxyphenols** *see* Butylated hydroxyanisole.

3-(N-*tert*-Butylmethylamino)-3-methyl-1-butyne *see* Butynamine.

N-*tert*-Butyl-1-methyl-3,3-diphenylpropylamine *see* Terodiline.

N-Butyl-2-methyl-N-(4-methyloxazol-2-yl)propionamide *see* Isamoxole.

4-Butyl-4-((4-methylpiperazin-1-yl)methyl)-1,2-diphenyl-3,5-pyrazolidinedione *see* Pipebuzone.

2-*sec*-Butyl-2-methyl-1,3-propanediol carbamate isopropylcarbamate *see* Nisobamate.

2-*sec*-Butyl-2-methyl-1,3-propanediol dicarbamate *see* Mebutamate.

N-*tert*-Butylnoradrenaline *see* Colterol.

'Butylnorsimpatol' *see* Bamethan.

3α-*tert*-Butyl-2,3,4,4aβ,8,9,13bα,14-octahydro-1H-benzo[6,7]cyclohepta-[1,2,3-de]pyrido[2,1-a]-isoquinolin-3-ol *see* Butaclamol.

N-*tert*-Butyloxycarbonyl-β-alanyl-L-tryptophyl-L-methionyl-L-aspartyl-L-phenylalanine amide *see* Pentagastrin.

BUTYL PARABEN (butyl p-hydroxybenzoate).

BUTYLPHENAMIDE* (N-butyl-3-phenylsalicylamide; 'bynamid').

1-(p-*tert*-Butylphenoxy)-3-(p-carboxyphenoxy)-2-propanol *see* Terbufibrol.

2-(p-*tert*-Butylphenoxy)cyclohexyl 2-propynyl sulfite *see* Propargite.

p-[3-(p-*tert*-Butylphenoxy)-2-hydroxypropoxy]benzoic acid *see* Terbufibrol.

2-(p-*tert*-BUTYLPHENOXY)ISOPROPYL 2-CHLOROETHYL SULFITE (2-chloroethyl 2-[4-(1,1-dimethylethyl)phenoxy]-1-methylethyl sulfite ester; R-88; 'aramite'; 'niagaramite'; 'ortho-mite').

N-[2-[(4-Butylphenyl)amino]-2-oxoethyl]-N-(carboxymethyl)glycine *see* Butilfenin.

2-(o-*tert*-Butyl-α-phenylbenzyloxy)-N,N-dimethylethylamine *see* Bufenadrine.

[[[(p-Butylphenyl)carbamoyl]methyl]imino]diacetic acid *see* Butilfenin.

α-(p-*tert*-Butylphenyl)-4-(diphenylmethyl)-1-piperazinebutanol *see* Trenizine.

α-(p-*tert*-Butylphenyl)-4-(hydroxydiphenylmethyl)-1-piperidinebutanol *see* Terfenadine.

Butyl 3-phenyl-3-piperid-1-ylpropionate *see* Butaverine.

4-Butyl-1-phenyl-3,5-pyrazolidinedione *see* Mofebutazone.

N-Butyl-3-phenylsalicylamide *see* Butylphenamide.

Butyl phthalate *see* Dibutyl phthalate.

5-Butylpicolinamide *see* Bupicomide.
5-Butylpicolinic acid *see* Fusaric acid.
N-**Butylpipecolic acid 2,6-dimethylanilide** *see* Bupivacaine.
1-Butyl-2′,6′-pipecoloxylidide *see* Bupivacaine.
2-*tert*-Butyl-α-(2-piperid-4-ylethyl)-4-quinoline-methanol *see* Quinacainol.
5-Butyl-2-pyridinecarboxamide *see* Bupicomide.
5-Butylpyridine-2-carboxylic acid *see* Fusaric acid.
Butylscopolamine *see* Scopolamine butyl bromide.
1-Butyl-3-sulfanilylurea *see* Carbutamide.
'Butylsympathol' *see* Bamethan.
6-Butyl-1,4,7,10-tetrahydro-4,10-dioxo-1,7-phen-anthroline-2,8-dicarboxylic acid *see* Bufrolin.
N-**(5-*tert*-Butyl-1,3,4-thiadiazol-2-yl)benzenesulfon-amide** *see* Glybuzole.
N-**(5-Butyl-1,3,4-thiadiazol-2-yl)-*p*-chlorobenzene-sulfonamide** *see* Butadiazamide.
*N*¹-**(5-*tert*-Butyl-1,3,4-thiadiazol-2-yl)sulfanilamide** *see* Glybuthiazol.
1-(4-*tert*-Butyl-2-thiazolyl)-4-methylpiperazine *see* Tebatizole.
2-[*p*-(Butylthio)-α-phenylbenzylthio]-*N*,*N*-dimethyl-ethylamine *see* Captodiame.
1-Butyl-3-*p*-toluenesulfonylurea *see* Tolbutamide.
1-Butyl-3-tosylurea *see* Tolbutamide.
Butyl *N*-(α,α,α-trifluoro-*m*-tolyl)anthranilate *see* Ufenamate.
1-Butyl-*N*-(2,4,6-trimethylphenyl)-2-pyrrolidine-carboxamide *see* Bumecaine.
N-*tert*-**Butyl-*N*,1,1-trimethyl-2-propynylamine** *see* Butynamine.
1-Butyl-2′,4′,6′-trimethyl-2-pyrrolidinecarboxanilide *see* Bumecaine.
Butyl vinyl ether polymer *see* Polyvinox.
1-Butyl-2-(2,6-xylylcarbamoyl)piperidine *see* Bupivacaine.
'Butyn' *see* Butacaine.
BUTYNAMINE* (*N*-*tert*-butyl-*N*,1,1-trimethyl-2-propynylamine; 3-(*N*-*tert*-butylmethylamino)-3-methyl-1-butyne).
2-Butynoic acid *see* Tetrolic acid.
BUTYRAMIDE (butyric acid amide; butanamide; ethylacetamide).
1-[[*p*-(2-Butyramidoethyl)phenyl]sulfonyl]-3-(3-cyclohexen-1-yl)-2-iminoimidazolidine *see* Glibutimine.
3-Butyramido-α-ethyl-2,4,6-triiodohydrocinnamic acid sodium salt *see* Sodium tyropanoate.
3-(3-Butyramido-2,4,6-triiodophenyl)-2-ethylacrylic acid *see* Bunamiodyl.
2-(3-Butyramido-3,4,6-triiodophenylmethylene)bu-tyric acid *see* Bunamiodyl.
BUTYRIC ACID (butanoic acid).
1-Butyric acid-7-(L-2-aminobutyric acid)-26-L-as-partic acid-27-L-valine-29-L-alaninecalcitonin (salmon) *see* Elcatonin.
1-Butyric acid-6-(L-2-aminobutyric acid)-7-glycine-oxytocin *see* Cargutocin.
1-Butyric acid-2-[3-(*p*-methoxyphenyl)-L-alanine]-oxytocin *see* Carbetocin.
'Butyron' *see* Buturon.
p-**BUTYROPHENETIDIDE** (*p*-ethoxybutyranil-

ide; *N*-(*p*-ethoxyphenyl)butyramide).
BUTYROPHENONE (1-phenyl-1-butanone; phenyl propyl ketone).
Butyrylacetic acid *see* 3-Oxohexanoic acid.
10-Butyryl-1,8-dihydroxyanthrone *see* Butantrone.
3′-(5-Butyryl-2,4-dihydroxy-3,3-dimethyl-6-oxo-1,4-cyclohexadien-1-ylmethyl)-2′,6′-dihydroxy-4′-methoxybutyrophenone *see* Desaspidin.
4-Butyryl-2-methylphloroglucinol-1-methyl ether *see* Aspidinol.
Butyrylperazine *see* Butaperazine.
'Butysedal' *see* Tetrabarbital.
Butyvinal *see* Vinylbital.
BUZEPIDE METIODIDE* (1-(3-carbamoyl-3,3-diphenylpropyl)hexahydro-1-methylazepi-nium iodide; 4-hexahydroazepin-1-yl-2,2-di-phenylbutyramide methiodide; 4-(*N*-hexameth-ylenimino)-2,2-diphenylbutyramide methiodide; metazepium iodide; diphexamide iodomethylate; FI-6146; R-661).
BUZEPIDE METIODIDE plus HALOPERIDOL ('vesadol').
BVU *see* Bromisoval.
BW-19C49 *see* Diethylthiambutene.
BW-29C48 *see* Pipanone.
BW-33T57 *see* Metisazone.
BW-47-83 *see* Cyclizine.
BW-48/80 *see* Compound 48/80.
BW-49-210 *see* Diaveridine.
BW-50-63 *see* Pyrimethamine.
BW-50-71 *see* Tioguanine.
BW-55-5 *see* Oxipurinol.
BW-56-72 *see* Trimethoprim.
BW-56-158 *see* Allopurinol.
BW-57C65 *see* Cloguanamil.
BW-57-223 *see* Lucanthone.
BW-57-322 *see* Azathioprine.
BW-57-323 *see* Tiamiprine.
BW-58-271 *see* Rolodine.
BW-61-32 *see* Stilbazium iodide.
BW-61-43 *see* Isopropylmethoxamine.
BW-62-415 *see* Bunamidine.
BW-63-90 *see* Butacetin.
BW-64-9 *see* Butaxamine.
BW-79T61 *see* Lucanthone.
BW-139C55 *see* Pentacynium chloride.
BW-291C51 *see* Forminitrazole.
BW-295C51 *see* Triprolidine.
BW-323 *see* Amfebutamone.
BW-349C59 *see* Moxipraquine.
BW-356C61 *see* Gloxazone.
BW-373C57 *see* Bretylium tosilate.
BW-378C48 *see* Dipipanone.
BW-467C60 *see* Betanidine.
BW-545C64 *see* Xylamidine tosilate.
BW-611C65 *see* Thenium closilate.
BW-720C *see* Buparvaquone.
BW-825C *see* Acrivastine.
BW-50197 *see* Metodiclorofen.
Bwy20 *see under* Scopolamine butyl bromide.
BX-311 *see* Cinoxolone.
BX-341 *see* Bifluranol.
BX-363A *see* Cicloxolone.

80

BX-428 *see* Terfluranol.
BX-430 *see* Pentafluranol.
BX-568A *see* Cinfenoac.
BX-591 *see* Acefluranol.
BX-650A *see* Ipsalazide.
BX-661A *see* Balsalazide.
By-123 *see under* Neomycin.

'Bykahepar' *see* Clanobutin.
'Byk-M 1' *see* Mephenesin.
'Bykomycin' *see under* Neomycin.
'Bykonox' *see* Vinylbital.
'Bynamid' *see* Butylphenamide.
BZ 55 *see* Carbutamide.

C

C-3 *see* Capobenic acid.
C-3 **Sankyo** *see* Bucumolol.
C 5 *see* Pentamethonium bromide.
C-6 *see* Hexamethonium bromide.
C 10 *see* Decamethonium bromide.
C-16 *see* Poligeenan.
C-45 *see* Belladonnin.
C-78 *see* Tulobuterol.
C-197 *see* Strophanthin.
C-209 *see under* Dexamethasone.
C-238 *see* Pridinol.
C-283 *see* Nitracrine.
C-325 *see* Pipoxizine.
C-330 *see under* Dimenhydrinate.
C-434 *see* Trimedoxime bromide.
C-1488 *see* Paromomycin.
C-1523 *see* Benzydamine.
C-1605 *see under* Benzydamine.
C-1656 *see* Clometacin.
C-2242 *see* Chlorotoluron.
C-2924 *see* Sodium auroallylthioureidobenzoate.
C-4311/b *see* Methylphenidate.
C-4675 *see* Pentapiperide.
C-5473 *see* Oxyphenonium bromide.
C-5511 *see* Ketobemidone.
C-5581 *see* Phenyltoloxamine.
C-5720 *see* Carprofen.
C-5968 *see* Hydralazine.
C-6866 *see* Chlormethine.
C-6989 *see* Fluorodifen.
C-7019 *see* Aziprotryne.
C-7115 *see* Ketobemidone.
C-7337 *see* Phentolamine.
C-7441 *see* Dihydralazine.
C-8514 *see* Chlorphenamidine.
C-9295 *see* Azamethonium bromide.
C-9333 *see* Amoscanate.
C-11925 *see* Phanquinone.
C-12669/A *see* Demecolcine.
C-13155 *see* Meladrazine.
C-15095 E *see* Thiambutosine.
C-17309 *see* Metandienone.
C-22598 *see* Chlormebuform.
C-193901 *see* Clonitazene.
CA-7 *see* Brinase.
Caa-40 *see* Isoxsuprine.
'Cabagin-U' *see* Vitamin U.
CABASTINE** ((±)-*trans*-1-[*cis*-4-cyano-4-(*p*-fluorophenyl)cyclohexyl]-3-methyl-4-phenylnipecotic acid).
  See also Levocabastine.

'Cabiol' *see* Benzyl benzoate.
Cabufocon A* *see* Cellaburate.
'Ca chel 330' *see* Calcium trisodium pentetate.
CACODYLIC ACID (dimethylarsinic acid).
'Cacodyl new' *see* Disodium methanearsonate.
CACTINOMYCIN*** (antibiotic from *Str. chrysomallus*; actinomycin C; HBF-386; NSC-18268).
CADAVERINE (pentamethylenediamine; 1,5-pentanediamine).
CADEXOMER IODINE*** (product of reaction of dextrin with epichlorohydrin coupled with ion exchange groups and iodine; dextrin-epichlorohydrin-iodine reaction product).
'Cadminate' *see* Cadmium succinate.
CADMIUM SUCCINATE ('cadminate').
CADMIUM SULFIDE ('capsebon').
CADRALAZINE*** (ethyl 6-[ethyl(2-hydroxypropyl)amino]-3-pyridazinecarbazate).
'Caducid' *see* Fluoresone.
Caerulein *see* Ceruletide.
CAFAMINOL*** (8-[(2-hydroxyethyl)methylamino]caffeine; 'rhinoptil').
CAFEDRINE** (7-[2-(2-hydroxy-1-methylphenethylamino)ethyl]theophylline; norephedrine-theophylline).
CAFEDRINE plus THEODRENALINE (H-835; 'akrinor'; 'praxinor'; 'voveran').
'Cafergot' *see under* Ergotamine tartrate.
Caffearin *see* Trigonelline.
CAFFEIC ACID (3,4-dihydroxycinnamic acid). *See also* Cynarine.
CAFFEINE (1,3,7-trimethylxanthine; coffein; guaranine; guarin; thein).
Caffeoylquinic acid *see* Chlorogenic acid.
'Cafide' *see* Butofilolol maleate.
'Cafilon' *see under* Phenmetrazine teoclate.
'Cafron' *see* Benactyzine.
'Caid' *see* Chlorophacinone.
Cajeputene *see* Limonene.
Calcacetosal *see* Calcium acetylsalicylate.
'Calcamine' *see* Dihydrotachysterol.
'Calcibromin' *see* Calcium bromide-lactobionate.
'Calcibronat' *see* Calcium bromide-lactobionate.
'Calcicol' *see* Calcium guaiacolsulfonate.
CALCIFEDIOL*** (9,10-secocholesta-5,7,10(19)-triene-3β,25-diol; U-32070; 'dedrogyl').
Calciferol* *see* Ergocalciferol.
'Calcimar' *see* Calcitonin.
CALCIMYCIN (A-23187; antibiotic A-23187).
CALCINAPHTHOL (calcium 2-naphthol-1-sul-

fonate; 'abrastol'; 'asaprol').

'Calciobrom' see Calcium bromide-lactobionate.

CALCIODOXYL BENZOATE* (calcium o-iodoxybenzoate; 'calsiod'; 'oxo-ate-B').

'Calciofon' see Calcium gluconate.

'Calciostab' see Calcium thiosulfate.

'Calciparin' see Heparin calcium.

'Calcitare' see Calcitonin.

Calcitetramate disodium see Sodium calcium edetate.

CALCITONIN*** (pig calcitonin; thyrocalcitonin; 'calcimar'; 'calcitare'; 'staporos').
See also Elcatonin; Human calcitonin; Salcatonin.

CALCITRIOL*** ((5Z,7E)-9,10-secocholesta-5,7,10(19)-triene-1α,3β,25-triol; 1α,25-dihydroxycholecalciferol; 1α,25-dihydroxycolecalciferol; 1α,25-dihydroxyvitamin D_3; Ro 21-5535; 'rocaltrol').

CALCIUM ACETYLSALICYLATE (calcacetosal).
See also Carbasalate calcium.

CALCIUM ALGINATE (calcium polymannuronate; 'calgitex'; 'coalgan'; 'goalgan'; 'kalipin').

CALCIUM AMINOSALICYLATE (calcium 4-aminosalicylate; 'PAC').

Calcium-4-benzamido-2-hydroxybenzoate see Calcium benzamidosalicylate.

CALCIUM BENZAMIDOSALICYLATE***
(calcium-4-benzamido-2-hydroxybenzoate; benzoylpas calcium; calcium benzoylpas).

Calcium benzoylpas* see Calcium benzamidosalicylate.

CALCIUM BROMIDE-LACTOBIONATE (Ca-$(C_{12}H_{21}O_{12})_2CaBr_2.6H_2O$; calcium galactoglyconate bromide).

CALCIUM BUCLOXATE (CB-804).

CALCIUM CARBAMOYLASPARTATE (calcium ureidosuccinate; 'pacilan').

Calcium carbaspirin* see Carbasalate calcium.

CALCIUM CARBIMIDE*** (calcium carbylamine; calcium cyanamide; calcium isocyanide; carbimide calcium; carbodimide calcium; nitrolime).

CALCIUM CARBIMIDE CITRATE (citrated calcium carbimide; 'abstem'; 'dipsan'; 'temposil').

Calcium carbylamine see Calcium carbimide.

CALCIUM CASEINATE* ('aciban').

'Calcium-chefaro' see Calcium glucoheptonate.

CALCIUM CLOFIBRATE*** (RU-19583; 'dabical').

'Calcium-corbiere' see Calcium glucoheptonate.

Calcium cyanamide see Calcium carbimide.

CALCIUM CYCLAMATE (calcium N-cyclohexylsulfamate; cyclamate; 'cyclan'; 'sucaryl-calcium').

Calcium N-cyclohexylsulfamate see Calcium cyclamate.

'Calcium-diasporal' see Calcium levulinate.

Calcium 2,2-dichlorovinyl methyl phosphate see Dichlorvos demethyl calcium.

Calcium 2,5-dihydroxybenzenesulfonate see Calcium dobesilate.

Calcium dioctyl sulfosuccinate see Docusate calcium.

Calcium disodium edetate see Sodium calcium edetate.

CALCIUM DOBESILATE*** (calcium 2,5-dihydroxybenzenesulfonate; dobesilate calcium; E-205; MD-205; 'dexium'; 'doxium').

'Calcium-drobena' see Calcium glucoheptonate.

CALCIUM 2-ETHYLBUTYRATE (calcium ethylbutanoate; 'ethanion').
See also under Hydroxyzine embonate.

CALCIUM FOLINATE*** (calcium N^5-formyltetrahydrofolate; leucovorin; citrovorum factor; NSC-3590; 'rescuvolin').

CALCIUM FRUCTOSE 1,6-DIPHOSPHATE ('candiolin'; 'glucofos').

Calcium galactoglyconate bromide see Calcium bromide-lactobionate.

CALCIUM GLUBIONATE*** (calcium gluconogalactobionate; calcium gluconolactobionate; $(C_{12}H_{21}O_{12}C_6H_{11}O_{17})Ca.H_2O$; (D-gluconato)-(lactobionato)calcium monohydrate).

Calcium D-glucarate see Calcium saccharate.

Calcium glucoheptogluconate see Calcium glucoheptonate.

CALCIUM GLUCOHEPTONATE** (calcium gluceptate; calcium glucoheptogluconate; calcium gluconate solution; calcium hexahydroxyheptonate).

CALCIUM GLUCONATE* (solid calcium gluconate; $C_{12}H_{22}O_{14}Ca.H_2O$; calcium gluconogalactogluconate; calcium glyconate).

Calcium gluconate solution see Calcium glucoheptonate.

Calcium gluconogalactobionate see Calcium glubionate.

Calcium gluconogalactogluconate see Calcium gluconate.

Calcium gluconolactobionate see Calcium glubionate.

CALCIUM GLUTAMATE ('vivacalcium').

Calcium glyconate see Calcium gluconate.

CALCIUM GUAIACOLSULFONATE ('calcicol'; 'gaiacyl').

Calcium hexahydroxyheptonate see Calcium glucoheptonate.

Calcium o-iodoxybenzoate see Calciodoxyl benzoate.

Calcium isocyanide see Calcium carbimide.

CALCIUM LEVULINATE ('calcium-diasporal'; 'calcium-pharmacon'; 'flanthin'; 'levucalcin'; 'mil-U-cal'; 'neocalcin').

CALCIUM MAGNESIUM PHYTATE (calcium magnesium inositolhexaphosphate; inositocalcium; phytocalcine).

CALCIUM MANDELATE ('amandacide'; 'camandeline'; 'camdelate'; 'eggopurin'; 'mandecal').

CALCIUM METHYL POLYGALACTURONATE SULFONATE(S) (G-31150; R-2055).

Calcium 2-naphthol-1-sulfonate see Calcinaphthol.

'Calcium-noury' see Sodium calcium edetate.

CALCIUM OLEATE ('collosol calcium').

CALCIUM PANTOTHENATE** (calcium salt of *N*-(2,4-dihydroxy-3,3-dimethylbutyryl)-β-alanine).

Calcium pentacemin trisodium* *see* Calcium trisodium pentetate.

'**Calcium-pharmacon**' *see* Calcium levulinate.

Calcium phosphate hydroxide *see* Hydroxyapatite.

CALCIUM PIDOLATE (calcium 5-oxopyrrolidine-2-carboxylate; calcium pyroglutamate; 'efical').

Calcium polycarbophil *see* Polycarbophil.

CALCIUM SACCHARATE*** (calcium D-glucarate; 'antacidin').

CALCIUM SODIUM FERRICLATE*** (calcium tetrasodium bis[pentaaqua-[D-gluconato(4−)]-tetra-μ-hydroxydioxotriferrate(3−)]; monocalcium tetrasodium bis[pentaaqua-[D-gluconato(4−)]tetra-μ-hydroxydioxotriferrate(3−)]; ferriclate calcium sodium; 'kelfer').

Calcium sulfaloxate *see* Sulfaloxate calcium.

Calcium tetrasodium bis[pentaaqua-[D-gluconato-(4−)]tetra-μ-hydroxydioxotriferrate(3−)] *see* Calcium sodium ferriclate.

Calcium theobromsal *see* Theobromine calcium salicylate.

CALCIUM THIOSULFATE ('calciostab'; 'tecesal').

Calcium trisodium (carboxymethylimino)bis(ethylenenitrilo)tetraacetic acid *see* Calcium trisodium pentetate.

CALCIUM TRISODIUM PENTETATE*** (calcium trisodium salt of diethylenetriaminepentaacetic acid; trisodium salt of 2,2'-carboxymethyliminobis(ethyleniminodiacetic acid) calcium chelate; calcium trisodium (carboxymethylimino)bis(ethylenenitrilo)tetraacetic acid; calcium pentacemin trisodium; pentetate calcium trisodium; pentacine; NSC-34249).

Calcium ureidosuccinate *see* Calcium carbamoylaspartate.

'**Caldorene**' *see* Mesulfen.

'**Calgam**' *see* Pangamic acid.

'**Calgitex**' *see* Calcium alginate.

'**Calgluchin**' *see* Calcium gluconate.

'**Calglucon**' *see* Calcium gluconate.

'**Calibene**' *see* Suxibuzone.

'**Calixin**' *see* Tridemorph.

Callicrein *see* Kallidinogenase.

'**Calmeran**' *see* Azacyclonol.

'**Calmonal**' *see* Meclozine.

'**Calmotusin**' *see* Clofedanol.

'**Calmpose**' *see* Diazepam.

Calomel *see* Mercurous chloride.

'**Calped**' *see* Phenylmercuric nitrate.

'**Calpol**' *see* Paracetamol.

'**Calsiod**' *see* Calciodoxyl benzoate.

'**Calsol**' *see* Tetrasodium edetate.

'**Calspirin**' *see* Calcium acetylsalicylate.

'**Calsprate**' *see* Calcium acetylsalicylate.

CALSULFHYDRYL* (aqueous dispersion of Ca complex salts with labile SH group; 'hydrosulfosol').

'**Calsynar**' *see* Salcatonin.

'**Calthor**' *see* Ciclacillin.

'**Calurin**' *see* Carbasalate calcium.

CALUSTERONE*** (17β-hydroxy-7β,17-dimethylandrost-4-en-3-one; NSC-88536; U-22550; 'methosarb'; 'riedemil').

CALYCOPTERIN (4',5'-dihydroxy-3,6,7,8-tetramethoxyflavone; 'thapsin').

CAM-807 *see* Bialamicol.

'**Camalon**' *see* Cyclarbamate.

'**Camandeline**' *see* Calcium mandelate.

'**Camatropin**' *see* Homatropine methyl bromide.

CAMAZEPAM*** (7-chloro-1,3-dihydro-3-hydroxy-1-methyl-5-phenyl-2*H*-1,4-benzodiazepin-2-one dimethylcarbamate ester; temazepam dimethylcarbamate; B-5833; Sb-5833; 'albego').

CAMBENDAZOLE*** (isopropyl 2-thiazol-4-yl-5-benzimidazolecarbamate; MK-905; 'bovicam'; 'porcam').

'**Cambimycin**' *see* Hachimycin.

'**Camcolit**' *see* Lithium carbonate.

'**Camdelate**' *see* Calcium mandelate.

'**Camesol 90**' *see* Dimethyl sulfoxide.

CAMIVERINE*** (2-phenyl-*N*-(2-pyrrolidin-1-ylethyl)glycine isopentyl ester; isopentyl 2-phenyl-2-[(2-pyrrolidin-1-ylethyl)amino]acetate).

'**Camoform**' *see* Bialamicol.

'**Camolar**' *see* Cycloguanil embonate.

'**Camoprim**' *see under* Amodiaquine.

CAMOSTAT** (*p*-guanidinobenzoic acid ester with (*p*-hydroxyphenyl)acetic acid ester with *N,N*-dimethylglycolamide; (dimethylcarbamoyl)methyl [*p*-(*p*-guanidinobenzoyloxy)phenyl]acetate; FOY-305).

CAMP *see* Adenosine 3',5'-phosphate.

'**Campanol**' *see* Polystyrenesulfonate potassium.

Camphane *see* Bornane.

2-Camphanol *see* Borneol.

Camphechlor *see* Campheclor.

CAMPHECLOR* (mixture of chlorinated derivatives of bornene; camphechlor; chlorcamphene; chlorinated camphene; chlorphen; kamfochlor; poliklorkamfen; polychlorcamphene).

Camphene *see* Bornene.

Camphetamide *see* Camphotamide.

'**Camphidonium**' *see* Trimethidinium methosulfate.

Camphocarbonic acid *see* 2-Oxo-3-bornanecarboxylic acid.

Camphocarboxylic acid *see* 2-Oxo-3-bornanecarboxylic acid.

Camphol *see* Borneol.

CAMPHOR (2-oxo-1,7,7-trimethylbicyclo[2.2.1]heptane; 2-bornanone; alcanfor).

CAMPHORAMINE (ammonium 2-oxobornane-3-carboxylate; ammonium camphocarbonate; ammonium camphocarboxylate).

3-Camphorcarboxylic acid *see* 2-Oxo-3-bornanecarboxylic acid.

CAMPHORSULFONIC ACID (2-oxobornane-10-sulfonic acid).

Camphorsulfonic acid esters and salts *see* Camsilate(s).

CAMPHOTAMIDE*** (3-(diethylcarbamoyl)-1-methylpyridinium camphorsulfonate; *N*'-meth-

ylnikethamide camphorsulfonate; camphetamide; camphetamine; camphramine).

Camphramine *see* Camphotamide.

CAMPTOTHECIN (2-ethyl-9,11-dihydro-8-(hydroxymethyl)-9-oxoindolizino[1,2-*b*]quinoline-7-
glycolic acid sodium salt; NSC-100880).

CAMSILATE(S)** (camphorsulfonate(s); camsyl-
ate(s)).

Camsylate(s)* *see* Camsilate(s).

CAMYLOFIN*** ([[2-(diethylamino)ethyl]-
amino]isopentyl phenylacetate isopentyl ester;
isoamyl *N*-(2-diethylaminoethyl)-2-phenylgly-
cinate; acamylophenine).

CAMYLOFIN plus BISMUTH NITRATE ('sedomuth').

CAMYLOFIN plus DIPYRONE ('avafortan').

'Camyna' *see* Tioxolone.

CANBISOL** ((±)-3-(1,1-dimethylheptyl)-
6aβ,7,8,9,10,10aα-hexahydro-6,6-dimethyl-6*H*-
dibenzo[*b,d*]pyran-1,9-diol).

'Candamide' *see* Lithium carbonate.

'Candaseptic' *see* Chlorocresol.

'Candeptin' *see* Candicidin.

'Canderel' *see* Aspartame.

CANDICIDIN*** (antibiotic from *Str. griseus*; A-
2701; NSC-94219; 'candeptin'; 'vanobid').

'Candiolin' *see* Calcium fructose 1,6-diphosphate.

Canescine *see* Deserpidine.

'Canesten' *see* Clotrimazole.

Canforemetina *see* Emetine camsilate.

CANNABINOL*** (6,6,9-trimethyl-3-pentyl-6*H*-
dibenzo[*b,d*]pyran-1-ol; 6,6,9-trimethyl-3-pentyl-
benzo[*c*]chromen-1-ol).

CANNABIS (*C. indica*; indian hemp; marihuana).

Cannabiscetin *see* Myricetin.

Cannogenic acid L-thevetoside *see* Perusitin.

Cannogenin L-thevetoside *see* Peruvoside.

'Canocyl' *see* Magnesium acetylsalicylate.

'Canogard' *see* Dichlorvos.

'Canopar' *see* Thenium closilate.

CANRENOATE POTASSIUM* (canrenoic acid
potassium salt; potassium canrenoate; aldadiene; CB-8109; SC-14266; 'kanrenol'; 'osyrol';
'sincomen'; 'soldactone'; 'venactone').

CANRENOIC ACID*** (17α-(2-carboxyethyl)-
17β-hydroxyandrosta-4,6-dien-3-one; 17β-hydr-
oxy-3-oxo-17α-pregna-4,6-diene-21-carboxylic
acid; 3-(17β-hydroxy-3-oxoandrosta-4,6-dien-
17-yl)propionic acid; 17β-hydroxy-17α-pregna-
4,6-diene-3-one-21-carboxylic acid).

Canrenoic acid lactone *see* Canrenone.

Canrenoic acid potassium salt *see* Canrenoate potassium.

CANRENONE** (17α-(2-carboxyethyl)-17β-hydr-
oxyandrosta-4,6-dien-3-one lactone; canrenoic
acid γ-lactone; RP 11614; SC-9376; 'phanurane').

'Cantabilin' *see* Hymecromone.

CANTHARIDIN (hexahydro-3α,7α-dimethyl-4,7-
epoxyisobenzofuran-1,3-dione).

CANTHAXANTHIN (β,β-carotene-4,4'-dione;
4,4'-dioxo-β-carotene; 'roxanthin red 10').

'Cantil' *see* Mepenzolate bromide.

'Cantor' *see* Minaprine.

'Cantrex' *see* Kanamycin.

'Cantrol' *see* 4-(4-Chloro-2-methylphenoxy)butyric
acid.

'Caparol' *see* Prometryn.

'Capastat' *see* Capreomycin.

'Capazine' *see* Prochlorperazine.

'Capben' *see* Sodium capobenate.

'Capellin' *see* Phenazone salicylate.

'Capla' *see* Mebutamate.

'Capmul 8210' *see* Octanoin.

CAPOBENIC ACID*** (trimethoxybenzoyl-6-
aminocaproic acid; 6-(3,4,5-trimethoxybenz-
amido)caproic acid; 6-(3,4,5-trimethoxybenz-
amido)hexanoic acid; C-3; 'C-tre').
See also Sodium capobenate.

'Capoten' *see* Captopril.

CAPREOMYCIN*** (antibiotic from *Str. capreo-
lus*; capreomycin sulfate).

Capric acid *see* Decanoic acid.

Caprine *see* Norleucine.

CAPROCHLORONE (L-4-(*o*-chlorobenzyl)-5-
oxo-4-phenylhexanoic acid; caproclorone).

'Caprocin' *see* Capreomycin.

Caproclorone *see* Caprochlorone.

'Caprodat' *see* Carisoprodol.

Caproic acid *see* Hexanoic acid.

'Caprokol' *see* Hexylresorcinol.

CAPROLACTAM (2-oxohexamethylenimine;
aminocaproic lactam; ε-caprolactam).

Caprolactam polymer *see* Policapram.

'Caprolest' *see* Aminocaproic acid.

Caprophenone *see* Hexanophenone.

'Caprosem' *see* Cloxotestosterone.

CAPROXAMINE*** ((*E*)-3'-amino-4'-methylhex-
anophenone *O*-(2-aminoethyl)oxime; Du-
22550).

Caprylic acid *see* Octanoic acid.

Caprylic alcohol *see* 1-Octanol.

CAPSAICIN (9-methylnon-6-enoic acid vanillylamide; decenoic acid vanillylamide).

'Capsebon' *see* Cadmium sulfide.

CAPTAFOL* (*N*-[(1,1,2,2'-tetrachloroethyl)thio]-
4-cyclohexenedicarboximide; *N*-(tetrachloroethylthio)-Δ⁴-tetrahydrophthalimide; 3a,4,7,7a-
tetrahydro-2-[(1,1,2,2-tetrachloroethyl)thio]-1*H*-
isoindole-1,3-(2*H*)-dione; 'difolatan'; 'folcid').

CAPTAFOL plus PYRIDINITRIL ('ciluan').

'Captagon' *see* Fenetylline.

CAPTAMINE** (2-(dimethylamino)ethanethiol;
N,N-dimethylmercaptamine; *N*-(2-mercapto-
ethyl)dimethylamine; NSC-45463).

CAPTAN* (3a,4,7,7a-tetrahydro-2-[(trichloromethyl)thio]-1*H*-isoindole-1,3(2*H*)dione; *N*-(trichloromethylthio)-4-cyclohexene-1,2-dicarbox-
imide; *N*-(trichloromethylthio)tetrahydrophthal-
imide; SR-406; 'orthocide-406'; 'vancide-89').

CAPTODIAME** (2-[*p*-(butylthio)-α-phenylbenz-
ylthio]-*N,N*-dimethylethylamine; N-68).

'Captodramine' *see* Captodiame.

CAPTOPRIL*** (1-[(2*S*)-3-mercapto-2-methyl-
propanoyl]pyrrolidine-2-carboxylic acid; 1-(3-
mercapto-2-methylpropionyl)-L-proline; SQ-

14225; 'acepril'; 'capoten'; 'lopirin'; 'tensobon').

CAPURIDE* (1-(2-ethyl-3-methylvaleryl)urea; McN-X-94; NSC-27178; 'pacinox').

'Capval' *see* Noscapine.

CAQ *see* Cloxiquine acetate.

2,2'-C-ara C *see* Ancitabine.

CARACEMIDE (*N*-acetyl-*N*,*O*-bis(methylcarbamoyl)hydroxylamine; *N*-[(methylamino)carbonyl]-*N*-[[(methylamino)carbonyl]oxy]acetamide; NSC-253272).

'Caradrin' *see* Proscillaridin.

'Caragard' *see* Terbumeton.

CARAMIPHEN* (2-(diethylamino)ethyl 1-phenylcyclopentanecarboxylate; caramiphen hydrochloride; merpanit; pantaphene; pentaphene; G-2747).

CARAMIPHEN EDISILATE (caramiphen edisylate; caramiphen ethanedisulfonate).

CARAZOLOL* (1-(carbazol-4-yloxy)-3-(isopropylamino)-2-propanol; 4-[2-hydroxy-3-(isopropylamino)propoxy]carbazole; 'conducton').

CARBACHOL* (carbacholine chloride; carbamoylcholine; carbocholine; choline carbamate; choline chloride carbamate).

Carbacholine chloride* *see* Carbachol.

'Carbadal' *see* Carbromal.

Carbadipimidine *see* Carpipramine.

CARBADOX (methyl 3-(2-quinoxalinylmethylene)carbazoate *N*¹,*N*⁴-dioxide; GS-6244; 'mecadox').

'Carbamat' *see* Isoprocarb.

CARBAMAZEPINE* (5*H*-dibenz[*b*,*f*]azepine-5-carboxamide; G-32883).

'Carbamed' *see* Carbachol.

CARBAMIC ACID (aminoformic acid).

Carbamic acid hydrazide *see* Semicarbazide.

Carbamide *see* Urea.

Carbamidine *see* Guanidine.

Carbamimidic acid *see* Pseudourea.

Carbamimidothioic acid *see* Pseudothiourea.

***N*-CARBAMOYLASPARTIC ACID** (ureidosuccinic acid).
See also Calcium carbamoylaspartate.

2-(2-Carbamoyl-1-aziridinyl)-2-(2-cyano-1-aziridinyl)propane *see* Azimexon.

Carbamoylbenzoic acids *see* Isophthalamic acid; Phthalamic acid; Terephthalamic acid.

4-Carbamoylbutyric acid *see* Glutaramic acid.

Carbamoylcarbamic acid *see* Allophanic acid.

4-Carbamoyl-1-[[2-carboxy-8-oxo-7-(2-phenyl-2-sulfoacetamido)-5-thia-1-azabicyclo[4.2.0]oct-2-en-3-yl]methyl]pyridinium hydroxide inner salt *see* Cefsulodin.

Carbamoylcefaloridine *see* Cefalonium.

Carbamoylcholine *see* Carbachol.

CARBAMOYLCYSTEINE (*S*-carbamoyl-L-cysteine; carbamylcysteine; NSC-102498; SCC).

Carbamoyldapsone *see* Amidapsone.

3-Carbamoyl-4-deacetyl-4-de(methoxycarbonyl)vincaleukoblastine *see* Vindesine.

(3-Carbamoyl-3,3-diphenylpropyl)diisopropylmethylammonium iodide *see* Isopropamide iodide.

(3-Carbamoyl-3,3-diphenylpropyl)ethyldimethylammonium bromide *see* Ambutonium bromide.

1-(3-Carbamoyl-3,3-diphenylpropyl)hexahydro-1-methylazepinium iodide *see* Buzepide metiodide.

1-(3-Carbamoyl-3,3-diphenylpropyl)-1-methylpiperidinium bromide *see* Fenpiverinium bromide.

Carbamoyldithiobenzenearsonous acid *S*,*S*-diester with thioglycolic acid *see* Thiacetarsamide.

1-(2-Carbamoylethyl)-4-phenylisonipecotic acid ethyl ester *see* Carperidine.

***N*-Carbamoylmaleamic acid** *see* Maleuric acid.

***N*-Carbamoylmalonamic acid** *see* Malonuric acid.

3(4*H*)-Carbamoylmethyl-2*H*-1,3-benzoxazin-2-one *see* Caroxazone.

***N*-(D-1-[(Carbamoylmethyl)carbamoyl]-3-methylbutyl]-*N*-methyl-L-2-pyrrolidinecarboxamide** *see* Pareptide.

Carbamoyl-β-methylcholine *see* Bethanechol.

4-(Carbamoylmethyl)-2,3-dihydro-3-oxo-1,4-benzoxazine *see* Paraxazone.

1-(*p*-Carbamoylmethylphenoxy)-3-isopropylamino-2-propanol *see* Atenolol.

3-Carbamoyl-1-methylpyridinium hydroxide *see* *N*¹-Methylnicotinamide.

1-Carbamoylmethyl-2-pyrrolidinone *see* Piracetam.

1-(2-Carbamoyloxyethyl)-2-methyl-5-nitroimidazole *see* Bamnidazole.

4-Carbamoyloxy-1-[3-(*p*-fluorobenzoyl)propyl]octahydroquinoline *see* Cicarperone.

4-Carbamoyloxy-1-[4-(*p*-fluorophenyl)-4-oxobutyl]decahydroquinoline *see* Cicarperone.

3-(Carbamoyloxymethyl)-7-[2-(2-furyl)-2-(methoxyimino)acetamido]-2-cephem-2-carboxylic acid *see* Cefuroxime.

3-(Carbamoyloxymethyl)-7*S*-methoxy-7*R*-(2-thienylacetamido)-2-cephem-2-carboxylic acid *see* Cefoxitin.

2-Carbamoylphenoxyacetic acid tetrahydrofuryl ester *see* Fenamifuril.

1-[2-(4-Carbamoylphenoxy)ethylamino]-3-(2-methylphenoxy)-2-propanol *see* Tolamolol.

4-(4-Carbamoyl-4-piperid-1-ylpiperid-1-yl)-2,2-diphenylbutyronitrile *see* Piritramide.

5-[3-(4-Carbamoyl-4-piperid-1-ylpiperid-1-yl)propyl]-3-chloro-10,11-dihydro-5*H*-dibenz[*b*,*f*]azepine *see* Clocapramine.

5-[3-[(4-Carbamoyl-4-piperid-1-yl)piperid-1-yl]propyl]-10,11-dihydro-5*H*-dibenz[*b*,*f*]azepine *see* Carpipramine.

10-[3-(4-Carbamoylpiperid-1-yl)propyl]-2-chlorophenothiazine *see* Pipamazine.

1-(1-Carbamoylpropyl)-2-pyrrolidinone *see* Etiracetam.

3-(4-Carbamoylpyrid-1-ylmethyl)-7-(thien-2-ylacetamido)-2-cephem-2-carboxylic acid *see* Cefalonium.

3-Carbamoyl-1-β-D-ribofuranosylpyridinium hydroxide 5'-ester with adenosine 5'-pyrophosphate inner salt *see* Nadide.

***O*-Carbamoylsalicylic acid lactam** *see* Carsalam.

***N*¹-Carbamoylsulfanilamide** *see* Sulfacarbamide.

7-(Carbamoyltetrahydro-3-hydroxy-5-methoxy-6,6-dimethylpyran-2-yloxy)-4-hydroxy-3-[4-hydroxy-

3-(3-methylbut-2-enyl)benzamido]-8-methyl-2H-chromen-2-one *see* Novobiocin.

'Carbamult' *see* Promecarb.

Carbamylcysteine *see* Carbamoylcysteine.

Carbamylurea *see* Biuret.

CARBANILAMIDE (phenylcarbamide; phenylurea; ureidobenzene).

CARBANILIC ACID (phenylcarbamic acid).

Carbanilic acid esters *see* Carbetamide; Cyclarbamate; Diperodon; Propham.

CARBANILIDE (1,3-diphenylurea).

CARBANOLATE* (6-chloro-3,4-xylyl methylcarbamate; 2-chloro-4,5-dimethylphenyl methylcarbamate; chlorxylam; 'banol').

CARBANTEL** (1-(*p*-chlorophenyl)-3-valerimidoylurea; *N*-[[(4-chlorophenyl)amino]carbonyl]-pentanimidamide).

CARBANTEL LAURYL SULFATE* (carbantel compound with dodecyl hydrogen sulfate; WIN-29194-6).

CARBARIL** (1-naphthyl methylcarbamate; carbaryl; ENT-23969; 'aasevin'; 'asevin'; 'aurex'; 'carylderm'; 'karbatox'; 'karbosep'; 'sevin').

CARBARSONE** (*p*-ureidobenzenearsonic acid; aminarsone).

Carbaryl* *see* Carbaril.

CARBASALATE CALCIUM*** (salicylic acid acetate calcium salt compound (1:1) with urea; calcium acetylsalicylate carbamide; calcium acetylsalicylate urea; calcium carbaspirin; carbaspirin calcium; 'calurin'; 'iromin').

Carbaspirin calcium* *see* Carbasalate calcium.

'Carbathion' *see* Metam-sodium.

CARBAZERAN*** (1-(6,7-dimethoxyphthalazin-1-yl)piperid-4-yl ethylcarbamate; UK-31557).

CARBAZIC ACID (hydrazinecarboxylic acid). *See also* Carbenzide; Tropabazate.

Carbazilquinone *see* Carboquone.

CARBAZOCHROME*** (3-hydroxy-1-methyl-5,6-indolinedione semicarbazone; adrenochrome semicarbazone; 'adrenoxyl'; 'cromadrenal'; 'cromosil').

CARBAZOCHROME plus TROXERUTIN ('fleboside').

CARBAZOCHROME SALICYLATE*** (mixture of carbazochrome with sodium salicylate; 'adrenosem'; 'adrestat').

CARBAZOCHROME SODIUM SULFONATE*** (5,6-dihydro-1-methyl-5,6-dioxo-3-indolinesulfonic acid 5-semicarbazone sodium salt; AC-17; 'adona').

CARBAZOCINE*** (1-(cyclopropylmethyl)octahydro-5,11b-iminoethano-11b*H*-benzo[*a*]carbazole).

CARBAZOLE (dibenzopyrrole; diphenylenimine).

1-(Carbazol-4-yloxy)-3-(isopropylamino)-2-propanol *see* Carazolol.

1-(Carbazol-4-yloxy)-3-[[2-(*o*-methoxyphenoxy)-ethyl]amino]-2-propanol *see* Carvedilol.

Carbazotic acid *see* Picric acid.

Carbazylquinone *see* Carboquone.

CARBENICILLIN*** (*N*-(2-carboxy-3,3-dimethyl-7-oxo-4-thia-1-azabicyclo[3.2.0]hept-6-yl)-2-2-phenylmalonamic acid; 6-(2-carboxy-2-phenylacetamido)penicillanic acid; α-carboxybenzylpenicillin; 6-(phenylmalonamido)penicillanic acid; carbenicillin sodium; carbenicillin potassium; BAY b-5369; BRL-2064; CP-15639-2; GS-3159; NSC-111071; 'anabactyl'; 'fugacillin'; 'geopen'; 'microcillin'; 'pyopen').

CARBENICILLIN plus CLOXACILLIN ('pyoclox').

Carbenicillin indanyl* *see* Carindacillin.

Carbenicillin phenyl sodium* *see* Carfecillin.

CARBENOXOLONE*** (3β-hydroxy-11-oxoolean-12-en-30-oic acid hydrogen succinate; (3β,20β)-3-(3-carboxy-1-oxopropoxy)-11-oxoolean-12-en-29-oic acid; enoxolone hydrogen succinate; carbenoxolone disodium; carbenoxolone sodium).

CARBENZIDE*** (ethyl 2-(α-methylbenzyl)-1-hydrazinecarboxylate; ethyl 3-(α-methylbenzyl)-carbazate).

CARBESILATE(S)** (*p*-carboxybenzenesulfonic acid, esters and salts).

CARBESTROL (3-ethyl-4-(*p*-methoxyphenyl)-2-methyl-3-cyclohexene-1-carboxylic acid; NSC-19962).

CARBETAMIDE* (2-[(anilinocarbonyl)oxy]-*N*-ethylpropionamide; *N*-ethyl-2-[[(phenylamino)-carbonyl]oxy]propanamide; 1-(ethylcarbamoyl)-ethyl carbanilate; carbethamide; 'legurame').

Carbetapentane *see* Pentoxyverine.

Carbethamide *see* Carbetamide.

CARBETHYL SALICYLATE* (ethyl salicylate carbonate; 'sal-ethyl carbonate').

Carbetidine *see* Etoxeridine.

CARBETIMER** (maleic anhydride-ethylene polymer ammonia reaction product).

CARBETOCIN*** (1-butyric acid-2-[3-(*p*-methoxyphenyl)-L-alanine]oxytocin).

'Carbicron' *see* Dicrotophos.

Carbidine (tr) *see* Dicarbine.

CARBIDOPA*** (2-(3,4-dihydroxybenzyl)-2-hydrazinopropionic acid; 3-(3,4-dihydroxyphenyl)-2-hydrazino-2-methylpropionic acid; α-hydrazino-3,4-dihydroxy-α-methylhydrocinnamic acid; α-hydrazino-α-methyldopa; hydrazinomethyldopa; α-methyldopa-hydrazine; MK-486; 'lodosyn'). *See also under* Levodopa.

CARBIFENE*** (2-ethoxy-*N*-methyl-*N*-[2-(methylphenethylamino)ethyl]-2,2-diphenylacetamide; carbiphene; carbiphene hydrochloride; etomide; etymide; NSC-106959; SQ-10269; 'bandol'; 'jubalon').

CARBIMAZOLE*** (1-(ethoxycarbonyl)-3-methyl-2-thioimidazole; ethyl 3-methyl-2-thioimidazoline-1-carboxylate; ethyl methimazolate; 1-methyl-2-imidazolethiol ethyl carbonate).

Carbimide calcium *see* Calcium carbimide.

Carbinamine *see* Methylamine.

Carbinol *see* Methanol.

CARBINOXAMINE*** (2-[*p*-chloro-α-(2-dimethylaminoethoxy)benzyl]pyridine; *p*-chloro-α-pyrid-2-ylbenzyl 2-dimethylaminoethyl ether; para-

carbinoxamine; carbinoxamine maleate).
See also under Rotoxamine.

Carbiphene* *see* Carbifene.

'Carbitol' *see* 2-(2-Ethoxyethoxy)ethanol.

'Carbocaine' *see* Mepivacaine.

Carbocholine *see* Carbachol.

CARBOCISTEINE*** (3-[(carboxymethyl)thio]-alanine; *S*-carboxymethylcysteine; AHR-3053; LJ-206; 'lisomucil'; 'loviscol'; 'muciclar'; 'mucodyne'; 'mucojet'; 'mucopront'; 'Pol 65'; 'rhinathiol'; 'transbronchin').

CARBOCISTEINE plus PRENOXDIAZINE ('libexin').

CARBOCISTEINE plus SOBREROL ('polimucil').

CARBOCISTEINE plus THEOPHYLLINE (MJ-12; 'thio-theo').

CARBOCLORAL*** (ethyl (2,2,2-trichloro-1-hydroxyethyl)carbamate; chloral urethan; ethyl trichloramate; trichloramate; CI-336; CN-16146; HY-185; NSC-33077).

CARBOCROMEN*** (ethyl 3-(2-diethylaminoethyl)-4-methylcoumarin-7-yloxyacetate; 3-[2-(diethylamino)ethyl]-7-(ethoxycarbonylmethoxy)-4-methylcoumarin; chromonar; A-27053; AG-3; Cassella-4489; NSC-110430).

Carbodimide calcium *see* Calcium carbimide.

CARBOFENOTION*** (*S*-[(*p*-chlorophenyl-thio)methyl] *O,O*-diethyl phosphorodithioate; carbophenothion; carbothion; nephocarp; R-1303; 'garrathion'; 'liro-trithion'; 'trithion').

CARBOFENOTION METHYL (*S*-[(*p*-chloro-phenylthio)methyl] *O,O*-dimethyl phosphorodithioate; carbophenothion methyl; 'methyltrithion').

CARBOFURAN* (2,3-dihydro-2,2-dimethylbenzofuran-7-yl methylcarbamate; NIA-10242; 'curaterr'; 'furadan').

N^4-(Carbo-2-hydroxyethoxy)sulfanilamide *see* Sulocarbilate.

Carbolane *see* Phosfolan.

Carbolic acid *see* Phenol.

'Carbolin' *see* Carbachol.

β-Carboline *see* 9*H*-Pyrido[3,4-*b*]indole.

γ-Carboline *see* 5*H*-Pyrido[4,3-*b*]indole

'Carbolith' *see* Lithium carbonate.

Carbolonium* *see* Hexcarbacholine bromide.

CARBOMER*** (acrylic acid polymer crosslinked with allyl sucrose; carpolene; 'carbopol').

Carbomethene *see* Ketene.

CARBOMYCIN*** (antibiotic from *Str. halstedii*; NSC-51001; 'magnamycin').

'Carbona' *see* Carbon tetrachloride.

Carbon dichloride *see* Tetrachloroethylene.

Carbon hexachloride *see* Hexachloroethane.

Carbonolol *see* Carteolol.

CARBON TETRACHLORIDE (tetrachloromethane).

Carbonyl chloride *see* Phosgene.

Carbonyldiamide *see* Urea.

Carbophenothion* *see* Carbofenotion.

Carbophos (tr) *see* Malathion.

CARBOPLATIN*** (*cis*-diammine(1,1-cyclobuta-

necarboxylato)platinum; CBDCA; JM-8; NSC-241240).

'Carbopol' *see* Carbomer.

CARBOPROST*** ((*E,Z*)-(1*R*,2*R*,3*R*,5*S*)-7-[3,5-dihydroxy-2-[(3*S*)-(3-hydroxy-3-methyl-1-octenyl)cyclopentyl]-5-heptenoic acid; (15*S*)-15-methyldinoprost; (15*S*)-15-methylprostaglandin $F_{2\alpha}$; (5*Z*,9α,11α,13*E*,15*S*)-9,11,15-trihydroxy-15-methylprosta-5-*cis*,13-*trans*-dien-1-oic acid; U-32921; 'prostin 15 M').

CARBOPROST METHYL* (carboprost methyl ester; U-36384).

CARBOPROST TROMETAMOL (carboprost tromethamine; U-26921E).

Carboprost tromethamine* *see* Carboprost trometamol.

CARBOQUONE*** (2,5-bis(1-aziridinyl)-3-(2-hydroxy-1-methoxyethyl)-6-methyl-*p*-benzoquinone carbamate ester; carbazilquinone; carbazylquinone; CS-310; NSC-134679).

'Carbostesin' *see* Bupivacaine.

Carbostibamide *see* Urea stibamine.

CARBOSTYRIL (2-quinolinol).

'Carbothiazol' *see* Maleylsulfathiazole.

Carbothion *see* Carbofenotion.

Carbothrone *see* Anthrone.

'Carbowaxes' *see* Macrogol(s).

5-Carboxamido-2-chlorobenzenesulfonamide *see* Sulclamide.

3-Carboxamido-4-hydroxy-α-[(1-methyl-3-phenyl-propylamino)methyl]benzyl alcohol *see* Labetalol.

1-(4-Carboxamidoimidazol-5-yl)-3,3-dimethyltriazene *see* Dacarbazine.

4-(4-Carboxamido-4-piperid-1-ylpiperid-1-yl)-4′-fluorobutyrophenone *see* Pipamperone.

10-[3-(4-Carboxamidopiperid-4-yl)propyl]-2-methyl-sulfonylphenothiazine *see* Metopimazine.

5-Carboxanilido-2,3-dihydro-6-methyl-1,4-oxathiin *see* Carboxin.

CARBOXIN* (5,6-dihydro-2-methyl-*N*-phenyl-1,4-oxathiin-3-carboxamide; 5-carboxanilido-2,3-dihydro-6-methyl-1,4-oxathiin; D-753; DCMO; 'vitavax').

CARBOXIN DIOXIDE (5-carboxanilido-2,3-dihydro-6-methyl-1,4-oxathiin 4,4-dioxide; oxycarboxin; DCMOD; F-461; 'plantavax').

Carboxin monoxide *see* Carboxin oxide.

CARBOXIN OXIDE (5-carboxanilido-2,3-dihydro-6-methyl-1,4-oxathiin 4-oxide; carboxin monoxide; F-831).

p-[2-(α-Carboxy-p-anisoyl)vinyl]benzoic acid *see* Cinfenoac.

1-(2-Carboxybenzamido)naphthalene *see* Naptalam.

p-Carboxybenzenesulfondiethylamide *see* Etebenecid.

p-Carboxybenzenesulfonic acid, esters and salts *see* Carbesilate(s).

1-(α-Carboxybenzyl)-1-methylpiperidinium iodide ester with diethyl(hydroxyethoxyethyl)methylammonium iodide *see* Piprocurarium iodide.

α-Carboxybenzylpenicillin *see* Carbenicillin.

6-(4-Carboxybutylthio)purine *see* Buthiopurine.

**1-[3-(2-Carboxybutyl)-2,4,6-triiodophenyl]pyrrolidin-2-one *see* Iolidonic acid.

N-(4-Carboxybutyryl)-L-alanyl-L-tyrosylglycyl-L-tryptophyl-L-leucyl-L-α-aspartylphenyl-L-alaninamide *see* Desglugastrin.

1-[[2-Carboxy-7-[2-(5-carboxyimidazole-4-carboxamido)-2-phenylacetamido]-8-oxo-5-thia-1-azabicyclo[4.2.0]oct-2-en-3-yl]methyl]-4-(2-sulfoethyl)-pyridinium hydroxide inner salt *see* Cefpimizole.

1-[(3-Carboxy-4-chlorophenyl)sulfonyl]-3,5-dimethylpiperidine *see* Tibric acid.

3β-(*cis*-2-Carboxycyclohexylcarbonyloxy)-11-oxo-olean-12-en-30-oic acid *see* Cicloxolone.

2-Carboxy-2′,6′-dichloro-3′-methyldiphenylamine *see* Meclofenamic acid.

(+)-*N*-Carboxy-9,10-dihydro-1-methyllysergamine benzyl ester *see* Metergoline.

(*S*)-α-Carboxy-2,3-dihydro-*N*,*N*,*N*-trimethyl-2-thioxo-1*H*-imidazole-4-ethanamium hydroxide inner salt *see* Thioneine.

9-(3-Carboxy-1,3-dihydroxypropyl)adenine *see* Eritadenine.

2-Carboxy-3,4-dimethoxybenzaldehyde isonicotinoylhydrazone *see* Opiniazide.

N-(2-Carboxy-3,3-dimethyl-7-oxo-4-thia-1-azabicyclo[3.2.0]hept-6-yl)-2-phenylmalonamic acid *see* Carbenicillin.

N-(2-Carboxy-3,3-dimethyl-7-oxo-4-thia-1-azabicyclo[3.2.0]hept-6-yl)-3-thiophenemalonamic acid *see* Ticarcillin.

2-Carboxy-1,1-dimethylpyrrolidinium iodide ester with choline iodide *see* Trepirium iodide.

*N*⁶-[D-2-(4-Carboxy-5,5-dimethylthiazolidin-2-yl)-*N*-(phenylacetyl)glycyl]-L-lysine monopotassium salt decapeptide *see* Benpenolisin.

3-[2-(1-Carboxyethoxy)ethoxy]-*N*-ethyl-2,4,6-triiodoacetanilide *see* Iolixanic acid.

3-(1-Carboxyethyl)benzophenone *see* Ketoprofen.

5-[[*p*-[(2-Carboxyethyl)carbamoyl]phenyl]azo]salicylic acid *see* Balsalazide.

2-[(2-Carboxyethyl)carbonyl]dibenzofuran *see* Furobufen.

5-(1-Carboxyethyl)-2-(*p*-chlorophenyl)benzoxazole *see* Benoxaprofen.

1-[4-(1-Carboxyethyl)-2-chlorophenyl]-3-pyrroline *see* Pirprofen.

2-Carboxyethyl dibenzofuran-2-yl ketone *see* Furobufen.

4-(3-Carboxy-1-ethyl-1,4-dihydro-4-oxoquinolin-7-yl)pyridine *see* Rosoxacin.

3-*O*-α-Carboxyethyl-D-glucosamine *see* Muramic acid.

17α-(2-Carboxyethyl)-17β-hydroxyandrosta-4,6-dien-3-one *see* Canrenoic acid.

17α-(2-Carboxyethyl)-17β-hydroxyandrosta-4,6-dien-3-one lactone *see* Canrenone.

2-(1-Carboxyethyl)-7-methoxy-10-methylphenothiazine *see* Protizinic acid.

1-[*p*-(1-Carboxyethyl)phenyl]cyclohexene *see* Tetriprofen.

4-(2-Carboxyethyl)phenyl tranexamate *see* Cetraxate.

2-(2-Carboxyethyl)-1,2,3,4-tetrahydro-6,7-dimethoxy-2-methyl-1-veratrylisoquinolinium benzene-sulfonate pentamethylene ester *see* Atracurium besilate.

2-[[(5-Carboxy-5-formamidopentyl)carbamoyl](2-phenylacetamido)methyl]-5,5-dimethyl-4-thiazolidinecarboxylic acid *see* Libecillide.

β-Carboxyglutaric acid *see* Tricarballylic acid.

S-(7-Carboxy-4-hexyl-9-oxoxanthen-2-yl)-*S*-methylsulfoximine *see* Sudexanox.

3-Carboxy-4-hydroxybenzenesulfonic acid *see* Sulfosalicylic acid.

2-(5-Carboxy-3-hydroxy-3-methylpentyl)-3,5,6-trimethylbenzoquinone lactone *see* Tocopheronic acid.

7β-[2-Carboxy-2-(4-hydroxyphenyl)acetamido]-7α-methoxy-3-[[(1-methyl-1*H*-tetrazol-5-yl)thio]methyl]-5-dethia-5-oxa-2-cephem-2-carboxylic acid *see* Latamoxef.

7-[2-Carboxy-2-(4-hydroxyphenyl)acetamido]-7-methoxy-3-[[(1-methyltetrazol-5-yl)thio]methyl]-8-oxo-5-oxa-1-azabicyclo[4.2.0]oct-2-ene-2-carboxylic acid *see* Latamoxef.

p-[(3-Carboxy-4-hydroxyphenyl)azo]hippuric acid *see* Ipsalazide.

3-(3-Carboxy-4-hydroxyphenyl)-4,5-dihydro-2-phenyl-3*H*-benz[*e*]indole *see* Fendosal.

(3-Carboxy-2-hydroxypropyl)trimethylammonium hydroxide inner salt *see* Carnitine.

7-[2-(5-Carboxyimidazole-4-carboxamido)-2-phenylacetamido]-3-[4-[(2-sulfoethyl)pyrid-1-yl]methyl]-2-cephem-2-carboxylic acid inner salt *see* Cefpimizole.

2-Carboxy-4-isopropenyl-3-pyrrolidineacetic acid *see* Kainic acid.

1-Carboxy-[2-(2-mercaptoimidazol-4(or-5)-yl)-ethyl]trimethylammonium hydroxide inner salt *see* Thioneine.

o-Carboxymethoxybenzaldehyde isonicotinoylhydrazone *see* Aconiazide.

N-[(2*S*,5*R*,6*S*)-2-Carboxy-6-methoxy-3,3-dimethyl-7-oxo-4-thia-1-azabicyclo[3.2.0]hept-2-yl]-3-thiophenemalonamic acid *see* Temocillin.

2-[4-[4-Carboxy-7-methoxy-3-[[(1-methyltetrazol-5-yl)thio]methyl]-3-cephem-7-ylcarbamoyl]-1,3-dithietan-2-ylidene]malonamic acid *see* Cefotetan.

N-[2-Carboxy-7-methoxy-3-[[(1-methyl-1*H*-tetrazol-5-yl)thio]methyl]-8-oxo-1-azabicyclo[4.2.0]oct-2-en-7-yl]-2-(*p*-hydroxyphenyl)malonamic acid *see* Latamoxef.

4-[[2-Carboxy-7-methoxy-3-[[(1-methyl-1*H*-tetrazol-5-yl)thio]methyl]-8-oxo-5-thia-1-azabicyclo-[4.2.0]oct-2-en-7-yl]carbamoyl]-1,3-dithietane-Δ²,ᵅ-malonamic acid *see* Cefotetan.

4-[2-[[4-(Carboxymethoxy)phenyl]carbonyl]ethenyl]-benzoic acid *see* Cinfenoac.

Carboxymethylcellulose *see* Carmellose.

3-(Carboxymethyl)-4-chlorobenzothiazol-3(2*H*)-one *see* Benazolin.

Carboxymethylcysteine *see* Carbocisteine.

N-(Carboxymethyl)-*N*-[2-[(2,6-diethylphenyl)-amino]-2-oxoethyl]glycine *see* Etifenin.

(Carboxymethyl)dimethyl(2-hydroxyethyl)ammonium hydroxide inner salt *see* Oxibetaine.

(Carboxymethyl)dimethyl(3-palmitamidopropyl)am-

89

monium hydroxide inner salt *see* Pendecamaine.

N-(Carboxymethyl)-*N*-[2-[(2,6-dimethylphenyl)-amino]-2-oxoethyl]glycine *see* Lidofenin.

(Carboxymethyl)(2-hydroxyethyl)dimethylammonium hydroxide inner salt *see* Oxibetaine.

Carboxymethyliminobis(ethylenenitrilodiacetic acid) *see* Pentetic acid.

N-(Carboxymethyl)-*N*-[2-[[4-(1-methylethyl)phenyl]amino]-2-oxoethyl]glycine *see* Iprofenin.

2-Carboxymethyl-10-methylphenothiazine *see* Metiazinic acid.

6-(5-Carboxy-3-methylpent-2-enyl)-7-hydroxy-5-methoxy-4-methylphthalide *see* Mycophenolic acid.

17β-(3-Carboxy-1-methylpropyl)etiocholanone *see* Cholanic acid.

1-Carboxymethyltheobromine *see* Theobromin-1-ylacetic acid.

7-(Carboxymethyl)theophylline *see* Theophyllin-7-ylacetic acid.

3-[(Carboxymethyl)thio]alanine *see* Carbocisteine.

2-[2-[(Carboxymethyl)thio]ethyl]-4-thiazolidinecarboxylic acid 2-ethyl ester *see* Letosteine.

N-Carboxy-3-morpholinosydnone imine ethyl ester *see* Molsidomine.

(3β,20β)-3-(3-Carboxy-1-oxopropoxy)-11-oxoolean-12-en-29-oic acid *see* Carbenoxolone.

1-[[2-Carboxy-8-oxo-7-[(2-thien-2-yl)-acetamido]-5-thia-1-azabicyclo[4.2.0]-oct-2-en-3-yl]methyl]pyridinium hydroxide inner salt *see* Cefaloridine.

N-(*p*-Carboxyphenethyl)-5-chloro-2-methylbenzamide *see* Meglitinide.

o-Carboxyphenoxyacetic acid hydroxymercuripropanolamide *see* Mercuderamide.

1-(2-Carboxyphenoxy)-3-hexyloxy-2-propanol *see* Exiproben.

6-(2-Carboxy-2-phenylacetamido)penicillanic acid *see* Carbenicillin.

9-(*o*-Carboxyphenyl)-6-hydroxy-3-isoxanthenone *see* Fluorescein.

1-[*N*-(1-Carboxy-3-phenylpropyl)alanyl]hexahydro-2-indolinecarboxylic acid 1-ethyl ester *see* Indolapril.

1-[*N*-[(*S*)-1-Carboxy-3-phenylpropyl]-L-alanyl]-L-proline *see* Enalaprilat.

1-[*N*-[(*S*)-1-Carboxy-3-phenylpropyl]-L-alanyl]-L-proline 1'-ethyl ester *see* Enalapril.

1-[*N*²-(1-Carboxy-3-phenylpropyl)-L-lysyl]-L-proline *see* Lisinopril.

4-Carboxy-α-phenyl-2-thiazolidineacetic acid ethyl ester *see* Leucogen.

3-(2-Carboxypropenyl)-2,2-dimethylcyclopropanecarboxylic acid *see* Chrysanthemumdicarboxylic acid.

N-(2-Carboxypropyl)-2,4,6-triiodo-3-(1-morpholinoethylideneamino)benzamide *see* Iomorinic acid.

(3-Carboxypropyl)trimethylammonium chloride methyl ester *see* Carpronium chloride.

6-(3-Carboxy-2-quinoxalinecarboxamido)penicillanic acid *see* Quinacillin.

3-Carboxyquinoxalin-2-yl-penicillin *see* Quinacillin.

2-(4-Carboxystyryl)-5-nitro-1-vinylimidazole *see* Stirimazole.

Carboxysulfamidochrysoidine *see* Sulfachrysoidine.

3-Carboxy-6,7,8,9-tetrahydro-1,6-dimethyl-4-oxo-4*H*-pyrido[1,2-*a*]pyrimidinium methyl sulfate ethyl ester *see* Rimazolium metilsulfate.

(α-Carboxy-3-thenyl)penicillin *see* Ticarcillin.

*N*¹-(Carboxythiazolyl)sulfanilamide *see* Sulfacarizole.

6-[2-Carboxy-2-(3-thienyl)acetamido]-6-methoxypenicillanic acid *see* Temocillin.

6-(α-Carboxy-α-thien-3-ylacetamido)penicillanic acid *see* Ticarcillin.

2-Carboxy-3'-(trifluoromethyl)diphenylamine *see* Flufenamic acid.

3-[Carboxy(trifluoromethylsulfonyl)amino]benzophenone ethyl ester *see* Triflumidate.

3-Carboxy-α,2,2-trimethylcyclopropaneacrylic acid *see* Chrysanthemumdicarboxylic acid.

2-Carboxy-1,1,6-trimethylpiperidinium iodide choline ester iodide *see* Dimecolonium iodide.

2-Carboxy-1,1,6-trimethylpiperidinium iodide ester with diethyl(2-hydroxyethyl)methyl)ammonium iodide *see* Dicolinium iodide.

N-Carboxy-L-tryptophyl-L-methionyl-L-α-aspartyl-3-phenyl-L-alaninamide *N*-*tert*-pentyl ester *see* Amogastrin.

Carboxyveratrylideneisoniazid *see* Opiniazide.

Carboxyverazid *see* Opiniazide.

CARBROMAL*** (1-(2-bromo-2-ethylbutyryl)-urea; acetylbromdiethylurea; bromadal; bromdiethylacetylurea; bromodiethylacetylurea; diethylbromacetylurea; uradal).

CARBROMAL plus BROMISOVAL ('sekundal').

CARBROMAL plus DIPHENHYDRAMINE ('betadorm').

CARBROMAL plus PROMETHAZINE ('doroma').

CARBUBARB*** (5-butyl-5-(2-carbamoyloxyethyl)barbituric acid carbamate ester; tylemal).

CARBURAZEPAM*** (7-chloro-1,2,3,5-tetrahydro-1-methyl-2-oxo-5-phenyl-4*H*-1,4-benzodiazepine-4-carboxamide).

CARBUTAMIDE*** (1-butyl-3-sulfanilylurea; *N*¹-(butylcarbamoyl)sulfanilamide; aminophenurobutane; nadizan; BZ 55; U-6987).

CARBUTAMIDE plus PHENFORMIN ('glucifrene').

CARBUTEROL*** (1-[5-(2-*tert*-butylamino-1-hydroxyethyl)-2-hydroxyphenyl]urea; 5-(2-*tert*-butylamino-1-hydroxyethyl)-*N*-carbamoyl-2-hydroxyaniline; α-[(*tert*-butylamino)methyl]-4-hydroxy-3-ureidobenzyl alcohol; SK&F-40383; 'bronsecur'; 'pirem').

'Carbyne' *see* Barban.

CARCAINUM CHLORIDE*** (dimethylbis-[(phenylcarbamoyl)methyl]ammonium chloride; QX-572).

'Carcholin' *see* Carbachol.

'Cardan' *see* Oxyphencyclimine.

'Cardelmycin' *see* Novobiocin.

'Cardibeltin' *see* Verapamil.

'Cardidigin' *see* Digitoxin.

'Cardilan' *see* Nicofuranose *and under* Potassium aspartate.

'Cardilate' *see* Erythrityl tetranitrate.
'Cardimone' *see* Adenosine phosphate.
'Cardine' *see* Visnadine.
'Cardiocap' *see* Carbocromen.
'Cardiodynamin' *see* Oxedrine.
'Cardiografin' *see* Meglumine diatrizoate.
'Cardio-green' *see* Indocyanine green.
'Cardiolipol' *see* Niceritrol.
'Cardiomone' *see* Adenosine phosphate.
'Cardioquin' *see* Quinidine polygalacturonate.
'Cardiorhythmine' *see* Ajmaline.
'Cardiorytmin' *see* Procainamide.
'Cardiotensin' *see under* Bemetizide.
'Cardioverina' *see* Papaverine.
'Cardivix' *see* Benziodarone.
'Cardiwell' *see* Erythrityl tetranitrate.
'Cardrase' *see* Ethoxzolamide.
'Cardrax' *see* Ethoxzolamide.
'Carduben' *see* Visnadine.
'Carena' *see* Aminophylline.
CARFECILLIN*** (*N*-(2-carboxy-3,3-dimethyl-7-oxo-4-thia-1-azabicyclo[3.2.0]hept-6-yl)-2-phenylmalonamic acid 1-phenyl ester; 6-[2-(phenoxycarbonyl)-2-phenylacetamido]penicillanic acid; carbenicillin phenyl sodium; carfenicillin; carfecillin sodium; BRL-3475; 'uticillin').
CARFENAZINE*** (1-[10-[3-(4-(2-hydroxyethyl)-1-piperazinyl)propyl]phenothiazin-2-yl]-1-propanone; 10-[3-[4-(2-hydroxyethyl)piperazin-1-yl]propyl]-2-propionylphenothiazine; carphenazine; carfenazine maleate; NSC-71755; Wy-2445).
Carfenicillin *see* Carfecillin.
CARFENTANIL*** (methyl 1-phenethyl-4-(*N*-phenylpropionamido)isonipecotate; methyl 4-[(1-oxopropyl)phenylamino]-1-(2-phenylethyl)-4-piperidinecarboxylate).
CARFENTANIL CITRATE* (R-33799).
CARFIMATE*** (α-ethynylbenzyl alcohol carbamate; 1-phenyl-2-propynyl carbamate; ethynyl phenyl carbinol carbamate; CFC).
CARGUTOCIN*** (1-butyric acid-6-(L-2-aminobutyric acid)-7-glycineoxytocin).
'Cariamyl' *see* Heptaminol theophyllineacetate.
'Caridan' *see* Oxyphencyclimine.
CARINAMIDE* (*p*-benzylsulfonamidobenzoic acid; *p*-(α-toluenesulfonamido)benzoic acid; caronamide).
CARINDACILLIN*** (*N*-(2-carboxy-3,3-dimethyl-7-oxo-4-thia-1-azabicyclo[3.2.0]hept-6-yl)-2-phenylmalonamic acid 1-indian-5-yl ester; 6-[2-[(indan-5-yloxy)carbonyl]-2-phenylacetamido]penicillanic acid; carbenicillin indanyl; indanylcarbenicillin; CP-15464; 'carindapen'; 'geocillin'; 'gu-pen').
'Carindapen' *see* Carindacillin.
'Caripeptic' *see* Papain.
'Carisoma' *see* Carisoprodol.
Carisoprodate* *see* Carisoprodol.
CARISOPRODOL*** (2-methyl-2-propyl-1,3-propanediol carbamate isopropylcarbamate; carisoprodate; isomeprobamate; isopropylmeprobamate; isoprotan; isoprothane).
'Caritol' *see* Diethylcarbamazine.

'Carlytene' *see* Moxisylyte.
CARMANTADINE** (1-adamant-1-ylazetidine-2-carboxylic acid; 1-tricyclo[3.3.1.1³,⁷]dec-1-yl-2-azetidinecarboxylic acid; Sch-15427).
CARMELLOSE*** (carboxymethylcellulose; poly(carboxymethyl)ether of cellulose; sodium carboxymethylcellulose; sodium cellulose glycolate; CMC).
See also Croscarmellose.
CARMETIZIDE** (methyl 6-chloro-3,4-dihydro-2-methyl-7-sulfamoyl-2*H*-1,2,4-benzothiadiazine-3-carboxylate 1,1-dioxide).
Carminomycin *see* Carubicin.
CARMOFUR*** (5-fluoro-*N*-hexyl-3,4-dihydro-2,4-dioxo-1(2*H*)-pyrimidinecarboxamide).
'Carmubris' *see* Carmustine.
'Carmurit' *see* Etoxazene.
CARMUSTINE*** (1,3-bis(2-chloroethyl)-1-nitrosourea; BCNU; NSC-409962; 'bicnu'; 'carmubris'; 'nitrumon').
'Carnacid-cor' *see* Pengitoxin.
CARNIDAZOLE** (*O*-methyl [2-(2-methyl-5-nitroimidazol-1-yl)ethyl]thiocarbamate; carnidazole hydrochloride; R-25831; R-28096; 'spartrix').
CARNITINE*** ((3-carboxy-2-hydroxypropyl)trimethylammonium hydroxide inner salt; 4-amino-3-hydroxybutyric acid trimethylbetaine; L-carnitine; vitamin Bt; 'nefrocarnit'; 'novain').
Carnitine carnitinate *see* Bicarnitine.
CARNOSINE (*N*-(β-alanyl)histidine; ignotine).
CAROCAINIDE*** (1-[4,7-dimethoxy-6-(2-pyrrolidin-1-ylethoxy)-5-benzofuranyl]-3-methylurea; MD-77027).
'Carofur' *see* Nifurprazine.
'Caroid' *see* Papain.
Caronamide *see* Carinamide.
'Carotaben' *see* Betacarotene.
β,β-Carotene *see* Betacarotene.
β,ε-Carotene-3,3'-diol dipalmitate *see* Xantofyl palmitate.
β,β-Carotene-4,4'-dione *see* Canthaxanthin.
CAROVERINE** (1-[2-(diethylamino)ethyl]-3-(*p*-methoxybenzyl)-2-(1*H*)-quinoxalinone; P-201-1).
CAROXAZONE*** (3(4*H*)-carbamoylmethyl-2*H*-1,3-benzoxazin-2-one; 2-oxo-2*H*-1,3-benzoxazine-3(4*H*)-acetamide; benzoxazone; FI-6654; 'timostenil').
CARPERIDINE*** (ethyl 1-(2-carbamoylethyl)-4-phenylisonipecotate).
CARPERONE*** (4'-fluoro-4-[4-(isopropylcarbamoyloxy)piperid-1-yl]butyrophenone; 4'-fluoro-4-(4-hydroxypiperid-1-yl)butyrophenone isopropylcarbamate; 1-[3-(*p*-fluorobenzoyl)propyl]-4-piperidinol isopropylcarbamate; AL-1021).
'Carphenamine' *see* Diphenhydramine.
Carphenazine* *see* Carfenazine.
'Carphenex' *see* Diphenhydramine.
Carphenol *see* Diphenan.
CARPINDOLOL*** (isopropyl (±)-4-[3-(*tert*-butylamino)-2-hydroxypropoxy]indole-2-carboxylate).

CARPIPRAMINE*** (5-[3-[(4-carbamoyl-4-piperid-1-yl)piperid-1-yl]propyl]-10,11-dihydro-5*H*-dibenz[*b*,*f*]azepine; 1'-[3-(10,11-dihydro-5*H*-dibenz[*b*,*f*]azepin-5-yl)propyl]-1,4-bipiperidine-4'-carboxamide; carbadipimidine; PZ-1511; RP-21679; 'defekton'; 'prazinil').

Carpolene *see* Carbomer.

CARPRAZIDIL*** (methyl 5-(3,6-dihydro-1(2*H*)-pyridyl)-2-oxo-2*H*-[1,2,4]oxadiazolo[2,3-*a*]pyrimidine-7-carbamate).

CARPROFEN*** ((±)-6-chloro-α-methylcarbazole-2-acetic acid; 2-(6-chlorocarbazol-2-yl)propionic acid; C-5720; Ro 20-5720; 'imadyl'; 'rimadyl').

CARPRONIUM CHLORIDE*** ((3-carboxypropyl)trimethylammonium chloride methyl ester; [3-(methoxycarbonyl)propyl]trimethylammonium chloride).

Carrageenan degradation product *see* Poligeenan.

Carrageenan emepronium salt *see* Emepronium carrageenate.

CARSALAM*** (2*H*-1,2-benzoxazine-2,4(3*H*)-dione; *O*-carbamoylsalicylic acid lactam; 3,4-dihydro-2*H*-1,3-benzoxazine-2,4-dione; oxyphenhydrazone).

'Carsil' *see* Silymarin.

CARTAP* (1,3-bis(carbamoylthio)-*N*,*N*-dimethyl-2-propylamine; *S*,*S*'-[2-(dimethylamino)-1,3-propanediyl] carbamothioate; NTD-2; 'padan').

CARTAZOLATE*** (ethyl 4-butylamino-1-ethyl-1*H*-pyrazolo[3,4-*b*]pyridine-5-carboxylate; SQ-65396).

CARTEOLOL*** (5-[3-(*tert*-butylamino)-2-hydroxypropoxy]-3,4-dihydrocarbostyril; 1-(*tert*-butylamino)-3-(3,4-dihydro-2(1*H*)-oxoquinolin-5-yl)-2-propanol; 5-[3-[(1,1-dimethylethyl)amino]-2-hydroxypropoxy]-3,4-dihydro-2(1*H*)-quinolinone; carbonolol; carteolol hydrochloride; Abbott 43326; OPC-1085; 'endak').

Carticaine* *see* Articaine.

CARTOX (tr) (carbon dioxide plus 10% ethylene oxide).

CARUBICIN*** ((1*S*,3*S*)-3-acetyl-1,2,3,4,6,11-hexahydro-3,5,10,12-tetrahydroxy-6,11-dioxo-1-naphthacenyl 3-amino-2,3,6-trideoxy-α-L-*lyxo*-hexopyranoside; (8*S*-*cis*)-8-acetyl-10-[(3-amino-2,3,6-trideoxy-α-L-*lyxo*-hexopyranosyl)oxy]-7,8,9,10-tetrahydro-1,6,8,11-tetrahydroxy-5,12-naphthacenedione; carubicin hydrochloride; carminomycin; NSC-1800/24; NSC-180024).

'Carudol' *see* Pyrazinobutazone.

CARUMONAM** ((*Z*)-[[[(2-aminothiazol-4-yl)[[(2*S*,3*S*)-2-(hydroxymethyl)-4-oxo-1-sulfoazetidin-3-yl]carbamoyl]methylene]amino]oxy]-acetic acid carbamate (ester)).

CARVACROL (2-methyl-5-isopropylphenol; 2-*p*-cymenol).

'Carvasin' *see* Isosorbide dinitrate.

CARVEDILOL** ((±)-1-(carbazol-4-yloxy)-3-[[2-(*o*-methoxyphenoxy)ethyl]amino]-2-propanol).

6,8-Carvomenthenediol *see* Sobrerol.

'Carylderm' *see* Carbaril.

'Caryolysin' *see* Chlormethine.

CARZENIDE*** (*p*-sulfamoylbenzoic acid; 'dirnate').

'Carzol' *see* Formetanate.

CASANTHRANOL (purified mixture of anthranol glycosides from *Cascara sagrada*; 'peristim').

'Casantin' *see* Diethazine.

'Cascapride' *see* Bromopride.

'Casmalon' *see* Cyclarbamate.

'Casoron' *see* Dichlobenil.

Cassella-4489 *see* Carbocromen.

Cassic acid *see* Rhein.

'Castrix' *see* Crimidine.

'Castron' *see* Pheniprazine.

'Catabex' *see* Dropropizine.

'Catalin' *see* Pirenoxine.

'Catanil' *see* Chlorpropamide.

'Catapres' *see* Clonidine.

'Catapresan' *see* Clonidine.

'Catapyrin' *see* Aminometradine.

'Catarase' *see* Chymotrypsin.

Catechin *see* Cianidanol.

Catechinic acid *see* Cianidanol.

(+)-Catechol *see* Cianidanol.

Catechuic acid *see* Cianidanol.

Catenulin *see* Paromomycin.

'Catergen' *see* Cianidanol.

'Cateudyl' *see* Methaqualone.

CATHINE** ((+)-*threo*-α-(1-aminoethyl)benzyl alcohol; (+)-norpseudoephedrine; katine; 'adiposettin'; 'amorphan'; 'exponcit'; 'fugoa'; 'minusin').

CATHINONE** ((*S*)-2-aminopropiophenone).

'Cathocin' *see* Novobiocin.

'Cathomycin' *see* Novobiocin.

'Catovit' *see* Prolintane.

'Catran' *see* Pheniprazine.

'Catron' *see* Pheniprazine.

'Catroniazid' *see* Pheniprazine.

'Caved S' *see* Deglycyrrhizinized liquorice.

'Caviject' *see* Fusidic acid.

'Cavinton' *see* Vinpocetine.

'Cavodil' *see* Pheniprazine.

'Cavoform' *see* Paraformaldehyde.

'Cavolax' *see* Dantron.

'Cavumbren' *see* Adipiodone.

'Caytine' *see* Protokylol.

CB-11 *see* Phenadoxone.

CB-154 *see* Bromocriptine.

CB-302 *see* Ferric fructose.

CB-304 *see* Azaribine.

CB-309 *see* Fenabutene.

CB-311 *see* Human growth hormone.

CB-313 *see* Mitotane.

CB-337 *see* Meglutol.

CB-804 *see* Calcium bucloxate.

CB-1048 *see* Chlornaphazine.

CB-1314 *see* Metochalcone.

CB-1348 *see* Chlorambucil.

CB-1639 *see* Cycloleucine.

CB-1664 *see* Aceprometazine.

CB-1678 *see* Propiomazine.

CB-1729 *see* *o*-Sarcolysin.

CB-2041 *see* Busulfan.

CB-2201 *see* Amfepentorex.
CB-2511 *see* Mannityl dimesilate.
CB-3007 *see* Sarcolysin.
CB-3025 *see* Melphalan.
CB-3026 *see* Medphalan.
CB-3208 *see* Formylmelphalan.
CB-3697 *see* Racefemine.
CB-4091 *see* Benfurodil hemisuccinate.
CB-4260 *see* Nortetrazepam.
CB-4261 *see* Tetrazepam.
CB-4306 *see* Clorazepate dipotassium.
CB-4857 *see* Menitrazepam.
CB-4984 *see* Acequinoline.
CB-8016 *see* Pentosan polysulfate.
CB-8049 *see* Diphenoxylate.
CB-8053 *see* Thiamphenicol.
CB-8073 *see* Diloxanide furoate.
CB-8080 *see* Etynodiol diacetate.
CB-8088 *see* Benfotiamine.
CB-8089 *see* Benperidol.
CB-8092 *see* Oxazepam.
CB-8102 *see* Bamifylline.
CB-8109 *see* Canrenoate potassium.
CB-8129 *see* Uric acid oxidase.
CB-10615 *see* Nifurmazole.
CB-11380 *see* Nifurizone.
CB-12025 *see* Nifuralide.
CB-12592 *see* Subendazole.
CB-30038 *see* Minaprine.
CBDCA *see* Carboplatin.
CCC *see* Chlormequat.
CCI-12933 *see* Minaxolone.
CCK-179 *see* Co-dergocrine.
CCN-52 *see* Cypermethrin.
CCNU *see* Lomustine.
CCRG-81010 *see* Mitozolomide.
CD-68 *see* Chlordane.
CD-3400 *see* Rescimetol.
CDAA *see* Allidochlor.
CDC *see* Chenodeoxycholic acid.
CDIB *see* Methyl clofenapate.
CDP-choline *see* Citicoline.
CDT *see* Simazine.
CE-264 *see* Alloclamide.
CE-305 *see* Flualamide.
CE-746 *see* Eprazinone.
'Cealysin' *see* Hexamethylolmelamine.
'Cebesine' *see* Oxybuprocaine.
'Cebutid' *see* Flurbiprofen.
'Cecekin' *see* Pancreozymin.
'Ceclor' *see* Cefaclor.
'Cedilanid' *see* Lanatoside C.
'Cedilanid D' *see* Deslanoside.
'Cedi-sanol' *see* Lanatoside C.
'Cedocard' *see* Isosorbide dinitrate.
'Cedona' *see* Deglycyrrhizinized liquorice.
'Cedopurin' *see* Methenamine mandelate.
Cedrarin *see* Orexin.
'Cedulamin' *see* Methenamine mandelate.
'Cedur' *see* Bezafibrate.
'Ceduran' *see under* Nitrofurantoin.
'CeeNU' *see* Lomustine.
CEFACETRILE** (3-acetoxymethyl-7-(2-cyano-

acetamido)-2-cephem-2-carboxylic acid; 7-(2-cyanoacetamido)-3-(hydroxymethyl)-2-cephem-2-carboxylic acid acetate; 7-(2-cyanoacetamido)-cephalosporanic acid; Ba-36278A; 'celospor').
'Cefacidal' *see* Cefazolin.
CEFACLOR*** ((6*R*,7*R*)-7-[(*R*)-2-amino-2-phenylacetamido]-3-chloro-2-cephem-2-carboxylic acid; 3-chloro-7-D-(2-phenylglycinamido)-3-cephem-4-carboxylic acid; compound 99638; 'alfatil'; 'ceclor'; 'distaclor'; 'panoral').
CEFADROXIL** ((6*R*,7*R*)-7-(*R*)-2-amino-2-[*p*-hydroxyphenyl)acetamido]-3-methyl-2-cephem-2-carboxylic acid; [6*R*-[6α,7β(*R*)]]-7-[[amino-(4-hydroxyphenyl)acetyl]amino]-3-methyl-2-cephem-2-carboxylic acid; BL-S578; MJF-11567-3; 'baxan'; 'bidocef'; 'duricef'; 'oracefal').
'Cefadyl' *see* Cefapirin.
CEFALEXIN** (7-((+)-2-amino-2-phenylacetamido)-3-methyl-2-cephem-2-carboxylic acid).
CEFALEXIN plus FLUCLOXACILLIN ('flucexin').
CEFALOGLYCIN** (7-(D-α-aminophenylacetamido)cephalosporanic acid; 7-(2-amino-2-phenylacetamido)-3-(hydroxymethyl)-2-cephem-2-carboxylic acid acetate inner salt; cephaloglycin).
'Cefaloject' *see* Cefapirin.
CEFALONIUM** (3-(4-carbamoylpyrid-1-ylmethyl)-7-(thien-2-ylacetamido)-2-cephem-2-carboxylic acid; carbamoylcefaloridine; cephalonium; compound 87/90).
CEFALORAM** (3-acetoxymethyl-7-(2-phenylacetamido)-2-cephem-2-carboxylic acid; 7-phenylacetamidocephalosporanic acid; cephaloram).
CEFALORIDINE** (1-[[2-carboxy-8-oxo-7-[(2-thien-2-yl)-acetamido]-5-thia-1-azabicyclo-[4.2.0]-oct-2-en-3-yl]methyl]pyridinium hydroxide inner salt; 3-(pyrid-1-ylmethyl)-7-(thien-2-ylacetamido)-2-cephem-2-carboxylic acid betaine; *N*-[7-(2-thienylacetamido)ceph-3-em-3-ylmethylpyridinium]-4-carboxylate; cephaloridine; Sch-11527).
CEFALOTIN** (3-acetoxymethyl-7-(2-thien-2-yl-acetamido)-2-cephem-2-carboxylic acid; 7-(2-thienylacetamido)cephalosporanic acid; cephalosporin 871; cephalothin; cefalotin sodium).
CEFAMANDOLE** (7-D-mandelamido-3-[[(1-methyl-1*H*-tetrazol-5-yl)thio]methyl]-2-cephem-2-carboxylic acid; cephamandole).
CEFAMANDOLE NAFATE* (formate ester sodium salt of cefamandole; 'kefadol'; 'mandokef'; 'mandol').
'Cefamezin' *see* Cefazolin.
CEFAPAROLE** ((6*R*,7*R*)-7-[(*R*)-2-amino-2-(*p*-hydroxyphenyl)acetamido]-3-[[(5-methyl-1,3,4-thiadiazol-2-yl)thio]methyl]-2-cephem-2-carboxylic acid).
CEFAPIRIN** (3-acetoxymethyl-7-[2-(pyrid-4-yl-thio)acetamido]-2-cephem-2-carboxylic acid; 3-hydroxymethyl-7-[2-(4-pyridylthio)acetamido]-2-cephem-2-carboxylic acid acetate; 7-[2-(pyrid-4-ylthio)acetamido]cephalosporanic acid; cepha-

pirin; BL-P1322; 'bristocef'; 'cefadyl'; 'cefalo-ject'; 'cefatrex'; 'cefatrexyl').

'Cefatrex' *see* Cefapirin.

'Cefatrexyl' *see* Cefapirin.

CEFATRIZINE** ((6*R*,7*R*)-7-[(*R*)-2-amino-2-(*p*-hydroxyphenylacetamido]-3-[*v*-triazol-4-yl-thio)methyl]-2-cephem-2-carboxylic acid; 7-[α-D-(*p*-hydroxyphenyl)glycylamino]-4-[(1*H*-1,2,3-triazol-4-ylthio)methyl]-2-cephem-2-carboxylic acid; BL-S640; S-640-P; SK&F-60771).

CEFAZAFLUR** ((6*R*,7*R*)-3-[[(1-methyl-1*H*-tetrazol-5-yl)thio]methyl]-7-[2-[(trifluoromethyl)thio]acetamido]-2-cephem-2-carboxylic acid; cefazaflur sodium; SK&F-59962).

CEFAZEDONE*** ((6*R*,7*R*)-7-[2-(3,5-dichloro-4-oxo-1-(4*H*)-pyridyl)acetamido]-3-[[(5-methyl-1,3,4-thiadiazol-2-yl)thio]methyl]-2-cephem-2-carboxylic acid; cefazedone sodium; EMD-30087; 'refosporin').

CEFAZOLIN** (3-[[(5-methyl-1,3,4-thiadiazol-2-yl)thio]methyl]-7-[2-(1*H*-tetrazol-1-yl)acet-amido]-2-cephem-2-carboxylic acid; cephazolin; cefazolin sodium; compound 46083; SK&F-41558; 'ancef'; 'cefacidal'; 'cefamezin'; 'celmet-in'; 'elzogram'; 'gramaxin'; 'kefzol'; 'totacef'; 'zolicef').

CEFAZOLIN plus DICLOXACILLIN** ('diri-men').

CEFBUPERAZONE*** ((6*R*,7*S*)-7-[(2*R*,3*S*)-2-(4-ethyl-2,3-dioxo-1-piperazinecarboxamido)-3-hydroxybutyramido]-7-methoxy-3-[[(1-methyl-1*H*-tetrazol-5-yl)thio]methyl]-2-cephem-2-carb-oxylic acid).

CEFETAMET*** ((6*R*,7*R*)-7-[2-(2-aminothiazol-4-yl)glyoxylamido]-3-methyl-2-cephem-2-carb-oxylic acid 7²-(*Z*)-(*O*-methyloxime)).

CEFETRIZOLE*** ((6*R*,7*R*)-7-[2-(2-thienyl)acet-amido]-3-[(*s*-triazol-3-ylthio)methyl]-2-cephem-2-carboxylic acid).

CEFMENOXIME*** ((6*R*,7*R*)-7-[2-(2-amino-thiazol-4-yl)glyoxylamido]-3-[[(1-methyl-1*H*-tetrazol-5-yl)thio]methyl]-2-cephem-2-carboxylic acid 7²-(*Z*)-(*O*-methyloxime); cefmenoxime hydrochloride; Abbott-50912; SCE-1365).

CEFMETAZOLE*** ((6*R*,7*S*)-7-[2-[(cyanomethyl)thio]acetamido]-7-methoxy-3-[[(1-methyl-1-tetrazol-5-yl)thio]methyl]-2-cephem-2-carboxylic acid; cefmetazole sodium; CS-1170).

'Cefobis' *see* Cefoperazone.

CEFODIZIME*** ((6*R*,7*R*)-7-[2-(2-aminothiazol-4-yl)glyoxylamido]-3-[[(5-(carboxymethyl)-4-methylthiazol-2-yl)thio]methyl]-2-cephem-2-carboxylic acid 7²-(*Z*)-(*O*-methyloxime)).

CEFONICID*** ([6*R*-[6α,7β(*R*)]]-7-[(hydroxy-phenylacetyl)amino]-3-[[[1-(sulfomethyl)-1*H*-tetrazol-5-yl]thio]methyl]-2-cephem-2-carboxylic acid; (6*R*,7*R*)-7-[(*R*)-mandelamido]-3-[[[1-(sul-fomethyl)-1*H*-tetrazol-5-yl]thio]methyl]-2-cephem-2-carboxylic acid; cefonicid disodium salt; cefonicid sodium; SK&F-D-75073).

CEFOPERAZONE*** ((6*R*,7*R*)-7-[(*R*)-2-(4-ethyl-2,3-dioxo-1-piperazinecarboxyamido)-2-(4-hydr-oxyphenyl)acetamido]-3-[[(1-methyl-1*H*-tetraz-

ol-5-yl)thio]methyl]-2-cephem-2-carboxylic acid; cefoperazone sodium; CP-52640; T-1551; 'cefo-bis'; 'wilprufen').

CEFORANIDE*** ((6*R*,7*R*)-7-[2-(α-amino-*o*-tol-yl)acetamido]-3-[[[1-(carboxymethyl)-1*H*-tetraz-ol-5-yl]thio]methyl]-2-cephem-2-carboxylic acid; 7-[*o*-(aminomethyl)phenylacetamido]-3-[[[1-(carboxymethyl)-1*H*-tetrazol-5-yl]thio]methyl]-2-cephem-2-carboxylic acid; BL-S786).

CEFOTAXIME*** ((6*R*,7*R*)-7-[2-(2-aminothiaz-ol-4-yl)glyoxylamido]-3-(hydroxymethyl)-2-cephem-2-carboxylic acid α-(*O*-methyloxime) acetate (ester); cefotaxime sodium; HR-756; RU-24756; 'claforan'; 'zariviz').

CEFOTETAN*** ((6*R*,6*S*)-4-[[2-carboxy-7-meth-oxy-3-[[(1-methyl-1*H*-tetrazol-5-yl)thio]methyl]-8-oxo-5-thia-1-azabicyclo[4.2.0]oct-2-en-7-yl]carbamoyl]-1,3-dithietane-Δ²,ᵃ-malonamic acid; 2-[4-[(7*S*)-4-carboxy-7-methoxy-3-[[(1-methyl-tetrazol-5-yl)thio]methyl]-3-cephem-7-ylcarb-amoyl]-1,3-dithietan-2-ylidene]malonamic acid; ICI-156834; YM-09330).

CEFOTIAM*** ((6*R*,7*R*)-7-[2-(2-aminothiazol-4-yl)acetamido]-3-[[[1-[2-(dimethylamino)ethyl]-1*H*-tetrazol-5-yl]thio]methyl]-2-cephem-2-carb-oxylic acid; cefotiam hydrochloride; Abbott 48999; CGP-14221/E; SCE-963; 'halospor'; 'spi-zef').

CEFOXAZOLE*** ((6*R*,7*R*)-7-[3-(*o*-chlorophen-yl)-5-methylisoxazole-4-carboxamido]-3-(hydr-oxymethyl)-2-cephem-2-carboxylic acid acetate; 7-[3-(*o*-chlorophenyl)-5-methylisoxazole-4-carb-oxamido]cephalosporanic acid; cephoxazole; 'ce-poxicillin cerate').

CEFOXITIN*** (3-(carbamoyloxymethyl)-7*S*-methoxy-7*R*-(2-thienylacetamido)-2-cephem-2-carboxylic acid; 3-hydroxymethyl-7-methoxy-7-(2-thien-2-ylacetamido)-2-cephem-2-carboxylic acid; cefoxitin sodium; L-620388; MK-306; 'me-foxin').

CEFPIMIZOLE** (1-[[(6*R*,7*R*)-2-carboxy-7-[(*R*)-2-(5-carboxyimidazole-4-carboxamido)-2-phenylacetamido]-8-oxo-5-thia-1-azabicyclo-[4.2.0]oct-2-en-3-yl]methyl]-4-(2-sulfoethyl)pyri-dinium hydroxide inner salt; 7-[2-(5-carboxyimi-dazole-4-carboxamido)-2-phenylacetamido]-3-[4-[(2-sulfoethyl)pyrid-1-yl]methyl]-2-cephem-2-carboxylic acid inner salt).

CEFPIRAMIDE*** ((6*R*,7*R*)-7-[(*R*)-2-(4-hydr-oxy-6-methylnicotinamido)-2-(*p*-hydroxyphen-yl)acetamido]-3-[[(1-methyl-1*H*-tetrazol-5-yl)-thio]methyl]-2-cephem-2-carboxylic acid; SM-1652).

CEFPIROME** (1-[[(6*R*,7*R*)-7-[2-(2-aminothiaz-ol-4-yl)glyoxylamido]-2-carboxy-8-oxo-5-thia-1-azabicyclo[4.2.0]oct-2-en-3-yl]methyl]-6,7-di-hydro-5*H*-1-pyrindinium hydroxide inner salt 7²-(*Z*)-(*O*-methyloxime); 7-[2-(2-aminothiazol-4-yl)glyoxylamido]-3-[(6,7-dihydro-5*H*-pyrindin-1-yl)methyl]-2-cephem-2-carboxylic acid inner salt 7²-(*O*-methyloxime)).

CEFRADINE*** (7-[2-amino-2-(1,4-cyclohexadi-en-1-yl)acetamido]-3-methyl-2-cephem-2-carboxylic acid; cephradine; SK&F-D-39304; SQ-11436; 'anspor'; 'eskacef'; 'forticef'; 'maxisporin'; 'sefril'; 'velosef').

CEFROTIL* ((6R,7R)-3-methyl-7-[2-[p-(1,4,5,6-tetrahydropyrimidin-2-yl)phenyl]acetamido]-2-cephem-2-carboxylic acid).

CEFROXADINE* ((6R,7R)-7-[(2R)-2-amino-2-(1,4-cyclohexadien-1-yl)acetamido]-3-methoxy-2-cephem-2-carboxylic acid; CGP-9000).

CEFSULODIN* (4-carbamoyl-1-[[(6R,7R)-2-carboxy-8-oxo-7-[(2R)-2-phenyl-2-sulfoacetamido]-5-thia-1-azabicyclo[4.2.0]oct-2-en-3-yl]methyl]pyridinium hydroxide inner salt; cefsulodin monosodium salt; cefsulodin sodium; Abbott 46811; CGP-7174/E; SCE-129; 'monaspor'; 'pseudocef'; 'pseudomonil').

CEFSUMIDE* ((6R,7R)-7-[(2R)-2-amino-2-(m-methanesulfonamidophenyl)acetamido]-3-methyl-2-cephem-2-carboxylic acid).

CEFTAZIDIME* (7-[2-(2-aminothiazol-4-yl)-1-(1-carboxy-1-methylethoxyimino)acetamido]-3-(1-pyridinomethyl)-3-cephem-4-carboxylate; 1-[[(6R,7R)-7-[2-(2-aminothiazol-4-yl)glyoxylamido]-2-carboxy-8-oxo-5-thia-1-azabicyclo-[4.2.0]oct-2-en-3-yl]methyl]pyridinium hydroxide inner salt 7^2-(Z)-[O-(1-carboxy-1-methylethyl)-oxime]; 7-[2-(2-aminothiazol-4-yl)glyoxylamido]-3-(pyrid-1-ylmethyl)-2-cephem-2-carboxylic acid betaine 7^2-(Z)-[O-(1-carboxy-1-methylethyl)oxime]; GR-20263).

CEFTEZOLE* ((6R,7R)-7-[2-(1H-tetrazol-1-yl)acetamido]-3-[(1,3,4-thiadiazol-2-ylthio)methyl]-2-cephem-2-carboxylic acid; 'celoslin').

CEFTIOLENE* ((6R,7R)-7-[2-(2-aminothiazol-4-yl)glyoxylamido]-3-[(E)-2-[[4-(formylmethyl)-1,4,5,6-tetrahydro-5,6-dioxo-as-triazin-3-yl]-thio]vinyl]-2-cephem-2-carboxylic acid 7^2-(Z)-(O-methyloxime)).

CEFTIOXIDE* ((5S,6R,7R)-7-[2-(2-amino-4-thiazolyl)glyoxylamido]-3-(hydroxymethyl)-2-cephem-2-carboxylic acid 7^2-(Z)-(O-methyloxime) acetate (ester), 5-oxide).

CEFTIZOXIME* ((6R,7R)-7-[2-(2-aminothiazol-4-yl)glyoxylamido]-2-cephem-2-carboxylic acid 7^2-(Z)-(O-methyloxime); 7-[2-(2-amino-thiazol-4-yl)-2-(methoxyimino)acetamido]-3-cephem-4-carboxylic acid; FK-749; FR-13749).

CEFTRIAXONE* ((6R,7R)-7-[2-(2-aminothiazol-4-yl)glyoxylamido]-3-[[(2,5-dihydro-6-hydroxy-2-methyl-5-oxo-as-triazin-3-yl)thio]methyl]-2-cephem-2-carboxylic acid 7^2-(Z)-(O-methyloxime); 7-[2-(2-aminothiazol-4-yl)-2-(methoxyimino)acetamido]-3-[[2,5-dihydro-6-hydroxy-2-methyl-5-oxo-1,2,4-triazin-3-yl)thio]methyl]-3-cephem-4-carboxylic acid; ceftriaxone disodium; ceftriaxone sodium; Ro 13-9904; 'rocephin').

CEFURACETIME* ((6R,7R)-7-[2-(2-furyl)-2-methoxyiminoacetamido]cephalosporanic acid; (Z)-(7R)-7-[2-(2-furyl)glyoxylamido]-3-(hydroxymethyl)-2-cephem-2-carboxylic acid mono-(O-methyloxime) acetate).

CEFUROXIME* ((6R,7R)-3-(carbamoyloxy-methyl)-7-[2Z)-2-(2-furyl)-2-(methoxyimino)-acetamido]-2-cephem-2-carboxylic acid; cefuroxime sodium; SN-107; 'ceplus'; 'zinacef').

'**Ceglunat**' see Lanatoside C.

'**Celadigal**' see Lanatoside C.

CELA S-1942 see Bromofos.

CELA S-2957 see Chlorthiophos.

'**Celbenin**' see Meticillin.

'**Celestamine**' see under Betamethasone.

'**Celestan soluble**' see Betamethasone sodium phosphate.

'**Celestene**' see Betamethasone.

'**Celestene-chronodose**' see under Betamethasone acetate.

'**Celestone**' see Betamethasone.

'**Celestone-soluspan**' see under Betamethasone acetate.

'**Celetil**' see under Ergotamine tartrate.

'**Celiomycin**' see Viomycin.

'**Celiopaste**' see Thallium sulfate.

CELIPROLOL* (3-[3-acetyl-4-[3-(tert-butyl-amino)-2-hydroxypropoxy]phenyl]-1,1-diethyl-urea; 1-[2-acetyl-4-[(diethylcarbamoyl)amino]-phenoxy]-3-(tert-butylamino)-2-propanol; celiprolol hydrochloride; ST-1396; 'selectol').

'**Celiptium**' see Elliptinium acetate.

CELLABURATE* (cellulose acetate butyrate; cabufocon A; 'meso-lens').

CELLACEFATE (a partial mixed acetate and hydrogen phthalate ester of cellulose; cellace-phate; cellulose; cellulose acetophthalate).

Cellacephate* see Cellacefate.

'**Cellase-1000**' see Cellulase.

'**Cellidrin**' see Allopurinol.

'**Cellon**' see Tetrachloroethane.

'**Cellosolve**' see 2-Ethoxyethanol.

'**Celluflex**' see Tricresyl phosphate.

CELLULASE* (concentrate of cellulose-splitting enzymes from Aspergillus niger; 'cellase-1000').

Cellulose see Cellacefate; Hypromellose; Methyl-cellulose; Oxidized cellulose; Oxidized regenerat-ed cellulose.

Cellulose acetate butyrate see Cellaburate.

Cellulose acetophthalate see Cellacefate.

Cellulose 2-hydroxyethyl ether reaction product with chloral see Celucloral.

Cellulose nitrate see Pyroxylin.

Cellulosic acid see Oxidized cellulose.

'**Celmetin**' see Cefazolin.

'**Celontin**' see Mesuximide.

'**Celoslin**' see Ceftezole.

'**Celospor**' see Cefacetrile.

'**Celpillina**' see Meticillin.

'**Celtacillin**' see Propicillin.

CELUCLORAL* (cellulose 2-hydroxyethyl ether reaction product with chloral; ML-1034).

'**Celuton**' see Sodium acexamate.

'**Censedal**' see Nealbarbital.

'**Centonuron**' see Bendroflumethiazide.

'**Centracid**' see Triclocarban.

'**Centractyl**' see Promazine.

'**Centrax**' see Prazepam.

Centrazene see Simtrazene.

'**Centrine**' see Dimevamide.

Centrophenoxine* see Meclofenoxate.
'Centroton' see Pyrovalerone.
'Centyl' see Bendroflumethiazide.
'Cepacilina' see Benzathine penicillin.
'Cepacol' see Cetylpyridinium.
'Cepentyl' see N-Cyclopentyllysergamide.
'Cepexin' see Cefalexin.
CEPH see Todralazine.
CEPHAELINE (7′,10,11-trimethoxyemetan-6′-ol; desmethylemetine; dihydropsychotrine).
Cephaeline methyl ether see Emetine.
'Cephalexin' see Cefalexin.
'Cephalmin' see Thioproperazine.
Cephaloglycin* see Cefaloglycin.
Cephalonium* see Cefalonium.
Cephaloram* see Cefaloram.
Cephaloridine* see Cefaloridine.
CEPHALOSPORANIC ACID (3-acetoxymethyl-2-cephem-2-carboxylic acid; 3-hydroxymethyl-2-cephem-2-carboxylic acid acetate).
CEPHALOSPORIN C* (3-acetoxymethyl-7-(5-amino-5-carboxyvaleramido)-2-cephem-2-carboxylic acid; 7-(5-amino-5-carboxyvaleramido)cephalosporanic acid; α-aminoadipic cephalosporin).
Cephalosporin N see Adicillin.
Cephalosporin 871 see Cefalotin.
Cephalothin* see Cefalotin.
Cephamandole* see Cefamandole.
Cephapirin* see Cefapirin.
Cephazolin* see Cefazolin.
2-CEPHEM-2-CARBOXYLIC ACID (8-oxo-5-thia-1-azabicyclo[4.2.0]oct-2-ene-2-carboxylic acid; 3-cephem-4-carboxylic acid).
3-Cephem-4-carboxylic acid see 2-Cephem-2-carboxylic acid.
Cephoxazole* see Cefoxazole.
Cephradine* see Cefradine.
'Cephulac' see Lactulose.
'Cepillina' see Meticillin.
'Ceplus' see Cefuroxime.
'Cepol' see Cefalexin.
'Ceporacin' see Cefalotin.
'Ceporan' see Cefaloridine.
'Ceporexin' see Cefalexin.
'Ceporin' see Cefaloridine.
'Cepovenin' see Cefalotin.
'Cepoxicillin cerate' see Cefoxazole.
'Cepraven' see Cefalonium.
Cerasine red see Oil scarlet.
'Cercine' see Diazepam.
'Cercobin' see Thiophanate.
Cerebronic acid see 2-Hydroxytetracosanoic acid.
Cerebrostenediol see Cholest-5-ene-3β,24-diol.
Cerebrostenolone see 24-Hydroxycholest-5-en-3-one.
Cerebrosterol see Cholest-5-ene-3β,24-diol.
'Cerebroxine' see Vincamine.
'Ceredon' see Benquinox.
'Cerenox' see Benquinox.
'Cerepar' see Cinnarizine.
'Ceresan' see Ethylmercuric chloride.
'Ceresan-M' see N-Ethylmercuri-p-toluenesulfon-

anilide.
CERM-370 see Amoproxan.
CERM-898 see Amixetrine.
CERM-1290 see Scopolamine methyl methosulfate.
CERM 1709 see Niaprazine.
CERM-1766 see Oxaflozane.
CERM-1841 see Flumexadol.
CERM-1875 see Fepromide.
CERM-1978 see Bepridil.
CERM-3024 see Zipeprol.
CERM-3209 see Papaverine adenylate.
'Ceropan' see Cefaloridine.
'Cerson' see Flumetasone pivalate.
'Certomycin' see Netilmicin.
'Certonal' see Methaqualone.
'Certonin' see Dehydrocholic acid.
'Certrol' see Ioxynil.
'Cerubidin' see Daunorubicin.
'Cerucal' see Metoclopramide.
Cerulein see Ceruletide.
CERULETIDE*** (5-oxo-L-prolyl-L-glutaminyl-L-aspartyl-L-tyrosyl-L-threonylglycyl-L-tryptophyl-L-methionyl-L-aspartyl-L-phenylalaninamide 4-(hydrogen sulfate) ester; caerulein; cerulein; 'takus').
'Cerutil' see Meclofenoxate.
'Cervantal' see under Ampicillin.
'Cervilame' see under Lomifylline.
'Cervilaxin' see Relaxin.
'Cervoxan' see Vinburnine.
'Cesamet' see Nabilone.
'Cescan-131' see Cesium(131Cs) chloride.
CESIUM(131Cs) CHLORIDE (radiocesium chloride; 'cescan-131').
'Cesol' see Praziquantel.
'Cestarsol' see Arecoline-acetarsol.
CETABEN*** (p-(hexadecylamino)benzoic acid; cetaben sodium; CL-203821; PHB).
CETACEUM (cetyl palmitate; parmaceti; spermaceti; 'hemotabs'; 'parmacetyl').
'Cetacillin' see Propicillin.
'Cetal' see Vincamine.
Cetalkon* see Cetalkonium chloride.
CETALKONIUM CHLORIDE*** (benzylcetyldimethylammonium; benzylhexadecyldimethylammonium chloride; cetalkon; NSC-32942). See also under Choline salicylate.
CETAMIFEN (tr) (ethanolamine 2-phenylbutyrate salt; cetamiphen).
Cetamiphen (tr) see Cetamifen.
CETAMOLOL** ((±)-2-[o-[3-(tert-butylamino)-2-hydroxypropoxy]phenoxy]-N-methylacetamide; cetamolol hydrochloride; AI-27303; 'betacor').
Cetanol see 1-Hexadecanol.
'Cetarin' see Racemorphan.
CETHEXONIUM CHLORIDE*** (hexadecyl(2-hydroxycyclohexyl)dimethylammonium chloride; 'biocidan').
CETIEDIL*** (2-(hexahydro-1H-azepin-1-yl)-ethyl α-cyclohexyl-3-thiopheneacetate; 2-hexamethyleniminoethyl α-cyclohexane-3-thiophene-

96

acetate; 2-hexamethyleniminoethyl α-thien-2-yl-cyclohexaneacetate; INO-502; 'stratene').

'Cetiprin' *see* Emepronium bromide.

'Cetiprin novum' *see* Emepronium carrageenate.

CETIRIZINE** ((±)-[2-[4-(*p*-chloro-α-phenyl-benzyl)piperazin-1-yl]ethoxy]acetic acid).

Cetobemidone* *see* Ketobemidone.

CETOCYCLINE*** (2-acetyl-4α-amino-4aβ,12a-dihydro-3,10,11,12aβ-tetrahydroxy-6,9-dimethyl-1,12(4*H*,5*H*)-naphthacenedione; cetotetrine; Abbott-40728).

CETOFENICOL*** (D-*threo-N*-[*p*-acetyl-β-hydroxy-α-(hydroxymethyl)phenethyl]-2,2-dichloroacetamide; 1-(*p*-acetylphenyl)-2-(dichloroacetamido)-1,3-propanediol; cetophenicol; W-3746).

CETOHEXAZINE*** (2,3-dihydro-4,6-dimethyl-3-pyridazinone; 4,6-dimethyl-3(2*H*)-pyridazinone; ketohexazine).

CETOMACROGOL(S)* (cetyl ethers of macrogols).

CETOMACROGOL 1000*** (polyethylene glycol 1000 monocetyl ester; polyethylene glycol 1000 monohexadecyl ether; 'texofor A.I.P').

Cetophenicol* *see* Cetofenicol.

'Ceto-sanol' *see* Lanatoside C.

CETOSTEARYLIC ALCOHOL* (mixture of 1-octadecanol and 1-hexadecanol).

Cetotetrine *see* Cetocycline.

CETOTIAMINE*** (*N*-(4-amino-2-methylpyrimidin-5-ylmethyl)-*N*-(4-hydroxy-2-mercapto-1-methyl-1-butenyl)formamide ethyl carbonate *S*-ester with ethyl thiocarbonate; *O*,*S*-dicarbethoxythiamine; *S*-ethoxycarbonylthiamine; DCET; SECT).

CETOXIME*** (2-(*N*-benzylanilino)acetamidoxime; cetoxime hydrochloride).

CETRAXATE*** (4-(2-carboxyethyl)phenyl tranexamate; *p*-hydroxyhydrocinnamic acid *trans*-4-(aminomethyl)cyclohexanecarboxylate; phloretic acid tranexamate ester; cetraxate hydrochloride; DV-1006).

CETRIMIDE*** (tetradecyltrimethylammonium bromide plus small amounts of dodecyl- and hexadecyl- trimethylammonium bromides).

CETRIMONIUM BROMIDE*** (hexadecyltrimethylammonium bromide; cetyltrimethylammonium bromide; cetrimide; CTAB).

CETRIMONIUM PENTACHLOROPHENATE (TCAP).

Cetyl alcohol *see* 1-Hexadecanol.

Cetylamine *see* Hexadecylamine.

Cetylic acid *see* Palmitic acid.

Cetyl palmitate *see* Cetaceum.

CETYLPYRIDINIUM BROMIDE*** (hexadecyl pyridinium bromide).

CETYLPYRIDINIUM *o*-THYMOTATE (hexadecylpyridinium 3-hydroxy-*p*-cymenecarboxylate; hexadecylpyridinium 3-isopropyl-6-methylsalicylate; 'pedyol').

Cetyltrimethylammonium bromide *see* Cetrimonium bromide.

'Cevanol' *see* Benactyzine.

CF-138C *see* Octafluorocyclobutane.

'CFC' *see* Carfimate.

CFC-12 *see* Dichlorodifluoromethane.

'CFT' *see* Diallate.

CG-21 *see* Fenyramidol oxyphenbutazone.

CG-201 *see* Bevonium metilsulfate.

CG-315 *see* Tramadol.

CG-635 *see* Etiroxate.

CG-3033 *see* Supidimide.

CG-3117 *see* Naproxen.

CGA-23654 *see* Nitroscanate.

CGP-2175 *see* Metoprolol.

CGP-7174/E *see* Cefsulodin.

CGP-7760 *see* Prenalterol.

CGP-9000 *see* Cefroxadine.

CGP-14221/E *see* Cefotiam.

CGS-5391B *see* Enolicam sodium.

CH-757 *see* Lormetazepam.

CH-3565 *see* Triclosan.

CH-13437 *see* Nafenopin.

CHALCONE (1,3-diphenyl-2-propen-1-one; phenyl styryl ketone).

CHANDONIUM IODIDE (17α-methyl-3β-pyrrolidin-1-yl-17-aza-D-homo-5-androstene dimethiodide; HS-310).

CHAULMESTROL (ethyl chaulmoograte).

CHAULMOOGRIC ACID (13-(2-cyclopenten-1-yl)tridecanoic acid; hydnocarpylacetic acid).

CHAULMOSULFONE*** (4,4'-bis[*p*-(13-cyclopentyltridecanamido)phenyl] sulfone; 4',4''-sulfonylbis(cyclopentanetridecananilide)).

'Chelaton' *see* Trisodium edetate.

'Chel DTPA' *see* Pentetic acid.

'Chelen' *see* Chloroethane.

CHELIDAMIC ACID (1,4-dihydro-4-oxo-2,6-pyridinedicarboxylic acid).

'Chelintox' *see* Sodium calcium edetate.

'Chemical mace' *see* 2-Chloroacetophenone.

'Chemiofuran' *see* Nitrofurantoin.

'Chemipen' *see* Pheneticillin.

'Chenar' *see* Chenodeoxycholic acid.

'Chendol' *see* Chenodeoxycholic acid.

Chenic acid *see* Chenodeoxycholic acid.

CHENODEOXYCHOLIC ACID*** (3α,7α-dihydroxy-5β-cholan-24-oic acid; 3,7-dihydroxycholanic acid; chenodiol; anthropodeoxycholic acid; chenic acid; gallodeoxycholic acid; CDC; 'chenar'; 'chendol'; 'chenofalk'; 'chenosaure'; 'chenossil'; 'cholanorm'; 'fluibil'; 'hekbilin').

Chenodiol* *see* Chenodeoxycholic acid.

'Chenofalk' *see* Chenodeoxycholic acid.

'Chenosaure' *see* Chenodeoxycholic acid.

'Chenossil' *see* Chenodeoxycholic acid.

Chenta *see* 1,2-Diaminocyclohexanetetraacetic acid.

'Chetovis' *see* Prasterone.

CHIA *see* Clorindanic acid.

Chick antidermatitis factor *see* Pantothenic acid.

Chillifolin* *see* Quillifoline.

Chin.... *see also* Quin.....

China green *see* Malachite green.

Chinaphthol *see* Quinaphthol.

Chindecamine* *see* Quindecamine.

Chinethazone* *see* Quinethazone.

CHINIOFON*** (mixture of 8-hydroxy-7-iodo-5-quinolinesulfonic acid with 20% of Na bicarb; iodoquinoline; meditrene; quiniofon; 'yatren').

Chinocide see Quinocide.

'Chinoderm' see Cloxiquine.

Chinoform see Clioquinol.

CHINOMETHIONAT* (6-methyl-1,3-dithiolo[4,5-*b*]quinoxalin-2-one; 6-methyl-2,3-quinoxalinedithiol cyclic *S,S*-dithiocarbonate; quinomethionate; 'forstan'; 'morestan').

CHINOPYRINE (compound of quinine-HCl with phenazone; quinopyrine).

'Chinoral' see Quinochloral.

'Chinosol' see 8-Quinolinol sulfate.

Chinothionat see Thioquinox.

'Chinoxone' see Oxycinchophen.

Chinurea see Quinurea.

Chitosamine see Glucosamine.

Chloditan (tr) see Mitotane.

Chlodofen (tr) see Feniodium chloride.

Chlopenadion see Clorindione.

Chlophedianol* see Clofedanol.

Chlopoxide see Chlordiazepoxide.

Chlopropham see Chlorpropham.

Chlor.... see also Clor.....

Chloracetophenone see 2-Chloroacetophenone.

Chloracetoxyquinoline see Cloxiquine acetate.

Chloracizin (tr) see Cloracizin.

Chloracon (tr) see Beclamide.

'Chloractil' see Chlorpromazine.

CHLORACYZINE*** (2-chloro-10-(3-diethylaminopropionyl)phenothiazine; 2-chlorophenothiazin-10-yl 2-diethylaminoethyl ketone).

'Chloradione' see Chlorophacinone.

CHLORAL (trichloroacetaldehyde).

CHLORAL BETAINE* (chloral hydrate betaine adduct; betain chloralum; cloral betaine; 'betachlor'; 'somilan'; 'somilar').

'Chloraldurat' see Chloral hydrate.

CHLORAL HYDRATE (trichloroacetaldehyde monohydrate).
See also Butylchloral hydrate; Chloral betaine; Dichloralphenazone.

CHLORAL HYDRATE ACETYLGLYCINAMIDE ('ansopal'; 'duphanox').

Chloral hydrocyanide see Chlorocyanohydrin.

CHLORALODOL*** (2-methyl-4-(2,2,2-trichloro-1-hydroxyethoxy)-2-pentanol; chlorhexadol).

Chloralosane see Chloralose.

CHLORALOSE** ((*R*)-1,2-*O*-(2,2,2-trichloroethylidene)-α-D-glucofuranose; anhydroglucochloral; chloralosane; α-chloralose; glucochloral; glucochloralose).

α-Chloralose see Chloralose.

CHLORALPHENAZONE (compound of 1 mol. phenazone with 1 mol. chloral hydrate; chloralantipyrine; 'hypnal').

Chloral reaction product with cellulose 2-hydroxyethyl ether see Celucloral.

Chloral urethan see Carbocloral.

CHLORAMBEN* (3-amino-2,5-dichlorobenzoic acid; 'amiben'; 'vegaben').

CHLORAMBUCIL*** (4-[*p*-[bis(2-chloroethyl)-amino]phenyl]butyric acid; chloraminophene; chlorbutin; CB-1348; NSC-3088).
See also Prednimustine.

'Chloramide' see Tosylchloramide sodium.

'Chloramin' see Chlormethine.

'Chloramine-t' see Tosylchloramide sodium.

Chloraminophene see Chlorambucil.

Chloramiphene see Clomifene.

CHLORAMPHENICOL*** (D-*threo*-2,2-dichloro-*N*-[β-hydroxy-α-(hydroxymethyl)-*p*-nitrophenethyl]acetamide; D(−)-*threo*-2-(dichloroacetamido)-1-(*p*-nitrophenyl)-1,3-propanediol; (−)-chloramphenicol;ǀchloronitromycin; levomycetin).

CHLORAMPHENICOL plus OLEANDOMYCIN ('chlotaon').

CHLORAMPHENICOL plus PREDNISONE ('cortiphenicol').

(+)-CHLORAMPHENICOL (dextramycin; dextromycetin).

DL-CHLORAMPHENICOL (synthomycin).

(−)-Chloramphenicol see Chloramphenicol.

CHLORAMPHENICOL HEMISUCCINATE SODIUM ('aquamycetin'; 'chlorocid S'; 'solnicol').

CHLORAMPHENICOL STEARATE (eusintomicine; eusynthomycin; 'madomicetina').
See also Cloramfenicol pantotenate complex.

Chloranautine see Dimenhydrinate.

CHLORANIFORMETHAN* (*N*-[1-(3,4-dichloroanilino)-2,2,2-trichloroethyl]formamide; *N*-(2,2,2-trichloro-1-formamidoethyl)aniline; BAY-79770; XXI/07; 'imugan').

CHLORANIL ('spergon'; 'vulklor').

CHLORANILIC ACID (2,5-dichloro-3,6-dihydroxy-*p*-benzoquinone).

CHLORANOCRYL* (*N*-(3,4-dichlorophenyl)-2-methyl-2-propenamide; *N*-(3,4-dichlorophenyl)-2-methylacrylamide; 'dicryl').

CHLORASQUIN (*N*-(*p*-[(2,4-diamino-5-chloroquinazolin-6-ylmethyl)amino]benzoyl]aspartic acid dihydrate; NSC-529861; SK-29861).

CHLORAZANIL*** (2-amino-4-(*p*-chloroanilino-*s*-triazine); chlorazinil; ASA-226).

Chlorazin see Chlorazine *and* Cycloguanil.

CHLORAZINE* (2-chloro-4,6-bis(diethylamino)-*s*-triazine; chlorazin; G-25804).

Chlorazinil see Chlorazanil.

CHLORAZODIN*** (1,1′-azobis(chloroformamidine); chloroazodin).

CHLORBENOXAMINE*** (1-[2-(*o*-chloro-α-phenylbenzyloxy)ethyl]-4-(*o*-methylbenzyl)piperazine; chlorbenzoxyethamine; UCB-1474).

CHLORBENSIDE* (1-chloro-4-[[(4-chlorophenyl)methyl]thio]benzene; 1-chloro-4-[(*p*-chlorobenzyl)thio]benzene; *p*-chlorobenzyl *p*-chlorophenyl sulfide; 4-chloro-α-[(*p*-chlorophenyl)-thio]toluene; 'chlorparacide'; 'chlorsulphacide'; 'mitox').

Chlorbenzilate see Chlorobenzilate.

CHLORBETAMIDE*** (*N*-(dichloroacetyl)-*N*-(2,4-dichlorobenzyl)-2-hydroxyethylamine;

WIN-5047).

CHLORBICYCLEN* (1,2,3,4,7,7-hexachloro-5,6-bis(chloromethyl)bicyclo[2.2.1]hept-2-ene; 1,4,5,6,7,7-hexachloro-5,6-bis(chloromethyl)norbornene; AC-12402; 'alodan').

CHLORBROMURON* (1-(4-bromo-3-chlorophenyl)-3-methoxy-3-methylurea; 'maloran').

CHLORBUFAM* (1-methyl-2-propynyl 3-chlorophenylcarbamate; 1-methylprop-2-ynyl *m*-chlorocarbanilate; BICP; biPC).

CHLORBUFAM plus CHLORIDAZON ('alicap').

CHLORBUFAM plus CYCLURON ('alinur').

Chlorbutanol *see* Chlorbutol.

Chlorbutin *see* Chlorambucil.

CHLORBUTOL* (1,1,1-trichloro-2-methyl-2-propanol; chlorobutanol; acetone-chloroform; chlorbutanol).

Chlorcamphene *see* Campheclor.

Chlorcholine *see* Chlormequat.

Chlorcinnazine *see* Clocinizine.

Chlorcyclamide (tr) *see* Chlorhexamide.

CHLORCYCLIZINE*** (1-[α-(*p*-chlorophenyl)-benzyl]-4-methylpiperazine; chlorocyclizine; AH-289).

'Chlordan' *see* Chlordane.

CHLORDANE* (1,2,4,5,6,7,8,8-octachloro-2,3,3a,4,7,7a-hexahydro-4,7-methanoindene; octachlor; CD-68; HCS-3260; M-40; M-410; 'chlordan'; 'chlor-kill'; 'octa-klor'; 'ortho-klor'; 'toxichlor'; 'velsicol 1068'; 'wydane').

CHLORDANE plus KEROSENE ('flit').

Chlordantoin* *see* Clodantoin.

CHLORDECONE* (decachlorooctahydro-1,3,4-metheno-2*H*-cyclobuta[*cd*]pentalen-2-one; decachloropentacyclodecan-4-one; 'kepone').

CHLORDIAZEPOXIDE*** (7-chloro-2-methyl-amino-5-phenyl-3*H*-1,4-benzodiazepine 4-oxide; chlopoxide; clopoxide; methaminodiazepoxide; chlordiazepoxide hydrochloride; NSC-115748; Ro 5-0690).

CHLORDIAZEPOXIDE plus CLIDINIUM BROMIDE ('librax'; 'libraxin'). *See also under* Amitriptyline.

Chlordimeform *see* Chlorphenamidine.

CHLORDIMORINE*** (3-chloro-4-[3-(4-morpholino)propoxy]biphenyl; 4-[3-(3-chloro-4-biphenylyloxy)propyl]morpholine).

Chlorepin *see* Clobazam.

'Chloresene' *see* Lindane.

Chlorethamine *see* Chlormethine.

Chlorethazine *see* Chlormethine.

Chlorethiazole *see* Clomethiazole.

CHLORETHOXYBUTAMOXANE (2-butyl-aminomethyl-8-(2-chloroethoxy)-1,4-benzodioxan).

Chloretin *see* Prynachlor.

'Chloretone' *see* Chlorbutol.

CHLORFENETHOL* (*p*-chloro-α-(*p*-chlorophenyl)-α-methylbenzyl alcohol; 4,4'-dichloro-α-methylbenzhydrol; bis(*p*-chlorophenyl) methyl carbinol; *p,p*'-dichlorodiphenyl methyl carbinol; CPAS; DCPC; DCPE; DMC; 'dimite'; 'micas-

in').

CHLORFENETHOL plus CHLORFENSULF-IDE ('milbax').

Chlorfenidim *see* Monuron.

Chlorfenisate *see* Clofibrate.

CHLORFENPROP-METHYL* (methyl 3-chloro-3-(*p*-chlorophenyl)propionate; methyl α,4-dichlorobenzenepropanoate; 'bidisin').

CHLORFENSON* (*p*-chlorophenyl *p*-chlorobenzenesulfonate; *p*-chlorophenyl closilate; chlorofenizon; difenson; metakson; ovex; ovochlor; CPCBS; PCPCBS; 'estonmite'; 'ovatran'; 'ovotran').

Chlorfenvinphos* *see* Clofenvinfos.

Chlorfluoran *see* Cryofluorane.

CHLORFLURAZOLE* (4,5-dichloro-2-(trifluoromethyl)-1*H*-benzimidazole; chloroflurazole; NC-2983).

Chlorftalidon *see* Chlortalidone.

Chlorguanide *see* Proguanil.

Chlorguanide triazine pamoate *see* Cycloguanil embonate.

Chlorhexadol* *see* Chloralodol.

'Chlorhexamed' *see* Chlorhexidine gluconate.

CHLORHEXAMIDE (1-(*p*-chlorophenylsulfonyl)-3-cyclohexylurea; chlorcyclamide).

CHLORHEXIDINE*** (1,1'-hexamethylenebis[5-(*p*-chlorophenyl)biguanide]; chlorohexidine; AY-5312).

CHLORHEXIDINE GLUCONATE* (chlorhexidine digluconate; 'chlorhexamed'; 'corsodyl'; 'hibiclens'; 'hibiscrub').

'Chlorhextol' *see* Polychlorinated biphenyl.

Chlorhistapyridamine *see* Chlorpheniramine.

Chlorhydroxyquinoline *see* Cloxiquine.

CHLORIDAZON* (5-amino-4-chloro-2-phenylpyridazin-3(2*H*)-one; pyrazon; PCA; 'pyramin'). *See also under* Chlorbufam.

Chloridine (tr) *see* Pyrimethamine.

Chloriguane *see* Proguanil.

Chlorimipramine *see* Clomipramine.

Chlorimpiphenine *see* Imiclopazine.

Chlorinat *see* Barban.

Chlorinated biphenyl *see* Polychlorinated biphenyl.

Chlorinated camphene *see* Campheclor.

CHLORINATED PHENOXYACETIC ACID (chiefly 2,4-dichlorophenoxyacetic acid and 2,4,5-trichlorophenoxyacetic acid; 'hormoslyr').

Chlorindanol* *see* Clorindanol.

'Chlorisept' *see* Cloxiquine.

CHLORISONDAMINE CHLORIDE*** (4,5,6,7-tetrachloro-2-[2-(dimethylamino)ethyl]-2-methylisoindolinium chloride methochloride; hisindamone; Su-3088; 'ecolid').

'Chlor-kill' *see* Chlordane.

CHLORMADINONE*** (6-chloro-6-dehydro-17α-hydroxyprogesterone; 6-chloro-17-hydroxy-pregna-4,6-diene-3,20-dione).

Δ¹-Chlormadinone *see* Delmadinone.

CHLORMADINONE ACETATE* (17α-acetoxy-6-chloro-6-dehydroprogesterone; NSC-92338).

CHLORMADINONE ACETATE plus ETHINYLESTRADIOL ('amenyl').

99

CHLORMADINONE ACETATE plus MES-TRANOL (S-3850; 'anconcen'; 'C-quens'; 'eunomin'; 'femigen'; 'gestamestrol'; 'gestranol'; 'ovosiston'; 'sequens'; 'volenyl').

CHLORMEBUFORM* (N-butyl-N'-(4-chloro-2-methylphenyl)-N-methylformamidine; C-22598; 'buformin'; 'ektomin').

Chlormeprazine see Prochlorperazine.

CHLORMEQUAT* ((2-chloroethyl)trimethylammonium chloride; 2-chloro-N,N,N-trimethylethanamium chloride; chlorcholine; chlorocholine chloride; CCC; 'cycocel').

CHLORMERODRIN* ((3-chloromercuri-2-methoxypropyl)urea; chlormeroprin; mercurylurée; chloromerodrin; promeran).

Chlormeroprin* see Chlormerodrin.

Chlormethazanone* see Chlormezanone.

CHLORMETHAZOLE* (2-(3,4-dichlorophenyl)-4-methyl-1,2,4-oxazolidine-3,5-dione; bioxone; methazole; 'probe'; 'tunic').

Chlormethazone see Chlormezanone.

Chlormethiazole* see Clomethiazole.

CHLORMETHINE* (N,N-bis(2-chloroethyl)-methylamine; methylbis-β-chloroethylamine; mechlorethamine; azotoyperite; chlorethamine; chlorethazine; chloromethine; embechine; embichin; kloretazin; N-lost; mustine; nitrogen mustard; stickstofflost; C-6866; HN2; MBA; NSC-762; SK-101).

CHLORMETHINE N-OXIDE (HN2O; MBAO; N-oxyd-lost; NSC-10107; XA-2).

Chlormethylenecycline see Clomocycline.

CHLORMEZANONE* (2-(p-chlorophenyl)-3-methyl-4-metathiazanone 1,1-dioxide; 2-(p-chlorophenyl)tetrahydro-3-methyl-4H-1,3-thiazin-4-one 1,1-dioxide; chlormethazanone; chlormethazone).

CHLORMEZAZONE plus ACETYLSALICYLIC ACID ('tranco-gesic').

CHLORMEZAZONE plus PARACETAMOL ('beserol'; 'lobak'; 'monatal').

CHLORMIDAZOLE* (1-(p-chlorobenzyl)-2-methylbenzimidazole; H-115).

CHLORNAPHAZINE* (bis(2-chloroethyl)-2-naphthylamine; chloronaphazine; chloronaphthine; cloronaftina; CB-1048; R-48).

Chlornidine see Clonidine.

2-CHLOROACETOPHENONE (chloracetophenone; phenacyl chloride; tear gas; C.N.; 'chemical mace').

17-(Chloroacetyl)ajmaline see Lorajmine.

N-(2-Chloroacetyl)diallylamine see Allidochlor.

N-(2-Chloroacetyl)-2,6-diethyl-N-(methoxymethyl)-aniline see Alachlor.

3-(p-Chloroanilino)-10-(p-chlorophenyl)-2,10-dihydro-2-isopropyliminophenazine see Clofazimine.

p-[2-(5-Chloro-o-anisamido)ethyl]benzoic acid see Meglitinide.

1-[p-[2-(5-Chloro-o-anisamido)ethyl]phenylsulfonyl]-3-cyclohexylurea see Glibenclamide.

1-[[p-[2-(5-Chloro-o-anisamido)ethyl]phenyl]sulfonyl]-3-methylurea see Glicondamide.

Chloroazodin* see Chlorazodin.

o-Chlorobenzalmalononitrile see o-Chlorobenzylidenemalononitrile.

2-(p-Chlorobenzamido)acetohydroxamic acid see Benurestat.

2-[p-[2-(p-Chlorobenzamido)ethyl]phenoxy]-2-methylpropionic acid see Bezafibrate.

2-(p-Chlorobenzamido)-3-indolepropionic acid see Benzotript.

4-Chloro-1,3-benzenedisulfonamide see Clofenamide.

p-Chlorobenzenesulfonic acid, esters and salts see Closilate(s).

CHLOROBENZILATE* (ethyl 2,2-bis(p-chlorophenyl)glycolate; ethyl 4,4'-dichlorobenzilate; ethyl 4-chloro-α-(4-chlorophenyl)-α-hydroxybenzeneacetate; chlorbenzilate; G-23922; 'folbex').

(Chlorobenzimidazolylmethyl)dimethylphenylethylenediamine see Midamaline.

6-Chloro-1,2-benzisothiazolin-3-one see Ticlatone.

6-Chloro-2H-1,2,4-benzothiadiazine-7-sulfonamide 1,1-dioxide see Chlorothiazide.

2-(5-Chloro-2H-benzotriazol-2-yl)-6-(1,1-dimethylethyl)-4-methylphenol see Bumetrizole.

5-Chloro-2-benzoxazolinone see Chlorzoxazone.

5-(p-Chlorobenzoyl)-1,4-dimethylpyrrole-2-acetic acid see Zomepirac.

4-(p-Chlorobenzoyl)-1-[3-(p-fluorobenzoyl)propyl]-piperidine see Cloroperone.

N-(p-Chlorobenzoyl)-N-(2-hydroxyethyl)-3-methyl-2-norbornanemethylamine see Clocanfamide.

1-(p-Chlorobenzoyl)-5-methoxy-2-methyl-3-indoleacetic acid see Indometacin.

3-(p-Chlorobenzoyl)-6-methoxy-2-methyl-1-indoleacetic acid see Clometacin.

1-(p-Chlorobenzoyl)-5-methoxy-2-methylindole-3-acetohydroxamic acid see Oxametacin.

2-[2-[1-(p-Chlorobenzoyl)-5-methoxy-2-methylindol-3-yl]acetamido]-2-deoxy-D-glucose see Glucametacin.

3-[4-[2-[[1-(p-Chlorobenzoyl)-5-methoxy-2-methylindol-3-yl]acetoxy]ethyl]piperazin-1-yl]propyl 4-benzamido-N,N-dipropylglutaramate see Proglumetacin.

O-[[1-(p-Chlorobenzoyl)-5-methoxy-2-methylindol-3-yl]acetyl]glycolic acid see Acemetacin.

N-[[-1-(p-Chlorobenzoyl)-5-methoxy-2-methylindol-3-yl]acetyl]-L-serine see Sermetacin.

N-(p-Chlorobenzoylmethyl)-3-(10,11-dihydro-5H-dibenz[b,f]azepin-5-yl)-N-methylpropylamine see Lofepramine.

2-(p-(p-Chlorobenzoyl)phenoxy)-2-methylpropionic acid isopropyl ester see Fenofibrate.

4-[4-(p-Chlorobenzoyl)piperid-1-yl]-4'-fluorobutyrophenone see Cloroperone.

1-(p-Chlorobenzoyl)-3-(1H-tetrazol-3-yl-methyl)indole see Intrazole.

N-(p-Chlorobenzoyl)-L-tryptophan see Benzotript.

Chlorobenztropine see Clobenztropine.

p-Chlorobenzyl p-chlorophenyl sulfide see Chlorbenside.

N-(o-Chlorobenzyl)dexamphetamine see Clobenzorex.

1-(*o*-Chlorobenzyl)-α-[(di-*sec*-butylamino)methyl]-pyrrole-2-methanol *see* Viminol.

2-(*p*-Chlorobenzyl)-1-(2-diethylaminoethyl)-5-nitrobenzimidazole *see* Clonitazene.

2-[(*p*-Chlorobenzyl)(2-dimethylaminoethyl)amino]-pyridine *see* Chloropyramine.

N-(*p*-Chlorobenzyl-*N'*,*N'*-dimethyl-*N*-pyrid-2-yl-ethylenediamine *see* Chloropyramine.

1-(*m*-Chlorobenzyl)-3-ethylurea *see* Lozilurea.

4-(*p*-Chlorobenzyl)-2-(hexahydro-1-methyl-1*H*-azepin-4-yl)-1(2*H*)-phthalazinone *see* Azelastine.

2-(*p*-Chlorobenzylidene)cyclohexanone *O*-[3-(di-isopropylamino)propyl]oxime *see* Erocainide.

o-CHLOROBENZYLIDENEMALONONI-TRILE (*o*-chlorobenzalmalononitrile; C.S.).

1-(*p*-Chlorobenzyl)-2-methylbenzimidazole *see* Chlormidazole.

(+)-*N*-(*o*-Chlorobenzyl)-α-methylphenethylamine *see* Clobenzorex.

4-(*o*-Chlorobenzyl)-5-oxo-4-phenylhexanoic acid *see* Caprochlorone.

3-[*p*-[(*m*-Chlorobenzyl)oxy]phenyl]-5-[(methyl-amino)methyl]-2-oxazolidinone *see* Almoxatone.

2-[4-(*p*-Chlorobenzyl)phenoxy]-2-methylbutyric acid ethyl ester *see* Beclobrate.

7-[3-[4-(*p*-Chlorobenzyl)piperazin-1-yl]propoxy]-3,4-dimethylcoumarin *see* Picumast.

N-[2-(*p*-Chlorobenzyl)prop-2-yl]carbamic acid ethyl ester *see* Cloforex.

1-(*p*-Chlorobenzyl)-2-pyrrolid-1-ylmethylbenzimid-azole *see* Clemizole.

1-[α-*N*-(*o*-Chlorobenzyl)pyrryl]-2-di-*sec*-butyl-aminoethanol *see* Viminol.

3-(*p*-Chlorobenzyl)quinolizidine *see* Cloquinozine.

4-(*p*-Chlorobenzyl)-1,4,6,7-tetrahydro-6,6-dimethyl-9*H*-imidazo[1,2-*a*]purin-9-one *see* Fenprinast.

5-(*o*-Chlorobenzyl)-4,5,6,7-tetrahydrothieno[3,2-*c*]-pyridine *see* Ticlopidine.

1-[(*p*-Chlorobenzyl)thio]-4-fluorobenzene *see* Fluorbenside.

2-[[(2'-Chlorobiphenyl-4-yl)carbonyl]methyl]acrylic acid *see* Itanoxone.

2-[(4'-Chlorobiphenyl-4-yl)methoxy]-2-methylpro-pionic acid *see* Clobuzarit.

2-(4'-Chlorobiphenyl-1-yloxy)-2-methylpropionic acid methyl ester *see* Methyl clofenapate.

4-[3-(3-Chloro-4-biphenylyloxy)propyl]morpholine *see* Chlordimorine.

2-Chloro-*N*,*N*-bis(2-chloroethyl)-1-propylamine *see* Novembichin.

4-Chloro-2,6-bis(5-chloro-2-hydroxybenzyl)phenol *see* Trichlorophen.

2-Chloro-4,6-bis(diethylamino)-*s*-triazine *see* Chlorazine.

2-Chloro-4,6-bis(ethylamino)-*s*-triazine *see* Simazine.

2-Chloro-4,6-bis(isopropylamino)-*s*-triazine *see* Propazine.

6-Chloro-*N*,*N'*-bis(1-methylethyl)-1,3,5-triazine-2,4-diamine *see* Propazine.

Chlorobutanol*** *see* Chlorbutol.

4-Chlorobut-2-yn-1-yl *m*-chlorocarbanilate *see* Bar-ban.

4-Chlorobut-2-yn-1-yl (*m*-chlorophenyl)carbamate *see* Barban.

'Chlorocain' *see* Mepivacaine.

Chlorocamphamide *see* Clocanfamide.

Chlorocanfamide *see* Clocanfamide.

m-Chlorocarbanilic acid esters *see* Barban; Chlor-bufan; Chlorprofam.

2-(6-Chlorocarbazol-2-yl)propionic acid *see* Carprofen.

'Chlorocarbon' *see* Carbon tetrachloride.

Chlorochin* *see* Chloroquine.

4'-Chloro-2'-(*o*-chlorobenzoyl)-2-(cyclopropyl-amino)-*N*-methylacetanilide *see* Ciprazafone.

3'-Chloro-4'-(*p*-chlorobenzoyl)-3,5-diiodosalicylanil-ide *see* Salantel.

o-Chloro-α-(*o*-chlorobenzyl)-α-hydroxyhydrocin-namic acid acetate (ester) 2-(2,2,6,6-tetramethyl-piperid-1-yl)ethyl ester *see* Tefenperate.

1-Chloro-4-[(*p*-chlorobenzyl)thio]benzene *see* Chlorbenside.

5'-Chloro-4'-(*p*-chloro-α-cyanobenzyl)-3,5-diiodo-2'-methylsalicylanilide *see* Closantel.

Chloro-(3-chloro-4-cyclohexylphenyl)acetic acid *see* Fenclorac.

3-[5-Chloro-α-(*p*-chloro-β-hydroxyphenethyl)-2-thenyl]-4-hydroxycoumarin *see* Tioclomarol.

6-Chloro-3-(chloromethyl)-3,4-dihydro-2-methyl-2*H*-1,2,4-benzothiodiazine-7-sulfonamide 1,1-di-oxide *see* Methyclothiazide.

3-Chloro-3-(3-chloro-2-nitrophenyl)pyrrole *see* Pyrrolnitrin.

5-Chloro-*N*-(2-chloro-4-nitrophenyl)salicylamide *see* Niclosamide.

5-Chloro-4-[2-(*p*-chlorophenoxy)acetamido]-*N*-[2-(diethylamino)ethyl]-*o*-anisamide *see* Cloxace-pride.

3'-Chloro-4'-(*p*-chlorophenoxy)-3,5-diiodosalicyl-anilide *see* Rafoxanide.

4-Chloro-5-[[2-[[3-(*o*-chlorophenoxy)-2-hydroxy-propyl]amino]ethyl]amino]-3(2*H*)-pyridazone *see* Ridazolol.

5'-Chloro-α⁴-(*p*-chlorophenyl)-α⁴-cyano-3,5-diiodo-2',4'-salicyloxylidide *see* Closantel.

N-[5-Chloro-4-[(4-chlorophenyl)cyanomethyl]-2-methylphenyl]-2-hydroxy-3,5-diiodobenzamide *see* Closantel.

7-Chloro-5-(*o*-chlorophenyl)-1,3-dihydro-2*H*-1,4-benzodiazepin-2-one *see* Delorazepam.

7-Chloro-5-(*o*-chlorophenyl)-1,3-dihydro-3-hydroxy-2*H*-1,4-benzodiazepin-2-one *see* Lorazepam.

7-Chloro-5-(*o*-chlorophenyl)-1,3-dihydro-3-hydroxy-1-methyl-2*H*-1,4-benzodiazepin-2-one *see* Lorme-tazepam.

7-Chloro-5-(*o*-chlorophenyl)-1,3-dihydro-3-hydroxy-2*H*-pyrido[3,2-*e*][1,4]diazepin-2-one *see* Lopiraze-pam.

7-Chloro-5-(*o*-chlorophenyl)-2,3-dihydro-1-methyl-1*H*-1,4-benzodiazepine-2-methanol *see* Tuclaze-pam.

7-Chloro-5-(*o*-chlorophenyl)-2,3-dihydro-2-oxo-1*H*-1,4-benzodiazepine-3-carboxylic acid ethyl ester *see* Ethyl dirazepate.

7-Chloro-5-(*o*-chlorophenyl)-1,3-dihydro-1-[2-(*p*-tolylsulfonyl)ethyl]-2*H*-1,4-benzodiazepin-2-one *see* Tolufazepam.

4-Chloro-α-(4-chlorophenyl)-α-hydroxybenzeneacetic acid ethyl ester *see* Chlorobenzilate.

4-Chloro-α-(4-chlorophenyl)-α-hydroxybenzeneacetic acid 1-methylethyl ester *see* Chloropropylate.

p-Chloro-α-(*p*-chlorophenyl)-α-methylbenzyl alcohol *see* Chlorfenethol.

8-Chloro-6-(*o*-chlorophenyl)-1-methyl-4*H*-imidazo[1,5-*a*][1,4]benzodiazepine *see* Climazolam.

1-Chloro-4-[[(4-chlorophenyl)methyl]thio]benzene *see* Chlorbenside.

8-Chloro-6-(*o*-chlorophenyl)-1-methyl-4*H*-*s*-triazolo[4,3-*a*][1,4]benzodiazepine *see* Triazolam.

3-Chloro-3-(*p*-chlorophenyl)propionic acid methyl ester *see* Chlorfenprop-methyl.

8-Chloro-6-(*o*-chlorophenyl)-4*H*-pyrido[2,3-*f*]-*s*-triazolo[4,3-*a*][1,4]diazepine *see* Zapizolam.

p-Chloro-α-(*p*-chlorophenyl)-α-pyrid-3-ylbenzyl alcohol *see* Parinol.

10-Chloro-11b-(*o*-chlorophenyl)-2,3,7,11b-tetrahydro-3-methyloxazolo[3,2-*d*][1,4]benzodiazepin-6(5*H*)-one *see* Mexazolam.

10-Chloro-11b-(*o*-chlorophenyl)-2,3,7,11b-tetrahydrooxazolo[3,2-*d*][1,4]benzodiazepin-6(5*H*)-one *see* Cloxazolam.

4-Chloro-α-[(*p*-chlorophenyl)thio]toluene *see* Chlorbenside.

4-Chloro-α-(4-chlorophenyl)-α-trichloromethylbenzenemethanol *see* Dicofol.

p-Chloro-α-(*p*-chlorophenyl)-α-(trichloromethyl)-benzyl alcohol *see* Dicofol.

4'-Chloro-5-[(7-chloro-4-quinolyl)amino]-3-[[(1,1-dimethylethyl)amino]methyl][1,1'-biphenyl]-2-ol *see* Tebuquine.

7-Chloro-2-(*o*-chlorostyryl)-4-[(4-diethylamino-1-methylbutyl)amino]quinoline *see* Aminoquinol.

Chlorocholine chloride *see* Chlormequat.

'Chlorocid S' *see* Chloramphenicol hemisuccinate sodium.

CHLOROCRESOL*** (4-chloro-3-methylphenol; chlorocresol sodium).

Chlorocrotylmercaptomethylpenicillin *see* Penicillin S.

CHLOROCYANOHYDRIN (chloral hydrocyanide; trichloroacetonitrile).

2-Chloro-6-(1-cyano-1-methylethylamino)-4-ethylamino-*s*-triazine *see* Cyanazine.

4'-Chloro-2-[(2-cyano-1-methylethyl)methylamino]-2-(*o*-fluorobenzoyl)-*N*-methylacetanilide *see* Alozafone.

5-Chloro-2-[[[[(2-cyano-1-methylethyl)methyl]amino]methyl]carbonyl]methylamino]-2'-fluorobenzophenone *see* Alozafone.

2-Chloro-8β-(cyanomethyl)-6-methylergoline *see* Lergotrile.

exo-3-Chloro-*endo*-6-cyano-2-norbornanone *O*-(methylcarbamoyl)oxime *see* 5-Chloro-6-oxo-2-norbornanecarbonitrile *o*-(methylcarbamoyl)oxime.

1-[*N*-(3-Chloro-4-cyanophenyl)carbamoyl]guanidine *see* Cloguanamil.

2,2'-[(2-Chloro-5-cyano-1,3-phenylene)diimino]-bis[2-oxoacetic acid] *see* Lodoxamide.

N,*N*'-(2-Chloro-5-cyano-*m*-phenylene)di(oxamic acid) *see* Lodoxamide.

Chlorocyclizine *see* Chlorcyclizine.

7-Chloro-5-cyclohexen-1-yl-1,3-dihydro-2*H*-1,4-benzodiazepin-2-one *see* Nortetrazepam.

7-Chloro-5-cyclohexen-1-yl-1,3-dihydro-1-methyl-2*H*-1,4-benzodiazepin-2-one *see* Tetrazepam.

5-Chloro-6-cyclohexyl-2(3*H*)-benzofuranone *see* Clofurac.

3-(3-Chloro-4-cyclohexylbenzoyl)propionic acid *see* Bucloxic acid.

6-Chloro-5-cyclohexyl-1-indancarboxylic acid *see* Clidanac.

6-Chloro-2-cyclohexyl-3-oxo-5-isoindolinesulfonamide *see* Clorexolone.

4-(3-Chloro-4-cyclohexylphenyl)-4-oxobutyric acid *see* Bucloxic acid.

5-Chloro-2-cyclohexyl-6-sulfamoylphthalimidine *see* Clorexolone.

6-Chloro-3-(cyclopentylmethyl)-3,4-dihydro-2*H*-1,2,4-benzothiadiazine-7-sulfonamide 1,1-dioxide *see* Cyclopenthiazide.

7-Chloro-1-[2-(cyclopropylmethoxy)ethyl]-1,3-dihydro-5-phenyl-2*H*-1,4-benzodiazepin-2-one *see* Iclazepam.

7-Chloro-2-[(cyclopropylmethyl)amino]-5-phenyl-3*H*-1,4-benzodiazepine-4-oxide *see* Cyprazepam.

7-Chloro-1-cyclopropylmethyl-1,3-dihydro-5-phenyl-2*H*-1,4-benzodiazepin-2-one *see* Prazepam.

7-Chloro-1-(cyclopropylmethyl)-5-(*o*-fluorophenyl)-1,3-dihydro-2*H*-1,4-benzodiazepin-2-one *see* Flutoprazepam.

6-Chloro-6-dehydro-17α-hydroxyprogesterone *see* Chlormadinone.

10-Chloro-11-demethoxyreserpine *see* Chloroserpidine.

7-Chloro-6-demethyl-6-deoxy-5-hydroxy-6-methylenetetracycline *see* Meclocycline.

Chlorodemethyldiazepam *see* Delorazepam.

7-Chloro-6-demethyltetracycline *see* Demeclocycline.

7(*S*)-Chloro-7-deoxylincomycin *see* Clindamycin.

10-Chlorodeserpidine *see* Chloroserpidine.

2-Chloro-10-[3-(1,4-diazabicyclo[4.2.0]nonan-4-yl)propionyl]phenothiazine *see* Azaclorzine.

2-[(8-Chlorodibenzo[*b*,*f*]thiepin-10-yl)oxy]-*N*,*N*-dimethylethylamine *see* Zotepine.

1-[(8-Chlorodibenz[*b*,*f*][1,4]oxazepin-10(11*H*)-yl)carbonyl]-2-(5-chlorovaleryl)hydrazine *see* Pinadoline.

cis-4-[3-(2-Chlorodibenz[*b*,*e*]oxepin-11-(6*H*)-ylidene)propyl]-1-piperazineethanol *see* Pinoxepin.

1-[*p*-Chloro-β-[(2,6-dichlorobenzyl)oxy]phenethyl]-imidazole *see* Orconazole.

6-Chloro-3-(dichloromethyl)-3,4-dihydro-1,2,4-benzothiadiazine-7-sulfonamide 1,1-dioxide *see* Trichlormethiazide.

5-Chloro-6-(2,3-dichlorophenoxy)-2-(methylthio)-benzimidazole *see* Triclabendazole.

5-Chloro-2-(2,4-dichlorophenoxy)phenol *see* Triclosan.

2-Chloro-1-(2,4-dichlorophenyl)vinyl diethyl phosphate *see* Clofenvinfos.

6-Chloro-1,6-didehydroretroprogesterone *see* Trengestone.

N-**[2-Chloro-1-[(diethoxyphosphinothioyl)thio]ethyl]phthalimide** *see* Dialifos.

6-Chloro-3(2*H***)-[[(diethoxyphosphinothioyl)thio]methyl]benzoxazol-2-one** *see* Phosalone.

2-Chloro-1-diethylaminocroton-3-yl dimethyl phosphate *see* Phosphamidon.

5-Chloro-2-[*p***-(2-diethylaminoethoxy)phenyl]benzothiazole** *see* Haletazole.

2-Chloro-1-[*p***-(2-diethylaminoethoxy)phenyl]-1,2-diphenylethylene** *see* Clomifene.

α-**Chloro-α'-[***p***-(2-diethylaminoethoxy)phenyl]stilbene** *see* Clomifene.

2-Chloro-4-diethylamino-6-ethylamino-*s***-triazine** *see* Trietazine.

2'-Chloro-2-[(2-diethylaminoethyl)ethylamino]acetanilide *see* Clodacaine.

7-Chloro-1-(2-diethylaminoethyl)-5-(*o***-fluorophenyl)-1,3-dihydro-2***H***-1,4-benzodiazepin-2-one** *see* Flurazepam.

6-Chloro-2-diethylamino-4-isopropylamino-*s***-triazine** *see* Ipazine.

6-Chloro-9-[4-(diethylamino)-1-methylbutylamino]-2-methoxyacridine *see* Mepacrine.

7-Chloro-4-(4-diethylamino-1-methylbutylamino)-3-methylquinoline *see* Sontoquine.

7-Chloro-4-[4-(diethylamino)-1-methylbutylamino]quinoline *see* Chloroquine.

7-Chloro-4-[3-[(diethylamino)methyl]-4-hydroxyanilino]quinoline *see* Amodiaquine.

2'-Chloro-2-[2-[(diethylamino)methyl]imidazol-1-yl]-5-nitrobenzophenone *see* Nizofenone.

(2-Chloro-3-diethylamino-1-methyl-3-oxo-1-propenyl) dimethyl phosphate *see* Phosphamidon.

2-Chloro-10-(3-diethylaminopropionyl)phenothiazine *see* Chloracyzine.

5-Chloro-7-(3-diethylaminopropylaminomethyl)-8-quinolinol *see* Clamoxyquine.

2-Chloro-10-(3-diethylaminopropyl)phenothiazine *see* Chlorproethazine.

6-Chloro-3-[[(diethylcarbamoyl)methyl]thio]pyridazine *see* Azintamide.

[2-Chloro-2-(diethylcarbamoyl)-1-methylvinyl] dimethyl phosphate *see* Phosphamidon.

4-Chloro-2,6-di(ethyleneimino)pyrimidine *see* Ethymidine.

4-Chloro-*N,N***-diethyl-***N***-heptylbenzenebutanaminium phosphate** *see* Clofilium phosphate.

2-Chloro-*N,N***-diethyl-3-hydroxycrotonamide dimethyl phosphate** *see* Phosphamidon.

6-Chloro-*N,N***-diethyl-***N'***-(1-methylethyl)-1,3,5-triazine-2,4-diamine** *see* Ipazine.

2-Chloro-*N***-(2,6-diethylphenyl)-***N***-(methoxymethyl)acetamide** *see* Alachlor.

6-Chloro-*N,N'***-diethyl-1,3,5-triazine-2,4-diamine** *see* Simazine.

9-Chloro-6α,11β-difluoro-21-hydroxy-16α-methylpregna-1,4-diene-3,20-dione *see* Halocortolone.

2-Chloro-2-(difluoromethoxy)-1,1,1-trifluoroethane

see Isoflurane.

2-Chloro-6α,9-difluoro-11β,17,21-trihydroxy-16α-methylpregna-1,4-diene-3,20-dione *see* Halometasone.

Chlorodifon *see* Tetradifon.

10-Chloro-5,10-dihydroarsacridine *see* Phenarsazine chloride.

6-Chloro-3,4-dihydro-2*H***-1,2,4-benzothiadiazine-7-sulfonamide 1,1-dioxide** *see* Hydrochlorothiazide.

1'-[3-(3-Chloro-10,11-dihydro-5*H***-dibenz-[***b,f***]azepin-5-yl)propyl][1,4'-bipiperidine]-4'-carboxamide** *see* Clocapramine.

4'-Chloro-2-[[3-(10,11-dihydro-5*H***-dibenz-[***b,f***]azepin-5-yl)propyl]methylamino]acetophenone** *see* Lofepramine.

1-(8-Chloro-10,11-dihydrodibenzo[*b,f***]-thiepin-10-yl)-4-methylpiperazine** *see* Clorotepine.

7-Chloro-2,3-dihydro-2,2-dihydroxy-5-phenyl-1*H***-1,4-benzodiazepine-3-carboxylic acid** *see* Clorazepic acid.

11-Chloro-8,12b-dihydro-2,8-dimethyl-12b-phenyl-4*H***[1,3]oxazino[3,2-***d***][1,4]benzodiazepine-4,7(6***H***)-dione** *see* Ketazolam.

S-**[2-Chloro-1-(1,3-dihydro-1,3-dioxo-2***H***-isoindol-2-yl)ethyl]** *O,O***-diethyl phosphorodithioate** *see* Dialifos.

6-Chloro-1β,2β-dihydro-17α-hydroxy-3'*H***-cyclopropa[1,2]pregna-4,6-diene-3,20-dione** *see* Cyproterone.

7-Chloro-1,3-dihydro-3-hydroxy-1-methyl-5-phenyl-2*H***-1,4-benzodiazepin-2-one** *see* Temazepam.

7-Chloro-1,3-dihydro-3-hydroxy-1-methyl-5-phenyl-2*H***-1,4-benzodiazepin-2-one dimethylcarbamate ester** *see* Camazepam.

7-Chloro-1,3-dihydro-3-hydroxy-5-phenyl-2*H***-1,4-benzodiazepin-2-one** *see* Oxazepam.

7-Chloro-3,4-dihydro-10-hydroxy-3-(α,α,α-trifluoro-*p***-tolyl)-1,9(2***H***)-acridandione** *see* Floxacrine.

6-Chloro-3,4-dihydro-3-isobutyl-2*H***-1,2,4-benzothiadiazine-7-sulfonamide 1,1-dioxide** *see* Butizide.

7-Chloro-3,3a-dihydro-2*H***,9***H***-isoxazolo[3,2-***b***]-[1,3]benzoxazin-9-one** *see* Seclazone.

6-Chloro-3,4-dihydro-3-(α-methylbenzyl)-2*H***-1,2,4-benzothiadiazine-7-sulfonamide 1,1-dioxide** *see* Bemetizide.

7-[[3-Chloro-6,11-dihydro-6-methyldibenzo[*c,f***][1,2]-thiazepin-11-yl]amino]heptanoic acid** *S,S***-dioxide** *see* Tianeptine.

7-Chloro-3,3a-dihydro-2-methyl-2*H***,9***H***-isoxazolo[3,2-***b***][1,3]benzoxazin-9-one** *see* Meseclazone.

7-Chloro-2,3-dihydro-1-methyl-5-phenyl-1*H***-1,4-benzodiazepine** *see* Medazepam.

7-(Chloro-1,3-dihydro-1-methyl-5-phenyl-2*H***-1,4-benzodiazepine-2-thione** *see* Sulazepam.

7-Chloro-1,3-dihydro-1-methyl-5-phenyl-2*H***-1,4-benzodiazepin-2-one** *see* Diazepam.

8-Chloro-10,11-dihydro-10-(4-methylpiperazin-1-yl)dibenzo[*b,f***]thiepine** *see* Clorotepine.

6-Chloro-3,4-dihydro-2-methyl-7-sulfamoyl-2*H***-1,2,4-benzothiadiazine-3-carboxylic acid 1,1-dioxide methyl ester** *see* Carmetizide.

6-Chloro-3,4-dihydro-2-methyl-3-[[(2,2,2-trifluoro-

ethyl)thio]methyl]-2*H*-1,2,4-benzothiadiazine-7-sulfonamide 1,1-dioxide *see* Polythiazide.

6-Chloro-3,4-dihydro-3-(5-norbornen-2-yl)-2*H*-1,2,4-benzothiadiazine-7-sulfonamide 1,1-dioxide *see* Cyclothiazide.

N-[2-[4-(5-Chloro-2,3-dihydro-2-oxo-1*H*-benzimidazol-1-yl)piperid-4-yl]ethyl]-4-fluorobenzamide *see* Halopemide.

2-Chloro-10-[3-[4-(dihydro-2(3*H*)-oxofuran-3-yl)-4-hydroxypiperid-1-yl]-propyl]phenothiazine *see* Furomazine.

7-Chloro-2,3-dihydro-2-oxo-5-phenyl-1*H*-1,4-benzodiazepine-3-carboxylic acid *see* Clorazepic acid.

7-Chloro-1,3-dihydro-5-phenyl-2*H*-1,4-benzodiazepin-2-one *see* Nordazepam.

7-Chloro-1,3-dihydro-5-phenyl-2*H*-1,4-benzodiazepin-2-one 4-oxide *see* Demoxepam.

8-Chloro-4,5-dihydro-1-phenyl-2*H*-1,5-benzodiazepin-2-one *see* Lofendazam.

7-Chloro-1,3-dihydro-5-phenyl-1-prop-2-ynyl-2*H*-1,4-benzodiazepin-2-one *see* Pinazepam.

7-Chloro-1,3-dihydro-5-phenyl-1-(2,2,2-trifluoroethyl)-2*H*-1,4-benzodiazepin-2-one *see* Halazepam.

6-Chloro-3,4-dihydro-3-succinimidomethyl-2*H*-1,2,4-benzothiadiazine-7-sulfonamide 1,1-dioxide *see* Sumetizide.

6-Chloro-3,4-dihydro-3-(trichloromethyl)-2*H*-1,2,4-benzothiadiazine-7-sulfonamide 1,1-dioxide *see* Teclothiazide.

6-Chloro-3,4-dihydro-3-[[(2,2,2-trifluoroethyl)-thio]methyl]-2*H*-1,2,4-benzothiadiazine-7-sulfonamide 1,1-dioxide *see* Epitizide.

6α-Chloro-17,21-dihydroxypregna-1,4-diene-3,11,20-trione *see* Chloroprednisone.

6-Chloro-3β,17-dihydroxypregna-4,6-dien-20-one *see* Clogestone.

7-Chloro-1-(2,3-dihydroxypropyl)-5-(*o*-fluorophenyl)-1,3-dihydro-2*H*-1,4-benzodiazepin-2-one *see* Proflazepam.

6-Chloro-4-(2,3-dihydroxypropyl)-2-methyl-2*H*-1,4-benzoxazin-3(4*H*)-one *see* Diproxadol.

4′-Chloro-3,5-diiodosalicylanilide acetate *see* Clioxanide.

Chlorodimeform *see* Chlorphenamidine.

Chlorodimenol *see* Clobutinol.

4′-Chloro-3,5-dimethoxy-4-(2-morpholinoethoxy)-benzophenone *see* Morclofone.

4-Chloro-4′-[(dimethoxyphosphinothioyl)oxy]azobenzene *see* Azothoate.

2-[*p*-Chloro-α-(2-dimethylaminoethoxy)benzyl]pyridine *see* Carbinoxamine; Rotoxamine.

8-Chloro-10-[2-(dimethylamino)ethoxy]dibenzo[*b*,*f*]-thiepin *see* Zotepine.

2-Chloro-α-(2-dimethylaminoethyl)benzhydrol *see* Clofedanol.

2-[*p*-Chloro-α-(2-dimethylaminoethyl)benzyl]pyridine *see* Chlorpheniramine.

8-Chloro-11-(2-dimethylaminoethyl)-6,11-dihydro-5*H*-benzo[5,6]cyclohepta-[1,2-*b*]pyridine *see* Closiramine.

7-Chloro-10-(2-dimethylaminoethyl)-5,10-dihydro-11*H*-dibenzo[*b*,*e*][1,4]-diazepin-11-one *see* Clobenzepam.

p-Chloro-α-(2-dimethylamino-1-methylethyl)-α-methylphenethyl alcohol *see* Clobutinol.

m-Chloro-α-[(dimethylamino)methyl]-β-phenylphenethylalcohol *see* Clemeprol.

8-Chloro-1-[(dimethylamino)methyl]-6-phenyl-4*H*-*s*-triazolo[4,3-*a*][1,4]benzodiazepine *see* Adinazolam.

2-Chloro-4-(dimethylamino)-6-methylpyrimidine *see* Crimidine.

2-Chloro-10-(3-dimethylaminopropionyl)phenothiazine *see* Cloracizin.

2-Chloro-9-(3-dimethylaminopropyl)acridan *see* Clomacran.

3-Chloro-5-[3-(dimethylamino)propyl]-10,11-dihydro-5*H*-dibenz[*b*,*f*]azepine *see* Clomipramine.

1-Chloro-5-[3-(dimethylamino)propylidene]-5*H*-dibenzo[*a*,*d*]cycloheptene *N*-oxide *see* Benzaprinoxide.

3-Chloro-11-[3-(dimethylamino)propylidene]-5,6-dihydromorphanthridine *see* Elanzepine.

2-Chloro-9-(3-dimethylaminopropylidene)thioxanthene *see* Chlorprothixene.

2-Chloro-10-(3-dimethylaminopropyl)phenothiazine *see* Chlorpromazine.

5-Chloro-1-(3-dimethylaminopropyl)-3-phenyl-2-benzimidazolinone *see* Clodazon.

4-Chloro-5-(dimethylamino)-2-[3-(trifluoromethyl)-phenyl]-3(2*H*)-pyridazinone *see* Metflurazon.

4-Chloro-6-(2,3-dimethylanilino)-2-[[[(2-hydroxyethyl)carbamoyl]methyl]thio]pyrimidine *see* Pirinixil.

[[4-Chloro-6-(2,3-dimethylanilino)pyrimidin-2-yl]-thio]acetic acid *see* Pirinixic acid.

6-Chloro-3-(1,2-dimethylbutyl)-3,4-dihydro-2*H*-1,2,4-benzothiadiazine-7-sulfonamide 1,1-dioxide *see* Mebutizide.

1-Chloro-*N*,*N*-dimethyl-5*H*-dibenzo[*a*,*d*]cyclohept-ene-Δ⁵,⁷-propylamine *N*-oxide *see* Benzaprinoxide.

6-Chloro-*N*-(1,1-dimethylethyl)-*N*′-ethyl-1,3,5-triazine-2,4-diamine *see* Terbuthylazine.

5-Chloro-3-(1,1-dimethylethyl)-6-methyl-2,4(1*H*,3*H*)-pyrimidinedione *see* Terbacil.

2-Chloro-4-(1,1-dimethylethyl)phenyl methyl methylphosphoramidate *see* Crufomate.

2-Chloro-*N*,*N*-dimethyl-5-[3-methyl-2-(phenylimino)-4-thiazolin-4-yl]benzenesulfonamide *see* Taltibride.

p-Chloro-α,α-dimethylphenethyl alcohol alanine ester *see* Alaproclate.

o-Chloro-α,α-dimethylphenethylamine *see* Clortermine.

p-Chloro-α,α-dimethylphenethylamine *see* Chlorphentermine.

2-(*p*-Chloro-α,α-dimethylphenethylamino)ethanol *see* Etolorex.

(*p*-Chloro-α,α-dimethylphenethyl)carbamic acid ethyl ester *see* Cloforex.

4-Chloro-3,5-dimethylphenol *see* Chloroxylenol.

2-Chloro-4,5-dimethylphenyl methylcarbamate *see* Carbanolate.

7-Chloro-1-(dimethylphosphinylmethyl)-1,3-di-

104

hydro-5-phenyl-2*H*-1,4-benzodiazepin-2-one *see* Fosazepam.

2-Chloro-5-[(3,5-dimethylpiperidino)sulfonyl]benzoic acid *see* Tibric acid.

4-Chloro-*N*-(*cis*-2,6-dimethylpiperid-1-yl)-3-sulfamoylbenzamide *see* Clopamide.

*N*¹-(5-Chloro-2,6-dimethylpyrimidin-4-yl)sulfanilamide *see* Sulfaclomide.

4-Chloro-2′,6′-dimethyl-5-sulfamoylsalicylanilide *see* Xipamide.

2-Chloro-*N*,*N*-dimethylthioxanthene-Δ⁹,ᵞ-propylamine *see* Chlorprothixene.

3′-Chloro-2,4′-dimethylvaleranilide *see* Pentanochlor.

1-CHLORO-2,4-DINITROBENZENE (dinitrochlorobenzene; DNCB).

4′-Chloro-2,6-dioxocyclohexanecarbothioanilide *see* Ontianil.

1-(*o*-Chloro-α,α-diphenylbenzyl)imidazole *see* Clotrimazole.

2-[*p*-(2-Chloro-1,2-diphenylvinyl)phenoxy]triethylamine *see* Clomifene; Enclomifene; Zuclomifene.

2-Chloro-*N*-*N*-dipropenylacetamide *see* Allidochlor.

5-Chloro-2,4-disulfamoyltoluene *see* Disulfamide.

4-Chloro-*N*-1,3-dithietan-2-ylidene-2-methylaniline *see* Nimidane.

1-Chloro-2,3-epoxypropane *see* Epichlorohydrin.

CHLOROETHANE (ethyl chloride; hydrochloric ether; muriatic ether).

2-CHLOROETHANOL (ethylene chlorohydrin; glycol chlorohydrin).

3-(2-Chloroethoxy)-6-cyano-9-fluoro-11β,16α, 17,21-tetrahydroxypregna-3,5-dien-20-one 16,17-acetonide 21-acetate *see* Cicortonide.

3-Chloro-*N*-ethoxy-2,6-dimethoxybenzenecarboximidic acid anhydride with benzoic acid *see* Benzoximate.

3-(2-Chloroethoxy)-9α-fluoro-6-formyl-11β,16α, 17α,21-tetrahydroxy-3,5-pregnadiene-20-one 16α,17α-acetonide 21-acetate *see* Formocortal.

3-(2-Chloroethoxy)-9-fluoro-11β,16α,17,21-tetrahydroxy-20-oxopregna-3,5-diene 6-carbonitrile cyclic 16,17-acetal with acetone 21-acetate *see* Cicortonide.

10-Chloro-3-ethoxymethyl-2,3,6,9-tetrahydro-9-oxo-*p*-dioxino[2,3-*g*]quinoline-8-carboxylic acid ethyl ester *see* Quincarbate.

2-Chloro-4-ethylamino-6-isopropylamino-*s*-triazine *see* Atrazine.

6-Chloro-2-ethylamino-4-methyl-4-phenyl-4*H*-3,1-benzoxazine *see* Etifoxine.

6-Chloro-2-ethylamino-4-phenyl-4*H*-3,1-benzothiazine *see* Etasuline.

2-[[4-Chloro-6-(ethylamino)-1,3,5-triazin-2-yl]amino]-2-methylpropionitrile *see* Cyanazine.

p-Chloro-α-ethylbenzyl alcohol *see* 1-(*p*-Chlorophenyl)-1-propanol.

3-(2-Chloroethyl)-2-[bis(2-chloroethyl)amino]tetrahydro-2*H*-1,3,2-oxazaphosphorine 2-oxide *see* Trofosfamide.

2-Chloroethyl *N*,*N*-bis(2-chloroethyl)-*N*′-(3-hydroxypropyl)phosphorodiamidate *see* Defosfamide.

3-(2-Chloroethyl)-2-(2-chloroethylamino)-2*H*-1,3,2-oxazaphosphorinane 2-oxide *see* Ifosfamide.

3-(2-Chloroethyl)-2-(2-chloroethylamino)tetrahydro-2*H*-1,3,2-oxazaphosphorine 2-oxide *see* Ifosfamide.

1-(2-Chloroethyl)-3-cyclohexyl-1-nitrosourea *see* Lomustine.

N-(2-Chloroethyl)dibenzylamine *see* Dibenamine.

6-Chloro-3-ethyl-3,4-dihydro-2*H*-1,2,4-benzothiadiazine-7-sulfonamide 1,1-dioxide *see* Ethiazide.

2-(2-Chloroethyl)-2,3-dihydro-4*H*-1,3-benzoxazin-4-one *see* Chlorthenoxazine.

3-(2-Chloroethyl)-3,4-dihydro-4-oxoimidazo[5,1-*d*]-*as*-tetrazine-8-carboxamide *see* Mitozolomide.

2-Chloroethyl 2-[4-(1,1-dimethylethyl)phenoxy]-1-methylethyl sulfite ester *see* 2-(*p*-*tert*-Butylphenoxy)isopropyl 2-chloroethyl sulfite.

1-(2-Chloroethyl)-3-(2,2-dimethylpropyl)-1-nitrosourea *see* Neptamustine.

1-(2-Chloroethyl)-3-[2-(dimethylsulfamoyl)ethyl]-1-nitrosourea *see* Tauromustine.

N-(2-Chloroethyl)-*N*-ethyl-2-methylbenzylamine *see* Xylamine.

N-(2-Chloroethyl)-*N*-ethyl-*o*-toluidine *see* Xylamine.

5-[(2-Chloroethyl)(2-fluoroethyl)amino]-6-methyluracil *see* Ftordopan.

1-(2-Chloroethyl)-3-(β-D-glucopyranosyl)-1-nitrosourea *see* Chlorozotocin.

7-Chloro-4-[4-[ethyl(2-hydroxyethyl)amino]-1-methylbutylamino]quinoline *see* Hydroxychloroquine.

1-(2-Chloroethyl)-3-(2-hydroxyethyl)-1-nitrosourea *see* Elmustine.

1-(2-Chloroethyl)-3-(2,3-*O*-isopropylidene-D-ribofuranosyl)-1-nitrosourea 5′-*p*-nitrobenzoate *see* Bofumustine.

2-[(2-Chloroethyl)methylamino]ethyl acetate *see* Acetylcholine mustard.

1-(2-Chloroethyl)-3-(4-methylcyclohexyl)-1-nitrosourea *see* Semustine.

6-Chloro-*N*-ethyl-*N*′-(1-methylethyl)-1,3,5-triazine-2,4-diamine *see* Atrazine.

N-(2-Chloroethyl)-*N*-(1-methyl-2-phenoxyethyl)benzylamine *see* Phenoxybenzamine.

5-(2-Chloroethyl)-4-methylthiazole *see* Clomethiazole.

1-(2-Chloroethyl)-3-neopentyl-1-nitrosourea *see* Neptamustine.

1-(2-CHLOROETHYL)-1-NITROSOUREA (NSC-47547).

2-[3-(2-Chloroethyl)-3-nitrosoureido]-2-deoxy-D-glucopyranose *see* Chlorozotocin.

1-Chloro-3-ethylpent-1-en-4-yn-3-ol *see* Ethchlorvynol.

5-Chloro-3-ethylpent-4-en-1-yn-3-ol *see* Ethchlorvynol.

Chloroethylphenamide *see* Beclamide.

3-[1-[*p*-(2-Chloroethyl)phenyl]butyl]-4-hydroxycoumarin *see* Clocoumarol.

3-[*p*-(2-Chloroethyl)-α-propylbenzyl]-4-hydroxycoumarin *see* Clocoumarol.

5-Chloro-*N*¹-[(1-ethylpyrrolidin-2-yl)methyl]-2-methoxysulfanilamide *see* Lorapride.

7-Chloro-1-[2-(ethylsulfonyl)ethyl]-5-(*o*-fluorophen-yl)-1,3-dihydro-2*H*-1,4-benzodiazepin-2-one *see* Elfazepam.

3-(2-Chloroethyl)tetrahydro-2-[(2-hydroxyethyl)-amino]-2*H*-1,3,2-oxazaphosphorine methanesul-fonate 2-oxide *see* Sufosfamide.

2-[[3-(2-Chloroethyl)tetrahydro-2*H*-1,3,2-oxaza-phosphorin-2-yl]amino]ethanol methanesulfonate (ester) *P*-oxide *see* Sufosfamide.

7-Chloro-2-ethyl-1,2,3,4-tetrahydro-4-oxo-6-quin-azolinesulfonamide *see* Quinethazone.

7-Chloro-2-ethyl-1,2,3,4-tetrahydro-6-sulfamoyl-quinazolin-4(3*H*)-one *see* Quinethazone.

Chloroethylthiamine *see* Beclotiamine.

(2-Chloroethyl)trimethylammonium chloride *see* Chlormequat.

17α-(Chloroethynyl)-17-hydroxy-19-androsta-4,9(10)-dien-3-one *see* Ethynerone.

Chlorofenizon *see* Chlorfenson.

5-Chloro-1-[3-[4-(*p*-fluorobenzoyl)piperid-1-yl]prop-yl]-2-benzimidazolinone *see* Milenperone.

9-(2-Chloro-6-fluorobenzyl)adenine *see* Arprinocid.

6-Chloro-3-(*p*-fluorobenzyl)-3,4-dihydro-2*H*-1,2,4-benzothiadiazine-7-sulfonamide 1,1-dioxide *see* Paraflutizide.

9-Chloro-6α-fluoro-11β,21-dihydroxy-16α-methyl-pregna-1,4-diene-3,20-dione *see* Clocortolone.

21-Chloro-9α-fluoro-11β,17α-dihydroxy-16α-meth-ylpregna-1,4-diene-3,20-dione *see* Clobetasol.

21-Chloro-9α-fluoro-11β-hydroxy-16α,17α-isoprop-ylidenedioxypregn-4-ene-3,20-dione *see* Halci-nonide.

21-Chloro-9α-fluoro-17α-hydroxy-16β-methyl-pregna-1,4-diene-3,11,20-trione *see* Clobetasone.

5-Chloro-1-[1-[3-(5-fluoro-2-oxo-1-benzimidazolin-yl)propyl]piperid-4-yl]-2-benzimidazolinone *see* Flumeridone.

2-[[*p*-Chloro-α-(*p*-fluorophenyl)benzyl]oxy]ethyl-amine *see* Halonamine.

7-Chloro-5-(*o*-fluorophenyl)-1,3-dihydro-3-hydroxy-1-(2-hydroxyethyl)-2*H*-1,4-benzodiazepin-2-one *see* Doxefazepam.

7-Chloro-5-(*o*-fluorophenyl)-2,3-dihydro-3-hydroxy-2-oxo-1*H*-1,4-benzodiazepine-1-propionitrile *see* Cinolazepam.

7-Chloro-5-(*o*-fluorophenyl)-1,3-dihydro-1-methyl-2*H*-1,4-benzodiazepin-2-one *see* Fludiazepam.

7-Chloro-5-(*o*-fluorophenyl)-2,3-dihydro-1-(methyl-carbamoyl)-2-oxo-1*H*-1,4-benzodiazepine-3-carb-oxylic acid ethyl ester *see* Ethyl carfluzepate.

7-Chloro-5-(*o*-fluorophenyl)-2,3-dihydro-2-oxo-1*H*-1,4-benzodiazepine-3-carboxylic acid ethyl ester *see* Ethyl loflazepate.

7-Chloro-5-(*o*-fluorophenyl)-2,3-dihydro-1-(2,2,2-trifluoroethyl)-1*H*-1,4-benzodiazepine *see* Fleta-zepam.

7-Chloro-5-(*o*-fluorophenyl)-1,3-dihydro-1-(2,2,2-trifluoroethyl)-2*H*-1,4-benzodiazepine-2-thione *see* Quazepam.

8-Chloro-6-(2-fluorophenyl)-1-methyl-4*H*-imi-dazo[1,5-*a*][1,4]-benzodiazepine *see* Midazolam.

6-[3-(2-Chloro-6-fluorophenyl)-5-methyl-4-isox-azolecarboxamido]penicillanic acid *see* Flucloxa-cillin.

3-(2-Chloro-6-fluorophenyl)-5-methylisoxazol-4-yl-penicillin *see* Flucloxacillin.

9-[(2-Chloro-6-fluorophenyl)methyl]-9*H*-purin-6-amine *see* Arprinocid.

10-Chloro-11b-(*o*-fluorophenyl)-2,3,7,11b-tetra-hydro-7-(2-hydroxyethyl)oxazolo-[3,2-*d*]-[1,4]benzodiazepin-6(5*H*)-one *see* Flutazolam.

1-Chloro-4-[[(4-fluorophenyl)thio]methyl]benzene *see* Fluorbenside.

4-Chloro-α-[(*p*-fluorophenyl)thio]toluene *see* Fluor-benside.

21-Chloro-9-fluoro-11β,16α,17-trihydroxypregn-4-ene-3,20-dione cyclic acetal with acetone *see* Hal-cinonide.

Chloroflurazole *see* Chlorflurazole.

CHLOROFORM (trichloromethane; formyl ter-chloride).

Chloroformyl chloride *see* Phosgene.

Chlorofos (tr) *see* Metrifonate.

4-Chloro-*N*-(2-furfuryl)-5-sulfamoylanthranilic acid *see* Furosemide.

CHLOROGENIC ACID (3-caffeoylquinic acid; 3-(3,4-dihydroxycinnamoyl)quinic acid).

Chloroguanide* *see* Proguanil.

Chloroguanil *see* Proguanil.

'Chlorohex' *see* Chlorhexidine.

10-Chloro-1,2,3,3a,4,5-hexahydro-6*H*-indolo[3,2,1-*de*][1,5]naphthyridin-6-one *see* Vicantril.

4-Chloro-*N*-(*endo*-hexahydro-4,7-methanoisoindol-in-2-yl)-3-sulfamoylbenzamide *see* Tripamide.

8-Chloro-1,2,3,4,10,10a-hexahydro-2-methyl-4a,10-(iminoethano)-4a*H*-[1]benzopyrano[3,2-*c*]pyridin-12-one *see* Lortalamine.

2-Chloro-10-[3-(hexahydropyrrolo[1,2-*a*]pyrazin-2(1*H*)-yl)propionyl]phenothiazine *see* Azaclorz-ine.

Chlorohexidine *see* Chlorhexidine.

CHLOROHYDRIN (3-chloro-1,2-propanediol; glycerol α-monochlorohydrin; U-5897).

Chlorohydrin dinitrate *see* Clonitrate.

4-Chloro-*N*-[2-(hydroxyamino)-2-oxoethyl]benz-amide *see* Benurestat.

2α-Chloro-17β-hydroxy-5α-androstan-3-one *O*-(*p*-nitrophenyl)oxime *see* Nisterime.

4-Chloro-17β-hydroxyandrost-4-en-3-one *see* Clos-tebol.

p-Chloro-α-hydroxybenzylphosphonic acid dimethyl ester dimethyl phosphate *see* Mifobate.

5-Chloro-2-hydroxydiphenylmethane *see* Clorofene.

4-Chloro-17β-hydroxyestr-4-en-3-one *see* Norclos-tebol.

7-Chloro-4-[4-(2-hydroxyethylamino)-1-methylbut-ylamino]quinoline *see* Cletoquine.

p-Chloro-*N*-(2-hydroxyethyl)-α,α-dimethylphen-ethylamine *see* Etolorex.

5-Chloro-2-[[2-(2-hydroxyethyl)methylamino]-*N*-methylacetamido]benzophenone *see* Oxazafone.

p-Chloro-*N*-(2-hydroxyethyl)-*N*-(3-methylnorborn-2-ylmethyl)benzamide *see* Clocanfamide.

2-Chloro-10-[3-[4-(2-hydroxyethyl)piperazin-1-yl]-propyl]phenothiazine *see* Perphenazine.

7-[5-Chloro-3-hydroxy-2-(3-hydroxy-4,4-dimethyl-

106

1-octenyl)cyclopentyl]-5-heptenoic acid *see* Nocloprost.

7-Chloro-4-hydroxy-5-indancarboxylic acid *see* Clorindanic acid.

2-CHLORO-4-(HYDROXYMERCURI)PHEN-OL (hydroxymercurichlorophenol; 'semesan'; 'uspulun').

2-Chloro-6-hydroxymercuriphenoxyacetic acid barbital salt *see* Merbaphen.

4-CHLORO-17β-HYDROXY-17-METHYL-1,4-ANDROSTADIEN-3-ONE (4-chlorometandienone; 'oral turinabol').

7α-Chloro-11β-hydroxy-16α-methyl-17,21-bis(1-oxopropoxy)pregna-1,4-diene-3,20-dione *see* Alclometasone dipropionate.

9-Chloro-11β-hydroxy-16β-methyl-17,21-bis(1-oxopropoxy)pregna-1,4-diene-3,20-dione *see* Beclometasone dipropionate.

3-Chloro-7-hydroxy-4-methylcoumarin bis(2-chloroethyl)phosphate *see* Haloxon.

6-Chloro-17-hydroxy-1α,2α-methylenepregna-4,6-diene-3,20-dione *see* Cyproterone.

6-Chloro-17α-hydroxy-16-methylenepregna-4,6-diene-3,20-dione acetate *see* Chloro-MDAP.

2-Chloro-5-[4-hydroxy-3-methyl-2-(methylimino)-thiazolidin-4-yl]benzenesulfonamide *see* Tizolemide.

6-Chloro-17-hydroxy-16α-methylpregna-4,6-diene-3,20-dione *see* Clomegestone.

7-Chloro-2-N-(hydroxymethyl)tetracycline *see* Clomocycline.

6-Chloro-17-hydroxy-19-norpregna-4,6-diene-3,20-dione *see* Amadinone.

21-Chloro-17-hydroxy-19-nor-17α-pregna-4,9-dien-20-yn-3-one *see* Ethynerone.

2-Chloro-5-(1-hydroxy-3-oxo-1-isoindolinyl)benzenesulfonamide *see* Chlortalidone.

Chloro(o-hydroxyphenyl)mercury *see* Mercufenol chloride.

6-Chloro-17-hydroxypregna-1,4-diene-3,20-dione *see* Cismadinone.

6-Chloro-17-hydroxypregna-4,6-diene-3,20-dione *see* Chlormadinone.

6-Chloro-17α-hydroxypregna-1,4,6-triene-3,20-dione *see* Delmadinone.

6α-Chloro-17-hydroxyprogesterone *see* Hydromadinone.

1-(3-Chloro-2-hydroxypropyl)-2-methyl-5-nitroimidazole *see* Ornidazole.

p-Chloro-β-(2-hydroxypropyl)-α-phenylhydrocinnamic acid δ-lactone *see* Lomevactone.

2-(p-Chloro-α-hydroxy-α-pyrid-2-ylbenzyl)-2-imidazoline *see* Dazadrol.

7-Chloro-4-(4-hydroxy-3-pyrrolidin-1-ylmethylanilino)quinoline *see* Amopyroquine.

Chlorohydroxyquinoline *see* Cloxiquine.

5-Chloro-4-(2-imidazolin-2-ylamino)-2,1,3-benzothiadiazole *see* Tizanidine.

4-Chloro-5-(2-imidazolin-2-ylamino)-6-methoxy-2-methylpyrimidine *see* Moxonidine.

4-Chloro-1-(2-imidazolin-2-ylmethyl)naphthalene *see* Clonazoline.

p-Chloro-α-(2-imidazolin-2-yl)-α-pyrid-2-ylbenzyl alcohol *see* Dazadrol.

3-Chloro-1-imidazol-1-yl-4-phenylisoquinoline *see* Climiqualine.

4-Chloro-2,2'-iminodibenzoic acid *see* Lobenzarit.

Chloroimipramine *see* Clomipramine.

7-Chloro-4-indanol *see* Clorindanol.

Chloroiodoquine *see* Clioquinol.

5-Chloro-7-iodo-8-quinolinol *see* Clioquinol.

Chloro-IPC *see* Chlorpropham.

5'-Chloro-2-[p-[(5-isobutylpyrimidin-2-yl)sulfamoyl]phenyl]-o-acetanisidide *see* Glicetanile.

2-Chloro-N-isopropylacetanilide *see* Propachlor.

o-Chloro-α-(isopropylaminomethyl)benzyl alcohol *see* Clorprenaline.

4-Chloro-2-(isopropylamino)-6-(4-methylpiperazin-1-yl)-5-(methylthio)pyrimidine *see* Iprozilamine.

1-[4-Chloro-2-(isopropylamino)-5-(methylthio)pyrimidin-6-yl]-4-methylpiperazine *see* Iprozilamine.

p-Chloro-α-isopropylbenzyl nicotinate *see* Nicoclonate.

4'-Chloro-N-(1-isopropylpiperid-4-yl)-2-phenylacetanilide *see* Lorcainide.

'Chlorol' *see* Dichloralphenazone.

Chlorolincomycin *see* Clindamycin.

CHLORO-MDAP (17α-acetoxy-6-chloro-6-dehydro-16-methylenepregesterone; 17α-acetoxy-6-chloro-16-methylenepregna-4,6-diene-3,20-dione; chlormethylenedehydroacetoxyprogesterone; 6-chloro-17α-hydroxy-16-methylenepregna-4,6-diene-3,20-dione acetate; 16-methylenechlormadinone; 'chlorsuperlutin').

CHLORO-MDAP plus MESTRANOL ('biogest'; 'sterolibrin').

(Chloromercuri)isobutylphenol *see* Mercurobutol.

(3-Chloromercuri-2-methoxypropyl)urea *see* Chlormerodrin.

o-(Chloromercuri)phenol *see* Mercufenol chloride.

Chloromerodrin *see* Chlormerodrin.

4-Chlorometandienone *see* 4-Chloro-17β-hydroxy-17-methyl-1,4-androstadien-3-one.

Chloromethapyrilene *see* Chloropyrilene.

Chloromethine *see* Chlormethine.

1-[p-[2-(5-Chloro-2-methoxybenzamido)ethyl]phenylsulfonyl]-3-cyclohexylurea *see* Glibenclamide.

1-[[p-[2-(5-Chloro-2-methoxybenzamido)ethyl]phenyl]sulfonyl]-3-methylurea *see* Glicondamide.

1-(5-Chloro-2-methoxybenzoyl)-3-[3-[4-(m-tolyl)piperazin-1-yl]propyl]urea *see* Ciltoprazine.

4-[6-(2-Chloro-4-methoxyphenoxy)hexyl]-3,5-heptanedione *see* Arildone.

4-[p-Chloro-N-(p-methoxyphenyl)benzamido]butyric acid *see* Clanobutin.

1-(3-Chloro-4-methoxyphenyl)-3,3-dimethylurea *see* Metoxuron.

N-(5-Chloro-2-methoxyphenyl)-4-[[[5-(2-methylpropyl)pyrimidin-2-yl]amino]sulfonyl]benzeneacetamide *see* Glicetanile.

4'-Chloro-5-methoxyvalerophenone (E)-O-(2-aminoethyl)oxime *see* Clovoxamine.

4'-Chloro-2-[(methylamino)methyl]benzhydrol *see* Setazindol.

p-Chloro-α-[2-(methylaminomethyl)phenyl]benzyl alcohol *see* Setazindol.

4-Chloro-2-(methylamino)-6-(4-methylpiperazin-1-yl)-5-(methylthio)pyrimidine *see* Mezilamine.

1-[4-Chloro-2-(methylamino)-5-(methylthio)pyrimidin-6-yl]-4-methylpiperazine *see* Mezilamine.

7-Chloro-2-methylamino-5-phenyl-3*H*-1,4-benzodiazepine 4-oxide *see* Chlordiazepoxide.

2-(3-Chloro-2-methylanilino)nicotinic acid *see* Clonixin.

p-[2-(5-Chloro-2-methylbenzamido)ethyl]benzoic acid *see* Meglitinide.

7-Chloro-3-methyl-2*H*-1,2,4-benzothiadiazine 1,1-dioxide *see* Diazoxide.

5-Chloro-3-methylbenzo[*b*]thiophene-2-acetic acid *see* Tianafac.

[[(*p*-Chloro-α-methylbenzylidene)amino]oxy]acetic acid 2-dimethylaminoethyl ester *see* Cloximate.

1-(4-Chloro-2-methylbenzyl)-1*H*-indazole-3-carboxylic acid *see* Tolnidamine.

(±)-6-Chloro-α-methylcarbazole-2-acetic acid *see* Carprofen.

3-Chloro-4-methylcoumarin-7-yl diethyl phosphate *see* Coroxon.

O-(3-Chloro-4-methylcoumarin-7-yl) *O,O*-diethyl phosphorothioate *see* Coumafos.

8-Chloro-α-methyl-3-dibenzofuranacetic acid *see* Furcloprofen.

p-Chloro-α-methyldiphenhydramine *see* Chlorphenoxamine.

2-Chloro-6-methylergoline-8β-acetonitrile *see* Lergotrile.

2-Chloro-*N*-(1-methylethyl)-*N*-phenylacetamide *see* Propachlor.

2-Chloro-5-[(2-methylindolin-1-yl)carbamoyl]benzenesulfonamide *see* Indapamide.

1-[(3-Chloro-2-methylindol-4-yl)oxy]-3-[(2-phenoxyethyl)amino]-2-propanol *see* Indopanolol.

4-Chloro-*N*-(2-methylindol-1-yl)-3-sulfamoylbenzamide *see* Indapamide.

4-Chloro-*N*-(1-methylisoindolin-2-yl)-3-sulfamoylbenzamide *see* Zidapamide.

(CHLOROMETHYL) METHYL ETHER (monochloromethyl ether; MCME).

α-(Chloromethyl)-2-methyl-5-nitroimidazole-1-ethanol *see* Ornidazole.

4-Chloro-*N*-methyl-3-(methylsulfamoyl)benzamide *see* Tiamizide.

3'-Chloro-α-[methyl(morpholinocarbonylmethyl)-amino]-*o*-benzotoluidide *see* Fominoben.

3'-Chloro-2'-[[methyl(morpholinocarbonylmethyl)-amino]methyl]benzanilide *see* Fominoben.

Chloromethyl 5-nitro-2-furyl ketone *see* Nifurmerone.

4-Chloro-1-methyl-5-nitroimidazole *see* Clomizole.

Chloromethyloxirane *see* Epichlorohydrin.

O-(3-Chloro-4-methyl-1-oxo-2*H*-1-benzopyran-7-yl) *O,O*-diethyl phosphorothioate *see* Coumafos.

2-Chloro-10-[3-[4-(2-(3-methyl-2-oxoimidazolidin-1-yl)ethyl)piperazin-1-yl]propyl]phenothiazine *see* Imiclopazine.

4-Chloro-3-methylphenol *see* Chlorocresol.

2-(4-CHLORO-2-METHYLPHENOXY)ACETIC ACID (2-M-4-C; MCP; MCPA; metaxon; 'agroxyl'; 'cornox'; 'dikotex'; 'mephanac'; 'methox-

one'; 'weedex').

See also Chlorinated phenoxyacetic acid.

4-(4-CHLORO-2-METHYLPHENOXY)BUTYRIC ACID (4-(MCB); MCPB; 4-(MCPB); 2,4-MCPB; 2M-4H-M; 'cantrol'; 'thitrol').

See also Sodium 4-(4-chloro-2-methylphenoxy)-butyrate.

2-(4-Chloro-2-methylphenoxy)propionic acid *see* Mecoprop.

7-Chloro-1-methyl-5-phenyl-1*H*-1,5-benzodiazepine-2,4(3*H*,5*H*)-dione *see* Clobazam.

p-Chloro-α-methyl-α-phenylbenzyl alcohol 2-(1-methylpyrrolidin-2-yl)ethyl ether *see* Clemastine.

2-(*p*-Chloro-α-methyl-α-phenylbenzyloxy)-*N,N*-dimethylethylamine *see* Chlorphenoxamine.

2-(*p*-Chloro-α-methyl-α-phenylbenzyloxy)-*N,N*-dimethylpropylamine *see* Mecloxamine.

1-[2-[(*p*-Chloro-α-methyl-α-phenylbenzyl)oxy]ethyl]-hexahydro-1*H*-azepine *see* Setastine.

2-[2-(*p*-Chloro-α-methyl-α-phenylbenzyloxy)ethyl]-1-methylpyrrolidine *see* Clemastine.

1-[2-[(*p*-Chloro-α-methyl-α-phenylbenzyl)oxy]ethyl]-octahydroazocine *see* Octastine.

2-(*p*-Chloro-α-methyl-α-phenylbenzyloxy)triethyl-amine *see* Clofenetamine.

N'-(4-Chloro-2-methylphenyl)-*N,N*-dimethylmeth-animidamide *see* Chlorphenamidine.

1-(3-Chloro-4-methylphenyl)-3,3-dimethylurea *see* Chlorotoluron.

N-(3-Chloro-4-methylphenyl)-2-methylpentanamide *see* Pentanochlor.

N-(3-Chloro-4-methylphenyl)-2-methylvaleramide *see* Pentanochlor.

trans-*N*-(6-Chloro-2-methylphenyl)-3-(1*H*-1-octa-hydropyrindin-1-yl)propionamide *see* Rodocaine.

8-Chloro-1-methyl-6-phenyl-4*H*-*s*-triazolo[4,3-*a*]-[1,4]benzodiazepine *see* Alprazolam.

8-Chloro-11-(4-methylpiperazin-1-yl)-5*H*-dibenzo-[*b,e*][1,4]diazepine *see* Clozapine.

2-Chloro-11-(4-methylpiperazin-1-yl)dibenzo[*b,f*]-[1,4]thiazepine *see* Clotiapine.

2-Chloro-11-(4-methylpiperazin-1-yl)-dibenz[*b,f*]-[1,4]oxazepine *see* Loxapine.

2-Chloro-10-[3-(4-methylpiperazin-1-yl)-propyl]-phenothiazine *see* Prochlorperazine.

7-Chloro-4-(4-methylpiperazin-1-yl)-10*H*-thieno-[3,2-*c*][1]benzazepine *see* Tilozepine.

2-Chloro-9-(1-methylpiperid-4-ylidene)xanthene *see* Clopipazan.

9α-Chloro-16β-methylprednisolone *see* Beclometasone.

6α-Chloro-16α-methylpregn-4-ene-3,20-dione *see* Clometerone.

6α-Chloro-16α-methylprogesterone *see* Clometerone.

2-Chloro-*N*-(1-methyl-2-propynyl)acetanilide *see* Prynachlor.

4-Chloro-*N*¹-methyl-*N*¹-(tetrahydro-2-methylfuryl)-*m*-benzenedisulfonamide *see* Mefruside.

2-(2-Chloro-4-methylthien-3-ylamino)-2-imidazoline *see* Tiamenidine.

3-Chloro-α-methyl-4-(2-thienylcarbonyl)benzene-acetic acid *see* Cliprofen.

108

p-Chloro-*N*-(2-morpholinoethyl)benzamide *see* Moclobemide.

2-Chloro-6-(2-morpholinoethylthio)pyridine *see* Fopirtoline.

3-Chloro-4-[3-(4-morpholino)propoxy]biphenyl *see* Chlordimorine.

'Chloromycetin' *see* Chloramphenicol.

'Chloronaftina' *see* Chlornaphazine.

4-Chloronandrolone *see* Norclostebol.

Chloronaphazine *see* Chlornaphazine.

Chloronaphthine *see* Chlornaphazine.

2-CHLORO-1,4-NAPHTHOQUINONE (antivitamin K_3).

2-(4-Chloro-1-naphthylmethyl)-2-imidazoline *see* Clonazoline.

2-[(1-Chloronaphth-2-yl)oxy]propionic acid methyl ester *see* Lonaprofen.

6-(7-Chloro-1,8-naphthyridin-2-yl)-2,3,6,7-tetrahydro-7-hydroxy-5*H*-*p*-dithiino[2,3-*c*]pyrrol-5-one 4-methyl-1-piperazinecarboxylate *see* Suriclone.

6-(7-Chloro-1,8-naphthyridin-2-yl)-2,3,6,7-tetrahydro-7-hydroxy-5*H*-*p*-dithiino[2,3-*c*]pyrrol-5-one 4-propionyl-1-piperazinecarboxylate ester *see* Suproclone.

'Chloronase' *see* Chlorpropamide.

CHLORONEB* (1,4-dichloro-2,5-dimethoxybenzene; 'demosan'; 'tersan SP').

2-Chloro-4-nitrobenzamide *see* Aklomide.

2-(*o*-Chloro-α-nitromethylbenzylthio)ethylamine *see* Nitralamine.

Chloronitromycin *see* Chloramphenicol.

2-CHLORO-4-NITROPHENOL ('nitrofungin').

O-(2-Chloro-4-nitrophenyl) *O*,*O*-dimethyl phosphorothioate *see* Dicapthon.

O-(3-Chloro-4-nitrophenyl) *O*,*O*-dimethyl phosphorothioate *see* Chlorothion.

O-(4-Chloro-3-nitrophenyl) *O*,*O*-dimethyl phosphorothioate *see* Phosnichlor.

4-Chloro-19-nortestosterone *see* Norclostebol.

trans-6′-Chloro-2,3,4,4a,5,6,7,7a-octahydro-1*H*-1-pyrindine-1-propiono-*o*-toluidide *see* Rodocaine.

4-(5-Chloro-2-oxobenzimidazolin-1-yl)-1-[3-(2-oxobenzimidazolin-1-ylpropyl]piperidine *see* Domperidone.

N-[2-[4-(5-Chloro-2-oxobenzimidazolin-1-yl)piperid-1-yl]ethyl]-*p*-fluorobenzamide *see* Halopemide.

5-Chloro-1-[1-[3-(2-oxo-1-benzimidazolinyl)propyl]piperid-4-yl]-2-benzimidazolinone *see* Domperidone.

4-Chloro-2-oxo-3(2*H*)-benzothiazoleacetic acid *see* Benazolin.

4-[(5-Chloro-2-oxobenzothiazolin-3-yl)acetyl]-1-piperazineethanol *see* Tiaramide.

S-[(6-Chloro-2-oxobenzoxazol-3(2*H*)-yl)methyl] *O*,*O*-diethyl phosphorodithioate *see* Phosalone.

5-CHLORO-6-OXO-2-NORBORNANECARBONITRILE *O*-(METHYLCARBAMOYL)OXIME (*exo*-3-chloro-*endo*-6-cyano-2-norbornanone *O*-(methylcarbamoyl)oxime; 'tranid').

Chloroperathiepine *see* Clorotepine.

CHLOROPHACINONE* (2-[(4-chlorophenyl)-phenylacetyl]-1*H*-indene-1,3(2*H*)-dione; 2-[(4-chlorophenyl)phenylacetyl]-1,3-indandione; ra-

viac; 'caid'; 'chloradione'; 'drat'; 'liphadione'; 'quick'; 'ratindan 3').

5-[3-[*N*-(*p*-Chlorophenacyl)methylamino]propyl]-10,11-dihydro-5*H*-dibenz[*b*,*f*]azepine *see* Lofepramine.

Chlorophenarsine *see* Dichlorophenarsine.

Chlorophene *see* Clorofene.

Chlorophenesin *see* Chlorphenesin.

1-(2-Chlorophenethyl)-*N*-cyclohexyl-4-hydroxy-*N*,α-dimethyl-4-piperidineacetamide *see* Pipramadol.

1-(2-Chlorophenethyl)-*N*-cyclohexyl-4-hydroxy-*N*,α,α-trimethyl-4-piperidineacetamide *see* Pipradimadol.

3-Chloro-*N*-phenethylpropionamide *see* Fenaclon.

1-(*p*-Chlorophenethyl)-1,2,3,4-tetrahydro-6,7-dimethoxy-2-methylisoquinoline *see* Metofoline.

Chlorophenindione *see* Clorindione.

Chloropheniramine *see* Chlorpheniramine.

Chlorophenothane *see* DDT.

2(1*H*)-[2-[(2-Chlorophenothiazin-10-yl)carbonyl]-ethyl]hexahydropyrrolo[1,2-*a*]pyrazine *see* Azaclorzine.

2-Chlorophenothiazin-10-yl 2-diethylaminoethyl ketone *see* Chloracyzine.

2-Chlorophenothiazin-10-yl 2-dimethylaminoethyl ketone *see* Cloracizin.

2-Chlorophenothiazin-10-yl 2-(hexahydropyrrolo[1,2-*a*]pyrazin-2(1*H*)-ylethyl ketone *see* Azaclorzine.

1-[3-(2-Chlorophenothiazin-10-yl)propyl]-4-(dihydro-2(3*H*)-oxofuran-3-yl)-4-hydroxypiperidine *see* Furomazine.

3-[1-[3-(2-Chlorophenothiazin-10-yl)propyl]-4-hydroxypiperid-4-yl]dihydro-2(3*H*)-furanone *see* Furomazine.

1-[2-[4-[3-(2-Chlorophenothiazin-10-yl)propyl]piperazin-1-yl]ethyl]-3-methyl-2-imidazolidinone *see* Imiclopazine.

2-[4-[3-(2-Chlorophenothiazin-10-yl)propyl]piperazin-1-yl]ethyl 3,4,5-trimethoxybenzoate *see* Metofenazate.

8-[3-(2-Chlorophenothiazin-10-yl)propyl]-1-thia-4,8-diazaspiro[4.5]decan-3-one *see* Spiclomazine.

Chlorophenoxamide *see* Clefamide.

2-(*p*-CHLOROPHENOXY)ACETIC ACID (4-CPA; 4-HFU; 'tomatotone').
See also Adafenoxate; Amphetamine *p*-chlorophenoxyacetate; Iproclozide; Meclofenoxate; Metformin *p*-chlorophenoxyacetate; Tocofenoxate.

p-Chlorophenoxyacetylcholine iodide *see* Meclofenoxate methiodide.

1-(*p*-Chlorophenoxyacetyl)-2-isopropylhydrazine *see* Iproclozide.

1-(*p*-Chlorophenoxyacetyl)-4-piperonylpiperazine *see* Fipexide.

2-(*p*-Chlorophenoxy)-*N*-(2-diethylaminoethyl)acetamide *see* Clofexamide.

β-(4-Chlorophenoxy)-α-(1,1-dimethylethyl)-1*H*-1,2,4-triazole-1-ethanol *see* Triadimenol.

1-(4-Chlorophenoxy)-3,3-dimethyl-1-(1*H*-1,2,4-triazol-1-yl)-2-butanone *see* Triadimefon.

109

[2-(*p*-Chlorophenoxy)ethyl]dodecyldimethylammonium bromide *see* Dodeclonium bromide.

7-[2-[4-(3-Chlorophenoxy)-3-hydroxy-1-butenyl]-3,5-dihydroxycyclopentyl]-2,5-heptadienoic acid methyl ester *see* Delprostenate.

7-[[4-(*m*-Chlorophenoxy)-3-hydroxy-1-butenyl]-3,5-dihydroxycyclopentyl]-5-heptenoic acid *see* Cloprostenol.

3-(*p*-Chlorophenoxy)-2-hydroxypropyl carbamate *see* Chlorphenesin carbamate.

7-[2-[[3-(*m*-Chlorophenoxy)-2-hydroxypropyl]thio]-3,5-dihydroxycyclopentyl]-5-heptenoic acid *see* Luprostiol.

1-[(*p*-Chlorophenoxy)-1-imidazol-1-yl]-3,3-dimethyl-2-butanone *see* Climbazole.

α-(*p*-Chlorophenoxy)isobutyric acid *see* Clofibric acid.

N-[2-(*p*-Chlorophenoxy)isobutyryl]-*N'*-(morpholinomethyl)urea *see* Plafibride.

1-(*p*-Chlorophenoxymethyl)-3,4-dihydroisoquinoline *see* Famotine.

6-[2-[2-(*p*-Chlorophenoxy)-2-methylpropionamido]-2-phenylacetamido]penicillanic acid *see* Fibracillin.

2-(*p*-Chlorophenoxy)-2-methylpropionic acid *see* Clofibric acid.

2-[2-(*p*-Chlorophenoxy)-2-methylpropionoxy]ethyl nicotinate *see* Etofibrate.

1-[2-(*p*-Chlorophenoxy)-2-methylpropionyl]-3-(morpholinomethyl)urea *see* Plafibride.

3-[2-(*p*-Chlorophenoxy)-2-methylpropionyl]-4-thiazolidinecarboxylic acid *see* Timofibrate.

1-(*p*-Chlorophenoxymethyl)-1,2,3,4-tetrahydro-6,7-isoquinolinediol *see* Clofeverine.

1-[*p*-(*p*-Chlorophenoxy)phenyl]-3,3-dimethylurea *see* Chloroxuron.

1-[(*p*-Chlorophenoxy)(pivaloyl)methyl]imidazole *see* Climbazole.

3-(*p*-Chlorophenoxy)-1,2-propanediol *see* Chlorphenesin.

2-(3-Chlorophenoxy)propionic acid *see* Cloprop.

16-(3-Chlorophenoxy)-9,11,15-trihydroxy-ω-tetranorprosta-5,13-dienoic acid *see* Cloprostenol.

6-(3-Chlorophenoxy)-9,11,15-trihydroxy-ω-tetranorprosta-2,5,13-trienoic acid methyl ester *see* Delprostenate.

16-(*m*-Chlorophenoxy)-9,11,15-trihydroxy-ω-tetranor-13-thiaprost-5-enoic acid *see* Luprostiol.

1-(2-Chloro-2-phenylacetyl)urea *see* Chlorphenacemide.

3-(*p*-Chlorophenyl)alanine *see* Fenclonine.

N-[[(4-Chlorophenyl)amino]carbonyl]-2,6-difluorobenzamide difluron *see* Diflubenzuron.

N-[[(4-Chlorophenyl)amino]carbonyl]pentanimidamide *see* Carbantel.

O-[4-[(4-Chlorophenyl)azo]phenyl] *O,O*-dimethyl phosphorothioate *see* Azothoate.

4-Chlorophenyl benzenesulfonate *see* Fenson.

α-(*p*-Chlorophenyl)-2-benzofuranmethanol *see* Cloridarol.

2-[2-(*p*-Chlorophenyl)benzoxazol-5-yl]propionic acid *see* Benoxaprofen.

1-(*p*-Chloro-α-phenylbenzyl)-4-cinnamylpiperazine

see Clocinizine.

1-(*p*-Chloro-α-phenylbenzyl)hexahydro-4-methyl-1*H*-1,4-diazepine *see* Homochlorcyclizine.

1-[α-(*p*-Chlorophenyl)benzyl]-4-*m*-methylbenzyl)piperazine *see* Meclozine.

1-[α-(*p*-Chlorophenyl)benzyl]-4-methylpiperazine *see* Chlorcyclizine.

1-[2-(*o*-Chloro-α-phenylbenzyloxy)ethyl]-4-(*o*-methylbenzyl)piperazine *see* Chlorbenoxamine.

4-[2-(*p*-Chloro-α-phenylbenzyloxy)ethyl]morpholine *see* Difencloxazine.

1-[2-(*p*-Chloro-α-phenylbenzyloxy)ethyl]piperidine *see* Cloperastine.

3-[α-(*p*-Chlorophenyl)benzyloxy]-2-methylpropionic acid *see* Clobuzarit.

3-(*p*-Chloro-α-phenylbenzyloxy)-1-methylpyrrolidine *see* Pyroxamine.

3-(*p*-Chloro-α-phenylbenzyloxy)tropane *see* Clobenztropine.

[2-[4-(*p*-Chloro-α-phenylbenzyl)piperazin-1-yl]ethoxy]acetic acid *see* Cetirizine.

2-[2-[4-(*p*-Chloro-α-phenylbenzyl)-1-piperazinyl]ethoxy]ethanol *see* Hydroxyzine.

2-[2-[2-[4-(*p*-Chloro-α-phenylbenzyl)piperazin-1-yl]ethoxy]ethoxy]ethanol *see* Etodroxizine.

1-[2-(*o*-Chloro-α-phenylbenzylthio)ethyl]-4-(*o*-methylbenzyl)piperazine *see* Bentipimine.

p-Chlorophenyl besilate *see* Fenson.

[4-(*p*-Chlorophenyl)butyl]diethylheptylammonium phosphate *see* Clofilium phosphate.

3-Chlorophenylcarbamic acid 1-methylethyl ester *see* Chlorpropham.

2-[[(*m*-Chlorophenyl)carbamoyl]amino]-1-methyl-2-imidazolin-4-one *see* Fenobam.

[4-(*m*-CHLOROPHENYLCARBAMOYLOXY)-2-BUTYNYL]TRIMETHYLAMMONIUM CHLORIDE ((4-hydroxy-2-butynyl)trimethylammonium chloride *m*-chlorophenylcarbamate; McN-A-343).

p-Chlorophenyl *p*-chlorobenzenesulfonate *see* Chlorfenson.

p-Chlorophenyl 2-(*p*-chlorophenoxy)-2-methylpropionate *see* Dulofibrate.

p-Chlorophenyl closilate *see* Chlorfenson.

4-Chloro-α-phenyl-*o*-cresol *see* Clorofene.

3-(*p*-Chlorophenyl)-1-cyanomethyl-4-iminoimidazolidin-2-one *see* Nimazone.

2-[1-(*p*-Chlorophenyl)cyclohexyloxy]triethylamine *see* Clofenciclan.

1-(*p*-Chlorophenyl)-1,2-cyclopropanedicarboximide *see* Ciproximide.

3-(*p*-Chlorophenyl)-5-cyclopropyl-2-methylpyrrolidine *see* Picilorex.

1-[2-(4-Chlorophenyl)-2-[(2,6-dichlorophenyl)methoxy]ethyl]-1*H*-imidazole *see* Orconazole.

1-[4-(4-Chlorophenyl)-2-[(2,6-dichlorophenyl)thio]butyl]imidazole *see* Butoconazole.

2-(*p*-Chlorophenyl)-1-[*p*-[2-(diethylamino)ethoxy]phenyl]-1-*p*-tolylethanol *see* Triparanol.

S-(*p*-Chlorophenyl) diethylcarbamothioate *see* Benthiocarb.

1-(*m*-Chlorophenyl)-4-[3-(3,4-diethyl-5-oxo-Δ²-1,2,4-triazolin-1-yl)propyl]piperazine *see* Etope-

110

ridone.

1-(*p*-Chlorophenyl)-3-(2,6-difluorobenzoyl)urea *see* Diflubenzuron.

5-(*p*-Chlorophenyl)-2,3-dihydro-5-hydroxy-5*H*-imidazo[2,1-*a*]isoindole *see* Mazindol.

5-(*p*-Chlorophenyl)-2,5-dihydro-3*H*-imidazo[2,1-*a*]-isoindol-5-ol *see* Mazindol.

5-(*o*-Chlorophenyl)-1,3-dihydro-3-methyl-7-nitro-2*H*-1,4-benzodiazepin-2-one *see* Meclonazepam.

6-(*o*-Chlorophenyl)-2,4-dihydro-2-[(4-methylpiperazin-1-yl)methylene]-8-nitro-1*H*-imidazo[1,2-*a*]-[1,4]benzodiazepin-1-one *see* Loprazolam.

5-(*o*-Chlorophenyl)-1,3-dihydro-7-nitro-2*H*-1,4-benzodiazepin-2-one *see* Clonazepam.

α-(*o*-Chlorophenyl)-α-[2-(diisopropylamino)ethyl]-1-piperidinebutyramide *see* Disobutamide.

1-(*o*-Chlorophenyl)-4-(3,4-dimethoxyphenethyl)piperazine *see* Mefeclorazine.

1-(*p*-Chlorophenyl)-4-dimethylamino-2,3-dimethyl-2-butanol *see* Clobutinol.

1-(*m*-Chlorophenyl)-3-(2-dimethylaminoethyl)-2-imidazolidinone *see* Imidoline.

1-(*m*-Chlorophenyl)-3-(dimethylamino)-1-phenyl-2-propanol *see* Clemeprol.

1-(*o*-Chlorophenyl)-3-(dimethylamino)-1-phenyl-1-propanol *see* Clofedanol.

1-(*m*-Chlorophenyl)-3-[2-(3,3-dimethyl-1-azetidinyl)ethyl]-2-imidazolidinone *see* Zetidoline.

N-(*p*-Chlorophenyl)-*N*,*N*-dimethylcarbamimidic acid ethyl ester *see* Trimeturon.

4-[4-(*p*-Chlorophenyl)-4-dimethylcarbamoylpiperid-1-yl]-4′-fluorobutyrophenone *see* Amiperone.

1-(*m*-Chlorophenyl)-2-[(1,1-dimethylethyl)amino]-1-propanone *see* Amfebutamone.

O-(*m*-CHLOROPHENYL) *O*,*O*-DIMETHYL PHOSPHOROTHIOATE ('neothiate').

1-(*p*-Chlorophenyl)-3,3-dimethylpseudourea *O*-methyl derivative *see* Trimeturon.

1-(*p*-Chlorophenyl)-2,5-dimethylpyrrole-3-acetic acid *see* Clopirac.

1-(*p*-Chlorophenyl)-3,3-dimethylurea *see* Monuron.

N-(*p*-Chlorophenyl)-2,2-dimethylvaleramide *see* Monalide.

5-(*o*-Chlorophenyl)-7-ethyl-1,3-dihydro-1-methyl-2*H*-thieno[2,3-*e*]-1,4-diazepin-2-one *see* Clotiazepam.

4-(*o*-Chlorophenyl)-2-ethyl-9-methyl-6*H*-thieno-[3,2-*f*]-*s*-triazolo[4,3-*a*][1,4]diazepine *see* Etizolam.

5-(4-Chlorophenyl)-6-ethyl-2,4-pyrimidinediamine *see* Pyrimethamine.

4-(*p*-Chlorophenyl)-1-[3-(*p*-fluorobenzoyl)propyl]-*N*,*N*-dimethylisonipecotamide *see* Amiperone.

4-(*p*-Chlorophenyl)-1-[3-(*p*-fluorobenzoyl)propyl]-4-piperidinol *see* Haloperidol.

4-(*o*-Chlorophenyl)-1-[3-(*p*-fluorobenzoyl)propyl]-4-(pyrrolidin-1-ylcarbonyl)piperidine *see* Haloperidide.

4-[[(4-Chlorophenyl)(5-fluoro-2-hydroxyphenyl)-methylidene]amino]butyramide *see* Progabide.

4-[4-(*p*-Chlorophenyl)-4′-fluoro-4-hydroxypiperid-1-yl]butyrophenone *see* Haloperidol.

4-(*p*-Chlorophenyl)-1-(*p*-fluorophenyl)pyrazole-3-acetic acid *see* Pirazolac.

4-[[α-(*p*-Chlorophenyl)-5-fluorosalicylidene]amino]-butyramide *see* Progabide.

5-(*p*-Chlorophenyl)-2-furanhydracrylic acid *see* Orpanoxin.

β-(4-Chlorophenyl)GABA *see* Baclofen.

3-Chloro-7-D-(2-phenylglycinamido)-3-cephem-4-carboxylic acid *see* Cefaclor.

1,1′-(*p*-Chlorophenylguanidinoformimidoyl)bispiperazine *see* Picloxydine.

2-(*p*-Chlorophenyl)-1,3,4,6,7,11b-hexahydro-9,10-dimethoxy-2*H*-benzo[*a*]quinolizine *see* Quillifoline.

4-(*p*-Chlorophenyl)-4-hydroxy-*N*,*N*-dimethyl-α,α-diphenyl-1-piperidinebutyramide *see* Loperamide.

2-[(*p*-Chlorophenyl)hydroxymethyl]benzofuran *see* Cloridarol.

4-[4-(*p*-Chlorophenyl)-4-hydroxypiperidino]-*N*,*N*-dimethyl-2,2-diphenylbutyramide *see* Loperamide.

4-[4-(*p*-Chlorophenyl)-4-hydroxypiperidino]-4′-fluorobutyrophenone *see* Haloperidol.

2-[[α-(*p*-Chlorophenyl)-α-hydroxy-*p*-tolyl]oxy]-2-methylpropionic acid *see* Fenirofibrate.

α-(*p*-Chlorophenyl)-α-(2-imidazolin-2-yl)-2-pyridinemethanol *see* Dazadrol.

(*o*-Chlorophenyl)imidazol-1-yldiphenylmethane *see* Clotrimazole.

1-(*p*-Chlorophenyl)-2-imino-3-methyl-4-imidazolidinone *see* Clazolimine.

3-(*p*-Chlorophenyl)-4-imino-2-oxo-1-imidazolidineacetonitrile *see* Nimazone.

2-(*p*-Chlorophenyl)-1,3-indandione *see* Clorindione.

1-(*o*-Chlorophenyl)-2-isopropylaminoethanol *see* Clorprenaline.

1-(*p*-Chlorophenyl)-5-isopropylbiguanide *see* Proguanil.

1-(3-Chloro-4-phenylisoquinolin-1-yl)imidazole *see* Climiqualine.

1-(*p*-Chlorophenyl)-3-methoxy-3-methylurea *see* Monolinuron.

2-(*o*-Chlorophenyl)-2-methylaminocyclohexanone *see* Ketamine.

2-(*p*-Chlorophenyl)-α-methyl-5-benzoxazoleacetic acid *see* Benoxaprofen.

2-(*m*-Chlorophenyl)-3-methyl-2,3-butanediol *see* Metaglycodol.

2-(*p*-Chlorophenyl)-3-methyl-2,3-butanediol *see* Phenaglycodol.

2-(*p*-Chlorophenyl)-3-methylbutyric acid α-cyano-*m*-phenoxybenzyl ester *see* Fenvalerate.

4-(*p*-Chlorophenyl)-5-methylimidazole *see* Lofemizole.

7-[3-(*o*-Chlorophenyl)-5-methylisoxazole-4-carboxamido]cephalosporanic acid *see* Cefoxazole.

7-[3-(*o*-Chlorophenyl)-5-methylisoxazole-4-carboxamido]-3-(hydroxymethyl)-2-cephem-2-carboxylic acid acetate *see* Cefoxazole.

6-[3-(*o*-Chlorophenyl)-5-methylisoxazol-4-ylcarboxamido]penicillanic acid *see* Cloxacillin.

1-(*p*-Chlorophenyl)-3-methyl-3-(1-methyl-2-propynyl)urea *see* Buturon.

1-(*m*-Chlorophenyl-3-(1-methyl-4-oxo-2-imidazolin-2-yl)urea *see* Fenobam.

111

2-(*p*-Chlorophenyl)-4-methyl-2,4-pentanediol *see* Fenpentadiol.

2-[(*p*-Chlorophenyl)-α-methyl-α-phenylmethoxy]propyldimethylamine *see* Mecloxamine.

2-(*p*-Chlorophenyl)-2-methylpropyl 1,2,3,6-tetrahydro-1,3-dimethyl-2,6-dioxopurine-7-acetate *see* Acefylline clofibrol.

2-(*p*-Chlorophenyl)-2-methylpropyl theophyllin-7-ylacetate *see* Acefylline clofibrol.

1-(*m*-Chlorophenyl)-4-[2-(5-methylpyrazol-3-yl)ethyl]piperazine *see* Mepiprazole.

1-(*o*-Chlorophenyl)-4-[2-(1-methylpyrazol-4-yl)ethyl]piperazine *see* Enpiprazole.

N^1-[1-(*m*-Chlorophenyl)-3-methylpyrazol-5-yl]sulfanilamide *see* Sulfaclorazole.

3-(*o*-Chlorophenyl)-2-methyl-4-quinazolinone *see* Mecloqualone.

4-[5-(*o*-Chlorophenyl)-1,2,4-oxadiazol-3-yl]pyridine *see* Pifexole.

3-[1-(4-Chlorophenyl)-3-oxobutyl]-4-hydroxy-2*H*-1-benzopyran-2-one *see* Coumachlor.

2-[*p*-(*o*-Chlorophenyl)phenacyl]acrylic acid *see* Itanoxone.

α-[*p*-(*p*-Chlorophenyl)phenoxy]isobutyric acid methyl ester *see* Methyl clofenapate.

[2-*p*-(*p*-Chlorophenyl)phenoxy]-2-methylpropionic acid methyl ester *see* Methyl clofenapate.

2-[(4-Chlorophenyl)phenylacetyl]-1,3-indandione *see* Chlorophacinone.

2-[(4-Chlorophenyl)phenylacetyl]-1*H*-indene-1,3(2*H*-dione *see* Chlorophacinone.

1-[4-(*p*-Chlorophenyl)-3-phenylbut-2-enyl]pyrrolidine *see* Pyrrobutamine.

2-[1-(*p*-Chlorophenyl)-1-phenylethoxy]-*N*,*N*-dimethylethylamine *see* Chlorphenoxamine.

2-[2-[1-(*p*-Chlorophenyl)-1-phenylethoxy]ethyl]-1-methylpyrrolidine *see* Clemastine.

1-[(4-Chlorophenyl)phenylmethyl]-4-(3-methylbenzyl)piperazine *see* Meclozine.

4-(*p*-Chlorophenyl)-5-[2-(4-phenylpiperazin-1-yl)ethyl]-1,3-dioxol-2-one *see* Clodoxopone.

3-(*p*-Chlorophenyl)-1-phenylpyrazole-4-acetic acid *see* Lonazolac.

4-(*p*-Chlorophenyl)-2-phenyl-5-thiazoleacetic acid *see* Fentiazac.

1-[3-[4-(*m*-Chlorophenyl)piperazin-1-yl]propyl]-3,4-diethyl-Δ²-1,2,4-triazolin-5-one *see* Etoperidone.

1-[3-[4-(*m*-Chlorophenyl)piperazin-1-yl]propyl]-3-ethyl-4-(2-phenoxyethyl)-Δ²-1,2,4-triazolin-5-one *see* Nefazodone.

3-[3-[4-(*m*-Chlorophenyl)piperazin-1-yl]propyl]quinazoline(1*H*,3*H*)-2,4-dione *see* Cloperidone.

2-[3-[4-(*m*-Chlorophenyl)piperazin-1-yl]propyl]-*s*-triazolo[4,3-*a*]pyridin-3(2*H*)-one *see* Trazodone.

1-(*p*-CHLOROPHENYL)-1-PROPANOL (*p*-chloro-α-ethylbenzyl alcohol).

α-(*p*-Chlorophenyl)-α-pyrid-2-yl-2-imidazoline-2-methanol *see* Dazadrol.

5-(*o*-Chlorophenyl)-3-pyrid-4-yl-1,2,4-oxadiazole *see* Pifexole.

4-[[4-(*o*-Chlorophenyl)](4-pyrrolidinamido)piperidino]-4′-fluorobutyrophenone *see* Haloperidide.

2-[*p*-(β-Chloro-α-phenylstyryl)phenoxy]triethyl-amine *see* Clomifene.

3-Chloro-4-(phenylsuccinimido)benzenesulfonamide *see* Suclofenide.

1-(*p*-Chlorophenylsulfonyl)-3-cyclohexylurea *see* Chlorhexamide.

1-(*p*-Chlorophenylsulfonyl)-3-[*p*-(dimethylamino)phenyl]urea *see* Glyparamide.

1-(*p*-Chlorophenylsulfonyl)-3-(hexahydro-1*H*-azepin-1-yl)urea *see* Glypinamide.

4-(*p*-Chlorophenylsulfonyl)-1,1-pentamethylenesemicarbazide *see* Chlorpentazide.

1-(*p*-Chlorophenylsulfonyl)-3-piperid-1-ylurea *see* Chlorpentazide.

1-(*p*-Chlorophenylsulfonyl)-3-propylurea *see* Chlorpropamide.

1-(*p*-Chlorophenylsulfonyl)-3-pyrrolidin-1-ylurea *see* Glyclopyramide.

4-(3-Chlorophenyl)-1,6,7,8-tetrahydro-1,3-dimethylpyrazolo[3,4-*e*][1,4]diazepine *see* Zometapine.

4-(*p*-Chlorophenyl)tetrahydro-6-methyl-3-phenyl-2*H*-pyran-2-one *see* Lomevactone.

2-(*p*-Chlorophenyl)tetrahydro-3-methyl-4*H*-1,3-thiazin-4-one 1,1-dioxide *see* Chlormezanone.

10-(*m*-Chlorophenyl)-2,3,4,10-tetrahydropyrimido[1,2-*a*]indol-10-ol *see* Ciclazindol.

2-(*p*-Chlorophenyl)thiazol-4-ylacetic acid *see* Fenclozic acid.

(*p*-Chlorophenyl)-2-thienyliodonium chloride *see* Tiodonium chloride.

S-[(*p*-Chlorophenylthio)methyl] *O*,*O*-diethyl phosphorodithioate *see* Carbofenotion.

S-[(*p*-Chlorophenylthio)methyl] *O*,*O*-dimethyl phosphorodithioate *see* Carbofenotion methyl.

2-[4-[(*p*-Chlorophenyl)thio]-3,5-xylyl]-*as*-triazine-3,5(2*H*,4*H*)-dione *see* Tiazuril.

(±)-2-[[α-(*p*-Chlorophenyl)-*p*-tolyl]oxy]-2-methylbutyric acid esters *see* Beclofibrate; Enclofibrate.

8-Chloro-6-phenyl-4*H*-*s*-triazolo[4,3-*a*][1,4]benzodiazepine *see* Estazolam.

p-Chlorophenyl 2,4,5-trichlorophenyl sulfone *see* Tetradifon.

6-Chloro-4-phenyl-1-(2,2,2-trifluoroethyl)-2(1*H*)-quinazolinone *see* Fluquazone.

2-(*p*-Chlorophenyl)-2-(α,α,α-trifluoro-*m*-toloxy)-acetic acid ester with *N*-(2-hydroxyethyl)acetamide *see* Halofenate.

1-(*p*-Chlorophenyl)-3-valerimidoylurea *see* Carbantel.

Chlorophos (tr) *see* Metrifonate.

CHLOROPICRIN (nitrochloroform; trichloronitromethane).

2-Chloro-11-piperazin-1-yldibenz[*b*,*f*][1,4]oxazepine *see* Amoxapine.

CHLOROPREDNISONE*** (6α-chloro-17,21-dihydroxypregna-1,4-diene-3,11,20-trione; chlorprednisone).

CHLOROPREDNISONE ACETATE* (chlorprednisone 21-acetate; 'topilan').

6-Chloro-9β,10α-pregna-1,4,6-triene-3,20-dione *see* Trengestone.

CHLOROPROCAINE*** (2-(diethylamino)ethyl 4-amino-2-chlorobenzoate; chlorprocaine).

Chloropromazine *see* Chlorpromazine.

3-Chloro-1,2-propanediol *see* Chlorohydrin.

3-Chloro-1,2-propanediol dinitrate *see* Clonitrate.

Chloropropham *see* Chlorpropham.

Chloroprophenpyridamine *see* Chlorpheniramine.

N-(3-Chloropropionyl)phenethylamine *see* Fenaclon.

CHLOROPROPYLATE* (isopropyl 2,2-bis(*p*-chlorophenyl)glycolate; isopropyl 4,4'-dichlorobenzilate; 1-methylethyl 4-chloro-α-(4-chlorophenyl)-α-hydroxybenzeneacetate; chlorpropylate; 'acaralate'; 'rospin').

γ-Chloropropylene oxide *see* Epichlorohydrin.

N-(3-Chloropropyl)-α-methylphenethylamine *see* Mefenorex.

5-(3-Chloropropyl)-4-methylthiazole *see* Cloprothiazole.

'Chloroptic' *see* Chloramphenicol.

CHLOROPYRAMINE*** (2-[(*p*-chlorobenzyl)(2-dimethylaminoethyl)amino]pyridine; *N*-(*p*-chlorobenzyl)-*N'*,*N'*-dimethyl-*N*-pyrid-2-ylethylenediamine; chlorpyramine; halopyramine; chlorotripelennamine; G-12114).

*N*¹-(6-Chloropyrazinyl)sulfanilamide *see* Sulfaclozine.

*N*¹-(6-Chloropyridazin-3-yl)sulfanilamide *see* Sulfachlorpyridazine.

2-(6-Chloropyridazin-3-ylthio]-*N*,*N*-diethylacetamide *see* Azintamide.

4-[3-(3-Chloro-10*H*-pyrido[3,2-*b*][1,4]benzothiazin-10-yl)propyl]-1-piperazineethanol *see* Cloxypendyl.

p-Chloro-α-pyrid-2-ylbenzyl 2-dimethylaminoethyl ether *see* Carbinoxamine; Rotoxamine.

1-(*p*-Chloro-α-pyrid-2-ylbenzyl)-4-[2-(2-hydroxyethoxy)ethyl]piperazine *see* Piclopastine.

4-(*p*-Chloro-α-pyrid-2-ylbenzylidene)-1-methylpiperidine *see* Cycliramine.

2-[2-[4-(*p*-Chloro-α-pyrid-2-ylbenzyl)piperazin-1-yl]ethoxy]ethanol *see* Piclopastine.

6-(5-Chloro-2-pyridyl)-6,7-dihydro-7-hydroxy-5*H*-pyrrolo[3,4-*b*]pyrazin-5-one 4-methylpiperazine-1-carboxylate ester *see* Zopiclone.

4-[2-(6-Chloropyrid-2-ylthio)ethyl]morpholine *see* Fopirtoline.

CHLOROPYRILENE*** (2-[(5-chloro-2-thenyl)(2-dimethylaminoethyl)amino]pyridine; chlorothen; chloromethapyrilene; chlorothenylpyramine).

3-Chloro-4-(3-pyrrolin-1-yl)hydratropic acid *see* Pirprofen.

2-[3-Chloro-4-(3-pyrrolin-1-yl)phenyl]propionic acid *see* Pirprofen.

CHLOROQUINE*** (7-chloro-4-[4-(diethylamino)-1-methylbutylamino]quinoline; chlorochin; RP 3377; SN-7618; W-7618; WIN-244).

CHLOROQUINE DIGENTISATE ('quinercyl').

Chloroquine di[8-hydroxy-7-iodo-5-quinolinesulfonate] *see* Cloquinate.

CHLOROQUINE DIPHOSPHATE (quingamine; 'delagil'; 'imagon'; 'tresochin').
See also under Broxyquinoline; Clioquinol; Cloqinate.

CHLOROQUINE DIPHOSPHATE plus GLYCOBIARSOL ('neoviacept').

CHLOROQUINE SILICATE ('resochin S').

CHLOROQUINE SULFATE ('nivaquine B').

CHLOROQUINE SULFATE plus DIIODOHYDROXYQUIN ('nivembin').

'Chloroquinol' *see* Halquinols.

5-Chloro-8-quinolinol *see* Cloxiquine.

2-[[4-(7-Chloroquinolin-4-yl)amino]pentylamino]ethanol *see* Cletoquine.

4-(7-Chloroquinolin-4-ylamino)-α-pyrrolidin-1-yl-*o*-cresol *see* Amopyroquine.

4-(7-Chloro-4-quinolylamino)-α-(diethylamino)-*o*-cresol *see* Amodiaquine.

N-(7-Chloro-4-quinolyl)anthranilic acid esters *see* Glafenine; Nicafenine.

2-Chloro-9-(quinuclidin-3-ylmethylene)thioxanthene *see* Nuclotixene.

'Chloros' *see* Sodium hypochlorite.

CHLOROSERPIDINE*** (10-chloro-11-demethoxyreserpine; 10-chlorodeserpidine).

6-Chloro-9-(1-D-sorbityl)isoalloxazine *see* Flavotine.

N-Chlorosuccinimide *see* Succinchlorimide.

4-Chloro-3-sulfamoylbenzamide *see* Sulclamide.

1-(4-Chloro-3-sulfamoylbenzamido)-2,6-dimethylpiperidine *see* Clopamide.

1-(4-Chloro-3-sulfamoylbenzamido)-2-methylindoline *see* Indapamide.

2-(4-Chloro-3-sulfamoylbenzamido)-1-methylisoindoline *see* Zidapamide.

4-Chloro-3-sulfamoylbenzoic acid 2,2-dimethylhydrazide *see* Alipamide.

p-(Chlorosulfamoyl)benzoic acid disodium salt *see* Monalazone disodium.

3-(4-Chloro-3-sulfamoylphenyl)-3-hydroxy-1-isoindolinone *see* Chlortalidone.

4-(4-Chloro-3-sulfamoylphenyl)-4-hydroxy-3-methyl-2-(methylimino)thiazolidine *see* Tizolemide.

3-(4-Chloro-2-sulfamoylphenyl)-3-hydroxyphthalimidine *see* Chlortalidone.

N-(2-Chloro-4-sulfamoylphenyl)-2-phenylsuccinimide *see* Suclofenide.

4-Chloro-5-sulfamoyl-2',6'-salicyloxylidide *see* Xipamide.

2-[[3-Chloro-4-sulfamoyl-6-(1*H*-tetrazol-5-yl)anilino]methyl]thiophene *see* Azosemide.

5-[4-Chloro-5-sulfamoyl-2-(2-thenylamino)phenyl]-1*H*-tetrazole *see* Azosemide.

Chlorosulthiadil *see* Hydrochlorothiazide.

4-Chlorotestosterone *see* Clostebol.

7-Chlorotetracycline *see* Chlortetracycline.

2-Chloro-1,2,3,3-tetrafluorocyclopropyl methyl ether *see* Aliflurane.

1-Chloro-1,2,3,4-tetrafluoro-3-methoxycyclopropane *see* Aliflurane.

4'-Chloro-1,2,3,4-tetrahydro-1,3-dioxo-4-isoquinolinecarboxanilide *see* Tesicam.

6-Chloro-2,3,4,5-tetrahydro-1-(*p*-hydroxyphenyl)-1*H*-3-benzazepine-7,8-diol *see* Fenoldopam.

8-Chloro-3,4,5,6-tetrahydro-6-[(1-isopropyl-2-imidazolin-2-yl)methyl]-2*H*-1,6-benzothiazocine *see*

Dazolicine.
8-Chloro-1,2,3,4-tetrahydro-5-methoxy-N,N-dimethyl-1-naphthylamine *see* Lometraline.
2-Chloro-5,9,10,14b-tetrahydro-5-methylisoquino[2,1-d][1,4]benzodiazepin-6(7H)-one *see* Clazolam.
8-Chloro-2,3,4,5-tetrahydro-2-methyl-5-[2-(6-methylpyrid-3-yl)ethyl]-1H-pyrido[4,3-b]indole *see* Dorastine.
7-Chloro-1,2,3,5-tetrahydro-1-methyl-2-oxo-5-phenyl-4H-1,4-benzodiazepine-4-carboxamide *see* Carburazepam.
2-Chloro-4′-(1,4,5,6-tetrahydro-4-methyl-6-oxopyridazin-3-yl)propionanilide *see* Amipizone.
7-Chloro-1,2,3,4-tetrahydro-2-methyl-4-oxo-3-o-tolyl-6-quinazolinesulfonamide *see* Metolazone.
6-Chloro-3a,4,9,9a-tetrahydro-2-methyl-4-phenylbenz[f]isoindoline *see* Losindole.
10-Chloro-2,3,7,11β-tetrahydro-2-methyl-11b-phenyloxazolo[3,2-d][1,4]benzodiazepin-6(5H)-one *see* Oxazolam.
7-Chloro-2,3,4,5-tetrahydro-4-oxo-5-phenyl-1H-1,5-benzodiazepine-1-carboxylic acid ethyl ester *see* Arfendazam.
7-Chloro-1,2,3,4-tetrahydro-4-oxo-2-phenyl-6-quinazolinesulfonamide *see* Fenquizone.
7-Chloro-1,2,3,4-tetrahydro-4-oxo-2-phenyl-6-sulfamoylquinazoline *see* Fenquizone.
Chlorotetrahydroxy[(2-hydroxy-5-oxo-2-imidazolin-4-yl)ureato]dialuminium *see* Alcloxa.
9-Chloro-7-(1H-tetrazol-5-yl)-5H-[1]benzopyrano[2,3-b]pyridin-5-one *see* Traxanox.
2-Chloro-5-(1H-tetrazol-5-yl)-N⁴-2-thenylsulfanilamide *see* Azosemide.
CHLOROTHALONIL* (2,4,5,6-tetrachloro-1,3-benzenedicarbonitrile; 1,3,4,5-tetrachloro-2,6-dicyanobenzene; 1,3,4,5-tetrachloro-2,6-dinitrilobenzene; tetrachloroisophthalonitrile; TPN; 'bravo'; 'DAC-2787'; 'daconil'; 'exotherm termil'; 'forturf'; 'termil').
Chlorothen* *see* Chloropyrilene.
'Chlorothene' *see* 1,1,1-Trichloroethane.
3-Chloro-4-(2-thenoyl)hydratropic acid *see* Cliprofen.
2-[(5-Chloro-2-thenyl)(2-dimethylaminoethyl)-amino]pyridine *see* Chloropyrilene.
Chlorothenylpyramine *see* Chloropyrilene.
8-Chlorotheophyllinate(s) *see* Teoclate(s).
CHLOROTHEOPHYLLINE (8-chlorotheophylline).
CHLOROTHEOPHYLLINE plus DIPHENHYDRAMINE ('betadorm A'; 'detensor').
CHLOROTHIAZIDE* (6-chloro-2H-1,2,4-benzothiadiazine-7-sulfonamide 1,1-dioxide; chlorthiazide).
See also under Methyldopa.
CHLOROTHIAZIDE SODIUM* ('lyovac diuril').
2-[3-Chloro-4-(thien-2-ylcarbonyl)phenyl]propionic acid *see* Cliprofen.
5-Chloro-2-thienyl imidazol-1-ylmethyl ketone (2,6-dichlorophenyl)hydrazone *see* Zinoconazole.
1-[2-[(2-Chloro-3-thienyl)methoxy]-2-(2,4-dichloro-

phenyl)ethyl]-1H-imidazole *see* Tioconazole.
CHLOROTHION (tr) (O-(3-chloro-4-nitrophenyl) O,O-dimethyl phosphorothioate; 'chlorthion').
3-(2-Chlorothioxanthen-9-ylidene)-N,N-dimethylpropylamine *see* Chlorprothixene.
3-[(2-Chlorothioxanthen-9-ylidene)methyl]quinuclidine; 2-chloro-9-(quinuclidin-3-ylmethylene)thioxanthene *see* Nuclotixene.
4-[3-(2-Chlorothioxanthen-9-ylidene)propyl]-N-methyl-1-piperazinepropionamide *see* Clotixamide.
4-[3-(2-Chlorothioxanthen-9-ylidene)propyl]-1-piperazineethanol *see* Clopenthixol; Zuclopenthixol.
4-[3-(2-Chlorothioxanthen-9-yl)propyl]-1-piperazinepropanol *see* Xanthiol.
5-Chlorotoluene-2,4-disulfonamide *see* Disulfamide.
2-(2-Chloro-p-toluidino)-2-imidazoline *see* Tolonidine.
2-(3-Chloro-o-toluidino)nicotinic acid *see* Clonixin.
4-(2-Chloro-m-toluidino)thiophene-3-carboxylic acid hydroxymethyl ester acetate *see* Aclantate.
CHLOROTOLURON* (1-(3-chloro-4-methylphenyl)-3,3-dimethylurea; 1-(m-chloro-p-tolyl)-3,3-dimethylurea; chlortoluron; C-2242; 'dicuran').
N-(3-Chloro-o-tolyl)anthranilic acid *see* Tolfenamic acid.
trans-1-[2-[N-(6-Chloro-o-tolyl)carboxamido]ethyl]-octahydro-1H-1-pyrindine *see* Rodocaine.
N′-(4-Chloro-o-tolyl)-N,N-dimethylformamidine *see* Chlorphenamidine.
1-(m-Chloro-p-tolyl)-3,3-dimethylurea *see* Chlorotoluron.
4-Chloro-o-tolyldithioimidocarbonic acid cyclic methylene ester *see* Nimidane.
1-(3-Chloro-p-tolyl)-4-[6-(p-tert-pentylphenoxy)hexyl]piperazine *see* Teroxalene.
CHLOROTRIANISENE* (1-chloro-1,2,2-tris-(p-methoxyphenyl)ethylene; 4,4′-dimethoxy-4′-(p-methoxyphenyl)stilbene; chlortrianisoestrol; NSC-10108).
1-Chloro-2-[2,2,2-trichloro-1-(4-chlorophenyl)ethyl]-benzene *see* o,p′-DDT.
[2-Chloro-1-(2,4,5-trichlorophenyl)vinyl] dimethyl phosphate *see* Stirofos.
6-Chloro-N,N′,N′-triethyl-1,3,5-triazine-2,4-diamine *see* Trietazine.
1-Chloro-2,2,2-trifluoroethyl difluoromethyl ether *see* Isoflurane.
2-Chloro-1,1,2-trifluoroethyl difluoromethyl ether *see* Enflurane.
4-[4-(4-Chloro-3-trifluoromethylphenyl)-4-hydroxypiperid-1-yl]-N,N-dimethyl-2,2-diphenylbutyramide *see* Fluperamide.
3-(2-Chloro-3,3,3-trifluoropropenyl)-2,2-dimethylcyclopropanecarboxylic acid α-cyano-3-phenoxybenzyl ester *see* Cyhalothrin.
4-(4-Chloro-α,α,α-trifluoro-m-tolyl)-1-[4,4-bis(p-fluorophenyl)butyl]-4-piperidinol *see* Penfluridol.
4-(4-Chloro-α,α,α-trifluoro-m-tolyl)-4-hydroxy-N,N-dimethyl-α,α-diphenyl-1-piperidinebutyramide *see* Fluperamide.
4-[4-(p-Chloro-α,α,α-trifluoro-m-tolyl)-4-hydroxy-

piperid-1-yl]-4′-fluorobutyrophenone *see* Clofluperol.

7α-Chloro-11β,17,21-trihydroxy-16α-methylpregna-1,4-diene-3,20-dione *see* Alclometasone.

9-Chloro-11β,17,21-trihydroxy-16β-methylpregna-1,4-diene-3,20-dione *see* Beclometasone.

6-Chloro-11β,17,21-trihydroxypregna-1,4,6-triene-3,20-dione *see* Cloprednol.

2-Chloro-10-[3-[4-(2-(3,4,5-trimethoxybenzoyloxy)-ethyl)piperazin-1-yl]propyl]phenothiazine *see* Metofenazate.

7-Chloro-4,6,2′-trimethoxy-6′-methylgris-2′-ene-3,4′-dione *see* Griseofulvin.

7-Chloro-2′,4,6-trimethoxy-6′-methylspiro(benzofuran-2(3H),1′-(2)-cyclohexene)-3,4-dione *see* Griseofulvin.

2-Chloro-N,N,N-trimethylethanamium chloride *see* Chlormequat.

2-Chloro-N,N,6-trimethyl-4-pyrimidinamine *see* Crimidine.

Chlorotripelennamine *see* Chloropyramine.

Chlorotriphenylstannane *see* Fentin chloride.

1-Chloro-1,2,2-tris(p-methoxyphenyl)ethylene *see* Chlorotrianisene.

1-(o-Chlorotrityl)imidazole *see* Clotrimazole.

β-Chlorovinyl ethynyl carbinol *see* Etchlorvynol.

'Chlorox' *see* Sodium hypochlorite.

4-(2-Chloro-9H-xanthen-9-ylidene)-1-methylpiperidine *see* Clopipazan.

CHLOROXINE* (5,7-dichloro-8-quinolinol; dichlorohydroxyquinoline; 'endiaton').
See also Halquinols.

CHLOROXURON* (1-[p-(p-chlorophenoxy)phenyl]-3,3-dimethylurea; chloroxyfenidim; kloroksifenidim; 'tenoran').

Chloroxyfenidim *see* Chloroxuron.

CHLOROXYLENOL* (4-chloro-3,5-dimethylphenol; PCMX; 'asterit'; 'scabintan').

[[4-Chloro-6-(2,3-xylidino)pyrimidin-2-yl]thio]acetic acid *see* Pirinixic acid.

2-[[4-Chloro-6-(2,3-xylidino)pyrimidin-2-yl]thio]-N-(2-hydroxyethyl)acetamide *see* Pirinixil.

6-Chloro-3,4-xylyl methylcarbamate *see* Carbanolate.

CHLOROZOTOCIN (1-(2-chloroethyl)-3-(β-D-glucopyranosyl)-1-nitrosourea; 2-[3-(2-chloroethyl)-3-nitrosoureido]-2-deoxy-D-glucopyranose; DCNU; NSC-178248).

CHLOROZOTOCIN TETRAACETATE (1-(2-chloroethyl)-1-nitroso-3-(tetraacetyl-β-D-2-glucopyranosyl)urea; NSC-114460).

'Chlorpactin' *see* Oxychlorosene.

'Chlorparacide' *see* Chlorbenside.

CHLORPENTAZIDE (4-(p-chlorophenylsulfonyl)-1,1-pentamethylenesemicarbazide; 1-(p-chlorophenylsulfonyl)-3-piperid-1-ylurea; HB-113).

Chlorpenthixol *see* Clopenthixol.

Chlorperazine *see* Prochlorperazine.

Chlorperphenazine *see* Perphenazine.

Chlorperphenthixene *see* Clopenthixol.

Chlorphedianol* *see* Clofedanol.

Chlorphen (tr) *see* Camphechlor.

CHLORPHENACEMIDE (1-(2-chloro-2-phenylacetyl)urea; 'comitiadon').

CHLORPHENACYL (tr) (p-[bis(2-chloroethyl)-amino]phenylacetic acid; NSC-71964).

Chlorphenacyl cholesteryl ester *see* Phenesterin.

Chlorphenacyl estradiol diester *see* Estradiol mustard.

CHLORPHENAMIDINE* (N′-(4-chloro-2-methylphenyl)-N,N-dimethylmethanimidamide; N′-(4-chloro-o-tolyl)-N,N-dimethylformamidine; chlordimeform; chlorodimeform; chlorphenamidine hydrochloride; C-8514; 'fundal'; 'galecron').

CHLORPHENAMIDINE plus FORMETANATE ('fundal forte').

Chlorphenamine* *see* Chlorpheniramine.

Chlorphenarsine *see* Dichlorophenarsine.

Chlorphencyclan *see* Clofenciclan.

CHLORPHENESIN* (3-(p-chlorophenoxy)-1,2-propanediol; glyceryl p-chlorophenyl ether; chlorophenesin; 'adermykon'; 'mycil').

CHLORPHENESIN CARBAMATE* (3-(p-chlorophenoxy)-2-hydroxypropyl carbamate; U-19646; 'maolate').

Chlorphenethanum *see* DDT.

Chlorphenindione *see* Clorindione.

CHLORPHENIRAMINE* (2-[p-chloro-α-(2-dimethylaminoethyl)benzyl]pyridine; chlorphenamine; chlorhistapyridamine; chloropheniramine; chloroprophenpyridamine; chlorpheniramine maleate; chlorprophenpyridamine).
See also Dexchlorpheniramine *and under* Cromoglicate disodium; Etilefrine; Pseudoephedrine.

Chlorphenisate *see* Clofibrate.

CHLORPHENOCTIUM AMSONATE* ((2,4-dichlorophenoxymethyl)dimethyloctylammonium salt of 4,4′-diaminostilbene-2,2′-disulfonic acid).

Chlorphenothane *see* DDT.

Chlorphenoxamide *see* Clefamide.

CHLORPHENOXAMINE* (p-chloro-α-methyldiphenhydramine; 2-[1-(p-chlorophenyl)-1-phenylethoxy]-N,N-dimethylethylamine; chlorphenoxamine hydrochloride).

CHLORPHENOXAMINE TEOCLATE (chlorphenoxamine 8-chlorotheophyllinate; chlorphenoxamine theoclate; 'rodavan').

CHLORPHENTERMINE* (p-chloro-α,α-dimethylphenethylamine; S-62; WX-2426).

Chlorphthalidone *see* Chlortalidone.

Chlorpiprazine *see* Perphenazine.

Chlorpiprozine *see* Perphenazine.

Chlorprednisone *see* Chloroprednisone.

Chlorprenaline *see* Clorprenaline.

Chlorprocaine* *see* Chloroprocaine.

CHLORPROETHAZINE* (2-chloro-10-(3-diethylaminopropyl)phenothiazine; RP 4909).

CHLORPROGUANIL* (1-(3,4-dichlorophenyl)-5-isopropylbiguanide; M-5943).

CHLORPROMAZINE* (2-chloro-10-(3-dimethylaminopropyl)phenothiazine; aminazin; aminosine; chloropromazine; clordelazine; cloropromazina; klorpromazine; chlorpromazine

115

hydrochloride; H-5746; HL-5746; RP 4560; SK&F-2601-A).

CHLORPROMAZINE SULFOXIDE (opromazine; 'secotil').

CHLORPROPAMIDE* (1-(p-chlorophenylsulfonyl)-3-propylurea; P-607).

CHLORPROPAMIDE plus METFORMIN ('diabiformine'; 'diabiphage').

CHLORPROPHAM* (isopropyl m-chlorocarbanilate; 1-methylethyl 3-chlorophenylcarbamate; chlopropham; chloropropham; chloro-IPC; klor-IFK; CIPC; 'metoxon').

Chlorprophenpyridamine see Chlorpheniramine.

Chlorpropylate see Chloropropylate.

CHLORPROTHIXENE* (trans isomer of 3-(2-chlorothioxanthen-9-ylidene)-N,N-dimethyl-propylamine; 2-chloro-9-(3-dimethylaminopropylidene)thioxanthene; 2-chloro-N,N-dimethyl-thioxanthene-$\Delta^{9,\gamma}$-propylamine; N-714; Ro 4-0403).

Chlorpyramine* see Chloropyramine.

CHLORPYRIFOS* (O,O-diethyl O-(3,5,6-trichloropyrid-2-yl) phosphorothioate; 3,5,6-trichloro-2-[(diethoxyphosphinothioyl)oxy]pyridine; Dowco 179; OMS-971; 'dursban').

CHLORPYRIFOS-METHYL* (O,O-dimethyl O-(3,5,6-trichloropyrid-2-yl) phosphorothioate; trichlormethylfos; Dowco 214).

CHLORQUINALDOL* (5,7-dichloro-2-methyl-8-quinolinol; dichlorohydroxyquinaldine; dichloroxyquinaldine).

CHLORQUINALDOL plus HALQUINOLS ('dignoquine').

CHLORQUINALDOL plus HYDROCORTISONE BUTYRATE ('locoid C').

Chlorquinol* see Halquinols.

CHLORQUINOX* (5,6,7,8-tetrachloroquinoxaline; 'lucel').

'Chlorsuccillin' see Suxamethonium chloride.

Chlorsudimeprylum see Clopamide.

'Chlorsulphacide' see Chlorbenside.

'Chlorsulthiadil' see Hydrochlorothiazide.

'Chlorsuperlutin' see Chloro-MDAP.

CHLORTALIDONE* (3-(4-chloro-2-sulfamoylphenyl)-3-hydroxyphthalimidine; 3-(4-chloro-3-sulfamoylphenyl)-3-hydroxy-1-isoindolinone; 2-chloro-5-(1-hydroxy-3-oxo-1-isoindolinyl)benzenesulfonamide; chlorthalidone; chlorftalidon; chlorphthalidone; clortalidone; phthalamudine; G-33182; NSC-69200).

See also under Atenolol; Clonidine; Oxprenolol; Reserpine.

'Chlorten' see Campheclor.

CHLORTETRACYCLINE* (7-chloro-4-(dimethylamino)-1,4,4a,5,5a,6,11,12a-octahydro-3,6,10,12,12a-pentahydroxy-6-methyl-1,11-dioxonaphthacene-2-carboxamide; 7-chlorotetracycline; biomitsin; biomycin; biovetin; biovit-40; A-377; NSC-13252).

CHLORTETRACYCLINE plus α-AMYLASE ('amycycline').

CHLORTHAL* (2,3,5,6-tetrachlorobenzene-1,4-dicarboxylic acid; 2,3,5,6-tetrachloroterephthalic acid).

CHLORTHAL-DIMETHYL* (dimethyl tetra-chloroterephthalate; DCPA; 'dacthal').

Chlorthalidone* see Chlortalidone.

CHLORTHENOXAZINE* (2-(2-chloroethyl)-2,3-dihydro-4-oxo-1,3-benzoxazine; 2-(2-chloroethyl)-2,3-dihydro-4H-1,3-benzoxazin-4-one; benzmethoxazone; AP-67).

CHLORTHIAMID* (2,6-dichlorobenzenecarbothiamide; 2,6-dichlorothiobenzamide; 'prefix').

Chlorthiazide* see Chlorothiazide.

'Chlorthion' see Chlorothion.

CHLORTHIOPHOS* (O-[2,5-dichloro-4-(methylthio)phenyl] O,O-diethyl phosphorothioate; CELA S-2957; S-2957).

Chlortoluron see Chlorotoluron.

'Chlortran' see Chlorbutol.

Chlortrianisoestrol* see Chlorotrianisene.

'Chlortride' see Chlorothiazide.

'Chlortrimeton' see Chlorpheniramine.

Chlorvalamide see Monalide.

Chlorxylam see Carbanolate.

'Chloryl' see Chloroethane.

'Chlorylen' see Trichloroethylene.

CHLORZOXAZONE* (5-chloro-2-benzoxazolinone).

Chlosudimeprimylum see Clopamide.

'Chlotaon' see under Chloramphenicol.

'Chlotride' see Chlorothiazide.

'Chloxyl' see 1,4-Bis(trichloromethyl)benzene.

'Chobile' see Cholic acid.

'Choladine' see Iopanoic acid.

Cholaic acid see Taurocholic acid.

Cholalic acid see Cholic acid.

CHOLANIC ACID (17β-(3-carboxy-1-methyl-propyl)etiocholanone; ursocholanic acid).

'Cholanorm' see Chenodeoxycholic acid.

'Cholebrine' see Iocetamic acid.

Cholecalciferol* see Colecalciferol.

Cholecystokinin see Pancreozymin.

'Choledyl' see Choline theophyllinate.

'Cholegyl' see Choline theophyllinate.

Choleic acid see Deoxycholic acid.

'Cholergol' see Choline orotate.

'Cholesolvin' see Simfibrate.

Cholesta-5,7-dien-3-ol see 7-Dehydrocholesterol.

CHOLEST-5-ENE-3β,24-DIOL (24-hydroxycholesterol; cerebrostenediol; cerebrosterol).

Cholest-5-en-3β-ol see Cholesterol.

Cholesterin see Cholesterol.

CHOLESTEROL (cholest-5-en-3β-ol; cholesterin; NSC-8798).

Cholesteryl p-[bis(2-chloroethyl)amino]phenylacetate see Phenesterin.

Cholestyramine* see Colestyramine.

CHOLIC ACID (3,7,12-trihydroxycholanic acid; cholalic acid; NSC-6135; 'chobile'; 'colalin'; 'felagol').

CHOLINE ((2-hydroxyethyl)trimethylammonium hydroxide; amanitine; bilineurine; bursine; fagine; gossypine; luridine; sincaline; vidine).

Choline acetate see Acetylcholine chloride.

Choline benzilate see Metocinium iodide.

Choline bromide hexamethylenedicarbamate *see* Hexcarbacholine bromide.

Choline carbamate *see* Carbachol.

CHOLINE CHLORIDE*** ((2-hydroxyethyl)trimethylammonium chloride).

CHOLINE CITRATE (choline dihydrogen citrate salt).

Choline cytidine 5′-pyrophosphate ester *see* Citicoline.

Choline dihydrogen citrate *see* Choline citrate.

CHOLINE GLUCONATE*** ((2-hydroxyethyl)-trimethylammonium D-gluconate).

CHOLINE GLYCEROPHOSPHATE*** (choline hydroxide (*R*)-2,3-dihydroxypropyl hydrogen phosphate inner salt; *sn*-glycero(3)phosphocholine).

Choline hydroxide 2,3-dihydroxypropyl hydrogen phosphate inner salt *see* Choline glycerophosphate.

Choline iodide benzilate *see* Metocinium iodide.

Choline iodide dimethylpipecolate methiodide *see* Dimecolonium iodide.

Choline iodide 1,1-dimethylpyrrolidinium iodide 2-carboxylate *see* Trepirium iodide.

Choline mesilate *see* Mesylcholine.

Choline methanesulfonate *see* Mesylcholine.

Choline 1,5-naphthalenedisulfonate dilactate diacetate *see* Aclatonium napadisilate.

Choline nitrate *see* Nitricholine perchlorate.

CHOLINE OROTATE ('cholergol').

'Cholinergol' *see* Carbachol.

CHOLINE SALICYLATE*** (choline salt of salicylic acid).

CHOLINE SALICYLATE plus CETALKONIUM CHLORIDE ('bonjela'; 'teejel').

CHOLINE SALICYLATE plus MAGNESIUM SALICYLATE (choline magnesium tris(salicylate); 'tegunor'; 'trisilate').

Choline salicylate magnesium sulfate complex *see* Salcolex.

CHOLINE STEARATE ('chomelan').

Choline suberate *see* Dicholine suberate.

CHOLINE THEOPHYLLINATE*** (oxtrimethylline; oxtriphylline; cholinophylline; theophylline cholinate).

Choline triethyl analog *see* Triethyl(2-hydroxyethyl)ammonium chloride.

Choline urocanoate (salt) *see* Murexine.

Choline xylyl ether bromide *see* Xylocholine.

Cholinophylline *see* Choline theophyllinate.

'Cholinvel' *see* Choline citrate.

'Choliopan' *see* Butropium bromide.

'Cholisate' *see* Choline salicylate.

'Cholit-ursan' *see* Ursodeoxycholic acid.

'Chologon' *see* Dehydrocholic acid.

'Cholografin' *see* Adipiodone sodium.

'Cholonerton' *see* Hymecromone.

'Cholospect' *see* Adipiodone meglumine.

'Choloview' *see* Iodoxamic acid.

'Cholovue' *see* Meglumine iodoxamate.

'Choloxin' *see* Dextrothyroxine sodium.

'Choloxon' *see* Dextrothyroxine sodium.

'Cholspasmin' *see* Hymecromone.

Cholylglycine *see* Glycocholic acid.

Cholyltaurine *see* Taurocholic acid.

'Chomelan' *see* Choline stearate.

Chondrodendrum tomentosum extract *see* Tubocurarine chloride.

CHONDROITINASE (chondroitin sulfatase; 'thiomucase').

See also under Chymotrypsin.

Chondroitin sulfatase *see* Chondroitinase.

CHONDROITIN SULFATE (chondroitinsulfuric acid; 'chonsurid'; 'structum').

Chondroitin sulfate B *see* Dermatan sulfate.

CHONDROITIN 4-SULFATE (chondroitin sulfate A; 'atheroitin').

CHONDROITIN 6-SULFATE (chondroitin sulfate C).

Chondrosamine *see* Galactosamine.

'Chonex' *see* Dehydrocholic acid.

'Chonsurid' *see* Chondroitin sulfate.

Chopramine *see* Lofepramine.

CHORIONIC GONADOTROPHIN*** (HCG; human chorionic gonadotrophin; pregnancy urine extract containing chiefly LH activity with little FSH activity).

'Choryl' *see* Carbachol.

'Chothyn' *see* Choline citrate.

CHQ *see* Halquinols.

CHROMAN (3,4-dihydro-1,2*H*-benzopyran).

'Chromaphon' *see* Coumithoate.

Chromatophore-expanding factor *see* Intermedin.

Chromene *see* 4*H*-1-Benzopyran.

2*H*-Chromen-2-one *see* Coumarin.

'Chromitope sodium' *see* Sodium chromate (^{51}Cr).

Chromium (III) sesquioxide *see* Dichromium trioxide.

'Chromium-Sandoz' *see* Dichromium trioxide.

CHROMOCARB*** (4-oxo-4*H*-1-benzopyran-2-carboxylic acid; chromone-2-carboxylic acid; atremon; LP-1).

CHROMOCARB DIETHYLAMINE (diethylamine chromone-2-carboxylate; 'fludarene').

CHROMOMYCIN (antibiotic from *Str. griseus*; 'toyomycin').

CHROMOMYCIN A$_3$ (NSC-58514).

Chromonar* *see* Carbocromen.

CHROMONE (4*H*-1-benzopyran-4-one; γ-benzopyrone).

Chromone-2-carboxylic acid *see* Chromocarb.

'Chromosmon' *see* Methylene blue.

CHROMOTROPIC ACID (4,5-dihydroxy-2,7-naphthalenedisulfonic acid; 1,8-naphthalenediol-3,6-disulfonic acid).

'Chronogest' *see* Flugestone.

'Chronogyn' *see* Danazol.

CHRYSANTHEMIC ACID (2,2-dimethyl-3-(2-methylpropenyl)cyclopropanecarboxylic acid; chrysanthemumic acid; chrysanthemummonocarboxylic acid).

See also Allethrin; Bioallethrin; Bioresmethrin; Cinerin I; Cismethrin; Cyclethrin; Dimethrin; Prothrin; Pyresmethrin; Resmethrin; Tetramethrin.

CHRYSANTHEMUMDICARBOXYLIC ACID

(3-carboxy-α,2,2-trimethylcyclopropaneacrylic acid; 3-(2-carboxypropenyl)-2,2-dimethylcyclopropanecarboxylic acid).
See also Cinerin II; Pyrethrin II.

Chrysanthemumdicarboxylic acid monomethyl ether *see* Pyrethric acid.

Chrysanthemumic acid *see* Chrysanthemic acid.

Chrysanthemummonocarboxylic acid *see* Chrysanthemic acid.

CHRYSAROBIN* (amorphous extract of *Andira aroba*; Goa powder).

Chrysatropic acid *see* Scopoletin.

Chrysazin *see* Dantron.

Chrysazin-3-carboxylic acid *see* Rhein.

CHRYSIN (5,7-dihydroxyflavone).

CHRYSOIDINE (2,4-diaminoazobenzene; 4-phenylazo-*m*-phenylenediamine).

CHRYSOIDINE-CITRATE COMPLEX ('azo-angin'; 'azohel').

CHRYSOIDINE DIHYDROIODIDE ('azoiodine'; 'azojod').

CHRYSOIDINE MONOTHIOCYANATE ('azorhodan'; 'dairin').

'Chrysomykine' *see* Chlortetracycline.

'Chryson' *see* Resmethrin.

CHRYSOPHANIC ACID (4,5-dihydroxy-2-methylanthraquinone; chrysophanol; methylchrysazin; 'rumicin').
See also Bismuth chrysophanate.

Chrysophanol *see* Chrysophanic acid.

'Chymar' *see* Chymotrypsin.

'Chymex' *see* Bentiromide.

'Chymolase' *see* Chymotrypsin.

CHYMOPAPAIN* (proteolytic enzyme from papaya latex; BAX-1526; NSC-107079; 'discase').

Chymopsin (tr) *see under* Chymotrypsin.

'Chymoral' *see* Chymotrypsin.

'Chymotest' *see* Chymotrypsin.

CHYMOTRYPSIN* (enzyme from mammalian pancreas; α-chymotrypsin).

CHYMOTRYPSIN plus CHONDROITINASE ('alphamucase').

CHYMOTRYPSIN plus TRYPSIN (chymopsin; 'brinastase'; 'fortivenat').

'Chymo-trypure' *see* Chymotrypsin.

'Chytryp' *see* Chymotrypsin.

CI-69 *see* Toluidine red.

CI-92 *see* Anazolene sodium.

CI-100 *see* Sulfadiasulfone sodium.

CI-107 *see* Argipressin tannate.

CI-301 *see* Bialamicol.

CI-336 *see* Carbocloral.

CI-337 *see* Azaserine.

CI-366 *see* Ethosuximide.

CI-379 *see* Benzilonium bromide.

CI-395 *see* Phencyclidine.

CI-400 *see* Eticyclidine.

CI-403-A *see* Pararosaniline embonate.

CI-406 *see* Oxymetholone.

CI-416 *see* Triclofenol piperazine.

CI-419 *see* Fenimide.

CI-427 *see* Prodilidine.

CI-433 *see* Clamoxyquine.

CI-440 *see* Flufenamic acid.

CI-456 *see* Tiamizide.

CI-473 *see* Mefenamic acid.

CI-501 *see* Cycloguanil embonate.

CI-505 *see* Dibutadiamin.

CI-515 *see* Guanoxyfen.

CI-546 *see* Alipamide.

CI-556 *see* Acedapsone.

CI-564 *see under* Cycloguanil embonate.

CI-572 *see* Profadol.

CI-581 *see* Ketamine.

CI-583 *see* Meclofenamic acid.

CI-628 *see* Nitromifene.

CI-633 *see* Clioxanide.

CI-634 *see* Tiletamine.

CI-636 *see* Sulfacitine.

CI-642 *see* Butirosin.

CI-661 *see* Oxiramide.

CI-662 *see* Brilliant green.

CI-673 *see* Vidarabine.

CI-683 *see* Ripazepam.

CI-686 *see* Trebenzomine.

CI-705 *see* Methaqualone.

CI-716 *see* Zolazepam.

CI-718 *see* Bentazepam.

CI-719 *see* Gemfibrozil.

CI-720 *see* Gemcadiol.

CI-744 *see under* Tiletamine.

CI-775 *see* Bevantolol.

CI-781 *see* Zometapine.

CI-787 *see* Tioperidone.

CI-808 *see* Vidarabine.

CI-825 *see* Pentostatin.

CI-845 *see* Pirmenol.

CI-867 *see* Piridicillin.

CI-871 *see* Piracetam.

CI-874 *see* Indeloxazine.

CI-880 *see* Amsacrine.

CI-882 *see* Sparfosate sodium.

CI-884 *see* Interferon.

CI-888 *see* Procaterol.

CI-897 *see* Tebuquine.

CI-898 *see* Trimetrexate.

CI-909 *see* Tiazofurine.

CI-919 *see* Enoxacin.

CI-922 *see* Methylene blue.

CI-925 *see* Tolonium chloride.

CIADOX** (cyanoacetic acid (quinoxalin-2-ylmethylene)hydrazide N^1,N^4-dioxide).

'Cianatil' *see* Cyamemazine.

CIANERGOLINE* ((α-*RS*)-α-cyano-6-methylergoline-8β-propionamide).

CIANIDANOL* ((2*R*,3*S*)-3,3',4',5,7-flavanpentol; 3,3',4',5,7-pentahydroxyflavan; catechin; catechinic acid; (+)-catechol; catechuic acid; cianidol; cyanidol; 'catergen'; 'NB/C').

CIANIDANOL RUTINOSIDE (cyaninoside; 'meralop').

Cianidol *see* Cianidanol.

CIANOPRAMINE* (5-[3-(dimethylamino)-propyl]-10,11-dihydro-5*H*-dibenz[*b,f*]azepine-3-carbonitrile; cyanimipramine; Ro 11-2465).

118

CIAPILOME*** (1-acetamido-5-cyanopyrimidin-4-one; *N*-(5-cyano-4-oxo-1(4*H*)-pyrimidinyl)-acetamide).

'Ciatyl' *see* Clopenthixol.

Ciba 1906 *see* Thiambutosine.

'Cibacalcin' *see* Human calcitonin.

'Cibalgin' *see under* Aminophenazone.

'Cibazole' *see* Sulfathiazole.

CIBENZOLINE*** (2-(2,2-diphenylcyclopropyl)-2-imidazoline; UP-33901).

Cic *see* Ciclopirox olamine.

CICARPERONE*** (4'-fluoro-4-(octahydro-4-hydroxy-1(2*H*)-quinolyl)butyrophenone carbamate ester; 4-carbamoyloxy-1-[3-(*p*-fluorobenzoyl)propyl]octahydroquinoline; 4-carbamoyloxy-1-[4-(*p*-fluorophenyl)-4-oxobutyl]decahydroquinoline; L-7810).

Cichorigenin *see* Esculetin.

CICLACILLIN** (6-(1-aminocyclohexanecarboxamido)penicillanic acid; (1-aminocyclohexyl)penicillin; cyclacillin; Wy-4508; 'calthor'; 'ultracillin'; 'wycil'; 'wypicil').

CICLACTATE*** (3,3,5-trimethylcyclohexyl lactate).

CICLAFRINE*** (*m*-(1-oxa-4-azaspiro[4.6]undec-2-yl)phenol; ciclafrine hydrochloride; Go-3026A; W-43026A).

CICLAZINDOL*** (10-(*m*-chlorophenyl)-2,3,4,10-tetrahydropyrimido[1,2-*a*]indol-10-ol; ciclazindol hydrochloride; Wy-23409).

CICLINDOLE*** (3-(dimethylamino)-1,2,3,4-tetrahydrocarbazole; 2,3,4,9-tetrahydro-*N*,*N*-dimethyl-1*H*-carbazol-3-amine; cyclindole; WIN-27147-2).

CICLIOMENOL*** (2-cyclohexyl-4-iodo-3,5-xylenol).

Ciclobarbital *see* Hexobarbital.

CICLOBENDAZOLE** (methyl 5-cyclopropylcarbonyl-2-benzimidazolecarbamate; cyclobendazole; R-17147).

'Ciclobiotic' *see* Metacycline.

CICLOFENAZINE*** (10-[3-(4-cyclopropylpiperazin-1-yl)propyl]-2-trifluoromethylphenothiazine; cyclophenazine; cyclophenazine hydrochloride).

CICLOHEXIMIDE*** (3-[(*R*)-2-[(1*S*,2*S*,5*S*)-3,5-dimethyl-2-oxocyclohexyl]-2-hydroxyethyl]glutarimide; cycloheximide; NSC-185; U-4527; 'actidione'; 'naramycin').

CICLONICATE*** (*trans*-3,3,5-trimethylcyclohexyl nicotinate).

CICLONIUM BROMIDE*** (diethylmethyl[2-(α-methyl-α-5-norbornen-2-ylbenzyloxy)ethyl]ammonium bromide; Asta-3746).

CICLONIUM BROMIDE plus DIPYRONE ('dolo-adamon').

Ciclonium iodide *see* Oxapium iodide.

CICLOPIROX*** (6-cyclohexyl-1-hydroxy-4-methylpyridin-2(1*H*)-one).

CICLOPIROX OLAMINE* (ciclopirox compound with 2-aminoethanol; ciclopirox ethanolamine salt; cic; HOE-296; 'batrafen').

CICLOPRAMINE*** (2,3,7,8-tetrahydro-3-(methylamino)-1*H*-quino[1,8-*ab*]benzazepine).

CICLOPROFEN*** (2-fluoren-2-ylpropionic acid; α-methylfluorene-2-acetic acid; SQ-20824).

CICLOPROLOL*** ((±)-1-[*p*-[2-(cyclopropylmethoxy)ethoxy]phenoxy]-3-(isopropylamino)-2-propanol; cycloprolol; cicloprolol hydrochloride; SL-75177-10).

CICLOSIDOMINE*** (*N*-(cyclohexylcarbonyl)-3-morpholinosydnone imine; ciclosidomine hydrochloride; PR-G 138-CL).

CICLOSPORIN** (cyclo[[(*E*)-(2*S*,3*R*,4*R*)-3-hydroxy-4-methyl-2-(methylamino)-6-octenoyl]-L-(2-aminobutyryl)-*N*-methylglycyl-*N*-methyl-L-leucyl-L-valyl-*N*-methyl-L-leucyl-L-alanyl-D-alanyl-*N*-methyl-L-leucyl-*N*-methyl-L-leucyl-*N*-methyl-L-valyl]; cyclosporine; cyclosporin A; 'sandimmun').

CICLOTATE(S)** (4-methylbicyclo[2.2.2]oct-2-ene-1-carboxylate(s)).

CICLOTIZOLAM*** (2-bromo-4-(*o*-chlorophenyl)-9-cyclohexyl-6*H*-thieno[3,2-*f*]-*s*-triazolo-[4,3-*a*][1,4]diazepine; WE 973-BS).

CICLOTROPIUM BROMIDE** ((8*r*)-3α-hydroxy-8-isopropyl-1α*H*,5α*H*-tropanium bromide α-phenylcyclopentaneacetate).

CICLOXILIC ACID*** (*cis*-2-hydroxy-2-phenylcyclohexanecarboxylic acid; 'plecton').

CICLOXOLONE*** (3β-(*cis*-2-carboxycyclohexylcarbonyloxy)-11-oxoolean-12-en-30-oic acid; 3β-hydroxy-11-oxoolean-12-en-30-oic acid hydrogen *cis*-1,2-cyclohexanedicarboxylate; cicloxolone disodium; BX-363A).

CICORTONIDE*** (3-(2-chloroethoxy)-6-cyano-9-fluoro-11β,16α,17,21-tetrahydroxypregna-3,5-dien-20-one 16,17-acetonide 21-acetate; 3-(2-chloroethoxy)-9-fluoro-11β,16α,17,21-tetrahydroxy-20-oxopregna-3,5-diene 6-carbonitrile cyclic 16,17-acetal with acetone 21-acetate).

CICROTOIC ACID*** (3-cyclohexyl-3-methylacrylic acid; 3-cyclohexylcrotonic acid; β-methylcyclohexaneacrylic acid; AD-106).

Cicutine *see* Coniine.

'Cidal' *see* Hexachlorophene *and* Triclosan.

CIDEFERRON*** (macromolecular complex of ferric hydroxide with dextrin and citric acid).

'Cidermex' *see under* Triamcinolone acetonide.

'Cidex' *see* Glutaral.

'Cidial' *see* Phenthoate.

'Cidomycin' *see* Gentamicin.

CIDOXEPIN*** (*cis*-11(6*H*)-[3-(dimethylamino)propylidene]dibenz[*b*,*e*]oxepine; *N*,*N*-dimethyldibenz[*b*,*e*]oxepin-*cis*-Δ$^{11(6H),\gamma}$-propylamine; P-4599).

'Ciergin' *see under* Mobecarb.

'Cifoform' *see* Clioquinol.

CIFOSTODINE** (cytidine cyclic 2',3'-(hydrogen phosphate); cyclic CMP).

CIGLITAZONE** ((±)-5-[*p*-[(1-methylcyclohexyl)methoxy]benzyl]-2,4-thiazolidinedione; ADD-3878; U-63287).

'Cignaethyl' *see* Dithranol.

'Cignolin' *see* Dithranol.

'Cigthranol' *see* Dithranol.

CIHEPTOLANE** (10,11-dihydro-*N*,*N*-dimethyl-spiro(5*H*-dibenzo[*a*,*d*]cycloheptene-5,2'-[1,3]dioxolane)-4'-methylamine; 4'-[(dimethylamino)methyl]-1,11-dihydrospiro[5*H*-dibenzo[*a*,*d*]cycloheptene-5,2'-[1,3]dioxolane]).

Cilag-61 *see* Hexamethylolmelamine.

CILASTATIN** ((*Z*)-7-[[(*R*)-2-amino-2-carboxyethyl]thio]-2-[(*S*)-2,2-dimethylcyclopropanecarboxamido]-2-heptenoic acid).

'Cillenta' *see* Benzathine penicillin.

'Cillimycin' *see* Lincomycin.

CILOBAMINE*** (*cis*-2-(3,4-dichlorophenyl)-3-(isopropylamino)bicyclo[2.2.2]octan-2-ol).

'Ciloprine' *see* Acediasulfone sodium.

Ciloprost *see* Iloprost.

CILOSTAMIDE*** (*N*-cyclohexyl-4-[(1,2-dihydro-2-oxo-6-quinolyl)oxy]-*N*-methylbutyramide; 6-(3-(*N*-cyclohexyl-*N*-methylcarbamoyl)propoxy)-2(1*H*)-quinolinone).

CILTOPRAZINE*** (1-(5-chloro-2-methoxybenzoyl)-3-[3-[4-(*m*-tolyl)piperazin-1-yl]propyl]-urea).

'Ciluan' *see under* Captafol.

'Cimedone' *see* Solasulfone.

CIMEMOXIN*** (1-(cyclohexylmethyl)hydrazine; cymemoxine; SD-206-03).

CIMEPANOL*** (1-cyclohexyl-2-methyl-1-propanol; α-isopropylcyclohexanemethanol).

CIMETIDINE*** (1-cyano-2-methyl-3-[2-[[(5-methylimidazol-4-yl)methyl]thio]ethyl]guanidine; 1-methyl-3-[2-(5-methylimidazol-4-ylmethylthio)ethyl]guanidine-2-carbonitrile; SK&F-92334; 'tagamet'; 'ulcerfen').

CIMETROPIUM BROMIDE** (8-(cyclopropylmethyl)-6β,7β-epoxy-3α-hydroxy-1α*H*,5α*H*-tropanium bromide (−)-(*S*)-tropate).

'Cimlac' *see* Aminoacridine.

CIMOXATONE*** (α-[*p*-[5-(methoxymethyl)-2-oxo-3-oxazolidinyl]phenoxy]-*m*-tolunitrile; 3-[4-[(3-cyanobenzyl)oxy]phenyl]-5-(methoxymethyl)-2-oxazolidinone; MD-780515).

CINAMETIC ACID*** (4-(2-hydroxyethoxy)-3-methoxycinnamic acid; ANP-3401; 'transoddi').

CINAMOLOL*** (3-[2-[2-hydroxy-3-(isopropylamino)propoxy]phenyl]acrylic acid methyl ester; methyl *o*-[2-hydroxy-3-(isopropylamino)propoxy]cinnamate).

CINANSERIN*** (2'-[[3-(dimethylamino)propyl]thio]cinnamanilide; cinanserin hydrochloride; NSC-125717; SQ-10643).

Cincaine *see* Cinchocaine.

CINCHOCAINE*** (2-butoxy-*N*-(2-diethylaminoethyl)cinchoninamide; cincaine; cinchocaine hydrochloride; dibucaine; quinocaine; sovkain).

Cinchol *see* β-Sitosterol.

Cinchonan-6',9-diol *see* Cupreine; Cupreidine.

Cinchonan-9-ol *see* Cinchonine; Cinchonidine.

CINCHONIDINE ((8α,9*R*)-cinchonan-9-ol; α-(5-vinylquinuclidin-2-yl)-4-quinolinemethanol; cinchonan-9-ol; α-(4-quinolyl)-5-vinyl-2-quinuclidinemethanol; cinchovatin; α-quinidine).

CINCHONINE ((9*S*)-cinchonan-9-ol; α-(5-vinyl-

quinuclidin-2-yl)-4-quinolinemethanol; cinchonan-9-ol; α-(4-quinolinyl)-5-vinyl-2-quinuclidinemethanol).

CINCHONINIC ACID (4-quinolinecarboxylic acid).

CINCHOPHEN*** (2-phenylcinchoninic acid; aciphenochinolinum; aminophan; quinophan).

Cinchovatin *see* Cinchonidine.

'Cinecol' *see* 2-Chloroethanol.

CINECROMEN*** (3,4,5-trimethoxycinnamic acid ester with 3-(2-hydroxy-3-morpholinopropyl)-4-methyl-7-(morpholinocarboxamido)coumarin).

Cinene *see* Limonene.

Cineol *see* Cineole.

CINEOLE (1,3,3-trimethyl-2-oxabicyclo[2.2.2]octane; cineol; eucalyptole).

CINEPAXADIL** (α-[[(8-acetyl-1,4-benzodioxan-5-yl)oxy]methyl]-4-(3,4,5-trimethyloxycinnamoyl)-1-piperazineethanol).

Cinepazate *see* Cinepazet.

CINEPAZET** (ethyl 4-(3,4,5-trimethoxycinnamoyl)piperazin-1-ylacetate; ethyl cinepazate; cinepazate; MD-6753).

CINEPAZET MALEATE* ('vascoril').

CINEPAZIC ACID*** (4-(3,4,5-trimethoxycinnamoyl)-1-piperazineacetic acid).
See also Cinepazet.

CINEPAZIDE*** (1-(pyrrolidin-1-ylcarbonylmethyl)-4-(3,4,5-trimethoxycinnamoyl)piperazine).

CINEPAZIDE MALEATE (MD-67350; 'vasodistal').

CINERIN I (2-(2-butenyl)-4-hydroxy-3-methyl-2-cyclopenten-1-one ester with 2,2-dimethyl-3-(2-methylpropenyl)cyclopropanecarboxylic acid; cinerolone ester of chrysanthemic acid).

CINERIN II (2-(2-butenyl)-4-hydroxy-3-methyl-2-cyclopenten-1-one ester with monomethyl ester of chrysanthemumdicarboxylic acid; cinerolone ester of chrysanthemumdicarboxylic acid monomethyl ester; cinerolone ester of pyrethric acid).

CINEROLONE (2-(2-butenyl)-4-hydroxy-3-methyl-2-cyclopenten-1-one).

CINFENINE** (*N*-[2-(diphenylmethoxy)ethyl]-*N*-methylcinnamylamine).

CINFENOAC*** (*p*-[2-(α-carboxy-*p*-anisoyl)vinyl]benzoic acid; 4-[2-[[4-(carboxymethoxy)phenyl]carbonyl]ethenyl]benzoic acid; cinfenoac sodium; BX-568A).

CINGESTOL*** (17α-ethynyl-5-estren-17-ol; 19-nor-17α-pregn-5-en-20-yl-17-ol).

CINITAPRIDE*** (4-amino-*N*-[1-(3-cyclohexen-1-ylmethyl)piperid-4-yl]-2-ethoxy-5-nitrobenzamide).

CINMETACIN*** (1-cinnamoyl-5-methoxy-2-methylindole-3-acetic acid).

'Cinnabene' *see* Cinnarizine.

CINNACAINE 3-(diethylamino)propyl cinnamate; 'apothesine').

CINNAMAVERINE*** (2-(diethylamino)ethyl 2,3-diphenylacrylate; 2-(diethylamino)ethyl 2-

phenylcinnamate).

CINNAMEDRINE* (*N*-cinnamyl-β-hydroxy-*N*,α-dimethylphenethylamine; 2-(cinnamylmethylamino)-1-phenyl-1-propanol; α[(1-cinnamylmethylamino)ethyl]benzyl alcohol).

CINNAMEIN (benzyl cinnamate).

Cinnamene *see* Styrene.

CINNAMIC ACID (phenylacrylic acid; phenylpropenoic acid).

1-Cinnamoyl-5-methoxy-2-methylindole-3-acetic acid *see* Cinmetacin.

Cinnamyl 3β-acetoxy-11-oxoolean-12-en-30-oate *see* Cinoxolone.

CINNAMYL ALCOHOL (3-phenyl-2-propen-1-ol; phenylallyl alcohol; styrone).

1′-Cinnamyl-2,6-dioxo-3-phenyl-3,4′-bipiperidine *see* Cinperene.

1-Cinnamyl-4-(2,6-dioxo-3-phenylpiperid-3-yl)piperidine *see* Cinperene.

1-Cinnamyl-4-(diphenylmethyl)piperazine *see* Cinnarizine.

N-**Cinnamyl-β-hydroxy-*N*,α-dimethylphenethylamine** *see* Cinnamedrine.

α[(1-Cinnamylmethylamino)ethyl]benzyl alcohol *see* Cinnamedrine.

2-(Cinnamylmethylamino)-1-phenyl-1-propanol *see* Cinnamedrine.

Cinnamyl methyl ketone *see* Benzylideneacetone.

N-**Cinnamyl-*N*-methyl-1-naphthalenemethylamine** *see* Naftifine.

3-[2-[(4-Cinnamylpiperazin-1-yl)methyl]benzimidazol-1-yl]-1-(2-furyl)-1-propanone *see* Fuprazole.

3-[2-[(4-Cinnamylpiperazin-1-yl)methyl]benzimidazol-1-yl]propiophenone *see* Cinprazole.

2-(1-Cinnamylpiperid-4-yl)-2-phenylglutarimide *see* Cinperene.

3-Cinnamyl-8-propionyl-3,8-diazabicyclo[3.2.1]octane *see* Azaprocin.

Cinnarazine *see* Cinnarizine.

CINNARIZINE* (*trans*-1-cinnamyl-4-(diphenylmethyl)piperazine; cinnarazine; cinnarazine hydrochloride; MD-516; R-516; R-1575).

CINNARIZINE plus DIPHENHYDRAMINE ('arlevert').

CINNARIZINE plus HEPTAMINOL THEOPHYLLINEACETATE (MD-1035; 'sureptil').

CINNARIZINE CLOFIBRATE* (compound (1:1) of cinnarizine with clofibric acid).

'**Cinnipirine**' *see* Cinnarizine.

CINNOFURADIONE* (2-tetrahydrofurfuryl-1*H*-benzo[*c*]pyrazolo[1,2-*a*]cinnoline-1,3(2*H*)-dione; cinofuron).

CINNOLINE (1,2-benzodiazine).

CINNOPENTAZONE* (2-pentyl-6-phenyl-1*H*-pyrazolo[1,2-*a*]cinnoline-1,3(2*H*)-dione; cintazone; AHR-3015; NSC-10285; Scha-306).

Cinnopropazone *see* Azapropazone.

'**Cinobac**' *see* Cinoxacin.

CINOCTRAMIDE (octahydro-1-(3,4,5-trimethoxycinnamoyl)azocine).

CINODINE* (cinodine hydrochloride; antibiotic BM-123-γ; BM-123-γ; CL-98984).

Cinofuron* *see* Cinnofuradione.

CINOLAZEPAM* (7-chloro-5-(*o*-fluorophenyl)-2,3-dihydro-3-hydroxy-2-oxo-1*H*-1,4-benzodiazepine-1-propionitrile).

'**Cinopal**' *see* Fenbufen.

'**Cinopenil**' *see* Meticillin.

CINOQUIDOX* (*N*-(2-cyanoethyl)-3-methyl-2-quinoxalinecarboxamide 1,4-dioxide).

CINOXACIN* (1-ethyl-1,4-dihydro-4-oxo-[1,3]dioxolo[4,5-*g*]cinnoline-3-carboxylic acid; 1-ethyl-4-oxo[1,3]dioxolo[4,5-*g*]cinnoline-3-carboxylic acid; azolinic acid; compound 64716; 'cinobac').

CINOXATE* (2-ethoxyethyl *p*-methoxycinnamate; 'giv tan F'; 'sundare').

CINOXOLONE* (cinnamyl 3β-acetoxy-11-oxoolean-12-en-30-oate; BX-311).

CINPERENE (1′-cinnamyl-2,6-dioxo-3-phenyl-3,4′-bipiperidine; 1-cinnamyl-4-(2,6-dioxo-3-phenylpiperid-3-yl)piperidine; 2-(1-cinnamylpiperid-4-yl)-2-phenylglutarimide; R-5046).

CINPRAZOLE* (1-(2-benzoylethyl)-2-[(4-cinnamylpiperazin-1-yl)methyl]benzimidazole; 1-[[1-(2-benzoylethyl)benzimidazol-2-yl]methyl]-4-cinnamylpiperazine; 3-[2-[(4-cinnamylpiperazin-1-yl)methyl]benzimidazol-1-yl]propiophenone).

CINPROPAZIDE (*N*-isopropyl-4-(3,4,5-trimethoxycinnamoyl)-1-piperazineacetamide; 1-(isopropylcarbamoylmethyl)-4-(3,4,5-trimethoxycinnamoyl)piperazine).

CINROMIDE* (*m*-bromo-*N*-ethylcinnamamide; (*E*)-3-(*m*-bromophenyl)-*N*-ethyl-2-propenamide).

Cintazone* *see* Cinnopentazone.

CINTRAMIDE* (3,4,5-trimethoxycinnamamide; cintriamide).

Cintriamide* *see* Cintramide.

'**CiNU**' *see* Lomustine.

'**Ciodrin**' *see* Crotoxyphos.

CIPC *see* Chlorpropham.

Cipermethrin *see* Cypermethrin.

CIPIONATE(S)* (3-cyclopentanepropionate(s); cypionate(s)).

CIPRAFAMIDE* (*N*-(*cis*-2,*trans*-3-diphenylcyclopropyl)-1-pyrrolidineacetamide).

CIPRAZAFONE (4′-chloro-2′-(*o*-chlorobenzoyl)-2-(cyclopropylamino)-*N*-methylacetanilide).

CIPREFADOL* ((−)-3-(2-(cyclopropylmethyl)-1,3,4,5,6 7,8,8a-octahydro-4aβ-isoquinolyl)phenol).

CIPREFADOL SUCCINATE* (ciprefadol butanedioate (1:1) salt; compound 113878).

CIPROCINONIDE* (21-[(cyclopropylcarbonyl)oxy]-6α,9-difluoro-11β-hydroxy-16α,17-[(1-methylethylidene)bis(oxy)]pregna-1,4-diene-3,20-dione; fluocinolone acetonide 21-cyclopropanecarboxylate; RS-2386).

CIPROFIBRATE* (2-[*p*-(2,2-dichlorocyclopropyl)phenoxy]-2-methylpropionic acid; WIN-35833).

CIPROFLOXACIN (1-cyclopropyl-6-fluoro-1,4-dihydro-4-oxo-7-piperazin-1-ylquinoline-3-carboxylic acid; ciprofloxacin hydrochloride; BAY o-9867; BAY q-3939).

CIPROPRIDE*** (*N*-[[1-(cyclopropylmethyl)pyr-rolidin-2-yl]methyl]-2-methoxy-5-sulfamoyl-benzamide; *N*-[(1-cyclopropylmethyl)pyrrolidin-2-yl)methyl]-5-sulfamoyl-*o*-anisamide).

CIPROQUAZONE*** (1-(cyclopropylmethyl)-6-methoxy-4-phenyl-2(1*H*)-quinazolinone; SL-573).

CIPROQUINATE*** (ethyl 6,7-bis(cyclopropyl-methoxy)-4-hydroxyquinoline-3-carboxylate; cy-proquinate; Su-18137; 'coxytrol').

CIPROSTENE** ((*Z*)-(3a*S*,5*R*,6*R*,6a*R*)-hexa-hydro-5-hydroxy-6-[(*E*)-(3*S*)-3-hydroxy-1-octen-yl]-3a-methyl-Δ$^{2(1H),δ}$-pentalenevaleric acid).

CIPROXIMIDE*** (1-(*p*-chlorophenyl)-1,2-cyclo-propanedicarboximide; cyproximide; CL-53415).

CIRAMADOL*** ((−)-[1α(*R**),2α]-3-[(dimethyl-amino)(2-hydroxycyclohexyl)methyl]phenol; (−)-(1*R**,2*R**)-2-[(*R**)-α-(dimethylamino)-*m*-hydroxybenzyl]cyclohexanol; Wy-15705).

CIRAZOLINE*** (2-[(*o*-cyclopropylphenoxy)-methyl]-2-imidazoline; LD-3098).

'Circanol' *see* Co-dergocrine.

'Circladin' *see* Bromindione.

'Circupon' *see* Etilefrine.

CIROLEMYCIN*** (antibiotic from *Str. bellus* var. *cirolerosis*; U-12241).

'Cirrcolina' *see* Choline citrate.

CISAPRIDE*** (*cis*-4-amino-5-chloro-*N*-[1-[3-(*p*-fluorophenoxy)propyl]-3-methoxypiperid-4-yl]-*o*-anisamide; R-51619).

Cisclomifene *see* Enclomifene.

Cisclomiphene *see* Enclomifene.

CISMADINONE*** (6-chloro-17-hydroxypregna-1,4-diene-3,20-dione).

CISMADINONE ACETATE* (cismadinone 17-acetate).

CISMETHRIN* (*cis*-(+)-5-benzylfuran-3-ylmeth-yl 2,2-dimethyl-3-(2-methyl-1-propenyl)cyclo-propanecarboxylate; *cis*-(+)-5-benzyl-3-furyl-methyl chrysanthemate; NRDC-119; OMS-1800; RU-12063).

CISPLATIN*** (*cis*-diamminedichloroplatinum; (SP-4-2)diamminedichloroplatinum; *cis*-dichlor-diammine platinum (II); *cis*-platinum (II) di-aminodichloride; cis-DDP; NSC-119875; 'neo-platin'; 'platinex'; 'platinol').

'Cistobil' *see* Iopanoic acid.

CITALOPRAM*** (1-[3-(dimethylamino)propyl]-1-(*p*-fluorophenyl)-5-phthalancarbonitrile; Lu-10-171).

'Citanest' *see* Prilocaine.

'Citarin' *see* Racemorphan *and* Sodium anhydro-methylene citrate *and* Tetramisole.

CITENAMIDE*** (5*H*-dibenzo[*a*,*d*]cyclohepotene-5-carboxamide; AY-15613).

CITENAZONE*** (5-cyano-2-thiophenecarbox-aldehyde thiosemicarbazone; 5-formyl-2-thio-phenecarbonitrile thiosemicarbazone; HOE-105).

'Citexal' *see* Methaqualone.

'Cithrol' *see* Macrogol stearate(s).

CITICOLINE** (choline cytidine 5'-pyrophos-phate ester; cytidine diphosphate choline; cyti-choline; CDP-choline).

'Citiolase' *see* Citiolone.

CITIOLONE*** (*N*-(tetrahydro-2-oxothien-3-yl)-acetamide; 2-acetamido-4-mercaptobutyric acid γ-thiolactone; α-acetamido-γ-thiobutyrolactone; acetylhomocysteine thiolactone; 'citiolase'; 'mu-corex'; 'thioxidrene').

'Citocillin' *see* Hydroxyprocaine-penicillin.

'Citracholin' *see* Choline citrate.

'Citramin' *see* Methenamine anhydromethylene-citrate.

'Citrazon' *see* Benzoximate.

Citrex (tr) *see* Dodine.

CITRIC ACID (2-hydroxy-1,2,3-propanetrioic acid; 'renacidin').

CITRIN (eriodictyol glucoside).

CITRININ (antibiotic from *Penicillium citrinum*; 4,6-dihydro-8-hydroxy-3,4,5-trimethyl-6-oxo-3*H*-2-benzopyran-7-carboxylic acid).

CITRODISALYL (methylenecitrodisalicylic acid; 'novaspirin'; 'salicitrin').

Citroformin *see* Methenamine anhydromethylene-citrate.

Citrohexal *see* Methenamine anhydromethylene-citrate.

Citrohexamine *see* Methenamine anhydromethyl-enecitrate.

'Citrola' *see* Dimethyl phthalate.

'Citromint' *see* Paraformaldehyde.

CITROPTEN (5,6-dihydroxycoumarin; limettin).

Citrovorum factor *see* Calcium folinate.

'Citrullamon' *see* Phenytoin.

CITRULLINE (2-amino-4-ureidovaleric acid; 5-ureidonorvaline).

CITRULLINE MALATE ('stimol').

CK-0383 *see* Verofylline.

CK-0569 *see* Ipexidine.

CL-2 *see* Pirenzepine.

CL 19 I *see* Iodocholesterol ^{131}I.

CL-68 *see* Clocortolone pivalate.

CL-369 *see* Ketamine.

CL-399 *see* Tiletamine.

CL-639-C *see* Dioxadrol.

CL-911-C *see* Dexoxadrol.

CL-912-C *see* Levoxadrol.

CL-1388R *see* Guanadrel.

CL-1848C *see* Etoxadrol.

CL-2422 *see* Guancidine.

CL-5279 *see* Aminitrozole.

CL-8490 *see* Methazolamide.

CL-10304 *see* Aminocaproic acid.

CL-11366 *see* Benzolamide.

CL-12625 *see* Natamycin.

CL-13494 *see* Sulfamethoxypyridazine.

CL-13900 *see* Puromycin.

CL-14377 *see* Methotrexate.

CL-16536 *see* Puromycin.

CL-19823 *see* Triamcinolone.

CL-22415 *see* Demecycline.

CL-25477 *see* Azatepa.

CL-26193 *see* Simtrazene.

CL-27071 *see* Descinolone acetonide.

CL-34433 *see* Triamcinolone hexacetonide.
CL-34699 *see* Amcinonide.
CL-36010 *see* Quinethazone.
CL-36467 *see* Levomepromazine.
CL-39743 *see* Levomepromazine.
CL-39808 *see* Tozalinone.
CL-40881 *see* Ethambutol.
CL-48156 *see* Imidoline.
CL-53381 *see* Triamcinolone acetonide sodium phosphate.
CL-53415 *see* Ciproximide.
CL-54131 *see* Piperamide.
CL-54998 *see* Brocresine.
CL-59112 *see* Roletamide.
CL-61965 *see* Triamcinolone acetonide sodium phosphate.
CL-62362 *see* Loxapine.
CL-64976 *see* Zilantel.
CL-65205 *see* Boxidine.
CL-65336 *see* Tranexamic acid.
CL-65562 *see* Triflocin.
CL-67772 *see* Amoxapine.
CL-71563 *see* Loxapine succinate.
CL-82204 *see* Fenbufen.
CL-84633 *see* Nimidane.
CL-88893 *see* Clazolimine.
CL-90748 *see* Azolimine.
CL-98984 *see* Cinodine.
CL-106359 *see* Triamcinolone acetonide sodium phosphate.
CL-112302 *see* Buprenorphine.
CL-203821 *see* Cetaben.
CL-205925 *see* Iprocinodine.
CL-206214 *see* Butamisole.
CL-206576 *see* Sulbenox.
CL-206797 *see* Cypothrin.
CL-216942 *see* Bisantrene.
CL-217658 *see* Imcarbofos.
CL-220075 *see* Bicifadine.
CL-227193 *see* Piperacillin.
CL-232315 *see* Mitoxantrone.
'Clafen' *see* Cyclophosphamide.
'Claforan' *see* Cefotaxime.
'Clairvan' *see* Etamivan.
CLAMIDOXIC ACID*** ([2-(3,4-dichlorobenz-amido)phenoxy]acetic acid; SNR-1804).
'Clamil' *see* Tolboxane.
'Clamoxyl' *see* Amoxicillin.
'Clamoxyquin' *see* Clamoxyquine.
CLAMOXYQUINE*** (5-chloro-7-(3-diethyl-aminopropylaminomethyl)-8-quinolinol; clam-oxyquin hydrochloride; CI-433; CN-17900-2B; NSC-20246; PAA-3854).
Clam poison *see* Saxitoxin.
CLANOBUTIN*** (4-[*p*-chloro-*N*-(*p*-methoxy-phenyl)benzamido]butyric acid; B-6518; 'byka-hepar').
CLANTIFEN** (4-(2,6-dichloroanilino)-3-thio-phenecarboxylic acid).
'Claradin' *see* Acetylsalicylic acid.
'Claresan' *see* Pyridoxine clofibrate.
'Clarin' *see* Heparin potassium.
'Clarmil' *see* Tolboxane.

Clavacin *see* Patulin.
Clavatin *see* Patulin.
Claviformin *see* Patulin.
'Claviton' *see* Tridihexethyl iodide.
CLAVULANIC ACID*** (*Z*-(2*R*,5*R*)-3-(2-hydr-oxyethylidene)-7-oxo-4-oxa-1-azabicyclo-[3.2.0]heptane-2-carboxylic acid; clavulanate potassium; BRL-14151).
See also under Amoxycillin.
CLAZOLAM*** ((+)-2-chloro-5,9,10,14b-tetra-hydro-5-methylisoquino[2,1-*d*][1,4]benzodiazep-in-6(7*H*)-one).
CLAZOLIMINE*** (1-(*p*-chlorophenyl)-2-imino-3-methyl-4-imidazolidinone; CL-88893).
CLEBOPRIDE*** (4-(4-amino-5-chloro-2-meth-oxybenzamido)-1-benzylpiperidine; 4-amino-*N*-(1-benzylpiperid-4-yl)-5-chloro-*o*-anisamide; 'gastridin').
CLEFAMIDE*** (2,2-dichloro-*N*-(2-hydroxy-ethyl)-*N*-[*p*-(*p*-nitrophenoxy)benzyl]acetamide; chlorophenoxamide; chlorphenoxamide; 'mebin-ol').
CLEMASTINE*** (*p*-chloro-α-methyl-α-phenyl-benzyl alcohol 2-(1-methylpyrrolidin-2-yl)ethyl ether; 2-[2-(*p*-chloro-α-methyl-α-phenylbenzyl-oxy)ethyl]-1-methylpyrrolidine; 2-[2-[1-(*p*-chlorophenyl)-1-phenylethoxy]ethyl]-1-methyl-pyrrolidine; meclastine; mecloprodine; 'agas-ten').
CLEMASTINE FUMARATE* (meclastine fumar-ate; HS-592; 'tavegil'; 'tavist').
CLEMEPROL** (*m*-chloro-α-[(dimethylamino)-methyl]-β-phenylphenethylalcohol; 1-(*m*-chlorophenyl)-3-(dimethylamino)-1-phenyl-2-propanol; clemeprol hydrochloride; BRL-14342).
CLEMIZOLE*** (1-(*p*-chlorobenzyl)-2-pyrrolid-1-ylmethylbenzimidazole; clemizole hydrochlor-ide; AL-20).
CLEMIZOLE PENICILLIN*** (penicillin G plus clemizole).
CLENBUTEROL*** (1-(4-amino-3,5-dichloro-phenyl)-2-*tert*-butylaminoethanol; 4-amino-α-(*tert*-butylaminomethyl)-3,5-dichlorobenzyl al-cohol; clenbuterol hydrochloride; NAB-365; 'spiropent'; 'ventipulmin').
'Clenil' *see* Beclometasone dipropionate.
CLENPIRIN** (1-butyl-2-(3,4-dichlorophenylimi-no)pyrrolidine; clenpyrin; FB b-6896).
Clenpyrin* *see* Clenpirin.
'Cleocin' *see* Clindamycin.
'Cleosin' *see* Clindamycin.
'Cleregil' *see* Deanol aceglumate.
CLETOQUINE*** (7-chloro-4-[4-(2-hydroxy-ethylamino)-1-methylbutylamino]quinoline; 2-[[4-(7-chloroquinolin-4-yl)amino]pentylamino]-ethanol).
'Cliacil' *see* Penicillin V.
CLIBUCAINE*** (2',4'-dichloro-3-piperid-1-yl-butyranilide).
CLIDANAC*** (6-chloro-5-cyclohexyl-1-indan-carboxylic acid; TAI-284).
CLIDINIUM BROMIDE*** (3-hydroxy-1-meth-

ylquinuclidinium bromide benzilate; Ro 2-3773). *See also under* Bromazepam; Chlordiazepoxide.

'Clift' *see* Meproscillarin.

CLIMAZOLAM** (8-chloro-6-(*o*-chlorophenyl)-1-methyl-4*H*-imidazo[1,5-*a*][1,4]benzodiazepine).

CLIMBAZOLE** (1-[(*p*-chlorophenoxy)-1-imidazol-1-yl]-3,3-dimethyl-2-butanone; 1-[(*p*-chlorophenoxy)(pivaloyl)methyl]imidazole; BAY e-6975; MEB-6401).

CLIMIQUALINE*** (3-chloro-1-imidazol-1-yl-4-phenylisoquinoline; 1-(3-chloro-4-phenylisoquinolin-1-yl)imidazole).

CLINDAMYCIN*** (methyl 7-chloro-6,7,8-trideoxy-6-(*trans*-1-methyl-4-propyl-L-2-pyrrolidinecarboxamido)-1-thio-L-*threo*-α-D-*galacto*-octopyranoside; chlorolincomycin; clinimycin; clindamycin hydrochloride; clinidamycin phosphate; U-21251; U-28508; 'cleocin'; 'cleosin'; 'dalacin C'; 'sobelin').

Clindamycin hexadecanoate *see* Clindamycin palmitate.

CLINDAMYCIN PALMITATE (clindamycin hexadecanoate; clindamycin palmitate hydrochloride; U-25179E).

'Clinibolin' *see* Nandrolone laurate.

Clinimycin *see* Clindamycin.

'Clinimycin' *see* Oxytetracycline.

'Clinium' *see* Lidoflazine.

CLINOFIBRATE*** (2,2'-[cyclohexylidenebis(*p*-phenyleneoxy)]bis[2-methylbutyric acid]).

CLINOLAMIDE** (*N*-cyclohexyllinoleamide; linolexamide; AC-32).

'Clinoril' *see* Sulindac.

'Clinovir' *see* Medroxyprogesterone acetate.

CLIOQUINOL** (5-chloro-7-iodo-8-quinolinol; chinoform; chloroiodoquine; iodochlorhydroxyquin; iodochlorhydroxyquinoline; quiniodochlor; quinoform).

CLIOQUINOL plus ASCORBIC ACID ('oralcer').

CLIOQUINOL plus CHLOROQUINE DIPHOSPHATE & CLIOQUINOL TETRACYCLINE ('tequinophil').

CLIOQUINOL plus FRAMYCETIN ('fraquinol').

CLIOQUINOL plus HYDROCORTISONE ('dioderm-C').

CLIOQUINOL plus PHANQUINONE & OXYPHENONIUM BROMIDE ('mexaform').

CLIOXANIDE*** (2-acetoxy-4'-chloro-3,5-diiodobenzanilide; 4'-chloro-3,5-diiodosalicylanilide acetate; CI-633; CN-58567; SYD-230).

CLIPROFEN*** (3-chloro-4-(2-thenoyl)hydratropic acid; 2-[3-chloro-4-(thien-2-ylcarbonyl)phenyl]propionic acid; 3-chloro-α-methyl-4-(2-thienylcarbonyl)benzeneacetic acid; R-25160).

'Cliquinol' *see* Clioquinol.

'Cliradon' *see* Ketobemidone.

'Clistin' *see* Carbinoxamine.

'Clitizina' *see* Menazone.

CLOBAZAM*** (7-chloro-1-methyl-5-phenyl-1*H*-1,5-benzodiazepine-2,4(3*H*,5*H*)-dione; chlorepin; clorepin; HR-376; HR-4723; LM-2717; RU-4723; 'frisium'; 'urbadan'; 'urbanyl').

CLOBAZAM plus NOMIFENSINE MALEATE (HOE-8476; 'psyton').

'Clobber' *see* Cypromid.

Clobedol *see* Clonitazene.

Clobenfurol *see* Cloridarol.

Clobenmetamide *see* Fominoben.

CLOBENOSIDE*** (ethyl 5,6-bis-*O*-(*p*-chlorobenzyl)-3-*O*-propyl-D-glucofuranoside).

CLOBENZEPAM*** (7-chloro-10-(2-dimethylaminoethyl)-5,10-dihydro-11*H*-dibenzo[*b*,*e*][1,4]diazepin-11-one; clobenzepam hydrochloride; 'tarpane').

CLOBENZOREX*** ((+)-*N*-(*o*-chlorobenzyl)-α-methylphenethylamine; *N*-(*o*-chlorobenzyl)dexamphetamine; SD-271-12).

CLOBENZTROPINE*** (3-(*p*-chloro-α-phenylbenzyloxy)tropane; chlorobenztropine; clobenztropine hydrochloride; FC-1; SL-6057).

CLOBENZTROPINE METHOBROMIDE (SL-6058).

CLOBETASOL*** (21-chloro-9α-fluoro-11β,17α-dihydroxy-16α-methylpregna-1,4-diene-3,20-dione).

CLOBETASOL PROPIONATE (clobetasol 17-propionate; GR2/925; 'dermovate'; 'dermoxin').

CLOBETASONE*** (21-chloro-9α-fluoro-17α-hydroxy-16β-methylpregna-1,4-diene-3,11,20-trione).

CLOBETASONE BUTYRATE (clobetasone 17-butyrate; GR2/1214; 'emovate'; 'eumovate').

CLOBETASONE BUTYRATE plus NYSTATIN ('trimovate').

CLOBUTINOL*** (*p*-chloro-α-(2-dimethylamino-1-methylethyl)-α-methylphenethyl alcohol; 1-(*p*-chlorophenyl)-4-dimethylamino-2,3-dimethyl-2-butanol; chlorodimenol; KAT-256; 'silomat').

CLOBUZARIT*** (2-[(4'-chlorobiphenyl-4-yl)methoxy]-2-methylpropionic acid; 3-[α-(*p*-chlorophenyl)benzyloxy]-2-methylpropionic acid; ICI-55897; 'clozic').

CLOCANFAMIDE*** (*p*-chloro-*N*-(2-hydroxyethyl)-*N*-(3-methylnorborn-2-ylmethyl)benzamide; *N*-(*p*-chlorobenzoyl)-*N*-(2-hydroxyethyl)-3-methyl-2-norbornanemethylamine; chlorocamphamide; chlorocanfamide; clorocanfamide).

CLOCAPRAMINE*** (5-[3-(4-carbamoyl-4-piperid-1-ylpiperid-1-yl)propyl]-3-chloro-10,11-dihydro-5*H*-dibenz[*b*,*f*]azepine; 1'-[3-(3-chloro-10,11-dihydro-5*H*-dibenz-[*b*,*f*]azepin-5-yl)propyl][1,4'-bipiperidine]-4'-carboxamide; Y-4153).

Clochinate *see* Cloquinate.

CLOCIGUANIL*** (4,6-diamino-1-(3,4-dichlorobenzyloxy)-1,2-dihydro-2,2-dimethyl-*s*-triazine; BRL-50216; WR-38839).

CLOCINIZINE*** (1-(*p*-chloro-α-phenylbenzyl)-4-cinnamylpiperazine; chlorcinnazine).

CLOCORTOLONE*** (9-chloro-6α-fluoro-11β,21-dihydroxy-16α-methylpregna-1,4-diene-3,20-dione).

CLOCORTOLONE ACETATE* (clocortolone 21-acetate; SH-818).

CLOCORTOLONE PIVALATE* (clocortolone 21-pivalate; clocortolone trimethylacetate; CL-68; SH-863; 'purantix').

Clocortolone trimethylacetate *see* Clocortolone pivalate.

CLOCOUMAROL** (3-[*p*-(2-chloroethyl)-α-propylbenzyl]-4-hydroxycoumarin; 3-[1-[*p*-(2-chloroethyl)phenyl]butyl]-4-hydroxycoumarin; DB-112).

CLODACAINE** (2'-chloro-2-[(2-diethylaminoethyl)ethylamino]acetanilide).

CLODANOLENE** (1-[[5-(3,4-dichlorophenyl)-furfurylidene]amino]hydantoin; clodanolene sodium; F-413; F-605).

Clodantocide* *see* Clodantoin.

CLODANTOIN** (5-(1-ethylpentyl)-3-(trichloromethylthio)hydantoin; chlordantoin; clodantocide; 'sporostacin').

CLODAZON** (5-chloro-1-(3-dimethylaminopropyl)-3-phenyl-2-benzimidazolinone; clodazon hydrochloride; AW-142446; HUF-2446).

CLODOXOPONE** (4-(*p*-chlorophenyl)-5-[2-(4-phenylpiperazin-1-yl)ethyl]-1,3-dioxol-2-one; LR-19731).

CLODRONIC ACID** (dichloromethane diphosphonic acid; (dichloromethylene)bis(phosphonic acid); (dichloromethylene)diphosphonic acid).

CLOFAZIMINE** (3-(*p*-chloroanilino)-10-(*p*-chlorophenyl)-2,10-dihydro-2-isopropyliminophenazine; riminophenazine; B-663; G-30320; NSC-141046; 'lamprene').

CLOFEDANOL** (2-chloro-α-(2-dimethylaminoethyl)benzhydrol; 1-(*o*-chlorophenyl)-3-dimethylamino-1-phenyl-1-propanol; chlophedianol; chlorphediol; clofedanol hydrochloride; Bayer-186; SK-74; SL-501).

CLOFEDANOL NOSCAPINE SUCCINATE (double succinate of clofedanol and noscapine; 'H-dulapine').

Clofelin (tr) *see* Clonidine.

CLOFENAMIC ACID** (*N*-(2,3-dichlorophenyl)anthranilic acid).

CLOFENAMIDE** (4-chloro-1,3-benzenedisulfonamide; monochlorphenamide).

Clofenapate *see* Methyl clofenapate.

CLOFENCICLAN** (2-[1-(*p*-chlorophenyl)-cyclohexyloxy]triethylamine; chlorphencyclan hydrochloride; KSW-786).

CLOFENETAMINE** (2-(*p*-chloro-α-methyl-α-phenylbenzyloxy)triethylamine).

Clofenotane** *see* DDT.

Clofenoxine *see* Meclofenoxate.

CLOFENOXYDE** (4',4'''-oxybis(2-chloroacetophenone)).

Clofenpyride *see* Nicofibrate.

CLOFENVINFOS** (2-chloro-1-(2,4-dichlorophenyl)vinyl diethyl phosphate; chlorfenvinphos; ENT-24969; GC-4072; SD-7859; 'birlane'; 'sapecron'; 'supona').

CLOFEVERINE** (1-(*p*-chlorophenoxymethyl)-1,2,3,4-tetrahydro-6,7-isoquinolinediol).

CLOFEXAMIDE** (2-(*p*-chlorophenoxy)-*N*-(2-diethylaminoethyl)acetamide; ANP-146).

CLOFEZONE** (equimolecular combination of clofexamide and phenylbutazone; ANP-3260).

CLOFIBRATE** (ethyl 2-(*p*-chlorophenoxy)-2-methylpropionate; ethyl clofibrate; klofibrat; chlorfenisate; chlorphenisate; CPIB; AY-61123; ICI-28257; NSC-79389).

CLOFIBRATE plus ANDROSTERONE ('atromid').

CLOFIBRATE plus DIPYRIDAMOLE ('persantinal').

CLOFIBRATE plus GLYCOSAMINOGLYCAN POLYSULFATE ('sinteroid').

CLOFIBRATE plus INOSITOL NICOTINATE ('angiokapsul').

CLOFIBRATE plus INOSITOL NICOTINATE & NICOTINIC ACID ('duplinal').

CLOFIBRATE plus NICOTINYL ALCOHOL ('liapten').

CLOFIBRATE plus PRACTOLOL ('eramid').

CLOFIBRIC ACID** (2-(*p*-chlorophenoxy)-2-methylpropionic acid; α-(*p*-chlorophenoxy)isobutyric acid; 'normolipem').

See also Binifibrate; Clofibrate; Clofibride; Dulofibrate; Etofibrate;Nicofibrate; Picafibrate; Salafibrate; Serfibrate; Simfibrate; Sitofibrate;Tiafibrate; Tocofibrate; Xantifibrate *and under* Aluminium; Calcium; Cinnarizine; Etofylline; Magnesium.

CLOFIBRIDE** (3-(dimethylcarbamoyl)propyl clofibrate; 4-hydroxy-*N*,*N*-dimethylbutyramide ester of clofibric acid; Mg-46; 'lipenan').

CLOFILIUM PHOSPHATE** (4-chloro-*N*,*N*-diethyl-*N*-heptylbenzenebutanaminium phosphate; [4-(*p*-chlorophenyl)butyl]diethylheptylammonium phosphate; LY-150378).

'Clofinit' *see* Clofibrate.

Clofinol *see* Nicofibrate.

'Clofipront' *see* Clofibrate.

'Clofiral' *see* Clofibrate.

'Clofirem' *see* Clofibrate.

Cloflucarban* *see* Halocarban.

CLOFLUPEROL** (4-[4-(*p*-chloro-α,α,α-trifluoro-*m*-tolyl)-4-hydroxypiperid-1-yl]-4'-fluorobutyrophenone; seperidol; seperidol hydrochloride; R-9298).

CLOFOCTOL** (2-(2,4-dichlorobenzyl)-4-(1,1,3,3-tetramethylbutyl)phenol; α-(2,4-dichlorophenyl)-4-(1,1,3,3-tetramethylbutyl)-*o*-cresol; 'octofene').

CLOFOREX** (ethyl (*p*-chloro-α,α-dimethylphenethyl)carbamate; ethyl [2-(*p*-chlorobenzyl)-prop-2-yl]carbamate; D-237).

CLOFURAC** (5-chloro-6-cyclohexyl-2(3*H*)-benzofuranone).

CLOGESTONE** (6-chloro-3β,17-dihydroxy-pregna-4,6-dien-20-one).

CLOGESTONE ACETATE* (clogestone diacetate; AY-11440).

CLOGUANAMIL** (1-amidino-3-(3-chloro-4-cyanophenyl)urea; 1-(*N*-(3-chloro-4-cyanophenyl)carbamoyl]guanidine; cloguanamile; BW-57C65).

Cloguanamile* *see* Cloguanamil.
CLOMACRAN*** (2-chloro-9-(3-dimethylamino-propyl)acridan; clomacran phosphate; SK&F-14336; 'devryl').
'Clomag' *see* Magnesium clofibrate.
CLOMEGESTONE*** (6-chloro-17-hydroxy-16α-methylpregna-4,6-diene-3,20-dione; 16α-methylchlormadinone).
CLOMEGESTONE ACETATE* (SH-741).
Clometacillin (tr) *see* Clometocillin.
CLOMETACIN*** (3-(p-chlorobenzoyl)-6-methoxy-2-methyl-1-indoleacetic acid; mindolic acid; C-1656; R-3939; 'duperan').
CLOMETERONE*** (6α-chloro-16α-methyl-pregn-4-ene-3,20-dione; 6α-chloro-16α-methyl-progesterone; clometherone).
Clometherone* *see* Clometerone.
CLOMETHIAZOLE*** (5-(2-chloroethyl)-4-methylthiazole; chlormethiazole; chlorethiazole; hemithiamine).
CLOMETHIAZOLE EDISILATE (clomethiazole edisylate; clomethiazole ethanedisulfonate; hemitiamine).
CLOMETOCILLIN*** (3,4-dichloro-α-methoxy-benzylpenicillin; 6-[2-(3,4-dichlorophenyl)-2-methoxyacetamido]penicillanic acid; clometacillin; clometocillin potassium).
'Clomid' *see* Clomifene.
Clomide *see* Aklomide.
CLOMIFENE*** (2-[p-(2-chloro-1,2-diphenylvinyl)phenoxy]triethylamine; 2-chloro-1-[p-(2-diethylaminoethoxy)phenyl]-1,2-diphenylethylene; α-chloro-α'-[p-(2-diethylaminoethoxy)phenyl]-stilbene; 2-[p-(β-chloro-α-phenylstyryl)phenoxy]-triethylamine; clomiphene; chloramiphene; clomifene citrate; MER-41; MRL-41; NSC-35770).
See also Enclomifene; Zuclomifene.
CLOMINOREX*** (2-amino-5-(p-chlorophenyl)-2-oxazoline; McN-1107).
Clomiphene* *see* Clomifene.
CLOMIPRAMINE*** (3-chloro-5-[3-(dimethyl-amino)propyl]-10,11-dihydro-5H-dibenz[b,f]-azepine; chloroimipramine; chlorimipramine; monochlorimipramine; clomipramine hydrochloride; G-34586).
CLOMIZOLE (tr) (4-chloro-1-methyl-5-nitroimidazole).
CLOMOCYCLINE*** (7-chloro-2-N-(hydroxy-methyl)tetracycline; chlormethylenecycline; methylolchlortetracycline).
CLONAZEPAM*** (5-(o-chlorophenyl)-1,3-dihydro-7-nitro-2H-1,4-benzodiazepin-2-one; LA-6; Ro 5-4023; 'clonopin'; 'iktorivil'; 'rivotril').
CLONAZOLINE*** (4-chloro-1-(2-imidazolin-2-ylmethyl)naphthalene; 2-(4-chloro-1-naphthyl-methyl)-2-imidazoline).
CLONIDINE*** (2-[(2,6-dichlorophenyl)imino]-imidazolidine; 2,6-dichloro-N-2-imidazolidinyl-ideneaniline; chlornidine; clofelin; clonidine hydrochloride; DCAI; ST-155; 'catapres'; 'catapresan'; 'dixarit'; 'hemiton'; 'isoglaucon'; 'namestin').
CLONIDINE plus CHLORTALIDONE ('combi-presan').
CLONIDINE plus CYCLOTHIAZIDE ('dima-pres').
CLONITAZENE*** (2-(p-chlorobenzyl)-1-(2-di-ethylaminoethyl)-5-nitrobenzimidazole; clobedol; C-193901).
CLONITRALIDE (niclosamide ethanolamine salt; Bayer-73; 'bayluscide').
CLONITRATE*** (3-chloro-1,2-propanediol dinitrate; chlorohydrin dinitrate; 'bangina'; 'dylate').
CLONIXERIL*** (2,3-dihydroxypropyl 2-(3-chloro-o-toluidino)nicotinate; Sch-12707).
CLONIXIN** (2-(3-chloro-2-methylanilino)nicotinic acid; 2-(3-chloro-o-toluidino)nicotinic acid; Sch-10304).
See also Clonixeril.
'Clonopin' *see* Clonazepam.
'Clont' *see* Metronidazole.
CLOPAMIDE*** (1-(4-chloro-3-sulfamoylbenz-amido)-2,6-dimethylpiperidine; 4-chloro-N-(cis-2,6-dimethylpiperid-1-yl)-3-sulfamoylbenz-amide; chlorsudimeprylum; chlosudimeprimyl-um; closudimeprimyl; DT-327).
See also under Pindolol; Reserpine.
'Clopane' *see* Cyclopentamine.
CLOPENTHIXOL*** (4-[3-(2-chlorothioxan-then-9-ylidene)propyl]-1-piperazineethanol; chlorpenthixol; chlorperphenthixene; AY-62021; N-746; NSC-64087).
cis-Clopenthixol *see* Zuclopenthixol.
Z-Clopenthixol *see* Zuclopenthixol.
CLOPERASTINE** (1-[2-(p-chloro-α-phenyl-benzyloxy)ethyl]piperidine; HT-11; Z-15042; 'hustazol'; 'seki').
CLOPERIDONE*** (3-[3-[4-(m-chlorophenyl)-piperazin-1-yl]propyl]quinazoline(1H,3H)-2,4-dione; cloperidone hydrochloride; MA-1337).
'Clophen' *see* Polychlorinated biphenyl.
CLOPIDOL*** (3,5-dichloro-2,6-dimethylpyrid-in-4-ol; meticlorpindol; 'coyden').
CLOPIMOZIDE*** (1-[4,4-bis(p-fluorophenyl)-butyl]-4-(5-chloro-2-oxobenzimidazolin-1-yl)-piperidine; 1-[1-[4,4-bis(p-fluorophenyl)butyl]-piperid-4-yl]-5-chlorobenzimidazolin-2-one; R-29764).
CLOPIPAZAN*** (4-(2-chloro-9H-xanthen-9-yl-idene)-1-methylpiperidine; 2-chloro-9-(1-methyl-piperid-4-ylidene)xanthene).
CLOPIPAZAN MESILATE (clopipazan mesyl-ate; clopipazan methanesulfonate; SK&F-69634).
CLOPIRAC** (1-(p-chlorophenyl)-2,5-dimethyl-pyrrole-3-acetic acid; BRL-13856; CP 172-AP; 'clopiran').
'Clopiran' *see* Clopirac.
'Clopixol' *see* Zuclopenthixol.
CLOPONONE*** ((±)-2,2-dichloro-N-[2-chloro-1-(p-chlorobenzoyl)ethyl]acetamide; (±)-2,2-di-chloro-N-[p-chloro-α-(chloromethyl)phenacyl]-acetamide).
CLOPONONE plus MYRALACT ('ginetris').
Clopoxide* *see* Chlordiazepoxide.

CLOPREDNOL** (6-chloro-11β,17,21-trihydroxypregna-1,4,6-triene-3,20-dione; RS-4691; 'syntestan').

CLOPROP* (2-(3-chlorophenoxy)propionic acid; 'frutone CPA').

CLOPROSTENOL*** ((±)-(Z)-7-[(1R*,2R*,3R*,5S*)-2-[(E)-(3R*)-4-(m-chlorophenoxy)-3-hydroxy-1-butenyl]-3,5-dihydroxycyclopentyl]-5-heptenoic acid; 16-(3-chlorophenoxy)-9,11,15-trihydroxy-ω-tetranorprosta-5,13-dienoic acid; cloprostenol sodium; ICI-80996; 'estrumate').

CLOPROTHIAZOLE** (5-(3-chloropropyl)-4-methylthiazole).

CLOQUINATE*** (chloroquine di[8-hydroxy-7-iodo-5-quinolinesulfonate]; chloroquine di(7-iodo-8-quinolinol-5-sulfonate); clochinate).

CLOQUINATE plus CHLOROQUINE DI-PHOSPHATE & DIIODOHYDROXYQUIN ('resotren').

CLOQUINOZINE*** (3-(p-chlorobenzyl)octahydroquinolizine; cloquinozine tartrate; QB-1).

Clor.... see also Chlor.....

CLORACETADOL*** (1-(p-acetamidophenoxy)-2,2,2-trichloroethanol; p-(2,2,2-trichloro-1-hydroxyethoxy)acetanilide; β,β,β-trichloro-α-hydroxy-p-acetophenetidide).

CLORACIZIN (tr) (2-chloro-10-(3-dimethylaminopropionyl)phenothiazine; 2-chlorophenothiazin-10-yl 2-dimethylaminoethyl ketone; chloracizin).

Cloral betaine*** see Chloral betaine.

CLORAMFENICOL PANTOTENATE COMPLEX*** (chloramphenicol pantothenate complex; PP-036; 'pantofenicol'; 'pantovernil').

'Cloramin' see Chlormethine.

CLORANOLOL*** (1-(tert-butylamino-3-(2,5-dichlorophenoxy)-2-propanol; GYKI-41099; 'tobanum').

CLORAZEPATE DIPOTASSIUM* (clorazepic acid potassium salt compound with potassium hydroxide; potassium 7-chloro-2,3-dihydro-2-oxo-5-phenyl-1H-1,4-benzodiazepine-3-carboxylate compound (1:1) with potassium hydroxide; clorazepate monopotassium (1:1) compound with potassium hydroxide; dipotassium clorazepate; potassium clorazepate; AB-35616; Abbott 35616; AH-3232; CB-4306; 'mendon'; 'tencilan'; 'tranxene'; 'tranxilene'; 'tranxilium').

CLORAZEPATE MONOPOTASSIUM* (potassium 7-chloro-2,3-dihydro-2-oxo-5-phenyl-1H-1,4-benzodiazepine-3-carboxylate; clorazepic acid potassium salt; monopotassium clorazepate; potassium clorazepate; 'azene').

Clorazepate monopotassium (1:1) compound with potassium hydroxide see Clorazepate dipotassium.

CLORAZEPIC ACID (7-chloro-2,3-dihydro-2,2-dihydroxy-5-phenyl-1H-1,4-benzodiazepine-3-carboxylic acid; 7-chloro-2,3-dihydro-2-oxo-5-phenyl-1H-1,4-benzodiazepine-3-carboxylic acid).

See also Clorazepate dipotassium; Clorazepate monopotassium.

Clordelazine see Chlorpromazine.

'Clordion' see Chlormadinone acetate.

Clorepin see Clobazam.

Cloresolone see Clorexolone.

CLORETATE*** (bis(2,2,2-trichloroethyl) carbonate; clorethate; SK&F-12866).

Clorethate* see Cloretate.

'Clorets' see Cloretate.

'Clorevan' see Chlorphenoxamine.

CLOREXOLONE** (6-chloro-2-cyclohexyl-3-oxo-5-isoindolinesulfonamide; cloresolone; M & B-8430).

CLORGILINE*** (N-[3-(2,4-dichlorophenoxy)-propyl]-N-methylprop-2-ynylamine; clorgyline; M & B-9302).

Clorgyline* see Clorgiline.

CLORIDAROL*** (α-benzofuran-2-yl-p-chlorobenzyl alcohol; 2-benzofuryl p-chlorophenyl carbinol; α-(p-chlorophenyl)-2-benzofuranmethanol; 2-[(p-chlorophenyl)hydroxymethyl]benzofuran; clobenfurol).

CLORIDAROL HEMISUCCINATE ('menacor').

CLORINDANIC ACID*** (7-chloro-4-hydroxy-5-indancarboxylic acid; CHIA).

CLORINDANOL*** (7-chloro-4-indanol; chlorindanol; lanesta; NSC-158565; WIN-19356).

CLORINDIONE*** (2-(p-chlorophenyl)-1,3-indandione; chlopenadion; chlorophenindione; chlorphenindione; G-25766; Mg-2522).

CLORMECAINE*** (2-(dimethylamino)ethyl 3-amino-4-chlorobenzoate).

Clorocanfamide see Clocanfamide.

CLOROFENE** (2-benzyl-4-chlorophenol; 5-chloro-2-hydroxydiphenylmethane; 4-chloro-α-phenyl-o-cresol; clorophene; chlorophene; septiphene; NSC-59989).

Cloronaftina see Chlornaphazine.

CLOROPERONE** (4-(p-chlorobenzoyl)-1-[3-(p-fluorobenzoyl)propyl]piperidine; 4-[4-(p-chlorobenzoyl)piperid-1-yl]-4'-fluorobutyrophenone; cloroperone hydrochloride; AHR-6134).

Clorophene* see Clorofene.

Cloropromazina see Chlorpromazine.

CLOROQUALONE** (3-(2,6-dichlorophenyl)-2-ethylquinazolin-4(3H)-one).

CLOROTEPINE** (8-chloro-10,11-dihydro-10-(4-methylpiperazin-1-yl)dibenzo[b,f]thiepine; 1-(8-chloro-10,11-dihydrodibenzo[b,f]-thiepin-10-yl)-4-methylpiperazine; chloroperathiepine; octoclothepin; 'clotepin').

'Clorpactin' see Oxychlorosene.

CLORPRENALINE*** (o-chloro-α-(isopropylaminomethyl)benzyl alcohol; 1-(o-chlorophenyl)-2-isopropylaminoethanol; chlorprenaline; isoprophenamine; clorprenaline hydrochloride; L-20025).

CLORSULON*** (4-amino-6-(trichlorovinyl)-m-benzenedisulfonamide; 4-amino-6-(trichloroethenyl)benzene-1,3-disulfonamide; MK-401).

Clortalidone see Chlortalidone.

CLORTERMINE*** (o-chloro-α,α-dimethylphenethylamine; SU-10568; 'voranil').

'**Clortran**' *see* Chlorbutol.

CLOSANTEL* (*N*-[5-chloro-4-[(4-chlorophenyl)cyanomethyl]-2-methylphenyl]-2-hydroxy-3,5-diiodobenzamide; 5'-chloro-4'-(*p*-chloro-α-cyanobenzyl)-3,5-diiodo-2'-methylsalicylanilide; 5'-chloro-α⁴-(*p*-chlorophenyl)-α⁴-cyano-3,5-diiodo-2',4'-salicyloxylidide; R-31520).

CLOSILATE(S)* (*p*-chlorobenzenesulfonic acid, esters and salts; closylate(s)).

'**Closina**' *see* Cycloserine.

CLOSIRAMINE* (8-chloro-11-(2-dimethylaminoethyl)-6,11-dihydro-5*H*-benzo[5,6]cyclohepta-[1,2-*b*]pyridine).

CLOSIRAMINE ACETURATE* (closiramine compound with *N*-acetylglycine; Sch-12169).

Clospirazine *see* Spiclomazine.

CLOSTEBOL* (4-chloro-17β-hydroxyandrost-4-en-3-one; 4-chlorotestosterone).

CLOSTEBOL ACETATE* ('macrobin'; 'steranabol'; 'turinabol').

CLOSTEBOL ACETATE plus NEOMYCIN ('trofodermin'; 'trophodermin').

'**Clostilbegyt**' *see* Clomifene.

Closudimeprimyl *see* Clopamide.

Closylate(s)* *see* Closilate(s).

'**Clotam**' *see* Tolfenamic acid.

'**Clotepin**' *see* Clorotepine.

Clothiapine* *see* Clotiapine.

Clothixamide* *see* Clotixamide.

CLOTIAPINE* (2-chloro-11-(4-methylpiperazin-1-yl)dibenzo[*b*,*f*][1,4]thiazepine; clothiapine; HF-2159; W-108/HF-2159).

CLOTIAZEPAM* (5-(*o*-chlorophenyl)-7-ethyl-1,3-dihydro-1-methyl-2*H*-thieno[2,3-*e*]-1,4-diazepin-2-one; Y-6047; 'trecalmo').

CLOTIOXONE* (2-phenyl-4-(trichloromethyl)-Δ²-1,3,4-oxadiazolin-5-one; RP 13607).

CLOTIXAMIDE* (4-[3-(2-chlorothioxanthen-9-ylidene)propyl]-*N*-methyl-1-piperazinepropionamide; clothixamide; clotixamide maleate; NSC-78714; P-4385B).

'**Clotride**' *see* Chlorothiazide.

CLOTRIMAZOLE* (1-(*o*-chloro-α,α-diphenylbenzyl)imidazole; (*o*-chlorophenyl)imidazol-1-yldiphenylmethane; 1-(*o*-chlorotrityl)imidazole; BAY b-5097; FB b-5097; 'canesten'; 'eparol'; 'gyne-lotrimin'; 'kanesten'; 'lotrimin'; 'mycelex'; 'mycosporin'; 'trimysten').
See also under Azidamfenicol.

CLOVOXAMINE* (4'-chloro-5-methoxyvalerophenone (*E*)-*O*-(2-aminoethyl)oxime).

CLOXACEPRIDE* (5-chloro-4-[2-(*p*-chlorophenoxy)acetamido]-*N*-[2-(diethylamino)ethyl]-*o*-anisamide).

CLOXACILLIN* (6-[3-(*o*-chlorophenyl)-5-methylisoxazol-4-ylcarboxamido]penicillanic acid; sodium cloxacillin; cloxacillin sodium salt; BRL-1621; P-25).

CLOXACILLIN plus HETACILLIN ('heclox'; 'varsaclox').
See also under Ampicillin.

'**Cloxamp**' *see under* Ampicillin.

CLOXAZOLAM* (10-chloro-11b-(*o*-chlorophenyl)-2,3,7,11b-tetrahydrooxazolo[3,2-*d*]-[1,4]benzodiazepin-6(5*H*)-one; 'olquadil'; 'sepazon').

CLOXESTRADIOL* (estradiol 17-trichlorohydroxyethyl ether; 3-hydroxy-17β-(2,2,2-trichloro-1-hydroxyethoxy)estra-1,3,5(10)-triene; 17β-(2,2,2-trichloro-1-hydroxyethoxy)estra-1,3,5(10)-trien-3-ol; (2,2,2-trichloro-1-hydroxyethyl) estradiol ether).

CLOXESTRADIOL ACETATE* (cloxestradiol diacetate; 'genovul').

Cloxifenol *see* Triclosan.

CLOXIMATE* ([[(*p*-chloro-α-methylbenzylidene)amino]oxy]acetic acid 2-dimethylaminoethyl ester).

CLOXIQUINE* (5-chloro-8-quinolinol; cloxyquin; chlorhydroxyquinoline; chlorohydroxyquinoline; 'chinoderm'; 'chlorisept'; 'dermofungine-A').
See also Halquinols.

CLOXIQUINE ACETATE (8-acetoxy-5-chloroquinoline; CAQ; chloracetoxyquinoline).

CLOXOTESTOSTERONE* (testosterone trichlorohydroxyethyl ether; 17β-(2,2,2-trichloro-1-hydroxyethoxy)androst-4-en-3-one; (2,2,2-trichloro-1-hydroxyethyl) testosterone ether; cloxotestosterone acetate).

'**Cloxypen**' *see* Cloxacillin.

CLOXYPENDYL* (4-[3-(3-chloro-10*H*-pyrido[3,2-*b*][1,4]benzothiazin-10-yl)propyl]-1-piperazineethanol; D-1262).

Cloxyquin* *see* Cloxiquine.

CLOZAPINE* (8-chloro-11-(4-methylpiperazin-1-yl)-5*H*-dibenzo[*b*,*e*][1,4]diazepine; HF-1854; LX-100-129; W-108/HF-1854; 'leponex').

'**Clozic**' *see* Clobuzarit.

CLY-503 *see* Simfibrate.

'**Clysodrast**' *see* Bisacodyl tannex.

CM-6912 *see* Ethyl loflazepate.

CM-9155 *see* Difluprednate.

CM-9164 *see* Midecamycin.

CMC *see* Carmellose.

CMP *see* Cytidylic acid.

CMP cyclic *see* Cifostodine.

CMPP *see* Mecoprop.

CMU *see* Monuron.

C.N. *see* 2-Chloroacetophenone.

CN-155 *see* Quinocide.

CN-1428 *see* Cyclarbamate.

CN-1883 *see* Acedapsone.

CN-2525-3-2 *see* Phencyclidine.

CN-3123 *see* Co-trifamole.

CN-5834-5931B *see* Triclofenol piperazine.

CN-10395 *see* Ethosuximide.

CN-14329-23A *see* Cycloguanil embonate.

CN-15573-23A *see* Pararosaniline embonate.

CN-15757 *see* Azaserine.

CN-16146 *see* Carbocloral.

CN-17900-2B *see* Clamoxyquine.

CN-20172-3 *see* Benzilonium bromide.

CN-27554 *see* Flufenamic acid.

CN-34799-5A *see* Guanoxyfen.

CN-35355 *see* Mefenamic acid.

CN-36337 *see* Tiamizide.
CN-38474 *see* Alipamide.
CN-38703 *see* Methaqualone.
CN-52372-2 *see* Ketamine.
CN-54521-2 *see* Tiletamine.
CN-55945 *see* Nitromifene.
CN-58567 *see* Clioxanide.
CO-405 *see* Butidrine.
'Coalgan' *see* Calcium alginate.
'Cobadex' *see* Hydrocortisone.
Cobalamins *see* Aquocobalamin; Cyancocobalamin; Hydroxocobalamin; Nitritocobalamin.
'Cobalion' *see* Cobamamide.
Coballamine *see* Cyanocobalamin.
Cobalt edetate *see* Dicobalt edetate.
Cobalt(2+) [(ethylenedinitrilo)tetraacetato]cobaltate(2−) *see* Dicobalt edetate.
COBALTOUS CHLORIDE Co 57* ($Co^{57}Cl_2$; 'cobatope-57').
COBALTOUS CHLORIDE Co 60* ('cobatope-60').
COBAMAMIDE** (inner salt of Co-(5'-deoxyadenosine-5') derivative of 3'-ester of cobinamide phosphate with 5,6-dimethyl-1,α-D-ribofuranosylbenzimidazole; 9-(5'-Co-5'-deoxy-β-D-ribofuranosyl)adenine derivative of α-(5,6-dimethylbenzimidazolyl)cobamide; 5,6-dimethylbenzimidazole-5-deoxyadenosylcobamide; 5,6-dimethylbenzimidazole cobamide coenzyme; dibencozide; adenosylcobamide; coenzyme B_{12}; 5-deoxyadenosylcobamide; dibencocid; dibencozamide; dimebencozamide; LM-176).
Cobamine *see* Cyanocobalamin.
'Coban' *see* Monensin.
'Cobantril' *see* Pyrantel embonate.
'Cobatope-57' *see* Cobaltous chloride Co 57.
'Cobatope-60' *see* Cobaltous chloride Co 60.
'Cobazymase' *see* Cobamamide.
Cobeminum *see* Cyanocobalamin.
'Coben' *see* Picoperine.
'Co-betaloc' *see under* Hydrochlorothiazide.
'Cobex' *see* Dinitramine.
COBH *see* Benquinox.
Cobinamide Co-methyl derivative hydroxide dihydrogen phosphate (ester), inner salt 3'-ester with 5,6-dimethyl-1-α-D-ribofuranosylbenzimidazole *see* Mecobalamin.
COBRA VENOM* ('cobrotoxin'; 'cobroxin'; 'nyloxin').
'Cobrentin' *see* Benzatropine.
'Cobrotoxin' *see* Cobra venom.
'Cobroxin' *see* Cobra venom.
Cocaethyline *see* Homococaine.
COCAINE (3-(benzoyloxy)-2-(methoxycarbonyl) tropane; L-ecgonine 3-benzoate 2-methyl ester; erythroxylin).
COCARBOXYLASE*** (thiamine pyrophosphate; diphosphothiamine; 'berolase'; 'interacton').
'Cocciden' *see* Beclotiamine.
Cocculin *see* Picrotoxin.
CODACTIDE** (1-D-serine-17-L-lysine-18-L-lysinamide-α$^{1-18}$-corticotrophin; Ba-41795).

Codehydrogenase I *see* Nadide.
Codehydrogenase II *see* Nadide phosphate.
CODEINE (7,8-didehydro-4,5α-epoxy-3-methoxy-17-methylmorphinan-6α-ol; methylmorphine; morphine 3-methyl ether; codeine phosphate).
β-Codeine *see* Neopine.
CODEINE METHYL BROMIDE (codeine methobromide; 'eucodin'; 'tecodin'; 'thekodin').
Codeinone (enol) methyl ether *see* Thebaine.
'Codelcortone-TBA' *see* Prednisolone tebutate.
'Codelsol' *see* Prednisolone sodium phosphate.
CO-DERGOCRINE* (mixture of dihydroergocornine, dihydroergocristine & dihydroergocryptine as mesilates or esilates; ergoloid mesylates; dihydroergotoxine; redergam; CCK-179).
CO-DERGOCRINE plus HYPERICIN ('sinedyston').
CO-DERGOCRINE plus LEUCINOCAINE ('bivelin').
CO-DERGOCRINE plus PAPAVERINE ('pol 35'; 'progeril'; 'progeryl').
CO-DERGOCRINE plus THIORIDAZINE (HM-51; 'visergil').
Codethyline *see* Ethylmorphine.
'Codhydrine' *see* Dihydrocodeine.
'Codidoxal' *see under* Doxycycline hyclate.
'Codinovo' *see* Hydrocodone.
'Codixocal' *see under* Doxycycline.
Cod-liver oil fatty acids, sodium salts *see* Sodium morrhuate.
Codorphone* *see* Conorfone.
CODOXIME*** (hydrocodone O-carboxymethyl-oxime).
'Codyl' *see* Codeine.
Coenzyme I *see* Nadide.
Coenzyme II *see* Nadide phosphate.
Coenzyme B_{12} *see* Cobamamide.
Coenzyme Q *see* Ubiquinone(s).
Coenzyme R *see* Biotin.
'Cofacodide' *see* Hydrocodone.
'Cofadicon' *see* Thebacon.
'Cofalaudid' *see* Hydromorphone.
'Coffearine' *see* Trigonelline.
Coffein *see* Caffeine.
COFISATIN*** (oxyphenisatin dehydrocholate (diester)).
'Coflavinase' *see* Flavin mononucleotide.
COFORMYCIN (3,6,7,8-tetrahydro-3-(β-D-erythro-pentofuranosyl)imidazo[4,5-d][1,3]diazepin-8-ol).
'Coforta' *see* Butafosfan.
'Co-fram' *see* Co-trifamole.
COGAZOCINE*** (3-(cyclobutylmethyl)-6-ethyl-1,2,3,4,5,6-hexahydro-11,11-dimethyl-2,6-methano-3-benzazocin-8-ol; 2-(cyclobutylmethyl)-5-ethyl-2'-hydroxy-9,9-dimethyl-6,7-benzomorphan).
'Cogentin' *see* Benzatropine.
'Cogesic' *see* Prodilidine.
'Cohydrin' *see* Dihydrocodeine.
'Colace' *see* Docusate sodium.
'Colalin' *see* Cholic acid.
Colamine *see* Ethanolamine.

Colaspase* see Asparaginase.

'Colcemid' see Demecolcine.

Colchamine see Demecolcine.

COLCHICINE (7-acetamido-6,7-dihydro-1,2,3,10-tetramethoxybenzo[a]heptalen-9(5H)-one; NSC-757).

'Colebenz' see Benzyl benzoate.

'Colebrina' see Iocetamic acid.

COLECALCIFEROL* (9,10-secocholesta-5,7,10(19)-trien-3-ol; cholecalciferol; vitamin D$_3$; natural vitamin D; oleovitamin D$_3$).

'Colectril' see Amiloride.

'Colesterinex' see Pyricarbate.

'Colestid' see Colestipol.

COLESTIPOL* (epichlorohydrin copolymer with diethylenetriamine; polyethylene polyamine polymer with (chloromethyl)oxirane; colestipol hydrochloride; U-26597A; 'colestid').

COLESTYRAMINE* (a styryldivinylbenzene copolymer containing quaternary ammonium groups; cholestyramine; MIC-135).

'Colfarit' see Acetylsalicylic acid.

COLFENAMATE* (N-(α,α,α-trifluoro-m-tolyl)-anthranilic acid ester with glycolamide; flufenamic acid ester with glycolamide; B-557).

COLFORSIN ((3R,4aR,5S,6S,6aS,-10S,10aR,10bS)-dodecahydro-5,6,10,10b-tetra-hydroxy-3,4a,7,7,10a-pentamethyl-3-vinyl-1H-naphtho[2,1-b]pyran-1-one 5-acetate; boforsin).

'Colidon' see Povidone.

'Colidosan' see Sodium ricinoleate.

COLIMECYCLINE* (reaction product of 1 mol. colistin with 3 mol. tetracycline in presence of formaldehyde; colistin tetracycline compound; tetracycline colistin compound; N,N',N'''-tris[[4-(dimethylamino)-1,4,4a,5,5a,6,11,12a-octahydro-3,5,6,10,12,12a-hexahydroxy-6-methyl-1,11-dioxo-2-naphthacenecarboxamido]-methyl]polymyxin E).

'Colimune' see Cromoglicate disodium.

Colimycin (tr) see Neomycin.

'Colimycin' see Colistin.

COLISTIMETHATE SODIUM (product of sulfomethylation of colistin sulfate with formaldehyde and sodium bisulfite; colistin sulfomethate; colistin mesilate; colistin methanesulfonate; W-1929).

COLISTIN (antibiotic from Bac. polymyxa var. colistinus; polymyxin E; colistin sulfate).

Colistin mesilate see Colistimethate sodium.

Colistin methanesulfonate see Colistimethate sodium.

Colistin sulfomethate* see Colistimethate sodium.

Colistin tetracycline compound see Colimecycline.

Collongite see Phosgene.

'Collosol calcium' see Calcium oleate.

'Colofac' see Mebeverine.

'Colofoam' see Hydrocortisone acetate.

'Colomenthol' see Menglytate.

'Colomycin' see Colistin.

'Colo-pleon' see Salazosulfapyridine.

'Colpotrophin' see Promestriene.

'Colprone' see Medrogestone.

COLTEROL* ((±)-α-[(tert-butylamino)methyl]-3,4-dihydroxybenzyl alcohol; N-tert-butyl-noradrenaline; (±)-4-[2-[(1,1-dimethylethyl)-amino]-1-hydroxyethyl]-1,2-benzenediol).

Colterol 3-acetate 4-p-anisate see Nisbuterol.

Colterol 3,4-di-p-toluate see Bitolterol.

COLTEROL MESILATE (colterol mesylate; colterol methanesulfonate (salt); WIN-5563-3).

Colterol mesylate* see Colterol mesilate.

'Coltromyl' see Thiocolchicoside.

'Coly-mycin' see Colistin.

'Combantrin' see Pyrantel embonate.

'Combelen' see Propionylpromazine.

'Combetin' see Strophanthin.

'Combipresan' see under Clonidine.

'Combistrep' see Streptoduocin.

'Comitiadon' see Chlorphenacemide.

'Compazine' see Prochlorperazine.

'Complamex' see Xantinol nicotinate.

'Complamin' see Xantinol nicotinate.

'Complexic acid' see Edetic acid.

'Complexon' see Trisodium edetate.

'Complexon IV' see 1,2-Diaminocyclohexanetetra-acetic acid.

'Comploment' see Pyridoxine.

COMPOUND 48/80 (formaldehyde condensation product of p-methoxy-N-methylphenethylamine; formaldehyde condensation product of N-methylhomoanisylamine; BW-48/80).

Compound 68-198 see Diamfenetide.

Compound 87/90 see Cefalonium.

Compound 87/312 see Nitrocefin.

Compound 469 see Isoflurane.

Compound 497 see Dieldrin.

Compound 1080 see Fluoroacetic acid.

Compound 46083 see Cefazolin.

Compound 48390 see Fosazepam.

Compound 53616 see Frentizole.

Compound 53858 see Fenoprofen.

Compound 56063 see Melizame.

Compound 57926 see Sinefungin.

Compound 64716 see Cinoxacin.

Compound 79891 see Narasin.

Compound 85287 see Nibroxane.

Compound 89218 see Nisoxetine.

Compound 90459 see Benoxaprofen.

Compound 90606 see Isamoxole.

Compound 93819 see Fluretofen.

Compound 99170 see Aprindine.

Compound 99638 see Cefaclor.

Compound 106990 see Nabidrox.

Compound 109514 see Nabilone.

Compound 110140 see Fluoxetine.

Compound 112531 see Vindesine.

Compound 113878 see Ciprefadol succinate.

Compound 113935 see Pentomone.

Compound 122587 see Drobuline.

Compound 133314 see Trioxifene mesilate.

'Compuron' see under Nicotinic acid.

(Cona-4,6-dienin-3β-yl)ethyldimethylammonium iodide see Stercuronium iodide.

'Conadil' see Sultiame.

'Concentrin' see Escin.

130

'Conceptrol' *see* Nonoxinol 9.
Conchinine *see* Quinidine.
'Concurat' *see* Tetramisole.
'Conditio' *see under* Potassium aspartate.
'Conducton' *see* Carazolol.
Conessi bark *see* Kurchi.
CONESSINE*** (3β-(dimethylamino)con-5-ene; neriine; roquessine; wrightine).
'Conestron' *see* Conjugated estrogens equine.
'Confortid' *see* Indometacin.
Congazone sodium* *see* Congo red.
'Congestan' *see under* Azatadine.
Congo blue *see* Trypan blue.
CONGO RED (4,4'-biphenylylbisazo(1-naphthylamine-4-sulfonic acid sodium salt); di-Na salt of 4,4'-bis(1-amino-4-sulfonaphth-2-ylazo)biphenyl; congazone sodium; direct red).
Conicine *see* Coniine.
CONIINE (2-propylpiperidine; cicutine; conicine).
CONJUGATED ESTROGENS plus NORGESTREL ('prempak').
CONJUGATED ESTROGENS plus OXAZEPAM ('ovaribran').
CONJUGATED ESTROGENS EQUINE* (estrogen sulfate; 'conestron'; 'dagynil'; 'menest'; 'premarin'; 'presomen'; 'SK-estrogens'; 'transannon').
'Conjuncain' *see* Oxybuprocaine.
'Conlumin' *see under* Norethisterone.
CONOPHARYNGINE (methyl 12,13-dimethoxyibogamine-18-carboxylate).
CONORFONE*** (17-(cyclopropylmethyl)-4,5α-epoxy-8β-ethyl-3-methoxymorphinan-6-one; codorphone; codorphone hydrochloride; conorfone hydrochloride; TR-5109).
'Conotrane' *see* Hydrargaphen.
'Conova' *see under* Etynodiol diacetate.
'Conovid' *see under* Noretynodrel.
Conquinine *see* Quinidine.
'Conray' *see* Meglumine iotalamate.
'Conray' *see* Iotalamic acid; Meglumine iotalamate; Sodium iotalamate.
'Conray 70' *see under* Meglumine iotalamate.
'Conray FL' *see under* Meglumine iotalamate.
'Conservasept' *see* Propham.
'Constaphyl' *see* Dicloxacillin.
'Contac' *see* Phenylpropanolamine.
'Contamex' *see* Ketazolam.
'Conteben' *see* Thioacetazone.
'Contergan' *see* Thalidomide.
'Continuin' *see* Etynodiol diacetate.
'Contramine' *see* Brocresine.
'Contrapar' *see* Gloxazone.
'Contrathion' *see* Pralidoxime mesilate.
'Contravul' *see* Sultiame.
'Contrical' *see* Aprotinin.
'Contristamine' *see* Chlorphenoxamine.
'Contrix 28' *see* Meglumine iotalamate.
'Contrykal' *see* Aprotinin.
'Contusol' *see* Heparin.
Convallatoxol *see* Strophanthidol L-rhamnoside.
'Convenil' *see* Butetamate.
'Convulex' *see* Valproic acid.

'Coomassie blue' *see* Anazolene sodium.
COPOVITHANE* (copolymer of 2-methylenetrimethylenebis(methylcarbamate) and 1-vinyl-2-pyrrolidone (approx 1:4); BAY i-7433).
Copper etc. *see* Cupr. ... etc.
'Coprol' *see* Docusate sodium.
'Coprolax' *see* Docusate sodium.
COPROSTANE (pseudocholestane).
Coprostanol *see* Coprosterol.
COPROSTEROL (coprostanol; stercorin).
'Coptin' *see* Co-trimazine.
'Co-ral' *see* Coumafos.
'Coramedan' *see* Digitoxin.
'Coramine' *see* Nikethamide.
Corazol (tr) *see* Pentetrazole.
CORBADRINE*** (α-(1-aminoethyl)protocatechuyl alcohol; 3,4-dihydroxynorephedrine; homoarterenol; isoadrenaline; α-methylnoradrenaline; α-methylnorepinephrine; nordefrin; norhomoepinephrine).
(−)-CORBADRINE (levonordefrin; 'neo-cobefrin').
Corconium (tr) *see* Dicholine suberate.
'Cordabromin' *see* Protheobromine.
'Cordalin' *see* Etofylline.
'Cordanum' *see* Talinolol.
'Cordarex' *see* Amiodarone.
'Cordarone' *see* Amiodarone.
Cordiamin *see* Nikethamide.
Cordianin *see* Allantoin.
'Cordilox' *see* Verapamil.
'Cordium' *see* Bepridil.
'Cordoxene' *see* Fenalcomine.
'Cordran' *see* Fludroxycortide.
CORDYCEPIN (adenine 3-deoxyriboside; 3'-deoxyadenosine).
'Coretal' *see* Oxprenolol.
'Corflazine' *see* Lidoflazine.
'Corgard' *see* Nadolol.
'Coriban' *see* Diamfenetide.
Cori ester *see* Glucose 1-phosphate.
'Corindolan' *see* Mepindolol.
'Corinfar' *see* Nifedipine.
Corkonium (tr) *see* Dicholine suberate.
'Corlan' *see* Hydrocortisone sodium succinate.
'Cormelian' *see* Dilazep.
'Cormelian digotab' *see under* β-Acetyldigoxin.
CORMETASONE** (6,6,9-trifluoro-11β,17,21-trihydroxy-16α-methylpregna-1,4-diene-3,20-dione; 6,6,9-trifluoro-16α-methylprednisolone; cormethasone).
CORMETASONE ACETATE (cormetasone 21-acetate; cormethasone acetate; RS-3694R).
Cormethasone* *see* Cormetasone.
'Cornocentin' *see* Ergometrine.
'Cornox' *see* 2-(4-Chloro-2-methylphenoxy)acetic acid.
'Cornox CWK' *see* Benazolin.
'Cornox RK' *see* Dichlorprop.
Corn sugar *see* Glucose.
'Corodenin' *see* Actinoquinol.
'Coronamide' *see* Carinamide.
'Corontin' *see* Prenylamine.

'**Corovliss**' *see* Isosorbide dinitrate.

COROXON (3-chloro-4-methylcoumarin-7-yl diethyl phosphate).

'**Corozate**' *see* Ziram.

'**Corrigast**' *see* Propantheline bromide.

'**Corsodyl**' *see* Chlorhexidine gluconate.

'**Cortef-fluid**' *see* Hydrocortisone cipionate.

'**Cortelan**' *see* Cortisone acetate.

'**Cortenema**' *see* Hydrocortisone.

'**Cortenil**' *see* Desoxycortone.

Cortexolone *see* Cortodoxone.

Cortexone *see* Desoxycortone.

'**Corthion**' *see* Parathion.

'**Corticoderm**' *see* Fluprednidene acetate.

CORTICOSTERONE (11β,21-dihydroxypregn-4-ene-3,20-dione; Kendall's compound B; Reichstein's substance H; NSC-9705).

CORTICOTROPHIN* (adrenocorticotrophin; corticotropin; ACTH).
See also Alsactide; Codactide; Norleusactide; Seractide; Tetracosactide; Tosactide;Tricosactide.

Corticotropin* *see* Corticotrophin.

'**Cortifan**' *see* Hydrocortisone.

'**Cortiphenicol**' *see under* Chloramphenicol.

'**Cortiron**' *see* Desoxycortone.

Cortisol *see* Hydrocortisone.

CORTISONE* (11-dehydro-17-hydroxycorticosterone; 17α,21-dihydroxypregn-4-ene-3,11,20-trione; Kendall's compound E; Reichstein's substance Fa; Wintersteiner's compound F; NSC-9703).

CORTISONE ACETATE* ('cortelan'; 'cortistab'; 'cortisyl').

'**Cortistab**' *see* Cortisone acetate.

CORTISUZOL** (11β,17,21-trihydroxy-6,16α-dimethyl-2'-phenyl-2'H-pregna-2,4,6-trieno[3,2-c]pyrazol-20-one 21-(m-sulfobenzoate)).

'**Cortisyl**' *see* Cortisone acetate.

CORTIVAZOL** (11β,17,21-trihydroxy-6,16α-dimethyl-2'-phenyl-2'H-pregna-2,4,6-trieno[3,2-c]pyrazol-20-one 21-acetate; NSC-80998; Ref-185).

CORTODOXONE** (11-deoxycortisone; 11-deoxy-17-hydroxycorticosterone; 11-desoxycortisone; 17,21-dihydroxypregn-4-ene-3,20-dione; 17,21-dihydroxyprogesterone; cortexolone; Reichstein's substance S; NSC-18317; SK&F-3050).

CORTOL (pregnane-3α,11β,17α,20α,20,21-pentol; α-cortol).

α-**Cortol** *see* Cortol.

β-**CORTOL** (pregnane-3α,11β,17α,20β,21-pentol).

CORTOLONE (3α,17α,20α,21-tetrahydroxypregnan-11-one; α-cortolone).

α-**Cortolone** *see* Cortolone.

β-**CORTOLONE** (3α,17α,20β,21-tetrahydroxypregnan-11-one).

'**Cortrosyn**' *see* Tetracosactide.

'**Corva-C**' *see* Oxedrine ascorbate.

'**Corvasymton**' *see* Oxedrine.

'**Corvaton**' *see* Molsidomine.

'**Corverum**' *see under* Diniprofylline.

Corynanthidine *see* Rauwolscine.

Corynine *see* Yohimbine.

'**Cosaldon**' *see under* Pentifylline.

'**Cosalgesic**' *see under* Dextropropoxyphene.

'**Cosban**' *see* 3,5-Xylyl methylcarbamate.

'**Coscopine**' *see* Noscapine.

'**Coscotabs**' *see* Noscapine.

'**Cosmegen**' *see* Dactinomycin.

'**Co-soltrim**' *see under* Trimethoprim.

Cosyntropin* *see* Tetracosactide.

'**Cotazym**' *see* Pancrelipase.

CO-TETROXAZINE* (tetroxoprim plus sulfadiazine (1:25); 'sterinor'; 'tibirox').

'**Cothera**' *see* Dimethoxanate.

'**Cotinazin**' *see* Isoniazid.

COTININE* ((−)-1-methyl-5-pyrid-3-ylpyrrolidin-2-one).

COTININE FUMARATE* (cotinine compound (2:1) with fumaric acid; 'scotine').

'**Cotofor**' *see* Dipropetryn.

'**Cotoran**' *see* Fluometuron.

'**Cotrane**' *see* Dimethoxanate.

CO-TRIFAMOLE* (trimethoprim plus sulfamoxole; CN-3123; 'co-fram'; 'supristol').

CO-TRIMAZINE* (trimethoprim plus sulfadiazine; 'coptin'; 'nibrisin'; 'scorprin'; 'septuryl').

CO-TRIMOXAZOLE* (trimethoprim plus sulfamethoxazole; Ro 6-2580/11).

COTRIPTYLINE* (3-(10,11-dihydro-5H-dibenzo[a,d]cyclohepten-5-ylidene)-1-dimethylamino-2-propanone; 5-[3-(dimethylamino)-2-oxopropylidene]-10,11-dihydro-5H-dibenzo[a,d]cycloheptene).

COUMACHLOR (3-(α-acetonyl-p-chlorobenzyl)-4-hydroxycoumarin; 3-[2-acetyl-1-(p-chlorophenyl)ethyl]-4-hydroxycoumarin; 3-[1-(4-chlorophenyl)-3-oxobutyl]-4-hydroxy-2H-1-benzopyran-2-one; 'ratilan'; 'tomorin').

'**Coumadin**' *see* Warfarin.

Coumafene *see* Warfarin.

COUMAFOS* (O-(3-chloro-4-methyl-1-oxo-2H-1-benzopyran-7-yl) O,O-diethyl phosphorothioate; O-(3-chloro-4-methylcoumarin-7-yl) O,O-diethyl phosphorothioate; coumaphos; Bayer 21199; 'asuntol'; 'baymix'; 'co-ral'; 'muscatox'; 'negasunt'; 'resitox').

COUMAFURYL* (3-(α-acetonylfurfuryl)-4-hydroxycoumarin; 3-(2-acetyl-1-furan-2-ylethyl)-4-hydroxycoumarin; 3-(1-furan-2-yl-3-oxobutyl)-4-hydroxy-2H-1-benzopyran-2-one; coumafuryl sodium; fumarin; furmarin; tomarin; 'fumasol').

COUMAMYCIN** (5-methylpyrrole-2-carboxylic acid diester with 3,3'-[(3-methylpyrrole-2,4-diyl)bis(carbonylimino)]bis[4-hydroxy-8-methyl-7-[(tetrahydro-3,4-dihydroxy-5-methoxy-6,6-dimethylpyran-2-yl)oxy]coumarin]; coumermicin; cumamycin; NSC-107412).

Coumaphos* *see* Coumafos.

Coumaran-3-one-2-spiro-1'-(cyclohex-2'-en-4'-one) *see* Gris-2'-ene-3,4'-dione.

o-**Coumaric acid** *see* trans-o-Hydroxycinnamic acid.

p-**Coumaric acid** *see* p-Hydroxycinnamic acid.

132

COUMARILIC ACID (2-benzofurancarboxylic acid; coumarylic acid).
COUMARIN (2H-1-benzopyran-2-one; benzo-α-pyrone; 2H-chromen-2-one; coumarinic acid lactone; coumarinic anhydride; cumarin; Tonka bean camphor).
COUMARIN plus TROXERUTIN ('venalot'). See also Melilotus officinalis extract.
Coumarinic acid see cis-o-Hydroxycinnamic acid.
Coumarinic acid lactone see Coumarin.
Coumarinic anhydride see Coumarin.
Coumarone see Benzofuran.
Coumarylic acid see Coumarilic acid.
COUMATETRALYL* (4-hydroxy-3-(1,2,3,4-tetrahydronaphth-1-yl)coumarin; 'racumin').
COUMAZOLINE*** (2-ethyl-3-(2-imidazolin-2-ylmethyl)benzofuran; 2-(2-ethylbenzofuran-3-ylmethyl)-2-imidazoline; L-5818).
Coumermycin* see Coumamycin.
COUMESTROL (2-(2,4-dihydroxyphenyl)-6-hydroxy-3-benzofurancarboxylic acid δ-lactone).
COUMETAROL*** (3,3'-(2-methoxyethylidene)-bis(4-hydroxycoumarin); cumetarol; cumetharol; cumethoxethan).
COUMITHOATE* (3-[(diethoxyphosphinothioyl)oxy]-6-oxo-6H-dibenzo[b,d]pyran; O,O-diethyl O-(3,4-tetramethylenecoumarin-7-yl) phosphorothioate; O,O-diethyl O-(7,8,9,10-tetrahydro-6-oxo-6H-dibenzo[b,d]pyran-3-yl phosphorothioate; 'chromaphon'; 'dition').
'Covalan' see Folescutol.
'Covatin' see Captodiame.
'Covatix' see Captodiame.
'Coxigon' see Benoxaprofen.
'Coxytrol' see Ciproquinate.
'Coyden' see Clopidol.
Cozymase see Nadide.
'Cozyme' see Dexpanthenol.
CP3H see Xibornol.
CP-73 see Norclostebol acetate.
CP 172-AP see Clopirac.
CP-271B see Talampicillin.
CP-1044-J3 see Bufexamac.
CP-1551-S see Milacemide.
CP-10188 see Fenclonine.
CP-10308-8 see Quinprenaline.
CP-10423-16 see Pyrantel embonate.
CP-10423-18 see Pyrantel.
CP-11332-1 see Quinazosin.
CP-12009-18 see Morantel tartrate.
CP-12252-1 see Tiotixene.
CP-12299-1 see Prazosin.
CP-12521-1 see Piquizil.
CP-12574 see Tinidazole.
CP-13608 see Tesicam.
CP-14368-1 see Lometraline.
CP-14445 see Oxantel.
CP-14445-16 see Oxantel embonate.
CP-14815-1 see Hoquizil.
CP-15464 see Carindacillin.
CP-15467-61 see Lithium carbonate.
CP-15639-2 see Carbenicillin.
CP-15973 see Sudoxicam.

CP-16171 see Piroxicam.
CP-16533-1 see Verapamil.
CP-18524 see Tibric acid.
CP-19106-1 see Trimazosin.
CP-22341 see Temodox.
CP-22665 see Flumizole.
CP-24314-1 see Pirbuterol.
CP-24314-14 see Pirbuterol acetate.
CP-24877 see Drinidene.
CP-25673 see Tiazuril.
CP-26154 see Tolimidone.
CP-27634 see Gliamilide.
CP-28720 see Glipizide.
CP-31081 see Polydextrose.
CP-32387 see Pirolate.
CP-33994-2 see Pirbenicillin.
CP-34089 see Sulprostone.
CP-36584 see Flutroline.
CP-38754 see Plauracin.
CP-44001 see Nantradol.
CP-45634 see Sorbinil.
CP-45899 see Sulbactam.
CP-47904 see Sulbactam pivoxil.
CP-48810-27 see Fanetizole mesilate.
CP-48867-09 see Ristianol.
CP-49952 see Sultamicillin.
CP-50556 see Levonantradol.
CP-51974 see Sertraline.
CP-52640 see Cefoperazone.
p-CPA see Fenclonine.
4-CPA see 2-(p-Chlorophenoxy)acetic acid.
CPAS see Chlorfenethol.
CPBS see Fenson.
CPCBS see Chlorfenson.
CPIB see Clofibrate.
'C-quens' see under Chlormadinone acetate.
CR-242 see Proglumide.
CR-242-B see under Proglumide.
CR-604 see Proglumetacin dimaleate.
CR-605 see Tiropramide.
CR-1639 see Dinocap.
'Crab-e-rad' see Disodium methanearsonate.
'Crabgrass killer' see Disodium methanearsonate.
'Crasnitin' see Asparaginase.
CRD-401 see Diltiazem.
Cream of tartar see Potassium hydrogen tartrate.
'Creatergyl' see Fosfocreatinine.
CREATINE (N-guanyl-N-methylglycine; methylglycocyamine; methylguanidoacetic acid).
CREATINEPHOSPHORIC ACID (N-[imino-(phosphonoamino)methyl]-N-methylglycine; N-(phosphonoamidino)sarcosine; creatine phosphate; phosphagen; phosphocreatine; phosphorylcreatine).
CREATININE (2-imino-1-methyl-4-imidazolin-one; 1-methylglycocyamidine; 1-methylhydantoin-2-imide).
Creatininephosphoric acid see Fosfocreatinine.
CREATINOLFOSFATE*** (1-(2-hydroxyethyl)-1-methylguanidine dihydrogen phosphate ester).
CREOSOL (2-methoxy-4-methylphenol; 2-methoxy-p-cresol; 4-methylguaiacol).
'Cresatin' see m-Cresyl acetate.

'**Crescormon**' *see* Human growth hormone.

CRESOL(S) (cresylic acid; hydroxytoluene(s); methylphenol(s)).
See also Tricresol; Tricresyl phosphate.

m-**Cresolsulfonic acid formaldehyde condensation product** *see* Methylenedi(*m*-cresolsulfonic acid)-polymer.

'**Cresopyrine**' *see* Acetylcresotic acid.

CRESOTAMIDE** (2-hydroxy-3-methylbenz-amide; 3-methylsalicylamide).
See also under Proxifezone.

2,3-Cresotic acid *see* Hydroxytoluic acid.

2,5-CRESOTIC ACID (2-hydroxy-5-methylbenzo-ic acid; 6-hydroxy-*m*-toluic acid; 5-methylsalicyl-ic acid; cresotinic acid; *p*-homosalicylic acid).

Cresotinic acid *see* 2,5-Cresotic acid.

o-**Cresotinic acid** *see* Hydroxytoluic acid.

Cresoxydiol *see* Mephenesin.

'**Crestomicina**' *see* Paromomycin.

m-**CRESYL ACETATE** (acetylmetacresol; meta-cresylacetate; *m*-tolyl acetate).

o-**Cresyl glyceryl ether** *see* Mephenesin.

Cresylic acid *see* Cresol(s).

'**Crillin**' *see* Pentapiperium metilsulfate.

'**Crill(s)**' *see* Polysorbate(s).

CRIMIDINE* (2-chloro-4-(dimethylamino)-6-methylpyrimidine; 2-chloro-*N*,*N*,6-trimethyl-4-pyrimidinamine; 'castrix').

Crinolol *see* Pacrinolol.

'**Crisalbine**' *see* Sodium aurotiosulfate.

CRISANTASPASE* (L-asparagine aminohydrol-ase from *Erwinia chrysanthemi*).

'**Cristerona**' *see* Androstanolone.

'**Cristodigin**' *see* Digitoxin.

CRL-40028 *see* Adrafinil.

'**Crodimyl**' *see* Methylchromone.

'**Crolax**' *see* Docusate sodium.

CROMACATE(S)** ((6-hydroxy-4-methylcou-marin-7-yloxy)acetic acid, esters and salts).

'**Cromadrenal**' *see* Carbazochrome.

CROMESILATE(S)** (6,7-dihydroxycoumarin-4-ylmethanesulfonic acid, esters and salts).

CROMITRILE** (($\pm$)-*p*-[2-hydroxy-3-[[4-oxo-2-(1*H*-tetrazol-5-yl)-4*H*-1-benzopyran-5-yl]oxy]-propoxy]benzonitrile).

'**Cromoformin**' *see* Phenformin.

CROMOGLICATE DISODIUM (cromoglicic acid disodium salt; cromolyn sodium; disodium cromoglycate; sodium cromoglycate; FPL-670; 'colimune'; 'inostral'; 'intal'; 'lomudal'; 'nal-crom'; 'opticrom'; 'rynacrom').

CROMOGLICATE DISODIUM plus CHLOR-PHENIRAMINE ('rinoglin').

CROMOGLICATE DISODIUM plus REPRO-TEROL ('aarane'; 'allergospasmin').

CROMOGLICIC ACID** (1,3-bis(2-carboxy-4-oxobenzopyran-5-yloxy)-2-propanol; 1,3-bis(2-carboxy-4-oxochromen-5-yloxy)propan-2-ol; 5,5'-(2-hydroxytrimethylenedioxy)bis-(4-oxo-4*H*-1-benzopyran-2-carboxylic acid; 4-oxo-4*H*-1-benzopyran-2-carboxylic acid 5,5'-diether (1,3) with glycerol; cromoglycic acid).
See also Cromoglicate disodium.

Cromoglycic acid* *see* Cromoglicic acid.

Cromolyn sodium* *see* Cromoglicate disodium.

'**Cromosil**' *see* Carbazochrome.

'**Croneton**' *see* Ethiofencarb.

'**Cronoformin**' *see* Phenformin.

CROPROPAMIDE** (*N*-[α-(*N*-crotonyl-*N*-pro-pylamino)butyryl]dimethylamine; 2-(crotonyl-propylamino)-*N*,*N*-dimethylbutyramide; *N*-[1-(dimethylcarbamoyl)propyl]-*N*-propylcroton-amide).
See also Prethcamide.

CROSCARMELLOSE** (carmellose cross-linked; croscarmellose sodium).

CROSS-LINKED DEXTRAN ('sephadex').

'**Crotalin**' *see* Rattlesnake venom.

'**Crotamitex**' *see* Crotamiton.

CROTAMITON** (*N*-ethyl-*N*-*o*-tolylcroton-amide; *N*-ethyl-*o*-crotonotoluidide).

CROTETAMIDE** (*N*-[α-(*N*-crotonyl-*N*-ethyl-amino)butyryl]dimethylamine; 2-(crotonylethyl-amino)-*N*,*N*-dimethylbutyramide; *N*-[1-(dimeth-ylcarbamoyl)propyl]-*N*-ethylcrotonamide; cro-tethamide).
See also Prethcamide.

Crotethamide* *see* Crotetamide.

CROTONAMIDE (2-butenamide; ethylideneacet-amide).

Croton-chloral hydrate *see* Butylchloral hydrate.

CROTONIAZIDE** (2-(2-butenylidene)-1-isoniazid; isonicotinic acid 2-butenylidenehydr-azide).

CROTONIC ACID (*trans*-2-butenoic acid; 3-methylacrylic acid).
See also Dinocap.

Crotonolic acid *see* Tiglic acid.

N-**[α-(*N*-Crotonyl-*N*-ethylamino)butyryl]dimethyl-amine** *see* Crotetamide.

2-(Crotonylethylamino)-*N*,*N*-dimethylbutyramide *see* Crotetamide.

N-**[α-(*N*-Crotonyl-*N*-propylamino)butyryl]dimethyl-amine** *see* Cropropamide.

2-(Crotonylpropylamino)-*N*,*N*-dimethylbutyramide *see* Cropropamide.

'**Crotothane**' *see* Dinocap.

CROTOXYPHOS* (α-methylbenzyl 3-hydroxy-crotonate dimethyl phosphate; 1-phenylethyl 3-(dimethoxyphosphinyloxy)-2-butenoate; 'cio-drin'; 'cyodrin'; 'rycovet fly repellent').

Crotylethylbarbituric acid *see* Barotal.

'**Croysulfone**' *see* Dapsone.

CRUFOMATE** (4-*tert*-butyl-2-chlorophenyl methyl *N*-methylphosphoramidate; 2-chloro-4-(1,1-dimethylethyl)phenyl methyl methylphos-phoramidate; 'ruelene').

'**Crylene**' *see* Pentapiperium metilsulfate.

CRYOFLUORANE** (1,2-dichloro-1,1,2,2-tetrafluoroethane; chlorfluoran).

'**Cryogenin**' *see* Phenicarbazide.

'**Cryptocillin**' *see* Oxacillin.

'**Cryptonol**' *see* 8-Quinolinol sulfate.

Crystallinic acid *see* Novobiocin.

CRYSTAL VIOLET* ([4-[bis[*p*-(dimethylamino)-phenyl]methylene]-2,5-cyclohexadien-1-ylidene)-

N-methylmethanaminium chloride; hexamethyl-pararosaniline; methylrosaniline chloride; *p*,*p'*,*p''*-tris(dimethylamino)triphenylmethane chloride; aniline violet; gentian violet; hexamethyl violet).

'Crystocillin' *see* Oxacillin.

'Crystoids' *see* Hexylresorcinol.

'Crystural' *see* Etoxazene.

C.S. *see* *o*-Chlorobenzylidenemalononitrile.

CS-310 *see* Carboquone.

CS-359 *see* Bucumolol.

CS-370 *see* Oxazolam.

CS-611 *see* Bumecaine.

CS-1170 *see* Cefmetazole.

CS-1507 *see* Drostanolone.

CSAG-144 *see* Mebeverine.

CT-871 *see* Bialamicol.

CT-1341 *see under* Alfadolone acetate.

CTAB *see* Cetrimonium bromide.

'C-total' *see under* Mobecarb.

CTR-6110 *see* Nitrodan.

'C-tre' *see* Capobenic acid.

CU-32-085 *see* Mesulergine.

'Cuemid' *see* Colestyramine.

'Cujec' *see* Cuproxoline.

CULARINE (7-methoxy-8-(*p*-methoxyphenoxy)-2-methylisoquinoline).

CUMALDEHYDE (*p*-isopropylbenzaldehyde).

Cumaldehyde thiosemicarbazone *see* Cutizone.

Cumamycin* *see* Coumamycin.

'Cumarene' *see* Dicoumarol.

Cumarin *see* Coumarin.

'Cumarina' *see* Warfarin.

[[(*p*-Cumenylcarbamoyl)methyl]imino]diacetic acid *see* Iprofenin.

Cumetarol* *see* Coumetarol.

Cumetharol* *see* Coumetarol.

Cumethoxethan *see* Coumetarol.

Cumic acid *see* *p*-Isopropylbenzoic acid.

'Cumid' *see* Dicoumarol.

'Cumopyran' *see* Cyclocoumarol.

'Cumopyrin' *see* Cyclocoumarol.

Cupradyl *see* Allocupreide sodium.

'Cupralene' *see* Allocupreide sodium.

Cupralyl *see* Allocupreide sodium.

'Cupramate' *see* Cupric dimethyldithiocarbamate.

CUPREIDINE ((9*S*)-cinchonan-6',9-diol; cinchonan-6',9-diol; 6'-hydroxycinchonine).

CUPREINE ((8α,9*R*)-cinchonan-6',9-diol; cinchonan-6',9-diol; 6'-hydroxycinchonidine; ultraquinine).

'Cuprelon' *see* Allocupreide sodium.

'Cuprenil' *see* Penicillamine.

Cupreol *see* β-Sitosterol.

'Cupri-aseptol' *see* Cupric 2-phenolsulfonate.

CUPRIC CHLORIDE (basic cupric chloride; 'bilitox').

CUPRIC DIMETHYLDITHIOCARBAMATE ('cupramate').

CUPRIC MORRHUATE (cupric salts of cod-liver oil fatty acids; 'gadusan').

CUPRIC 2-PHENOLSULFONATE (2-phenolsulfonic acid cupric salt; cupric sulfocarbolate; 'cu-pri-aseptol').

Cupric sulfocarbolate *see* Cupric 2-phenolsulfonate.

'Cuprimine' *see* Penicillamine.

'Cuprimyl' *see* Cuproxoline.

CUPRIMYXIN** (bis(6-methoxy-1-phenazinol-5,10-dioxidato-*O*¹,*O*¹⁰)copper; Ro 7-4488/1; 'unitop').

'Cuprion' *see* Allocupreide.

CUPROXOLINE*** (bis(dihydrogen 8-hydroxy-5,7-quinolinedisulfinato)copper compound with diethylamine (1:4); cuproxyquinoline diethylamine disulfonate; 'cujec'; 'cuprimyl'; 'dicupreine').

Cuproxyquinoline diethylamine disulfonate *see* Cuproxoline.

Curacaolin *see* Barbaloin.

'Curaglymol' *see* Hexachlorophene.

'Curamil' *see* Pyrazophos.

'Curantyl' *see* Dipyridamole.

Curare *see* Tubocurarine chloride.

Curarexine methylsulfate *see* Laudexium metilsulfate.

'Curaterr' *see* Carbofuran.

'Curatin' *see* Doxepin.

Curling factor *see* Griseofulvin.

'Cutheparin' *see* Magnesium heparinate.

'Cutilene' *see* Mesulfen.

'Cutisan' *see* Triclocarban.

Cutisone *see* Cutizone.

CUTIZONE (tr) (*p*-isopropylbenzaldehyde thiosemicarbazone; cumaldehyde thiosemicarbazone; cutisone; kutizon; SHCH-58).

'Cuvalit' *see* Lisuride maleate.

'Cuxacillin' *see* Amoxicillin.

CV-57533 *see* Xenyhexenic acid.

CV-58903 *see* Xenazoic acid.

CVMP *see* Stirofos.

CY-39 *see* Psilocybine.

CY-116 *see* Aminocaproic acid.

CY-153 *see* Acexamic acid.

CYACETACIDE*** (cyanoacetic acid hydrazide; cyanacetylhydrazide; cyanacetohydrazide; cyacetazide; cyanazide; cyanizide; cyanoethydrazide; AB-42).

Cyacetazide* *see* Cyacetacide.

'Cyaceticid' *see* Cyacetacide.

CYAMEMAZINE*** (2-cyano-10-(3-dimethylamino-2-methylpropyl)phenothiazine; 10-[3-(dimethylamino)-2-methylpropyl]phenothiazine-2-carbonitrile; cyamepromazine; kyamepromazin; RP 7204).

Cyamepromazine* *see* Cyamemazine.

Cyamopsis tetragonoloba polysaccharide *see* Guar gum.

Cyanacetohydrazide *see* Cyacetacide.

Cyanacetylhydrazide *see* Cyacetacide.

Cyanatoacetic acid *see* Cyanoacetic acid.

CYANATRYN (6-[(1-cyano-1-methylethyl)amino]-4-(ethylamino)-2-methylthio-*s*-triazine; WL-63611).

Cyanazide *see* Cyacetacide.

CYANAZINE* (2-chloro-6-(1-cyano-1-methylethylamino)-4-ethylamino-*s*-triazine; 2-[[4-chloro-6-(ethylamino)-1,3,5-triazin-2-yl]amino]-2-methylpropionitrile; SD-15418; WL-19805; 'bladex'; 'fortrol'; 'radikill').

Cyanidol *see* Cianidanol.

Cyanimipramine *see* Cianopramine.

Cyaninoside *see* Cianidanol rutinoside.

Cyanizide *see* Cyacetacide.

7-(2-Cyanoacetamido)cephalosporanic acid *see* Cefacetrile.

7-(2-Cyanoacetamido)-3-(hydroxymethyl)-2-cephem-2-carboxylic acid acetate *see* Cefacetrile.

CYANOACETIC ACID (cyanacetic acid; cyanatoacetic acid; malonic acid mononitrile; malononitrile).

Cyanoacetic acid hydrazide *see* Cyacetacide.

Cyanoacetic acid (quinoxalin-2-ylmethylene)hydrazide N^1,N^4**-dioxide** *see* Ciadox.

2-Cyanoacrylic acid esters *see* Bucrilate; Enbucrilate; Flucrilate; Mecrilate; Ocrilate.

1-[1-(2-Cyanoaziridin-1-yl)-1-methylethyl]-2-aziridinecarboxamide *see* Azimexon.

Cyanobenzene *see* Benzonitrile.

N-(α-Cyanobenzyl)amphetamine *see* Amfetaminil.

O-(α-Cyanobenzylimino) *O,O*-diethyl phosphorothioate *see* Phoxim.

3-[4-[(3-Cyanobenzyl)oxy]phenyl]-5-(methoxymethyl)-2-oxazolidinone *see* Cimoxatone.

CYANOCOBALAMIN*** (5,6-dimethylbenzimidazolylcyanocobamide; cycobemin; vitamin B_{12}; antipernicious anemia factor; aquocobinamide cyanide; coballamine; cobamine; cobeminum; extrinsic factor; LLD factor).

CYANOCOBALAMIN (⁵⁷Co) (radiocyanocobalamin; 'racobalamin-57'; 'rubratope-57').

CYANOCOBALAMIN (⁵⁸Co) (radiocyanocobalamin).

CYANOCOBALAMIN (⁶⁰Co) (radiocycobemin; radiocyanocobalamin; 'rubratope-60').

2-Cyano-1-[2-[[[2-[(diaminomethylene)amino]thiazol-4-yl]methyl]thio]ethyl]-3-methylguanidine *see* Tiotidine.

2-Cyano-1,4-dihydro-6-methyl-4-(*m*-nitrophenyl)-3,5-pyridinedicarboxylic acid 5-isopropyl 3-methyl ester *see* Nivadipine.

2-Cyano-10-(3-dimethylamino-2-methylpropyl)-phenothiazine *see* Cyamemazine.

1-Cyano-3-(1,1-dimethylpropyl)guanidine *see* Guancidine.

2-Cyano-3,3-diphenylacrylic acid esters *see* Etocrilene; Octocrilene.

4-[2-[(5-Cyano-5,5-diphenylpentyl)methylamino]-ethyl]-4methylmorpholinium chloride methochloride *see* Pentacynium chloride.

N-(5-Cyano-5,5-diphenylpentyl)-*N,N,N*′-trimethyl-ethyl-1-ammonium-2-morpholinium chloride *see* Pentacynium chloride.

1′-(3-Cyano-3,3-diphenylpropyl)-1,4′-bipiperidine-4′-carboxamide *see* Piritramide.

1-(3-Cyano-3,3-diphenylpropyl)-4-(2-oxo-3-propionylbenzimidazolin-1-yl)piperidine *see* Bezitramide.

1-(3-Cyano-3,3-diphenylpropyl)-4-phenylisonipecotic acid *see* Difenoxin.

N-[[1-(3-Cyano-3,3-diphenylpropyl)-4-phenylisonipecotoyl]oxy]succinimide *see* Difenoximide.

1-(3-Cyano-3,3-diphenylpropyl)-4-phenylpiperidine-4-carboxylic acid *see* Difenoxin.

1-(3-Cyano-3,3-diphenylpropyl)-4-piperid-1-ylisonipecotamide *see* Piritramide.

1-[1-(3-Cyano-3,3-diphenylpropyl)piperid-4-yl]-3-propionyl-2-benzimidazolinone *see* Bezitramide.

Cyanoethane *see* Propionitrile.

Cyanoethydrazide *see* Cyacetacide.

N-(2-Cyanoethyl)amphetamine *see* Fenproporex.

Cyanoethylene *see* Acrylonitrile.

2-Cyanoethyl *N*-[[(methylamino)carbonyl]oxy]eth-animidothioate *see* Thiocarboxim.

2-Cyanoethyl *N*-(methylcarbamoyloxy)acetimido-thioate *see* Thiocarboxim.

N-(2-Cyanoethyl)-3-methyl-2-quinoxalinecarbox-amide 1,4-dioxide *see* Cinoquidox.

CYANOFENPHOS* (*O*-(*p*-cyanophenyl) *O*-ethyl phenylphosphonothioate; CYP; S-4087; 'surecide').

Cyanoferrates (II) *see* Ferrocyanides.

Cyanoferrates (III) *see* Ferricyanides.

α-Cyano-4-fluoro-3-phenoxybenzyl 3-(β,4-dichloro-styryl)-2,2-dimethylcyclopropanecarboxylate *see* Flumethrin.

α-Cyano-4-fluoro-3-phenoxybenzyl 3-(2,2-dichloro-vinyl)-2,2-dimethylcyclopropanecarboxylate *see* Cyfluthrin.

8-[*cis*-4-Cyano-4-(*p*-fluorophenyl)cyclohexyl]-1-(*p*-fluorophenyl)-4-oxo-1,3,8-triazaspiro[4.5]decane-3-acetamide *see* Icospiramide.

trans-1-[*cis*-4-Cyano-4-(*p*-fluorophenyl)cyclohexyl]-3-methyl-4-phenylisonipecotic acid *see* Cabastine; Levocabastine.

Cyanoformic acid methyl ester *see* Methyl cyanoformate.

δ-Cyano-3,3a,4,5,6,6a-hexahydro-5-hydroxy-4-(3-hydroxy-4-methyl-1-octenyl)-2-*H*-cyclopenta[*b*]-furan-Δ²⁶-valeric acid *see* Nileprost.

2-Cyano-10-[3-(4-hydroxypiperid-1-yl)propyl]-phenothiazine *see* Periciazine.

2α-Cyano-17β-hydroxy-4,4-17-trimethylandrost-5-en-3-one *see* Cyanoketone.

4-Cyano-2-iodo-6-nitrophenol *see* Nitroxinil.

CYANOKETONE (2α-cyano-17β-hydroxy-4,4-17-trimethylandrost-5-en-3-one; WIN-19578).

α-Cyano-6-methylergoline-8β-propionamide *see* Cianergoline.

6-[(1-Cyano-1-methylethyl)amino]-4-(ethylamino)-2-methylthio-*s*-triazine *see* Cyanatryn.

2-Cyano-1-[2-[[(5-methylimidazol-4-yl)methyl]thio]-ethyl]-3-(2-propynyl)guanidine *see* Etintidine.

1-Cyano-2-methyl-3-[2-[[(5-methylimidazol-4-yl)-methyl]thio]ethyl]guanidine *see* Cimetidine.

2-Cyano-10-[3-(4-methylpiperazin-1-yl)propyl]-phenothiazine *see* Cyanperazine.

7-[2-[(Cyanomethyl)thio]acetamido]-7-methoxy-3-[[(1-methyl-1*H*-tetrazol-5-yl)thio]methyl]-2-cephem-2-carboxylic acid *see* Cefmetazole.

Cyanomycin *see* Pyocyanine.

N-(5-Cyano-4-oxo-1(4*H*)-pyrimidinyl)acetamide *see* Ciapilome.

1-Cyano-3-*tert*-pentylguanidine *see* Guancidine.

α-Cyano-*m*-phenoxybenzyl esters *see* Cyhalothrin; Cypermethrin; Cypothrin; Deltamethrin; Fenvalerate.

1-(2-Cyanophenoxy)-3-[(2-indol-3-yl-1,1-dimethylethyl)amino]-2-propanol *see* Bucindolol.

1-(2-Cyanophenoxy)-3-(*tert*-pentylamino)-2-propanol *see* Penirolol.

Cyano(3-phenoxyphenyl)methyl 2-(4-chlorophenyl)-3-methylbutyrate *see* Fenvalerate.

O-(*p*-Cyanophenyl) O,O-dimethyl phosphorothioate *see* Cyanophos.

O-(*p*-Cyanophenyl) O-ethyl phenylphosphonothioate *see* Cyanofenphos.

CYANOPHOS* (*O*-(*p*-cyanophenyl) *O,O*-dimethyl phosphorothioate; CYAP; S4084; 'cyanox').

2-Cyano-1-pyrid-4-yl-3-(1,2,2-trimethylpropyl)guanidine *see* Pinacidil.

N'-**Cyanosulfanilamide** *see* Sulcymide.

5-Cyano-2-thiophenecarboxaldehyde thiosemicarbazone *see* Citenazone.

'Cyanox' *see* Cyanophos.

CYANPERAZINE (2-cyano-10-[3-(4-methylpiperazin-1-yl)propyl]phenothiazine).

'Cyantin' *see* Nitrofurantoin.

CYANURIC ACID (2,4,6-trihydroxy-*s*-triazine; *s*-triazinetriol; tricyanic acid; trihydroxycyanidine).

Cyanurotriamide *see* Melamine.

CYAP *see* Cyanophos.

'Cyasorb 5411' *see* Octrizole.

'Cybis' *see* Nalidixic acid.

CYCASIN (methylazoxymethanol glucoside; MAM).

Cyclacillin* *see* Ciclacillin.

'Cycladiene' *see* Dienestrol.

'Cyclaine' *see* Hexylcaine.

Cyclamate *see* Calcium cyclamate; Sodium cyclamate.

CYCLAMIC ACID* (cyclohexanesulfamic acid; *N*-cyclohexylsulfamic acid; hexamic acid).
See also under Aminophenazone; Calcium; Sodium; Tetracycline.

Cyclamide (tr) *see* Glycyclamide.

Cyclamidomycin *see* Desdanine.

'Cyclamycin' *see* Troleandomycin.

'Cyclan' *see* Calcium cyclamate.

CYCLANDELATE*** (3,3,5-trimethylcyclohexyl mandelate; cyclomandol; BS-572).

Cyclandelate nicotinate *see* Micinicate.

CYCLARBAMATE*** (1,1-cyclopentanedimethanol dicarbanilate; CN-1428).

Cyclazenin *see* Guanacline.

CYCLAZOCINE*** (3-cyclopropylmethyl-1,2,3,4,5,6-hexahydro-6,11-dimethyl-2,6-methano-3-benzazocin-8-ol; 2-cyclopropylmethyl-2'-hydroxy-5,9-dimethyl-6,7-benzomorphan; 3-cyclopropylmethyl-6,11-dimethyl-6,7-benzomorphan-8-ol; NSC-107492; WIN-20740).

CYCLAZODONE*** (2-cyclopropylamino-5-phenyl-2-oxazolin-4-one; LD-3695).

CYCLETHRIN* (3-(2-cyclopenten-1-yl)-2-methyl-4-oxo-2-cyclopenten-1-yl) 2,2-dimethyl-3-(2-methyl-1-propenyl)cyclopropanecarboxylate).

CYCLEXANONE** (2-cyclopenten-1-yl-2-(2-morpholinoethyl)cyclopentanone).

Cyclic AMP *see* Adenosine 3',5'-phosphate.

Cyclic CMP *see* Cifostodine.

Cyclic methylene (4-chloro-*o*-tolyl)dithioimidocarbonate *see* Nimidane.

Cyclindole* *see* Ciclindole.

'Cyclipen' *see* Penimepicycline.

CYCLIRAMINE*** (4-(*p*-chloro-α-pyrid-2-ylbenzylidene)-1-methylpiperidine; NSC-70933; Sch-2544).

CYCLIZINE*** ((±)-1-(diphenylmethyl)-4-methylpiperazine; cyclizine dihydrochloride; BW-47-83).
See also under Dipipanone.

2,2'-Cyclo-1β-D-arabinofuranosylcytosine *see* Ancitabine.

2,2'-Cyclo-ara C *see* Ancitabine.

CYCLOATE (*S*-ethyl cyclohexylethylcarbamidothioate; 'ro-neet').

CYCLOBARBITAL*** (5-cyclohexen-1-yl-5-ethylbarbituric acid; tetrahydrophenobarbital; cyclohexemal; ethylhexabital; hexemal; cyclobarbital calcium).

'Cyclobarbitone' *see* Cyclobarbital.

Cyclobendazole* *see* Ciclobendazole.

CYCLOBENZAPRINE*** ([3-(5*H*-dibenzo[*a,d*]cyclohepten-5-ylidene)propyl]dimethylamine; cyclobenzaprine hydrochloride; MK-130; RP 9715).

'Cyclobral' *see* Cyclandelate.

CYCLOBUTOIC ACID** (3-cyclohexyl-3-hydroxybutyric acid; β-hydroxy-β-methylcyclohexanepropionic acid).

2-Cyclobutylamino-1-(3,4-dihydroxyphenyl)ethanol *see* Norbudrine.

α-Cyclobutylaminomethyl-3,4-dihydroxybenzyl alcohol *see* Norbudrine.

17-(Cyclobutylmethyl)-4,5a-epoxymorphinan-3,6a,14-triol *see* Nalbuphine.

3-(Cyclobutylmethyl)-6-ethyl-1,2,3,4,5,6-hexahydro-11,11-dimethyl-2,6-methano-3-benzazocin-8-ol *see* Cogazocine.

2-(Cyclobutylmethyl)-5-ethyl-2'-hydroxy-9,9-dimethyl-6,7-benzomorphan *see* Cogazocine.

17-(Cyclobutylmethyl)-8β-methyl-6-methylenemorphinan-3-ol *see* Xorphanol.

17-(Cyclobutylmethyl)morphinan-3,14-diol *see* Butorphanol.

12-Cyclobutylmethyl-7,7a,8,9-tetrahydro-3,7a-dihydroxy-6*H*-8,9*c*-iminoethanophenanthro[4,5-*bcd*]furan-5-(4a*H*)-ol *see* Nalbuphine.

N-**Cyclobutylnoradrenaline** *see* Norbudrine.

CYCLOBUTYROL*** (α-ethyl-1-hydroxycyclohexaneacetic acid; 2-(1-hydroxycyclohexyl)butyric acid; cyclobutyrol sodium; 'hebucol').

CYCLOBUTYROL CALCIUM ('lipotrin').

'Cyclocaine' *see* Isobutamben.

'Cyclocapron' *see* Tranexamic acid.

Cyclocarbothiamine *see* Cycotiamine.

CYCLOCOUMAROL* (3,5-dihydro-2-methoxy-

2-methyl-4-phenylpyrano[3,2-c](1)benzopyran-5-one; Link's compound 63; BL-5).

'Cyclocur' *see under* Estradiol valerate.

2,2′-Cyclocytarabine *see* Ancitabine.

Cyclocytidine *see* Ancitabine.

'Cyclodan' *see* Endosulfan.

CYCLOFENIL*** (bis(p-acetoxyphenyl)cyclohexylidenemethane; bis(p-hydroxyphenyl)cyclohexylidenemethane diacetate; 4,4′-(cyclohexylidenemethylene)diphenol diacetate; cyclofenil; F-6066; H-3452; ICI-48213).

Cyclofenyl *see* Cyclofenil.

'Cycloform' *see* Isobutamben.

'Cyclogesin' *see* Isobutamben.

'Cyclogest' *see* Progesterone.

'Cyclogol' *see* Cetomacrogol(s).

CYCLOGUANIL (4,6-diamino-1-(p-chlorophenyl)-1,2-dihydro-2,2-dimethyl-s-triazine; chlorazin; proguanil metabolite).

CYCLOGUANIL EMBONATE*** (cycloguanil compound (2:1) with 4,4′-methylenebis[3-hydroxy-2-naphthoic acid]; chlorguanide triazine pamoate; cycloguanil pamoate; CI-501; CN-14329-23A; NSC-77830; PAM-MR-807-23A; 'camolar').

CYCLOGUANIL EMBONATE plus ACEDAPSONE (CI-564; 'dapolar').

Cycloguanil pamoate* *see* Cycloguanil embonate.

'Cyclogyl' *see* Cyclopentolate.

5-Cyclohepten-1-yl-5-ethylbarbituric acid *see* Heptabarb.

1-Cycloheptyl-3-(p-toluenesulfonyl)urea *see* Heptolamide.

2,5-Cyclohexadiene-1,4-dione *see* p-Benzoquinone.

1,1′-(2,5-Cyclohexadiene-1,4-diylidenedinitrilo)dipyrrole *see* Azarole.

6-(α-D-Cyclohexa-1,4-dienylglycylamino)penicillanic acid *see* Epicillin.

Cyclohexamine *see* Eticyclidine.

CYCLOHEXANE (hexamethylene; hexanaphthene).

cis-**[1,1-Cyclohexanebis(methylamine)](sulfato)platinum** *see* Spiroplatin.

Cyclohexanecarbamic acid 1,1-diphenyl-2-propynyl ester *see* Enpromate.

Cyclohexanehexol *see* Inositol.

Cyclohexanehexol hexaphosphate *see* Phytic acid.

Cyclohexanepentol *see* Quercitol.

Cyclohexanepropionic acid 2-(dimethylamino)ethyl ester *see* Cyprodenate.

Cyclohexanesulfamic acid *see* Cyclamic acid.

Cyclohexemal* *see* Cyclobarbital.

1-Cyclohexene-1,2-dicarboximidomethyl 2,2-dimethyl-3-(2-methylpropenyl)cyclopropanecarboxylate *see* Tetramethrin.

5-(1-Cyclohexen-1-yl)-1,3-dihydro-1-methyl-7-nitro-2H-1,4-benzodiazepin-2-one *see* Menitrazepam.

5-Cyclohexen-1-yl-1,5-dimethylbarbituric acid *see* Hexobarbital.

5-Cyclohexen-1-yl-5-ethylbarbituric acid *see* Cyclobarbital.

(R)-3-Cyclohexenylglyoxylic acid *see* Ketomycin.

p-(1-Cyclohexen-1-yl)hydratropic acid *see* Tetriprofen.

(3-Cyclohexen-1-ylhydroxymethyl)phosphinic acid *see* Fosmenic acid.

N-[p-[[3-(3-Cyclohexen-1-yl)-2-iminoimidazolidin-1-yl]sulfonyl]phenethyl]butyramide *see* Glibutimine.

5-Cyclohexen-1-yl-5-methylbarbituric acid *see* Norhexobarbital.

3-(3-Cyclohexen-1-ylmethyl)-1,8-dimethylxanthine *see* Mexafylline.

17β-Cyclohexen-1-yloxyestra-1,3,5(10)-trien-3-ol propionate *see* Orestrate.

2-(p-(Cyclohexen-1-yl)phenyl)propionic acid *see* Tetriprofen.

1-(3-Cyclohexen-1-yl-3-phenylpropyl)-1-methylpiperidinium methylsulfate *see* Fenclexonium metilsulfate.

Cycloheximide* *see* Cicloheximide.

Cyclohexitol *see* Inositol.

N-[2-[4-[[[(Cyclohexylamino)carbonyl]amino]sulfonyl]phenyl]ethyl]-5-methylpyrazine-2-carboxamide *see* Glipizide.

2-Cyclohexylamino-1-methylethyl benzoate *see* Hexylcaine.

1-Cyclohexylamino-2-propyl benzoate *see* Hexylcaine.

2-(α-Cyclohexylbenzyl-N,N,N′,N′-tetraethyl-1,3-propanediamine *see* Feclemine.

2-(Cyclohexylcarbonyl)-1,3,4,6,7,11b-hexahydro-2H-pyrazino[2,1-a]isoquinolin-4-one *see* Praziquantel.

1-(Cyclohexylcarbonyl)-4-methylpiperazine *see* Pexantel.

N-(Cyclohexylcarbonyl)-3-morpholinosydnone imine *see* Ciclosidomine.

N-[3-(Cyclohexylcarbonyl)propyl]-N-ethyl-p-methoxyamphetamine *see* Secoverine.

3-Cyclohexylcrotonic acid *see* Cicrotoic acid.

1-Cyclohexylcyclohexanecarboxylic acid *see* [Bicyclohexyl]-1-carboxylic acid.

3-Cyclohexyl-6,7-dihydro-1H-cyclopentapyrimidine-2,4(3H,5H)-dione *see* Lenacil.

1-Cyclohexyl-3-[p-[2-(3,4-dihydro-7-methoxy-4,4-dimethyl-1,3-dioxo-2(1H)-isoquinolyl)ethyl]phenylsulfonyl]urea *see* Gliquidone.

N-Cyclohexyl-4-[(1,2-dihydro-2-oxo-6-quinolyl)oxy]-N-methylbutyramide *see* Cilostamide.

N-Cyclohexyl-N′,N″-dimethylenephosphorothioic triamide *see* Hexaphosphamide.

2-Cyclohexyl-3,5-dimethylphenol *see* Cyclomenol.

3-Cyclohexyl-N,N-dimethyl-3-phenylpropylamine *see* Gamfexine.

2-Cyclohexyl-4,6-dinitrophenol *see* Dinex.

Cyclohexylethylcarbamothioic acid S-ethyl ester *see* Cycloate.

1-Cyclohexyl-3-[p-[2-(1-ethyl-4-isopentyloxy-3-methyl-1H-pyrazolo[3,4-b]pyridine-5-carboxamido)ethyl]phenylsulfonyl]urea *see* Glicaramide.

1-Cyclohexyl-4-[ethyl(p-methoxy-α-methylphenethyl)amino]-1-butanone *see* Secoverine.

4-Cyclohexyl-3-ethyl-1,2,4-triazole *see* Hexazole.

Cyclohexyl 4′-[3-(p-fluorobenzoyl)propyl]-1-piperazinecarboxylate *see* Fenaperone.

2-Cyclohexyl-*N*-hexylethylamine *see* Hecylamine.
p-Cyclohexylhydratropic acid *see* Hexaprofen.
3-Cyclohexyl-3-hydroxybutyric acid *see* Cyclobutoic acid.
1-Cyclohexyl-3-[(β-hydroxy-α-methylphenethyl)-amino]-1-propanone *see* Alifedrine.
6-Cyclohexyl-1-hydroxy-4-methylpyridin-2(1*H*)-one *see* Ciclopirox.
2-Cyclohexyl-3-hydroxy-1,4-naphthoquinone *see* Parvaquone.
7-[2-(5-Cyclohexyl-3-hydroxy-1-pentenyl)-3,5-dihydroxycyclopentyl]-5-heptenoic acid methyl ester *see* Alfaprostol.
4-(β-Cyclohexyl-β-hydroxyphenethyl)-1,1-dimethylpiperazinium methylsulfate *see* Hexocyclium metilsulfate.
1-(3-Cyclohexyl-3-hydroxy-3-phenylpropyl)-1-methylpyrrolidinium chloride *see* Tricyclamol chloride.
(3-Cyclohexyl-3-hydroxy-3-phenylpropyl)trimethylammonium chloride *see* Tridihexethyl chloride.
(3-Cyclohexyl-3-hydroxy-3-phenylpropyl)trimethylammonium iodide *see* Tridihexethyl iodide.
2,2'-[Cyclohexylidenebis(*p*-phenyleneoxy)]bis[2-methylbutyric acid] *see* Clinofibrate.
cis-(Cyclohexylidenedimethylenediamine-*N*,*N'*)(sulfato)platinum *see* Spiroplatin.
4,4'-(Cyclohexylidenemethylene)diphenol diacetate *see* Cyclofenil.
1-Cyclohexyl-3-indan-5-ylsulfonylurea *see* Glyhexamide.
2-Cyclohexyl-4-iodo-3,5-xylenol *see* Cicliomenol.
N-Cyclohexyllinoleamide *see* Clinolamide.
Cyclohexylmandelic acid *see* α-Phenylcyclohexaneglycolic acid.
3-Cyclohexyl-3-methylacrylic acid *see* Cicrotoic acid.
1-Cyclohexyl-2-methylaminopropyl 5-ethyl-5-phenylbarbiturate *see* Barbexaclone.
6-(3-(*N*-Cyclohexyl-*N*-methylcarbamoyl)propoxy)-2(1*H*)-quinolinone *see* Cilostamide.
1-(Cyclohexylmethyl)hydrazine *see* Cimemoxin.
1-Cyclohexyl-3-[[*p*-[2-(5-methyl-3-isoxazolecarboxamido)ethyl]phenyl]sulfonyl]urea *see* Glisolamide.
Cyclohexyl 4-methylpiperazin-1-yl ketone *see* Pexantel.
1-Cyclohexylmethylpiperidine *see* Leptacline.
1-Cyclohexyl-2-methyl-1-propanol *see* Cimepanol.
1-Cyclohexyl-*N*-methyl-2-propylamine *see* Propylhexedrine.
1-Cyclohexyl-3-[[*p*-[2-(5-methylpyrazine-2-carboxamido)ethyl]phenyl]sulfonyl]urea *see* Glipizide.
1-Cyclohexyl-2-(2-methylquinolin-4-yl)-3-thiazol-2-ylguanidine *see* Timegadine.
1-Cyclohexyl-3-(*p*-methylthiobenzenesulfonyl)urea *see* Thiohexamide.
2-(8-Cyclohexyloctyl)-3-hydroxy-1,4-naphthoquinone *see* Menoctone.
1-Cyclohexyl-3-[[*p*-[2-(1-oxo-2-isoindolinecarboxamido)ethyl]phenyl]sulfonyl]urea *see* Glisindamide.
p-Cyclohexyloxybenzoic acid methylpiperidylpropyl ester *see* Cyclomethycaine.

4-[(4-Cyclohexyloxycarbonyl)piperazin-1-yl]-4'-fluorobutyrophenone *see* Fenaperone.
1-(*o*-Cyclohexylphenoxy)-3-isopropylamino-2-propanol *see* Exaprolol.
2-(2-Cyclohexyl-2-phenylacetoxyethyl)dimethylsulfonium iodide *see* Hexasonium iodide.
1-(2-Cyclohexyl-2-phenyl-1,3-dioxolan-4-ylmethyl)-1-methylpiperidinium iodide *see* Oxapium iodide.
α-Cyclohexyl-α-phenyl-1-piperidinepropanol *see* Trihexyphenidyl.
2-(*p*-Cyclohexylphenyl)propionic acid *see* Hexaprofen.
α-Cyclohexyl-α-phenyl-1-pyrrolidinepropanol *see* Procyclidine.
N-Cyclohexyl-1-piperazineacetamide *see* Esaprazole.
1-Cyclohexylpropyl carbamate *see* Procymate.
N-Cyclohexylsulfamic acid *see* Cyclamic acid.
5-(Cyclohexylthio)-2-benzimidazolecarbamic acid methyl ester *see* Dribendazole.
α-Cyclohexyl-3-thiopheneacetic acid 2-(hexahydro-1*H*-azepin-1-yl)ethyl ester *see* Cetiedil.
1-Cyclohexyl-3-*p*-toluenesulfonylurea *see* Glycyclamide.
2-Cyclohexyl-3,5-xylenol *see* Cyclomenol.
'Cyclokapron' *see* Tranexamic acid.
CYCLOLEUCINE (1-aminocyclopentanecarboxylic acid; CB-1639; NSC-1026).
Cyclomandol *see* Cyclandelate.
CYCLOMENOL*** (2-cyclohexyl-3,5-xylenol; 2-cyclohexyl-3,5-dimethylphenol).
CYCLOMETHONE (cyclooctadecane-1,10-bis-(trimethylammonium iodide); Lu-274).
CYCLOMETHYCAINE*** (3-(2-methylpiperid-1-yl)propyl *p*-cyclohexyloxybenzoate).
'Cyclon A' *see* Methyl cyanoformate.
Cyclonamine* *see* Etamsylate.
Cyclonium iodide *see* Oxapium iodide.
Cyclooctadecane-1,10-bis(trimethylammonium iodide) *see* Cyclomethone.
1-Cyclooctyl-3,3-dimethylurea *see* Cycluron.
1-Cyclooctyl-3-*p*-toluenesulfonylurea *see* Glyoctamide.
Cyclo-3-oxapentamethylenebiguanide *see* Moroxydine.
'Cyclopal' *see* Cyclopentobarbital.
'Cyclopen' *see* Cyclopentobarbital.
Cyclopentacycloheptene *see* Azulene.
Cyclopentadrin *see* Cyclopentamine.
CYCLOPENTAMINE*** (1-cyclopentyl-2-(methylamino)propane; *N*,α-dimethylcyclopentaneethylamine; cyclopentadrin; cyclopentamine hydrochloride).
Cyclopentaneacetic acid dimethylaminoethyl ester *see* Cyclopentolate.
1,1-Cyclopentanedimethanol dicarbanilate *see* Cyclarbamate.
3-Cyclopentanepropionic acid, esters and salts *see* Cipionate(s).
Cyclopentanone 2α,3α-epithio-5α-androstan-17β-yl methyl acetal *see* Mepitiostane.
3-(2-Cyclopenten-1-yl)-2-methyl-4-oxo-2-cyclopenten-1-yl) 2,2-dimethyl-3-(2-methyl-1-propenyl)-

cyclopropanecarboxylate *see* Cyclethrin.

2-Cyclopenten-1-yl-2-(2-morpholinoethyl)cyclopentanone *see* Cyclexanone.

17β-Cyclopenten-1-yloxyandrosta-1,4-dien-3-one *see* Quinbolone.

13-(2-Cyclopenten-1-yl)tridecanoic acid *see* Chaulmoogric acid.

11-(2-Cyclopenten-1-yl)undecanoic acid *see* Hydnocarpic acid.

CYCLOPENTHIAZIDE* (6-chloro-3-(cyclopentylmethyl)-3,4-dihydro-2*H*-1,2,4-benzothiadiazine-7-sulfonamide 1,1-dioxide; Su-8341). *See also under* Oxprenolol.

CYCLOPENTOBARBITAL (5-allyl-5-cyclopenten-1-ylbarbituric acid).

CYCLOPENTOLATE* (2-(dimethylamino)-ethyl 1-hydroxy-α-phenylcyclopentaneacetate; cyclopentolate hydrochloride; GT 75; 'cyclogyl'; 'cyplegin'; 'minims'; 'mydrilate'; 'zyklolat').

1-Cyclopentyl-3-[[*p*-[2-(*o*-anisamido)ethyl]phenyl]sulfonyl]urea *see* Glipentide.

N-**CYCLOPENTYLLYSERGAMIDE** (lysergic acid cyclopentylamide; 'cepentyl').

1-Cyclopentyl-3-[*p*-[2-(*o*-methoxybenzamido)ethyl]phenylsulfonyl]urea *see* Glipentide.

1-Cyclopentyl-2-(methylamino)propane *see* Cyclopentamine.

3-Cyclopentyloxy-16α,17-dihydroxy-19-nor-17α-pregna-1,3,5(10)-trien-20-yne *see* Nilestriol.

3-Cyclopentyloxyestratriene-16α,17β-diol *see* Quinestradol.

3-Cyclopentyloxy-17α-ethynylestra-1,3,5(10)-trien-17β-ol *see* Quinestrol.

3-(Cyclopentyloxy)-17-hydroxypregna-3,5-dien-20-one *see* Pentagestrone.

4-[3-(Cyclopentyloxy)-4-methoxyphenyl]-2-pyrrolidinone *see* Rolipram.

3-Cyclopentyloxy-17-methylandrosta-3,5-dien-17β-ol *see* Penmesterol.

3-Cyclopentyloxy-19-nor-17α-pregna-3,5-dien-20-yn-17-ol *see* Quingestanol.

3-Cyclopentyloxy-19-nor-17α-pregna-1,3,5(10)-trien-20-yne-16α,17-diol *see* Nilestriol.

3-Cyclopentyloxy-19-nor-17α-pregna-1,3,5(10)-trien-20-yn-17β-ol *see* Quinestrol.

3-Cyclopentyloxypregna-3,5-dien-20-one *see* Quingestrone.

1-Cyclopentyl-1-phenyl-3-piperid-1-yl-1-propanol *see* Cycrimine.

3-[*N*-(4-Cyclopentylpiperazin-1-yl)formimidoyl]rifamycin *see* Rifapentine.

17β-(3-Cyclopentylpropionoxy)-4-hydroxyestr-4-en-3-one *see* Oxabolone cipionate.

α-Cyclopentyl-2-thiopheneglycolic acid 2-(diethylamino)ethyl ester methobromide *see* Penthienate.

1-Cyclopentyl-3-*p*-toluenesulfonylurea *see* Tolpentamide.

Cyclophenazine* *see* Ciclofenazine.

CYCLOPHOSPHAMIDE* (2-[bis(2-chloroethyl)amino]tetrahydro-2*H*-1,3,2-oxazaphosphorine 2-oxide; *N*,*N*-bis(2-chloroethyl)-*N'*-(3-hydroxypropyl)phosphorodiamidic acid intramolecular ester; cyclophosphamide monohydrate; B-518; NSC-26271).

CYCLOPREGNOL* (6β-hydroxy-3,5-cyclopregnan-20-one; 'neurosterone').

Cycloprolol* *see* Cicloprolol.

CYCLOPROPANE* (trimethylene).

2-Cyclopropylamino-5-phenyl-2-oxazolin-4-one *see* Cyclazodone.

5-Cyclopropylcarbonyl-2-benzimidazolecarbamic acid methyl ester *see* Ciclobendazole.

21-[(Cyclopropylcarbonyl)oxy]-6α,9-difluoro-11β-hydroxy-16α,17-[(1-methylethylidene)bis(oxy)]pregna-1,4-diene-3,20-dione *see* Ciprocinonide.

1-Cyclopropyl-6-fluoro-1,4-dihydro-4-oxo-7-piperazin-1-ylquinoline-3-carboxylic acid *see* Ciprofloxacin.

22-Cyclopropyl-7α-((*R*)-1-hydroxy-1-methylpropyl)-6,14-*endo*-ethenotetrahydrothebaine *see* Homprenorphine.

21-Cyclopropyl-7α-((*S*)-1-hydroxy-1,2,2-trimethylpropyl)-6,14-*endo*-ethano-6,7,8,14-tetrahydrooripavine *see* Buprenorphine.

1-[*p*-[2-(Cyclopropylmethoxy)ethoxy]phenoxy]-3-(isopropylamino)-2-propanol *see* Cicloprolol.

1-[4-[2-(Cyclopropylmethoxy)ethyl]phenoxy]-3-(isopropylamino)-2-propanol *see* Betaxolol.

α-Cyclopropyl-α-(*p*-methoxyphenyl)-5-pyrimidinemethanol *see* Ancymidol.

17-(Cyclopropylmethyl)-7,8-dihydro-7-(1-hydroxy-1-methylethyl)-6-*O*-methyl-6,14-ethano-17-normorphine *see* Diprenorphine.

17-(Cyclopropylmethyl)-3,4-dihydroxymorphinan *see* Oxilorphan.

3-Cyclopropylmethyl-6,11-dimethyl-6,7-benzomorphan-8-ol *see* Cyclazocine.

3-Cyclopropylmethyl-6,11-dimethyl-2,6-methano-6,7-benzomorphan *see* Volazocine.

17-(Cyclopropylmethyl)-4,5α-epoxy-3,14-dihydroxymorphinan-6-one *see* Naltrexone.

17-(Cyclopropylmethyl)-4,5α-epoxy-8β-ethyl-3-methoxymorphinan-6-one *see* Conorfone.

8-(Cyclopropylmethyl)-6β,7β-epoxy-3α-hydroxy-1α*H*,5α*H*-tropanium bromide (−)-(*S*)-tropate *see* Cimetropium bromide.

17-(Cyclopropylmethyl)-4,5α-epoxy-6-methylenemorphinan-3,14-diol *see* Nalmefene.

3-Cyclopropylmethyl-6-ethyl-1,2,3,4,5,6-hexahydro-11,11-dimethyl-2,6-methano-3-benzazocin-8-ol *see* Gemazocine.

2-(Cyclopropylmethyl)-5-ethyl-2'-hydroxy-9,9-dimethyl-6,7-benzomorphan *see* Gemazocine.

3-Cyclopropylmethyl-1,2,3,4,5,6-hexahydro-*cis*-6,11-dimethyl-2,6-methano-3-benzazocine *see* Volazocine.

3-Cyclopropylmethyl-1,2,3,4,5,6-hexahydro-6,11-dimethyl-2,6-methano-3-benzazocin-8-ol *see* Cyclazocine.

3-(Cyclopropylmethyl)-1,2,3,4,5,6-hexahydro-11-methoxy-6-methyl-2,6-methano-3-benzazocin-8-ol *see* Moxazocine.

2-(Cyclopropylmethyl)-2'-hydroxy-5,9-dimethyl-6,7-benzomorphan *see* Cyclazocine.

2-(Cyclopropylmethyl)-2'-hydroxy-5,9-dimethyl-8-oxo-6,7-benzomorphan *see* Ketazocine.

2-(Cyclopropylmethyl)-2'-hydroxy-9-methoxy-5-methyl-6,7-benzomorphan *see* Moxazocine.

N-Cyclopropylmethyl-7α-(1-hydroxy-1-methylethyl)-O^6-methyldihydro-*endo*-ethanonormorphine *see* Diprenorphine.

N-Cyclopropylmethyl-7α-(1(R)-hydroxy-1-methylpropyl)-6,14-*endo*-ethenotetrahydronorthebaine *see* Homprenorphine.

N-(Cyclopropylmethyl)-3-hydroxymorphinan *see* Cyclorphan.

17-(Cyclopropylmethyl)-4-hydroxymorphinan-6-one *see* Ketorfanol.

1-(Cyclopropylmethyl)-6-methoxy-4-phenyl-2(1H)-quinazolinone *see* Ciproquazone.

N-Cyclopropylmethyl-19-methylnorvinol *see* Cyprenorphine.

17-(Cyclopropylmethyl)morphinan-3,14-diol *see* Oxilorphan.

17-(Cyclopropylmethyl)morphinan-3-ol *see* Cyclorphan.

1-(Cyclopropylmethyl)octahydro-5,11b-iminoethano-11bH-benzo[a]carbazole *see* Carbazocine.

(−)-3-(2-(Cyclopropylmethyl)-1,3,4,5,6 7,8,8a-octahydro-4aβ-isoquinolyl)phenol *see* Ciprefadol.

N-[[1-(Cyclopropylmethyl)pyrrolidin-2-yl]methyl]-2-methoxy-5-sulfamoylbenzamide *see* Cipropride.

N-[(1-Cyclopropylmethyl)pyrrolidin-2-yl)methyl]-5-sulfamoyl-*o*-anisamide *see* Cipropride.

3-(Cyclopropylmethyl)-3,4,5,6-tetrahydro-8-hydroxy-6,11-dimethyl-2,6-methano-3-benzazocin-1(2H)-one *see* Ketazocine.

N-Cyclopropylmethyl-6,7,8,14-tetrahydro-7α-(1-hydroxy-1-methylethyl)-6,14-*endo*-ethenonororipavine *see* Cyprenorphine.

13-(Cyclopropylmethyl)-4,4a,5,6-tetrahydro-3H-5,10b-(iminoethano)-1H-naphtho[1,2-c]pyran-9-ol *see* Proxorphan.

1-(o-Cyclopropylphenoxy)-3-isopropylamino-2-propanol *see* Procinolol.

2-[(o-Cyclopropylphenoxy)methyl]-2-imidazoline *see* Cirazoline.

10-[3-(4-Cyclopropylpiperazin-1-yl)propyl]-2-trifluoromethylphenothiazine *see* Ciclofenazine.

CYCLOPYRRONIUM BROMIDE*** (1-ethyl-3-hydroxy-1-methylpyrrolidinium bromide α-cyclopentylphenylacetate).

CYCLOQUINE (tr) (4-[3,5-bis(diethylaminomethyl)-4-hydroxyanilino]-7-chloroquinoline).

CYCLORPHAN* (N-(cyclopropylmethyl)-3-hydroxymorphinan; 17-(cyclopropylmethyl)morphinan-3-ol; Ro 4-6711).

'Cycloryl' *see* Sodium dodecyl sulfate.

CYCLOSERINE*** (D-4-amino-3-isoxazolidinone; MK-65; PA-94).

'Cyclospasmol' *see* Cyclandelate *and* Drofenine.

Cyclosporin A *see* Ciclosporin.

Cyclosporine* *see* Ciclosporin.

'Cycloteriam' *see under* Cyclothiazide.

CYCLOTHIAZIDE*** (6-chloro-3,4-dihydro-3-(5-norbornen-2-yl)-2H-1,2,4-benzothiadiazine-7-sulfonamide 1,1-dioxide; MDi-193).

CYCLOTHIAZIDE plus TRIAMTERENE ('cycloteriam').

See also under Clonidine.

Cyclouron *see* Cycluron.

CYCLOVALONE*** (2,6-divanillylidenecyclohexanone; 'beveno').

See also under Tiratricol.

Cyclo-(L-valyl-L-ornithyl-L-leucyl-D-phenylalanyl-L-propyl-L-valyl-L-ornithyl-L-leucyl-D-phenylalanyl-L-prolyl) *see* Gramicidin S.

Cyclozanin* *see* Guanacline.

CYCLURON* (1-cyclooctyl-3,3-dimethylurea; cyclouron; OMU).

See also under Chlorbufam.

Cycobemin* *see* Cyanocobalamin.

'Cycocel' *see* Chlormequat.

CYCOTIAMINE*** (N-(4-amino-2-methylpyrimidin-5-ylmethyl)-N-[1-(2-oxo-1,3-oxathian-4-ylidene)ethyl]formamide; cyclocarbothiamine).

CYCRIMINE*** (1-cyclopentyl-1-phenyl-3-piperid-1-yl-1-propanol; cycrimine hydrochloride).

'Cycvalon' *see* Cyclovalone.

'Cydril' *see* Levamfetamine succinate.

CYFLUTHRIN* (α-cyano-4-fluoro-3-phenoxybenzyl *cis-trans*-3-(2,2-dichlorovinyl)-2,2-dimethylcyclopropanecarboxylate; 'baytroid').

'Cyfos' *see* Ifosfamide.

'Cygon' *see* Dimethoate.

CYHALOTHRIN* ((RS)-α-cyano-3-phenoxybenzyl (Z)-(1RS,3RS)-3-(2-chloro-3,3,3-trifluoropropenyl)-2,2-dimethylcyclopropanecarboxylate; PP-563).

CYHEPTAMIDE*** (10,11-dihydro-5H-dibenzo-[a,d]cycloheptene-5-carboxamide; AY-8682; BS-7029; ICI-51426).

CYHEPTROPINE*** (10,11-dihydro-5H-dibenzo[a,d]cycloheptene-5-carboxylic acid tropine ester).

CYHEXATIN* (tricyclohexylhydroxystannane; tricyclohexylhydroxytin; 'plictran').

'Cylan' *see* Phosfolan.

'Cylert' *see under* Pemoline.

'Cylopal' *see* Cyclopentobarbital.

Cymarin *see* Strophanthin.

Cymarol *see* Strophanthidol D-cymaroside.

'Cymbi' *see* Ampicillin.

'Cymbush' *see* Cypermethrin.

Cymemoxine* *see* Cimemoxin.

CYMENE(S) (isopropyltoluene(s)).

p-Cymene-2,5-diol *see* Thymohydroquinone.

p-Cymene-2,5-dione *see* Thymoquinone.

2-p-Cymenol *see* Carvacrol.

3-p-Cymenol *see* Thymol.

'Cymetox' *see under* Demephion-O.

'Cymidon' *see* Ketobemidone.

CYN *see* Cynarine.

CYNARINE*** (3,4-dihydroxycinnamic acid 1-carboxy-4,5-dihydroxy-1,3-cyclohexylene ester; 1,3-dicaffeylquinic acid; CYN; 'anghirol'; 'listrocol').

'Cynem' *see* Thionazin.

'Cynkotox' *see* Zineb.

'Cynomel' *see* Liothyronine.

'Cyodrin' *see* Crotoxyphos.

'Cyolane' *see* Phosfolan.

CYP *see* Cyanofenphos.

CYPENAMINE* (2-phenylcyclopentylamine).

CYPERMETHRIN* (3-(2,2-dichlorovinyl)-2,2-dimethylcyclopropanecarboxylic acid ester with *m*-phenoxymandelonitrile; cyano(3-phenoxyphenyl)methyl 3-(2,2-dichloroethenyl)-2,2-dimethylcyclopropanecarboxylate; cipermethrin; CCN-52; FMC-30980; NRDC-149; WL-43467; 'barricade'; 'cymbush'; 'ripcord'; 'rycopel').

Cypionate(s)* *see* Cipionate(s).

'Cyplegin' *see* Cyclopentolate.

CYPOTHRIN* (cyano(3-phenoxyphenyl)methyl 3,3-dimethylspiro[cyclopropane-1,1'-(1*H*)indene]-2-carboxylate; 3,3-dimethylspiro[cyclopropane-1,1'-(1*H*)indene]-2-carboxylic acid ester with *m*-phenoxymandelonitrile; CL-206797).

CYPRAZEPAM* (7-chloro-2-[(cyclopropylmethyl)amino]-5-phenyl-3*H*-1,4-benzodiazepine-4-oxide; W-3623).

CYPRENORPHINE* (*N*-cyclopropylmethyl-6,7,8,14-tetrahydro-7α-(1-hydroxy-1-methylethyl)-6,14-*endo*-ethenonororipavine; *N*-cyclopropylmethyl-19-methylnorvinol; M-285).

'Cyprex' *see* Dodine.

Cyprodemanol* *see* Cyprodenate.

CYPRODENATE* (2-(dimethylamino)ethyl cyclohexanepropionate; cyprodemanol; cyprodenate maleate; LB-125; RD-406).

CYPROHEPTADINE* (4-(5-dibenzo[*a,d*]cyclohepten-5-ylidene)-1-methylpiperidine; cyproheptadine hydrochloride).

CYPROLIDOL* (α,α-diphenyl-2-pyrid-4-ylcyclopropanemethanol; α-(2-pyrid-4-ylcyclopropyl)benzhydrol; cyprolidol hydrochloride; IN-1060; NSC-84973).

CYPROMID* (3,4-dichloro-*N*-(cyclopropylcarbonyl)aniline; *N*-(3,4-dichlorophenyl)cyclopropanecarboxamide; 'clobber').

'Cypromin' *see* Rolicyprine.

Cyproquinate* *see* Ciproquinate.

CYPROTERONE* (6-chloro-17-hydroxy-1α,2α-methylenepregna-4,6-diene-3,20-dione; 6-chloro-1β,2β-dihydro-17α-hydroxy-3'*H*-cyclopropa[1,2]pregna-4,6-diene-3,20-dione; 1α,2α-methylenechlormadinone; SH-881; SH-80881).

CYPROTERONE ACETATE (NSC-81430; SH-714; 'androcur'; 'sinovir').

CYPROTERONE ACETATE plus ETHINYLESTRADIOL (SH-B-209-AB; 'diane').

Cyproximide* *see* Ciproximide.

CYSTAFOS (tr) (2-aminoethyl sodium thiophosphate; mercaptamine *S*-phosphate; cystaphos).

'Cystamin' *see* Methenamine.

CYSTAMINE (2,2'-dithiobisethylamine; cystinamine; decarboxycystine; L-1591).

Cystaphos *see* Cystafos.

CYSTATHIONINE (2-amino-4-(2-amino-2-carboxyethylthio)butyric acid).

Cysteamine* *see* Mercaptamine.

CYSTEIC ACID (3-sulfoalanine).

Cysteinamine *see* Mercaptamine.

CYSTEINE (2-amino-3-mercaptopropionic acid; β-mercaptoalanine; NSC-8746; 'cysthion').

'Cysthion' *see* Cysteine.

Cystinamine *see* Cystamine.

CYSTINE* (β,β'-dithiodialanine; dicysteine; 'nephrin').

'Cystit' *see* Nitrofurantoin.

'Cystogen' *see* Methenamine.

'Cystografin' *see under* Meglumine diatrizoate.

'Cystorelin' *see* Gonadorelin acetate.

CYTARABINE* (4-amino-1-arabinofuranosyl-1,2-dihydro-2-pyrimidinone; 1-β-D-arabinofuranosylcytosine; cytosine arabinoside; ara-C; aracytidine; cytarabine hydrochloride; AC-1075; NSC-63878; U-19920A).

Cytarabine 5'-(1-adamantanecarboxylate) *see* Adamantoylcytarabine.

CYTARABINE 5'-PHOSPHATE (arabinofuranosylcytosine monophosphate; ara-CMP).

'Cytellin' *see under* β-Sitosterol.

'Cytembena' *see* Bromebric acid.

CYTHIOATE (*O,O*-dimethyl *O*-(*p*-sulfamoylphenyl) phosphorothioate; 'proban').

'Cythion' *see* Malathion.

Cyticholine *see* Citicoline.

CYTIDINE (cytosine riboside).

Cytidine cyclic 2',3'-(hydrogen phosphate) *see* Cifostodine.

Cytidine diphosphate choline *see* Citicoline.

Cytidinephosphoric acid *see* Cytidylic acid.

CYTIDYLIC ACID (cytidinephosphoric acid; cytosylic acid; CMP).
See also Cifostodine.

'Cytimun' *see* Sufosfamide.

CYTISINE ((1*R-cis*)-1,2,3,4,5,6-hexahydro-1,5-methano-8*H*-pyrido[1,2-*a*][1,5]diazocin-8-one; baptitoxine; cytiton; laburnine; sophorine; ulexine).

Cytiton (tr) *see* Cytisine.

CYTOCHROME C (hematin-protein; myohematin).

'Cytoflav' *see* Flavin mononucleotide.

'Cytogran' *see* Buthiopurine.

'Cytoleukon' *see* Busulfan.

'Cytomel' *see* Liothyronine.

'Cytonal' *see* Fosfestrol.

'Cytosar' *see* Cytarabine.

CYTOSINE (4-amino-2-(1*H*)-pyrimidinone).

Cytosine arabinoside *see* Cytarabine.

Cytosine riboside *see* Cytidine.

'Cytospaz' *see* Hyoscyamine.

'Cytostasan' *see* Bendamustine.

'Cytostasin' *see* Hexestrol 4,4'-diphosphate.

'Cytostatin' *see* Hexestrol 4,4'-diphosphate.

Cytosylic acid *see* Cytidylic acid.

'Cytoval' *see* Bromebric acid.

'Cytoxan' *see* Cyclophosphamide.

'Cytrol' *see* Amitrole.

'Cytrolane' *see* Mephosfolan.

D

2,4-D *see* 2,4-Dichlorophenoxyacetic acid.
D-6 *see* Dicholine suberate.
D-15-14 *see* Octamoxin.
D-25 *see* Fenticlor.
D-26 *see* Bithionol.
D-32 *see* Xibenolol.
D-40TA *see* Estazolam.
D-40 *see* Iodoxyl.
D-41 *see* Tromantadine.
D-47 *see* Sulbentine.
D-50 *see* Pyrazinamide.
D-00079 *see* Anoxomer.
D-109 *see* Hexylcaine.
D-138 *see* Norgestimate.
D-145 *see* Memantine.
D-201 *see* Isothipendyl.
D-206 *see* Prothipendyl.
D-237 *see* Cloforex.
D-254 *see* Pipazetate.
D-301 *see* Benzoxonium chloride.
D-365 *see* Verapamil.
D-563 *see* Oxyfedrine.
D-600 *see* Gallopamil.
D-753 *see* Carboxin.
D-775 *see* Homofenazine.
D-860 *see* Tolbutamide.
D-1201 *see* Prothrin.
D-1262 *see* Cloxypendyl.
D-1593 *see* Tiamizide.
D-1601 *see* Moprolol.
D-1721 *see* Alipamide.
D-1959 *see* Reproterol.
D-2083 *see* Desonide.
D-8955 *see* Tinofedrine.
D-12524 *see* Lopirazepam.
DA-398 *see* Epirizole.
DA-688 *see* Gefarnate.
DA-708 *see* Teflurane.
DA-808 *see* Nafcaproic acid.
DA-893 *see* Roflurane.
DA-914 *see* Nafiverine.
DA-992 *see* Naftypramide.
DA-1128 *see* Meprophenidol.
DA-1773 *see* Sodium picosulfate.
DA-2370 *see* Feprazone.
'Daartil' *see* Normethadone.
DAB *see* *p*-(Dimethylamino)azobenzene.
'Dabical' *see* Calcium clofibrate.
'Dabrosan' *see* Allopurinol.
'DAC-2787' *see* Chlorothalonil.
DACARBAZINE* (1-(4-carboxamidoimidazol-

5-yl)-3,3-dimethyltriazene; 5-(3,3-dimethyl-1-tri-azeno)imidazole-4-carboxamide; DIC; DTIC; NSC-45388; 'DTIC-DOME').
DACEMAZINE* (10-(*N*,*N*-dimethylglycyl)-phenothiazine).
DACISTEINE* (*N*-acetyl-L-cysteine acetate (ester); acetylcysteine acetate).
'Daconil' *see* Chlorothalonil.
'Dactarin' *see* Miconazole.
'Dacthal' *see* Chlorthal-dimethyl.
'Dactil' *see* Piperidolate.
DACTINOMYCIN* (actinomycin D; meracti-nomycin; NSC-3053; 'cosmegen').
DACURONIUM BROMIDE* ((3α,17β-dihydr-oxy-5α-androstan-2β,16β-ylene)bis(1-methylpip-eridinium bromide) 3-acetate; 2β,16β-dipiperid-1-yl-5α-androstane-3α,17β-diol 3-acetate di-methobromide; NB-68).
DAD *see* Dianhydrogalactitol.
DADA *see* Diisopropylamine dichloroacetate.
DADDS *see* Acedapsone.
DADPS *see* Dapsone.
DAEP *see* *S*-2-Acetamidoethyl *O*,*O*-dimethyl phosphorodithioate.
DAES *see* Diethylstilbestrol.
'Daflon' *see under* Diosmin.
Daftazol (tr) *see* Amiphenazole.
'Dagenan' *see* Sulfapyridine.
'Dagicide' *see* Lindane.
'Dagralax' *see* Dantron.
'Dagynil' *see* Conjugated estrogens equine.
Dahlin *see* Inulin.
DAIDZEIN (4′,7-dihydroxyisoflavone).
DAIDZIN (daidzein 7-glucoside).
'Daimeton' *see* Sulfamonomethoxine.
'Dairin' *see* Chrysoidine monothiocyanate.
'Daitol' *see* Etersalate.
'Daktacort' *see under* Miconazole.
'Daktarin' *see* Miconazole.
'Dalacin' *see* Streptovarycin.
'Dalacin C' *see* Clindamycin.
DALANATED INSULIN (insulin derivative ob-tained by removal of C-terminal alanine from B-chain; dealanated-insulin; SN-44).
DALAPON* (2,2-dichloropropionic acid; 'dow-pon'; 'radapon').
Dalapon trichlorophenoxyethyl ester *see* Erbon.
DALBERGIN (6-hydroxy-7-methoxy-4-phenyl-coumarin).
DALEDALIN* (3-methyl-3-[3-(methylamino)-propyl]-1-phenylindoline; UK-3557).

DALEDALIN TOSILATE (daledalin tosylate; UK-3557-15).
'Dalmadorm' see Flurazepam.
'Dalmane' see Flurazepam.
'Dalnate' see Tolindate.
'Dalysep' see Sulfalene.
'Dalzic' see Practolol.
DAM see Diacetyl monoxime.
DAMASCENINE (methyl 3-methoxy-2-methyl-aminobenzoate; methyl 3-methoxy N-methyl-anthranilate; methyldamascenine; nigelline).
Dambose see Inositol.
'D-amfetasul' see Dexamphetamine.
DAMINOZIDE* (butanedioic acid mono-2,2-dimethylhydrazide; succinic acid dimethylhydrazide; 'alar'; 'B-nine').
DAMOTEPINE* (10-[(dimethylamino)methyl]-dibenzo[b,f]thiepin; N,N-dimethyldibenzo[b,f]-thiepin-10-methylamine; GP-41299).
'Damoxicil' see Amoxicillin.
DAN-268 see Magnesium oxoglurate.
DAN-523 see Tameticillin.
DAN-10510 see Azidocillin.
'Danatrol' see Danazol.
DANAZOL* (17α-pregna-2,4-dien-20-yno[2,3-d]isoxazol-17-ol; WIN-17757; 'chronogyn'; 'danatrol'; 'danocrine'; 'danol'; 'isoxozol'; 'winobanin').
'Daneral' see Pheniramine p-aminosalicylate.
DANITRACEN* (4-(9,10-dihydro-9-hydroxy-anthr-10-ylidene)-1-methylpiperidine; 9,10-di-hydro-10-(1-methylpiperid-4-ylidene)-9-anthrol; WA-335).
'Danivac' see Dantron.
DANK see Dihydroxyaluminium sodium carbonate.
'Dano' see Amitriptylinoxide.
'Danocrine' see Danazol.
'Danol' see Danazol.
DANT see Alcuronium chloride.
'Dantafur' see Nitrofurantoin.
'Dantamacrin' see Dantrolene.
Danthron* see Dantron.
'Dantrium' see Dantrolene.
DANTROLENE* (1-[5-(p-nitrophenyl)-2-fur-furylideneamino]hydantoin; F-368; F-440).
DANTRON* (1,8-dihydroxyanthraquinone; danthron; anthrapurol; antrapurol; chrysazin; dianthone).
DANTRON plus DOCUSATE CALCIUM ('dioxidan').
DANTRON plus POLOXAMER ('dorbanex').
'Danzen' see Serrapeptase.
'Daonil' see Glibenclamide.
'Dapanone' see Phenisonone.
DAPHNETIN (7,8-dihydroxycoumarin).
DAPIPRAZOLE* (5,6,7,8-tetrahydro-3-[2-(4-o-tolylpiperazin-1-yl)ethyl]-s-triazolo[4,3-a]pyridine).
'Dapocel' see Diisopropylamine dichloroacetate.
'Dapolar' see under Cycloguanil embonate.
'Dapotum' see Fluphenazine enantate.
'Dapotum D' see Fluphenazine decanoate.

DAPSONE* (4,4'-diaminodiphenyl sulfone; bis(p-aminophenyl) sulfone; p,p'-sulfodianiline; diaphenylsulfone; diphenason; sulfone-mere; DADPS; DDS; F-1358; NSC-6091). See also under Pyrimethamine.
DAPSONEDISULFONIC ACID DISODIUM SALT ('avlosulfone-EOS').
DAPT see Amiphenazole.
'Daptazole' see Amiphenazole.
'Daquin' see Chlorazanil.
'Daramin' see Saccharin ammonium salt.
'Daranide' see Diclofenamide.
'Daraprim' see Pyrimethamine.
'Darbid' see Isopropamide iodide.
'Darcil' see Pheneticillin.
'Dardanim' see Deanol aceglumate.
'Darebon' see under Reserpine.
'Darenthin' see Bretylium tosilate.
'Daricon' see Oxyphencyclimine.
'Daritran' see under Meprobamate.
'Darkinal' see under Batroxobin.
DARODIPINE* (diethyl 4-(4-benzofurazanyl)-1,4-dihydro-2,6-dimethyl-3,5-pyridinedicarb-oxylate; dazodipine).
'Darovermex' see Piperazine.
'Darstine' see Piperphenamine.
'Dartal' see Thiopropazate.
'Dartalan' see Thiopropazate.
'Dartan' see Thiopropazate.
'Darvisul' see Phenolsulfazole.
'Darvocet-N' see Dextropropoxyphene napsilate.
'Darvon' see Dextropropoxyphene.
'Darvon-N' see Dextropropoxyphene napsilate.
'Dasanil' see Fensulfothion.
DAT see Acetiamine.
DATC see Diallate and Tiocarlide.
DATISCETIN (2',3,5,7-tetrahydroxyflavone).
DATISCIN (datiscetin rutoside; datiscoside).
Datura stramonium see Stramonium.
Daturine see Hyoscyamine.
Dau ET-14 see Fenclofos.
Dau ET-57 see Fenclofos.
'Daunoblastin' see Daunorubicin.
Daunomycin see Daunorubicin.
DAUNORUBICIN* ((1S,3S)-3-acetyl-1,2,3,4,6,11-hexahydro-3,5,12-trihydroxy-10-methoxy-6,11-dioxo-1-naphthacenyl 3-amino-2,3,6-trideoxy-α-L-lyxo-hexopyranoside; dauno-mycin; rubidomycin; daunorubicin hydrochloride; FI-6339; NDC 0082-4155; NSC-82151; NSC-83142; RP 13057).
Daunorubicin benzoylhydrazone see Zorubicin.
DAUNORUBICIN OXIME (NSC-143491).
DAUNORUBICIN SEMICARBAZONE (NSC-143114).
DAUNOSAMINYLDAUNORUBICIN (NSC-140781).
'Davosine' see Sulfamethoxypyridazine.
'Daxid' see Xanthiol.
'Daxolin' see Loxapine succinate.
DAZADROL* (p-chloro-α-(2-imidazolin-2-yl)-α-pyrid-2-ylbenzyl alcohol; 2-(p-chloro-α-hydr-oxy-α-pyrid-2-ylbenzyl)-2-imidazoline; α-(p-

chlorophenyl)-α-(2-imidazolin-2-yl)-2-pyridine-
methanol; α-(*p*-chlorophenyl)-α-pyrid-2-yl-2-
imidazoline-2-methanol; dazadrol maleate (1:1)
salt; Sch-12650).

DAZIDAMINE*** (2-benzyl-3-[[3-(dimethylamino)propyl]thio]-2*H*-indazole).

DAZMEGREL** (3-(imidazol-1-ylmethyl)-2-
methylindole-1-propionic acid).

Dazodipine *see* Darodipine.

DAZOLICINE*** (8-chloro-3,4,5,6-tetrahydro-6-
[(1-isopropyl-2-imidazolin-2-yl)methyl]-2*H*-1,6-
benzothiazocine; UCB-B-192).

DAZOMET* (tetrahydro-3,5-dimethyl-2*H*-1,3,5-
thiadiazine-2-thione; thiazon; tiazon; DMTT;
'basamid'; 'mylone').

DAZOPRIDE** (4-amino-5-chloro-*N*-(1,2-di-
ethylpyrazolidin-4-yl)-*o*-anisamide).

DAZOXIBEN*** (*p*-[2-(1*H*-imidazol-1-yl)ethoxy]-
benzoic acid; dazoxiben hydrochloride; UK-
37248).

2,4-DB *see* 4-(2,4-Dichlorophenoxy)butyric acid.

DB-112 *see* Clocoumarol.

DB-136 *see* Furidarone.

DB-139 *see* Pyrazinobutazone.

DB-2041 *see* Meglumine iocarmate.

DBCP *see* 1,2-Dibromo-3-chloropropane.

DBD *see* Mitolactol.

DBED *see* Benzathine.

DBI *see* Phenformin.

DBM *see* Mitobronitol.

DBMA *see* Dibemethine.

DBP *see* Dibutyl phthalate.

DBPC *see* Butylated hydroxytoluene.

'Db-retard' *see* Phenformin.

DBS *see* Dibromsalicil.

DBV *see* Buformin.

DCA *see* Desoxycortone.

DCAI *see* Clonidine.

DCBAG *see* Guanabenz.

DCDE *see* Diponium bromide.

2,3-DCDT *see* Diallate.

DCET *see* Cetotiamine.

DCF *see* Mefeclorazine *and* Pentostatin.

DCH-21 *see* Exiproben.

DCI (3,4-dichloro-α-(isopropylaminomethyl)benz-
yl alcohol; 1-(3,4-dichlorophenyl)-2-isopropyl-
aminoethanol; dichlorodideoxyisoprenaline; dichlorisoprenaline; dichloroisoproterenol).

DCMO *see* Carboxin.

DCMOD *see* Carboxin dioxide.

DCMU *see* Diuron.

DCNU *see* Chlorozotocin.

DCP *see* Amiloride.

DCPA *see* Chlorthal-dimethyl.

DCPC *see* Chlorfenethol.

DCPE *see* Chlorfenethol.

DCR-515 *see under* Reserpine.

DCS-90 *see* Dihydroergocristine.

DD-234 *see* Scopolamine methyl methosulfate.

'DDAVP' *see* Desmopressin acetate.

DDD (1,1-dichloro-2,2-bis(*p*-chlorophenyl)ethane;
1,1'-(2,2-dichloroethylene)bis(4-chlorobenzene);
p,p'-DDD; TDE; 'rhothane').

o,p'-**DDD*** *see* Mitotane.

p,p'-**DDD** *see* DDD.

DDDM *see* Dichlorophen.

DDE (1,1-dichloro-2,2-bis(*p*-chlorophenyl)ethyl-
ene; 1,1'-(2,2-dichloroethylidene)bis(4-chloro-
benzene); p,p'-DDE).

p,p'-**DDE** *see* DDE.

DDGA *see* Dodine.

DDM *see* Dichlorophen.

DDMP *see* Metodiclorofen.

cis-**DDP** *see* Cisplatin.

DDS *see* Dapsone.

DDT* (1,1,1-trichloro-2,2-bis(*p*-chlorophenyl)eth-
ane; 1,1'-(2,2,2-trichloroethylene)bis(4-chloro-
benzene); 1-chloro-2-[2,2,2-trichloro-1-(*p*-
chlorophenyl)ethyl]benzene; 1,1,1-trichloro-2-(*o*-
chlorophenyl)-2-(*p*-chlorophenyl)ethane; clofenotane; dicophane; chlorophenothane; chlorphenethanum; chlorphenothane; gesarol; parachlorocide; pentachlorin; penticidum; *p,p'*-
DDT).

DDT plus DIMETHOATE ('vantal').

DDT plus LINDANE (BHC plus DDT; 'ditox L';
'omyl'; 'trix'; 'zoralin').

DDT plus LINDANE & METHOXYCHLOR ('tritox').

o,p'-**DDT** (1-chloro-2-[2,2,2-trichloro-1-(4-chloro-
phenyl)ethyl]benzene; 2,2,2-trichloro-1-(*o*-
chlorophenyl)-1-*p*-chlorophenyl)ethane).

p,p'-**DDT** *see* DDT.

DDVF *see* Dichlorvos.

DDVP *see* Dichlorvos.

**4-Deacetyl-3-[(1-carboxy-2-indol-3-ylethyl)carb-
amoyl]-3-de(methoxycarbonyl)vincaleukoblastine,
ethyl ester** *see* Vintriptol.

Deacetyldigilanide C *see* Deslanoside.

Deacetyllanatoside C *see* Deslanoside.

N-**Deacetyl-*N*-methylcolchicine** *see* Demecolcine.

N-**DEACETYLTHIOCOLCHICINE** (NSC-9170;
R-261-P; 'thiocolciran').

**Deacetylvinblastine 4-(*N*,*N*-dimethylglycinate)
(ester)** *see* Vinglycinate.

Dealanated-insulin *see* Dalanated insulin.

1-Deamino-8-D-arginine vasopressin *see* Desmopressin.

1-DEAMINO-2-ISOLEUCINE OXYTOCIN (1-
(3-mercaptopropionic acid)-2-isoleucine oxytocin).

Deaminooxytocin *see* Demoxytocin.

'Deaner' *see* Deanol *p*-acetamidobenzoate.

Deanil pyrisuccinate *see* Pirisudanol.

DEANOL* (2-(dimethylamino)ethanol).
See also below and Amindocate; Botiacrine;
Clormecaine; Cloximate; Cyclopentolate; Cypro-
denate; Denaverine; Dimenoxadol; Dicarfen;
Hydroxytetracaine; Indocate; Meclofenoxate;
Namoxyrate; Pargeverine; Tetracaine; Warfarin-
deanol.

DEANOL ACEGLUMATE** (2-(dimethylamino)ethyl hydrogen *N*-acetylglutamate; demanol aceglumate; 'cleregil'; 'dardanim'; 'otrun';
'risatarun').

DEANOL *p*-ACETAMIDOBENZOATE (2-(di-

methylamino)ethyl *p*-acetamidobenzoate; 'deaner'; 'diforene').

DEANOL BENZILATE (2-(dimethylamino)ethyl
benzilate; benzacine; 'diphemin'; 'labotropine').

DEANOL HEMISUCCINATE (S-167; 'tonibral').

**Deanol 3-hydroxy-4-(hydroxymethyl)-2-methylpyr-
id-5-ylmethyl succinate** *see* Pirisudanol.

DEANOL PHOSPHATE (phosphoryldimethylaminoethanol; 'panclar'; 'panklar').

DEANOL PIDOLATE (2-(dimethylamino)ethyl 5-
oxopyrrolidine-2-carboxylate; deanol pyroglutamate).

DEANOL PIDOLATE plus HEPTAMINOL ('debrumyl').

Deanol pyridoxine succinate *see* Pirisudanol.

Deanol pyrisuccinate *see* Pirisudanol.

Deanol pyroglutamate *see* Deanol pidolate.

DEANOL TARTRATE (2-(dimethylamino)ethyl
hydrogen tartrate; deanol bitartrate; 'atrol'; 'dimethanen'; 'paxanol'; 'stimulest').

'**Deanxit**' *see under* Flupentixol.

'**Deapril-st**' *see* Co-dergocrine.

7-Deazaadenosine *see* Tubercidin.

DEAZAAMINOPTERIN (*N*-[*p*-[(2,4-diaminoqui-
nazolin-6-ylmethyl)amino]benzoyl]glutamic
acid; NSC-529860).

'**Deazin**' *see* Bromelains.

'**Debecylina**' *see* Benzathine penicillin.

'**Debekacyl**' *see* Dibekacin.

'**Debendrin**' *see* Diphenhydramine.

'**Debetrol**' *see* Dextrothyroxine sodium.

'**Debinyl**' *see* Phenformin.

'**Deblaston**' *see* Pipemidic acid.

DEBOXAMET* (5-methoxy-2-methylindole-3-
acetohydroxamic acid).

'**Debridat**' *see* Trimebutine maleate.

'**Debrisan**' *see* Dextranomer.

Debrisochin* *see* Debrisoquine.

DEBRISOQUINE* (3,4-dihydro-3(1*H*)-isoqui-
nolinecarboxamidine; 2-amidino-1,2,3,4-tetra-
hydroisoquinoline; debrisochin; isocaramidine;
Ro 5-3307/B1).

'**Debrumyl**' *see under* Deanol pidolate.

'**Debrycen**' *see* Primycin.

Decacalcium dihydroxide hexakis(orthophosphate)
see Hydroxyapatite.

**1,1',2,2',3,3',4,4',5,5'-Decachlorobi[2,4-cyclopenta-
dien-1-yl]** *see* Dienochlor.

**Decachlorooctahydro-1,3,4-metheno-2*H*-cyclobuta-
[*cd*]pentalen-2-one** *see* Chlordecone.

DECADONIUM IODIDE (tr) (decamethylene-
1,10-bis(adamant-1-yldimethylammonium iodide)).

'**Decadron**' *see* Dexamethasone.

'**Decadron-LA**' *see* Dexamethasone acetate.

'**Deca-durabolin**' *see* Nandrolone decanoate.

**1,2,3,4,4a,6,7,11b,12,13a-Decahydro-9,10-dimeth-
oxy-13*H*-dibenzo[*a,f*]quinolizin-13-one oxime** *see*
Benolizime.

**Decahydro-2-hydroxy-2,4b-dimethyl-7-oxo-1-phen-
anthrenepropionic acid δ-lactone** *see* Testolactone.

**1,2,3,4,4aβ,5,6,6a,11bβ,13bβ-Decahydro-4,4,6aβ,9-
tetramethyl-13*H*-benzo[*a*]-furo[2,3,4-*m,n*]-
xanthen-11-ol** *see* Siccanin.

**3,4,5,6,7,8,9,10,11,12-Decahydro-7,14,16-trihydr-
oxy-3-methyl-1*H*-2-benzoxacyclotetradecin-1-one
(3*S*,7*R*)-** *see* Zeranol.

**3,4,5,6,7,8,9,10,11,12-Decahydro-7,14,16-trihydr-
oxy-3-methyl-1*H*-2-benzoxacyclotetradecin-1-one
(3*S*,7*S*)-** *see* Taleranol.

**Decahydro-4a,7,9-trihydroxy-2-methyl-6,8-bis-
(methylamino)pyrano[2,3-*b*][1,4]benzodioxin-4-
one** *see* Spectinomycin.

'**Decalcinor**' *see* Disodium edetate.

DECAMETHONIUM BROMIDE* (decameth-
ylenebis(trimethylammonium bromide); C 10).

Decamethrin *see* Deltamethrin.

**Decamethylene-1,10-bis(adamant-1-yldimethylam-
monium iodide)** *see* Decadonium iodide.

**1,1'-Decamethylenebis(4-aminoquinaldinium acet-
ate)** *see* Dequalinium acetate.

**1,1'-Decamethylenebis(4-aminoquinaldinium chlor-
ide)** *see* Dequalinium chloride.

**1,1'-Decamethylenebis[1,4-dihydro-4-(octylimino)-
pyridine]** *see* Octenidine.

**Decamethylenebis[dimethyl(2-thymyloxyethyl)am-
monium bromide]** *see* Deditonium bromide.

**Decamethylenebis(methylcarbamic acid) ester with
(*m*-hydroxyphenyl)trimethylammonium bromide**
see Demecarium bromide.

**N,N'-Decamethylenebis[[*m*-[(methylcarbamoyl)-
oxy]phenyl]trimethylammonium bromide]** *see* Demecarium bromide.

**2,2'-Decamethylenebis(1,2,3,4-tetrahydro-6,7-di-
methoxy-1-veratrylisoquinolinium methylsulfate)**
see Laudexium metilsulfate.

Decamethylenebis(trimethylammonium bromide) *see*
Decamethonium bromide.

4,4'-(Decamethylenediimino)diquinaldine *see* Quindecamine.

2,2'-(Decamethylenedithio)diethanol *see* Tiadenol.

2,2'-(Decamethylenedithio)diethanol bis(clofibrate)
see Tiafibrate.

**2-(Decamethyltetracontadecaenyl)-5,6-dimethoxy-
3-methyl-*p*-benzoquinone** *see* Ubidecarenone.

Decanedioic acid *see* Sebacic acid.

DECANOIC ACID (capric acid; decylic acid).

'**Decapryn**' *see* Doxylamine.

Decarboxycysteine *see* Mercaptamine.

Decarboxycystine *see* Cystamine.

'**Decaris**' *see* Levamisole.

'**Decaserpil**' *see* Methoserpidine.

'**Decaserpine**' *see* Methoserpidine.

'**Decaserpyl**' *see* Methoserpidine.

'**Decasone**' *see* Dexamethasone.

Decaspiride *see* Fenspiride.

'**Deccox**' *see* Decoquinate.

DECENOIC ACID (decylenic acid).

'**Decentan**' *see* Perphenazine enantate.

DECIMEMIDE* (4-decyloxy-3,5-dimethoxy-
benzamide).

'**Decis**' *see* Deltamethrin.

DECITROPINE* (3α-(5*H*-dibenzo[*a,d*]cyclo-
hepten-5-yloxy)tropane).

DECLENPERONE* (1-[3-[4-(4-fluorobenzoyl)-

piperid-1-yl]propyl]-2-benzimidazolinone; R-33204).

'**Declinax**' *see* Debrisoquine.

'**Declomycin**' *see* Demeclocycline.

DECLOXIZINE*** (1-(diphenylmethyl)-4-[2-(2-hydroxyethoxy)ethyl]piperazine; 2-[2-[4-(diphenylmethyl)piperazin-1-yl]ethoxy]ethanol; UCB-1402).

'**Decme**' *see* Dihydroergocristine.

'**Decofilina**' *see* Etamiphyllin dehydrocholate.

DECOMINOL*** (1-amino-3-(decyloxy)-2-propanol).

'**Deconamine**' *see under* Pseudoephedrine.

DECOQUINATE*** (ethyl 6-decyloxy-7-ethoxy-4-hydroxyquinoline-3-carboxylate; HC-1528; M & B-15497; 'deccox').

'**Decorpa**' *see* Guar gum.

'**Decortilen**' *see* Prednylidene.

'**Decortisyl**' *see* Prednisone.

DECTAFLUR*** (9-octadecenylamine hydrofluoride; SK&F-38094).

'**Dectan**' *see* Dexamethasone troxundate.

'**Dectancyl**' *see* Dexamethasone.

Decylenic acid *see* Decenoic acid.

Decyl(2-hydroxyethyl)dimethylammonium bromide 1-adamantanecarboxylate *see* Amantanium bromide.

Decylic acid *see* Decanoic acid.

4-Decyloxy-3,5-dimethoxybenzamide *see* Decimemide.

6-Decyloxy-7-ethoxy-4-hydroxyquinoline-3-carboxylic acid ethyl ester *see* Decoquinate.

'**Dedetane**' *see* DDT.

'**Dedevap**' *see* Dichlorvos.

Dediton* *see* Deditonium bromide.

DEDITONIUM BROMIDE*** (decamethylenebis[dimethyl(2-thymyloxyethyl)ammonium bromide]; dediton).

'**Dedrogyl**' *see* Calcifediol.

'**Dedyl**' *see* Diisopropylamine dichloroacetate.

12,13-Deepoxy-12,13-didehydro-4′-deoxycirramycin A₁ *see* Repromicin.

Deet *see* Diethyltoluamide.

DEF *see* Tributyl phosphorotrithioate.

'**Defekton**' *see* Carpipramine.

'**Defencin**' *see* Isoxsuprine.

DEFEROXAMINE** (30-amino-3,14,25-trihydroxy-3,9,14,20,25-pentaazatriacontane-2,10,13,21,24-pentaone; N-[5-[3-[(5-aminopentyl)hydroxycarbamoyl]propionamido]pentyl]-3-[[5-(N-hydroxyacetamido)pentyl]carbamoyl]propionylhydroxamic acid; desferrioxamine; deferoxamine hydrochloride; Ba-29837; NSC-527604).

DEFEROXAMINE MESILATE (deferoxamine mesylate; deferoxamine methanesulfonate; DFOM; Ba-33122; 'desferal'; 'desferol').

'**Defibrase**' *see* Batroxobin.

DEFIBROTIDE*** (polydeoxyribonucleotides of bovine lung (mol. wts between 45000 and 55000)).

'**Defilin**' *see* Docusate sodium.

'**Deflamene**' *see* Formocortal.

'**Deflamon**' *see under* Metronidazole.

DEFLAZACORT*** (11β,21-dihydroxy-2′-methyl-5′βH-pregna-1,4-dieno[17,16-d]oxazole-3,20-dione 21-acetate; azacort; DL-458-IT; L-5458; MDL-458).

'**Defluina**' *see under* Ajmalicine.

DEFOSFAMIDE*** (2-chloroethyl N,N-bis(2-chloroethyl)-N′-(3-hydroxypropyl)phosphorodiamidate; dephosphamide).

'**Defungit**' *see* Bensuldazic acid.

'**Degalol**' *see* Deoxycholic acid.

DEGLYCYRRHIZINIZED LIQUORICE ('caved S'; 'cedona'; 'rucedal'; 'ulcedal').

'**Degranol**' *see* Mannomustine.

'**Degripol**' *see* Propyphenazone.

'**Dehacodin**' *see* Dihydrocodeine.

'**Dehydranone**' *see* Dehydroacetic acid.

DEHYDROACETIC ACID (2-acetyl-5-hydroxy-3-oxo-4-hexenoic acid δ-lactone; 3-acetyl-6-methyl-2H-pyran-2,4(3H)-dione; methylacetopyronone).

Dehydroandrosterone *see* Prasterone.

Dehydrobenzperidol *see* Droperidol.

7-DEHYDROCHOLESTEROL (cholesta-5,7-dien-3-ol; provitamin D₃).

24-Dehydrocholesterol *see* Desmosterol.

DEHYDROCHOLIC ACID*** (3,7,12-triketocholanic acid; 3,7,12-trioxo-5β-cholan-24-oic acid; dehydrocholate sodium).
See also Cofisatin.

11-DEHYDROCORTICOSTERONE (17-(2-hydroxy-1-oxoethyl)-4-androstene-3,11-dione; 21-hydroxy-4-pregnene-3,11,20-trione; Kendall's compound A; NSC-9702).

Dehydrocortisol *see* Prednisolone.

2,2′-Dehydrodimorphine *see* Pseudomorphine.

DEHYDROEMETINE*** (3-ethyl-1,6,7,11b-tetrahydro-9,10-dimethoxy-2-(1,2,3,4-tetrahydro-6,7-dimethoxyisoquinolin-1-ylmethyl)-4H-benzo[a]quinolizine; DHE; BT-436; Ro 1-9334).

Dehydroepiandrosterone *see* Prasterone.

11-Dehydro-17-hydroxycorticosterone *see* Cortisone.

6-Dehydro-17α-hydroxy-16-methyleneprogesterone acetate *see* MDAP.

Dehydroimipramine *see* Depramine.

5,6-Dehydroisoandrosterone *see* Prasterone.

Dehydropempidine *see* Dropempine.

6-Dehydro-9β,10α-progesterone *see* Dydrogesterone.

3-DEHYDRORETINOL (vitamin A₂).

6-Dehydroretroprogesterone *see* Dydrogesterone.

Dehydrostilbestrol *see* Dienestrol.

'**Dekadin**' *see* Dequalinium chloride.

'**Dekelmin**' *see* Metyridine.

'**Deladroxate**' *see under* Algestone acetofenide.

'**Deladroxone**' *see* Algestone acetofenide.

'**Delagil**' *see* Chloroquine diphosphate.

'**Delakmin**' *see* 25-Hydroxycolecalciferol.

'**Delalutin**' *see* Hydroxyprogesterone caproate.

'**Delan**' *see* Dithianon.

DELANTERONE*** (1α-methylandrosta-4,16-

dien-3-one).
'**Delatestryl**' *see* Testosterone enantate.
'**Delaxin**' *see* Methocarbamol.
'**Delazin**' *see* Promazine.
'**Delcaine**' *see* Pseudococaine.
'**Delegol**' *see* o-Benzylphenol.
DELERGOTRILE* (6-methylergoline-8α-aceto-
   nitrile).
'**Delestrec**' *see* Estradiol undecylate.
'**Delestrogen**' *see* Estradiol valerate.
DELFANTRINE* (N^1,N^1-dimethyl-3-(4-methyl-
   piperazin-1-ylcarbonyl)sulfanilamide; Ba-
   32968).
'**Delfen**' *see* Nonoxinol 9.
'**Delgesic**' *see* Lysine acetylsalicylate.
'**Delichol**' *see* Choline citrate.
'**Delimmun**' *see* Inosine pranobex.
'**Delinal**' *see* Oxyclipine.
'**Delipoderm**' *see* Promestriene.
'**Delladec**' *see* Dexamethasone acetate.
DELMADINONE* (6-chloro-17α-hydroxy-
   pregna-1,4,6-triene-3,20-dione; Δ¹-chlormadin-
   one; 'tandak').
DELMADINONE ACETATE* (RS-1301; 'es-
   trex').
'**Delmeson**' *see* Fluorometholone.
DELMETACIN* (1-benzoyl-2-methylindole-3-
   acetic acid; demetacin).
'**Delnav**' *see* Dioxation.
DELORAZEPAM* (7-chloro-5-(o-chlorophen-
   yl)-1,3-dihydro-2H-1,4-benzodiazepin-2-one;
   chlorodemethyldiazepam; Ro 5-3027; RV-
   12165).
DELOXOLONE* (3β-hydroxyolean-9(11)-en-30-
   oic acid hydrogen succinate).
m-**Delphene** *see* Diethyltoluamide.
'**Delphicort**' *see* Triamcinolone.
'**Delpregnen**' *see under* Megestrol acetate.
DELPROSTENATE* (methyl (2E,5Z)-7-
   [(1R,2R,3R,5S)-2[(E)(3R)-4-(3-chlorophenoxy)-
   3-hydroxy-1-butenyl]-3,5-dihydroxycyclopent-
   yl]-2,5-heptadienoate; methyl 6-(3-chlorophen-
   oxy)-9,11,15-trihydroxy-ω-tetranorprosta-
   2,5,13-trienoate).
'**Delprosyn**' *see* Propicillin.
'**Delspectin**' *see* Spectinomycin.
Delta-E *see* Prednisone.
Delta-F *see* Prednisolone.
'**Delta-asverin**' *see* Tipepidine.
'**Delta-butazolidine**' *see under* Phenylbutazone.
Deltacortisone *see* Prednisone.
'**Deltacortone**' *see* Prednisone.
'**Delta-elmedal**' *see under* Phenylbutazone.
'**Deltafluorene**' *see* Dexamethasone.
Deltahydrocortisone *see* Prednisolone.
DELTAMETHRIN* (3-(2,2-dibromoethenyl)-2,2-
   dimethylcyclopropanecarboxylic acid ester with
   m-phenoxymandelonitrile; (S)-cyano(3-phen-
   oxyphenyl)methyl (1R,3R)-3-(2,2-dibromoethen-
   yl)-2,2-dimethylcyclopropanecarboxylate; 3-
   (2,2-dibromovinyl)-2,2-dimethylcyclopropane-
   carboxylic acid α-cyano-3-phenoxybenzyl ester;
   decamethrin; NRDC-161; OMS-1998; 'decis').

'**Deltamide**' *see* Diethyltoluamide.
'**Deltamin**' *see* Metformin.
'**Deltamine**' *see* Pemoline.
'**Deltan berna**' *see* Dimethyl sulfoxide.
'**Deltaplasma**' *see* Dextran.
'**Deltoin**' *see* Metetoin.
'**Deltyl**' *see* Barbipyrine.
'**Delursan**' *see* Ursodeoxycholic acid.
'**Deluteval**' *see under* Estradiol valerate.
'**Delvinal**' *see* Vinbarbital.
'**Delvosteron**' *see* Proligestone.
'**Delysid**' *see* Lysergide.
'**Dema**' *see* Chlormethine.
'**Demalon**' *see* 17β-Hydroxy-1α,17-dimethylandros-
   tan-3-one.
Demanol aceglumate* *see* Deanol aceglumate.
'**Demasorb**' *see* Dimethyl sulfoxide.
'**Demazin**' *see under* Pseudoephedrine.
DEMBROXOL** (*trans*-4-[(3,5-dibromosalicyl)-
   amino]cyclohexanol).
DEMECARIUM BROMIDE* ((*m*-hydroxy-
   phenyl)trimethylammonium bromide deca-
   methylenebis(methylcarbamate); N,N'-deca-
   methylenebis[[*m*-[(methylcarbamoyl)oxy]phen-
   yl]trimethylammonium bromide]; demecastigmine; BC-48).
Demecastigmine* *see* Demecarium bromide.
DEMECLOCYCLINE* (7-chloro-6-demethyl-
   tetracycline; demethylchlortetracycline; demeclocycline hydrochloride; DMCT; 'declomycin';
   'ledermycin'; 'mexocine').
DEMECLOCYCLINE plus TRIAMCINOLONE
   ('ledermix').
   See also under Tetracycline.
DEMECOLCINE* (6,7-dihydro-1,2,3,10-tetra-
   methoxy-7-(methylamino)-5H-benzo[*a*]heptalen-
   9-one; N-deacetyl-N-methylcolchicine; colchamine; omain; C-12669/A; NSC-3096).
DEMECYCLINE* (6-demethyltetracycline; desmethyltetracycline; CL-22415).
DEMEGESTONE* (19-demethyl-17α-methyl-
   pregna-4,9-diene-3,20-dione; 17-methyl-19-nor-
   pregna-4,9-diene-3,20-dione; 17α-methyl-Δ⁹-19-
   norprogesterone; R-2453; 'lutionex').
DEMELVERINE* (N-methyldiphenethyl-
   amine).
Demephion *see under* Demephion-O.
DEMEPHION-O* (O,O-dimethyl O-[2-(methylthio)ethyl] phosphorothioate).
DEMEPHION-O plus DEMEPHION-S (demephion; 'atlasetox'; 'cymetox').
DEMEPHION-S* (O,O-dimethyl S-[2-(methylthio)ethyl] phosphorothioate; methyl demeton
   methyl; M-82; 'tinox').
'**Demerol**' *see* Pethidine.
'**Demeso**' *see* Dimethyl sulfoxide.
Demetacin *see* Delmetacin.
Demethyl.... *see also* Desmethyl.....
Demethylchlortetracycline* *see* Demeclocycline.
6-Demethyl-6-deoxy-7-dimethylaminotetracycline
   see Minocycline.
**6-Demethyl-6-deoxy-5-hydroxy-6-methylenetetra-
   cycline** *see* Metacycline.

148

6-Demethyl-6-deoxy-7-nitrotetracycline *see* Nitrocycline.

6-Demethyl-6-deoxytetracycline *see* Sancycline.

Demethyldiazepam *see* Nordazepam.

Demethyldiazepam oxide *see* Demoxepam.

4′-Demethylepipodophyllotoxin 9-(4,6-O-ethylidene-β-D-glucopyranoside) *see* Etoposide.

4′-Demethylepipodophyllotoxin 9-(4,6-O-2-thenylidene-β-D-glucopyranoside) *see* Teniposide.

N-Demethyl-N-formylleurosine *see* Vinformide.

19-Demethyl-17α-methylpregna-4,9-diene-3,20-dione *see* Demegestone.

N-Demethylorphenadrine *see* Tofenacin.

Demethylpapaverine *see* Papaveroline.

6-Demethyltetracycline *see* Demecycline.

Demeton *see under* Demeton-O.

DEMETON-O* (*O,O*-diethyl *O*-[2-(ethylthio)-ethyl] phosphorothioate; mercaptophossystox; merkaptofos; thionosystox).

DEMETON-O plus DEMETON-S (demeton; diethyl ethylthioglycol thiophosphate; mercaptophas; Bayer-8196; E-1059; 'systox'; 'vnuran').

DEMETON-S* (*O,O*-diethyl *S*-[2-(ethylthio)ethyl] phosphorothioate; isodemeton; isosystox; merkaptofos tiolovyj; thiolosystox).
See also under Demeton-O.

Demeton-methyl *see under* Demeton-O-methyl.

DEMETON-O-METHYL* (*O*-[2-(ethylthio)ethyl] *O,O*-dimethyl phosphorothioate; methylmercaptophos; metil-merkaptofos).

DEMETON-O-METHYL plus DEMETON-S-METHYL (demeton-methyl; methyl-demeton; 'metaisosystox'; 'meta-systemox'; 'metasystox'; 'methylsystox').

DEMETON-S-METHYL* (*S*-[2-(ethylthio)ethyl] *O,O*-dimethyl phosphorothioate; isodemeton methyl; methyl isodemeton; methylisosystox; metil-merkaptofos tiolovyj; 'metaisosystox(i)'; 'metasystox(i)').
See also under Demeton-O-methyl.

DEMETON-S-METHYLSULFON* (demeton-*S*-methylsulphone; *S*-[2-(ethylsulfonyl)ethyl] *O,O*-dimethyl phosphorothioate; dioxydemeton-*S*-methyl; methylisosystoxsulfon; 'metaisosystoxsulfon').
See also under Azinphos-methyl.

Demeton-S-methylsulfoxide *see* Oxydemeton-methyl.

Demeton-S-methylsulphone *see* Demeton-S-methylsulfon.

'Demetrim' *see* Prazepam.

'Demetrin' *see* Prazepam.

DEMEXIPTILINE* (5*H*-dibenzo[*a,d*]cyclohepten-5-one *O*-[2-(methylamino)ethyl]oxime).

'Demidone' *see* Hydroxypethidine.

'Demigran' *see* Flumedroxone.

DEMOCONAZOLE* ((*E*)-1-[2,4-dichloro-β-[2-[4-chlorophenoxy]ethoxy]styryl]imidazole).

'Demosan' *see* Chloroneb.

'Demotil' *see* Diphemanil metilsulfate.

DEMOXEPAM* (7-chloro-1,3-dihydro-5-phenyl-2*H*-1,4-benzodiazepin-2-one 4-oxide; demethyldiazepam oxide; nordazepam oxide;

NSC-46077; Ro 5-2092).

DEMOXYTOCIN* (1-(3-mercaptopropionic acid)oxytocin; deaminooxytocin; ODA-914; 'sandopart').

'Demulen' *see under* Etynodiol diacetate.

'Demycin' *see* Buclosamide.

DENA *see* Diethylnitrosamine.

Denaton* *see* Denatonium benzoate.

DENATONIUM BENZOATE* (benzyldiethyl(2,6-xylylcarbamoylmethyl)ammonium benzoate; denaton; lidocaine benzyl benzoate; NSC-157658; THS-839).

DENAVERINE* (2-(dimethylamino)ethyl 2-(2-ethylbutoxy)-2,2-diphenylacetate; denaverine hydrochloride; X-60; 'spasmalgan').

'Dendrid' *see* Idoxuridine.

'Denka antisprout' *see* Propham.

DENOFUNGIN* (antibiotic from *Str. hygroscopicus*; U-28009).

'De-nol' *see* Bismuth subcitrate.

DENOPAMINE ((−)-(*R*)-α-[[(3,4-dimethoxyphenethyl)amino]methyl]-*p*-hydroxybenzyl alcohol).

DENPIDAZONE* (4-butyl-1,2-dihydro-5-hydroxy-1,2-diphenyl-3,6-pyridazinedione).

'Dentromin' *see* Pemoline.

DENZIMOL* ((±)-α-(*p*-phenethylphenyl)imidazole-1-ethanol; *N*-[2-[4-(2-phenylethyl)phenyl]-2-hydroxyethyl]imidazole; denzimol hydrochloride; Rec 15-1533).

'Deosan' *see* Sodium hypochlorite.

6′-Deoxo-9,10α-dihydro-β-ergocriptine *see* Desocriptine.

9-Deoxo-16,16-dimethyl-9-methylenedinoprostone *see* Meteneprost.

1-De(5-oxo-L-proline)-2-de-L-glutamine-5-L-methioninecaerulein *see* Sincalide.

Deoxy.... *see also* Desoxy.....

3′-Deoxyadenosine *see* Cordycepin.

5-Deoxyadenosylcobamide *see* Cobamamide.

DEOXYCHOLIC ACID (3,12-dihydroxycholanic acid; choleic acid).

2′-Deoxycoformycin *see* Pentostatin.

11-Deoxycortisone *see* Cortodoxone.

Deoxycortone* *see* Desoxycortone.

17-Deoxydexamethasone *see* Desoximetasone.

12-Deoxyerythromycin *see* Berythromycin.

O-3-Deoxy-3-(ethylamino)-4-C-methyl-β-L-arabinopyranosyl-(1→4)-O-[2,6-diamino-2,3,4,6-tetradeoxy-α-D-glycero-hex-4-enopyranosyl-(1→6)]-2-deoxy-L-streptamine *see* Etisomicin.

2′-DEOXY-5-ETHYLURIDINE (EDU; 'edurid').

21-Deoxy-F-4 *see* Descinolone.

2′-Deoxy-5-fluorouridine *see* Floxuridine.

5′-Deoxy-5-fluorouridine *see* Doxifluridine.

11-Deoxy-17-hydroxycorticosterone *see* Cortodoxone.

3-Deoxy-17α-hydroxy-6α-methylprogesterone *see* Anagestone.

6-Deoxy-5-hydroxytetracycline *see* Doxycycline.

2′-Deoxy-5-iodouridine *see* Idoxuridine.

4′-Deoxyleurocristine *see* Vinepidine.

3-[6-(O-6-Deoxy-α-L-mannopyranosyl)-β-D-gluco-

149

pyranosyloxy]-3′,4′,5,7-tetrahydroxyflavylium chloride *see* Keracyanin.

1-Deoxy-1-methylamino-D-glucitol *see* Meglumine.

3β-[(6-Deoxy-4-*O*-methyl-α-L-mannopyranosyl)-oxy]-14-hydroxybufa-4,20,22-trienolide *see* Meproscillarin.

O-3-Deoxy-4-*C*-methyl-3-(methylamino)-β-L-arabinopyranosyl-(1→4)-*O*-(2,6-diamino-2,3,4,6-tetradeoxy-α-D-glycero-hex-4-enopyranosyl-(1→6))-2-deoxy-*N*³-ethyl-L-streptamine *see* Netilmicin.

O-3-Deoxy-4-*C*-methyl-3-(methylamino)-β-L-arabinopyranosyl-(1→1)-*O*-[2,6-diamino-2,3,4,6-tetradeoxy-α-D-glycero-hex-4-enopyranosyl-(1→3)]-4,6-diamino-4,5,6-trideoxy-D-myo-inositol *see* Pentisomicin.

2-Deoxy-2-(3-methyl-3-nitrosoureido)-D-glucopyranose *see* Streptozocin.

21-Deoxy-21-(4-methylpiperazin-1-yl)prednisolone *see* Mazipredone.

2-Deoxy-2-nicotinamido-β-D-glucopyranose 1,3,4,6-tetranicotinate *see* Glunicate.

6-Deoxyoxytetracycline *see* Doxycycline.

3-(2-Deoxy-β-D-*erythro*-pentofuranosyl)-3,6,7,8-tetrahydroimidazo[4,5-*d*][1,3]diazepin-8-ol *see* Pentostatin.

2-Deoxyphenytoin *see* Doxenitoin.

21-Deoxyprednisolone *see* Deprodone.

DEOXYPYRIDOXINE (4-deoxypyridoxine; 5-hydroxy-4,6-dimethyl-3-pyridinemethanol; NSC-3063).

DEOXYRIBONUCLEASE (dornase).
See also Pancreatic dornase; Streptodornase.

2-Deoxy-2-(tetracyclinylmethylamino)-β-D-glucopyranose *see* Meglucycline.

21-Deoxytriamcinolone *see* Descinolone.

2′-Deoxy-5-(trifluoromethyl)uridine *see* Trifluridine.

11-Deoxy-11,16,16-trimethyldinoprostone *see* Trimoprostil.

14-Deoxyvincaminic acid 2-hydroxypropyl ester *see* Vinpoline.

2,4-DEP (2-(2,4-dichlorophenoxy)ethanol phosphite (3:1); 'falone').

'Depakene' *see* Valproic acid.

'Depamide' *see* Valpromide.

'Depasan' *see* Sparteine.

'Depen' *see* Penicillamine.

'Depepsen' *see* Sodium amylosulfate.

'Depersolon' *see* Mazipredone.

ɟ-De(L-phenylalanine)insulin *see* Insulin defalan.

Dephosphamide* *see* Defosfamide.

'Depigman' *see* Monobenzone.

'Depixol' *see* Flupentixol decanoate.

'Depleil' *see* Teclothiazide.

'Deplet' *see* Teclothiazide.

'Depo-clinovir' *see* Medroxyprogesterone acetate.

'Depocural' *see* Clemizole penicillin.

'Depodillar' *see* Paramethasone acetate.

'Depo-estradiol' *see* Estradiol cipionate.

'Depoestromon' *see* Dianisylhexene.

'Depofemin' *see* Estradiol cipionate.

'Depo-medrol' *see* Methylprednisolone acetate.

'Depo-medrone' *see* Methylprednisolone acetate.

'Deponit' *see* Glyceryl trinitrate.

'Depo-nortestonate' *see* Nandrolone cipionate.

'Depo-prodasone' *see* Medroxyprogesterone acetate.

Depoprogesterone *see* Medroxyprogesterone acetate.

'Depo-provera' *see* Medroxyprogesterone acetate.

'Deposiston' *see* Ethinylestradiol 3-isopropylsulfonate.

'Depostat' *see* Gestonorone caproate.

'Deposteron' *see* Testosterone undecenate.

'Deposul' *see* Sulfadimethoxine.

'Depot-oestromenine' *see* Dianisylhexene.

'Depot-ostromon' *see* Dianisylhexene.

'Depovernil' *see* Sulfamethoxypyridazine.

'Depoviron' *see* Testosterone cipionate.

DEPRAMINE*** (5-[3-(dimethylamino)propyl]-5*H*-dibenz[*b,f*]azepine; balipramine; dehydroimipramine).

DEPRAMINE FUMARATE (G-31406).

'Deprelin' *see* Succinonitrile.

'Deprenaline' *see* Selegiline.

'Deprenon' *see* Acetergamine.

Deprenyl *see* Selegiline.

'Depressan' *see* Dihydralazine.

'Deprex' *see* Dibenzepin.

'Depridol' *see* Methadone.

'Deprinol' *see* Imipramine.

DEPRODONE** (11β,17α-dihydroxypregna-1,4-diene-3,20-dione; 21-deoxyprednisolone; desolone).

DEPRODONE PROPIONATE (deprodone 17-propionate; RD-20000).

'Deprol' *see under* Meprobamate.

'Depronal' *see* Dextropropoxyphene.

'Depropanex' *see* Kallidinogenase.

DEPROSTIL*** ((1*R*,2*S*)-2-(3-hydroxy-3-methyloctyl)-5-oxocyclopentaneheptanoic acid; 15-hydroxy-15-methyl-9-oxoprostan-1-oic acid; AY-22469).

'Depsococaine' *see* Pseudococaine.

DEPTROPINE*** (3-[(10,11-dihydro-5*H*-dibenzo[*a,d*]cyclohepten-5-yl)oxy]tropane; brontine; dibenzheptropine; detropine citrate; BS-6987).

'Dequadin' *see* Dequalinium chloride.

DEQUALINIUM ACETATE (1,1′-decamethylenebis(4-aminoquinaldinium acetate); 'salvicyclin').

DEQUALINIUM CHLORIDE*** (1,1′-decamethylenebis(4-aminoquinaldinium chloride); dequalon; BAQD-10).

Dequalon* *see* Dequalinium chloride.

'Dequavagyn' *see* Dequalinium chloride.

'Deracil' *see* Thiouracil.

'Dereuma' *see under* Aminophenazone.

'Derfon' *see* Amfepramone.

'Deripen' *see* Ampicillin.

'Dermafos' *see* Fenclofos.

'Dermairol' *see* Tretinoin.

'Dermalar' *see* Fluocinolone acetonide.

'Dermastatin' *see* Viridofulvin.

DERMATAN SULFATE (chondroitin sulfate B; β-heparin; 'beparin').

'Dermatol' *see* Bismuth gallate.
'Dermofungine-A' *see* Cloxiquine.
'Dermofungine-B' *see* Dichlorobenzododecinium chloride.
'Dermol' *see* Bismuth chrysophanate.
'Dermonistat' *see* Miconazole.
'Dermovate' *see* Clobetasol propionate.
'Dermoxin' *see* Clobetasol propionate *and* Tolnaftate.
'Deroctyl' *see* Glibenclamide.
'Deronil' *see* Dexamethasone.
'DES' *see* Diethylstilbestrol.
2,4-DES *see* Disul.
'Desace' *see* Deslanoside.
Desacetyl.... *see* Deacetyl.....
'Desaci' *see* Deslanoside.
Desaglybuzole* *see* Glybuzole.
'Desalfa' *see* Dexamethasone isonicotinate.
DESASPIDIN*** (3'-(5-butyryl-2,4-dihydroxy-3,3-dimethyl-6-oxo-1,4-cyclohexadien-1-ylmethyl)-2',6'-dihydroxy-4'-methoxybutyrophenone).
Deschlorbiomycin *see* Tetracycline.
DESCINOLONE*** (9-fluoro-11β,16α,17-trihydroxypregna-1,4-diene-3,20-dione; 21-deoxytriamcinolone; 21-deoxy-F-4; NSC-44827).
DESCINOLONE ACETONIDE* (descinolone cyclic 16,17-acetal with acetone; CL-27071; NSC-44827).
'Desclidium' *see* Viquidil.
'Descresept' *see* Aristolochic acid.
DESDANINE (*trans*-3-(1-pyrrolin-2-yl)acrylamide; cyclamidomycin; pyracrimycin A).
'Desenovis' *see* Xenyhexenic acid.
'Deseril' *see* Methysergide.
'Desernil' *see* Methysergide.
'Deserol' *see* Bromazine.
'Deseronil' *see* Dexamethasone acetate.
DESERPIDINE*** (trimethoxybenzoate of methyl 11-demethoxyreserpate; 11-desmethoxyreserpine; canescine).
'Desferal' *see* Deferoxamine mesilate.
'Desferol' *see* Deferoxamine mesilate.
Desferrioxamine* *see* Deferoxamine.
Desfluorotriamcinolone acetonide *see* Desonide.
Desglucolanatoside C *see* β-Acetyldigoxin.
DESGLUGASTRIN*** (N-(4-carboxybutyryl)-L-alanyl-L-tyrosylglycyl-L-tryptophyl-L-leucyl-L-α-aspartylphenyl-L-alaninamide).
'Desibyl' *see* Ox bile.
DESIPRAMINE*** (10,11-dihydro-5-(3-methylaminopropyl)-5H-dibenz[b,f]azepine; desmethylimipramine; norimipramine; DMI; AW-1151129; EX-4355; G-35020; JB-8181; NSC-114901).
Desitriptyline *see* Nortriptyline.
DESLANOSIDE*** (deacetyldigilanide C; deacetyllanatoside C; purpurea glycoside C).
Desmeth.... *see also* Demeth.....
Desmethoxykhellin *see* Visnagin.
11-Desmethoxy-10-methoxyreserpine *see* Methoserpidine.
11-Desmethoxyreserpine *see* Deserpidine.

Desmethylamitriptyline *see* Nortriptyline.
N-Desmethylcodeine *see* Norcodeine.
Desmethyldopan *see* Uramustine.
Desmethylemetine *see* Cephaeline.
Desmethylimipramine *see* Desipramine.
DESMETHYLMORAMIDE*** (1-(4-morpholino-2,2-diphenylbutyryl)pyrrolidine).
N-Desmethylmorphine *see* Normorphine.
Desmethylpipazuroylguanidine *see* Amiloride.
Desmethylprothiadene *see* Northiadene.
8-Desmethylpseudotropine *see* Norpseudotropine.
Desmethyltetracycline *see* Demecycline.
8-Desmethyltropine *see* Nortropine.
'Desmodure-15' *see* Naphthalene 1,5-diisocyanate.
'Desmodur T' *see* Toluene diisocyanate.
'Desmoid' *see* Methylene blue.
DESMOPRESSIN*** (1-deamino-8-D-arginine vasopressin; 1-(3-mercaptopropionic acid)-8-D-arginine vasopressin; 'adiuretin').
DESMOPRESSIN ACETATE* (desmopressin monoacetate; 'DDAVP').
DESMOPRESSIN DIACETATE ('desurin'; 'minirin'; 'minurin').
DESMOSTEROL (24-dehydrocholesterol).
DESOCRIPTINE*** (6'-deoxo-9,10α-dihydro-β-ergocriptine).
'Desogen' *see* Dofamium chloride *and* Toloconium chloride.
DESOGESTREL*** (13-ethyl-11-methylene-18,19-dinor-17α-pregn-4-en-20-yn-17-ol; 17α-ethinyl-18-methyl-11-methylene-4-estren-17-ol; Org-2969).
DESOGESTREL plus ETHINYLESTRADIOL ('marvelon'; 'oviol'; 'varnoline').
Desolone *see* Deprodone.
'Desomidine' *see* Hexamidine.
DESOMORPHINE*** (4,5-epoxy-3-hydroxy-N-methylmorphinan; dihydrodesoxymorphine).
DESONIDE** (11β,16α,17,21-tetrahydroxypregna-1,4-diene-3,20-dione cyclic 16,17-acetal with acetone; 11β,21-dihydroxy-16α,17α-isopropylidenedioxypregna,1,4-diene-3,20-dione; 16α-hydroxyprednisolone 16,17-acetonide; desfluorotriamcinolone acetonide; prednacinolone acetonide; D-2083; 'reticus'; 'sterax'; 'tridesilon'; 'tridesonit').
'Desopimon' *see* Chlorphentermine.
DESOXIMETASONE*** (9-fluoro-11β,21-dihydroxy-16α-methylpregna-1,4-diene-3,20-dione; 9α-fluoro-16α-methyl-17-deoxyprednisolone; 17-deoxydexamethasone; desoxymethasone; A-41304; HOE-304; R-2113; 'flubason'; 'ibaril'; 'topicorte'; 'topisolone').
DESOXIMETASONE plus NEOMYCIN ('stiedex').
Desoxy.... *see also* Deoxy.....
Desoxyalizarin *see* Anthrarobin.
11-Desoxycorticosterone *see* Desoxycortone.
11-Desoxycortisone *see* Cortodoxone.
DESOXYCORTONE*** (21-hydroxy-4-pregnene-3,20-dione; 21-hydroxyprogesterone; 11-desoxycorticosterone; deoxycortone; cortexone; Kendall's dioxy compound B; Reichstein's sub-

stance Q; DCA; DOC; NSC-11319).
See also under Nandrolone phenpropionate.

Desoxyephedrine *see* Methamphetamine.

2'-Desoxy-5-fluorouridine *see* Floxuridine.

Desoxyhexahydroephedrine *see* Propylhexedrine.

Desoxymethasone* *see* Desoximetasone.

Desoxynorephedrine *see* Amphetamine.

3-Desoxy-19-nortestosterone *see* Allylestrenol.

Desoxyphenobarbital *see* Primidone.

'De-squaman' *see* Pyrithione zinc.

'Dessin' *see* Dinobuton.

DESTHIOBIOTIN (5-methyl-2-oxo-4-imidazoli-dinehexanoic acid; dethiobiotin; NSC-3085).

'Destolit' *see* Ursodeoxycholic acid.

N-Desulfo-N-(2-sulfobenzoyl)heparin *see* o-Sulfo-benzheparide.

'Desuric' *see* Benzbromarone.

'Desurin' *see* Desmopressin diacetate.

DESYLAMINE (2-amino-2-phenylacetophenone; α-phenylphenacylamine).

'Desyrel' *see* Trazodone.

DET *see* Diethyltoluamide.

DETA *see* Diethyltoluamide.

DETAJMIUM BITARTRATE*** (4-[3-(diethyl-amino)-2-hydroxypropyl]ajmalinium hydrogen tartrate; 'tachmalcor').

'Detal' *see* Dinitro-o-cresol.

'Detamide' *see* Diethyltoluamide.

DETANOSAL** (2-(diethylamino)ethyl salicylate).

'Deteclo' *see under* Tetracycline.

'Detensor' *see under* Chlorotheophylline.

DETERENOL*** ((±)-p-hydroxy-α-[(isopropyl-amino)methyl]benzyl alcohol; (±)-1-(p-hydroxy-phenyl)-2-isopropylaminoethanol; deterenol hydrochloride; AL-842).

DETF *see* Metrifonate.

Dethiobiotin *see* Desthiobiotin.

Dethylandiamine *see* Thenyldiamine.

'Dethyrone' *see* Dextrothyroxine sodium.

'Detigon' *see* Clofedanol.

DETOMIDINE*** (4-(2,3-dimethylbenzyl)imid-azole).

DETORUBICIN*** (doxorubicin 3²-glyoxylate 2-(diethyl acetal)).

'Detraine' *see* Propanocaine.

DETRALFATE*** (dextran sulfate sodium salt aluminium complex).

DETROTHYRONINE*** (D-3-[4-(4-hydroxy-3-iodophenoxy)-3,5-diiodophenyl]alanine; D-3,3',5-triiodothyronine).

'Detrovel' *see* Estil.

'Deturgylone' *see* Prednazoline.

'Deumacard' *see* Pentetrazole.

'De-ursil' *see* Ursodeoxycholic acid.

'Develin' *see* Dextropropoxyphene.

'Devincal' *see* Vincamine.

'Devincan' *see* Vincamine.

'Devoran' *see* Lindane.

'Devrinol' *see* Napropamide.

'Devryl' *see* Clomacran.

'Dexabolin' *see under* Dexamethasone.

'Dexacillin' *see* Epicillin.

'Dexa-cortancyl' *see* Dexamethasone acetate.

'Dexa-cortisyl' *see* Dexamethasone.

'Dexambutol' *see* Ethambutol.

'Dexamed' *see* Dexamphetamine.

'Dexameth' *see* Dexamethasone.

DEXAMETHASONE*** (9α-fluoro-11β,17α,21-trihydroxy-16α-methyl-1,4-pregnadiene-3,20-di-one; 9α-fluoro-16α-methylprednisolone; Δ¹-de-hydro-9α-fluoro-16α-methylhydrocortisone; de-xadecadrol; hexadecadrol; dexamethasone disodium phosphate; dexamethasone sulfate; MK-125; NSC-34521).

DEXAMETHASONE plus BENZYL NICOTIN-ATE ('rheumasit').

DEXAMETHASONE plus ETHYLESTRENOL ('dexabolin').

DEXAMETHASONE plus INDOMETACIN (C-209; 'inflacine').
See also under Azidamfenicol.

DEXAMETHASONE ACETATE* (dexamethas-one 21-acetate; 'decadron-LA'; 'delladec'; 'dese-ronil'; 'dexa-cortancyl'; 'dexolone'; 'duphar-cort').

DEXAMETHASONE ISONICOTINATE (dexa-methasone 21-isonicotinate; dexamethasone 4-pyridinecarboxylate; HE-111; 'auxiloson'; 'aux-isone'; 'desalfa'; 'voren').

DEXAMETHASONE LINOLEATE (dexameth-asone 21-linoleate; ISF-2073; 'linoderm').

DEXAMETHASONE PIVALATE (dexamethas-one trimethylacetate; 'opticortenol').

DEXAMETHASONE PIVALATE plus PHENYLMERCURIC BORATE (Z-1141C; 'exosterol').

DEXAMETHASONE PIVALATE plus PREDN-ISOLONE ('opticortenol-S').

Dexamethasone 4-pyridinecarboxylate *see* Dexa-methasone isonicotinate.

DEXAMETHASONE SODIUM m-SULFO-BENZOATE ('dexa-sol'; 'hubersona'; 'sisotox').

DEXAMETHASONE SUCCINATE (dexameth-asone hydrogen succinate; 'betafluorene').

Dexamethasone trimethylacetate *see* Dexamethas-one pivalate.

DEXAMETHASONE TROXUNDATE* (dexa-methasone 3,6,9-trioxaundecanoate; 'dectan').

DEXAMISOLE** ((+)-2,3,5,6-tetrahydro-6-phenylimidazo[2,1-b]thiazole; dexamisole hydro-chloride; R-12563).
See also Levamisole; Tetramisole.

DEXAMPHETAMINE** ((+)-amphetamine; (+)-α-methylphenethylamine; dextroamphet-amine; dexamphetamine sulfate; NSC-73713).

DEXAMPHETAMINE plus AMOBARBITAL ('dexamyl').

'Dexamyl' *see under* Dexamphetamine.

'Dexascheroson' *see* Dexamethasone.

'Dexa-sol' *see* Dexamethasone sodium m-sulfo-benzoate.

'Dexawin' *see* Racefenicol.

Dexbenzetimide *see* Dexetimide.

DEXBROMPHENIRAMINE*** ((+)-2-p-bromo-α-(2-dimethylaminoethyl)benzyl]pyrid-

ine; (+)-3-(p-bromophenyl)-N,N-dimethyl-3-pyrid-2-ylpropylamine; dexbrompheniramine maleate).
See also Brompheniramine.

DEXCHLORPHENIRAMINE*** ((+)-2-[p-chloro-α-(2-dimethylaminoethyl)benzyl]pyridine; (+)-3-(p-chlorophenyl)-N,N-dimethyl-2-pyrid-2-ylpropylamine; dexchlorpheniramine maleate).
See also Chlorpheniramine; and under Betamethasone.

DEXCLAMOL*** ((+)-2,3,4,4aβ,8,9,13bα,14-octahydro-3α-isopropyl-1H-benzo[6,7]cyclohepta[1,2,3-de]pyrido[2,1-a]isoquinolin-3-ol; dexclamol hydrochloride; AY-24169).

'Dexedrine' see Dexamphetamine.

DEXETIMIDE** ((+)-benzetimide; dexbenzetimide; R-16470; 'tremblex').
See also Benzetimide.

DEXETOZOLINE*** ((+)-ethyl (Z)-(S)-3-methyl-4-oxo-5-piperid-1-yl-Δ^{2,α}-thiazolidineacetate).

DEXIMAFEN*** (2,3,5,6-tetrahydro-5-phenyl-1H-imidazo[1,2-a]imidazole; R-26333).
See also Imafen.

DEXINDOPROFEN*** ((+)-(S)-p-(1-oxoisoindolin-2-yl)hydratropic acid; (+)-4-(1,3-dihydro-1-oxo-2H-isoindol-2-yl)-α-methylbenzeneacetic acid).

'Dexium' see Calcium dobesilate.

DEXIVACAINE*** ((+)-1-methyl-2',6'-pipecoloxylidide; mepivacaine (+)-isomer).

DEXLOFEXIDINE*** ((+)-(S)-2-[1-(2,6-dichlorophenoxy)ethyl]-2-imidazoline).

Dexnorgestrel see Levonorgestrel.

Dexnorgestrel acetime see Norgestimate.

'Dexol' see Sodium perborate.

'Dexolone' see Dexamethasone acetate.

'Dexon' see Fenaminosulf and Polyglycolic acid.

DEXOXADROL*** ((+)-2,2-diphenyl-4-piperid-2-yl-1,3-dioxolane; dexoxadrol hydrochloride; CL-911-C; NSC-526062; U-22559A).

DEXPANTHENOL*** (D-(+)-2,4-dihydroxy-N-(3-hydroxypropyl)-3,3-dimethylbutyramide; pantothenol).

Dexphenmetrazine see Phenmetrazine.

DEXPROPRANOLOL*** ((+)-1-[2-hydroxy-3-(isopropylamino)propoxy]naphthalene; (+)-propranolol; dexpropranolol hydrochloride; AY-20694; ICI-47319).
See also Propranolol.

DEXPROXIBUTENE*** ((+)-3-[(dimethylamino)methyl]-1,2-diphenyl-3-buten-2-ol propionate).
See also Proxibutene.

'Dextelan' see Dexamethasone.

DEXTILIDINE** ((+)-ethyl trans-2-dimethylamino-1-phenyl-3-cyclohexene-1-carboxylate).

'Dextim' see Methamphetamine.

Dextrafer (tr) see Iron dextran injection.

Dextramycin (tr) see (+)-Chloramphenicol.

DEXTRAN*** (polysaccharide formed by Leuconostoc mesenteriodides; gemodex; polyglucin;

polyglukina; PVTD; sinkol).
See also below and Cross-linked dextran; Polidexide sulfate.

DEXTRAN 40* (low molecular weight dextran; reoisodex; reopoliglukin; 'fluidex'; 'infukoll M-40'; 'LMO'; 'lomodex'; 'rheomacrodex'; 'rheotran').

DEXTRAN 60 ('schiwadex 60').

DEXTRAN 70* ('gentran'; 'hyskor'; 'macrodex').

DEXTRAN 75 ('longasteril 75').

(Dextran)(glucoheptonic acid)hydroxyoxoiron see Gleptoferron.

DEXTRANOMER*** (dextran cross-linked with epichlorohydrin; dextran 2,3-dihydroxypropyl 2-hydroxy-1,3-propanediyl ether; 'debrisan').

DEXTRAN SULFATE ('dexulate'; 'polyran').
See also Detralfate; and under Betamethasone valerate.

'Dextraven' see Dextran.

DEXTRIFERRON*** (iron-dextrin complex; 'astrafer'; 'ferrigen').

Dextrin-epichlorohydrin-iodine reaction product see Cadexomer iodine.

Dextroamphetamine* see Dexamphetamine.

'Dextrococaine' see Pseudococaine.

DEXTROFEMINE*** ((+)-α-methyl-N-(1-methyl-2-phenoxyethyl)phenethylamine; (+)-threo-3,5-dimethyl-1,6-diphenyl-1-oxa-4-azahexane).
See also Racefemine.

DEXTROMETHORPHAN** ((+)-cis-1,3,4,9,10,10a-hexahydro-6-methoxy-11-methyl-2H-10,4a-iminoethanophenanthrene; 3-methoxy-N-methylmorphinan; dextromethorphan hydrobromide; Ro 1-5470/5; Ro 1-5479).
See also under Paracetamol.

DEXTROMORAMIDE** ((+)-1-(3-methyl-4-morpholino-2,2-diphenylbutyryl)pyrrolidine; (+)-4-(2-methyl-4-oxo-3,3-diphenyl-4-pyrrolidin-1-ylbutyl)morpholine; pyrrolamidole; dextromoramide bitartrate; R-875; SK&F-5137).

Dextromycetin (tr) see (+)-Chloramphenicol.

'Dextrone' see Diquat.

'Dextrone X' see Paraquat.

Dextronic acid see Gluconic acid.

DEXTROPROPOXYPHENE** ((+)-4-[(dimethylamino)methyl]-1,2-diphenyl-2-butanol propionate; (+)-(1S,2R)-1-benzyl-3-(dimethylamino)-2-methyl-1-phenylpropyl propionate; (+)-propoxyphene; dextropropoxyphene hydrochloride; propoxyphene hydrochloride).

DEXTROPROPOXYPHENE plus ACETYLSALICYLIC ACID ('dolasan').

DEXTROPROPOXYPHENE plus PARACETAMOL ('cosalgesic'; 'diantalvic'; 'distalgesic').
See also Levopropoxyphene and under Azapropazone; Proxifezone.

DEXTROPROPOXYPHENE NAPSILATE (propoxyphene napsilate; S-9700; 'darvocet-N'; 'darvon-N').

DEXTROPROPOXYPHENE THEOBROMIN-1-YLACETATE (Z-867; 'lenigesal').

DEXTRORPHAN** ((+)-cis-1,3,4,9,10,10a-hexahydro-11-methyl-2*H*-10,4a-iminoethanophen-anthren-6-ol; 3-hydroxy-*N*-methylmorphinan; Ro 1-6794).

Dextrose *see* Glucose.

Dextrosulfenidol *see* Thiamphenicol.

DEXTROTHYROXINE* (D-3-[4-(4-hydroxy-3,5-diiodophenoxy)-3,5-diiodophenyl]alanine; D-3,3′,5,5′-tetraiodothyronine; DT-5).

DEXTROTHYROXINE SODIUM* (dextrothyroxine sodium salt; sodium dextrothyroxine).

'Dexulate' *see* Dextran sulfate.

DEZAGUANINE (6-amino-1,5-dihydro-4*H*-imidazo[4,5-*c*]pyridin-4-one).

'Dezentan' *see* Perphenazine.

DEZOCINE* ((−)-13β-amino-5,6,7,8,9,10,11α,12-octahydro-5α-methyl-5,11-methanobenzocyclodecen-3-ol; Wy-16225).

DF-69 *see under* Ajmalicine.

DF-118 *see* Dihydrocodeine.

DFDT *see* 1,1,1-Trichloro-2,2-bis(*p*-fluorophenyl)-ethane.

DFOM *see* Deferoxamine mesilate.

DFP *see* Isoflurophate.

DFUR *see* Doxifluridine.

'D₂H' *see* Proxibarbal.

DH-524 *see* Fenmetozole.

DH-581 *see* Probucol.

DHA *see* Prasterone.

'DHA' *see* Dehydroacetic acid.

DHA 245 *see* Amiphenazole.

DHAQ *see* Mitoxantrone.

'DH-codeine' *see* Dihydrocodeine.

DHE *see* Dehydroemetine.

DHE-45 *see* Dihydroergotamine.

DHE-145 *see* Dihydroergocristine.

DHK-135 *see* Dihydroergocryptine.

DHO-180 *see* Dihydroergocornine.

'Diabesulf' *see* Carbutamide.

'Diabeta' *see* Glibenclamide.

'Diabetal' *see* Carbutamide.

'Diabetasi' *see* Chlorpropamide.

'Diabetol' *see* Tolbutamide.

'Diabetoral' *see* Chlorpropamide.

'Diabiformine' *see under* Chlorpropamide.

'Diabinese' *see* Chlorpropamide.

'Diabiphage' *see under* Chlorpropamide.

'Diaboral' *see* Glycyclamide.

'Diabtyl' *see under* Batroxobin.

'Diabuton' *see* Tolbutamide.

Diacarb (tr) *see* Acetazolamide.

Diacephine *see* Diamorphine.

DIACEREIN (9,10-dihydro-4,5-dihydroxy-9,10-dioxo-2-anthroic acid diacetate).

DIACETAMATE* (*p*-acetamidophenyl acetate).

4,4′-Diacetamidodiphenyl sulfone *see* Acedapsone.

3,5-Diacetamido-2,4,6-triiodobenzoic acid *see* Diatrizoic acid.

α,5-Diacetamido-2,4,6-triiodo-*m*-toluic acid *see* Iodamide.

2,5-Diacetamidovaleric acid *see* Bisorcic.

DIACETAZOTOL (*N*,*N*-diacetyl-4-(*o*-tolylazo)-*o*-toluidine; 4-(diacetylamino)-2′,3-dimethylazo-benzene; 2-(diacetylamino)-5-(*o*-tolylazo)tolu-ene; 4-(*o*-tolylazo)-*o*-diacetotoluidide; dimazene; amidoazotoluene diacetate; diacetotoluide; di-acetylaminoazotoluene; periphermium; 'di-mazon'; 'epidon'; 'pellidol').

DIACETOLOL* (*N*-[3-acetyl-4-[2-hydroxy-3-[(1-methylethyl)amino]propoxy]phenyl]acet-amide; 3′-acetyl-4′-[2-hydroxy-3-(isopropyl-amino)propoxy]acetanilide; diacetolol hydro-chloride; EU-4891; M & B-16942A).

DIACETONE ALCOHOL (4-hydroxy-4-methyl-2-pentanone; 'tyranton').

Diacetotoluide *see* Diacetazotol.

2,3-Diacetoxybenzoic acid *see* Dipyrocetyl.

4,4′-Diacetoxy-5,5′-difluoro-(1-ethyl-2-methylethyl-ene)di-*m*-phenylene diacetate *see* Acefluranol.

Diacetoxydiphenylisatin *see* Acetphenolisatin.

Diacetyl *see* 2,3-Butanedione.

3,6-Di-*O*-acetyl-17-allyl-17-normorphine *see* Di-acetylnalorphine.

Diacetylaminoazotoluene *see* Diacetazotol.

4-(Diacetylamino)-2′,3-dimethylazobenzene *see* Diacetazotol.

2-(Diacetylamino)-5-(*o*-tolylazo)toluene *see* Diacetazotol.

3-Diacetylamino-2,4,6-triiodobenzoic acid *see* Docetrizoic acid.

Diacetylcholine *see* Suxamethonium chloride.

Diacetyldapsone *see* Acedapsone.

Diacetyldiaphenylsulfone *see* Acedapsone.

DIACETYLDIHYDROMORPHINE (dihydrohe-roin; paralaudin).

2,6-Diacetyl-7,9-dihydroxy-8,9a-dimethyldibenzofu-ran-1,3-dione *see* Usnic acid.

Diacetyldihydroxyphenylisatin *see* Acetphenolisat-in.

Diacetyldiphenolisatin *see* Acetphenolisatin.

DIACETYL MONOXIME (2,3-butanedione monoxime; DAM; NSC-660).

Diacetylmorphine *see* Diamorphine.

DIACETYLNALORPHINE* ((−)-(5*R*,6*S*)-9a-allyl-4,5-epoxymorphin-7-ene-3,6-diyl diacetate; 3,6-di-*O*-acetyl-17-allyl-17-normorphine; na-lorphine diacetate).

N²,N⁵-Diacetyl-L-ornithine *see* Bisorcic.

Diacetylpyrocatecholcarboxylic acid *see* Dipyrocet-yl.

Diacetylthiamine *see* Acetiamine.

1α,7α-Diacetylthio-17β-hydroxy-17-methylandrost-4-en-3-one *see* Tiomesterone.

N,N-Diacetyl-4-(*o*-tolylazo)-*o*-toluidine *see* Diacetazotol.

'Diacid' *see* Carbromal.

'Diacromone' *see* Methylchromone.

'Di-ademil' *see* Hydroflumethiazide.

Diadonium diiodide *see* Diadonium iodide.

DIADONIUM IODIDE (tr) (bis[2-(*N*-adamant-1-yl-*N*-methylamino)ethyl] succinate dimethiod-ide; (3,8-dioxa-4,7-dioxodecamethylene-1,10)bis-(adamant-1-yldimethylammonium iodide); suc-cinic acid bis[2-(*N*-adamant-1-yl-*N*-methyl-amino)ethyl] ester dimethiodide; diadonium di-iodide).

'Diadril' *see* Meclozine.

'**Diafen**' *see* Diphenylpyraline.
'**Diaginol**' *see* Sodium acetrizoate.
'**Diagnex blue**' *see* Azuresin.
'**Diakarmon**' *see* Sorbitol.
'**Dial**' *see* Allobarbital.
'**Dialar**' *see* Diazepam.
'**Dialicor**' *see* Etafenone.
Dialifor* *see* Dialifos.
DIALIFOS* (*S*-[2-chloro-1-(1,3-dihydro-1,3-di-oxo-2*H*-isoindol-2-yl)ethyl] *O*,*O*-diethyl phosphorodithioate; *N*-[2-chloro-1-[(diethoxyphosphinothioyl)thio]ethyl]phthalimide; dialifor; 'torak').
DIALLATE* (*S*-(2,3-dichloro-2-propenyl) bis(1-methylethyl)carbamothioate; *S*-(2,3-dichloroallyl) diisopropylcarbamothioate; di-allate; DATC; 2,3-DCDT; 'avadex'; 'CFT').
Di-allate* *see* Diallate.
Diallylacetic acid *see* 2-Allyl-4-pentenoic acid.
Diallylbarbital *see* Allobarbital.
5,5-Diallylbarbituric acid *see* Allobarbital.
5,5'-Diallyl-α,α'-bis(diethylamino)-*m*,*m*'-bitolyl-4,4'-diol *see* Bialamicol.
Diallylbis(diethylaminomethyl)biphenol *see* Bialamicol.
N,*N*'-**Diallylbisnortoxiferine dichloride** *see* Alcuronium chloride.
N,*N*-**Diallyl-2-chloroacetamide** *see* Allidochlor.
DIALLYLMELAMINE (4,6-diamino-2-(diallylamino)-*s*-triazine; U-7720).
Diallylmelamine *N*-oxide *see* Oxonazine.
N,*N*'-**Diallylnortoxiferinium dichloride** *see* Alcuronium chloride.
Diallymal* *see* Allobarbital.
'**Dialose plus**' *see* Oxyphenisatine.
DIALURIC ACID (5-hydroxybarbituric acid; tartronylurea).
Diamantane *see* Adamantane.
'**Diamethine**' *see* Dimethyltubocurarine chloride.
DIAMFENETIDE** (2,2'-bis(4-acetamidophenoxy)ethyl ether; β,β'-oxybis(*p*-acetophenetidide); oxybis(*p*-ethoxyacetanilide); diamphenethide; oxybisphenacetin; compound 68-198; 'coriban').
'**Diamicron**' *see* Gliclazide.
DIAMIDE (1,1'-azobis(*N*,*N*-dimethylformamide); bis(dimethylcarbamoyl)diimide; diazenedicarboxylic acid bis(dimethylamide); *N*,*N*,*N*',*N*'-tetramethylazoformamide).
4,4'-Diamidinodiphenoxypropane *see* Propamidine.
4,4'-Diamidinodiphenyl ether *see* Phenamidine.
'**Diamine blue**' *see* Trypan blue.
DIAMINE OXIDASE (histaminase; 'torantil'; 'torantyl').
3,6-Diaminoacridine *see* Proflavine.
2,4-Diamino-5-(4-amino-3,5-dimethoxybenzyl)pyrimidine *see* Aditeren.
6,9-Diamino-1-(6-amino-9*H*-purin-9-yl)-1,5,6,7,8,9-hexadeoxy-β-D-*ribo*-decofuranuronic acid *see* Sinefungin.
2,4-Diaminoazobenzene *see* Chrysoidine.
Diaminobenzpyrylum *see* Tripelennamine.
4,4'-Diaminobiphenyl *see* Benzidine.
2,4-Diamino-5-(4-bromo-3,5-dimethoxybenzyl)pyr-

imidine *see* Brodimoprim.
2',6'-Diamino-2-butoxy-3,3'-azopyridine *see* Neotropin.
Diaminocaproic acid *see* Lysine.
2,6-Diamino-3-carboguanidino-5-chloropyrazine *see* Amiloride.
*N*⁴-**(2,4-Diamino-6-carboxyphenylazo)sulfanilamide** *see* Sulfachrysoidine.
4,6-Diamino-1-(*p*-chlorophenyl)-1,2-dihydro-2,2-dimethyl-*s*-triazine *see* Cycloguanil.
2,4-Diamino-5-(*p*-chlorophenyl)-6-ethylpyrimidine *see* Pyrimethamine.
2,4-Diamino-5-(*p*-chlorophenyl)-9-methyl-1,3,5-triazaspiro[5.5]undeca-1,3-diene *see* Spirazine.
(3,5-Diamino-6-chloropyrazinoyl)guanidine *see* Amiloride.
N-(*p*-[(2,4-**Diamino-5-chloroquinazolin-6-ylmethyl)-amino]benzoyl]aspartic acid dihydrate** *see* Chlorasquin.
1,2-DIAMINOCYCLOHEXANETETRAACETIC ACID (chenta; 'complexon IV'; 'komplexon IV').
4,6-Diamino-2-(diallylamino)-*s*-triazine *see* Diallylmelamine.
4,6-Diamino-2-(diallylamino)-*s*-triazine *N*²-oxide *see* Oxonazine.
4,6-Diamino-1-(3,4-dichlorobenzyloxy)-1,2-dihydro-2,2-dimethyl-*s*-triazine *see* Clociguanil.
2,4-Diamino-5-(3,4-dichlorophenyl)-6-methylpyrimidine *see* Metodiclorofen.
O-[2,6-**Diamino-2,6-dideoxy-α-D-glucopyranosyl-(1→4)]-*O*-[β-D-ribofuransoyl-(1→5)]-2-deoxystreptamine** *see* Ribostamycin.
O-[2,6-**Diamino-2,6-dideoxy-α-D-glucopyranosyl-(1→4)]-*O*-[β-D-xylofuranosyl-(1→5)]-*N*¹-(4-amino-2-hydroxybutyryl)-2-deoxystreptamine** *see* Butirosin.
O-(2,6-**Diamino-2,6-dideoxy-β-L-idopyranosyl-(1→3)-*O*-β-D-ribofuranosyl)-(1→5)-*O*-[2-amino-2-deoxy-α-D-glucopyranosyl-(1→4)]-2-deoxystreptamine** *see* Paromomycin.
O-2,6-**Diamino-2,6-dideoxy-β-L-idopyranosyl-(1→3)-*O*-β-D-ribofuranosyl-(1→5)-*O*-[2,6-di-amino-2,6-dideoxy-α-D-glucopyranosyl-(1→4)]-2-deoxy-D-streptamine** *see* Framycetin.
2,4-Diamino-5-(3,5-diethoxy-4-pyrrol-1-ylbenzyl)-pyrimidine *see* Epiroprim.
4,6-Diamino-1,2-dihydro-2,2-dimethyl-1-[*p*-(methylthio)phenyl]-*s*-triazine *see* Methiotriazamine.
3,3'-Diamino-4,4'-dihydroxyarsenobenzene *see* Arsphenamine.
3,3'-Diamino-4,4'-dihydroxyarsenobenzenemethylenesulfoxylic acid *see* Neoarsphenamine.
2,4-Diamino-5-(3,4-dimethoxybenzyl)pyrimidine *see* Diaveridine.
2,4-Diamino-5-[3,5-dimethoxy-4-(2-methoxyethoxy)benzyl]pyrimidine *see* Tetroxoprim.
2,4-Diamino-5-(3,4-dimethoxy-6-methylbenzyl)pyrimidine *see* Ormetoprim.
2,4-Diamino-5-[3,5-dimethoxy-4-(methylthio)benzyl]pyrimidine *see* Metioprim.
2,4-Diamino-5-[4-(dimethylamino)-3,5-dimethoxybenzyl]pyrimidine *see* Aditoprim.

4,4'-Diaminodiphenyl sulfone *see* Dapsone.
6,9-Diamino-2-ethoxyacridine *see* Ethacridine.
Diaminoethoxyazobenzene *see* Etoxazene.
3,8-Diamino-5-ethyl-6-phenylphenanthridinium bromide *see* Homidium bromide.
L-2,6-Diamino-*N*-hexadecylhexanamide *see* Lycetamine.
2,6-Diaminohexanoic acid *see* Lysine.
4,6-Diamino-2-hydroxy-1,3-cyclohexene 3,6'-diamino-3,6'-dideoxydi-α-D-glucoside *see* Kanamycin.
[[15-(3,6-Diamino-4-hydroxyhexanamido)-3-(hexahydro-2-iminopyrimidin-4'-yl)-9,12-bis(hydroxymethyl)-2,5,8,11,14-pentaoxo-1,4,7,10,13-pentaazacyclohexadec-6-ylidene]methyl]urea *see* Enviomycin.
3-[[[2-[(Diaminomethylene)amino]thiazol-4-yl]methyl]thio]-*N*-sulfamoylpropionamidine *see* Famotidine.
N-(Diaminomethylene)-2-(2,5-dimethyl-3-pyrrolin-1-yl)acetamide *see* Rolgamidine.
3,8-Diamino-5-methyl-6-phenylphenanthridinium bromide *see* Dimidium bromide.
N-[*p*-[(2,4-Diamino-5-methylquinazolin-6-ylmethyl)amino]benzoyl]-L-aspartic acid *see* Methasquin.
2,4-Diamino-5-methyl-6-[(3,4,5-trimethoxyanilino)methyl]quinazoline *see* Trimetrexate.
2,4-Diamino-4-(6-methylveratryl)pyrimidine *see* Ormetoprim.
2,4-DIAMINOPHENOL ('acrol'; 'amidol'; 'dianol').
2,6-Diamino-3-phenylazopyridine *see* Phenazopyridine.
N⁴-(2,4-Diaminophenylazo)sulfanilamide *see* Sulfamidochrysoidine.
2,4-Diamino-5-phenylthiazole *see* Amiphenazole.
N-(Diaminophosphinyl)-*p*-fluorobenzamide *see* Flurofamide.
N-(Diaminophosphinyl)-*o*-toluamide *see* Tolfamide.
2,4-Diamino-6-piperid-1-ylpyrimidine 3-oxide *see* Minoxidil.
Di(aminopropyl)tetramethylenediamine *see* Spermine.
N-[*p*-[(2,4-Diamino-6-pteridin-6-ylmethyl)methylamino]benzoyl]glutamic acid *see* Methotrexate.
N-[*p*-[(2,4-Diaminopterid-6-ylmethyl)amino]benzoyl]glutamic acid sodium salt *see* Aminopterin sodium.
N-[*p*-[(2,4-Diaminoquinazolin-6-ylmethyl)amino]benzoyl]aspartic acid *see* Quinaspar.
N-[*p*-[(2,4-Diaminoquinazolin-6-ylmethyl)-amino]benzoyl]glutamic acid *see* Deazaaminopterin.
Di-5-aminosalicylic acid *see* Azodisalicylic acid.
4,4'-Diaminostilbene-2,2'-disulfonic acid *see* Amsonic acid.
4,4'-Diamino-2-sulfamoyldiphenyl sulfone *see* Sulfamoyldapsone.
3,5-Diamino-2-(*p*-sulfamoylphenylazo)benzoic acid *see* Sulfachrysoidine.
O-(2,6-Diamino-2,3,4,6-tetradeoxy-α,D-glycerohex-4-enopyranosyl-(1→4)-O-(3-deoxy-4-C-methyl-3-methylamino-β,L-arabinopyranosyl)-(1→6))-2-deoxy-D-streptamine *see* Sisomicin.

O-2,6-Diamino-2,3,4,6-tetradeoxy-α-D-*erythro*-hexapyranosyl-(1→4)-O-[3-deoxy-4-C-methyl-3-(methylamino)-β-L-arabinopyranosyl-(1→6)]-2-deoxystreptamine *see* Gentamicin.
1,3-Diamino-2,4,5,6-tetrahydroxycyclohexane *see* Streptamine.
2-[*p*-[(4,6-Diamino-*s*-triazin-2-yl)amino]phenyl]-1,3,2-dithiaarsolane-4,5-dicarboxylic acid dipotassium salt *see* Melarsonyl potassium.
S-(4,6-Diamino-*s*-triazin-2-ylmethyl) O,O-dimethyl phosphorodithioate *see* Menazon.
3,5-Diamino-1,2,4-triazole *see* Guanazole.
2,4-Diamino-5-(3,4,5-trimethoxybenzyl)pyrimidine *see* Trimethoprim.
Diaminovaleric acid *see* Ornithine.
2,4-Diamino-5-veratrylpyrimidine *see* Diaveridine.
***cis*-Diammine(1,1-cyclobutanecarboxylato)platinum** *see* Carboplatin.
***cis*-Diamminedichloroplatinum** *see* Cisplatin.
DIAMOCAINE* (1-(2-anilinoethyl)-4-(2-diethylaminoethoxy)-4-phenylpiperidine).
DIAMOCAINE CYCLAMATE* (diamocaine dicyclamate; R-10948).
Diamond green G *see* Brilliant green.
DIAMORPHINE* (acetomorphine; diacephine; diacetylmorphine; diaphorm; heroin; morphacetinum; morphine diacetate).
'Diamox' *see* Acetazolamide.
Diamphenethide* *see* Diamfenetide.
'Diampicicol' *see* Ampicillin guaiacyldiethylaminoacetate.
'Diamplicil' *see under* Ampicillin.
DIAMPROMIDE* (N-[2-(N-methylphenethylamino)propyl]propionanilide; diampromide sulfate).
'Diampron' *see* Amicarbalide.
Diamthazole* *see* Dimazole.
'Dianabol' *see* Metandienone.
Dianat (tr) *see* Dicamba.
'Diandrone' *see* Prasterone.
'Diane' *see under* Cyproterone acetate.
1,4:3,6-Dianhydo-2-deoxy-2-[[3-(1,2,3,6-tetrahydro-1,3-dimethyl-2,6-dioxopurin-7-yl)propyl]amino]-L-iditol 5-nitrate *see* Teopranitol.
Dianhydrodulcitol *see* Dianhydrogalactitol.
DIANHYDROGALACTITOL (dianhydrodulcitol; DAD; NSC-132313).
1,4:3,6-Dianhydroiditol *see* Isoidide.
1,4:3,6-Dianhydromannitol *see* Isomannide.
1,4:3,6-Dianhydrosorbitol *see* Isosorbide.
'Dianil blue' *see* Trypan blue.
3,3'-Dianisolebis-4,4'-(3,5-diphenyltetrazolium chloride) *see* Tetrazolium blue.
DIANISYLHEXENE (α,α'-diethyl-4,4'-dimethoxystilbene; dimestrol; 'depoestromon'; 'depotoestromenine'; 'depot-ostromon'; 'synthila').
DIANISYLNEOPENTANE (1,1-bis(*p*-methoxyphenyl)-2,2-dimethylpropane).
1,3-Dianisyl-2-phenethylguanidine *see* Guanicaine.
2,2-Di-*p*-anisyl-1,1,1-trichloroethane *see* Methoxychlor.
'Dianol' *see* 2,4-Diaminophenol.
'Diantalvic' *see under* Dextropropoxyphene.

156

Dianthone *see* Dantron.
'Diantil' *see* Chlorbetamide.
Diapamide* *see* Tiamizide.
'Diaparene' *see* Methylbenzethonium chloride.
'Diaphene' *see* Dibromsalan.
Diaphenylsulfone *see* Dapsone.
'Diaphine' *see* Xenysalate.
Diaphorm *see* Diamorphine.
'Diapid' *see* Lypressin.
'Diaquone' *see* Dantron.
DIARBARONE*** (*N*-[2-(diethylamino)ethyl]-4-hydroxy-2-oxo-2*H*-chromen-3-carboxamide; *N*-[2-(diethylamino)ethyl]-4-hydroxy-4-oxo-(2*H*)-1-benzopyran-3-carboxamide).
'Diarsed' *see under* Diphenoxylate.
Di-5-ASA *see* Azodisalicylic acid.
Diasatin *see* Acetphenolisatin.
'Diasone' *see* Aldesulfone sodium.
'Diaspasmyl' *see* Propyromazine bromide.
'Diasprin' *see* Succinylsalicylic acid.
Diastase* *see* α-Amylase.
'Diathesin' *see* Salicyl alcohol.
DIATHYMOSULFONE*** (di[4-(4-hydroxy-2-methyl-5-isopropylphenylazo)phenyl] sulfone; 6,6'-[sulfonylbis(*p*-phenyleneazo)]dithymol; thymosulfone; timosulfone).
DIATHYMOSULFONE SILVER (thymolated silver sulfone; J-51).
'Diatox' *see* Dapsone.
'Diatox argentique' *see* Diathymosulfone silver.
DIATRIZOIC ACID* (3,5-diacetamido-2,4,6-triiodobenzoic acid; amidotrizoic acid; NSC-61815; 'odiston').
See also Ethyl cartrizoate; Meglumine diatrizoate; Propyl docetrizoate; Sodium diatrizoate.
DIAVERIDINE*** (2,4-diamino-5-(3,4-dimethoxybenzyl)pyrimidine; 2,4-diamino-5-veratrylpyrimidine; BW-49-210; NSC-408735).
DIAVERIDINE plus SULFADIMETHOXINE ('mesulene').
22,25-DIAZACHOLESTANOL (17-[1-[2-(dimethylamino)ethyl]aminoethyl]androstanol; SC-11952).
20,25-Diazacholesterol *see* Azacosterol.
Diazacycloheptane *see* Hexahydro-1*H*-1,4-diazepine.
Diazacycloheptatriene *see* Diazepine.
Diazenedicarboxylic acid bis(dimethylamide) *see* Diamide.
DIAZEPAM*** (7-chloro-1,3-dihydro-1-methyl-5-phenyl-2*H*-1,4-benzodiazepin-2-one; duxen; methyldiazepinone; LA-111; NSC-77518; Ro 5-2807; Wy-3467).
See also under Phenytoin; Verapamil.
DIAZEPINE (diazacycloheptatriene).
Diazil (tr) *see* Benactyzine.
1,2-Diazine *see* Pyridazine.
1,3-Diazine *see* Pyrimidine.
1,4-Diazine *see* Pyrazine.
Diazinon* *see* Dimpylate.
DIAZIQUONE*** (diethyl 2,5-bis(1-aziridinyl)-3,6-dioxo-1,4-cyclohexadiene-1,4-dicarbamate; 2,5-bis(1-aziridinyl)-*p*-benzoquinone-3,6-dicarb-

amic acid diethyl ester; 2,5-diethylenimino-1,4-benzoquinone-3,6-dicarbamic acid diethyl ester; NSC-182986).
O-Diazoacetyl-L-serine *see* Azaserine.
4,4'-(Diazoamino)benzamidine *see* Diminazene.
DIAZOAMINOBENZENE (1,3-diphenyltriazene).
Diazo bleu* *see* Evans blue.
1,2-Diazole *see* Pyrazole.
1,3-Diazole *see* Imidazole.
'Diazolina' *see* Morinamide.
Diazoline *see* Mebhydrolin.
'Diazon' *see* Aldesulfone sodium.
6-Diazo-5-oxonorleucine *see* DON.
DIAZOXIDE*** (7-chloro-3-methyl-2*H*-1,2,4-benzothiadiazine 1,1-dioxide; NSC-64198; Sch-6783; SRG-95213).
DIAZOXON (4-(diethoxyphosphinyloxy)-2-isopropyl-6-methylpyrimidine; diethyl (2-isopropyl-6-methylpyrimidin-4-yl) phosphate; diethyl [6-methyl-2-(1-methylethyl)pyrimidin-4-yl] phosphate).
Dibazole (tr) *see* Bendazol.
'Dibein' *see* Phenformin.
DIBEKACIN*** (*O*-3-amino-3-deoxy-α-D-glucopyranosyl-(1→4)-*O*-[2,6-diamino-2,3,4,6-tetradeoxy-α-D-*erythro*-hexopyranosyl-(1→6)]-2-deoxy-L-streptamine; 3',4'-dideoxykanamycin B; DKB; 'debekacyl'; 'icacin'; 'orbicin'; 'panimycin').
DIBEMETHINE*** (*N*,*N*-dibenzylmethylamine; diphenylisopropylamine; DBMA; L-566).
'Dibenal' *see* Sulfadiazine.
DIBENAMINE (*N*-(2-chloroethyl)dibenzylamine; sympatholytin).
'Dibencil' *see* Benzathine penicillin.
'Dibencillin' *see* Benzathine penicillin.
Dibencocid *see* Cobamamide.
Dibencozamide *see* Cobamamide.
'Dibencozan' *see* Cobamamide.
Dibencozide* *see* Cobamamide.
Dibenthiamine* *see* Bentiamine.
'Dibenyline' *see* Phenoxybenzamine.
11*H*-Dibenz[*b,e*]azepine *see* Morphanthridine.
5*H*-Dibenz[*b,f*]azepine-5-carboxamide *see* Carbamazepine.
4-[3-(5*H*-Dibenz[*b,f*]azepin-5-yl)propyl]hexahydro-1*H*-1,4-diazepine-1-ethanol *see* Homopipramol.
4-[3-(5*H*-Dibenz[*b,f*]azepin-5-yl)propyl]-1-(2-hydroxyethyl)homopiperazine *see* Homopipramol.
4-[3-(5*H*-Dibenz[*b,f*]azepin-5-yl)propyl]-1-piperazineethanol *see* Opipramol.
DIBENZEPIN*** (10-[2-(dimethylamino)ethyl]-5,10-dihydro-5-methyldibenzo[*b,e*][1,4]diazepin-11-one; HF-1927).
Dibenzheptropine* *see* Deptropine.
Dibenzo[*b,e*]bicyclo[2.2.2]octadiene *see* 9,10-Ethanoanthracene.
5*H*-Dibenzo[*a,d*]cycloheptene-5-carboxamide *see* Citenamide.
5*H*-Dibenzo[*a,d*]cyclohepten-5-one *O*-[2-(methylamino)ethyl]oxime *see* Demexiptiline.
**4-(5*H*-Dibenzo[*a,d*]cyclohepten-5-ylidene)-*N*,*N*-di-

methyl-2-butynylamine *see* Intriptyline.
4-(5-Dibenzo[a,d]cyclohepten-5-ylidene)-1-methyl-piperidine *see* Cyproheptadine.
[3-(5H-Dibenzo[a,d]cyclohepten-5-ylidene)propyl]dimethylamine *see* Cyclobenzaprine.
3α-(5H-Dibenzo[a,d]cyclohepten-5-yloxy)tropane *see* Decitropine.
DIBENZO-p-DIOXIN (diphenylene dioxide; phendioxin).
DIBENZOFURAN (biphenylene oxide; diphenylene oxide).
Dibenzoparadiazine *see* Phenazine.
Dibenzoparathiazine *see* Phenothiazine.
Dibenzopyrazine *see* Phenazine.
Dibenzo[b,e]pyridine *see* Acridine.
Dibenzo-γ-pyrone *see* Xanthone.
Dibenzopyrrole *see* Carbazole.
3-Dibenzo[b,e]thiepin-11(6H)-ylidene-1αH,5αH-tropane *see* Tropatepine.
Dibenzoxine *see* Noxiptiline.
Dibenzoyl *see* Benzil.
Dibenzoyl disulfide *see* Bensulfene.
Dibenzoyl peroxide *see* Benzoyl peroxide.
Dibenzoylthiamin *see* Bentiamine.
Dibenzthion *see* Sulbentine.
1,3-Dibenzyldecahydro-2-oxoimidazo[4,5-c]thieno-[1,2-a]thiolium 10-camphorsulfonate *see* Trimetaphan camsilate.
N,N'-Dibenzylethylenediamine *see* Benzathine.
'Dibenzyline' *see* Phenoxybenzamine.
Dibenzylmethylamine *see* Dibemethine.
3,5-Dibenzyltetrahydro-1,3,5-thiadiazine-2-thione *see* Sulbentine.
(DIBENZYLTIN)-S,S'-BIS(ISOOCTYL THIO-GLYCOLATE) ('ergoterm TGO').
'Dibenzyran' *see* Phenoxybenzamine.
'Dibestil' *see* Diethylstilbestrol.
'Dibotin' *see* Phenformin.
'Dibrom' *see* Naled.
'Dibromdulcitol' *see* Mitolactol.
'Dibromin' *see* 5,5-Dibromobarbituric acid.
Dibrominum *see* 5,5-Dibromobarbituric acid.
5,5-DIBROMOBARBITURIC ACID (dibrominum; 'dibromin').
4,4'-Dibromobenzilic acid isopropyl ester *see* Bromopropylate.
3,5-Dibromo-N-(p-bromobenzyl)salicylamide *see* Bensalan.
1,2-DIBROMO-3-CHLOROPROPANE (DBCP; 'fumazone'; 'nemazon').
3,4'-Dibromo-5-chlorothiosalicylanilide acetate *see* Brotianide.
5,6β-Dibromo-5α-cholestan-3β-ol acetate *see* Acebrochol.
[[4,6-Dibromo-α-(cyclohexylmethylamino)-o-tolyl]oxy]acetic acid ethyl ester *see* Oxabrexine.
2',4'-Dibromo-α-(cyclohexylmethylamino)-o-vanillotoluidide acetate *see* Brovanexine.
3,5-Dibromo-N^α-cyclohexyl-N^α-methyltoluene-α,2-diamine *see* Bromhexine.
1,2-Dibromo-2,2-dichloroethyl dimethyl phosphate *see* Naled.
1,6-Dibromo-1,6-dideoxydulcitol *see* Mitolactol.

1,6-Dibromo-1,6-dideoxy-D-galactitol *see* Mitolactol.
1,6-Dibromo-1,6-dideoxy-D-mannitol *see* Mitobronitol.
Dibromodihydroxybenzil *see* Dibromsalicil.
Dibromodulcit *see* Mitolactol.
3,5-Dibromo-4-hydroxybenzaldehyde O-(2,4-dinitrophenyl)oxime *see* Bromofenoxim.
3,4'-Dibromo-6-hydroxybenzanilide *see* Dibromsalan.
3,5-Dibromo-4-hydroxybenzonitrile *see* Bromoxynil.
3,5-Dibromo-N^α-(trans-4-hydroxycyclohexyl)toluene-α,2-diamine *see* Ambroxol.
2',7-Dibromo-4-hydroxymercurifluorescein *see* Merbromin.
3,5-Dibromo-4-hydroxyphenyl 2-ethylbenzofuran-3-yl ketone *see* Benzbromarone.
Dibromohydroxyquinoline *see* Broxyquinoline.
2-[[(6,8-Dibromo-9H-indeno[2,1-d]pyrimidin-9-ylidene)amino]oxy]-N-(2-dimethylaminoethyl)propionamide *see* Brindoxime.
N-[2-[[(6,8-Dibromo-9H-indeno[2,1-d]pyrimidin-9-ylidene)amino]oxy]propionyl]-N',N'-dimethylethylenediamine *see* Brindoxime.
Dibromomannitol *see* Mitobronitol.
Dibromomethyldihydroxyquinoline *see* Broxaldine.
5,7-Dibromo-2-methyl-8-quinolinol *see* Broquinaldol.
5,7-Dibromo-2-methyl-8-quinolinol benzoate *see* Broxaldine.
6,8-Dibromo-9-oxo-9H-indeno[2,1-d]pyrimidine O-[1-[[(2-dimethylaminoethyl)amino]carbonyl]ethyl]oxime *see* Brindoxime.
2,2'-Dibromopropamidine *see* Dibrompropamidine.
Di(bromopropionyl)piperazine *see* Pipobroman.
'Dibromoquin' *see* Broxyquinoline.
5,7-Dibromo-8-quinolinol *see* Broxyquinoline.
trans-4-[(3,5-Dibromosalicyl)amino]cyclohexanol *see* Dembroxol.
3,5-Dibromosalicylanilide *see* Metabromsalan.
4',5-Dibromosalicylanilide *see* Dibromsalan.
3,5-Dibromo-N-tetrahydrofurfurylsalicylamide *see* Fursalan.
3,5-Dibromo-3'-(trifluoromethyl)salicylanilide *see* Flusalan.
3,5-Dibromo-α,α,α-trifluorosalicylotoluidide *see* Flusalan.
3-(2,2-Dibromovinyl)-2,2-dimethylcyclopropanecarboxylic acid α-cyano-3-phenoxybenzyl ester *see* Deltamethrin.
DIBROMPROPAMIDINE*** (4,4'-(trimethylenedioxy)bis(3-bromobenzamidine); 2,2'-dibromopropamidine; dibrompropamidine isetionate).
DIBROMSALAN** (3-bromo-6-hydroxybenz-p-bromanilide; 3,4'-dibromo-6-hydroxybenzanilide; 4',5-dibromosalicylanilide; NSC-20527).
DIBROMSALAN plus TRIBROMSALAN ('ASC-4'; 'hilomid'; 'hitreman'; 'mitenyl'; 'temasept I').
DIBROMSALICIL (DBS; dibromodihydroxybenzil; dibromsalicyl; 'dibrosal'; 'respectol').
Dibromsalicyl *see* Dibromsalicil.

158

'Dibrosal' *see* Dibromsalicil.
DIBROSPIDIUM CHLORIDE** (3,12-bis(3-bromopropionyl)-3,12-diaza-6,9-diazoniadispiro[5.2.5.2]hexadecane dichloride).
Dibucaine *see* Cinchocaine.
DIBUDINATE(S)** (2,6-di-*tert*-butylnaphthalene-1,5-disulfonic acid, esters and salts).
'Dibuline' *see* Dibutoline.
DIBUPROL*** (1,3-dibutoxy-2-propanol; 7-hydroxy-5,9-dioxatridecane).
DIBUPYRONE** (4-(isobutylamino)-2,3-dimethyl-1-phenyl-5-pyrazolin-3-one methanesulfonate; (antipyrinylisobutylamino)methane sulfonate; isobutylphenazone methanesulfonate; dibupyrone sodium).
DIBUSADOL*** (*N*-[4-(diethylamino)butyl]salicylamide acetate; dibusadol citrate; B-862).
DIBUTADIAMIN (*N-tert*-butyl-1,4-butanediamine; CI-505).
Dibutamide *see* Ambucetamide.
DIBUTOLINE (ethyl(2-hydroxyethyl)dimethylammonium sulfate dibutylcarbamate).
'Dibutox' *see* Dinoseb.
1,3-Dibutoxy-2-propanol *see* Dibuprol.
3-(Dibutylamino)-1-[1,3-dichloro-6-(trifluoromethyl)-9-phenanthryl]-1-propanol *see* Halofantrine.
5-(2-Dibutylaminoethylamino)-3-phenyl-1,2,4-oxadiazole *see* Butalamine.
2-Dibutylamino-4′-methoxyacetanilide *see* Ambucetamide.
3-[p-(3-Dibutylaminopropoxy)benzoyl]-2-ethylindolizine *see* Butoprozine.
2-[4-[3-(Dibutylamino)propoxy]-3,5-dimethylbenzoyl]chromone *see* Bucromarone.
p-[3-(Dibutylamino)propoxy]phenyl 2-ethyl-3-indolizinyl ketone *see* Butoprozine.
3-Dibutylaminopropyl p-aminobenzoate *see* Butacaine.
N,N′-Dibutyl-N,N′-bis(morpholinocarbonyl)ethylenediamine *see* Dimorpholamine.
Dibutyl 1-(butylamino)cyclohexylphosphonate *see* Aminophon.
2,6-Di-tert-butyl-p-cresol *see* Butylated hydroxytoluene.
N,N′-Dibutyl-N,N′-di(carboxymorpholide)ethylenediamine *see* Dimorpholamine.
N,N-Dibutyl-4-hexyloxy-1-naphthamidine *see* Bunamidine.
4-(3,5-Di-tert-butyl-4-hydroxyphenoxy)-3,5-diiodohydrocinnamic acid *see* Hinderin.
3,5-Di-tert-butyl-4-hydroxytoluene *see* Butylated hydroxytoluene.
Di-tert-butylmethylphenol *see* Butylated hydroxytoluene.
2,6-Di-tert-butyl-4-methylphenyl methylcarbamate *see* Terbucarb.
2,6-Di-tert-butylnaphthalene-1,5-disulfonic acid, esters and salts *see* Dibudinate(s).
3,7-Di-tert-butylnaphthalene-1,5-disulfonic acid, esters and salts *see* Bunapsilate(s).
2,6-Di-tertbutylnaphthalene-1-sulfonic acid esters and salts *see* Ethyl dibunate; Sodium dibunate.

Dibutyl p-nitrophenyl phosphate *see* Nibufin.
6,8-Di-tert-butyl-4-oxo-4H-1-benzopyran-2-carboxylic acid *see* Terbucromil.
DIBUTYL PHTHALATE (butyl phthalate; DBP).
DIBUTYL SUCCINATE ('tabutrex').
p-Dibutylsulfamoylbenzoic acid *see* Butacid.
DIC *see* Dacarbazine.
DICA *see* Lonidamine.
1,3-Dicaffeylquinic acid *see* Cynarine.
Dicaine (tr) *see* Tetracaine.
DICAMBA* (3,6-dichloro-2-methoxybenzoic acid; dianat; 'banvel'; 'mediben').
DICAMBA-METHYL (methyl 3,6-dichloro-2-methoxybenzoate; disugran; 'racuza').
'Di-captan' *see* Dicapthon.
DICAPTHON* (*O*-(2-chloro-4-nitrophenyl) *O,O*-dimethyl phosphorothioate; 'di-captan'; 'noltran').
Dicaptol (tr) *see* Dimercaprol.
Dicarbamoyldiimide *see* Azoformamide.
3,3-Dicarbethoxy-N,N-diethyl-4-phenyl-1-butylamine *see* Diethyl benzyl(2-diethylaminoethyl)-malonate.
O,S-Dicarbethoxythiamine *see* Cetotiamine.
DICARBINE*** (2,3,4,4a,5,9b-hexahydro-2,8-dimethyl-1H-pyrid[4,3-b]indole; hexahydro-3,6-dimethyl-γ-carboline; carbidine).
DICARFEN*** (2-(dimethylamino)ethyl N,N-diphenylcarbamate ester; deanol diphenylcarbamate; SD-25).
Dicarnitine *see* Bicarnitine.
'Dicarzol' *see* Formetanate.
'Dicel' *see* Fenproporex.
'Dicertan' *see* Papaverine adenylate.
'Dicestal' *see* Dichlorophen.
'Dicetel' *see* Pinaverium bromide.
DICHLOBENIL* (2,6-dichlorobenzonitrile; 'casoron').
DICHLOFENTHION* (*O*-(2,4-dichlorophenyl) *O,O*-diethyl phosphorothioate; V-C-13; 'nemacide').
DICHLOFLUANID* (1,1-dichloro-N-[(dimethylamino)sulfonyl]-1-fluoro-N-phenylmethanesulfenamide; dichlorofluanid; 'elvaron'; 'euparen').
DICHLONE* (2,3-dichloro-1,4-naphthoquinone; 'phygon').
DICHLORALPHENAZONE* (compound of 1 mol. phenazone and 2 mol. chloral hydrate; dichloralantipyrine).
DICHLORAMINE (N,N-dichloro-p-toluenesulfonamide; dichloramine *T*).
cis-**Dichlordiammine platinum (II)** *see* Cisplatin.
'Dichloren' *see* Chlormethine.
Dichloresul *see* Disul.
'Di-chloricide' *see* p-Dichlorobenzene.
DICHLORISONE*** (9α,11β-dichloro-17α,21-dihydroxypregna-1,4-diene-3,20-dione; dichlorisone acetate).
Dichlorisoprenaline *see* DCI.
'Dichlorman' *see* Dichlorvos.
DICHLORMATE* (3,4-dichlorobenzyl methylcarbamate; 'rowmate'; 'sirmate').
DICHLORMEZANONE*** (2-(3,4-dichloro-

159

phenyl)-2,3,5,6-tetrahydro-3-methyl-4H-1,3-thiazin-4-one 1,1-dioxide; WIN-12267).

2-Dichloroacetamido-1-(p-methylsulfonylphenyl)-1,3-propanediol see Thiamphenicol.

2-(Dichloroacetamido)-1-(p-nitrophenyl)-1,3-propanediol see Chloramphenicol.

N-(Dichloroacetyl)-N-(2,4-dichlorobenzyl)-2-hydroxyethylamine see Chlorbetamide.

(±)-threo-**N-(2,2-Dichloroacetyl)-β-hydroxy-α-hydroxymethyl-p-methylsulfonylphenethylamine** see Racefenicol.

1-(Dichloroacetyl)-1,2,3,4-tetrahydro-6-quinolinyl 2-furoate see Quinfamide.

S-(2,3-Dichloroallyl) diisopropylcarbamothioate see Diallate.

[2-(2,6-Dichloroanilino)ethyl]guanidine see Guanclofine.

2-(2,3-Dichloroanilino)nicotinic acid see Diclonixin.

o-**(2,6-Dichloroanilino)phenylacetic acid** see Diclofenac.

2-(3,4-Dichloroanilino)quinolizinium bromide see Nolinium bromide.

4-(2,6-Dichloroanilino)-3-thiophenecarboxylic acid see Clantifen.

N-[1-(3,4-Dichloroanilino)-2,2,2-trichloroethyl]formamide see Chloraniformethan.

2,6-Dichlorobenzaldehyde (4-amino-4H-1,2,4-triazol-3-yl)hydrazone see Nebidrazine.

[2-(3,4-Dichlorobenzamido)phenoxy]acetic acid see Clamidoxic acid.

p-**DICHLOROBENZENE** ('di-chloricide'; 'paramoth').

2,6-Dichlorobenzenecarbothiamide see Chlorthiamid.

4,4'-Dichlorobenzilic acid, esters see Chlorobenzilate; Chloropropylate.

DICHLOROBENZODODECINIUM CHLORIDE ((3,4-dichlorobenzyl)dodecyldimethylammonium chloride; 'dermofungine-B'; 'riseptin').

2,6-Dichlorobenzonitrile see Dichlobenil.

S-(5,7-Dichlorobenzoxazol-2-ylmethyl) O,O-diethyl phosphorodithioate see Benoxafos.

2,4-DICHLOROBENZYL ALCOHOL ('dybenal'; 'rapidosept').

(3,4-Dichlorobenzyl)dodecyldimethylammonium chloride see Dichlorobenzododecinium chloride.

1-(2,6-Dichlorobenzylideneamino)guanidine see Guanabenz.

1-[(2,6-Dichlorobenzylidene)amino]-3-hydroxyguanidine see Guanoxabenz.

1-(2,4-Dichlorobenzyl)-1H-indazole-3-carboxylic acid see Lonidamine.

3,4-Dichlorobenzyl methylcarbamate see Dichlormate.

2-(2,4-Dichlorobenzyl)-4-(1,1,3,3-tetramethylbutyl)phenol see Clofoctol.

1,1-Dichloro-2,2-bis(p-chlorophenyl)ethane see DDD.

1,1-Dichloro-2,2-bis(p-chlorophenyl)ethanol see Hydroxy-DDD.

1,1-Dichloro-2,2-bis(p-chlorophenyl)ethylene see DDE.

1,1-DICHLORO-2,2-BIS(p-ETHYLPHENYL)-ETHANE (1,1'-(2,2'-dichloroethylene)bis(4-ethylbenzene); Q-137; 'perthane').

3,4-Dichlorocarbanilic acid methyl ester see Swep.

4,6-Dichloro-2-(o-chloroanilino)-s-triazine see Anilazine.

1-[2,4-Dichloro-β-(p-chlorobenzyloxy)phenethyl]imidazole see Econazole.

1-[2,4-Dichloro-β-[(p-chlorobenzyl)thio]phenethyl]imidazole see Sulconazole.

2,2-Dichloro-N-[2-chloro-1-(p-chlorobenzoyl)ethyl]acetamide see Cloponone.

2,2-Dichloro-N-[p-chloro-α-(chloromethyl)phenacyl]acetamide see Cloponone.

1-[2,4-Dichloro-β-[2-(p-chlorophenoxy)ethoxy]-α-methylstyryl]imidazole see Omoconazole.

1-[2,4-Dichloro-β-[2-(4-chlorophenoxy)ethoxy]styryl]imidazole see Democonazole.

1-[2,4-Dichloro-β-[3-(p-chlorophenoxy)propoxy]phenethyl]imidazole see Zoficonazole.

1,1-Dichloro-2-(o-chlorophenyl)-2-(p-chlorophenyl)ethane see Mitotane.

1-[2,4-Dichloro-β-(p-chlorophenyl)cinnamyl]imidazole see Aliconazole.

4,6-Dichloro-N-(2-chlorophenyl)-1,3,5-triazin-2-amine see Anilazine.

1-[2,4-Dichloro-β-[(2-chloro-3-thenyl)oxy]phenethyl]imidazole see Tioconazole.

Dichloro(2-chlorovinyl)arsine see Lewisite.

6,7-Dichloro-3-(3-cyclopenten-1-yl)-2H-1,2,4-benzothiadiazine 1,1-dioxide see Pazoxide.

2,2'-Dichloro-α-cyclopropylbenzhydrol see Proclonol.

3,4-Dichloro-N-(cyclopropylcarbonyl)aniline see Cypromid.

2-[p-(2,2-Dichlorocyclopropyl)phenoxy]-2-methylpropionic acid see Ciprofibrate.

2,10-Dichloro-12H-dibenzo[d,g][1,3]-dioxocin-6-carboxylic acid methyl ester see Treloxinate.

1,3-Dichloro-α-[2-(dibutylamino)ethyl]-6-(trifluoromethyl)-9-phenanthrenemethanol see Halofantrine.

1-[2,4-Dichloro-β-[(2,4-dichlorobenzyl)oxy]phenethyl]-3-(p-fluorophenacyl)imidazolium chloride see Fludazonium chloride.

1-[2,4-Dichloro-β-(2,4-dichlorobenzyloxy)phenethyl]imidazole see Miconazole.

1-[2,4-Dichloro-β-(2,6-dichlorobenzyloxy)phenethyl]imidazole see Isoconazole.

1-[2,4-Dichloro-β-[(2,4-dichlorobenzyl)oxy]phenethyl]-3-phenethylimidazolium chloride see Sepazonium chloride.

4,4'-Dichloro-α-dichloromethylbenzhydrol see Hydroxy-DDD.

Dichlorodideoxyisoprenaline see DCI.

3,5-Dichloro-N-(2-diethylaminoethyl)-o-anisamide see Diclometide.

3,5-Dichloro-N-(2-diethylaminoethyl)-2-methoxybenzamide see Diclometide.

9,11-Dichloro-6,21-difluoro-16,17-dihydroxypregna-1,4-diene-3,20-dione 16,17-acetonide see Tralonide.

2,2-Dichloro-1,1-difluoroethyl methyl ether see Methoxyflurane.

2,2-Dichloro-1,1-difluoroethyl methyl sulfide *see* Methioflurane.

DICHLORODIFLUOROMETHANE (CFC-12; FC-12; fluorocarbon 12).

Dichlorodifluoromethoxyethane *see* Methoxyflurane.

6,7-Dichloro-1,5-dihydroimidazo[2,1-*b*]quinazolin-2(3*H*)-one *see* Anagrelide.

[(6,7-Dichloro-2,3-dihydro-2-methyl-1-oxo-2-phenyl-1*H*-inden-5-yl)oxy]acetic acid *see* Indacrinone.

2,5-Dichloro-3,6-dihydroxy-*p*-benzoquinone *see* Chloranilic acid.

ab-**Dichloro-*ce*-dihydroxy-*df*-bis(isopropylamine)-platinum** *see* Iproplatin.

5,5′-Dichloro-2,2′-dihydroxy-3,3′-dinitrobiphenyl *see* Niclofolan.

Dichlorodihydroxydiphenylmethane *see* Dichlorophen.

Dichlorodihydroxydiphenyl sulfide *see* Fenticlor.

9,11β-Dichloro-17,21-dihydroxy-16α-methylpregna-1,4-diene-3,20-dione *see* Meclorisone.

9α,11β-Dichloro-17α,21-dihydroxypregna-1,4-diene-3,20-dione *see* Dichlorisone.

1,4-Dichloro-2,5-dimethoxybenzene *see* Chloroneb.

1,1-Dichloro-*N*-[(dimethylamino)sulfonyl]-1-fluoro-*N*-phenylmethanesulfenamide *see* Dichlofluanid.

Dichlorodimethyl ether *see* Bis(chloromethyl) ether.

2,4-Dichloro-3,5-dimethylphenol *see* Dichloroxylenol.

3,5-Dichloro-*N*-(1,1-dimethyl-2-propynyl)benzamide *see* Propyzamide.

3,5-Dichloro-2,6-dimethylpyridin-4-ol *see* Clopidol.

4,4′-Dichloro-6,6′-dinitro-*o,o*-biphenol *see* Niclofolan.

5,5′-Dichloro-3,3′-dinitro-2,2′-biphenol *see* Niclofolan.

4,6′-Dichloro-4′,6-dinitro-2,2′-methylenediphenol *see* Nitroclofene.

p,p′-**Dichlorodiphenyl methyl carbinol** *see* Chlorfenethol.

1,2-Dichloro-3,5-disulfamoylbenzene *see* Diclofenamide.

2,2-Dichloroethenyl dimethyl phosphate *see* Dichlorvos.

2,2-Dichloro-*N*-(2-ethoxyethyl)-*N*-[(p-nitrophenoxy)benzyl]acetamide *see* Etofamide.

2,3-Dichloro-4-(2-ethylacryloyl)phenoxyacetic acid *see* Etacrynic acid.

1,1-DICHLOROETHYLENE (vinylidene chloride).

1,2-DICHLOROETHYLENE (ethylene chloride; Dutch liquid; 'brocide').

1,1′-(2,2-Dichloroethylene)bis(4-chlorobenzene) *see* DDD.

1,1′-(2,2′-Dichloroethylene)bis(4-ethylbenzene) *see* 1,1-Dichloro-2,2-bis(*p*-ethylphenyl)ethane.

1,1′-(2,2-Dichloroethylidene)bis(4-chlorobenzene) *see* DDE.

Dichlorofenidim *see* Diuron.

Dichlorofluanid *see* Dichlofluanid.

9α,11β-Dichloro-6α-fluoro-21-hydroxy-16α,17α-isopropylidenedioxypregna-1,4-diene-3,20-dione

see Fluclorolone acetonide.

9α,11β-Dichloro-6α-fluoro-16α,17α,21-trihydroxy-pregna-1,4-diene-3,20-dione *see* Fluclorolone.

2,6-Dichloro-*N*-(2-guanidinoethyl)aniline *see* Guanclofine.

2,4′-Dichloro-4-(2-hydroxy-3,5-diiodobenzamido)-benzophenone *see* Salantel.

2,2-Dichloro-*N*-(2-hydroxyethyl)-*N*-[p-(p-nitrophenoxy)benzyl]acetamide *see* Clefamide.

2,2-Dichloro-*N*-[β-hydroxy-α-(hydroxymethyl)-p-(methylsulfonyl)phenethyl]acetamide *see* Racefenicol; Thiamphenicol.

2,2-Dichloro-*N*-[β-hydroxy-α-(hydroxymethyl)-p-nitrophenethyl]acetamide *see* Chloramphenicol.

2,2-Dichloro-4′-hydroxy-*N*-methylacetanilide *see* Diloxanide.

2′,5-Dichloro-2-hydroxy-4′-nitrobenzanilide *see* Niclosamide.

Dichlorohydroxyquinaldine *see* Chlorquinaldol.

Dichlorohydroxyquinoline *see* Chloroxine.

2,6-Dichloro-*N*-2-imidazolidinylideneaniline *see* Clonidine.

2′,4′-Dichloro-2-imidazol-1-ylacetophenone *O*-(2,4-dichlorobenzyl)oxime *see* Oxiconazole.

O-(2,5-**Dichloro-4-iodophenyl)** *O,O*-**dimethyl phosphorothioate** *see* Iodofenphos.

Dichloroisocyanuric acid *see* Troclosene.

(4,7-Dichloro-2-isoindolinyl)guanidine *see* Aganodine.

3,4-Dichloro-α-(isopropylaminomethyl)benzyl alcohol *see* DCI.

Dichloroisoproterenol *see* DCI.

Dichloromethane diphosphonic acid *see* Clodronic acid.

3,6-Dichloro-2-methoxybenzoic acid *see* Dicamba.

3,4-Dichloro-α-methoxybenzylpenicillin *see* Clometocillin.

2,3-Dichloro-4-methoxyphenyl 2-furyl ketone *o*-[2-(diethylamino)ethyl]oxime *see* Diclofurime.

4,4′-Dichloro-α-methylbenzhydrol *see* Chlorfenethol.

trans-**2,10-Dichloro-12-methyl-12*H*-dibenzo[*d,g*]-[1,3]dioxocin-6-carboxylic acid ethyl ester** *see* Ponfibrate.

(Dichloromethylene)bis(phosphonic acid) *see* Clodronic acid.

2,3-Dichloro-4-(2-methylenebutyryl)phenoxyacetic acid *see* Etacrynic acid.

(Dichloromethylene)diphosphonic acid *see* Clodronic acid.

[(6,7-Dichloro-2-methyl-1-oxo-2-phenylindan-5-yl)-oxy]acetic acid *see* Indacrinone.

2-[(2,6-Dichloro-3-methylphenyl)amino]benzoic acid *see* Meclofenamic acid.

5,7-Dichloro-2-methyl-8-quinolinol *see* Chlorquinaldol.

O-[2,5-**Dichloro-4-(methylthio)phenyl]** *O,O*-**diethyl phosphorothioate** *see* Chlorthiophos.

3′,4′-DICHLORO-2-METHYLVALERANILIDE (*N*-(3,4-dichlorophenyl)-2-methylpentanamide; *N*-(3,4-dichlorophenyl)-2-methylvaleramide; 'karsil').

2,3-Dichloro-1,4-naphthoquinone *see* Dichlone.

161

2,6-Dichloro-4-nitroaniline *see* Dicloran.

2,4-Dichloro-4′-nitrodiphenyl ether *see* Nitrofen.

2,4-Dichloro-1-(*p*-nitrophenoxy)benzene *see* Nitrofen.

2′,5-Dichloro-4′-nitrosalicylanilide *see* Niclosamide.

7-[2-(3,5-Dichloro-4-oxo-1-(4*H*)-pyridyl)acetamido]-3-[[(5-methyl-1,3,4-thiadiazol-2-yl)thio]methyl]-2-cephem-2-carboxylic acid *see* Cefazedone.

DICHLOROPHEN*** (dichlorodihydroxydiphenylmethane; 2,2′-methylenebis(4-chlorophenol); dichlorophene; dichlosal; di-phenthane-70; DDDM; DDM; G-4).

DICHLOROPHENARSINE*** (2-amino-4-(dichloroarsino)phenol; arsphendichloride; chlorophenarsine; chlorphenarsine; dichlorphenarsine; M-4000; RP 2591).

Dichlorophene *see* Dichlorophen.

DICHLOROPHENOBARBITAL (5-(3,5-dichlorophenyl)-5-ethylbarbituric acid).

2,4-DICHLOROPHENOXYACETIC ACID (2,4-D; 'dikonirit'; 'esteron 44′; 'pielik'; 'weedar'). *See also* Butyl 2,4-dichlorophenoxyacetate; Chlorinated phenoxyacetic acid; Dimethylamine 2,4-dichlorophenoxyacetate; *and under* Ioxynil.

4-(2,4-DICHLOROPHENOXY)BUTYRIC ACID (2,4-DB; 'embutox').

1-[2-(2,4-Dichlorophenoxy)-4,4-dimethyl-3-oxopentyl]imidazole *see* Valconazole.

2-(2,4-Dichlorophenoxy)ethanol phosphite *see* 2,4-DEP.

1-[2-(2,6-Dichlorophenoxy)ethylamino]guanidine *see* Guanoclor.

2-(2,4-Dichlorophenoxy)ethyl hydrogen sulfate *see* Disul.

2-[1-(2,6-Dichlorophenoxy)ethyl]-2-imidazoline *see* Dexlofexidine; Levlofexidine; Lofexidine.

2-(2,4-Dichlorophenoxy)-1-imidazol-1-yl-4,4-dimethyl-3-pentanone *see* Valconazole.

2-(3,4-Dichlorophenoxymethyl)-2-imidazoline *see* Fenmetozole.

2-(2,4-Dichlorophenoxy)phenylacetic acid *see* Fenclofenac.

(2,4-Dichlorophenoxy)propionic acid *see* Dichlorprop.

N-[3-(2,4-Dichlorophenoxy)propyl]-N-methylprop-2-ynylamine *see* Clorgiline.

(2,6-Dichlorophenylacetyl)guanidine *see* Guanfacine.

N-(2,6-Dichlorophenyl)-*o*-aminophenylacetic acid *see* Diclofenac.

N-(2,3-Dichlorophenyl)anthranilic acid *see* Clofenamic acid.

2,4-Dichlorophenyl benzenesulfonate *see* Dichlorophenyl besilate.

DICHLOROPHENYL BESILATE (2,4-dichlorophenyl benzenesulfonate; 'genite').

N-(3,4-Dichlorophenyl)cyclopropanecarboxamide *see* Cypromid.

1-[2-(2,4-Dichlorophenyl)-2-(2,4-dichlorophenylmethoxy)ethyl]-1*H*-imidazole *see* Miconazole.

1-[2-(2,4-Dichlorophenyl)-2-(2,6-dichlorophenylmethoxy)ethyl]-1*H*-imidazole *see* Isoconazole.

O-**(2,4-Dichlorophenyl)** *O,O*-diethyl phosphorothioate *see* Dichlofenthion.

4-(2,3-Dichlorophenyl)-1,4-dihydro-2,6-dimethylpyridine-3,5-dicarboxylic acid ethyl methyl ester *see* Felodipine.

3-(3,5-Dichlorophenyl)-5,5-dimethyl-2,4-oxazolidinedione *see* Dichlozoline.

1-(3,4-Dichlorophenyl)-3,3-dimethylurea *see* Diuron.

1-[[2-(2,4-Dichlorophenyl)-1,3-dioxolan-2-yl]methyl]-1*H*-1,2,4-triazole *see* Azaconazole.

N-(3,4-Dichlorophenyl)-N-[1-(ethoxycarbonyl)ethyl]benzamide *see* Benzoylprop-ethyl.

5-(3,5-Dichlorophenyl)-5-ethylbarbituric acid *see* Dichlorophenobarbital.

O-**(2,4-Dichlorophenyl)** *O*-ethyl *S*-propyl phosphorodithioate *see* Prothiofos.

3-(2,6-Dichlorophenyl)-2-ethylquinazolin-4(3*H*)-one *see* Cloroqualone.

1-[[5-(3,4-Dichlorophenyl)furfurylidene]amino]hydantoin *see* Clodanolene.

1-(2,4-Dichlorophenyl)-2-(*N*-imidazolyl)ethyl 4-phenylthiobenzyl ether *see* Fenticonazole.

cis-*p*-[[[2-(2,4-Dichlorophenyl)-2-(imidazol-1-ylmethyl)-1,3-dioxolan-4-yl]methyl]thio]carbanilic acid ethyl ester *see* Tubulozole.

2-[(2,6-Dichlorophenyl)imino]imidazolidine *see* Clonidine.

cis-**2-(3,4-Dichlorophenyl)-3-(isopropylamino)bicyclo[2.2.2]octan-2-ol** *see* Cilobamine.

1-(3,4-Dichlorophenyl)-2-isopropylaminoethanol *see* DCI.

1-(3,4-Dichlorophenyl)-5-isopropylbiguanide *see* Chlorproguanil.

3-(3,5-Dichlorophenyl)-N-isopropyl-2,4-dioxoimidazolidine-1-carboxamide *see* Iprodione.

6-[2-(3,4-Dichlorophenyl)-2-methoxyacetamido]penicillanic acid *see* Clometocillin.

1-(3,4-Dichlorophenyl)-1-(*p*-methoxybenzoyl)-3,3-dimethylurea *see* Anisuron.

1-(3,4-Dichlorophenyl)-3-methoxy-3-methylurea *see* Linuron.

N-(3,4-Dichlorophenyl)-2-methylacrylamide *see* Chloranocryl.

2-[(2,6-Dichlorophenyl)methylene]-N-hydroxyhydrazinecarboximidamide *see* Guanoxabenz.

6-[3-(2,6-Dichlorophenyl)-5-methyl-4-isoxazolecarboxamido]penicillanic acid *see* Dicloxacillin.

2-(3,4-Dichlorophenyl)-4-methyl-1,2,4-oxazolidine-3,5-dione *see* Chlormethazole.

N-(3,4-Dichlorophenyl)-2-methylpentanamide *see* 3′,4′-Dichloro-2-methylvaleranilide.

N-(3,4-Dichlorophenyl)-2-methyl-2-propenamide *see* Chloranocryl.

6-[[1-(2,6-Dichlorophenyl)-4-methylpyrazol-5-yl]carboxamido]penicillanic acid *see* Prazocillin.

N-(3,4-Dichlorophenyl)-2-methylvaleramide *see* 3′,4′-Dichloro-2-methylvaleranilide.

3-(3,5-Dichlorophenyl)-5-methyl-5-vinyloxazolidine-2,4-dione *see* Vinclozolin.

α-(2,4-Dichlorophenyl)-α-phenyl-5-pyrimidinemethanol *see* Triarimol.

5-[2-[4-(3,5-Dichlorophenyl)piperazin-1-yl]ethyl]-4-

(*p*-fluorophenyl)-4-oxazolin-2-one *see* Lodiperone.

N-[3-[4-(2,5-Dichlorophenyl)piperazin-1-yl]propyl]acetamide *see* Acaprazine.

N-(3,4-Dichlorophenyl)propionamide *see* Propanil.

1-[[2-(2,4-Dichlorophenyl)-4-[(2-propynyloxy)methyl]-1,3-dioxolan-2-yl]methyl]imidazole *see* Parconazole.

2,6-Dichloro-4-phenyl-3,5-pyridinedicarbonitrile *see* Pyridinitril.

4-(3,4-Dichlorophenyl)-1,2,3,4-tetrahydro-7-methoxy-2-methylisoquinoline *see* Diclofensine.

4-(3,4-Dichlorophenyl)-1,2,3,4-tetrahydro-*N*-methyl-1-naphthylamine *see* Sertraline.

2-(3,4-Dichlorophenyl)-2,3,5,6-tetrahydro-3-methyl-4*H*-1,3-thiazin-4-one 1,1-dioxide *see* Dichlormezanone.

4-(3,4-Dichlorophenyl)-1,2,3,4-tetrahydronaphth-1-yl(methyl)amine *see* Sertraline.

α-(3,4-Dichlorophenyl)-4-(1,1,3,3-tetramethylbutyl)-*o*-cresol *see* Clofoctol.

1-[2,4-Dichloro-β-[[*p*-(phenylthio)benzyl]oxy]phenethyl]imidazole *see* Fenticonazole.

S-[(2,5-Dichlorophenylthio)methyl] *O*,*O*-diethyl phosphorodithioate *see* Phenkapton.

cis-1-[*p*-[[2-(2,4-Dichlorophenyl)-2-(1*H*-1,2,4-triazol-1-ylmethyl)-1,3-dioxolan-4-yl]methoxy]phenyl]-4-isopropylpiperazine *see* Terconazole.

2′,4′-Dichloro-3-piperid-1-ylbutyranilide *see* Clibucaine.

Dichloroprop *see* Dichlorprop.

S-(2,3-Dichloro-2-propenyl) bis(1-methylethyl)carbamothioate *see* Diallate.

3′,4′-Dichloropropionanilide *see* Propanil.

2,2-Dichloropropionic acid *see* Dalapon.

2,2-Dichloropropionic acid trichlorophenoxyethyl ester *see* Erbon.

p,*p*′-Dichloro-α-pyrid-3-ylbenzhydrol *see* Parinol.

5,7-Dichloro-8-quinolinol *see* Chloroxine.

3-(β,4-Dichlorostyryl)-2,2-dimethylcyclopropanecarboxylic acid α-cyano-4-fluoro-3-phenoxybenzyl ester *see* Flumethrin.

p-(*N*,*N*-Dichlorosulfamoyl)benzoic acid *see* Halazone.

1,2-Dichloro-1,1,2,2-tetrafluoroethane *see* Cryofluorane.

2-[2,6-Dichloro-*N*-(tetrahydro-2*H*-pyran-2-yl)anilino]-2-imidazoline *see* Piclonidine.

2-[2,3-Dichloro-4-(2-thenoyl)phenoxy]acetic acid *see* Tienilic acid.

2,6-Dichlorothiobenzamide *see* Chlorthiamid.

N,*N*-Dichloro-*p*-toluenesulfonamide *see* Dichloramine.

N-(2,6-Dichloro-*m*-tolyl)anthranilic acid *see* Meclofenamic acid.

3,5-Dichloro-*s*-triazine-2,4,6(1*H*,3*H*,5*H*)-trione *see* Troclosene.

4,5-Dichloro-2-(trifluoromethyl)-1*H*-benzimidazole *see* Chlorflurazole.

5,6-Dichloro-2-(trifluoromethyl)-1*H*-benzimidazole-1-carboxylic acid phenyl ester *see* Fenazaflor.

4,4′-Dichloro-3-(trifluoromethyl)carbanilide *see* Halocarban.

3-(2,2-Dichlorovinyl)-2,2-dimethylcyclopropanecarboxylic acid esters *see* Cyfluthrin; Cypermethrin; Permethrin.

2,2-Dichlorovinyl dimethyl phosphate *see* Dichlorvos.

2,2-Dichlorovinyl methyl octyl phosphate *see* Vincofos.

Dichlorovos *see* Dichlorvos.

DICHLOROXYLENOL*** (2,4-dichloro-3,5-dimethylphenol).

Dichloroxyquinaldine *see* Chlorquinaldol.

Dichlorphenamide* *see* Diclofenamide.

Dichlorphenarsine *see* Dichlorophenarsine.

Dichlorphos *see* Dichlorvos.

DICHLORPROP* ((2,4-dichlorophenoxy)propionic acid; dichloroprop; 2,4-DP; 'cornox RK').

'Dichlor-stapenor' *see* Dicloxacillin.

DICHLORVOS*** (2,2-dichloroethenyl dimethyl phosphate; 2,2-dichlorovinyl dimethyl phosphate; dichlorovos; dichlorphos; DDVF; DDVP; NSC-6738; SD-1750).

DICHLORVOS plus DICHLORVOS DEMETHYL CALCIUM ('krecalvin').

DICHLORVOS plus FENITROTHION ('nuvan staykill').

DICHLORVOS plus IODOFENPHOS ('nuvan top').

DICHLORVOS DEMETHYL CALCIUM (calcium 2,2-dichlorovinyl methyl phosphate). *See also under* Dichlorvos.

Dichlosal *see* Dichlorophen.

'Dichlotride' *see* Hydrochlorothiazide.

DICHLOZOLINE* (3-(3,5-dichlorophenyl)-5,5-dimethyl-2,4-oxazolidinedione; MW-274115; S-55009; 'solex').

DICHOLINE SUBERATE (suberoylbis(choline); suberyldicholine; choline suberate; corconium; corkonium; korkonium; subecholine; D-6).

DICHROMIUM TRIOXIDE* (chromium (III) sesquioxide; 'chromium-Sandoz').

Dichystrol *see* Dihydrotachysterol.

DICIFERRON** ((3,5,5-trimethylhexanoyl)ferrocene).

'Dicinon' *see* Etamsylate.

DICIRENONE** (17-hydroxy-3-oxo-17α-pregn-4-ene-7α,21-dicarboxylic acid γ-lactone isopropyl ester).

'Diclocil' *see* Dicloxacillin.

'Dicloeta' *see under* Dicloxacillin.

DICLOFENAC*** (*o*-(2,6-dichloroanilino)phenylacetic acid; *N*-(2,6-dichlorophenyl)-*o*-aminophenylacetic acid; diclofenac sodium; GP-45840; 'voltaren'; 'voltarol').

DICLOFENAMIDE*** (1,2-dichloro-3,5-disulfamoylbenzene; dichlorphenamide).

DICLOFENSINE*** ((±)-4-(3,4-dichlorophenyl)-1,2,3,4-tetrahydro-7-methoxy-2-methylisoquinoline; moxifensine; Ro 8-4650).

Diclofibrate *see* Simfibrate.

DICLOFURIME*** (2,3-dichloro-4-methoxyphenyl 2-furyl ketone (*E*)-*O*-[2-(diethylamino)ethyl]oxime).

DICLOFURIME MESILATE (diclofurime methanesulfonate; ANP-4364).

DICLOMETIDE* (3,5-dichloro-*N*-(2-diethylaminoethyl)-2-methoxybenzamide; 3,5-dichloro-*N*-(2-diethylaminoethyl)-*o*-anisamide).

Diclonium bromide *see* Nolinium bromide.

DICLONIXIN* (2-(2,3-dichloroanilino)nicotinic acid).

DICLORALUREA* (1,3-bis(2,2,2-trichloro-1-hydroxyethyl)urea; SK&F-1995).

DICLORAN* (2,6-dichloro-4-nitroaniline; 'allisan'; 'botran').

'Diclotride' *see* Hydrochlorothiazide.

DICLOXACILLIN* (6-[3-(2,6-dichlorophenyl)-5-methyl-4-isoxazolecarboxamido]penicillanic acid; sodium dicloxacillin; BRL-1702; P-1011; R-13423).

DICLOXACILLIN plus HETACILLIN ('dicloeta').
See also under Ampicillin; Cefazolin.

'Dicloxypen' *see* Dicloxacillin.

'Dico' *see* Hydrocodone.

DICOBALT EDETATE* (cobalt(2+) [(ethylenedinitrilo)tetraacetato]cobaltate(2-); cobalt edetate; 'kelocyanor').

'Dicodid' *see* Hydrocodone.

DICOFOL* (1,1,1-trichloro-2,2-bis(*p*-chlorophenyl)ethanol; 4-chloro-α-(4-chlorophenyl)-α-trichloromethylbenzenemethanol; *p*-chloro-α-(*p*-chlorophenyl)-α-(trichloromethyl)benzyl alcohol; DTMC; hydroxy-DDT; 'keltan'; 'kelthane').

Dicoline (tr) *see* Dicolinium iodide.

DICOLINIUM IODIDE* (2-carboxy-1,1,6-trimethylpiperidinium iodide ester with diethyl(2-hydroxyethyl)methylammonium iodide; diethyl(2-hydroxyethyl)methylammonium iodide dimethylpipecolate methiodide; dicoline).

'Diconal' *see under* Dipipanone.

'Dicopal' *see* Prochlorperazine.

Dicophane* *see* DDT.

'Dicorantil' *see* Disopyramide.

Dicoumarin *see* Dicoumarol.

DICOUMAROL* (3,3'-methylenebis(4-hydroxycoumarin); dicumarol; biscumarol; bishydroxycoumarin; dicoumarin).

'Dicoumoxyl' *see* Coumetarol.

DICRESULENE* (3,3'-methylenebis[6-hydroxy-*p*-toluenesulfonic acid]).

'Dicrotalin' *see* Rattlesnake venom.

DICROTOPHOS* (3-(dimethoxyphosphinyloxy)-*N*,*N*-dimethyl-*cis*-crotonamide; dimethyl [1-(dimethylcarboxamido)-1-propen-2-yl] phosphate; 3-(dimethylamino)-1-methyl-3-oxo-1-propenyl dimethyl phosphate; 2-(dimethylcarbamoyl)-1-methylvinyl dimethyl phosphate; 2-(dimethylcarboxamido)-1-methylvinyl dimethyl phosphate; 1-(dimethylcarboxamido)-1-propen-2-yl dimethyl phosphate; 3-hydroxy-*N*,*N*-dimethyl-*cis*-crotonamide dimethyl phosphate; 'bidrin'; 'carbicron'; 'ektafos').

'Dicryl' *see* Chloranocryl.

'Dictyzide' *see* Cyacetacide.

'Dicumacyl' *see* Ethyl biscoumacetate.

'Dicuman' *see* Dicoumarol.

Dicumarol* *see* Dicoumarol.

'Dicumol' *see* Dicoumarol.

'Dicumoxane' *see* Coumetarol.

'Dicupreine' *see* Cuproxoline.

'Dicuran' *see* Chlorotoluron.

'Dicusat' *see* Warfarin.

sym-**Dicyanoethane** *see* Succinonitrile.

2-(2,2-Dicyclohexylethyl)piperidine *see* Perhexiline.

2,2-Dicyclohexyl-1-piperid-2-ylethylene *see* Hexadiline.

2-(2,2-Dicyclohexylvinyl)piperidine *see* Hexadiline.

Dicyclomine* *see* Dicycloverine.

DICYCLOPENTADIENYLIRON (ferrocene).

(2-Dicyclopentylacetoxyethyl)diethyloctylammonium bromide *see* Penoctonium bromide.

(2-Dicyclopentylacetoxyethyl)trimethylammonium bromide *see* Diponium bromide.

DICYCLOVERINE* (2-(diethylamino)ethyl 1-cyclohexylcyclohexanecarboxylate; 2-(diethylamino)ethyl (bicyclohexyl)-1-carboxylate; dicyclomine; JL-998; M-33536).

'Dicynene' *see* Etamsylate.

'Dicynone' *see* Etamsylate.

Dicysteine *see* Cystine.

'Didakene' *see* Tetrachloroethylene.

'Didandin' *see* Diphenadione.

3α-[(6,11-Didehydrodibenzol[*b*,*e*]thiepin-11-yl)oxy]-8*r*-propyl-1α*H*-tropanium bromide *see* Tipetropium bromide.

7,8-Didehydro-4,5α-epoxy-3-methoxy-17-methylmorphinan-6α-ol *see* Codeine.

8,14-Didehydro-4,5α-epoxy-3-methoxy-17-methylmorphinan-6α-ol *see* Neopine.

6,7-Didehydro-4,5α-epoxy-3-methoxy-17-methylmorphinan-8β-ol *see* Pseudocodeine.

7,8-Didehydro-4,5-epoxy-17-methylmorphinan-3,6-diol *see* Morphine.

9,10-Didehydro-*N*-[(*S*)-2-hydroxy-1-methylethyl]-1,6-dimethylergoline-8β-carboxamide *see* Propisergide.

3-(9,10-Didehydro-6-methylergolin-8a-yl)-1,1-diethylurea *see* Lisuride.

16,17-Didehydro-19α-methyloxayohimban-16-carboxylic acid methyl ester *see* Ajmalicine.

9,10-Didehydro-6-methyl-8β-[(pyrid-2-ylthio)methyl]ergoline *see* Tiomergine.

2,10-Di(demethoxy)-2-glucosyloxy-10-methylthiocolchicine *see* Thiocolchicoside.

1,4-Dideoxy-1,4-bis[(2-hydroxyethyl)amino]erythritol 1,4-dimethanesulfonate *see* Ritrosulfan.

1,4-Dideoxy-1,4-bis[(2-mesyloxyethyl)amino]erythritol *see* Ritrosulfan.

3β-[(Dideoxy-β-D-*ribo*-hexopyranosyl-(1→4)-*O*-2,6-dideoxy-β-D-*ribo*-hexopyranosyl-(1→4)-2,6-dideoxy-β-D-*ribo*-hexopyranosyl]oxy]-14,16β-dihydroxy-5β-card-20(22)-enolide 3',3'',3''',4''',16-pentaformate *see* Gitoformate.

3',4'-Dideoxykanamycin B *see* Dibekacin.

3β-[*O*-(2,6-Dideoxy-4-*O*-methyl-D-*ribo*-hexopyranosyl)-(1→4)-*O*-(2,6-dideoxy-D-*ribo*-hexopyranosyl)-(1→4)-2,6-dideoxy-D-*ribo*-hexopyranosyl-

oxy]-12β,14-dihydroxy-5β,14β-card-20(22)-enol-ide *see* Metildigoxin.

3-(2,6-Dideoxy-3-*O*-methyl-α-L-*arabino*-hexopyranosyloxy)-8,8-epoxymethano-11-hydroxy-2,4,6,10,12,13-hexamethyl-9-oxo-5-[3,4,6-trideoxy-3-(dimethylamino)-β-D-*xylo*-hexopyranosyloxy]tridecan-13-olide *see* Oleandomycin.

4-[(2,6-Dideoxy-3*C*-methyl-α-L-*ribo*-hexopyranosyloxy)oxy]-14-ethyl-12,13-dihydroxy-3,5,7,9,11,13-hexamethyl-7-[[2,3,6-trideoxy-3-(dimethylamino)-α-L-*ribo*-hexopyranosyl]oxy]-6-[[3,4,6-trideoxy-3-(dimethylamino)-β-D-*xylo*-hexopyranosyl]oxy]oxacyclotetradecane-2,10-dione *see* Megalomycin.

O-4,6-Dideoxy-4-[[4,5,6-trihydroxy-3-(hydroxymethyl)-2-cyclohexen-2-yl]amino]-α-D-glucopyranosyl(1→4)-*O*-α-D-glucopyranosyl)-(1→4)-D-glucopyranoside *see* Acarbose.

'Didione' *see* Ethadione.

'Didrate' *see* Dihydrocodeine.

'Didrex' *see* Benzphetamine.

'Didronel' *see* Etidronate disodium.

'Didropantin' *see* Dihydrostreptomycin.

Didropyridine *see* Pyrithyldione.

'Didrothenate' *see* Dihydrostreptomycin.

DIDROVALTRATE*** (1,4a,5,7a-tetrahydro-1,6-dihydroxyspiro[cyclopenta[*c*]pyran-7(6*H*),2'-oxirane]-4-methanol 6-acetate 1,4-diisovalerate; 3,4,5,6-tetrahydro-3,4-dihydroxyspiro(benzofuran-2(3*H*),2'-oxirane)-6-methanol 6-acetate 3,4-diisovalerate).

See also Valepotriate.

'Didroxane' *see* Dichlorophen.

DIEDI *see* Diisopropylamine dichloroacetate.

DIELDRIN** (product containing 85% of 1,2,3,4,10,10-hexachloro-6,7-epoxy-1,4,4a,5,6,7,8,8a-octahydro-1,4-*exo*-5,8-*endo*-dimethanonaphthalene; compound 497; HEOD).

Diemal* *see* Barbital.

DIENESTROL*** (4,4'-(diethylideneethylene)diphenol; 3,4-bis(*p*-hydroxyphenyl)-2,4-hexadiene; dienoestrol; dehydrostilbestrol).

DIENOCHLOR* (1,1',2,2',3,3',4,4',5,5'-decachlorobi(2,4-cyclopentadien-1-yl); 'pentac').

Dienoestrol* *see* Dienestrol.

DIENOGEST*** (17-hydroxy-3-oxo-19-nor-17α-pregna-4,9-diene-21-nitrile).

1,2:3,4-Diepoxybutane ethylenimine polymer *see* Polyetadene.

Diepoxypiperazine *see* Epoxypropylpiperazine.

1,2:15,16-Diepoxy-4,7,10,13-tetraoxahexadecane *see* Etoglucid.

'Diepropon' *see* Amfepramone.

Dietamfenazole *see* Ditazole.

Dietamiphylline* *see* Etamiphyllin.

DIETHADIONE*** (5,5-diethyldihydro-2*H*-1,3-oxazine-2,4-(3*H*)-dione; 5,5-diethyltetrahydro-1,3-oxazine-2,4-dione; dietroxine; 'dioxone'; 'ledosten'; 'toce').

Diethamphenazole *see* Ditazole.

DIETHANOLAMINE (2,2'-iminodiethanol; diolamine).

DIETHAZINE*** (10-[2-(diethylamino)ethyl]-phenothiazine; dinezin; eazamine; RP 2987).

DIETHAZINE ETHIODIDE (triethyl(2-phenothiazin-10-ylethyl)ammonium iodide; RP 3580).

Diethchinalphion *see* Quinalphos.

Diethion *see* Ethion.

'Diethoxin' *see* Parethoxycaine.

1-(3,4-Diethoxybenzyl)-6,7-diethoxyisoquinoline *see* Ethaverine.

1-(3,4-Diethoxybenzyl)-6,7-diisopropoxyisoquinoline *see* Diproteverine.

1-(3,4-Diethoxybenzylidene)-6,7-diethoxy-1,2,3,4-tetrahydroisoquinoline *see* Drotaverine.

1,1-Diethoxyethane *see* Acetal.

DIETHOXYMETHANE (ethylal).

1,3-Diethoxy-5-(2-morpholinoethoxy)benzene *see* Floredil.

4-[2-(3,5-Diethoxyphenoxy)ethyl]morpholine *see* Floredil.

2-(3,5-Diethoxyphenoxy)triethylamine *see* Amifloverine.

α-[[(Diethoxyphosphinothioyl)oxy]imino]benzeneacetonitrile *see* Phoxim.

3-[(Diethoxyphosphinothioyl)oxy]-6-oxo-6*H*-dibenzo[*b,d*]pyran *see* Coumithoate.

3-[(Diethoxyphosphinothioyl)oxy]-1-phenyl-1*H*-1,2,4-triazole *see* Phentriazophos.

2-[(Diethoxyphosphinothioyl)oxy]quinoxaline *see* Quinalphos.

[[[(Diethoxyphosphinothioyl)thio]acetyl]methyl]carbamic acid ethyl ester *see* Mecarbam.

2-(Diethoxyphosphinylimino)-1,3-dithiolane *see* Phosfolan.

4-(Diethoxyphosphinyloxy)-2-isopropyl-6-methylpyrimidine *see* Diazoxon.

[[2-(Diethoxyphosphinyl)thio]ethyl]dimethylamine *see* Amiton.

(2-Diethoxyphosphinylthioethyl)trimethylammonium iodide *see* Ecothiopate iodide.

4,4'-Diethoxythiocarbanilide *see* Etocarlide.

Diethylacetal *see* Acetal.

N-(2,6-Diethylacetanilido)iminodiacetic acid *see* Etifenin.

Diethylamine chromone-2-carboxylate *see* Chromocarb diethylamine.

Diethylamine 1,4-dihydroxybenzene-3-sulfonate *see* Etamsylate.

Diethylamine diphenolsulfonate *see* Etamsylate.

Diethylamine 4-hydroxycyclohexadien-1-one-sulfonate *see* Etamsylate.

2-[2-(Diethylamino)acetamido]-*m*-toluic acid methyl ester *see* Tolycaine.

2-(DIETHYLAMINO)ACETIC ACID (*N,N*-diethylglycine).

2-(Diethylamino)acetic acid prednisolone ester *see* Prednisolamate.

2-(Diethylamino)acetomeside *see* Trimecaine.

2-(Diethylamino)-2',6'-acetoxylidide *see* Lidocaine.

N-[2-(Diethylamino)acetyl]-6-(methoxycarbonyl)-*o*-toluidine *see* Tolycaine.

10-[(DIETHYLAMINO)ACETYL]PHENOTHIAZINE (difasin; diphasin; diphazin).

N-[4-(Diethylamino)butyl]salicylamide acetate *see*

Dibusadol.

4-(Diethylamino)-2-butynyl α-phenylcyclohexane-glycolate *see* Oxybutynin.

3-(Diethylamino)butyranilide *see* Octacaine.

3-(Diethylamino)-1,2-dimethylpropyl *p*-aminobenzoate *see* Dimethocaine.

3-(Diethylamino)-1,2-dimethylpropyl *p*-butoxybenzoate ethiodide *see* Quateron.

3-(Diethylamino)-1,2-dimethylpropyl *p*-isobutoxybenzoate *see* Ganglefene.

3-(Diethylamino)-2,2-dimethylpropyl tropate *see* Amprolium.

3-(Diethylamino)-1,1-dithien-2-ylbut-1-ene *see* Diethylthiambutene.

2-(Diethylamino)ethanol ribonucleate *see* Ribaminol.

2-[2-(Diethylamino)ethoxy]benzanilide *see* Salverine.

3-[4-[2-(Diethylamino)ethoxy]benzoyl]-2-ethylbenzofuran *see* Etabenzarone.

5-[2-(Diethylamino)ethoxy]-1,3-diethoxybenzene *see* Amifloverine.

6-[2-(Diethylamino)ethoxy]-2-(dimethylamino)-benzothiazole *see* Dimazole.

2-[2-(Diethylamino)ethoxy]diphenylmethane *see* Etoloxamine.

2-[2-(Diethylamino)ethoxy]ethyl 3-amino-4-butoxybenzoate *see* Betoxycaine.

2-[2-(Diethylamino)ethoxy]ethyl 2-ethyl-2-phenylbutyrate *see* Oxeladin.

2-[2-(Diethylamino)ethoxy]ethyl 2-phenylbutyrate *see* Butamirate.

2-[2-(Diethylamino)ethoxy]ethyl 1-phenylcyclopentanecarboxylate *see* Pentoxyverine.

2-[2-(Diethylamino)ethoxy]ethyl phenylethylacetate *see* Butamirate.

2-[2-(Diethylamino)ethoxy]ethyl α-phenyl-1-piperidineacetate dimethiodide *see* Piprocurarium iodide.

4-[2-(Diethylamino)ethoxy]-α-hydroxy-4′-methoxy-α-phenylbibenzyl *see* Ethamoxytriphetol.

9-[2-(Diethylamino)ethoxy]-4-hydroxy-7-methyl-5*H*-furo[3,2-*g*][1]benzopyran-5-one *see* Amikhelline.

2-[3-[2-(Diethylamino)ethoxy]-2-hydroxypropoxy]-anisole *see* Guafecainol.

1-[2-(Diethylamino)ethoxy]-3-(*o*-methoxyphenoxy)-2-propanol *see* Guafecainol.

3-[*o*-[2-(Diethylamino)ethoxy]phenoxy]-4-phenyl-3-buten-2-one *see* Zocainone.

4-[2-(Diethylamino)ethoxy]phenyl 2-ethylbenzofuran-3-yl ketone *see* Etabenzarone.

1-[*p*-[2-(Diethylamino)ethoxy]phenyl]-2-(*p*-methoxyphenyl)-1-phenylethanol *see* Ethamoxytriphetol.

1-[*o*-[2-(Diethylamino)ethoxy]phenyl]-2-methyl-5-phenylpyrrole *see* Leiopyrrole.

2-[2-(Diethylamino)ethoxy]phenyl phenethyl ketone *see* Etafenone.

4-[2-(Diethylamino)ethoxy]phenyl phenethyl ketone *see* Dietifen.

2′-[2-(Diethylamino)ethoxy]-3-phenylpropiophenone *see* Etafenone.

4′-[2-(Diethylamino)ethoxy]-3-phenylpropiophenone

see Dietifen.

α-[2-[2-(Diethylamino)ethoxy]phenyl]toluene *see* Etoloxamine.

***p*-[2-(Diethylamino)ethoxy]stilbene ethiodide** *see* Stilonium iodide.

2-(Diethylamino)ethyl *p*-aminobenzoate *see* Procaine.

2-(Diethylamino)ethyl 3-amino-2-butoxybenzoate *see* Metabutoxycaine.

2-(Diethylamino)ethyl 4-amino-2-butoxybenzoate *see* Ambucaine.

2-(Diethylamino)ethyl 4-amino-3-butoxybenzoate *see* Oxybuprocaine.

2-(Diethylamino)ethyl 4-amino-2-chlorobenzoate *see* Chloroprocaine.

1-[[2-(Diethylamino)ethyl]amino]-3,4-dihydroisoquinoline *see* Iquindamine.

1-[[2-(Diethylamino)ethyl]amino]-4-hydroxymethylthioxanthone *see* Hycanthone.

[[2-(Diethylamino)ethyl]amino]isopentyl phenylacetate *see* Camylofin.

1-[[2-(Diethylamino)ethyl]amino]-4-methylthioxanthen-9-one *see* Lucanthone.

2-(Diethylamino)ethyl 4-amino-1-naphthoate *see* Naphthocaine.

2-(Diethylamino)ethyl 3-amino-4-propoxybenzoate *see* Proxymetacaine.

2-(Diethylamino)ethyl 4-amino-2-propoxybenzoate *see* Propoxycaine.

2-(Diethylamino)ethyl *p*-aminosalicylate *see* Hydroxyprocaine.

2-(Diethylamino)ethyl *p*-aminothiolobenzoate *see* Thiocaine.

2-(Diethylamino)ethyl benzilate *see* Benactyzine.

2-(DIETHYLAMINO)ETHYL BENZOATE (bencaine).

3-[2-(Diethylamino)ethyl]-2*H*-1,3-benzoxazine-2,4(3*H*)-dione *see* Letimide.

α-[2-(Diethylamino)ethyl]benzyl benzoate *see* Propanocaine.

2-(Diethylamino)ethyl 4-benzyl-1-piperidinecarboxylate *see* Benrixate.

2-(Diethylamino)ethyl [bicyclohexyl]-1-carboxylate *see* Dicycloverine.

***S*-[2-(Diethylamino)ethyl] 2-[4-biphenyl]thiobutyrate** *see* Xenthiorate.

4′-[[2-(Diethylamino)ethyl]carbamoyl]acetanilide *see* Acecainide.

2-(Diethylamino)ethyl 1-cyclohexylcyclohexanecarboxylate *see* Dicycloverine.

2-(Diethylamino)ethyl α-cyclopentyl-2-thiopheneglycolate methobromide *see* Penthienate.

2-(Diethylamino)ethyl di(azodibenzoate) *see* Azoprocaine.

***S*-[2-(Diethylamino)ethyl] *O*,*O*-diethyl phosphorothioate** *see* Amiton.

2-(Diethylamino)ethyl 2-[3,5-diiodo-4-(3-iodo-4-methoxyphenoxy)phenyl]acetate *see* Tyromedan.

2-(Diethylamino)ethyl diphenylacetate *see* Adiphenine.

2-(Diethylamino)ethyl 2,3-diphenylacrylate *see* Cinnamaverine.

2-(Diethylamino)ethyl 2,2-diphenylpropionate *see*

166

Aprofene.

2-(Diethylamino)ethyl diphenylpropylacetate *see* Proadifen.

N-**(2-Diethylaminoethyl)**-*S,S*-**diphenylsulfoximide** *see* Suloxifen.

S-**2-Diethylaminoethyl diphenylthioacetate** *see* Tifenamil.

S-**[2-(Diethylamino)ethyl] diphenylthiocarbamate** *see* Fencarbamide.

2-(Diethylamino)ethyl diphenylvalerate *see* Proadifen.

2-(Diethylamino)ethyl *p*-ethoxybenzoate *see* Parethoxycaine.

1-[2-(Diethylamino)ethyl]-2-(*p*-ethoxybenzyl)-5-nitrobenzimidazole *see* Etonitazene.

3-[2-(Diethylamino)ethyl]-7-(ethoxycarbonylmethoxy)-4-methylcoumarin *see* Carbocromen.

1-[2-[2-(Diethylamino)ethyl]ethylamino]ethyl *p*-aminobenzoate *see* Amoxecaine.

5-[2-(Diethylamino)ethyl]-3-(α-ethylbenzyl)-1,2,4-oxadiazole *see* Proxazole.

N-**[2-(Diethylamino)ethyl]-2-ethyl-2-phenylmalonamic acid ethyl ester** *see* Fenalamide.

5-[2-(Diethylamino)ethyl]-4-(*p*-fluorophenyl)-4-oxazolin-2-one *see* Fluzoperine.

Diethylaminoethyl guaiacyl ether *see* Guaiactamine.

2-(Diethylamino)ethyl 2-hydroxybiphenyl-3-carboxylate *see* Xenysalate.

N-**[2-(Diethylamino)ethyl]-4-hydroxy-4-oxo-(2*H*)-1-benzopyran-3-carboxamide** *see* Diarbarone.

N-**[2-(Diethylamino)ethyl]-4-hydroxy-2-oxo-2*H*-chromen-3-carboxamide** *see* Diarbarone.

4-[2-(Diethylamino)ethyl]-5-imino-3-phenyl-1,2,4-oxadiazoline *see* Imolamine.

2-(Diethylamino)ethyl 1-isopentylcyclohexanecarboxylate *see* Isomylamine.

2-(Diethylamino)ethyl *p*-isopropylbenzoate *see* Isopropylcaine.

1-[2-(Diethylamino)ethyl]-3-(*p*-methoxybenzyl)-2-(1*H*)-quinoxalinone *see* Caroverine.

N-**[2-(Diethylamino)ethyl]-2-methoxy-5-(methylsulfonyl)benzamide** *see* Tiapride.

N-**[2-(Diethylamino)ethyl]-2-(*p*-methoxyphenoxy)-acetamide** *see* Mefexamide.

N-**[2-(Diethylamino)ethyl]-α-methyl-4-biphenylacetamide** *see* Bifepramide.

3-[2-(Diethylamino)ethyl]-4-methylcoumarin-7-yloxyacetic acid ethyl ester *see* Carbocromen.

2-(Diethylamino)ethyl α-methyl-2,5-endomethylene-1,2,5,6-tetrahydrobenzhydryl ether methobromide *see* Ciclonium bromide.

N-**[2-(Diethylamino)ethyl]-5-(methylsulfonyl)-*o*-anisamide** *see* Tiapride.

2-(Diethylamino)ethyl nicotinate *see* Nicametate.

2-(Diethylamino)ethyl *p*-nicotinoylaminobenzoate *see* Nicotinoylprocaine.

10-[2-(Diethylamino)ethyl]phenothiazine *see* Diethazine.

2-(2-Diethylaminoethyl)-3-phenyl-2-benzofuranone *see* Amolanone.

2-(Diethylamino)ethyl 2-phenylbutyrate *see* Butetamate.

2-(Diethylamino)ethyl 2-phenylcinnamate *see* Cinnamaverine.

2-(Diethylamino)ethyl α-phenylcyclohexaneacetate *see* Drofenine.

2-(Diethylamino)ethyl α-phenylcyclohexaneglycolate methobromide *see* Oxyphenonium bromide.

2-(Diethylamino)ethyl 1-phenylcyclopentanecarboxylate *see* Caramiphen.

2-(Diethylamino)ethyl phenylethylacetate *see* Butetamate.

2-[2-(Diethylamino)ethyl]-2-phenylglutarimide *see* Phenglutarimide.

N-**[2-(Diethylamino)ethyl]-2-phenylglycine isoamyl ester** *see* Camylofin.

5-[2-(Diethylamino)ethyl]-3-phenyl-1,2,4-oxadiazole *see* Oxolamine.

2-[2-(Diethylamino)ethyl]-3-phenylphthalimidine *see* Ubisindine.

2-(Diethylamino)ethyl α-phenyl-1-piperidineacetate *see* Bietamiverine.

5-[2-(Diethylamino)ethyl]-3-(1-phenylpropyl)-1,2,4-oxadiazole *see* Proxazole.

2-(Diethylamino)ethyl 3-phenylsalicylate *see* Xenysalate.

2-(Diethylamino)ethyl 2-phenylvalerate *see* Propivane.

2-(Diethylamino)ethyl 2-quinuclidinecarboxylate dimethiodide *see* Dioquin.

1-[2-(Diethylamino)ethyl]reserpine *see* Bietaserpine.

N-**[2-(Diethylamino)ethyl]salicylamide** *see* Saletamide.

2-(Diethylamino)ethyl salicylate *see* Detanosal.

2-(Diethylamino)ethyl tetrahydro-α-(1-naphthylmethyl)-2-furanpropionate *see* Naftidrofuryl.

7-[2-(Diethylamino)ethyl]theophylline *see* Etamiphyllin.

[[2-(Diethylamino)ethyl]thio]acetic acid 8-ester with octahydro-5,8-dihydroxy-4,6,9,10-tetramethyl-6-vinyl-3a,9-propano-3a*H*-cyclopentacycloocten-1(4*H*)-one *see* Tiamulin.

2-(Diethylamino)ethyl 2-(trifluoromethyl)phenothiazin-10-yl ketone *see* Fluacizine.

2-(Diethylamino)ethyl *o*-xylylcyclopentanecarboxylate *see* Metcaraphen.

4-(Diethylamino)-2-(*o*-hydroxyphenyl)-2-phenylbutyric acid lactone *see* Amolanone.

4-[3-(Diethylamino)-2-hydroxypropyl]ajmalinium hydrogen tartrate *see* Detajmium bitartrate.

N-**[3-(Diethylamino)-2-hydroxypropyl]-3-methoxy-1-phenylindole-2-carboxamide** *see* Eproxindine.

7-(Diethylamino)-4-hydroxy-6-propyl-3-quinolinecarboxylic acid methyl ester *see* Amquinate.

2-(Diethylamino)isopropyl 2,2-diphenylacetate *see* Methyladiphenine.

2-[(DIETHYLAMINO)METHYL]-1,4-BENZODIOXAN (F-883; 'prosympal').

α-[(Diethylamino)methyl]benzyl alcohol benzoate ester *see* Elucaine.

4-[4-(Diethylamino)-1-methylbutylamino]-6-methoxy-2-(4-nitrostyryl)quinoline *see* Trichomonacide.

8-[4-(Diethylamino)-1-methylbutylamino]-6-methoxyquinoline 4,4′-methylene-bis(3-hydroxy-2-

naphthoate) *see* Pamaquine.

2-(Diethylamino)-1-methylethyl *cis*-1-hydroxy[bicyclohexyl]-2-carboxylate *see* Rociverine.

6-[(Diethylamino)methyl]-3-methylflavone *see* Flavamine.

O-[2-(Diethylamino)-6-methylpyrimidin-4-yl] *O*,*O*-diethyl phosphorothioate *see* Pirimiphos ethyl.

O-[2-(Diethylamino)-6-methylpyrimidin-4-yl] *O*,*O*-dimethyl phosphorothioate *see* Pirimiphos methyl.

7-(Diethylamino)-5-methyl-*s*-triazolo[1,5-*a*]pyrimidine *see* Trapidil.

α-[*p*-(Diethylamino)phenyl]-α-[4-(diethylimino)-cyclohexa-2,5-dienylidene]toluene-2,5-disulfonic acid sodium salt *see* Isosulfan blue.

[4-[α-[*p*-(Diethylamino)phenyl]-2,5-disulfobenzylidene]-2,5-cyclohexadien-1-ylidene]diethylammonium hydroxide inner salt *see* Isosulfan blue.

N-[4-[[4-(Diethylamino)phenyl]phenylmethylene]-2,5-cyclohexadien-1-ylidene]-*N*-ethylethanaminium sulfate *see* Brilliant green.

3-(Diethylamino)-1-phenyl-1-propanone *O*-[[(4-methoxyphenyl)amino]carbonyl]oxime *see* Anidoxime.

3-(Diethylamino)-1-phenylpropyl benzoate *see* Propanocaine.

1-(Diethylamino)-2-propanol *see* Dimepranol.

10-[3-(Diethylamino)propionyl]-2-(trifluoromethyl)-phenothiazine *see* Fluacizine.

2-(Diethylamino)propiophenone *see* Amfepramone.

3-(Diethylamino)propiophenone *O*-[(*p*-methoxyphenyl)carbamoyl] oxime *see* Anidoxime.

8-[[3-(Diethylamino)propyl]amino]-6-methoxyquinoline *see* Plasmocid.

2-[*N*-[3-(Diethylamino)propyl]anilino]-1-methoxyindan *see* Moxaprindine.

2-(Diethylamino)propyl benzilate *see* Metamizil.

3-(Diethylamino)propyl cinnamate *see* Cinnacaine.

3-(Diethylamino)propyl 2,2-diphenylacetate *see* Arpenal.

3-(Diethylamino)propyl 2,2-diphenylacetate methyl methosulfate *see* Mesfenal.

3-(Diethylamino)propyl 2-ethoxy-2,2-diphenylacetate *see* Etpenal.

10-[(Diethylamino)propyl]phenothiazine *see* Profenamine.

3-(Diethylamino)propyl 2-phenylbicyclo[2.2.1]heptane-2-carboxylate *see* Bornaprine.

N-[3-(Diethylamino)propyl]-*N*-phenyl-2-indanamine *see* Aprindine.

2-Diethylamino-2',4',6'-trimethylacetanilide *see* Trimecaine.

Diethylammonium 2,5-dihydroxybenzenesulfonate *see* Etamsylate.

3-(8,8-Diethyl-2-aza-8-germaspiro[4.5]dec-2-yl)-propyldimethylamine *see* Spirogermanium.

5,5-Diethylbarbituric acid *see* Barbital.

Diethyl 4-(4-benzofurazanyl)-1,4-dihydro-2,6-dimethyl-3,5-pyridinedicarboxylate *see* Darodipine.

Diethyl (*p*-benzothiazol-2-ylbenzyl)phosphonate *see* Fostedil.

DIETHYL BENZYL(2-DIETHYLAMINO-ETHYL)MALONATE (3,3-dicarbethoxy-*N*,*N*-diethyl-4-phenyl-1-butylamine; 'spasmocalm'; 'spazmokalm').

Diethyl 2,5-bis(1-aziridinyl)-3,6-dioxo-1,4-cyclohexadiene-1,4-dicarbamate *see* Diaziquone.

1,2-Diethyl-1,3-bis(*p*-hydroxyphenyl)-3-methylpropane *see* Benzestrol.

Diethylbromacetylurea *see* Carbromal.

DIETHYLCARBAMAZINE*** (*N*,*N*-diethyl-4-methyl-1-piperazinecarboxamide; 1-(diethylcarbamoyl)-4-methylpiperazine; ditrazin; L-84; RP 3799).

Diethylcarbamothioic acid *S*-(*p*-chlorophenyl)ester *see* Benthiocarb.

Diethylcarbamothioic acid *S*-ethyl ester *see* Ethiolate.

6-(Diethylcarbamoyl)-3-cyclohexene-1-carboxylic acid compound with 4-(2-dimethylaminoethylamino)-6-methoxyquinoline *see* Quinetalate.

1-[1-(Diethylcarbamoyl)ethoxy]naphthalene *see* Napropamide.[4-[(Diethylcarbamoyl)methoxy]-3-methoxyphenyl]acetic acid propyl ester *see* Propanidid.

1-(Diethylcarbamoyl)-4-methylpiperazine *see* Diethylcarbamazine.

3-(Diethylcarbamoyl)-1-methylpyridinium camphorsulfonate *see* Camphotamide.

N-(Diethylcarbamoylmethyl)-3,4,5-trimethoxybenzamide *see* Tricetamide.

1-(Diethylcarbamoyl)-1,2,3,4,5,6,7,8-octahydro-6,6-dimethyl-8-oxo-3-phenyl-2-naphthoic acid *see* Fenaftic acid.

1-[2-[4-(Diethylcarbamoyl)piperazin-1-yl]ethyl]-3-tetradecylimidazolidin-2-one *see* Impacarzine.

O,*O*-Diethyl *O*-1,4-diazinyl phosphorothioate *see* Thionazin.

Diethyl 1′,4′-dihydro-2′,6′-dimethyl-2-(methylthio)[3,4′-bipyridine]-3′,5′-dicarboxylate *see* Mesudipine.

Diethyl 1,4-dihydro-2,6-dimethyl-1-(2-morpholinoethyl)-4-(α,α,α-trifluoro-*o*-tolyl)-3,5-pyridinedicarboxylate *see* Flordipine.

5,5-Diethyldihydro-2*H*-1,3-oxazine-2,4-(3*H*)-dione *see* Diethadione.

α,α′-Diethyl-4,4′-dihydroxybibenzyl *see* Hexestrol.

α,α′-Diethyl-4,4′-dihydroxy-3,3′-dimethylbibenzyl *see* Methestrol.

Diethyl [(dimethoxyphosphinothioyl)thio]succinate *see* Malathion.

α,α′-Diethyl-4,4′-dimethoxystilbene *see* Dianisylhexene.

8,8-Diethyl-*N*,*N*-dimethyl-2-aza-8-germaspiro-[4.5]decane-2-propanamine *see* Spirogermanium.

*N*³,*N*³-Diethyl-2,4-dinitro-6-(trifluoromethyl)-*m*-phenylenediamine *see* Dinitramine.

Diethyl dithiobis(thionoformate) *see* Dixanthogen.

Diethyldithiocarbamic acid sodium salt *see* Dithiocarb.

S,*S*-Diethyl 1,3-dithioisophthalate *see* Ditophal.

Diethyl 1,3-dithiolan-2-ylidenephosphoramidate *see* Phosfolan.

Diethyldixanthogen *see* Dixanthogen.

N,*N*-Diethylenebis(*N*,*N*′-diethylenephosphoric diamide) *see* Dipin.

N,N'-Diethylenebis(*N,N'*-diethylenephosphorothioic diamide) *see* Thiodipin.

Diethylenediamine *see* Piperazine.

4,4'-(1,2-Diethylene)di-*o*-cresol *see* Methestrol.

4,4'-(1,2-Diethylene)diphenol *see* Hexestrol.

DIETHYLENE GLYCOL (3-oxapentane-1,5-diol; 2,2'-oxydiethanol-diglycol; diglycol).

Diethylene glycol monoethyl ether *see* 2-(2-Ethoxyethoxy)ethanol.

DIETHYLENE GLYCOL MONOLAURATE ('diglycol laurate'; 'glaurin').

Diethylene imidoxide *see* Morpholine.

Diethylene oximide *see* Morpholine.

Diethylenetriaminepentaacetic acid *see* Pentetic acid.

2,5-Diethylenimino-1,4-benzoquinone-3,6-dicarbamic acid diethyl ester *see* Diaziquone.

Diethyl ether *see* Ether.

O,O-Diethyl *S*-[2-(ethylsulfinyl)ethyl] phosphorodithioate *see* Oxydisulfoton.

O,O-Diethyl *S*-[(ethylthio)ethyl] phosphorodithioate *see* Disulfoton.

O,O-Diethyl *O*-[2-(ethylthio)ethyl] phosphorothioate *see* Demeton-O.

O,O-Diethyl *S*-[2-(ethylthio)ethyl] phosphorothioate *see* Demeton-S.

Diethyl ethylthioglycol thiophosphate *see under* Demeton-O.

O,O-Diethyl *S*-(ethylthiomethyl) phosphorodithioate *see* Phorate.

N,N-Diethylglycine *see* 2-(Diethylamino)acetic acid.

N,N-Diethylglycine ester with 4'-hydroxyacetanilide *see* Propacetamol.

N,N-Diethylhexahydro-2-hydroxy-9,10-dimethoxybenzo[*a*]quinolizine-3-carboxamide acetate *see* Benzquinamide.

Diethyl(3-hydroxybutyl)methylammonium iodide 5-bromo-2-furoate *see* Fubrogonium iodide.

Diethyl(2-hydroxyethyl)methylammonium bromide benzilate *see* Methylbenactyzium bromide.

Diethyl(2-hydroxyethyl)methylammonium bromide 3-methyl-2-phenylvalerate *see* Valethamate bromide.

Diethyl(2-hydroxyethyl)methylammonium bromide *p*-[*o*-(octyloxy)benzamido]benzoate *see* Otilonium bromide.

Diethyl(2-hydroxyethyl)methylammonium bromide α-phenylcyclohexaneglycolate *see* Oxyphenonium bromide.

Diethyl(2-hydroxyethyl)methylammonium bromide α-phenyl-2-thiopheneglycolate *see* Oxitefonium bromide.

Diethyl(2-hydroxyethyl)methylammonium bromide 9-xanthenecarboxylate *see* Methantheline bromide.

Diethyl(2-hydroxyethyl)methylammonium iodide dimethylpipecolate methiodide *see* Dicolinium iodide.

Diethyl(2-hydroxyethyl)octylammonium bromide dicyclopentylacetate *see* Penoctonium bromide.

α,α'-Diethyl-4-hydroxy-4-methoxystilbene *see* Mestilbol.

Diethyl *N*-hydroxynaphthylimido phosphate *see* Naftalofos.

N,N-Diethyl-β-hydroxyphenethylamine benzoate ester *see* Elucaine.

Diethyl(3-hydroxypropyl)methylammonium iodide 2,4-diphenyl-1,3-cyclobutanedicarboxylate *see* Truxicurium iodide.

Diethyl(3-hydroxypropyl)methylammonium methosulfate diphenylacetate *see* Mesfenal.

1,1-Diethyl-3-hydroxypyrrolidinium bromide benzilate *see* Benzilonium bromide.

Diethyl-IDA *see* Etifenin.

4,4'-(Diethylideneethylene)diphenol *see* Dienestrol.

N,N'-Diethylimidazole-4,5-dicarboxamide *see* Etimizole.

O,O-Diethyl *S*-(isopropylcarbamoylmethyl) phosphorodithioate *see* Prothoate.

Diethyl (2-isopropyl-6-methylpyrimidin-4-yl) phosphate *see* Diazoxon.

O,O-Diethyl *O*-(2-isopropyl-6-methylpyrimidin-4-yl) phosphorothioate *see* Dimpylate.

N,N-Diethylleucinyl *p*-aminobenzoate *see* Leucinocaine.

Diethyl lodoxamide *see* Lodoxamide ethyl.

N,N-Diethyllysergamide *see* Lysergide.

Diethyl mercaptosuccinate *S*-ester with *O,O*-dimethyl phosphorodithioate *see* Malathion.

N,N-Diethyl-*N'*-(1-methoxy-2-indanyl)-*N'*-phenyl-1,3-propanediamine *see* Moxaprindine.

N-(β,β-Diethyl-*m*-methoxyphenethyl)-4-hydroxybutyramide *see* Embutramide.

N,N-Diethyl-2-[2-methoxy-4-[(propoxycarbonyl)methyl]phenoxy]acetamide *see* Propanidid.

N,N-Diethyl-2-(3-methoxy-4-propylphenoxy)acetamide *see* Propinal.

5,5-Diethyl-1-methylbarbituric acid *see* Metharbital.

N,N-Diethyl-1-methyl-3,3-dithien-2-ylallylamine *see* Diethylthiambutene.

Diethyl (4-methyl-1,3-dithiolan-2-ylidene)phosphoramidate *see* Mephosfolan.

N,N-Diethyl-*N'*-(6-methylergolin-8α-yl)sulfamide *see* Etisulergine.

1,1-Diethyl-3-(6-methylergolin-8α-yl)urea *see* Terguride.

O,O-Diethyl *S*-[2-[(1-methylethyl)amino]-2-oxoethyl] phosphorodithioate *see* Prothoate.

N,N-Diethyl-1-methylimidazole-4,5-dicarboxamide *see* Antitheine.

3,3-Diethyl-1-(6-methylisoergolen-8-yl)urea *see* Lisuride.

Diethyl [6-methyl-2-(1-methylethyl)pyrimidin-4-yl] phosphate *see* Diazoxon.

O,O-Diethyl *O*-[6-methyl-2-(1-methylethyl)pyrimidin-4-yl] phosphorothioate *see* Dimpylate.

Diethylmethyl[2-(α-methyl-α-5-norbornen-2-ylbenzyloxy)ethyl]ammonium bromide *see* Ciclonium bromide.

Diethyl [[[2-[[[[(4-methylphenyl)sulfonyl]amino]carbonyl]amino]phenyl]amino]thioxomethyl]phosphoramidate *see* Uredofos.

Diethylmethyl[2-[[4-[*p*-(phenylthio)phenyl]3*H*-1,5-benzodiazepin-2-yl]thio]ethyl]ammonium iodide see Tibezonium iodide.

N,*N*-Diethyl-4-methyl-1-piperazinecarboxamide *see* Diethylcarbamazine.

3,3-Diethyl-5-methyl-2,4-piperidinedione *see* Methyprylon.

DIETHYL 3-METHYLPYRAZOL-5-YL PHOSPHATE (parasoxon; parazoxon; G-24483).

3,3-Diethyl-5-methyl-2,4(1*H*,3*H*)-pyridinedione *see* Ethypicone.

O,*O*-Diethyl *O*-(4-methylsulfinylphenyl) phosphorothioate *see* Fensulfothion.

N,*N'*-Diethyl-6-(methylthio)-1,3,5-triazine-2,4-diamine *see* Simetryne.

4,4'-(1,2-Diethyl-3-methyltrimethylene)diphenol *see* Benzestrol.

Diethyl naphthyloximido phosphate *see* Naftalofos.

N,*N*-Diethyl-2-(naphth-1-yloxy)propionamide *see* Napropamide.

N,*N*-Diethylnicotinamide *see* Nikethamide.

O,*O*-Diethyl *O*-(α-nitrilobenzylimino)phosphorothioate *see* Phoxim.

Diethyl (*p*-nitrophenyl) phosphate *see* Paraoxon.

O,*O*-Diethyl *O*-(*p*-nitrophenyl) phosphorothioate *see* Parathion.

DIETHYLNITROSAMINE (*N*-nitrosodiethylamine; DENA).

Diethylolthioglycine *see* *N*,*N*-Bis(2-hydroxyethyl)glycine.

5,5-Diethyl-1,3-oxazine-2,4-dione *see* Diethadione.

O,*O*-Diethyl *S*-(4-oxobenzotriazin-3-ylmethyl) phosphorodithioate *see* Azinphos-ethyl.

N,*N*-Diethyl-4-[2-(2-oxo-3-tetradecylimidazolidin-1-yl)ethyl]-1-piperazinecarboxamide *see* Impacarzine.

2,2-Diethyl-4-pentenoic amide *see* Valdetamide.

5,5-Diethyl-1-phenylbarbituric acid *see* Phetharbital.

[[[(2,6-Diethylphenyl)carbamoyl]methyl]imino]diacetic acid *see* Etifenin.

Diethyl [1,2-phenylenebis(iminocarbonothioyl)]bis-(carbamate) *see* Thiophanate.

Diethyl 4,4'-*o*-phenylenebis(3-thioallophanate) *see* Thiophanate.

O,*O*-Diethyl *O*-(1-phenyl-1*H*-1,2,4-triazol-3-yl) phosphorothioate *see* Phentriazophos.

3,3-Diethyl-2,4-piperidinedione *see* Dihyprylone.

Diethylpropion* *see* Amfepramone.

1,1-Diethyl-3-(6-propylergolin-8α-yl)urea *see* Proterguride.

O,*O*-Diethyl *O*-pyrazinyl phosphorothioate *see* Thionazin.

3,3-Diethyl-2,4(1*H*,3*H*)-pyridinedione *see* Pyrithyldione.

O,*O*-Diethyl *O*-quinoxalin-2-yl phosphorothioate *see* Quinalphos.

N,*N*-Diethylrifamycin B amide *see* Rifamide.

trans-α,α'-Diethyl-4,4'-stilbenediol *see* Diethylstilbestrol.

DIETHYLSTILBESTROL*** (*trans*-3,4-bis(*p*-hydroxyphenyl)-3-hexene; *trans*-α,α'-diethyl-4,4'-stilbenediol; stilbestrol; stilboestrol; DAES; NSC-3070).
See also Dianisylhexene; Fosfestrol; Furostil-

bestrol; Mestilbol; Stilpalmitate.

p-Diethylsulfamoylbenzoic acid *see* Etebenecid.

5,5-Diethyltetrahydro-1,3-oxazine-2,4-dione *see* Diethadione.

O,*O*-Diethyl *O*-(7,8,9,10-tetrahydro-6-oxo-6*H*-dibenzo[*b*,*d*]pyran-3-yl phosphorothioate *see* Coumithoate.

1,8-Diethyl-1,3,4,9-tetrahydropyrano-[3,4-*b*]indole-1-acetic acid *see* Etodolac.

3,3-Diethyl-1,2,3,4-tetrahydropyridine-2,4-dione *see* Pyrithyldione.

O,*O*-Diethyl *O*-(3,4-tetramethylenecoumarin-7-yl) phosphorothioate *see* Coumithoate.

3,3'-Diethylthiadicarbocyanine iodide *see* Dithiazanine iodide.

DIETHYLTHIAMBUTENE*** (*N*,*N*-diethyl-1-methyl-3,3-dithien-2-ylallylamine; 3-(diethylamino)-1,1-dithien-2-ylbut-1-ene; BW-19C49).

5,5-Diethyl-2-thiobarbituric acid *see* Thiobarbital.

Diethyl [thio[*o*-[3-(*p*-tolylsulfonyl)ureido]phenyl]-carbamoyl]phosphoramidate *see* Uredofos.

DIETHYLTOLUAMIDE* (*N*,*N*-diethyl-*m*-toluamide; *m*-delphene; BAS-3179F; DET; DETA; m-DET).

*N*¹-(4,6-Diethyl-*s*-triazin-2-yl)sulfanilamide *see* Sulfasymazine.

O,*O*-Diethyl *O*-(3,5,6-trichloropyrid-2-yl) phosphorothioate *see* Chlorpyrifos.

3,9-Diethyl-6-tridecanol sodium sulfate *see* Sodium heptadecyl sulfate.

*N*⁴,*N*⁴-Diethyl-α,α,α-trifluoro-3,5-dinitrotoluene-2,4-diamine *see* Dinitramine.

N,*N*-Diethyl-α-(3,4,5-trimethoxybenzamido)acetamide *see* Tricetamide.

N',*N'*-Diethyl-*N*-(3,4,5-trimethoxybenzoyl)glycinamide *see* Tricetamide.

9-(3,3-Diethylureido)-4,6,6a,7,8,9-hexahydro-7-methylindolo[4,3-*f*,*g*]quinoline *see* Lisuride.

N,*N*-DIETHYLVALERAMIDE (valeric acid diethylamide; 'valyl'; 'xalyl').

N,*N*-Diethylvanillamide *see* Etamivan.

Diethylxanthogen *see* Dixanthogen.

Diethyxime (tr) *see* Dietixim.

DIETIFEN*** (4-[2-(diethylamino)ethoxy]phenyl phenethyl ketone; 4'-[2-(diethylamino)ethoxy]-3-phenylpropiophenone; 'epilin').

DIETIXIM (tr) (*p*-bromobenzothiohydroxamic acid *S*-(2-diethylaminoethyl)ester; diethyxime).

'Dietrol' *see* Phendimetrazine.

Dietroxine *see* Diethadione.

Difacil *see* Adiphenine.

Difamizole *see* Difenamizole.

2-Difarnesyl-3-methyl-1,4-naphthoquinone *see* Farnoquinone.

Difasin (tr) *see* 10-(Diethylaminoacetyl)phenothiazine *and* Promethazine.

Difazin (tr) *see* 10-(Dimethylaminoacetyl)phenothiazine *and* Promethazine.

'Difco-M' *see* Phytohemagglutinin.

DIFEBARBAMATE*** (1,3-bis(3-butoxy-2-hydroxypropyl)phenobarbital dicarbamate ester).
See also under Febarbamate.

DIFEMERINE*** (2-(dimethylamino)-1,1-dimethylethyl benzilate ester; 'luostyl').

DIFEMETOREX*** (2-(diphenylmethyl)-1-piperidineethanol).

DIFENAMIZOLE*** (2-(dimethylamino)-*N*-(1,3-diphenylpyrazol-5-yl)propionamide; 5-[2-(dimethylamino)propionamido]-1,3-diphenylpyrazole; difamizole; diphenamizole; AP-14; 'pasalin').

Difenatsin *see* Diphenadione.

'Difenax' *see* Diphenpyramide.

DIFENCLOXAZINE*** (4-[2-(*p*-chloro-α-phenylbenzyloxy)ethyl]morpholine; diphencloxazine; LD-2630).

DIFENIDOL** (α,α-diphenyl-1-piperidinebutanol; 1,1-diphenyl-4-piperid-1-yl-1-butanol; diphenidol hydrochloride; SK&F-478).

DIFENIDOL EMBONATE (difenidol pamoate; SK&F-478-J).

Difenin (tr) *see* Phenytoin.

Difenoxilic acid *see* Difenoxin.

DIFENOXIMIDE*** (*N*-[[1-(3-cyano-3,3-diphenylpropyl)-4-phenylisonipecotoyl]oxy]succinimide; 4-[(2,5-dioxopyrrolidin-1-yloxy)carbonyl]-α,α,4-triphenyl-1-piperidinebutanenitrile; difenoximide hydrochloride; SC-26100).

DIFENOXIN*** (1-(3-cyano-3,3-diphenylpropyl)-4-phenylisonipecotic acid; 1-(3-cyano-3,3-diphenylpropyl)-4-phenylpiperidine-4-carboxylic acid; difenoxilic acid; difenoxin hydrochloride; McN-JR-15403-11; R-15403; 'lyspafen').
See also Butoxylate; Diphenoxylate; Fetoxilate.

Difenpiramide *see* Diphenpyramide.

Difenson *see* Chlorfenson.

DIFENZOQUAT* (1,2-dimethyl-3,5-diphenyl-1*H*-pyrazolium methyl sulfate; 'avenge'; 'finaven').

Difesyl (tr) *see* Difezil.

DIFETARSONE*** (*N*,*N*'-ethylene-1,2-diarsanilic acid; *N*,*N*'-ethylenebis[4-aminophenylarsonic acid]; *N*,*N*'-bis(*p*-arsonophenyl)ethylenediamine; diphetarsone; difetarsone disodium; RP-4763; 'amebarsin'; 'bemarsal'; 'rodameb').

DIFETEROL*** (2-[[2-(diphenylmethoxy)ethyl]methylamino]-1-phenyl-1-propanol; α-[1-[[2-(diphenylmethoxy)ethyl]methylamino]ethyl]benzyl alcohol; 'pandryl P').

DIFEZIL (tr) ((3-acetyl-5-chloro-2-hydroxybenzyl)-diethyl(2-phenoxyethyl)ammonium 3-hydroxy-2-naphthoate; difesyl; diphesyl).

'Diflam' *see* Benzydamine.

DIFLORASONE** (6α,9-difluoro-11β,17,21-trihydroxy-16β-methylpregna-1,4-diene-3,20-dione; 6α,9-difluoro-16β-methylprednisolone; 6α-fluorobetamethasone).

DIFLORASONE DIACETATE* (U-34865; 'florone').

DIFLUANAZINE*** (1-(2-anilinoethyl)-4-[4,4-bis(*p*-fluorophenyl)butyl]piperazine; difluanine hydrochloride; McN-JR-7242-11; R-7242).

Difluanine* *see* Difluanazine.

DIFLUBENZURON* (1-(*p*-chlorophenyl)-3-(2,6-difluorobenzoyl)urea; *N*-[[(4-chlorophenyl)amino]carbonyl]-2,6-difluorobenzamide diflu-

ron; DU-112307; Ph 60-40; Th-6040; 'dimilin').

DIFLUCORTOLONE*** (6α,9-difluoro-11β,21-dihydroxy-16α-methylpregna-1,4-diene-3,20-dione; 6α,9-difluoro-16α-methyl-1-dehydrocorticosterone).

DIFLUCORTOLONE PIVALATE* (diflucortolone 21-pivalate; SH-968).

DIFLUCORTOLONE VALERATE (Ro 10-7614; 'nerisone'; 'temetex'; 'travocort').

DIFLUMIDONE*** (3'-benzoyl-1,1-difluoromethanesulfonanilide; diflumidone sodium; BA-4164-8; MBR-4164-8; R-807).

DIFLUNISAL*** (2',4'-difluoro-4-hydroxy-3-biphenylcarboxylic acid; 5-(2,4-difluorophenyl)salicylic acid; MK-647; SV-108; 'diflusal'; 'dolobid'; 'fluniget'; 'unisal').

6α,9-Difluoro-11β,21-dihydroxy-16α-methylpregna-1,4-diene-3,20-dione *see* Diflucortolone.

1,1-DIFLUOROETHANE (FC-152a; fluorocarbon 152a; 'genetron 152A').

2',4'-Difluoro-4-hydroxy-3-biphenylcarboxylic acid *see* Diflunisal.

6α,9-Difluoro-11β-hydroxy-21,21-dimethoxy-16α,17-[(1-methylethylidene)bis(oxy)]pregna-1,4-diene-3,20-dione *see* Flumoxonide.

6α,9-Difluoro-11β-hydroxy-16α,17-[(1-methylethylidene)bis(oxy)]-21-(1-oxopropoxy)pregna-1,4-diene-3,20-dione *see* Procinonide.

6α,9α-Difluoro-16α-hydroxyprednisolone *see* Fluocinolone.

4-[*o*-(Difluoromethoxy)phenyl]-1,4-dihydro-2,6-dimethyl-3,5-pyridinedicarboxylic acid dimethyl ester *see* Riodipine.

6α,9-Difluoro-16α-methyl-1-dehydrocorticosterone *see* Diflucortolone.

6α,9α-Difluoro-16α-methylprednisolone *see* Flumetasone.

6α,9-Difluoro-16β-methylprednisolone *see* Diflorasone.

3,3'-Difluoro-4,4'-[1-methyl-2-(2,2,2-trifluoroethyl)ethylene]diphenol *see* Pentafluranol.

2-(2,4-Difluorophenyl)-4,5-bis(*p*-methoxyphenyl)imidazole *see* Fenflumizole.

5-(2,4-Difluorophenyl)salicylic acid *see* Diflunisal.

6α,9-Difluoroprednisolone 21-acetate 17-butyrate *see* Difluprednate.

Difluorotetrachloroethane *see* 1,1,2,2-Tetrachloro-1,2-difluoroethane.

6,8-Difluoro-2,3,4,9-tetrahydro-*N*,*N*-dimethyl-1*H*-carbazol-3-amine *see* Flucindole.

6α,9α-Difluoro-11β,16α,17α,21-tetrahydroxypregna-1,4-diene-3,20-dione *see* Fluocinolone.

6α,9-Difluoro-11β,16α,17-trihydroxy-3,20-dioxopregna-1,4-dien-21-al 21-(dimethylacetal) cyclic 16,17-acetal with acetone *see* Flumoxonide.

6α,9α-Difluoro-11β,17α,21-trihydroxy-16α-methylpregna-1,4-diene-3,20-dione *see* Flumetasone.

6α,9-Difluoro-11β,17,21-trihydroxy-16β-methylpregna-1,4-diene-3,20-dione *see* Diflorasone.

6α,9-Difluoro-11β,17,21-trihydroxypregna-1,4-diene-3,20-dione 21-acetate 17-butyrate *see* Difluprednate.

DIFLUPREDNATE*** (6α,9-difluoro-11β,17,21-

171

trihydroxypregna-1,4-diene-3,20-dione 21-acetate 17-butyrate; 6α,9-difluoroprednisolone 21-acetate 17-butyrate; CM-9155; W-6309; 'epitopic').

'Diflupyl' see Isoflurophate.

'Diflurex' see Tienilic acid.

Diflurophate* see Isoflurophate.

'Diflusal' see Diflunisal.

DIFO see Dimefox.

'Difolatan' see Captafol.

'Diforene' see Deanol p-acetamidobenzoate.

DIFTALONE** (phthalazino[2,3-b]phthalazine-5,12(7H,14H)-dione; diphtalone; L-5418; 'aladione').

'Digacin' see Digoxin.

Digenic acid see Kainic acid.

'Digenin' see Kainic acid.

'Digilong' see Digitoxin.

'Digimed' see Digitoxin.

'Digimerck' see Digitoxin.

'Diginorgin' see Digitalin.

'Digipan' see Digitoxin.

'Digisidin' see Digitoxin.

DIGITALIN (mixture of amorphous glycosides from digitalis; 'diginorgin').

Digitalin crystalline see Digitoxin.

'Digitaline' see Digitoxin.

ψ-Digitonin see Gitalin crystalline.

DIGITOXIGENIN (3β,14β-dihydroxy-5β-card-20(22)-enolide; 'thevetigenin').

DIGITOXIGENIN HEMISUCCINATE (AY-17611).

Digitoxigenin 3-tridigitoxoside see Digitoxin.

DIGITOXIN*** (digitoxigenin 3-tridigitoxoside; digitalin crystalline; digitoxoside).

ψ-Digitoxin see Gitoxin.

Digitoxoside see Digitoxin.

DIGLYCOCOLL HYDRIODIDE IODINE* ('bursoline').

Diglycol see Diethylene glycol.

DIGLYCOLIC ACID (2,2-oxydiacetic acid).

Diglycolic acid bis(3-carboxy-2,4,6-triiodoanilide) see Ioglycamic acid.

'Diglycol laurate' see Diethylene glycol monolaurate.

N,N'-Diglycoloyldi(3-carboxy-2,4,6-triiodoaniline) see Ioglycamic acid.

3,3'-(Diglycoloyldiimino)bis(2,4,6-triiodobenzoic acid) see Ioglycamic acid.

'Dignoquine' see under Chlorquinaldol.

DIGOXIN*** (3β,12,14-trihydroxy-5β-card-20(22)-enolide 3-tridigitoxoside; 12-hydroxydigitoxin).

Diguanide see Biguanide.

1,3-Diguanidino-2,4,5,6-tetrahydroxycyclohexane see Streptidine.

2,4-Diguanidino-3,5,6-trihydroxycyclohexyl-5-deoxy-2-O-(2-deoxy-2-methylamino-α-L-glucopyranosyl)-3-formyl-β-L-lyxo-pentafuranoside see Streptomycin.

2,4-Diguanidino-3,5,6-trihydroxycyclohexyl-5-deoxy-2-o-[2-deoxy-2-(methylamino)-α-L-glucopyranosyl]-3-(hydroxymethyl)-β-L-lyxo-pentanofura-

noside see Dihydrostreptomycin.

N-(4-Diguanidopiperazin-1-ylmethyl)tetracycline see Guamecycline.

Diguanyl see Proguanil.

Diguanyldiazoaminobenzene see Diminazene.

1,3-Diguanyl-4-lauryloxybenzene see Lauroguadine.

Dihexiverine see Dihexyverine.

Dihexyl sodium sulfosuccinate see Sodium dihexyl sulfosuccinate.

DIHEXYVERINE*** (2-piperid-1-ylethyl [bicyclohexyl]-1-carboxylate; dihexiverine; JL-1078).

'Dihydergot-plus' see under Dihydroergotamine.

1,4-Dihydracryloylpiperazine dimethanesulfonate see Piposulfan.

'Dihydral' see Dihydrotachysterol.

DIHYDRALAZINE*** (1,4-dihydrazinophthalazine; dihydralazine bis(methanesulfonate); dihydralazine mesylate; C-7441).
See also under Oxprenolol.

Dihydrazinophthalazine see Dihydralazine.

'Dihydrin' see Dihydrocodeine.

Dihydroampicillin see Epicillin.

Dihydrobaikiaine see Pipecolic acid.

1,3-Dihydro-2-benzazole see Isoindoline.

4-(9,10-Dihydro-4H-benzo[4,5]cyclohepta[1,2-b]thien-4-ylidene)-1-methylpiperidine see Pizotifen.

2-(2,3-Dihydro-1,4-benzodioxin-2-yl)-2-imidazoline see Idazoxan.

1-(2,3-Dihydro-1,4-benzodioxin-6-yl)-3-(3-phenylpyrrolidin-1-yl)-1-propanone see Proroxan.

3,4-Dihydro-1,2H-benzopyran see Chroman.

3,4-Dihydro-2,1H-benzopyran see Isochroman.

3,4-Dihydro-1,2H-benzothiopyran see Thiochroman.

3,4-Dihydro-2H-1,3-benzoxazine-2,4-dione see Carsalam.

Dihydrobenzthiazide see Hydrobentizide.

Dihydrochlorothiazide see Hydrochlorothiazide.

DIHYDROCODEINE*** (4,5-epoxy-6-hydroxy-3-methoxy-N-methylmorphinan; 5,6,7,7a,8,9-hexahydro-3-methoxy-10-methyl-4aH-8,9c-iminoethanophenanthro[4,5-bcd]furan-5-ol; dihydroneopine; drocode; DF-118).

Dihydrocodeine 6-nicotinate see Nicodicodine.

Dihydrocodeinone see Hydrocodone.

Dihydrocodeinone enol acetate see Thebacon.

Dihydrodesoxymorphine see Desomorphine.

9,10-Dihydro(8a,10a)diazoniaphenanthrene dibromide see Diquat.

10,11-DIHYDRO-5H-DIBENZ[b,f]AZEPINE (2,2'-iminobibenzyl; iminodibenzyl).

1'-[3-(10,11-Dihydro-5H-dibenz[b,f]azepin-5-yl)-propyl]-1,4-bipiperidine-4'-carboxamide see Carpipramine.

3-(10,11-Dihydro-5H-dibenz[b,f]azepin-5-yl)quinuclidine see Quinupramine.

10,11-Dihydro-5H-dibenzo[a,d]cycloheptene-5-carboxamide see Cyheptamide.

10,11-Dihydro-5H-dibenzo[a,d]cycloheptene-5-carboxylic acid tropine ester see Cyheptropine.

10,11-Dihydro-5H-dibenzo[a,d]cyclohepten-5-one
O-[2-(dimethylamino)ethyl]oxime see Noxiptiline.

7-[(10,11-Dihydro-5H-dibenzo[a,d]cyclohepten-5-yl)amino]heptanoic acid see Amineptine.

3-(10,11-Dihydro-5H-dibenzo[a,d]cyclohepten-5-ylidene)-1-dimethylamino-2-propanone see Cotriptyline.

3-(10,11-Dihydro-5H-dibenzo[a,d]cyclohepten-5-ylidene)-1-ethyl-2-methylpyrrolidine see Piroheptine.

2-(10,11-Dihydro-5H-dibenzo[a,d]cyclohepten-5-yloxy)-N,N-dimethylacetamide see Oxitriptyline.

4-(10,11-Dihydro-5H-dibenzo[a,d]cyclohepten-5-yloxy)-1-methylpiperidine see Hepzidine.

3-[(10,11-Dihydro-5H-dibenzo[a,d]cyclohepten-5-yl)oxy]tropane see Deptropine.

1a,10b-Dihydrodibenzo[a,e]cyclopropa[c]cyclohepten-6(1H)-one O-(2-aminoethyl)oxime see Mariptiline.

10,11-DIHYDRODIBENZO[b,f][1,4]THIAZEPINE (1-aza-4-thia-2,3,5,6-dibenzocycloheptadiene; homophenothiazine).

Dihydrodiethylstilbestrol see Hexestrol.

9,10-Dihydro-4,5-dihydroxy-9,10-dioxo-2-anthroic acid diacetate see Diacerein.

3α,4-Dihydro-3,4-dihydroxyspiro[benzofuran-2(3H),2'-oxirane]-6-methanol 6-acetate 3,4-diisovalerate see Valtrate.

1,7a-Dihydro-1,6-dihydroxyspiro[cyclopenta[c]pyran-7(6H),2'-oxirane]-4-methanol 4-acetate 1,6-diisovalerate see Valtrate.

1,7a-Dihydro-1,6-dihydroxyspiro[cyclopenta[c]pyran-7(6H),2'-oxirane]-4-methanol 4-acetate 1(or 6)-isovalerate 6(or 1)-(3-hydroxy-3-methylbutyrate) acetate see Acevaltrate.

8,9-Dihydro-4,11-dimethoxy-9-methylene-5-oxospiro[5H-furo[3',2':6,7][1]benzopyrano[3,2-c]pyridine-7(6H),1'-piperidinium] chloride see Azaspirium chloride.

1,4-Dihydro-7,8-dimethoxy-4-oxopyrimido[4,5-b]quinoline-2-carboxylic acid ethyl ester see Pirolate.

2,3-Dihydro-2,2-dimethylbenzofuran-7-yl methylcarbamate see Carbofuran.

10,11-Dihydro-N,N-dimethyl-5H-dibenzo[a,d]cycloheptene-Δ⁵,ᵞ-propylamine see Amitriptyline.

9,10-Dihydro-10,10-dimethyl-9-[3-(methylamino)propylidene]anthracene see Litracen.

3,7-Dihydro-1,8-dimethyl-3-(2-methylbutyl)-1H-purine-2,6-dione see Verofylline.

4,9-Dihydro-1,3-dimethyl-4-[(4-methylpiperazin-1-yl)acetyl]pyrazolo[4,3-b][1,5]benzodiazepin-10(1H)-one see Zolenzepine.

1',4'-Dihydro-2',6'-dimethyl-2-(methylthio)[3,4'-bipyridine]-3',5'-dicarboxylic acid diethyl ester see Mesudipine.

1,4-Dihydro-2,6-dimethyl-1-(2-morpholinoethyl)-4-(α,α,α-trifluoro-o-tolyl)-3,5-pyridinedicarboxylic acid diethyl ester see Flordipine.

1,4-Dihydro-2,6-dimethyl-4-(2-nitrophenyl)pyridine-3,5-dicarboxylic acid, esters see Nifedipine; Nisoldipine.

1,4-Dihydro-2,6-dimethyl-4-(3-nitrophenyl)pyridine-3,5-dicarboxylic acid, esters see Nicardipine; Niludipine; Nimodipine; Nitrendipine.

3,7-Dihydro-6,7-dimethyl-5-phenylpyrrolo[3,4-e]-1,4-diazepin-2(1H)-one see Premazepam.

2,3-Dihydro-4,6-dimethyl-3-pyridazinone see Cetohexazine.

10,11-Dihydro-N,N-dimethylspiro(5H-dibenzo[a,d]-cycloheptene-5,2'-[1,3]dioxolane)-4'-methylamine see Ciheptolane.

Dihydro-m-dioxin see 1,3-Dioxane.

S-[(1,3-Dihydro-1,3-dioxo-2H-isoindol-2-yl)methyl] O,O-dimethyl phosphorodithioate see Phosmet.

Dihydro-p-dioxole see 1,3-Dioxolane.

5,10-Dihydro-5,10-dioxonaphtho[2,3-b]1,4-dithiin-2,3-dicarbonitrile see Dithianon.

6,7-Dihydrodipyrido[1,2-a:2',1'-c]pyrazinediium dibromide see Diquat.

DIHYDROERGOCORNINE (DHO-180).

DIHYDROERGOCRISTINE (dihydroergocristine mesilate; dihydroergocristine methanesulfonate; DCS-90; DHE-145).
See also under Ajmalicine; Reserpine.

DIHYDROERGOCRYPTINE (DHK-135).

DIHYDROERGOCRYPTINE MESILATE (dihydroergocryptine methanesulfonate; 'vasobral').

DIHYDROERGOTAMINE*** (9,10-dihydro-12'-hydroxy-2'-methyl-5'α-(phenylmethyl)ergotaman-3',6',18-trione; dihydroergatamine tartrate; dihydroergotamine mesilate; dihydroergotamine methanesulfonate; DHE-45).

DIHYDROERGOTAMINE plus ETILEFRINE ('dihydergot-plus').

DIHYDROERGOTAMINE plus TROXERUTIN ('venelbin').

Dihydroergotoxine see Co-dergocrine.

1-(9,10-Dihydro-9,10-ethanoanthryl)-4-methylpiperazine see Trazitiline.

Dihydroethaverine see Drotaverine.

Dihydroflavone see Flavanone.

Dihydroflumethiazide see Hydroflumethiazide.

Dihydrofolliculin see Estradiol.

α-Dihydrofucosterol see β-Sitosterol.

Dihydrogen [N,N-bis[2-[bis(carboxymethyl)amino]ethyl]glycinato(5−)]gadolinate(2−) see Gadopentetic acid.

3,4-Dihydroharmine see Harmaline.

Dihydroheroin see Diacetyldihydromorphine.

4-(9,10-Dihydro-9-hydroxyanthr-10-ylidene)-1-methylpiperidine see Danitracen.

Dihydrohydroxycodeinone see Oxycodone.

14,15-Dihydro-14β-hydroxy-(3α,16α)-eburnamenine-14-carboxylic acid methyl ester see Vincamine.

2-[2,3-Dihydro-7-hydroxy-2-(4-hydroxy-3-methoxyphenyl)-3-(hydroxymethyl)benzofuran-5-yl]-3,5,7-trihydroxy-4-chromanone see Silicristin.

5,6-Dihydro-1-(2-hydroxy-3-isopropylaminopropoxy)naphthalene see Idropranolol.

15α,16α-Dihydro-17-hydroxy-7α-mercapto-3-oxo-3'H-cyclopropa[15,16]-17α-pregna-1,4,15-triene-21-carboxylic acid γ-lactone acetate see Mespirenone.

173

7,8-Dihydro-14-hydroxy-N-(3-methyl-2-butenyl)-normorphinone see Nalmexone.

3,4-Dihydro-7-hydroxy-1-methyl-β-carboline see Harmalol.

3,4-Dihydro-1-(hydroxymethyl)-5,7-dimethyl-4-oxo-6-phthalazinecarboxylic acid ethyl ester see Oxagrelate.

7,8-Dihydro-14-hydroxymorphine see Hydromorphinol.

2,3-Dihydro-3α-hydroxynortropidine see Nortropine.

2,3-Dihydro-3β-hydroxynortropidine see Norpseudotropine.

6,7-Dihydro-17-hydroxy-3-oxo-3′H-cyclopropa[6,7]-17α-pregna-4,6-diene-21-carboxylic acid potassium salt see Prorenoate potassium.

6,11-Dihydro-N-(2-hydroxy-3-phenoxypropyl)-N-methyldibenz[b,e]oxepin-11-ethylamine see Doxaminol.

10,11-Dihydro-10-[4-(3-hydroxypropyl)piperazin-1-yl]-8-(methylthio)dibenzo[b,f]thiepin see Oxyprothepine.

Dihydro-14-hydroxy-6β-thebainol 4-methyl ether see Oxymethebanol.

4,6-Dihydro-8-hydroxy-3,4,5-trimethyl-6-oxo-3H-2-benzopyran-7-carboxylic acid see Citrinin.

4,5-Dihydroimidazole see 2-Imidazoline.

2,3-Dihydroindene see Indan.

N-(2,3-Dihydro-1H-inden-2-yl)-N′,N′-diethyl-N-phenyl-1,3-propanediamine see Aprindine.

1,3-Dihydroisobenzofuran see Phthalan.

3,4-Dihydro-6-isobutyl-5-methyl-4-oxothieno[2,3-d]-pyrimidine-2-carboxylic acid see Tiprinast.

Dihydroisoperparine see Drotaverine.

3,4-Dihydro-3(1H)-isoquinolinecarboxamidine see Debrisoquine.

DIHYDROLYSERGAMINE (8β-aminomethyl-6-methyl-10a-ergoline).

4′,5′-Dihydro-7α-mercaptospiro[androst-4-ene-17,2′(3′H)-furan]-3-one acetate see Spiroxasone.

3,4-Dihydro-7-methoxy-1-methyl-β-carboline see Harmaline.

5,6-Dihydro-4-methoxy-6-(3,4-methylenedioxystyryl)-2-pyrone see Methysticin.

1,3-Dihydro-1-(methoxymethyl)-7-nitro-5-phenyl-2H-1,4-benzodiazepin-2-one see Motrazepam.

3,5-Dihydro-2-methoxy-2-methyl-4-phenylpyrano[3,2-c][1]benzopyran-5-one see Cyclocoumarol.

3,4-Dihydro-7-methoxy-1-methyl-9H-pyrid[3,4-b]indole see Harmaline.

4,9-Dihydro-7-methoxy-1-methyl-3H-pyrido[3,4-b]indole see Harmaline.

5,8-Dihydro-5-methoxy-8-oxo-1,3-dioxolo[4,5-g]quinoline-7-carboxylic acid see Miloxacin.

3,4-Dihydro-1-(p-methoxyphenoxymethyl)isoquinoline see Memotine.

4,5-Dihydro-6-[2-(p-methoxyphenyl)benzimidazol-5-yl]-5-methyl-3(2H)-pyridazinone see Pimobendan.

5,6-Dihydro-4-methoxy-6-(2-phenylethenyl)-2H-pyran-2-one see Kawain.

1-[2-[p-(3,4-Dihydro-6-methoxy-2-phenylnaphth-1-yl)phenoxy]ethyl]pyrrolidine see Nafoxidine.

3,4-Dihydro-2-(p-methoxyphenyl)-1-naphthyl p-[2-(1-pyrrolidinyl)ethoxy]phenyl ketone see Trioxifene.

5,6-Dihydro-4-methoxy-6-(2-phenylvinyl)-α-pyrone see Kawain.

5,6-Dihydro-4-methoxy-6-styryl-2-pyrone see Kawain.

3,12-Dihydro-6-methoxy-3,3,12-trimethyl-7H-pyrano[2,3-c]acridin-7-one see Acronine.

5,6-Dihydro-5-(3-methylaminopropyl)-11H-dibenz[b,e]azepine see Mezepine.

10,11-Dihydro-5-(3-methylaminopropyl)-5H-dibenz[b,f]azepine see Desipramine.

10,11-Dihydro-5-(3-methylaminopropylidene)-5H-dibenzo[a,d]cycloheptene see Nortriptyline.

1a,10b-Dihydro-6-[3-(methylamino)propylidene]dibenzo[a,e]cyclopropa[c]cycloheptene see Octriptyline.

6,11-Dihydro-11-[3-(methylamino)propylidene]dibenzo[b,e]thiepin see Northiadene.

10,11-Dihydro-N-methyl-5H-dibenzo[a,d]cycloheptene-Δ5,γ-propylamine see Nortriptyline.

1a,10b-Dihydro-N-methyldibenzo[a,e]cyclopropa[c]-cyclohepten-Δ6(1H),γ-propylamine see Octriptyline.

N-[3-(6,11-Dihydro-6-methyl-5,5-dioxidodibenzo-[1,2,5]thiadiazepin-11-yl)propyl]-N,α-dimethyl-phenethylamine see Pretiadil.

5,6-Dihydro-1-methyl-5,6-dioxo-3-indolinesulfonic acid 5-semicarbazone sodium salt see Carbazochrome sodium sulfonate.

(2,5-Dihydro-5-methyl-2-furan)glycine see Furanomycin.

10,11-Dihydro-5-methyl-10-(methylamino)-5H-dibenz[b,f]azepine see Metapramine.

6,11-Dihydro-6-methyl-11[3-[methyl(α-methylphenethyl)amino]propyl]dibenzo[1,2,5]thiadiazepine 5,5-dioxide see Pretiadil.

4,9-Dihydro-3-methyl-4-[(4-methylpiperazin-1-yl)-acetyl]-10H-thieno[3,4-b][1,5]benzodiazepin-10-one see Telenzepine.

7,8-Dihydro-O³-methyl-O⁶-nicotinoylmorphine see Nicodicodine.

1,3-Dihydro-1-methyl-7-nitro-5-phenyl-2H-1,4-benzodiazepin-2-one see Nimetazepam.

1,6-Dihydro-2-methyl-6-oxo-[3,4′-bipyridine]-5-carbonitrile see Milrinone.

3,6-Dihydro-1(2H)-[2-(3-methyl-2-oxooxazolidin-5-yl)ethyl]-4-phenylpyridine see Fenpipalone.

4,5-Dihydro-5-methyl-4-oxo-5-phenyl-2-furoic acid see Acifran.

5,6-Dihydro-2-methyl-N-phenyl-1,4-oxathiin-3-carboxamide see Carboxin.

5,11-Dihydro-11-[(4-methylpiperazin-1-yl)acetyl]-6H-pyrido[2,3-b][1,4]benzodiazepin-6-one see Pirenzepine.

10,11-Dihydro-10-(4-methylpiperazin-1-yl)dibenzo[b,f]thiepin see Perathiepine.

9,10-Dihydro-9-(4-methylpiperazin-1-yl)-9,10-ethanoanthracene see Trazitiline.

10,11-Dihydro-10-(4-methylpiperazin-1-yl)-8-(methylthio)dibenzo[b,f]thiepin see Metitepine.

9,10-Dihydro-10-(1-methylpiperid-4-ylidene)-9-anthrol see Danitracen.

174

6,11-Dihydro-11-(1-methylpiperid-4-ylidene)-5*H*-benzo[5,6]cyclohepta[1,2-*b*]pyridine see Azatadine.

9,10-Dihydro-4-(1-methylpiperid-4-ylidene)-4*H*-benzo[4,5]cyclohepta[1,2-*b*]thiophene see Pizotifen.

4,9-Dihydro-4-(1-methylpiperid-4-ylidene)-10*H*-benzo[4,5]cyclohepta[1,2-*b*]thiophen-10-one see Ketotifen.

6,11-Dihydro-11-(1-methylpiperid-4-ylidene)dibenzo[*b,e*]thiepin see Perithiadene.

3,4-Dihydro-1-methyl-9*H*-pyrid[3,4-*b*]indol-7-ol see Harmalol.

4,9-Dihydro-1-methyl-3*H*-pyrid[3,4-*b*]indol-7-ol see Harmalol.

1-[2-(3,6-Dihydro-4-methyl-1(2*H*)-pyridyl)ethyl]-guanidine see Guanacline.

4,5α-Dihydro-2α-methyltestosterone see Drostanolone.

1-[10,11-Dihydro-8-(methylthio)dibenzo[*b,f*]thiepin-10-yl]-4-methylpiperazine see Metitepine.

6,11-Dihydro-6-methyl-11-(1α*H*,5α*H*-tropan-3α-yloxy)dibenzo[*c,f*][1,2]thiazepine 5,5-dioxide see Zepastine.

Dihydromorphine see Paramorphan.

Dihydromorphinone see Hydromorphone.

2,3-Dihydro-1-(morpholinoacety)-3-phenyl-4(1*H*)-quinazolinone see Moquizone.

1-(5,6-Dihydronaphth-2-yloxy)-3-isopropylamino-2-propanol see Idropranolol.

Dihydroneopine see Dihydrocodeine.

6,7-Dihydro-3-(5-nitro-2-furyl)-5*H*-imidazo[2,1-*b*]-thiazolium chloride see Furazolium chloride.

1,3-Dihydro-7-nitro-5-phenyl-2*H*-1,4-benzodiazepin-2-one see Nitrazepam.

1,3-Dihydro-7-nitro-5-phenyl-2*H*-1,4-benzodiazepin-2-one-3-carboxylic acid potassium salt see Potassium nitrazepate.

Dihydronorguiaretic acid see Nordihydroguaiaretic acid.

2,3-Dihydronortropidine see Nortropane.

Dihydronovobiocin tetracycline compound see Tetracycline dihydronovobiocin sodium phytate.

Dihydrooxazole see Oxazoline.

2,3-Dihydro-3-oxobenzisosulfonazole see Saccharin.

2,3-Dihydro-3-oxo-4*H*-1,4-benzoxazine-4-acetamide see Paraxazone.

10,11-Dihydro-10-oxo-5*H*-dibenz[*b,f*]azepine-5-carboxamide see Oxcarbazepine.

6,11-Dihydro-11-oxodibenzo[*b,e*]thiepin-3-acetic acid see Tiopinac.

6,11-Dihydro-11-oxodibenz[*b,e*]oxepin-2-acetic acid see Isoxepac.

6,11-Dihydro-11-oxodibenz[*b,e*]oxepin-3-acetic acid see Oxepinac.

2,3-Dihydro-3-oxoindole see Pseudoindoxyl.

1,3-Dihydro-3-oxo-1-isobenzofuranyl 6-[(aminophenylacetyl)amino]penicillanate see Talampicillin.

1,3-Dihydro-3-oxo-1-isobenzofuranyl 2-[[3-(trifluoromethyl)phenyl]amino]-3-pyridinecarboxylate see Talniflumate.

4-(1,3-Dihydro-1-oxo-2*H*-isoindol-2-yl)-α-methyl-benzeneacetic acid see Indoprofen.

1,4-Dihydro-4-oxo-2,6-pyridinedicarboxylic acid see Chelidamic acid.

3,4-Dihydro-3-pentyl-6-(trifluoromethyl)-2*H*-1,2,4-benzothiadiazine-7-sulfonamide 1,1-dioxide see Penflutizide.

'Dihydroperparin' see Drotaverine.

1,3-Dihydro-1-[1-(2-phenoxyethyl)piperid-4-yl]-2*H*-benzimidazol-2-one see Oxiperomide.

1,2-Dihydro-3-(phenoxymethyl)pyrido[3,4-*e*]-1,2,4-triazine see Oxifungin.

5-(4,5-Dihydro-2-phenyl-3*H*-benz[*e*]indol-3-yl)salicylic acid see Fendosal.

3,4-Dihydro-2-phenyl-2*H*-1-benzopyran see Flavan.

2,3-Dihydro-2-phenyl-4*H*-1-benzopyran-4-one see Flavanone.

2,3-Dihydro-α-[1-[(4-phenylbutyl)amino]ethyl]benzo[*b*]thiophene-5-methanol see Tibalosin.

4,5-Dihydro-1-phenyl-1,4-epoxy-1*H*,3*H*-[1,4]oxazepino[4,3-*a*]benzimidazole see Oxapadol.

5,6-Dihydro-6-phenylimidazo[2,1-*b*]thiazole see Antafenite.

5-[2-(3,6-Dihydro-4-phenyl-1(2*H*)-pyridyl)ethyl]-3-methyl-2-oxazolidinone see Fenpipalone.

1,2-Dihydro-5-phenyl-6,7-tetramethylene-3*H*-thieno[2,3-*e*][1,4]diazepin-2-one see Bentazepam.

2,3-Dihydro-1,4-phthalazinedione see Phthalhydrazide.

3,6-Dihydro-5-(*o*-propoxyphenyl)-7*H*-v-triazolo[4,5-*d*]pyrimidin-7-one see Zaprinast.

Dihydropropranolol see Idropranolol.

Dihydropsychotrine see Cephaeline.

Dihydropyrazole see Pyrazoline.

Dihydropyridinium see Pyrithyldione.

5-(3,6-Dihydro-1(2*H*)-pyridyl)-2-oxo-2*H*-[1,2,4]oxadiazolo[2,3-*a*]pyrimidine-7-carbamic acid methyl ester see Carprazidil.

2,3-Dihydroquercetin see Taxifolin.

Dihydroquinine see Hydroquinine.

10,11-Dihydro-5-quinuclidin-3-yl-5*H*-dibenz[*b,f*]azepine see Quinupramine.

1,9-Dihydro-9-β-D-ribofuranosyl-6*H*-purin-6-one see Inosine.

2,3-Dihydrospiro(naphthalene-1(4*H*),3'-piperidine)-2',4,6'-trione see Alonimid.

22,23-Dihydrostigmasterol see β-Sitosterol.

Dihydrostilbestrol see Hexestrol.

DIHYDROSTREPTOMYCIN*** (2,4-diguanidino-3,5,6-trihydroxycyclohexyl 5-deoxy-2-*O*-[2-deoxy-2-(methylamino)-α-L-glucopyranosyl]-3-(hydroxymethyl)-β-L-*lyxo*-pentanofuranoside).

DIHYDROSTREPTOMYCIN plus PROCAINE-PENICILLIN ('ambocillin'; 'mixtencillin'; 'retromyopen').
See also Streptoduacin.

DIHYDROSTREPTOMYCIN AMINOSALICYLATE ('pasomycin').

DIHYDROSTREPTOMYCIN PANTOTHENATE ('enterastrept').

DIHYDROTACHYSTEROL*** (9,10-seco-ergosta-5,7,22-trien-3β-ol; 24-methyl-9,10-secocholesta-5,7,22-trien-3β-ol; dichystrol).

Dihydrotestosterone see Androstanolone.

5α-Dihydrotestosterone *see* Androstanolone.
6,7-Dihydro-1,2,3,10-tetramethoxy-7-(methyl-amino)-5H-benzo[a]heptalen-9-one *see* Demecolcine.
Dihydrotheelin *see* Estradiol.
5,6-Dihydro-6-thien-2-ylimidazo[2,1-b]thiazole *see* Antienite.
3,6-Dihydro-α-(o-toloxymethyl)-1(2H)-pyridinethanol *see* Tolpronine.
3,4-Dihydro-6-(trifluoromethyl)-2H-1,2,4-benzothiadiazine-7-sulfonamide 1,1-dioxide *see* Hydroflumethiazide.
10,11-Dihydro-N,N,β-trimethyl-5H-dibenzo[a,d]-cycloheptene-5-propylamine *see* Butriptyline.
1,3-Dihydro-N,3,3-trimethyl-1-phenylbenzo[c]thiophene-1-propylamine *see* Talsupram.
4,8-Dihydro-1,3,8-trimethyl-4-phenylpyrazolo[3,4-b][1,4]diazepine-5,7(1H,6H)-dione *see* Zomebazam.
(±)-cis-9,10-Dihydro-N,N,10-trimethyl-2-(trifluoromethyl)-9-anthracenepropylamine *see* Fluotracen.
Dihydrovitamin K₁ *see* Phytonadiol.
Dihydroxyacetaldehyde *see* Glyoxal.
DIHYDROXYACETONE (1,3-dihydroxy-2-propanone).
Dihydroxyacetophenones *see* Quinacetophenone; Resacetophenone.
Dihydroxy aluminium aminoacetate *see* Aluminium glycinate.
DIHYDROXYALUMINIUM SODIUM CARBONATE (DANK; 'kompensan'; 'rolaids').
4,4′-(3α,17β-Dihydroxy-5α-androstan-2β,16β-ylene)bis(1,1-dimethylpiperazinium) dibromide diacetate *see* Pipecuronium bromide.
(3α,17β-Dihydroxy-5α-androstan-2β,16β-ylene)-bis(1-methylpiperidinium bromide) 3-acetate *see* Dacuronium bromide.
(3α,17β-Dihydroxy-5α-androstan-2β,16β-ylene)-bis(1-methylpiperidinium bromide) 3,17-diacetate *see* Pancuronium bromide.
Dihydroxyanthranol *see* Anthrarobin.
1,8-Dihydroxyanthranol *see* Dithranol.
1,4-Dihydroxyanthraquinone *see* Quinizarine.
1,8-Dihydroxyanthraquinone *see* Dantron.
4,5-Dihydroxyanthraquinone-2-carboxylic acid *see* Rhein.
m-Dihydroxybenzene *see* Resorcinol.
o-Dihydroxybenzene *see* Pyrocatechol.
p-Dihydroxybenzene *see* Hydroquinone.
2,5-Dihydroxy-p-benzenedisulfonic acid *see* Persilic acid.
2,5-Dihydroxybenzenesulfonic acid calcium salt *see* Calcium dobesilate.
2,5-Dihydroxybenzenesulfonic acid diethylamine salt *see* Etamsylate.
2,5-Dihydroxybenzenesulfonic acid 5-p-toluenesulfonate *see* Sultosilic acid.
2,2′-Dihydroxybenzil *see* Salicil.
2,5-Dihydroxybenzoic acid *see* Gentisic acid.
2,3-Dihydroxybenzoic acid diacetate *see* Dipyrocetyl.
Dihydroxybenzoic acids *see* Gentisic acid; Protoca-techuic acid; Pyrocatechuic acid; Resorcylic acids.
3,4-Dihydroxybenzyl alcohol *see* Protocatechuyl alcohol.
1-(3,4-Dihydroxybenzyl)-6,7-dimethoxyisoquinoline dinicotinate *see* Niceverine.
2-(3,4-Dihydroxybenzyl)-2-hydrazinopropionic acid *see* Carbidopa.
1-(3,4-Dihydroxybenzyl)-6,7-isoquinolinediol *see* Papaveroline.
1-(3,4-Dihydroxybenzyl)-1,2,3,4-tetrahydro-6,7-di-hydroxyisoquinoline *see* Tetrahydropapaveroline.
5,5′-Dihydroxy-5,5′-bibarbituric acid *see* Alloxantin.
1,4-Dihydroxy-5,8-bis[[2-[(2-hydroxyethyl)amino]-ethyl]amino]anthraquinone *see* Mitoxantrone.
2,5-Dihydroxy-3,6-bis(p-hydroxyphenyl)-p-benzo-quinone *see* Atromentin.
3β,14β-Dihydroxybufa-4,20,22-trienolide 3-rhamno-glucoside *see* Scillaren A.
3,14-Dihydroxybufa-4,20,22-trienolide 3-rhamno-side *see* Proscillaridin.
D-DIHYDROXYBUSULFAN (D-threo-1,2,3,4-butanetetrol 1,4-bis-(methanesulfonate) ester; D-threitol 1,4-dimethanesulfonate; D-threityl 1,4-dimesilate; NSC-39068).
L-Dihydroxybusulfan *see* Treosulfan.
2,3-Dihydroxy-2-butenyl 6-(2-amino-2-phenylacet-amido)penicillanate cyclic carbonate *see* Lenam-picillin.
3β,14β-Dihydroxy-5β-card-20(22)-enolide *see* Digitoxigenin.
3β,14β-Dihydroxy-5β-card-20(22)-enolide 3-(4‴-acetyltridigitoxoside) *see* Acetyldigitoxin.
3,6-Dihydroxycholanic acid *see* Hyodeoxycholic acid.
3,7-Dihydroxycholanic acid *see* Chenodeoxycholic acid; Ursodeoxycholic acid.
3,12-Dihydroxycholanic acid *see* Deoxycholic acid.
3α,7α-Dihydroxy-5β-cholan-24-oic acid *see* Cheno-deoxycholic acid.
1α,25-Dihydroxycholecalciferol *see* Calcitriol.
3,4-Dihydroxycinnamic acid *see* Caffeic acid.
3,4-Dihydroxycinnamic acid 1-carboxy-4,5-dihydr-oxy-1,3-cyclohexylene ester *see* Cynarine.
1α,25-Dihydroxycolecalciferol *see* Calcitriol.
5,6-Dihydroxycoumarin *see* Citropten.
6,7-Dihydroxycoumarin *see* Esculetin.
7,8-Dihydroxycoumarin *see* Daphnetin.
6,7-Dihydroxycoumarin-4-ylmethanesulfonic acid, esters and salts *see* Cromesilate(s).
2,3-Dihydroxy-2-cyclopenten-1-one *see* Reductic acid.
6β,14-Dihydroxy-3,4-dimethoxy-17-methylmorphi-nan *see* Drotebanol.
D-(+)-4-(2,4-Dihydroxy-3,3-dimethylbutyramido)-butyric acid *see* Hopantenic acid.
2,4-Dihydroxy-3,3-dimethylbutyric acid *see* Pantoic acid.
N-(2,4-Dihydroxy-3,3-dimethylbutyryl)-β-alanine *see* Pantothenic acid.
2-[(2,4-Dihydroxy-3,3-dimethylbutyryl)amino]eth-anesulfonic acid *see* Pantoyltaurine.

3,5-Dihydroxy-6,6-dimethyl-2,4-cyclohexadien-1-one *see* Filixic acid.

3,6-Dihydroxy-6,*N*-dimethyl-4,5-epoxymorphinan *see* Methyldihydromorphine.

11α,15-Dihydroxy-16,16-dimethyl-9-methylene-5-*cis*,13-*trans*-prostadienoic acid *see* Meteneprost.

11,15-Dihydroxy-16,16-dimethyl-9-oxoprosta-2,13-dienoic acid methyl ester *see* Gemeprost.

11β,21-Dihydroxy-3,20-dioxo-4-pregnen-18-al *see* Aldosterone.

2,5-DIHYDROXY-3,6-DIPHENYL-*p*-BENZO-QUINONE (polyporic acid; polyporin; NSC-44175).

3α-17β-Dihydroxy-2β,16β-dipiperidino-5α-androstane 3,17-diacetate 16β-methobromide *see* Vecuronium bromide.

1,16-Dihydroxy-3,14-dithiahexadecane *see* Tiadenol.

4,17β-Dihydroxyestr-4-en-3-one 17-cyclopentanepropionate *see* Oxabolone cipionate.

Dihydroxyestrin *see* Estradiol.

5,7-Dihydroxyflavone *see* Chrysin.

11β,17α-Dihydroxy-*D*-homopregna-1,4-diene-3,20-dione 17α-butyrate *see* Domoprednate.

1,8-Dihydroxy-3-(hydroxymethyl)anthraquinone *see* Aloe-emodin.

7-[3,5-Dihydroxy-2-(3-hydroxy-3-methyl-1-octenyl)-cyclopentyl]-4,5-heptadienoic acid methyl ester *see* Prostalene.

7-[3,5-Dihydroxy-2-(3-hydroxy-3-methyl-1-octenyl)-cyclopentyl]-5-heptenoic acid *see* Carboprost.

3,5-Dihydroxy-α-(*p*-hydroxy-α-methylphenethylaminomethyl)benzyl alcohol *see* Fenoterol.

7-[3α,5α-Dihydroxy-2β-[3(*S*)-hydroxy-*trans*-oct-1-enyl]cyclopent-1-yl]-*cis*-hept-5-enoic acid *see* Dinoprost.

Dihydroxy-[(2-hydroxy-5-oxo-2-imidazolin-4-yl)-ureato]aluminium *see* Aldioxa.

7-[3,5-Dihydroxy-2-(3-hydroxy-4-phenoxy-1-butenyl)cyclopentyl]-4,5-heptanedioic acid methyl ester *see* Fenprostalene.

5,7-Dihydroxy-2-(4-hydroxyphenyl)chromone *see* Apigenin.

3,5-Dihydroxy-α-[[-2-(*p*-hydroxyphenyl)-1-methylethyl]aminomethyl]benzyl alcohol *see* Fenoterol.

(±)-2,3-Dihydroxy-*N*-[3-(*p*-hydroxyphenyl)-1-methylpropyl]phenethylamine *see* Dobutamine.

2,4-Dihydroxy-*N*-(3-hydroxypropyl)-3,3-dimethylbutyramide *see* Dexpanthenol; Panthenol.

7-[3,5-Dihydroxy-2-[3-hydroxy-4-(3-thienyloxy)-1-butenyl]cyclopentyl]-5-heptenoic acid *see* Tiaprost.

7-[3,5-Dihydroxy-2-[3-hydroxy-4-[(α,α,α-trifluoro-*m*-tolyl)oxy]-1-butenyl]cyclopentyl]-5-heptenoic acid *see* Fluprostenol.

5,5′-Dihydroxyhydurilic acid *see* Alloxantin.

4′,7-Dihydroxyisoflavone *see* Daidzein.

3,4-Dihydroxy-α-isopropylaminomethylbenzyl alcohol *see* Isoprenaline.

3,5-Dihydroxy-α-isopropylaminomethylbenzyl alcohol *see* Orciprenaline.

3′,4′-Dihydroxy-2-isopropylaminopropiophenone *see* Phenisonone.

3,4-Dihydroxy-α-(1-isopropylaminopropyl)benzyl alcohol *see* Isoetarine.

11β,21-Dihydroxy-16α,17α-isopropylidenedioxypregna-1,4-diene-3,20-dione *see* Desonide.

4-(6,7-Dihydroxyisoquinolin-1-ylmethyl)pyrocatechol *see* Papaveroline.

5,6-Dihydro-2-(2,6-xylidino)-4*H*-1,3-thiazine *see* Xylazine.

Dihydroxymalonic acid *see* Mesoxalic acid.

11β,17-Dihydroxy-21-mercaptopregn-4-ene-3,20-dione *see* Tixocortol.

2,2′-Dihydroxy-4-methoxybenzophenone *see* Dioxybenzone.

16α,17α-Dihydroxy-3-methoxyestra-1,3,5(10)-triene *see* Epimestrol.

4′,5′-Dihydroxy-7-methoxyflavone *see* Genkwanin.

5,7-Dihydroxy-4′-methoxyflavone *see* Acacetin.

2′,6′-Dihydroxy-4′-methoxy-3′-methylbutyrophenone *see* Aspidinol.

3,17-Dihydroxy-11β-methoxy-19-nor-17α-pregna-1,3,5(10)-trien-20-yne *see* Moxestrol.

3,4-Dihydroxy-α-[4-(*o*-methoxyphenyl)piperazin-1-ylmethyl]benzyl alcohol *see* Pipratecol.

3′,4′-Dihydroxy-2-(methylamino)acetophenone *see* Adrenalone.

3,4-Dihydroxy-α-[1-(methylamino)ethyl]benzyl alcohol *see* Dioxifedrine.

3,4-Dihydroxy-α-[(methylamino)methyl]benzyl alcohol *see* Epinephrine; Racepinefrine.

18,20-Dihydroxy-3β-(methylamino)pregn-5-ene *see* Paravallarinol.

4,17β-Dihydroxy-17-methylandrosta-1,4-dien-3-one *see* Enestebol.

4,17β-Dihydroxy-17-methylandrost-4-en-3-one *see* Oxymesterone.

4,5-Dihydroxy-2-methylanthraquinone *see* Chrysophanic acid.

6,7-Dihydroxy-4-methylcoumarin bis(hydrogen sulfate) *see* Sulmarin.

5,6-Dihydroxy-1-methylindoxyl *see* Adrenolutin.

5,7-Dihydroxy-4′-methylisoflavone *see* Biochanin A.

Di[4-(4-hydroxy-2-methyl-5-isopropylphenylazo)-phenyl] sulfone *see* Diathymosulfone.

3,4-Dihydroxy-α-[(α-methyl-3,4-methylenedioxy-phenethylamino)methyl]benzyl alcohol *see* Protokylol.

11α,17β-Dihydroxy-17-methyl-3-oxoandrosta-1,4-diene-2-carboxaldehyde *see* Formebolone.

11β,17β-Dihydroxy-17-methyl-3-oxoandrosta-1,4-diene-2-carboxylic acid *see* Roxibolone.

11,15-Dihydroxy-15-methyl-9-oxo-13-thiaprostanoic acid *p*-benzamidophenyl ester *see* Tiprostanide.

3,4-Dihydroxy-α-methylphenylalanine *see* Methyldopa.

11β,17-Dihydroxy-21-(4-methylpiperazin 1-yl)-pregna-1,4-diene-3,20-dione *see* Mazipredone.

17,21-Dihydroxy-16β-methylpregna-1,4-diene-3,11,20-trione *see* Meprednisone.

11β,21-Dihydroxy-2′-methyl-5′β*H*-pregna-1,4-dieno[17,16-*d*]oxazole-3,20-dione 21-acetate *see* Deflazacort.

Dihydroxy(6-methyl-8-quinolinolato)bismuth *see*

Mebiquine.

5,5-Di(hydroxymethyl)-2-(trichloromethyl)-1,3-di-oxane *see* Penthrichloral.

3,5-Dihydroxy-3-methylvaleric acid *see* Mevalonic acid.

6,7-Dihydroxy-4-morpholinomethylcoumarin *see* Folescutol.

4,5-Dihydroxy-2,7-naphthalenedisulfonic acid *see* Chromotropic acid.

2,6-Dihydroxy-3-nitro-3′,5′-bis(trifluoromethyl)-benzanilide diacetate *see* Flurantel.

3,4-Dihydroxynorephedrine *see* Corbadrine.

6α,8α-Dihydroxy-3-oxoeudesma-1,4-dien-12-oic acid 12,6-lactone *see* Artemisin.

11α,15-Dihydroxy-9-oxo-5-*cis*,13-*trans*-prostadie-noic acid *see* Dinoprostone.

11,15-Dihydroxy-9-oxoprost-13-en-1-oic acid *see* Alprostadil.

11,16-Dihydroxy-9-oxoprost-13-enoic acid methyl ester *see* Misoprostol.

3,4-Dihydroxyphenanthrene *see* Morphol.

N-**(3,4-Dihydroxyphenethyl)-1-adamantanecarbox-amide** *see* Dopamantine.

3,4-Dihydroxyphenethylamine *see* Dopamine.

β,4-Dihydroxyphenethylamine *see* Octopamine.

7-[3,5-Dihydroxy-2-[[2-(phenoxymethyl)-1,3-dioxo-lan-2-yl]vinyl]cyclopentyl]-5-heptenoic acid *see* Etiproston.

2,5-Dihydroxyphenylacetic acid *see* Homogentisic acid.

3,4-Dihydroxyphenylacetic acid *see* Homoprotoca-techuic acid.

3-(3,4-Dihydroxyphenyl)alanine *see* Dopa.

Dihydroxyphenylhexane *see* Hexylresorcinol.

3-(3,4-Dihydroxyphenyl)-2-hydrazino-2-methylpro-pionic acid *see* Carbidopa.

2-(2,4-Dihydroxyphenyl)-6-hydroxy-3-benzofuran-carboxylic acid δ-lactone *see* Coumestrol.

7-[2[2-(3,4-Dihydroxyphenyl)-2-hydroxyethyl-amino]ethyl]theophylline *see* Theodrenaline.

7-[3-[2-(3,5-Dihydroxyphenyl)-2-hydroxyethyl-amino]propyl]theophylline *see* Reproterol.

1-[2-(3,4-Dihydroxyphenyl)-2-hydroxyethyl]-4-(*o*-methoxyphenyl)piperazine *see* Pipratecol.

1-(3,4-Dihydroxyphenyl)-2-isopropylamino-1-butan-ol *see* Isoetarine.

Dihydroxyphenylmethenylbenzyl alcohol *see* Phenolphthalol.

α-(3,4-Dihydroxyphenyl)-4-(2-methoxyphenyl)-1-piperazineethanol *see* Pipratecol.

3-(3,4-Dihydroxyphenyl)-2-methylalanine *see* Meth-yldopa.

α-(3,4-Dihydroxyphenyl)-2-piperidinemethanol *see* Rimiterol.

1-(3α,17β-Dihydroxy-2β-piperid-1-yl-5α-androstan-16β-yl)-1-methylpiperidinium bromide diacetate *see* Vecuronium bromide.

erythro-**3,4-Dihydroxy-α-piperid-2-ylbenzyl alcohol** *see* Rimiterol.

11β,17α-Dihydroxypregna-1,4-diene-3,20-dione *see* Deprodone.

17α,21-Dihydroxypregna-1,4-diene-3,11,20-trione *see* Prednisone.

3,17-Dihydroxypregna-3,5-dien-20-one-3-cyclopent-yl ether *see* Pentagestrone.

3α,21-Dihydroxy-5α-pregnane-11,20-dione *see* Alfa-dolone.

11β,21-Dihydroxypregn-4-ene-3,20-dione *see* Corti-costerone.

16α,17-Dihydroxypregn-4-ene-3,20-dione *see* Al-gestone.

17,21-Dihydroxypregn-4-ene-3,20-dione *see* Cor-todoxone.

14,17-Dihydroxypregn-4-ene-3,20-dione cyclic acet-al with propionaldehyde *see* Proligestone.

11β,21-Dihydroxypregn-4-ene-3,18,20-trione *see* Aldosterone.

17α,21-Dihydroxypregn-4-ene-3,11,20-trione *see* Cortisone.

16α,17-Dihydroxyprogesterone *see* Algestone.

17,21-Dihydroxyprogesterone *see* Cortodoxone.

14,17-Dihydroxyprogesterone cyclic acetal with pro-pionaldehyde *see* Proligestone.

2,3-Dihydroxypropanal *see* Glyceraldehyde.

1,3-Dihydroxy-2-propanone *see* Dihydroxyacetone.

2,3-Dihydroxypropionaldehyde *see* Glyceraldehyde.

2,3-Dihydroxypropyl *N*-(7-chloroquinolin-4-yl)an-thranilate *see* Glafenine.

2,3-Dihydroxypropyl 2-(3-chloro-*o*-toluidino)nico-tinate *see* Clonixeril.

1-(2,3-Dihydroxypropyl)-3,5-diiodo-4-pyridone *see* Iopydol.

3-(2,3-Dihydroxypropyl)-2-methyl-4-(3*H*)-quinazo-linone *see* Diproqualone.

7-(2,3-Dihydroxypropyl)theophylline *see* Dipro-phylline.

7-(2,3-Dihydroxypropyl)theophylline bis(nicotinate ester) *see* Diniprofylline.

2,3-Dihydroxypropyl *N*-(8-trifluoromethylquinolin-4-yl)anthranilate *see* Floctafenine.

(Dihydroxypropyl)trimethylammonium iodide for-mal *see* Oxapropanium iodide.

4,6-Dihydroxypyrazolo[3,4-*d*]pyrimidine *see* Oxipu-rinol.

4,8-Dihydroxyquinaldic acid *see* Xanthurenic acid.

2,3-Dihydroxysuccinic acid *see* Tartaric acid.

4′,5′-Dihydroxy-3,6,7,8-tetramethoxyflavone *see* Calycopterin.

3,4-Dihydroxythiophene-2,5-dicarboxylic acid di-propyl ester *see* Protiofate.

3,5-Dihydroxytoluene *see* Orcinol.

2,5-Dihydroxy-α-toluic acid *see* Homogentisic acid.

Dihydroxytrimethoxyfuchsone *see* Rubrophen.

6-(6,10-Dihydroxyundecyl)-β-resorcylic acid lactone *see* Zeranol.

1α,25-Dihydroxyvitamin D$_3$ *see* Calcitriol.

DIHYPRYLONE* (3,3-diethyl-2,4-piperidinedi-one; piperidione; Nu-1510).

'Dihytamin' *see* Dihydroergocristine.

'Dihyzin' *see* Dihydralazine.

3,3′-Di-2-imidazolin-2-ylcarbanilide *see* Imidocarb.

Diindogen *see* Indigotin.

Diiodobrassidic acid ethyl ester *see* Iodobrassid.

Diiodobuphenine *see* Bufeniode.

Diiododithymol *see* Dithymol diiodide.

DIIODOHYDROXYQUIN* (5,7-diiodo-8-quinolinol; diiodohydroxyquinoline; dijodoxichinoline; diodoxyquinoline; iodoxine; SS-578).

DIIODOHYDROXYQUIN plus TETRACYCLINE ('diocyclin').
See also under Chloroquine sulfate;
Cloquinate.

Diiodohydroxyquinoline* see Diiodohydroxyquin.

3,5-Diiodo-4-(3-iodo-4-methoxyphenoxy)phenylacetic acid diethylaminoethyl ester see Tyromedan.

Diiodomethanesulfonic acid sodium salt see Dimethiodal sodium.

3,5-Diiodo-1-methylchelidamic acid sodium salt see Iodoxyl.

2,6-Diiodo-4-nitrophenol see Disophenol.

3,5-Diiodo-4-oxo-1-pyridineacetic acid salts see Diodone; Iodopyridone; Propyliodone.

2,6-DIIODO-1-PHENOL-4-SULFONIC ACID
(3,5-diiodo-p-phenolsulfonic acid; soziodolic acid).

3,5-Diiodo-p-phenolsulfonic acid see 2,6-Diiodo-1-phenol-4-sulfonic acid.

3,5-Diiodo-4-pyridone see Iopydone.

'Diiodoquin' see Diiodohydroxyquin.

5,7-Diiodo-8-quinolinol see Diiodohydroxyquin.

Diiodostearic acid ethyl ester see Iodetryl.

3,5-DIIODOTYROSINE (2-amino-3-(4-hydroxy-3,5-diiodophenyl)propionic acid; 4-hydroxy-3,5-diiodophenylalanine; iodogorgoic acid; iodogorgonic acid).

Diiodo-β-tyrosine see Betazine.

4,4'-Diisoamyloxythiocarbanilide see Tiocarlide.

Diisobutyrylthiamine see Sulbutiamine.

2,3-Diisocyanatotoluene see Toluene diisocyanate.

DIISOPROMINE* (N,N-diisopropyl-3,3-diphenylpropylamine; disopromine).

N-[2-[(Diisopropoxyphosphinothioyl)thio]ethyl]benzenesulfonamide see Bensulide.

DIISOPROPYLAMINE DICHLOROACETATE
(DADA; DIEDI; diisopropylamine dichloroethanoate; DIPA; IS-401; 'dapocel'; 'dedyl'; 'disotat'; 'kalodil'; 'tensicor').

2'-(2-Diisopropylaminoethoxy)butyrophenone see Ketocaine.

o-(2-Diisopropylaminoethoxy)-α-propylbenzyl alcohol see Ketocainol.

N-[2-(Diisopropylamino)ethyl]-2-oxo-1-pyrrolidineacetamide see Pramiracetam.

α-(2-Diisopropylaminoethyl)-α-phenyl-2-pyridineacetamide see Disopyramide.

4-Diisopropylamino-2-phenyl-2-pyrid-2-ylbutyramide see Disopyramide.

Diisopropylcarbamothioic acid S-(2,3-dichloro-2-propenyl) ester see Diallate.

Diisopropylcarbamothioic acid S-(2,3,3-trichloro-2-propenyl) ester see Triallate.

2,2-Diisopropyl-1,3-dioxolane-4-methanol see Promoxolane.

N,N-Diisopropyl-3,3-diphenylpropylamine see Diisopromine.

Diisopropyl 1,3-dithiole-$\Delta^{2,\alpha}$-malonate see Malotilate.

Diisopropylfluo(ro)phosph(on)ate see Isoflurophate.

N,N'-Diisopropyl-3,4-furazandicarboxamide 2-oxide see Ipramidil.

2,3:4,6-Di-O-isopropylidene-α-L-xylo-hexulofuranosonic acid see Diprogulic acid.

Diisopropylmethanoldioxolane see Promoxolane.

O,O-DIISOPROPYL O-p-NITROPHENYL PHOSPHATE ('mioticol'; 'propicol').

2,6-Diisopropylphenol see Propofol.

[[[(2,6-Diisopropylphenyl)carbamoyl]methyl]imino]diacetic acid see Disofenin.

Diisopropylphosphorodiamidic fluoride see Mipafox.

Diisopropyl phosphorofluoridate see Isoflurophate.

Dijodoxichinoline see Diiodohydroxyquin.

3,5-Diketocaproic acid see Triacetic acid.

Diklorfenidim (tr) see Diuron.

'Dikonirit' see 2,4-Dichlorophenoxyacetic acid.

'Dikotex' see 2-(4-Chloro-2-methylphenoxy)acetic acid.

'Dilabil' see Dehydrocholic acid.

'Dilabron' see Isoetarine.

'Dilanacin' see Digoxin.

'Dilangil' see Mannityl hexanitrate.

'Dilangio' see Bencyclane.

'Dilantin' see Phenytoin.

'Dilar' see Paramethasone acetate.

'Dilasmyl' see Choline theophyllinate.

'Dilatal' see Buphenine.

'Dilatol' see Buphenine.

'Dilatropon' see Buphenine.

'Dilaudid' see Hydromorphone.

'Dilavase' see Isoxsuprine.

DILAZEP* (tetrahydro-1H-1,4-diazepine-1,4(5H)-dipropanol 3,4,5-trimethoxybenzoate diester; biopropazepan bis(3,4,5-trimethoxybenzoate); THDT; Asta C-4898; 'cormelian').
See also under β-Acetyldigoxin.

'Dilcit' see Inositol nicotinate.

DILEVALOL ((−)-5-[(1R)-1-hydroxy-2-[[(1R)-1-methyl-3phenylpropyl]amino]ethyl]salicylamide; R,R-labetalol; dilevalol hydrochloride; Sch-19927).

'Dilexan' see under Phloroglucinol.

'Dillar' see Paramethasone acetate.

DILMEFONE* (2',4'-dimethoxy-3-pyrid-4-ylacrylophenone; 4-[2-(2,4-dimethoxybenzoyl)vinyl]pyridine).

'Diloderm' see Dichlorisone.

'Dilombrin' see Dithiazanine iodide.

'Dilor' see Diprophylline.

'Dilospan' see Phloroglucinol.

'Dilosyn' see Methdilazine.

'Dilovasan' see Isoxsuprine.

DILOXANIDE* (2,2-dichloro-4'-hydroxy-N-methylacetanilide; RD-3803; 'entamide').

DILOXANIDE FUROATE (CB-8073; 'furamide').

DILTIAZEM ((+)-5-(2-dimethylaminoethyl)-cis-2,3-dihydro-3-hydroxy-2-(p-methoxyphenyl)-1,5-benzothiazepin-4(5H)-one acetate ester; 5-[2-(dimethylamino)ethyl]-2,3,4,5-tetrahydro-2-(4-methoxyphenyl)-4-oxo-1,5-benzothiazepin-3-yl acetate; diltiazem hydrochloride; CRD-401; 'an-

179

ginyl'; 'dilzem'; 'herbesser'; 'tildiem').

'Diluran' see Acetazolamide.

'Dilvasene' see Oxapropanium iodide.

'Dilydrin' see Buphenine.

'Dilzem' see Diltiazem.

DIMABEFYLLINE*** (7-[p-(dimethylamino)-benzyl]theophylline; LJ-278).

'Dimaestad' see Deanol.

Dimagnesium tetraaluminium hydroxide oxide sulfate hydrate see Almadrate sulfate.

'Dimalone' see Dimethyl carbate.

DIMANTINE*** (N,N-dimethyloctadecylamine; dymanthine; GS-1339; NSC-5547; 'thelmesan').

'Dimapres' see under Clonidine.

'Dimapyrin' see Aminophenazone.

Dimazene* see Diacetazotol.

DIMAZOLE** (6-[2-(diethylamino)ethoxy]-2-(dimethylamino)benzothiazole; diamthazole; dimazole dihydrochloride; Ro 2-2453).

'Dimazon' see Diacetazotol.

'Dimeate' see Thiometon.

Dimebencozamide see Cobamamide.

DIMECAMINE*** (3-dimethylamino-2,2,3-trimethylnorbornane; N,N,2,3,3-pentamethyl-2-norbornanamine; methylmecamylamine).

Dimecoline (tr) see Dimecolonium iodide.

DIMECOLONIUM IODIDE*** (2-carboxy-1,1,6-trimethylpiperidinium iodide choline ester iodide; choline iodide dimethylpipecolate methiodide; dimecoline; dimekolin; dimelin).

'Dimecron' see Phosphamidon.

DIMECROTIC ACID*** (2,4-dimethoxy-β-methylcinnamic acid; 3-(2,4-dimethoxyphenyl)-3-methylacrylic acid; 3-(2,4-dimethoxyphenyl)-3-methylpropenoic acid; 3-(2,4-dimethoxyphenyl)-crotonic acid).
See also Magnesium dimecrotate.

'Dimedion' see Ethadione.

Dimeditiapramine see Tiapamil.

Dimedrol (tr) see Diphenhydramine.

DIMEFADANE*** (N,N-dimethyl-3-phenyl-1-indanamine; SK&F-1340).

DIMEFLINE*** (8-[(dimethylamino)methyl]-7-methoxy-3-methylflavone; DW-62; NSC-114650; Rec-7-0267).

DIMEFOX* (bis(dimethylamido)fluorophosphate; bis(dimethylamino)fluorophosphine oxide; tetramethylphosphorodiamidic fluoride; BFP; BFPO; DIFO; DMF; 'hanane'; 'pestox XIV'; 'terra-sytam').

Dimekolin (tr) see Dimecolonium iodide.

DIMELAZINE*** (10-(1,3-dimethylpyrrolidin-3-ylmethyl)phenothiazine; diprothazine; mepyrrotazine).

Dimelin see Dimecolonium iodide.

'Dimelor' see Acetohexamide.

DIMEMORFAN** (3,17-dimethylmorphinan; N,3-dimethylmorphinan; AT-17; 'astomin').

'Dimenformon' see Estradiol.

DIMENHYDRINATE*** (2-diphenylmethoxy-N,N-dimethylethylamine compound with 8-chlorotheophylline; diphenhydramine 8-chloro-theophyllinate; diphenhydramine teoclate; chlor-

anautine).

DIMENHYDRINATE plus SCOPOLAMINE (C-330; 'gestadramine').

DIMENOXADOL*** (2-(dimethylamino)ethyl ethoxydiphenylacetate; dimenoxadole; esthocin; estocin).

Dimenoxadole* see Dimenoxadol.

DIMEPHEPTANOL*** (6-(dimethylamino)-4,4-diphenyl-3-heptanol; methadol; NIH-2933).
See also Alphamethadol; Betamethadol.

Dimepheptanol acetate see Acetylmethadol.

DIMEPRANOL** (1-(dimethylamino)-2-propan-ol).

Dimepranol p-acetamidobenzoate inosine complex see Inosine pranobex.

DIMEPREGNEN*** (3β-hydroxy-6α,16α-dimethyl-4-pregnen-20-one; ST-1411).

Dimepropion* see Metamfepramone.

DIMEPROZAN*** (9-[3-(dimethylamino)propylidene]-2-methoxyxanthene; 2-methoxy-N,N-dimethyl-Δ⁹,γ-xanthenepropylamine; dimeprozine).

Dimeprozine* see Dimeprozan.

'Dimeray' see Meglumine iocarmate.

DIMERCAPROL*** (2,3-dimercaptopropanol; British antilewisite; dicaptol; BAL).

Dimercaptopropane sodium sulfonate see Unithiol.

2,3-Dimercaptopropanol see Dimercaprol.

2,3-Dimercaptosuccinic acid see Succimer.

Dimerin (tr) see Methyprylon.

'Dimer X' see Meglumine iocarmate.

DIMESNA*** (disodium 2,2'-dithiodiethanesulfonate).

DIMESONE** (9α-fluoro-11β,21-dihydroxy-16α,17-dimethylpregna-1,4-diene-3,20-dione).

Dimestrol (tr) see Dianisylhexene.

Dimesyldideoxyerythritol see Ritrosulfan.

'Dimetabrone' see Brofoxine.

DIMETACRINE*** (10-[3-(dimethylamino)propyl]-9,9-dimethylacridan; dimethacrin; dimetacrine tartrate; SD-709).

DIMETAMFETAMINE** (N,N-dimethylamphetamine; (S)-N,N,α-trimethylphenethylamine; 'metromin'; 'metrotonin').

DIMETAN* (5,5-dimethyl-1-oxocyclohex-2-en-3-yl dimethylcarbamate; 1-hydroxy-5,5-dimethyl-1-cyclohexen-3-one dimethylcarbamate; G-19258).

'Dimetane' see Brompheniramine.

Dimetazine see Mebolazine.

Dimethacrin see Dimetacrine.

DIMETHADIONE*** (5,5-dimethyl-2,4-oxazolidinedione; AC-1198; Bax-1400-Z; DMO; NSC-30152).

'Dimethanen' see Deanol tartrate.

Dimethanesulfonylmannitol see Mannityl dimesilate.

DIMETHAZAN*** (7-[2-(dimethylamino)ethyl]-1,3-dimethylxanthine; 7-[2-(dimethylamino)-ethyl]theophylline).

Dimethenthoate see Phenthoate.

Dimethicone* see Dimeticone.

Dimethindene* see Dimetindene.

DIMETHIODAL SODIUM*** (diiodomethane-sulfonic acid sodium salt).

DIMETHIRIMOL* (5-butyl-2-(dimethylamino)-4-hydroxy-6-methylpyrimidine; 'milcurb').

Dimethisoquin* *see* Quinisocaine.

DIMETHISTERONE*** (6α,21-dimethylethister-one; 17α-ethynyl-6α,21-dimethyltestosterone; 17α-ethynyl-17-hydroxy-6α,21-dimethylandrost-4-en-3-one; 17β-hydroxy-6α-methyl-17-(1-pro-pynyl)androst-4-en-3-one).

DIMETHISTERONE plus ETHINYLESTRADI-OL ('oracon').

DIMETHOATE* (2-[(dimethoxyphosphinothio-yl)thio]-*N*-methylacetamide; *O,O*-dimethyl *S*-[2-(methylamino)-2-oxoethyl] phosphorodithioate; *O,O*-dimethyl *S*-(methylcarbamoylmethyl) phos-phorodithioate; fosfamid; phosphamide; Bi-58; HC-8014bis; 'amidofos'; 'cygon'; 'fostion MM'; 'perfekthion'; 'rogor'; 'roxion'). *See also under* DDT.

O-**Dimethoate** *see* Omethoate.

DIMETHOCAINE* (3-(diethylamino)-1,2-di-methylpropyl *p*-aminobenzoate).

DIMETHOLIZINE*** (1-(*o*-methoxyphenyl)-4-(3-methoxypropyl)piperazine; dimetholizine phosphate; HT-1479).

Dimethothiazine* *see* Dimetotiazine.

DIMETHOXANATE*** (2-[2-(dimethylamino)-ethyl]ethyl 10-phenothiazinecarboxylate; di-methoxanate hydrochloride).

Dimethoxon *see* Omethoate.

1,10-Dimethoxy-6aα-aporphine-2,9-diol *see* Bold-ine.

3,4-Dimethoxybenzaldehyde *see* Veratraldehyde.

6-(2,6-Dimethoxybenzamido)penicillanic acid *see* Meticillin.

7-(3,4-Dimethoxybenzoyloxy)-3-ethyl-1-(*p*-meth-oxyphenyl)-2-methyl-3-azaheptane *see* Mebever-ine.

4-[2-(2,4-Dimethoxybenzoyl)vinyl]pyridine *see* Di-lmefone.

3,4-Dimethoxybenzyl alcohol *see* Veratryl alcohol.

3,4-Dimethoxybenzylamine *see* Veratrylamine.

1-(3,4-Dimethoxybenzyl)-6,7-dimethoxyisoquinoline *see* Papaverine.

2-(3,4-Dimethoxybenzyl)-4-(diphenylmethyl)-1,2-di-methylpiperazine *see* Benderizine.

3,4-DIMETHOXYBENZYLHYDRAZINE (ve-trazin).

4-(3,4-Dimethoxybenzylideneamino)-6,7-dimethoxy-quinoline *see* Leniquinsin.

3,3′-(3,3′-Dimethoxy-4,4′-biphenylene)bis(2,5-di-phenyl-2*H*-tetrazolium chloride) *see* Tetrazolium blue.

N-**(3,4-Dimethoxycinnamoyl)anthranilic acid** *see* Tranilast.

2-(3,6-Dimethoxy-2,4-dimethylbenzyl)-2-imidazol-ine *see* Domazoline.

2,5-Dimethoxy-α,4-dimethylphenethylamine *see* 2,5-Dimethoxy-4-methylamphetamine.

3,4-Dimethoxy-*N,N*-dimethyl-α-(3-phenylpropyl)-benzylamine *see* Vetrabutine.

Dimethoxy-DT *see* Methoxychlor.

12,13-Dimethoxyibogamine-18-carboxylic acid methyl ester *see* Conopharyngine.

4-(6,7-Dimethoxyisoquinolin-1-ylmethyl)pyroca-techol *see* Papaverine.

4-[(6,7-Dimethoxyisoquinolin-1-yl)methyl]pyroca-techol dinicotinate *see* Niceverine.

Dimethoxymethane *see* Methylal.

5-[[3,5-Dimethoxy-4-(2-methoxyethoxy)phenyl]-methyl]-2,4-pyrimidinediamine *see* Tetroxoprim.

5,6-Dimethoxy-3-[2-[4-(*o*-methoxyphenyl)piperazin-1-yl]ethyl]-2-methylindole *see* Milipertine.

6,7-Dimethoxy-2-[2-[4-(*o*-methoxyphenyl)piperazin-1-yl]ethyl]-4(3*H*)-quinazolinone *see* Peraquinsin.

4,4′-Dimethoxy-4′-(*p*-methoxyphenyl)stilbene *see* Chlorotrianisene.

2,5-DIMETHOXY-4-METHYLAMPHET-AMINE (2-amino-1-(2,5-dimethoxy-4-methyl-phenyl)propane; 2,5-dimethoxy-α,4-dimethyl-phenethylamine; 1-(2,5-dimethoxy-4-methyl-phenyl)-2-propylamine; DOM; STP).

2,4-Dimethoxy-α-methylbenzhydrol *see* Fenocinol.

2,4-Dimethoxy-β-methylcinnamic acid *see* Dime-crotic acid.

5,8-Dimethoxy-2-methyl-6,7-furanochromone *see* Khellin.

4,9-Dimethoxy-7-methyl-5*H*-furo[3,2-*g*][1]benzopyr-an-5-one *see* Khellin.

1-[2-(5,6-Dimethoxy-2-methylindol-3-yl)ethyl]-4-(*o*-methoxyphenyl)piperazine *see* Milipertine.

1-[2-(5,6-Dimethoxy-2-methylindol-3-yl)ethyl]-4-phenylpiperazine *see* Oxypertine.

3,4-Dimethoxy-17-methylmorphinan-6β,14-diol *see* Drotebanol.

Dimethoxymethylphenobarbital *see* Eterobarb.

5,6-Dimethoxy-2-methyl-3-[2-(4-phenylpiperazin-1-yl)ethyl]indole *see* Oxypertine.

1-(2,5-Dimethoxy-4-methylphenyl)-2-propylamine *see* 2,5-Dimethoxy-4-methylamphetamine.

2,3-Dimethoxy-*N*-[(1-methylpyrrolidin-2-yl)methyl]-5-(methylsulfamoyl)benzamide *see* Sulverapride.

4,5-Dimethoxy-2-(methylsulfinyl)toluene *see* Tol-mesoxide.

5-[3,5-Dimethoxy-4-(methylthio)benzoyl]pyrimidine-2,4-diylamine *see* Metioprim.

4,9-Dimethoxy-7-[(methylthio)methyl]-5*H*-furo[3,2-*g*][1]benzopyran-5-one *see* Timefurone.

1-(6,7-Dimethoxy-4(3*H*)-oxoquinazolin-2-yl)-4-(*o*-methoxyphenyl)piperazine *see* Peraquinsin.

Dimethoxyphenecillin *see* Meticillin.

3,4-Dimethoxyphenethylamine *see* Homoveratryl-amine.

p-**[3-[(3,4-Dimethoxyphenethyl)amino]-2-hydroxy-propoxy]-β-methylcinnamonitrile** *see* Pacrinolol.

α-[[(3,4-Dimethoxyphenethyl)amino]methyl]-*p*-hydr-oxybenzyl alcohol *see* Denopamine.

1-[(3,4-Dimethoxyphenethyl)amino]-3-(*m*-tolyloxy)-2-propanol *see* Bevantolol.

N-**(3,4-Dimethoxyphenethyl)-2-(3,4-dimethoxyphen-yl)-*N*-methyl-1,3-dithiane-2-propylamine 1,1,3,3-tetraoxide** *see* Tiapamil.

2-(3,4-Dimethoxyphenethylimino)-1-methylpyrrolid-ine *see* Mixidine.

5-[(3,4-Dimethoxyphenethyl)methylamino]-2-(3,4-

181

dimethoxyphenyl)-2-isopropylvaleronitrile *see* Verapamil.

5-[*N*-(3,4-Dimethoxyphenethyl)methylamino]-2-isopropyl-2-(3,4,5-trimethoxyphenyl)valeronitrile *see* Gallopamil.

2-[3-[(3,4-Dimethoxyphenethyl)methylamino]propyl]-5,6-dimethoxyphthalimidine *see* Falipamil.

2-(3,5-Dimethoxyphenoxy)ethanol *see* Floverine.

3-(2,4-Dimethoxyphenyl)crotonic acid *see* Dimecrotic acid.

3-[4-[3-[[2-(3,4-Dimethoxyphenyl)ethyl]amino]-2-hydroxypropoxy]phenyl]-3-methylacrylonitrile *see* Pacrinolol.

1-(3,4-Dimethoxyphenyl)-5-ethyl-7,8-dimethoxy-4-methyl-5*H*-2,3-benzodiazepine *see* Tofisopam.

(±)-1-(2,5-Dimethoxyphenyl)-2-glycinamidoethanol *see* Midodrine.

2-(3,4-Dimethoxyphenyl)-2-isopropyl-2-[3-(*N*-methylhomoveratrylamino)propyl]acetonitrile *see* Verapamil.

3-(2,4-Dimethoxyphenyl)-3-methylacrylic acid *see* Dimecrotic acid.

3-(2,4-Dimethoxyphenyl)-3-methylpropenoic acid *see* Dimecrotic acid.

Dimethoxyphenylpenicillin *see* Meticillin.

1-(2,4-Dimethoxyphenyl)-1-phenylethanol *see* Fenocinol.

5,6-Dimethoxy-3-[2-(4-phenylpiperazin-1-yl)ethyl]-indole-2-carboxylic acid ethyl ester *see* Alpertine.

2-[(Dimethoxyphosphinothioyl)thio]-*N*-methylacetamide *see* Dimethoate.

4-[[(Dimethoxyphosphinothioyl)thio]methyl]-2-methoxy-1,3,4-thiadiazol-5-one *see* Methidathion.

2-[[(Dimethoxyphosphinothioyl)thio]methyl]phthalimide *see* Phosmet.

6-[[(Dimethoxyphosphinothioyl)thio]methyl]-1,3,5-triazine-2,4-diamine *see* Menazon.

2-[(Dimethoxyphosphinothioyl)thio]-2-phenylacetic acid ethyl ester *see* Phenthoate.

[(Dimethoxyphosphinothioyl)thio]succinic acid diethyl ester *see* Malathion.

3-(Dimethoxyphosphinyloxy)crotonic acid, esters *see* Crotoxyphos; Mevinphos.

3-(Dimethoxyphosphinyloxy)-*N*,*N*-dimethyl-*cis*-crotonamide *see* Dicrotophos.

5,6-Dimethoxyphthalaldehydic acid *see* Opianic acid.

5,6-Dimethoxyphthalaldehydic acid isonicotinoyl-hydrazone *see* Opiniazide.

1-(6,7-Dimethoxyphthalazin-1-yl)piperid-4-yl ethylcarbamate *see* Carbazeran.

Dimethoxyphthalide *see* Meconin.

4,5-Dimethoxyphthalide *see* Pseudomeconin.

5,6-Dimethoxyphthalide *see* *m*-Meconin.

5-(6,7-Dimethoxyphthalidyl)-5,6,7,8-tetrahydro-4-methoxy-6-methyl-1,3-dioxolo[4,5-*g*]isoquinoline *see* Noscapine.

1-(6,7-Dimethoxy-3-phthalidyl)-1,2,3,4-tetrahydro-8-methoxy-2-methyl-6,7-methylenedioxyisoquinoline *see* Noscapine.

1-[4,7-Dimethoxy-6-(2-piperid-1-ylethoxy)-5-benzofuranyl]-3-methylurea *see* Murocainide.

6,7-Dimethoxy-1-protocatechuylisoquinoline dinico-tinate *see* Niceverine.

2′,4′-Dimethoxy-3-pyrid-4-ylacrylophenone *see* Dilmefone.

Dimethoxypyrimidylsulfanilamide isomers *see* Sulfadimethoxine; Sulfadoxine; Sulfamoprine.

1-[4,7-Dimethoxy-6-(2-pyrrolidin-1-ylethoxy)-5-benzofuranyl]-3-methylurea *see* Carocainide.

4-(6,7-Dimethoxyquinazolin-4-yl)piperazine-1-carboxylic acid 2-hydroxy-2-methylpropyl ester *see* Hoquizil.

6,7-Dimethoxy-2-[4-(tetrahydrofuran-2-carbonyl)-piperazin-1-yl]quinazolin-4-ylamine *see* Terazosin.

3,5-Dimethoxytoluene *see* Elemicin.

6,7-Dimethoxy-1-(3,4,5-triethoxyphenyl)isoquinoline *see* Octaverine.

6,7-Dimethoxy-4-veratrylideneaminoquinoline *see* Leniquinsin.

6,7-Dimethoxy-1-veratrylisoquinoline *see* Papaverine.

Dimethpyrindene *see* Dimetindene.

DIMETHRIN* (2,4-dimethylbenzyl 2,2-dimethyl-3-(2-methyl-1-propenyl)cyclopropanecarboxylate; 2,4-dimethylbenzyl chrysanthemate; (2,4-dimethylphenyl)methyl 2,2-dimethyl-3-(2-methyl-1-propenyl)cyclopropanecarboxylate; 2,4-xylylmethyl 2,2-dimethyl-3-(2-methylpropenyl)-cyclopropanecarboxylate; ENT-21170).

ar,*ar*-Dimethylacetanilide(s) *see* Acetoxylidide(s).

O,*S*-Dimethyl acetylphosphoramidothioate *see* Acephate.

9,9-Dimethylacridan-10-carbothioic acid 2-dimethylaminoethyl thioester *see* Botiacrine.

2,3-Dimethylacrylic acid *see* Tiglic acid.

3,3-Dimethylacrylic acid *see* Senecioic acid.

2,3-Dimethylacrylic acid tropine ester *see* Tropigline.

β,β-Dimethylacryloylcholine *see* Senecioylcholine.

*N*¹-(3,3-Dimethylacryloyl)sulfanilamide *see* Sulfadicramide.

3,5-Dimethyl-1-adamantanamine *see* Memantine.

α,α-Dimethyl-1-adamantaneethylamine *see* Somantadine.

Dimethylamantadine *see* Memantine.

Dimethylamido ethoxy phosphoryl cyanide *see* Tabun.

DIMETHYLAMINE 2,4-DICHLOROPHEN-OXYACETATE ('herbatox D-500').

DIMETHYLAMINE TRICHLOROBENZOATE (2,3,6-trichlorobenzoic acid dimethylamine salt; 'benzabor'; 'benzac'; 'trysben 200').

Dimethylaminoacetaldehyde diphenylacetal *see* Medifoxamine.

6-(Dimethylamino)acetylgluconic acid *see* Pangamic acid.

4-(Dimethylamino)antipyrine *see* Aminophenazone.

p-(DIMETHYLAMINO)AZOBENZENE (*N*,*N*-dimethyl-*p*-phenylazoaniline; butter yellow; DAB).

p-(Dimethylamino)benzoic acid 2-ethylhexyl ester *see* Padimate O.

p-(Dimethylamino)benzoic acid pentyl ester mixture *see* Padimate.

7-[*p*-(Dimethylamino)benzyl]theophylline *see* Dimabefylline.

3-[[(Dimethylamino)carbonyl]amino]phenyl (1,1-dimethylethyl)carbamate *see* Karbutilate.

1-[(Dimethylamino)carbonyl]-5-methyl-1*H*-pyrazol-3-yl dimethylcarbamate *see* Dimetilan.

3β-(Dimethylamino)con-5-ene *see* Conessine.

3-(Dimethylamino)-6,8-difluoro-1,2,3,4-tetrahydrocarbazole *see* Flucindole.

3-(Dimethylamino)-2,3-dihydro-2-methylbenzopyran *see* Trebenzomine.

3-(Dimethylamino)-1,2-dihydro-7-methyl-1,2-(propylmalonyl)-1,2,4-benzotriazine *see* Azapropazone.

5-[4-(Dimethylamino)-3,5-dimethoxybenzyl]pyrimidine-2,4-diamine *see* Aditoprim.

N-[3-(Dimethylamino)-1,3-dimethylbutyl]-6,7-dimethoxy-2,1-benzoxathian-3-carboxamide 1,1-dioxide *see* Tisocromide.

2-(Dimethylamino)-1,1-dimethylethyl benzilate ester *see* Difemerine.

4-(Dimethylamino)-α,2-dimethylphenethylamine *see* Amiflamine.

trans-4-(Dimethylamino)-*N*-(2,6-dimethylphenyl)-1-(2-hydroxycyclohexyl)-4-piperidinecarboxamide *see* Transcainide.

4-(Dimethylamino)-3,5-dimethylphenyl methylcarbamate *see* Mexacarbate.

4-(Dimethylamino)-2,3-dimethyl-1-phenyl-3-pyrazolin-5-one *see* Aminophenazone.

6-(Dimethylamino)-2-[2-(2,5-dimethyl-1-phenyl-3-pyrrolyl)vinyl]-1-methylquinolinium chloride *see* Pyrvinium chloride.

3-(Dimethylamino)-1,2-dimethylpropyl *p*-aminobenzoate *see* Butamin.

2-(Dimethylamino)-5,6-dimethylpyrimidin-4-yl dimethylcarbamate *see* Pirimicarb.

3-[(Dimethylamino)-*m*-dioxan-5-ylmethyl]pyridine *see* Doxpicomine.

6-(Dimethylamino)-4,4-diphenyl-3-heptanol *see* Alphamethadol; Dimepheptanol.

6-(Dimethylamino)4,4-diphenyl-3-heptanone *see* Methadone; Levomethadone.

6-(Dimethylamino)-4,4-diphenyl-3-hexanone *see* Normethadone.

2-(Dimethylamino)-*N*-(1,3-diphenylpyrazol-5-yl)-propionamide *see* Difenamizole.

4-(Dimethylamino)-2,2-diphenylvaleramide *see* Dimevamide.

3-(Dimethylamino)-1,1-dithien-2-yl-1-butene *see* Dimethylthiambutene.

4-(Dimethylamino)-1,2-dithiolane *see* Nereistoxin.

2-(Dimethylamino)ethanethiol *see* Captamine.

2-(Dimethylamino)ethanol *see* Deanol.

α,α'-(Dimethylamino)ethanol-4,4'-biacetophenone *see* Hemicholinium.

N-[*p*-(2-Dimethylaminoethoxy)benzyl]-3,4,5-trimethoxybenzamide *see* Trimethobenzamide.

5-[2-(Dimethylamino)ethoxy]carvacryl isopropyl carbonate *see* Iproxamine.

2-[α-(2-Dimethylaminoethoxy)-2,6-diethylbenzyl]pyridine *see* Pytamine.

1-[6-[2-(Dimethylamino)ethoxy]-4,7-dimethoxybenzofuran-5-yl]-3-(*p*-methoxyphenyl)-2-propen-1-one *see* Mecinarone.

6-[2-(Dimethylamino)ethoxy]-4,7-dimethoxy-5-[3-(*p*-methoxyphenyl)-1-oxoprop-2-enyl]benzofuran *see* Mecinarone.

2-[2-(Dimethylamino)ethoxy]ethyl 10-phenothiazinecarboxylate *see* Dimethoxanate.

2-[2-(Dimethylamino)ethoxy]ethyl 1-phenylcyclopentanecarboxylate *see* Minepentate.

11α-(Dimethylamino)-2β-ethoxy-3α-hydroxy-5α-pregnan-20-one *see* Minaxolone.

4-[2-(Dimethylamino)ethoxy]-5-isopropyl-2-methylphenyl isopropyl carbonate *see* Iproxamine.

2-[α-(2-Dimethylaminoethoxy)-α-methylbenzyl]pyridine *see* Doxylamine.

trans-1-[*p*-[2-(Dimethylamino)ethoxy]phenyl]-1,2-diphenylbut-1-ene *see* Tamoxifen.

trans-α-[*p*-[2-(Dimethylamino)ethoxy]phenyl]-α'-ethylstilbene *see* Tamoxifen.

4-[2-(Dimethylamino)ethoxy]-1(2*H*)-phthalazinone oxime *see* Taloximine.

4-[2-(Dimethylamino)ethoxy]-*N*-(3,4,5-trimethoxybenzoyl)benzylamine *see* Trimethobenzamide.

2-(Dimethylamino)ethyl *p*-acetamidobenzoate *see* Deanol p-acetamidobenzoate.

2-(Dimethylamino)ethyl 3-amino-4-chlorobenzoate *see* Clormecaine.

17-[1-[2-(Dimethylamino)ethyl]aminoethyl]androstanol *see* 22,25-Diazacholestanol.

4-[[2-(Dimethylamino)ethyl]amino]-6-methoxyquinoline compound with diethylcarbamoylcyclohexenecarboxylic acid *see* Quinetalate.

2-(Dimethylamino)ethyl benzilate *see* Deanol benzilate.

2-(Dimethylamino)ethyl 1-benzyl-2,3-dimethylindole-5-carboxylate *see* Indocate.

2-[α-[2-(Dimethylamino)ethyl]benzyl]pyridine *see* Pheniramine.

2-(Dimethylamino)ethyl 2-(*p*-biphenylyl)butyrate *see* Namoxyrate.

2-(Dimethylamino)ethyl *p*-butylaminobenzoate *see* Tetracaine.

2-(Dimethylamino)ethyl 4-butylaminosalicylate *see* Hydroxytetracaine.

2-(Dimethylamino)ethyl *p*-chlorophenoxyacetate *see* Meclofenoxate.

2-(Dimethylamino)ethyl cyclohexanepropionate *see* Cyprodenate.

S-[2-(Dimethylamino)ethyl] *O,O*-diethyl phosphorothioate methiodide *see* Ecothiopate iodide.

5-[2-(Dimethylamino)ethyl]-*cis*-2,3-dihydro-3-hydroxy-2-(*p*-methoxyphenyl)-1,5-benzothiazepin-4(5*H*)-one acetate *see* Diltiazem.

10-[2-(Dimethylamino)ethyl]-5,10-dihydro-5-methyldibenzo[*b,e*][1,4]diazepin-11-one *see* Dibenzepin.

5-[2-(Dimethylamino)ethyl]-2,3-dihydro-2-phenyl-1,5-benzothiazepin-4(5*H*)-one *see* Tiazesim.

2-(Dimethylamino)ethyl 6-(2,6-dimethoxybenzamido)penicillanate *see* Tameticillin.

S-[2-(Dimethylamino)ethyl] 9,9-dimethyl-10-acridancarbothioate *see* Botiacrine.

2-(Dimethylamino)ethyl 1-(2-dimethylaminoethyl)-2,3-dimethylindole-5-carboxylate *see* Amindocate.

1-[2-(Dimethylamino)ethyl]-2,3-dimethylindole-5-carboxylic acid dimethylaminoethyl ester *see* Amindocate.

7-[2-(Dimethylamino)ethyl]-1,3-dimethylxanthine *see* Dimethazan.

2-(Dimethylamino)ethyl *N,N*-diphenylcarbamate *see* Dicarfen.

2-(Dimethylamino)ethyl diphenyl(2-propynyloxy)-acetate *see* Pargeverine.

2-(Dimethylamino)ethyl ethoxydiphenylacetate *see* Dimenoxadol.

2-(Dimethylamino)ethyl 2-(2-ethylbutoxy)-2,2-diphenylacetate *see* Denaverine.

1-[2-(Dimethylamino)ethyl]-9-ethyl-1,3,4,9-tetra-hydro-1-methylthiopyrano[3,4-*b*]indole *see* Tandamine.

2-(Dimethylamino)ethyl hydrogen *N*-acetylglutamate *see* Deanol aceglumate.

2-(Dimethylamino)ethyl hydrogen tartrate *see* Deanol tartrate.

2-(Dimethylamino)ethyl [5-hydroxy-4-(hydroxy-methyl)-6-methylpyrid-3-yl]methyl succinate *see* Pirisudanol.

1-[2-(Dimethylamino)ethyl]-3-(1-hydroxyiminoprop-yl)indole *see* Etoprindole.

2-(Dimethylamino)ethyl 1-hydroxy-α-phenylcyclo-pentaneacetate *see* Cyclopentolate.

4'-[[1-(Dimethylamino)ethylidene]amino]-2-meth-oxyacetanilide *see* Amidantel.

2-[1-[2-[2-(Dimethylamino)ethyl]inden-3-yl]ethyl]-pyridine *see* Dimetindene.

1-[2-(Dimethylamino)ethyl]indol-3-yl ethyl ketone oxime *see* Etoprindole.

3-[2-(Dimethylamino)ethyl]indol-4-yl hydrogen phosphate *see* Psilocybine.

α-[2-(Dimethylamino)ethyl]-α-isopropyl-1-naphthal-eneacetamide *see* Naftypramide.

2-[[2-(Dimethylamino)ethyl](*p*-methoxybenzyl)-amino]pyridine *see* Mepyramine.

2-[[2-(Dimethylamino)ethyl](*p*-methoxybenzyl)-amino]thiazole *see* Zolamine.

1-[[2-(Dimethylamino)ethyl]methylamino]-3-phenyl-indole *see* Binedaline.

5-(Dimethylamino)-3-ethyl-2-methylindole *see* Medmain.

2-(Dimethylamino)ethyl 1-methylpyrrolidine-2-carb-oxylate dimethiodide *see* Hygronium.

N-[2-(Dimethylamino)ethyl]-3-nitronaphthalimide *see* Mitonafide.

2-(Dimethylamino)ethyl 5-oxopyrrolidine-2-carb-oxylate *see* Deanol pidolate.

3-[[2-(Dimethylamino)ethyl]oxyimino]-1,2:4,5-di-benzocyclohepta-1,4-diene *see* Noxiptiline.

β-(Dimethylamino)-β-ethylphenethyl alcohol 3,4,5-trimethoxybenzoate *see* Trimebutine.

p-[2-(Dimethylamino)ethyl]phenol *see* Hordenine.

10-[2-(Dimethylamino)ethyl]phenothiazine *see* Fenethazine.

1-[2-(Dimethylamino)ethyl]-1-phenylindene *see* Indriline.

4-(Dimethylamino)-2-ethyl-2-phenylvaleronitrile *see* Etaminile.

1-[2-(Dimethylamino)ethyl]-3-propionylindole oxime *see* Etoprindole.

6-[2-(Dimethylamino)ethyl]pyrido[2,3-*b*][1,5]benzo-thiazepin-5(6*H*)-one *see* Bepiastine.

2-[2-(Dimethylamino)ethyl]-3-(1-pyrid-2-ylethyl)ind-ene *see* Dimetindene.

5-[2-(Dimethylamino)ethyl]-2,3,4,5-tetrahydro-2-(4-methoxyphenyl)-4-oxo-1,5-benzothiazepin-3-yl acetate *see* Diltiazem.

1-[2-(Dimethylamino)ethyl]-1,3,4,9-tetrahydro-1-methylindeno[2,1-*c*]pyran *see* Pirandamine.

2-(Dimethylamino)ethyl 1,3,4,5-tetrahydrothiopyra-no[4,3-*b*]indole-8-carboxylate *see* Tipindole.

2-[[2-(Dimethylamino)ethyl]-3-thenylamino]pyridine *see* Thenyldiamine.

7-[2-(Dimethylamino)ethyl]theophylline *see* Dimeth-azan.

N-[2-(Dimethylamino)ethyl]-*N*-trifluoromethylcarb-anilic acid ethyl ester *see* Flubanilate.

2-[α-(Dimethylamino)-*m*-hydroxybenzyl]cyclohex-anol *see* Ciramadol.

trans-4-(Dimethylamino)-1-(2-hydroxycyclohexyl)-2',6'-isonipecotoxylidide *see* Transcainide.

3-[(Dimethylamino)(2-hydroxycyclohexyl)methyl]-phenol *see* Ciramadol.

1-(Dimethylamino)-2-hydroxyethyl 2-oxonorborn-ane-3-carboxylate *see* Ethyl camphoramine.

5-[4-(Dimethylamino)isobutyl]-10,11-dihydro-5*H*-di-benzo[*a,d*]cycloheptene *see* Butriptyline.

Dimethylaminoisopropanol *p*-acetamidobenzoate *see* Inosine pranobex.

4-(Dimethylamino)-2-isopropyl-2-phenylvaleronitrile *see* Isoaminile.

(Dimethylaminoisopropyl)thiophenylpyridylamine *see* Isothipendyl.

2-(Dimethylamino)-*N*-[[(methylamino)carbonyl]-oxy]-2-oxoethanimidothioic acid methyl ester *see* Oxamyl.

7-(Dimethylamino)-3-(methylamino)phenazthionium chloride *see* Azure B.

4-(DIMETHYLAMINO)-3'-METHYLAZO-BENZENE (*N,N*-dimethyl-*p*-(*m*-tolylazo)anil-ine; 3'-meDAB; methyl butter yellow; 3'-methyl-DAB).

10-[(Dimethylamino)methyl]dibenzo[*b,f*]thiepin *see* Damotepine.

4'-[(Dimethylamino)methyl]-1,11-dihydrospiro[5*H*-dibenzo[*a,d*]cycloheptene-5,2'-[1,3]dioxolane] *see* Ciheptolane.

α-[(Dimethylamino)methyl]-3,4-dihydroxybenzyl al-cohol *see* *N*-Methylepinephrine.

4-[(Dimethylamino)methyl]-1,2-dioxolane methiod-ide *see* Oxapropanium iodide.

4-(Dimethylamino)-3-methyl-1,2-diphenyl-2-butanol propionate *see* Dextropropoxyphene; Levoprop-oxyphene.

3-[(Dimethylamino)methyl]-1,2-diphenyl-3-buten-2-ol propionate *see* Dexproxibutene; Proxibutene.

6-(Dimethylamino)-5-methyl-4,4-diphenyl-3-hexan-one *see* Isomethadone.

3-[(Dimethylamino)methyleneamino]-2,4,6-triiodo-hydrocinnamic acid *see* Iopodic acid.

3-[(Dimethylamino)methyleneamino]-2,4,6-triiodo-

184

hydrocinnamic acid ethyl ester *see* Ethyl iopodate.

3-[(Dimethylamino)methyleneamino]-2,4,6-triiodohydrocinnamic acid sodium salt *see* Sodium iopodate.

6-[2-(Dimethylamino)-2-methylethyl]-6,11-dihydro-5*H*-pyrido[2,3-*b*]benzodiazepin-5-one *see* Propizepine.

1-[2-(Dimethylamino)-1-methylethyl]-2-phenylcyclohexanol acetate ester *see* Nexeridine.

10-[2-(Dimethylamino)-1-methylethyl]-2-propionylphenothiazine *see* Propiomazine.

N-[2-[[5-[(Dimethylamino)methyl]furfuryl]thio]ethyl]-*N'*-methyl-2-nitro-1,1-ethenediamine *see* Ranitidine.

3-[(Dimethylamino)methyl]indole *see* Gramine.

8-[(Dimethylamino)methyl]-7-methoxy-3-methylflavone *see* Dimefline.

trans-2-[(Dimethylamino)methyl]-1-(*m*-methoxyphenyl)cyclohexanol *see* Tramadol.

1-[(Dimethylamino)methyl]-1-methylpropyl benzoate *see* Amylocaine.

3-(Dimethylamino)-1-methyl-3-oxo-1-propenyl dimethyl phosphate *see* Dicrotophos.

4-(Dimethylamino)-3-methylphenyl methylcarbamate *see* Aminocarb.

5-[3-(Dimethylamino)-2-methylpropyl]-10,11-dihydro-5*H*-dibenz[*b,f*]azepine *see* Trimipramine.

5-[3-(Dimethylamino)-1-methylpropyl]-10,11-dihydro-5*H*-dibenzo[*a,d*]cycloheptene *see* Butriptyline.

10-[3-(Dimethylamino)-2-methylpropyl]-2-ethylphenothiazine *see* Etymemazine.

10-[3-(Dimethylamino)-2-methylpropyl]-2-methoxyphenothiazine *see* Levomepromazine.

10-[3-(Dimethylamino)-2-methylpropyl]-2-(methylthio)phenothiazine *see* Methiomeprazine.

10-[3-(Dimethylamino)-2-methylpropyl]phenothiazine *see* Alimemazine.

10-[3-(Dimethylamino)-2-methylpropyl]phenothiazine-2-carbonitrile *see* Cyamemazine.

5-(Dimethylamino)-9-methyl-2-propyl-1*H*-pyrazolo[1,2-*a*][1,2,4]benzotriazine-1,3(2*H*)-dione *see* Azapropazone.

10-[3-(Dimethylamino)-2-methylpropyl]-2-trifluoromethylphenothiazine *see* Trifluomeprazine.

O-[2-(Dimethylamino)-6-methylpyrimidin-4-yl] *O,O*-diethyl phosphorothioate *see* Pyrimitate.

N-[2-[[[2-[(Dimethylamino)methyl]thiazol-4-yl]methyl]thio]ethyl]-*N'*-methyl-2-nitro-1,1-ethenediamine *see* Nizatidine.

4-(Dimethylamino)-3,4,5,6,11,12,13,14-octahydro-3,5,8,10,13-pentahydroxy-11-methoxy-6,13-dimethyl-2,6-epoxy-2*H*-naphthaceno[1,2-*b*]oxocin-9,16-dione *see* Menogaril.

4-(Dimethylamino)-1,4,4a,5,5a,6,11,12a-octahydro-3,6,10,12,12a-pentahydroxy-6-methyl-1,11-dioxonaphthacene-2-carboxamide *see* Tetracycline.

5-[3-(Dimethylamino)-2-oxopropylidene]-10,11-dihydro-5*H*-dibenzo[*a,d*]cycloheptene *see* Cotriptyline.

Dimethylaminophenazone *see* Aminophenazone.

2-(Dimethylamino)-2-phenylbutyl 3,4,5-trimethoxybenzoate *see* Trimebutine.

2-(Dimethylamino)-1-phenyl-3-cyclohexene-1-carboxylic acid ethyl ester *see* Tilidine.

[*p*-(Dimethylamino)phenyl]diazenesulfonic acid sodium salt *see* Fenaminosulf.

2-(Dimethylamino)-5-phenyl-2-oxazolin-4-one *see* Tozalinone.

2-[3-(Dimethylamino)-1-phenylpropylidene]norbornane *see* Heptaverine.

3β-(Dimethylamino)-5α-pregnane-18,20α-diol diacetate ester *see* Stevaladil.

S,S'-[2-(Dimethylamino)-1,3-propanediyl] carbamothioate *see* Cartap.

1-(Dimethylamino)-2-propanol *see* Dimepranol.

5-[2-(Dimethylamino)propionamido]-1,3-diphenylpyrazole *see* Difenamizole.

2-(Dimethylamino)propiophenone *see* Metamfepramone.

4-[3-(Dimethylamino)propoxy]-1,2,2,6,6-pentamethylpiperidine *see* Pemerid.

4-[[3-(Dimethylamino)propyl]amino]-7-iodoquinoline *see* Iometin.

9-[[3-(Dimethylamino)propyl]amino]-1-nitroacridine *see* Nitracrine.

10-[2-(Dimethylamino)propyl]-1-azaphenothiazine *see* Isothipendyl.

10-[3-(Dimethylamino)propyl]-1-azaphenothiazine *see* Prothipendyl.

[3-(Dimethylamino)propyl]carbamic acid propyl ester *see* Propamocarb.

5-[3-(Dimethylamino)propyl]-5*H*-dibenz[*b,f*]azepine *see* Depramine.

2-[3-(Dimethylamino)propyl]-8,8-diethyl-2-aza-8-germaspiro[4.5]decane *see* Spirogermanium.

5-[3-(Dimethylamino)propyl]-5,6-dihydro-11*H*-dibenz[*b,e*]azepine *see* Prazepine.

5-[3-(Dimethylamino)propyl]-10,11-dihydro-5*H*-dibenz[*b,f*]azepine *see* Imipramine.

5-[3-(Dimethylamino)propyl]-10,11-dihydro-5*H*-dibenz[*b,f*]azepine-3-carbonitrile *see* Cianopramine.

5-[3-(Dimethylamino)propyl]-5,11-dihydro-10*H*-dibenz[*b,f*]azepin-10-one *see* Ketimipramine.

5-[3-(Dimethylamino)propyl]-5,6-dihydro-11-methylene-11*H*-dibenzo[*b,e*]azepine *see* Enprazepine.

(±)-*cis*-9-[3-(Dimethylamino)propyl]-9,10-dihydro-10-methyl-2-(trifluoromethyl)anthracene *see* Fluotracen.

N-[3-(Dimethylamino)propyl]-5,6-dihydromorphanthridine *see* Prazepine.

10-[3-(Dimethylamino)propyl]-9,9-dimethylacridan *see* Dimetacrine.

10-[3-(Dimethylamino)propyl]-2-dimethylsulfamoylphenothiazine *see* Dimetotiazine.

1-[3-(Dimethylamino)propyl]-3,4-diphenylpyrazole *see* Fezolamine.

1-[3-(Dimethylamino)propyl]-1-(*p*-fluorophenyl)-5-phthalancarbonitrile *see* Citalopram.

5-[3-(Dimethylamino)propyl]-6,7,8,9,10,11-hexahydrocyclooct[*b*]indole *see* Iprindole.

6-[3-(Dimethylamino)propylidene][12*H*]benzofuro[3,2-*c*][1]benzoxepine *see* Oxetorone.

5-[3-(Dimethylamino)propylidene]dibenzocycloheptene *see* Proheptatriene.

185

cis-11(6*H*)-[3-(Dimethylamino)propylidene]dibenz-[*b,e*]oxepine *see* Cidoxepin.

trans-11(6*H*)-[3-(Dimethylamino)propylidene]dibenz[*b,e*]oxepine *see* Doxepin.

5-[3-(Dimethylamino)propylidene]-10,11-dihydrodibenzo[*a,d*]cycloheptene *see* Amitriptyline.

11-[3-(Dimethylamino)propylidene]-6,11-dihydrodibenzo[*b,e*]thiepin *see* Dosulepin.

9-[3-(Dimethylamino)propylidene]-9,10-dihydro-10,10-dimethylanthracene *see* Melitracen.

11-[3-(Dimethylamino)propylidene]-5,6-dihydro-5-methylmorphanthridine *see* Elantrine.

9-[3-(Dimethylamino)propylidene]-2-methoxyxanthene *see* Dimeprozan.

9-[3-(Dimethylamino)propylidene]thioxanthene *see* Prothixene.

2-[2-(Dimethylamino)propyl]-2-isopropyl-2-phenylacetonitrile *see* Isoaminile.

10-[3-(Dimethylamino)propyl]-2-methoxyphenothiazine *see* Methopromazine.

9-[3-(Dimethylamino)propyl]-2-methoxythioxanthen-9-ol *see* Meprotixol.

17β-[[3-(Dimethylamino)propyl]methylamino]androst-4-en-3β-ol *see* Azacosterol.

5-[3-(Dimethylamino)propyl]phenanthridinone *see* Fantridone.

10-[2-(Dimethylamino)propyl]phenothiazine *see* Promethazine.

10-[3-(Dimethylamino)propyl]phenothiazine *see* Promazine.

1-[10-[2-(Dimethylamino)propyl]phenothiazin-2-yl]-1-propanone *see* Propiomazine.

4'-[4-[3-(Dimethylamino)propyl]piperazin-1-yl]acetamide *see* Piperamide.

10-[2-(Dimethylamino)propyl]-2-propionylphenothiazine *see* Propiomazine.

10-[3-(Dimethylamino)propyl]-2-propionylphenothiazine *see* Propionylpromazine.

10-[2-(Dimethylamino)propyl]-10*H*-pyrido[3,2-*b*]-[1,4]benzothiazine *see* Isothipendyl.

10-[3-(Dimethylamino)propyl]-10*H*-pyrido[3,2-*b*]-[1,4]benzothiazine *see* Prothipendyl.

(+)-3-[3-(Dimethylamino)propyl]-1,3,8,8-tetramethyl-3-azabicyclo[3.2.1]octane methyl sulfate methosulfate *see* Trimethidinium methosulfate.

4-[3-(Dimethylamino)propyl]-4*H*-thieno[3,2-*b*]-[1]benzazepine *see* Tienopramine.

2'-[[3-(Dimethylamino)propyl]thio]cinnamanilide *see* Cinanserin.

10-[3-(Dimethylamino)propyl]-2-(trifluoromethyl)-phenothiazine *see* Triflupromazine.

2-(Dimethylamino)pyrazine *see* Ampyzine.

2-[1-[3-[[2-[(Dimethylamino)sulfonyl]-10*H*-phenothiazin-10-yl]propyl]piperidin-4-yl]ethyl]hexadecanoate *see* Pipotiazine palmitate.

O-[*p*-(Dimethylamino)sulfonyl]phenyl *O,O*-dimethyl phosphorothioate *see* Famphur.

3-(Dimethylamino)-1,2,3,4-tetrahydrocarbazole *see* Ciclindole.

4-(Dimethylamino)-*m*-tolyl methylcarbamate *see* Aminocarb.

4-(Dimethylamino)-*o*-tolylphosphinic acid *see* Toldimfos.

3-(Dimethylamino)-2,2,3-trimethylnorbornane *see* Dimecamine.

2-(Dimethylamino)-3,5,6-trimethylpyrazine *see* Triampyzine.

3-(Dimethylamino)-1,1,2-tris(*p*-methoxyphenyl)-1-propene *see* Aminoxytriphene.

4-(Dimethylamino)-3,5-xylyl methylcarbamate *see* Mexacarbate.

N,N-Dimethylamphetamine *see* Dimetamfetamine.

3,4-Dimethylamphetamine *see* Xylopropamine.

1,3-DIMETHYLAMYLAMINE (methylhexanamine; 'forthane').

Dimethylandrostanolone *see* 17β-Hydroxy-1α,17-dimethylandrostan-3-one.

'Dimethylane' *see* Promoxolane.

ar,ar-Dimethylaniline *see* Xylidine.

2-(2,6-Dimethylanilino)-5,6-dihydro-4*H*-1,3-thiazine *see* Xylazine.

2-(2,3-Dimethylanilino)nicotinic acid *see* Nixylic acid.

2-(2,6-Dimethylanilino)nicotinic acid *see* Metanixin.

Dimethylarsinic acid *see* Cacodylic acid.

ar,ar-Dimethylbenzamide *see* Xylamide.

7,12-DIMETHYLBENZ[*a*]ANTHRACENE (9,10-dimethyl-1,2-benzanthracene; DMBA).

Dimethylbenzene *see* Xylene.

3,3'-Dimethylbenzidine *see* *o*-Tolidine.

5,6-Dimethylbenzimidazole cobamide coenzyme *see* Cobamamide.

5,6-Dimethylbenzimidazole-5-deoxyadenosylcobamide *see* Cobamamide.

α-(5,6-Dimethylbenzimidazol-2-yl)cobamide methyl *see* Mecobalamin.

5,6-Dimethylbenzimidazolylcyanocobamide *see* Cyanocobalamin.

2,2-Dimethyl-1,3-benzodioxol-4-yl methylcarbamate *see* Bendiocarb.

N,N-Dimethylbenzofuro[3,2-*c*][1]benzoxepin-Δ^{6(12H),γ}-propylamine *see* Oxetorone.

*N*¹-(3,4-Dimethylbenzoyl)sulfanilamide *see* Sulfadimethylbenzoylamide.

*p,*α-DIMETHYLBENZYL ALCOHOL (*p*-tolyl methyl carbinol).
See also Tocamphyl.

2,4-Dimethylbenzyl chrysanthemate *see* Dimethrin.

2,4-Dimethylbenzyl 2,2-dimethyl-3-(2-methyl-1-propenyl)cyclopropanecarboxylate *see* Dimethrin.

4-(2,3-Dimethylbenzyl)imidazole *see* Detomidine.

1-(2,4-Dimethylbenzyl)-1*H*-indazole-3-carboxylic acid *see* Xinidamine.

1,1-Dimethylbiguanide *see* Metformin.

1,1'-Dimethyl-4,4'-bipyridinium dichloride *see* Paraquat.

Dimethylbis[(phenylcarbamoyl)methyl]ammonium chloride *see* Carcainum chloride.

N,N'-Dimethyl-*N,N*'-bis[3-(3,4,5-trimethoxybenzoyloxy)propyl]ethylenediamine *see* Hexobendine.

3,3-Dimethyl-2-butanol *see* Pinacolyl alcohol.

1-[2-(1,3-Dimethyl-but-2-enylidene)hydrazino]-phthalazine *see* Budralazine.

3,3-DIMETHYLBUTYL ACETATE (acetylcarbocholine).

3,3-Dimethylbut-2-yl methylphosphorofluoridate *see*

Soman.

Dimethylcaramiphen *see* Metcaraphen.

Dimethylcarbamic acid esters *see* Camazepam; Pirimicarb; Pitenodil.

Dimethylcarbamodithioic acid salts *see* Ferbam; Ziram.

m-**(Dimethylcarbamoylamino)phenyl** *tert*-**butylcarbamate** *see* Karbutilate.

5-[(Dimethylcarbamoyl)methoxy]-10,11-dihydro-5*H*-**dibenzo[***a,d***]cycloheptene** *see* Oxitriptyline.

(Dimethylcarbamoyl)methyl [*p***-(***p***-guanidinobenzoyloxy)phenyl]acetate** *see* Camostat.

1-Dimethylcarbamoyl-5-methylpyrazol-3-yl dimethylcarbamate *see* Dimetilan.

2-(Dimethylcarbamoyl)-1-methylvinyl dimethyl phosphate *see* Dicrotophos.

1-[2-(Dimethylcarbamoyloxy)ethyl]-4-[3-(2-thenoyl)propyl]piperazine *see* Pitenodil.

3-(Dimethylcarbamoyl)propyl clofibrate *see* Clofibride.

N-**[1-(Dimethylcarbamoyl)propyl]-***N*-**ethylcrotonamide** *see* Crotetamide.

N-**[1-(Dimethylcarbamoyl)propyl]-***N*-**propylcrotonamide** *see* Cropropamide.

DIMETHYL CARBATE (dimethyl 5-norbornene-2,3-dicarboxylate; RP-50; 'dimalone').

2-(Dimethylcarboxamido)-1-methylvinyl dimethyl phosphate *see* Dicrotophos.

1-(Dimethylcarboxamido)-1-propen-2-yl dimethyl phosphate *see* Dicrotophos.

Dimethyl (*p***-chloro-α-hydroxybenzyl)phosphonate dimethyl phosphate** *see* Mifobate.

N,α-**Dimethylcyclohexaneethylamine** *see* Propylhexedrine.

2,2-Dimethyl-1,3,5-cyclohexanetrione *see* Filixic acid.

N,α-**Dimethylcyclopentaneethylamine** *see* Cyclopentamine.

3,3-Dimethylcysteine *see* Penicillamine.

N,*N*-**Dimethyldibenzo[***b,e***]oxepin-Δ**¹¹⁽⁶ᴴ⁾,γ-**propylamine** *see* Cidoxepin; Doxepin.

N,*N*-**Dimethyldibenzo[***b,f***]thiepin-10-methylamine** *see* Damotepine.

N,*N*-**Dimethyldibenzo[***b,e***]thiepin-Δ**¹¹⁽⁶ᴴ⁾,γ-**propylamine** *see* Dosulepin.

Dimethyl 4-[*o***-(difluoromethoxy)phenyl]-1,4-dihydro-2,6-dimethyl-3,5-pyridinedicarboxylate** *see* Riodipine.

Dimethyl 1,4-dihydro-2,6-dimethyl-4-(2-nitrophenyl)pyridine-3,5-dicarboxylate *see* Nifedipine.

Dimethyl [1-(dimethylcarboxamido)-1-propen-2-yl] phosphate *see* Dicrotophos.

1-[3-[(1,3-Dimethyl-2,4-dioxopyrimidin-6-yl)amino]propyl]-4-(*o***-methoxyphenyl)piperazine** *see* Urapidil.

N,*N*-**Dimethyl-2,2-diphenoxyethylamine** *see* Medifoxamine.

N,*N*-**Dimethyl-2,2-diphenylacetamide** *see* Diphenamid.

Dimethyldiphenylene disulfide *see* Mesulfen.

(+)-*N*,*N*-**Dimethyl-1,2-diphenylethylamine** *see* (+)-*N*,*N*-Dimethyl-α-phenylphenethylamine.

(−)-*N*,*N*-**Dimethyl-1,2-diphenylethylamine** *see* Le-

fetamine.

N,*N*-**Dimethyl-2-(diphenylmethoxy)ethylamine-***N*-**oxide 2-oxo-10-bornanesulfonate** *see* Amoxydramine camsilate.

3,5-Dimethyl-1,6-diphenyl-1-oxa-4-azahexane *see* Dextrofemine; Racefemine.

(+)-*threo*-**3,5-Dimethyl-1,6-diphenyl-1-oxa-4-azahexane** *see* Dextrofemine.

1,2-Dimethyl-3,5-diphenyl-1*H*-**pyrazolium methyl sulfate** *see* Difenzoquat.

1,4-Dimethyl-1,4-diphenyl-2-tetrazene *see* Simtrazene.

1,1′-Dimethyl-4,4′-dipyridylium dichloride *see* Paraquat.

Dimethyldithiocarbamic acid salts *see* Cupric dimethyldithiocarbamate; Ferbam; Ziram.

N,*N*-**Dimethylene oxide bis(pyridinium-4-aldoxime) dichloride** *see* Obidoxime chloride.

Dimethylenimine *see* Aziridine.

N′-**(1,6-Dimethylergolin-8α-yl)-***N*,*N*-**dimethylsulfamide** *see* Mesulergine.

Dimethylergometrine *see* Methysergide.

Dimethylergonovine *see* Methysergide.

α,α′-**Dimethylethanolamino-4,4′-biacetophenone** *see* Hemicholinium.

6α,21-Dimethylethisterone *see* Dimethisterone.

O,*O*-**Dimethyl** *O*-**(6-ethoxy-2-ethylpyrimidin-4-yl)-phosphorothioate** *see* Etrimfos.

4-[2-[(1,1-Dimethylethyl)amino]-1-hydroxyethyl]-1,2-benzenediol *see* Colterol.

4-[2-[(1,1-Dimethylethyl)amino]-1-hydroxyethyl]-1,2-phenylene bis(4-methylbenzoate) *see* Bitolterol.

5-[3-[(1,1-Dimethylethyl)amino]-2-hydroxypropoxy]-3,4-dihydro-2(1*H***)-quinolinone** *see* Carteolol.

α′-**[(1,1-Dimethylethyl)aminomethyl]-4-hydroxy-1,3-benzenedimethanol** *see* Salbutamol.

2-(1,1-Dimethylethyl)-4,6-dinitrophenol *see* Dinoterb.

N-**(1,1-Dimethylethyl)-***N*′-**ethyl-6-methoxy-1,3,5-triazine-2,4-diamine** *see* Terbumeton.

N-**(1,1-Dimethylethyl)-***N*′-**ethyl-6-(methylthio)-1,3,5-triazine-2,4-diamine** *see* Terbutryn.

2-[4-(1,1-Dimethylethyl)phenoxy]cyclohexyl 2-propynyl sulfite *see* Propargite.

α-**[4-(1,1-Dimethylethyl)phenyl]-4-(hydroxydiphenylmethyl)-1-piperidinebutanol** *see* Terfenadine.

2,5-Dimethyl-3-furyl 4-hydroxy-3,5-diiodophenyl ketone *see* Furidarone.

N,*N*-**Dimethylglycolamide [***p***-(***p***-guanidinobenzoyloxy)phenyl]acetate** *see* Camostat.

10-(*N*,*N*-**Dimethylglycyl)phenothiazine** *see* Dacemazine.

7-(1,2-Dimethylheptyl)-2,2-dimethyl-4-pyrid-4-yl-2*H*-**1-benzopyran-5-ol** *see* Nonabine.

3-(1,1-Dimethylheptyl)-6aβ,7,8,9,10,10aα-hexahydro-6,6-dimethyl-6*H*-**dibenzo[***b,d***]pyran-1,9-diol** *see* Canbisol.

3-(1,1-Dimethylheptyl)-6aα,7,8,9,10,10aβ-hexahydro-6,6-dimethyl-6*H*-**dibenzo[***b,d***]pyran-1,9-diol** *see* Nabidrox.

3-(1,1-Dimethylheptyl)-6,6a,7,8,10,10a-hexahydro-

1-hydroxy-6,6-dimethyl-9*H*-dibenzo[*b*,*d*]pyran-9-one *see* Nabilone.

8-(1,2-Dimethylheptyl)-1,3,4,5-tetrahydro-5,5-dimethyl-2-(2-propynyl)-2*H*-[1]benzopyrano[4,3-*c*]pyridin-10-yl α,2-dimethyl-1-piperidinebutyrate *see* Menabitan.

8-(1,2-Dimethylheptyl)-1,3,4,5-tetrahydro-5,5-dimethyl-2-(2-propynyl)-2*H*-[1]benzopyrano[4,3-*c*]pyridin-10-yl 1-piperidinebutyrate *see* Nabitan.

8-(1,2-Dimethylheptyl)-1,2,3,5-tetrahydro-5,5-dimethylthiopyrano[2,3-*c*][1]benzopyran-10-ol *see* Tinabinol.

3-(1,2-Dimethylheptyl)-7,8,9,10-tetrahydro-6,6,9-trimethyl-6*H*-dibenzo[*b*,*d*]pyran-1-yl hexahydro-1*H*-azepine-1-butyrate *see* Nabazenil.

Dimethylhexestrol *see* Methestrol.

1,5-Dimethylhexylamine *see* Octodrine.

N-(1,5-Dimethylhexyl)isopentylamine *see* Octamylamine.

1,1-DIMETHYLHYDRAZINE (unsymmetrical dimethylhydrazine; UDMH).

*N*¹-(3,4-Dimethylisoxazol-5-yl)sulfanilamide *see* Sulfafurazole.

*N*¹-(4,5-Dimethylisoxazol-3-yl)sulfanilamide *see* Sulfatroxazole.

Dimethylmeperidine *see* Trimeperidine.

N,*N*-Dimethylmercaptamine *see* Captamine.

2,3-Dimethyl-4-(methanesulfonylamino)-1-phenyl-3-pyrazolin-5-one *see* Sulfamidopyrine sodium.

Dimethyl [[2-(2-methoxyacetamido)-4-(phenylthio)-phenyl]imidocarbonyl]dicarbamate *see* Febantel.

2,2-Dimethyl-3-[2-(methoxycarbonyl)-1-propenyl]-cyclopropanecarboxylic acid *see* Pyrethric acid.

N,*N*-Dimethyl-*N*'-[3-[[(methylamino)carbonyl]oxy]-phenyl]methanimidamide *see* Formetanate.

O,*O*-Dimethyl *S*-[[2-[1-(methylaminocarboxy)ethyl]-thio]ethyl]phosphorothioate *see* Vamidothion.

O,*O*-Dimethyl *S*-[2-(methylamino)-2-oxoethyl] phosphorodithioate *see* Dimethoate.

O,*O*-Dimethyl *S*-[2-(methylamino)-2-oxoethyl] phosphorothioate *see* Omethoate.

2,3-Dimethyl-4-(methylamino)-1-phenyl-3-pyrazolin-5-one *see* Noramidopyrine.

9,9-Dimethyl-10-(3-methylaminopropyl)acridan *see* Monometacrine.

3,3-Dimethyl-1-(3-methylaminopropyl)-1-phenyl-phthalan *see* Talopram.

3,3-Dimethyl-1-(3-methylaminopropyl)-1-phenyl-thiophthalan *see* Talsupram.

N,*N*-Dimethyl-2-(*p*-methylbenzhydroxyloxy)ethyl-amine *see* *p*-Methyldiphenhydramine.

1,8-Dimethyl-3-(2-methylbutyl)xanthine *see* Verofylline.

O,*O*-Dimethyl *S*-[[2-[1-(methylcarbamoyl)ethyl]-thio]ethyl] phosphorothioate *see* Vamidothion.

O,*O*-Dimethyl *S*-(methylcarbamoylmethyl) phosphorodithioate *see* Dimethoate.

O,*O*-Dimethyl *S*-(methylcarbamoylmethyl) phosphorothioate *see* Omethoate.

Dimethyl (2-methylcarbamoyl-1-methylvinyl) phosphate *see* Monocrotophos.

N,*N*-Dimethyl-*N*'-[*m*-(methylcarbamoyloxy)phenyl]formamidine *see* Formetanate.

Dimethyl (1-methylcarboxamido-1-propen-2-yl) phosphate *see* Monocrotophos.

Dimethyl[2-(*N*-methyldodecanamido)ethyl](phenyl-carbamoylmethyl)ammonium chloride *see* Dofamium chloride.

3,3-Dimethyl-2-methylenebicyclo[2.2.1]heptane *see* Bornene.

4,4-Dimethyl-1-[(3,4-methylenedioxy)phenyl]-1-penten-3-ol *see* Stiripentol.

3,3-Dimethyl-2-methylenenorbornane *see* Bornene.

N,*N*-Dimethyl-*N*'-(6-methylergolin-8α-yl)sulfamide *see* Disulergine.

O,*O*-Dimethyl *S*-[2-[[1-methyl-2-(methylamino)-2-oxoethyl]thio]ethyl] phosphorothioate *see* Vamidothion.

Dimethyl 1-methyl-3-methylamino-3-oxo-1-propenyl phosphate *see* Monocrotophos.

N,*N*-Dimethyl-2-(*o*-methyl-α-phenylbenzyloxy)-ethylamine *see* Orphenadrine.

1,1-Dimethyl-2-[(*p*-methyl-α-phenylbenzyloxy)meth-yl]piperidinium bromide *see* Pirdonium bromide.

2,3-Dimethyl-4-(3-methyl-2-phenylmorpholinometh-yl)-1-phenyl-3-pyrazolin-5-one *see* Morazone.

*N*¹,*N*¹-Dimethyl-3-(4-methylpiperazin-1-ylcarbon-yl)sulfanilamide *see* Delfantrine.

N,*N*-Dimethyl-9-[3-(4-methylpiperazin-1-yl)propyl-idene]thioxanthene-2-sulfonamide *see* Tiotixene.

N,*N*-Dimethyl-10-[3-(4-methylpiperazin-1-yl)prop-yl]-2-phenothiazinesulfonamide *see* Thioproperazine.

2,2-Dimethyl-3-(2-methylpropenyl)cyclopropane-carboxylic acid *see* Chrysanthemic acid.

O,*O*-Dimethyl *O*-[2-(methylthio)ethyl] phosphoro-thioate *see* Demephion-O.

O,*O*-Dimethyl *S*-[2-(methylthio)ethyl] phosphoro-thioate *see* Demephion-S.

3,5-Dimethyl-4-(methylthio)phenyl methylcarbam-ate *see* Methiocarb.

O,*O*-Dimethyl *O*-[*p*-(methylthio)-*m*-tolyl] phospho-rothioate *see* Fenthion.

N,3-Dimethylmorphinan *see* Dimemorfan.

3,17-Dimethylmorphinan *see* Dimemorfan.

O,*O*-Dimethyl *S*-(2-morpholino-2-oxoethyl) phos-phorodithioate *see* Morphothion.

O,*O*-Dimethyl *S*-(2-morpholin-4-ylacetyl) phospho-rodithioate *see* Morphothion.

7α,17-Dimethylnandrolone *see* Mibolerone.

N,*N*'-Dimethyl-2-naphthaleneacetamidine *see* Napactadine.

2,3-Dimethyl-4-nicotinamido-1-phenyl-3-pyrazolin-5-one *see* Nifenazone.

1,2-Dimethyl-5-nitroimidazole *see* Dimetridazole.

α,2-Dimethyl-5-nitroimidazole-1-ethanol *see* Secnidazole.

5,6-Dimethyl-2-nitroindan-1,3-dione *see* Nivimedone.

O,*O*-Dimethyl *O*-(*p*-nitrophenyl) phosphorothioate *see* Parathion-methyl.

O,*S*-Dimethyl *O*-(*p*-nitrophenyl) phosphorothioate *see* Parathion isomethyl.

DIMETHYLNITROSAMINE (*N*-nitrosodimeth-ylamine; DMN).

Dimethyl (*p*-nitro-*m*-tolyl) phosphate *see* Fenitrooxon.

O,O-Dimethyl O-(p-nitro-m-tolyl) phosphorothioate *see* Fenitrothion.

O,O-DIMETHYL S-(p-NITRO-m-TOLYL) PHOSPHOROTHIOATE ('isosumithion').

2-(4,8-Dimethyl-3,7-nonadienyl)-6-methyl-2,6-octadiene-1,8-diol *see* Plaunotol.

Dimethyl 5-norbornene-2,3-dicarboxylate *see* Dimethyl carbate.

5-(3,3-Dimethyl-2-norbornylidene)-3-penten-2-one *see* Bornelone.

6,6-Dimethyl-2-norpinene *see* Apopinene.

2-[2-(6,6-Dimethylnorpinen-2-yl)ethoxy]triethylamine *see* Myrtecaine.

7α,17-Dimethyl-19-nortestosterone *see* Mibolerone.

Dimethyloctadecylamine *see* Dimantine.

2-(3,7-Dimethyl-2-octadienyl)hydroquinone *see* Geroquinol.

3,7-Dimethyl-2,6-octadienyl trimethyltetradecatrienoate *see* Gefarnate.

3,5-Dimethyl-N-(4,6,6a,7,8,9,10,10a-octahydro-4,7-dimethylindolo[4,3-fg]quinolin-9-yl)pyrazole-1-carboxamide *see* Metoquizine.

1,1-Dimethyl-3-(octahydro-4,7-methano-1H-inden-5-yl)urea *see* Noruron.

Dimethylolurea *see* 1,3-Bis(hydroxymethyl)urea.

5,5-Dimethyl-2,4-oxazolidinedione *see* Dimethadione.

N¹-[(4,5-Dimethyloxazol-2-yl)amidino]sulfanilamide *see* Sulfaguanole.

N¹-(4,5-Dimethyloxazol-2-yl)sulfanilamide *see* Sulfamoxole.

O,O-Dimethyl S-(4-oxobenzotriazin-3-ylmethyl) phosphorodithioate *see* Azinphos-methyl.

5,5-Dimethyl-1-oxocyclohex-2-en-3-yl dimethylcarbamate *see* Dimetan.

3-[2-(3,5-Dimethyl-2-oxocyclohexyl)-2-hydroxyethyl]glutarimide *see* Cicloheximide.

3,7-Dimethyl-1-(5-oxohexyl)xanthine *see* Pentoxifylline.

1,7-DIMETHYL-2-OXO-7-NORBORNANE-CARBOXALDEHYDE (π-oxocamphor; 8-oxocamphor).

4-(4,4-Dimethyl-3-oxopentyl)-1,2-diphenylpyrazolidine-3,5-dione *see* Tribuzone.

6-(2,2-Dimethyl-5-oxo-4-phenylimidazolidin-1-yl)penicillanic acid *see* Hetacillin.

3-[[(2,3-Dimethyl-5-oxo-1-phenyl-3-pyrazolin-4-yl)amino]methyl]-4-isopropyl-2-methyl-1-phenyl-3-pyrazolin-5-one *see* Bisfenazone.

[[(2,3-Dimethyl-5-oxo-1-phenyl-3-pyrazolin-4-yl)methyl]amino]methanesulfonic acid sodium salt *see* Dipyrone.

2-(2,2-Dimethyl-1-oxopropyl)-1H-indene-1,3(2H)-dione *see* Pindone.

3,3-Dimethyl-7-oxo-4-thia-1-azabicyclo[3.2.0]heptane-2-carboxylic acid *see* Penicillanic acid.

[[(3,3-Dimethyl-7-oxo-4-thia-1-azabicyclo-[3.2.0]hept-2-yl)carbonyl]oxy]methyl 6-[(aminophenylacetyl)amino]-3,3-dimethyl-7-oxo-4-thia-1-azabicyclo[3.2.0]heptane-2-carboxylate S,S-dioxide *see* Sultamicillin.

Dimethyloxychinizin *see* Phenazone.

N,N-Dimethyl(3-palmitamidopropyl)aminoacetic acid *see* Pendecamaine.

Dimethylpapaveroline dinicotinate *see* Niceverine.

N,α-Dimethyl-p-pentylphenethylamine *see* Amfepentorex.

α,α-Dimethylphenethylamine *see* Phentermine.

(+)-N,α-Dimethylphenethylamine *see* Methamphetamine.

N,β-Dimethylphenethylamine *see* Phenpromethamine.

2,α-Dimethylphenethylamine *see* Ortetamine.

5′-[2-[(α,α-Dimethylphenethyl)amino]-1-hydroxyethyl]-2′-hydroxymethanesulfonanilide *see* Zinterol.

5-(2,5-Dimethylphenoxy)-2,2-dimethylvaleric acid *see* Gemfibrozil.

Dimethyl(2-phenoxyethyl)-2-thenylammonium p-chlorobenzenesulfonate *see* Thenium closilate.

[2-(2,6-Dimethylphenoxy)ethyl]trimethylammonium bromide *see* Xylocholine.

5-(3,5-Dimethylphenoxymethyl)oxazolidin-2-one *see* Metaxalone.

2,6-Dimethyl-1-[4-(2-phenoxy-2-phenylacetamido)-butyl]piperidine *see* Oxiramide.

[2-(2,6-Dimethylphenoxy)propyl]trimethylammonium chloride *see* β-Methylxylocholine.

N-(2,3-Dimethylphenyl)anthranilic acid *see* Mefenamic acid.

N,N-Dimethyl-p-phenylazoaniline *see* p-(Dimethylamino)azobenzene.

N,N-Dimethyl-α-phenylbenzeneacetamide *see* Diphenamid.

N,N-Dimethyl-γ-phenylcyclohexanepropylamine *see* Gamfexine.

N′-(2,6-Dimethylphenyl)-N,N-diethylglycinamide *see* Lidocaine.

N′-(2,4-Dimethylphenyl)-N-[N-(2,4-dimethylphenyl)formimidoyl]-N-methylformamidine *see* Amitraz.

N′-(2,4-Dimethylphenyl)-N-[[(2,4-dimethylphenyl)imino]methyl]-N-methylmethanimidamide *see* Amitraz.

Dimethyl [1,2-phenylenebis(iminocarbonothioyl)]bis(carbamate) *see* Thiophanate-methyl.

Dimethyl 4,4′-(o-phenylene)bis(3-thioallophanate) *see* Thiophanate-methyl.

N-(2,6-Dimethylphenyl)-N′-[imino(methylamino)-methyl]urea *see* Lidamidine.

N,N-Dimethyl-3-phenyl-1-indanamine *see* Dimefadane.

N,N-Dimethyl-1-phenylindene-1-ethylamine *see* Indriline.

(2,4-Dimethylphenyl)methyl 2,2-dimethyl-3-(2-methyl-1-propenyl)cyclopropanecarboxylate *see* Dimethrin.

3,4-Dimethyl-2-phenylmorpholine *see* Phendimetrazine.

N,N-Dimethyl-γ-phenyl-Δ²,⁷-norbornanepropylamine *see* Heptaverine.

(+)-N,N-DIMETHYL-α-PHENYLPHENE-THYLAMINE ((+)-1-(dimethylamino)-1,2-diphenylethane; (+)-N,N-dimethyl-1,2-diphenylethylamine; (+)-N,N-dimethylstilbylamine; 'α-

189

spa').

(−)-*N*,*N*-Dimethyl-α-phenylphenethylamine *see* Lefetamine.

1,1-DIMETHYL-4-PHENYLPIPERAZINIUM IODIDE (DMPP).

1,3-Dimethyl-4-phenyl-4-propionoxyazacycloheptane *see* Proheptazine.

1,3-Dimethyl-4-phenyl-4-propionoxypiperidine *see* Alphaprodine; Betaprodine.

β-1,3-Dimethyl-4-phenyl-4-propionoxypiperidine *see* Betaprodine.

N-(2,6-Dimethylphenyl)-1-propylpiperidine-2-carboxamide *see* Ropivacaine.

N,N-Dimethyl-α-(3-phenylpropyl)veratrylamine *see* Vetrabutine.

2,3-Dimethyl-1-phenyl-3-pyrazolin-5-one *see* Phenazone.

2,6-Dimethyl-α-phenyl-α-2-pyridyl-1-piperidine-butanol *see* Pirmenol.

N,N-Dimethyl-3-phenyl-3-pyrid-2-ylpropylamine *see* Pheniramine.

1,2-Dimethyl-3-phenyl-3-pyrrolidyl propionate *see* Prodilidine.

2,3-Dimethyl-1-phenyl-4-stearamido-3-pyrazolin-5-one *see* Stampyrine.

Dimethylphenylsuccinimide *see* Mesuximide.

N,N-Dimethyl-N'-phenyl-N'-(2-thenyl)ethylenedi-amine *see* Methaphenilene.

N,N-Dimethyl-2-(α-phenyl-*o*-toloxy)ethylamine *see* Phenyltoloxamine.

N,N-Dimethyl-3-phenyl-3-*p*-tolyl-1-propylamine *see* Tolpropamine.

1,1-Dimethyl-3-phenylurea *see* Fenuron.

O,S-Dimethyl phosphoramidothioate *see* Methamidophos.

O,O-Dimethyl phosphorodithioate *S*-ester with 3-(mercaptomethyl)-1,2,3-benzotriazine-4(3*H*)-one *see* Azinphos-methyl.

2',6'-Dimethylphthalanilic acid *see* Ftaxilide.

DIMETHYL PHTHALATE (methyl phthalate).

O,O-Dimethyl *S*-(phthalimidomethyl) phosphorodithioate *see* Phosmet.

2,5-Dimethylpiperazine *see* Lupetazine.

2,6-Dimethylpiperidine *see* Nanofin.

α-[3-(2,6-Dimethyl-1-piperidinyl)propyl]-α-phenyl-2-pyridinemethanol *see* Pirmenol.

N-[4-(2,6-Dimethylpiperid-1-yl)butyl]-2-phenoxy-2-phenylacetamide *see* Oxiramide.

2,4'-Dimethyl-3-piperid-1-ylpropiophenone *see* Tolperisone.

6,17-Dimethylpregna-4,6-diene-3,20-dione *see* Medrogestone.

2,2-Dimethylpropane *see* Neopentane.

2,2-Dimethylpropionic acid *see* Pivalic acid.

4-[2-(2,2-Dimethylpropionyl)ethyl]-1,2-diphenyl-3,5-pyrazolidinedione *see* Tribuzone.

Dimethylpropranolol *see* Pranolium chloride.

2,2'-Dimethyl-2-(propylamino)propionanilide *see* Quatacaine.

m-(1,3-Dimethyl-4-propylpiperid-4-yl)phenol *see* Picenadol.

(−)-*N*,α-Dimethyl-*N*-prop-2-ynylphenethylamine *see* Selegiline.

5-[(1,1-Dimethyl-2-propynyl)sulfamoyl]-*N*-[(1-ethyl-pyrrolidin-2-yl)methyl]-*o*-anisamide *see* Tinisulpride.

1,3-Dimethylpurin-2-one-6-thione *see* 6-Thiotheophylline.

9-(3,5-Dimethylpyrazole-1-carboxamido)-4-ethyl-octahydro-7-methylindolo[4,3-*fg*]quinoline *see* Toquizine.

N,N'-Dimethylpyrazole-3,4-dicarboxamide *see* Ethipyrole.

4,6-Dimethyl-3(2*H*)-pyridazinone *see* Cetohexazine.

5,11-Dimethyl-6*H*-pyrido[4,3-*b*]carbazole *see* Ellipticine.

3,5-Dimethyl-*N*-(pyrid-4-ylmethyl)benzamide *see* Picobenzide.

N,N-Dimethyl-*N'*-pyrid-2-yl-*N'*-then-2-ylethylenedi-amine *see* Methapyrilene.

N,N-Dimethyl-*N'*-pyrid-2-yl-*N'*-then-3-ylethylenedi-amine *see* Thenyldiamine.

5-[*p*-(4,6-Dimethylpyrimidin-2-ylsufamoyl)phenyl-azo]salicyclic acid *see* Salazosulfadimidine.

N¹-(2,6-Dimethylpyrimid-4-yl)sulfanilamide *see* Sulfasomidine.

N¹-(4,6-Dimethylpyrimid-2-yl)sulfanilamide *see* Sulfadimidine.

2,5-Dimethyl-1-pyrrolidinepropanol salicylate *see* Pranosal.

10-(1,3-Dimethylpyrrolidin-3-ylmethyl)phenothiazine *see* Dimelazine.

Dimethylquinolinyl methyl sulfate urea *see* Quinuronium sulfate.

N,N-Dimethyl-10-quinuclidin-3-ylphenothiazine-2-sulfonamide *see* Quisultazine.

7,8-Dimethyl-10-(1-ribityl)isoalloxazine *see* Riboflavin.

N,N-Dimethylserotonin *see* Bufotenine.

Dimethylsiloxane polymer *see* Dimeticone.

3,3-Dimethylspiro[cyclopropane-1,1'-(1*H*)indene]-2-carboxylic acid ester with *m*-phenoxymandeloni-trile *see* Cypothrin.

N,N-Dimethylspiro[dibenz[*b*,*e*]oxepin-11(6*H*),2'-[1,3]dioxolane]-4'-methylamine *see* Spiroxepin.

(+)-*N*,*N*-Dimethylstilbylamine *see* (+)-*N*,*N*-Dimethyl-α-phenylphenethylamine.

(−)-*N*,*N*-Dimethylstilbylamine *see* Lefetamine.

2,2-Dimethyl-5-styryloxazolidin-4-one *see* Methastyridone.

Dimethylsulfadiazine *see* Sulfadimidine.

2-(Dimethylsulfamoyl)-10-[3-(1-methylpiperazin-4-yl)propyl]phenothiazine *see* Thioproperazine.

1-[3-[2-(Dimethylsulfamoyl)phenothiazin-10-yl]-propyl]-4-(2-hydroxyethyl)piperidine *see* Pipotiazine.

O,O-Dimethyl O-(*p*-sulfamoylphenyl) phosphoro-thioate *see* Cythioate.

3,4-Dimethyl-*N*-sulfanilylbenzamide *see* Sulfadimethylbenzoylamide.

Dimethylsulfapyrimidine *see* Sulfadimidine.

2-[7-[1,1-Dimethyl-3-(4-sulfobutyl)benz[*e*]indolin-2-ylidene]-1,3,5-heptatrienyl]-1,1-dimethyl-3-(4-sul-fobutyl)-1*H*-benz[*e*]indolium hydroxide *see* Indocyanine green.

DIMETHYLSULFOLANE (2,4-dimethylsulfol-

ane; 3,3-bis(ethylsulfonyl)pentane; 2,4-dimethyl-tetrahydrothiophene 1,1-dioxide).
DIMETHYLSULFONAL (bis(ethylsulfonyl)di-ethylmethane; 3,3-bis(ethylsulfonyl)pentane).
Dimethylsulfonyloxybutane *see* Busulfan.
DIMETHYL SULFOXIDE*** (methyl sulfoxide; dimexide; DMSO; DM-70; DM-90; NSC-763; SQ-9453).
See also under Idoxuridine.
7α,17-Dimethyltestosterone *see* Bolasterone.
Dimethyl tetrachloroterephthalate *see* Chlorthal-dimethyl.
DIMETHYLTHIAMBUTENE*** (3-(dimethyl-amino)-1,1-dithien-2-yl-1-butene; *N*,*N*,1-tri-methyl-3,3-dithien-2-ylallylamine).
2,7-Dimethylthianthrene *see* Mesulfen.
1-[4-(2,4-Dimethylthiazol-5-yl)butyl]-4-(4-methyl-thiazol-2-yl)piperazine *see* Peratizole.
m,*N*-**Dimethylthiocarbanilic acid** *O*-indan-5-yl ester *see* Tolindate.
m,*N*-**Dimethylthiocarbanilic acid** *O*-(1,2,3,4-tetra-hydro-1,4-methanonaphth-6-yl) ester *see* Tolci-clate.
asym-**Dimethylthionine chloride** *see* Azure A.
N,*N*-**Dimethylthioxanthene-Δ⁹,⁷-propylamine** *see* Prothixene.
1,3-Dimethyl-6-thioxanthine *see* 6-Thiotheophyl-line.
Dimethyltoluthionine chloride *see* Tolonium chlor-ide.
N,*N*-**Dimethyl-*p*-(*m*-tolylazo)aniline** *see* 4-(Dimeth-ylamino)-3′-methylazobenzene.
5-(3,3-Dimethyl-1-triazeno)imidazole-4-carbox-amide *see* Dacarbazine.
Dimethyl (2,2,2-trichloro-1-hydroxyethyl)phosphon-ate *see* Metrifonate.
Dimethyl (2,2,2-trichloro-1-hydroxyethyl)phosphon-ate butyrate *see* Butonate.
O,*O*-**Dimethyl** *O*-(2,4,5-trichlorophenyl) phosphoro-thioate *see* Fenclofos.
Dimethyl (3,5,6-trichloropyrid-2-yl) phosphate *see* Fospirate.
O,*O*-**Dimethyl** *O*-(3,5,6-trichloropyrid-2-yl) phos-phorothioate *see* Chlorpyrifos-methyl.
α,α-**Dimethyltricyclo[3.3.1.1³,⁷]decane-1-ethanamine** *see* Somantadine.
2,6-Dimethyl-4-tridecylmorpholine *see* Tridemorph.
1,1-Dimethyl-3-(*m*-trifluoromethylphenyl)urea *see* Fluometuron.
1,1-Dimethyl-3-(α,α,α-trifluoro-*m*-tolyl)urea *see* Fluometuron.
4,5-Dimethyl-2-(1,7,7-trimethyl bicyclo[2.2.1]hept-2-yl)phenol *see* Xibornol.
3,7-Dimethyl-9-(2,6,6-trimethyl-1-cyclohexen-1-yl)-nona-(*all-trans*)-2,4,6,8-tetraenal *see* Retinal.
3,7-Dimethyl-9-(2,6,6-trimethyl-1-cyclohexen-1-yl)-nona-2,4,6,8-tetraenoic acid *see* Isoretinoin; Tre-tinoin.
3,7-Dimethyl-9-(2,6,6-trimethyl-1-cyclohexen-1-yl)-nona-2,4,6,8-tetraen-1-ol *see* Retinol.
DIMETHYLTUBOCURARINE CHLORIDE*** (metocurine chloride; tubocurarine dimethyl ether; 'diamethine'; 'mecostrin'; 'metubine').

N,*N*-**Dimethyltyramine** *see* Hordenine.
Dimethylurethamide *see* Meturedepa.
Dimethylurethimine *see* Meturedepa.
1,3-Dimethylxanthine *see* Theophylline.
1,7-Dimethylxanthine *see* Paraxanthine.
3,7-Dimethylxanthine *see* Theobromine.
2,2-Dimethyl-5-(2,5-xylyloxy)valeric acid *see* Gem-fibrozil.
'**Dimethylyn**' *see* Promoxolane.
DIMETICONE** (dimethylsiloxane polymer; methylpolysiloxane; polydimethylsiloxane; di-methicone; polysilane; polysiloxane; silicone; si-lidone).
See also Simethicone *and under* Algeldrate.
DIMETICONE 350 ('dymasyl').
DIMETILAN* (1-[(dimethylamino)carbonyl]-5-methyl-1*H*-pyrazol-3-yl dimethylcarbamate; 1-dimethylcarbamoyl-5-methylpyrazol-3-yl di-methylcarbamate; OMS-479; 'snip').
'**Dimetina**' *see* Phenbenzamine.
DIMETINDENE*** (2-[1-[2-[2-(dimethylamino)-ethyl]inden-3-yl]ethyl]pyridine; 2-[2-(dimethyl-amino)ethyl]-3-(1-pyrid-2-ylethyl)indene; di-methindene; dimethpyrindene; NSC-107677; Su-6518).
See also under Phenylephrine.
Dimetiotazine* *see* Dimetotiazine.
DIMETIPIRIUM BROMIDE*** (1-(2-hydroxy-ethyl)-1,2,5-trimethylpyrrolidinium bromide benzilate).
DIMETOFRINE*** (4-hydroxy-3,5-dimethoxy-α-methylaminomethylbenzyl alcohol; 1-(4-hydr-oxy-3,5-dimethoxyphenyl)-2-methylaminoethan-ol; SM-14; 'pressamina').
DIMETOTIAZINE*** (10-[2-(dimethylamino)-propyl]-2-dimethylsulfamoylphenothiazine; di-methothiazine; dimetiotazine; fonazine; IL-6302; RP 8599).
DIMETOTIAZINE MESILATE (dimetotiazine methanesulfonate; fonazine mesylate).
DIMETRIDAZOLE** (1,2-dimethyl-5-nitroimid-azole; RP 8595; 'emtryl'; 'entryl').
DIMEVAMIDE*** (4-(dimethylamino)-2,2-di-phenylvaleramide; aminopentamide; BL-139).
Dimexide (tr) *see* Dimethyl sulfoxide.
'**Dimid**' *see* Diphenamid.
DIMIDIUM BROMIDE* (3,8-diamino-5-methyl-6-phenylphenanthridinium bromide; 'trypad-ine').
'**Dimilin**' *see* Diflubenzuron.
'**Diminal**' *see* Vinbarbital.
DIMINAZENE*** (4,4′-(diazoamino)benzamid-ine; 1,3-bis(*p*-amidinophenyl)triazene; diguanyl-diazoaminobenzene).
'**Dimite**' *see* Chlorfenethol.
'**Dimitronal**' *see* Cinnarizine.
'**Dimocillin**' *see* Meticillin.
'**Dimorlin**' *see* Dextromoramide.
DIMORPHOLAMINE* (*N*,*N*′-dibutyl-*N*,*N*′-bis-(morpholinocarbonyl)ethylenediamine; *N*,*N*′-di-butyl-*N*,*N*′-di(carboxymorpholide)ethylenedi-amine; Th-1064).
'**Dimorphone**' *see* Hydromorphone.

'Dimotane' *see* Brompheniramine.
'Dimothyn' *see* Aluminium glycinate.
DIMOXAMINE* (2-amino-1-(2,5-dimethoxy-4-methylphenyl)butane; 1-(2,5-dimethoxy-4-methylphenyl)-2-butylamine; (*R*)-α-ethyl-2,5-dimethoxy-4-methylphenethylamine; dimoxamine hydrochloride; BL-3912A).
DIMOXYLINE*** (1-(4-ethoxy-3-methoxybenzyl)-6,7-dimethoxy-3-methylisoquinoline; dioxyline; dimoxyline phosphate).
'Dimp' *see* Dimethyl phthalate.
'Dimplex' *see* Hexachlorophene.
DIMPYLATE*** (*O*,*O*-diethyl *O*-(2-isopropyl-6-methylpyrimidin-4-yl) phosphorothioate; *O*,*O*-diethyl *O*-[6-methyl-2-(1-methylethyl)pyrimidin-4-yl] phosphorothioate; diazinon; G-24480).
DIM-SA *see* Succimer.
'Dimyril' *see* Isoaminile.
'Dinacrin' *see* Isoniazid.
DINAZAFONE*** (2'-benzoyl-4'-chloro-*N*-methyl-2-[(2-methylallyl)amino]acetanilide).
'Dindevan' *see* Phenindamine.
'Di-neumobron' *see* Tipepidine.
DINEX* (2-cyclohexyl-4,6-dinitrophenol; dinitro-*o*-cyclohexylphenol; DNOCHP; pedinex; SN-46).
DINEX DICYCLOHEXYLAMINE (dinex dicyclohexylamine derivative; dinex bis(cyclohexanamine) derivative; 'dynone II').
DINEX SODIUM ('anobesina').
Dinezin (tr) *see* Diethazine.
3,6-Dinicotinoylmorphine *see* Nicomorphine.
1,3-Dinicotinoyloxy-2-propanol clofibrate *see* Binifibrate.
'Dinile' *see* Succinonitrile.
'Dinintel' *see* Clobenzorex.
DINIPROFYLLINE*** (7-(2,3-dihydroxypropyl)-theophylline bis(nicotinate ester); diprophylline dinicotinate).
DINIPROFYLLINE plus PHENOBARBITAL ('corverum').
DINITOLMIDE** (3,5-dinitro-*o*-toluamide; 2-methyl-3,5-dinitrobenzene; 'salcostat'; 'whitsyn T'; 'zoalene'; 'zoamix').
DINITRAMINE (*N*³,*N*³-diethyl-2,4-dinitro-6-(trifluoromethyl)-*m*-phenylenediamine; *N*⁴,*N*⁴-diethyl-α,α,α-trifluoro-3,5-dinitrotoluene-2,4-diamine; 'cobex').
3,5-Dinitrobenzamide *see* Nitromide.
Dinitrochlorobenzene *see* 1-Chloro-2,4-dinitrobenzene.
DINITRO-*O*-CRESOL (2-methyl-4,6-dinitrophenol; 4,6-dinitro-*o*-cresol; DNC; DNOC; K-III; K-IV).
4,6-Dinitro-*o*-cresol *see* Dinitro-*o*-cresol.
Dinitro-*o*-cyclohexylphenol *see* Dinex.
3,5-Dinitro-*N*⁴,*N*⁴-dipropylsulfanilamide *see* Oryzalin.
Dinitrogen monoxide *see* Nitrous oxide.
2,6-Dinitro-4-octylphenyl 2-butenoate *see* Dinocap.
2,6-Dinitro-4-octylphenyl crotonate *see* Dinocap.
1-(3,5-Dinitrosalicoyl)-2-(5-nitrofurfurylidene)hydrazine *see* Nifursol.

3,5-Dinitrosalicylic acid 2-(5-nitrofurfurylidene)-hydrazide *see* Nifursol.
3-(2,4-Dinitrostyryl)-7-(thien-2-ylacetamido)-2-cephem-2-carboxylic acid *see* Nitrocefin.
3,5-Dinitro-*o*-toluamide *see* Dinitolmide.
2,4'-Dinitro-4-(trifluromethyl)diphenyl ether *see* Fluorodifen.
DINOBUTON* (2-*sec*-butyl-4,6-dinitrophenyl isopropyl carbonate; 1-methylethyl [2-(1-methylpropyl)-4,6-dinitrophenyl] carbonate; dinoseb isopropyl carbonate; 'acrex'; 'dessin').
DINOCAP* (2,6-dinitro-4-octylphenyl 2-butenoate with admixture of 2,4-dinitro-6-octylphenyl 2-butenoate; 2,6-dinitro-4-octylphenyl and 2,4-dinitro-6-octylphenyl crotonates; DNOPC; CR-1639; 'arathane'; 'crotothane'; 'iscothane'; 'karathane'; 'mildex').
DINOPROP* (2-isopropyl-3-methyl-4,6-dinitrophenol; 2-methyl-3-(1-methylethyl)-4,6-dinitrophenol; DNOIPP; DNPP; 'motylkopielik').
DINOPROST*** (7-[3α,5α-dihydroxy-2β-[3(*S*)-hydroxy-*trans*-oct-1-enyl]cyclopent-1-yl]-*cis*-hept-5-enoic acid; 9α,11α,15-trihydroxy-5-*cis*-13-*trans*-prostadienoic acid; prostaglandin F₂α; U-14583; 'enzaprost F'; 'prostin F2 alpha').
DINOPROST TROMETAMOL (dinoprost tromethamine; U-14583E; 'lutalyse').
Dinoprost tromethamine* *see* Dinoprost trometamol.
DINOPROSTONE*** (11α,15-dihydroxy-9-oxo-5-*cis*-13-*trans*-prostadienoic acid; 7-[3α-hydroxy-2β-[3(*S*)-hydroxy-*trans*-oct-1-enyl]-5-oxo-cyclopent-1-yl]-*cis*-hept-5-enoic acid; prostaglandin E₂; U-12062; 'prostin E₂').
20,21-Dinor-16α-eburnamine *see* Vindeburnol.
DINOSEB* (6-*sec*-butyl-2,4-dinitrophenol; 6-(1-methylpropyl)-2,4-dinitrophenol; DNBP; DNIBF; 'dibutox'; 'gebutox').
DINOSEB ACETATE ('aretit'; 'ivosit').
Dinoseb isopropyl carbonate *see* Dinobuton.
Dinoseb 3-methyl-2-butenoate *see* Binapacryl.
Dinoseb senecioate *see* Binapacryl.
DINOSEB TROLAMINE (dinoseb compound with 2,2',2''-nitrilotriethanol; DNOSBP; DNSBP; 'elgetol 313'; 'premerge').
DINOTERB* (2-*tert*-butyl-4,6-dinitrophenol; 2-(1,1-dimethylethyl)-4,6-dinitrophenol; DNTBP).
DINSED*** (*N*,*N*'-ethylenebis(3-nitrobenzenesulfonamide; *N*,*N*'-bis(3-nitrobenzenesulfonyl)-ethylenediamine; NSC-5109).
'Dinuclan' *see* Salsalate.
'Dinyl' *see* Biphenyl.
Diochin (tr) *see* Dioquin.
2,2'-[[3-(Dioctadecylamino)propyl]imino]diethanol *see* Avridine.
'Dioctylal' *see* Docusate sodium.
Dioctyl sulfosuccinate *see* Docusate sodium.
'Diocyclin' *see under* Diiodohydroxyquin.
'Diocyl' *see* Dicycloverine.
'Dioderm' *see* Hydrocortisone.
'Dioderm-C' *see under* Clioquinol.
DIODONE** (3,5-diiodo-4-oxo-1(4*H*)-pyridineacetic acid diethanolamine salt; iodopyracet; RP

3203).

DIODONE MEGLUMINE* (diodone methylglucamine; 'pyelombrine M').

'Diodoquin' *see* Diiodohydroxyquin.

Diodoxyquinoline *see* Diiodohydroxyquin.

'Diodrast' *see* Diodone.

Diolamine* *see* Diethanolamine.

'Diolan' *see* Ethylmorphine.

'Diomax' *see* Acetazolamide.

'Dionine' *see* Ethylmorphine.

'Dionosil' *see* Propyliodone.

DIOQUIN (tr) (2-(diethylamino)ethyl 2-quinuclidinecarboxylate dimethiodide; diochin).

Dioscorea polystacha, steroid saponins *see* Polisaponin.

DIOSMIN** (3',5,7-trihydroxy-4'-methoxyflavone 7-[6-*O*-(6-deoxy-α-L-mannopyranosyl)-β-D-glucopyranoside]; 3',5,7-trihydroxy-4'-methoxyflavone 7-[6-(β-L-rhamnosido)-D-glucoside]; 3',5,7-trihydroxy-4'-methoxyflavone rutinoside; SE-4601; 'diovenor'; 'tovene').

DIOSMIN plus HESPERIDIN ('daflon').

'Diothane' *see* Diperodon.

'Diothoid' *see* Diperodon.

'Diothyl' *see* Pyrimitate.

'Diotroxin' *see* Liotrix.

'Diovac' *see* Docusate sodium.

'Diovenor' *see* Diosmin.

'Diovocyclin' *see* Estradiol dipropionate.

DIOXACARB* (*o*-(1,3-dioxolan-2-yl)phenyl methylcarbamate; dioxicarb; dioxocarb; 'eleocron'; 'elocron'; 'famid').

(3,8-Dioxa-4,7-dioxodecamethylene-1,10)bis(adamant-1-yldimethylammonium iodide) *see* Diadonium iodide.

DIOXADROL*** ((±)-2-(2,2-diphenyl-1,3-dioxolan-4-yl)piperidine; DL-2,2-diphenyl-4-piperid-2-yl-1,3-dioxolane; dioxadrol hydrochloride; oxadrol; CL-639-C).

See also Dexoxadrol; 'Levoxadrol.

3,14-Dioxahexadecamethylene-1,16-bis[(carbopropoxymethyl)dimethylammonium bromide] *see* Prodeconium bromide.

Dioxahexadekanium bromide *see* Prodeconium bromide.

DIOXAMATE*** (2-methyl-2-nonyl-1,3-dioxolan-4-ylmethyl carbamate; A-2655).

1,3-DIOXANE (dihydro-*m*-dioxin).

1,4-DIOXANE (tetrahydro-*p*-dioxin).

1,4-Dioxane-2,5-dione, polymer with 3,6-dimethyl-1,4-dioxane-2,5-dione *see* Polyglactin(s).

p-**Dioxanedithiol bisdiethyl phosphorodithioate** *see* Dioxation.

S,S',5,5'-p-**Dioxane-2,3-diyl bis(*O,O*-diethylphosphorodithioate** *see* Dioxation.

S,S'-**1,4-Dioxane-2,3-diyl-*O,O,O',O'*-tetraethyl phosphorodithioate** *see* Dioxation.

10-[3-[4-(2-*m*-Dioxan-2-ylethyl)piperazin-1-yl]propyl]phenothiazine *see* Oxaprazine.

10-[3-[4-(2-*m*-Dioxanylethyl)piperazin-1-yl]propyl]-2-(trifluoromethyl)phenothiazine *see* Oxaflumazine.

3,6-Dioxaoctane-1,8-diol *see* Triethylene glycol.

DIOXAPHETYL BUTYRATE*** (ethyl 4-morpholino-2,2-diphenylbutyrate; ethyl α,α-diphenyl-4-morpholinebutyrate).

(1,4-Dioxaspiro[4.5]dec-2-ylmethyl)guanidine *see* Guanadrel.

Dioxathion *see* Dioxation.

DIOXATION*** (*S,S'*-diester of *p*-dioxane-2,3-dithiol with *O,O*-diethylphosphorodithioate; mixture of *cis* and *trans* forms of dioxation; *S,S',5,5'-p*-dioxane-2,3-diyl bis(*O,O*-diethylphosphorodithioate; *p*-dioxanedithiol bisdiethyl phosphorodithioate; *S,S'*-1,4-dioxane-2,3-diyl-*O,O,O'O'*-tetraethyl phosphorodithioate; dioxathion; AC-528).

'Dioxatrine' *see* Benzetimide.

DIOXETHEDRIN*** (α-[1-(ethylamino)ethyl]-3,4-dihydroxybenzyl alcohol; α-[1-(ethylamino)ethyl]protocatechuyl alcohol; *N*-ethylcorbadrine).

Dioxicarb *see* Dioxacarb.

'Dioxidan' *see under* Dantron.

DIOXIDINE (tr) (quinoxaline-2,3-dimethanol 1,4-dioxide).

Dioxidine diacetate *see* Quinoxidine.

5-(10,10-Dioxido-9-oxothioxanthen-3-yl)tetrazole *see* Doxantrazole.

DIOXIFEDRINE*** (3,4-dihydroxy-α-[1-(methylamino)ethyl]benzyl alcohol).

m-**DIOXIN** ($C_4H_6O_2$).

p-**DIOXIN** ($C_4H_4O_2$).

Dioxine *see* 2,3,7,8-Tetrachlorodibenzo-*p*-dioxin.

2-[4-[4-(7,9-Dioxo-8-azaspiro[4.5]dec-8-yl)butyl]piperazin-1-yl]pyrimidine *see* Buspirone.

4-[4-(7,9-Dioxo-8-azaspiro[4.5]dec-7-yl)butyl]-1-pyrimidin-2-ylpiperazine *see* Buspirone.

1,3-Dioxo-1*H*-benz[*de*]isoquinoline-2(3*H*)-acetic acid *see* Alrestatin.

Dioxocarb *see* Dioxacarb.

4,4'-Dioxo-β-carotene *see* Canthaxanthin.

2,2'-(3,11-Dioxo-4,10-dioxatridecylenebis[6,7-dimethoxy-1-(3,4-dimethoxybenzyl)-1,2,3,4-tetrahydro-2-methylisoquinolinium] dibenzenesulfonate *see* Atracurium besilate.

3,5-Dioxohexanoic acid *see* Triacetic acid.

(2,5-Dioxoimidazolin-4-yl)urea *see* Allantoin.

1,3-DIOXOLANE (dihydro-*p*-dioxole).

7-[(1,3-Dioxolan-2-yl)methyl]theophylline *see* Doxofylline.

(1,3-Dioxolan-4-ylmethyl)trimethylammonium iodide *see* Oxapropanium iodide.

o-**(1,3-Dioxolan-2-yl)phenyl methylcarbamate** *see* Dioxacarb.

1-[2-(1,3-Dioxolo[4,5-*f*]indol-7-yl)ethyl]-4-(*o*-methoxyphenyl)piperazine *see* Solypertine.

'Dioxone' *see* Diethadione.

N-**(2,6-Dioxopiperid-3-yl)-2,3-norbornanedicarboximide** *see* Taglutimide.

N-**(2,6-Dioxopiperid-3-yl)phthalimide** *see* Thalidomide.

9,9-Dioxopromethazine *see* Promethazine S,S-dioxide.

4,6-Dioxo-10-propyl-4*H*,6*H*-benzo[1,2-*b*:5,4-*b'*]dipyran-2,8-dicarboxylic acid *see* Ambicromil.

2,5-Dioxopyrrolidine *see* Succinimide.

4-[(2,5-Dioxopyrrolidin-1-yloxy)carbonyl]-α,α,4-triphenyl-1-piperidinebutanenitrile *see* Difenoximide.

N,N'-(1,16-Dioxo-4,7,10,13-tetraoxahexadecane-1,16-diyl)di(3-amino-2,4,6-triiodobenzoic acid) *see* Iodoxamic acid.

3,3'-[(1,14-Dioxo-3,6,9,12-tetraoxatetradecane-1,14-diyl)diimino]bis[2,4,6-triiodobenzoic acid] *see* Iotetric acid.

DIOXYBENZONE*** (2,2'-dihydroxy-4-methoxybenzophenone; NSC-56769).

Dioxydemeton-S-methyl *see* Demeton-S-methylsulfon.

Dioxyline *see* Dimoxyline.

'Dioxyline' *see* Benzoxiquine.

DIPA *see* Diisopropylamine dichloroacetate.

'Dipar' *see* Phenformin.

'Di-paralene' *see* Chlorcyclizine.

'Dipasic' *see* Pasiniazid.

'Dipaxin' *see* Diphenadione.

Dipenine bromide* *see* Diponium bromide.

Dipentene *see* Limonene.

Diperocaine *see* Diperodon.

DIPERODON*** (3-piperid-1-ylpropyl 1,2-dicarbanilate; diperocaine).

'Diphacil' *see* Adiphenine.

'Diphacin' *see* Diphenadione.

Diphacinone* *see* Diphenadione.

'Diphantoin' *see* Phenytoin.

Diphasin (tr) *see* 10-(Diethylaminoacetyl)phenothiazine *and* Promethazine.

Diphazin (tr) *see* 10-(Diethylaminoacetyl)phenothiazine *and* Promethazine.

'Diphebuzol' *see* Phenylbutazone.

DIPHEMANIL METILSULFATE*** (4-(diphenylmethylene)-1,1-dimethylpiperidinium methylsulfate; diphenmethanil).

'Diphemin' *see* Deanol benzilate.

'Diphenacin' *see* Diphenadione.

DIPHENADIONE** (2-(diphenylacetyl)-1,3-indandione; diphacinone; difenatsin; PID; U-1363).

DIPHENAMID* (N,N-dimethyl-2,2-diphenylacetamide; N,N-dimethyl-α-phenylbenzeneacetamide).

Diphenamizole *see* Difenamizole.

DIPHENAN*** (p-benzylphenyl carbamate; α-phenyl-p-cresyl carbamate; benzylphenylurethan; carphenol).

Diphenason *see* Dapsone.

'Diphenatil' *see* Diphemanil metilsulfate.

DIPHENAZINE (1,4-bis(3-phenylprop-2-yl)piperazine; 1,4-bis(α-methylphenethyl)piperazine; 1,4-bis(phenylisopropyl)piperazine; 'quietidine').

Diphencloxazine *see* Difencloxazine.

Diphenetholine *see* Bibenzonium bromide.

N,N'-Di-p-phenetylacetamidine *see* Phenacaine.

Diphenhexenic acid *see* Xenyhexenic acid.

DIPHENHYDRAMINE*** (2-(diphenylmethoxy)-N,N-dimethylethylamine; anautine; benzhydramine; dimedrol; PM-255; S-51).
See also under Carbromal; Chlorotheophylline;

Cinnarizine; Methaqualone; Prenoxdiazine; Valdetamide.

Diphenhydramine aminoxide camphorsulfonate *see* Amoxydramine camsilate.

Diphenhydramine aminoxide camsylate *see* Amoxydramine camsilate.

DIPHENHYDRAMINE ASCORBATE ('antamin').

DIPHENHYDRAMINE 8-BROMOTHEOPHYLLINATE (bromanautine).

Diphenhydramine 8-chlorotheophyllinate *see* Dimenhydrinate.

Diphenhydramine teoclate *see* Dimenhydrinate.

DIPHENHYDRAMINE THEOPHYLLINATE (etanautine; 'nautamine').

'Diphenidol' *see* Difenidol.

Diphenin (tr) *see* Phenytoin.

Diphenmethanil* *see* Diphemanil metilsulfate.

DIPHENOXYLATE*** (4-ethoxycarbonyl α,α,4-triphenyl-1-piperidinebutyronitrile; ethyl 1-(3-cyano-3,3-diphenylpropyl)-4-phenylisonipecotate; ethyl difenoxilate; CB-8049; FH-049-E; R-1132).

DIPHENOXYLATE plus ATROPINE ('diarsed'; 'lofene'; 'lomotil'; 'reasec'; 'retardin').

DIPHENPYRAMIDE (2-biphenyl-4-yl-N-pyrid-2-ylacetamide; N-pyrid-2-ylbiphenylacetamide; difenpiramide; 'difenax').

Di-phenthane-70 *see* Dichlorophen.

'Diphentoin' *see* Phenytoin.

Diphenyl (the compound) *see* Biphenyl.

2,2-Diphenylacetic acid esters *see* Adiphenine; Anicaine; Arpenal; Mesfenal; Methyldiphenine; Pinolcaine.

2-(Diphenylacetyl)-1,3-indandione *see* Diphenadione.

Diphenylaminechlorarsine *see* Phenarsazine chloride.

1-(p,α-Diphenylbenzyl)imidazole *see* Bifonazole.

Diphenylbutazone *see* Phenylbutazone.

1,3-Diphenyl-2-buten-1-one *see* Dypnone.

2-[p-(1,2-Diphenyl-1-butenyl)phenoxy]-N,N-dimethylethylamine *see* Tamoxifen.

Diphenylcarbamic acid dimethylaminoethyl ester *see* Dicarfen.

Diphenylcarbinol *see* Benzhydrol.

2,4-Diphenyl-1,3-cyclobutanedicarboxylic acid *see* Truxillic acid.

2,2-Diphenylcyclopropanecarboxylic acid ester with 1-piperidineethanol *see* Pituxate.

2-(2,2-Diphenylcyclopropyl)-2-imidazoline *see* Cibenzoline.

3-[[(2,2-Diphenylcyclopropyl)methyl]amino]propyl 3,4,5-trimethoxybenzoate *see* Ecipramidil.

N-(cis-2,trans-3-Diphenylcyclopropyl)-1-pyrrolidineacetamide *see* Ciprafamide.

Diphenyl diketone *see* Benzil.

2-(2,2-Diphenyl-1,3-dioxolan-4-yl)piperidine *see* Dioxadrol.

Diphenylene dioxide *see* Dibenzo-p-dioxin.

Diphenylene ketone oxide *see* Xanthone.

Diphenylenemethane *see* Fluorene.

Diphenylene oxide *see* Dibenzofuran.

194

Diphenylenimine *see* Carbazole.
1,2-Diphenylethane *see* Bibenzyl.
1,2-Diphenylethene *see* Stilbene.
2-(1,1-Diphenylethoxy)-*N*,*N*-dimethylethylamine *see* Moxastine.
[2-(1,2-Diphenylethoxy)ethyl]trimethylammonium bromide *see* Bibenzonium bromide.
1,2-Diphenylethylamine *see* Stilbylamine.
1,2-Diphenylethylene *see* Stilbene.
3-(2,2-Diphenylethyl)-5-(2-piperid-1-ylethyl)-1,2,4-oxadiazole *see* Prenoxdiazine.
Diphenylglycolic acid *see* Benzilic acid.
Diphenylglyoxal *see* Benzil.
3,4-Diphenylhexamethylenebis(trimethylammonium iodide) *see* Paramyon.
5,5-Diphenylhydantoin *see* Phenytoin.
Diphenylhydracrylic acid acetohydrazide *see* Diphoxazide.
1,2-Diphenylhydrazine *see* Hydrazobenzene.
5,5-Diphenyl-4-imidazolidinone *see* Doxenitoin.
Diphenyl ketone *see* Benzophenone.
Diphenylmethanol *see* Benzhydrol.
2-(Diphenylmethoxy)-*N*,*N*-dimethylethylamine *see* Diphenhydramine.
2′-(Diphenylmethoxy)-*N*,1-dimethyl-2-phenoxydiethylamine *see* Prenoverine.
α-[1-[[2-(Diphenylmethoxy)ethyl]methylamino]ethyl]benzyl alcohol *see* Difeterol.
2-[[2-(Diphenylmethoxy)ethyl]methylamino]-1-phenyl-1-propanol *see* Difeterol.
N-[2-(Diphenylmethoxy)ethyl]-*N*-methylcinnamylamine *see* Cinfenine.
3-(Diphenylmethoxy)-8-ethylnortropane *see* Etybenzatropine.
1-[2-(Diphenylmethoxy)ethyl]piperidine *see* Perastine.
4-(Diphenylmethoxy)-1-methylpiperidine *see* Diphenylpyraline.
3-(Diphenylmethoxy)tropane *see* Benzatropine.
4-(Diphenylmethyl)-1,2-dimethyl-2-veratrylpiperazine *see* Benderizine.
2-(Diphenylmethylene)butylamine *see* Etifelmine.
3-(Diphenylmethylene)-1,1-diethyl-2-methylpyrrolidinium bromide *see* Prifinium bromide.
4-(Diphenylmethylene)-1,1-dimethylpiperidinium methylsulfate *see* Diphemanil metilsulfate.
3′,4′-[(Diphenylmethylene)dioxy]-3,5,7-flavantriol *see* Bencianol.
3-(Diphenylmethylene)-1-ethylpyrrolidine *see* Pridefine.
4-(Diphenylmethylene)-1-[2-[2-(2-hydroxyethoxy)ethoxy]ethyl]piperidine *see* Pipoxizine.
2-[2-[2-[4-(Diphenylmethylene)piperid-1-yl]ethoxy]ethoxy]ethanol *see* Pipoxizine.
1-(Diphenylmethyl)-4-(*p*-hydroxybenzyl)piperazine *see* Belarizine.
1-(Diphenylmethyl)-4-[2-(2-hydroxyethoxy)ethyl]piperazine *see* Decloxizine.
1-(Diphenylmethyl)-4-(3,4-methylenedioxyphenyl)piperazine *see* Medibazine.
1-(Diphenylmethyl)-4-methylpiperazine *see* Cyclizine.
1-(Diphenylmethyl)-4-[[(6-methylpyrid-2-yl)methyl-

ene]amino]piperazine *see* Ropizine.
4-(Diphenylmethyl)-1-(*N*-octylformimidoyl)piperidine *see* Fenoctimine.
1-(Diphenylmethyl)-4-[3-(2-oxobenzimidazolin-1-yl)propyl]piperazine *see* Oxatomide.
(1-(Diphenylmethyl)-4-[3-(2-phenyl-1,3-dioxolan-2-yl)propyl]piperazine *see* Dotarizine.
α-[4-(Diphenylmethyl)piperazin-1-yl]-*p*-cresol *see* Belarizine.
2-[2-[4-(Diphenylmethyl)piperazin-1-yl]ethoxy]ethanol *see* Decloxizine.
1-[3-[4-(Diphenylmethyl)piperazin-1-yl]propyl]-2-benzimidazolinone *see* Oxatomide.
2-(Diphenylmethyl)-1-piperidineethanol *see* Difemetorex.
2-[(Diphenylmethyl)sulfinyl]acetohydroxamic acid *see* Adrafinil.
4,5-Diphenyl-2-oxazolepropionic acid *see* Oxaprozin.
2,2′-(4,5-Diphenyloxazol-2-ylimino)diethanol *see* Ditazole.
1,2-Diphenyl-4-(2-phenylsulfinylethyl)-3,5-pyrazolidinedione *see* Sulfinpyrazone.
3,3-Diphenyl-3′-(phenylthio)dipropylamine *see* Tiopropamine.
(Diphenylphosphinyl)acetic acid hydrazide *see* Fosenazide.
2,5-Diphenylpiperazine dipenicillin *g see* Phenyracillin.
α,α-Diphenyl-1-piperidinebutanol *see* Difenidol.
α,α-Diphenyl-2-piperidinemethanol *see* Pipradrol.
α,α-Diphenyl-4-piperidinemethanol *see* Azacyclonol.
α,α-Diphenyl-2-piperidinepropionic acid ethyl ester *see* Pifenate.
2,2-Diphenyl-4-piperidinobutyramide *see* Fenpipramide.
Diphenylpiperidinopropane *see* Fenpiprane.
1,1-Diphenyl-3-piperidino-1-propanol *see* Pridinol.
1,1-Diphenyl-2-piperidino-1-propanol *see* Diphepanol.
2,2-Diphenyl-4-piperid-1-ylbutyramide *see* Fenpipramide.
2,2-Diphenyl-4-piperid-2-yl-1,3-dioxolane *see* Dexoxadrol; Dioxadrol; Levoxadrol.
2,2-Diphenyl-2-(2-piperid-1-ylethyl)acetamide *see* Fenpipramide.
5,5-Diphenyl-2-(2-piperid-1-ylethyl)-1,3-dioxolan-4-one *see* Pipoxolan.
4,4-Diphenyl-6-piperid-1-yl-3-heptanone *see* Dipipanone.
4,4-Diphenyl-6-piperid-1-yl-3-hexanone *see* Norpipanone.
3,3-Diphenyl-1-piperid-1-ylpropane *see* Fenpiprane.
1,1-Diphenyl-2-piperid-1-ylpropyl salicylate *see* Diphepanol.
1,2-Diphenyl-4-(2-pivaloylethyl)-3,5-pyrazolidinedione *see* Tribuzone.
1,3-Diphenyl-2-propen-1-one *see* Chalcone.
Diphenylpropionic acid diethylaminoethyl ester *see* Aprofene.
Diphenylpropoxyacetic acid 1-methylpiperid-4-yl ester *see* Propiverine.

Diphenylpropylacetic acid diethylaminoethyl ester *see* Proadifen.

3-[(3,3-Diphenylpropyl)amino]propyl 3,4,5-trimeth-oxybenzoate *see* Mepramidil.

***N*-(3,3-Diphenylpropyl)amphetamine** *see* Prenylamine.

1-(3,3-Diphenylpropyl)cyclohexamethylenimine *see* Prozapine.

1-(3,3-Diphenylpropyl)hexahydroazepine *see* Prozapine.

1-(3,3-Diphenylpropyl)hexamethylenimine *see* Prozapine.

***N*-(3,3-Diphenylpropyl)-α-methylbenzylamine** *see* Fendiline.

***N*-(3,3-Diphenylpropyl)-α-methylcyclohexaneethylamine** *see* Droprenilamine.

***N*-(3,3-Diphenylpropyl)-α-methylphenethylamine** *see* Prenylamine.

1-(3,3-Diphenylpropyl)piperidine *see* Fenpiprane.

1,1-Diphenyl-2-propynyl cyclohexanecarbamate *see* Enpromate.

Diphenyl(propynyloxy)acetic acid dimethylaminoethyl ester *see* Pargeverine.

DIPHENYLPYRALINE*** (4-(diphenylmethoxy)-1-methylpiperidine; P-253).
See also Piprinhydrinate *and under* Phenylephrine.

1,2-DIPHENYL-3,5-PYRAZOLIDINEDIONE ('phenopyrazone').
See also under Aminophenazone.

α,α-Diphenyl-2-pyrid-4-ylcyclopropanemethanol *see* Cyprolidol.

2,3-Diphenyl-1-[3-(4-pyrid-2-ylpiperazin-1-yl)propyl]-3-pyrazolin-5-one *see* Revenast.

1,1-Diphenyl-4-pyrrolidin-1-ylbut-2-yn-1-ol *see* Butinoline.

α,α-Diphenyl-3-quinuclidinemethanol *see* Quifenadine.

Diphenylthioacetic acid esters *see* Diprofene; Tifenamil.

Diphenylthiocarbazone *see* Dithizone.

Diphenylthioloacetic acid esters *see* Diprofene; Thiphenamil.

1,3-Diphenylthiourea *see* Thiocarbanilide.

1,3-Diphenyltriazene *see* Diazoaminobenzene.

5,5-Diphenyl-3-(2,2,2-trichloro-1-hydroxyethyl)-4-imidazolidinone *see* Triclodazol.

1,2-Diphenyl-4-(4,4,4-trimethyl-3-oxobutyryl)-3,5-pyrazolidinedione *see* Tribuzone.

1,3-Diphenylurea *see* Carbanilide.

Diphenylvaleric acid diethylaminoethyl ester *see* Proadifen.

Diphenylyl.... *see* Biphenylyl.....

DIPHEPANOL* (1,1-diphenyl-2-piperid-1-yl-propyl salicylate; Ho-10682).

Diphesatine* *see* Acetphenolisatin.

Diphesyl (tr) *see* Difezil.

Diphetarsone* *see* Difetarsone.

Diphexamide iodomethylate *see* Buzepide metiodide.

'Diphone' *see* Dapsone.

'Diphos' *see* Etidronic acid.

DIPHOSGENE (trichloromethyl chloroformate;

perstoff; superpalite; surpalite).

Diphosphonate *see* Etidronate disodium.

Diphosphopyridine nucleotide *see* Nadide.

Diphosphothiamine *see* Cocarboxylase.

DIPHOXAZIDE*** (acetylhydrazide of 3,3-diphenylhydracrylic acid; 1-acetyl-2-(3-hydroxy-3,3-diphenylpropionyl)hydrazine).

Diphtalone *see* Diftalone.

'Dipidolor' *see* Piritramide.

DIPIN (tr) (1,4-bis(diaziridinylphosphinylidyne)-piperazine; *N,N'*-diethylenebis(*N,N'*-diethylene-phosphoric diamide); piperazine-1,4-diphosphoric acid tetraethylenimide; 1,4-piperazinedi-ylbis[bis(1-aziridinyl)phosphine oxide]; tetraethylenimide piperazine diphosphate).

DIPIPANONE*** (4,4-diphenyl-6-piperid-1-yl-3-heptanone; piperidyl amidone; dipipanone hydrochloride; BW-378C48).

DIPIPANONE plus CYCLIZINE ('diconal').

2,2',2'',2'''-[(4,8-Dipiperidinopyrimido[5,4-*d*]pyr-imidine-2,6-diyl)dinitrilo]tetraethanol *see* Dipyridamole.

Dipiperidyl *see* Bipiperidine.

2β,16β-Dipiperid-1-yl-5α-androstane-3α,17β-diol 3-acetate dimethobromide *see* Dacuronium bromide.

2β,16β-Dipiperid-1-yl-5α-androstane-3α,17β-diol di-acetate dimethobromide *see* Pancuronium bromide.

2β,16β-Dipiperid-1-yl-5α-androstane-3α,17β-diol 3,17-diacetate 16β-methobromide *see* Vecuronium bromide.

'Dipiperon' *see* Pipamperone.

DIPIPROVERINE*** (2-piperid-1-ylethyl phenylpiperidylacetate; LD-935; P-4).

Dipivalylepinephrine *see* Dipivefrine.

Dipivefrin* *see* Dipivefrine.

DIPIVEFRINE*** ((±)-3,4-dihydroxy-α-[(methylamino)methyl]benzyl alcohol 3,4-dipivalate; (±)-4-[1-hydroxy-2-(methylamino)ethyl]-1,2-phenylene bis(2,2-dimethylpropanoate); dipivefrin; epinephrine 3,4-dipivalate; dipivalylepinephrine; DPE; K-30081; 'epifrin'; 'glaucothil').

DIPIVEFRINE plus PILOCARPINE ('thilo-adren').

DIPLACIN (tr) (1,3-bis(2-platineciumethoxy)-benzene dichloride; 4,4'-[*m*-phenylenebis(oxy-ethylene)]bis[hexahydro-1-hydroxy-7-(hydroxy-methyl)pyrrolizinium chloride]; diplatsin).

Diplatsin *see* Diplacin.

'Diplosal' *see* Salsalate.

'Diplosal acetate' *see* Acetylsalicylsalicylic acid.

'Dipodolor' *see* Piritramide.

Dipon* *see* Diponium bromide.

DIPONIUM BROMIDE*** (triethyl(2-hydroxy-ethyl)ammonium bromide dicyclopentylacetate; (2-dicyclopentylacetoxyethyl)trimethylammon-ium bromide; dipenine bromide; dipon; DCDE; HL-267; Sa-267; THPP).

Dipotassium clorazepate*** *see* Clorazepate dipotassium.

DIPRAFENONE*** ((±)-2'-[2-hydroxy-3-(*tert*-pentylamino)propoxy]-3-phenylpropiophenone).

'**Dipramid**' *see* Isopropamide iodide.
Diprazin (tr) *see* Promethazine.
DIPRENORPHINE* (21-cyclopropyl-6,7,8,14-tetrahydro-7α-(1-hydroxy-1-methylethyl)-6,14-*endo*-ethanooripavine; (6*R*,7*R*,14*S*)-17-(cyclopropylmethyl)-7,8-dihydro-7-(1-hydroxy-1-methylethyl)-6-*O*-methyl-6,14-ethano-17-normorphine; diprenorphine hydrochloride; M-5050; 'revivon').
DIPROBUTINE* (3-amino-3-propylheptane; 1,1-dipropylbutylamine).
'**Diproderm**' *see* Betamethasone dipropionate.
'**Diprofarn**' *see* Dipyrone.
DIPROFENE* (dipropylaminoethyl diphenyl-thioloacetate; diprophen).
'**Diprogenta**' *see under* Betamethasone dipropionate.
DIPROGULIC ACID* (2,3:4,6-di-*O*-isopropyl-idene-α-L-*xylo*-hexulofuranosonic acid).
DIPROLEANDOMYCIN* (oleandomycin 4',11-dipropionate).
DIPROPAMINE (phenylenebis(oxypropylene)bis-(ethyldimethylammonium iodide)).
DIPROPETRYN* (6-(ethylthio)-2,4-bis(isoprop-ylamino)-*s*-triazine; 'cotofor').
Diprophen (tr) *see* Diprofene.
DIPROPHYLLINE* (7-(2,3-dihydroxypropyl)-theophylline; dyphyllin; glyfillin; glyphillin; hy-philline).
DIPROPHYLLINE plus 7-(2-HYDROXYPROP-YL)THEOPHYLLINE ('neophylline').
Diprophylline dinicotinate *see* Diniprofylline.
Dipropiomazine *see* Propionylpromazine.
3,5-Dipropionamido-2,4,6-triiodobenzoic acid *see* Diprotrizoic acid.
Dipropylacetamide *see* Valpromide.
Dipropylacetic acid *see* Valproic acid.
4-(Dipropylamino)-3,5-dinitrobenzenesulfonamide *see* Oryzalin.
Dipropylaminoethyl diphenylthioloacetate *see* Di-profene.
5,5-DIPROPYLBARBITURIC ACID (propylbar-bital).
1,1-Dipropylbutylamine *see* Diprobutine.
Dipropylcarbamothioic acid *S*-**ethyl ester** *see* Ethyl dipropylcarbamothioate.
Dipropylcarbamothioic acid *S*-**propyl ester** *see* Ver-nolate.
Dipropyl 3,4-dihydroxy-2,5-thiophenedicarboxylate *see* Protiofate.
Dipropylenediamine *see* Lupetazine.
Dipropyline *see* Alverine.
p-**(Dipropylsulfamoyl)benzoic acid** *see* Probenecid.
N,*N*-**Dipropyl-*p*-toluenesulfonamide** *see* Ditol-amide.
2,2-Dipropylvaleramide *see* Valdipromide.
DIPROQUALONE** (3-(2,3-dihydroxypropyl)-2-methyl-4-(3*H*)-quinazolinone).
DIPROQUALONE CAMSILATE plus ETH-ENZAMIDE ('algopriv').
'**Diprosalic**' *see under* Betamethasone dipropionate.
'**Diprosone**' *see* Betamethasone dipropionate.
DIPROTEVERINE** (1-(3,4-diethoxybenzyl)-6,7-

diisopropoxyisoquinoline).
Diprothazine *see* Dimelazine.
DIPROTRIZOIC ACID (3,5-dipropionamido-2,4,6-triiodobenzoic acid).
See also Sodium diprotrizoate.
'**Diprovex**' *see* Estradiol dipropionate.
DIPROXADOL* (6-chloro-4-(2,3-dihydroxy-propyl)-2-methyl-2*H*-1,4-benzoxazin-3(4*H*)-one).
'**Dipsan**' *see* Calcium carbimide citrate.
'**Dipterex**' *see* Metrifonate.
'**Dipterex-ER**' *see under* Metrifonate.
DIPYRIDAMOLE* (2,6-bis[bis(2-hydroxy-ethyl)amino]-4,8-bis(1-piperidyl)pyrimido[5,4-*d*]pyrimidine; 2,2',2'',2'''-[(4,8-dipiperidinopyr-imido[5,4-*d*]pyrimidine-2,6-diyl)dinitrilo]tetra-ethanol; NSC-515776; RA-8).
DIPYRIDAMOLE plus ACETYLSALICYLIC ACID ('asasantin').
DIPYRIDAMOLE plus OXAZEPAM ('persum-bran').
Dipyridyl (the compound) *see* Bipyridine.
N,*N*'**-(1,2-Di-4-pyridylethylene)bis[*o*-toluamide]** *see* Tolpadol.
Di(pyrid-4-ylmethyl)amine *see* Gapicomine.
3-(Dipyrid-2-ylmethylene)-α,α-dipyrid-2-yl-1,4-cyclopentadiene-1-methanol *see* Pyrinoline.
'**Di-pyrin**' *see* Aminophenazone.
DIPYRITHIONE* (2,2'-dithiodipyridine 1,1'-dioxide; 2,2'-thiodipyridine 1,1'-dioxide; OMDS; 'omadine disulfide').
DIPYROCETYL* (2,3-diacetoxybenzoic acid; diacetylpyrocatecholcarboxylic acid; 2,3-di-hydroxybenzoic acid diacetate).
DIPYRONE* ([[(2,3-dimethyl-5-oxo-1-phenyl-3-pyrazolin-4-yl)methyl]amino]methanesulfonic acid sodium salt; 4-(methylamino)phenazone methanesulfonic acid sodium salt; sodium (anti-pyrinylmethylamino)methanesulfonate; meta-mizole; noramidopyrine methanesulfonate sodi-um; sodium noramidopyrine methanesulfonate; analgin; methampyrone; methapyrone; methyl-melubrin; noramidazophen; novamidazophen; novaminsulfon; oxiquinazine; sulpyrin; NSC-73205).
See also under Camylofin; Ciclonium bromide; Drofenine; Metixene.
Dipyroxime (tr) *see* Trimedoxime bromide.
1,4-Dipyrrolidin-1-yl-2-butyne *see* Tremorine.
DIQUAT* (9,10-dihydro-8a,10a-diazoniaphen-anthrene dibromide; 6,7-dihydrodipyrido[1,2-*a*:2',1'-*c*]pyrazinediium dibromide; FB/2; 'aqua-cide'; 'dextrone'; 'reglone').
'**Diquel**' *see* Etymemazine.
'**Diquinol**' *see* Ethaverine.
Diquinolylurea bismethosulfate *see* Quinuronium sulfate.
'**Diratyl**' *see* Hydroflumethiazide.
Direct red *see* Congo red.
'**Drema**' *see* Hydrochlorothiazide.
'**Dirian**' *see* Brotianide.
'**Dirimen**' *see under* Cefazolin.
'**Dirnate**' *see* Carzenide.

'Dironyl' *see* Lisuride.
'Dirytmin' *see* Disopyramide.
'Disadine' *see* Povidone-iodine.
'Disalcid' *see* Salsalate.
Disalicylic acid *see* Salsalate.
'Disalunil' *see* Hydrochlorothiazide.
'Disaluril' *see* Hydrochlorothiazide.
'Disalyl' *see* Salsalate.
'Disamide' *see* Disulfamide.
'Discase' *see* Chymopapain.
'Disepron' *see* Spiclomazine.
'Disipal' *see* Orphenadrine.
DISOBUTAMIDE*** (α-(*o*-chlorophenyl)-α-[2-(diisopropylamino)ethyl]-1-piperidinebutyr-amide; SC-31828).
'Disoderm' *see* Dichlorisone.
Disodium aurothiomalate *see* Sodium aurothiomalate.
Disodium [(benzylamidino)amidino]phosphoramidate *see* Benfosformin.
Disodium cromoglycate* *see* Cromoglicate disodium.
Disodium 2,2'-dithiodiethanesulfonate *see* Dimesna.
DISODIUM EDETATE* (disodium salt of ethylenediaminetetraacetic acid; disodium dihydrogen edetate; sodium edetate).
See also Sodium calcium edetate; Tetrasodium edetate.
Disodium endothal *see* Endothal sodium.
Disodium 1,2-ethanediylbis(carbamodithioate) *see* Nabam.
Disodium ethylenebis(carbamodithioate) *see* Nabam.
Disodium etidronate *see* Etidronate disodium.
DISODIUM HYDROGEN CITRATE (acid sodium citrate; 'alkacitron').
Disodium medronate *see* Medronate disodium.
DISODIUM METHANEARSONATE (sodium metharsinite; sodium monomethylarsonate).
Disodium methylenediphosphonate *see* Medronate disodium.
Disodium 4,4'-pyrid-2-ylmethylenedi(phenyl sulfate) *see* Sodium picosulfate.
Disodium 2,2'-thiobis(4,6-dichlorophenoxide) *see* Sodium bitionolate.
DISOFENIN*** ([[[(2,6-diisopropylphenyl)carbamoyl]methyl]imino]diacetic acid; *N*-[2-[[2,6-bis(1-methylethyl)phenyl]amino]-2-oxoethyl]-*N*-(carboxymethyl)glycine).
DISOGLUSIDE*** ((25*R*)-3β-(β-D-glucopyranosyloxy)spirost-5-ene).
'Disomer' *see* Dexbrompheniramine.
'Disonate' *see* Docusate sodium.
DISOPHENOL (2,6-diiodo-4-nitrophenol; 'ancylol').
Disoprofol *see* Propofol.
Disopromine* *see* Diisopromine.
DISOPYRAMIDE*** (α-(2-diisopropylaminoethyl)-α-phenyl-2-pyridineacetamide; 4-diisopropylamino-2-phenyl-2-pyrid-2-ylbutyramide; B-712; H-3292; RU-3292; SC-7031).
DISOPYRAMIDE PHOSPHATE* (SC-13957; 'norpace').

'Disorat' *see* Metipranolol.
'Disotat' *see* Diisopropylamine dichloroacetate.
'Dispamil' *see* Papaverine.
'Disparolene' *see* Chlorpropamide.
'Dispasmol' *see* Phenbenzamine ethobromide.
'Dispermin' *see* Piperazine.
'Dispril' *see* Calcium acetylsalicylate.
'Disprin' *see* Calcium acetylsalicylate.
'Distaclor' *see* Cefaclor.
'Distalgesic' *see under* Dextropropoxyphene.
'Distamine' *see* Penicillamine.
Distamycin A *see* Stallimycin.
'Distaneurine' *see* Clomethiazole edisilate.
DISTIGMINE BROMIDE*** (3-hydroxy-1-methylpyridinium bromide hexamethylenebis(*N*-methylcarbamate); hexamethylene-1,6-bis[1-methyl-3-(methylcarbamoyloxy)pyridinium bromide]; hexamarium bromide; BC-51).
'Disto-5' *see* Bithionoloxide.
'Distol-8' *see* Tetrasodium edetate.
'Distolon' *see* Niclofolan.
'Distowet' *see* Hexachloroethane.
'Distrapax' *see* Clomethiazole edisilate.
'Distreptaze' *see under* Streptodornase.
Distylin *see* Taxifolin.
Disugran* *see* Dicamba-methyl.
DISUL* (2-(2,4-dichlorophenoxy)ethyl hydrogen sulfate; dichloresul; 2,4-DES; 'SES').
DISULERGINE*** (*N*,*N*-dimethyl-*N*'-(6-methyl-ergolin-8α-yl)sulfamide; sulergine).
DISULFAMIDE** (5-chloro-2,4-disulfamoyltoluene; 5-chlorotoluene-2,4-disulfonamide; disulphamide; tolclotide).
'Disulfine blue' *see* Isosulfan blue.
DISULFIRAM*** (bis(diethylthiocarbamyl) disulfide; ethyldithiuram; ethyl thiurad; tetraethylthiuram disulfide; teturam; tiuram; TTD).
*N*⁴-(1,3-Disulfo-3-phenylpropyl)sulfanilamide disodium salt *see* Sulfasolucin.
DISULFORMIN (tr) (formaldehyde condensation product of *N*⁴-sulfanilylsulfanilamide).
DISULFOTON* (*O*,*O*-diethyl *S*-[(ethylthio)ethyl] phosphorodithioate; dithiodemeton; ethylthiometon; thiodemeton; thiometon ethyl; M-74; 'disyston'; 'dithio-systox'; 'frumin'; 'thiosystox').
'Disulone' *see* Dapsone.
Disulph.... *see also* Disulf.....
Disulphamide* *see* Disulfamide.
'Disyncran' *see* Methdilazine.
'Di-syston' *see* Disulfoton.
'Disyston-S' *see* Oxydisulfoton.
'Ditaven' *see* Digitoxin.
DITAZOLE*** (2,2'-(4,5-diphenyloxazol-2-ylimino)diethanol; dietamfenazole; diethamphenazole; S-222; 'ageroplas').
DITERCALINIUM CHLORIDE*** (2,2'-([4,4'-bipiperidine]-1,1'-diyldiethylene)bis[10-methoxy-7*H*-pyrido[4,3-*c*]carbazolium]dichloride).
'Diteriam' *see under* Benzthiazide.
Ditetrazolium chloride *see* Tetrazolium blue.
'Dithane 1740' *see* Nabam.
'Dithane A-40' *see* Nabam.
'Dithane D-14' *see* Nabam.

'Dithane M-22' see Maneb.
'Dithane M-45' see Mancozeb.
'Dithane manganese' see Maneb.
'Dithane S31' see under Maneb.
'Dithane-ultra' see Mancozeb.
'Dithane Z 78' see Zineb.
DITHIANON* (5,10-dihydro-5,10-dioxonaph-tho[2,3-b]1,4-dithiin-2,3-dicarbonitrile; 'delan').
DITHIAZANINE IODIDE*** (3-ethyl-2-[5-(3-ethylbenzothiazolin-2-ylidene)-1,3-pentadienyl]-benzothiazolium iodide; 3,3'-diethylthiadicarbo-cyanine iodide).
α-[1-[1-(3,3-Dithien-3-ylallyl)amino]ethyl]benzyl al-cohol see Tinofedrine.
Dithien-2-ylglycolic acid ester with 6,6,9-trimethyl-9-azabicyclo[3.3.1]nonan-3β-ol see Mazaticol.
3-(dithien-2-ylmethylene)-5-methoxy-1,1-dimethyl-piperidinium bromide see Timepidium bromide.
3-(Dithien-2-ylmethylene)-1-methylpiperidine see Tipepidine.
3-(Di-2-thienylmethylene)octahydro-5-methyl-2H-quinolizinium bromide see Tiquizium bromide.
Dithio see Sulfotep.
4,4'-Dithiobis(2-aminobutyric acid) see Homocyst-ine.
2,2'-Dithiobisethylamine see Cystamine.
N,N'-[Dithiobis[2-(2-hydroxyethyl)-1-methylvinyl-ene]]bis[N-[(4-amino-2-methyl-5-pyrimidinyl)-methyl]formamide] see Thiamine disulfide.
N,N'-[Dithiobis[2-(2-hydroxyethyl)-1-methylvinyl-ene]]bis[N-[(4-amino-2-methyl-5-pyrimidinyl)-methyl]formamide] diisobutyrate(ester) see Sulbu-tiamine.
N,N'-[Dithiobis[(2-isobutyryloxyethyl)-1-methylvin-ylene]]bis[N-[(4-amino-2-methylpyrimidin-5-yl)-methyl]formamide] see Sulbutiamine.
Dithiobis(thionoformic acid) diethyl ester see Di-xanthogen.
DITHIOCARB (sodium diethyldithiocarbamate; DTC; U-14624; 'imuthiol').
Dithiodemeton see Disulfoton.
β,β'-Dithiodialanine see Cystine.
2,2'-Dithiodi(ethanesulfonic acid) disodium salt see Dimesna.
1,1'-(Dithiodiethylene)bis[3-(2-chloroethyl)-1(or3)-nitrosourea] see Ditiomustine.
3,3'-Dithiodimethylenebis(5-hydroxy-6-methyl-4-pyridinemethanol) see Pyritinol.
2,2'-Dithiodipyridine 1,1'-dioxide see Dipyrithione.
1,3-Dithioisophthalic acid S,S-diethyl ester see Di-tophal.
1,2-Dithiolane-3-pentanoic acid see Thioctic acid.
1,3-Dithiolan-2-ylidenephosphoramidic acid diethyl ester see Phosfolan.
5-(1,2-Dithiolan-3-yl)valeric acid see Thioctic acid.
1,3-Dithiole-Δ²,ᵅ-malonic acid diisopropyl ester see Malotilate.
Dithioloisophthalic acid diethyl ester see Ditophal.
1,3-Dithiolo[4,5-b]quinoxaline-2-thione see Thioqui-nox.
Dithiomethon see Thiometon.
Dithiometon see Thiometon.
Dithion see Sulfotep.

Dithione see Sulfotep.
Dithiophos (tr) see Sulfotep.
Dithiophosphoric acid see Phosphorodithioic acid.
Dithiopropylthiamine see Prosultiamine.
'Dithio-systox' see Disulfoton.
Dithio-TEPP see Sulfotep.
DITHIZONE (diphenylthiocarbazone; phenylazo-thionoformic acid phenylhydrazide).
DITHRANOL*** (1,8,9-anthratriol; 1,8-dihydr-oxyanthranol; 1,8,9-trihydroxyanthracene; an-thralin).
DITHRANOL plus UREA ('psoradexan').
DITHRANOL TRIACETATE (1,8,9-triacetoxy-anthracene).
DITHYMOL DIIODIDE (bis(thymol iodide); bithymoldiiodide; diiododithymol; iodothymol).
Ditilin (tr) see Suxamethonium chloride.
Ditiobisfenol see Probucol.
DITIOMUSTINE*** (1,1'-(dithiodiethylene)bis[3-(2-chloroethyl)-1(or3)-nitrosourea]).
'Dition' see Coumithoate.
DITOLAMIDE*** (N,N-dipropyl-p-toluenesul-fonamide; A-17624).
Di-p-tolyliodonium chloride see Toliodium chloride.
DITOPHAL** (S,S-diethyl 1,3-dithioisophthalate; ETIP; ICI-15688; 'etisul').
'Ditox' see DDT.
'Ditox L' see under DDT.
'Ditran' see 1-Ethylpiperid-3-yl phenylcyclopent-aneglycolate.
Ditrazin (tr) see Diethylcarbamazine.
'Ditripentat' see Calcium trisodium pentetate.
'Ditrone' see Phenylbutazone megallate.
'Ditropan' see Oxybutynin.
Ditropyl isatropate see Belladonnin.
'Ditrosal' see Dinitro-o-cresol.
'Ditubin' see Isoniazid.
Diu-60 see Bemetizide.
'Diube' see under Atenolol.
'Diucardin' see Hydroflumethiazide.
'Diucomb' see under Bemetizide.
'Diumide' see Furosemide.
'Diuramide' see Acetazolamide.
'Diurexan' see Xipamide.
'Diuril' see Chlorothiazide.
'Diurilix' see Chlorothiazide.
DIURON* (1-(3,4-dichlorophenyl)-3,3-dimethyl-urea; dichlorofenidim; diklorfenidim; DCMU; DMU; 'karmex').
'Diutazol' see Acetazolamide.
DIVABUTEROL** ((±)-5-[2-(tert-butylamino)-1-hydroxyethyl]-m-phenylene dipivalate).
'Divanil' see Cyclovalone.
2,6-Divanillylidenecyclohexanone see Cyclovalone.
'Divanon' see Cyclovalone.
'Divarine' see Dipyrone.
'Divascan' see Iprazochrome.
'Diveronal' see Quinuronium sulfate.
'Dividol' see Viminol p-hydroxybenzoate.
'Divimax' see under Spirgetine.
Diviminol see Viminol.
Divinylbenzene-methacrylic acid polymer see Pola-crilin.

Divinylene sulfide *see* Thiophene.
Divinyl ether *see* Vinyl ether.
Divinyl oxide *see* Vinyl ether.
Dixamone bromide* *see* Methantheline bromide.
DIXANTHOGEN*** (*O,O*-diethyl ester of dithio-bis(thionoformic acid); bis(ethylxanthogen); diethyl dithiobis(thionoformate); diethyldixanthogen; diethylxanthogen; xanthogen).
'Dixarit' *see* Clonidine.
'Dixeran' *see* Melitracen.
2-[2-(Di-2,6-xylylmethoxy)ethoxy]-*N*,*N*-dimethylethylamine *see* Xyloxemine.
1-[Di(2,6-xylyl)methoxy]-3-(isopropylamino)-2-propanol *see* Xipranolol.
DIXYRAZINE* (10-[3-[4-(2-(2-hydroxyethoxy)-ethyl)piperazin-1-yl]-2-methylpropyl]phenothiazine; UCB-3412; 'esocalm'; 'esucos'; 'metronal'; 'roscal').
DJ-1550 *see* Sulfametoxydiazine.
DJENKOLIC ACID (3,3′-methylenedithiobis(2-aminopropionic acid); 3,3′-methylenedithiodialanine).
DKB *see* Dibekacin.
DL-150 *see* Oxdralazine.
DL-152 *see* Bietaserpine.
DL-164 *see* Tiodonium chloride.
DL-181-IT *see* Premazepam.
DL-308-IT *see* Zetidoline.
DL-458-IT *see* Deflazacort.
DL-473-IT *see* Rifapentine.
DL-507-IT *see* Teicoplanin.
DL-588 *see* Napactadine.
DL-809-IT *see* Isoprazone.
DL-832 *see* Glaucine.
DL-1777 *see* Medazomide.
DL-8280 *see* Ofloxacin.
DM *see* Phenarsazine chloride.
DM-70 (tr) *see* Dimethyl sulfoxide.
DM-90 (tr) *see* Dimethyl sulfoxide.
DMBA *see* 7,12-Dimethylbenz[*a*]anthracene.
DMC *see* Chlorfenethol.
DMCT *see* Demeclocycline.
DMDT *see* Methoxychlor.
DMF *see* Dimefox.
DMI *see* Desipramine.
DMN *see* Dimethylnitrosamine.
DMO *see* Dimethadione.
DMPEA *see* Homoveratrylamine.
DMPP *see* 1,1-Dimethyl-4-phenylpiperazinium iodide.
DMPS *see* Unithiol.
DMS *see* Succimer.
DMSA *see* Succimer.
DMSO *see* Dimethyl sulfoxide.
DMSP *see* Fensulfothion.
DMTT *see* Dazomet.
DMU *see* Diuron.
DNBP *see* Dinoseb.
DNC *see* Dinitro-*o*-cresol.
DNCB *see* 1-Chloro-2,4-dinitrobenzene.
DNIBF *see* Dinoseb.
DNOC* *see* Dinitro-*o*-cresol.
DNOCHP *see* Dinex.

DNOIPP *see* Dinoprop.
DNOPC *see* Dinocap.
DNOSBP *see* Dinoseb trolamine.
DNPP *see* Dinoprop.
DNSBP *see* Dinoseb trolamine.
DNTBP *see* Dinoterb.
DNTP *see* Parathion.
'Doberol' *see* Toliprolol.
Dobesilate calcium *see* Calcium dobesilate.
'Dobesin' *see* Amfepramone.
'Dobren' *see* Sulpiride.
'Dobrizon' *see* Methaqualone.
'Doburil' *see* Cyclothiazide.
DOBUTAMINE*** ((±)-2,3-dihydroxy-*N*-[3-(*p*-hydroxyphenyl)-1-methylpropyl]phenethylamine; (±)-4-[2-[3-(*p*-hydroxyphenyl)-1-methylpropylamino]ethyl]pyrocatechol; dobutamine hydrochloride; 'dobutrex').
'Dobutrex' *see* Dobutamine.
DOC *see* Desoxycortone.
'Doca' *see* Desoxycortone.
'Docabolin' *see under* Nandrolone phenpropionate.
DOCETRIZOIC ACID* (3-diacetylamino-2,4,6-triiodobenzoic acid).
See also Propyl docetrizoate.
'Dociretic' *see under* Bendroflumethiazide.
'Dociton' *see* Propranolol.
'Doclizid-t' *see* Chlorazanil.
DOCONAZOLE*** (*cis*-1-[[4-[(4-biphenylyl-oxy)methyl]-2-(2,4-dichlorophenyl)-1,3-dioxolan-2-yl]methyl]imidazole; R-34000).
Docosanoic acid *see* Behenic acid.
cis-**13-Docosenoic acid** *see* Erucic acid.
trans-**13-Docosenoic acid** *see* Brassidic acid.
DOCUSATE CALCIUM (calcium dioctyl sulfosuccinate; 'surfak').
See also under Dantron.
DOCUSATE SODIUM*** (sodium dioctyl sulfosuccinate; sulfosuccinic acid bis(2-ethylhexyl)ester sodium salt).
DOCUSATE SODIUM plus SORBITOL ('yal').
'Dodat' *see* DDT.
Dodecachlorooctahydro-1,3,4-metheno-1*H*-cyclobuta[*c,d*]pentalene *see* Mirex.
Dodecahydrobenz[*g*]indolo[2,3-*a*]quinolizine *see* Yohimban.
1,2,3,4,4a,4b,5,6,7,9,10,10a-Dodecahydro-2-hydroxy-2,4b-dimethyl-7-oxo-1-phenanthrenepropionic acid δ-lactone *see* Testolactone.
Dodecahydro-3-hydroxy-6-(hydroxymethyl)-3,3a,6-trimethyl(11*H*)benz[*e*]indene-7-acetic acid δ lactone *see* Oxandrolone.
Dodecahydro-7,14-methano-2*H*,6*H*-dipyrido[1,2-*a*:1′,2′-*e*][1,5]diazocine *see* Sparteine.
Dodecahydro-13-methylbenz[*g*]indolo[2,3-*a*]quinolizine *see* Mimbane.
Dodecahydro-1α,2α,4β,10α,11β-pentahydroxy-3α,8,11aβ-trimethyl-5*H*-1,11cβ-(epoxymethano)-phenanthro[10,1-*bc*]pyran-5-one 4-(2-hydroxy-2-methylbutyrate) *see* Glaucarubin.
Dodecahydro-5,6,10,10b-tetrahydroxy-3,4a,7,7,10a-pentamethyl-3-vinyl-1*H*-naphtho[2,1-*b*]pyran-1-one 5-acetate *see* Colforsin.

Dodecanoic acid *see* Lauric acid.

[2-(*N*-Dodecanoyl-*N*-methylamino)ethyl]dimethyl-(phenylcarbamoylmethyl)ammonium chloride *see* Dofamium chloride.

1-[*N*-(2-Dodecanoyloxyethyl)carbamoylmethyl]pyridinium chloride *see* Lapirium chloride.

DODECARBONIUM CHLORIDE (benzyl[(dodecylcarbamoyl)methyl]dimethylammonium chloride; 'straminol'; 'urolocide').

DODECLONIUM BROMIDE*** ([2-(*p*-chlorophenoxy)ethyl]dodecyldimethylammonium bromide; GR-412).

N-[2-(Dodecylamino)ethylamino]ethylglycine *see* Dodicin.

Dodecyldimethyl(2-phenoxyethyl)ammonium bromide *see* Domiphen bromide.

Dodecylguanidine acetate *see* Dodine.

1-Dodecylhexahydro-2*H*-azepin-2-one *see* Laurocapram.

2-DODECYLISOQUINOLINIUM BROMIDE (laurylisoquinolinium bromide; 'isothan Q15').

1,1'-(4-Dodecyloxy-*m*-phenylene)diguanidine *see* Lauroguadine.

3-(Dodecyloxy)propylamine *see* Laurixamine.

1-DODECYLPYRIDINIUM BROMIDE (laurylpyridinium bromide; 'isothan Q4'; 'laurosept').

Dodecyl sodium sulfate *see* Sodium dodecyl sulfate.

Dodecyl sulfate(s) *see* Laurilsulfate(s).

DODECYL SULFOACETATE (lauryl sulfoacetate; 'lowila').

α-[2-(Dodecylthio)ethyl]-ω-hydroxypoly(oxy-1,2-ethanediyl) *see* Laureth 10S.

DODECYLTRIPHENYLPHOSPHONIUM BROMIDE (DTPB; 'mycal'; 'myxal').

DODICIN* (*N*-[2-(dodecylamino)ethylamino]ethylglycine; 2,5,8-triazaeicosane-1-carboxylic acid; 'tego 103S').

DODINE* (dodecylguanidine acetate; citrex; doguadine; DDGA; 'bilobran'; 'cyprex'; 'melprex').

DOFAMIUM CHLORIDE*** (dimethyl[2-(*N*-methyldodecanamido)ethyl](phenylcarbamoylmethyl)ammonium chloride; [2-(*N*-dodecanoyl-*N*-methylamino)ethyl]dimethyl(phenylcarbamoylmethyl)ammonium chloride; 'desogen').

'Dogmatyl' *see* Sulpiride.

Doguadine *see* Dodine.

'Doktacillin' *see* Ampicillin.

'Dolantin' *see* Pethidine.

'Dolargan' *see* Pethidine.

'Dolasan' *see under* Dextropropoxyphene.

'Dolene' *see* Dextropropoxyphene.

'Dolgit' *see* Ibuprofen.

'Dolicaine' *see* Lidocaine.

'Dolicur' *see* Dimethyl sulfoxide.

'Dolipol' *see* Tolbutamide.

'Dolisina' *see* Pethidine.

'Dolitrone' *see* Phenythilone.

'Dolo-adamon' *see under* Ciclonium bromide.

'Dolobid' *see* Diflunisal.

'Dolocontral' *see* Pethidine.

'Dolophine' *see* Methadone.

'Dolo-prolixan' *see under* Azapropazone.

'Dolorphen' *see* Dextropropoxyphene.

'Dolo-tanderil' *see under* Oxyphenbutazone.

'Doloxene' *see* Dextropropoxyphene.

DOM *see* 2,5-Dimethoxy-4-methylamphetamine.

'Domar' *see* Pinazepam.

DOMAZOLINE** (2-(3,6-dimethoxy-2,4-dimethylbenzyl)-2-imidazoline; doxazoline; Sch-1366D).

'Domeform' *see* Clioquinol.

'Dominal' *see* Prothipendyl.

'Dominil' *see* Oxyphencyclimine.

DOMIODOL** (2,3-[(2-iodoethylene)dioxy]-1-propanol; 2-(iodomethyl)-1,3-dioxolane-4-methanol).

DOMIPHEN BROMIDE*** (dodecyldimethyl(2-phenoxyethyl)ammonium bromide; phenododecinium bromide; PDDB; NSC-39415; 'bradosol'; 'domittol').

'Domistan' *see* Histapyrrodine.

'Domittol' *see* Domiphen bromide.

DOMOPREDNATE*** (11β,17α-dihydroxy-*D*-homopregna-1,4-diene-3,20-dione 17α-butyrate).

DOMOXIN** (1-(1,4-benzodioxan-2-ylmethyl)-1-benzylhydrazine; IS-2596).

DOMPERIDONE*** (5-chloro-1-[1-[3-(2-oxo-1-benzimidazolinyl)propyl]piperid-4-yl]-2-benzimidazolinone; 4-(5-chloro-2-oxobenzimidazolin-1-yl)-1-[3-(2-oxobenzimidazolin-1-ylpropyl]piperidine; KW-5338; R-33812; 'motilium').

DON (6-diazo-5-oxonorleucine; NSC-7365).

'Dona' *see* Glucosamine sulfate.

'Donalgin' *see* Niflumic acid.

Donaxine *see* Gramine.

'Donorest' *see* Fentiazac.

DOOTC *see* Doxycycline.

DOPA (3-(3,4-dihydroxyphenyl)alanine; dopalanine).

See also Levodopa.

DOPAC *see* Homoprotocatechuic acid.

'Dopaflex' *see* Levodopa.

'Dopal' *see* Levodopa.

Dopalanine *see* Dopa.

'Dopalfher' *see* Levodopa.

DOPAMANTINE** (*N*-(3,4-dihydroxyphenethyl)-1-adamantanecarboxamide; *N*-(1-adamantanecarbonyl)-3,4-dihydroxyphenethylamine; Sch-15507).

'Dopamet' *see* Methyldopa.

DOPAMINE** (4-(2-aminoethyl)pyrocatechol; 3,4-dihydroxyphenethylamine; 3-hydroxytyramine; ASL-279; 'dynatra'; 'intropin'; 'revivan').

DOPAN (tr) (5-[bis(2-chloroethyl)amino]-6-methyluracil; NSC-44629).

'Dopar' *see* Levodopa.

'Dopasol' *see* Levodopa.

'Dopastral' *see* Levodopa.

'Dopegyt' *see* Methyldopa.

'Dopergin' *see* Lisuride maleate.

DOPEXAMINE** (4-[2-[[6-(phenethylamino)hexyl]amino]ethyl]pyrocatechol; dopexamine hydrochloride; FPL-60278 AR).

'Dopram' *see* Doxapram.

DOQUALAST*** (11-oxo-11*H*-pyrido[2,1-*b*]quinazoline-2-carboxylic acid).

DORASTINE** (8-chloro-2,3,4,5-tetrahydro-2-methyl-5-[2-(6-methylpyrid-3-yl)ethyl]-1*H*-pyrido[4,3-*b*]indole; dorastine dihydrochloride; Ro 5-9110/1).

'**Doraxamin**' *see* Aluminium glycinate.

'**Dorbane**' *see* Dantron.

'**Dorbanex**' *see under* Dantron.

'**Dorevane**' *see* Propiomazine.

'**Dorex**' *see* Oxeladin.

'**Doriden**' *see* Glutethimide.

'**Dorithricin**' *see* Dihydroergotamine.

'**Dormethan**' *see* Dextromethorphan.

'**Dormicum**' *see* Midazolam.

'**Dormin**' *see* Ethallymal.

'**Dormisan**' *see* Cyclopentobarbital.

'**Dormison**' *see* Methylpentynol.

'**Dormodor**' *see* Flurazepam.

'**Dormogen**' *see* Methaqualone.

'**Dormuphar**' *see* Dichloralphenazone.

'**Dormutil**' *see* Methaqualone.

Dornase *see* Deoxyribonuclease.

'**Dornavac**' *see* Pancreatic dornase.

'**Dornokinase**' *see under* Streptodornase.

'**Dornwal**' *see* Amphenidone.

'**Doroma**' *see under* Carbromal.

'**Dorsacaine**' *see* Oxybuprocaine.

'**Dorsedin**' *see under* Metixene.

'**Dorsiflex**' *see* Mephenoxalone.

'**Doryl**' *see* Carbachol.

'**Dosanex**' *see* Metoxuron.

'**Doseval**' *see* Methyprylon.

DOSULEPIN*** (11-[3-(dimethylamino)propylidene]-6,11-dihydrodibenzo[*b*,*e*]thiepin; *N*,*N*-dimethyldibenzo[*b*,*e*]thiepin-Δ$^{11(6H),\gamma}$-propylamine; dothiepin; 'prothiaden').

DOSULEPIN plus EMBRAMINE ('prothidryl').

DOTARIZINE** (1-(diphenylmethyl)-4-[3-(2-phenyl-1,3-dioxolan-2-yl)propyl]piperazine).

DOTEFONIUM BROMIDE*** (1-methyl-1-[2-(*N*-methyl-α-thien-2-ylmandelamido)ethyl]pyrrolidinium bromide; H-4132).

Dothiepin* *see* Dosulepin.

'**Dovenix**' *see* Nitroxinil.

'**Dovine**' *see* Prolonium iodide.

Dowco 179 *see* Chlorpyrifos.

Dowco 214 *see* Chlorpyrifos-methyl.

'**Dowicide**' *see* *o*-Phenylphenol.

'**Dowmycin E**' *see* Erythromycin stearate.

'**Dowpon**' *see* Dalapon.

DOXAMINOL*** (6,11-dihydro-*N*-(2-hydoxy-3-phenoxypropyl)-*N*-methyldibenz[*b*,*e*]oxepin-11-ethylamine; BM-10188).

DOXANTRAZOLE* (5-(10,10-dioxido-9-oxothioxanthen-3-yl)tetrazole; 3-tetrazol-5-ylthioxanthen-9-one 10,10-dioxide).

DOXAPRAM*** (1-ethyl-4-(2-morpholinoethyl)-3,3-diphenyl-2-pyrrolidinone; doxapram hydrochloride; AHR-619).

DOXAPROST*** ((1*R**,2*R**)-2-[(*E*)-3-hydroxy-3-methyl-1-octenyl]-5-oxocyclopentaneheptanoic acid; AY-24559).

'**Doxapryl**' *see* Doxapram.

Doxazoline *see* Domazoline.

DOXAZOSIN** (1-(4-amino-6,7-dimethoxyquinazolin-2-yl)-4-(1,4-benzodioxan-2-ylcarbonyl)-piperazine; UK-33274).

DOXEFAZEPAM*** (7-chloro-5-(*o*-fluorophenyl)-1,3-dihydro-3-hydroxy-1-(2-hydroxyethyl)-2*H*-1,4-benzodiazepin-2-one).

DOXENITOIN*** (5,5-diphenyl-4-imidazolidinone; 2-deoxyphenytoin; LG-1; SK&F-2599; 'glior').

DOXEPIN** (*trans*-11(6*H*)-[3-(dimethylamino)-propylidene]dibenz[*b*,*e*]oxepine; *N*,*N*-dimethyldibenz[*b*,*e*]oxepin-*trans*-Δ$^{11(6H),\gamma}$-propylamine; MF-10; NSC-108160; P-3693A).

See also Cidoxepin.

'**Doxergan**' *see* Oxomemazine.

DOXIBETASOL*** (9α-fluoro-11β,17α-dihydroxy-16β-methylpregna-1,4-diene-3,20-dione; doxybetasol).

DOXIBETASOL PROPIONATE (doxibetasol 27-propionate; GR2/443).

DOXIFLURIDINE*** (5'-deoxy-5-fluorouridine; 5-fluoro-5'-deoxyuridine; DFUR; Ro 21-9738).

'**Doxinate**' *see* Docusate sodium.

'**Doxitard**' *see* Doxycycline hyclate.

'**Doxium**' *see* Calcium dobesilate.

DOXOFYLLINE*** (7-[(1,3-dioxolan-2-yl)methyl]theophylline).

'**Doxol**' *see* Docusate sodium.

DOXORUBICIN*** ((1*S*,3*S*)-3-glycoloyl-1,2,3,4,6,11-hexahydro-3,5,12-trihydroxy-10-methoxy-6,11-dioxo-1-naphthacenyl-3-amino-2,3,6-trideoxy-α-L-*lyxo*-hexopyranoside; (8*S*,10*S*)-10-[(3-amino-2,3,6-trideoxy-α-L-*lyxo*-hexopyranosyl)oxy]-8-glycolyl-7,8,9,10-tetrahydro-6,8,11-trihydroxy-1-methoxy-5,12-naphthacenedione; 14-hydroxydaunorubicin; adriamycin; NSC-123127; 'adriablastina').

Doxorubicin 3²-glyoxylate 2-(diethyl acetal) *see* Detorubicin.

DOXPICOMINE*** ((−)-3-[(dimethylamino)-*m*-dioxan-5-ylmethyl]pyridine; doxpicomine hydrochloride; doxpicomin hydrochloride; LY-108380).

Doxpicomin hydrochloride* *see* Doxpicomine.

'**Doxy**' *see* Doxycycline.

Doxybetasol* *see* Doxibetasol.

DOXYCYCLINE*** (6-deoxy-5-hydroxytetracycline; 6-deoxyoxytetracycline; DOOTC; NSC-56228).

DOXYCYCLINE plus CODEINE ('codixocal'; 'vibratussal').

Doxycycline hemiethanolate hydrochloride *see* Doxycycline hyclate.

DOXYCYCLINE HYCLATE (doxycycline hemiethanolate hydrochloride; GS-3065; 'doxitard'; 'vibramycin').

DOXYCYCLINE HYCLATE plus CODEINE ('codidoxal').

DOXYLAMINE*** (2-[α-(2-dimethylaminoethoxy)-α-methylbenzyl]pyridine; histadoxylamine; doxylamine succinate; doxylammonium succinate).

'Doxytrex' *see* Doxycycline.
Dp *see* Mazipredone.
2,4-DP *see* Dichlorprop.
DPA *see* Propanil.
DPA *see* Algestone acetofenide *and* Propanil.
DPE *see* Dipivefrine.
DPN *see* Nadide.
DPX-8 *see* Pipethanate.
Dracylic acid *see* Benzoic acid.
'Drainasept' *see* Taurolidine.
'Dramamine' *see* Dimenhydrinate.
'Dramcillin S' *see* Pheneticillin.
'Drano liquid' *see* 1,1,1-Trichloroethane.
'Dranyl' *see* Hydroflumethiazide.
'Drat' *see* Chlorophacinone.
'Draza' *see* Methiocarb.
DRAZIDOX** (3-methylquinoxaline-2-carboxylic acid hydrazide 1,4-dioxide).
'Drazine' *see* Fenoxypropazine.
'Drenison' *see* Fludroxycortide.
'Drenusil' *see* Polythiazide.
DRIBENDAZOLE*** (methyl 5-(cyclohexylthio)-2-benzimidazolecarbamate).
'Dricol' *see* Amidefrine mesilate.
DRINIDENE*** (2-(aminomethylene)indan-1-one; CP-24877).
'Drinupal' *see* Proguanil.
'Driol' *see* Osalmid.
DROBULINE*** (($\pm$)-1-(isopropylamino)-4,4-diphenyl-2-butanol; ($\pm$)-α-[[(1-methylethyl)-amino]methyl]-γ-phenylbenzenepropanol; compound 122587).
'Drocarbil' *see* Arecoline-acetarsol.
DROCINONIDE*** (9-fluoro-11β,16α,17,21-tetrahydroxy-5α-pregnane-3,20-dione cyclic 16,17-acetal with acetone).
DROCLIDINIUM BROMIDE*** (3-hydroxy-1-methylquinuclidinium bromide α-phenylcyclohexaneglycolate).
Drocode *see* Dihydrocodeine.
'Drocort' *see* Fludroxycortide.
'Droctil' *see* Exiproben.
DROFENINE** (2-(diethylamino)ethyl α-phenylcyclohexaneacetate; hexahydroadiphenine; 'cyclospasmol'; 'trasentine-A'; 'trasentin-6H').
DROFENINE plus DIPYRONE ('spasmatol').
'Drofenite' *see* Tetramisole.
'Drolban' *see* Drostanolone.
'Droleptan' *see* Droperidol.
'Drometil' *see* Azosulfamide.
DROMETRIZOLE*** (2-(2*H*-benzotriazol-2-yl)-4-methylphenol; 2-(2*H*-benzotriazol-2-yl)-*p*-cresol; 'tinuvin P').
'Dromisol' *see* Dimethyl sulfoxide.
'Dromoran' *see* Levorphanol.
Dromostanolone* *see* Drostanolone.
DRONABINOL** ((6a*R*,10a*R*)-6a,7,8,10a-tetrahydro-6,6,9-trimethyl-3-pentyl-6*H*-dibenzo[*b,d*]pyran-1-ol; Δ^1-tetrahydrocannabinol; Δ^9-tetrahydrocannabinol; SP-104).
'Droncit' *see* Praziquantel.
DROPEMPINE** (1,2,3,6-tetrahydro-1,2,2,6,6-pentamethylpyridine; dehydropempidine; 'abdo-

man').
DROPERIDOL*** (4'-fluoro-4-[1,2,3,6-tetrahydro-4-(2-oxobenzimidazolin-1-yl)pyrid-1-yl]-butyrophenone; 1-[1-[3-(*p*-fluorobenzoyl)prop-yl]-1,2,3,6-tetrahydropyrid-4-yl]-2-benzimidazolinone; 1-[1-[4-(*p*-fluorophenyl)-4-oxobutyl]-1,2,3,6-tetrahydropyrid-4-yl]-2-benzimidazolinone; dehydrobenzperidol; McN-JR-4749; R-4749).
DROPERIDOL plus FENTANYL ('innovar'; 'inoval'; 'thalamonal').
See also under Ketamine
Dropranolol *see* Idropranolol.
DROPRENILAMINE*** (*N*-(3,3-diphenylprop-yl)-α-methylcyclohexaneethylamine; hexahydroprenylamine).
DROPROPIZINE*** (3-(4-phenylpiperazin-1-yl)-1,2-propanediol; hydropropizine; idropropizina; UCB-1967).
DROSOPHILIN A (2,3,5,6-tetrachloro-4-hydroxyanisole; 2,3,5,6-tetrachloro-4-methoxyphenol).
DROSTANOLONE*** (17β-hydroxy-2α-methylandrostan-3-one; 4,5α-dihydro-2α-methyltestosterone; dromostanolone; drostanolone propionate; CS-1507; NSC-12198).
DROTAVERINE*** (1-(3,4-diethoxybenzylidene)-6,7-diethoxy-1,2,3,4-tetrahydroisoquinoline; dihydroethaverine; dihydroisoperparine; nospanum).
DROTEBANOL*** (6β,14-dihydroxy-3,4-dimethoxy-17-methylmorphinan; 3,4-dimethoxy-17-methylmorphinan-6β,14-diol).
DROXACIN** (5-ethyl-2,3,5,8-tetrahydro-8-oxofuro[2,3-*g*]quinoline-7-carboxylic acid; droxacin sodium; SH-263).
'Droxaryl' *see* Bufexamac.
DROXICAINIDE*** (($\pm$)-1-(2-hydroxyethyl)-2',6'-pipecoxylidide; 1-(2-hydroxyethyl)pipecolic acid 2,6-dimethylanilide).
'Droxolan' *see* Deoxycholic acid.
'Droxone' *see* Algestone acetofenide.
DROXYPROPINE*** (1-[2-(2-hydroxyethoxy)-ethyl]-4-phenyl-4-propionylpiperidine).
'Drylin' *see* Co-trimoxazole.
'Dryptal' *see* Furosemide.
DS-36 *see* Sulfamonomethoxine.
DS-103-282 *see* Tizanidine.
DSDP *see* Amiton.
DSE *see* Nabam.
DSM *see* Mannityl dimesilate.
DS substance *see* Serotonin.
DT-5 *see* Dextrothyroxine.
DT-327 *see* Clopamide.
DTC *see* Dithiocarb.
DTIC *see* Dacarbazine.
'DTIC-DOME' *see* Dacarbazine.
DTMC *see* Dicofol.
DTP *see* Prosultiamine.
DTPA *see* Pentetic acid.
DTPB *see* Dodecyltriphenylphosphonium bromide.
DTS *see* Succimer.
Du-21220 *see* Ritodrine.

203

DU-21445 *see* Tiprenolol.
Du-22550 *see* Caproxamine.
DU-23187 *see* Quincarbate.
DU-112307 *see* Diflubenzuron.
'Dualar' *see* Benzodepa.
DUAZOMYCIN*** (antibiotic from *Str. ambofaciens*; duazomycin A; NSC-51097).
Duazomycin A *see* Duazomycin.
Duazomycin B *see* Azotomycin.
Duazomycin C *see* Ambomycin.
Duboisine *see* Hyoscyamine.
'Dubronax' *see* Dapsone.
'Ducolax' *see* Bisacodyl.
'Dugro' *see* Ronidazole.
'Dulcin' *see* Phenetylurea.
Dulcite *see* Dulcitol.
DULCITOL (dulcite; dulcose; euonymit; melampyrin; melampyrit).
10-D-Dulcityl-7,8-dimethylisoalloxazine *see* Galactoflavin.
'Dulcolan' *see* Bisacodyl.
'Dulcolax' *see* Bisacodyl.
Dulcose *see* Dulcitol.
DULOFIBRATE*** (*p*-chlorophenyl 2-(*p*-chlorophenoxy)-2-methylpropionate; clofibric acid *p*-chlorophenyl ester).
'Dulsivac' *see* Docusate sodium.
'Dumitone' *see* Dapsone.
'Dumolid' *see* Nitrazepam.
'Duobiocin' *see* Co-trimoxazole.
'Duodorm' *see* Dichloralphenazone.
'Duogastrone' *see* Carbenoxolone.
'Duolip' *see* Etofylline clofibrate.
'Duoluton' *see under* Norgestrel.
DUOMETACIN*** (3-(*p*-anisoyl)-6-methoxy-2-methylindole-1-acetic acid; 6-methoxy-3-(*p*-methoxybenzoyl)-2-methylindole-1-acetic acid; R-4444).
'Duomycin' *see* Chlortetracycline.
'Duo-tran' *see under* Fentonium bromide.
'Duperan' *see* Clometacin.
'Duphalac' *see* Lactulose.
'Duphanox' *see* Chloral hydrate acetylglycinamide.
'Duphar' *see* Tetradifon.
'Duphar antisprout' *see* Propham.
'Dupharcort' *see* Dexamethasone acetate.
'Duphaspasmin' *see* Mebeverine.
'Duphaston' *see* Dydrogesterone.
'Duplexcillin' *see under* Ampicillin.
'Duplinal' *see under* Clofibrate.
'Duplocillin' *see* Benzathine penicillin.
'Duponol C' *see* Sodium dodecyl sulfate.
DUPRACETAM*** (1,2-bis[(2-oxo-1-pyrrolidinyl)acetyl]hydrazine).
'Durabol' *see* Nandrolone cyclohexanecarboxylate.
'Durabolin' *see* Nandrolone phenpropionate.
'Duraboral' *see* Ethylestrenol.
'Duracaine' *see* Procaine.
'Duranest' *see* Etidocaine.
Durapatite* *see* Hydroxyapatite.
'Duraphenicol' *see* Chloramphenicol.
'Durasulf' *see* Sulfametomidine.
'Durasuline' *see* Protamine zinc insulin.

'Dura-tab' *see* Quinidine gluconate.
'Duratrimet' *see* Co-trimoxazole.
'Durenate' *see* Sulfametoxydiazine.
'Duricef' *see* Cefadroxil.
'Durisan' *see* Sulfaperin.
'Duroliopaque' *see* Ethyl iodostearate.
'Duromine' *see* Phentermine resin.
'Duropenin' *see* Benzathine penicillin.
'Durotan' *see under* Reserpine.
'Dursban' *see* Chlorpyrifos.
'Dusodril' *see* Naftidrofuryl.
'Duspatal' *see* Mebeverine.
Dutch liquid *see* 1,2-Dichloroethylene.
'Du-ter' *see* Fentin hydroxide.
'Duvadilan' *see* Isoxsuprine.
'Duvaline' *see* Pyricarbate.
'Duvaron' *see* Dydrogesterone.
Duxen *see* Diazepam.
'Duxil' *see under* Ajmalicine.
DV-714 *see* Leiopyrrole.
DV-1006 *see* Cetraxate.
DW-61 *see* Flavoxate.
DW-62 *see* Dimefline.
DW-75 *see* Norleusactide.
'Dyazide' *see under* Hydrochlorothiazide.
'Dybar' *see* Fenuron.
'Dybenal' *see* 2,4-Dichlorobenzyl alcohol.
'Dyclone' *see* Dyclonine.
DYCLONINE*** (4′-butoxy-3-piperid-1-ylpropiophenone; dylocaine; dyclonine hydrochloride).
DYDROGESTERONE*** (9β,10α-pregna-4,6-diene-3,20-dione; 6-dehydro-9β,10α-progesterone; 6-dehydroretroprogesterone; isopregnenone; NSC-92336).
Dyflos* *see* Isoflurophate.
'Dyfonate' *see* Fonophos.
'Dygratal' *see* Dihydrotachysterol.
'Dykanol' *see* Polychlorinated biphenyl.
'Dylate' *see* Clonitrate.
Dylocaine* *see* Dyclonine.
'Dylox' *see* Metrifonate.
Dymanthine* *see* Dimantine.
'Dymasyl' *see* Dimeticone 350.
'Dymelor' *see* Acetohexamide.
'Dymid' *see* Diphenamid.
'Dynacaine' *see* Pyrrocaine.
'Dynalin' *see* Tiamulin.
'Dynaltone' *see* Aralkonium chloride.
'Dynamutilin' *see* Tiamulin.
'Dynamyxin' *see* Sulfomyxin.
'Dynapen' *see* Dicloxacillin.
'Dynatra' *see* Dopamine.
'Dyneric' *see* Clomifene.
'Dynese' *see* Magaldrate.
'Dynium' *see* Aralkonium chloride.
'Dynocard' *see* Gitoformate.
'Dynone II' *see* Dinex dicyclohexylamine.
'Dynothel' *see* Dextrothyroxine sodium.
'Dyphonate' *see* Fonophos.
Dyphyllin *see* Diprophylline.
'Dyphylline' *see* Theophylline.
DYPNONE (1,3-diphenyl-2-buten-1-one; β-meth-

ylchalcone).
'Dyren' *see* Triamterene.
'Dyrene' *see* Anilazine.
'Dyrenium' *see* Triamterene.
'Dysedon' *see* Oxomemazine.
'Dysenterol' *see* Clioquinol.
'Dysmalgine' *see* Dextrofemine.

'Dyspas' *see* Dicycloverine.
'Dytac' *see* Triamterene.
'Dyta-urese' *see* Spironolactone.
'Dytenzide' *see under* Hydrochlorothiazide.
'Dythol' *see* Cholesterol.
'Dytide' *see under* Benzthiazide.
'Dytransin' *see* Ibufenac.

E

E-3 *see* Lachesine.
E-39 *see* Inproquone.
E-106 *see* Furfenorex.
E-106-E *see* Furfenorex cyclamate.
E-111 *see* Propylhexedrine.
E-141 *see* Etamsylate.
E-142 *see* Anidoxime.
E-171 *see* Lysine acetylsalicylate.
E-205 *see* Calcium dobesilate.
E-212 *see* Toyocamycin.
E-217 *see* Thalidomide.
E-250 *see* Selegiline.
E-438 *see* Sulfasomizole.
E-600 *see* Paraoxon.
E-605 *see* Parathion.
E-614 *see* Tripamide.
E-643 *see* Bunazosin.
E-1059 *see under* Demeton-O.
E-2663 *see* Bentiromide.
E-3314 *see* Schradan.
E-9002 *see* Naftalofos.
EA-166 *see* Guanoxyfen.
EA-3054 *see* Bioallethrin.
EACA *see* Aminocaproic acid.
'Eatan' *see under* Methaqualone.
'Eatan N' *see* Nitrazepam.
Eazamine *see* Diethazine.
'Ebesal' *see* Allocupreide sodium.
'Ebimar' *see* Poligeenan.
'Ebrantil' *see* Urapidil.
EBSELEN** (2-phenyl-1,2-benzisoselenazolin-3-one).
'Ebufac' *see* Ibuprofen.
Eburnamenine-14-carboxylic acid methyl ester *see* Apovincamine.
Eburnamonine *see* Vinburnine.
'Ebutol' *see* Ethambutol.
E.C.3.2.1.23 *see* Tilactase.
E.C.3.2.1.35 *see* Hyalosidase.
EC-50 *see* Fenitrothion.
Ecarazine *see* Todralazine.
'Ecatox' *see* Parathion.
'Ecatril' *see* Dibenzepin.
Ecboline *see* Ergotoxine.
ECGONINE (tropine-2-carboxylic acid).
L-Ecgonine 3-benzoate 2-methyl ester *see* Cocaine.
Echothiopate *see* Ecothiopate iodide.
Echothiophosphate *see* Ecothiopate iodide.
Ecinamine *see* Etifelmine.
ECIPRAMIDIL*** (3-[[(2,2-diphenylcyclopropyl)methyl]amino]propyl 3,4,5-trimethoxybenzoate).
'Eclabron' *see* Guaifylline.
'Ecloril' *see* Chlorambucil.
'Ecolid' *see* Chlorisondamine chloride.
'Ecomytrin' *see* Amfomycin.
ECONAZOLE*** (1-(2,4-dichloro-β-(*p*-chlorobenzyloxy)phenethyl)imidazole; 2,4,4'-trichloro-α-(imidazol-1-ylmethyl)-α,α'-ditolyl ether; econazole nitrate; R-14827; SQ-13050; 'ecostatin'; 'epi-pevaryl'; 'gyno-pevaryl'; 'ifenec'; 'pevaryl').
See also under Triamcinolone acetonide.
'Econopred' *see* Prednisolone acetate.
'Ecostatin' *see* Econazole.
Ecostigmine* *see* Ecothiopate iodide.
ECOTHIOPATE IODIDE*** ((2-diethoxyphosphinylthioethyl)trimethylammonium iodide; *S*-[2-(dimethylamino)ethyl] *O,O*-diethyl phosphorothioate methiodide; ecostigmine; echothiopate; echothiophosphate; MI-217; MJ-217; 'phospholine').
'Ecoval 70' *see* Betamethasone valerate.
'Ectodex' *see* Amitraz.
'Ectoral' *see* Fenclofos.
ECTYLUREA*** (1-(2-ethyl-*cis*-crotonyl)urea).
'Eczecidin' *see* Clioquinol.
Edathamil* *see* Edetic acid.
'Edecrin' *see* Etacrynic acid.
'Edemo' *see* *O*-Ethyl *S*-(2-diethylaminoethyl)phosphonothioate.
'Edemox' *see* Acetazolamide.
Edetate disodium calcium *see* Sodium calcium edetate.
Edetate sodium* *see* Tetrasodium edetate.
Edetate trisodium* *see* Trisodium edetate.
EDETIC ACID*** (ethylenebis(iminodiacetic acid); ethylenediaminetetraacetic acid; (ethylenedinitrilo)tetraacetic acid; tetra(carboxymethyl)-ethylenediamine; edathamil; EDTA; tetracemin; 'complexic acid'; 'komplexic acid'; 'versenic acid').
See also Dicobalt edetate; Disodium edetate; Piperazine calcium edetate; Sodium calcium edetate; Tetrasodium edetate; Trisodium edetate.
EDETOL** (1,1',1'',1'''-(ethylenedinitrilo)tetra-2-propanol; 1,1',1'',1'''-(1,2-ethanediyldinitrilo)-tetrakis[2-propanol]; 'quadrol').
EDIFENPHOS* (*O*-ethyl *S,S*-diphenyl phosphorodithioate; 'hinosan').
EDISILATE(S)** (ethane-1,2-disulfonate(s); edisylate(s)).

206

Edisylate(s)* *see* Edisilate(s).

'Ediwal' *see under* Levonorgestrel.

EDOGESTRONE* (17-acetoxy-3,3-ethylenedi-oxy-6-methylpregn-5-en-20-one; 3,3-ethylenedi-oxy-17-hydroxy-6-methylpregn-5-en-20-one acetate; 17-hydroxy-6-methylpregn-5-ene-3,20-dione cyclic 3-(ethylene acetal) acetate; Ph-218).

EDPA *see* Etifelmine.

Edrofuradene *see* Nifurdazil.

Edrophone* *see* Edrophonium chloride.

EDROPHONIUM CHLORIDE* (ethyl(*m*-hydroxyphenyl)dimethylammonium chloride; edrophone; Ro 2-3198).

EDTA *see* Edetic acid.

EDU *see* 2'-Deoxy-5-ethyluridine.

'Edurid' *see* 2'-Deoxy-5-ethyluridine.

EF-185 *see* Framycetin.

'Efcortesol' *see* Hydrocortisone sodium phosphate.

'Efektolol' *see* Propranolol.

'Effectin' *see* Bitolterol mesilate.

'Efferalgan' *see under* Paracetamol.

'Effilon' *see* Amfepramone.

'Effortil' *see* Etilefrine.

'Efical' *see* Calcium pidolate.

'Efitard' *see* Procaine-penicillin.

EFLOXATE* (ethyl (4-oxo-2-phenyl-4*H*-1-benzopyran-7-yloxy)acetate; ethyl 7-flavonoxy-acetate; oxyflavyl).

'Efosin' *see under* Fenpipramide.

'Efsiomycin' *see* Fluvomycin.

'Eftapan' *see* Eprazinone.

'Eftolon' *see* Sulfaphenazole.

'Efudex' *see* Fluorouracil.

'Efudix' *see* Fluorouracil.

'Egacen' *see* Hyoscyamine.

'Eggopurin' *see* Calcium mandelate.

'Eglonyl' *see* Sulpiride.

'Egmol' *see* Phenolphthalol.

EGTA *see* Egtazic acid.

EGTAZIC ACID ([ethylenebis(oxyethylenenitri-lo)]tetraacetic acid; 3,12-bis(carboxymethyl)-6,9-dioxa-3,12-diazatetradecanedioic acid; EGTA).

Egyt-13 *see* Benzonatate.

Egyt-201 *see* Bencyclane.

Egyt-475 *see* Piberaline.

Egyt-739 *see* Guanazodine.

EHDP *see* Etidronate disodium.

EHIDA *see* Etifenin.

Ehrlich 5 *see* Oxophenarsine.

Ehrlich 594 *see* Acetarsol.

Ehrlich 606 *see* Arsphenamine.

Eicosanoic acid *see* Arachidic acid.

5,8,11,14-Eicosatetraenoic acid *see* Arachidonic acid.

EICOSA-5,8,11,14-TETRAYNOIC ACID (tetra-ynoic acid).

'Ekaprol' *see* Aminocaproic acid.

'Ekatin' *see* Thiometon.

'Ekatin F' *see* Morphothion.

'Ekatin M' *see* Morphothion.

'Eketebin' *see* Protionamide.

'Ekomine' *see* Atropine methonitrate.

'Ektafos' *see* Dicrotophos.

'Ektomin' *see* Chlormebuform.

'Ekvacillin' *see* Cloxacillin.

EL-241 *see* Parinol.

EL-273 *see* Triarimol.

EL-531 *see* Ancymidol.

EL-857 *see* Apramycin.

EL-974 *see* Ticarbodine.

'Eladigal' *see* Lanatoside C.

ELAIDIC ACID (*trans*-9-octadecenoic acid).

'Elamol' *see* Tofenacin.

'Elan' *see* Fenyramidol.

'Elancoban' *see* Monensin.

'Elantan' *see* Isosorbide mononitrate.

ELANTRINE (11-[3-(dimethylamino)propylid-ene]-5,6-dihydro-5-methylmorphanthridine; EX-10029).

ELANZEPINE (3-chloro-11-[3-(dimethyl-amino)propylidene]-5,6-dihydromorphanthrid-ine).

'Elarzone' *see* Pipebuzone.

'Elavil' *see* Amitriptyline.

ELCATONIN* (1-butyric acid-7-(L-2-aminobu-tyric acid)-26-L-aspartic acid-27-L-valine-29-L-alaninecalcitonin (salmon)).

'Elcosal' *see* Aluminium glycinate.

'Elcosine' *see* Sulfasomidine.

ELD-950 *see* Eledoisin.

'Eldepryl' *see* Selegiline.

ELDEXOMER (starch hydrolysate etherified with epichlorohydrin in the presence of excess alkali).

'Eldisine' *see* Vindesine.

'Eldopal' *see* Levodopa.

Eldrin *see* Rutoside.

Elecamphane camphor *see* Alantolactone.

'Electopen' *see under* Ampicillin.

'Electrocortin' *see* Aldosterone.

ELEDOISIN (5-oxo-L-prolyl-L-prolyl-L-seryl-L-lysyl-L-aspartyl-L-alanyl-L-phenylalanyl-L-isoleucylglycyl-L-leucyl-L-methionamide; ELD-950).

ELEMICIN (3,5-dimethoxytoluene; orcinol di-methyl ether).

'Elenium' *see* Chlordiazepoxide.

'Eleocron' *see* Dioxacarb.

'Eleparon' *see* Heparin.

'Eleudron' *see* Sulfathiazole.

ELFAZEPAM (7-chloro-1-[2-(ethylsulfonyl)-ethyl]-5-(*o*-fluorophenyl)-1,3-dihydro-2*H*-1,4-benzodiazepin-2-one; SK&F-72517).

'Elgetol 30' *see* Dinitro-*o*-cresol.

'Elgetol 313' *see* Dinoseb trolamine.

'Elipol' *see* Dinitro-*o*-cresol.

'Elipten' *see* Aminoglutethimide.

'Eliptin' *see* Aminoglutethimide.

'Elisal' *see* Sultiame.

'Elixophylline' *see* Theophylline.

'Elkapin' *see* Etozolin.

'Elkosin' *see* Sulfasomidine.

ELLAGIC ACID* (2,3,7,8-tetrahydroxy[1]ben-zopyrano[5,4,3-*cde*][1]benzopyran-5,10-dione; hexahydroxydiphenic acid dilactone; benzoaric acid; 'gallogen').

'Ellatun' see Tramazoline.

ELLIPTICINE (5,11-dimethyl-6*H*-pyrido[4,3-*b*]-carbazole; NSC-71795).

ELLIPTINIUM ACETATE* (9-hydroxy-2,5,11-trimethyl-6*H*-pyrido[4,3-*b*]carbazolium acetate; 9-hydroxy-2-methylellipticinium acetate; NSC-264127; 'celiptium').

ELMUSTINE* (1-(2-chloroethyl)-3-(2-hydroxyethyl)-1-nitrosourea; HECNU; NSC-29485).

'Elobromo' see Mitolactol.

'Elocron' see Dioxacarb.

'Elorgan' see Pentoxifylline.

'Elorine' see Tricyclamol chloride.

'Elozell' see under Potassium aspartate.

'Elrodorm' see Glutethimide.

'Elronon' see Noxiptiline.

'Elsan' see Phenthoate.

'Elsix' see Hexetidine.

'Elspar' see Asparaginase.

'Elsyl' see Metizoline.

'Elthon' see under Verapamil.

'Eltrianyl' see Co-trimoxazole.

'Eltroxin' see Levothyroxine sodium.

ELUCAINE (*N*,*N*-diethyl-β-hydroxyphenethylamine benzoate ester; α-[(diethylamino)methyl]-benzyl alcohol benzoate ester).

'Elugan' see Dimeticone.

'Elvanol' see Polyvinyl alcohol.

'Elvaron' see Dichlofluanid.

'Elycaine' see Butacaine.

'Elyzol' see Metronidazole.

'Elzogram' see Cefazolin.

'Emanil' see Idoxuridine.

'Emasol' see Polysorbate 20.

'Embacillin' see Ampicillin.

'Embaclox' see Cloxacillin.

'Embacycline' see Oxytetracycline.

'Embadol' see Tiomesterone.

'Embanox' see Butylated hydroxyanisole.

EMBAY 8440 see Praziquantel.

'Embazin' see Sulfaquinoxaline.

Embechine (tr) see Chlormethine.

Embichin (tr) see Chlormethine.

Embichin 7 (tr) see Novembichin.

'Embikhin' (tr) see Chlormethine.

EMBONATE(S) (4,4'-methylenebis(3-hydroxy-2-naphthoic acid), esters and salts; pamoate(s)).

EMBRAMINE* (2-(*p*-bromo-α-methyl-α-phenylbenzyloxy)-*N*,*N*-dimethylethylamine; 2-[1-(*p*-bromophenyl)-1-phenylethoxy]-*N*,*N*-dimethylethylamine; mebromphenhydramine; embramine hydrochloride).
See also under Dosulepin.

EMBRAMINE TEOCLATE (embramine 8-chlorotheophyllinate; embramine theoclate).

'Embramycin' see Embramine.

'Embutox' see 4-(2,4-Dichlorophenoxy)butyric acid.

EMBUTRAMIDE* (*N*-(β,β-diethyl-*m*-methoxyphenethyl)-4-hydroxybutyramide; *N*-[2-ethyl-2-(3-methoxyphenyl)butyl]-4-hydroxybutyramide).

'Emcol E-607' see Lapirium chloride.

'Emcortina' see Fluprednidene acetate.

'Emcyt' see Estramustine phosphate sodium.

EMD-9806 see Pramiverine.

EMD-15700 see Nitrefazole.

EMD-19698 see Peratizole.

EMD-30087 see Cefazedone.

EMD-33512 see Bisoprolol fumarate.

'Emdabol' see Tiomesterone.

'Emdecassol' see under Asiaticoside.

'Emedan' see Carbutamide.

EMEPRONIUM BROMIDE* (ethyldimethyl(1-methyl-3,3-diphenylpropyl)ammonium bromide).

EMEPRONIUM CARRAGEENATE* (carrageenan emepronium salt; 'cetiprin novum').

Emerald green see Brilliant green.

'Emergil' see Flupentixol.

'Emeside' see Ethosuximide.

'Emete-con' see Benzquinamide.

'Emeteral' see Prochlorperazine.

'Emeticon' see Benzquinamide.

EMETINE (6',7',10,11-tetramethoxyemetan; cephaeline methyl ether; ipecine; methylcephaeline; NSC-33669).

EMETINE CAMSILATE (emetine camphorsulfonate; emetine camsylate; canforemetina).

'Emetoplix' See Emetine camsilate.

EMILIUM TOSILATE* (*N*-ethyl-3-methoxy-*N*,*N*-dimethylbenzenemethanamium salt with 4-methylbenzenesulfonic acid; ethyl (*m*-methoxybenzyl)dimethylammonium *p*-toluenesulfonate; emilium tosylate).

'Emivan' see Etamivan.

'Emmenin' see Estradiol gluconate.

'Emodella' see Emodin.

EMODIN (1,3,8-trihydroxy-6-methylanthraquinone; archin; frangula-emodin; frangulic acid; rheum emodin).

Emodin rhamnoside see Frangulin A.

EMORFAZONE* (4-ethoxy-2-methyl-5-morpholinopyridazin-3(2*H*)-one; M-73101).

'Emostat' see Mepesulfate.

'Emovate' see Clobetasone butyrate.

'Emphysin' see Quinetalate.

'Empicol' see Sodium dodecyl sulfate.

EMPT see Fenfluramine.

EMQ see Ethoxyquin.

'Emtryl' see Dimetridazole.

'Emulax' see Docusate sodium.

EMYLCAMATE* (1-ethyl-1-methylpropyl carbamate; 3-methyl-3-pentyl carbamate; methyl diethyl carbinol urethan; *tert*-hexanol carbamate; KABI-925; MK-250).

EN-141 see Josamycin.

EN-313 see Moracizine.

EN-970 see Fluquazone.

EN-1010 see Pyrrocaine.

EN-1620A see Nalmexone.

EN-1639A see Naltrexone.

EN-1661L see Bisobrin lactate.

EN-1733A see Molindone.

EN-2234-A see Nalbuphine.

EN-15304 see Naloxone.

ENALAPRIL* (1-[*N*-[(*S*)-1-carboxy-3-phenyl-propyl]-L-alanyl]-L-proline 1'-ethyl ester; enalaprilat ethyl ester).
ENALAPRIL MALEATE* (MK-421).
ENALAPRILAT* (1-[*N*-[(*S*)-1-carboxy-3-phenyl-propyl]-L-alanyl]-L-proline; MK-422).
Enallachrome *see* Esculin.
ENALLYLPROPYMAL* (5-allyl-5-isopropyl-1-methylbarbituric acid; enallylpropymal sodium; 'narconumal').
Enallynymal* *see* Methohexital.
ENANTATE(S)* (enanthate(s); heptanoate(s); heptylate(s); hexane-1-carboxylate(s); oenanthate(s)).
Enanthal *see* Heptyl aldehyde.
Enanthaldehyde *see* Heptyl aldehyde.
ENANTHIC ACID (1-hexanecarboxylic acid; heptanoic acid; heptylic acid; oenanthic acid).
See also Enantate(s).
Enanthol *see* Heptyl aldehyde.
'Enavid' *see under* Noretynodrel.
ENBUCRILATE* (butyl 2-cyanoacrylate; 'fimomed'; 'finomed'; 'histoacryl').
ENCAINIDE* ((±)-4-methoxy-2'-[2-(1-methyl-piperid-2-yl)ethyl]benzanilide; (±)-2'-[2-(1-methylpiperid-2-yl)ethyl]-*p*-anisanilide; encainide hydrochloride; MJ-9067).
'Encephabol' *see* Pyritinol.
ENCIPRAZINE* ((±)-4-(*o*-methoxyphenyl)-α-[(3,4,5-trimethoxyphenoxy)methyl]-1-piperazine-ethanol).
ENCLOMIFENE* ((*E*)-2-[*p*-(2-chloro-1,2-di-phenylvinyl)phenoxy]triethylamine; 2-[*p*-(2-chloro-*trans*-1,2-diphenylvinyl)phenoxy]triethyl-amine; enclomiphene; cisclomifene; cisclomi-phene; RIMI-16289).
See also Clomifene; Zuclomifene.
Enclomiphene* *see* Enclomifene.
'Encordin' *see* Peruvoside.
ENCYPRATE* (ethyl *N*-benzylcyclopropane-carbamate; A-19757; MO-1255).
'Endak' *see* Carteolol.
'Endep' *see* Amitriptyline.
'Endercin' *see* Etacrynic acid.
'Endiaton' *see* Chloroxine.
Endiemal* *see* Metharbital.
'Endifasept' *see* 2-Phenoxyethanol.
'Endiran' *see* Osalmid.
'Endobil' *see* Iodoxamic acid *and* Meglumine iodo-xamate.
'Endocaine' *see* Pyrrocaine.
'Endogan' *see* Endosulfan.
'Endografin' *see* Adipiodone meglumine.
'Endoiodine' *see* Prolonium iodide.
1,4-Endomethylenecyclohexane *see* Norbornane.
1,4-Endomethylene-2-cyclohexene *see* Norbornene.
1,4-Endomethylene-Δ⁵-cyclohexene-2,3-dicarboxylic acid *see* 5-Norbornene-2,3-dicarboxylic acid.
3,6-Endomethylene-1,2,3,6-tetrahydrophthalic acid *see* 5-Norbornene-2,3-dicarboxylic acid.
Endomid *see* Endomide.
ENDOMIDE* (*N,N,N',N'*-tetraethyl-5-norborn-ene-*trans*-2,3-dicarboxamide; endomid; K-509;

'analeptan').
See also under Bamethan.
'Endomirabil' *see* Meglumine iodoxamate.
ENDOMYCIN* (antibiotic from *Streptomyces endus*).
Endophenolphthalein *see* Acetphenolisatin.
'Endosan' *see* Binapacryl.
'Endosprin' *see* Lysine acetylsalicylate.
ENDOSULFAN* (6,7,8,9,10,10-hexachloro-1,5,5a,6,9,9a-hexahydro-6,9-methano-2,4,3-benzodioxathiepin 3-oxide; 1,2,3,4,7,7-hexa-chloro-5,6-bis(hydroxymethyl)norbornene sulf-ite; hexachloronorbornene 5,6-bis(oxymethyl-ene) sulfite).
'Endothal' *see* Endothal sodium.
Endothall *see* Endothal sodium.
ENDOTHAL SODIUM* (7-oxa-3,6-endomethyl-enehexahydrophthalic acid disodium salt; *endo-endo*-7-oxabicyclo[2.2.1]heptane-2,3-dicarboxyl-ic acid disodium salt; disodium endothal; en-dothall; 'endothal').
See also under Propham.
ENDOTHION* (*S*-(5-methoxy-4-oxo-4*H*-pyran-2-ylmethyl) *O,O*-dimethyl phosphorothioate; 'farming S').
'Endoton' *see* Prolonium iodide.
'Endoverine' *see* Papaverine mandelate.
'Endoxan' *see* Cyclophosphamide.
'Endoxana' *see* Cyclophosphamide.
'Endoyodina' *see* Prolonium iodide.
ENDRALAZINE* (6-benzoyl-3-hydrazino-5,6,7,8-tetrahydropyrido[4,3-*c*]pyridazine).
ENDRALAZINE MESILATE (endralazine mesyl-ate; endralazine methanesulfonate; BQ-22-708; 'miretilan').
'Endrate' *see* Disodium edetate; Tetrasodium edet-ate.
ENDRIN* (1,2,3,4,10,10-hexachloro-6,7-epoxy-1,4,4a,5,6,7,8,8a-octahydro-1,4-*endo*-5,8-*endo*-dimethanonaphthalene; 3,4,5,6,9,9-hexachloro-1a,2,2a,5,6,6a,7,7a-octahydro-2,7:3,6-dimeth-anonaphth[2,3-*b*]oxirene; compound 269; nen-drin).
ENDRISONE* (11β-hydroxy-6α-methylpregna-1,4-diene-3,20-dione; endrysone; 'aldrisone').
Endrysone* *see* Endrisone.
Enduracidin *see* Enramycin.
'Enduron' *see* Methyclothiazide.
'Enduxan' *see* Cyclophosphamide.
'Enelfa' *see* Paracetamol.
'Enelone' *see* Pregnenolone acetate.
'Energer' *see* Isocarboxazid.
'Eneril' *see* Paracetamol.
ENESTEBOL* (4,17β-dihydroxy-17-methylan-drosta-1,4-dien-3-one).
ENFENAMIC ACID* (*N*-phenethylanthranilic acid).
ENFLURANE* (2-chloro-1,1,2-trifluoroethyl difluoromethyl ether; methylflurether; NSC-115944; 'ethrane').
'Enheptin-a' *see* Aminitrozole.
Enhexymal* *see* Hexobarbital.
ENIBOMAL* (5-(2-bromoallyl)-5-isopropyl-1-

209

methylbarbituric acid; narcobarbital; enibomal sodium).

ENICLOBRATE*** (pyrid-3-ylmethyl ($\pm$)-2-[[α-(p-chlorophenyl)-p-tolyl]oxy]-2-methylbutyrate; Sgd-33374).

'Enide' *see* Diphenamid.

'Enidran' *see* Osalmid.

'Enidrel' *see under* Norethisterone.

ENILCONAZOLE*** (($\pm$)-1-[β-(allyloxy)-2,4-dichlorophenethyl]imidazole).

Enimal *see* Hexobarbital.

'Enirant' *see* Dihydroergocristine.

ENISOPROST** (($\pm$)-methyl (Z)-7-[(1R,2R,3R)-3-hydroxy-2-[(E)-(4RS)-4-hydroxy-4-methyl-1-octenyl]-5-oxocyclopentyl]-4-heptenoate).

ENOCITABINE*** (N-(1-β-D-arabinofuranosyl-1,2-dihydro-2-oxopyrimidin-4-yl)docosanamide).

ENOLICAM*** (3',4',7-trichloro-2,3-dihydro-5-hydroxy-1-benzothiepin-4-carboxanilide 1,1-dioxide).

ENOLICAM SODIUM* (enolicam monosodium salt; CGS-5391B).

'Enovid' *see under* Noretynodrel.

ENOXACIN** (1-ethyl-6-fluoro-1,4-dihydro-4-oxo-7-piperazin-1-yl-1,8-naphthyridine-3-carboxylic acid; AT-2266; CI-919).

ENOXOLONE*** (3-hydroxy-11-oxoolean-12-en-30-oic acid; glycyrrhetic acid; glycyrrhetin; glycyrrhetinic acid; rhetinic acid).

Enoxolone glycoside *see* Glycyrrhizic acid.

Enoxolone hydrogen succinate *see* Carbenoxolone.

'Enpac' *see* Lactobacillus acidophilus cultures.

Enphenemal* *see* Methylphenobarbital.

ENPIPRAZOLE*** (1-(o-chlorophenyl)-4-[2-(1-methylpyrazol-4-yl)ethyl]piperazine; enpiprazole dihydrochloride; H-3608).

ENPRAZEPINE** (5-[3-(dimethylamino)propyl]-5,6-dihydro-11-methylene-11H-dibenzo[b,e]azepine).

Enprofen *see* Furaprofen.

ENPROFYLLINE*** (3-propylxanthine).

ENPROMATE*** (1,1-diphenyl-2-propynyl cyclohexanecarbamate; NSC-112682).

ENPROSTIL** (methyl 7-[(1R*,2R*,3R*)-3-hydroxy-2-[(E)-(3R*)-3-hydroxy-4-phenoxy-1-butenyl]-5-oxocyclopentyl]-4,5-heptadienoate).

ENRAMYCIN*** (antibiotic from *Str. fungicidicus*; enduracidin).

'Ensawan' *see* Endosulfan.

'Ensidon' *see* Opipramol.

'Ensign' *see* Citicoline.

ENT-7169 *see* Alloxan.

ENT-16275 *see* Bioallethrin.

ENT-20852 *see* Butonate.

ENT-21170 *see* Dimethrin.

ENT-23969 *see* Carbaril.

ENT-24915 *see* Tepa.

ENT-24969 *see* Clofenvinfos.

ENT-25567 *see* Naftalofos.

ENT-26316 *see* Apholate.

ENT-29106 *see* Nimidane.

'Entacyl' *see* Piperazine.

'Entamide' *see* Diloxanide.

'Entefur' *see* Nifuraldezone.

Enteramine *see* Serotonin.

'Enterastrept' *see* Dihydrostreptomycin pantothenate.

'Enterfram' *see* Framycetin.

'Enterobiol' *see* Nitroxoline.

'Enterocura' *see* Sulfaguanole.

'Enterokin' *see* Clioquinol.

'Enteromide' *see* Sulfaloxate calcium.

'Entero-norm' *see* Albumin tannate.

'Enteroquinol' *see* Clioquinol.

'Entero-septol' *see* Clioquinol.

'Enterotonin' *see* Carbachol.

'Enterovioform' *see* Clioquinol.

'Enterozol' *see* Clioquinol.

'Entex' *see* Fenthion.

'Entizol' *see* Metronidazole.

'Entobex' *see* Phanquinone.

'Entodon' *see* Prolonium iodide.

'Entonox' *see* Nitrous oxide.

'Entrophen' *see* Acetylsalicylic acid.

'Entryl' *see* Dimetridazole.

ENTSUFON** (2-[2-[2-[p-(1,1,3,3-tetramethylbutyl)phenoxy]ethoxy]ethoxy]ethanesulfonic acid; entsufon sodium).

'Entumine' *see* Clotiapine.

'Enturen' *see* Sulfinpyrazone.

'Enturon' *see* Sulfinpyrazone.

'Envacar' *see* Guanoxan.

ENVIOMYCIN** (stereoisomer of [[15-(3,6-diamino-4-hydroxyhexanamido)-3-(hexahydro-2-iminopyrimidin-4-yl)-9,12-bis(hydroxymethyl)-2,5,8,11,14-pentaoxo-1,4,7,10,13-pentaazacyclohexadec-6-yl-idene]methyl]urea; tuberactinomycin N).

ENVIRADENE** ((E)-2-amino-1-(isopropylsulfonyl)-6-(1-phenylpropenyl)benzimidazole; (E)-1-[(1-methylethyl)sulfonyl]-6-(1-phenyl-1-propenyl)-1H-benzimidazol-2-amine; LY-127123).

ENVIROXIME*** ((E)-2-amino-6-benzoyl-1-(isopropylsulfonyl)benzimidazole oxime; 2-amino-1-(isopropylsulfonyl)-6-benzimidazole phenyl ketone oxime).
See also Viroxime.

'Enzactin' *see* Triacetin.

'Enzaprost F' *see* Dinoprost.

'Enzeon' *see* Chymotrypsin.

'Enzopride' *see* Nadide.

'Eoden' *see* Heptaminol.

'Epadyn-U' *see* Vitamin U.

'Eparol' *see* Clotrimazole.

'Eparsulfo' *see* Magnesium methynotrithioglycolate.

EPEG *see* Etoposide.

EPERISONE** (4'-ethyl-2-methyl-3-piperid-1-ylpropiophenone).

EPHEDRINE ((−)-α-[1-(methylamino)ethyl]benzyl alcohol; (−)-2-(methylamino)-1-phenyl-1-propanol; ephedrine hydrochloride; ephedrine sulfate).
See also Pseudoephedrine; Racephedrine.

EPHENAMINE (2-hydroxy-N-methyl-1,2-diphenylethylamine).

L-EPHENAMINE PENICILLIN (L-ephenamine salt of penicillin G).

Epiandrosterone *see* 3β-Hydroxy-5α-androstan-17-one.

EPICAINIDE* (*N*-[(1-ethylpyrrolidin-2-yl)-methyl]-2-hydroxy-2,2-diphenylacetamide; *N*-[(1-ethylpyrrolidin-2-yl)methyl]benzilamide).

Epichlorhydrine *see* Epichlorohydrin.

EPICHLOROHYDRIN (1-chloro-2,3-epoxypropane; chloromethyloxirane; γ-chloropropylene oxide; epichlorhydrine).

Epichlorohydrin copolymer with diethylenetriamine *see* Colestipol.

Epichlorohydrin dextran reaction products *see* Dextranomer; Polidexide sulfate.

Epichlorohydrin starch reaction products *see* Anilomer; Eldexomer.

EPICILLIN* (6-[D-2-amino-2-(1,4-cyclohexadien-1-yl)acetamido]penicillanic acid; (6*R*)-6-(α-D-cyclohexa-1,4-dienylglycylamino)penicillanic acid; dihydroampicillin; SQ-11302; 'dexacillin'; 'florispec'; 'spectacillin').

'Epiclase' *see* Phenacemide.

'Epi-clear' *see* Benzoyl peroxide.

'Epidine' *see* Trimethadione.

'Epido' *see* Phenylmercuric nitrate.

'Epidon' *see* Diacetazotol.

'Epidosin' *see* Valethamate bromide.

'Epidropal' *see* Allopurinol.

EPIESTRIOL* (1,3,5(10)-estratriene-3β,16β,17β-triol; 16-epiestriol; epioestriol).

'Epifrin' *see* Dipivefrine.

Epihydrin alcohol *see* Glycidol.

'Epileptasid' *see* Rattlesnake venom.

'Epilim' *see* Valproic acid.

'Epilin' *see* Dietifen.

EPIMESTROL* (16α,17α-dihydroxy-3-methoxyestra-1,3,5(10)-triene; 3-methoxyestra-1,3,5(10)-triene-16α,17α-diol; NSC-55975; Org-817; 'stimovul').

'Epimide' *see* Phensuximide.

'Epi-monistat' *see* Miconazole.

'Epinal' *see* Epinephryl borate.

Epinefrina *see* Epinephrine.

EPINEPHRINE* ((−)-3,4-dihydroxy-α-[(methylamino)methyl]benzyl alcohol; adrenaline; epinefrina; epirenamine; levorenin; NSC-62786; 'adrenalin').

Epinephrine 3,4-dipivalate *see* Dipivefrine.

EPINEPHRYL BORATE* ((−)-4-[1-hydroxy-2-(methylamino)ethyl]-*m*-phenylene cyclic borate; 'epinal'; 'eppy').

'Epinoval' *see* Valdetamide.

'Epinyl' *see* Ethadione.

Epioestriol* *see* Epiestriol.

'Epi-pevaryl' *see* Econazole.

'Epipevisone' *see under* Triamcinolone acetonide.

'Epipol' *see* Dinitro-*o*-cresol.

EPIPROPIDINE* (1,1'-bis(2,3-epoxypropyl)-4,4'-bipiperidine; epoxypropidine; NSC-56308).

Epirenamine *see* Epinephrine.

EPIRIZOLE (5-methoxy-1-(4-methoxy-6-methylpyrimidin-2-yl)-3-methylpyrazole; 4-methoxy-2-(5-methoxy-3-methylpyrazol-1-yl)-6-methylpyrimidine; mepirizole; methopyrimazole; DA-398; 'mebron').

EPIROPRIM* (2,4-diamino-5-(3,5-diethoxy-4-pyrrol-1-ylbenzyl)pyrimidine).

EPIRUBICIN ((1*S*,3*S*)-3-glycoloyl-1,2,3,4,6,11-hexahydro-3,5,12-trihydroxy-10-methoxy-6,11-dioxonaphthacen-1-yl 3-amino-2,3,6-trideoxy-α-L-*arabino*-hexopyranoside; (8*S*,10*S*)-10-[(3-amino-2,3,6-trideoxy-α-L-*arabino*-hexopyranosyl)oxy]-8-glycoloyl-7,8,9,10-tetrahydro-6,8,11-trihydroxy-1-methoxy-5,12-naphthacenedione; pidorubicin; epirubicin hydrochloride).

'Episol' *see* Haletazole.

EPITESTOSTERONE (17α-hydroxyandrost-4-en-3-one).

Epithiazide* *see* Epitizide.

2α,3α-Epithio-5α-androstan-17β-ol *see* Epitiostanol.

EPITIOSTANOL (2α,3α-epithio-5α-androstan-17β-ol; NSC-194684; S-10275; 'thiodrol').

Epitiostanol 1-methoxycyclopentyl ether *see* Mepitiostane.

EPITIZIDE* (6-chloro-3,4-dihydro-3-[[(2,2,2-trifluoroethyl)thio]methyl]-2*H*-1,2,4-benzothiadiazine-7-sulfonamide 1,1-dioxide; epithiazide; NSC-108164; P-2105).

'Epitopic' *see* Difluprednate.

EPN *see* *O*-Ethyl *O*-(*p*-nitrophenyl) phenylphosphonothioate.

'Epodyl' *see* Etoglucid.

'Eponate' *see* Epipropidine.

EPOPROSTENOL* ((5*Z*,9α,11α,13*E*,15*S*)-6,9-epoxy-11,15-dihydroxyprosta-5,13-dien-1-oic acid; (*Z*)-(3a*R*,4*R*,5*R*,6a*S*)-hexahydro-5-hydroxy-4-[(*E*)-(3*S*)-3-hydroxy-1-octenyl]-2*H*-cyclopenta[*b*]furan-Δ²,δ-valeric acid; epoprostenol sodium; PGI₂; PGX; prostacyclin; prostaglandin I₂; prostaglandin X; U-53217).

Epoprostenol sodium* *see* Epoprostenol.

'Eporal' *see* Dapsone.

EPOSTANE (4α,5-epoxy-3,17β-dihydroxy-4,17-dimethyl-5α-androst-2-ene-2-carbonitrile).

4α,5-Epoxy-3,17β-dihydroxy-4,17-dimethyl-5α-androst-2-ene-2-carbonitrile *see* Epostane.

4,5-Epoxy-3,14-dihydroxy-*N*-methyl-6-oxomorphinan *see* Oxymorphone.

6,7-Epoxy-4,5-dihydroxy-2-octenoic acid δ-lactone acetate *see* Asperlin.

6,9-Epoxy-11,15-dihydroxyprosta-5,13-dien-1-oic acid *see* Epoprostenol.

4-(1,2-Epoxy-1,6-dimethylhex-4-enyl)-5-methoxy-1-oxaspiro[2.5]oct-6-yl hydrogen deca-2,4,6,8-tetraendioate *see* Fumagillin.

21,23-Epoxy-19,24-dinor-17α-chola-1,3,5(10),7,20,22-hexaene-3,17-diol 3-acetate *see* Estrofurate.

6β,7β-Epoxy-8-ethyl-3α-hydroxy-1α*H*,5α*H*-tropanium bromide (−)-tropate *see* Oxitropium bromide.

2,3-Epoxy-2-ethyl-3-propylpropionic acid *see* Oxanamide.

12,13-Epoxy-6-(formylmethyl)-3-hydroxy-4,8,12,14-tetramethyl-9-oxo-5-[3,4,6-trideoxy-3-(dimethylamino)-β-D-*xylo*-hexopyranosyloxy]-heptadec-10-en-15-olide *see* Rosaramicin.

14,15β-Epoxy-3β-hydroxy-5β-bufa-10,22-dienolide *see* Bufogenin.

4,5-Epoxy-3-hydroxy-5,*N*-dimethyl-6-oxo-morphinan *see* Metopon.

4,5-Epoxy-6-hydroxy-3-methoxy-*N*-methylmorphinan *see* Dihydrocodeine.

4,5-Epoxy-14-hydroxy-3-methoxy-*N*-methyl-6-oxomorphinan *see* Oxycodone.

4,5-Epoxy-6-hydroxy-3-methoxymorphin-7-ene *see* Norcodeine.

5-(2,3-Epoxy-5-hydroxy-4-methylhexyl)tetrahydro-3,4-dihydroxy-β-methyl-2*H*-pyran-2-crotonic acid, ester with 9-hydroxynonanoic acid *see* Pseudomonic acid.

9-[4-[5-(2,3-Epoxy-5-hydroxy-4-methylhexyl)tetrahydro-3,4-dihydroxypyran-2-yl]-3-methylbut-2-enoyloxy]nonanoic acid *see* Pseudomonic acid.

4,5-Epoxy-3-hydroxy-*N*-methylmorphinan *see* Desomorphine.

4,5-Epoxy-3-hydroxy-*N*-methyl-6-oxomorphinan *see* Hydromorphone.

4α,5-Epoxy-17β-hydroxy-3-oxo-5α-androstane-2α-carbonitrile *see* Trilostane.

Epoxymethamine bromide *see* Scopolamine methyl bromide.

4,5-Epoxy-3-methoxy-*N*-methyl-6-oxomorphinan *see* Hydrocodone.

Epoxypiperazine *see* Epoxypropylpiperazine.

2,3-Epoxy-1-propanol *see* Glycidol.

Epoxypropidine* *see* Epipropidine.

2,3-Epoxypropionic acid *see* Glycidic acid.

6-(1,2-Epoxypropyl)-5,6-dihydro-5-hydroxy-2*H*-pyran-2-one acetate *see* Asperlin.

1,2-Epoxypropylphosphonic acid *see* Fosfomycin.

EPOXYPROPYLPIPERAZINE (1,4-bis(2,3-epoxypropyl)piperazine; diepoxypiperazine; epoxypiperazine).

L-Epoxytropine tropate *see* Scopolamine.

'Eppy' *see* Epinephryl borate.

EPRAZINONE* (3-[4-(β-ethoxyphenethyl)piperazin-1-yl]-2-methylpropiophenone; CE-746; 'eftapan'; 'mucitux').

EPROXINDINE* ((±)-*N*-[3-(diethylamino)-2-hydroxypropyl]-3-methoxy-1-phenylindole-2-carboxamide).

EPROZINOL* (1-(3-hydroxy-3-phenylpropyl)-4-(β-methoxyphenethyl)piperazine; 4-(β-methoxyphenethyl)-α-phenyl-1-piperazinepropanol; 'eupneron').

Epsom salts *see* Magnesium sulfate.

'Eptam' *see* *S*-Ethyl dipropylcarbamothioate.

'Eptapur' *see* Buturon.

EPTAZOCINE* (2,3,4,5,6,7-hexahydro-1,4-dimethyl-1,6-methano-1*H*-benzazonin-10-ol).

EPTC *see* *S*-Ethyl dipropylcarbamothioate.

'Equa' *see* Aspartame.

'Equavert' *see* Buclizine.

'Equigard' *see* Dichlorvos.

'Equilibrin' *see* Amitriptylinoxide.

'Equilid' *see* Sulpiride.

EQUILIN (3-hydroxyestra-1,3,5(10),7-tetraen-17-one).

'Equilox' *see* Haloxon.

'Equimate' *see* Fluprostenol.

Equine gonadotrophin *see* Serum gonadotrophin.

'Equipax' *see* Procymate.

'Equipertine' *see* Oxypertine.

'Equipoise' *see* Hydroxyzine embonate.

'Equiproxen' *see* Naproxen.

'Equiverm' *see* Mebendazole.

'Equizole' *see* Tiabendazole.

ER-72 *see under* Benzydamine.

ER-105 *see under* Glycyclamide.

ER-115 *see* Temazepam.

'Eradacin' *see* Rosoxacin.

'Eradex' *see* Thioquinox.

'Eraldin' *see* Practolol.

'Eramid' *see under* Clofibrate.

'Erantin' *see* Dextropropoxyphene.

'Erasol' *see* Chlormethine.

'Eraverm' *see* Piperazine.

'Eraxan' *see* Magnesium peroxide.

'Erbaprelina' *see* Pyrimethamine.

'Erbocain' *see* Fomocaine.

ERBON* (2-(2,4,5-trichlorophenoxy)ethyl 2,2-dichloropropionate; dalapon trichlorophenoxyethyl ester; 'baron'; 'novon').

'Ercefuryl' *see* Nifuroxazide.

'Ercoquin' *see* Hydroxychloroquine.

Ergadenylic acid *see* Adenosine phosphate.

Ergam (tr) *see* Ergotoxine.

'Ergenyl' *see* Valproic acid.

Ergine *see* Lysergamide.

Ergobasine *see* Ergometrine.

ERGOCALCIFEROL* (24-methyl-9,10-secocholesta-5,7,10(19),22-tetraen-3β-ol; 9,10-secoergosta-5,7,10(19),22-tetraen-3β-ol; calciferol; vitamin D_2; irradiated ergosterol; oleovitamin D_2; viosterol).

α-ERGOCRYPTINE (12′-hydroxy-2′-(1-methylethyl)-5′-(2-methylpropyl)ergotaman-3′,6′,18-trione; ergokryptine).

'Ergoklinine' *see* Ergometrine.

Ergokryptine *see* α-Ergocryptine.

ERGOLINE (4,6,6a,7,8,9,10,10a-octahydroindolo[4,3-*fg*]quinoline).

Ergoloid mesylates* *see* Co-dergocrine.

ERGOMETRINE* (*N*-[1-(hydroxymethyl)-ethyl]lysergamide; lysergic acid propanolamide; ergobasine; ergonovine; ergotocine; ergometrine maleate; ergometrine tartrate).

'Ergomimet' *see* Dihydroergotamine.

Ergonovine* *see* Ergometrine.

'Ergont' *see* Dihydroergotamine.

'Ergostetrine' *see* Ergometrine.

ERGOTAMINE* (12′-hydroxy-2′-methyl-5′-(phenylmethyl)ergotaman-3′,6′,18-trione).

ERGOTAMINE TARTRATE* ('exmigra'; 'femergin'; 'gynergen'; 'lingraine').

ERGOTAMINE TARTRATE plus CAFFEINE ('cafergot'; 'celetil').

'Ergoterm TGO' *see* (Dibenzyltin)-*S*,*S*′-bis(isooctyl thioglycolate).

Ergothioneine *see* Thioneine.

Ergothionone *see* Thioneine.

Ergotocine *see* Ergometrine.

ERGOTOXINE (mixture of ergocornine, ergocristine and ergocryptine; ecboline; ergam).

'Ergotrate' *see* Ergometrine.

'Ergotren' *see* Dihydroergocristine.

ERICOLOL** ((±)-3-[2-[3-(*tert*-butylamino)-2-hydroxypropoxy]-4-chlorophenyl]-2-cyclopenten-1-one).

Erinit (tr) *see* Pentaerythrityl tetranitrate.

ERIODICTIN (eriodictyol rhamnoside).

ERIODICTYOL (3′,4′,5,7-tetrahydroxyflavanone; vitamin(s) P).

Eriodictyol glucoside *see* Citrin.

Eriodictyol 3′-methyl ether *see* Homoeriodictyol.

Eriodictyol rhamnoside *see* Eriodictin.

Eriodictyonone *see* Homoeriodictyol.

ERITADENINE (4-aden-9-yl-2,3-dihydroxybutyric acid; 4-(6-aminopurin-9-yl)-2,3-dihydroxybutyric acid; 4-(6-aminopurin-9-yl)-4-deoxy-D-erythronic acid; 9-(3-carboxy-1,3-dihydroxypropyl)adenine; lentysine).

Erithrityl tetranitrate* *see* Erythrityl tetranitrate.

Eritrityl tetranitrate** *see* Erythrityl tetranitrate.

'Ermetrine' *see* Ergometrine.

EROCAINIDE** ((*E*)-2-(*p*-chlorobenzylidene)-cyclohexanone (*E*)-*O*-[3-(diisopropylamino)-propyl]oxime).

'Erracalma' *see* Dextromoramide.

ERUCIC ACID (*cis*-13-docosenoic acid).

'Ervasin' *see* Acetylcresotic acid.

'Erycin' *see* Erythromycin.

'Erycinum' *see* Erythromycin.

Erycorbin *see* Isoascorbic acid.

'Erypar' *see* Erythromycin stearate.

'Erysan' *see* Chlornaphazine.

Erythorbic acid *see* Isoascorbic acid.

'Erythran' *see* Prednisolone palmitate.

Erythrite *see* Erythritol.

ERYTHRITOL (*erythro*-1,2,3,4-butanetetrol; antierythrite; erythrite; erythroglucin; erythrol; phycite; phycitol).

Erythritol anhydride polyethylenimine polymer *see* Polyetadene.

ERYTHRITYL TETRANITRATE* (erithrityl tetranitrate; eritrityl tetranitrate; erythryl nitrate; nitroerythrol; NSC-106566).

'Erythrocin' *see* Erythromycin.

Erythroglucin *see* Erythritol.

Erythrol *see* Erythritol.

ERYTHROMYCIN*** (14-ethyl-7,12,13-trihydroxy-3,5,7,9,11,13-hexamethyl-2,10-dioxo-6-[[3,4,6-trideoxy-3-(dimethylamino)-β-D-*xylo*-hexopyranosyl]oxy]oxacyclotetradec-4-yl 2,6-dideoxy-3-*C*-methyl-3-*O*-methyl-α-L-*ribo*-hexopyranoside).

ERYTHROMYCIN plus AMMONIUM SULFOBITUMINATE ('akne-mycin').

ERYTHROMYCIN plus BROMHEXINE ('synergomycin').

ERYTHROMYCIN plus TETRACYCLINE

('macrocycline').
See also under Benzydamine.

ERYTHROMYCIN ESTOLATE* (erythromycin propionate ester lauryl sulfate; PELS; 'ery-toxinal'; 'ilosone'; 'lauritran').

ERYTHROMYCIN ESTOLATE plus TETRACYCLINE ('laucetin'; 'lautecin').

ERYTHROMYCIN ETHYLSUCCINATE ((2-ethylsuccinyl)erythromycin; 'abbotticine'; 'erythroped'; 'paediathrocin'; 'pantomycin'; 'pediamycin'; 'pediathrocin').

ERYTHROMYCIN PROPIONATE ('propiocin').
See also Erythromycin estolate.

ERYTHROMYCIN STEARATE ('bristamycin'; 'dowmycin E'; 'erypar'; 'ethril'; 'gallimycin'; 'qidmycin').

Erythromycin B *see* Berythromycin.

'Erythroped' *see* Erythromycin ethylsuccinate.

'Erythrotil' *see* Erythromycin.

Erythroxylin *see* Cocaine.

Erythryl nitrate *see* Erythrityl tetranitrate.

'Ery-toxinal' *see* Erythromycin estolate.

ES-304 *see* Nicofuranose.

ES-902 *see* Pimefylline nicotinate.

'Esafosfina' *see* Fructose 1,6-diphosphate.

'Esantene' *see* Inositol nicotinate.

ESAPRAZOLE*** (*N*-cyclohexyl-1-piperazineacetamide).

Esb-3 *see* Sulfaclozine.

'Esbatal' *see* Betanidine.

'Esberiven' *see* Melilotus officinalis extract.

'Esbuphon' *see* Norfenefrine.

'Escalol' *see* Padimate.

ESCIN (*Aesculus hippocastanum* component; escin sodium).

'Escorpal' *see* Fencarbamide.

'Escosyl' *see* Esculin.

ESCULAMINE*** (8-[bis(2-hydroxyethyl)-aminomethyl]-6,7-dihydroxy-4-methylcoumarin).

ESCULETIN (6,7-dihydroxycoumarin; aesculetin; cichorigenin; esculetol).

Esculetin 6-glucoside *see* Esculin.

Esculetol *see* Esculetin.

ESCULIN (esculetin 6-glucoside; aesculin; biocolorin; enallachrome; esculoside; polychrome).

'Esculol' *see* Padimate.

Esculoside *see* Esculin.

'Esentil' *see* Dicycloverine.

Eseridine *see* Physostigmine *N*-oxide.

Eserine *see* Physostigmine.

'Esfar' *see* Bucloxic acid.

'Esiclene' *see* Formebolone.

'Esidrex' *see* Hydrochlorothiazide.

'Esidrix' *see* Hydrochlorothiazide.

ESILATE(S)** (esylate(s); ethanesulfonate(s)).

'Esimil' *see under* Guanethidine monosulfate.

'Esiodine' *see* Prolonium iodide.

'Esiteren' *see under* Hydrochlorothiazide.

'Eskacef' *see* Cefradine.

'Eskalith' *see* Lithium carbonate.

'Eskaserp' *see* Reserpine.

'Eskazinyl' *see* Trifluoperazine.

'**Esmarin**' *see* Trichlormethiazide.
'**Esmodil**' *see* Meprochol.
ESMOLOL** (($\pm$)-methyl *p*-[2-hydroxy-3-(isopropylamino)propoxy]hydrocinnamate; ($\pm$)-methyl 4-[2-hydroxy-3-[(1-methylethyl)amino]propoxy]benzenepropanoate; esmolol hydrochloride; ASL-8052).
'**Esocalm**' *see* Dixyrazine.
'**Esoderm**' *see* DDT.
'**Esoiodine**' *see* Prolonium iodide.
'**Esopin**' *see* Homatropine methyl bromide.
ESORUBICIN*** ((8*S*,10*S*)-10-[[(2*S*,4*R*,6*S*)-4-aminotetrahydro-6-methyl-2*H*-pyran-2-yl]oxy]-8-glycoloyl-7,8,9,10-tetrahydro-6,8,11-trihydroxy-1-methoxy-5,12-naphthacenedione).
'**Esparin**' *see* Promazine.
'**Espectrin**' *see* Co-trimoxazole.
'**Esperan**' *see* Oxapium iodide.
'**Espiran**' *see* Fenspiride.
Esproquin* *see* Esproquine.
ESPROQUINE** (2-[(3-ethylsulfinyl)propyl]-1,2,3,4-tetrahydroisoquinoline; esproquin hydrochloride; NC-7197).
'**Essavan**' *see* Escin.
ESTAZOLAM** (8-chloro-6-phenyl-4*H*-*s*-triazolo[4,3-*a*][1,4]benzodiazepine; D-40TA; 'kainever'; 'nuctalon').
'**Esteron 44**' *see* 2,4-Dichlorophenoxyacetic acid.
Esthocin (tr) *see* Dimenoxadol.
ESTIL (2-(4-allyl-2-methoxyphenoxy)-*N*,*N*-diethylacetamide; G-29595; 'detrovel'; 'eunal').
Estocin (tr) *see* Dimenoxadol.
ESTOLATE(S)** (propionate lauryl sulfate(s)).
Estomycin *see* Paromomycin.
'**Estonate**' *see* DDT.
'**Estonmite**' *see* Chlorfenson.
'**Estonox**' *see* Campheclor.
'**Estopen**' *see* Penethamate hydriodide.
'**Estracyt**' *see* Estramustine.
ESTRADIOL*** (*cis*-1,3,5(10)-estratriene-3,17β-diol; β-estradiol; dihydrofolliculin; dihydrotheelin; dihydroxyestrin; NSC-20293).
ESTRADIOL BENZOATE*** (estradiol 3-benzoate; benzestrofol; NSC-9566).
ESTRADIOL BENZOATE plus TESTOSTERONE ISOBUTYRATE ('folvirin').
Estradiol 3,17-bis[*p*-[bis(2-chloroethyl)amino]phenyl]acetate *see* Estradiol mustard.
Estradiol 3-[bis(2-chloroethyl)carbamate] *see* Estramustine.
ESTRADIOL CIPIONATE (estradiol cyclopentanepropionate; 'depo-estradiol'; 'depofemin').
Estradiol 17-cyclohexen-1-yl ether 3-propionate *see* Orestrate.
Estradiol cyclopentanepropionate *see* Estradiol cipionate.
ESTRADIOL DIPROPIONATE ('agofollin'; 'diovocyclin'; 'diprovex'; 'follicyclin'; 'ovocyclin P'; 'progynon-DP').
ESTRADIOL ENANTATE (estradiol 17-heptanoate; estradiol enanthate; SQ-16150).
See also under Algestone acetofenide.
Estradiol enanthate* *see* Estradiol enantate.

ESTRADIOL GLUCONATE ('emmenin').
Estradiol 17-heptanoate *see* Estradiol enantate.
Estradiol 17β-methyl ether 3-propyl ether *see* Promestriene.
ESTRADIOL MUSTARD (estradiol 3,17-bis[*p*-[bis(2-chloroethyl)amino]phenyl]acetate; chlorphenacyl estradiol diester; NSC-112259).
Estradiol 17-nicotinate 3-propionate *see* Estrapronicate.
ESTRADIOL PIVALATE (estradiol trimethylacetate; 'estrotate').
Estradiol polyphosphate *see* Polyestradiol phosphate.
Estradiol 17-trichlorohydroxyethyl ether *see* Cloxestradiol.
Estradiol trimethylacetate *see* Estradiol pivalate.
Estradiol 17-undecanoate *see* Estradiol undecylate.
ESTRADIOL UNDECYLATE*** (estradiol 17-undecanoate; SQ-9993; 'delestrec').
ESTRADIOL VALERATE*** (estradiol 17-valerate; NSC-17590; 'atladiol'; 'delestrogen'; 'progynova').
ESTRADIOL VALERATE plus 17α-HYDROXY-16-METHYLENEPREGNA-4,6-DIENE-3,20-DIONE CAPROATE ('lutofollin').
ESTRADIOL VALERATE plus HYDROXYPROGESTERONE CAPROATE ('gravibindan').
ESTRADIOL VALERATE plus NORGESTREL ('cyclocur'; 'progylut').
ESTRADIOL VALERATE plus PROGESTERONE HYDROXYHEXANOATE (NSC-77622; 'deluteval').
ESTRADIOL VALERATE plus TESTOSTERONE ENANTATE ('deladumone').
See also under Prasterone enantate.
'**Estradurin**' *see* Polyestradiol phosphate.
ESTRAMUSTINE*** (estradiol 3-[bis(2-chloroethyl)carbamate]; estramustine phosphate; Leo-275; NSC-89199; Ro 21-8837; 'estracyt').
ESTRAMUSTINE PHOSPHATE SODIUM* (estramustine 17-(dihydrogen phosphate) disodium salt; Ro 21-8837/001; 'emcyt').
ESTRANE (19-norandrostane).
ESTRAPRONICATE*** (estradiol 17-nicotinate 3-propionate).
Estra-1,3,5(10)-triene-3,17β-diol *see* Estradiol.
Estra-1,3,5(10)-triene-3,16α,17β-triol *see* Estriol.
Estra-1,3,5(10)-triene-3,16β,17β-triol *see* Epiestriol.
ESTRAZINOL*** (DL-*trans*-3-methoxy-8-aza-19-nor-17α-pregna-1,3,5(10)-trien-20-yn-17-ol; estrazinol hydrobromide; W-4454A).
Estr-4-ene-3β,17-diol *see* Bolandiol.
'**Estrex**' *see* Delmadinone acetate.
ESTRIOL (1,3,5(10)-estratriene-3β,16α,17β-triol; follicular hormone hydrate; folliculin hydrate; theelol; trihydroxyestrin; NSC-12169).
Estriol 3-cyclopentyl ether *see* Quinestradol.
ESTRIOL SUCCINATE*** (estriol 16,17-bis-(hydrogen succinate); estriol dihemisuccinate; 'sinapause'; 'styptanon'; 'synapause').
ESTROFURATE*** (21,23-epoxy-19,24-dinor-17α-chola-1,3,5(10),7,20,22-hexaene-3,17-diol 3-

acetate; 17α-(3-furyl)estra-1,3,5(10),7-tetraene-3,17-diol 3-acetate; AY-11483).

Estrogen sulfate *see* Conjugated estrogens equine.

ESTRONE* (3-hydroxyestra-1,3,5(10)-trien-17-one; follicular hormone; folliculin; ketohydroxyestratriene; theelin).

ESTRONE ACETATE ('hogival').

Estropiprate* *see* Piperazine estrone sulfate.

'Estrotate' *see* Estradiol pivalate.

'Estrovis' *see* Quinestrol.

'Estrumate' *see* Cloprostenol.

'Estulic' *see* Guanfacine.

'Esucos' *see* Dixyrazine.

Esylate(s)* *see* Esilate(s).

ET-394 *see* Tribromsalan.

ET-495 *see* Piribedil.

ETABENZARONE* (3-[4-[2-(diethylamino)ethoxy]benzoyl]-2-ethylbenzofuran; 4-[2-(diethylamino)ethoxy]phenyl 2-ethylbenzofuran-3-yl ketone; benzarone diethylaminoethyl ether; L-2642).

'Etacortin' *see* Fluprednidene acetate.

ETACRYNIC ACID* (2,3-dichloro-4-(2-ethylacryloyl)phenoxyacetic acid; 2,3-dichloro-4-(2-methylenebutyryl)phenoxyacetic acid; ethacrynic acid; MK-595; NSC-85791).
See also Sodium etacrynate.

ETAFEDRINE* ((−)-2-(ethylmethylamino)-1-phenylpropan-1-ol; (−)-α-(1-ethylmethylaminoethyl)benzyl alcohol; N-ethylephedrine; etafedrine hydrochloride).

ETAFENONE* (2′-[2-(diethylamino)ethoxy]-3-phenylpropiophenone; 2-[2-(diethylamino)ethoxy]phenyl phenethyl ketone; baksacor; KCA; LG-11457; SA-1; 'baxacor'; 'dialicor').

Etafurazone* *see* Nifursemizone.

Etambutol *see* Ethambutol.

Etamid (tr) *see* Probenecid.

Etamifyllin *see* Etamiphyllin.

ETAMINILE* (4-(dimethylamino)-2-ethyl-2-phenylvaleronitrile; OM-977).

ETAMIPHYLLIN* (7-[2-(diethylamino)ethyl]-theophylline; dietamiphylline; etamifyllin; etamiphylline; R-3588).

ETAMIPHYLLIN CAMSILATE (etamiphyllin camphorsulfonate; 'millophylline').

ETAMIPHYLLIN DEHYDROCHOLATE ('decofilina').

Etamiphylline* *see* Etamiphyllin.

Etamiphyllin (7-hydroxy-4-methyl-2-oxo-1-benzopyran-6-yloxy)acetate *see* Metescufylline.

ETAMIVAN* (N,N-diethylvanillamide; vanillic acid diethylamide; ethamivan; NSC-406087).

ETAMOCYCLINE* (ethylenebis[(methylimino)methylene]bistetracycline).

Etampromide *see* Propetamide.

ETAMSYLATE* (diethylammonium 2,5-dihydroxybenzenesulfonate; diethylamine 1,4-dihydroxybenzene-3-sulfonate; diethylamine diphenolsulfonate; diethylamine 4-hydroxycyclohexadien-1-one-sulfonate; cyclonamine; ethamsylate; E-141; MD-154).

'Etamucin' *see* Hyaluronic acid.

'Etamycin' *see* Viridofulvin.

Etanautine *see* Diphenhydramine theophyllinate.

Etaperazine (tr) *see* Perphenazine.

'Etaphylline' *see* Acefylline piperazine.

'Etapirazin' *see* Perphenazine.

ETAQUALONE* (3-(o-ethylphenyl)-2-methyl-4(3H)-quinazolinone).

ETASULINE* (6-chloro-2-ethylamino-4-phenyl-4H-3,1-benzothiazine).

ETAZEPINE* ((±)-11-ethoxy-5,11-dihydro-5-methyl-6H-dibenz[b,e]azepin-6-one).

'Etazine' *see* Secbumeton.

Etazol (tr) *see* Sulfaethidole.

ETAZOLATE* (ethyl 1-ethyl-4-(isopropylidenehydrazino)-1H-pyrazolo[3,4-b]pyridine-5-carboxylate; SQ-20009).

ETEBENECID* (p-carboxybenzenesulfondiethylamide; p-diethylsulfamoylbenzoic acid; ethebenecid; 'urelim').

Etenzamide* *see* Ethenzamide.

Eterilate *see* Etersalate.

ETEROBARB* (5-ethyl-1,3-bis(methoxymethyl)-5-phenylbarbituric acid; dimethoxymethylphenobarbital; EX-12-095; RMI-16238; 'antilon').

ETERSALATE* (2-(p-acetamidophenoxy)ethyl salicylate acetate (ester); β-hydroxy-p-acetophenetidide salicylate acetate; eterilate; eterylate; phenacetin acetylsalicylate; 'daitol').

Eterylate *see* Etersalate.

ETHACRIDINE* (6,9-diamino-2-ethoxyacridine).

ETHACRIDINE LACTATE (lactacridine; lactoacridine).

Ethacrynate sodium* *see* Sodium etacrynate.

Ethacrynic acid* *see* Etacrynic acid.

ETHADIONE* (3-ethyl-5,5-dimethyl-2,4-oxazolidinedione; 'didione'; 'dimedion'; 'epinyl'; 'neoabsentol').

Ethal *see* 1-Hexadecanol.

ETHALLYMAL* (5-allyl-3-ethylbarbituric acid; 'dormin').

ETHAMBUTOL* ((+)-N,N′-bis(1-hydroxymethylpropyl)ethylenediamine; (+)-2,2′-ethylenediiminodi-1-butanol; etambutol; CL-40881).

ETHAMBUTOL plus ISONIAZID ('miazide'; 'mynah').

Ethamicort *see* Hydrocortamate.

Ethamid (tr) *see* Probenecid.

Ethaminal *see* Pentobarbital.

Ethaminol *see* Monoethanolamine oleate.

Ethamivan* *see* Etamivan.

ETHAMOXYTRIPHETOL (2-(p-anisyl)-1-[p-(2-diethylaminoethoxy)phenyl]-1-phenylethanol; 4-[2-(diethylamino)ethoxy]-α-hydroxy-4′-methoxy-α-phenylbibenzyl; 1-[p-[2-(diethylamino)ethoxy]phenyl]-2-(p-methoxyphenyl)-1-phenylethanol; Mer-25).

Ethamsylate* *see* Etamsylate.

Ethanal *see* Acetaldehyde.

Ethanedial *see* Glyoxal.

Ethane diamide *see* Oxamide.

Ethanediamine *see* Ethylenediamine.

Ethanedioic acid *see* Oxalic acid.
1,1-ETHANEDIOL (ethylidene glycol).
1,2-Ethanediol *see* Ethylene glycol.
ETHANE-1,2-DISULFONIC ACID (ethylene disulfonate; 'allergosil').
See also Edisilate(s).
1,2-Ethanediylbis(carbamodithioic acid) salts *see* Mancozeb; Maneb; Nabam; Zineb.
1,2-Ethanediylbis(phenylmethyl)bis[(diethoxyphosphinyl)carbonimidodithioate] *see* Zilantel.
1,1',1'',1'''-(1,2-Ethanediyldinitrilo)tetrakis[2-propanol] *see* Edetol.
Ethane-1-hydroxy-1,1-diphosphonic acid *see* Etidronic acid.
Ethane nitrile *see* Acetonitrile.
Ethanesulfonic acid, esters and salts *see* Esilate(s).
ETHANETHIOL (ethylmercaptan).
'Ethanion' *see* Calcium 2-ethylbutyrate.
9,10-ETHANOANTHRACENE (dibenzo[b,e]bicyclo[2.2.2]octadiene).
Ethanoic acid *see* Acetic acid.
ETHANOL (ethyl alcohol; alcohol).
ETHANOLAMINE (2-aminoethanol; olamine; colamine).
ETHANOLAMINE ACETYLLEUCINATE (monoethanolamine salt of DL-N-acetylleucine; RP 7452; 'tanganil').
ETHANOLAMINE IOXITALAMATE (ioxitalamic acid ethanolamine salt).
ETHANOLAMINE IOXITALAMATE plus MEGLUMINE IOXITALAMATE ('vasobrix').
ETHANOLAMINE NICOTINATE (ethanolamine salt of nicotinic acid; 'nicamin').
Ethanolamine nitrate *see* Itramin.
Ethanolamine oleate *see* Monoethanolamine oleate.
Ethanolamine 2-phenylbutyrate salt *see* Cetamifen.
2-Ethanolsulfonic acid *see* Isethionic acid.
Ethanone *see* Acetaldehyde.
Ethanoylaminoethanoic acid *see* Aceturic acid.
Ethaperazine (tr) *see* Perphenazine.
'Ethapirazine' *see* Perphenazine.
'Ethaquin' *see* Ethaverine.
Ethasulfate sodium* *see* Sodium etasulfate.
'Ethavan' *see* Homovanillin.
ETHAVERINE*** (1-(3,4-diethoxybenzyl)-6,7-diethoxyisoquinoline; ethylpapaverine; ethaverine hydrochloride).
Ethazole (tr) *see* Sulfaethidole.
Ethchlorovynol *see* Ethchlorvynol.
ETHCHLORVYNOL*** (1-chloro-3-ethylpent-1-en-4-yn-3-ol; 5-chloro-3-ethylpent-4-en-1-yn-3-ol; β-chlorovinyl ethynyl carbinol; ethchlorovynol; 'arvynol'; 'normoson'; 'placidyl'; 'serenesil').
Ethebenecid* *see* Etebenecid.
Ethene *see* Ethylene.
Ethenol homopolymer *see* Polyvinyl alcohol.
Ethenone *see* Ketene.
Ethenylbenzene *see* Styrene.
6-Ethenyldecahydro-5-hydroxy-4,6,9,10-tetramethyl-1-oxo-3a,9-propano-3aH-cyclopentacyclo-octen-8-yl [[2-(diethylamino)ethyl]thio]acetate *see* Tiamulin.
Ethenyl-p-diethoxydiphenylamidine *see* Phenacaine.

Ethenyloxyethene *see* Vinyl ether.
ETHENZAMIDE*** (o-ethoxybenzamide; salicylamide ethyl ether; etenzamide).
See also under Diproqualone camsilate.
ETHER (diethyl ether; ethyl ether).
See also Vinycombinum.
Ether hydrochloric *see* Chloroethane.
Ether muriatic *see* Chloroethane.
ETHIAZIDE*** (6-chloro-3-ethyl-3,4-dihydro-2H-1,2,4-benzothiadiazine-7-sulfonamide 1,1-dioxide).
Ethidium bromide* *see* Homidium bromide.
Ethimizole (tr) *see* Etimizole.
ETHINAMATE*** (1-ethynylcyclohexyl carbamate).
Ethine *see* Acetylene.
ETHINYLESTRADIOL (17-ethynylestradiol; NSC-10973).
See also Chlormadinone acetate; Cyproterone acetate; Desogestrel; Dimethisterone; Etynodiol diacetate; Levonorgestrel; Medroxyprogesterone acetate; Megestrol acetate; Norethisterone; Norethisterone acetate; Norgestrienone.
ETHINYLESTRADIOL plus LYNESTRENOL ('fisioquens'; 'minilyn'; 'ovenon'; 'ovoresta'; 'pregnon 28'; 'yermonil').
ETHINYLESTRADIOL plus QUINGESTANOL (S-602-1; 'relovis').
Ethinylestradiol 3-cyclopentyl ether *see* Quinestrol.
ETHINYLESTRADIOL 3-ISOPROPYLSULFONATE (J-96; 'deposiston').
Ethinylestradiol 3-methyl ether *see* Mestranol.
Ethinylestrenol *see* Lynestrenol.
17α-Ethinyl-18-methyl-11-methylene-4-estren-17-ol *see* Desogestrel.
Ethinylnortestosterone *see* Norethisterone.
17α-Ethinyltestosterone *see* Ethisterone.
Ethinyl trichloride *see* Trichloroethylene.
Ethinyltrienolone *see* Norgestrienone.
Ethioamide *see* Ethionamide.
'Ethiodan' *see* Iofendylate.
ETHIODIZED (131I) OIL*** (ethyl esters of radioiodinated fatty acids; radioethiodized oil).
ETHIOFENCARB* (2-[(ethylthio)methyl]phenyl methylcarbamate; HOX-1901; 'croneton').
ETHIOLATE* (diethylcarbamothioic acid S-ethyl ester; 'prefox').
ETHION (bis[S-(diethoxyphosphinothioyl)mercapto]methane; ethyl methylene phosphorodithioate; O,O,O',O'-tetraethyl-S,S'-methylene diphosphorodithioate; diethion; 'niagara-1240'; 'nialate'; 'niallate').
ETHIONAMIDE*** (2-ethylisonicotinthioamide; 2-(ethyl)thioisonicotinamide; ethioamide; ethionizine; etina; thianide; Th-1314).
ETHIONAMIDE SULFOXIDE (Th-1405).
ETHIONINE (2-amino-4-(ethylthio)butyric acid; NSC-751).
Ethionizine *see* Ethionamide.
Ethiophos *see* Amifostine.
ETHIPYROLE (tr) (N,N'-dimethylpyrazole-3,4-dicarboxamide; etipyrole).
ETHIRIMOL* (5-butyl-2-(ethylamino)-6-methyl-

4-pyrimidinol; 'milstem').

Ethiron (tr) *see* AET.

ETHISTERONE*** (17-ethynyl-17β-hydroxyandrost-4-en-3-one; 17α-ethinyltestosterone; 17α-ethynyltestosterone; 17-hydroxy-17α-pregn-4-en-20-yn-3-one; pregneninolone; pregneninonol; pregnin; NSC-9565).

ETHISTERONE ACETATE (ethisterone 17-acetate; SC-8470).

Ethizine *see* Fenethazine.

Ethmozine *see* Moracizine.

ETHOATE-METHYL* (*S*-[2-(ethylamino)-2-oxoethyl] *O,O*-dimethyl phosphorodithioate; *S*-(ethylcarbamoylmethyl) *O,O*-dimethyl phosphorodithioate; fitios).

Ethobrome *see* Bromethol.

'Ethodin' *see* Ethacridine lactate.

Ethoform* *see* Benzocaine.

ETHOFUMESATE* (2-ethoxy-2,3-dihydro-3,3-dimethylbenzofuran-5-yl methanesulfonate; 'nortran').

Ethoglucid* *see* Etoglucid.

ETHOHEPTAZINE*** (4-(ethoxycarbonyl)-1-methyl-4-phenylhexamethylenimine; ethyl DL-1-methyl-4-phenylazacycloheptane-4-carboxylate; ethyl hexahydro-1-methyl-4-phenylazepine-4-carboxylate; Wy-401).

ETHOHEXADIOL* (2-ethyl-1,3-hexanediol; Rutgers-612).

Ethomids *see* Macrogol di(polyoxyethylene) fatty acid amides.

Ethomorphine *see* Ethylmorphine.

ETHOMOXANE*** (DL-2-[(butylamino)methyl]-8-ethoxy-1,4-benzodioxan; ethoxybutamoxane; ethomoxane hydrochloride).

Ethonam* *see* Etonam.

Ethonamidate *see* Etonam nitrate.

ETHOPABATE (methyl 4-acetamido-2-ethoxybenzoate).

ETHOPROP* (*O*-ethyl *S,S*-dipropyl phosphorodithioate; ethoprophos; phosethoprop; prophos; V-C 9-104; 'mocap').

Ethopropazine* *see* Profenamine.

Ethoprophos *see* Ethoprop.

Ethosalamide* *see* Etosalamide.

'Ethosalicyl' *see* Ethenzamide.

Ethosuccimide *see* Ethosuximide.

ETHOSUXIMIDE*** (2-ethyl-2-methylsuccinimide; 3-ethyl-3-methyl-2,5-pyrrolidinedione; ethosuccimide; piknolepsin; pyknolepsin; CI-366; CN-10395; H-490; NSC-64013; PM-671).

ETHOSUXIMIDE plus MEPACRINE ('acrisuxin').

ETHOTOIN*** (3-ethyl-5-phenylhydantoin; AC-695; 'peganone').

Ethotrimeprazine *see* Etymemazine.

'Ethovan' *see* Homovanillin.

Ethoxarine *see* Oxamarin.

Ethoxazene* *see* Etoxazene.

Ethoxazolamide *see* Ethoxzolamide.

ETHOXAZORUTOSIDE*** (morpholinoethylrutoside; oxarutin).

Ethoxide (tr) *see* Etocarlide.

Ethoxolamide *see* Ethoxzolamide.

4'-Ethoxyacetanilide *see* Phenacetin.

Ethoxyacetic acid *p*-menthyl ester *see* Menglytate.

N^4-(2-Ethoxyacetyl)-N^1-(5-methylisoxazol-3-yl)sulfanilamide *see* Sulfacecole.

p-Ethoxyaniline *see* p-Phenetidine.

2-(p-Ethoxyanilino)-N-propylpropionamide *see* Propetamide.

o-Ethoxybenzamide *see* Ethenzamide.

Ethoxybenzene *see* Phenetole.

o-Ethoxybenzoic acid (1-carboxyethylidene)hydrazide *see* Ruvazone.

p-Ethoxybenzoic acid diethylaminoethyl ester *see* Parethoxycaine.

α-[(6-Ethoxybenzothiazol-2-yl)thio]hydratropic acid *see* Tazasubrate.

Ethoxybutamoxane* *see* Ethomoxane.

p-Ethoxybutyranilide *see* p-Butyrophenetidide.

S-[[[(Ethoxycarbonyl)amino]methylcarbonyl]methyl] O,O-diethyl phosphorodithioate *see* Mecarbam.

S-[α-(Ethoxycarbonyl)benzyl] O,O-dimethyl phosphorodithioate *see* Phenthoate.

S-[α-(Ethoxycarbonyl)benzyl]O,O-dimethyl phosphorothioate *see* Phenthoate oxon.

2-[α-(Ethoxycarbonyl)benzyl]thiazolidine-4-carboxylic acid *see* Leucogen.

18-[4-(Ethoxycarbonyl)-3,5-dimethoxybenzoyl]reserpic acid methyl ester *see* Syrosingopine.

1-[2-[2-(Ethoxycarbonyl)-5,6-dimethoxyindol-3-yl]ethyl]-4-phenylpiperazine *see* Alpertine.

4-(Ethoxycarbonyl)-1,3-dimethyl-4-phenylhexamethylenimine *see* Metethoheptazine.

2-(Ethoxycarbonylmethylene)-3-methyl-5-piperid-1-yl-4-thiazolidinone *see* Etozolin.

4-(Ethoxycarbonyl)-1-methyl-4-phenylhexamethylenimine *see* Ethoheptazine.

2-[2-[(Ethoxycarbonylmethyl)thio]ethyl]thiazolidine-4-carboxylic acid *see* Letosteine.

1-(Ethoxycarbonyl)-3-methyl-2-thioimidazole *see* Carbimazole.

N-(Ethoxycarbonyl)-3-morpholinosydnone imine *see* Molsidomine.

p-(Ethoxycarbonyl)phenyl 6-guanidinohexanoate *see* Gabexate.

3-(Ethoxycarbonyl)-6,7,8,9-tetrahydro-1,6-dimethyl-4-oxohomopyrimidazole methyl sulfate *see* Rimazolium metilsulfate.

3-(Ethoxycarbonyl)-6,7,8,9-tetrahydro-1,6-dimethyl-4-oxo-4H-pyrido[1,2-a]pyrimidinium methyl sulfate *see* Rimazolium metilsulfate.

5-(Ethoxycarbonyl)-1-(1,2,3,4-tetrahydronaphth-1-yl)imidazole *see* Etonam.

S-Ethoxycarbonylthiamine *see* Cetotiamine.

4-Ethoxycarbonyl α,α,4-triphenyl-1-piperidinebutyronitrile *see* Diphenoxylate.

p-Ethoxychrysoidine *see* Etoxazene.

Ethoxyd (tr) *see* Etocarlide.

2-Ethoxy-2,3-dihydro-3,3-dimethylbenzofuran-5-yl methanesulfonate *see* Ethofumesate.

11-Ethoxy-5,11-dihydro-5-methyl-6H-dibenz[b,e]azepin-6-one *see* Etazepine.

6-Ethoxy-1,2-dihydro-2,2,4-trimethylquinoline *see* Ethoxyquin.

3-Ethoxy-1,1-dihydroxy-2-butanone *see* Ketoxal.

2-Ethoxy-2,2-diphenylacetic acid 3-diethylamino-propyl ester *see* Etpenal.

'Ethoxydrazone' *see* Ruvazone.

2-ETHOXYETHANOL (ethylene glycol mono-ethyl ether; 'cellosolve').

6-(2-Ethoxyethoxy)benzamide *see* Etosalamide.

2-(2-ETHOXYETHOXY)ETHANOL (diethylene glycol monoethyl ether; 'carbitol').

[2-(2-Ethoxyethoxy)ethoxy]acetic acid, esters and salts *see* Troxundate(s).

5-[1-[2-(2-Ethoxyethoxy)ethoxy]ethyl]-1,2-benzodioxole *see* Sesamex.

1-[(2-Ethoxyethoxy)ethoxy]-2-(3,4-methylenedioxyphenyl)ethane *see* Sesamex.

(1-Ethoxyethyl)glyoxal *see* 3-Ethoxy-2-oxobutyraldehyde.

(1-Ethoxyethyl)glyoxal bisthiosemicarbazone *see* Gloxazone.

2-Ethoxyethyl *p*-methoxycinnamate *see* Cinoxate.

p-Ethoxy-α-hydroxyacetanilide *see* Fenacetinol.

3-Ethoxy-4-hydroxybenzaldehyde *see* Homovanillin.

4-ETHOXY-3-HYDROXYBENZALDEHYDE (ethylisovanillin).

4'-Ethoxy-3'-hydroxybutyranilide *see* Bucetin.

7-[2-(5-Ethoxy-3-hydroxy-4,4-dimethyl-1-pentenyl)-5-oxo-3-cyclopenten-1-yl]-5-heptenoic acid *see* Penprostene.

Ethoxyhydroxyzine *see* Etodroxizine.

Ethoxylated *tert*-octylphenol formaldehydepolymer *see* Tyloxapol.

1-(4-Ethoxy-3-methoxybenzyl)-6,7-dimethoxy-3-methylisoquinoline *see* Dimoxyline.

Ethoxymethyl *N*-(2,6-dichloro-*m*-tolyl)anthranilate *see* Terofenamate.

2-Ethoxy-4'-[(5-methylisoxazol-3-yl)sulfamoyl]acetanilide *see* Sulfacecole.

Ethoxymethyl meclofenamate *see* Terofenamate.

2-Ethoxy-*N*-methyl-*N*-[2-(methylphenethylamino)ethyl]-2,2-diphenylacetamide *see* Carbifene.

4-Ethoxy-2-methyl-5-morpholinopyridazin-3(2*H*)-one *see* Emorfazone.

6-(2-Ethoxy-1-naphthamido)penicillanic acid *see* Nafcillin.

2-Ethoxynaphth-1-yl-penicillin *see* Nafcillin.

3-ETHOXY-2-OXOBUTYRALDEHYDE ((1-ethoxyethyl)glyoxal; β-ethoxy-α-ketobutyraldehyde).

3-Ethoxy-2-oxobutyraldehyde bis(thiosemicarbazone) *see* Gloxazone.

3-[4-(β-Ethoxyphenethyl)piperazin-1-yl]-2-methylpropiophenone *see* Eprazinone.

o-ETHOXYPHENOL (ethyl 2-hydroxyphenyl ether; guethol).

2-(*o*-Ethoxyphenoxymethyl)morpholine *see* Viloxazine.

2-(2-Ethoxyphenoxymethyl)tetrahydro-1,4-oxazine *see* Viloxazine.

3-(*o*-Ethoxyphenoxy)-1,2-propanediol *see* Guaietolin.

N-(*p*-Ethoxyphenyl)acetamide *see* Phenacetin.

4-(*p*-Ethoxyphenylazo)-*m*-phenylenediamine *see* Etoxazene.

2-(*p*-Ethoxyphenyl)-1,3-bis(*p*-methoxyphenyl)guanidine *see* Guanicaine.

N-(*p*-Ethoxyphenyl)butyramide *see* *p*-Butyrophenidide.

N-(*p*-Ethoxyphenyl)glycolamide *see* Fenacetinol.

N-(*p*-Ethoxyphenyl)lactamide *see* Lactylphenetidin.

p-(α-Ethoxy-*p*-phenylphenacylamino)benzoic acid *see* Xenazoic acid.

N-(*p*-Ethoxyphenyl)succinimide *see* Phenetylsuccinimide.

1-(*p*-Ethoxyphenyl)urea *see* Phenetylurea.

N^1-(6-Ethoxypyridazin-3-yl)sulfanilamide *see* Sulfaethoxypyridazine.

ETHOXYQUIN* (6-ethoxy-1,2-dihydro-2,2,4-trimethylquinoline; polyethoxyquinoline; EMQ; 'santoquin'; 'stop-scald').

8-Ethoxy-5-quinolinesulfonic acid *see* Actinoquinol.

'Ethoxysclerol' *see* Polidocanol.

1-Ethoxy-6-sulfamoyl-2,1,3-benzothiadiazole *see* Ethoxzolamide.

N^1-(4-Ethoxy-1,2,5-thiadiazol-3-yl)sulfanilamide *see* Sulfatrozole.

5-Ethoxy-3-(trichloromethyl)-1,2,4-thiadiazole *see* ETMT.

Ethoxyzolamide *see* Ethoxzolamide.

ETHOXZOLAMIDE* (1-ethoxy-6-sulfamoyl-2,1,3-benzothiadiazole; ethoxazolamide; ethoxolamide; ethoxyzolamide; 'cardrase'; 'cardrax'; 'glaucotensil').

Ethpenal *see* Etpenal.

'Ethrane' *see* Enflurane.

'Ethril' *see* Erythromycin stearate.

'Ethumine' *see* Clotiapine.

Ethybenztropine* *see* Etybenzatropine.

Ethychlordiphene *see* Etofamide.

'Ethycholine' *see* Suxamethonium chloride.

'Ethycyclin' *see* Ethinylestradiol.

'Ethydan' *see* Vinycombinum.

'Ethyl' *see* Tetraethyllead.

Ethylacetamide *see* Butyramide.

Ethyl 2-acetamido-3-[*p*-[bis(2-chloroethyl)amino]phenyl]propionate *see* Phenaphan.

3-(*N*-Ethylacetamido)-2,4,6-triiodohydrocinnamic acid *see* Iprocemic acid.

2-[2-[3-(*N*-Ethylacetamido)-2,4,6-triiodophenoxy]ethoxy]propionic acid *see* Iolixanic acid.

ETHYL ACETRIZOATE (ethyl 3-acetamido-2,4,6-triiodobenzoate; 'bronchiol').

Ethyl *trans*-α-acetyl-1-methyl-5-nitroimidazole-2-acrylate *see* Propenidazole.

5-(2-Ethylacryloyl)-6-methylbenzofuran-2-carboxylic acid *see* Furacrinic acid.

'Ethyladrianol' *see* Etilefrine.

Ethylal *see* Diethoxymethane.

Ethyl alcohol *see* Ethanol.

3-(Ethylamino)-1,2-benzisothiazole *see* Etisazole.

Ethyl *p*-aminobenzoate *see* Benzocaine.

Ethyl *m*-aminobenzoate mesilate *see* Tricaine.

Ethyl 2-amino-6-benzyl-4,5,6,7-tetrahydrothieno[2,3-*c*]pyridine-3-carboxylate *see* Tinoridine.

Ethyl 2-amino-3-(3,4-dihydroxyphenyl)-2-methylpropionate *see* Methyldopate.

α-[1-(Ethylamino)ethyl]-3,4-dihydroxybenzyl alcohol *see* Dioxethedrin.

α-[1-(Ethylamino)ethyl]protocatechuyl alcohol *see* Dioxethedrin.

Ethyl 2-amino-6-[(*p*-fluorobenzyl)amino]-3-pyridinecarbamate *see* Flupirtine.

m-[2-(Ethylamino)-1-hydroxyethyl]phenol *see* Etilefrine.

2-(Ethylamino)-4-isopropylamino-6-methoxy-*s*-triazine *see* Atraton.

2-(Ethylamino)-4-isopropylamino-6-(methylthio)-*s*-triazine *see* Ametryn.

α-[(Ethylamino)methyl]-3-hydroxybenzyl alcohol *see* Etilefrine.

4-[(Ethylamino)methyl]-2-methyl-5-[(methylthio)methyl]-3-pyridinol *see* Tamitinol.

2-[1-(Ethylamino)-2-oxocyclohexyl]thiophene *see* Tiletamine.

S-[2-(Ethylamino)-2-oxoethyl] *O,O*-dimethyl phosphorodithioate *see* Ethoate-methyl.

2-(Ethylamino)-4-oxo-5-phenyl-2-oxazoline *see* Fenozolone.

Ethyl 1-(*p*-aminophenethyl)-4-phenylisonipecotate *see* Anileridine.

2-(Ethylamino)-3-phenylnorbornane *see* Fencamfamin.

2-(Ethylamino)-5-phenyl-2-oxazolin-4-one *see* Fenozolone.

2-(Ethylamino)-2-thien-2-ylcyclohexanone *see* Tiletamine.

2-(Ethylamino)-1-(3-trifluoromethylphenyl)propane *see* Fenfluramine.

N-Ethylamphetamine *see* Etilamfetamine.

17β-Ethyl-5α-androstane *see* 5α-Pregnane.

17β-Ethyl-5β-androstane *see* 5β-Pregnane.

Ethyl 1-(3-anilinopropyl)-4-phenylisonipecotate *see* Piminodine.

Ethyl apovincamin-22-oate *see* Vinpocetine.

Ethyl 2-benzimidazolecarbamate *see* Lobendazole.

2-Ethylbenzofuran-3-yl 4-hydroxy-3,5-diiodophenyl ketone *see* Benziodarone.

2-Ethylbenzofuran-3-yl 4-hydroxyphenyl ketone *see* Benzarone.

2-(2-Ethylbenzofuran-3-ylmethyl)-2-imidazoline *see* Coumazoline.

Ethyl *O*-benzoyl-3-chloro-2,6-dimethoxybenzohydroxamate *see* Benzoximate.

Ethyl *N*-benzoyl-*N*-(3,4-dichlorophenyl)-L-alanine *see* Benzoylprop-ethyl.

Ethyl *m*-benzoyl-*N*-(trifluoromethylsulfonyl)carbanilate *see* Triflumidate.

α-Ethylbenzyl alcohol *see* 1-Phenyl-1-propanol.

Ethyl *N*-benzylcyclopropanecarbamate *see* Encyprate.

3-(α-Ethylbenzyl)-4-hydroxycoumarin *see* Phenprocoumon.

Ethyl 1-(2-benzyloxyethyl)-4-phenylisonipecotate *see* Benzethidine.

α-Ethyl-4-biphenylacetic acid *see* Xenbucin.

Ethyl bis(1-aziridinyl)phosphinylcarbamate *see* Uredepa.

Ethyl 5,6-bis-*O*-(*p*-chlorobenzyl)-3-*O*-propyl-D-glucofuranoside *see* Clobenoside.

Ethyl *p*-[2-[*p*-(bis(2-chloroethyl)amino)phenyl]acetamido]benzoate *see* Phenastezin.

Ethyl 2-[*p*-[bis(2-chloroethyl)amino]phenylacetamido]-4-(methylthio)butyrate *see* Phenamet.

Ethyl 3-[*p*-[bis(2-chloroethyl)amino]phenyl]-2-nicotinoylaminopropionate *see* Nicosin.

Ethyl 2,2-bis(*p*-chlorophenyl)glycolate *see* Chlorobenzilate.

ETHYL BISCOUMACETATE*** (ethyl ester of 3,3′-carboxymethylenebis(4-hydroxycoumarin); Et ester of 2,2-bis(4-hydroxy-3-coumarinyl)acetic acid; Et ester of bis(4-hydroxy-2-oxo-2*H*-1-benzopyran-3-yl)acetic acid; ethyldicumarin; neodicumarin; pelentan; BOEA; G-11765).

Ethyl 6,7-bis(cyclopropylmethoxy)-4-hydroxyquinoline-3-carboxylate *see* Ciproquinate.

Ethyl [bis(2,2-dimethylaziridinyl)phosphinyl]carbamate *see* Meturedepa.

3-Ethyl-2,4-bis(*p*-hydroxyphenyl)hexane *see* Benzestrol.

5-Ethyl-1,3-bis(methoxymethyl)-5-phenylbarbituric acid *see* Eterobarb.

S-Ethyl bis(2-methylpropyl)carbamothioate *see* Butylate.

1-Ethyl-2,6-bis(*p*-pyrrolidin-1-ylstyryl)pyridinium iodide *see* Stilbazium iodide.

'Ethyl butex' *see* Ethyl paraben.

2-(2-Ethylbutoxy)-2,2-diphenylacetic acid 2-dimethylaminoethyl ester *see* Denaverine.

Ethyl 4-(butylamino)-1-ethyl-6-methyl-1*H*-pyrazolo[3,4-*b*]pyridine-5-carboxylate *see* Tracazolate.

Ethyl 4-butylamino-1-ethyl-1*H*-pyrazolo[3,4-*b*]pyridine-5-carboxylate *see* Cartazolate.

ETHYL BUTYLETHYLMALONAMATE (2-but-2-yl-2-ethylmalonamic acid ethyl ester; 'butesamid').

2-Ethylbutyric acid calcium salt *see* Calcium 2-ethylbutyrate.

ETHYL CAMPHORAMINE (2-hydroxy-*N,N*-dimethylethylamine camphocarbonate; 1-(dimethylamino)-2-hydroxyethyl 2-oxonorbornane-3-carboxylate).

Ethyl carbamate *see* Urethan.

1-(Ethylcarbamoyl)ethyl carbanilate *see* Carbetamide.

Ethyl 1-(2-carbamoylethyl)-4-phenylisonipecotate *see* Carperidine.

S-(Ethylcarbamoylmethyl) *O,O*-dimethyl phosphorodithioate *see* Ethoate-methyl.

4-[*N*-(Ethylcarbonyl)anilino]-4-(methoxymethyl)-1-(2-thien-2-ylethyl)piperidine *see* Sufentanil.

4-[4-(Ethylcarbonyl)-4-piperid-1-ylpiperid-1-yl]-4′-fluorobutyrophenone *see* Propyperone.

Ethyl 4-carboxy-α-phenyl-2-thiazolidineacetate *see* Leucogen.

ETHYL CARFLUZEPATE*** (ethyl 7-chloro-5-(*o*-fluorophenyl)-2,3-dihydro-2-(methylcarbamoyl)-2-oxo-1*H*-1,4-benzodiazepine-3-carboxylate).

ETHYL CARTRIZOATE*** (ethyl (3,5-diacetamido-2,4,6-triiodobenzoyloxy)acetate; ethyl diatrizoate ethyl carbonate).

Ethyl chaulmoograte *see* Chaulmestrol.

Ethyl chloride *see* Chloroethane.
Ethyl *N*-[2-(*p*-chlorobenzyl)prop-2-yl]carbamate *see* Cloforex.
Ethyl 7-chloro-5-(*o*-chlorophenyl)-2,3-dihydro-2-oxo-1*H*-1,4-benzodiazepine-3-carboxylate *see* Ethyl dirazepate.
Ethyl 4-chloro-α-(4-chlorophenyl)-α-hydroxybenzeneacetate *see* Chlorobenzilate.
Ethyl (*p*-chloro-α,α-dimethylphenethyl)carbamate *see* Cloforex.
Ethyl 10-chloro-3-ethoxymethyl-2,3,6,9-tetrahydro-9-oxo-*p*-dioxino[2,3-*g*]quinoline-8-carboxylate *see* Quincarbate.
Ethyl 7-chloro-5-(*o*-fluorophenyl)-2,3-dihydro-2-(methylcarbamoyl)-2-oxo-1*H*-1,4-benzodiazepine-3-carboxylate *see* Ethyl carfluzepate.
Ethyl 7-chloro-5-(*o*-fluorophenyl)-2,3-dihydro-2-oxo-1*H*-1,4-benzodiazepine-3-carboxylate *see* Ethyl loflazepate.
Ethyl 2-(*p*-chlorophenoxy)-2-methylpropionate *see* Clofibrate.
Ethyl (±)-2-[[α-(*p*-chlorophenyl)-*p*-tolyl]oxy]-2-methylbutyrate *see* Beclobrate.
Ethyl 7-chloro-2,3,4,5-tetrahydro-4-oxo-5-phenyl-1*H*-1,5-benzodiazepine-1-carboxylate *see* Arfendazam.
24β-Ethyl-Δ⁵-cholesten-3β-ol *see* β-Sitosterol.
Ethyl cinepazate *see* Cinepazet.
Ethyl clofibrate *see* Clofibrate.
N-Ethylcorbadrine *see* Dioxethedrin.
N-Ethyl-*o*-crotonotoluidide *see* Crotamiton.
1-(2-Ethyl-*cis*-crotonyl)urea *see* Ectylurea.
Ethyl cyanide *see* Propionitrile.
Ethyl 2-cyano-3,3-diphenylacrylate *see* Etocrilene.
Ethyl 1-(3-cyano-3,3-diphenylpropyl)-4-phenylisonipecotate *see* Diphenoxylate.
S-Ethyl cyclohexylethylcarbamidothioate *see* Cycloate.
Ethyl 6-decyloxy-7-ethoxy-4-hydroxyquinoline-3-carboxylate *see* Decoquinate.
Ethyl (3,5-diacetamido-2,4,6-triiodobenzoyloxy)acetate *see* Ethyl cartrizoate.
Ethyl diatrizoate ethyl carbonate *see* Ethyl cartrizoate.
Ethyl [[4,6-dibromo-α-(cyclohexylmethylamino)-*o*-tolyl]oxy]acetate *see* Oxabrexine.
ETHYL DIBUNATE*** (ethyl 3,6-di-*tert*-butylnaphthalene-1-sulfonate; dibunate; NDR-304).
Ethyl 4,4′-dichlorobenzilate *see* Chlorobenzilate.
Ethyl *trans*-2,10-dichloro-12-methyl-12*H*-dibenzo-[*d,g*][1,3]dioxocin-6-carboxylate *see* Ponfibrate.
Ethyl *cis*-*p*-[[[2-(2,4-dichlorophenyl)-2-(imidazol-1-ylmethyl)-1,3-dioxolan-4-yl]methyl]thio]carbanilate *see* Tubulozole.
Ethyldicumarin *see* Ethyl biscoumacetate.
Ethyl 2-[(diethoxyphosphinothioyl)oxy]-5-methylpyrazolo[1,5-*a*]pyrimidine-6-carboxylate *see* Pyrazophos.
Ethyl [[[(diethoxyphosphinothioyl)thio]acetyl]methyl]carbamate *see* Mecarbam.
Ethyl *N*-(2-diethylaminoethyl)-2-ethyl-2-phenylmalonate *see* Fenalamide.
Ethyl 3-(2-diethylaminoethyl)-4-methylcoumarin-7-yloxyacetate *see* Carbocromen.

O-ETHYL *S*-(2-DIETHYLAMINOETHYL)-PHOSPHONOTHIOATE (ethoxy (2-diethylaminoethylthio)phosphine oxide; 'edemo').
S-Ethyl diethylcarbamothioate *see* Ethiolate.
Ethyl difenoxilate *see* Diphenoxylate.
α-Ethyl-5,5′-difluoro-α′-methylbibenzyl 3,3′,4,4′-tetrayl tetraacetate *see* Acefluranol.
2-Ethyl-2,3-dihydro-5-benzofuranacetic acid *see* Furofenac.
Ethyl 1,4-dihydro-7,8-dimethoxy-4-oxopyrimido-[4,5-*b*]quinoline-2-carboxylate *see* Pirolate.
9-Ethyl-6,9-dihydro-4,6-dioxo-10-propyl-4*H*-pyrano[3,2-*g*]quinoline-2,8-dicarboxylic acid *see* Nedocromil.
Ethyl 3,4-dihydro-1-(hydoxymethyl)-5,7-dimethyl-4-oxo-6-phthalazinecarboxylate *see* Oxagrelate.
2-Ethyl-9,11-dihydro-8-(hydroxymethyl)-9-oxoindolizino[1,2-*b*]quinoline-7-glycolic acid sodium salt *see* Camptothecin.
3-Ethyl-6,7-dihydro-2-methyl-5-(morpholinomethyl)indol-4(5*H*)-one *see* Molindone.
1-Ethyl-1,4-dihydro-7-methyl-4-oxo-1,8-naphthyridine-3-carboxylic acid *see* Nalidixic acid.
1-Ethyl-4,6-dihydro-3-methyl-8-phenylpyrazolo[4,3-*e*][1,4]diazepin-5(1*H*)-one *see* Ripazepam.
6-[2-[2-[5-(6-Ethyl-3,6-dihydro-5-methyl-2*H*-pyran-2-yl)-3-methyl-1,4-hexadienyl]-3-methylcyclopropyl]vinyl]tetrahydro-4,5-dihydroxy-2*H*-pyran-2-acetic acid *see* Ambruticin.
1-Ethyl-1,4-dihydro-4-oxo[1,3]dioxolo[4,5-*g*]cinnoline-3-carboxylic acid *see* Cinoxacin.
5-Ethyl-5,8-dihydro-8-oxo-1,3-dioxolo[4,5-*g*]quinoline-7-carboxylic acid *see* Oxolinic acid.
8-Ethyl-5,8-dihydro-5-oxo-2-piperazin-1-ylpyrido[2,3-*d*]pyrimidine-6-carboxylic acid *see* Pipemidic acid.
1-Ethyl-1,4-dihydro-4-oxo-7-pyrid-4-yl-3-quinolinecarboxylic acid *see* Rosoxacin.
*N*¹-(1-Ethyl-1,2-dihydro-2-oxopyrimidin-4-yl)sulfanilamide *see* Sulfacitine.
8-Ethyl-5,8-dihydro-5-oxo-2-pyrrolidin-1-ylpyrido[2,3-*d*]pyrimidine-6-carboxylic acid *see* Piromidic acid.
4-Ethyl-3,4-dihydro-4-phenyl-1(2*H*)-isoquinolinethione *see* Tisoquone.
5-Ethyldihydro-5-phenyl-4,6(1*H*,5*H*)-pyrimidinedione *see* Primidone.
4-Ethyl-3,4-dihydro-4-phenylthioisocarbostyril *see* Tisoquone.
Ethyl 9,10-diiodobrassidate *see* Iodobrassid.
Ethyl diiodostearate *see* Iodetryl.
α-Ethyl-2,5-dimethoxy-4-methylphenethylamine *see* Dimoxamine.
Ethyl 5,6-dimethoxy-3-[2-(4-phenylpiperazin-1-yl)-ethyl]indole 2-carboxylate *see* Alpertine.
Ethyl 2-[(dimethoxyphosphinothioyl)thio]-2-phenylacetate *see* Phenthoate.
4-Ethyl-6,7-dimethoxyquinazoline *see* Quazodine.
Ethyl *N*-[2-(dimethylamino)ethyl]-*m*-trifluoromethylcarbanilate *see* Flubanilate.
Ethyl 2-(dimethylamino)-2-phenyl-3-cyclohexene-1-carboxylate *see* Tilidine.

N-Ethyl-*N*,1-dimethyl-3,3-dithien-2-yl-allylamine *see* Ethylmethylthiambutene.

Ethyldimethyl(1-methyl-3,3-diphenylpropyl)ammonium bromide *see* Emepronium bromide.

3-Ethyl-5,5-dimethyl-2,4-oxazolidinedione *see* Ethadione.

5-Ethyl-3,5-dimethyl-2,4-oxazolidinedione *see* Paramethadione.

Ethyl dimethylphosphoramidocyanidate *see* Tabun.

7-[2-(4-Ethyl-2,3-dioxo-1-piperazinecarboxamido)-3-hydroxybutyramido]-7-methoxy-3-[[(1-methyl-1*H*-tetrazol-5-yl)thio]methyl]-2-cephem-2-carboxylic acid *see* Cefbuperazone.

7-[2-(4-Ethyl-2,3-dioxo-1-piperazinecarboxamido)-2-(4-hydroxyphenyl)acetamido]-3-[[(1-methyl-1*H*-tetrazol-5-yl)thio]methyl]-2-cephem-2-carboxylic acid *see* Cefoperazone.

6-[2-(4-Ethyl-2,3-dioxo-1-piperazinecarboxamido)-2-phenylacetamido]penicillanic acid *see* Piperacillin.

N-Ethyl-3,3′-diphenyldipropylamine *see* Alverine.

Ethyl α,α-diphenyl-4-morpholinebutyrate *see* Dioxaphetyl butyrate.

O-Ethyl *S*,*S*-diphenyl phosphorodithioate *see* Edifenphos.

Ethyl α,α-diphenyl-2-piperidinepropionate *see* Pifenate.

2-Ethyl-3,3-diphenylpropen(2)ylamine *see* Etifelmine.

S-ETHYL DIPROPYLCARBAMOTHIOATE (EPTC; 'eptam').

O-Ethyl *S*,*S*-dipropyl phosphorodithioate *see* Ethoprop.

ETHYL DIRAZEPATE* (ethyl 7-chloro-5-(*o*-chlorophenyl)-2,3-dihydro-2-oxo-1*H*-1,4-benzodiazepine-3-carboxylate).

Ethyldithiuram *see* Disulfiram.

ETHYLENE (ethene).

Ethylenebis(dithiocarbamic acid) salts *see* Mancozeb; Maneb; Nabam; Zineb.

Ethylenebis(iminodiacetic acid) *see* Edetic acid.

3,3′-Ethylenebis(methylimino)di-1-propanol 3,4,5-trimethoxybenzoate diester *see* Hexobendine.

Ethylenebis[(methylimino)(2-ethylethylene)]bis(3,4,5-trimethoxybenzoate) *see* Butobendine.

Ethylenebis[(methylimino)methylene]bistetracycline *see* Etamocycline.

N,*N*′-Ethylenebis(3-nitrobenzenesulfonamide *see* Dinsed.

[Ethylenebis(oxyethylenenitrilo)]tetraacetic acid *see* Egtazic acid.

3,3′-[Ethylenebis(oxyethyleneoxyethylenecarbonylimino)]bis(2,4,6-triiodobenzoic acid) *see* Iodoxamic acid.

3,3′-[Ethylenebis(oxyethyleneoxymethylenecarbonylimino)]bis(2,4,6-triiodobenzoic acid) *see* Iotetric acid.

N,*N*-Ethylenecarbamic acid *see* 1-Aziridinecarboxylic acid.

Ethylene chloride *see* 1,2-Dichloroethylene.

Ethylene chlorohydrin *see* 2-Chloroethanol.

ETHYLENEDIAMINE (1,2-diaminoethane; ethanediamine).

Ethylenediaminetetraacetic acid *see* Edetic acid.

N,*N*′-Ethylene-1,2-diarsanilic acid *see* Difetarsone.

cis-1,2-Ethylenedicarboxylic acid *see* Maleic acid.

trans-1,2-Ethylenedicarboxylic acid *see* Fumaric acid.

Ethylene dichloride *see* 1,2-Dichloroethane.

Ethylene dicyanide *see* Succinonitrile.

2,2′-Ethylenediiminobis(ethylamine) *see* Trientine.

2,2′-Ethylenediiminodi-1-butanol *see* Ethambutol.

(Ethylenedinitrilo)tetraacetic acid *see* Edetic acid.

1,1′,1″,1‴-(Ethylenedinitrilo)tetra-2-propanol *see* Edetol.

1,2-Ethylenedioxybenzene *see* 1,4-Benzodioxan.

4,4′-Ethylenedioxybis(*N*-hexyl-*N*-methylbenzylamine) *see* Symetine.

3,3-Ethylenedioxy-17-hydroxy-6-methylpregn-5-en-20-one acetate *see* Edogestrone.

Ethylene disulfonate *see* Ethane-1,2-disulfonic acid.

ETHYLENE GLYCOL (1,2-ethanediol; glycol).

Ethylene glycol monoethyl ether *see* 2-Ethoxyethanol.

Ethylene glycol monophenyl ether *see* 2-Phenoxyethanol.

Ethylene glycol monosalicylate *see* Glycol salicylate.

Ethylene glycol salicylate *see* Glycol salicylate.

Ethylene glycol terephthalic acid polymer *see* Pegoterate.

Ethylene imine *see* Aziridine.

Ethylene iminoquinone *see* Inproquone.

Ethylene lactic acid *see* Hydracrylic acid.

Ethylene-maleic anhydride polymer *see* Maletamer.

ETHYLENE OXIDE (oxirane).

1,4-Ethylenepiperidine *see* Quinuclidine.

Ethylenesulfonic acid polymer sodium salt *see* Sodium apolate.

Ethylenimine *see* Aziridine.

N-Ethylephedrine *see* Etafedrine.

17α-Ethylestrane *see* 19Nor-17α-pregnane

17β-Ethylestrane *see* 19-Norpregnane.

17α-Ethylestr-4-ene-3,17-diol 3-propionate *see* Propetandrol.

ETHYLESTRENOL* (17α-ethyl-4-estren-17-ol; 17α-ethyl-17β-hydroxyestr-4-ene; 19-nor-17α-pregn-4-en-17-ol; ethylnandrol; ethyloestrenol). *See also under* Dexamethasone.

17α-Ethyl-4-estren-17-ol *see* Ethylestrenol.

17α-Ethyl-5-estren-17-ol *see* Bolenol.

Ethyl ether *see* Ether.

Ethylethoxyphosphoryl *p*-nitrophenolate *see* Armin.

3-Ethyl-2-[5-(3-ethylbenzothiazolin-2-ylidene)-1,3-pentadienyl]benzothiazolium iodide *see* Dithiazanine iodide.

5-Ethyl-5-(1-ethylbutyl)barbituric acid *see* Tetrabarbital.

5-Ethyl-5-(1-ethylbutyl)-2-thiobarbituric acid *see* Thiotetrabarbital.

Ethyl 6-[ethyl(2-hydroxypropyl)amino]-3-pyridazinecarbazate *see* Cadralazine.

Ethyl 1-ethyl-4-(isopropylidenehydrazino)-1*H*-pyrazolo[3,4-*b*]pyridine-5-carboxylate *see* Etazolate.

Ethyl 3-ethyl-4-oxo-5-piperid-1-yl-Δ^{2,α}-thiazolidineacetate *see* Piprozolin.

1-Ethyl-2-[3-(1-ethyl-2(1*H*)-quinolylidene)propenyl]-quinolinium chloride *see* Quinaldine blue.

α-Ethyl-6-[5-[2-(5-ethyltetrahydro-5-hydroxy-6-methyl-2*H*-pyran-2-yl)-15-hydroxy-2,10,12-tri-methyl-1,6,8-trioxadispiro[4.1.5.3]pentadec-13-en-9-yl]-2-hydroxy-1,3-dimethyl-4-oxo-heptyl]-tetrahydro-3,5-dimethyl-2*H*-pyran-2-acetic acid *see* Narasin.

α-Ethyl-6-[5-[2-(5-ethyltetrahydro-5-hydroxy-6-methyl-2*H*-pyran-2-yl)-15-hydroxy-2,10,12-tri-methyl-1,6,8-trioxadispiro[4.1.5.3]pentadec-13-en-9-yl]-2-hydroxy-1,3-dimethyl-4-oxoheptyl]-tetrahydro-5-methyl-2*H*-pyran-2-acetic acid *see* Salinomycin.

6-[7(*R*)-[5(*S*)-Ethyl-5-(5(*R*)-ethyltetrahydro-5-hydr-oxy-6(*S*)-methyl-2*H*-pyran-2(*R*)-yl)tetrahydro-3(*S*)-methyl-2(*S*)-furyl]-4-(*S*)-hydroxy-3(*R*),5(*S*)-dimethyl-6-oxononyl]-2,3-cresotic acid *see* Lasa-locid.

13β-Ethyl-17α-ethynyl-17-hydroxygona-4,9,11-tri-en-3-one *see* Gestrinone.

13β-Ethyl-17α-ethynyl-17-hydroxygon-4-en-3-one *see* Norgestrel.

17β-Ethyletioallocholane *see* 5α-Pregnane.

17β-Ethyletiocholane *see* 5β-Pregnane.

Ethyl 7-flavonoxyacetate *see* Efloxate.

Ethyl fluclozepate *see* Ethyl loflazepate.

Ethyl 8-fluoro-5,6-dihydro-5-methyl-6-oxo-4*H*-imi-dazo[1,5-*a*][1,4]benzodiazepine-3-carboxylate *see* Flumazepil.

1-Ethyl-6-fluoro-1,4-dihydro-7-(4-methylpiperazin-1-yl)-4-oxo-3-quinolinecarboxylic acid *see* Peflo-xacin.

1-Ethyl-6-fluoro-1,4-dihydro-4-oxo-7-piperazin-1-yl-1,8-naphthyridine-3-carboxylic acid *see* Eno-xacin.

1-Ethyl-6-fluoro-1,4-dihydro-4-oxo-7-piperazin-1-ylquinoline-3-carboxylic acid *see* Norfloxacin.

Ethyl *p*-fluorophenyl sulfone *see* Fluoresone.

Ethyl glycol salicylate *see* Glycol salicylate.

Ethyl green *see* Brilliant green.

'Ethyl-gusathion' *see* Azinphos-ethyl.

'Ethyl guthion' *see* Azinphos-ethyl.

Ethylhexabital *see* Cyclobarbital.

Ethylhexadecyldimethylammonium ethyl sulfate *see* Mecetronium etilsulfate.

S-Ethyl hexahydro-1*H*-azepine-1-carbothioate *see* Molinate.

Ethyl hexahydro-1,3-dimethyl-4-phenylazepine-4-carboxylate *see* Metethoheptazine.

6-Ethyl-1,2,3,4,5,6-hexahydro-3-[(1-hydroxycyclo-propyl)methyl]-11,11-dimethyl-2,6-methano-3-benzazocin-8-ol *see* Bremazocine.

13a-Ethyl-2,3,5,6,13a,13b-hexahydro-1*H*-indolo-[3,2,1-*de*]pyrido[3,2,1-*ij*][1,5]naphthyridine-12-carboxylic acid methyl ester *see* Apovincamine.

m-(3-Ethylhexahydro-1-methyl-1*H*-azepin-3-yl)-phenol *see* Meptazinol.

2-Ethyl-1,3,4,6,7,11b-hexahydro-10-methyl-2*H*-benzo[*a*]quinolizin-2-ol *see* Tolquinzole.

Ethyl hexahydro-1-methyl-4-phenylazepine-4-carb-oxylate *see* Ethoheptazine.

(1*R*,2*R*,4*S*)-2-Ethyl-1,2,3,4,6,11-hexahydro-2,5,7-trihydroxy-6,11-dioxo-4-[[2,3,6-trideoxy-4-*O*-[2,6-dideoxy-4-*O*-(tetrahydro-6-methyl-5-oxo-2-*N*-pyran-2-yl)-α-L-*lyxo*-hexopyranoyl]-3-(dimeth-ylamino)-α-L-*lyxo*-hexopyranosyl]oxy]-1-naph-thacenecarboxylic acid methyl ester *see* Aclaru-bicin.

2-Ethyl-1,3-hexanediol *see* Ethohexadiol.

2-Ethyl-1-hexanol sodium sulfate *see* Sodium eta-sulfate.

5-Ethyl-5-hexylbarbituric acid *see* Hexethal.

N-(2-Ethylhexyl)bicyclo[2.2.1]hept-5-ene-2,3-di-carboximide *see* (Ethylhexyl)norbornenedicarbo-ximide.

2-Ethylhexyl 2-cyano-3,3-diphenylacrylate *see* Oc-tocrilene.

2-Ethylhexyl *p*-dimethylaminobenzoate *see* Padim-ate O.

2-Ethylhexyl diphenyl phosphate *see* Octicizer.

N-(2-Ethylhexyl)-3,6-endomethylenetetrahydro-phthalimide *see* (Ethylhexyl)norbornenedicarbox-imide.

N-(2-Ethylhexyl)-3-hydroxybutyramide *see* Butoct-amide.

(ETHYLHEXYL)NORBORNENEDICARBOX-IMIDE (*N*-(2-ethylhexyl)-3,6-endomethylene-tetrahydrophthalimide; *N*-(2-ethylhexyl)-3a,4,7,7a-tetrahydro-4,7-methano-1*H*-isoindole-1,3(2*H*)-dione; *N*-(2-ethylhexyl)bicyclo-[2.2.1]hept-5-ene-2,3-dicarboximide; *N*-octylbi-cycloheptenedicarboximide; MGK-264; 'octac-ide 264'; 'Van Dyke 264').

2-Ethylhexyl sodium sulfate *see* Sodium etasulfate.

N-(2-Ethylhexyl)-3a,4,7,7a-tetrahydro-4,7-meth-ano-1*H*-isoindole-1,3(2*H*)-dione *see* (Ethylhexyl)-norbornenedicarboximide.

5-Ethyl-5-hexyl-2-thiobarbituric acid *see* Thiohex-ethal.

Ethyl(hydrogen 2-mercapto-5-benzoxazolecarboxyl-ato)mercury sodium salt *see* Otimerate sodium.

Ethyl *p*-hydroxybenzoate *see* Ethyl paraben.

Ethyl *p*-hydroxybenzoate 6-guanidinohexanoate *see* Gabexate.

2-Ethyl-3-(4-hydroxybenzoyl)benzofuran *see* Benz-arone.

24-Ethyl-3β-hydroxy-5,22-cholestadiene *see* Stig-masterol.

α-Ethyl-1-hydroxycyclohexaneacetic acid *see* Cyclobutyrol.

5-Ethyl-2-[(1-hydroxycyclopropyl)methyl]-2'-hydr-oxy-9,9-dimethyl-6,7-benzomorphan *see* Brem-azocine.

2-Ethyl-3-(4-hydroxy-3,5-diiodobenzoyl)benzofuran *see* Benziodarone.

2-Ethyl-3-(4-hydroxy-3,5-diiodobenzoyl)coumarone *see* Benziodarone.

Ethyl 4-hydroxy-6,7-diisobutoxyquinoline-3-carb-oxylate *see* Buquinolate.

Ethyl 5-hydroxy-1,2-dimethylindole-3-carboxylate *see* Mecarbinate.

6-[7-Ethyl-4-hydroxy-3,5-dimethyl-6-oxo-7-[5-(5-ethyltetrahydro-5-hydroxypyran-2-yl)tetrahydro-2-furyl]heptyl]-3-methylsalicylic acid *see* Lasalo-cid.

13-Ethyl-17-hydroxy-18,19-dinor-17α-pregna-4,5-dien-20-yn-3-one *see* Gestodene.

13-Ethyl-17-hydroxy-18,19-dinor-17α-pregna-4,9,11-trien-20-yn-3-one *see* Gestrinone.

13-Ethyl-17-hydroxy-18,19-dinor-17α-pregn-4-en-3-one *see* Norboletone.

13β-Ethyl-17-hydroxy-18,19-dinor-17α-pregn-4-en-20-yn-3-one *see* Norgestrel.

(+)-13-Ethyl-17-hydroxy-18,19-dinor-17α-pregn-4-en-20-yn-3-one oxime acetate *see* Norgestimate.

Ethyl(3-hydroxy-3,3-diphenylpropyl)dimethylammonium bromide carbamate *see* Ambutonium bromide.

17α-Ethyl-17β-hydroxyestr-4-ene *see* Ethylestrenol.

17α-Ethyl-17β-hydroxyestr-5-ene *see* Bolenol.

17β-Ethyl-17α-hydroxyestr-4-ene-3,20-dione *see* Gestonorone.

16β-Ethyl-17β-hydroxyestr-4-en-3-one *see* Oxendolone.

17α-Ethyl-17β-hydroxyestr-4-en-3-one *see* Norethandrolone.

Ethyl 1-hydroxyethyl carbonate ampicillin ester *see* Bacampicillin.

Ethyl(2-hydroxyethyl)dimethylammonium chloride benzilate *see* Lachesine.

Ethyl(2-hydroxyethyl)dimethylammonium chloride succinate *see* Suxethonium chloride.

Ethyl(2-hydroxyethyl)dimethylammonium sulfate dibutylcarbamate *see* Dibutoline.

Ethyl 1-[2-(2-hydroxyethyl)ethyl]-4-phenylisonipecotate *see* Etoxeridine.

1-Ethyl-1-(2-hydroxyethyl)piperidinium bromide benzilate *see* Pipethanate ethobromide.

1-Ethyl-1-(2-hydroxyethyl)pyrrolidinium *p*-toluenesulfonate 3,4,5-trimethoxybenzoate *see* Troxypyrrolium tosilate.

13β-Ethyl-3-(hydroxyimino)-18,19-dinor-17-pregn-4-en-20-yn-17β-yl acetate *see* Norgestimate.

3-Ethyl-7-hydroxy-1-(*p*-methoxyphenyl)-2-methyl-3-azaheptane 3,4-dimethoxybenzoate *see* Mebeverine.

1-Ethyl-3-hydroxy-1-methylpiperidinium bromide benzilate *see* Pipenzolate bromide.

2-Ethyl-2-(hydroxymethyl)-1,3-propanediol trinitrate *see* Propatylnitrate.

1-[[2-Ethyl-(2-hydroxy-2-methylpropyl)amino]ethylamino]-4-methylthioxanthen-9-one *see* Becantone.

1-Ethyl-3-hydroxy-1-methylpyrrolidinium bromide α-cyclopentylphenylacetate *see* Cyclopyrronium bromide.

17α-Ethyl-17-hydroxy-19-norandrost-4-en-3-one *see* Norethandrolone.

8-Ethyl-5-hydroxy-4-oxo-6-vinyl-4*H*-1-benzopyran-2-carboxylic acid *see* Evicromil.

β-Ethyl-β-hydroxyphenethyl carbamate *see* Oxyfenamate.

Ethyl 1-(β-hydroxyphenethyl)-4-phenylpiperidine-4-carboxylate *see* Oxpheneridine.

α-Ethyl-1-hydroxy-4-phenylcyclohexaneacetic acid *see* Fencibutirol.

Ethyl(*m*-hydroxyphenyl)dimethylammonium chloride *see* Edrophonium chloride.

Ethyl 1-(2-hydroxy-2-phenylethyl)-4-phenylisonipecotate *see* Oxpheneridine.

3-Ethyl-3-(*m*-hydroxyphenyl)-1-methylhexahydroazepine *see* Meptazinol.

3-Ethyl-3-(*m*-hydroxyphenyl)-1-methylhexamethylenamine *see* Meptazinol.

Ethyl 4-(*m*-hydroxyphenyl)-1-methylisonipecotate *see* Hydroxypethidine.

Ethyl (*m*-hydroxyphenylmethylpiperidyl)ketone *see* Ketobemidone.

Ethyl 1-(3-hydroxy-3-phenylpropyl)-4-phenylisonipecotate *see* Phenoperidine.

6-[Ethyl(2-hydroxypropyl)amino]-3-pyridinecarbazic acid ethyl ester *see* Cadralazine.

1-Ethyl-1-(3-hydroxypropyl)piperidinium iodide 2,4-diphenyl-1,3-cyclobutanedicarboxylate *see* Truxipicurium iodide.

3-Ethyl-7-hydroxy-2,8,12,16-tetramethyl-5,13-dioxo-9-[[3,4,6-trideoxy-3-(dimethylamino)-β-D-*xylo*-hexopyranosyl]oxy]-4,17-dioxabicyclo-[14.1.0]heptadec-14-ene-10-acetaldehyde *see* Rosaramicin.

16-Ethyl-4-hydroxy-5,9,13,15-tetramethyl-2,10-dioxo-6-[[3,4,6-trideoxy-3-(dimethylamino)-β-D-*xylo*-hexopyranosyl]oxy]oxacyclohexadeca-11,13-diene-7-acetaldehyde *see* Repromicin.

Ethylideneacetamide *see* Crotonamide.

Ethylidene diethyl ether *see* Acetal.

9-[(4,6-*o*-Ethylidene-β-*d*-glucopyranosyl)oxy]-5,8,8a,9-tetrahydro-5-(4-hydroxy-3,5-dimethoxyphenyl)furo[3',4':6,7]naphtho[2,3-*d*]-1,3-dioxol-6(5a*H*)-one *see* Etoposide.

Ethylidene glycol *see* 1,1-Ethanediol.

2-Ethyl-3-(2-imidazolin-2-ylmethyl)benzofuran *see* Coumazoline.

Ethyl 10-(*p*-iodophenyl)undecanoate *see* Iofendylate.

Ethyl iodophenylundecylate *see* Iofendylate.

ETHYL IODOSTEARATE (mixture of ethyl esters of 9- and 10-iodostearic acids; 'duroliopaque').

ETHYL IOPODATE (3-[(dimethylamino)methyleneamino]-2,4,6-triiodohydrocinnamic acid ethyl ester; SH-617-L).

5-Ethyl-5-isoamylbarbituric acid *see* Amobarbital.

5-Ethyl-5-isoamyl-2-thiobarbituric acid *see* Thioethamyl.

Ethylisobutrazine *see* Etymemazine.

2-Ethylisonicotinthioamide *see* Ethionamide.

5-Ethyl-5-isopentylbarbituric acid *see* Amobarbital.

5-Ethyl-5-isopentyl-2-thiobarbituric acid *see* Thioethamyl.

5-Ethyl-5-isopropylbarbituric acid *see* Probarbital sodium.

1-Ethyl-4-(isopropylidenehydrazino)-1*H*-pyrazolo[3,4-*b*]pyridine-5-carboxylic acid ethyl ester *see* Etazolate.

Ethylisovanillin *see* 4-Ethoxy-3-hydroxybenzaldehyde.

ETHYL LOFLAZEPATE*** (ethyl 7-chloro-5-(*o*-fluorophenyl)-2,3-dihydro-2-oxo-1*H*-1,4-benzodiazepine-3-carboxylate; ethyl fluclozepate; CM-6912; 'victan').

Ethylmercaptan *see* Ethanethiol.
ETHYLMERCURIC CHLORIDE ('ceresan').
See also Mercuran.
ETHYLMERCURIC PHOSPHATE (NIUIF-1; 'ruberon').
p-**(Ethylmercurithio)benzenesulfonic acid** *see* Sodium timerfonate.
N-**ETHYLMERCURI-*p*-TOLUENESULFON-ANILIDE** ('ceresan-M').
Ethyl methimazolate *see* Carbimazole.
Ethyl (*m*-methoxybenzyl)dimethylammonium *p*-toluenesulfonate *see* Emilium tosilate.
N-**Ethyl-3-methoxy-*N*,*N*-dimethylbenzenemethanamium salt with 4-methylbenzenesulfonic acid** *see* Emilium tosilate.
β-**Ethyl-6-methoxy-α,α-dimethyl-2-naphthalenepropionic acid** *see* Methallenestril.
N-**Ethyl-6-methoxy-*N'*-(1-methylethyl)-1,3,5-triazine-2,4-diamine** *see* Atraton.
4-**[Ethyl(*p*-methoxy-α-methylphenethyl)amino]butyl veratrate** *see* Mebeverine.
N-**Ethyl-6-methoxy-*N'*-(1-methylpropyl)-1,3,5-triazine-2,4-diamine** *see* Secbumeton.
N-**[2-Ethyl-2-(3-methoxyphenyl)butyl]-4-hydroxybutyramide** *see* Embutramide.
3-**Ethyl-4-(*p*-methoxyphenyl)-2-methyl-3-cyclohexene-1-carboxylic acid** *see* Carbestrol.
4-**[*N*-Ethyl-2-(*p*-methoxyphenyl)-1-methylethylamino]butyl 3,4-dimethoxybenzoate** *see* Mebeverine.
1-**Ethyl-2-[[(2-methoxy-5-sulfamoylphenyl)carbamoyl]methyl]pyrrolidine** *see* Isosulpride.
S-**Ethyl 11-methoxy-3,9,11-trimethyldodeca-2,4-dienethioate** *see* Triprene.
N-**Ethyl-9-(4-methoxy-2,3,6-trimethylphenyl)-3,7-dimethyl-2,4,6,8-nonatetraenamide** *see* Motretinide.
Ethyl (*all-trans*)-9-(4-methoxy-2,3,6-trimethylphenyl)-3,7-dimethyl-2,4,6,8-nonatetraenoate *see* Etretinate.
5-**Ethyl-5-(2-methylallyl)-2-thiobarbituric acid** *see* Methallatal.
3-**(Ethylmethylamino)-1,1-dithien-2-ylbut-1-ene** *see* Ethylmethylthiambutene.
α-**(1-Ethylmethylaminoethyl)benzyl alcohol** *see* Etafedrine.
2-**Ethyl-2-methylaminoindan-1,3-dione** *see* Metindione.
2-**(Ethylmethylamino)-1-phenylpropan-1-ol** *see* Etafedrine.
Ethyl 3-(α-methylbenzyl)carbazate *see* Carbenzide.
Ethyl 2-(α-methylbenzyl)-1-hydrazinecarboxylate *see* Carbenzide.
Ethyl (+)-1-(α-methylbenzyl)imidazole-5-carboxylate *see* Etomidate.
5-**Ethyl-5-(1-methyl-1-butenyl)barbituric acid** *see* Vinbarbital.
5-**Ethyl-5-(1-methylbutyl)barbituric acid** *see* Pentobarbital.
5-**Ethyl-5-(3-methylbutyl)barbituric acid** *see* Amobarbital.
5-**Ethyl-5-(1-methylbutyl)-2-thiobarbituric acid** *see* Thiopental.

5-**Ethyl-5-(3-methylbutyl)-2-thiobarbituric acid** *see* Thioethamyl.
Ethyl methyl 4-(2,3-dichlorophenyl)-1,4-dihydro-2,6-dimethylpyridine-3,5-dicarboxylate *see* Felodipine.
Ethyl methyl 1,4-dihydro-2,6-dimethyl-4-(3-nitrophenyl)-3,5-pyridinedicarboxylate *see* Nitrendipine.
13-**Ethyl-11-methylene-18,19-dinor-17α-pregn-4-en-20-yn-17-ol** *see* Desogestrel.
Ethyl methylene phosphorodithioate *see* Ethion.
4,4'-**(1-Ethyl-2-methylethylene)bis[6-fluoropyrocatechol] tetraacetate** *see* Acefluranol.
erythro-4,4'-**(1-Ethyl-2-methylethylene)di(2-fluorophenol)** *see* Bifluranol.
N-**Ethyl-*N'*-(1-methylethyl)-6-(methylthio)-1,3,5-triazine-2,4-diamine** *see* Ametryn.
β-**Ethyl-β-methylglutarimide** *see* Bemegride.
2-**Ethyl-5-[1-methyl-2-(1-methyl-5-nitroimidazol-2-yl)vinyl]-1,3,4-thiadiazole** *see* Tivanidazole.
Ethyl 3-methyl-4-(methylthio)phenyl isopropylphosphoramidate *see* Fenamiphos.
Ethyl 2-(2-methyl-5-nitroimidazol-1-yl)ethyl sulfone *see* Tinidazole.
Ethyl 3-methyl-4-oxo-5-piperid-1-yl-Δ^{2,α}-thiazolediacetate *see* Dexetozoline; Etozolin.
Ethyl 3-methyl-4-oxo-5-piperid-1-ylthiazolidinylidene-2-acetate *see* Dexetozoline; Etozolin.
N-**Ethyl-α-methylphenethylamine** *see* Etilamfetamine.
α-**Ethyl-*p*-[2-(α-methylphenethylamino)ethoxy]benzyl alcohol** *see* Fenalcomine.
Ethyl 1-methyl-4-phenylazacycloheptane-4-carboxylate *see* Ethoheptazine.
Ethyl-1-methyl-5-phenylbarbituric acid *see* Methylphenobarbital.
Ethyl 6-methyl-2-phenylcinchoninate *see* Neocinchophen.
5-**Ethyl-6-methyl-4-phenyl-3-cyclohexane-1-carboxylic acid** *see* Fenestrel.
5-**Ethyl-1-methyl-5-phenylhydantoin** *see* Metetoin.
5-**Ethyl-3-methyl-5-phenylhydantoin** *see* Mephenytoin.
Ethyl 1-methyl-4-phenylisonipecotate *see* Pethidine.
Ethyl 1-methyl-4-phenylpiperidine-4-carboxylate *see* Pethidine.
3-**Ethyl-1-methyl-4-phenyl-4-propionoxypiperidine** *see* Alphameprodine; Betameprodine.
3-**Ethyl-2-methyl-2-phenylsuccinimide** *see* Fenimide.
4-**Ethyl-1-(1-methylpiperid-4-yl)-3-phenyl-3-pyrazolin-5-one** *see* Piperylone.
4'-**Ethyl-2-methyl-3-piperid-1-ylpropiophenone** *see* Eperisone.
5-**Ethyl-5-(1-methylpropyl)barbituric acid** *see* Secbutabarbital.
1-**Ethyl-1-methylpropyl carbamate** *see* Emylcamate.
5-**Ethyl-5-(1-methylpropyl)-2-thiobarbituric acid** *see* Thiobutabarbital.
1-**Ethyl-1-methyl-2-propyn-1-ol** *see* Methylpentynol.
1-**Ethyl-1-methyl-2-propynyl phthalate** *see* Ftalofyne.

3-Ethyl-3-methyl-2,5-pyrrolidinedione *see* Ethosuximide.

2-Ethyl-2-methylsuccinimide *see* Ethosuximide.

ETHYLMETHYLTHIAMBUTENE*** (*N*-ethyl-*N*,1-dimethyl-3,3-dithien-2-yl-allylamine; 3-(ethylmethylamino)-1,1-dithien-2-ylbut-1-ene).

Ethyl 3-methyl-2-thioimidazoline-1-carboxylate *see* Carbimazole.

***N*-Ethyl-α-methyl-*m*-trifluoromethylphenethylamine** *see* Fenfluramine.

***N*-Ethyl-α-methyl-*m*-[(trifluoromethyl)thio]phenethylamine** *see* Tiflorex.

7-Ethyl-2-methyl-4-undecanol sodium sulfate *see* Sodium tetradecyl sulfate.

2-Ethyl-3-methylvaleramide *see* Valnoctamide.

1-(2-Ethyl-3-methylvaleryl)urea *see* Capuride.

ETHYLMORPHINE* (morphine ethyl ether; codethyline; ethomorphine).

Ethyl 4-morpholino-2,2-diphenylbutyrate *see* Dioxaphetyl butyrate.

1-Ethyl-4-(2-morpholinoethyl)-3,3-diphenyl-2-pyrrolidinone *see* Doxapram.

Ethyl 1-(2-morpholinoethyl)-1-phenylisonipecotate *see* Morpheridine.

Ethyl 10-(3-morpholinopropyl)phenothiazine-2-carbamate *see* Moracizine.

Ethylnandrol *see* Ethylestrenol.

2-Ethyl-2-naphth-1-ylbutyric acid *see* Nafcaproic acid.

2-[(2-Ethyl-5-nitroimidazol-1-yl)ethyl]carbamothioic acid *O*-methyl ester *see* Sulnidazole.

Ethyl *p*-nitrophenyl benzenethiophosphate *see* *O*-Ethyl *O*-(*p*-nitrophenyl) phenylphosphonothioate.

Ethyl *p*-nitrophenyl ethylphosphonate *see* Armin.

***O*-ETHYL *O*-(*p*-NITROPHENYL) PHENYLPHOSPHONOTHIOATE** (ethyl *p*-nitrophenyl benzenethiophosphate; ethyl *p*-nitrophenyl thionobenzenephosphate; EPN).

Ethyl *p*-nitrophenyl thionobenzenephosphate *see* *O*-Ethyl *O*-(*p*-nitrophenyl) phenylphosphonothioate.

1-Ethyl-3-(5-nitrothiazol-2-yl)urea *see* Nithiazide.

Ethylnorantitheine (tr) *see* Etimizole.

Ethylnorphenylephrine *see* Etilefrine.

17-Ethyl-19-nortestosterone *see* Norethandrolone.

13α-Ethyl-2,3,5,6,12,13,13a,13b-octahydro-12-hydroxy-1*H*-indolo[3,2,1-*de*]pyrido[3,2,1-*ij*]-[1,5]naphthyridine-12-carboxylic acid methyl ester *see* Vincamine.

***N*-(4-Ethyl-4,6,6a,7,8,9,10,10a-octahydro-7-methylindolo[4,3-*fg*]quinolin-9-yl)-3,5-dimethylpyrazole-1-carboxamide** *see* Toquizine.

Ethyloestrenol* *see* Ethylestrenol.

1-Ethyl-4-oxo[1,3]dioxolo[4,5-*g*]cinnoline-3-carboxylic acid *see* Cinoxacin.

Ethyl (4-oxo-2-phenyl-4*H*-1-benzopyran-7-yloxy)-acetate *see* Efloxate.

3-Ethyl-4-oxo-5-piperid-1-yl-Δ²,α-thiazolidineacetic acid ethyl ester *see* Piprozolin.

16-Ethyl-14-oxopyridocantinone *see* Vinburnine.

α-Ethyl-2-oxo-1-pyrrolidineacetamide *see* Etiracetam.

***N*-[1-[2-(4-Ethyl-5-oxo-2-tetrazolin-1-yl)ethyl]-4-(methoxymethyl)piperid-4-yl]propionanilide** *see* Alfentanil.

Ethylpapaverine *see* Ethaverine.

ETHYL PARABEN (ethyl *p*-hydroxybenzoate).

5-(1-Ethylpentyl)-3-(trichloromethylthio)hydantoin *see* Clodantoin.

Ethylphenacemide *see* Pheneturide.

Ethyl 1-phenethyl-4-phenylisonipecotate *see* Pheneridine.

Ethylphenylacetamide *see* 2-Phenylbutyramide.

Ethylphenylacetic acid *see* 2-Phenylbutyric acid.

1-(α-Ethyl-α-phenylacetyl)urea *see* Pheneturide.

***N*-Ethyl-2-[[(phenylamino)carbonyl]oxy]propanamide** *see* Carbetamide.

5-Ethyl-5-phenylbarbituric acid *see* Phenobarbital.

2-Ethyl-2-phenylbutyric acid diethylaminoethoxyethyl ester *see* Oxeladin.

***N*-Ethyl-1-phenylcyclohexylamine** *see* Eticyclidine.

(+)-2-(2-Ethyl-2-phenyl-1,3-dioxolan-4-yl)piperidine *see* Etoxadrol.

***O*-Ethyl *S*-phenyl ethylphosphonodithioate** *see* Fonophos.

2-Ethyl-2-phenylglutarimide *see* Glutethimide.

3-Ethyl-5-phenylhydantoin *see* Ethotoin.

Ethyl 4-phenylisonipecotate *see* Norpethidine.

Ethyl phenyl ketone *see* Propiophenone.

5-Ethyl-6-phenylmetathiazine-2,4-dione *see* Phenythilone.

3-(*o*-Ethylphenyl)-2-methyl-4(3*H*)-quinazolinone *see* Etaqualone.

***N*-Ethyl-3-phenyl-2-norbornanamine** *see* Fencamfamin.

3-Ethyl-3-phenylpiperazine-2,6-dione *see* Iminophenimide.

(+)-2-Ethyl-2-phenyl-4-piperid-2-yl-1,3-dioxolane *see* Etoxadrol.

***N*-Ethyl-2-phenyl-*N*-(pyrid-4-ylmethyl)hydracrylamide** *see* Tropicamide.

Ethyl 4-phenyl-1-[2-(tetrahydrofurfuryloxy)ethyl]-isonipecotate *see* Furethidine.

2-Ethyl-2-phenylthiamorpholine-3,5-dione *see* Phenythilone.

5-Ethyl-5-phenyl-2-thiobarbituric acid *see* Thiophenobarbital.

Ethylphosphonodithioic acid *O*-ethyl *S*-phenyl ester *see* Fonophos.

Ethylphosphonothioic acid *O*-ethyl *O*-(2,4,5-trichlorophenyl) ester *see* Trichloronat.

Ethyl 3-phthalazin-1-ylcarbazate *see* Todralazine.

Ethyl 2-phthalazin-1-ylhydrazinecarboxylate *see* Todralazine.

2-Ethyl-3-(β-piperidino-*p*-phenetidino)phthalimidine *see* Etomidoline.

1-Ethylpiperid-3-yl benzilate methobromide *see* Pipenzolate bromide.

***N*-Ethyl-3-piperidyl cyclopentylmandelate** *see* 1-Ethylpiperid-3-yl phenylcyclopentaneglycolate.

1-Ethylpiperid-3-yl diphenylacetate *see* Piperidolate.

2-Ethyl-3-[*p*-(2-piperid-1-ylethoxy)anilino]isoindolin-1-one *see* Etomidoline.

2-Ethyl-3-[*p*-(2-piperid-1-ylethoxy)anilino]phthal-

imidine see Etomidoline.

1-Ethyl-4-piperidylidene-1,1′-dithienylmethane see Pipendyl methane.

1-ETHYLPIPERID-3-YL PHENYLCYCLO-PENTANEGLYCOLATE (N-ethyl-3-piperidyl cyclopentylmandelate; JB-329; 'ditran').

N′-Ethylpodophyllohydrazide see Mitopodozide.

2-(N-Ethylpropylamino)-2′,6′-butyroxylidide see Etidocaine.

N-[2-(N-Ethylpropylamino)butyryl]-2,6-xylidine see Etidocaine.

2-(N-Ethylpropylamino)-2′,6′-dimethylbutyranilide see Etidocaine.

2-(Ethylpropylamino)ethyl benzilate see Benaprizine.

N-(1-Ethylpropyl)-3,4-dimethyl-2,6-dinitroaniline see Pendimethalin.

Ethyl 3-O-propylglucofuranoside 5,6-disalicylate see Salprotoside.

Ethyl protal see Homovanillin.

Ethylprotocatechuic aldehyde see Homovanillin.

Ethyl N-[5-(purin-6-ylthio)valeryl]glycinate see Butocin.

N-Ethyl-N-pyrid-4-ylmethyltropamide see Tropicamide.

Ethyl pyrophosphate see Tetraethyl pyrophosphate.

Ethyl pyrophosphorothionate see Pyrophos.

N-[(1-Ethylpyrrolidin-2-yl)methyl]benzilamide see Epicainide.

N-(1-Ethylpyrrolidin-2-ylmethyl)-5-(ethylsulfonyl)-o-anisamide see Sultopride.

N-(1-Ethylpyrrolidin-2-ylmethyl)-5-(ethylsulfonyl)-2-methoxybenzamide see Sultopride.

N-[(1-Ethylpyrrolidin-2-yl)methyl]-2-hydroxy-2,2-diphenylacetamide see Epicainide.

N-(1-Ethylpyrrolidin-2-ylmethyl)-2-methoxy-5-sulfamoylbenzamide see Sulpiride.

N-(1-Ethylpyrrolidin-2-ylmethyl)-5-sulfamoyl-o-anisamide see Sulpiride.

O-Ethyl O-quinolin-8-yl phenylphosphonothioate see Quintiofos.

ETHYL SALICYLATE ('sal-ethyl').

Ethyl salicylate carbonate see Carbethyl salicylate.

N¹-Ethylsisomicin see Netilmicin.

ETHYLSTIBAMINE* (diethylamine salt of p-aminobenzenestibonic acid; stibosamine; Bayer-693; 'neostibosan').

(2-Ethylsuccinyl)erythromycin see Erythromycin ethylsuccinate.

1-Ethyl-5′-sulfamoyl-2-pyrrolidineacet-o-anisidide see Isosulpride.

1-Ethyl-N-sulfanilylcytosine see Sulfacitine.

S-[2-(Ethylsulfinyl)ethyl] O,O-dimethyl phosphorothioate see Oxydemeton-methyl.

2-[(3-Ethylsulfinyl)propyl]-1,2,3,4-tetrahydroisoquinoline see Esproquine.

Ethylsulfonal see Methylsulfonal.

p-Ethylsulfonylbenzaldehyde thiosemicarbazone see Subathizone.

S-[2-(Ethylsulfonyl)ethyl] O,O-dimethyl phosphorothioate see Demeton-S-methylsulfon.

1-(2-Ethylsulfonylethyl)-2-methyl-5-nitroimidazole see Tinidazole.

3-Ethyl-1,6,7,11b-tetrahydro-9,10-dimethoxy-2-(1,2,3,4-tetrahydro-6,7-dimethoxyisoquinolin-1-ylmethyl)-4H-benzo[a]quinolizine see Dehydroemetine.

5-[(4-Ethyl-2,3,4,5-tetrahydrofuran-5-on-3-yl)methyl]-1-methylimidazole see Pilocarpine.

3-Ethyl-2,3,3a,4-tetrahydro-1H-indolo[3,2,1-de]-[1,5]naphthyridine-6-carboxylic acid methyl ester see Vinconate.

6-Ethyl-2,3,6,9-tetrahydro-3-methyl-2,6-dioxothiazolo[5,4-f]quinoline-8-carboxylic acid see Tioxacin.

2-Ethyl-1,2,3,4-tetrahydro-2-methylisoquinolinium p-toluenesulfonate see Trethinium tosilate.

Ethyl 1-(1,2,3,4-tetrahydronaphth-1-yl)imidazole-5-carboxylate see Etonam.

5-Ethyl-2,3,5,8-tetrahydro-8-oxofuro[2,3-g]quinoline-7-carboxylic acid see Droxacin.

2-Ethyltetrahydro-2-phenyl-1,4-thiazine-3,5-dione see Phenythilone.

2-[5-Ethyltetrahydro-5-[tetrahydro-3-methyl-5-(tetrahydro-6-hydroxy-6-hydroxymethyl-3,5-dimethylpyran-2-yl)-2-furyl]-2-furyl]-9-hydroxy-β-methoxy-α,γ,2,8-tetramethyl-1,6-dioxaspiro-[4.5]decane-7-butyric acid see Monensin.

9-Ethyl-1,3,4,9-tetrahydro-N,N,1-trimethylthiopyrano[3,4-b]indole-1-ethanamine see Tandamine.

N¹-(5-Ethyl-1,3,4-thiadiazol-2-yl)sulfanilamide see Sulfaethidole.

6-(Ethylthio)-2,4-bis(isopropylamino)-s-triazine see Dipropetryn.

16α-ETHYLTHIO-6-DEHYDRORETROPRO-GESTERONE (16α-(ethylthio)dydrogesterone; 16α-ethylthio-9β,10α-pregna-4,6-diene-3,20-dione; retroprogestagen; Ro 6-3129).

16α-(Ethylthio)dydrogesterone see 16α-Ethylthio-6-dehydroretroprogesterone.

S-[2-(Ethylthio)ethyl] O,O-dimethyl phosphorodithioate see Thiometon.

O-[2-(Ethylthio)ethyl] O,O-dimethyl phosphorothioate see Demeton-O-methyl.

S-[2-(Ethylthio)ethyl] O,O-dimethyl phosphorothioate see Demeton-S-methyl.

2-(Ethyl)thioisonicotinamide see Ethionamide.

2-[(Ethylthio)methyl]phenyl methylcarbamate see Ethiofencarb.

2-(Ethylthio)-10-[3-(4-methylpiperazin-1-yl)propyl]-phenothiazine see Thiethylperazine.

Ethylthiometon see Disulfoton.

Ethyl thiurad see Disulfiram.

N-Ethyl-N-o-tolylcrotonamide see Crotamiton.

Ethyl 3,5,6-tri-O-benzyl-D-glucurofuranoside see Tribenoside.

Ethyl trichloramate see Carbocloral.

Ethyl (2,2,2-trichloro-1-hydroxyethyl)carbamate see Carbocloral.

O-Ethyl O-(2,4,5-trichlorophenyl) ethylphosphonothioate see Trichloronat.

N-Ethyl-m-(trifluoromethyl)amphetamine see Fenfluramine.

α-Ethyl-α-[m-(trifluoromethyl)phenyl]benzyl alcohol see Flumecinol.

α-Ethyl-3-(trifluromethyl)benzhydrol see Flumecinol.

**14-Ethyl-7,12,13-trihydroxy-3,5,7,9,11,13-hexam-
ethyl-2,10-dioxo-6-[[3,4,6-trideoxy-3-(dimethylamino)-β-D-*xylo*-hexopyranosyl]oxy]oxacyclo-
tetradec-4-yl 2,6-dideoxy-3-*C*-methyl-3-*O*-
methyl-α-L-*ribo*-hexopyranoside** *see* Erythromycin.

**4-[Ethyl-[2,4,6-triiodo-3-(methylamino)phenyl]-
amino]-4-oxobutanoic acid** *see* Iosumetic acid.

N-**Ethyl-2′,4′,6′-triiodo-3′-(methylamino)succinanil-
ic acid** *see* Iosumetic acid.

α-**Ethyl-2,4,6-triiodo-3-(2-oxopyrrolidin-1-yl)hydro-
cinnamic acid** *see* Iolidonic acid.

**2-Ethyl-3-[2,4,6-triiodo-3-(2-oxopyrrolidin-1-yl)-
phenyl]propionic acid** *see* Iolidonic acid.

**1-Ethyl-1-[2-(3,4,5-trimethoxybenzoyloxy)ethyl]pyr-
rolidinium** *p*-toluenesulfonate *see* Troxypyrrolium
tosilate.

**Ethyl 4-(3,4,5-trimethoxycinnamoyl)piperazin-1-yl-
acetate** *see* Cinepazet.

Ethyl 3,7,11-trimethyl-2,4-dodecadienoate *see*
Hydroprene.

**8-Ethyl-3-(tropoyloxy)-6,7-epoxytropanium bro-
mide** *see* Oxitropium bromide.

α-**Ethyltryptamine** *see* Etryptamine.

Ethyl urethan *see* Urethan.

Ethyl vanillin *see* Homovanillin.

ETHYL VINYL ETHER ('vinamar').

'Ethymal' *see* Ethosuximide.

Ethymemazine *see* Etymemazine.

ETHYMIDINE (tr) (2,4-bis(1-aziridinyl)-6-chloro-
pyrimidine; 4-chloro-2,6-di(ethyleneimino)pyr-
imidine; etimidin; A-1).

Ethymisol *see* Etimizole.

ETHYNERONE*** (21-chloro-17-hydroxy-19-
nor-17α-pregna-4,9-dien-20-yn-3-one; 17α-
(chloroethynyl)-17-hydroxy-19-androsta-
4,9(10)-dien-3-one; etynerone).

Ethynodiol* *see* Etynodiol.

17-Ethynylandrostane *see* Pregn-20-yne.

α-**Ethynylbenzyl alcohol carbamate** *see* Carfimate.

1-Ethynylcyclohexyl carbamate *see* Ethinamate.

**1-[3-(1-Ethynylcyclohexyloxy)-2-hydroxypropyl]-4-
(*p*-fluorophenyl)piperazine** *see* Fluciprazine.

**1-(1-Ethynylcyclohexyloxy)-3-[4-(*o*-methoxyphen-
yl)piperazin-1-yl]-2-propanol** *see* Mociprazine.

α-**[(1-Ethynylcyclohexyloxy)methyl]-4-(*p*-fluoro-
phenyl)-1-piperazineethanol** *see* Fluciprazine.

α-**[[(1-Ethynylcyclohexyl)oxy]methyl]-4-(*o*-meth-
oxyphenyl)-1-piperazineethanol** *see* Mociprazine.

α-**[[(1-Ethynylcyclohexyl)oxy]methyl]-4-(α,α,α-tri-
fluoro-*m*-tolyl)-1-piperazineethanol** *see* Tercipraz-
ine.

17α-Ethynyl-3β,17β-dihydroxyestr-4-ene *see* Etynodiol.

17α-Ethynyl-3β,17-dihydroxy-11β-methylestr-4-ene
see Metynodiol.

17α-Ethynylestr-4-ene-3β,17β-diol *see* Etynodiol.

17α-Ethynylestr-4-en-17β-ol *see* Lynestrenol.

17α-Ethynyl-6α,21-dimethyltestosterone *see* Dimethisterone.

17α-Ethynyl-5-estren-17-ol *see* Cingestol.

17α-Ethynyl-5(10)-estren-17-ol *see* Tigestol.

4′-Ethynyl-2-fluorobiphenyl *see* Fluretofen.

17-Ethynyl-17β-hydroxyandrost-4-en-3-one *see* Ethisterone.

**17α-Ethynyl-17-hydroxy-6α,21-dimethylandrost-4-
en-3-one** *see* Dimethisterone.

17α-Ethynyl-17-hydroxyestra-4,9,11-trien-3-one *see*
Norgestrienone.

17α-Ethynyl-17-hydroxy-5(10)-estren-3-one *see*
Noretynodrel.

17-Ethynyl-17β-hydroxyestr-4-en-3-one *see* Norethisterone.

**17α-Ethynyl-17-hydroxy-7α-methyl-5(10)-estren-3-
one** *see* Tibolone.

17-Ethynyl-17β-hydroxy-19-norandrost-4-en-3-one
see Norethisterone.

17-Ethynyl-11β-methoxyestradiol *see* Moxestrol.

17-Ethynyl-3-methoxy-1,3,5(10)-estratrien-17β-ol
see Mestranol.

Ethynyl methyl carbinol *see* Methylpentynol.

17α-Ethynyl-11β-methylestr-4-ene-3β,17-diol *see*
Metynodiol.

**17α-Ethynyl-11β-methyl-19-norandrost-4-ene-
3β,17-diol** *see* Metynodiol.

17α-Ethynyl-19-norandrost-4-ene-3β,17-diol *see*
Etynodiol.

17α-Ethynyl-19-nortestosterone *see* Norethisterone.

Ethynyl phenyl carbinol carbamate *see* Carfimate.

17α-Ethynyltestosterone *see* Ethisterone.

ETHYPICONE*** (3,3-diethyl-5-methyl-
2,4(1*H*,3*H*)-pyridinedione; 3,3-diethyl-1,2,3,4-
tetrahydro-5-methyl-2,4-dioxopyridine; de-
hydromethyprylone).

Ethypropymal* *see* Probarbital sodium.

Ethyrone (tr) *see* AET.

Ethysine (tr) *see* Fenethazine.

Ethyzine (tr) *see* Fenethazine.

Etian *see* 5β-Androstane.

ETIBENDAZOLE*** (methyl 5-[2-(*p*-fluorophen-
yl)-1,3-dioxolan-2-yl]-2-benzimidazolecarbam-
ate; R-34803).

'Etibi' *see* Ethambutol.

Eticlordifene *see* Etofamide.

'Eticol' *see* Paraoxon.

ETICYCLIDINE** (*N*-ethyl-1-phenylcyclohexyl-
amine; cyclohexamine; CI-400).

ETIDOCAINE*** ((+)-2-(*N*-ethylpropylamino)-
2′,6′-butyroxylidide; (+)-2-(*N*-ethylpropyl-
amino)-2′,6′-dimethylbutyranilide; (+)-*N*-[2-(*N*-
ethylpropylamino)butyryl]-2,6-xylidine; W-
19053; 'duranest').

'Etidron' *see* Etidronate disodium.

ETIDRONATE DISODIUM* (disodium etidronate; diphosphonate; EHDP; 'didronel'; 'etidron').

ETIDRONIC ACID*** ((1-hydroxyethylidene)di-
phosphonic acid; ethane-1-hydroxy-1,1-diphos-
phonic acid; 'diphos').

ETIFELMINE*** (2-(diphenylmethylene)butyl-
amine; 2-ethyl-3,3-diphenylpropen(2)ylamine;
ecinamine; EDPA; NA-III; 'gilutensin').

ETIFENIN** (*N*-(carboxymethyl)-*N*-[2-[(2,6-di-
ethylphenyl)amino]-2-oxoethyl]glycine; *N*-(2,6-
diethylacetanilido)iminodiacetic acid; [[[(2,6-di-

ethylphenyl)carbamoyl]methyl]imino]diacetic acid; diethyl-IDA; EHIDA; 'hepatobida').

ETIFOXINE*** (6-chloro-2-ethylamino-4-methyl-4-phenyl-4*H*-3,1-benzoxazine; HOE-36801).

ETILAMFETAMINE*** (*N*-ethyl-α-methylphenethylamine; *N*-ethylamphetamine).

ETILEFRINE*** (α-[(ethylamino)methyl]-3-hydroxybenzyl alcohol; *m*-[2-(ethylamino)-1-hydroxyethyl]phenol; ethylnorphenylephrine; fetanol; phethanol; M-1-36).
See also under Dihydroergotamine.

ETILEFRINE PIVALATE** ((±)-etilefrine 3-pivalate; etilefrine trimethylacetate).

'Etilon' *see* Parathion.

Etimidin (tr) *see* Ethymidine.

ETIMIZOLE (tr) (*N*,*N'*-diethylimidazole-4,5-dicarboxamide; ethimizole; ethylnorantitheine; IEM-163).

Etina *see* Ethionamide.

ETINTIDINE*** (2-cyano-1-[2-[[(5-methylimidazol-4-yl)methyl]thio]ethyl]-3-(2-propynyl)guanidine; etinidine hydrochloride; BL-5641).

Etioallocholane *see* 5α-Androstane.

Etiocholane *see* 5β-Androstane.

Etiocholanone *see* 3α-Hydroxy-5β-androstan-17-one.

'Etiol' *see* Malathion.

'Etionizina' *see* Ethionamide.

ETIP *see* Ditophal.

ETIPIRIUM IODIDE*** (1-(2-hydroxyethyl)-1-methylpyrrolidinium iodide benzilate).

ETIPROSTON*** ((*Z*)-7-[(1*R*,2*R*,3*R*,5*S*)-3,5-dihydroxy-2-[(*E*)-2-[2-(phenoxymethyl)-1,3-dioxolan-2-yl]vinyl]cyclopentyl]-5-heptenoic acid).

Etipyrole *see* Ethipyrole.

ETIRACETAM*** (1-(1-carbamoylpropyl)-2-pyrrolidinone; (+)-α-ethyl-2-oxo-1-pyrrolidineacetamide).

Etiron (tr) *see* AET.

ETIROXATE** (α-methyl-DL-thyroxine ethyl ester; CG-635; 'skleronorm').

ETISAZOLE*** (3-(ethylamino)-1,2-benzisothiazole; BAY Va-9387; 'netrosella').

Etisine (tr) *see* Fenethazine.

ETISOMICIN** (*O*-3-deoxy-3-(ethylamino)-4-*C*-methyl-β-L-arabinopyranosyl-(1→4)-*O*-[2,6-diamino-2,3,4,6-tetradeoxy-α-D-*glycero*-hex-4-enopyranosyl-(1→6)]-2-deoxy-L-streptamine; BAY vl-4718).

'Etisul' *see* Ditophal.

ETISULERGINE*** (*N*,*N*-diethyl-*N'*-(6-methylergolin-8α-yl)sulfamide).

Etizin (tr) *see* Fenethazine.

ETIZOLAM*** (4-(*o*-chlorophenyl)-2-ethyl-9-methyl-6*H*-thieno[3,2-*f*]-*s*-triazolo[4,3-*a*][1,4]diazepine).

Etmozine (tr) *see* Moracizine.

ETMT (5-ethoxy-3-(trichloromethyl)-1,2,4-thiadiazole; 'terrazole').

ETOCARLIDE*** (4,4'-diethoxythiocarbanilide; ethoxide; ethoxyd; etoxid).

Etoclofene *see* Terofenamate.

ETOCRILENE*** (ethyl 2-cyano-3,3-diphenyl-acrylate; etocrylene; 'uvinul N-35').

Etocrylene* *see* Etocrilene.

ETODOLAC*** (1,8-diethyl-1,3,4,9-tetrahydropyrano-[3,4-*b*]indole-1-acetic acid; etodolic acid; AY-24236).

Etodolic acid *see* Etodolac.

ETODROXIZINE*** (2-[2-[2-[4-(*p*-chloro-α-phenylbenzyl)piperazin-1-yl]ethoxy]ethoxy]ethanol; etodroxizine maleate; ethoxyhydroxyzine; UCB-1414).
See also under Methaqualone.

ETOFAMIDE*** (2,2-dichloro-*N*-(2-ethoxyethyl)-*N*-[(*p*-nitrophenoxy)benzyl]acetamide; ethychlordiphene; eticlordifene; 'kitnos').

ETOFENAMATE*** (2-(2-hydroxyethoxy)ethyl *N*-(α,α,α-trifluoro-*m*-tolyl)anthranilate; flufenamic acid ester with 2-(2-hydroxyethoxy)ethanol; B-577; TV-485; 'rheumon').

ETOFIBRATE** (2-[2-(*p*-chlorophenoxy)-2-methylpropionoxy]ethyl nicotinate; 2-hydroxyethyl nicotinate 2-(*p*-chlorophenoxy)-2-methylpropionate ester; 2-(nicotinoyloxy)ethyl clofibrate; 'lipo-Merz').

ETOFORMIN*** (1-butyl-2-ethylbiguanide; SHE 199).

ETOFURADINE*** (*N*-benzofuran-2-ylmethyl-*N'*,*N'*-dimethyl-*N*-pyrid-2-ylethylenediamine).

ETOFYLLINE*** (7-(2-hydroxyethyl)theophylline; etophylline; oxyethyltheophylline).

ETOFYLLINE plus THEOPHYLLINE-EPHEDRINE ('peripherin').

ETOFYLLINE CLOFIBRATE*** (2-theophyllin-7-ylethyl 2-(*p*-chlorophenoxy)-2-methylpropionate; theofibrate; ML-1024; 'duolip').

ETOFYLLINE NICOTINATE (He-682; 'actemil'; 'hesotanol'; 'hesotin').

Etofylline pyridoxol salt hydrogen sulfate ester *see* Pyridofylline.

ETOGLUCID*** (1,2:15,16-diepoxy-4,7,10,13-tetraoxahexadecane; triethylene glycol diglycidyl ether; ethoglucid; AY-62013; ICI-32865; 'epodyl').

ETOLOREX*** (2-(*p*-chloro-α,α-dimethylphenethylamino)ethanol; *p*-chloro-*N*-(2-hydroxyethyl)-α,α-dimethylphenethylamine).

ETOLOXAMINE*** (2-(α-phenyl-*o*-toloxy)triethylamine; α-[2-[2-(diethylamino)ethoxy]phenyl]toluene; 2-[2-(diethylamino)ethoxy]diphenylmethane; etoloxamine hydrochloride; 'AH3').

ETOMIDATE*** (ethyl (+)-1-(α-methylbenzyl)-imidazole-5-carboxylate; R-7405; R-16659; R-26490; RP-7405).

Etomide *see* Carbifene.

ETOMIDOLINE** (2-ethyl-3-(β-piperidino-*p*-phenetidino)phthalimidine; 2-ethyl-3-[*p*-(2-piperid-1-ylethoxy)anilino]isoindolin-1-one; 2-ethyl-3-[*p*-(2-piperid-1-ylethoxy)anilino]phthalimidine; amidoline; K-2680).

ETONAM*** (5-(ethoxycarbonyl)-1-(1,2,3,4-tetrahydronaphth-1-yl)imidazole; ethyl 1-(1,2,3,4-tetrahydronaphth-1-yl)imidazole-5-carboxylate; ethonam).

ETONAM NITRATE (ethonamidate; R-10100).

228

ETONITAZENE* (1-[2-(diethylamino)ethyl]-2-(*p*-ethoxybenzyl)-5-nitrobenzimidazole; Ba-20684; NIH-7607).

ETOPERIDONE* (1-(*m*-chlorophenyl)-4-[3-(3,4-diethyl-5-oxo-Δ²-1,2,4-triazolin-1-yl)propyl]piperazine; 1-[3-[4-(*m*-chlorophenyl)piperazin-1-yl]propyl]-3,4-diethyl-Δ²-1,2,4-triazolin-5-one; ST-1191; 'staff').

'**Etophylate**' *see* Acefylline piperazine.

Etophylline *see* Etofylline.

ETOPOSIDE* (5*R*-(5α,5aβ,8aα,9β(*R**))-9-[(4,6-*O*-ethylidene-β-D-glucopyranosyl)oxy]-5,8,8a,9-tetrahydro-5-(4-hydroxy-3,5-dimethoxyphenyl)-furo[3',4':6,7]naphtho[2,3-*d*]-1,3-dioxol-6(5a*H*)-one; 4'-demethylepipodophyllotoxin 9-(4,6-*O*-ethylidene-β-D-glucopyranoside); EPEG; NSC-141540; VP-16-213; 'vepesid').

ETOPRINDOLE* (1-[2-(dimethylamino)ethyl]-3-(1-hydroxyiminopropyl)indole; 1-[2-(dimethylamino)ethyl]-3-propionylindole oxime; 1-[2-(dimethylamino)ethyl]indol-3-yl ethyl ketone oxime).

Etoquinol *see* Actinoquinol.

ETORPHINE* (6,7,8,14-tetrahydro-7α-(1-hydroxy-1-methylbutyl)-6,14-*endo*-ethenooripavine; 19-propylnorvinol; propylorvinol; etorphine hydrochloride; M-99).

ETORPHINE plus ACEPROMAZINE ('immobilon').

ETORPHINE plus LEVOMEPROMAZINE ('immobilon').

Etorphine acetate *see* Acetorphine.

ETOSALAMIDE* (6-(2-ethoxyethoxy)benzamide; salicylamide-2-ethoxyethyl ether; ethosalamide).

'**Etosalicil**' *see* Ethenzamide.

'**Etoscol**' *see* Hexoprenaline.

'**Etossidrazone**' *see* Ruvazone.

'**Etoval**' *see* Butethal.

ETOXADROL* ((+)-2-(2-ethyl-2-phenyl-1,3-dioxolan-4-yl)piperidine; (+)-2-ethyl-2-phenyl-4-piperid-2-yl-1,3-dioxolane; CL-1848C; 'thoxan').

ETOXAZENE* (4-(*p*-ethoxyphenylazo)-*m*-phenylenediamine; 4-(*p*-phenetylazo)-*m*-phenylenediamine; ethoxazene; diaminoethoxyazobenzene; *p*-ethoxychrysoidine; NSC-7214; SQ-2128).

ETOXERIDINE* (ethyl ester of 1-[2-(2-hydroxyethoxy)ethyl]-4-phenylisonipecotic acid; carbetidine; UCB-2073; Wy-2039).

Etoxid (tr) *see* Etocarlide.

ETOZOLIN* (3-methyl-4-oxo-5-piperidino-Δ²,α-thiazolidineacetic acid ethyl ester; ozolinone ethyl ester; 2-(ethoxycarbonylmethylene)-3-methyl-5-piperid-1-yl-4-thiazolidinone; W-2900A; 'elkapin').
See also Dexetozoline.

ETPENAL (tr) (3-(diethylamino)propyl 2-ethoxy-2,2-diphenylacetate; ethpenal).

'**Etrafon**' *see under* Amitriptyline.

'**Etrenol**' *see* Hycanthone mesilate.

ETRETIN ** ((*all-trans*)-9-(4-methoxy-2,3,6-tri-methylphenyl)-3,7,dimethyl-2,4,6,8-nonatetra-enoic acid; 3-methoxy-15-apo-φ-caroten-15-oic acid; Ro 10-1670).

ETRETINATE* (ethyl (*all-trans*)-9-(4-methoxy-2,3,6-trimethylphenyl)-3,7-dimethyl-2,4,6,8-nonatetraenoate; 3-methoxy-15-apo-φ-caroten-15-oic acid ethyl ester; Ro 10-9359; 'tigason').

'**Etriflogin**' *see under* Benzydamine.

ETRIMFOS (*O*,*O*-dimethyl *O*-(6-ethoxy-2-ethyl-pyrimidin-4-yl)phosphorothioate).

'**Etrofolan**' *see* Isoprocarb.

'**Etrolene**' *see* Fenclofos.

Etruscomycin *see* Lucimycin.

'**Etrynit**' *see* Propatylnitrate.

ETRYPTAMINE* (3-(2-aminobutyl)indole; α-ethyltryptamine; etryptamine acetate; NSC-63963; U-17312E).

ETTN *see* Propatylnitrate.

Ettriol nitrate *see* Propatylnitrate.

'**Etumine**' *see* Clotiapine.

ETYBENZATROPINE* (3-(diphenylmethoxy)-8-ethylnortropane; ethybenztropine; methyl-benztropine; tropethydryline; UK-738).

ETYMEMAZINE* (10-[3-(dimethylamino)-2-methylpropyl]-2-ethylphenothiazine; ethotrime-prazine; ethylisobutrazine; ethymemazine; RP 6484).

Etymide *see* Carbifene.

Etynerone *see* Ethynerone.

ETYNODIOL ** (17α-ethynyl-3β,17β-dihydroxy-estr-4-ene; 17α-ethynylestr-4-ene-3β-17β-diol; 17α-ethynyl-19-norandrost-4-ene-3β,17β-diol; 19-nor-17α-pregn-4-en-20-yne-3β,17β-diol; ethynodi-ol).

ETYNODIOL ACETATE (etynodiol 17-acetate; SC-12222).

ETYNODIOL DIACETATE (etynodiol 3,17-di-acetate; CB-8080; SC-11800; 'continuin'; 'femu-len'; 'lumetrodiol'; 'lutometrodiol').

ETYNODIOL DIACETATE plus ETHINYLES-TRADIOL ('bisecurin'; 'conova'; 'demulen').

ETYNODIOL DIACETATE plus MESTRANOL ('metrulen'; 'ovulen'; 'planor').

Etyprenaline* *see* Isoetarine.

EU-1063 *see* Proquinolate.

EU-1085 *see* Leniquinsin.

EU-1093 *see* Buquinolate.

EU-1806 *see* Naftidrofuryl oxalate.

Eu-2200 *see* Inosine.

EU-2826 *see* Benurestat.

EU-2972 *see* Nolinium bromide.

EU-3325 *see* Triafungin.

EU-3421 *see* Oxifungin.

EU-4200 *see* Piribedil.

EU-4891 *see* Diacetolol.

EU-4906 *see* Sitogluside.

EU-16738 *see* Bunaftine.

'**Eubetin**' *see* Chlorpropamide.

'**Eubine**' *see* Oxycodone.

Eucalyptole *see* Cineole.

'**Eucast**' *see* Nicametate.

EUCATROPINE* (1,2,2,6-tetramethyl-4-piperidinol mandelate; 'euphthalmine').

Euchema spinosum degradation product *see* Poligeenan.

'**Euchinin**' *see* Quinine ethyl carbonate.

'**Eucilat**' *see* Benfurodil hemisuccinate.

'**Euclidan**' *see* Nicametate.

'**Eucodin**' *see* Codeine methyl bromide.

'**Eucol**' *see* Arginine oxoglurate.

'**Euctan**' *see* Tolonidine.

'**Eucupine**' *see* Euprocin.

'**Eudan**' *see* Mephebarbital.

'**Eudatin**' *see* Pargyline.

'**Eudemine**' *see* Diazoxide.

'**Eudragit-S**' *see* Fisalamine.

'**Eudyna**' *see* Tretinoin.

Euflavinium** *see* Acriflavinium chloride.

Eugallol *see* Gallacetophenone.

Eugenic acid *see* Eugenol.

EUGENOL (4-allyl-2-methoxyphenol; eugenic acid).

'**Euglucin**' *see* Chlorpentazide.

'**Euglucon**' *see* Glibenclamide.

'**Euglycin**' *see* Metahexamide.

'**Eugynon**' *see under* Levonorgestrel.

'**Euhypnos**' *see* Temazepam.

'**Eukraton**' *see* Bemegride.

'**Eulion**' *see* Imidazole clofibrate.

'**Eulipos**' *see* Dextrothyroxine sodium.

'**Eumicton**' *see* Acetazolamide.

'**Eumotol**' *see* Bumadizone calcium.

'**Eumovate**' *see* Clobetasone butyrate.

'**Eumydrine**' *see* Atropine methonitrate.

'**Eunal**' *see* Estil.

'**Eunarcon**' *see* Enibomal.

'**Eunasin**' *see* Metizoline.

'**Eunephran**' *see* Butizide.

'**Eunerpan**' *see* Melperone.

'**Eunoctin**' *see* Nitrazepam.

'**Eunomin**' *see under* Chlormadinone acetate.

Euonymit *see* Dulcitol.

'**Euparen**' *see* Dichlofluanid.

'**Eupatal**' *see* Alantolactone.

'**Eupaverin**' *see* Moxaverine.

'**Euphagin**' *see* Benzocaine.

'**Euphoramin**' *see under* Methamphetamine.

'**Euphthalmine**' *see* Eucatropine.

'**Euphylline**' *see* Aminophylline.

'**Eupneron**' *see* Eprozinol.

'**Euporphin**' *see* Apomorphine methyl bromide.

'**Eupramin**' *see* Imipramine.

'**Euprax**' *see* Albuton.

EUPROCIN*** (isoamylhydrocupreine; O^6-isopentyl hydrocupreine; WL-287; 'eucupine').

'**Euquinine**' *see* Quinine ethyl carbonate.

'**Eurax**' *see* Crotamiton.

'**Euraxil**' *see* Crotamiton.

'**EureCor**' *see* Isosorbide dinitrate.

'**Euresol**' *see* Resorcinol acetate.

'**Eurinol**' *see* Trichlormethiazide.

'**Eusaprim**' *see* Co-trimoxazole.

'**Eusidon**' *see* Opipramol.

Eusintomicine *see* Chloramphenicol stearate.

'**Euspiran**' *see* Isoprenaline.

'**Euspirax**' *see* Choline theophyllinate.

'**Eustidil**' *see* Haloxon.

Eusynthomycin *see* Chloramphenicol stearate.

'**Euthroid**' *see* Liotrix.

'**Euthyral**' *see under* Levothyroxine sodium.

'**Euthyrox**' *see* Levothyroxine sodium.

'**Eutizon**' *see* Isoniazid.

'**Eutonal**' *see* Nitrous oxide.

'**Eutonyl**' *see* Pargyline *and under* Nitrous oxide.

'**Eutrophyl**' *see* α-Tocopherylquinone.

'**Euvaderm**' *see* Betamethasone benzoate.

'**Euvasculin**' *see under* Bamethan.

'**Euvernil**' *see* Sulfacarbamide.

'**Euvitol**' *see* Fencamfamin.

E-V-A-16 *see* Indanazoline.

'**Evacalm**' *see* Diazepam.

'**Evadyne**' *see* Butriptyline.

EVANS BLUE** (tetrasodium salt of 4,4'-bis[7-(8-amino-1-hydroxy-5,7-disulfonaphth-2-ylazo)]-3,3'-bitolyl; azovan blue; diazo bleu; T-1824).

'**Evaspirine**' *see* Fenyramidol.

'**Eventin**' *see* Propylhexedrine.

EVICROMIL* (8-ethyl-5-hydroxy-4-oxo-6-vinyl-4*H*-1-benzopyran-2-carboxylic acid; 8-ethyl-5-hydroxy-4-oxo-6-vinylchromene-2-carboxylic acid).

'**Evipal**' *see* Hexobarbital.

'**Evramicina**' *see* Troleandomycin.

'**Evramycin**' *see* Troleandomycin.

'**Evronal**' *see* Secobarbital.

EX-12-095 *see* Eterobarb.

EX-4355 *see* Desipramine.

EX-4810 *see* Ambuside.

EX-4883 *see* Rolicyprine.

EX-10029 *see* Elantrine.

EX-10781 *see* Metizoline.

'**Exacyl**' *see* Tranexamic acid.

'**Ex-adipos**' *see* Phentermine.

EXALAMIDE*** (*o*-(hexyloxy)benzamide).

'**Exalgin**' *see* *N*-Methylacetanilide.

'**Exangit**' *see* Benzonatate.

EXAPROLOL*** (1-(*o*-cyclohexylphenoxy)-3-isopropylamino-2-propanol; Mg-8823).

'**Exelmin**' *see* Piperazine.

EXEPANOL** ((±)-*cis*-2,3,4,5-tetrahydro-3-(methylamino)-1-benzoxepin-5-ol).

'**Exhelm II**' *see* Morantel tartrate.

EXIFONE*** (2,3,3',4,4',5'-hexahydroxybenzophenone).

EXIPROBEN*** (1-(2-carboxyphenoxy)-3-hexyloxy-2-propanol; 2-(3-hexyloxy-2-hydroxyprop-oxy)benzoic acid; DCH-21; X-40; 'droctil').

'**Exirel**' *see* Pirbuterol.

'**Exluto**' *see* Lynestrenol.

'**Exluton**' *see* Lynestrenol.

'**Exmigra**' *see* Ergotamine tartrate.

'**Exna**' *see* Benzthiazide.

'**Exofene**' *see* Hexachlorophene.

'**Exolan**' *see* Dithranol triacetate.

'**Exomycol**' *see* Phenylmercuric borate.

'**Exopon**' *see* Cyclexanone.

'**Exosterol**' *see under* Dexamethasone pivalate.

'**Exosulfonyl**' *see* Succisulfone diethanolamine salt.

'**Exotherm termil**' *see* Chlorothalonil.

EXP-105-1 *see* Amantadine.
EXP-126 *see* Rimantadine.
EXP-338 *see* Midaflur.
EXP-999 *see* Metopimazine.
'Expandex' *see* Dextran.
Expansin *see* Patulin.
'Expansolin' *see* Tretoquinol.
'Exponcit' *see* Cathine.

'Extencillin' *see* Benzathine penicillin.
'Exton reagent' *see* Sulfosalicylic acid.
'Extovyl' *see* Betahistine dimesilate.
Extraline (tr) *see* N-Methylaniline.
'Extramycin' *see* Sisomicin.
'Extranase' *see* Bromelains.
Extrinsic factor *see* Cyanocobalamin.
'Exurate' *see* Benzbromarone.

F

F-1 *see* Nitrofurfuryl methyl ether.
F-2 *see* Zearalenone.
F-19 *see* Amikhelline.
F-26 *see* Nidroxyzone.
F-28 *see* Furaguanidine.
F-30 *see* Nitrofurantoin.
F-35 *see* Furazidin.
F-60 *see* Furazolidone.
F-70 *see* Oxitefonium bromide.
F-74 *see* Furaniozid.
F-75 *see* Prazocillin.
F-139 *see* Butonate.
F-151 *see* Methafurylene.
F-309 *see* Suramin sodium.
F-368 *see* Dantrolene.
F-413 *see* Clodanolene.
F-440 *see* Dantrolene.
F-461 *see* Carboxin dioxide.
F-605 *see* Clodanolene.
F-691 *see* Furodazole.
F-710 *see* Plasmocid.
F-776 *see* Orpanoxin.
F-831 *see* Carboxin oxide.
F-853 *see* Nitrafudam.
F-883 *see* 2-[(Diethylamino)methyl]-1,4-benzodi-oxan.
F-933 *see* Piperoxan.
F-1052 *see* Butamoxane.
F-1162 *see* Sulfanilamide.
F-1358 *see* Dapsone.
F-1379 *see* Itanoxone.
F-1399 *see* Acedapsone.
F-1500 *see* Succisulfone.
F-1983 *see* Pyrovalerone.
F-2249 *see* Oxapropanium iodide.
F-2559 *see* Gallamine triethiodide.
F-6066 *see* Cyclofenil.
Fa-402 *see* Fentonium bromide.
'Fabahistin' *see* Mebhydrolin napadisilate.
'Fabianol' *see* Amikacin.
'FAC' *see* Prothoate.
'Factrel' *see* Gonadorelin.
FAD *see* Flavin-adenine dinucleotide.
Fagarol *see* Sesamin.
'Falicaine' *see* Propipocaine.
'Falicor' *see* Prenylamine.
'Falignost' *see* Iomeglamic acid.
'Fali-lepsin' *see* Phenobarbital-norpseudoephedrine.
FALIPAMIL*** (2-[3-[(3,4-dimethoxyphenethyl)-methylamino]propyl]-5,6-dimethoxyphthalimid-

ine; AQ-A39).
'Falithrom' *see* Phenprocoumon.
'Falmonox' *see* Teclozan.
'Falone' *see* 2,4-DEP.
'Famid' *see* Dioxacarb.
FAMOTIDINE*** ([1-amino-3-[[[2-[(diamino-methylene)amino]thiazol-4-yl]methyl]thio]prop-ylidene]sulfamide; 3-[[[2-[(diaminomethylene)-amino]thiazol-4-yl]methyl]thio]-*N*-sulfamoylpro-pionamidine; L-643341; MK-208; YM-11170).
FAMOTINE*** (1-(*p*-chlorophenoxymethyl)-3,4-dihydroisoquinoline; famotine hydrochloride; UK-2054).
FAMPHUR* (*O*-[*p*-(dimethylamino)sulfonyl]-phenyl *O*,*O*-dimethyl phosphorothioate; 'war-bex').
FAMPROFAZONE*** (4-isopropyl-2-methyl-3-[*N*-methyl-*N*-(α-methylphenethyl)aminomethyl]-1-phenyl-3-pyrazolin-5-one; *N*-(4-isopropyl-2-methyl-5-oxo-1-phenyl-3-pyrazolin-3-ylmethyl)-*N*-methylamphetamine).
FAMPROFAZONE plus PROPYPHENAZONE ('gevodin').
'Fanasil' *see* Sulfadoxine.
'Faneron' *see* Bromofenoxim.
FANETIZOLE*** (phenethyl(4-phenylthiazol-2-yl)amine; 2-(phenethylamino)-4-phenylthiazole).
FANETIZOLE MESILATE (fanetizole methane-sulfonate; fanetizole mesylate; CP-48810-27).
Fankinon *see* Phanquinone.
'Fansidar' *see under* Pyrimethamine.
Fanthridone* *see* Fantridone.
'Fantorin' *see* Stibophen.
FANTRIDONE*** (5-[3-(dimethylamino)propyl]-phenanthridinone; fanthridone; AGN-616).
'Fanzil' *see* Sulfadoxine.
FAOP *see* Pralidoxime phenacyl chloride.
'Fargo' *see* Triallate.
'Farial' *see* Indanazoline.
'Farlutal' *see* Medroxyprogesterone acetate.
'Farmidone' *see* Propyphenazone.
'Farmiglucina' *see* Paromomycin.
'Farming S' *see* Endothion.
'Farmiserina' *see* Cycloserine.
FARNESOL (3,7,11-trimethyl-2,6,10-dodecatrien-1-ol).
1-Farnesyl-4-piperonylpiperazine *see* Pifarnine.
FARNOQUINONE (2-difarnesyl-3-methyl-1,4-naphthoquinone; 3-(3,7,11,15,19,23-hexamethyl-2,6,10,14,18,22-tetracosahexaenyl)-2-methyl-1,4-naphthoquinone; 2-methyl-3-*all-trans*-tetrapren-

yl-1,4-naphthoquinone; vitamin K$_2$; menaquin-one-4; pharnoquinone).

Fasciolin see Hexachloroethane.

'**Fasciophene**' see Hexachlorophene.

'**Fasigyn**' see Tinidazole.

Fast green see Malachite green.

Fast green J see Brilliant green.

'**Fastin**' see Phentermine.

'**Fat Ponceau R**' see Scarlet red.

'**Faustan**' see Diazepam.

FAZADINIUM BROMIDE*** (1,1'-azobis(3-methyl-2-phenyl-1H-imidazo[1,2-a]pyridinium bromide); phenazidinium; AH-8165D; 'faza-don').

'**Fazadon**' see Fazadinium bromide.

'**Fazol**' see Isoconazole.

FB/2 see Diquat.

FBA-1420 see Propanidid.

FBA-1464 see Guanacline.

FBA-1500 see Mefruside.

FBA-4059 see Brotianide.

FBA-4503 see Propiram.

FB b-4231 see Glisoxepide.

FB b-5097 see Clotrimazole.

FB b-6366 see Asparaginase.

FB b-6896 see Clenpirin.

FC-1 see Clobenztropine.

FC-11 see Trichlorofluoromethane.

FC-12 see Dichlorodifluoromethane.

FC-152a see 1,1-Difluoroethane.

FC-318 see Octafluorocyclobutane.

'**F-cortef**' see Fludrocortisone.

FEBANTEL*** (dimethyl [[2-(2-methoxyacet-amido)-4-(phenylthio)phenyl]imidocarbonyl]di-carbamate; 2'-(2,3-bismethoxycarbonylguanidi-no)-2-methoxy-5'-(phenylthio)-2-methoxyacet-anilide; BAY h-5757; BAY Vh-5757; 'bayverm'; 'rintal').

FEBARBAMATE*** (1-(2-butoxy-2-hydroxy-propyl)-5-ethyl-5-phenylbarbituric acid carb-amate ester; phenobamate; Go-560).

FEBARBAMATE plus DIFEBARBAMATE & PHENOBARBITAL ('atrium 300'; 'tetrabam-ate').

'**Febramine**' see Cetoxime.

FEBRIFUGINE (tr) (3-(3-hydroxypiperid-2-yl-acetonyl)-4(3H)-quinazolinone).

'**Febrilix**' see Paracetamol.

'**Febrimin**' see Phenicarbazide.

'**Febrinina**' see Aminophenazone.

FEBUPROL*** (1-butoxy-3-phenoxy-2-propanol; H-33; 'valbil').

'**Febutol**' see Fenyramidol oxyphenbutazone.

FEBUVERINE*** (1,4-piperazinediethanol di(2-phenylbutyrate) ester; 1,4-bis(2-phenylbutyryl-oxyethyl)piperazine; phebutazine; PG-430).

'**Febuzine isopirin**' see under 4-(Isopropylamino)-phenazone.

'**Fecatest**' see o-Tolidine.

FECLEMINE*** (2-(α-cyclohexylbenzyl-N,N,N',N'-tetraethyl-1,3-propanediamine; fenet-amine; phenecyclamine; phenetamine; UCB-1545).

FECLEMINE EMBONATE ('licaran').

FECLOBUZONE*** (4-butyl-4-hydroxymethyl-1,2-diphenyl-3,5-pyrazolidinedione p-chloro-benzoate ester; AE-9).

'**Fectrim**' see Co-trimoxazole.

FEDRILATE*** (1-methyl-3-morpholinopropyl tetrahydro-4-phenyl-2H-pyran-4-carboxylate; fenhydropyxylate; UCB-3928; 'tussefane').

'**Feguanide**' see Phenformin.

'**Felagol**' see Cholic acid.

'**Feldene**' see Piroxicam.

'**Felicur**' see 1-Phenyl-1-propanol.

FELIPYRINE*** (1-phenyl-3-piperid-1-ylpyr-rolidin-2-one).

'**Felkreon**' see Ox bile.

'**Felmane**' see Flurazepam.

FELODIPINE*** (ethyl methyl 4-(2,3-dichloro-phenyl)-1,4-dihydro-2,6-dimethylpyridine-3,5-dicarboxylate).

'**Felogen**' see 6-(1-Hydroxyethyl)norbornene acid succinate.

'**Felotrast**' see Phenobutiodil.

Fel tauri see Ox bile.

'**Felviten**' see Anethole trithione.

FELYPRESSIN*** (2-phenylalanine-8-lysine va-sopressin; PLV-2; 'octapressin').

'**Femergin**' see Ergotamine tartrate.

'**Femex**' see Naproxen.

'**Femigen**' see under Chlormadinone acetate.

'**Feminor sequential**' see under Noretynodrel.

FEMOXETINE*** ((+)-trans-3-[(p-methoxy-phenoxy)methyl]-1-methyl-4-phenylpiperidine; FG-4963).

'**Femulen**' see Etynodiol diacetate.

Fen.... see also Phen.....

FENABUTENE*** (p-(2-buten-2-yl)phenyl acet-ate; p-(1-methylpropenyl)phenyl acetate; CB-309; 'isotyl AO12').

FENACETINOL** (p-ethoxy-α-hydroxyacetanil-ide; N-(p-ethoxyphenyl)glycolamide; p-glycolo-phenetidide; N-glycoloyl-p-phenetidine; α-hydr-oxyphenacetin; PM-1952).

FENACLON** (3-chloro-N-phenethylpropion-amide; N-(3-chloropropionyl)phenethylamine; fenacon; fenakon; phenacon).

Fenacon see Fenaclon.

FENADIAZOLE*** (2-(o-hydroxyphenyl)-1,3,4-oxadiazole; o-(1,3,4-oxadiazol-2-yl)phenol; JL-512).

Fenafan (tr) see Phenaphan.

FENAFTIC ACID*** (1-(diethylcarbamoyl)-1,2,3,4,5,6,7,8-octahydro-6,6-dimethyl-8-oxo-3-phenyl-2-naphthoic acid).

Fenakon (tr) see Fenaclon.

FENALAMIDE*** (ethyl N-(2-diethylamino-ethyl)-2-ethyl-2-phenylmalonate; phenylethyl-malonic acid monoethyl ester diethylamino-ethylamide; Sch-5706).

FENALCOMINE*** (α-ethyl-p-[2-(α-methylphen-ethylamino)ethoxy]benzyl alcohol; N-[2-[p-(1-hydroxypropyl)phenoxy]ethyl]-α-methylphen-ethylamine; fenalcomine hydrochloride; 'cordox-ene').

'Fenam' *see* Isoxsuprine.
Fenamet (tr) *see* Phenamet.
FENAMIFURIL*** (tetrahydrofurfuryl (2-carbamoylphenoxy)acetate).
Fenamin (tr) *see* Amphetamine.
FENAMINOSULF* (sodium [*p*-(dimethylamino)-phenyl]diazenesulfonate; 'dexon').
FENAMIPHOS* (ethyl 3-methyl-4-(methylthio)-phenyl isopropylphosphoramidate; 'nemacur P').
FENAMISAL*** (phenyl 4-aminosalicylate; *p*-aminosalol; phenyl-PAS; FR-7; NSC-40144).
'Fenamizol' *see* Amiphenazole.
FENAMOLE** (5-amino-1-phenyl-1*H*-tetrazole; PAT; AL-0559; NSC-25413; P-463).
FENAPERONE*** (cyclohexyl 4'-[3-(*p*-fluorobenzoyl)propyl]-1-piperazinecarboxylate; 4-[(4-cyclohexyloxycarbonyl)piperazin-1-yl]-4'-fluorobutyrophenone).
'Fenarol' *see* Hydroxyzine.
Fenasal (tr) *see* Niclosamide.
Fenasprate *see* Benorilate.
Fenastezin (tr) *see* Phenastezin.
Fenatin (tr) *see* Phenatin.
FENAZAFLOR* (phenyl 5,6-dichloro-2-(trifluoromethyl)-1*H*-benzimidazole-1-carboxylate; fenoflurazole; NC-5016; 'lovozal').
FENBENDAZOLE*** (methyl 5-(phenylthio)-2-benzimidazolecarbamate; HOE-881V; 'panacur').
FENBENICILLIN*** (6-(2-phenoxy-2-phenylacetamido)penicillanic acid; α-phenoxybenzylpenicillin; phenbenicillin; fenbenicillin potassium; 'penspek').
'Fenbiotic' *see* Chloramphenicol.
'Fen-bridal' *see* Promethazine.
FENBUFEN* (3-(4-biphenylylcarbonyl)propionic acid; γ-oxo[1,1'-biphenyl]-4-butanoic acid; CL-82204; 'cinopal'; 'lederfen').
Fenbutazona *see* Phenylbutazone.
FENBUTRAZATE*** (2-(3-methyl-2-phenylmorpholino)ethyl 2-phenylbutyrate; phenbutrazate; R-381).
FENCAMFAMIN*** (2-(ethylamino)-3-phenylnorbornane; *N*-ethyl-3-phenyl-2-norbornanamine; fencamfamin hydrochloride; H-610).
FENCARBAMIDE*** (2-(diethylamino)ethanethiol diphenylcarbamate; *S*-[2-(diethylamino)ethyl] diphenylthiocarbamate; phenacarbamide; phencarbamide; Bayer-1355; Wh-3363).
Fencarol (tr) *see* Quifenadine.
Fenchlorfos *see* Fenclofos.
Fenchlorophos* *see* Fenclofos.
Fenchlorphos* *see* Fenclofos.
FENCIBUTIROL** (α-ethyl-1-hydroxy-4-phenylcyclohexaneacetic acid; 2-(1-hydroxy-4-phenylcyclohexyl)butyric acid; Mg-4833; 'biligen'; 'hepasil'; 'verecolene').
FENCLEXONIUM METILSULFATE*** (1-(3-cyclohexen-1-yl-3-phenylpropyl)-1-methylpiperidinium metilsulfate; HOE-019).
FENCLOFENAC** (2-(2,4-dichlorophenoxy)-phenylacetic acid; R-67408; RX-67408; 'flenac').

FENCLOFOS*** (*O,O*-dimethyl *O*-(2,4,5-trichlorophenyl) phosphorothioate; fenchlorfos; fenchlorophos; fenchlorphos; phenchlorphos; ronnel; Dau ET-14; Dau ET-57).
FENCLONINE*** (DL-3-(*p*-chlorophenyl)alanine; p-CPA; CP-10188; H-69/17; NSC-77370).
FENCLORAC*** (chloro-(3-chloro-4-cyclohexylphenyl)acetic acid; WHR-539).
FENCLOZIC ACID*** (2-(*p*-chlorophenyl)thiazol-4-ylacetic acid; ICI-54450; 'myalex').
FENDILINE** (*N*-(3,3-diphenylpropyl)-α-methylbenzylamine; phenoxan; HK-137; 'sensit').
FENDIZOATE(S)** (2-[(2'-hydroxybiphenyl-4-yl)carbonyl]benzoic acid, esters and salts).
FENDOSAL*** (3-(3-carboxy-4-hydroxyphenyl)-4,5-dihydro-2-phenyl-3*H*-benz[*e*]indole; 5-(4,5-dihydro-2-phenyl-3*H*-benz[*e*]indol-3-yl)salicylic acid; 'alnovin').
FENERITROL*** (pentaerythritol tetrakis-(2-phenylbutyrate); SD-149-01).
'Fenesina' *see* Butetamate.
Fenesterin (tr) *see* Phenesterin.
FENESTREL** (5-ethyl-6-methyl-4-phenyl-3-cyclohexane-1-carboxylic acid).
Fenetamine *see* Feclemine.
FENETHAZINE*** (10-[2-(dimethylamino)-ethyl]phenothiazine; ethizine; ethysine; ethyzine; etisine; etizin; fenethiazine; phenetazine; phenethazine; RP 3015; SC-1627).
Fenethiazine *see* Fenethazine.
Fenethylazocine *see* Phenazocine.
Fenethylline* *see* Fenetylline.
FENETRADIL** (1-(isobutoxymethyl)-2-(4-methylpiperazin-1-yl)ethyl 2-phenylbutyrate).
FENETYLLINE*** (7-[2-(1-methyl-2-phenylethylamino)ethyl]theophylline; 7-[2-(α-methylphenethylamino)ethyl]theophylline; amfetyline; amphetyline; fenethylline hydrochloride; R-720-11; 'captagon').
FENFLUMIZOLE*** (2-(2,4-difluorophenyl)-4,5-bis(*p*-methoxyphenyl)imidazole).
FENFLURAMINE*** (*N*-ethyl-α-methyl-*m*-trifluoromethylphenethylamine; *N*-ethyl-*m*-(trifluoromethyl)amphetamine; 2-(ethylamino)-1-(3-trifluoromethylphenyl)propane; phenfluramine; AHR-965; AHR-3002; EMPT; S-768).
FENHARMANE*** (1-benzyl-2,3,4,9-tetrahydro-1*H*-pyrid[3,4-*b*]indole; fenoharman).
'Fenhydren' *see* Phenindione.
Fenhydropyxylate *see* Fedrilate.
Fenidim (tr) *see* Fenuron.
'Fenidina' *see* Phenacetin.
'Fenidrone' *see* Oxycinchophen.
Fenigama (tr) *see* 4-Amino-3-phenylbutyric acid.
'Fenilin' *see* Phenindione.
'Fenilor' *see under* Broxyquinoline.
FENIMIDE** (3-ethyl-2-methyl-2-phenylsuccinimide; CI-419; PM-1807).
'Fenina' *see* Phenacetin.
FENIODIUM CHLORIDE*** (bis(2,4-dichlorophenyl)iodonium chloride; chlodofen).
Feniodol *see* Pheniodol sodium.
FENIPENTOL*** (α-butylbenzyl alcohol; 1-

234

phenyl-1-pentanol; PC-1).

FENIPENTOL CAMPHORATE (phenylamyl camphorate; phenylpentyl camphorate; 'flubilar').

FENIROFIBRATE*** ((±)-2-[[α-(*p*-chlorophenyl)-α-hydroxy-*p*-tolyl]oxy]-2-methylpropionic acid).

FENISOREX** ((+)-*cis*-3-aminomethyl-7-fluoro-1-phenylisochroman; (+)-*cis*-7-fluoro-1-phenylisochroman-3-ylmethylamine).

'Fenistil' *see* Dimetindene.

FENITRON (tr) (2-(azacycloheptyl)ethyl *m*-nitrophenyl ketone; 3-hexahydroazepin-1-yl-3′-nitropropiophenone; 3-hexamethylenimino-3′-nitropropiophenone; phenitron).

FENITROOXON (dimethyl (*p*-nitro-*m*-tolyl) phosphate; 'sumioxon').

FENITROTHION* (*O,O*-dimethyl *O*-(*p*-nitro-*m*-tolyl) phosphorothioate; methylnitrophos; BAY-41831; Bayer-41831; EC-50; HC-8057; OMS-43; 'accothion'; 'folithion'; 'metathion'; 'owadofos'; 'sumithion'; 'tik-20′).
See also under Dichlorvos.

FENITROTHION plus FENVALERATE ('sumicombi').

Fenizin (tr) *see* Phenelzine.

Fenizon *see* Fenson.

Fenmedifam *see* Phenmedipham.

FENMETOZOLE** (2-(3,4-dichlorophenoxymethyl)-2-imidazoline; DH-524).

FENMETRAMIDE*** (5-methyl-3-oxo-6-phenylmorpholine; 5-methyl-6-phenyl-3-morpholinone; phenmetramide; McN-1075).

FENOBAM** (1-(*m*-chlorophenyl)-3-(1-methyl-4-oxo-2-imidazolin-2-yl)urea; 2-[[(*m*-chlorophenyl)carbamoyl]amino]-1-methyl-2-imidazolin-4-one; McN-3377).

FENOCINOL** (2,4-dimethoxy-α-methylbenzhydrol; 1-(2,4-dimethoxyphenyl)-1-phenylethanol; 'pancreabil').

FENOCTIMINE*** (4-(diphenylmethyl)-1-(*N*-octylformimidoyl)piperidine; fenoctimine sulfate).

FENOFIBRATE*** (isopropyl 2-[*p*-(*p*-chlorobenzoyl)phenoxy]-2-methylpropionate; procetofene; proketofen; LF-178; 'fenolibs'; 'lipanthyl'; 'lipantyl').

Fenoflurazole *see* Fenazaflor.

Fenoharman *see* Fenharmane.

Fenolactina *see* Lactylphenetidin.

FENOLDOPAM** (6-chloro-2,3,4,5-tetrahydro-1-(*p*-hydroxyphenyl)-1*H*-3-benzazepine-7,8-diol).

FENOLDOPAM MESILATE (fenoldopam methanesulfonate; fenoldopam mesylate; SK&F-82526-J).

'Fenolibs' *see* Fenofibrate.

Fenolovo (tr) *see* Fentin hydroxide.

Fenoperidine *see* Phenoperidine.

Fenophosphon *see* Trichloronat.

Fenoprain *see* Propafenone.

FENOPROFEN** ((±)-*m*-phenoxyhydratropic acid; 2-(3-phenoxyphenyl)propionic acid; compound 53858; 'fepron'; 'nalfon').

FENOPROFEN CALCIUM ('fenopron'; 'nalgesic'; 'progesic').

'Fenopron' *see* Fenoprofen calcium.

FENOPROP* (2-(2,4,5-trichlorophenoxy)propionic acid; 2,4,5-TP; silvex; fenoprop esters; fenoprop potassium; 'kuron'; 'kurosal').

'Fenostil' *see* Dimetindene.

FENOTEROL*** (3,5-dihydroxy-α-[[2-(*p*-hydroxyphenyl)-1-methylethyl]aminomethyl]benzyl alcohol; 3,5-dihydroxy-α-(*p*-hydroxy-α-methylphenethylaminomethyl)benzyl alcohol; hydroxyphenylorciprenaline; Th-1165a; 'berotec'; 'partusisten').

FENOTEROL plus IPRATROPIUM BROMIDE ('berodual').

FENOVERINE*** (phenothiazin-10-yl 4-piperonylpiperazin-1-ylmethyl ketone; 1-(phenothiazin-10-ylmethylcarbonyl)-4-piperonylpiperazine; 10-[(4-piperonylpiperazin-1-yl)acetyl]phenothiazine; 'spasmopriv').

'Fenoverm' *see* Phenothiazine.

Fenoxazol *see* Pemoline.

FENOXAZOLINE*** (2-(2-isopropylphenoxymethyl)-2-imidazoline).
See also Prednazoline.

FENOXEDIL*** (2-(*p*-butoxyphenoxy)-*N*-(2,5-diethoxyphenyl)-*N*-(2-diethylaminoethyl)acetamide; *N*-[2-(*p*-butoxyphenoxy)acetyl]-*N*-(2,5-diethoxyphenyl)-*N′,N′*-diethylethylenediamine; ANP-3548; 'suplexedil').

Fenoxypen *see* Penicillin V.

FENOXYPROPAZINE*** (1-(1-methyl-2-phenoxyethyl)hydrazine; phenoxypropazine; HP-1275; 'drazine').

FENOZOLONE*** (2-(ethylamino)-4-oxo-5-phenyl-2-oxazoline; 2-(ethylamino)-5-phenyl-2-oxazolin-4-one; LD-3394; 'ordinator').

FENPENTADIOL*** (2-(*p*-chlorophenyl)-4-methyl-2,4-pentanediol; RD-292).

FENPERATE*** (2-piperid-1-ylethyl α-benzyl-α-hydroxyhydrocinnamate acetate (ester); 2-piperid-1-ylethyl α-acetoxy-α-benzylhydrocinnamate).

FENPIPALONE** (3,6-dihydro-1(2*H*)-(2-(3-methyl-2-oxooxazolidin-5-yl)ethyl)-4-phenylpyridine; 5-[2-(3,6-dihydro-4-phenyl-1(2*H*)-pyridyl)ethyl]-3-methyl-2-oxazolidinone; AHR-1680).

FENPIPRAMIDE*** (2,2-diphenyl-2-(2-piperid-1-ylethyl)acetamide; 2,2-diphenyl-4-piperid-1-ylbutyramide; 2,2-diphenyl-4-piperidinobutyramide; Ho-9980; R-14; U-0229; 'resantin').

FENPIPRAMIDE plus FENPIPRANE ('efosin').

FENPIPRANE*** (3,3-diphenyl-1-piperid-1-ylpropane; diphenylpiperidinopropane; 1-(3,3-diphenylpropyl)piperidine; Ho-10116).
See also under Fenpipramide.

FENPIVERINIUM BROMIDE*** (1-(3-carbamoyl-3,3-diphenylpropyl)-1-methylpiperidinium bromide).

FENPRINAST*** (4-(*p*-chlorobenzyl)-1,4,6,7-tetrahydro-6,6-dimethyl-9*H*-imidazo[1,2-*a*]purin-9-one; fenprinast hydrochloride).

235

FENPROPOREX* (N-(2-cyanoethyl)amphet-amine; DL-3-(α-methylphenethylamino)propio-nitrile; 'dicel'; 'suralgon').

FENPROSTALENE* (methyl (±)-7-[(R,2R,3R,5S)-3,5-dihydroxy-2-(E)-(3R)-(3-hydroxy-4-phenoxy-1-butenyl)cyclopentyl]-4,5-heptadienoate; methyl 9,11,15-trihydroxy-16-phenoxy-ω-tetranorprosta-4,5,13-trienoate; RS-84043).

FENQUIZONE (7-chloro-1,2,3,4-tetrahydro-4-oxo-2-phenyl-6-quinazolinesulfonamide; 7-chloro-1,2,3,4-tetrahydro-4-oxo-2-phenyl-6-sul-famoylquinazoline; 'idrolone').

FENRETINIDE ((all-trans)-4'-hydroxyretinanil-ide; tretinoin p-hydroxyanilide).

FENSON* (4-chlorophenyl benzenesulfonate; p-chlorophenyl besilate; fenizon; CPBS; PCBS; PCI; PCPBS; 'murvesco'; 'nitricide').

FENSPIRIDE* (8-phenethyl-1-oxa-3,8-diaza-spiro[4.5]decan-2-one; decaspiride; JP-428; NAT-333; NDR-5998A; 'espiran'; 'pneumorel'; 'respiride'; 'viarespan').

FENSULFOTHION* (O,O-diethyl O-(4-methyl-sulfinylphenyl) phosphorothioate; DMSP; Bayer-25141; 'dasanil'; 'terracur P').

'Fentanest' see Fentanyl.

FENTANYL* (N-(1-phenethylpiperid-4-yl)pro-pionanilide; 1-phenethyl-4-(N-propionylanilino)-piperidine; phentanyl; fentanyl citrate; McN-JR-4263-49; R-4263).
See also under Droperidol.

Fentathienyl* see Sufentanil.

'Fentazin' see Perphenazine.

FENTHION* (O,O-dimethyl O-[p-(methylthio)-m-tolyl] phosphorothioate; Bayer-29493; Bayer S-1752; 'baycid'; 'bayten'; 'baytex'; 'entex'; 'lebay-cid'; 'mercaptophos'; 'queleton'; 'tiguvon').

FENTIAZAC* (4-(p-chlorophenyl)-2-phenyl-5-thiazoleacetic acid; BR-700; Wy-21894; 'donor-est'; 'flogene'; 'norvedan').

FENTICLOR* (bis(5-chloro-2-hydroxyphenyl) sulfide; dichlorodihydroxydiphenyl sulfide; 2,2'-thiobis(4-chlorophenol); D-25; HL-1050; NSC-4112; S-7; 'novex'; 'ovitrol').

FENTICLOR plus TRIAMCINOLONE ('fenti-derm').

FENTICONAZOLE* (1-[2,4-dichloro-β-[[p-(phenylthio)benzyl]oxy]phenethyl]imidazole; 1-(2,4-dichlorophenyl)-2-(N-imidazolyl)ethyl 4-phenylthiobenzyl ether; fenticonazole nitrate; Rec 15/1476).

'Fentiderm' see under Fenticlor.

FENTIN* (triphenyltin).

FENTIN ACETATE* (acetoxytriphenylstannane; 'brestan').

FENTIN CHLORIDE* (chlorotriphenylstannane; TPTC).

FENTIN HYDROXIDE* (hydroxytriphenylstan-nane; triphenylhydroxytin; fenolovo; TPTH; 'duter').

FENTONIUM BROMIDE* (3α-hydroxy-8-(p-phenylphenacyl)-1αH,5αH-tropanium bromide (−)-tropate; hyoscyamine (4'-phenylphenacyl)

bromide; Fa-402; Z-326; 'ketoscilium'; 'ulce-sium').

FENTONIUM BROMIDE plus PERPHENAZ-INE (FZ-484; 'duo-tran').

'Fentrinol' see Amidefrine mesilate.

FENURON* (1,1-dimethyl-3-phenylurea; fenidim; 'dybar').

FENURON TRICHLOROACETATE ('urab').

FENVALERATE (2-(p-chlorophenyl-2-isopropyl-acetic acid ester with m-phenoxymandelonitrile; 2-(p-chlorophenyl)-3-methylbutyric acid α-cya-no-m-phenoxybenzyl ester; cyano(3-phenoxy-phenyl)methyl 2-(4-chlorophenyl)-3-methyl-butyrate; OMS-2000; S-5602; WL-43775; 'bel-mark'; 'sumicidin'; 'sumifive').

FENYRAMIDOL* (α-[(2-pyridylamino)meth-yl]benzyl alcohol; phenyramidol; fenyramidol hydrochloride; IN-511; MJ-505; NSC-17777).

FENYRAMIDOL OXYPHENBUTAZONE (CG-21; 'febutol').

FENYRIPOL* (α-[(pyrimidin-2-ylamino)meth-yl]benzyl alcohol; fenyripol hydrochloride; IN-836; NSC-43183).

FEPENTOLIC ACID (α-butyl-5-carboxy-2-hydroxybenzyl alcohol; α-butyl-α-hydroxy-4,3-cresotic acid; 4-hydroxy-3-(1-hydroxypentyl)-benzoic acid; RCM-258).

FEPITRIZOL* (5-[2-(hydroxymethyl)phenyl]-1-methyl-3-pyrid-3-yl-1H-1,2,4-triazole; o-(1-methyl-3-pyrid-3-yl-1H-1,2,4-triazol-5-yl)benzyl alcohol).

FEPRACET (tr) (p-amino-N-(1-methyl-2-phenyl-ethyl)phenylacetamide; p-aminophenylacetic acid phenylisopropylamide; N-(p-aminophenyl-acetyl)amphetamine; amphetamine p-amino-phenylacetate; fepratset; phepracet; IEM-366).

FEPRADINOL ((±)-α-[[(2-hydroxy-1,1-dimeth-ylethyl)amino]methyl]benzyl alcohol).

Fepratset (tr) see Fepracet.

FEPRAZONE (4-(3-methyl-2-butenyl)-1,2-di-phenyl-3,5-pyrazolidinedione; 4-prenyl-1,2-di-phenyl-3,5-pyrazolidinedione; phenylprenazone; prenazone; DA-2370; 'methrazone'; 'metrazone'; 'zepelin').
See also under Bromhexine.

FEPROMIDE* (3,4,5-trimethoxy-N-(1-phen-oxymethyl-2-pyrrolidin-1-ylethyl)benzamide; CERM-1875).

'Fepron' see Fenoprofen.

FEPROSIDNINE* (3-(α-methylphenethyl)syd-none imine).

FER-1443 see Ticlatone.

FERBAM* (ferric dimethylcarbamodithioate; ferric dimethyldithiocarbamate; S,S',S''-tris(dimethyl-carbamodithioato)iron; 'ferberk'; 'fermate'; 'fer-radow'; 'fuklasin ultra'; 'karbam black').

'Ferberk' see Ferbam.

Ferbitol (tr) see Iron sorbitex.

'Fermate' see Ferbam.

'Fermine' see Dimethyl phthalate.

'Fernasan' see Thiram.

'Ferradow' see Ferbam.

Ferric.... see also Iron.....

236

Ferric chloride-phenazone compound *see* Ferripyrine.

FERRIC (^{59}Fe) CITRATE INJECTION*** (sterile solution containing radioactive iron, sodium citrate and sodium chloride).

Ferric cyanoferrate *see* Prussian blue.

Ferric dimethylcarbamodithioate *see* Ferbam.

Ferric dimethyldithiocarbamate *see* Ferbam.

Ferric ferrocyanide *see* Prussian blue.

FERRIC FRUCTOSE*** (fructose-iron complex compound with potassium (2:1); CB-302; 'ferritose').

Ferricholinate *see* Ferrocholinate.

Ferric hydroxide compound with dextrin & citric acid *see* Cideferron.

Ferriclate calcium sodium* *see* Calcium sodium ferriclate.

FERRICYANIDES (cyanoferrates (III)).

'Ferridextran' *see* Iron dextran injection.

'Ferrigen' *see* Dextriferron.

Ferriheme chloride *see* Hemin.

Ferriheme hydroxide *see* Hematin.

Ferriporphyrin chloride *see* Hemin.

Ferriporphyrin hydroxide *see* Hematin.

FERRIPYRINE (ferric chloride-phenazone compound; ferropyrine).

Ferritetraceminnatrium* *see* Sodium feredetate.

'Ferritose' *see* Ferric fructose.

Ferrocene *see* Dicyclopentadienyliron.

'Ferrochel' *see* Ferrocholinate.

FERROCHOLINATE*** (chelate of ferric hydroxide with choline dihydrogen citrate; ferricholinate; iron choline citrate; 'ferrochel'; 'ferrolip').

'Ferrocontin' *see* Ferroglycine sulfate.

FERROCYANIDES (cyanoferrates (II)).

FERROGLYCINE SULFATE (iron-glycine complex; orferon; 'ferrocontin'; 'ferronord'; 'plesmet').

Ferroheme *see* Heme.

'Ferrolip' *see* Ferrocholinate.

'Ferronascin' *see* Sodium dipantoylferrate.

'Ferronord' *see* Ferroglycine sulfate.

FERROPOLIMALER*** (maleic acid polymer with methylvinyl ether iron (ferrous) salt; iron polymalether; 'tetucur').

Ferroporphyrin *see* Heme.

Ferropyrine *see* Ferripyrine.

FERROTRENINE*** (bis(*N*-ethylidenethreoninato) hydrogen diaquoferrate (II); hydrogen bis(*N*-ethylidenethreoninato) diaquoferrate (II)).

Ferrous... *see also* Iron......

Ferrous sodium pantoate *see* Sodium dipantoylferrate.

FERTIRELIN*** (5-oxo-L-prolyl-L-histidyl-L-tryptophyl-L-seryl-L-tyrosylglycyl-L-leucyl-L-arginyl-*N*-ethyl-L-prolinamide).

'Fertodur' *see* Cyclofenil.

FERULIC ACID (4-hydroxy-3-methoxycinnamic acid).
    See also Magnesium ferulate; Rescimetol.

'Fe-3-specific' *see* *N,N*-Bis(2-hydroxyethyl)glycine.

Fetanol (tr) *see* Etilefrine.

FETOXILATE*** (2-phenoxyethyl 1-(3-cyano-3,3-diphenylpropyl)-4-phenylisonipecotate; 2-phenoxyethyl difenoxilate; fetoxylate hydrochloride; McN-JR-13558-11; R-13558).

Fetoxylate* *see* Fetoxilate.

FEXICAINE*** (2-(*p*-butoxyphenoxy)-*N*-(*o*-methoxyphenyl)-*N*-(2-pyrrolidin-1-ylethyl)acetamide; 1-[2-[[2-(*p*-butoxyphenoxy)acetyl]-(*o*-methoxyphenyl)amino]ethyl]pyrrolidine; *N*-(2-(*p*-butoxyphenoxy)acetyl)-*N*-(2-pyrrolidin-1-ylethyl)-*o*-anisidine).

'Feximac' *see* Bufexamac.

FEXNIDAZOLE*** (1-methyl-2-[[*p*-(methylthio)phenoxy]methyl]-5-nitroimidazole).

FEZATIONE*** (3-(*p*-methylbenzylideneamino)-4-phenyl-4-thiazoline-2-thione).

FEZOLAMINE*** (1-[3-(dimethylamino)propyl]-3,4-diphenylpyrazole).

FG-4963 *see* Femoxetine.

FG-5111 *see* Melperone.

FGA *see* Flugestone acetate.

FH-049-E *see* Diphenoxylate.

FI-5631 *see* Methopromazine.

FI-5852 *see* Oxabolone cipionate.

FI-5853 *see* Paromomycin.

FI-6146 *see* Buzepide metiodide.

FI-6337 *see* Metergoline.

FI-6339 *see* Daunorubicin.

FI-6426 *see* Stallimycin.

FI-6642 *see* Metiazinic acid.

FI-6654 *see* Caroxazone.

FI-6714 *see* Nicergoline.

FI-6820 *see* Brofoxine.

FI-6927 *see* Pipotiazine palmitate.

FI-7302 *see under* Amoxicillin.

'Fibocil' *see* Aprindine.

'Fiboran' *see* Aprindine.

FIBRACILLIN** (D-6-[2-[2-(*p*-chlorophenoxy)-2-methylpropionamido]-2-phenylacetamido]penicillanic acid; 'fibrapen').

Fibrafylline *see* Acefylline clofibrol.

'Fibrapen' *see* Fibracillin.

'Fibrase' *see* Pentosan polysulfate.

FIBRIN ADHESIVE (human fibrinogen concentrate; 'tissucol').

FIBRINOGEN (human fibrinogen; 'fibrogen'; 'parenogen').

FIBRINOGEN (^{125}I)*** (fibrinogen I 125; human fibrinogen labeled with iodine 125; 'ibrin'; 'sensor').

FIBRINOLYSIN (HUMAN)** ('actase'; 'thrombolysin').
    See also Brinase; Plasmin.

'Fibrogen' *see* Fibrinogen.

'Ficam' *see* Bendiocarb.

'Ficoid' *see* Fluocortolone caproate.

FIGLU *see* Formiminoglutamic acid.

'Filair' *see* Terbutaline.

'Filariol' *see* Bromofos-ethyl.

FILENADOL*** (($\pm$)-*erythro*-α-methyl-β-[3,4-(methylenedioxy)phenyl]-4-morpholineethanol).

Filicic acid *see* Filixic acid.

Filicin *see* Filixic acid.

Filicinic acid *see* Filixic acid.

Filimarisin *see* Filipin.
FILIPIN* (3,5,7,9,11,13,15,26,27-nonahydroxy-2-(1-hydroxyhexyl)-16-methyl-16,18,20,22,24-octacosapentaenoic acid 1,27-lactone; 4,6,8,10,12,14,16,27-octahydroxy-3-(1-hydroxyhexyl)-17,28-dimethyloxacyclooctacosa-17,19,21,23,25-pentaen-2-one; filimarisin; NSC-3364; NSC-208642; U-5956).
FILIXIC ACID (3,5-dihydroxy-6,6-dimethyl-2,4-cyclohexadien-1-one; 2,2-dimethyl-1,3,5-cyclohexanetrione; filicic acid; filicin; filicinic acid).
'**Filon**' *see* Phenmetrazine teoclate.
'**Filoral**' *see* Choline theophyllinate.
'**Fimomed**' *see* Enbucrilate.
'**Finajet**' *see* Trenbolone acetate.
'**Finalgon**' *see under* Nicoboxil.
'**Finalin**' *see* Methylbenactyzium bromide.
'**Finaplex**' *see* Trenbolone acetate.
'**Finaven**' *see* Difenzoquat.
'**Finimal**' *see* Paracetamol.
'**Finlepsin**' *see* Carbamazepine.
'**Finomed**' *see* Enbucrilate.
'**Finovakil**' *see* Fluoroacetic acid.
'**Finquel**' *see* Tricaine.
'**Fintozid**' *see* Pasiniazid.
FIPEXIDE* (1-(*p*-chlorophenoxyacetyl)-4-piperonylpiperazine; 'vigilor').
FISALAMINE* (5-aminosalicylic acid; *m*-aminosalicylic acid; 5-ASA; 'asacol'; 'eudragit-S').
'**Fisiogamma**' *see* Oxybate sodium.
'**Fisioquens**' *see under* Ethinylestradiol.
'**Fisohex**' *see* Hexachlorophene.
'**Fisostina**' *see* Furtrethonium tosilate.
'**Fissancort**' *see* Dexamethasone.
Fitios *see* Ethoate-methyl.
FK-749 *see* Ceftizoxime.
FK-880 *see* Sulpiride.
FK-1160 *see* Tiaramide.
FK-1320 *see* Glipizide.
FL-113 *see* Ipriflavone.
FL-1039 *see* Pivmecillinam.
FL-1060 *see* Mecillinam.
FLA-136 *see* Nebidrazine.
'**Flabellin**' *see* Meticillin.
'**Flac**' *see* Fluoroacetic acid.
'**Flagecidin**' *see* Anisomycin.
'**Flagentyl**' *see* Secnidazole.
'**Flagyl**' *see* Metronidazole.
'**Flamanil**' *see* Pifoxime.
FLAMENOL* (5-methoxyresorcinol).
'**Flamilon**' *see* Suxibuzone.
'**Flammazin**' *see* Sulfadiazine silver.
'**Flanthin**' *see* Calcium levulinate.
FLAVAMINE* (6-[(diethylamino)methyl]-3-methylflavone; flavamine hydrochloride; Rec-7-0052).
FLAVAN (3,4-dihydro-2-phenyl-2*H*-1-benzopyran; 2-phenylchroman).
3,3',4,4',5,7-Flavanhexol *see* Leucocianidol.
FLAVANONE (2,3-dihydro-2-phenyl-4*H*-1-benzopyran-4-one; 2-phenyl-4-chromanone; dihydroflavone).
3,3',4',5,7-Flavanpentol *see* Cianidanol.

Flavin *see* Quercetin.
FLAVIN-ADENINE DINUCLEOTIDE (riboflavin 5'-adenosine diphosphate; FAD; isoalloxazine-adenine dinucleotide).
FLAVIN MONONUCLEOTIDE (riboflavin 5'-phosphate sodium salt; alloxazine mononucleotide; 'A.M.N'; 'coflavinase'; 'cytoflav'; 'hyryl').
FLAVODIC ACID* (5,7-bis(carboxymethoxy)-flavone; [(4-oxo-2-phenyl-4*H*-1-benzopyran-5,7-diyl)dioxy]diacetic acid).
FLAVODIC ACID SODIUM SALT ('pericel').
FLAVODILOL* ((±)-7-[2-hydroxy-3-(propylamino)propoxy]flavone).
'**Flavomycin**' *see* Bambermycin.
FLAVONE (2-phenyl-4*H*-1-benzopyran-4-one; 2-phenylchromone).
7-Flavonoxyacetic acid ethyl ester *see* Efloxate.
'**Flavoquine**' *see* Amodiaquine.
'**Flavoteben**' *see* *N*'-(*p*-Hydroxybenzylidene)isoniazid.
FLAVOTINE (6-chloro-9-(1-D-sorbityl)isoalloxazine).
FLAVOVIOLET (3-hydroxy-6,7-dimethyl-2-(1-ribityloxy)quinoxaline).
FLAVOXATE* (2-piperid-1-ylethyl 3-methyl-4-oxo-2-phenyl-4*H*-1-benzopyran-8-carboxylate; 2-piperid-1-ylethyl 8-methylflavonecarboxylate; AK-123; DW-61; NSC-114649; Rec-7-0040).
'**Flavugal**' *see* Cyclovalone.
'**Flaxedil**' *see* Gallamine triethiodide.
FLAZALONE* (3-(*p*-fluorobenzoyl)-4-(*p*-fluorophenyl)-4-hydroxy-1-methylpiperidine; *p*-fluorophenyl 4-(*p*-fluorophenyl)-4-hydroxy-1-methyl-piperid-3-yl ketone; flumefenine; NSC-102629; R-760).
'**Fleboside**' *see under* Carbazochrome.
FLECAINIDE* (*N*-(piperid-2-ylmethyl)-2,5-bis(2,2,2-trifluoroethoxy)benzamide).
FLECAINIDE ACETATE* (flecainide monoacetate salt; R-818; 'tambocor').
'**Flectadol**' *see* Lysine acetylsalicylate.
'**Flectar**' *see* Butixirate.
'**Flemoxin**' *see* Amoxicillin.
'**Flenac**' *see* Fenclofenac.
FLETAZEPAM* (7-chloro-5-(*o*-fluorophenyl)-2,3-dihydro-1-(2,2,2-trifluoroethyl)-1*H*-1,4-benzodiazepine; Sch-15698).
'**Flexartal**' *see* Carisoprodol.
'**Flexeril**' *see* Cyclobenzaprine.
'**Flexin**' *see* Zoxazolamine.
'**Flibol e**' *see* Metrifonate.
'**Flit**' *see under* Chlordane.
FLO-1347 *see* Tiapride.
FLOCTAFENINE* (2,3-dihydroxypropyl *N*-(8-trifluoromethylquinolin-4-yl)anthranilate; R-4318; RU-15750; 'idalon'; 'idarac').
'**Flogar**' *see* Oxametacin.
'**Flogene**' *see* Fentiazac.
'**Floginax**' *see* Naproxen.
'**Flonatril**' *see* Clorexolone.
FLOPROPIONE* (2',4',6'-trihydroxypropiophenone; phloropropiophenone; RP-13907).
FLORANTYRONE* (4-(fluoranthren-8-yl)-4-

oxobutyric acid; γ-oxo-8-fluoranthrenebutyric acid; SC-1674).

'Floraquin' *see* Diiodohydroxyquin.

FLORDIPINE* (diethyl 1,4-dihydro-2,6-dimethyl-1-(2-morpholinoethyl)-4-(α,α,α-trifluoro-*o*-tolyl)-3,5-pyridinedicarboxylate).

FLOREDIL* (1,3-diethoxy-5-(2-morpholinoethoxy)benzene; 4-[2-(3,5-diethoxyphenoxy)ethyl]-morpholine).

FLORENAL (tr) (9-oxofluoren-2-ylglyoxal bisulfite compound; fluorenal).

Floretione *see* Fluoresone.

FLORIFENINE ** (2-pyrrolidin-1-ylethyl *N*-[7-(trifluoromethyl)-4-quinolyl]anthranilate).

Florimycin (tr) *see* Viomycin.

'Florinef' *see* Fludrocortisone.

'Florisil' *see* Magnesium trisilicate.

'Florispec' *see* Epicillin.

'Florocycline' *see* Tetracycline.

'Florone' *see* Diflorasone diacetate.

Floropipamide *see* Pipamperone.

Floropipetone *see* Propyperone.

'Floropryl' *see* Isoflurophate.

'Flosin' *see* Indoprofen.

'Flosint' *see* Indoprofen.

FLOTRENIZINE* ((±)-4-[bis(*p*-fluorophenyl)methyl]-α-(*p-tert*-butylphenyl)-1-piperazinebutanol).

FLOVERINE ** (2-(3,5-dimethoxyphenoxy)ethanol; 5-(2-hydroxyethyl)-1,3-dimethoxybenzene).

Floxacillin* *see* Flucloxacillin.

FLOXACRINE* (7-chloro-3,4-dihydro-10-hydroxy-3-(α,α,α-trifluoro-*p*-tolyl)-1,9(2*H*)-acridandione; HOE-991).

'Floxapen' *see* Flucloxacillin.

FLOXURIDINE* (2′-deoxy-5-fluorouridine; 2′-desoxy-5-fluorouridine; 5-fluoro-2′-deoxyuridine; FUDR; NSC-27640).

FLUACIZINE* (2-(diethylamino)ethyl 2-(trifluoromethyl)phenothiazin-10-yl ketone; 10-[3-(diethylamino)propionyl]-2-(trifluoromethyl)-phenothiazine; fluoracizine; ftoracizine).

FLUALAMIDE* (2-allyloxy-*N*-(2-diethylaminoethyl)-4-trifluoromethylbenzamide; 2-allyloxy-*N*-(2-diethylaminoethyl)-α,α,α-trifluoro-*p*-toluamide; CE-305).

'Fluamoxina' *see* Amoxicillin.

FLUANISONE* (4′-fluoro-4-[4-(*o*-methoxyphenyl)piperazin-1-yl]butyrophenone; 1-[3-(*p*-fluorobenzoyl)propyl]-4-(*o*-methoxyphenyl)piperazine; metorin; MD-2028; R-2028; R-2167).

'Fluanxol' *see* Flupentixol.

'Fluaton' *see* Fluorometholone.

FLUAZACORT* (9-fluoro-11β,21-dihydroxy-2′-methyl-5′β*H*-pregna-1,4-dieno[17,16-*d*]oxazole-3,20-dione 21-acetate; fluazacortenol; L-64000; 'azacortid').

Fluazacortenol *see* Fluazacort.

FLUBANILATE* (ethyl *N*-[2-(dimethylamino)-ethyl]-*m*-trifluoromethylcarbanilate; flubanilate hydrochloride).

'Flubason' *see* Desoximetasone.

FLUBENDAZOLE* (methyl 5-(*p*-fluorobenzo-yl)-2-benzimidazolecarbamate; R-17889; 'fluvermal').

Flubenisolone* *see* Betamethasone.

'LUBEPRIDE* (1-(*p*-fluorobenzyl)-2-[(2-methoxy-5-sulfamoylbenzamido)methyl]pyrrolidine; *N*-[[1-(*p*-fluorobenzyl)pyrrolidin-2-yl]methyl]-5-sulfamoyl-*o*-anisamide).

'Flubilar' *see* Fenipentol camphorate.

Flubuperone *see* Melperone.

FLUCARBRIL* (1-methyl-2-oxo-6-(trifluoromethyl)quinoline).

FLUCETOREX ** (α-[[α-methyl-*m*-(trifluoromethyl)phenethyl]carbamoyl]-*p*-acetanisidide; *p*-[[[α-methyl-*m*-(trifluoromethyl)phenethyl]carbamoyl]methoxy]acetanilide; PM-3944).

'Flucexin' *see under* Cefalexin.

FLUCINDOLE* (6,8-difluoro-2,3,4,9-tetrahydro-*N*,*N*-dimethyl-1*H*-carbazol-3-amine; 3-(dimethylamino)-6,8-difluoro-1,2,3,4-tetrahydrocarbazole; WIN-35150).

FLUCIPRAZINE ** (1-[3-(1-ethynylcyclohexyloxy)-2-hydroxypropyl]-4-(*p*-fluorophenyl)piperazine; α-[(1-ethynylcyclohexyloxy)methyl]-4-(*p*-fluorophenyl)-1-piperazineethanol).

FLUCLOROLONE* (9α,11β-dichloro-6α-fluoro-16α,17α,21-trihydroxypregna-1,4-diene-3,20-dione).

FLUCLOROLONE ACETONIDE* (fluclorolone cyclic 16,17-acetal with acetone; 9α,11β-dichloro-6α-fluoro-21-hydroxy-16α,17α-isopropylidenedioxypregna-1,4-diene-3,20-dione; flucloronide; RS-2252; 'topilar').

Flucloronide* *see* Fluclorolone acetonide.

FLUCLOXACILLIN* (6-[3-(2-chloro-6-fluorophenyl)-5-methyl-4-isoxazolecarboxamido]penicillanic acid; 3-(2-chloro-6-fluorophenyl)-5-methylisoxazol-4-ylpenicillin; floxacillin; BRL-2039).

See also under Amoxicillin; Ampicillin; Cefalexin.

'Flucort' *see* Flumetasone.

FLUCRILATE* (2,2,2-trifluoro-1-methylethyl 2-cyanoacrylate; flucrylate; BA-4197; MBR-4197).

Flucrylate* *see* Flucrilate.

FLUCYTOSINE* (4-amino-5-fluoro-1,2-dihydropyrimidin-2-one; 5-fluorocytosine; Ro 2-9915; 'alcobon'; 'ancobon'; 'ancotil').

FLUCYTOSINE ARABINOSIDE (arabinofuranosyl-5-fluorocytosine; ara-FC).

FLUCYTOSINE DEOXYRIBOSIDE (5-fluoro-2′-deoxycytidine).

FLUDALANINE* (3-fluoro-D-alanine-2-*d*).

FLUDARABINE ** (9-β-D-arabinofuranosyl-2-fluoroadenine).

FLUDARABINE PHOSPHATE* (2-fluoro-9-(5-*O*-phosphono-β-D-arabinofuranosyl)-9*H*-purin-6-amine; fludarabine dihydrogen phosphate; 2-fluoro-ARA-AMP; NSC-312887).

'Fludarene' *see* Chromocarb diethylamine.

FLUDAZONIUM CHLORIDE* (1-[2,4-dichloro-β-[(2,4-dichlorobenzyl)oxy]phenethyl]-3-(*p*-fluorophenacyl)imidazolium chloride; R-

23633).
'Fluderma' *see* Formocortal.
'Fludex' *see* Indapamide.
FLUDIAZEPAM* (7-chloro-5-(*o*-fluorophenyl)-1,3-dihydro-1-methyl-2*H*-1,4-benzodiazepin-2-one; ID-540).
'Fludilat' *see* Bencyclane.
FLUDOREX (β-methoxy-*N*-methyl-*m*-trifluoromethylphenethylamine; WIN-11464).
FLUDOXOPONE* (4-(*p*-fluorophenyl)-5-[2-(4-phenylpiperazin-1-yl)ethyl]-1,3-dioxol-2-one).
'Fludrocortisate' *see* Fludrocortisone.
FLUDROCORTISONE* (9α-fluoro-11β,17α,21-trihydroxypregn-4-ene-3,20-dione; fluohydrisone; fluohydrocortisone; fluorhydrocortisone; fluorocortisol; fluorocortisone; fludrocortisone acetate; StC-1400).
'Fludrocortone' *see* Fludrocortisone.
'Fludrone' *see* Fludrocortisone.
FLUDROXYCORTIDE* (6α-fluoro-16α,17-dihydroxycorticosterone cyclic 16,17-acetal with acetone; 6α-fluoro-11β,16α,17,21-tetrahydroxypregn-4-ene-3,20-dione cyclic 16,17-acetal with acetone; 6α-fluoro-11β,21-dihydroxy-16α,17α-isopropylidenedioxypregn-4-ene-3,20-dione; fluorandrenolone; flurandrenolide; flurandrenolone).
Fluenethyl *see* Fluenetil.
FLUENETIL* (2-fluoroethyl [1,1'-biphenyl]-4-acetate; 2-fluoroethyl biphenylylacetate; 2-fluoroethyl xenylacetate; fluenethyl; 'lambrol').
FLUFENAMIC ACID* (*N*-(α,α,α-trifluoro-*m*-tolyl)anthranilic acid; 2-carboxy-3'-(trifluoromethyl)diphenylamine; B-306; CI-440; CN-27554; INF-1837; McN-R-1238; NSC-82699; TVX-916).
See also Aluminium flufenamate; Colfenamate; Etofenamate; Prefenamate; Ufenamate.
Flufenazine* *see* Fluphenazine.
FLUFENISAL* (4-acetoxy-4'-fluorobiphenyl-3-carboxylic acid; 4'-fluoro-4-hydroxy-3-biphenylcarboxylic acid acetate).
FLUFOSAL (2-hydroxy-4-(trifluoromethyl)-benzoic acid dihydrogen phosphate; α,α,α-trifluoro-2,4-cresotic acid dihydrogen phosphate).
FLUFYLLINE* (7-[2-[4-(*p*-fluorobenzoyl)piperid-1-yl]ethyl]theophylline).
FLUGESTONE* (9α-fluoro-11β,17α-dihydroxyprogesterone; 9-fluoro-11β,17-dihydroxypregn-4-ene-3,20-dione; fluorogestone; flurogestone).
FLUGESTONE ACETATE (flugestone 17-acetate; FGA; NSC-65411; SC-9880).
'Fluibil' *see* Chenodeoxycholic acid.
'Fluibron' *see* Ambroxol.
'Fluidemin' *see* Bromindione.
'Fluidex' *see* Dextran 40.
'Fluimucil' *see* Acetylcysteine.
FLUINDAROL* (2-(α,α,α-trifluoro-*p*-tolyl)-1,3-indandione).
FLUINDIONE* (2-(*p*-fluorophenyl)-1,3-indandione).
'Fluitran' *see* Trichlormethiazide.

'Flukanide' *see* Rafoxanide.
'Flumamine' *see* Metformin.
FLUMAZEPIL (ethyl 8-fluoro-5,6-dihydro-5-methyl-6-oxo-4*H*-imidazo[1,5-*a*][1,4]benzodiazepine-3-carboxylate; Ro-15-1788).
'Flumazine' *see* Fluphenazine.
FLUMECINOL* (α-ethyl-3-(trifluromethyl)-benzhydrol; α-ethyl-α-[*m*-(trifluoromethyl)phenyl]benzyl alcohol; 1-phenyl-1-[3-(trifluoromethyl)phenyl]-1-propanol; ziksorin; zykzorin; 'zixoryn').
FLUMEDROXONE* (17-hydroxy-6α-(trifluoromethyl)pregn-4-ene-3,20-dione; 17-hydroxy-6α-(trifluoromethyl)progesterone; WG-537).
Flumefenine *see* Flazalone.
FLUMEQUINE* (9-fluoro-6,7-dihydro-5-methyl-1-oxo-1*H*,5*H*-benzo[*ij*]quinolizine-2-carboxylic acid; R-802; 'apurone').
FLUMERIDONE* (5-chloro-1-[1-[3-(5-fluoro-2-oxo-1-benzimidazolinyl)propyl]piperid-4-yl]-2-benzimidazolinone; R-45486).
FLUMETASONE* (6α,9α-difluoro-11β,17α,21-trihydroxy-16α-methylpregna-1,4-diene-3,20-dione; 6α,9α-difluoro-16α-methylprednisolone; flumethasone; NSC-54702; RS-2177; U-10974).
FLUMETASONE PIVALATE (NSC-107680; 'cerson'; 'fluvet'; 'locacorten'; 'locorten'; 'losalen').
FLUMETASONE PIVALATE plus SALICYLIC ACID & COAL TAR ('psocorten').
Flumethasone* *see* Flumetasone.
FLUMETHIAZIDE* (6-(trifluoromethyl)-2*H*-1,2,4-benzothiadiazine-7-sulfonamide 1,1-dioxide; trifluoromethylthiazide; 'ademil').
'Flumetholon' *see* Fluorometholone.
FLUMETHRIN* (α-cyano-4-fluoro-3-phenoxybenzyl 3-(β,4-dichlorostyryl)-2,2-dimethylcyclopropanecarboxylate; BAY vl-6045).
FLUMETRAMIDE* (6-(α,α,α-trifluoro-*p*-tolyl)-3-morpholinone; McN-1564).
FLUMEXADOL* (α,α,α-trifluoro-*m*-morpholin-2-yltoluene; 2-(α,α,α-trifluoro-*m*-tolyl)morpholine; CERM-1841).
FLUMEZAPINE (7-fluoro-2-methyl-4-(4-methylpiperazin-1-yl)-10*H*-thieno[2,3-*b*][1,5]benzodiazepine; LY-120363).
'Flumidin' *see* Moroxydine.
FLUMINOREX* (2-amino-5-(α,α,α-trifluoro-*p*-tolyl)-2-oxazoline; McN-1231).
FLUMIZOLE* (4,5-bis(*p*-methoxyphenyl)-2-trifluoromethylimidazole; CP-22665).
Flumoperon *see* Trifluperidol.
'Flumoxil' *see under* Amoxicillin.
FLUMOXONIDE (6α,9-difluoro-11β,16α,17-trihydroxy-3,20-dioxopregna-1,4-dien-21-al 21-(dimethylacetal) cyclic 16,17-acetal with acetone; 6α,9-difluoro-11β-hydroxy-21,21-dimethoxy-16α,17-[(1-methylethylidene)bis(oxy)]pregna-1,4-diene-3,20-dione; RS-40584).
FLUNAMINE (2-[bis(*p*-fluorophenyl)methoxy]ethylamine).
FLUNARIZINE* (1-[bis(*p*-fluorophenyl)methyl]-4-cinnamylpiperazine; flunarizine hydro-

240

chloride; R-14950; 'sibelium').

FLUNIDAZOLE*** (2-(*p*-fluorophenyl)-1-(2-hydroxyethyl)-5-nitroimidazole; 2-(*p*-fluorophenyl)-5-nitroimidazole-1-ethanol; MK-915).

'Fluniget' *see* Diflunisal.

FLUNISOLIDE*** (6α-fluoro-11β,16α,17,21-tetrahydroxypregna-1,4-diene-3,20-dione cyclic 16,17-acetal with acetone; RS-3999; 'syntaris'; 'val-679').

FLUNISOLIDE ACETATE* (RS-1320).

FLUNITRAZEPAM*** (5-(*o*-fluorophenyl)-1,3-dihydro-1-methyl-7-nitro-2*H*-1,4-benzodiazepin-2-one; Ro 5-4200; 'narcozep'; 'rohypnol'; 'roipnol'; 'rophynal').

FLUNIXIN** (2-[2-methyl-3-(trifluoromethyl)anilino)nicotinic acid; 2-[[2-methyl-3-(trifluoromethyl)phenyl]amino]-3-pyridinecarboxylic acid; 2-(α³,α³,α³-trifluoro-2,3-xylidino)nicotinic acid).

FLUNIXIN MEGLUMINE* (flunixin methylglucamine salt; Sch-14714; 'banamine').

Flunixin methylglucamine salt *see* Flunixin meglumine.

FLUNOXAPROFEN*** (2-(*p*-fluorophenyl)-α-methyl-5-benzoxazoleacetic acid).

FLUOCINOLONE* (6α,9α-difluoro-11β,16α,17α,21-tetrahydroxypregna-1,4-diene-3,20-dione; 6α,9α-difluoro-16α-hydroxyprednisolone).

FLUOCINOLONE ACETONIDE*** (fluocinolone cyclic 16,17-acetal with acetone; NSC-92339; RS-1401 AT).

Fluocinolone acetonide 21-acetate *see* Fluocinonide.

Fluocinolone acetonide 21-cyclopropanecarboxylate *see* Ciprocinonide.

Fluocinolone acetonide 21-propionate *see* Procinonide.

Fluocinolone cyclic 16,17-acetal with acetone *see* Fluocinolone acetonide.

FLUOCINONIDE*** (fluocinolone acetonide 21-acetate; NSC-101791; RS-410 FAPG; 'lidex'; 'metosine'; 'metosyn'; 'novoter'; 'topsym'; 'topsyne').

FLUOCORTIN** (6α-fluoro-11β-hydroxy-16α-methyl-3,20-dioxopregna-1,4-dien-21-oic acid).

FLUOCORTIN BUTYL* (butyl 6α-fluoro-11β-hydroxy-16α-methyl-3,20-dioxopregna-1,4-dien-21-oate; fluocortin butyl ester; SH K-203; 'vaspit').

FLUOCORTIN BUTYL plus ISOCONAZOLE ('bi-vaspit').

FLUOCORTOLONE*** (6α-fluoro-11β,21-dihydroxy-16α-methylpregna-1,4-diene-3,20-dione; 6α-fluoro-16α-methyl-1,2-dehydrocorticosterone; SH-742).

FLUOCORTOLONE CAPROATE* (fluocortolone hexanoate; SH-770; 'ficoid'; 'ultralan').

FLUOCORTOLONE PIVALATE (fluocortolone trimethylacetate).

FLUOCORTOLONE PIVALATE plus FLUOCORTOLONE OCTANOATE ('ultracur').

Fluohydrisone *see* Fludrocortisone.

Fluohydrocortisone *see* Fludrocortisone.

FLUOMETURON* (1,1-dimethyl-3-(α,α,α-tri-fluoro-*m*-tolyl)urea; 1,1-dimethyl-3-(*m*-trifluoromethylphenyl)urea; 'cotoran').

'Fluon' *see* Politef.

'Fluonid' *see* Fluocinolone acetonide.

Fluopromazine* *see* Triflupromazine.

Fluoracizine *see* Fluacizine.

Fluorafur *see* Tegafur.

'Fluorakil' *see* Fluoroacetic acid.

Fluorandrenolone *see* Fludroxycortide.

FLUORANIL (tetrafluorobenzoquinone(s)).

FLUORBENSIDE* (1-chloro-4-[[(4-fluorophenyl)thio]methyl]benzene; 4-chloro-α-[(*p*-fluorophenyl)thio]toluene; 1-[(*p*-chlorobenzyl)thio]-4-fluorobenzene; 'fluoroparacide'; 'fluorosulphacide').

Fluordopan (tr) *see* Ftordopan.

Fluorenal *see* Florenal.

FLUORENE (diphenylenemethane; 2,2'-methylenebiphenyl).

FLUORENYLACETAMIDE (2-acetamidofluorene; 2-acetylaminofluorene).

FLUORENYLACETOHYDROXAMIC ACID (*N*-fluoren-2-yl-*N*-hydroxyacetamide; 2-(*N*-hydroxyacetamido)fluorene; *N*-hydroxy-2-acetylaminofluorene).

_N_-Fluoren-2-yl-_N_-hydroxyacetamide *see* Fluorenylacetohydroxamic acid.

α-Fluoren-9-ylidene-_p_-toluamidine *see* Renytoline.

2-Fluoren-2-ylpropionic acid *see* Cicloprofen.

FLUORESCEIN (9-(*o*-carboxyphenyl)-6-hydroxy-3-isoxanthenone; resorcinolphthalein; 'thilorbin').

FLUORESCEIN DISODIUM (uranin; 'obiturin').

FLUORESONE** (ethyl *p*-fluorophenyl sulfone; floretione; 'bripadon'; 'caducid').

'Fluorformylon' *see* Formocortal.

Fluorhydrocortisone* *see* Fludrocortisone.

Fluormetolon* *see* Fluorometholone.

FLUOROACETAMIDE (2-fluoroacetamide; 'fussol').

FLUOROACETIC ACID (2-fluoroacetic acid (or its salts); compound 1080; 'finovakil'; 'flac'; 'fluorakil'; 'fluoron'; 'fluron'; 'furatol'; 'megatox'; 'vitax F-15').

_N_-(2-FLUOROACETYL)-_N_-METHYL-1-NAPHTHYLAMINE (2-fluoro-*N*-methyl-*N*-naphth-1-yl-acetamide; *N*-methyl-*N*-naphth-1-ylfluoroacetamide; MNFA; 'nissol').

3-Fluoro-D-alanine-2-_d_ *see* Fludalanine.

7-Fluoroancitabine *see* Flurocitabine.

7-Fluoro-2,2'-anhydro-1-β-D-arabinofuranosylcytosine *see* Flurocitabine.

2-Fluoro-ARA-AMP *see* Fludarabine phosphate.

1-[1-[2-[(_p_-Fluorobenzoyl)amino]ethyl]piperid-4-yl]-benzimidazolin-2-one *see* Halopemide.

5-(_p_-Fluorobenzoyl)-2-benzimidazolecarbamic acid methyl ester *see* Flubendazole.

3-(_p_-Fluorobenzoyl)-4-(_p_-fluorophenyl)-4-hydroxy-1-methylpiperidine *see* Flazalone.

3-[4-[4-(_p_-Fluorobenzoyl)piperid-1-yl]butyl]-2,4(1_H_,3_H_)-quinazolinedione *see* Butanserin.

6-[2-[4-(_p_-Fluorobenzoyl)piperid-1-yl]ethyl]-2,3-di-hydro-7-methyl-5_H_-thiazolo[3,2-_a_]pyrimidin-5-

one *see* Setoperone.

3-[2-[4-(*p*-Fluorobenzoyl)piperid-1-yl]ethyl]-2-methyl-4*H*-pyrido[1,2-*a*]pyrimidin-4-one *see* Pirenperone.

3-[2-[4-(*p*-Fluorobenzoyl)piperid-1-yl]ethyl]-2,4(1*H*,3*H*)-quinazolinedione *see* Ketanserin.

7-[2-[4-(*p*-Fluorobenzoyl)piperid-1-yl]ethyl]theophylline *see* Flufylline.

3-[2-[4-(*p*-Fluorobenzoyl)piperid-1-yl]ethyl]-2-thio-2,4(1*H*,3*H*)-quinazolinedione *see* Altanserin.

1-[3-[4-(4-Fluorobenzoyl)piperid-1-yl]propyl]-2-benzimidazolinone *see* Declenperone.

7-[3-[4-(*p*-Fluorobenzoyl)piperid-1-yl]propyl]theophylline *see* Fluprofylline.

3-[3-(*p*-Fluorobenzoyl)propyl]-3-azabicyclo[3.2.2]nonane *see* Nonaperone.

1′-[3-(*p*-Fluorobenzoyl)propyl][1,4′-bipiperidine]-4′-carboxamide *see* Pipamperone.

8-[3-(*p*-Fluorobenzoyl)propyl]-1-(*p*-fluorophenyl)-1,3,8-triazaspiro[4.5]decan-4-one *see* Fluspiperone.

2-[3-(*p*-Fluorobenzoyl)propyl]hexahydropyrrolo[1,2-*a*]pyrazine *see* Azabuperone.

1-[3-(*p*-Fluorobenzoyl)propyl]-4-(6-methoxy-2-methylindol-3-yl)piperidine *see* Mindoperone.

1-[3-(*p*-Fluorobenzoyl)propyl]-4-(*o*-methoxyphenyl)piperazine *see* Fluanisone.

8-[3-(*p*-Fluorobenzoyl)propyl]-2-methyl-2,8-diazaspiro[4.5]decane-1,3-dione *see* Roxoperone.

1-[3-(*p*-Fluorobenzoyl)propyl]-4-methylpiperidine *see* Melperone.

8-[3-(*p*-Fluorobenzoyl)propyl]-1-oxo-4-phenyl-2,4,8-triazaspiro[4.5]decane *see* Spiperone.

8-[3-(*p*-Fluorobenzoyl)propyl]-1-phenyl-1,3,8-triazaspiro[4.5]decan-4-one *see* Spiperone.

4-[3-(*p*-Fluorobenzoyl)propyl]-1-piperazinecarboxylic acid cyclohexyl ester *see* Fenaperone.

1-[3-(*p*-Fluorobenzoyl)propyl]piperidine *see* Primaperone.

1-[3-(*p*-Fluorobenzoyl)propyl]-4-piperidinol isopropylcarbamate *see* Carperone.

1-[1-[3-(*p*-Fluorobenzoyl)propyl]piperid-4-yl]-2-benzimidazolinone *see* Benperidol.

1-[3-(*p*-Fluorobenzoyl)propyl]-4-piperid-1-ylisonipecotamide *see* Pipamperone.

1′-[3-(*p*-Fluorobenzoyl)propyl]-4′-propionyl-1,4′-bipiperidine *see* Propyperone.

1-[3-(*p*-Fluorobenzoyl)propyl]-4-pyrid-2-ylpiperazine *see* Azaperone.

1-[3-(*p*-Fluorobenzoyl)propyl]-4-(pyrrolidin-1-ylcarbonyl)-4-*m*-tolylpiperidine *see* Meperidide.

1-[1-[3-(*p*-Fluorobenzoyl)propyl]-1,2,3,6-tetrahydropyrid-4-yl]-2-benzimidazolinone *see* Droperidol.

1-[3-(*p*-Fluorobenzoyl)propyl]-4-(2-thioxobenzimidazolin-1-yl)piperidine *see* Timiperone.

1-[3-(*p*-Fluorobenzoyl)propyl]-4-(*p*-tolyl)-4-piperidinol *see* Moperone.

1-[3-(*p*-Fluorobenzoyl)propyl]-4-(*m*-trifluoromethylphenyl)-4-piperidinol *see* Trifluperidol.

1-(*p*-Fluorobenzyl)-2-[[1-(4-methoxyphenethyl)piperid-4-yl]amino]benzimidazole *see* Astemizole.

1-(*p*-Fluorobenzyl)-2-[(2-methoxy-5-sulfamoylbenzamido)methyl]pyrrolidine *see* Flubepride.

N-[[1-(*p*-Fluorobenzyl)pyrrolidin-2-yl]methyl]-5-sulfamoyl-*o*-anisamide *see* Flubepride.

6α-Fluorobetamethasone *see* Diflorasone.

(±)-2-(2-Fluoro-4-biphenyl)propionic acid *see* Flurbiprofen.

2-(3′-Fluoro-4-biphenylyl)propionic acid *see* Fluprofen.

(±)-8-Fluoro-α,5-bis(*p*-chlorophenyl)-1,3,4,5-tetrahydro-2*H*-pyrido[4,3-*b*]indole-2-butanol *see* Flutroline.

'Fluoroblastin' *see* Fluorouracil.

Fluorocarbon 11 *see* Trichlorofluoromethane.

Fluorocarbon 12 *see* Dichlorodifluoromethane.

Fluorocarbon 152a *see* 1,1-Difluoroethane.

Fluorocortisol *see* Fludrocortisone.

Fluorocortisone* *see* Fludrocortisone.

5-Fluorocytosine *see* Flucytosine.

5-Fluoro-2′-deoxycytidine *see* Flucytosine deoxyriboside.

5-Fluoro-5′-deoxyuridine *see* Doxifluridine.

2-[(8-Fluorodibenz[*b,f*]oxepin-10-yl)thio]-N-methylethylamine *see* Fluradoline.

FLUORODIFEN* (2,4′-dinitro-4-(trifluromethyl)diphenyl ether; 2-nitro-1-(*p*-nitrophenoxy)-4-(trifluoromethyl)benzene; α,α,α-trifluoro-3-nitro-4-(*p*-nitrophenoxy)toluene; C-6989; 'preforan').

9-Fluoro-1′,4′-dihydro-11β,21-dihydroxy-2′β*H*-naphtho[2′,3′:16,17]pregna-1,4-diene-3,20-dione *see* Naflocort.

6-Fluoro-1,4-dihydro-1-(methylamino)-7-(4-methylpiperazin-1-yl)-4-oxo-3-quinolinecarboxylic acid *see* Amifloxacin.

9-Fluoro-2,3-dihydro-3-methyl-10-(4-methylpiperazin-1-yl)-7-oxo-7*H*-pyrido[1,2,3-*de*]-1,4-benzoxazine-6-carboxylic acid *see* Ofloxacin.

9-Fluoro-6,7-dihydro-5-methyl-1-oxo-1*H*,5*H*-benzo[*ij*]quinolizine-2-carboxylic acid *see* Flumequine.

8-Fluoro-5,6-dihydro-5-methyl-6-oxo-4*H*-imidazo[1,5-*a*][1,4]benzodiazepine-3-carboxylic acid ethyl ester *see* Flumazepil.

N-[(8-Fluoro-2,3-dihydro-1-methyl-5-phenyl-1*H*-1,4-benzodiazepin-2-yl)methyl]-3-furamide *see* Lufuradom.

6-Fluoro-2,3-dihydrospiro[4*H*-1-benzopyran-4,4′-imidazolidine]-2′,5′-dione *see* Sorbinil.

6α-Fluoro-16α,17-dihydroxycorticosterone cyclic 16,17-acetal with acetone *see* Fludroxycortide.

9α-Fluoro-11β,21-dihydroxy-16α,17-dimethylpregna-1,4-diene-3,20-dione *see* Dimesone.

6α-Fluoro-11β,21-dihydroxy-16α,17α-isopropylidenedioxypregn-4-ene-3,20-dione *see* Fludroxycortide.

9α-Fluoro-11β,21-dihydroxy-16α,17α-isopropylidenedioxypregna-1,4-diene-3,20-dione *see* Triamcinolone acetonide.

9-Fluoro-11β,17α-dihydroxy-17-lactoylandrost-1,4-dien-3-one *see* Fluperolone.

9α-Fluoro-11β,17β-dihydroxy-17α-methylandrost-4-en-3-one *see* Fluoxymesterone.

9-Fluoro-11β,17-dihydroxy-16β-methyl-3-oxoandrosta-1,4-diene-17β-carbothioic acid methyl ester *see* Timobesone.

242

6α-Fluoro-11β,21-dihydroxy-16α-methylpregna-1,4-diene-3,20-dione *see* Fluocortolone.

9α-Fluoro-11β,17α-dihydroxy-6α-methylpregna-1,4-diene-3,20-dione *see* Fluorometholone.

9α-Fluoro-11β,17α-dihydroxy-16β-methylpregna-1,4-diene-3,20-dione *see* Doxibetasol.

9-Fluoro-11β,21-dihydroxy-16α-methylpregna-1,4-diene-3,20-dione *see* Desoximetasone.

9-Fluoro-11β,21-dihydroxy-2′-methyl-5′βH-pregna-1,4-dieno[17,16-d]oxazole-3,20-dione 21-acetate *see* Fluazacort.

9-Fluoro-11β,17-dihydroxypregn-4-ene-3,20-dione *see* Flugestone.

9α-Fluoro-11β,17α-dihydroxyprogesterone *see* Flugestone.

Fluorodopan *see* Ftordopan.

8-Fluoroerythromycin *see* Flurithromycin.

2-Fluoroethyl [1,1′-biphenyl]-4-acetate *see* Fluenetil.

2-Fluoroethyl biphenylylacetate *see* Fluenetil.

8-(2-Fluoroethyl)-3α-hydroxy-1αH,5αH-tropanium bromide benzilate *see* Flutropium bromide.

2-Fluoroethyl xenylacetate *see* Fluenetil.

'Fluorofen' *see* Triflupromazine.

4′-Fluoro-4-[4-(p-fluorobenzoyl)piperid-1-yl]butyrophenone *see* Lenperone.

FLUOROFORM (trifluoromethane; 'genetron 23′).

Fluoroformylon *see* Formocortal.

5-Fluoro-1-(2-furanidyl)uracil *see* Tegafur.

Fluorogestone* *see* Flugestone.

4′-Fluoro-4-(3,4,6,7,12,12a-hexahydropyrazino-[1′,2′:1,6]pyrido[3,4-b]indol-2(1H)-yl)butyrophenone *see* Biriperone.

4′-Fluoro-4-(hexahydropyrrolo[1,2-a]pyrazin-2(1H)-yl)-butyrophenone *see* Azabuperone.

5-Fluoro-N-hexyl-3,4-dihydro-2,4-dioxo-1(2H)-pyrimidinecarboxamide *see* Carmofur.

4′-Fluoro-4-hydroxy-3-biphenylcarboxylic acid acetate *see* Flufenisal.

6-Fluoro-9-[3-[4-(2-hydroxyethyl)piperazin-1-yl]-propyl]2-(trifluoromethyl)thioxanthene *see* Teflutixol.

6-Fluoro-9-[3-[4-(2-hydroxyethyl)piperid-1-yl]propylidene]-2-(trifluoromethyl)thioxanthene *see* Piflutixol.

6α-Fluoro-16α-hydroxyhydrocortisone acetonide *see* Fludroxycortide.

6α-Fluoro-11β-hydroxy-16α-methyl-3,20-dioxopregna-1,4-dien-21-oic acid *see* Fluocortin.

6α-Fluoro-11β-hydroxy-16α-methyl-3,20-dioxopregna-1,4-dien-21-oic acid butyl ester *see* Fluocortin butyl.

9α-Fluoro-11β-hydroxy-17α-methyltestosterone *see* Fluoxymesterone.

4′-Fluoro-4-(4-hydroxypiperid-1-yl)butyrophenone isopropylcarbamate *see* Carperone.

9α-Fluoro-16α-hydroxyprednisolone *see* Triamcinolone.

4′-Fluoro-4-(4-hydroxy-4-p-tolylpiperid-1-yl)butyrophenone *see* Moperone.

4′-Fluoro-4-[4-hydroxy-4-(m-trifluoromethylphenyl)piperid-1-yl]butyrophenone *see* Trifluperidol.

4′-Fluoro-4-[4-hydroxy-4-(α,α,α-trifluoro-m-tolyl)-

piperid-1-yl]butyrophenone *see* Trifluperidol.

5-Fluoro-N-(2-imidazolin-2-yl)-o-toluidine *see* Flutonidine.

4′-Fluoro-4-[4-(isopropylcarbamoyloxy)piperid-1-yl]butyrophenone *see* Carperone.

'Fluoromar' *see* Fluroxene.

FLUOROMETHOLONE*** (9α-fluoro-6α-methyl-21-deoxyprednisolone; 9α-fluoro-11β,17α-dihydroxy-6α-methylpregna-1,4-diene-3,20-dione; fluormetolon).

FLUOROMETHOLONE ACETATE (fluorometholone 17-acetate; NSC-47438; U-17323).

N-(5-Fluoro-2-methoxy-α-methylbenzyl)-2-[p-[(5-isobutylpyrimidin-2-yl)sulfamoyl]phenyl]acetamide *see* Gliflumide.

4′-Fluoro-4-[4-(6-methoxy-2-methylindol-3-yl)piperid-1-yl]butyrophenone *see* Mindoperone.

4′-Fluoro-4-[4-[2-[(p-methoxy-α-phenylbenzyl)oxy]-ethyl]piperazin-1-yl]butyrophenone *see* Mobenzoxamine.

4′-Fluoro-4-[4-(o-methoxyphenyl)piperazin-1-yl]butyrophenone *see* Fluanisone.

(±)-2-Fluoro-α-methyl[1,1′-biphenyl]-4-acetic acid *see* Flurbiprofen.

9α-Fluoro-16α-methyl-17-deoxyprednisolone *see* Desoximetasone.

9α-Fluoro-6α-methyl-21-deoxyprednisolone *see* Fluorometholone.

4′-Fluoro-3-(2-methyl-1,3-dioxo-2,8-diazaspiro-[4.5]dec-8-yl)butyrophenone *see* Roxoperone.

9-Fluoro-16-methyleneprednisolone *see* Fluprednidene.

9α-Fluoro-2-methylhydrocortisone *see* Methylfludrocortisone.

7-Fluoro-2-methyl-4-(4-methylpiperazin-1-yl)-10H-thieno[2,3-b][1,5]benzodiazepine *see* Flumezapine.

5-Fluoro-2-methyl-1-[p-(methylsulfinyl)benzylidene]-indene-3-acetic acid *see* Sulindac.

2-Fluoro-N-methyl-N-naphth-1-yl-acetamide *see* N-(2-Fluoroacetyl)-N-methyl-1-naphthylamine.

3-Fluoro-6-(4-methylpiperazin-1-yl)morphanthridine *see* Fluperlapine.

4′-Fluoro-4-(4-methylpiperid-1-yl)butyrophenone *see* Melperone.

6α-Fluoro-16α-methylprednisolone *see* Paramethasone.

9α-Fluoro-16α-methylprednisolone *see* Dexamethasone.

9α-Fluoro-16β-methylprednisolone *see* Betamethasone.

9α-Fluoro-21-methylprednisolone *see* Fluperolone.

Fluoromethyl 2,2,2-trifluoro-1-(trifluoromethyl)-ethyl ether *see* Sevoflurane.

'Fluoron' *see* Fluoroacetic acid.

4′-Fluoro-4-(octahydro-4-hydroxy-1(2H)-quinolyl)-butyrophenone carbamate ester *see* Cicarperone.

4′-Fluoro-4-[4-(2-oxobenzimidazolin-1-yl)piperid-1-yl]butyrophenone *see* Benperidol.

'Fluoroparacide' *see* Fluorbenside.

'Fluorophene' *see* Flusalan.

1-[p-[2-[(p-Fluorophenethyl)oxy]ethoxy]phenoxy]-3-(isopropylamino)-2-propanol *see* Flusoxolol.

8-[3-(p-Fluorophenoxy)propyl]-1-phenyl-1,3,8-tri-
azaspiro[4.5]decan-4-one see Spiramide.

N-[[5-(o-Fluorophenyl)-2,3-dihydro-1-methyl-1H-
1,4-benzodiazepin-2-yl]methyl]-3-thiophenecarb-
oxamide see Tifluadom.

5-(o-Fluorophenyl)-1,3-dihydro-1-methyl-7-nitro-
2H-1,4-benzodiazepin-2-one see Flunitrazepam.

4-(p-Fluorophenyl)-3,6-dihydropyrid-1(2H)-yl 1-(2-
hydroxyethyl)-5-methylpyrazol-4-yl ketone see
Flupranone.

3-[4-(p-Fluorophenyl)-3,6-dihydro-1(2H)-pyridyl]-1-
[1-(2-hydroxyethyl)-5-methylpyrazol-4-yl]-1-pro-
panone see Flupranone.

4-(o-Fluorophenyl)-6,8-dihydro-1,3,8-trimethylpyr-
azolo[3,4-e][1,4]diazepin-7(1H)-one see Zolazepam.

5-(2-(p-Fluorophenyl)-1,3-dioxolan-2-yl)-2-benzimi-
dazolecarbamic acid methyl ester see Etibendazole.

p-Fluorophenyl 4-(p-fluorophenyl)-4-hydroxy-1-
methylpiperid-3-yl ketone see Flazalone.

2-(p-Fluorophenyl)-1-(2-hydroxyethyl)-5-nitroimid-
azole see Flunidazole.

2-(p-Fluorophenyl)-1,3-indandione see Fluindione.

7-Fluoro-1-phenylisochroman-3-ylmethylamine see
Fenisorex.

4-(p-Fluorophenyl)-1-isopropyl-7-methyl-2(1H)-qui-
nazolinone see Fluproquazone.

α-(p-Fluorophenyl)-4-(o-methoxyphenyl)-1-piperaz-
inebutanol see Anisopirol.

4-(p-Fluorophenyl)-5-[2-[4-(o-methoxyphenyl)pip-
erazin-1-yl]ethyl]-4-oxazolin-2-one see Zoloperone.

2-(p-Fluorophenyl)-α-methyl-5-benzoxazoleacetic
acid see Flunoxaprofen.

4-(p-Fluorophenyl)-3-[[3,4-(methylenedioxy)phen-
oxy]methyl]piperidine see Paroxetine.

1-[(4-Fluorophenyl)methyl]-N-[1-[2-(4-methoxy-
phenyl)ethyl]-4-piperidinyl]benzimidazol-2-amine
see Astemizole.

2-(p-Fluorophenyl)-5-nitroimidazole-1-ethanol see
Flunidazole.

1-[1-[4-(p-Fluorophenyl)-4-oxobutyl]-1,2,3,6-tetra-
hydropyrid-4-yl]-2-benzimidazolinone see Droperidol.

8-[4-(p-Fluorophenyl)-3-pentenyl]-1-phenyl-1,3,8-tri-
azaspiro[4.5]decan-4-one see Spirilene.

4-(p-Fluorophenyl)-5-[2-(4-phenylpiperazin-1-yl)-
ethyl]-1,3-dioxol-2-one see Fludoxopone.

N-[3-[4-(p-Fluorophenyl)piperazin-1-yl]-1-methyl-
propyl]nicotinamide see Niaprazine.

5-[[4-(p-Fluorophenyl)piperid-3-yl]methoxy]-1,3-
benzodioxole see Paroxetine.

2′-(p-Fluorophenyl)-2′H-17α-pregna-2,4-dien-20-
yno[3,2-c]pyrazol-17-ol see Nivacortol.

1-[(p-Fluorophenyl)sulfonyl]-4-[p-[[7-(trifluoromethyl)-4-quinolyl]amino]benzoyl]piperazine see
Losulazine.

4-[3-(p-Fluorophenyl)-6-(trifluoromethyl)-1-indan-
yl]-1-piperazineethanol see Tefludazine.

2-Fluoro-9-(5-O-phosphono-β-D-arabinofuranosyl)-
9H-purin-6-amine see Fludarabine phosphate.

4′-Fluoro-4-piperid-1-ylbutyrophenone see Primaperone.

4′-Fluoro-4-(4-piperid-1-yl-4-propionylpiperid-1-yl)-
butyrophenone see Propyperone.

'Fluoroplex' see Fluorouracil.

6α-Fluoroprednisolone see Fluprednisolone.

9-Fluoroprednisolone see Isoflupredone.

4′-Fluoro-4-(4-pyrid-2-ylpiperazin-1-yl)butyrophen-
one see Azaperone.

4′-Fluoro-4-(4-pyrrolidinamido-4-m-tolylpiperid-1-
yl)butyrophenone see Meperidide.

Fluorosalan* see Flusalan.

6-Fluorospiro[chroman-4,4′-imidazolidine]-2′,5′-di-
one see Sorbinil.

4′-Fluoro-4-[spiro(5-oxo-3-phenylimidazolidin-4,4′-
piperidin)-1′-yl]butyrophenone see Spiperone.

'Fluorosulphacide' see Fluorbenside.

5-Fluoro-1-(tetrahydro-2-furanyl)-2,4-(1H,3H)-pyr-
imidinedione see Tegafur.

5-Fluoro-1-(tetrahydro-2-furyl)uracil see Tegafur.

7-Fluoro-2,3,3a,9a-tetrahydro-3-hydroxy-6-imino-
6H-furo[2′,3′:4,5]oxazolo[3,2-a]pyrimidine-2-
methanol see Flurocitabine.

4′-Fluoro-4-[1,2,3,6-tetrahydro-4-(2-oxobenzimid-
azolin-1-yl)pyrid-1-yl]butyrophenone see Droperidol.

9α-Fluoro-11β,16α,17,21-tetrahydroxypregna-1,4-
diene-3,20-dione see Triamcinolone.

6α-Fluoro-11β,16α,17,21-tetrahydroxypregna-1,4-
diene-3,20-dione acetonide see Flunisolide.

9-Fluoro-11β,16α,17,21-tetrahydroxy-5α-pregnane-
3,20-dione cyclic 16,17-acetal with acetone see
Drocinonide.

6α-Fluoro-11β,16α,17,21-tetrahydroxypregn-4-ene-
3,20-dione cyclic 16,17-acetal with acetone see
Fludroxycortide.

4′-Fluoro-4-[4-(2-thioxobenzimidazolin-1-yl)piperid-
1-yl]butyrophenone see Timiperone.

2-(5-Fluoro-o-toluidino)-2-imidazoline see Flutonidine.

1-[3-[6-Fluoro-2-(trifluoromethyl)thioxanthen-9-yl-
idene]propyl]-4-piperidineethanol see Piflutixol.

4-[3-[6-Fluoro-2-(trifluoromethyl)thioxanthen-9-yl]-
propyl]-1-piperazineethanol see Teflutixol.

9-Fluoro-11β,17,21-trihydroxy-16-methylene-
pregna-1,4-diene-3,20-dione see Fluprednidene.

6α-Fluoro-11β,17,21-trihydroxy-16α-methylpregna-
1,4-diene-3,20-dione see Paramethasone.

9α-Fluoro-11β,17,21-trihydroxy-21-methylpregna-
1,4-diene-3,20-dione see Fluperolone.

9α-Fluoro-11β,17α,21-trihydroxy-16α-methyl-1,4-
pregnadiene-3,20-dione see Dexamethasone.

9α-Fluoro-11β,17,21-trihydroxy-16β-methylpregna-
1,4-diene-3,20-dione see Betamethasone.

9-Fluoro-11β,17,21-trihydroxypregna-1,4-diene-
3,20-dione see Isoflupredone.

9-Fluoro-11β,16α,17-trihydroxypregna-1,4-diene-
3,20-dione see Descinolone.

9α-Fluoro-11β,17α,21-trihydroxypregn-4-ene-3,20-
dione see Fludrocortisone.

FLUOROURACIL*** (5-fluorouracil; fluracil;
NSC-19893; Ro 2-9757).

5-Fluorouracil see Fluorouracil.

Fluoroxene see Fluroxene.

2-(3'-Fluoroxenyl)propionic acid *see* Fluprofen.
'Fluosol DA' *see under* Perfluamine.
'Fluosterone' *see* Fluoxymesterone.
Fluostigmine* *see* Isoflurophate.
'Fluotestin' *see* Fluoxymesterone.
'Fluothane' *see* Halothane.
FLUOTRACEN* ((±)-*cis*-9,10-dihydro-*N,N*,10-trimethyl-2-(trifluoromethyl)-9-anthracenepropylamine; (±)-*cis*-9-[3-(dimethylamino)propyl]-9,10-dihydro-10-methyl-2-(trifluoromethyl)anthracene; fluotracen hydrochloride; SK&F-28175).
FLUOXETINE* ((±)-*N*-methyl-3-phenyl-3-[(α,α,α-trifluoro-*p*-tolyl)oxy]propylamine; *N*-methyl-3-phenyl-3-[(*p*-trifluoromethyl)phenoxy]propylamine; (±)-α,α,α-trifluoro-*p*-[3-(methylamino)-1-phenylpropoxy]toluene; compound 110140).
Fluoximesterone* *see* Fluoxymesterone.
Fluoxiprednisolone* *see* Triamcinolone.
FLUOXYMESTERONE* (9α-fluoro-11β,17β-dihydroxy-17α-methylandrost-4-en-3-one; 9α-fluoro-11β-hydroxy-17α-methyltestosterone; fluoximesterone; NSC-12165).
Fluoxyprednisolone *see* Triamcinolone.
Flupenthixol* *see* Flupentixol.
FLUPENTIXOL* (9-[3-[4-(2-hydroxyethyl)piperazin-1-yl]propylidene]-2-trifluoromethylthioxanthene; flupenthixol; LC-44; N-7009).
FLUPENTIXOL plus MELITRACEN ('deanxit').
FLUPENTIXOL DECANOATE ('depixol').
FLUPERAMIDE* (4-[4-(4-chloro-3-trifluoromethylphenyl)-4-hydroxypiperid-1-yl]-*N,N*-dimethyl-2,2-diphenylbutyramide; 4-(4-chloro-α,α,α-trifluoro-*m*-tolyl)-4-hydroxy-*N,N*-dimethyl-α,α-diphenyl-1-piperidinebutyramide; R-18910).
FLUPERLAPINE* (3-fluoro-6-(4-methylpiperazin-1-yl)morphanthridine; NB-106-689).
FLUPEROLONE* (9α-fluoro-11β,17,21-trihydroxypregna-1,4-diene-3,20-dione; 9-fluoro-11β,17α-dihydroxy-17-lactoylandrost-1,4-dien-3-one; 9α-fluoro-21-methylprednisolone; fluperolone acetate; P-1742).
FLUPHENAZINE* (10-[3-[4-(2-hydroxyethyl)piperazin-1-yl]propyl]-2-(trifluoromethyl)phenothiazine; 4-[3-[2-(trifluoromethyl)phenothiazin-2-yl]propyl]-1-piperazineethanol; flufenazine; fluphenazine hydrochloride).
FLUPHENAZINE plus NORTRIPTYLINE ('motipress'; 'motival').
FLUPHENAZINE DECANOATE ('dapotum D'; 'lyogen'; 'modecate').
FLUPHENAZINE ENANTATE ('dapotum').
FLUPIMAZINE* (10-[3-[4-(2-hydroxyethoxy)piperid-1-yl]propyl]-2-(trifluoromethyl)phenothiazine; 2-[[1-[3-[2-(trifluoromethyl)phenothiazin-10-yl]propyl]piperid-4-yl]oxy]ethanol; 4-(2-hydroxyethoxy)-1-[3-[2-(trifluoromethyl)phenothiazin-10-yl]propyl]piperidine).
FLUPIRTINE* (ethyl 2-amino-6-[(*p*-fluorobenzyl)amino]-3-pyridinecarbamate).
FLUPRANONE* (3-[4-(*p*-fluorophenyl)-3,6-dihydro-1(2*H*)-pyridyl]-1-[1-(2-hydroxyethyl)-5-methylpyrazol-4-yl]-1-propanone; 4-(*p*-fluorophenyl)-3,6-dihydropyrid-1(2*H*)-yl 1-(2-hydroxyethyl)-5-methylpyrazol-4-yl ketone;
FLUPRAZINE* ([2-[4-(α,α,α-trifluoro-*m*-tolyl)piperazin-1-yl]ethyl]urea).
FLUPREDNIDENE* (9-fluoro-11β,17,21-trihydroxy-16-methylenepregna-1,4-diene-3,20-dione; 9-fluoro-16-methyleneprednisolone; fluprednilidene; fluprednylidene).
FLUPREDNIDENE ACETATE (fluprednidene-21-acetate; FPA; StC-1106; 'corticoderm'; 'emcortina'; 'etacortin').
Fluprednilidene *see* Fluprednidene.
FLUPREDNISOLONE* (6α-fluoro-11β,17,21-trihydroxypregna-1,4-diene-3,20-dione; 6α-fluoroprednisolone; fluprednisolone acetate; NSC-47439; U-7800).
Fluprednylidene *see* Fluprednidene.
FLUPROFEN* (2-(3'-fluoro-4-biphenylyl)propionic acid; 2-(3'-fluoroxenyl)propionic acid; BTS-17345; RD-17435).
FLUPROFYLLINE (7-[3-[4-(*p*-fluorobenzoyl)piperid-1-yl]propyl]theophylline).
FLUPROQUAZONE* (4-(*p*-fluorophenyl)-1-isopropyl-7-methyl-2(1*H*)-quinazolinone; RF-46-790).
FLUPROSTENOL* ((±)-*Z*-7-[(1*R*,2*R*,3*R*,5*S*)-3,5-dihydroxy-2-[(*E*)-(3*R*)-3-hydroxy-4-[(α,α,α-trifluoro-*m*-tolyl)oxy]-1-butenyl]cyclopentyl]-5-heptenoic acid; 9α,11α,15α-trihydroxy-16-[3-(trifluoromethyl)phenoxy]-17,18,19,20-tetranor-5-*cis*-13-*trans*-prostadienoic acid; fluoprostenol sodium; ICI-80008; ICI-81008; 'equimate').
FLUQUAZONE (6-chloro-4-phenyl-1-(2,2,2-trifluoroethyl)-2(1*H*)-quinazolinone; EN-970).
Fluracil* *see* Fluorouracil.
FLURADOLINE* (2-[(8-fluorodibenz[*b,f*]oxepin-10-yl)thio]-*N*-methylethylamine; fluradoline hydrochloride; HP-494; P-762494A).
Flurandrenolide* *see* Fludroxycortide.
Flurandrenolone* *see* Fludroxycortide.
FLURANTEL* (2,6-dihydroxy-3-nitro-3',5'-bis-(trifluoromethyl)benzanilide diacetate (ester)).
FLURAZEPAM* (7-chloro-1-(2-diethylaminoethyl)-5-(*o*-fluorophenyl)-1,3-dihydro-2*H*-1,4-benzodiazepin-2-one; flurazepam hydrochloride; ID-480; NSC-78559; Ro 5-6901).
FLURBIPROFEN* ((±)-2-(2-fluoro-4-biphenylyl)propionic acid; (±)-2-fluoro-α-methyl[1,1'-biphenyl]-4-acetic acid; BTS-18322; FP-70; U-27182; 'cebutid'; 'froben').
Flurecol *see* Flurenol.
FLURENOL* (9-hydroxy-9*H*-fluorene-9-carboxylic acid; flurecol).
FLURENOL-BUTYL (butyl 9-hydroxy-9*H*-fluorene-9-carboxylate; 'aniten').
FLURETOFEN (4'-ethynyl-2-fluorobiphenyl; compound 93819).
'Fluril' *see* Fluorouracil.
FLURITHROMYCIN* ((8*S*)-8-fluoroerythromycin).
'Flurobate' *see* Betamethasone benzoate.

FLUROCITABINE* (7-fluoro-2,2′-anhydro-1-
β-D-arabinofuranosylcytosine;
(2*R*,3*R*,3a*S*,9a*R*)-7-fluoro-2,3,3a,9a-tetrahydro-
3-hydroxy-6-imino-6*H*-furo[2′,3′:4,5]oxazo-
lo[3,2-*a*]pyrimidine-2-methanol; 7-fluoroancitab-
ine; AAFC).

FLUROFAMIDE* (*N*-(diaminophosphinyl)-*p*-
fluorobenzamide).

Flurogestone see Flugestone.

'Fluron' see Fluoroacetic acid.

Flurothyl* see Flurotyl.

FLUROTYL* (bis(2,2,2-trifluoroethyl) ether;
hexafluorodiethyl ether; flurothyl; HFE; SK&F-
6539; 'indokolon').

Flurotyl isomer see Hexafluoroisopropyl methyl
ether.

FLUROXENE (2,2,2-trifluoroethyl vinyl ether;
fluoroxene; 'fluoromar').

Fluroxyspiramine see Spiramide.

FLUSALAN* (3,5-dibromo-3′-(trifluoromethyl)salicylanilide; 3,5-dibromo-α,α,α-trifluorosalicylotoluidide; fluorosalan).

FLUSOXOLOL ((*S*)-1-[*p*-[2-[(*p*-fluorophenethyl)oxy]ethoxy]phenoxy]-3-(isopropylamino)-2-propanol; Ro 31-1411).

FLUSPIPERONE* (8-[3-(*p*-fluorobenzoyl)-propyl]-1-(*p*-fluorophenyl)-1,3,8-triazaspiro-[4.5]decan-4-one; R-28930).

FLUSPIRILENE* (8-[4,4-bis(*p*-fluorophenyl)-butyl]-1-phenyl-1,3,8-triazaspiro[4.5]-decan-4-one; spirodiflamine; McN-JR-6218; R-6218).

FLUTAMIDE* (2-methyl-4′-nitro-3′-(trifluoromethyl)propionanilide; 4′-nitro-3′-(trifluoromethyl)isobutyranilide; α,α,α-trifluoro-2-methyl-4′-nitro-*m*-propionotoluamide; α′,α′,α′-trifluoro-4′-nitroisobutyro-*m*-toluidide; niftolid; Sch-13521; 'sebatrol').

FLUTAZOLAM* (10-chloro-11b-(*o*-fluorophenyl)-2,3,7,11b-tetrahydro-7-(2-hydroxyethyl)oxazolo-[3,2-*d*][1,4]benzodiazepin-6(5*H*)-one).

FLUTIAZIN* (8-(trifluoromethyl)phenothiazine-1-carboxylic acid; SK&F-22908).

FLUTIZENOL* (4-[3-[4-(2-hydroxyethyl)piperazin-1-yl]propyl]-6-trifluoromethyl-4*H*-thieno-[2,3-*b*][1,4]benzothiazine; 4-[3-(6-trifluoromethyl-4*H*-thieno[2,3-*b*][1,4]benzothiazin-4-yl-propyl]-l-piperazineethanol).

'Flutone' see Triamcinolone acetonide.

FLUTONIDINE (5-fluoro-*N*-(2-imidazolin-2-yl)-*o*-toluidine; 2-(5-fluoro-*o*-toluidino)-2-imidazoline; ST-600).

FLUTOPRAZEPAM* (7-chloro-1-(cyclopropylmethyl)-5-(*o*-fluorophenyl)-1,3-dihydro-2*H*-1,4-benzodiazepin-2-one).

'Flutra' see Trichlormethiazide.

FLUTROLINE* ((±)-8-fluoro-α,5-bis(*p*-chlorophenyl)-1,3,4,5-tetrahydro-2*H*-pyrido[4,3-*b*]indole-2-butanol; CP-36584).

FLUTROPIUM BROMIDE ((8*r*)-8-(2-fluoroethyl)-3α-hydroxy-1α*H*,5α*H*-tropanium bromide benzilate).

'Fluvermal' see Flubendazole.

'Fluversin' see Suloctidil.

'Fluvet' see Flumetasone pivalate.

FLUVOMYCIN (polypeptide antibiotic from *Bac. subtilis*; 'efsiomycin'; 'riomycin'; 'vivicil').

FLUVOXAMINE* (5-methoxy-4′-(trifluoromethyl)valerophenone (*E*)-*O*-(2-aminoethyl)oxime).

FLUZINAMIDE (*N*-methyl-3-[(α,α,α-trifluoro-*m*-tolyl)oxy]-1-azetidinecarboxamide; AHR-8559).

FLUZOPERINE* (5-[2-(diethylamino)ethyl]-4-(*p*-fluorophenyl)-4-oxazolin-2-one).

FM-24 see Bornaprolol.

FMC-30980 see Cypermethrin.

FMC-33297 see Permethrin.

'Fobex' see Benactyzine.

'Focusan' see Tolnaftate.

Folacin see Folic acid.

'Folbex' see Chlorobenzilate.

'Folcid' see Captafol.

FOLESCUTOL* (6,7-dihydroxy-4-morpholinomethylcoumarin; 4-(morpholinomethyl)esculetin; LD-2988; 'covalan').

'Folex' see Tributyl phosphorotrithioite.

FOLIC ACID* (*N*-[*p*-[[(2-amino-4-hydroxy-6-pteridyl)methyl]amino]benzoyl]-L-(+)-glutamic acid; pteroylglutamic acid; vitamin B$_c$; vitamin M; folacin; *Lactobacillus casei* factor; NSC-3073).

'Folidol E' see Parathion.

'Folidol M' see Parathion methyl.

'Foligan' see Allopurinol.

'Folimat' see Omethoate.

FOLINIC ACID (*N*^{5}-formyltetrahydrofolic acid). *See also* Calcium folinate.

'Folithion' see Fenitrothion.

Follicle stimulating hormone, human see Human menopausal gonadotrophin.

Follicular hormone see Estrone.

Folliculin see Estrone.

Folliculin hydrate see Estriol.

Folliculostatin see Inhibin.

'Follicyclin' see Estradiol dipropionate.

'Follinett' see *under* Norgestrel.

'Follistrel' see Levonorgestrel.

Follotropin see Human menopausal gonadotrophin.

'Folosan' see Tecnazene.

FOLPET (2-(trichloromethylthio)-1*H*-isoindole-1,3-(2*H*)-dione; *N*-(trichloromethylthio)phthalimide; 'ortho-phaltan'; 'phaltan').

'Folvirin' see *under* Estradiol benzoate.

FOMINOBEN* (*N*-[2-[(6-benzamido-2-chlorobenzyl)methylamino]acetyl]morpholine; 3′-chloro-2′-[[methyl(morpholinocarbonylmethyl)-amino]methyl]benzanilide; 3′-chloro-α-[methyl(morpholinocarbonylmethyl)amino]-*o*-benzotoluidide; clobenmetamide; PB-89; 'noleptan'; 'terion').

See also under Bromhexine.

FOMOCAINE (4-(3-morpholinopropyl)benzyl phenyl ether; 4-[3-(4-phenoxymethylphenyl)propyl]morpholine; P-652).

246

Fonazine* see Dimetotiazine.
'Fonderma' see Pyrithione sodium.
'Fonlipol' see Tiadenol.
FONOPHOS* (*O*-ethyl *S*-phenyl ethylphosphono-
dithioate; 'dyfonate'; 'dyphonate').
'Fontamide' see Sulfathiourea.
'Fontilix' see Meticrane.
'Fonurit' see Acetazolamide.
'Fonzylane' see Buflomedil.
Food blue 3 see Isosulfan blue.
FOPIRTOLINE*** (2-chloro-6-(2-morpholino-
ethylthio)pyridine; 4-[2-(6-chloropyrid-2-ylthio)-
ethyl]morpholine).
'Foralamin' see Methafurylene.
'Forane' see Isoflurane.
'Forapin' see Bee venom.
'Fordiuran' see Bumetanide.
'Fordonal' see Thiazolinobutazone.
'Forenol' see Niflumic acid.
'Forhistal' see Dimetindene.
'Forit' see Oxypertine.
Formal see Methylal.
FORMALDEHYDE (formalin; formol; methanal;
methyl aldehyde; methylene oxide; oxomethane;
oxymethylene).
Formaldehydeacetamide see Formicin.
Formaldehydeaniline see Formaniline.
Formalin see Formaldehyde.
FORMAMIDE (methenamide).
FORMAMIDE OXIME (isouretin; isuretin).
FORMAMIDINE (methanimidamide).
2-Formamido-5-nitrothiazole see Forminitrazole.
Formamine see Methenamine.
'Formamint' see Paraformaldehyde.
Formamol see Methenamine anhydromethylene-
citrate.
FORMANILIDE (*N*-phenylformamide).
FORMANILINE (formaldehydeaniline).
'Formanol' see Methenamine anhydromethylene-
citrate.
Formchlorazin see Triforine.
FORMEBOLONE** (11α,17β-dihydroxy-17-
methyl-3-oxoandrosta-1,4-diene-2-carboxalde-
hyde; 2-formyl-11α,17β-dihydroxy-17α-methyl-
androsta-1,4-dien-3-one; formyldienolone; 'esi-
clene').
Formetamide see Formetorex.
FORMETANATE* (*N*,*N*-dimethyl-*N*'-[3-[[(meth-
ylamino)carbonyl]oxy]phenyl]methanimidamide;
N,*N*-dimethyl-*N*'-[*m*-(methylcarbamoyloxy)-
phenyl]formamidine; 'carzol'; 'dicarzol').
See also under Chlorphenamidine.
FORMETOREX*** (*N*-formyl-α-methylphen-
ethylamine; *N*-(α-methylphenethyl)formamide;
formetamide).
FORMIC ACID (aminic acid).
FORMICIN (formaldehydeacetamide; methylalacetamide).
'Formiloxine' see Gitoformate.
**3-[[2-(Formimidoylamino)ethyl]thio]-6-(1-hydroxy-
ethyl)-7-oxo-1-azabicyclo[3.2.0]hept-2-ene-2-
carboxylic acid** see Imipenem.
N-**Formimidoylthienamycin** see Imipenem.

FORMIMINOGLUTAMIC ACID (*N*-formimido-
ylglutamic acid; FIGLU).
'Formin' see Methenamine.
FORMINITRAZOLE*** (2-formamido-5-nitro-
thiazole; BW-291C51; 'aroxine').
'Forminitrol' see Paraformaldehyde.
'Formitrol' see Paraformaldehyde.
FORMOCORTAL*** (3-(2-chloroethoxy)-9α-
fluoro-11β,16α,17α,21-tetrahydroxy-20-oxo-3,5-
pregnadiene-6-carboxaldehyde cyclic 16,17-acet-
al with acetone 21-acetate; 21-acetoxy-3-(2-
chloroethoxy)-9α-fluoro-6-formyl-11β-hydroxy-
16α,17α-isopropylidenedioxypregna-3,5-dien-20-
one; 3-(2-chloroethoxy)-9α-fluoro-6-formyl-
11β,16α,17α,21-tetrahydroxy-3,5-pregnadiene-
20-one 16α,17α-acetonide 21-acetate; fluoroformylon).
Formol see Formaldehyde.
FORMONETIN (7-hydroxy-4'-methoxyisoflav-
one; formononetin; ononein).
Formononetin see Formonetin.
FORMOTEROL*** ((±)-2'-hydroxy-5'-[(*RS*)-1-
hydroxy-2-[[(*RS*)-*p*-methoxy-α-methylphen-
ethyl]amino]ethyl]formanilide).
FORMOTHION* (*S*-(*N*-formyl-*N*-methylcarba-
moylmethyl) *O*,*O*-dimethyl phosphorodithioate;
S-(2-formylmethylamino)-2-oxoethyl *O*,*O*-di-
methyl phosphorodithioate; isoformothion; 'anfix'; 'anthio'; 'antio').
FORMYCIN A (7-amino-3-(β-D-ribofuranosyl)-
pyrazolo[4,3-*d*]pyrimidine).
FORMYCIN B (7-hydroxy-3-(β-D-ribofuranosyl)-
pyrazolo[4,3-*d*]pyrimidine; larusin).
4'-Formylacetanilide thiosemicarbazone see Thioacetazone.
16-Formylacetylgitoxin see Acetylgitaloxin.
o-**Formylbenzoic acid** see Phthalaldehydic acid.
p-**Formylbenzoic acid** see Benzaldehyde-4-carb-
oxylic acid.
Formyldienolone see Formebolone.
**2-Formyl-11α,17β-dihydroxy-17α-methylandrosta-
1,4-dien-3-one** see Formebolone.
18-Formyl-11β,21-dihydroxypregn-4-ene-3,20-dione
see Aldosterone.
Formylformic acid see Glyoxylic acid.
16-Formylgitoxigenin see Gitaloxigenin.
16-Formylgitoxin see Gitaloxin.
2-(2-Formylhydrazino)-4-(5-nitro-2-furyl)thiazole
see Nifurthiazole.
[3-(*N*-Formylhydroxylamino)propyl]phosphinic acid
see Fosmidomycin.
**4-Formyl-3-hydroxy-(5-hydroxymethyl)-2-methyl-
pyridine** see Pyridoxal.
FORMYLMELPHALAN (L-3-[*p*-[bis-(2-chloro-
ethyl)amino]phenyl]-*N*-formylalanine; N-form-
ylmelphalan; CB-3208; NSC-37024).
Formylmerphalan see Formylsarcolysin.
S-**(2-Formylmethylamino)-2-oxoethyl *O*,*O*-dimethyl
phosphorodithioate** see Formothion.
S-**(*N*-Formyl-*N*-methylcarbamoylmethyl) *O*,*O*-di-
methyl phosphorodithioate** see Formothion.
**10-(Formylmethyl)-7,13-dihydroxy-8-methoxy-3,12-
dimethyl-5-oxo-4,17-dioxabicyclo[14.1.0]hepta-**

dec-14-en-9-yl 3,6-dideoxy-4-O-(2,6-dideoxy-3-C-methyl-α-L-*ribo*-hexopyranosyl)-3-(dimethylamino)-β-D-glucopyranoside 4'',7'-dipropionate see Maridomycin.

7-(Formylmethyl)-4,10-dihydroxy-5-methoxy-9,16-dimethyl-2-oxooxacyclohexadeca-11,13-dien-6-yl 3,6-dideoxy-4-O-(2,6-dideoxy-3-C-methyl-α-L-*ribo*-hexopyranosyl)-3-(dimethylamino)-β-D-glucopyranoside 4'-acetate 4''-isovalerate see Josamycin.

7-(Formylmethyl)-4,10-dihydroxy-5-methoxy-9,16-dimethyl-2-oxooxacyclohexadeca-11,13-dien-6-yl 3,6-dideoxy-4-O-(2,6-dideoxy-3-C-methyl-α-L-*ribo*-hexopyranosyl)-3-(dimethylamino)-β-D-glucopyranoside 4,4''-dipropionate see Midecamycin.

N-Formyl-α-methylphenethylamine see Formetorex.

2-Formyl-1-methylpyridinium chloride oxime see Pralidoxime chloride.

2-Formyl-1-methylpyridinium iodide oxime see Pralidoxime iodide.

o-Formylphenoxyacetic acid isonicotinoylhydrazone see Aconiazide.

2-Formylpyridine see Picolinaldehyde.

FORMYLSARCOLYSIN (DL-3-[*p*-[bis(2-chloroethyl)amino]phenyl]-*N*-formylalanine; formylmerphalan; MP-506; NSC-39274). See also Formylmelphalan.

Formyl terchloride see Chloroform.

N⁵-Formyltetrahydrofolic acid see Folinic acid.

5-Formyl-2-thiophenecarbonitrile thiosemicarbazone see Citenazone.

6-Formyl-4,7,9-trihydroxyphenazine-1-carboxylic acid methyl ester see Lomofungin.

FORSKOLIN (17β-acetoxy-8,13-epoxy-1α,6β,9α-trihydroxylabd-14-en-11-one).

'Forstan' see Chinomethionat.

'Fortagesic' see under Paracetamol.

'Fortal' see Pentazocine.

'Fortapen' see Ampicillin.

'Fortasept' see Lauralkonium chloride.

'Fortecortin' see Dexamethasone.

'Forthane' see 1,3-Dimethylamylamine.

'Forticef' see Cefradine.

'Fortivenat' see under Chymotrypsin.

'Fortizyme' see α-Amylase.

'Fortombrine' see Sodium acetrizoate.

'Fortombrine M' see Meglumine acetrizoate.

'Fortral' see Pentazocine.

'Fortralin' see Pentazocine.

'Fortrol' see Cyanazine.

'Forturf' see Chlorothalonil.

Fosarbin see Pyrophos.

FOSAZEPAM*** (7-chloro-1-(dimethylphosphinylmethyl)-1,3-dihydro-5-phenyl-2*H*-1,4-benzodiazepin-2-one; compound 48390; HR-930).

FOSCARNET SODIUM*** (phosphonoformic acid trisodium salt).

'Foschlor' see Metrifonate.

FOSCOLIC ACID*** (2,2'-phosphinicodilactic acid; phoscolic acid; PDLA).

FOSENAZIDE*** ((diphenylphosphinyl)acetic acid hydrazide).

Fosfakol (tr) see Paraoxon.

Fosfamid (tr) see Dimethoate.

'Fosferno' see Parathion.

FOSFESTROL*** (*trans*-α,α'-diethyl-4,4'-stilbenediol bis(dihydrogen phosphate); stilbestrol diphosphate; NSC-10481; ST-52).

'Fosfocin' see Fosfomycin.

FOSFOCREATININE*** ((1-methyl-4-oxo-2-imidazolidinylidene)phosphoramidic acid; creatininephosphoric acid; phosphocreatinine; 'creatergyl').

Fosfolan see Phosfolan.

FOSFOMYCIN*** ((−)(1*R*,2*S*)-1,2-epoxypropylphosphonic acid; phosphonomycin; MK-955; 'fosfocin').

FOSFOMYCIN plus AMOXICILLIN ('moxiprim').

FOSFOMYCIN plus CEFALEXIN ('kufaprim').

FOSFONET SODIUM*** (phosphonoacetic acid disodium salt monohydrate; Abbott-38642).

FOSFOSAL*** (2-phosphonobenzoic acid; salicylic acid dihydrogen phosphate).

'Fosfostimol' see Adenosine phosphates.

'Fosfothion' see Malathion.

'Fosgran' see Metrifonate.

'Fosgren' see Metrifonate.

FOSMENIC ACID*** ((3-cyclohexen-1-ylhydroxymethyl)phosphinic acid).

FOSMIDOMYCIN*** ([3-(*N*-hydroxyformamido)propyl]phosphonic acid; [3-(*N*-formylhydroxylamino)propyl]phosphinic acid; fosmidomycin monosodium salt).

FOSPIRATE*** (dimethyl (3,5,6-trichloropyrid-2-yl) phosphate; 'torelle').

'Fossyol' see Metronidazole.

FOSTEDIL*** (diethyl (*p*-benzothiazol-2-ylbenzyl)phosphonate; KB-944).

'Fosten' see Aprotinin.

'Fostion' see Prothoate.

'Fostion MM' see Dimethoate.

'Foston' see Toldimfos.

FOTRETAMINE*** (2,2,4,4,6-pentakis(1-aziridinyl)-2,2,4,4,6,8-hexahydro-6-morpholino-1,3,5,2,4,6,-triazatriphosphorine).

'Fouadin' see Stibophen.

'Fovane' see Benzthiazide.

'Foxalin' see Digitoxin.

Fox green see Indocyanine green.

'Foy' see Gabexate mesilate.

FOY-305 see Camostat.

FP-70 see Flurbiprofen.

FPA see Fluprednisolone acetate.

FPL-670 see Cromoglicate disodium.

FPL-59002 KP see Nedocromil.

FPL-60278 AR see Dopexamine.

FR-7 see Fenamisal.

FR-33 see Roxoperone.

FR-005759 see Pyrrolnitrin.

FR-13749 see Ceftizoxime.

FRABUPROFEN*** (2-[4-(α,α,α-trifluoro-*m*-tolyl)piperazin-1-yl]ethyl (±)-*p*-isobutylhydratropate).

'Fragivix' see Benzarone.

'Framidal' *see* Framycetin.
FRAMYCETIN*** (*O*-2,6-diamino-2,6-dideoxy-β-L-idopyranosyl(1→3)-*O*-β-D-ribofuranosyl-(1→5)-*O*-[2,6-diamino-2,6-dideoxy-α-D-glucopyranosyl-(1→4)]-2-deoxy-D-streptamine; neomycin B; EF-185; 'actilin'; 'enterfram'; 'framidal'; 'framygen'; 'soframycin').
See also under Clioquinol.
Framycin (tr) *see* Neomycin.
'Framygen' *see* Framycetin.
'Francaine' *see* Procaine teoclate.
Frangula-emodin *see* Emodin.
Frangulic acid *see* Emodin.
FRANGULIN (frangulin A plus frangulin B; avornin).
FRANGULIN A (1,3,8-trihydroxy-6-methylanthraquinone L-rhamnoside; emodin rhamnoside; franguloside; rhamnoxanthin).
FRANGULIN B (1,6,8-trihydroxy-3-methylanthraquinone 6-(D-apicofuranoside)).
Franguloside *see* Frangulin A.
'Franocide' *see* Diethylcarbamazine.
'Frantin' *see* Bephenium embonate.
'Fraquinol' *see under* Clioquinol.
'Fraustan' *see* Diazepam.
'Frekentine' *see* Amfepramone.
'Frenactyl' *see* Benperidol.
'Frenodosa' *see* Amyl nitrite.
'Frenolon' *see* Metofenazate.
'Frenolyse' *see* Tranexamic acid.
FRENTIZOLE*** (6-methoxy-2-[(phenylcarbamoyl)amino]benzothiazole; 1-(6-methoxybenzothiazol-2-yl)-3-phenylurea; compound 53616).
'Freon 12' *see* Dichlorodifluoromethane.
'Freon 112' *see* Tetrachlorodifluoroethane.
'Freon 113' *see* 1,1,2,2-Tetrachloro-1,2-difluoroethane *and* 1,1,2-Trichloro-1,2,2-trifluoroethane.
'Freon 114' *see* Cryofluorane.
'Freon C-138' *see* Octafluorocyclobutane.
'Frescon' *see* Trifenmorph.
Frey inhibitor *see* Aprotinin.
'Frideron' *see* Zeranol.
'Frigen 12' *see* Dichlorodifluoromethane.
'Frigen 112' *see* Tetrachlorodifluoroethane.
'Frigen-113' *see* 1,1,2-Trichloro-1,2,2-trifluoroethane.
'Frigen 114' *see* Cryofluorane.
'Frigiderm' *see* Cryofluorane.
'Fringanor' *see* Phendimetrazine embonate.
'Frisium' *see* Clobazam.
'Froben' *see* Flurbiprofen.
'Fruchol' *see* Magnesium ferulate.
'Fructergyl' *see under* Ascorbic acid.
Fructofuranose tetranicotinate *see* Nicofuranose.
FRUCTOSE (D-fructose; laevulose; levulose).
FRUCTOSE 1,6-DIPHOSPHATE (Harden-Young ester; 'esafosfina').
See also Calcium fructose 1,6-diphosphate.
Fructose nicotinate *see* Nicofuranose.
FRUCTOSE 6-PHOSPHATE (hexose monophosphate; Neuberg ester).
Fructose tetranicotinate *see* Nicofuranose.
'Frugalan' *see* Furfenorex.

'Frumin' *see* Disulfoton.
Frusemide* *see* Furosemide.
'Frutone CPA' *see* Cloprop.
FSH *see* Human menopausal gonadotrophin.
FT-81 *see* Bendroflumethiazide.
FT-207 *see* Tegafur.
Ftalicetimida *see* Phthalylsulfacetamide.
Ftalofos (tr) *see* Phosmet.
FTALOFYNE*** (1-ethyl-1-methyl-2-propynyl phthalate; methylpentynol phthalate; phthalofyne; NSC-25614; 'whipicide').
FTAXILIDE*** (2',6'-dimethylphthalanilic acid; *N*-(2,6-xylyl)phthalamic acid).
F₃TDR *see* Trifluridine.
FTIVAZIDE*** (4-hydroxy-3-methoxybenzaldehyde isonicotinoylhydrazone; *N'*-vanillideneisoniazid; vanillin isonicotinoylhydrazone; phthivazid).
Ftoracizine (tr) *see* Fluacizine.
Ftorafur (tr) *see* Tegafur.
FTORDOPAN (tr) (5-[(2-chloroethyl)(2-fluoroethyl)amino]-6-methyluracil; fluordopan; fluorodopan).
FTORMETAZINE*** (2-(4-methylpiperazin-1-yl)ethyl 2-trifluoromethylphenothiazin-10-yl ketone; 10-[3-(4-methylpiperazin-1-yl)propionyl]-2-trifluoromethylphenothiazine).
Ftoroplast (tr) *see* Politef.
Ftorotan (tr) *see* Halothane.
FTORPROPAZINE*** (2-[4-(2-hydroxyethyl)-piperazin-1-yl]ethyl 2-trifluoromethylphenothiazin-10-yl ketone; 10-[3-[4-(2-hydroxyethyl)-piperazin-1-yl]propionyl]-2-trifluoromethyl-phenothiazine).
'Fuadin' *see* Stibophen.
'Fua-med' *see* Nitrofurantoin.
FUBERIDAZOLE* (2-furan-2-yl-1*H*-benzimidazole; 'voronit').
FUBROGONIUM IODIDE*** ([3-(5-bromo-2-furoyloxy)butyl]diethylmethylammonium iodide; diethyl(3-hydroxybutyl)methylammonium iodide 5-bromo-2-furoate; fubromegan).
Fubromegan (tr) *see* Fubrogonium iodide.
FUCHSINE (mixture of hydrochlorides of pararosaniline and rosaniline; magenta; rosein; rubin; 'solferino').
FUCHSINE SULFONATE (acid fuchsine; mixture of NH₄ or Na salts of fuchsine di- and trisulfonic acids).
'Fucidin' *see* Fusidic acid.
'Fuclasin' *see* Ziram.
FUDR *see* Floxuridine.
'Fugacillin' *see* Carbenicillin.
'Fugillin' *see* Fumagillin.
'Fugipaverin' *see* Alverine.
'Fugoa' *see* Cathine.
'Fuklasin' *see* Ziram.
'Fuklasin ultra' *see* Ferbam.
'Fulcin' *see* Griseofulvin.
Fulmicoton* *see* Pyroxylin.
'Fulvicin' *see* Griseofulvin.
FUMAGILLIN*** (4-(1,2-epoxy-1,6-dimethylhex-4-enyl)-5-methoxy-1-oxaspiro[2.5]oct-6-yl

hydrogen deca-2,4,6,8-tetraenedioate; antibiotic from *Aspergillus fumigatus*; NSC-9168).

FUMARIA OFFICINALIS EXTRACT (AN-1320; 'oddibil').

FUMARIC ACID (*trans*-1,2-ethylenedicarboxylic acid; allomaleic acid; boletic acid).

Fumarin see Coumafuryl.

'**Fumasol**' *see* Coumafuryl.

'**Fumazone**' *see* 1,2-Dibromo-3-chloropropane.

'**Fumidil**' *see* Fumagillin.

FUMIGATIN (6-hydroxy-5-methoxy-*p*-toluquinone).

'**Fumigrain**' *see* Acrylonitrile.

'**Fumite TCNB**' *see* Tecnazene.

FUMOXICILLIN** ((2*S*,5*R*,6*R*)-6-[(*R*)-2-(furfurylideneamino)-2-(*p*-hydroxyphenyl)acetamido]-penicillanic acid; furoxicillin).

'**Fundal**' *see* Chlorphenamidine.

'**Fundal forte**' *see under* Chlorphenamidine.

'**Fungi-ban**' *see* Bis(tributyltin) oxide.

Fungicidin see Nystatin.

'**Fungifos**' *see* Tolciclate.

'**Fungifral**' *see* Hedaquinium chloride.

FUNGIMYCIN* (perimycin; NC-1968; WX-2412).

'**Fungiplex**' *see* Sulbentine.

'**Fungitin**' *see* Amphotericin B.

'**Fungizone**' *see* Amphotericin B.

FUNTUMIDINE (3α-aminoallopregnan-2-ol; 3α-amino-5α-pregnan-2-ol).

FUPRAZOLE* (3-[2-[(4-cinnamylpiperazin-1-yl)methyl]benzimidazol-1-yl]-1-(2-furyl)-1-propanone).

Furacilin see Nitrofural.

'**Furacin**' *see* Nitrofural.

FURACRINIC ACID* (5-(2-ethylacryloyl)-6-methylbenzofuran-2-carboxylic acid; 6-methyl-5-(2-methylenebutyryl)-2-benzofurancarboxylic acid; GP-48674).

FURACRYLIN (tr) (1-[(5-nitro-2-furyl)acrylideneamino]-1,3,4-triazole).

'**Furadan**' *see* Carbofuran.

'**Furadantin**' *see* Nitrofurantoin.

'**Furadantoin**' *see* Nitrofurantoin.

Furadoine see Nitrofurantoin.

Furadonin (tr) *see* Nitrofurantoin.

'**Furadroxyl**' *see* Nidroxyzone.

FURAFYLLINE* (3-furfuryl-1,8-dimethylxanthine).

Furagin (tr) *see* Furazidin.

FURAGUANIDINE (tr) (1-(5-nitro-2-furfurylideneamino)guanidine; F-28; 'guanofuracin').

FURALAZINE* (3-amino-6-[2-(5-nitro-2-furyl)-vinyl]-*as*-triazine; 3-amino-6-(5-nitrofurfurylidenemethyl)-1,2,4-triazine; furatrizine; nifuralazin; nitrofuralazin).

2-FURALDEHYDE (furfural; furfuraldehyde; furfurol(e); pyromucic aldehyde).

Furaloxon (tr) *see* Nidroxyzone.

FURALTADONE* (5-(4-morpholinomethyl)-3-[(5-nitrofurfurylidene)amino]-2-oxazolidinone; 5-(morpholinomethyl)furazolidone; furmethonol; NF-260).

See also Levofuraltadone.

'**Furamazone**' *see* Nifuraldezone.

'**Furamicid**' *see* Nitrofurfuryl methyl ether.

'**Furamide**' *see* Diloxanide furoate.

Furamon (tr) *see* Furtrethonium iodide.

FURAN (furfuran).

'**Furanace**' *see* Nifurpirinol.

2-Furancarboxylic acid see Furoic acid.

FURANIOZID (tr) (5-nitro-2-furaldehyde isonicotinoylhydrazone; isonicotinic acid (5-nitrofurfurylidene)hydrazide; nitrofurfurylideneisoniazid; F-74).

2-Furanmethanol see Furfuryl alcohol.

6,7-Furanochromone see 5*H*-Furo[3,2-*g*][1]benzopyran-5-one.

FURANOMYCIN (α-amino-2,5-dihydro-5-methyl-2-furanacetic acid; (2,5-dihydro-5-methyl-2-furan)glycine).

'**Furanthril**' *see* Furosemide.

'**Furantocompren**' *see* Nitrofurantoin.

'**Furantoin**' *see* Nitrofurantoin.

2-Furan-2-yl-1*H*-benzimidazole see Fuberidazole.

3-(1-Furan-2-yl-3-oxobutyl)-4-hydroxy-2*H*-1-benzopyran-2-one see Coumafuryl.

FURAPROFEN* ((±)-α-methyl-3-phenyl-7-benzofuranacetic acid; 2-(3-phenylbenzofuran-7-yl)propionic acid; enprofen; R-803).

'**Furaspore**' *see* Nitrofurfuryl methyl ether.

'**Furatin**' *see* Nitrofurantoin.

'**Furatol**' *see* Fluoroacetic acid.

Furatrizine see Furalazine.

Furaxone (tr) *see* Furazolidone.

FURAZABOL** (17β-hydroxy-17α-methyl-5α-androstano[2,3-*c*]furazan; 17α-methyl-5α-androstano[2,3-*c*]furazan-17β-ol; androfurazanol).

FURAZIDIN (tr) (1-[3-(5-nitro-2-furyl)allylideneamino]hydantoin; furagin; F-35).

Furazole* see Furazolium chloride.

FURAZOLIDONE* (3-(5-nitrofurfurylideneamino)-2-oxazolidinone; nifurazolidone; furaxone; F-60).

FURAZOLIUM CHLORIDE* (6,7-dihydro-3-(5-nitro-2-furyl)-5*H*-imidazo[2,1-*b*]thiazolium chloride; furazole; NF-963; 'novofur').

FURAZOLIUM TARTRATE* (NF-1425).

Furazosin* see Prazosin.

'**Furbenal**' *see* Nitrofurfuryl methyl ether.

FURBUCILLIN** (6-((*R*)-2-hydroxy-4-methylvaleramido)penicillanic acid 2-furoate ester; 6-((*R*)-2-furoyloxy-4-methylvaleramido)penicillanic acid).

FURCLOPROFEN* ((+)-8-chloro-α-methyl-3-dibenzofuranacetic acid).

'**Furedeme**' *see* Furterene.

Furenapyridazine see Nifurprazine.

Furenazine see Nifurprazine.

'**Furesis**' *see* Furosemide.

FURETHIDINE* (ethyl 4-phenyl-1-[2-(tetrahydrofurfuryloxy)ethyl]isonipecotate).

FURFENOREX* ((+)-*N*-furfuryl-*N*,α-dimethylphenethylamine; (+)-*N*-methyl-*N*-(1-phenylprop-2-yl)-2-furfurylamine; E-106).

FURFENOREX CYCLAMATE (furfurenox

250

cyclohexylsulfamate; E-106-E; SD-27115).

Furfural see 2-Furaldehyde.

Furfuraldehyde see 2-Furaldehyde.

Furfuran see Furan.

Furfurol(*e*) see 2-Furaldehyde.

FURFURYL ALCOHOL (2-furanmethanol).

2-(Furfurylamino)-4-phenoxy-5-sulfamoylbenzene-sulfonic acid see Sulosemide.

N-**Furfuryl-*N*,α-dimethylphenethylamine** see Furfenorex.

N-**Furfuryl-*N'*,*N'*-dimethyl-*N*-pyrid-2-ylethylenedi-amine** see Methafurylene.

3-Furfuryl-1,8-dimethylxanthine see Furafylline.

N'-**[1-(2-Furfuryl)ethylidene]isoniazed** see Menazone.

1-Furfurylideneacetone 2-isonicotinoylhydrazone see Larusan.

6-[2-(Furfurylideneamino)-2-(*p*-hydroxyphenyl)acet-amido]penicillanic acid see Fumoxicillin.

6-[2-[3-(Furfurylideneamino)-2-oxo-1-imidazolidine-carboxamido]-2-(*p*-hydroxyphenyl)acetamido]-penicillanic acid see Fuzlocillin.

*N*¹-**(2-Furfurylidene-1-methylethylidene)isoniazid** see Larusan.

2-Furfuryl methyl ketone isonicotinoylhydrazone see Menazone.

Furfuryltrimethylammonium benzenesulfonate see Furtrethonium besilate.

Furfuryltrimethylammonium iodide see Furtrethonium iodide.

Furfuryltrimethylammonium *p*-toluenesulfonate see Furtrethonium tosilate.

FURIDARONE*** (2,5-dimethyl-3-furyl 4-hydr-oxy-3,5-diiodophenyl ketone; 3-(4-hydroxy-3,5-diiodobenzoyl)-2,5-dimethylfuran; furodiarone; DB-136).

'**Furidin**' see Thiofuradene.

'**Furiton**' see Nihydrazone.

Furmarin see Coumafuryl.

'**Furmethide**' see Furtrethonium iodide.

Furmethonol see Furaltadone.

FURMETHOXADONE*** (5-methyl-3-(5-nitro-2-furfurylideneamino)-2-oxazolidinone; 5-meth-ylfurazolidone; nitrofuradoxadone).

5*H*-FURO[3,2-*g*][1]BENZOPYRAN-5-ONE (6,7-furanochromone; furo-2',3',6,7-chromone).

7*H*-Furo[3,2-*g*][1]benzopyran-7-one see Psoralen.

FUROBUFEN** (2-[(2-carboxyethyl)carbonyl]di-benzofuran; 2-carboxyethyl dibenzofuran-2-yl ketone; γ-oxo-2-dibenzofuranbutyric acid; AY-21367).

FURODAZOLE*** (2-(2-furyl)-7-methyl-1*H*-imi-dazo[4,5-*f*]quinolin-9-ol; F-691).

Furodiarone see Furidarone.

FUROFENAC*** (2-ethyl-2,3-dihydro-5-benzofu-ranacetic acid).

2-FUROIC ACID (2-furancarboxylic acid; brenzschleimsaure; pyromucic acid).
See also Diloxanide furoate; Quinfamide; Furo-stilbestrol.

FUROMAZINE*** (2-chloro-10-[3-[4-(dihydro-2(3*H*)-oxofuran-3-yl)-4-hydroxypiperid-1-yl]-propyl]phenothiazine; 1-[3-(2-chlorophenothiaz-in-10-yl)propyl]-4-(dihydro-2(3*H*)-oxofuran-3-yl)-4-hydroxypiperidine; 3-[1-[3-(2-chlorophe-nothiazin-10-yl)propyl]-4-hydroxypiperid-4-yl]di-hydro-2(3*H*)-furanone).

Furo[*b*]monazole see Oxazole.

'**Furophen**' see Nitrofurantoin.

FUROSEMIDE*** (4-chloro-*N*-(2-furfuryl)-5-sul-famoylanthranilic acid; frusemide; fursemide; LB-502).
See also under Reserpine.

FUROSEMIDE plus PENBUTEROL ('betase-mid').

FUROSTILBESTROL*** (*trans*-3,4-bis[4-(2-furoyloxy)phenyl]hex-3-ene; diethylstilbestrol di(2-furoate); stilbestrol 2-furancarboxylate; stil-bestrol furoate).

Furoxicillin see Fumoxicillin.

'**Furoxone**' see Furazolidone.

6-((*R*)-2-Furoyloxy-4-methylvaleramido)penicillanic acid see Furbucillin.

FURSALAN** (3,5-dibromo-*N*-tetrahydrofurfur-ylsalicylamide).

Fursemide see Furosemide.

FURSULTIAMINE*** (*N*-(4-amino-2-methylpyr-imidin-5-ylmethyl)-*N*-[4-hydroxy-1-methyl-2-(tetrahydrofurfuryldithio)-1-butenyl]formamide; thiamine tetrahydrofurfuryl disulfide; TTFD).

FURTERENE*** (6-(2-furyl)-2,4,7-triaminopte-ridine; 2,4,7-triamino-6-(2-furyl)pteridine; 'fure-deme').

FURTRETHONIUM BESILATE (furfuryltri-methylammonium benzenesulfonate; benz-amon).

FURTRETHONIUM IODIDE*** (furfuryltri-methylammonium iodide; furamon; 'furmeth-ide').

FURTRETHONIUM TOSILATE (furfuryltri-methylammonium *p*-toluenesulfonate; 'fisosti-na').

17α-(3-Furyl)estra-1,3,5(10),7-tetraene-3,17-diol 3-acetate see Estrofurate.

FURYLFURAMIDE (2-(2-furyl)-2-(5-nitro-2-fur-furylidene)acetamide; 2-(2-furyl)-3-(5-nitro-2-furyl)acrylamide; AF-2).

7-[2-(2-Furyl)glyoxylamido]-3-(hydroxymethyl)-2-cephem-2-carboxylic acid mono-(*O*-methylox-ime), acetate see Cefuracetime.

7-[2-(2-Furyl)-2-methoxyiminoacetamido]cephalo-sporanic acid see Cefuracetime.

2-(2-Furyl)-7-methyl-1*H*-imidazo[4,5-*f*]quinolin-9-ol see Furodazole.

2-(2-Furyl)-2-(5-nitro-2-furfurylidene)acetamide see Furylfuramide.

2-(2-Furyl)-3-(5-nitro-2-furyl)acrylamide see Furyl-furamide.

6-(2-Furyl)-2,4,7-triaminopteridine see Furterene.

FUSAFUNGINE*** (antibiotic from a fusarium of *Lateritium wr* section; S-314).

'**Fusagit**' see Fusidate silver.

'**Fusarex**' see Tecnazene.

FUSARIC ACID (5-butylpicolinic acid; 5-butyl-pyridine-2-carboxylic acid).

Fusaric acid amide see Bupicomide.

251

'Fusid' *see* Furosemide.
FUSIDATE SILVER (silver fusidate; 'fusagit').
FUSIDATE SODIUM (fusidic acid sodium salt; SQ-16360).
FUSIDIC ACID*** (*cis*-3α,11α,16β-trihydroxy-4α,8,14-trimethyl-18-nor-5α,8α,9β,13α,14β-cholesta-17(20),24-dien-21-oic acid 16-acetate; 3α,11α,16β-trihydroxy-29-nor-8α,9β,13α,14β-dammara-17(20),24-dien-21-oic acid 16-acetate; ZN-6).
'Fussol' *see* Fluoroacetamide.
'Futraful' *see* Tegafur.

FUZLOCILLIN** ((2*S*,5*R*,6*R*)-6-[(2*R*)-2-[3-[(*E*)-furfurylideneamino]-2-oxo-1-imidazolidinecarb-oxamido]-2-(*p*-hydroxyphenyl)acetamido]peni-cillanic acid; BAY vk-4999).
FW-152 *see* Hydroxy-DDD.
FWH-399 *see* Troxonium tosilate.
FX-501 *see* Xenytropium bromide.
'Fybogel' *see* Psyllium.
'Fyracyl' *see* Magnesium acetylsalicylate.
Fytic acid*** *see* Phytic acid.
FZ-484 *see under* Fentonium bromide.

G

G-4 *see* Dichlorophen.
'G-11' *see* Hexachlorophene.
G-469 *see* Nicothiazone.
G-491 *see* Tiabendazole.
G-605 *see* Sulfoniazid.
G-610 *see* Trichlorophen.
G-728 *see* Arginine pidolate.
G-867 *see* Sulfadimethylbenzoylamide.
G-2747 *see* Caramiphen.
G-3012 *see* Metcaraphen.
G-5668 *see* Prethcamide.
G-7225 *see* Mecloralurea.
G-11765 *see* Ethyl biscoumacetate.
G-12114 *see* Chloropyramine.
G-13289 *see* Sulfaproxyline.
G-13871 *see* Phenylbutazone.
G-19258 *see* Dimetan.
G-22008 *see* 3-Methyl-1-phenylpyrazol-5-yl dimethylcarbamate.
G-22150 *see* Imipramine.
G-22355 *see* Imipramine.
G-23350 *see* Acenocoumarol.
G-23922 *see* Chlorobenzilate.
G-24480 *see* Dimpylate.
G-24483 *see* Diethyl 3-methylpyrazol-5-yl phosphate.
G-25178 *see* Prodeconium bromide.
G-25766 *see* Clorindione.
G-25804 *see* Chlorazine.
G-26872 *see* Phenbutazone sodium glycerate.
G-27202 *see* Oxyphenbutazone.
G-28315 *see* Sulfinpyrazone.
G-29595 *see* Estil.
G-30027 *see* Atrazine.
G-30320 *see* Clofazimine.
G-31150 *see* Calcium methyl polygalacturonate sulfonate(s).
G-31406 *see* Depramine fumarate.
G-32883 *see* Carbamazepine.
G-33040 *see* Opipramol.
G-33182 *see* Chlortalidone.
G-34162 *see* Ametryn.
G-34586 *see* Clomipramine.
G-35020 *see* Desipramine.
G-35359 *see* Ketimipramine.
GABA *see* 4-Aminobutyric acid.
GABAPENTIN*** (1-(aminomethyl)cyclohexaneacetic acid).
'Gabbromycin' *see* Paromomycin.
'Gabbroral' *see* Paromomycin.
GABEXATE*** (ethyl *p*-hydroxybenzoate 6-gua-

nidinohexanoate; *p*-(ethoxycarbonyl)phenyl 6-guanidinohexanoate).
GABEXATE MESILATE (gabexate methanesulfonate; 'foy').
GABOB *see* 4-Amino-3-hydroxybutyric acid.
GABOXADOL*** (4,5,6,7-tetrahydroisoxazolo[5,4-*c*]pyridin-3-ol; THIP; Lu-2-030).
'Gadexyl' *see* Pipradrol.
Gadolinium diethylenetriaminepentaacetic acid *see* Gadopentetic acid.
GADOPENTETIC ACID** (dihydrogen [*N*,*N*-bis[2-[bis(carboxymethyl)amino]ethyl]glycinato(5-)]gadolinate(2-); gadolinium diethylenetriaminepentaacetic acid).
'Gadusan' *see* Cupric morrhuate.
GAGPS *see* Glycosaminoglycan polysulfate(s).
Gaiactamine* *see* Guaiactamine.
'Gaiacyl' *see* Calcium guaiacolsulfonate.
'Gaiamar' *see* Guaifenesin.
Gaiazulene *see* Guaiazulene.
Gaietamine *see* Guaiactamine.
Galactaric acid *see* Mucic acid.
Galactin *see* Prolactin.
GALACTOFLAVIN (10-D-dulcityl-7,8-dimethyl-isoalloxazine; NSC-3099).
4-*O*-β-D-Galactopyranosyl-D-fructose *see* Lactulose.
GALACTOSAMINE (chondrosamine).
β-D-Galactosidase *see* Tilactase.
GALANGIN (3,5,7-trihydroxyflavone).
GALANTAMINE*** (1,2,3,4,6,7,7a,11c-octahydro-9-methoxy-2-methylbenzofuro[4,3,2-*efg*]-benzazocin-6-ol; galanthamine; nivaline).
Galanthamine *see* Galantamine.
GALASCORBIN (tr) (potassium ascorbate flavonoid complex; vitamin C plus vitamin P).
'Galatone' *see* Gluconiazone.
'Galatur' *see* Iprindole.
'Galecron' *see* Chlorphenamidine.
'Galidor' *see* Bencyclane.
'Gallabis' *see* Bismuth gallate.
GALLACETOPHENONE (2',3',4'-trihydroxyacetophenone; 4-acetylpyrogallol; alizarin yellow; eugallol; pyrogallol monoacetate).
GALLAMINE TRIETHIODIDE*** (1,2,3-tris[2-(diethylamino)ethoxy]benzene triethiodide; (phenenyltrisoxyethylene)tris(trimethylammonium iodide); pyrogallol 1,2,3-tris(diethylaminoethyl ether) triethiodide; gallammonium iodide; bencurine iodide; benzcurine iodide; pyrolaxon; sinocurarine; F-2559; RP 3697).

Gallammonium iodide* *see* Gallamine triethiodide.
GALLIC ACID (3,4,5-trihydroxybenzoic acid; pyrogallol-5-carboxylic acid; pyrogallic acid).
'Gallimycin' *see* Erythromycin stearate.
GALLIUM (^{67}Ga) CITRATE*** (radiogallium citrate).
Gallodeoxycholic acid *see* Chenodeoxycholic acid.
'Gallogen' *see* Ellagic acid.
GALLOPAMIL*** (5-[*N*-(3,4-dimethoxyphenethyl)methylamino]-2-isopropyl-2-(3,4,5-trimethoxyphenyl)valeronitrile; isopropyl[3-(*N*-methyl-*N*-homoveratrylamino)propyl](3,4,5-trimethoxyphenyl)acetonitrile; methoxyverapamil; D-600; 'procorum').
Gallotannic acid *see* Tannins.
GALOSEMIDE*** (3-(propionamidosulfonyl)-4-[*m*-(trifluoromethyl)anilino]pyridine; *N*-[[4-(α,α,α-trifluoro-*m*-toluidino)pyrid-3-yl]sulfonyl]-propionamide).
'Gamanil' *see* Lofepramine.
'Gamaquil' *see* Phenprobamate.
Gamatran *see* Alverine.
'Gamefar' *see* Pamaquine.
Gametocidum *see* Pamaquine.
GAMFEXINE*** (3-cyclohexyl-*N*,*N*-dimethyl-3-phenylpropylamine; *N*,*N*-dimethyl-γ-phenyl-cyclohexanepropylamine; WIN-1344).
'Gamibetol' *see* 4-Amino-3-hydroxybutyric acid.
'Gamiso' *see* Lindane.
'Gamma 666' *see* Lindane.
Gamma benzene hexachloride* *see* Lindane.
'Gammacorten' *see* Dexamethasone.
Gamma-OH *see* Oxybate sodium.
Gammaphos *see* Amifostine.
'Gammexane' *see* Lindane.
GAMOLENIC ACID*** (*cis,cis,cis*-octadeca-6,9,12-trienoic acid).
'Gamonil' *see* Lofepramine.
'Gamophen' *see* Hexachlorophene.
'Ganda' *see* Guanethidine monosulfate.
GANGLEFENE*** (3-diethylamino-1,2-dimethyl-propyl ester of *p*-isobutoxybenzoic acid; ganglerone).
Ganglerone (tr) *see* Ganglefene.
'Ganibetol' *see* 4-Amino-3-hydroxybutyric acid.
'Ganlion' *see* Azamethonium bromide.
'Gantanol' *see* Sulfamethoxazole.
'Gantrisin' *see* Sulfafurazole.
'Gantrosan' *see* Sulfafurazole.
GAPICOMINE** (di(pyrid-4-ylmethyl)amine; 4,4'-(iminodimethylene)dipyridine; 4-(pyrid-5-yl-methylaminomethyl)pyridine).
GAPICOMINE CITRATE ('bicordin').
'Garamycin' *see* Gentamicin.
Garantose *see* Saccharin.
'Gardenal' *see* Phenobarbital.
'Gardol' *see* Sodium *N*-lauroylsarcosinate.
'Gardona' *see* Stirofos.
'Gargilon' *see* Dequalinium chloride.
Garlic *see* Allium sativum.
'Garoin' *see under* Phenytoin.
'Garrathion' *see* Carbofenotion.
'Gastomag' *see* Magnesium trisilicate.

'Gastracid-test' *see* Phenazopyridine.
'Gastramine' *see* Betazole.
'Gastrazid' *see* Phenazopyridine.
'Gastridin' *see* Clebopride.
Gastrin-like pentapeptide *see* Pentagastrin.
Gastrin-like tetrapeptide *see* Tetragastrin.
'Gastripon' *see* Xenytropium bromide.
'Gastrix' *see* Oxyphencyclimine.
'Gastrixone' *see* Trantelinium bromide.
'Gastrodiagnost' *see* Pentagastrin.
'Gastrografin' *see* Meglumine diatrizoate.
'Gastronerton' *see* Metoclopramide.
'Gastronilo' *see* Zolimidine.
'Gastropin' *see* Xenytropium bromide.
'Gastropulgit' *see* Attapulgite.
'Gastrosil' *see* Metoclopramide.
'Gastrotest' *see* Phenazopyridine.
'Gastrovit' *see* Magnesium hydroxide.
'Gastrozepin' *see* Pirenzepine.
'Gatalone' *see* Gluconiazone.
'Gatinar' *see* Lactulose.
'Gatnon' *see* Benzthiazuron.
Gaultheria oil *see* Methyl salicylate.
GB *see* Sarin.
GB-94 *see* Mianserin.
GC-4072 *see* Clofenvinfos.
'Geabol' *see* Metandienone.
'Gebutox' *see* Dinoseb.
'Gecolate' *see* Guaifenesin.
GEFARNATE*** (*trans*-3,7-dimethyl-2,6-octadienyl trimethyltetradecatrienoate; geranyl farnesylacetate; DA-688).
'Gefarnil' *see* Gefarnate.
'Gefarnyl' *see* Gefarnate.
Geksan (tr) *see* Lindane.
'Gelafusal' *see* Gelatin solution.
GELATIN BROMOTANNATE (bromtannigel; 'bromocoll').
GELATIN SOLUTION ('gelafusal'; 'gelifundin'). *See also* Polygeline.
GELATIN SPONGE ('marbagelan').
'Gelifundin' *see* Gelatin solution.
'Geloverm' *see* Hexylresorcinol.
'Gelstaph' *see* Cloxacillin.
'Gelvatol' *see* Polyvinyl alcohol.
GEMAZOCINE*** (3-cyclopropylmethyl-6-ethyl-1,2,3,4,5,6-hexahydro-11,11-dimethyl-2,6-methano-3-benzazocin-8-ol; 2-(cyclopropylmethyl)-5-ethyl-2'-hydroxy-9,9-dimethyl-6,7-benzomorphan; R-15497).
GEMCADIOL*** (2,2,9,9-tetramethyl-1,10-decanediol; CI-720).
GEMEPROST*** (methyl (*E*)-7-[(1*R*,2*R*,3*R*)-3-hydroxy-2-[(*E*)-(3*R*)-3-hydroxy-4,4-dimethyl-1-octenyl]-5-oxocyclopentyl]-2-heptenoate; methyl 11,15-dihydroxy-16,16-dimethyl-9-oxoprosta-2,13-dienoate; ONO-802; SC-37681).
Gemfa (tr) *see* Hempa.
GEMFIBROZIL*** (5-(2,5-dimethylphenoxy)-2,2-dimethylvaleric acid; 2,2-dimethyl-5-(2,5-xylyloxy)valeric acid; CI-719; 'gevilon').
Gemodex (tr) *see* Dextran.
'Gemodez' *see* Povidone.

'Gemonil' *see* Metharbital.
'Gemora' *see* Butaverine.
'Genabil' *see* Menbutone.
'Genabilene' *see* Menbutone.
'Genabol' *see* Norboletone.
'Genacort' *see* Hydrocortisone.
Genatropine *see* Atropine *N*-oxide.
'Genebile' *see* Menbutone.
'Geneserine' *see* Physostigmine *N*-oxide.
'Geneticin' *see* Gentamicin.
'Genetron 23' *see* Fluoroform.
'Genetron-113' *see* 1,1,2-Trichloro-1,2,2-trifluoro-ethane.
'Genetron 152A' *see* 1,1-Difluoroethane.
'Genicide' *see* Xanthone.
'Geniphene' *see* Campheclor.
GENISTEIN (4',5,7-trihydroxyisoflavone; prunetol).
Genistein 4-methyl ether *see* Biochanin A.
'Genite' *see* Dichlorophenyl besilate.
GENKWANIN (4',5'-dihydroxy-7-methoxyflavone; puddmetin).
'Genomorphine' *see* Morphine *N*-oxide.
'Genoscopolamine' *see* Scopolamine *N*-oxide.
'Genostrychnine' *see* Strychnine *N*-oxide.
'Genovul' *see* Cloxestradiol acetate.
'Genoxal' *see* Cyclophosphamide.
'Gentallin' *see* Gentamicin.
'Gentalyn' *see* Gentamicin.
GENTAMICIN*** (*O*-2,6-diamino-2,3,4,6-tetra-deoxy-α-D-*erythro*-hexapyranosyl-(1→4)-*O*-[3-deoxy-4-*C*-methyl-3-(methylamino)-β-L-arabi-nopyranosyl-(1→6)]-2-deoxystreptamine; gentamicin sulfate; gentamycin; gentomycin; NSC-82261; Sch-9724).
See also under Betamethasone dipropionate.
GENTAMICIN plus POLYMETHYL METH-ACRYLATE (spheres) ('septopal').
'Gentamidon' *see* Aminophenazone gentisate.
Gentamycin *see* Gentamicin.
'Gentamytrex' *see* Gentamicin.
Gentian violet *see* Crystal violet.
GENTISIC ACID*** (2,5-dihydroxybenzoic acid; 5-hydroxysalicylic acid).
See also Sodium gentisate.
'Gentisod' *see* Sodium gentisate.
'Gentisone' *see* Gentamicin.
Gentomycin *see* Gentamicin.
'Gentran' *see* Dextran 70.
'Gentron 12' *see* Dichlorodifluoromethane.
'Geocillin' *see* Carindacillin.
'Geomycin' *see* Gentamicin.
'Geopen' *see* Carbenicillin.
GEPEFRINE*** ((+)-(*S*)-*m*-(2-aminopropyl)-phenol; (+)-*m*-hydroxy-α-methylphenethyl-amine; α-methyl-*m*-tyramine; (+)-*m*-hydroxy-amphetamine; 'pressionorm').
Geranyl farnesylacetate *see* Gefarnate.
2-Geranylhydroquinone *see* Geroquinol.
6-Geranyl-7-hydroxycoumarin *see* Ostruthin.
'Gerdaxyl' *see* Medifoxamine.
'Germa-medica' *see* Hexachlorophene.
'Germanin' *see* Suramin sodium.

'Germed' *see* Dipyridamole.
'Germicidin' *see* Metacycline.
'Germidine' *see* Cetylpyridinium bromide.
'Germinol' *see* Benzalkonium chloride.
'Germitol' *see* Benzalkonium chloride.
'Gernebcin' *see* Tobramycin.
'Gerodyl' *see* Pipradrol.
'Gerontine' *see* Spermine.
GEROQUINOL*** (2-(3,7-dimethyl-2-octadien-yl)hydroquinone; 2-geranylhydroquinone).
'Gerovital H3' *see* Procaine.
'Gesabel' *see* Ipazine.
'Gesagard' *see* Prometryn.
'Gesamil' *see* Propazine.
'Gesapax' *see* Ametryn.
'Gesapon' *see* DDT.
'Gesaprim' *see* Atrazine.
'Gesaran' *see* Methoprotryn.
'Gesaran 207' *see under* Methoprotryn.
'Gesaran 211' *see under* Methoprotryn.
'Gesaran 2079' *see under* Methoprotryn.
'Gesarex' *see* DDT.
Gesarol *see* DDT.
'Gesatop' *see* Simazine.
GESTACLONE*** (17β-acetyl-6-chloro-1β,1a,2β,8β,9α,10,11,12,13,14α,15,16β,16a,17-tetradecahydro-10β,13β-dimethyl-3*H*-dicyclo-propa(1,2:16,17)cyclopenta[*a*]phenanthren-3-one; SH-1040).
GESTADIENOL*** (17-hydroxy-19-norpregna-4,6-diene-3,20-dione).
GESTADIENOL ACETATE (Ba-31458).
'Gestadramine' *see under* Dimenhydrinate.
'Gestafortin' *see* Chlormadinone acetate.
'Gestamestrol' *see under* Chlormadinone acetate.
'Gestamin' *see* Atraton.
'Gestanin' *see* Allylestrenol.
'Gestanon' *see* Allylestrenol.
'Gestapuran' *see* Medroxyprogesterone acetate.
'Gestatron' *see* Dydrogesterone.
GESTODENE*** (13-ethyl-17-hydroxy-18,19-di-nor-17α-pregna-4,5-dien-20-yn-3-one; SH B-331).
'Gestogan' *see* Chlormadinone acetate.
GESTONORONE (17β-ethyl-17α-hydroxyestr-4-ene-3,20-dione; 17α-hydroxy-19-norpregn-4-ene-3,20-dione; 17α-hydroxy-19-norprogesterone; gestronol; norhydroxyprogesterone).
GESTONORONE CAPROATE*** (gestonorone hexanoate; NSC-84054; SH-582; 'depostat').
Gestonorone hexanoate *see* Gestonorone caproate.
'Gestranol' *see under* Chlormadinone acetate.
Gestrienone *see* Norgestrienone.
GESTRINONE** (13β-ethyl-17α-ethynyl-17-hydroxygona-4,9,11-trien-3-one; 13-ethyl-17-hydroxy-18,19-dinor-17α-pregna-4,9,11-trien-20-yn-3-one; A-46745; R-2323; RU-2323).
Gestronol* *see* Gestonorone.
'Getryl' *see* Febarbamate.
'Gevelina' *see* Properidine.
'Gevilon' *see* Gemfibrozil.
'Gevodin' *see under* Famprofazone.
'Gewo-339' *see* Pasiniazid.

255

'Gexane' see Lindane.
GHBA see 4-Hydroxybutyric acid.
α-GHI see Acarbose.
GHRH see Somatomedin.
'Gichtex' see Allopurinol.
Gigantic acid see Penicillin F.
'Gilurytmal' see Ajmaline.
'Gilustenon' see Glyceryl trinitrate.
'Gilutensin' see Etifelmine.
'Gimid' see Glutethimide.
'Gina' see Propatylnitrate.
'Ginapect' see Propatylnitrate.
'Ginebatin' see Bacitracin.
'Ginetris' see under Cloponone.
'Gingicaine' see Tetracaine.
'Gingivit' see Dichlorophen.
GINK (tr) see Isoniazid.
GINKGO BILOBA EXTRACT ('ginkor'; 'tana-kan'; 'tebonin').
'Ginkor' see Ginkgo biloba extract.
GINSENG (Panax quinquefolium root; Panax gin-seng; hiyaku).
GINSENG plus TROMETAMOL ('panabolide').
GIPARMEN*** (4-methyl-7-(2-propynyloxy)cou-marin).
GIRACTIDE*** (1-glycine-18-L-argininamide-α$^{1-18}$-corticotrophin; renactide).
'Girostan' see Thiotepa.
'Gitalide' see Gitalin amorphous.
'Gitaligin' see Gitalin amorphous.
GITALIN AMORPHOUS** ('gitalide'; 'gitaligin'; 'verodigen').
GITALIN CRYSTALLINE (ψ-digitonin; pseudo-digitonin).
GITALOXIGENIN (16-formylgitoxigenin).
Gitaloxigenin monodigitoxoside see Lanadoxin.
Gitaloxigenin tridigitoxoside see Gitaloxin.
GITALOXIN*** (16-formylgitoxin; gitaloxigenin tridigitoxoside; gitoxin 16-formate).
GITOFORMATE*** (3β-[(dideoxy-β-D-ribo-hexopyranosyl-(1→4)-O-2,6-dideoxy-β-D-ribo-hexopyranosyl-(1→4)-2,6-dideoxy-β-D-ribo-hexopyranosyl)oxy]-14,16β-dihydroxy-5β-card-20(22)-enolide 3',3'',3''',4''',16-pentaformate; gi-toxin pentaformate; pentaformylgitoxin; AC-2770; 'dynocard'; 'formiloxine').
GITOXIGENIN (Δ^{20,22}-3,14,16,21-tetrahydronor-cholenic acid lactone).
GITOXIN (anhydrogitalin; bigitalin; ψ-digitoxin; pseudodigitoxin).
Gitoxin 16-formate see Gitaloxin.
Gitoxin pentaformate see Gitoformate.
'Gittalun' see Doxylamine.
'Giv tan F' see Cinoxate.
'Gix' see 1,1,1-Trichloro-2,2-bis(p-fluorophenyl)-ethane.
GL-7 see Glycol salicylate.
'Glacialin' see Boroglyceride.
GLADIOLIC ACID (4-methoxy-5-methyl-o-phthalaldehyde-3-carboxylic acid).
GLAFENINE*** (2,3-dihydroxypropyl N-(7-chloroquinolin-4-yl)anthranilate; glaphenine; R-1707; 'glifanan').

Glaphenine* see Glafenine.
'Glarubin' see Glaucarubin.
Glauber salt see Sodium sulfate.
'Glaucadrin' see under Aceclidine.
GLAUCARUBIN (1,2,3,3aβ,4,6a-β,7,7aα,10,11,11a,11bα-dodecahydro-1α,2α,4β,10α,11β-pentahydroxy-3α,8,11aβ-trimethyl-5H-1,11cβ-(epoxymethano)phenanthro[10,1-bc]-pyran-5-one 4-(2-hydroxy-2-methylbutyrate); α-kirondrin; MK-53; 'glarubin'; 'glaumeba').
GLAUCINE (1,2,9,10-tetramethoxy-6aα-aporph-ine; boldine dimethyl ether; (±)-glaucine phos-phate; DL-832).
'Glaucomide' see Acetazolamide.
Glaucostat see Aceclidine.
'Glaucotensil' see Ethoxzolamide.
'Glaucothil' see Dipivefrine.
'Glaumarin' see Carbachol.
'Glaumeba' see Glaucarubin.
'Glaurin' see Diethylene glycol monolaurate.
'Glaxoridin' see Cefaloridine.
GLAZIOVINE*** (alkaloid from Ocotea glaziovii; PM-297; 'suavedol').
GL enzyme see Hyalosidase.
GLEPTOFERRON*** ((dextran)(glucoheptonic acid)hydroxyoxoiron; iron heptonate; 'gleptosil'; 'heptomer').
'Gleptosil' see Gleptoferron.
GLIAMILIDE*** (endo-1-[[4-[2-(2-methoxynico-tinamido)ethyl]piperid-1-yl]sulfonyl]-3-(5-nor-bornen-2-ylmethyl)urea; CP-27634).
'Glianimon' see Benperidol.
GLIBENCLAMIDE*** (1-[p-[2-(5-chloro-2-meth-oxybenzamido)ethyl]phenylsulfonyl]-3-cyclohex-ylurea; 1-[p-[2-(5-chloro-o-anisamido)ethyl]-phenylsulfonyl]-3-cyclohexylurea; glybencl-amide; glybenzcyclamide; glyburide; HB-419; U-26452).
GLIBENCLAMIDE plus PHENFORMIN ('bi-eu-glucon').
'Glibenese' see Glipizide.
GLIBORNURIDE*** (1-(2-endo-hydroxy-3-endo-bornyl)-3-(p-toluenesulfonyl)urea; Ro 6-4563; 'glitrim'; 'gluborid'; 'glutril').
GLIBUTIMINE** (1-[[p-(2-butyramidoethyl)-phenyl]sulfonyl]-3-(3-cyclohexen-1-yl)-2-imino-imidazolidine; N-[p-[[3-(3-cyclohexen-1-yl)-2-iminoimidazolidin-1-yl]sulfonyl]phenethyl]bu-tyramide; glybutamide; GP-51084; 'glucidol').
GLICARAMIDE** (1-cyclohexyl-3-[p-[2-(1-ethyl-4-isopentyloxy-3-methyl-1H-pyrazolo[3,4-b]pyr-idine-5-carboxamido)ethyl]phenylsulfonyl]urea).
GLICETANILE*** (5'-chloro-2-[p-[(5-isobutyl-pyrimidin-2-yl)sulfamoyl]phenyl]-o-acetanisid-ide; N-(5-chloro-2-methoxyphenyl)-4-[[[5-(2-methylpropyl)pyrimidin-2-yl]amino]sulfonyl]-benzeneacetamide; glicetanile sodium; glidanile; SH-1051).
GLICLAZIDE*** (1-(3-azabicyclo[3.3.0]oct-3-yl)-3-(p-toluenesulfonyl)urea; Se-1702; 'diamicron').
GLICONDAMIDE*** (1-[[p-[2-(5-chloro-2-meth-oxybenzamido)ethyl]phenyl]sulfonyl]-3-methyl-urea; 1-[[p-[2-(5-chloro-o-anisamido)ethyl]phen-

256

yl]sulfonyl]-3-methylurea).

'Glicotron' *see* Tolbutamide.

Glidanile *see* Glicetanile.

GLIDAZAMIDE*** (1-(hexahydro-1*H*-azepin-1-yl)-3-(indan-5-ylsulfonyl)urea).

'Glidiabet' *see* Glibenclamide.

Glidiazine* *see* Glymidine sodium.

'Glido' *see under* Betamethasone.

'Glifanan' *see* Glafenine.

GLIFLUMIDE*** (*N*-(5-fluoro-2-methoxy-α-methylbenzyl)-2-[*p*-[(5-isobutylpyrimidin-2-yl)-sulfamoyl]phenyl]acetamide; (−)-(*S*)-4-[*N*-(5-isobutylpyrimidin-2-yl)sulfamoyl]phenylacetic acid 1-(5-fluoro-2-methoxyphenyl)ethylamide; SH-31168; Z-28200).

'Glimid' *see* Glutethimide.

'Glior' *see* Doxenitoin.

'Glipasol' *see* Glybuthiazol.

GLIPENTIDE** (1-[*p*-[2-(*o*-anisamido)ethyl]benzenesulfonyl]-3-cyclopentylurea; 1-cyclopentyl-3-[[*p*-[2-(*o*-anisamido)ethyl]phenyl]sulfonyl]urea; 1-cyclopentyl-3-[*p*-[2-(*o*-methoxybenzamido)-ethyl]phenylsulfonyl]urea; glypentide; UR-661; 'staticum').

GLIPIZIDE** (1-cyclohexyl-3-[[*p*-[2-(5-methyl-pyrazine-2-carboxamido)ethyl]phenyl]sulfonyl]-urea; *N*-[2-[4-[[[(cyclohexylamino)carbonyl]-amino]sulfonyl]phenyl]ethyl]-5-methylpyrazine-2-carboxamide; glydiazinamide; CP-28720; FK-1320; K-4024; 'glibenese'; 'minidiab'; 'minodiab').

'Gliptide' *see* Sulglicotide.

GLIQUIDONE*** (1-cyclohexyl-3-[*p*-[2-(3,4-di-hydro-7-methoxy-4,4-dimethyl-1,3-dioxo-2(1*H*)-isoquinolyl)ethyl]phenylsulfonyl]urea; ARDF-26; M-5276; 'glurenorm').

GLISAMURIDE*** (1-methyl-3-[*p*-[[3-(4-methyl-cyclohexyl)ureido]sulfonyl]phenethyl]-1-pyrid-2-ylurea).

GLISINDAMIDE*** (1-cyclohexyl-3-[[*p*-[2-(1-oxo-2-isoindolinecarboxamido)ethyl]phenyl]sul-fonyl]urea).

GLISOLAMIDE*** (1-cyclohexyl-3-[[*p*-[2-(5-methyl-3-isoxazolecarboxamido)ethyl]phenyl]-sulfonyl]urea).

GLISOXEPIDE*** (1-(hexahydro-1*H*-azepin-1-yl)-3-[[*p*-[2-(5-methyl-3-isoxazolecarboxamido)-ethyl]phenyl]sulfonyl]urea; 3-[4-(hexahydroazep-in-1-ylureidosulfonyl)phenethylcarbamoyl]-5-methylisoxazole; 4-[4-[3-(5-methylisoxazole-3-carboxamido)ethyl]benzenesulfonyl]-1,1-hexa-methylenesemicarbazide; BAY b-4231; BS-4231; FB b-4231; RP 22410; 'pro-diaban').

'Glissitol' *see* Ox bile.

'Glistelone' *see* Prednisolone steaglate.

'Glitisol' *see* Thiamphenicol.

'Glitrim' *see* Glibornuride.

'Globacillin' *see* Azidocillin.

'Globenicol' *see* Chloramphenicol.

'Globociclina' *see* Metacycline.

'Globucid' *see* Sulfaethidole.

Globulariacintrin *see* Rutoside.

'Glofil-125' *see* Sodium iotalamate (^{125}I).

GLOMERULOTROPHIN (1,2,3,4-tetrahydro-6-methoxy-1-methyl-9*H*-pyrid[3,4-*b*]indole).

Glonoin *see* Glyceryl trinitrate.

GLOXAZONE*** (3-ethoxy-2-oxobutyraldehyde bis(thiosemicarbazone); (1-ethoxyethyl)glyoxal bisthiosemicarbazone; kethoxal bis(thiosemi-carbazone); KTS; BW-356C61; NSC-82116; 'contrapar').

GLPS *see* Sulglicotide.

'Gluborid' *see* Glibornuride.

GLUCAGON*** (hyperglycemic-glycogenolytic factor of pancreas; HGF).

'Glucal' *see* Calcium gluconate.

Glucaldrate *see* Potassium glucaldrate; Sodium glucaldrate.

GLUCALOX*** (polymerized complex of glycerol and aluminium hydroxide; glycalox; 'manalox AG').

GLUCAMETACIN*** (2-[2-[1-(*p*-chlorobenzoyl)-5-methoxy-2-methylindol-3-yl]acetamido]-2-de-oxy-D-glucose; indometacin amide deoxyglucose derivative).

GLUCAMINE (1-amino-1-deoxy-D-glucitol).

'Glucantime' *see* Meglumine antimonate.

D-Glucaric acid *see* Saccharic acid.

'Glucaron' *see* Aceglatone.

Glucaspaldrate *see* Sodium glucaspaldrate.

GLUCEPTATE(S)** (glucoheptonate(s)).

GLUCEPTATE SODIUM* (D-glycero-D-gulo-heptonic acid monosodium salt; sodium gluco-heptonate).

'Glucidol' *see* Glibutimine.

'Glucidoral' *see* Carbutamide.

'Glucifrene' *see under* Carbutamide.

'Glucinan' *see* Metformin *p*-chlorophenoxyacetate.

'Glucirenan' *see* Metformin *p*-chlorophenoxyacet-ate.

D-Glucitol *see* Sorbitol.

'Glucobasin' *see* Adenosine triphosphate.

'Glucobiogen' *see* Calcium gluconate.

Glucochloral *see* Chloralose.

Glucochloralose *see* Chloralose.

Glucodiazine *see* Glymidine sodium.

'Glucodigin' *see* Digitoxin.

'Glucoenergan' *see* Fencamfamin.

'Glucofos' *see* Calcium fructose 1,6-diphosphate.

Glucofuranoic acid lactone *see* Glucurolactone.

Glucofuranoside *see* Tribenoside.

D-Glucofuranuronic acid *see* Glucuronic acid.

Glucoheptonate(s) *see* Gluceptate(s).

Glucohexitol *see* Sorbitol.

(D-Gluconato)(lactobionato)calcium monohydrate *see* Calcium glubionate.

GLUCONIAZONE (glyconiazide; isoniazid glucu-ronolactone).

GLUCONIC ACID (dextronic acid; D-gluconic acid; glycogenic acid; glyconic acid; maltonic acid; pentahydroxyhexanoic acid).
    See also Calcium gluconate; Glusoferron; Mag-nesium gluconate; Potassium gluconate; Sodium antimonylgluconate; Sodium stibogluconate.

D-Gluconic acid polymer with D-glucitol, iron (fer-ric) salt *see* Glusoferron.

257

N-Gluconoyl-3-[(2-hydroxyethyl)carbamoyl]-5-(*N*-methylacetamido)-2,4,6-triiodoaniline *see* Ioglunide.

'Glucophage' *see* Metformin.

'Glucopostin' *see* Phenformin.

Glucoproscillaridin A *see* Scillaren A.

α-D-Glucopyranosyl-β-D-fructofuranoside *see* Sucrose.

3β-(β-D-Glucopyranosyloxy)-14,23-dihydroxy-24-nor-5β,14β-chol-20(22)-en-21-oic acid γ-lactone *see* Actodigin.

3β-(β-D-Glucopyranosyloxy)spirost-5-ene *see* Disogluside.

3β-(β-D-Glucopyranosyloxy)stigmast-5-ene *see* Sitogluside.

β-D-Glucopyranuronamide *see* Glucuronamide.

D-Glucosaccharic acid *see* Saccharic acid.

1,4-Glucosaccharolactone *see* Saccharic acid 1,4-lactone.

Glucosaccharonic acid *see* Isoascorbic acid.

GLUCOSAMINE** (2-amino-2-deoxy-β-D-glucopyranose; 2-amino-2-deoxy-D-glucose; chitosamine; glucosamine hydrochloride; NSC-758).

Glucosaminedesoxystreptamine ribosediaminohexose *see* Paromomycin.

GLUCOSAMINE SULFATE ('dona').

GLUCOSE (α-D-glucopyranose; dextrose; D-glucose; corn sugar; glycose; saccharum amylaceum; starch sugar; traubenzucker).

GLUCOSE 1-PHOSPHATE (Cori ester).

GLUCOSE 6-PHOSPHATE (Robinson ester).

'Glucosulfa' *see under* Metformin.

GLUCOSULFAMIDE*** (glucose sodium bisulfite compound of N^1-hydroxymethylsulfanilamide; glycosulfamide).

GLUCOSULFONE*** (*N,N'*-di(glucose sodium sulfonate) of 4,4'-diaminodiphenyl sulfone; *p,p'*-sulfonyldianiline *N,N'*-di(D-glucose sodium bisulfite compound); P-501; SN-166).

1-D-Glucos-2-yl-3-methyl-3-nitrosourea *see* Streptozocin.

'Glucotard' *see* Guar gum.

'Glucoxy' *see* Glucurolactone.

GLUCUROLACTONE*** (γ-lactone of D-glucofuranuronic acid; glucofuranoic acid lactone; glucuronolactone; 'guronsan').

GLUCURONAMIDE*** (β-D-glucopyranuronamide).

'Glucurone' *see* Glucurolactone.

GLUCURONIC ACID (D-glucofuranuronic acid).

Glucurono-2-amino-2-deoxyglucoglucan sulfate *see* Sulodexide.

Glucuronolactone *see* Glucurolactone.

Glucuronylglucosaminoglycan sulfate *see* Sulodexide.

'Gludiase' *see* Glybuzole.

Gluk.... *see* Gluc.....

'Glumal' *see* Aceglutamide aluminium.

'Glumol' *see* Aceglutamide aluminium.

'Glumorin' *see* Kallidinogenase.

GLUNICATE** (2-deoxy-2-nicotinamido-β-D-glucopyranose 1,3,4,6-tetranicotinate).

'Gluquinate' *see* Quinidine gluconate.

'Glurenorm' *see* Gliquidone.

'Gluronazid' *see* Gluconiazone.

'Gluside' *see* Saccharin.

GLUSOFERRON*** (D-gluconic acid polymer with D-glucitol, iron (ferric) salt).

'Glutadenyl' *see* Adenosine phosphate.

GLUTAMIC ACID*** (2-aminoglutaric acid; 2-aminopentanedioic acid; glutaminic acid; glutamic acid hydrochloride).
See also Arginine glutamate; Calcium glutamate; Sodium glutamate.

Glutamic acid lactam *see* Pidolic acid.

Glutamic acid monoamide *see* Glutamine.

GLUTAMINE (glutamic acid monoamide; NSC-97925).

L-Glutamine *see* Levoglutamide.

Glutaminic acid *see* Glutamic acid.

L-Glutamyl-L-cysteinyl glycine *see* Glutathione.

Glutamyltaurine *see* Glutaurine.

GLUTARAL*** (glutaraldehyde; pentanedial; 'alhydex'; 'cidex'; 'glutarol').

Glutaraldehyde *see* Glutaral.

GLUTARAMIC ACID (4-carbamoylbutyric acid; glutaric acid monoamide).

GLUTARANILIC ACID (4-(phenylcarbamoyl)butyric acid; *N*-phenylglutaramic acid).

GLUTARIC ACID (pentanedioic acid).

Glutaric acid monoamide *see* Glutaramic acid.

GLUTARIMIDE (2,6-piperidinedione).

'Glutarol' *see* Glutaral.

GLUTATHIONE (L-glutamyl-L-cysteinyl glycine; glutathione sodium; GSH; 'thation'; 'triptide').

GLUTAURINE** (glutamyltaurine; *N*-(2-sulfoethyl)-L-glutamine).

'Glutavene' *see* Sodium glutamate.

GLUTETHIMIDE*** (2-ethyl-2-phenylglutarimide).

Glutimic acid *see* Pidolic acid.

Glutiminic acid *see* Pidolic acid.

'Glutrex' *see* Tetracycline glucosamine.

'Glutril' *see* Glibornuride.

Glybenclamide *see* Glibenclamide.

Glybenzcyclamide *see* Glibenclamide.

'Glyboral' *see* Boroglyceride.

'Glybrom' *see* Pyrabrom.

Glyburide* *see* Glibenclamide.

Glybutamide* *see* Glibutimine.

GLYBUTHIAZOL*** (N^1-(5-*tert*-butyl-1,3,4-thiadiazol-2-yl)sulfanilamide; sulfatertiobutylthiadiazole; RP 2259; Th-1395).

GLYBUZOLE*** (*N*-(5-*tert*-butyl-1,3,4-thiadiazol-2-yl)benzenesulfonamide; desaglybuzole; AN-1324; RP 7891).

Glycalox* *see* Glucalox.

'Glycamide' *see* 4,5-Imidazoledicarboxamide.

Glycarbylamide *see* 4,5-Imidazoledicarboxamide.

GLYCARSAMIDE (*N*-glycoloylarsanilic acid; *N*-glycolylarsanilic acid).
See also Tryparsamide.

GLYCERALDEHYDE (2,3-dihydroxypropanal; 2,3-dihydroxypropionaldehyde; NSC-67934).

Glycerides oleiques polyoxyethylenes *see* Peglicol 5 oleate.

Glycerin *see* Glycerol.
GLYCEROL*** (1,2,3-propanetriol; glycerin).
Glycerol α-monobromohydrin *see* Bromohydrin.
Glycerol α-monochlorohydrin *see* Chlorohydrin.
Glycerol α-monoiodohydrin *see* Iodohydrin.
Glycero(3)phosphocholine *see* Choline glycerophosphate.
Glyceryl 2-(acetylsalicylate) 1,3-di(clofibrate) *see* Salafibrate.
Glyceryl *p*-chlorophenyl ether *see* Chlorphenesin.
Glyceryl guaiacolate *see* Guaifenesin.
Glyceryl 1-octanoate *see* Octanoin.
GLYCERYL SALICYLATE (glyceryl monosalicylate; glycosal; saliceral).
Glyceryl triacetate *see* Triacetin.
Glyceryl trilinoleate *see* Trilinolein.
GLYCERYL TRINITRATE (glonoin; nitroglycerin; nitroglycerol; trinitrine; trinitroglycerin).
Glycide *see* Glycidol.
GLYCIDIC ACID (2,3-epoxypropionic acid; oxiranecarboxylic acid).
GLYCIDOL (2,3-epoxy-1-propanol; epihydrin alcohol; glycide).
(±)-α-(Glycinamidomethyl)-2,5-dimethoxybenzyl alcohol *see* Midodrine.
GLYCINE (aminoacetic acid; glycocoll; sucre de gelatine).
1-Glycine-18-L-argininamide-α$^{1-18}$-corticotrophin *see* Giractide.
Glycine-*p*-phenetidine *see* Phenocoll.
GLYCLOPYRAMIDE*** (1-(*p*-chlorophenylsulfonyl)-3-pyrrolidin-1-ylurea).
GLYCOBIARSOL*** (bismuthyl *N*-glycolylarsanilate; bismuthoxy *p*-*N*-glycolylarsanilate; bismuth glycolylarsanilate; WIN-1011).
See also under Chloroquine diphosphate.
GLYCOCHOLIC ACID (cholylglycine; glycinecholic acid conjugate).
Glycocoll *see* Glycine.
GLYCOCYAMINE (*N*-amidinoglycine; guanidoacetic acid).
Glycodiazine *see* Glymidine sodium.
GLYCOGEN (animal starch; hepatin).
Glycogenic acid *see* Gluconic acid.
Glycol *see* Ethylene glycol.
GLYCOLALDEHYDE (hydroxyacetaldehyde).
Glycolamide ester with flufenamic acid *see* Colfenamate.
Glycol chlorohydrin *see* 2-Chloroethanol.
Glycoleucine *see* Norleucine.
GLYCOLIC ACID (2-hydroxyacetic acid; glycollic acid).
See also Acemetacin; Pleuromulin; Polyglactin(s); Polyglycolic acid.
Glycollic acid *see* Glycolic acid.
***p*-Glycolophenetidide** *see* Fenacetinol.
***N*-Glycoloylarsanilic acid** *see* Glycarsamide.
3-Glycoloyl-1,2,3,4,6,11-hexahydro-3,5,12-trihydroxy-6-11-dioxonaphthacen-1-yl 3-amino-2,3,6-trideoxy-α-L-*lyxo*-hexopyranoside *see* Medorubicin.
3-Glycoloyl-1,2,3,4,6,11-hexahydro-3,5,12-trihydroxy-10-methoxy-6,11-dioxonaphthacene-1-yl 3-amino-2,3,6-trideoxy-α-L-*arabino*-hexopyranoside *see* Epirubicin.
3-Glycoloyl-1,2,3,4,6,11-hexahydro-3,5,12-trihydroxy-10-methoxy-6,11-dioxo-1-naphthacenyl-3-amino-2,3,6-trideoxy-α-L-*lyxo*-hexopyranoside *see* Doxorubicin.
***N*-Glycoloyl-*p*-phenetidine** *see* Fenacetinol.
GLYCOL SALICYLATE (2-hydroxyethyl salicylate; ethylene glycol monosalicylate; ethylene glycol salicylate; ethyl glycol salicylate; monoglycol salicylate; GL-7).
***N*-Glycolylarsanilic acid** *see* Glycarsamide.
Glycolyltheophylline sodium *see* Sodium theophyllin-7-ylacetate.
Glycolylurea *see* Hydantoin.
Glyconiazide *see* Gluconiazone.
Glyconic acid *see* Gluconic acid.
Glycopyrrolate* *see* Glycopyrronium bromide.
GLYCOPYRRONIUM BROMIDE*** (3-hydroxy-1,1-dimethylpyrrolidinium bromide α-phenylcyclopentaneglycolate; glycopyrrolate; AHR-504).
Glycosal *see* Glyceryl salicylate.
GLYCOSAMINOGLYCAN POLYSULFATE(S) (mucopolysaccharide polysulfate; GAGPS; 'arteparon'; 'ateroid').
See also Chondroitin sulfate; Dermatan sulfate; Heparin; *and under* Clofibrate.
Glycose *see* Glucose.
Glycosulfamide *see* Glucosulfamide.
'Glycotron' *see* Tolbutamide.
GLYCYCLAMIDE*** (1-cyclohexyl-3-*p*-toluenesulfonylurea; cyclamide; tolhexamide; K-38; K-386).
GLYCYCLAMIDE plus METFORMIN (ER-105).
4-Glycylamidobenzenearsonic acid sodium salt *see* Tryparsamide.
Glycyl-*N*-[4-chloro-2-(2-chlorobenzoyl)phenyl]-*N*-methylglycinamide *see* Lorzafone.
***N*-[*N*-(*N*-Glycylglycyl)glycyl]-8-lysinevasopressin** *see* Terlipressin.
'Glycylpressin' *see* Terlipressin.
Glycyrrhetic acid *see* Enoxolone.
Glycyrrhetin *see* Enoxolone.
Glycyrrhetinic acid *see* Enoxolone.
Glycyrrhiza *see* Liquorice.
GLYCYRRHIZIC ACID (enoxolone glycoside; glycyrrhizin; glycyrrhizinic acid; retinic acid).
Glycyrrhizin *see* Glycyrrhizic acid.
Glycyrrhizinic acid *see* Glycyrrhizic acid.
Glydanile *see* Glicetanile.
Glydiazinamide *see* Glipizide.
Glyfillin *see* Diprophylline.
GLYHEXAMIDE*** (1-cyclohexyl-3-indan-5-ylsulfonylurea; NSC-106960; SQ-15860).
Glyhexylamide* *see* Metahexamide.
Glykresin* *see* Mephenesin.
'Glymaxil' *see* Sodium glucaldrate.
GLYMIDINE SODIUM*** ([*N*-[5-(2-methoxyethoxy)pyrimidin-2-yl]benzenesulfonamido]sodium; glidiazine; glucodiazine; glycodiazine; sodium glymidine; SH-717).
'Glyo 6' *see* Piridoxilate.

GLYOCTAMIDE*** (1-cyclooctyl-3-*p*-toluene-sulfonylurea).

GLYODIN* (2-heptadecyl-4,5-dihydro-1*H*-imidazole acetate; 'glyoxide').

GLYOXAL (dihydroxyacetaldehyde; ethanedial; oxalaldehyde).

Glyoxalic acid *see* Glyoxylic acid.

Glyoxalidine *see* Imidazolidine.

Glyoxaline *see* Imidazole.

Glyoxaline-5-alanine *see* Histidine.

'Glyoxide' *see* Glyodin.

trans-**3-Glyoxylamidoacrylamide oxime** *see* Zedalan.

Glyoxyldiureide *see* Allantoin.

GLYOXYLIC ACID (oxoacetic acid; formylformic acid; glyoxalic acid; ketoacetic acid).

Glyoxylic acid doxorubicin 3²-ester 2-(diethyl acetal) *see* Detorubicin.

Glyoxyloylurea *aldehydo*-[bis(*p*-chlorophenyl) acetal] *see* Urefibrate.

GLYPARAMIDE* (1-(*p*-chlorophenylsulfonyl)-3-[*p*-(dimethylamino)phenyl]urea; P-1306).

'Glyped' *see* Triacetin.

Glypentide *see* Glipentide.

Glyphenarsine *see* Tryparsamide.

Glyphillin* *see* Diprophylline.

GLYPHOSATE* (*N*-(phosphonomethyl)glycine; MON-0573).

GLYPINAMIDE*** (1-(*p*-chlorophenylsulfonyl)-3-(hexahydro-1*H*-azepin-1-yl)urea; azepinamide; U-12504).

Glypressin *see* Terlipressin.

GLYPROTHIAZOL*** (*N*¹-(5-isopropyl-1,3,4-thiadiazol-2-yl)sulfanilamide; sulfaisopropyl-thiadiazole; RP 2254; VK-57).

Glyptide sulfate *see* Sulglicotide.

'Glysal' *see* Glycol salicylate.

GLYSOBUZOLE*** (*N*-(5-isobutyl-1,3,4-thiadiazol-2-yl)-*p*-methoxybenzenesulfonamide; isobuzole; 'stabinol').

'Glyvenol' *see* Tribenoside.

GMP *see* Guanylic acid.

GNOSCOPINE (DL-narcotine; DL-noscapine; α-gnoscopine).
    See also Noscapine.

'GnRH serono' *see* Gonadorelin.

Go-560 *see* Febarbamate.

Go-919 *see* Piprozolin.

Go-1213 *see* Atolide.

Go-1261 *see* Tilidine.

Go-1733 *see* Suloxifen oxalate.

Go-2782 *see* Iproxamine.

Go-3026A *see* Ciclafrine.

'Goalgan' *see* Calcium alginate.

Goa powder *see* Chrysarobin.

GOBAB *see* 3-Amino-4-hydroxybutyric acid.

Go/CGP-4540 *see* Amoscanate.

'Godalax' *see* Bisacodyl.

'Godamed' *see under* Acetylsalicylic acid.

'Goedecke 3282' *see* Oxonazine.

Goetsch's vitamin *see* Vitamin T-complex.

GOHBA *see* 4-Hydroxybutyric acid.

GOITRIN (5-vinyl-2-oxazolidinethione).

'Golaval' *see* Cloponone.

GOLD (¹⁹⁸Au) COLLOIDAL** (colloidal radiogold; radioaurum; radiogold, colloidal; 'aurcoloid-198'; 'aureotope').

Gold mercaptoacetanilide *see* Aurothioglycanide.

Gold sodium allylthioureidobenzoate *see* Sodium auroallylthioureidobenzoate.

Gold sodium thiomalate *see* Sodium aurothiomalate.

Gold sodium thiosulfate *see* Sodium aurotiosulfate.

Gold thioglucose *see* Aurothioglucose.

GONADORELIN*** (luteinizing hormone releasing factor (sheep, pig or other species); L-pyroglutamyl-L-histidyl-L-tryptophyl-L-seryl-L-tyrosylglycyl-L-leucyl-L-arginyl-L-prolylglycinamide; 5-oxo-L-prolyl-L-histidyl-L-tryptophyl-L-seryl-L-tyrosylglycyl-L-leucyl-L-arginyl-L-prolylglycinamide; LH-RH; AY-24031; HOE-471; ICI-88262; 'factrel'; 'GnRH serono'; 'kryptocur'; 'luliberine'; 'relefact LH-RH').

GONADORELIN plus PROTIRELIN ('relefact LH-RH/TRH').

GONADORELIN ACETATE* (gonadorelin acetate (salt) hydrate; Abbott 41070; 'cystorelin'; 'ovarelin').

Gonadotrophins *see* Chorionic gonadotrophin; Human menopausal gonadotrophin; Human pituitary gonadotrophin; Serum gonadotrophin.

'Gondafin' *see* Glymidine sodium.

'Gondafon' *see* Glymidine sodium.

Gonosan *see* Kawain.

'Gontochin' *see* Chloroquine.

'Gophicide' *see* *O*,*O*-Bis(*p*-chlorophenyl) *N*-acetimidoylphosphoramidothioate.

'Gordox' *see* Aprotinin.

GOSSYPETIN (3,3',4',5,7,8-hexahydroxyflavone).

GOSSYPOL (1,1',6,6',7,7'-hexahydroxy-5,5'-diisopropyl-3,3'-dimethyl[2,2'-binaphthalene]-8,8'-dicarboxaldehyde).

'Goutin' *see* Sodium anhydromethylenecitrate.

GP-121 *see* Phencyclidine.

GP-41299 *see* Damotepine.

GP-41353 *see* Triclosan.

GP-45840 *see* Diclofenac.

GP-48674 *see* Furacrinic acid.

GP-51084 *see* Glibutimine.

GPA-878 *see* Metazamide.

GR2/234 *see* Alfaxalone.

GR2/443 *see* Doxibetasol propionate.

GR2/541 *see* Betamethasone acibutate.

GR2/925 *see* Clobetasol propionate.

GR2/1214 *see* Clobetasone butyrate.

GR2/1574 *see* Alfadolone.

GR-62 *see* Isoxsuprine.

GR-412 *see* Dodeclonium bromide.

GR-20263 *see* Ceftazidime.

'Gracidin' *see* Phenmetrazine.

'Gramaxin' *see* Cefazolin.

GRAMICIDIN S*** (antibiotic from *Bac. brevis*; cyclo(L-valyl-L-ornithyl-L-leucyl-D-phenylalanyl-L-propyl-L-valyl-L-ornithyl-L-leucyl-D-phenylalanyl-L-prolyl); 'gramoderm'; 'gromidin').

GRAMINE (3-[(dimethylamino)methyl]indole; donaxine).

'**Gramoderm**' *see* Gramicidin S.

'**Gramoxone**' *see* Paraquat.

Granatan *see* Granatanine.

GRANATANINE (9-azabicyclo[3.3.1]nonane; granatan).

Granatol *see* Granatoline.

GRANATOLINE (9-azabicyclo[3.3.1]nonan-3-ol; granatol).

'**Grandaxin**' *see* Tofisopam.

'**Gratibain**' *see* Ouabain.

Gratus strophanthin *see* Ouabain.

'**Gravibindan**' *see under* Estradiol valerate.

'**Gravol**' *see* Dimenhydrinate.

'**Gravosan**' *see* Clomifene.

Green of bitter almonds *see* Malachite green.

'**Grenolon**' *see* Perphenazine.

'**Gricin**' *see* Griseofulvin.

'**Grifulvin**' *see* Griseofulvin.

'**Grillocin**' *see* Zinc ricinoleate.

'**Grisactin**' *see* Griseofulvin.

GRISEIN (antibiotic from *Streptomyces griseus*, identical with albomycin (q.v.)).

GRIS-2'-ENE-3,4'-DIONE (coumaran-3-one-2-spiro-1'-(cyclohex-2'-en-4'-one)).

GRISEOFULVIN* (7-chloro-2',4,6-trimethoxy-6'-methylspiro(benzofuran-2(3*H*),1'-(2)-cyclo-hexene)-3,4-dione; 7-chloro-4,6,2'-trimethoxy-6'-methylgris-2'-ene-3,4'-dione; curling factor; NSC-34533).

'**Grisovin**' *see* Griseofulvin.

'**Grofas**' *see* Quindoxin.

'**Gromidin**' *see* Gramicidin S.

GROWTH HORMONE (somatotrophin; somatotropin; STH).

See also Human growth hormone.

Growth hormone release inhibiting factor *see* Somatostatin.

Growth hormone releasing hormone *see* Somatomedin.

GS-95 *see* Thiethylperazine.

GS-385 *see* Suclofenide.

GS-1339 *see* Dimantine.

GS-2147 *see* Sancycline.

GS-2876 *see* Metacycline.

GS-2989 *see* Meclocycline.

GS-3065 *see* Doxycycline hyclate.

GS-3159 *see* Carbenicillin.

GS-6244 *see* Carbadox.

GS-6742 *see* Sulfomyxin.

GS-7443 *see* Mequidox.

GS-14254 *see* Secbumeton.

GS-15329 *see* Terbuthylazine.

GS-23654 *see* Nitroscanate.

GSH *see* Glutathione.

GT 41 *see* Busulfan.

GT 75 *see* Cyclopentolate.

GTP *see* Guanosine triphosphate.

'**G-tril**' *see* Febarbamate.

GUABENXAN* ((1,4-benzodioxan-6-ylmethyl)-guanidine; 6-(guanidinomethyl)-1,4-benzodi-

oxan; guabenxan sulfate).

GUABENXAN plus BEMETIZIDE ('tensigradyl').

'**Guacetin**' *see* Guaiacetin.

GUACETISAL* (guaiacyl acetylsalicylate; *o*-methoxyphenyl salicylate acetate).

GUAFECAINOL* (2-[3-[2-(diethylamino)eth-oxy]-2-hydroxypropoxy]anisole; 1-[2-(diethyl-amino)ethoxy]-3-(*o*-methoxyphenoxy)-2-pro-panol; 'brufacaine').

GUAIACETIN (sodium phenone acetate; sodium pyrocatechol acetate; 'guacetin').

'**Guaiacillin**' *see* Ampicillin guaiacolsulfonate.

GUAIACOL (*o*-methoxyphenol).

Guaiacol glyceryl ether *see* Guaifenesin.

Guaiacolsulfonic acid salts *see* Calcium guaiacolsulfonate; Sulfogaiacol.

GUAIACTAMINE* (2-(*o*-methoxyphenoxy)tri-ethylamine; diethylaminoethyl guaiacyl ether; gaiactamine; gaietamine).

Guaiacyl acetylsalicylate *see* Guacetisal.

'**Guaiamar**' *see* Guaifenesin.

GUAIAPATE* (1-[2-[2-(2-(*o*-methoxyphen-oxy)ethoxy)ethoxy]ethyl]piperidine; Mg-5454).

GUAIAZULENE (7-isopropyl-1,4-dimethylazul-ene; gaiazulene; AZ-8; 'azulon'; 'stomalene').

Guaiazulene soluble *see* Sodium gualenate.

Guaicuran *see* Guaifenesin.

GUAIETOLIN* (3-(*o*-ethoxyphenoxy)-1,2-pro-panediol).

GUAIFENESIN* (3-(*o*-methoxyphenoxy)-1,2-propanediol; guaiphenesin; glyceryl guaiacolate; guaiacol glyceryl ether; guaicuran; My-301; XL-90).

See also Guaifylline; Methocarbamol; *and under* Noscapine; Pseudoephedrine.

GUAIFYLLINE** (3-(*o*-methoxyphenoxy)-1,2-propanediol compound with theophylline; guai-phenesin theophylline derivative; guaithylline; 'eclabron').

GUAIMESAL** ((±)-2-(*o*-methoxyphenoxy)-2-methyl-1,3-benzodioxan-4-one).

Guaiphenesin* *see* Guaifenesin.

Guaithylline* *see* Guaifylline.

'**Guajacuran**' *see* Guaifenesin.

Gualenate *see* Sodium gualenate.

GUAMECYCLINE** (*N*-(4-(amidinoamidino)-piperazin-1-yl-methyl)tetracycline; *N*-(4-diguani-dopiperazin-1-ylmethyl)tetracycline; *N*-(4-guani-dinoformimidoylpiperazin-1-ylmethyl)tetracycl-ine; 'guanamycin'; 'xantociclina').

GUANABENZ* (1-(2,6-dichlorobenzylidene-amino)guanidine; DCBAG; 'rexitine').

GUANABENZ plus MEFRUSIDE ('rexitine plus').

GUANABENZ ACETATE (BR-750; NSC-68982; Wy-8678).

GUANACLINE** (1-[2-(3,6-dihydro-4-methyl-1(2*H*)-pyridyl)ethyl]guanidine; 1-(2-guanidino-ethyl)-1,2,3,6-tetrahydro-4-picoline; cyclazenin; cyclozanin; B-1464; FBA-1464).

GUANACLINE plus METHYLDOPA ('tadip').

GUANADREL* ((1,4-dioxaspiro[4.5]dec-2-yl-methyl)guanidine; CL-1388R; U-28288D; 'ana-

261

rel').

Guanamprazine *see* Amiloride.

'Guanamycin' *see* Guamecycline.

'Guanatol' *see* Proguanil.

GUANAZODINE*** (1-(octahydroazocin-2-yl-methyl)guanidine; 2-(guanidylmethyl)hepta-methylenimine; 2-(guanidylmethyl)octahydro-azocine; 1-(2-heptamethyleniminomethyl)guan-idine; guanidinomethylazacyclooctane; Egyt-739; 'sanegyt').

GUANAZOLE (3,5-diamino-1,2,4-triazole; NSC-1895).

Guanazolo *see* Azaguanine.

GUANCIDINE** (1-cyano-3-(1,1-dimethylprop-yl)guanidine; 1-cyano-3-*tert*-pentylguanidine; guancydine; CL-2422).

GUANCLOFINE*** (2,6-dichloro-*N*-(2-guanidi-noethyl)aniline; [2-(2,6-dichloroanilino)ethyl]-guanidine).

Guancydine* *see* Guancidine.

'Guaneran' *see* Tiamiprine.

GUANETHIDINE*** (1-[2-(1-azacyclooctyl)-ethyl]guanidine; 1-[(2-hexahydro-1(2*H*)-azocin-yl)ethyl]guanidine; guanizol; isobarin; octadine; octatensin; oktadin).

GUANETHIDINE MONOSULFATE* (guaneth-idine hydrogen sulfate; 'ganda').

GUANETHIDINE MONOSULFATE plus HYDROCHLOROTHIAZIDE ('esimil').

GUANETHIDINE SULFATE* (NSC-29863; Su-5864).

GUANFACINE*** (*N*-amidino-2-(2,6-dichloro-phenyl)acetamide; *N*-(aminoiminomethyl)-2,6-dichlorobenzeneacetamide; (2,6-dichlorophenyl-acetyl)guanidine; guanfacine hydrochloride; BS-100-141; 'estulic').

GUANICAINE (1,3-dianisyl-2-phenethylguanid-ine; 2-(*p*-ethoxyphenyl)-1,3-bis(*p*-methoxyphen-yl)guanidine; guanicaine hydrochloride; pheno-dianisyl).

GUANIDINE (aminoformamidine; carbamidine; iminourea; uramine).

p-**Guanidinobenzoic acid ester with (*p*-hydroxyphen-yl)acetic acid ester with *N,N*-dimethylglycolamide** *see* Camostat.

4-Guanidinobutyramide *see* Tiformin.

N-(**2-Guanidinoethyl)aza-6-spiro[2.5]-octane** *see* Spirgetine.

1-(2-Guanidinoethyl)-1,2,3,6-tetrahydro-4-picoline *see* Guanacline.

N-(**Guanidinoformimidoyl)morpholine** *see* Mor-oxydine.

N-(**4-Guanidinoformimidoylpiperazin-1-ylmethyl)-tetracycline** *see* Guamecycline.

6-Guanidinohexanoic acid *p*-(ethoxycarbonyl)phenyl ester *see* Gabexate.

Guanidinomethylazacyclooctane *see* Guanazodine.

2-(Guanidinomethyl)-1,4-benzodioxan *see* Guano-xan.

6-(Guanidinomethyl)-1,4-benzodioxan *see* Guaben-xan.

Guanidoacetic acid *see* Glycocyamine.

Guanidotaurine *see* Taurocyamine.

2-(Guanidylmethyl)heptamethylenimine *see* Guan-azodine.

2-(Guanidylmethyl)octahydroazocine *see* Guan-azodine.

GUANINE (2-amino-6-hydroxypurine; 2-amino-hypoxanthine).

GUANINE ARABINOSIDE (arabinofuranosyl-guanine; ara-G).

GUANINE PROPIONATE (6-hydroxy-2-(α-pro-pionamido)purine).

Guanine riboside *see* Guanosine.

Guanisochin* *see* Guanisoquine.

Guanisoquin* *see* Guanisoquine.

GUANISOQUINE*** (7-bromo-3,4-dihydro-2(1*H*)-isoquinolinecarboxamidine sulfate; guan-isochin; guanisoquin; P-3896).

Guanizol *see* Guanethidine.

GUANOCLOR*** (1-[2-(2,6-dichlorophenoxy)-ethylamino]guanidine; 1-[2-(2,6-dichlorophen-oxy)ethyl]-2-guanylhydrazine; NSC-108163; P-1029).

GUANOCTINE*** (*tert*-octylguanidine; (1,1,3,3-tetramethylbutyl)guanidine; A-7283; BP-1184).

'Guanofuracin' *see* Furaguanidine.

GUANOSINE (guanine riboside; vernine).

Guanosine monophosphate *see* Guanylic acid.

Guanosine phosphate *see* Guanylic acid.

GUANOSINE TRIPHOSPHATE (GTP).

GUANOXABENZ** (1-[(2,6-dichlorobenzylid-ene)amino]-3-hydroxyguanidine; 2-[(2,6-dichlo-rophenyl)methylene]-*N*-hydroxyhydrazinecarbo-ximidamide; 'benzerial').

GUANOXAN*** ((1,4-benzodioxan-2-ylmethyl)-guanidine; 2-(guanidinomethyl)-1,4-benzodi-oxan; P-1003; 'envacar').

GUANOXYFEN*** (1-(3-phenoxypropyl)guanid-ine; guanoxyfen sulfate; CI-515; CN-34799-5A; EA-166; HP-1598).

Guanylhydrazine *see* Aminoguanidine.

GUANYLIC ACID (guanosine monophosphate; guanosine phosphate; GMP).

N-**Guanyl-*N*-methylglycine** *see* Creatine.

Guaranine *see* Caffeine.

GUAR GUM (*Cyamopsis tetragonoloba* polysac-charide; 'decorpa'; 'glucotard'; 'prefil').
See also under Attapulgite.

Guarin *see* Caffeine.

'Guastil' *see* Sulpiride.

'Guayanesin' *see* Guaifenesin.

'Gubernal' *see* Alprenolol.

Guethol *see* *o*-Ethoxyphenol.

L-Gulitol *see* Sorbitol.

'Gumbix' *see* *p*-Aminomethylbenzoic acid.

'Gu-pen' *see* Carindacillin.

'Guronsan' *see* Glucurolactone.

'Gusathion' *see* Azinphos-methyl.

'Gusathion A' *see* Azinphos-ethyl.

'Gusathion-MS' *see under* Azinphos-methyl.

'Guthion' *see* Azinphos-methyl.

'Gutron' *see* Midodrine.

'Guttalax' *see* Sodium picosulfate.

GUVACINE (1,2,5,6-tetrahydronicotinic acid).

GUVACOLINE (methyl 1,2,5,6-tetrahydronicotin-

ate).
GYKI-41099 *see* Cloranolol.
'Gyn' *see* Magnesium gluconate.
'Gyne-lotrimin' *see* Clotrimazole.
'Gynergen' *see* Ergotamine tartrate.
'Gynesin' *see* Trigonelline.
'Gyno-daktarin' *see* Miconazole.

'Gyno-monistat' *see* Miconazole.
'Gyno-pevaryl' *see* Econazole.
'Gynophase' *see under* Norethisterone acetate.
'Gyno-rest' *see* Dydrogesterone.
'Gyno-sterosan' *see* Chlorquinaldol.
'Gynotherax' *see* Chlorquinaldol.
'Gynovlar' *see under* Norethisterone acetate.

H

H *see* Mustard gas.
H-3 *see* Procaine.
H-9/88 *see* Metirosine.
H-33 *see* Febuprol.
H-44/68 *see* Metirosine methyl ester.
H-56/28 *see* Alprenolol.
H-69/17 *see* Fenclonine.
H-80/62 *see* Prenalterol.
H-88/32 *see* Oxidopamine.
H-93/26 *see* Metoprolol.
H-102/09 *see* Zimeldine.
H-104/08 *see* Pamatolol.
H-115 *see* Chlormidazole.
H-133/22 *see* Prenalterol.
H-149/94 *see* Picoprazole.
H-168/68 *see* Omeprazole.
H-224 *see* Buformin.
H-365 *see* Paroxypropione.
H-490 *see* Ethosuximide.
H-610 *see* Fencamfamin.
H-835 *see under* Cafedrine.
H-990 *see* Oxymetazoline.
H-3292 *see* Disopyramide.
H-3452 *see* Cyclofenil.
H-3608 *see* Enpiprazole.
H-3774 *see* Alibendol.
H-4007 *see* Mepiprazole.
H-4132 *see* Dotefonium bromide.
H-4170 *see* Tolpiprazole.
H-5746 *see* Chlorpromazine.
H-6706 *see* Metflurazon.
H-733293 *see* Acesulfame.
HACHIMYCIN** (antibiotic from *Str. hachjoensis*; hashimycin; 'cambimycin'; 'trichomycin'; 'trichonat'; 'trichosept').
'Haelan' *see* Fludroxycortide.
Haem.... *see also* Hem.....
'Haemaccel' *see* Polygeline.
Haffkynine *see* Mepacrine.
'Haflutan' *see* Clofenamide.
'Halan' *see* Halothane.
'Halane' *see* Troclosene sodium.
HALAZEPAM*** (7-chloro-1,3-dihydro-5-phenyl-1-(2,2,2-trifluoroethyl)-2*H*-1,4-benzodiazepin-2-one; Sch-12041; 'paxipam').
HALAZONE** (*p*-(*N*,*N*-dichlorosulfamoyl)benzoic acid; *p*-sulfondichloramidobenzoic acid; halazone sodium; pantocide; 'pantosept').
'Halciderm' *see* Halcinonide.
'Halcimat' *see* Halcinonide.
HALCINONIDE*** (21-chloro-9-fluoro-11β,16α,17-trihydroxypregn-4-ene-3,20-dione cyclic 16,17-acetal with acetone; 21-chloro-9α-fluoro-11β-hydroxy-16α,17β-isopropylidenedioxypregn-4-ene-3,20-dione; SQ-18566; 'halciderm'; 'halcimat'; 'halcort'; 'halog').
'Halcion' *see* Triazolam.
'Halcort' *see* Halcinonide.
'Haldol' *see* Haloperidol.
'Haldrate' *see* Paramethasone acetate.
'Haldrone' *see* Paramethasone acetate.
'Halenol' *see* Dichlorophen.
HALETAZOLE*** (5-chloro-2-[*p*-(2-diethylaminoethoxy)phenyl]benzothiazole; halethazole; 'episol').
Halethazole* *see* Haletazole.
'Halidor' *see* Bencyclane.
'Halinone' *see* Bromindione.
'Haloanisone' *see* Fluanisone.
HALOCARBAN*** (4,4'-dichloro-3-(trifluoromethyl)carbanilide; cloflucarban).
HALOCORTOLONE** (9-chloro-6α,11β-difluoro-21-hydroxy-16α-methylpregna-1,4-diene-3,20-dione).
Halocrinic acid *see* Brocrinat.
HALOFANTRINE*** (3-(dibutylamino)-1-[1,3-dichloro-6-(trifluoromethyl)-9-phenanthryl]-1-propanol; 1,3-dichloro-α-[2-(dibutylamino)ethyl]-6-(trifluoromethyl)-9-phenanthrenemethanol; halofantrine hydrochloride; WR-171669).
HALOFENATE*** (2-(*p*-chlorophenyl)-2-(α,α,α-trifluoro-*m*-toloxy)acetic acid ester with *N*-(2-hydroxyethyl)acetamide; 2-acetamidoethyl 2-(4-chlorophenyl)-2-(3-trifluoromethylphenoxy)-acetate; MK-185; 'livipas').
HALOFUGINONE*** ((±)-*trans*-7-bromo-6-chloro[3-(3-hydroxypiperid-2-yl)acetonyl]-4(3*H*)-quinazolinone; 7-bromo-6-chlorofebrifugine; halofuginone hydrochloride; RU-19100; 'stenorol').
'Halog' *see* Halcinonide.
Halogabide *see* Progabide.
HALOMETASONE*** (2-chloro-6α,9-difluoro-11β,17,21-trihydroxy-16α-methylpregna-1,4-diene-3,20-dione).
'Halon' *see* Dichlorodifluoromethane.
HALONAMINE** (2-[[*p*-chloro-α-(*p*-fluorophenyl)benzyl]oxy]ethylamine).
HALOPEMIDE*** (*N*-[2-[4-(5-chloro-2,3-dihydro-2-oxo-1*H*-benzimidazol-1-yl)piperid-4-yl]ethyl]-4-fluorobenzamide; *N*-[2-[4-(5-chloro-2-oxobenzimidazolin-1-yl)piperid-1-yl]ethyl]-*p*-

264

fluorobenzamide; 1-[1-[2-[(p-fluorobenzoyl)-amino]ethyl]piperid-4-yl]benzimidazolin-2-one; R-34301).

HALOPENIUM CHLORIDE* ((p-bromobenzyl) [3-(4-chloro-2-isopropyl-5-methylphenoxy)-propyl]dimethylammonium chloride; halopone).

HALOPERIDIDE (4-(o-chlorophenyl)-1-[3-(p-fluorobenzoyl)propyl]-4-(pyrrolidin-1-ylcarbonyl)piperidine; 4-[[4-(o-chlorophenyl)](4-pyrrolidinamido)piperidino]-4'-fluorobutyrophenone; haloperidide oxalate; R-3201).

HALOPERIDOL* (4-(p-chlorophenyl)-1-[3-(p-fluorobenzoyl)propyl]-4-piperidinol; 4-[4-(p-chlorophenyl)-4'-fluoro-4-hydroxyperid-1-yl]-butyrophenone; 4-[4-(p-chlorophenyl)-4-hydroxypiperidino]-4'-fluorobutyrophenone; McN-JR-1625; R-1625).

HALOPERIDOL plus ISOPROPAMIDE IODIDE ('vesalium').
See also under Buzepide metiodide.

Halopone* *see* Halopenium chloride.

HALOPREDONE* (2-bromo-6β,9-difluoro-prednisolone; 2-bromo-6β,9-difluoro-11β,17,21-trihydroxypregna-1,4-diene-3,20-dione).

HALOPREDONE ACETATE* (halopredone 17,21-diacetate).

HALOPROGESTERONE* (17α-bromo-6α-fluoro-4-pregnene-3,20-dione; 17α-bromo-6α-fluoroprogesterone; 'prohalone').

HALOPROGIN* (3-iodo-2-propynol 2,4,5-trichlorophenyl ether; 2,4,5-trichloro-1-(3-iodo-2-propyn-1-yl-oxy)benzene; M-1028(Meiji); NSC-100071).

HALOPROPANE (3-bromo-1,1,2,2-tetrafluoro-propane).

Halopyramine* *see* Chloropyramine.

'Halospor' *see* Cefotiam.

'Halotestin' *see* Fluoxymesterone.

'Halotex' *see* Haloprogin.

HALOTHANE* (2-bromo-2-chloro-1,1,1-tri-fluoroethane; ftorotan).

HALOXAZOLAM* (10-bromo-11b-(o-fluoro-phenyl)-2,3,7,11b-tetrahydrooxazolo[3,2-d]-[1,4]benzodiazepin-6(5H)-one).

HALOXON* (bis(2-chloroethyl) (3-chloro-4-methylcoumarin-7-yl) phosphate; 3-chloro-7-hydroxy-4-methylcoumarin bis(2-chloroethyl) phosphate).

HALQUINOLS* (mixture of 5-chloro, 7-chloro-and 5,7-dichloro-8-quinolinols; chlorquinol; CHQ; SQ-1640).
See also Chloroxine; *and under* Chlorquinaldol; Triamcinolone.

'Hamovannad' *see* Inositol nicotinate.

HAMYCIN (antibiotic from *Str. pimprina*).

'Hanane' *see* Dimefox.

'Hansolar' *see* Acedapsone.

'Hapamine' *see* Histamine azoprotein complex.

HAQ *see* Ametantrone diacetate.

Harden-Young ester *see* Fructose 1,6-diphosphate.

HARMALINE (4,9-dihydro-7-methoxy-1-methyl-3H-pyrido[3,4-b]indole; 3,4-dihydro-7-methoxy-1-methyl-9H-pyrid[3,4-b]indole; 3,4-dihydro-

harmine; 3,4-dihydro-7-methoxy-1-methyl-β-carboline; harmalol methyl ether; O-methylhar-malol).

HARMALOL (4,9-dihydro-1-methyl-3H-pyrid[3,4-b]indol-7-ol; 3,4-dihydro-1-methyl-9H-pyrid[3,4-b]indol-7-ol; 3,4-dihydro-7-hydroxy-1-methyl-β-carboline).

Harmalol methyl ether *see* Harmaline.

HARMAN (1-methyl-9H-pyrido[3,4-b]indole; 3-methyl-4-carboline; 2-methyl-β-carboline; aribine; loturin; passiflorin).

HARMINE (7-methoxyharman; banisterine; leucoharmine; telepathine; yageine).

'Harmogen' *see* Piperazine estrone sulfate.

'Harmonyl' *see* Deserpidine.

'Harnosal' *see under* Sulfaethidole.

'Harolan' *see* Benzbromarone.

'Harvatrate' *see* Atropine methonitrate.

'Harzol' *see* β-Sitosterol.

Hashimycin *see* Hachimycin.

'Hasivin' *see* Oxymetazoline.

'Haurymellin' *see* Metformin.

'Havapen' *see* Penamecillin.

'Havidote' *see* Sodium calcium edetate.

'Hazol' *see* Oxymetazoline.

HB-113 *see* Chlorpentazide.

HB-115 *see* Nifurprazine.

HB-419 *see* Glibenclamide.

HBF-386 *see* Cactinomycin.

HBT *see* Tioxolone.

HC-3 *see* Hemicholinium.

HC-606 *see* Hexcarbacholine bromide.

HC-1528 *see* Decoquinate.

HC-8014bis *see* Dimethoate.

HC-8056 *see* Parathion-methyl.

HC-8057 *see* Fenitrothion.

HC-8059 *see* Malathion.

HC-8061 *see* Parathion isomethyl.

HC-20511 *see* Ketotifen fumarate.

HCC *see* 25-Hydroxycolecalciferol.

HCG *see* Chorionic gonadotrophin.

HCS-3260 *see* Chlordane.

'6-HD' *see* Oxidopamine.

HDP *see* Oxidronic acid.

'H-dulapine' *see* Clofedanol noscapine succinate.

HE-111 *see* Dexamethasone isonicotinate.

He-682 *see* Etofylline nicotinate.

'Healon' *see* Hyaluronic acid.

'Hebaral' *see* Hexethal.

'Hebucol' *see* Cyclobutyrol.

'Heclox' *see under* Cloxacillin.

HECNU *see* Elmustine.

HECYLAMINE (2-cyclohexyl-N-hexylethylamine; 2-hexylaminoethylcyclohexane).

HEDAQUINIUM CHLORIDE* (2,2'-hexadeca-methylenebis(isoquinolinium chloride); B1 Q16).

'Hedex' *see* Paracetamol.

HEDONAL (methyl propyl carbinol carbamate; pentyl carbamate).

'Hedulin' *see* Phenindione.

'Hekbilin' *see* Chenodeoxycholic acid.

'Helcosol' *see* Bismuth gallate.

265

Helenien *see* Xantofyl palmitate.
Helenin *see* Alantolactone.
'Helfergin' *see* Meclofenoxate.
'Helfo-dopa' *see* Levodopa.
HELIOMYCIN*** (antibiotic from *Actinomyces flavochromogenes* var. *heliomycini*).
'Heliophan' *see* Homosalate.
'Helixor' *see* Viscum album.
'Helmatac' *see* Parbendazole.
'Helmex' *see* Pyrantel embonate.
'Helmezine' *see* Piperazine.
'Helmicid' *see* Piperazine.
'Helminal' *see* Kainic acid.
'Helminthex' *see* Piperazine.
'Helmitol' *see* Methenamine anhydromethylenecitrate.
'Helmodym-88' *see* Rare earth levulinates.
'Helmox' *see* Cyacetacide.
HEMATIN (ferriheme hydroxide; ferriporphyrin hydroxide; hydroxyhemin; 'phenodin').
Hematin reduction product *see* Heme.
HEMATOPORPHYRIN (2,4-bis(1-hydroxyethyl)-1,3,5,8-tetramethylporphine-6,7-dipropionic acid; 'hemedomine'; 'photodyn'; 'porfyron').
HEME (ferrous complex of 1,3,5,8-tetramethyl-2,4-divinyl porphine-6,7-dipropionic acid; ferroheme; ferroporphyrin; hematin reduction product; protoheme).
'Hemedomine' *see* Hematoporphyrin.
'Hemeran' *see* Calcium methyl polygalacturonate sulfonate(s).
HEMICHOLINIUM (4',4"-biacetophenone-2',2"-bis[(2-hydroxyethyl)dimethylammonium]; α,α'-(dimethylamino)ethanol-4,4'-biacetophenone; α,α'-dimethylethanolamino-4,4'-biacetophenone; HC-3).
'Hemi-daonil' *see* Glibenclamide.
Hemiglobin *see* Methemoglobin.
3,4,5-Hemimellitinol *N*-methylcarbamate ester *see* 3,4,5-Trimethylphenyl methylcarbamate.
HEMIN (ferrichloride of 2,4-divinyl-1,3,5,8-tetramethylporphine-6,7-dipropionic acid; ferriheme chloride; ferriporphyrin chloride; Teichman's-crystals).
'Hemineurine' *see* Clomethiazole edisilate.
'Heminevrine' *see* Clomethiazole edisilate.
Hemithiamine *see* Clomethiazole.
Hemitiamine (tr) *see* Clomethiazole edisilate.
'Hemiton' *see* Clonidine.
'Hemoced' *see* Etamsylate.
'Hemodyn I' *see* Povidone.
'Hemo-pak' *see* Oxidized cellulose.
'Hemostat' *see* Mepesulfate.
'Hemostop' *see* Naftazone.
'Hemotabs' *see* Cetaceum.
HEMPA (hexamethylphosphoric triamide; gemfa; hexamethylphosphamide; hexamethylphosphoramide; HMPA; HMPT; 'hexametapol').
Hendecanoic acid *see* Undecanoic acid.
Hendecenoic acid *see* Undecenoic acid.
Heneicosafluorotripropylamine *see* Perfluamine.
HEOD *see* Dieldrin.

'Hepadial' *see* Magnesium dimecrotate.
'Hepaldine' *see* Timonacic.
'Hepa-Merz' *see* Ornithine aspartate.
'Heparcholine' *see* Choline.
'Heparegene' *see* Timonacic.
HEPARIN*** (heparin sodium; mucoitin sodium polysulfate).
See also Magnesium heparinate *and under* Batroxobin.
HEPARIN CALCIUM ('calciparin').
'Heparin-degranol' *see* Mannomustine heparinate.
HEPARIN POTASSIUM ('clarin'; 'panhepin').
Heparin sodium *see* Heparin.
β-Heparin *see* Dermatan sulfate.
'Heparlipon' *see* Thioctic acid.
'Heparoid' *see* Mepesulfate.
'Hepartest' *see* Sulfobromphthalein.
'Hepasil' *see* Fencibutirol.
'Hep-a-stat' *see* Nitarsone.
'Hepasulfol' *see* Anethole trithione.
Hepatin *see* Glycogen.
'Hepatobida' *see* Etifenin.
'Hepatolite' *see* Butilfenin.
'Hepatoscan' *see* Lidofenin.
'Hepatotestbrom' *see* Sulfobromphthalein.
'Hepoid' *see* Sodium polyanhydromannuronic sulfate.
'Heporal' *see* Anethole trithione.
HEPRONICATE*** (2-hexyl-2-hydroxymethyl-1,3-propanediol trinicotinate).
'Hepsan' *see* Acetylmethionine choline salt.
Heptaaluminium heptadecahydroxide bis(sulfate) *see* Alusulf.
HEPTABARB*** (5-cyclohepten-1-yl-5-ethylbarbituric acid; heptabarbital; heptabarbitone; heptamal).
Heptabarbital* *see* Heptabarb.
Heptabarbitone* *see* Heptabarb.
HEPTACHLOR* (1,4,5,6,7,8,8-heptachloro-3a,4,7,7c-tetrahydro-4,7-methanoindene).
Heptachlorotetrahydromethanoindene *see* Heptachlor.
2-Heptadecyl-4,5-dihydro-1*H*-imidazole acetate *see* Glyodin.
'Heptadrine' *see* Tuaminoheptane.
Heptaldehyde *see* Heptyl aldehyde.
Heptamal* *see* Heptabarb.
HEPTAMETHYLENIMINE (azacyclooctane; octahydroazocine; perhydroazocine).
1-(2-Heptamethyleniminomethyl)guanidine *see* Guanazodine.
'Heptamine' *see* Octodrine *and* Tuaminoheptane.
HEPTAMINOL*** (6-amino-2-methyl-2-heptanol; heptaminol hydrochloride; RP 2831).
See also under Deanol pidolate.
Heptaminol acefyllinate *see* Heptaminol theophyllineacetate.
HEPTAMINOL ADENOSINE PHOSPHATE* ('ampecyclal').
HEPTAMINOL THEOPHYLLINEACETATE (heptaminol acefyllinate; heptaminol theophylline ethanoate; TEH; MD-6260; 'cariamyl'; 'theo-heptylon').

See also under Cinnarizine.

Heptaminol theophylline ethanoate *see* Heptaminol theophyllineacetate.

'**Heptanal**' *see* Methadone.

1-Heptanecarboxylic acid *see* ∪ctanoic acid.

1,7-Heptanedicarboxylic acid *see* Azelaic acid.

Heptanedioic acid *see* Pimelic acid.

Heptanoic acid *see* Enanthic acid.

HEPTAVERINE*** (*N,N*-dimethyl-γ-phenyl-Δ$^{2,\gamma}$-norbornanepropylamine; 2-[3-(dimethylamino)-1-phenylpropylidene]norbornane).

'**Heptedrine**' *see* Tuaminoheptane.

Heptobarbital *see* Mephebarbital.

HEPTOLAMIDE*** (1-cycloheptyl-3-(*p*-toluenesulfonyl)urea).

'**Heptomer**' *see* Gleptoferron.

HEPTYL ALDEHYDE (enanthal; enanthaldehyde; enanthol; heptaldehyde; oenanthaldehyde).

2-Heptylamine *see* Tuaminoheptane.

Heptylic acid *see* Enanthic acid.

Heptylpenicillin *see* Penicillin K.

'**Hepzide**' *see* Nithiazide.

HEPZIDINE*** (4-(10,11-dihydro-5*H*-dibenzo-[*a,d*]cyclohepten-5-yloxy)-1-methylpiperidine; BS-7051).

'**Heraclene**' *see* Cobamamide.

'**Heraldium**' *see* Mecloralurea.

'**Herban**' *see* Noruron.

'**Herbatox D-500**' *see* Dimethylamine 2,4-dichlorophenoxyacetate.

'**Herbesser**' *see* Diltiazem.

HERBIPOLIN (2-amino-6-hydroxy-7,7-dimethylpurine).

'**Hercules 528**' *see* Dioxation.

'**Herkol**' *see* Dichlorvos.

Heroin *see* Diamorphine.

'**Herperal**' *see* Stallimycin.

'**Herpid**' *see under* Idoxuridine.

'**Herplex**' *see* Idoxuridine.

'**Heruclin**' *see* Histidine.

'**Herulcin**' *see* Histidine.

'**Hesotanol**' *see* Etofylline nicotinate.

'**Hesotin**' *see* Etofylline nicotinate.

'**Hespan**' *see* Hetastarch.

'**Hespander**' *see* Hetastarch.

HESPERETIN (3′,5,7-trihydroxy-4′-methoxyflavanone; hesperitin).

Hesperetin 7-rhamnoglucoside *see* Hesperidin.

HESPERIDIN (hesperetin 7-rhamnoglucoside; vitamin P).

Hesperitin *see* Hesperetin.

'**Hetabiotic**' *see* Hetacillin.

HETACILLIN** (6-(2,2-dimethyl-5-oxo-4-phenyl-imidazolidin-1-yl)penicillanic acid; penicinate; phenazacillin; hetacillin potassium; BL-P804; BRL-804).

See also Sarpicillin; *and under* Cloxacillin; Dicloxacillin.

HETAFLUR*** (hexadecylamine hydrofluoride; SK&F-2208).

HETASTARCH* (2-hydroxyethyl starch; 'hespan'; 'hespander'; 'volex').

Heteroauxin *see* 3-Indoleacetic acid.

HETERONIUM BROMIDE*** ((±)-3-hydroxy-1,1-dimethylpyrrolidinium bromide α-phenyl-2-thiopheneglycolate; (±)-1-methylpyrrolidin-3-yl α-phenyl-α-(2-thienyl)glycolate methobromide).

'**Hetolin**' *see* 3,3,3-Tris(*p*-chlorophenyl)propionic acid 4-methylpiperazide.

HETP *see* Hexaethyl tetraphosphate.

'**Hetrazan**' *see* Diethylcarbamazine.

'**Hetrum**' *see* Heteronium bromide.

'**Hexabalm**' *see* Hexachlorophene.

Hexabendine *see* Hexobendine.

'**Hexabolan**' *see* Trenbolone cyclohexylmethylcarbonate.

'**Hexabrix**' *see under* Meglumine ioxaglate.

HEXACAMPHAMINE* (methenamine (+)-camphorate; 'amphotropine'; 'arocan'; 'zymarocan').

Hexacarbacholine *see* Hexcarbacholine bromide.

'**Hexachloran**' *see* Lindane.

Hexachlorane (tr) *see* Lindane.

HEXACHLOROBENZENE (Julin's carbon chloride; perchlorobenzene).

1,2,3,4,7,7-Hexachloro-5,6-bis(chloromethyl)bicyclo[2.2.1]hept-2-ene *see* Chlorbicyclen.

1,4,5,6,7,7-Hexachloro-5,6-bis(chloromethyl)norbornene *see* Chlorbicyclen.

1,2,3,4,7,7-Hexachloro-5,6-bis(hydroxymethyl)norbornene sulfite *see* Endosulfan.

Hexachlorocyclohexane *see* Lindane.

Hexachlorodihydroxydiphenylmethane *see* Hexachlorophene.

1,2,3,4,10,10-Hexachloro-6,7-epoxy-1,4,4a,5,6,7,8,8a-octahydro-1,4-*endo*-5,8-*endo*-dimethanonaphthalene *see* Endrin.

HEXACHLOROETHANE (carbon hexachloride; fasciolin; perchloroethane).

1,2,3,4,10,10-Hexachloro-1,4,4a,5,8,8a-hexahydro-1,4:5,8-dimethanonaphthalene *see* Aldrin.

6,7,8,9,10,10-Hexachloro-1,5,5a,6,9,9a-hexahydro-6,9-methano-2,4,3-benzodioxathiepin 3-oxide *see* Endosulfan.

Hexachloronorbornene 5,6-bis(oxymethylene) sulfite *see* Endosulfan.

3,4,5,6,9,9-Hexachloro-1a,2,2a,5,6,6a,7,7a-octahydro-2,7:3,6-dimethanonaphth[2,3-*b*]oxirene *see* Dieldrin *and* Endrin.

Hexachlorophane* *see* Hexachlorophene.

HEXACHLOROPHENE*** (2,2′-methylenebis(3,4,6-trichlorophenol); hexachlorodihydroxydiphenylmethane; hexachlorophane; AT-7).

HEXACHLOROPHENE plus PHENYLMERCURIC BORATE ('remanex').

HEXACHLOROPHENE PHOSPHATE (hexachlorophene monophosphate; Ph-1503).

Hexachloro-*p*-xylene *see* 1,4-Bis(trichloromethyl)benzene.

Hexacitramine *see* Methenamine anhydromethylenecitrate.

'**Hexacol**' *see* Alloclamide.

'**Hexacycline**' *see* Tetracycline phosphate complex.

Hexacyclonate *see* Sodium hexacyclonate.

HEXACYCLONIC ACID (4-hydroxy-3,3-pentamethylenebutyric acid; 1-(hydroxymethyl)cyclo-

hexaneacetic acid; β,β-pentamethylene-γ-hydroxybutyric acid).
See also Sodium hexacyclonate.
HEXACYPRONE* (1-benzyl-2-oxocyclohexanepropionic acid).
Hexadecadrol *see* Dexamethasone.
2,2'-Hexadecamethylenebis(isoquinolinium chloride) *see* Hedaquinium chloride.
Hexadecanamide *see* Palmitamide.
Hexadecanoic acid *see* Palmitic acid.
1-HEXADECANOL (cetanol; cetyl alcohol; ethal).
HEXADECYLAMINE (cetylamine).
Hexadecylamine hydrofluoride *see* Hetaflur.
p-**(Hexadecylamino)benzoic acid** *see* Cetaben.
α-**Hexadecylcitric acid** *see* Agaric acid.
Hexadecyl(2-hydroxycyclohexyl)dimethylammonium chloride *see* Cethexonium chloride.
Hexadecyl[2-[(*p*-methoxybenzyl)-2-pyrimidinylamino]ethyl]dimethylammonium bromide *see* Tonzonium bromide.
Hexadecyl pyridinium bromide *see* Cetylpyridinium bromide.
Hexadecylpyridinium 3-hydroxy-*p*-cymenecarboxylate *see* Cetylpyridinium o-thymotate.
Hexadecylpyridinium 3-isopropyl-6-methylsalicylate *see* Cetylpyridinium o-thymotate.
Hexadecyltrimethylammonium bromide *see* Cetrimonium bromide. .
2,4-Hexadienoic acid *see* Sorbic acid.
HEXADILINE* (2,2-dicyclohexyl-1-piperid-2-ylethylene; 2-(2,2-dicyclohexylvinyl)piperidine; hexadylamine; MRL-38).
HEXADIMETHRINE BROMIDE*
(*N*,*N*,*N'*,*N'*-tetramethyl-1,6-hexanediamine polymer with 1,3-dibromopropane; polymer of *N*,*N*,*N'*,*N'*-tetramethyl-*N*-trimethylenehexamethylenediammonium dibromide; *N*,*N*,*N'*,*N'*-tetramethylhexamethylenediamine trimethylene bromide polymer; 'polybrene').
Hexadiphane *see* Prozapine.
Hexadiphensulfonium* *see* Hexasonium iodide.
HEXADISTIGMINE (hexamethylene-1,6-bis[[*m*-(*N*-methylcarbamoyloxy)phenyl]trimethylammonium bromide]; BC-40).
'Hexadrol' *see* Dexamethasone.
Hexadylamine *see* Hexadiline.
HEXAETHYL TETRAPHOSPHATE (HETP; hexastigmine).
Hexafluorenium* *see* Hexafluronium bromide.
Hexafluorodiethyl ether *see* Flurotyl.
HEXAFLUOROISOPROPYL METHYL ETHER (flurotyl isomer; 'isoindokolon').
HEXAFLURONIUM BROMIDE* (hexamethylenebis(fluoren-9-yldimethylammonium bromide); hexafluorenium; IN-117; NSC-19477).
HEXAHOMOSERINE (2-amino-6-hydroxyhexanoic acid; α-amino-ε-hydroxycaproic acid; 6-hydroxynorleucine).
Hexahydroadiphenine *see* Drofenine.
Hexahydroaminoethanophenanthrene *see* Morphinan.
Hexahydroazepine *see* Hexamethylenimine.
2,3,4,5,6,7-Hexahydro-1*H*-azepine-1-aceto-2',6'-

xylidide *see* Pincainide.
Hexahydro-1*H*-azepine-1-carbothioic acid *S*-ethyl ester *see* Molinate.
Hexahydro-1*H*-azepine-1-carboxylic acid ester with 2-bromo-6-methylergoline-8β-methanol *see* Brazergoline.
4-Hexahydroazepin-1-yl-2,2-diphenylbutyramide methiodide *see* Buzepide metiodide.
2-(Hexahydro-1*H*-azepin-1-yl)ethyl α-cyclohexyl-3-thiopheneacetate *see* Cetiedil.
1-(2-Hexahydroazepin-1-ylethyl)-2-oxocyclohexanecarboxylic acid benzyl ester *see* Amicibone.
1-(Hexahydro-1*H*-azepin-1-yl)-3-(indan-5-ylsulfonyl)urea *see* Glidazamide.
6-[[(Hexahydro-1*H*-azepin-1-yl)methylene]amino]penicillanic acid *see* Mecillinam.
(2*S*,5*R*,6*R*)-6-[(Hexahydroazepin-1-ylmethylene)-amino]penicillanic acid pivaloyloxymethyl ester *see* Pivmecillinam.
1-(Hexahydro-1*H*-azepin-1-yl)-3-[[*p*-[2-(5-methyl-3-isoxazolecarboxamido)ethyl]phenyl]sulfonyl]urea *see* Glisoxepide.
3-Hexahydroazepin-1-yl-3'-nitropropiophenone *see* Fenitron.
1-(Hexahydro-1*H*-azepin-1-yl)-3-(*p*-toluenesulfonyl)urea *see* Tolazamide.
3-[4-(Hexahydroazepin-1-ylureidosulfonyl)phenethylcarbamoyl]-5-methylisoxazole *see* Glisoxepide.
1-[(2-Hexahydro-1(2*H*)-azocinyl)ethyl]guanidine *see* Guanethidine.
1,2,3,4,5,6-Hexahydro-2,3'-bipyridine *see* Anabasine.
Hexahydrodesoxyephedrine *see* Propylhexedrine.
HEXAHYDRO-1*H*-1,4-DIAZEPINE (1,4-diazacycloheptane; homopiperazine).
6,6aα,12,12aα,13aα,14-Hexahydro-4,8-dimethoxy-6,6-dimethyl-5aα*H*,13*H*-[1]benzopyrano[3,2-*b*]xanthen-13-one *see* Pentomone.
4'-(1,2,3,4,4a,10b-Hexahydro-8,9-dimethoxy-2-methylbenzo[*c*][1,6]naphthyridin-6-yl)acetanilide *see* Benafentrine.
Hexahydro-3,6-dimethyl-γ-carboline *see* Dicarbine.
Hexahydro-3α,7α-dimethyl-4,7-epoxyisobenzofuran-1,3-dione *see* Cantharidin.
2,3,4,5,6,7-Hexahydro-1,4-dimethyl-1,6-methano-1*H*-benzazonin-10-ol *see* Eptazocine.
1,2,3,4,5,6-Hexahydro-6,11-dimethyl-3-(3-methyl-2-butenyl)-2,6-methano-3-benzazocin-8-ol *see* Pentazocine.
8,9,10,11,11a,12-Hexahydro-8,10-dimethyl-7a*H*-naphtho[1',2':5,6]pyrano[3,2-*c*]pyridin-7a-ol *see* Naranol.
N-**(1,2,3,4,4a,9b-Hexahydro-8,9b-dimethyl-3-oxo-4-dibenzofuranyl)-4-methyl-1-piperazinepropionamide** *see* Taziprinone.
1,2,3,4,5,6-Hexahydro-6,11-dimethyl-3-phenethyl-2,6-methano-3-benzazocin-8-ol *see* Phenazocine.
Hexahydro-1,3-dimethyl-4-phenylazepine-4-carboxylic acid ethyl ester *see* Metethoheptazine.
Hexahydro-1,2-dimethyl-4-phenylazepine-4-carboxylic acid methyl ester *see* Metheptazine.
Hexahydro-1,3-dimethyl-4-phenylazepin-4-ol pro-

pionate ester *see* Proheptazine.

2,3,4,4a,5,9b-Hexahydro-2,8-dimethyl-1*H*-pyr-id[4,3-*b*]indole *see* Dicarbine.

Hexahydro-1,3-dioxo-2*H*-isoindol-2-ylmethyl chrysanthemate *see* Tetramethrin.

Hexahydro-α,α-diphenylpyrrolo[1,2-*a*]pyrazine-2(1*H*)-butyramide *see* Pirolazamide.

Hexahydro-5-hydroxy-4-(3-hydroxy-4-methyl-1-octen-6-ynyl)-Δ²⁽¹ᴴ⁾,δ-pentalenevaleric acid *see* Iloprost.

Hexahydro-5-hydroxy-4-(3-hydroxy-1-octenyl)-2*H*-cyclopenta[*b*]furan-Δ²,δ-valeric acid *see* Epoprostenol.

4-[[3,3a,4,5,6,6a-Hexahydro-5-hydroxy-4-(3-hydroxy-1-octenyl)cyclopenta[*b*]pyrrol-2-yl]thio]butyric acid methyl ester *see* Tilsuprost.

Hexahydro-5-hydroxy-6-(3-hydroxy-1-octenyl)-3a-methyl-Δ²⁽¹ᴴ⁾,δ-pentalenevaleric acid *see* Ciprostene.

2,3,5,6,7,7aα-Hexahydro-7β-hydroxy-1*H*-pyrrolizine-1β-methanol *see* Platynecine.

1,2,3,4,5,6-Hexahydro-8-hydroxy-3,6,11-trimethyl-2,6-methanobenzazocine *see* Metazocine.

1-(1,2,3,4,5,6-Hexahydro-8-hydroxy-3,6,11-trimethyl-2,6-methano-3-benzazocin-11-yl)-3-octanone *see* Tonazocine.

1,3,4,6,7,11b-Hexahydro-3-isobutyl-9,10-dimethoxy-2*H*-benzo[*a*]quinolizin-2-one *see* Tetrabenazine.

1,2,3,4,5,6-Hexahydro-2,6-methano-3-benzazocine *see* 6,7-Benzomorphan.

1-(3a,4,5,6,7,7a-Hexahydro-4,7-methanoindan-5-yl)-3,3-dimethylurea *see* Noruron.

1,2,3,4,5,6-Hexahydro-1,5-methano-8*H*-pyrido[1,2-*a*][1,5]diazocin-8-one *see* Cytisine.

(+)-*cis*-1,3,4,9,10,10a-Hexahydro-6-methoxy-11-methyl-2*H*-10,4a-iminoethanophenanthrene *see* Dextromethorphan.

5,6,7,7a,8,9-Hexahydro-3-methoxy-10-methyl-4a*H*-8,9c-iminoethanophenanthro[4,5-*bcd*]furan-5-ol *see* Dihydrocodeine.

Hexahydro-4-methoxy-8-methyl-7a-(piperid-1-ylmethyl)-2,5-methanocyclopenta-*m*-dioxin-7-ol *see* Valperinol.

1,2,3,4,10,14b-Hexahydro-2-methyldibenzo[*c,f*]pyrazino[1,2-*a*]azepine *see* Mianserin.

(+)-*cis*-1,3,4,9,10,10a-Hexahydro-11-methyl-2*H*-10,4a-iminoethanophenanthren-6-ol *see* Dextrorphan.

2-(Hexahydro-1-methylindolin-3-yl)ethyl benzilate *see* Metindizate.

4,6,6a,7,8,9-Hexahydro-7-methylindolo[4,3-*fg*]quinoline-9-carboxylic acid diethylamide *see* Lysergide.

Hexahydro-1-methyl-4-phenylazepinecarboxylic acid ethyl ester *see* Ethoheptazine.

2,3,3a,4,5,6-Hexahydro-8-methyl-1*H*-pyrazino-[3,2,1-*jk*]carbazole *see* Pirlindole.

1,2,3,7,8,8a-Hexahydro-7-methyl-8-[2-(tetrahydro-4-hydroxy-6-oxo-2*H*-pyran-2-yl)ethyl]naphth-1-yl 2-methylbutyrate *see* Mevastatin.

*N*⁶-[5-(Hexahydro-2-oxo-1*H*-thieno[3,4-*d*]imidazol-in-4-yl)-1-oxopentyl]lysine *see* Biocytin.

5-(Hexahydro-2-oxo-1*H*-thieno[3,4-*d*]imidazol-4-yl)-2-pentenoic acid *see* Lidimycin.

1,3,6,7,8,9-Hexahydro-5-phenyl-2*H*-(1)-benzothieno[2,3-*e*]-1,4-diazepin-2-one *see* Bentazepam.

Hexahydropicolinic acid *see* Pipecolic acid.

Hexahydroprenylamine *see* Droprenilamine.

Hexahydropyrazine *see* Piperazine.

1,3,4,6,7,11b-Hexahydro-2*H*-pyrazino[2,1-*a*]isoquinoline *see* Azaquinzole.

Hexahydropyridine *see* Piperidine.

Hexahydro-2,4,6-pyrimidinetrione *see* Barbituric acid.

10-(3-(Hexahydropyrrolo[1,2-*a*]pyrazin-2-(1*H*)-yl)-propionyl)-2-trifluoromethylphenothiazine *see* Azaftozine.

Hexahydro-4-[3-(2-trifluoromethylphenothiazin-10-yl)propyl]-(1*H*)1,4-diazepine-1-ethanol *see* Homofenazine.

1,2,3,4,5,6-Hexahydro-6,11,11-trimethyl-3-(3-methyl-2-butenyl)-2,6-methano-3-benzazocin-8-ol *see* Ibazocine.

2,3,3',4,4',5'-Hexahydroxybenzophenone *see* Exifone.

1β,3β,5,11α,14,19-Hexahydroxy-5β-card-20(22)-enolide 3-L-rhamnoside *see* Ouabain.

Hexahydroxycyclohexane *see* Inositol.

1,1',6,6',7,7'-Hexahydroxy-5,5'-diisopropyl-3,3'-dimethyl[2,2'-binaphthalene]-8,8'-dicarboxaldehyde *see* Gossypol.

4,5,7,4',5',7'-Hexahydroxy-2,2'-dimethylnaphthodianthrone *see* Hypericin.

Hexahydroxydiphenic acid dilactone *see* Ellagic acid.

3,3',4',5,5',7-Hexahydroxyflavone *see* Myricetin.

3,3',4',5,7,8-Hexahydroxyflavone *see* Gossypetin.

3,3',4',5,6,7-Hexahydroxyflavone *see* Quercetagetin.

5,6,9,17,19,21-Hexahydroxy-23-methoxy-2,4,12,16,18,20,22-heptamethyl-2,7-(epoxypentadeca(1,11,13)trienimino)-naphtho[2,1-*b*]furan-1,11(2*H*)-dione 21-acetate *see* Rifamycin.

Hexakis(μ-acetato)-μ-4-oxotetrazinc *see* Zinc acetate basic.

Hexakis(1-aziridinyl) phosphonitrilate *see* Apholate.

N,N,N',N',N'',N'''-Hexakis(2-hydroxyethyl)-2,4,6-triiodo-1,3,5-benzenetricarboxamide *see* Iosimide.

Hexakis(hydroxymethyl)melamine *see* Hexamethylolmelamine.

Hexakis(1-methyl-2-phenylpropyl)distannoxane *see* Neostanox.

'Hexaklor' *see* Lindane.

'Hexal' *see* Methenamine sulfosalicylate.

'Hexalet' *see* Methenamine sulfosalicylate.

'Hexalgon' *see* Norpipanone.

'Hexaloid' *see* Methenamine.

'Hexamandelate' *see* Methenamine mandelate.

Hexamarium bromide *see* Distigmine bromide.

'Hexametapol' *see* Hempa.

Hexamethonium benzenesulfonate *see* Hexamethonium besilate.

HEXAMETHONIUM BESILATE (hexametho-

269

nium benzenesulfonate; hexonium B).

HEXAMETHONIUM BROMIDE*** (hexamethylene-1,6-bis(trimethylammonium bromide); hexonium; C-6; PP-4420).

HEXAMETHONIUM NICOTINATE (hexonate).

2,2,4,6,6,8-Hexamethyl-4,8-diphenylcyclotetrasiloxane *see* Quadrosilan.

Hexamethylenamine *see* Methenamine.

Hexamethylene *see* Cyclohexane.

Hexamethylenebis[(2-carbamoyloxyethyl)dimethylammonium bromide] *see* Hexcarbacholine bromide.

1,1′-Hexamethylenebis[5-(p-chlorophenyl)biguanide] *see* Chlorhexidine.

Hexamethylene-1,6-bis[dimethyl[1-methyl-3-(2,2,6-trimethylcyclohexyl)propyl]ammonium chloride] *see* Triclobisonium chloride.

1,1′-Hexamethylenebis[5-(2-ethylhexyl)biguanide] *see* Alexidine.

Hexamethylenebis(fluoren-9-yldimethylammonium bromide) *see* Hexafluronium bromide.

α,α′-[Hexamethylenebis(iminomethylene)]bis(3,4-dihydroxybenzyl alcohol) *see* Hexoprenaline.

Hexamethylene-1,6-bis[[m-(N-methylcarbamoyloxy)phenyl]trimethylammonium bromide] *see* Hexadistigmine.

Hexamethylene-1,6-bis[1-methyl-3-(methylcarbamoyloxy)pyridinium bromide] *see* Distigmine bromide.

N,N′-Hexamethylenebis(noradrenaline) *see* Hexoprenaline.

Hexamethylene-1,6-bis(trimethylammonium bromide) *see* Hexamethonium bromide.

4,4′-Hexamethylenedioxydibenzamidine *see* Hexamidine.

6-[N,N-(1,6-Hexamethylene)formamidino]penicillanic acid *see* Mecillinam.

Hexamethylenetetramine *see* Methenamine.

1,1-Hexamethylene-4-(p-toluenesulfonyl)semicarbazide *see* Tolazamide.

HEXAMETHYLENIMINE (azacycloheptane; hexahydroazepine; perhydroazepine).

4-(N-Hexamethylenimino)-2,2-diphenylbutyramide methiodide *see* Buzepide metiodide.

2-Hexamethyleniminoethyl α-cyclohexane-3-thiopheneacetate *see* Cetiedil.

2-Hexamethyleniminoethyl α-thien-2-ylcyclohexaneacetate *see* Cetiedil.

3-Hexamethylenimino-3′-nitropropiophenone *see* Fenitron.

Hexamethylmelamine *see* Altretamine.

HEXAMETHYLOLMELAMINE (2,4,6-tris[di-(hydroxymethyl)amino]triazine; hexakis(hydroxymethyl)melamine; trimethylolmelamine; Cilag-61; 'cealysin').

Hexamethylpararosaniline *see* Crystal violet.

Hexamethylphosphamide *see* Hempa.

Hexamethylphosphoramide *see* Hempa.

Hexamethylphosphoric triamide *see* Hempa.

HEXAMETHYLTEPA (tris(2,2-dimethylaziridin-1-yl)phosphine oxide; tepa-132).

Hexamethyltetracosahexaene *see* Squalene.

3-(3,7,11,15,19,23-Hexamethyl-2,6,10,14,18,22-

tetracosahexaenyl)-2-methyl-1,4-naphthoquinone *see* Farnoquinone.

Hexamethyl violet *see* Crystal violet.

Hexamic acid *see* Cyclamic acid.

Hexamidin (tr) *see* Primidone.

HEXAMIDINE*** (4,4′-hexamethylenedioxydibenzamidine; hexamidine di(ethanol-2-sulfonate); hexamidine diisethionate; hexamidine isetionate; RP-2535).
See also under Benzydamine.

Hexamine* *see* Methenamine.

Hexanaphthene *see* Cyclohexane.

1-Hexanecarboxylic acid *see* Enanthic acid.

1,6-Hexanedicarboxylic acid *see* Suberic acid.

'Hexanicit' *see* Inositol nicotinate.

'Hexanicotol' *see* Inositol nicotinate.

'Hexanitrin' *see* Mannityl hexanitrate.

'Hexanitrol' *see* Mannityl hexanitrate.

Hexanitromannitol *see* Mannityl hexanitrate.

HEXANOIC ACID (1-pentanecarboxylic acid; butylacetic acid; caproic acid).

tert-**Hexanol carbamate** *see* Emylcamate.

HEXANOPHENONE (pentyl phenyl ketone; caprophenone).

HEXAPHOSPHAMIDE (tr) (bis(1-aziridinyl)-(cyclohexylamino)phosphine sulfide; N-cyclohexyl-N′,N′′-dimethylenephosphorothioic triamide).

'Hexapneumine' *see* Biclotymol.

HEXAPRADOL*** (α-(1-aminohexyl)benzhydrol).

HEXAPROFEN** (p-cyclohexylhydratropic acid; 2-(p-cyclohexylphenyl)propionic acid; BTS-13622).

HEXAPROPYMATE*** (1-(2-propynyl)cyclohexyl carbamate; propargylcyclohexanol carbamate; L-2013; 'merinax'; 'modirax').

Hexasone* *see* Hexasonium iodide.

HEXASONIUM IODIDE*** (2-(2-cyclohexyl-2-phenylacetoxyethyl)dimethylsulfonium iodide; (2-hydroxyethyl)dimethylsulfonium iodide α-phenylcyclohexaneacetate; hexadiphensulfonium; hexasone; 'thiospasmin').

'Hexastat' *see* Altretamine.

Hexastigmine *see* Hexaethyl tetraphosphate.

'Hexatrione' *see* Triamcinolone hexacetonide.

'Hexaverm' *see* Lindane.

'Hexayodina' *see* Prolonium iodide.

HEXAZOLE* (4-cyclohexyl-3-ethyl-1,2,4-triazole).

HEXCARBACHOLINE BROMIDE*** (hexamethylenebis[(2-carbamoyloxyethyl)dimethylammonium bromide]; choline bromide hexamethylenedicarbamate; carbolonium; hexacarbacholine; HC-606).

'Hexchloran' *see* Lindane.

HEXEDINE*** (2,6-bis(2-ethylhexyl)hexahydro-7α-methyl-1H-imidazo[1,5-c]imidazole; W-4701).

Hexemal* *see* Cyclobarbital.

Hexenal (tr) *see* Hexobarbital.

3-Hexenoic acid *see* Hydrosorbic acid.

δ-Hexenolactone *see* Parasorbic acid.

270

Hexenolide *see* Parasorbic acid.

Hex-2-enonic acid γ-lactone *see* Isoascorbic acid.

HEXESTROL*** (α,α'-diethyl-4,4'-dihydroxybibenzyl; 4,4'-(1,2-diethylene)diphenol; dihydrodiethylstilbestrol; dihydrostilbestrol; hexoestrol; sinestrol; synestrol; NSC-9894).

HEXESTROL 4,4'-DIPHOSPHATE ('cytostasin'; 'cytostatin').

HEXETHAL* (5-ethyl-5-hexylbarbituric acid; 'hebaral'; 'ortal').

HEXETIDINE*** (5-amino-1,3-bis(2-ethylhexyl)-hexahydro-5-methylpyrimidine).

'Hexetril' *see* Hexetidine.

Hexicide *see* Lindane.

HEXOBARBITAL*** (5-cyclohexen-1-yl-1,5-dimethylbarbituric acid; enhexymal; ciclobarbital; enimal; hexenal; hexobarbital sodium; methexenyl; methylcyclobarbital; methylhexabital; methylhexobarbital).

HEXOBENDINE*** (*N*,*N*'-dimethyl-*N*,*N*'-bis[3-(3,4,5-trimethoxybenzoyloxy)propyl]ethylenediamine; 3,3'-ethylenebis(methylimino)di-1-propanol 3,4,5-trimethoxybenzoate diester; hexabendine; hexobendine dihydrochloride; ST-7090).

HEXOCYCLIUM METILSULFATE*** (4-(β-cyclohexyl-β-hydroxyphenethyl)-1,1-dimethylpiperazinium methylsulfate; 'tral').

Hexoestrol* *see* Hexestrol.

'Hexo-imotryl' *see under* Benzydamine.

Hexol *see* Inositol.

'Hexomilone' *see* Hexamidine.

Hexonate (tr) *see* Hexamethonium nicotinate.

'Hexone' *see* Hexamethonium bromide.

Hexonium (tr) *see* Hexamethonium bromide.

Hexonium B (tr) *see* Hexamethonium besilate.

'Hexopal' *see* Inositol nicotinate.

HEXOPRENALINE*** (*N*,*N*'-bis[2-(3,4-dihydroxyphenyl)-2-hydroxyethyl]hexamethylenediamine; α,α'-[hexamethylenebis(iminomethylene)]bis(3,4-dihydroxybenzyl alcohol); *N*,*N*'-hexamethylenebis(noradrenaline); hexoprenalinehydrochloride; ST-1512; 'etoscol'; 'ipradol').

HEXOPYRRONIUM BROMIDE*** (3-hydroxy-1,1-dimethylpyrrolidinium bromide α-phenylcyclohexaneglycolate; AHR-483).

'Hexoral' *see* Hexetidine.

'Hex-o-san' *see* Hexachlorophene.

'Hexyclan' *see* Lindane.

'Hexydal' *see* Methenamine mandelate.

Hexydaline *see* Methenamine mandelate.

2-Hexylaminoethylcyclohexane *see* Hecylamine.

4-Hexylbenzene-1,3-diol *see* Hexylresorcinol.

HEXYLCAINE*** (2-cyclohexylamino-1-methylethyl benzoate; D-109; 'cyclaine').

1-Hexyl-3,7-dimethylxanthine *see* Pentifylline.

2-Hexyl-5-hydroxycyclopentaneheptanoic acid *see* Rosaprostol.

2-Hexyl-2-hydroxymethyl-1,3-propanediol trinicotinate *see* Hepronicate.

1-Hexyl-4-(*N*-isobutylbenzimidoyl)piperazine *see* Bucainide.

Hexyl methyl carbinol *see* 2-Octanol.

1-Hexyl-4-[*N*-(2-methylpropyl)benzimidoyl]piperazine *see* Bucainide.

o-**(Hexyloxy)benzamide** *see* Exalamide.

p-**HEXYLOXYHYDROCINNAMIC ACID** (3-(*p*-hexyloxyphenyl)propionic acid).

See also Nandrolone (*p*-hexyloxy)hydrocinnamate; Testosterone 3-*p*-(hexyloxy)hydrocinnamate.

2-(3-Hexyloxy-2-hydroxypropoxy)benzoic acid *see* Exiproben.

9-(*p*-Hexyloxyphenyl)-10-methylacridinium chloride *see* Phenacridan chloride.

3-(*p*-Hexyloxyphenyl)propionic acid *see* *p*-Hexyloxyhydrocinnamic acid.

HEXYLRESORCINOL* (4-hexylbenzene-1,3-diol; 4-hexylresorcinol; 6-hexylresorcinol; dihydroxyphenylhexane; ST-37).

See also Acrisorcin.

3-Hexyl-7,8,9,10-tetrahydro-6,6,9-trimethyl-6*H*-dibenzo[*b*,*d*]pyran-1-ol *see* Pyrahexyl.

1-Hexyltheobromine *see* Pentifylline.

Hexyphenidyl* *see* Trihexyphenidyl.

Heyden-611 *see* Stibophen potassium.

HF-241 *see* Bufeniode.

HF-1854 *see* Clozapine.

HF-1927 *see* Dibenzepin.

HF-2159 *see* Clotiapine.

HF-2333 *see* Perlapine.

HFE *see* Flurotyl.

4-HFU *see* 2-(*p*-Chlorophenoxy)acetic acid.

HFU-81723 *see* Tiamulin.

HFZ *see* Homofenazine.

HGF *see* Glucagon.

HH-50 *see* Nonivamide.

HH-197 *see* Butamirate citrate.

HHDN *see* Aldrin.

HHG *see* Human pituitary gonadotrophin.

HI-56 *see under* Ampicillin.

5-HIAA *see* 5-Hydroxyindoleacetic acid.

HIBENZATE(S)** (2-(4-hydroxybenzoyl)benzoate(s); 4'-hydroxybenzophenone-2-carboxylate(s); benzhydrate(s)).

'Hibiclens' *see* Chlorhexidine gluconate.

'Hibicon' *see* Beclamide.

'Hibiscrub' *see* Chlorhexidine gluconate.

'Hibitane' *see* Chlorhexidine.

'Hiconcil' *see* Amoxicillin.

HIDA *see* Lidofenin.

'Hidacian' *see* Cyacetacide.

'Hidrea' *see* Hydroxycarbamide.

'Hidrix' *see* Hydroxycarbamide.

'Hi-enterol' *see* Clioquinol.

'Hi-glucon' *see* Calcium glucoheptonate.

'Hilomid' *see under* Dibromsalan.

HINDERIN (4-(3,5-di-*tert*-butyl-4-hydroxyphenoxy)-3,5-diiodohydrocinnamic acid).

Hinokitiol *see* β-Thujaplicin.

'Hinosan' *see* Edifenphos.

Hiochic acid *see* Mevalonic acid.

'Hioxyl' *see* Hydrogen peroxide.

'Hippocras' *see* Magnesium orotate.

'Hippodine' *see* Sodium iodohippurate.

'Hippramine' *see* Methenamine hippurate.

'Hippuran' *see* Sodium iodohippurate.
HIPPURIC ACID (*N*-benzoylglycine).
  See also Methenamine hippurate.
'Hipputope' *see* Sodium iodohippurate (^{131}I).
'Hipputope I-125' *see* Sodium iodohippurate (^{125}I).
'Hiprex' *see* Methenamine hippurate.
Hisfen (tr) *see* Hisphen.
Hisindamone (tr) *see* Chlorisondamine chloride.
'Hismanal' *see* Astemizole.
HISPHEN (tr) (*N*-[*p*-[bis(2-chloroethyl)amino]-
  phenylacetyl]-L-histidine methyl ester; methyl 2-
  [*p*-[bis(2-chloroethyl)amino]phenylacetamido]-3-
  imidazol-4-ylpropionate; hisfen; MD-2).
'Hispril' *see* Diphenylpyraline.
'Histabromazine' *see* Bromazine.
'Histabutazine' *see* Buclizine.
Histadoxylamine *see* Doxylamine.
'Histadur' *see* Chlorpheniramine.
HISTAGLOBIN (tr) (histamine-γ-globulin com-
  plex; 'biobasal AG').
'Histalog' *see* Betazole.
'Histamethine' *see* Meclozine.
Histametizine* *see* Meclozine.
Histaminase *see* Diamine oxidase.
HISTAMINE (4-(2-aminoethyl)imidazole; 4-imi-
  dazoleethylamine).
HISTAMINE AZOPROTEIN COMPLEX ('hap-
  amine'; 'lertigon').
Histamine-γ-globulin complex *see* Histaglobin.
Histapyridamine *see* Pheniramine.
HISTAPYRRODINE*** (*N*-phenyl-*N*-(2-pyr-
  rolid-1-ylethyl)benzylamine; 1-(2-*N*-benzylanili-
  noethyl)pyrrolidine).
'Histaspan' *see* Chlorpheniramine.
Histazylamine *see* Thonzylamine.
HISTIDINE* (2-amino-3-imidazolylpropionic
  acid; glyoxaline-5-alanine; histidine hydrochlor-
  ide).
'Histoacryl' *see* Enbucrilate.
'Histol' *see* Chlorphenoxamine.
'Histostat' *see* Nitarsone.
'Histryl' *see* Diphenylpyraline.
'Hitreman' *see under* Dibromsalan.
Hiyaku *see* Ginseng.
HK-137 *see* Fendiline.
HL-267 *see* Diponium bromide.
HL-523 *see* Tiformin.
HL-781 *see* Tetroxoprim.
HL-1050 *see* Fenticlor.
HL-5746 *see* Chlorpromazine.
HLS-831 *see* Tolbutamide.
HM-11 *see* Pheniprazine.
HM-51 *see under* Co-dergocrine.
HMD *see* Oxymetholone.
HMDP *see* Oxidronic acid.
HMG *see* Human menopausal gonadotrophin.
HMPA *see* Hempa.
HMPT *see* Hempa.
HMS *see* Medrysone.
HN2 *see* Chlormethine.
HN3 *see* Trichlormethine.
Ho-.... *see also* HOE-.....
Ho-1/93 *see* Tretamine.

Ho-2374 *see* 1,2,3,4-Tetranitrocarbazole.
Ho-9980 *see* Fenpipramide.
Ho-10116 *see* Fenpiprane.
Ho-10446 *see* Hydroxypethidine.
Ho-10495 *see* Norpipanone.
Ho-10582 *see* Normethadone.
Ho-10600 *see* Phenadoxone.
Ho-10682 *see* Diphepanol.
Ho-10720 *see* Ketobemidone.
Ho-10820 *see* Methadone.
Ho-11513 *see* Pheniramine.
Ho-16842 *see* Bitoscanate.
HOE-.... *see also* Ho-.....
HOE-019 *see* Fenclexonium metilsulfate.
HOE-39-893d *see* Penbutolol.
HOE-42-440 *see* Tiamenidine.
HOE-045 *see* Articaine.
HOE-069 *see* Secretin.
HOE-095K *see* Acesulfame.
HOE-105 *see* Citenazone.
HOE-118 *see* Piretanide.
HOE-193 *see* Bisbendazole.
HOE-280 *see* Ofloxacin.
HOE-296 *see* Ciclopirox olamine.
Hoe-296V *see* Resorantel.
HOE-304 *see* Desoximetasone.
HOE-440 *see* Tiamenidine.
HOE-467 *see* Tendamistat.
HOE-471 *see* Gonadorelin.
Hoe-473 *see* Aclantate.
HOE-740 *see* Tizolemide.
HOE-757 *see* Toprilidine.
HOE-766 *see* Buserelin acetate.
HOE-881V *see* Fenbendazole.
HOE-893D *see* Penbutolol.
HOE-984 *see* Nomifensine maleate.
HOE-991 *see* Floxacrine.
HOE-8476 *see under* Clobazam.
HOE-16842 *see* Bitoscanate.
HOE-36801 *see* Etifoxine.
HOE-36984 *see* Nomifensine maleate.
HOE-40045 *see* Articaine.
'Hog' *see* Phencyclidine.
'Hoggar' *see* Doxylamine.
'Hogival' *see* Estrone acetate.
Holarrhena antidysenterica bark *see* Kurchi.
'Holfidal' *see* 1,2,3,4-Tetranitrocarbazole.
'Hollicide' *see* Bis(tributyltin) oxide.
'Holocaine' *see* Phenacaine.
'Holoxan' *see* Ifosfamide.
'Homactid' *see* Tosactide.
'Homapin' *see* Homatropine methyl bromide.
HOMARYLAMINE*** (*N*-methyl-3,4-methylene-
  dioxyphenethylamine; 4-[2-(methylamino)ethyl]-
  1,2-methylenedioxybenzene; homarylamine
  hydrochloride; MK-7).
'Homatromide' *see* Homatropine methyl bromide.
HOMATROPINE (mandelyl tropeine; tropine
  mandelate).
HOMATROPINE METHYL BROMIDE*** (8-
  methyltropinium bromide mandelate; novatrop-
  ine).
Homatropine phenacyl chloride *see* Phenactropi-

272

nium chloride.

HOMIDIUM BROMIDE*** (3,8-diamino-5-ethyl-6-phenylphenanthridinium bromide; ethidium bromide).

HOMIDIUM CHLORIDE (ethidium chloride; 'novidium').

Homoacridan see Morphanthridine.

HOMOANSERINE (N-(4-aminobutyryl)-1-methylhistidine).

Homoarterenol see Corbadrine.

HOMOCARNOSINE (N-(4-aminobutyryl)histidine).

HOMOCHLORCYCLIZINE*** (1-(p-chloro-α-phenylbenzyl)hexahydro-4-methyl-1H-1,4-diazepine; 'homoclomin').

HOMOCHOLINE ((3-hydroxypropyl)trimethylammonium ion).

'Homoclomin' see Homochlorcyclizine.

HOMOCOCAINE (ecgonine 3-benzoate 2-ethyl ester; cocaethylin).

Homocodeine see Pholcodine.

HOMOCYSTEINE (2-amino-4-mercaptobutyric acid).

HOMOCYSTINE (4,4'-dithiobis(2-aminobutyric acid)).

HOMOERIODICTYOL (4',5,7-trihydroxy-3'-methoxyflavone; eriodictyol 3'-methyl ether; eriodictyonone).

HOMOFENAZINE*** (hexahydro-4-[3-(2-trifluoromethylphenothiazin-10-yl)propyl]-(1H)1,4-diazepine-1-ethanol; 10-[2-[4-(2-hydroxyethyl)-1,4-diazacyclohept-1-yl]propyl]-2-trifluoromethylphenothiazine; 1-(2-hydroxyethyl)-4-[3-(2-trifluoromethyl)phenothiazin-10-ylpropyl]homopiperazine; homofenazine hydrochloride; HFZ; D-775).

HOMOFOLIC ACID (N-[4-[[2-(2-amino-1,4-dihydro-4-oxopteridin-6-yl)ethyl]amino]benzoyl]-L-glutamic acid; NSC-79249).

HOMOGENTISIC ACID (2,5-dihydroxy-α-toluic acid; 2,5-dihydroxyphenylacetic acid; alcapton; alcaptonic acid).

Homomenthyl salicylate see Homosalate.

Homomyrtenyloxytriethylamine see Myrtecaine.

Homopantothenic acid see Hopantenic acid.

Homophenothiazine see 10,11-Dihydrodibenzo[b,f]-[1,4]thiazepine.

Homopiperazine see Hexahydro-1H-1,4-diazepine.

Homopiperazine-1,4-dipropanol see Biopropazepan.

Homopiperidine see Azepine.

HOMOPIPRAMOL*** (4-[3-(5H-dibenz[b,f]-azepin-5-yl)propyl]-1-(2-hydroxyethyl)homopiperazine; 4-[3-(5H-dibenz[b,f]azepin-5-yl)propyl]-hexahydro-1H-1,4-diazepine-1-ethanol).

Homoproline see Pipecolic acid.

HOMOPROTOCATECHUIC ACID (3,4-dihydroxyphenylacetic acid; DOPAC).

Homopyrimidazole see 4H-Pyrido[1,2-a]pyrimidine.

HOMOSALATE*** (3,3,5-trimethylcyclohexyl salicylate; homomenthyl salicylate; 'heliophan').

p-Homosalicylic acid see 2,5-Cresotic acid.

HOMOSERINE (2-amino-4-hydroxybutyric acid).

Homosulfamide see Mafenide.

Homosulfamine see Mafenide.

Homosulfanilamide see Mafenide.

HOMOTAURINE (3-aminopropanesulfonic acid).

HOMOVANILLIC ACID (4-hydroxy-3-methoxyphenylacetic acid).

HOMOVANILLIDENEISONIAZID (N'-homovanillideneisoniazid; homovanillin isonicotinoylhydrazone).

HOMOVANILLIN (3-ethoxy-4-hydroxybenzaldehyde; ethylprotocatechuic aldehyde; ethyl protal; ethyl vanillin).

Homovanillin isonicotinoylhydrazone see Homovanillideneisoniazid.

HOMOVERATRYLAMINE (3,4-dimethoxyphenethylamine; DMPEA).

1-Homoveratrylamino-3-m-toloxy-2-propanol see Bevantolol.

HOMPRENORPHINE*** (22-cyclopropyl-7α-((R)-1-hydroxy-1-methylpropyl)-6,14-endo-ethenotetrahydrothebaine; N-cyclopropylmethyl-7α-(1(R)-hydroxy-1-methylpropyl)-6,14-endo-ethenotetrahydronorthebaine; R&S 5205-M).

'Honvan' see Fosfestrol.

HOPA see Hopantenic acid.

HOPANTENIC ACID*** (D-(+)-4-(2,4-dihydroxy-3,3-dimethylbutyramido)butyric acid; homopantothenic acid; HOPA).

HOQUIZIL*** (2-hydroxy-2-methylpropyl 4-(6,7-dimethoxyquinazolin-4-yl)piperazine-1-carboxylate; CP-14815-1).

HORDENINE (p-[2-(dimethylamino)ethyl]phenol; N,N-dimethyltyramine; p-hydroxy-N,N-dimethylphenethylamine; anhaline).

'Horizon' see Amitriptyline.

'Hormoformin' see Prasterone.

'Hormofort' see Hydroxyprogesterone caproate.

'Hormoslyr' see Chlorinated phenoxyacetic acid.

Horse chestnut see Aesculus hippocastanum.

'Hostacaine' see Butanilicaine.

'Hostaginan' see Prenylamine.

'Hostathion' see Phentriazophos.

HOX-1901 see Ethiofencarb.

HP-213 see Salinazid.

HP-494 see Fluradoline.

HP-549 see Isoxepac.

HP-1275 see Fenoxypropazine.

HP-1598 see Guanoxyfen.

HPC see Oxycinchophen.

HPEK see Tetroquinone.

HP-FSH see Human pituitary gonadotrophin.

HPG see Human pituitary gonadotrophin.

HPP see Allopurinol.

HR-376 see Clobazam.

HR-458 see Loprazolam mesilate.

HR-756 see Cefotaxime.

HR-930 see Fosazepam.

HR-4723 see Clobazam.

HS see Mustard gas.

HS-3 see Obidoxime chloride.

HS-310 see Chandonium iodide.

HS-592 see Clemastine fumarate.

Hsp-2986 see Pramiverine.

5-HT see Serotonin.
HT-11 see Cloperastine.
HT-1479 see Dimetholizine.
5-HTP see Oxitriptan.
'Hubersona' see Dexamethasone sodium *m*-sulfobenzoate.
'Hudorex' see Hydrochlorothiazide.
HUF-2446 see Clodazon.
'Humachtid' see Tosactide.
HUMAN CALCITONIN (synthetic human calcitonin; 'cibacalcin').
Human chorionic gonadotrophin see Chorionic gonadotrophin.
Human α¹⁻²⁸ corticotrophin see Tosactide.
HUMAN GROWTH HORMONE (somatropin; CB-311; 'asellacrin'; 'crescormon').
See also Growth hormone.
Human insulin* see Insulin human.
HUMAN MENOPAUSAL GONADOTROPHIN (follicle stimulating hormone, human; menotrophine; menotropins; follotropin; FSH; HMG; 'humegon'; 'pergonal'; 'pregova').
See also Urofollitrophin.
HUMAN PITUITARY GONADOTROPHIN (HHG; HP-FSH; HPG).
'Humatin' see Paromomycin.
'Humegon' see Human menopausal gonadotrophin.
'Humorsol' see Demecarium bromide.
'Humulin' see Insulin human.
'Humycin' see Paromomycin.
'Hungazin' see Atrazine.
'Hustazol' see Cloperastine.
HWA-285 see Propentofylline.
HY-185 see Carbocloral.
HYALOBIURONIC ACID (2-amino-2-deoxy-3-*O*-β-D-glucopyranosyl-D-glucose).
HYALOSIDASE** (hyaluronoglucosaminidase; GL enzyme; E.C.3.2.1.35).
HYALURONIC ACID (hyaluronate sodium; 'etamucin'; 'healon').
HYALURONIDASE(S)*** (diffusing factor; hyaluronate glycanohydrolase; lidase; lydasa; mesomucinase; spreading factor).
See also Hyalosidase.
Hyaluronoglucosaminidase see Hyalosidase.
'Hyamate' see Buramate.
'Hyamine 10X' see Methylbenzethonium chloride.
'Hyamine 1622' see Benzethonium chloride.
'Hyamine 3500' see Benzalkonium chloride.
'Hyamine 3528' see Octriphenate.
'Hybamate' see Buramate.
HYCANTHONE*** (1-[[2-(diethylamino)ethyl]-amino]-4-hydroxymethylthioxanthone; hydroxylucanthone; NSC-134434; WIN-24933).
HYCANTHONE MESILATE (hycanthone methanesulfonate; 'etrenol').
'Hycodan' see Hydrocodone.
HYDANTOIN (2,4-(3*H*,5*H*)imidazolidinedione; glycolylurea).
'Hydantoinal' see Phenytoin.
'Hydeltrasol' see Prednisolone sodium phosphate.
'Hydeltra-TBA' see Prednisolone tebutate.

'Hydergin' see Co-dergocrine.
'Hydergine' see Co-dergocrine.
HYDNOCARPIC ACID (11-(2-cyclopenten-1-yl)-undecanoic acid).
Hydnocarpylacetic acid see Chaulmoogric acid.
HYDRABAMINE PENICILLIN (*N*,*N*'-bis(dehydroabietyl)ethylenediamine-dipenicillin G; 'compocillin').
HYDRACARBAZINE*** (6-hydrazino-3-pyridinecarboxamide; Th-1325).
HYDRACARBAZINE plus PEMPIDINE (Th-2516; 'normatensyl').
'Hydracoll' see Algeldrate.
HYDRACRYLIC ACID (3-hydroxypropionic acid; ethylene lactic acid).
Hydracrylic acid β-lactone see Propiolactone.
'Hydral' see Chloral hydrate.
HYDRALAZINE*** (1-hydrazinophthalazine; apressin; hydralazine hydrochloride; hydralazine sulfate; hydrallazine; Ba-5968; C-5968).
See also under Hydrochlorothiazide.
Hydrallazine see Hydralazine.
Hydramitrazine see Meladrazine.
'Hydraphen' see Hydrargaphen.
HYDRARGAPHEN*** (phenylmercuric salt of dinaphthylmethanedisulfonic acid; 3,3'-methylenebis(2-naphthalenesulfonic acid) phenylmercuric salt; 'conotrane'; 'hydraphen'; 'instrumer').
HYDRATROPIC ACID (2-phenylpropionic acid; 2-methyl-2-phenylacetic acid; Th-4082).
Hydrazinecarboxylic acid see Carbazic acid.
Hydrazine yellow see Tartrazine.
α-Hydrazino-3,4-dihydroxy-α-methylhydrocinnamic acid see Carbidopa.
3-Hydrazino-6-[(2-hydroxypropyl)methylamino]pyridazine see Pildralazine.
Hydrazinomethyldopa see Carbidopa.
α-Hydrazino-α-methyldopa see Carbidopa.
2-Hydrazinooctane see Octamoxin.
Hydrazinophthalazine see Hydralazine.
2,2'-[(6-Hydrazinopyridazin-3-yl)imino]diethanol see Oxdralazine.
1-[(6-Hydrazinopyridazin-3-yl)methylamino]-2-propanol see Pildralazine.
6-Hydrazino-3-pyridinecarboxamide see Hydracarbazine.
1-Hydrazino-4-pyrid-4-ylmethylphthalazine see Picodralazine.
HYDRAZOBENZENE (1,2-diphenylhydrazine).
'Hydrea' see Hydroxycarbamide.
'Hydrenox' see Hydroflumethiazide.
'Hydril' see Hydrochlorothiazide.
'Hydrion' see Ambuside.
Hydroaminacridine see Tacrine.
Hydroaminacrine see Tacrine.
HYDROBENTIZIDE*** (3-[(benzylthio)methyl]-6-chloro-3,4-dihydro-2*H*-1,2,4-benzothiadiazine-7-sulfonamide 1,1-dioxide; dihydrobenzthiazide; hydrobenzthiazide).
Hydrobenzthiazide see Hydrobentizide.
Hydrobutamine see Butidrine.
Hydrochloric ether see Chloroethane.
HYDROCHLOROTHIAZIDE*** (6-chloro-3,4-

dihydro-2H-1,2,4-benzothiadiazine-7-sulfonamide 1,1-dioxide; chlorosulthiadil; dihydrochlorothiazide; hypothiazide).

HYDROCHLOROTHIAZIDE plus METOPROLOL TARTRATE ('co-betaloc').

HYDROCHLOROTHIAZIDE plus METOPROLOL TARTRATE & HYDRALAZINE ('treloc').

HYDROCHLOROTHIAZIDE plus PROPRANOLOL ('inderide').

HYDROCHLOROTHIAZIDE plus SPIRONOLACTONE ('risicordin').

HYDROCHLOROTHIAZIDE plus TRIAMTERENE ('dyazide'; 'dytenzide'; 'esiteren'; 'slimin'; 'triamthiazid'; 'turfa').

HYDROCHLOROTHIAZIDE plus TRIAMTERENE & PROPRANOLOL ('betathiazid').
See also under Amiloride; Bietaserpine; Guanethidine monosulfate; Methyldopa; Metoprolol.

HYDROCINNAMIC ACID (3-phenylpropionic acid; benzenepropanoic acid; 2-benzylacetic acid).

'Hydrocodeine' *see* Dihydrocodeine.

'Hydrocodin' *see* Dihydrocodeine.

HYDROCODONE* (4,5-epoxy-3-methoxy-N-methyl-6-oxomorphinan; dihydrocodeinone; hydrocodone bitartrate; hydrocon).

Hydrocodone O-carboxymethyloxime *see* Codoxime.

Hydrocodone enol acetate *see* Thebacon.

Hydrocon *see* Hydrocodone.

HYDROCORTAMATE* (hydrocortisone 21-(2-diethylaminoacetate); ethamicort).

HYDROCORTISONE* (11β,17α,21-trihydroxypregn-4-ene-3,20-dione; 17-hydroxycorticosterone; antiinflammatory hormone; compound F; cortisol; NSC-10483).
See also under Miconazole.

HYDROCORTISONE plus OXYTETRACYCLINE ('terra-cortril').

HYDROCORTISONE plus UREA ('hydrodexan').

HYDROCORTISONE ACETATE (hydrocortisone 21-acetate; NSC-741).

Hydrocortisone 1-[(1-benzyl-1H-indazol-3-yloxy)-acetate] *see* Bendacort.

Hydrocortisone 21-*tert*-butylacetate *see* Hydrocortisone tebutate.

HYDROCORTISONE BUTYRATE (hydrocortisone 17-butyrate; 'locoid').

HYDROCORTISONE CIPIONATE (hydrocortisone cyclopentylpropionate; hydrocortisone cypionate; 'cortef-fluid').

Hydrocortisone diethylaminoacetate *see* Hydrocortamate.

Hydrocortisone hemisuccinate *see* Hydrocortisone sodium succinate.

HYDROCORTISONE SODIUM PHOSPHATE (hydrocortisone 21-phosphate sodium; 'actocortin'; 'efcortesol').

HYDROCORTISONE SODIUM SUCCINATE (hydrocortisone 21-succinate sodium; hydrocortisone hemisuccinate; 'buccalsone'; 'corlan'; 'solucortef').

HYDROCORTISONE TEBUTATE (hydrocortisone 21-*tert*-butylacetate).

'Hydrodexan' *see* Hydrocortisone.

'Hydro-diuril' *see* Hydrochlorothiazide.

HYDROFLUMETHIAZIDE* (3,4-dihydro-6-(trifluoromethyl)-2H-1,2,4-benzothiadiazine-7-sulfonamide 1,1-dioxide; dihydroflumethiazide; metflorylthiadiazine; trifluoromethylhydrothiazide).

HYDROFLUMETHIAZIDE plus SPIRONOLACTONE ('aldactide').

Hydrogen bis(N-ethylidenethreoninato) diaquoferrate (II) *see* Ferrotrenine.

HYDROGEN PEROXIDE (hydrogen dioxide; NSC-19892).
See also Urea hydrogen peroxide.

α-Hydro-ω-hydroxypoly(oxyethylene)poly(oxypropylene) poly(oxyethylene) block copolymer(s); methyloxirane polymer(s) with oxirane *see* Poloxamer.

HYDROMADINONE* (6α-chloro-17-hydroxyprogesterone).

'Hydromedin' *see* Etacrynic acid.

'Hydromerfene' *see* Phenylmercuric borate.

'Hydromet' *see* Methyldopa.

HYDROMORPHINOL** (7,8-dihydro-14-hydroxymorphine).

HYDROMORPHONE* (4,5-epoxy-3-hydroxy-N-methyl-6-oxomorphinan; dihydromorphinone; laudacon; morficon; morphicon).

'Hydromox' *see* Quinethazone.

'Hydronol' *see* Isosorbide.

'Hydroperit' *see* Urea hydrogen peroxide.

HYDROPRENE (ethyl 3,7,11-trimethyl-2,4-dodecadienoate).

Hydropropizine *see* Dropropizine.

HYDROQUININE (dihydroquinine).

HYDROQUININE plus THIAMINE ('inhibin').

Hydroquinol *see* Hydroquinone.

HYDROQUINONE (p-dihydroxybenzene; hydroquinol; quinol).

HYDROQUINONE β-D-GLUCOPYRANOSIDE (arbutin; ursin; 'uvasol').

Hydroquinone monobenzyl ether *see* Monobenzone.

Hydroquinone monomethyl ether *see* Mequinol.

'Hydro-saluric' *see* Hydrochlorothiazide.

'Hydrosarpan' *see* Ajmalicine.

'Hydrosarpan 711' *see under* Ajmalicine.

HYDROSORBIC ACID (3-hexenoic acid).

'Hydrosulfosol' *see* Calsulfhydryl.

HYDROTALCITE* (aluminium magnesium hydroxide carbonate hydrate; 'altacite'; 'talcit'; 'ultracit').

'Hydro-tonuron' *see* Hydrochlorothiazide.

Hydrotrichlorothiazide *see* Trichlormethiazide.

Hydroxamethocaine* *see* Hydroxytetracaine.

HYDROXINDASATE* (5-acetoxy-3-(2-aminoethyl)-1-(p-methoxybenzyl)-2-methylindole; hydroxindasol acetate).

HYDROXINDASOL* (3-(2-aminoethyl)-1-(p-methoxybenzyl)-2-methylindol-5-ol; 3-(2-aminoethyl)-5-hydroxy-1-(p-methoxybenzyl)-2-methyl-

275

indole).

Hydroxindasol acetate *see* Hydroxindasate.

'Hydroxobase' *see* Hydroxocobalamin.

HYDROXOCOBALAMIN*** (α-(5,6-dimethyl-benzimidazolyl)hydroxocobamide; hydroxocobemine; hydroxycobalamin; hydroxycobalamine; OH-cobalamin; vitamin B_{12a}).

HYDROXOCOBALAMIN plus MECOBALAMIN ('lyomethyl').

Hydroxocobemine* *see* Hydroxocobalamin.

Hydroxyacetaldehyde *see* Glycolaldehyde.

N-**Hydroxyacetamide** *see* Acetohydroxamic acid.

2-(*N*-Hydroxyacetamido)fluorene *see* Fluorenyl-acetohydroxamic acid.

3′-Hydroxyacetanilide *see* Metacetamol.

4′-Hydroxyacetanilide *see* Paracetamol.

4′-Hydroxyacetanilide salicylate *see* Acetaminosalol.

2-Hydroxyacetic acid *see* Glycolic acid.

HYDROXYACETONE (1-hydroxy-2-propanone; acetol; acetyl carbinol).

Hydroxyacetone salicylate *see* Salicyl acetol.

β-Hydroxy-*p*-acetophenetidide salicylate acetate *see* Etersalate.

2-HYDROXYACETOPHENONE (benzoyl carbinol).

N-**Hydroxy-2-acetylaminofluorene** *see* Fluorenyl-acetohydroxamic acid.

β-Hydroxyalanine *see* Serine.

HYDROXYAMPHETAMINE*** (*p*-(2-amino-propyl)phenol; *p*-hydroxy-α-methylphenethyl-amine; α-methyltyramine; norpholedrine; oxamphetamine).

(+)-*m*-Hydroxyamphetamine *see* Gepefrine.

17β-Hydroxyandrosta-1,4-dien-3-one *see* Boldenone.

3α-HYDROXY-5β-ANDROSTAN-17-ONE (etiocholanone; 5-isoandrosterone).

3β-HYDROXY-5α-ANDROSTAN-17-ONE (epiandrosterone; 3-hydroxyetioallocholan-17-one; isoandrosterone).

17β-Hydroxy-5α-androstan-3-one *see* Androstanolone.

3β-Hydroxyandrost-5-en-17-one *see* Prasterone.

17α-Hydroxyandrost-4-en-3-one *see* Epitestosterone.

17β-Hydroxyandrost-4-en-3-one *see* Testosterone.

17β-Hydroxy-5α-androst-1-en-3-one 1-methoxy-cyclohexyl ether *see* Mesabolone.

p-**Hydroxyanisole** *see* Mequinol.

9-Hydroxyanthracene *see* 9-Anthrol.

HYDROXYAPATITE* (calcium phosphate hydroxide; decacalcium dihydroxide hexakis(orthophosphate); durapatite; hydroxylapatite; WIN-40350).

HYDROXYAPATITE plus peptide mixture ('ossopan').

3α-Hydroxy-8-azabicyclo[3.2.1]octane-8-carboxylic acid phenyl ester carbazate (ester) *see* Tropabazate.

5-Hydroxybarbituric acid *see* Dialuric acid.

o-**Hydroxybenzaldehyde** *see* Salicylaldehyde.

p-**Hydroxybenzaldehyde isonicotinoylhydrazone** *see*

N′-(*p*-Hydroxybenzylidene)isoniazide.

o-**Hydroxybenzamide** *see* Salicylamide.

o-**Hydroxybenzoic acid** *see* Salicylic acid.

p-**Hydroxybenzoic acid esters** *see* Parabens.

p-**Hydroxybenzoic acid ethyl ester 6-guanidinohexanoate** *see* Gabexate.

4′-Hydroxybenzophenone-2-carboxylate(s) *see* Hibenzate(s).

4-Hydroxy-1,3-benzoxathiol-2-one *see* Tioxolone.

2-(4-Hydroxybenzoyl)benzoic acid, esters and salts *see* Hibenzate(s).

O-(2-**Hydroxybenzoyl)salicylic acid** *see* Salsalate.

o-**Hydroxybenzyl alcohol** *see* Salicyl alcohol.

p-[(*o*-**Hydroxybenzylidene)imino]phenetole** *see* Salicylidene-*p*-phenetidine.

N′-(*p*-**HYDROXYBENZYLIDENE)ISONIAZID** (*p*-hydroxybenzaldehyde isonicotinoylhydrazone; 'flavoteben').

p-**Hydroxybenzylpenicillin** *see* Penicillin X.

cis-1-**Hydroxy[bicyclohexyl]-2-carboxylic acid 2-(diethylamino)-1-methylethyl ester** *see* Rociverine.

2-Hydroxybiphenyl *see* *o*-Phenylphenol.

2-[(2′-Hydroxybiphenyl-4-yl)carbonyl]benzoic acid, esters and salts *see* Fendizoate(s).

3-Hydroxy-4,5-bis(hydroxymethyl)-α-picoline *see* Pyridoxine.

Hydroxybis(*p*-isobutylhydratropato)aluminium *see* Ibuprofen aluminum.

Hydroxybis[α-methyl-4-(2-methylpropyl)benzene-acetato-*O*]aluminium *see* Ibuprofen aluminum.

1-(2-*endo*-Hydroxy-3-*endo*-bornyl)-3-(*p*-toluenesulfonyl)urea *see* Glibornuride.

Hydroxybutanedioic acid *see* Malic acid.

3-Hydroxy-2-butanone *see* Acetoin.

1-(3-Hydroxybutyl)-4-[6-(6-methoxyquinolin-8-yl-amino)hexyl]piperazine *see* Moxipraquine.

(4-Hydroxy-2-butynyl)trimethylammonium chloride *m*-chlorophenylcarbamate *see* [4-(*m*-Chlorophenylcarbamoyloxy)-2-butynyl]trimethylammonium chloride.

4-Hydroxybutyraldehyde *see* Aldol.

4-HYDROXYBUTYRIC ACID (GHBA; GOH-BA).

4-Hydroxybutyric acid acetate *see* Aceburic acid.

4-Hydroxybutyric acid sodium salt *see* Oxybate sodium.

3-Hydroxy-*p*-butyrophenetidide *see* Bucetin.

HYDROXYCARBAMIDE*** (hydroxyurea; NSC-32065; SQ-1089).

HYDROXYCHLOROQUINE*** (7-chloro-4-[4-[ethyl(2-hydroxyethyl)amino]-1-methylbutyl-amino]quinoline; oxichlorochin; oxychloroquine; SN-8137).

3-Hydroxycholanic acid *see* Lithocholic acid.

1α-Hydroxycholecalciferol *see* Alfacalcidol.

25-Hydroxycholecalciferol *see* 25-Hydroxycolecalciferol.

24-HYDROXYCHOLEST-5-EN-3-ONE (cerebrostenolone).

24-Hydroxycholesterol *see* Cholest-5-ene-3β,24-diol.

6′-Hydroxycinchonidine *see* Cupreine.

6′-Hydroxycinchonine *see* Cupreidine.

276

3-Hydroxycinchophen *see* Oxycinchophen.

cis-o-**HYDROXYCINNAMIC ACID** (coumarinic acid).

trans-o-**HYDROXYCINNAMIC ACID** (*o*-coumaric acid).

p-**HYDROXYCINNAMIC ACID** (*p*-coumaric acid).

Hydroxycobalamin *see* Hydroxocobalamin.

Hydroxycodeine *see* Neopine.

1α-Hydroxycolecalciferol *see* Alfacalcidol.

25-HYDROXYCOLECALCIFEROL (25-hydroxycholecalciferol; vitamin D$_4$; HCC; 'delakmin').

17-Hydroxycorticosterone *see* Hydrocortisone.

7-Hydroxycoumarin *see* Umbelliferone.

3-Hydroxy-*cis*-crotonic acid dimethyl phosphate methyl ester *see* Mevinphos.

2-Hydroxy-2,4,6-cycloheptatrien-1-one *see* Tropolone.

4-Hydroxy-2,5-cyclohexadien-1-one-4-sulfonic acid diethylamine salt *see* Etamsylate.

2-Hydroxy-1,1,3,3-cyclohexanetetramethanol tetranicotinate *see* Nicomol.

HYDROXYCYCLOHEXIMIDE (3-[2-hydroxy-2-(5-hydroxy-3,5-dimethyl-2-oxocyclohexyl)ethyl]-glutarimide; NSC-39147; U-9361; 'resactin A'; 'streptovitacin A').

2-(1-Hydroxycyclohexyl)butyric acid *see* Cyclobutyrol.

6β-Hydroxy-3,5-cyclopregnan-20-one *see* Cyclopregnol.

3-Hydroxy-2-*p*-cymenecarboxylic acid *see* *o*-Thymotic acid.

14-Hydroxydaunorubicin *see* Doxorubicin.

HYDROXY-DDD (1,1-dichloro-2,2-bis(*p*-chlorophenyl)ethanol; 4,4′-dichloro-α-dichloromethylbenzhydrol; FW-152).

Hydroxy-DDT *see* Dicofol.

N-(3-Hydroxydecanoyl)serine *see* Serratamic acid.

2-(10-Hydroxydecyl)-5,6-dimethoxy-3-methyl-*p*-benzoquinone *see* Idebenone.

m-Hydroxydexamphetamine *see* Gepefrine.

12-Hydroxydigitoxin *see* Digoxin.

14-Hydroxydihydrocodeinone *see* Oxycodone.

Hydroxydihydromorphinone *see* Oxymorphone.

3-Hydroxy-4,5-di(hydroxymethyl)-2-methylpyridine *see* Pyridoxine.

4-Hydroxy-3,5-diiodobenzonitrile *see* Ioxynil.

3-(4-Hydroxy-3,5-diiodobenzoyl)-2,5-dimethylfuran *see* Furidarone.

4-Hydroxy-3,5-diiodo-α-[1-(1-methyl-3-phenylpropylamino)ethyl]benzyl alcohol *see* Bufeniode.

3-[4-(4-Hydroxy-3,5-diiodophenoxy)-3,5-diiodophenyl]alanine *see* Dextrothyroxine; Levothyroxine; Thyroxine.

4-Hydroxy-3,5-diiodophenylalanine *see* 3,5-Diiodotyrosine.

3-(4-Hydroxy-3,5-diiodophenyl)-β-alanine *see* Betazine.

4-Hydroxy-6,7-diisobutoxyquinoline-3-carboxylic acid ethyl ester *see* Buquinolate.

4-Hydroxy-6,7-diisopropoxy-3-quinolinecarboxylic acid methyl ester *see* Proquinolate.

4-Hydroxy-3,5-dimethoxybenzoic acid *see* Syringic acid.

4-Hydroxy-3,5-dimethoxy-α-methylaminomethylbenzyl alcohol *see* Dimetofrine.

1-(4-Hydroxy-3,5-dimethoxyphenyl)-2-methylaminoethanol *see* Dimetofrine.

18β-Hydroxy-11,17α-dimethoxy-3β,20α-yohimban-16β-carboxylic acid *see* Reserpic acid.

17β-HYDROXY-1α,17-DIMETHYLANDROSTAN-3-ONE (dimethylandrostanolone; 'demalon').

17β-Hydroxy-2α,17-dimethyl-5α-androstan-3-one azine *see* Mebolazine.

17β-Hydroxy-7α,17-dimethylandrost-4-en-3-one *see* Bolasterone.

17β-Hydroxy-7β,17-dimethylandrost-4-en-3-one *see* Calusterone.

4-Hydroxy-*N*,*N*-dimethylbutyramide ester of clofibric acid *see* Clofibride.

3-Hydroxy-*N*,*N*-dimethyl-*cis*-crotonamide dimethyl phosphate *see* Dicrotophos.

1-Hydroxy-5,5-dimethyl-1-cyclohexen-3-one dimethylcarbamate *see* Dimetan.

17-Hydroxy-6β,7β:15β,16β-dimethylene-3-oxo-17α-pregna-1,4-diene-21-carboxylic acid γ-lactone *see* Spirorenone.

3-Hydroxy-6,*N*-dimethyl-4,5-epoxymorphin-6-ene *see* Methyldesorphine.

17β-Hydroxy-7α,17-dimethylestr-4-en-3-one *see* Mibolerone.

17β-Hydroxy-16,16-dimethylestr-4-en-3-one *see* Metogest.

2-Hydroxy-*N*,*N*-dimethylethylamine camphocarbonate *see* Ethyl camphoramine.

α-[[(2-Hydroxy-1,1-dimethylethyl)amino]methyl]-benzyl alcohol *see* Fepradinol.

(−)-5-(1-Hydroxy-1,5-dimethylhex-4-en-1-yl)-2-methyl-1-cyclohexene *see* Levomenol.

5-Hydroxy-1,2-dimethylindole-3-carboxylic acid ethyl ester *see* Mecarbine.

2′-Hydroxy-5,9-dimethyl-2-(3-methyl-2-butenyl)-6,7-benzomorphan *see* Pentazocine.

2-Hydroxy-*N*,*N*-dimethyl-*N*-(1-methylethyl)-3-(1-naphthalenyloxy)-1-propanaminium chloride *see* Pranolium chloride.

11α-Hydroxy-17,17-dimethyl-18-norandrosta-4,13-dien-3-one *see* Nordinone.

7-[2-(3-Hydroxy-4,4-dimethyl-1-octenyl)-3-methyl-5-oxocyclopentyl]-5-heptenoic acid *see* Trimoprostil.

5-(3-Hydroxy-4,4-dimethyl-1-pentenyl)-1,3-benzodioxole *see* Stiripentol.

p-Hydroxy-*N*,*N*-dimethylphenethylamine *see* Hordenine.

2′-Hydroxy-5,9-dimethyl-2-phenethyl-6,7-benzomorphan *see* Phenazocine.

3-Hydroxy-1,1-dimethylpiperidinium bromide benzilate *see* Mepenzolate bromide.

4-Hydroxy-1,1-dimethylpiperidinium bromide benzilate *see* Parapenzolate bromide.

4-Hydroxy-1,1-dimethylpiperidinium methylsulfate 3-methyl-2-phenylvalerate ester *see* Pentapiperium metilsulfate.

3β-Hydroxy-6α,16α-dimethyl-4-pregnen-20-one *see*

Dimepregnen.

11β-Hydroxy-16α,17α-dimethyl-17-propionylandrosta-1,4-dien-3-one *see* Rimexolone.

α-(1-Hydroxy-2,2-dimethylpropyl)-3,4-(methylenedioxy)styrene *see* Stiripentol.

5-Hydroxy-4,6-dimethyl-3-pyridinemethanol *see* Deoxypyridoxine.

1-Hydroxy-4,6-dimethylpyridin-2(1*H***)-one** *see* Metipirox.

3-Hydroxy-1,1-dimethylpyrrolidinium bromide benzilate *see* Benzopyrronium bromide.

erythro-**3-Hydroxy-1,1-dimethylpyrrolidinium bromide α-cyclopentylmandelate** *see* Ritropirronium bromide.

3-Hydroxy-1,1-dimethylpyrrolidinium bromide α-phenylcyclohexaneglycolate *see* Hexopyrronium bromide.

3-Hydroxy-1,1-dimethylpyrrolidinium bromide α-phenylcyclopentaneglycolate *see* Glycopyrronium bromide.

3-Hydroxy-1,1-dimethylpyrrolidinium bromide α-phenyl-2-thiopheneglycolate *see* Heteronium bromide.

3-Hydroxy-6,7-dimethyl-2-(1-ribityloxy)quinoxaline *see* Flavoviolet.

4-Hydroxy-*N*,*N*-dimethyltryptamine *see* Psilocin.

5-Hydroxy-*N*,*N*-dimethyltryptamine *see* Bufotenine.

HYDROXYDIONE SODIUM SUCCINATE***
(21-hydroxy-5β-pregnane-3,20-dione 21-(sodium hemisuccinate); sodium 21-(3-carboxypropionyloxy)pregnane-3,20-dione; pregnocin; 'presuren'; 'viadril').

7-Hydroxy-5,9-dioxatridecane *see* Dibuprol.

2-[[(3-Hydroxy-11,29-dioxoolean-12-en-29-yl)oxy]methyl]-1,1-dimethylpyrrolidinium methylsulfate *see* Roxolonium metilsulfate.

2-Hydroxy-1,2-diphenylethanone *see* Benzoin.

trans-**[4-(Hydroxydi-2-thienylmethyl)cyclohexyl]trimethylammonium bromide** *see* Thihexinol methylbromide.

6-HYDROXYDOPA (2,4,5-trihydroxyphenylalanine).

6-Hydroxydopamine *see* Oxidopamine.

p-**HYDROXYEPHEDRINE** (*p*-hydroxy-α-(1-methylaminoethyl)benzyl alcohol; 1-(*p*-hydroxyphenyl)-2-methylamino-1-propanol; 'methylsympatol'; 'suprifen').

3-Hydroxyestra-1,3,5(10),7-tetraen-17-one *see* Equilin.

3-Hydroxyestra-1,3,5(10)-trien-17-one *see* Estrone.

17β-Hydroxyestra-4,9,11-trien-3-one *see* Trenbolone.

17β-Hydroxyestr-4-en-3-one *see* Nandrolone.

17β-Hydroxyestr-4-en-3-one 1-adamantanecarboxylate *see* Bolmantalate.

2-Hydroxyethanesulfonic acid *see* Isethionic acid.

2-Hydroxyethanethiol *see* 2-Mercaptoethanol.

8α-Hydroxy-6,10-ethano-5-azoniaspiro-[4.5]decane chloride benzilate *see* Trospium chloride.

1-[2-(2-Hydroxyethoxy)ethyl]-4-phenylisonipecotic acid ethyl ester *see* Etoxeridine.

1-[2-(2-Hydroxyethoxy)ethyl]-4-phenyl-4-propionylpiperidine *see* Droxypropine.

10-[3-[4-(2-(2-Hydroxyethoxy)ethyl)piperazin-1-yl]-2-methylpropyl]phenothiazine *see* Dixyrazine.

2-(2-Hydroxyethoxy)ethyl *N*-(α,α,α-trifluoro-*m*-tolyl)anthranilate *see* Etofenamate.

4-(2-Hydroxyethoxy)-3-methoxycinnamic acid *see* Cinametic acid.

9-[(2-Hydroxyethoxy)methyl]guanine *see* Aciclovir.

10-[3-[4-(2-Hydroxyethoxy)piperid-1-yl]propyl]-2-(trifluoromethyl)phenothiazine *see* Flupimazine.

4-(2-Hydroxyethoxy)-1-[3-[2-(trifluoromethyl)phenothiazin-10-yl]propyl]piperidine *see* Flupimazine.

***N*-(2-Hydroxyethyl)acetamide 2-(*p*-chlorophenyl)-2-(α,α,α-trifluoro-*m*-toloxy)acetate ester** *see* Halofenate.

3′-[*N*-(2-Hydroxyethyl)acetamido]-2′,4′,6′-triiodo-5′-(methylcarbamoyl)-D-gluconanilide *see* Ioglucol.

1-(2-Hydroxyethyl)aziridine *see* 1-Aziridineethanol.

2-Hydroxyethyl benzylcarbamate *see* Buramate.

6-(1-Hydroxyethyl)bicyclo[2.2.1]hept-2-ene *see* 6-(1-Hydroxyethyl)norbornene.

1-[(2-Hydroxyethyl)carbamoylmethyl]pyridinium chloride laurate *see* Lapirium chloride.

3′-[(2-Hydroxyethyl)carbamoyl]-2′,4′,6′-triiodo-5′-(*N*-methylacetamido)-D-gluconanilide *see* Ioglunide.

***N*-(2-Hydroxyethyl)cinnamamide** *see* Idrocilamide.

10-[2-[4-(2-Hydroxyethyl)-1,4-diazacyclohept-1-yl]propyl]-2-trifluoromethylphenothiazine *see* Homofenazine.

[4-(2-Hydroxyethyl)diethylenediaminomethyl]tetracycline *see* Pipacycline.

(2-Hydroxyethyl)diisopropylmethylammonium bromide xanthene-9-carboxylate *see* Propantheline bromide.

5-(2-Hydroxyethyl)-1,3-dimethoxybenzene *see* Floverine.

(2-Hydroxyethyl)dimethyl-[1-(10-phenothiazinylmethyl)ethyl]ammonium chloride *see* Promethazine hydroxyethyl chloride.

(2-Hydroxyethyl)dimethylsulfonium chloride succinylbis ester *see* Succinyldisulfocholine.

(2-Hydroxyethyl)dimethylsulfonium iodide α-phenylcyclohexaneacetate *see* Hexasonium iodide.

(2-Hydroxyethyl)dimethylsulfonium iodide α-phenylcyclohexaneglycolate *see* Oxysonium iodide.

2-(1-Hydroxyethyl)-β-(hydroxymethyl)-3-methyl-5-benzofuranacrylic acid γ-lactone hydrogen succinate *see* Benfurodil hemisuccinate.

(1-Hydroxyethylidene)diphosphonic acid *see* Etidronic acid.

3-(2-Hydroxyethylidene)-7-oxo-4-oxa-1-azabicyclo[3.2.0]heptane-2-carboxylic acid *see* Clavulanic acid.

2,2′-(2-Hydroxyethylimino)bis-[*N*-(α,α-dimethylphenethyl)-*N*-methylacetamide] *see* Oxetacaine.

6-(1-Hydroxyethyl)-3-[[2-[(iminomethyl)amino]ethyl]thio]-7-oxo-1-azabicyclo[3.2.0]hept-2-ene-2-carboxylic acid *see* Imipenem.

3-(2-Hydroxyethyl)indole *see* Tryptophol.

8-[(2-Hydroxyethyl)methylamino]caffeine *see* Cafaminol.

1-(2-Hydroxyethyl)-1-methylguanidine dihydrogen phosphate ester *see* Creatinolfosfate.

1-(2-Hydroxyethyl)-2-methyl-5-nitroimidazole *see* Metronidazole.

1-(2-Hydroxyethyl)-1-methylpyrrolidinium iodide benzilate *see* Etipirium iodide.

N-(2-Hydroxyethyl)-3-methyl-2-quinoxalinecarboxamide 1,4-dioxide *see* Olaquindox.

2-Hydroxyethyl 3-methylquinoxaline-2-carboxylate 2,4-dioxide *see* Temodox.

N-(2-Hydroxyethyl)nicotinamide esters *see* Nicafenine; Nicorandil; Picafibrate.

2-Hydroxyethyl nicotinate 2-(*p*-chlorophenoxy)-2-methylpropionate ester *see* Etofibrate.

1-(2-Hydroxyethyl)-3-(5-nitrofurfurylideneamino)-2-imidazolidinone *see* Nifurdazil.

N-(2-Hydroxyethyl)-α-(5-nitro-2-furyl)nitrone *see* Nifuratrone.

6-(1-HYDROXYETHYL)NORBORNENE (6-(1-hydroxyethyl)bicyclo[2.2.1]hept-2-ene; hydroxyethylnorcamphene).

6-(1-HYDROXYETHYL)NORBORNENE ACID SUCCINATE ('felogen').

Hydroxyethylnorcamphene *see* 6-(1-Hydroxyethyl)-norbornene.

2,2′-[[3-(2-Hydroxyethyl)octadecylaminopropyl]imino]diethanol dihydrofluoride *see* Olaflur.

N-(2-Hydroxyethyl)palmitamide *see* Palmidrol.

1-(2-Hydroxyethyl)pipecolic acid 2,6-dimethylanilide *see* Droxicainide.

1-(2-Hydroxyethyl)-2′,6′-pipecoxylidide *see* Droxicainide.

N-[[4-(2-Hydroxyethyl)piperazin-1-yl]carboxymethyl]tetracycline *see* Apicycline.

2-[4-(2-Hydroxyethyl)piperazin-1-yl]ethyl 2-trifluoromethylphenothiazin-10-yl ketone *see* Ftorpropazine.

N-[4-(2-Hydroxyethyl)piperazin-1-yl-methyl]tetracycline *see* Pipacycline.

10-[3-[4-(2-Hydroxyethyl)piperazin-1-yl]propionyl]-2-trifluoromethylphenothiazine *see* Ftorpropazine.

3-[4-(2-Hydroxyethyl)piperazin-1-yl]propyl DL-4-benzamido-*N*,*N*-dipropylglutaramate 1-(*p*-chlorobenzoyl)-5-methoxy-2-methylindole-3-acetate *see* Proglumetacin.

5-[3-[3-(2-Hydroxyethyl)piperazin-1-yl]propyl]dibenz[*b*,*f*]azepine *see* Opipramol.

9-[3-[4-(2-Hydroxyethyl)piperazin-1-yl]propylidene]-2-trifluoromethylthioxanthene *see* Flupentixol.

10-[3-[4-(2-Hydroxyethyl)piperazin-1-yl]propyl]-2-propionylphenothiazine *see* Carfenazine.

10-[3-[4-(2-Hydroxyethyl)piperazin-1-yl]propyl]-2-(trifluoromethyl)phenothiazine *see* Fluphenazine.

4-[3-[4-(2-Hydroxyethyl)piperazin-1-yl]propyl]-6-trifluoromethyl-4*H*-thieno-[2,3-*b*][1,4]benzothiazine *see* Flutizenol.

10-[4-[3-(2-Hydroxyethyl)piperid-1-yl]propyl]-*N*,*N*-dimethylphenothiazine 2-sulfonamide *see* Pipotiazine.

10-[3-[4-(2-Hydroxyethyl)piperid-1-yl]propyl]phenothiazin-2-yl methyl ketone *see* Piperacetazine.

N-Hydroxyethylpromethazine *see* Promethazine hydroxyethyl chloride.

1-(2-Hydroxyethyl)-4-[3-(pyrido[3,2-*b*]-[1,4]benzothiazin-10-yl)propyl]piperazine *see* Oxypendyl.

7-*O*-(2-Hydroxyethyl)rutoside *see* Monoxerutin.

2-Hydroxyethyl salicylate *see* Glycol salicylate.

2-Hydroxyethyl starch *see* Hetastarch.

2-Hydroxyethyl *p*-sulfamoylcarbanilate *see* Sulocarbilate.

4-(2-Hydroxyethyl)-α-tetracyclinyl-1-piperazineacetic acid *see* Apicycline.

N-(2-Hydroxyethyl)tetradecylamine lactate *see* Myralact.

7-(2-Hydroxyethyl)theophylline *see* Etofylline.

1-(2-Hydroxyethyl)-4-[3-(2-trifluoromethyl)phenothiazin-10-ylpropyl]homopiperazine *see* Homofenazine.

N-(2-Hydroxyethyl)-2,4,6-triiodo-5-[2-[2,4,6-triiodo-3-(*N*-methylacetamido)-5-(methylcarbamoyl)-benzamido]acetamido]isophthalamic acid *see* Ioxaglic acid.

(2-Hydroxyethyl)trimethylammonium chloride succinate *see* Suxamethonium chloride.

(2-Hydroxyethyl)trimethylammonium hydroxide *see* Choline.

(2-Hydroxyethyl)trimethylammonium iodide benzilate *see* Metocinium iodide.

1-(2-Hydroxyethyl)-1,2,5-trimethylpyrrolidinium bromide benzilate *see* Dimetipirium bromide.

3-Hydroxyetioallocholan-17-one *see* 3β-Hydroxy-5α-androstan-17-one.

8β-Hydroxy-4α*H*-eudesm-5-en-12-oic acid γ-lactone *see* Alantolactone.

5-Hydroxyflavone *see* Primuletin.

9-Hydroxy-9*H*-fluorene-9-carboxylic acid *see* Flurenol.

[3-(*N*-Hydroxyformamido)propyl]phosphonic acid *see* Fosmidomycin.

4-Hydroxy-4*H*-furo[3,2-*c*]pyran-2(6*H*)-one *see* Patulin.

3-HydroxyGABA *see* 4-Amino-3-hydroxybutyric acid.

Hydroxyhemin *see* Hematin.

2-(7-Hydroxyheptyl)-3-(3-oxo-4-phenoxybutyl)-cyclopentanone *see* Oxoprostol.

5-Hydroxy-2-hexenoic acid lactone *see* Parasorbic acid.

p-Hydroxyhydrocinnamic acid *see* Phloretic acid.

p-Hydroxyhydrocinnamic acid *trans*-4-(aminomethyl)cyclohexanecarboxylate *see* Cetraxate.

7-[3-Hydroxy-2-(3-hydroxy-4,4-dimethyl-1-octenyl)-5-methylenecyclopentyl]-5-heptenoic acid *see* Meteneprost.

7-[3-Hydroxy-2-(3-hydroxy-4,4-dimethyl-1-octenyl)-5-oxocyclopentyl]-2-heptenoic acid methyl ester *see* Gemeprost.

3-[2-Hydroxy-2-(5-hydroxy-3,5-dimethyl-2-oxocyclohexyl)ethyl]glutarimide *see* Hydroxycycloheximide.

7-[2-Hydroxy-3-[(2-hydroxyethyl)methylamino]-propyl]theophylline compound with 2-(*p*-chloro-

279

phenoxy)-2-methylpropionic acid *see* Xantifibrate.

7-[2-Hydroxy-3-[(2-hydroxyethyl)methylamino]-propyl]theophylline compound with nicotinic acid *see* Xantinol nicotinate.

4-Hydroxy-2-(7-hydroxyheptyl)-3-(4-hydroxy-4-methyl-1-octenyl)cyclopentanone *see* Rioprostil.

8-Hydroxy-5-[(1-hydroxy-2-isopropylamino)butyl]-carbostyril *see* Procaterol.

2′-Hydroxy-5′-(1-hydroxy-2-isopropylaminoethyl)-methanesulfonanilide *see* Soterenol.

4-Hydroxy-9-[2-hydroxy-3-(isopropylamino)prop-oxy]-7-methyl-5*H*-furo[3,2-*g*][1]benzopyran-5-one *see* Iprocrolol.

o-(6-Hydroxy-5-hydroxymercuri-2,7-diiodo-3-oxo-(3*H*)xanthen-9-yl)benzenesulfonic acid sodium salt *see* Meralein sodium.

o-[[2-Hydroxy-3-(hydroxymercuri)propyl]carbamoyl]phenoxyacetic acid *see* Mercuderamide.

2′-Hydroxy-5′-[1-hydroxy-2-[(*p*-methoxy-α-methyl-phenethyl)amino]ethyl]formanilide *see* Formoterol.

2′-Hydroxy-5′-[1-hydroxy-2-(*p*-methoxyphenethyl-amino)propyl]methanesulfonanilide *see* Mesuprine.

17β-Hydroxy-2-hydroxymethylene-17-methyl-5α-androstan-3-one *see* Oxymetholone.

2-Hydroxy-1-(hydroxymethyl)ethyl acetylsalicylate diclofibrate *see* Salafibrate.

8-Hydroxy-5-[1-hydroxy-2-[(1-methylethyl)amino]-butyl]-2(1*H*)-quinolinone *see* Procaterol.

2-Hydroxy-1-(hydroxymethyl)ethyl salicylate 2-acetate bis[2-(*p*-chlorophenoxy)-2-methylpropion-ate] *see* Salafibrate.

3-Hydroxy-2-[(2-hydroxy-2-methylheptyl)thio]-5-oxocyclopentaneheptanoic acid ester with 4′-hydroxybenzanilide *see* Tiprostanide.

7-[3-Hydroxy-2-[(2-hydroxy-2-methylheptyl)thio]-5-oxocyclopentyl]heptanoic acid *p*-benzamidophenyl ester *see* Tiprostanide.

3-Hydroxy-5-(hydroxymethyl)-2-methylisonicotinaldehyde *see* Pyridoxal.

3-Hydroxy-5-(hydroxymethyl)-2-methylisonicotinic acid *see* Pyridoxic acid.

2-[(5-HYDROXY-4-HYDROXYMETHYL-6-METHYLPYRID-3-YL)METHOXY]GLY-COLIC ACID (5-hydroxy-6-methyl-3,4-pyrid-inedimethanol 3-ether with glycolic acid; pyridoxine 3-ether with glycolic acid).
See also Piridoxilate.

3-Hydroxy-2-(4-hydroxy-4-methyl-1-octenyl)-5-oxocyclopentaneheptanoic acid methyl ester *see* Misoprostol.

7-[3-Hydroxy-2-[(3*R*)-(3-hydroxy-3-methyl-1-octen-yl)]-5-oxocyclopentyl]-5-heptenoic acid *see* Arbaprostil.

7-[3-Hydroxy-2-(4-hydroxy-4-methyl-1-octenyl)-5-oxocyclopentyl]-4-heptenoic acid methyl ester *see* Enisoprost.

1-(4-Hydroxy-3-hydroxymethylphenyl)-2-(4-meth-oxy-α-methylphenethylamino)ethanol *see* Salmefamol.

5-Hydroxy-2-hydroxymethyl-4-pyrone *see* Kojic

acid.

3-Hydroxy-2-[(*E*)-(3*S*)-3-hydroxy-1-octenyl]-5-oxo-cyclopentaneheptanoic acid *see* Alprostadil.

7-[3α-Hydroxy-2β-[3(*S*)-hydroxy-*trans*-oct-1-enyl]-5-oxo-cyclopent-1-yl]-*cis*-hept-5-enoic acid *see* Dinoprostone.

4-Hydroxy-3-(1-hydroxypentyl)benzoic acid *see* Fepentolic acid.

p-Hydroxy-α-[1-(*p*-hydroxyphenethylamino)ethyl]-benzyl alcohol *see* Ritodrine.

7-[3-Hydroxy-2-(3-hydroxy-4-phenoxy-1-butenyl)-5-oxocyclopentyl]-4,5-heptadienoic acid methyl ester *see* Enprostil.

7-[3-Hydroxy-2-(3-hydroxy-4-phenoxy-1-butenyl)-5-oxocyclopentyl]-*N*-(methylsulfonyl)-5-hepten-amide *see* Sulprostone.

N-[2-[[2-Hydroxy-3-(*p*-hydroxyphenoxy)propyl]-amino]ethyl]morpholine-4-carboxamide *see* Xamoterol.

p-Hydroxy-α-[[[3-(*p*-hydroxyphenyl)-1-methylprop-yl]amino]methyl]benzyl alcohol *see* Butopamine.

5-Hydroxyimidazole-4-carboxamide riboside *see* Mizoribine.

Hydroxyimine *see* 1-Aziridineethanol.

2-[*p*-[3-(Hydroxyimino)cyclohexyl]phenyl]propionic acid *see* Ximoprofen.

4-[[*p*-[1-(Hydroxyimino)ethyl]phenoxy]acetyl]mor-pholine *see* Mofoxime.

1-[[*p*-[1-(Hydroxyimino)ethyl]phenoxy]acetyl]pip-eridine *see* Pifoxime.

2-[(Hydroxyimino)methyl]-1-methylpyridinium chloride *see* Pralidoxime chloride.

2-[(Hydroxyimino)methyl]-1-methylpyridinium iod-ide *see* Pralidoxime iodide.

3-Hydroxyindole *see* Indoxyl.

5-HYDROXYINDOLEACETIC ACID (5-hydr-oxyindol-3-ylacetic acid; 5-HIAA).

o-[2-Hydroxy-3-[(2-indol-3-yl-1,1-dimethylethyl)-amino]propoxy]benzonitrile *see* Bucindolol.

4-Hydroxy-3-iodo-5-nitrobenzonitrile *see* Nitroxinil.

4-(4-Hydroxy-3-iodophenoxy)-3,5-diiodobenzoic acid acetate *see* Acetiromate.

4-(4-Hydroxy-3-iodophenoxy)-3,5-diiodohydrocin-namic acid *see* Thyropropic acid.

[4-(4-Hydroxy-3-iodophenoxy)-3,5-diiodophenyl]-acetic acid *see* Tiratricol.

3-[4-(4-Hydroxy-3-iodophenoxy)-3,5-diiodophenyl]-alanine *see* Detrothyronine; Liothyronine; Rathyronine.

3-[4-(4-Hydroxy-3-iodophenoxy)-3,5-diiodophenyl]-propionic acid *see* Thyropropic acid.

1-(2-Hydroxy-3-isobutoxypropyl)-4-methylpiperaz-ine 2-phenylbutyrate ester *see* Fenetradil.

8-Hydroxyisocoumarin-4-yl hydroxymethyl ketone *see* Oosponol.

4-(2-Hydroxy-3-isopentyloxypropyl)morpholine 3,4,5-trimethoxybenzoate *see* Amoproxan.

4′-[1-Hydroxy-2-(isopropylamino)ethyl]methanesul-fonanilide *see* Sotalol.

5-[1-Hydroxy-2-(isopropylamino)ethyl]-8-quinolinol *see* Quinprenaline.

m-Hydroxy-α-[(isopropylamino)methyl]benzyl alco-

hol *see* Metaterol.
p-Hydroxy-α-[(isopropylamino)methyl]benzyl alcohol *see* Deterenol.
4-Hydroxy-α-[(isopropylamino)methyl]-3-(methanesulfonamido)benzyl alcohol *see* Soterenol.
4-Hydroxy-α-[(isopropylamino)methyl]-3-methoxybenzyl alcohol *see* Metiprenaline.
8-Hydroxy-α-[(isopropylamino)methyl]-5-quinolinemethanol *see* Quinprenaline.
4′-[2-Hydroxy-3-(isopropylamino)propoxy]acetanilide *see* Practolol.
7-[2-Hydroxy-3-(isopropylamino)propoxy]-2-benzofuranyl methyl ketone *see* Befunolol.
4-[2-Hydroxy-3-(isopropylamino)propoxy]carbazole *see* Carazolol.
8-[2-Hydroxy-3-(isopropylamino)propoxy]-3-chromanol 3-nitrate *see* Nipradilol.
o-[2-Hydroxy-3-(isopropylamino)propoxy]cinnamic acid methyl ester *see* Cinamolol.
p-[2-Hydroxy-3-(isopropylamino)propoxy]hydrocinnamic acid methyl ester *see* Esmolol.
4-[2-Hydroxy-3-(isopropylamino)propoxy]indole *see* Pindolol.
4-[2-Hydroxy-3-(isopropylamino)propoxy]-2-methylindole *see* Mepindolol.
1-[2-Hydroxy-3-(isopropylamino)propoxy]naphthalene *see* Propranolol.
[*p*-[2-Hydroxy-3-(isopropylamino)propoxy]phenethyl]carbamic acid methyl ester *see* Pamatolol.
1-[*p*-[2-Hydroxy-3-(isopropylamino)propoxy]phenethyl]-3-isopropylurea *see* Pafenolol.
p-[2-Hydroxy-3-(isopropylamino)propoxy]phenylacetamide *see* Atenolol.
3-[2-[2-Hydroxy-3-(isopropylamino)propoxy]phenyl]acrylic acid methyl ester *see* Cinamolol.
3-[2-Hydroxy-3-(isopropylamino)propoxy]-2-phenylphthalimidine *see* Nofecainide.
2-[2-Hydroxy-3-(isopropylamino)propoxy]thiazole *see* Tazolol.
4-[2-Hydroxy-3-(isopropylamino)propoxy]-2,3,6-trimethylphenyl acetate *see* Metipranolol.
3-Hydroxy-3-isopropyl-5,6-indolinedione 5-semicarbazone *see* Iprazochrome.
1-Hydroxy-2-isopropyl-5-methylbenzene *see* Thymol.
4-(α-Hydroxyisopropyl)-1-methylcyclohexen-6-ol *see* Sobrerol.
β-Hydroxy-*p*-(isopropylthio)-α-methyl-*N*-octylphenethylamine *see* Suloctidil.
3α-Hydroxy-8-isopropyl-1α*H*,5α*H*-tropanium bromide α-phenylcyclopentaneacetate *see* Ciclotropium bromide.
3α-Hydroxy-8-isopropyl-1α*H*,5α*H*-tropanium bromide 2-propylvalerate *see* Sintropium bromide.
3α-Hydroxy-8-isopropyl-1α*H*,5α*H*-tropanium bromide (±)-tropate *see* Ipratropium bromide.
Hydroxyisosparteine *see* Retamine.
HYDROXYLAMINE (oxammonium).
Hydroxylapatite *see* Hydroxyapatite.
Hydroxylucanthone *see* Hycanthone.
Hydroxymalonic acid *see* Tartronic acid.
17-Hydroxy-7-mercapto-3-oxo-17α-pregn-4-ene-21-carboxylic acid γ-lactone 7-acetate *see* Spirono-

lactone.
Hydroxymercurichlorophenol *see* 2-Chloro-4-(hydroxymercuri)phenol.
4-Hydroxymercuri-2,7-diiodoresorcinolsulfonphthalein *see* Meralein sodium.
1-(3-Hydroxymercuri-2-methoxypropyl)biuret *see* Merbiurelidin.
3-(3-Hydroxymercuri-2-methoxypropyl)camphoramic acid sodium salt plus theophylline *see* Mercurophylline.
o-[*N*-(3-Hydroxymercuri-2-methoxypropyl)carbamoyl]phenoxyacetic acid sodium salt and/or its theophylline derivative *see* Mersalyl.
8-[3-(Hydroxymercuri)-2-methoxypropyl]coumarin-3-carboxylic acid sodium salt with theophylline *see* Mercumatilin sodium.
1-(3-Hydroxymercuri-2-methoxypropyl)-3-succinylurea theophylline derivative *see* Meralluride.
1-Hydroxymercuri-2-propanol *see* Merisopol.
Hydroxymesterone *see* Medrysone.
2′-Hydroxy-4′-methoxyacetophenone *see* Peonol.
4-Hydroxy-3-methoxybenzaldehyde *see* Vanillin.
4-Hydroxy-3-methoxybenzaldehyde isonicotinoylhydrazone *see* Ftivazide.
4-Hydroxy-3-methoxybenzamide *see* Vanillamide.
6-Hydroxy-4-methoxy-5-benzofuranacrylic acid δ-lactone *see* Bergapten.
4-Hydroxy-3-methoxybenzoic acid *see* Vanillic acid.
2-Hydroxy-4-methoxybenzophenone *see* Oxybenzone.
N-(4-Hydroxy-3-methoxybenzyl)nonamide *see* Nonivamide.
4-Hydroxy-3-methoxycinnamic acid *see* Ferulic acid.
7-Hydroxy-6-methoxycoumarin *see* Scopoletin.
7-Hydroxy-4′-methoxyflavone *see* Pratol.
7-Hydroxy-4′-methoxyisoflavone *see* Formonetin.
4-Hydroxy-3-methoxymandelic acid *see* Vanilmandelic acid.
4-Hydroxy-3-methoxy-α-methylaminomethylbenzyl alcohol *see* Metanephrine.
2-Hydroxy-4-methoxy-4′-methylbenzophenone *see* Mexenone.
6-(4-Hydroxy-6-methoxy-7-methyl-3-oxophthalan-5-yl)-4-methyl-4-hexenoic acid *see* Mycophenolic acid.
4-Hydroxy-α-[(*p*-methoxy-α-methylphenethylamino)methyl]-*m*-xylene-α,α′-diol *see* Salmefamol.
4-Hydroxy-α-[1-(*p*-methoxyphenethylamino)ethyl]-5-(methylsulfonamido)benzyl alcohol *see* Mesuprine.
5-[1-Hydroxy-2-[[2-(*o*-methoxyphenoxy)ethyl]amino]ethyl]-*o*-toluenesulfonamide *see* Amosulalol.
4-Hydroxy-3-methoxyphenylacetic acid *see* Homovanillic acid.
4-(4-Hydroxy-3-methoxyphenyl)-2-butanone *see* Zingerone.
6-Hydroxy-7-methoxy-4-phenylcoumarin *see* Dalbergin.
2-(4-Hydroxy-3-methoxyphenyl)ethyl methyl ketone *see* Zingerone.

281

4-Hydroxy-3-methoxyphenylglycolic acid *see* Vanilmandelic acid.

6-Hydroxy-3-methoxy-7-phenyl-2,6-heptadienoic acid δ-lactone *see* Kawain.

4-Hydroxy-α-[[[3-(p-methoxyphenyl)-1-methylpropyl]amino]methyl]-3-(methylsulfinyl)benzyl alcohol *see* Sulfinalol.

1-(2-Hydroxy-3-methoxy-3-phenylpropyl)-4-(2-methoxy-2-phenylethyl)piperazine *see* Zipeprol.

1-(2-Hydroxy-3-methoxypropyl)-2-nitroimidazole *see* Misonidazole.

6-Hydroxy-5-methoxy-p-toluquinone *see* Fumigatin.

β-(Hydroxymethoxy)tricarballylic acid γ-lactone *see* Anhydromethylenecitric acid.

p-Hydroxy-α-(1-methylaminoethyl)benzyl alcohol *see* p-Hydroxyephedrine.

3′-(1-Hydroxy-2-methylaminoethyl)methanesulfonanilide|methanesulfonate *see* Amidefrine mesilate.

4-[1-Hydroxy-2-(methylamino)ethyl]-1,2-phenylene bis(2,2-dimethylpropanoate) *see* Dipivefrine.

4-[1-Hydroxy-2-(methylamino)ethyl]-m-phenylene cyclic borate *see* Epinephryl borate.

3-[1-Hydroxy-2-(methylamino)ethyl]phenyl pivalate *see* Pivenfrine.

m-Hydroxy-α-(methylaminomethyl)benzyl alcohol *see* Phenylephrine.

p-Hydroxy-α-(methylaminomethyl)benzyl alcohol *see* Oxedrine.

Hydroxymethyl 6-(2-amino-2-phenylacetamido)-3,3-dimethyl-7-oxo-4-thia-1-azabicyclo-[3.2.0]heptane-2-carboxylate 3,3-dimethyl-7-oxo-4-thia-1-azabicyclo[3.2.0]heptane-2-carboxylate (ester) S,S-dioxide *see* Sultamicillin.

Hydroxymethyl 6-(α-aminophenylacetamido)penicillanate penicillanate (ester) S,S-dioxide *see* Sultamicillin.

Hydroxymethyl 6-D(−)-(α-aminophenylacetamido)penicillinate pivalate *see* Pivampicillin.

20-Hydroxy-3β-(methylamino)-5-pregnene-18-carboxylic acid lactone *see* Paravallarine.

4′-(1-Hydroxy-2-methylaminopropyl)methanesulfonanilide *see* Metalol.

17β-Hydroxy-17-methylandrosta-1,4-dien-3-one *see* Metandienone.

17β-Hydroxy-17α-methyl-5α-androstano[2,3-c]furazan *see* Furazabol.

17β-Hydroxy-1α-methyl-5α-androstan-3-one *see* Mesterolone.

17β-Hydroxy-2α-methylandrostan-3-one *see* Drostanolone.

17β-Hydroxy-17-methyl-5α-androstan-3-one *see* Mestanolone.

17β-Hydroxy-2α-methyl-5α-androstan-3-one azine *see* Bolazine.

17β-Hydroxy-1-methyl-5α-androst-1-en-3-one *see* Metenolone.

17β-Hydroxy-2-methyl-5α-androst-1-en-3-one *see* Stenbolone.

17β-Hydroxy-17-methylandrost-4-en-3-one *see* Methyltestosterone.

17β-Hydroxy-17-methyl-4-androsteno[3,2-c]pyrazole *see* Hydroxystenozole.

2-Hydroxy-3-methylbenzamide *see* Cresotamide.

2-Hydroxy-3-methylbenzoic acid *see* Hydroxytoluic acid.

2-Hydroxy-5-methylbenzoic acid *see* 2,5-Cresotic acid.

N-[2-Hydroxy-1-(methylcarbamoyl)ethyl]-2,4,6-triiodo-5-(2-methoxyacetamido)isophthalamic acid *see* Ioseric acid.

4′-[[(Hydroxymethyl)carbamoyl]sulfamoyl]phthalanilic acid *see* Sulfaloxic acid.

3-Hydroxymethyl-2-cephem-2-carboxylic acid acetate *see* Cephalosporanic acid.

3-(Hydroxymethyl)chrysazin *see* Aloe-emodin.

7-Hydroxy-4-methylcoumarin *see* Hymecromone.

(6-Hydroxy-4-methylcoumarin-7-yloxy)acetic acid, esters and salts *see* Cromacate(s).

3-Hydroxy-N-methyl-cis-crotonamide dimethyl phosphate *see* Monocrotophos.

1-(Hydroxymethyl)cyclohexaneacetic acid *see* Hexacyclonic acid.

β-Hydroxy-β-methylcyclohexanepropionic acid *see* Cyclobutoic acid.

2-Hydroxymethyl-2,3-dimethylpentyl carbamate isopropylcarbamate *see* Nisobamate.

2-Hydroxymethyl-2,3-dimethylpentyl dicarbamate *see* Mebutamate.

2-Hydroxymethyl-1,1-dimethylpiperidinium methyl sulfate benzilate *see* Bevonium metilsulfate.

2-Hydroxymethyl-1,1-dimethylpyrrolidinium bromide α-phenylcyclohexaneglycolate *see* Oxypyrronium bromide.

2-(Hydroxymethyl)-1,1-dimethylpyrrolidinium methylsulfate benzilate *see* Poldine metilsulfate.

2-(Hydroxymethyl)-1,1-dimethylpyrrolidinium methylsulfate 3β-hydroxy-11-oxoolean-12-en-30-oate *see* Roxolonium metilsulfate.

2-Hydroxy-N-methyl-1,2-diphenylethylamine *see* Ephenamine.

1-(8-Hydroxy-6-methyldodeca-2,4,6-trienoyl)-2-pyrrolidone *see* Pecilocin.

9-Hydroxy-2-methylellipticinium acetate *see* Elliptinium acetate.

2-Hydroxy-2-(3,4-methylenedioxyphenyl)acetamidine *see* Olmidine.

(Hydroxymethylene)diphosphonic acid *see* Oxidronic acid.

17α-Hydroxy-16-methylenepregna-4,6-diene-3,20-dione acetate *see* MDAP.

5-Hydroxy-6-methylenetetracycline *see* Metacycline.

6-Hydroxy-5-methylene-1-(1,2,3-trihydroxy-2-methylpropyl)-2-oxa-7,9-diazabicyclo[4.2.2]decane-8,10-dione *see* Bicozamycin.

3-Hydroxy-17α-methylestra-1,3,5(10)-trien-17-one *see* Almestrone.

17β-Hydroxy-17-methylestra-4,9,11-trien-3-one *see* Metribolone.

17β-Hydroxy-7α-methylestr-4-en-3-one *see* Trestolone.

17β-Hydroxy-17-methylestr-4-en-3-one *see* Methylestrenolone.

4-[2-Hydroxy-3-[(1-methylethyl)amino]propoxy]-benzenepropanoic acid methyl ester *see* Esmolol.

N-[1-(Hydroxymethyl)ethyl]lysergamide *see* Ergometrine.

5-(1-Hydroxy-1-methylethyl)-2-methyl-2-cyclohexen-1-ol *see* Sobrerol.

D-(+)-2-(1-Hydroxy-1-methylethyl)-1-methylpiperidine diphenylacetate (ester) *see* Pinolcaine.

12'-Hydroxy-2'-(1-methylethyl)-5'-(2-methylpropyl)ergotaman-3',6',18-trione *see* α-Ergocryptine.

3-Hydroxy-3-methylglutaric acid *see* Meglutol.

Hydroxymethylgramicidin *see* Methocidin.

6-Hydroxy-6-methyl-2-heptylamine *see* Heptaminol.

3-Hydroxy-1-methyl-5,6-indolinedione *see* Adrenochrome.

3-Hydroxy-1-methyl-5,6-indolinedione semicarbazone *see* Carbazochrome.

7-[3-[[2-Hydroxy-3-[(2-methylindol-4-yl)oxy]propyl]amino]butyl]theophylline *see* Teoprolol.

7-(Hydroxymethyl)-4-methoxybenzopyran-5-one *see* Khellol.

8β-(Hydroxymethyl)-10-methoxy-1,6-dimethylergoline 5-bromonicotinate *see* Nicergoline.

2-(Hydroxymethyl)-5-methoxy-6,7-furanochromone *see* Khellol.

7-(Hydroxymethyl)-4-methoxy-5*H*-furo-[3,2-*g*]-(1)benzopyran-5-one glucoside *see* Khelloside.

3-(Hydroxymethyl)-7-methoxy-7-(2-thien-2-ylacetamido)-2-cephem-2-carboxylic acid *see* Cefoxitin.

3-[[[1-(Hydroxymethyl)-2-(methylamino)-2-oxoethyl]amino]carbonyl]-2,4,6-triiodo-5-[(methoxyacetyl)amino]benzoic acid *see* Ioseric acid.

5-[1-Hydroxy-2-[[1-methyl-3-[3,4-(methylenedioxy)phenyl]propyl]amino]ethyl]salicylamide *see* Medroxalol.

17-Hydroxy-6-methyl-16-methylenepregna-4,6-diene-3,20-dione *see* Melengestrol.

4-Hydroxy-2-methyl-*N*-(5-methylisoxazol-3-yl)-2*H*-1,2-benzothiazine-3-carboxamide 1,1-dioxide *see* Isoxicam.

2-(HYDROXYMETHYL)-2-METHYL-1-PENTANOL (2-methyl-2-propyl-1,3-propanediol).

See also Lorbamate; Tolboxane; Tybamate.

5-(Hydroxymethyl)-3-(3-methylphenyl)oxazolidin-2-one *see* Toloxatone.

2-(Hydroxymethyl)-3-methylquinoxaline 1,4-dioxide *see* Mequidox.

1-(Hydroxymethyl)-3-methyl-2-thiourea *see* Noxytiolin.

5-(Hydroxymethyl)-6-methyluracil *see* Pentoxyl.

3-Hydroxy-*N*-methylmorphinan *see* Dextrophan; Levophanol; Racemorphan.

2-Hydroxy-3-methyl-1,4-naphthoquinone *see* Phthiocol.

5-Hydroxy-2-methyl-1,4-naphthoquinone *see* Plumbagin.

7-[2-(4-Hydroxy-6-methylnicotinamido)-2-(*p*-hydroxyphenyl)acetamido]-3-[[(1-methyl-1*H*-tetrazol-5-yl)thio]methyl]-2-cephem-2-carboxylic acid *see* Cefpiramide.

Hydroxymethylnitrofurantoin *see* Nifurtoinol.

3-(Hydroxymethyl)-1-[(5-nitrofurfurylidene)amino]hydantoin *see* Nifurtoinol.

3-(Hydroxymethyl)-1-[3-(5-nitro-2-furyl)allylideneamino]hydantoin *see* Nifurmazole.

2-(Hydroxymethyl)-6-[2-(5-nitro-2-furyl)vinyl]pyridine *see* Nifurpirinol.

17β-Hydroxy-17α-methyl-19-norandrosta-4,9,11-trien-3-one *see* Metribolone.

17β-Hydroxy-17-methyl-4-norandrost-4-en-3-one *see* Methylestrenolone.

17β-Hydroxy-17-methyl-*B*-norandrost-4-en-3-one *see* Benorterone.

17-Hydroxy-6-methyl-19-norpregna-4,6-diene-3,20-dione *see* Nomegestrol.

17-Hydroxy-11β-methyl-19-norpregn-4-ene-3,20-dione acetate *see* Norgestomet.

17-Hydroxy-7α-methyl-19-nor-17α-pregn-5(10)-en-20-yn-3-one *see* Tibolone.

2-[(*E*)-3-Hydroxy-3-methyl-1-octenyl]-5-oxocyclopentaneheptanoic acid *see* Doxaprost.

2-(3-Hydroxy-3-methyloctyl)-5-oxocyclopentaneheptanoic acid *see* Deprostil.

17β-Hydroxy-17-methyl-2-oxa-5α-androstan-3-one *see* Oxandrolone.

[(7-Hydroxy-4-methyl-2-oxo-2*H*-1-benzopyran-6-yl)oxy]acetic acid *see* Metesculetol.

1-[(4-Hydroxy-7-methyl-5-oxo-5*H*-furo[3,2-*g*]-[1]benzopyran-9-yl)oxy]-3-(isopropylamino)-2-propanol *see* Iprocrolol.

15-Hydroxy-15-methyl-9-oxoprostan-1-oic acid *see* Deprostil.

4-Hydroxy-3-methyl-2-(2,4-pentadienyl)-2-cyclopenten-1-one *see* Pyrethrolone.

4-Hydroxy-4-methyl-2-pentanone *see* Diacetone alcohol.

1-Hydroxy-5-methylphenazinium hydroxide inner salt *see* Pyocyanine.

(+)-*m*-Hydroxy-α-methylphenethylamine *see* Gepefrine.

p-Hydroxy-α-methylphenethylamine *see* Hydroxyamphetamine.

7-[2-(2-Hydroxy-1-methylphenethylamino)ethyl]theophylline *see* Cafedrine.

3-(β-Hydroxy-α-methylphenethylamino)-3'-methoxypropiophenone *see* Oxyfedrine.

1-[2-[[2-Hydroxy-3-(2-methylphenoxy)propyl]amino]ethyl]-5-methyl-2,4-pyrimidinedione *see* Primidolol.

1-(3-Hydroxy-5-methyl-4-phenylhexyl)-1-methylpiperidinium bromide *see* Piperphenamine.

12'-Hydroxy-2'-methyl-5'-(phenylmethyl)ergotaman-3',6',18-trione *see* Ergotamine.

5-[2-(Hydroxymethyl)phenyl]-1-methyl-3-pyrid-3-yl-1*H*-1,2,4-triazole *see* Fepitrizol.

p-Hydroxy-α-[1-(1-methyl-3-phenylpropylamino)ethyl]benzyl alcohol *see* Buphenine.

5-[1-Hydroxy-2-[(1-methyl-3-phenylpropyl)amino]ethyl]salicylamide *see* Dilevalol; Labetalol.

11β-Hydroxy-6α-methylpregna-1,4-diene-3,20-dione *see* Endrisone.

17-Hydroxy-6-methylpregna-4,6-diene-3,20-dione *see* Megestrol.

11β-Hydroxy-6α-methylpregn-4-ene-3,20-dione *see* Medrysone.

17α-Hydroxy-6α-methylpregn-4-ene-3,20-dione *see*

Medroxyprogesterone.

17-Hydroxy-6-methylpregn-5-ene-3,20-dione cyclic 3-(ethylene acetal) acetate *see* Edogestrone.

17α-Hydroxy-6α-methylpregn-4-en-20-one *see* Anagestone.

11β-Hydroxy-6α-methylprogesterone *see* Medrysone.

17α-Hydroxy-6α-methylprogesterone *see* Medroxyprogesterone.

2-Hydroxy-2-methylpropyl 4-(4-amino-6,7,8-trimethoxyquinazolin-2-yl)piperazine-1-carboxylate *see* Trimazosin.

2-Hydroxy-2-methylpropyl 4-(6,7-dimethoxyquinazolin-4-yl)piperazine-1-carboxylate *see* Hoquizil.

N-[1-(Hydroxymethyl)propyl]lysergamide *see* Methylergometrine.

N-[1-(Hydroxymethyl)propyl]-1-methyl-D-lysergamide *see* Methysergide.

Hydroxymethyl 2-propylvalerate pivalate *see* Valproate piroxil.

17β-Hydroxy-6α-methyl-17-(1-propynyl)androst-4-en-3-one *see* Dimethisterone.

2-(Hydroxymethyl)pyrazolo[1,5-c]quinazolin-5(6H)-one *see* Pirquinozol.

3-Hydroxy-2-methyl-4,5-pyridinedimethanol *see* Pyridoxine.

5-Hydroxy-6-methyl-3,4-pyridinedimethanol 3-ether with glycolic acid *see* 2-[(5-Hydroxy-4-hydroxymethyl-6-methylpyrid-3-yl)methoxy]glycolic acid.

3-Hydroxy-1-methylpyridinium bromide dimethylcarbamate *see* Pyridostigmine bromide.

3-Hydroxy-1-methylpyridinium bromide hexamethylenebis(N-methylcarbamate) *see* Distigmine bromide.

4-Hydroxy-2-methyl-N-pyrid-2-yl-2H-1,2-benzothiazine-3-carboxamide 1,1-dioxide *see* Piroxicam.

6-(Hydroxymethyl)pyrid-2-ylmethyl 2-(p-chlorophenoxy)-2-methylpropionate *see* Pirifibrate.

4-Hydroxy-2-methyl-N-pyrid-2-yl-2H-thieno[2,3-e]-1,2-thiazine-3-carboxamide 1,1-dioxide *see* Tenoxicam.

3-Hydroxymethyl-7-[2-(4-pyridylthio)acetamido]-2-cephem-2-carboxylic acid acetate *see* Cefapirin.

3-Hydroxy-1-methylquinuclidinium bromide benzilate *see* Clidinium bromide.

3-Hydroxy-1-methylquinuclidinium bromide α-phenylcyclohexaneglycolate *see* Droclidinium bromide.

14-Hydroxy-3β-(4-O-methyl-α-L-rhamnopyranosyloxy)-14β-bufa-4,20,22-trienolide *see* Meproscillarin.

N¹-Hydroxymethylsulfanilamide glucose sodium bisulfite compound *see* Glucosulfamide.

4-Hydroxy-2-methyl-N-thiazol-2-yl-2H-1,2-benzothiazine-3-carboxamide 1,1-dioxide *see* Sudoxicam.

5-(Hydroxymethyl)-3-m-tolyloxazolidin-2-one *see* Toloxatone.

1-Hydroxy-4-methyl-6-(2,4,4-trimethylpentyl)-2(1H)-pyridone *see* Piroctone.

2-[4-(Hydroxymethylureidosulfonyl)phenylcarbamoyl]benzoic acid *see* Sulfaloxic acid.

6-((R)-2-Hydroxy-4-methylvaleramido)penicillanic acid 2-furoate *see* Furbucillin.

3-Hydroxymorphinan *see* Norlevorphanol.

7-Hydroxy-4-morpholinomethylcoumarin *see* Oxazorone.

2'-Hydroxy-3-morpholinopropiophenone *see* Romifenone.

3-(2-Hydroxy-3-morpholinopropyl)-4-methyl-7-(4-morpholinecarboxamido)coumarin trimethoxycinnamate ester *see* Cinecromen.

3-(2-Hydroxy-3-morpholinopropyl)-6,7,8-trimethoxy-1,2,3-benzotriazin-4(3H)-one 3,4,5-trimethoxybenzoate ester *see* Razinodil.

Hydroxymycin *see* Paromomycin.

6-Hydroxy-2-naphthalenepropionic acid *see* Allenoic acid.

N-Hydroxynaphthalimide diethyl phosphate *see* Naftalofos.

3-HYDROXY-2-NAPHTHOIC ACID ('bona').

3-Hydroxy-2-naphthoic acid (3-acetyl-5-chloro-2-hydroxybenzyl)dimethyl(2-phenoxyethyl)ammonium salt *see* Difezil.

3-Hydroxy-2-naphthoic acid benzyldimethyl(2-phenoxyethyl)ammonium salt *see* Bephenium hydroxynaphthoate.

5-Hydroxy-1,4-naphthoquinone *see* Juglone.

2-(2-Hydroxynaphth-1-yl)cyclohexanone *see* Naphthonone.

3-Hydroxy-4-naphth-1-yloxybutyramidoxime *see* Nadoxolol.

(±)-1-[3-[[2-Hydroxy-3-(1-naphthyloxy)propyl]amino]-3-methylbutyl]-2-benzimidazolinone *see* Adimolol.

(2-Hydroxy-3-naphth-1-yloxypropyl)isopropyldimethylammonium chloride *see* Pranolium chloride.

6-[2-(4-Hydroxy-1,5-naphthyridine-3-carboxamido)-2-phenylacetamido]penicillanic acid *see* Apalcillin.

2-Hydroxy-2',6'-nicotinoxylidide *see* Isonixin.

4-Hydroxy-3-nitrobenzenearsonic acid *see* Roxarsone.

p-Hydroxy-N²-(5-nitro-2-furfurylidene)benzohydrazide *see* Nifuroxazide.

8-Hydroxy-4-nitroquinoline *see* Nitroxoline.

2-Hydroxynonadecane-1,2,3-tricarboxylic acid *see* Agaric acid.

17β-Hydroxy-19-norandrosta-4,9,11-trien-3-one *see* Trenbolone.

m-Hydroxynorephedrine *see* Metaraminol.

6-Hydroxynorleucine *see* Hexahomoserine.

17-Hydroxy-19-norpregna-4,6-diene-3,20-dione *see* Gestadienol.

17-Hydroxy-19-nor-17α-pregna-4,9,11-trien-20-yn-3-one *see* Norgestrienone.

17α-Hydroxy-19-norpregn-4-ene-3,20-dione *see* Gestonorone.

17-Hydroxy-19-norpregn-4-en-3-one *see* Norethandrolone.

20β-Hydroxy-19-norpregn-4-en-3-one *see* Oxogestone.

17-Hydroxy-19-nor-17α-pregn-5(10)-en-20-yn-3-one *see* Noretynodrel.

17β-Hydroxy-19-norpregn-4-en-20-yn-3-one *see* Norethisterone.

17α-Hydroxy-19-norprogesterone *see* Gestonorone.

12-Hydroxy-9-octadecenoic acid *see* Ricinoleic acid.

2-Hydroxy-4-(octyloxy)benzophenone *see* Octabenzone.

3β-Hydroxyolean-9(11)-en-30-oic acid hydrogen succinate *see* Deloxolone.

3-(17β-Hydroxy-3-oxoandrosta-4,6-dien-17-yl)propionic acid *see* Canrenoic acid.

17-(2-Hydroxy-1-oxoethyl)-4-androstene-3,11-dione *see* 11-Dehydrocorticosterone.

17-Hydroxy-3-oxo-19-nor-17α-pregna-4,9-diene-21-nitrile *see* Dienogest.

3-Hydroxy-11-oxoolean-12-en-30-oic acid *see* Enoxolone.

3β-Hydroxy-11-oxoolean-12-en-30-oic acid hydrogen *cis*-1,2-cyclohexanedicarboxylate *see* Cicloxolone.

3-Hydroxy-11-oxoolean-12-en-30-oic acid hydrogen succinate *see* Carbenoxolone.

4-Hydroxy-3-(3-oxo-1-phenylbutyl)-2*H*-1-benzopyran-2-one *see* Warfarin.

3-(3-Hydroxy-1-oxo-2-phenylpropoxy)-8-methyl-8-(1-methylethyl)-8-azoniabicyclo[3.2.1]octane bromide *see* Ipratropium bromide.

17β-Hydroxy-3-oxo-17α-pregna-4,6-diene-21-carboxylic acid *see* Canrenoic acid.

17-Hydroxy-3-oxo-17α-pregn-4-ene-7α,21-dicarboxylic acid γ-lactone isopropyl ester *see* Dicirenone.

17-Hydroxy-3-oxo-17α-pregn-4-ene-7,21-dicarboxylic acid 7-methyl ester 21-potassium salt *see* Mexrenoate potassium.

15α-Hydroxy-9-oxo-10,13-*trans*-prostadienoic acid *see* Prostaglandin A₁.

15-Hydroxy-9-oxo-5-*cis*-8(12),13-*trans*-prostatrienoic acid *see* Prostaglandin B₂.

3-Hydroxy-4-oxo-1(4*H*)-pyran-2,6-dicarboxylic acid *see* Meconic acid.

3-Hydroxy-4-oxo-1(4*H*)-pyridinealanine *see* Mimosine.

1-Hydroxy-5-oxo-5*H*-pyrido[3,2-*a*]phenoxazine-3-carboxylic acid *see* Pirenoxine.

4-Hydroxy-2-oxo-1-pyrrolidineacetamide *see* Oxiracetam.

1-(8-Hydroxy-2-oxoquinolin-5-yl)-2-isopropylamino-1-butanol *see* Procaterol.

p-[2-Hydroxy-3-[[4-oxo-2-(1*H*-tetrazol-5-yl)-4*H*-1-benzopyran-5-yl]oxy]propoxy]benzonitrile *see* Cromitrile.

6-(10-Hydroxy-6-oxo-*trans*-1-undecenyl)-β-resorcylic acid lactone *see* Zearalenone.

4-Hydroxy-2,4-pentadienoic acid γ-lactone *see* Protoanemonin.

4-Hydroxy-3,3-pentamethylenebutyric acid *see* Hexacyclonic acid.

o-[2-Hydroxy-3-(*tert*-pentylamino)propoxy]benzonitrile *see* Penirolol.

2′-[2-Hydroxy-3-(*tert*-pentylamino)propoxy]-3-

phenylpropiophenone *see* Diprafenone.

HYDROXYPETHIDINE*** (ethyl 4-(*m*-hydroxyphenyl)-1-methylisonipecotate; bemidone; Ho-10446; WIN-771).

α-Hydroxyphenacetin *see* Fenacetinol.

3-Hydroxy-*N*-phenacylmorphinan *see* Levophenacylmorphan.

Hydroxyphenamate *see* Oxyfenamate.

4-Hydroxyphenethylamine *see* Tyramine.

2-(*p*-Hydroxyphenethylamino)-1-(*p*-hydroxyphenyl)propan-1-ol *see* Ritodrine.

2-(β-Hydroxyphenethylamino)pyrimidine *see* Fenyripol.

β-Hydroxyphenethyl carbamate *see* Styramate.

α-(*p*-Hydroxyphenethyl)-4,7-dimethoxy-6-(2-piperid-1-ylethoxy)-5-benzofuranmethanol *see* Piprofurol.

2-(β-Hydroxyphenethyl)-1-methyl-6-phenacylpiperidine *see* Lobeline.

2-[6-(β-Hydroxyphenethyl)-1-methylpiperid-2-yl]acetophenone *see* Lobeline.

7-Hydroxyphenothiazin-3-one *see* Thionol.

1-(*p*-Hydroxyphenoxy)-3-(isopropylamino)-2-propanol *see* Prenalterol.

β-(4-Hydroxyphenoxy)phenethylamine *see* Thyronamine.

2-[4-(4-Hydroxyphenoxy)phenyl]acetic acid *see* Thyroacetic acid.

3-[4-(4-Hydroxyphenoxy)phenyl]alanine *see* Thyronine.

1-Hydroxy-16-phenoxy-ω-tetranorprostane-9,15-dione *see* Oxoprostol.

5-(*m*-Hydroxyphenoxy)-1*H*-tetrazole *see* Melizame.

α-Hydroxyphenylacetic acid *see* Mandelic acid.

α-Hydroxy-α-phenylacetophenone *see* Benzoin.

7-[(Hydroxyphenylacetyl)amino]-3-[[[1-(sulfomethyl)-1*H*-tetrazol-5-yl]thio]methyl]-2-cephem-2-carboxylic acid *see* Cefonicid.

3-(*p*-Hydroxyphenyl)alanine *see* Tyrosine.

3-(*p*-Hydroxyphenyl)-β-alanine *see* β-Tyrosine.

p-Hydroxyphenylbutazone *see* Oxyphenbutazone.

4-(*o*-Hydroxyphenyl)-3-buten-2-one *see* Salicylideneacetone.

2-Hydroxy-2-phenylbutyl carbamate *see* Oxyfenamate.

3-Hydroxy-2-phenylcinchoninic acid *see* Oxycinchophen.

cis-2-Hydroxy-2-phenylcyclohexanecarboxylic acid *see* Cicloxilic acid.

2-(1-Hydroxy-4-phenylcyclohexyl)butyric acid *see* Fencibutirol.

6-[4-(*p*-Hydroxyphenyl)-2,2-dimethyl-5-oxoimidazolidin-1-yl]penicillanic acid *see* Oxetacillin.

3-(*m*-Hydroxyphenyl)-2,3-dimethyl-1-phenacylpiperidine *see* Myfadol.

2-[3-(*m*-Hydroxyphenyl)-2,3-dimethylpiperid-1-yl]acetophenone *see* Myfadol.

2-(*m*-Hydroxyphenyl)ethanolamine *see* Norfenefrine.

2-(*p*-Hydroxyphenyl)ethanolamine *see* Octopamine.

2-(*p*-Hydroxyphenyl)ethylamine *see* Tyramine.

2-Hydroxy-2-phenylethyl carbamate *see* Styramate.

3-Hydroxy-*N*-(2-phenylethyl)morphinan *see* Phenomorphan.

L-2-(*p*-Hydroxyphenyl)glycine *see* Oxfenicine.

6-[α-D-(*p*-Hydroxyphenyl)glycylamino]penicillanic acid *see* Amoxicillin.

7-[α-D-(*p*-Hydroxyphenyl)glycylamino]-4-[(1*H*-1,2,3-triazol-4-ylthio)methyl]-2-cephem-2-carboxylic acid *see* Cefatrizine.

6-[2-(*p*-Hydroxyphenyl)-2-[3-[4-hydroxy-2-(*p*-sulfamoylanilino)pyrimidin-5-yl]ureido]acetamido]penicillanic acid *see* Piroxicillin.

1-(*p*-Hydroxyphenyl)-2-isopropylaminoethanol *see* Deterenol.

3-(1-Hydroxy-1-phenylisopropylamino)-3'-methoxypropiophenone *see* Oxyfedrine.

1-(*p*-Hydroxyphenyl)-2-methylamino-1-propanol *see* *p*-Hydroxyephedrine.

1-(*p*-Hydroxyphenyl)-2-(1-methyl-2-phenoxyethylamino)-1-propanol *see* Isoxsuprine.

1-(*p*-Hydroxyphenyl)-2-(1-methyl-3-phenylpropylamino)-1-propanol *see* Buphenine.

1-[4-(*m*-Hydroxyphenyl)-1-methylpiperid-4-yl]-1-propanone *see* Ketobemidone.

4-(*m*-Hydroxyphenyl)-1-methyl-4-propionylpiperidine *see* Ketobemidone.

(±)-4-[2-[3-(*p*-Hydroxyphenyl)-1-methylpropylamino]ethyl]pyrocatechol *see* Dobutamine.

3-(*m*-Hydroxyphenyl)-1-methyl-3-propylpyrrolidine *see* Profadol.

***o*-Hydroxyphenyl-2-morpholinoethyl ketone** *see* Romifenone.

Hydroxyphenylorciprenaline *see* Fenoterol.

2-(*o*-Hydroxyphenyl)-1,3,4-oxadiazole *see* Fenadiazole.

3α-Hydroxy-8-(*p*-phenylphenacyl)-1α*H*,5α*H*-tropanium bromide (−)-tropate *see* Fentonium bromide.

2-Hydroxy-2-phenylpropionamide *see* Atrolactamide.

2-Hydroxy-2-phenylpropionic acid *see* Atrolactic acid.

3-Hydroxy-2-phenylpropionic acid *see* Tropic acid.

4-Hydroxy-3-(1-phenyl-2-propionylethyl)coumarin sodium salt *see* Nafarin.

4-Hydroxy-3-(1-phenylpropyl)coumarin *see* Phenprocoumon.

1-(3-Hydroxy-3-phenylpropyl)-4-(β-methoxyphenethyl)piperazine *see* Eprozinol.

1-(3-Hydroxy-3-phenylpropyl)-4-phenylisonipecotic acid ethyl ester *see* Phenoperidine.

***N*-(*p*-Hydroxyphenyl)salicylamide** *see* Osalmid.

4-(3-Hydroxy-3-phenyl-3-thien-2-ylpropyl)-4-methylmorpholinium iodide *see* Tiemonium iodide.

2-[[*N*-(*m*-Hydroxyphenyl)-*p*-toluidino]methyl]-2-imidazoline *see* Phentolamine.

(*m*-Hydroxyphenyl)trimethylammonium bromide decamethylenebis(methylcarbamate) *see* Demecarium bromide.

(*m*-Hydroxyphenyl)trimethylammonium bromide dimethylcarbamate *see* Neostigmine bromide.

3-Hydroxyphthalide ampicillin ester *see* Talampicillin.

3-Hydroxyphthalide indometacin ester *see* Talmetacin.

3-(3-Hydroxypiperid-2-ylacetonyl)-4(3*H*)-quinazolinone *see* Febrifugine.

3-(1-Hydroxy-2-piperid-1-ylethyl)-5-phenylisoxazole *see* Perisoxal.

10-[3-(4-Hydroxypiperid-1-yl)-2-methylpropyl]-2-methoxyphenothiazine *see* Perimetazine.

10-[2-(4-Hydroxypiperid-1-yl)propyl]phenothiazine-1-carbonitrile *see* Periciazine.

α-Hydroxypiperonylformamidine *see* Olmidine.

4-Hydroxypiracetam *see* Oxiracetam.

Hydroxypolyethoxydodecane *see* Polidocanol.

16α-Hydroxyprednisolone 16,17-acetonide *see* Desonide.

17β-Hydroxy-17α-pregna-4,6-diene-3-one-21-carboxylic acid *see* Canrenoic acid.

3α-Hydroxy-5α-pregnane-11,20-dione *see* Alfaxalone.

3α-Hydroxy-5β-pregnane-11,20-dione *see* Renanolone.

21-Hydroxy-5β-pregnane-3,20-dione 21-(sodium hemisuccinate) *see* Hydroxydione sodium succinate.

21-Hydroxy-4-pregnene-3,20-dione *see* Desoxycortone.

21-Hydroxy-4-pregnene-3,11,20-trione *see* 11-Dehydrocorticosterone.

3β-Hydroxypregn-5-en-20-one *see* Pregnenolone.

17-Hydroxy-17α-pregn-4-en-20-yn-3-one *see* Ethisterone.

HYDROXYPROCAINE* (2-(diethylamino)-ethyl *p*-aminosalicylate; oxiprocaine; oxyprocaine; pascain).

HYDROXYPROCAINE-PENICILLIN ('citocillin').

HYDROXYPROGESTERONE* (17α-hydroxyprogesterone).

HYDROXYPROGESTERONE ACETATE* ('prodox').

HYDROXYPROGESTERONE CAPROATE* (hydroxyprogesterone hexanoate; NSC-17592). *See also under* Estradiol valerate.

17α-Hydroxyprogesterone *see* Hydroxyprogesterone.

21-Hydroxyprogesterone *see* Desoxycortone.

3-Hydroxypropane-1-sulfonic acid salicylate ester *see* Sulprosal.

1-Hydroxy-1,2,3-propanetrioic acid *see* Isocitric acid.

2-Hydroxy-1,2,3-propanetrioic acid *see* Citric acid.

1-Hydroxy-2-propanone *see* Hydroxyacetone.

6-Hydroxy-2-(α-propionamido)purine *see* Guanine propionate.

4'-Hydroxypropionanilide *see* Parapropamol.

3-Hydroxypropionic acid *see* Hydracrylic acid.

***p*-Hydroxypropiophenone** *see* Paroxypropione.

2-HYDROXYPROPIOPHENONE (lactophenone).

4'-Hydroxypropiophenone *see* Paroxypropione.

7-[2-Hydroxy-3-(propylamino)propoxy]flavone *see* Flavodilol.

2'-[2-Hydroxy-3-(propylamino)propoxy]-3-phenylpropiophenone *see* Propafenone.

17β-Hydroxy-17-propylandrost-4-en-3-one *see* Topterone.

2-Hydroxypropyl 14-deoxyvincaminate *see* Vinpoline.

1-(2-Hydroxypropyl)-2-methyl-5-nitroimidazole *see* Secnidazole.

1-(3-Hydroxypropyl)-2-methyl-4-nitroimidazole *see* Ternidazole.

N-**[2-[*p*-(1-Hydroxypropyl)phenoxy]ethyl]-α-methylphenethylamine** *see* Fenalcomine.

5-(2-Hydroxypropyl)-5-(2-propenyl)-2,4,6(1*H*,3*H*,5*H*)-pyrimidinetrione *see* Proxibarbal.

1-(2-Hydroxypropyl)theobromine *see* Protheobromine.

7-(2-Hydroxypropyl)theophylline *see* Proxyphylline.

(2-Hydroxypropyl)trimethylammonium chloride acetate *see* Methacholine chloride.

(2-Hydroxypropyl)trimethylammonium chloride carbamate *see* Bethanechol.

(2-Hydroxypropyl)trimethylammonium ion *see* β-Methylcholine.

(3-Hydroxypropyl)trimethylammonium ion *see* Homocholine.

6-Hydroxypurine *see* Hypoxanthine.

4-Hydroxypyrazole-3-carboxamide 5-riboside *see* Pirazofurin.

4-Hydroxypyrazolopyrimidine *see* Allopurinol.

HYDROXYPYRIDINE TARTRATE*** (3-pyridinol tartaric ester; 3-hydroxypyridine tartrate; pyrid-3-yl tartrate).

1-Hydroxy-2(1*H*)-pyridinethione *see* Pyrithione.

5-(α-Hydroxy-α-pyrid-2-ylbenzyl)-7-(α-pyrid-2-ylbenzylidene)norborn-5-ene-2,3-dicarboxamide *see* Norbormide.

4-Hydroxyquinaldic acid *see* Kynurenic acid.

8-Hydroxyquinoline *see* 8-Quinolinol.

4′-Hydroxyretinanilide *see* Fenretinide.

14β-Hydroxy-3β-(rhamnoglucosyloxy)-bufa-4,20,22-trienolide *see* Scillaren A.

14-Hydroxy-3β-rhamnosyloxybufa-4,20,22-trienolide *see* Proscillaridin.

5-Hydroxy-1-β-D-ribofuranosylimidazole-4-carboxamide *see* Mizoribine.

4-Hydroxy-5-β-D-ribofuranosyl-1*H*-pyrazole-3-carboxamide *see* Pirazofurin.

7-Hydroxy-3-(β-D-ribofuranosyl)pyrazolo[4,3-*d*]-pyrimidine *see* Formycin B.

4′-Hydroxysalicylanilide *see* Osalmid.

5-Hydroxysalicylic acid *see* Gentisic acid.

8-Hydroxysantonin *see* Artemisin.

3α-Hydroxyspiro[1α*H*,5α*H*-nortropane-8,1′-pyrrolidinium]chloride benzilate *see* Trospium chloride.

HYDROXYSTENOZOLE*** (17β-hydroxy-17-methyl-4-androsteno[3,2-*c*]pyrazole).

HYDROXYSTILBAMIDINE*** (2-hydroxy-4,4′-stilbenedicarboxamidine).

2-Hydroxy-4,4′-stilbenedicarboxamidine *see* Hydroxystilbamidine.

Hydroxysuccinic acid *see* Malic acid.

HYDROXYTETRACAINE*** (2-(dimethyl-amino)ethyl 4-butylaminosalicylate; hydroxamethocaine).

2-HYDROXYTETRACOSANOIC ACID (cere-

bronic acid).

5-Hydroxytetracycline *see* Oxytetracycline.

trans-**3-Hydroxy-β-(1,4,5,6-tetrahydro-1-methylpyr-imid-2-yl)styrene** *see* Oxantel.

4-Hydroxy-3-(1,2,3,4-tetrahydronaphth-1-yl)coumarin *see* Coumatetralyl.

o-**[2-Hydroxy-3-(2,2,5,5-tetramethylpyrrolidin-1-yl)propoxy]toluene** *see* Lotucaine.

N-**[3-(2-Hydroxy-2-thien-2-ylethyl)-4-thiazolin-2-yl-idene]acetamide** *see* Antazonite.

p-**[2-[[2-Hydroxy-3-(*o*-toloxy)propyl]amino]ethoxy]-benzamide** *see* Tolamolol.

1-[2-[[2-Hydroxy-3-(*o*-toloxy)propyl]amino]ethyl]-thymine *see* Primidolol.

N-**[2-Hydroxy-3-(*m*-toloxy)propyl]-3,4-dimethoxy-phenethylamine** *see* Bevantolol.

N-**[2-Hydroxy-3-(*m*-toloxy)propyl]homoveratryl-amine** *see* Bevantolol.

1-[2-Hydroxy-3-(*o*-toloxy)propyl]-2,2,5,5-tetra-methylpyrrolidine *see* Lotucaine.

Hydroxytoluene(s) *see* Cresol(s).

HYDROXYTOLUIC ACID*** (2-hydroxy-3-methylbenzoic acid; 2,3-cresotic acid; *o*-cresotin-ic acid; 2-hydroxy-*m*-toluic acid; hydroxytoluin-ic acid; 3-methylsalicylic acid).

α-Hydroxy-α-toluic acid *see* Mandelic acid.

2-Hydroxy-*m*-toluic acid *see* Hydroxytoluic acid.

6-Hydroxy-*m*-toluic acid *see* 2,5-Cresotic acid.

1-Hydroxy-4-toluidinoanthraquinone-*m*-sulfonic acid *see* Solway purple.

Hydroxytoluinic acid *see* Hydroxytoluic acid.

Hydroxytricarballylic acids *see* Citric acid; Isocitric acid.

3-Hydroxy-17β-(2,2,2-trichloro-1-hydroxyethoxy)-estra-1,3,5(10)-triene *see* Cloxestradiol.

14-Hydroxy-3β-[(2,3,6-trideoxy-α-L-*erythro*-hexo-pyranosyl)oxy]-5β-card-20(22)-enolide *see* Ramnodigin.

2-Hydroxytriethylamine ribonucleate *see* Ribaminol.

2-Hydroxy-4-(trifluoromethyl)benzoic acid dihydro-gen phosphate *see* Flufosal.

17-Hydroxy-6α-(trifluoromethyl)pregn-4-ene-3,20-dione *see* Flumedroxone.

17-Hydroxy-6α-(trifluoromethyl)progesterone *see* Flumedroxone.

2-(3-Hydroxy-2,4,6-triiodobenzyl)butyric acid *see* Iophenoxic acid.

Hydroxytrimethonium iodide *see* Prolonium iodide.

6-Hydroxy-β,2,7-trimethyl-5-benzofuranacrylic acid δ-lactone *see* Trioxysalen.

2′-Hydroxy-2,5,9-trimethyl-6,7-benzomorphan *see* Metazocine.

5-Hydroxy-α,α,4-trimethyl-3-cyclohexene-1-metha-nol *see* Sobrerol.

3-Hydroxy-3,7,11-trimethyldodecanoic acid *see* Trethocanic acid.

2-Hydroxytrimethylene-1,3-bis(trimethylammonium iodide) *see* Prolonium iodide.

5,5′-(2-Hydroxytrimethylenedioxy)bis-(4-oxo-4*H*-1-benzopyran-2-carboxylic acid) *see* Cromoglicic acid.

2′-Hydroxy-5,9,9-trimethyl-2-(3-methyl-2-butenyl)-

6,7-benzomorphan *see* Ibazocine.

2′-Hydroxy-2,5,9-trimethyl-9-(3-oxooctyl)-6,7-benzomorphan *see* Tonazocine.

15-Hydroxy-11,16,16-trimethyl-9-oxoprosta-5,13-dien-1-oic acid *see* Trimoprostil.

1-(4-Hydroxy-2,3,5-trimethylphenoxy)-3-(isopropylamino)-2-propanol 4-acetate *see* Metipranolol.

11β-Hydroxy-16α,17α,21-trimethylpregna-1,4-diene-3,20-dione *see* Rimexolone.

9-Hydroxy-2,5,11-trimethyl-6*H*-pyrido[4,3-*b*]carbazolium acetate *see* Elliptinium acetate.

17α-Hydroxy-19,21,24-trinorchola-4,9,11,22-tetraen-3-one *see* Altrenogest.

Hydroxytriphenylstannane *see* Fentin hydroxide.

3-Hydroxytropane *see* Tropine.

5-Hydroxytryptamine *see* Serotonin.

5-Hydroxytryptophan *see* Oxitriptan.

3-Hydroxytyramine *see* Dopamine.

4-Hydroxy-5,6-undecadiene-8,10-diynoic acid γ-lactone *see* Nemotin.

Hydroxyurea *see* Hydroxycarbamide.

γ-Hydroxyvinylacrylic acid γ-lactone *see* Protoanemonin.

17β-Hydroxy-17α-vinyl-5(10)-estren-3-one *see* Norgesterone.

17β-Hydroxy-17α-vinylestr-4-en-3-one *see* Norvinisterone.

17β-Hydroxy-17α-vinyl-19-norandrost-4-en-3-one *see* Norvinisterone.

4-Hydroxy-3-(3,5-xylyl)coumarin *see* Xylocoumarol.

17α-Hydroxyyohimban-16α-carboxylic acid *see* Yohimbic acid.

HYDROXYZINE*** (2-[2-[4-(*p*-chloro-α-phenylbenzyl)-1-piperazinyl]ethoxy]ethanol; hydroxizine; hydroxyzine dihydrochloride; UCB-4492).
See also under Brallobarbital.

HYDROXYZINE EMBONATE (hydroxyzine 4,4′-methylenebis(3-hydroxynaphthalene-4-carboxylate); hydroxyzine pamoate).

HYDROXYZINE EMBONATE plus CALCIUM 2-ETHYLBUTYRATE ('sedocalene').

Hydroxyzine pamoate *see* Hydroxyzine embonate.

HYDURILIC ACID (5,5′-bibarbituric acid).

HYGRONIUM (tr) (2-(dimethylamino)ethyl 1-methylpyrrolidine-2-carboxylate dimethiodide).

'Hygroton' *see* Chlortalidone.

'Hykinone' *see* Menadione sodium bisulfite.

HYMECROMONE*** (7-hydroxy-4-methylcoumarin; 4-methylumbelliferone; LM-94).

'Hyminal' *see* Methaqualone.

'Hymorphan' *see* Hydromorphone.

HYOCHOLIC ACID (3,6,7-trihydroxycholanic acid).

HYODEOXYCHOLIC ACID (3,6-dihydroxycholanic acid).

'Hyodur' *see* Dimethyl sulfoxide.

'Hyosan' *see* Dichlorophen.

HYOSCINE (DL-6,7-epoxytropine tropate; DL-atroscine).
See also Scopolamine.

Hyoscine amine oxide *see* Scopolamine *N*-oxide.

HYOSCYAMINE (atropine L-isomer; daturine;

duboisine; L-hyoscyamine).

D-Hyoscyamine *see* Atropine.

L-Hyoscyamine *see* Hyoscyamine.

Hyoscyamine (4′-phenylphenacyl) bromide *see* Fentonium bromide.

'Hypaque' *see* Meglumine diatrizoate; Sodium diatrizoate.

'Hyperforat' *see* Hypericin.

HYPERICIN (4,5,7,4′,5′,7′-hexahydroxy-2,2′-dimethylnaphthodianthone).
See also under Co-dergocrine.

HYPERIN (quercetin 3-galactoside; hyperoside).

'Hyperol' *see* Urea hydrogen peroxide.

Hyperoside *see* Hyperin.

'Hyperpax' *see* Methyldopa.

'Hyperstat' *see* Diazoxide.

'Hypertane' *see* Ethiazide.

Hypertensin *see* Angiotensin.

'Hypertensin-Ciba' *see* Angiotensinamide.

'Hypertonal' *see* Diazoxide.

Hyphilline* *see* Diprophylline.

'Hypnal' *see* Chloralphenazone.

'Hypnazol' *see* Fenadiazole.

'Hypnodil' *see* Metomidate.

'Hypnomidate' *see* Etomidate.

Hypnone *see* Acetophenone.

'Hypnorex' *see* Lithium carbonate.

'Hypnotrol' *see* Secobarbital.

'Hypnovel' *see* Midazolam.

Hypo *see* Sodium thiosulfate.

HYPOGLYCIN A (L-2-amino-3-(2-methylenecyclopropyl)propionic acid).

HYPOGLYCIN B (L-glutamyl dipeptide with hypoglycin A).

'Hypoglycone' *see* Tolbutamide.

Hyponitrous acid anhydride *see* Nitrous oxide.

α-Hypophamine *see* Oxytocin.

β-Hypophamine *see* Vasopressin.

'Hyposan' *see* Sodium hypochlorite.

'Hypostamine' *see* Tritoqualine.

'Hyposterol' *see* 2-Phenylbutyramide.

Hyposulfite *see* Sodium thiosulfate.

'Hyposulphene' *see* Sodium thiosulfate.

HYPOTAURINE (2-aminoethanesulfinic acid).

Hypothiazide (tr) *see* Hydrochlorothiazide.

'Hypotrol' *see* Secobarbital.

'Hypovase' *see* Prazosin.

HYPOXANTHINE (6-hydroxypurine; 6(1*H*)-purinone; sarcine; sarkin).

Hypoxanthine riboside *see* Inosine.

'Hyprenan' *see* Prenalterol.

HYPROLOSE*** (cellulose 2-hydroxypropyl ether).

HYPROMELLOSE*** (a partial mixed methyl and hydroxypropyl ether of cellulose).

'Hyptor' *see* Methaqualone.

'Hyryl' *see* Flavin mononucleotide.

'Hyskor' *see* Dextran 70.

'Hystryl' *see* Diphenylpyraline.

'Hytacherol' *see* Dihydrotachysterol.

'Hytakerol' *see* Dihydrotachysterol.

'Hyton' *see* Pemoline.

'Hytrast' *see under* Iopydol.

'Hyvar' *see* Isocil.
'Hyvar X' *see* Bromacil.
'Hyzyd' *see* Isoniazid.

I

IA-307 *see* Sulfadiasulfone sodium.
IAA *see* 3-Indoleacetic acid.
'Iatropur' *see* Triamterene.
'Ibaril' *see* Desoximetasone.
IBAZOCINE** (1,2,3,4,5,6-hexahydro-6,11,11-trimethyl-3-(3-methyl-2-butenyl)-2,6-methano-3-benzazocin-8-ol; 2'-hydroxy-5,9,9-trimethyl-2-(3-methyl-2-butenyl)-6,7-benzomorphan).
IBC *see* Bucrilate.
'IBD 20' *see* Isosorbide dinitrate.
Ibenzmethyzin* *see* Procarbazine.
IBH-194 *see* Isonixin.
'Ibistacin' *see* Ribostamycin.
'Ibition' *see* Thiobarbital.
IBOGAINE (alkaloid from *Tabernanthe iboga*; ibogine; 'bogadin-TM').
IBOPAMINE*** (4-[2-(methylamino)ethyl]-*o*-phenylene diisobutyrate; 4-[2-(methylamino)-ethyl]pyrocatechol diisobutyrate; *N*-methyldop-amine diisobutyrate; SB-7505; SK&F-100168).
'Ibosure' *see* Ibuprofen.
IBOTENIC ACID (α-amino-3-hydroxy-5-isox-azoleacetic acid).
'Ibrin' *see* Fibrinogen (^{125}I).
Ibrotal* *see* Ibrotamide.
IBROTAMIDE*** (2-bromo-*N*-ethyl-*N*-isopropyl-acetamide; ibrotal).
'Ibudros' *see* Ibuproxam.
IBUFENAC*** (*p*-isobutylphenylacetic acid; RD-11654).
IBUPROFEN*** (2-(*p*-isobutylphenyl)propionic acid; *p*-isobutylhydratropic acid; B-80; IP-82; McN-R-1451; RD-13621; U-18573; UCB-79171).
IBUPROFEN ALUMINUM* (hydroxybis[α-methyl-4-(2-methylpropyl)benzeneacetato-*O*]-aluminium; hydroxybis(*p*-isobutylhydratro-pato)aluminium; U-18573G).
IBUPROFEN GUAIACOL ESTER (*o*-methoxy-phenyl 2-(*p*-isobutylphenyl)propionate; AF-2259).
IBUPROFEN-LYSINE (lysine salt of ibuprofen; 'saren').
IBUPROXAM*** (*p*-isobutylhydratropohydro-xamic acid; 2-(*p*-isobutylphenyl)propionohydro-xamic acid; 'ibudros').
IBUTEROL** (5-(2-*tert*-butylamino-1-hydroxy-ethyl-*m*-phenylene diisobutyrate; 5-(2-*tert*-butyl-amino-1-hydroxyethyl)resorcinol diisobutyrate).
IBUVERINE*** (isobutyl α-phenylcyclohexane-glycolate).

IBX *see* Xibornol.
Ibylcaine* *see* Butethamine.
'Icacin' *see* Dibekacin.
ICG *see* Indocyanine green.
Ichthammol *see* Ammonium sulfobituminate.
Ichthammonium *see* Ammonium sulfobituminate.
Ichthium *see* Ammonium sulfobituminate.
Ichthosulfol *see* Ammonium sulfobituminate.
ICI-350 *see* Aminochlorthenoxazine.
ICI-8173 *see* Quindoxin.
ICI-15688 *see* Ditophal.
ICI-24223 *see* Isobutyltritylamine.
ICI-28257 *see* Clofibrate.
ICI-29661 *see* Pyrimitate.
ICI-32525 *see* Sulfamonomethoxine.
ICI-32865 *see* Etoglucid.
ICI-33828 *see* Metallibure.
ICI-35868 *see* Propofol.
ICI-38174 *see* Pronetalol.
ICI-45520 *see* Propranolol.
ICI-45673 *see* Toliprolol.
ICI-46474 *see* Tamoxifen citrate.
ICI-46683 *see* Oxyclozanide.
ICI-47319 *see* Dexpropranolol.
ICI-48213 *see* Cyclofenil.
ICI-50123 *see* Pentagastrin.
ICI-50172 *see* Practolol.
ICI-51426 *see* Cyheptamide.
ICI-54450 *see* Fenclozic acid.
ICI-54594 *see* Brofezil.
ICI-55052 *see* Nequinate.
ICI-55695 *see* Methyl clofenapate.
ICI-55897 *see* Clobuzarit.
ICI-58834 *see* Viloxazine.
ICI-59118 *see* Razoxane.
ICI-66082 *see* Atenolol.
ICI-74917 *see* Bufrolin.
ICI-80008 *see* Fluprostenol.
ICI-80996 *see* Cloprostenol.
ICI-81008 *see* Fluprostenol.
ICI-88262 *see* Gonadorelin.
ICI-118587 *see* Xamoterol fumarate.
ICI-125211 *see* Tiotidine.
ICI-136753 *see* Tracazolate.
ICI-156834 *see* Cefotetan.
ICI-US 457 *see* Octazamide.
ICLAZEPAM*** (7-chloro-1-[2-(cyclopropyl-methoxy)ethyl]-1,3-dihydro-5-phenyl-2*H*-1,4-benzodiazepin-2-one).
ICN-542 *see* Ribaminol.
ICN-1229 *see* Ribavirin.

ICOSPIRAMIDE** ((±)-8-[*cis*-4-cyano-4-(*p*-fluorophenyl)cyclohexyl]-1-(*p*-fluorophenyl)-4-oxo-1,3,8-triazaspiro[4.5]decane-3-acetamide).

ICRF-159 *see* Razoxane.

'Icteryl' *see* Menbutone.

ID-480 *see* Flurazepam.

ID-530 *see* Nimetazepam.

ID-540 *see* Fludiazepam.

'Idalon' *see* Floctafenine.

'Idarac' *see* Floctafenine.

IDARUBICIN*** ((1*S*,3*S*)-3-acetyl-1,2,3,4,6,11-hexahydro-3,5,12-trihydroxy-6,11-dioxonaph-thacen-1-yl 3-amino-2,3,6-trideoxy-α-L-*lyxo*-hexopyranoside; (7*S*,9*S*)-9-acetyl-7-[(3-amino-2,3,6-trideoxy-α-L-*lyxo*-hexopyranosyl)oxy]-7,8,9,10-tetrahydro-6,9,11-trihydroxy-5,12-naphthacenedione).

IDAZOXAN** ((±)-2-(1,4-benzodioxan-2-yl)-2-imidazoline; (±)-2-(2,3-dihydro-1,4-benzodiox-in-2-yl)-2-imidazoline; idazoxan hydrochloride; RX-781094).

'Ideaxan' *see* Piracetam.

IDEBENONE** (2-(10-hydroxydecyl)-5,6-dimeth-oxy-3-methyl-*p*-benzoquinone).

'Idemin' *see under* Meprobamate.

'Idexur' *see* Idoxuridine.

'Idogenabil' *see* Menbutone.

'Idoxene' *see* Idoxuridine.

IDOXURIDINE*** (2′-deoxy-5-iodouridine; IDU; iododeoxyuridine; IUDR; allergan-211; NSC-39661; SK&F-14287).

IDOXURIDINE plus DIMETHYL SULFOXIDE ('herpid'; 'iduridine'; 'ophthalmadine').

'Idril' *see* 8-Quinolinol sulfate.

Idrobutamina *see* Butidrine.

IDROCILAMIDE** (*N*-(2-hydroxyethyl)cinnam-amide; LCB-29; 'brolitene'; 'srilane').

'Idroestril' *see* Diethylstilbestrol.

'Idrolone' *see* Fenquizone.

'Idro P-3' *see* Oxamarin.

IDROPRANOLOL** (5,6-dihydro-1-(2-hydroxy-3-isopropylaminopropoxy)naphthalene; 1-(5,6-dihydronaphth-2-yloxy)-3-isopropylamino-2-propanol; dihydropropranolol; dropranolol).

Idropropizina *see* Dropropizine.

IDU *see* Idoxuridine.

'Idulian' *see* Azatadine.

'Iduridine' *see under* Idoxuridine.

'Iduviran' *see* Idoxuridine.

IEM-163 *see* Etimizole.

IEM-366 *see* Fepracet.

'Ifenec' *see* Econazole.

IFENPRODIL*** (4-benzyl-1-[3-hydroxy-3-(*p*-hydroxyphenyl)prop-2-yl]piperidine; 4-benzyl-α-(*p*-hydroxyphenyl)-β-methyl-1-piperidineethan-ol; 2-(4-benzylpiperid-1-yl)-1-(*p*-hydroxyphen-yl)-1-propanol; α-[1-(4-benzylpiperid-1-yl)ethyl]-*p*-hydroxybenzyl alcohol).

IFENPRODIL TARTRATE (RC 61-91; 'vadilex').

IFK (tr) *see* Propham.

IFOSFAMIDE*** (*N*,3-bis(2-chloroethyl)tetra-hydro-2*H*-1,3,2-oxazaphosphorin-2-amine 2-oxide; 3-(2-chloroethyl)-2-(2-chloroethylamino)-2*H*-1,3,2-oxazaphosphorinane 2-oxide; 3-(2-chloroethyl)-2-(2-chloroethylamino)tetrahydro-2*H*-1,3,2-oxazaphosphorine 2-oxide; isofosf-amide; isophosphamide; Asta-4942; MJF-9325; NSC-109724; Z-4942; 'cyfos'; 'holoxan'; 'iso-en-doxan'; 'mitoxana').

'Igepal CA' *see* Octoxinol.

'Igepal CO' *see* Nonoxinol(s).

Ignotine *see* Carnosine.

'Igran' *see* Terbutryn.

'Igroton' *see* Chlortalidone.

IHP *see* Xibornol.

IIH P-S10 *see* Prolactin.

I-K-1 *see* Metofoline.

'Ikapharm' *see* Phenmetrazine.

'Ikaran' *see* Dihydroergotamine.

'Iktorivil' *see* Clonazepam.

IL-5902 *see* Spiramycin.

IL-6001 *see* Trimipramine.

IL-6302 *see* Dimetotiazine.

IL-17803 *see* Acebutolol.

IL-19552 *see* Pipotiazine palmitate.

'Ildamen' *see* Oxyfedrine.

'Iletin' *see* Insulin zinc suspension.

'Iliadin' *see* Oxymetazoline.

'Ilidar' *see* Azapetine.

'Ilopan' *see* Dexpanthenol.

ILOPROST*** ((*E*)-(3a*S*,4*R*,5*R*,6a*S*)-hexahydro-5-hydroxy-4-[(*E*)-(3*S*,4*RS*)-3-hydroxy-4-methyl-1-octen-6-ynyl]-$\Delta^{2(1H),\delta}$-pentalenevaleric acid; ci-loprost).

'Ilosone' *see* Erythromycin estolate.

'Ilotycin' *see* Erythromycin.

'Ilozoft' *see* Docusate sodium.

'Ilube' *see under* Acetylcysteine.

ILUDIN M (antibiotic from *Clitocybe illudens*; NSC-400978).

ILUDIN S (NSC-400979).

'Ilvin' *see* Brompheniramine.

IMA *see* Isopropylmethoxamine.

'Imadyl' *see* Carprofen.

IMAFEN*** (2,3,5,6-tetrahydro-5-phenyl-1*H*-imi-dazo[1,2-*a*]imidazole; imafen hydrochloride; R-25540).

'Imagon' *see* Chloroquine diphosphate.

'Imagotan' *see* Sulforidazine.

'Imakol' *see* Oxomemazine.

'Imap' *see* Fluspirilene.

'Imbaral' *see* Sulindac.

'Imbretil' *see* Hexcarbacholine bromide.

'Imbrilon' *see* Indometacin.

IMCARBOFOS*** (tetraethyl [(2-methoxy-*p*-phenylene)bis[imino(thiocarbonyl)]]diphosphor-amidate; CL-217658).

Imequin *see* 2,2,6,6-Tetramethylquinuclidine meth-iodide.

'Imeson' *see* Nitrazepam.

'Imesonal' *see* Secobarbital.

IMET-3993 *see* Bendamustine.

IMEXON*** (4-imino-1,3-diazabicyclo[3.1.0]hex-an-2-one).

'Imferdex' *see* Iron dextran injection.

'Imferon' *see* Iron dextran injection.

IMICLOPAZINE*** (2-chloro-10-[3-[4-(2-(3-methyl-2-oxoimidazolidin-1-yl)ethyl)piperazin-1-yl]propyl]phenothiazine; 1-[2-[4-[3-(2-chlorophenothiazin-10-yl)propyl]piperazin-1-yl]ethyl]-3-methyl-2-imidazolidinone; chlorimpiphenine; Astra-4241).

'Imidaline' *see* Phentolamine.

Imidamin *see* Antazoline.

'Imidan' *see* Phosmet.

IMIDAZOLE (1,3-diazole; glyoxaline; iminazole).

4-Imidazoleacrylic acid *see* Urocanic acid.

Imidazoleacryloylcholine *see* Murexine.

IMIDAZOLE CLOFIBRATE ('eulion').

4,5-IMIDAZOLEDICARBOXAMIDE (glycarbylamide; 'glycamide').

4,5-Imidazoledicarboxylic acid diethyldiamide *see* Etimizole.

2-IMIDAZOLEETHYLAMINE (2-(2-aminoethyl)imidazole; 2-isohistamine).

4-Imidazoleethylamine *see* Histamine.

IMIDAZOLIDINE (glyoxalidine; tetrahydroglyoxaline).

2,4-Imidazolidinedione *see* Hydantoin.

Imidazolidinetrione *see* Parabanic acid.

2-IMIDAZOLINE (4,5-dihydroimidazole).

4-(2-Imidazolin-2-ylamino)-2-methyl-2H-indazole *see* Indanidine.

3-(2-Imidazolin-2-ylmethyl)-2-methylbenzo[b]thiophene *see* Metizoline.

3-(2-Imidazolin-2-ylthio)indole *see* Tinazoline.

Imidazolinylureidoaluminium compounds *see* Alcloxa; Aldioxa.

2-Imidazol-1-yl-2'-acetonaphthone *see* Nafimidone.

1-(4-Imidazol-4(5)-ylbutyl)-3-methylthiourea *see* Burimamide.

p-[2-(1H-Imidazol-1-yl)ethoxy]benzoic acid *see* Dazoxiben.

1-(2-Imidazol-4-yl-1-methylethyl)-3-[2-[[(5-methylimidazol-4-yl)methyl]thio]ethyl]guanidine *see* Sopromidine.

3-(Imidazol-1-ylmethyl)-2-methylindole-1-propionic acid *see* Dazmegrel.

2-(1H-Imidazol-1-yl)-1-(2-naphthalenyl)ethanone *see* Nafimidone.

3-Imidazol-1-yl-1-pentylallyl nicotinate *see* Nicogrelate.

N-(p-Imidazol-4-ylphenyl)-N'-isopropylformamidine *see* Mifentidine.

1-(3-Imidazol-4-ylpropyl)-3-[2-[[(5-methylimidazol-4-yl)methyl]thio]ethyl]guanidine *see* Impromidine.

Imidazolylthioguanine *see* Tiamiprine.

p-Imidazo[1,2-a]pyridin-2-ylhydratropic acid *see* Miroprofen.

2-[p-(Imidazo[1,2-a]pyridin-2-yl)phenyl]propionic acid *see* Miroprofen.

7H-Imidazo[4,5-d]pyrimidine *see* Purine.

IMIDECYL IODINE* (complex of 2-alkyl-(C$_7$H$_{15}$ to C$_{17}$H$_{35}$)-1-carboxymethyl-1-(2-hydroxyethyl)-2-imidazolinium chloride with 3,6,9,12,15,18,21,24,27,30,33,36,39-tridexaoxapentaconan-1-ol and iodine; 'amfodyne'; 'amphodyne').

'Imidin' *see* Naphazoline.

IMIDOCARB*** (3,3'-bis(2-imidazolin-2-yl)carbanilide; 3,3'-di-2-imidazolin-2-ylcarbanilide; imidocarb hydrochloride; 'imizol').

IMIDOLINE** (1-(m-chlorophenyl)-3-(2-dimethylaminoethyl)-2-imidazolidinone; CL-48156).

Imidolol *see* Adimolol.

Iminazole *see* Imidazole.

2,2'-Iminobibenzyl *see* 10,11-Dihydro-5H-dibenz-[b,f]azepine.

4-Imino-1,3-diazabicyclo[3.1.0]hexan-2-one *see* Imexon.

2,2'-Iminodiethanol *see* Diethanolamine.

4,4'-(Iminodimethylene)dipyridine *see* Gapicomine.

3,3'-Iminodi-1-propanol dimesilate *see* Improsulfan.

(1-Iminoethyl)phosphoramidothioic acid O,O-bis(p-chlorophenyl) ester *see* Phosacetim.

2-Imino-1-methyl-4-imidazolinone *see* Creatinine.

2-Imino-3-methyl-1-phenyl-4-imidazolidinone *see* Azolimine.

IMINOPHENIMIDE*** (3-ethyl-3-phenylpiperazine-2,6-dione).

2-Imino-5-phenyl-4-oxazolidinone *see* Pemoline.

N-[Imino(phosphonoamino)methyl]-N-methylglycine *see* Creatinephosphoric acid.

Iminopromazine *see* Aminopromazine.

5-Imino-2,2,4,4-tetrakis(trifluoromethyl)imidazolidine *see* Midaflur.

Iminourea *see* Guanidine.

Imipemide* *see* Imipenem.

IMIPENEM** ((5R,6S)-3-[[2-(formimidoylamino)ethyl]thio]-6-[(R)-1-hydroxyethyl]-7-oxo-1-azabicyclo[3.2.0]hept-2-ene-2-carboxylic acid; [5R-[5α,6α(R*)]]-6-(1-hydroxyethyl)-3-[[2-[(iminomethyl)amino]ethyl]thio]-7-oxo-1-azabicyclo[3.2.0]hept-2-ene-2-carboxylic acid; imipemide; imipemide monohydrate; N-formimidoylthienamycin; MK-0787).

IMIPRAMINE*** (5-[3-(dimethylamino)propyl]-10,11-dihydro-5H-dibenz[b,f]azepine; imipramine hydrochloride; imizine; melipramine; psychoforine; G-22150; G-22355).

Imipramine N-oxide *see* Imipraminoxide.

IMIPRAMINOXIDE*** (imipramine N-oxide; 'imiprex').

'Imiprex' *see* Imipraminoxide.

Imizine (tr) *see* Imipramine.

'Imizol' *see* Imidocarb.

'Immenoctal' *see* Secobarbital.

'Immenox' *see* Secobarbital.

'Immobilon' *see under* Etorphine.

'Immunoviral' *see* Inosine pranobex.

'Immunox' *see* Thymopentin.

'Imodium' *see* Loperamide.

IMOLAMINE*** (4-[2-(diethylamino)ethyl]-5-imino-3-phenyl-1,2,4-oxadiazoline; LA-1211).

'Imotryl' *see* Benzydamine.

IMP *see* Inosinic acid.

IMPACARZINE*** (N,N-diethyl-4-[2-(2-oxo-3-tetradecylimidazolidin-1-yl)ethyl]-1-piperazinecarboxamide; 1-[2-[4-(diethylcarbamoyl)piperazin-1-yl]ethyl]-3-tetradecylimidazolidin-2-one).

'Imperacin' *see* Oxytetracycline.

Imperatorin see Pentosalen.
'Impletol' see Procaine-caffeine complex.
'Impromen' see Bromperidol.
IMPROMIDINE* (1-(3-imidazol-4-ylpropyl)-3-[2-[[(5-methylimidazol-4-yl)methyl]thio]ethyl]-guanidine; impromidine hydrochloride; impromidine trihydrochloride; SK&F-92676-A3).
IMPROSULFAN* (3,3'-iminodi-1-propanol dimesilate; NSC-102627; Yoshi 864).
IMPROSULFAN TOSILATE (NSC-140117).
'Impruvol' see Butylated hydroxytoluene.
'Impugan' see Furosemide.
'Impulsin' see Palmidrol.
'Imugan' see Chloraniformethan.
IMURACETAM* (1,3-bis[(2-oxopyrrolidin-1-yl)methyl]urea).
'Imuran' see Azathioprine.
'Imurel' see Azathioprine.
'Imuthiol' see Dithiocarb.
IN-29-5931 see Triclofenol piperazine.
IN-73 see Isoniazid.
IN-117 see Hexafluronium bromide.
IN-379 see Pimetine.
IN-391 see Methindethyrium.
IN-461 see Benzindopyrine.
IN-511 see Fenyramidol.
IN-836 see Fenyripol.
IN-1060 see Cyprolidol.
'Inactin' see Thiobutabarbital.
'Inaktin' see Thiobutabarbital.
'Inamycin' see Novobiocin.
'Inappetyl' see Benzphetamine.
'Inapsine' see Droperidol.
'Incidal' see Mebhydrolin napadisilate.
In:Cn see Poly I:C.
Indacrinic acid see Indacrinone.
INDACRINONE ((±)-[(6,7-dichloro-2-methyl-1-oxo-2-phenylindan-5-yl)oxy]acetic acid; (±)-[(6,7-dichloro-2,3-dihydro-2-methyl-1-oxo-2-phenyl-1H-inden-5-yl)oxy]acetic acid; indacrinic acid; MK-196).
'Indalitan' see Clorindione.
Indalone see Butopyronoxyl.
INDALPINE* (4-(2-indol-3-ylethyl)piperidine; 3-(2-piperid-4-ylethyl)indole; LM-5008).
INDAN (2,3-dihydroindene).
INDANAZOLINE* (2-(4-indanylamino)-2-imidazoline; E-V-A-16; 'farial').
INDANIDINE (4-(2-imidazolin-2-ylamino)-2-methyl-2H-indazole; indanidine hydrochloride; Sgd-101/75).
INDANOREX (2-(1-aminopropyl)-2-indanol).
1,2,3-Indantrione hydrate see Ninhydrin.
2-(4-Indanylamino)-2-imidazoline see Indanazoline.
Indanylcarbenicillin see Carindacillin.
O-Indan-5-yl m,N-dimethylthiocarbanilate see Tolindate.
6-[2-[(Indan-5-yloxy)carbonyl]-2-phenylacetamido]penicillanic acid see Carindacillin.
INDAPAMIDE* (3-(aminosulfonyl)-4-chloro-N-(2,3-dihydro-2-methyl-1H-indol-1-yl)benzamide; 1-(4-chloro-3-sulfamoylbenzamido)-2-methylindoline; 2-chloro-5-[(2-methylindolin-1-yl)carbamoyl]benzenesulfonamide; 4-chloro-N-(2-methylindol-1-yl)-3-sulfamoylbenzamide; S-1520; SE-1520; 'fludex'; 'natrilix'; 'tertensif'). See also under Atenolol.
INDECAINIDE* (9-[3-(isopropylamino)propyl]fluorene-9-carboxamide; ricainide).
INDELOXAZINE* ((±)-2-[(inden-7-yloxy)methyl]morpholine; indeloxazine hydrochloride; CI-874; YM-08054-1).
INDENOLOL* (4(or 7)-[2-hydroxy-3-(isopropylamino)propoxy]indene; 1-(inden-4(or 7)-yloxy)-3-(isopropylamino)-2-propanol; indenolol hydrochloride; Sch-28316Z; YB-2).
1-(Inden-4(or 7)-yloxy)-3-(isopropylamino)-2-propanol see Indenolol.
2-[(Inden-7-yloxy)methyl]morpholine see Indeloxazine.
'Inderal' see Propranolol.
'Inderetic' see under Bendroflumethiazide.
'Inderex' see under Bendroflumethiazide.
'Inderide' see under Hydrochlorothiazide.
Indican see Indoxyl β-D-glucoside; Indoxylsulfuric acid.
Indicarmin see Indigo carmine.
Indigo blue see Indigotin.
INDIGO CARMINE (indigotin-5,5'-disulfonic acid disodium salt; carminum coeruleum; indicarmin; soluble indigo blue).
INDIGOTIN (2,2'-bipseudoindoxyl; diindogen; indigo blue).
Indigotin-5,5'-disulfonic acid disodium salt see Indigo carmine.
Indium disodium pentetate see Pentetate indium disodium In-111.
Indium trisodium pentetate see Pentetate indium trisodium In-111.
'Indobloc' see Propranolol.
INDOBUFEN* ((±)-2-[p-(1-oxoisoindolin-2-yl)phenyl]butyric acid; K-3920).
INDOCATE (2-(dimethylamino)ethyl 1-benzyl-2,3-dimethylindole-5-carboxylate; deanol ester of 1-benzyl-2,3-dimethylindole-5-carboxylic acid).
'Indocid' see Indometacin.
'Indocin' see Indometacin.
INDOCYANINE GREEN* (2-[7-[1,1-dimethyl-3-(4-sulfobutyl)benz[e]indolin-2-ylidene]-1,3,5-heptatrienyl]-1,1-dimethyl-3-(4-sulfobutyl)-1H-benz[e]indolium hydroxide internal salt sodium salt; Fox green; tricarbocyanine-II; ICG).
'Indocybin' see Psilocybine.
'Indokolon' see Flurotyl.
INDOLAPRIL ((2S,3aS,7aS)-1-[(S)-N-[(S)-1-carboxy-3-phenylpropyl]alanyl]hexahydro-2-indolinecarboxylic acid 1-ethyl ester).
INDOLE (1-benzazole; 2,3-benzopyrrole; ketole).
3-INDOLEACETIC ACID (heteroauxin; IAA).
2,3-Indoledione see Isatin.
Indole-3-ethanol see Tryptophol.
3-Indoleethylamine see Tryptamine.
2-Indolinone see Oxindole.
3-Indolinone see Pseudoindoxyl.
INDOLMYCIN (tr) (5-(1-indol-3-ylethyl)-2-meth-

293

ylaminooxazolin-4-one; antibiotic PAA 155; PAA-155).

Ψ-Indolone *see* (3*H*)Pseudoindol-3-one.

2-(3*H*)-Indolone *see* Oxindole.

5-(1-Indol-3-ylethyl)-2-methylaminooxazolin-4-one *see* Indolmycin.

4-(2-Indol-3-ylethyl)piperidine *see* Indalpine.

***N*-[1-(2-Indol-3-ylethyl)piperid-4-yl]benzamide** *see* Indoramin.

Indol-4-yloxy-3-isopropylamino-2-propanol *see* Pindolol.

'Indomee' *see* Indometacin.

INDOMETACIN*** (1-(*p*-chlorobenzoyl)-5-methoxy-2-methyl-3-indoleacetic acid; indomethacin; McN-R-1166).

INDOMETACIN plus ZOLIMIDINE ('solitacin'). *See also* Acemetacin; Glucametacin; Meglumine indometacinate; Oxametacin; Proglumetacin; Sermetacin; Talmetacin; *and under* Dexamethasone.

Indometacin hydroxylamide *see* Oxametacin.

Indometacin meglumine *see* Meglumine indometacinate.

Indometacin 3-pyridylmethyl thioester *see* Pimetacin.

INDOMETHACIN TROPINE ESTER (tropine indometacinate; 'tropesin').

Indomethacin* *see* Indometacin.

Indopan (tr) *see* 2-Methyltryptamine.

INDOPANOLOL*** ((±)-1-[(3-chloro-2-methyl-indol-4-yl)oxy]-3-[(2-phenoxyethyl)amino]-2-propanol).

INDOPINE*** (3-[2-(1-phenethylpiperid-4-yl)-ethyl]indole).

INDOPROFEN*** (*p*-(1-oxoisoindolin-2-yl)hydratropic acid; 2-[*p*-(1-carboxyethyl)phenyl]isoindolin-1-one; 2-[*p*-(1-carboxyethyl)phenyl]phthalimidine; 4-(1,3-dihydro-1-oxo-2*H*-isoindol-2-yl)-α-methylbenzeneacetic acid; K-4277; 'flosin'; 'flosint').

INDORAMIN*** (4-benzamido-1-(2-indol-3-yl-ethyl)-piperidine; 3-[2-(4-benzamidopiperid-1-yl)ethyl]-indole; *N*-[1-(2-indol-3-ylethyl)piperid-4-yl]benzamide; indoramin hydrochloride; Wy-21901; 'baratol').

INDORENATE*** (methyl (±)-α-(aminomethyl)-5-methoxyindole-3-acetate).

'Indorm' *see* Propiomazine.

'Indosmos' *see* Indometacin.

Indoxamic acid *see* Oxametacin.

INDOXOLE** (2,3-bis(*p*-methoxyphenyl)indole; U-22020).

INDOXYL (3-hydroxyindole; indol-3-ol).

INDOXYL β-D-GLUCOSIDE (indican).

3-INDOXYLSULFURIC ACID (indican).

INDRILINE*** (*N*,*N*-dimethyl-1-phenylindene-1-ethylamine; 1-[2-(dimethylamino)ethyl]-1-phenylindene; MJ-1986).

'Indunox' *see* Etodroxizine.

'Indusil T' *see* Cobamamide.

'Inerteen' *see* Polychlorinated biphenyl.

'Inezin' *see* *S*-Benzyl *O*-ethyl phenylphosphonothioate.

INF *see* Menazone.

INF-1837 *see* Flufenamic acid.

INF-3355 *see* Mefenamic acid.

INF-4668 *see* Meclofenamic acid.

'Infectomycin' *see* Amoxicillin.

'Infecundin' *see under* Noretynodrel.

'Inferno' *see* Amiton.

'Infiltrina' *see* Dimethyl sulfoxide.

'Inflacine' *see under* Dexamethasone.

'Inflamase' *see* Prednisolone sodium phosphate.

'Inflanefran' *see* Prednisolone acetate.

'Inflaryl' *see* Niflumic acid.

Inflatine *see* Lobeline.

'Infukoll M-40' *see* Dextran 40.

'Infundin' *see* Oxytocin.

Ingalan (tr) *see* Methoxyflurane.

'Ingasan CF₃' *see* Halocarban.

'INGH' *see* Gluconiazone.

INH *see* Isoniazid.

Inhalan (tr) *see* Methoxyflurane.

'INHA-PAS' *see* Pasiniazid.

'INHG' *see* Gluconiazone.

INHIBIN (folliculostatin).

'Inhibin' *see under* Hydroquinine.

'Inhibostamin' *see* Tritoqualine.

'Inhiston' *see* Pheniramine.

INHM *see* Isoniazid mesilate.

INHS *see* Salinazid.

INICARONE*** (3-isonicotinoyl-2-isopropyl-benzofuran; 2-isopropylbenzofuran-3-yl pyrid-4-yl ketone).

'Inimur' *see* Nifuratel.

'Iniprol' *see* Aprotinin.

'Initard' *see under* Isophane insulin.

Inkasan (tr) *see* Metralindole.

'Innovan' *see under* Droperidol.

'Innovar' *see under* Droperidol.

INO-502 *see* Cetiedil.

'Inofal' *see* Sulforidazine.

'Inolin' *see* Tretoquinol.

'Inophylline' *see* Aminophylline.

INOSINE*** (1,9-dihydro-9-β-D-ribofuranosyl-6*H*-purin-6-one; hypoxanthine riboside; oxiamin; Eu-2200; 'atorel'; 'trophicardyl').

'Inosine' *see* Phytic acid.

Inosine 1-(dimethylamino)-2-propanol *p*-acetamidobenzoate *see* Inosine pranobex.

Inosine monophosphate *see* Inosinic acid.

INOSINE PRANOBEX* (dimepranol *p*-acetamidobenzoate inosine complex; *p*-acetamidobenzoic acid inosine dimethylamino-2-propanol complex; dimethylaminoisopropanol inosine *p*-acetamidobenzoate; inosine 1-(dimethylamino)-2-propanol *p*-acetamidobenzoate; methisoprinol; NP-113; NPT-10381; 'delimmun'; 'immunoviral'; 'inosiplex'; 'isoprinosine'; 'pranosine'; 'viruxan').

INOSINE TRIPHOSPHATE (inosine triphosphoric acid; ITP).

INOSINIC ACID (inosine 5'-phosphate; inosine monophosphate; IMP).

'Inosiplex' *see* Inosine pranobex.

Inosite *see* Inositol.

Inositocalcium *see* Calcium magnesium phytate.

INOSITOL (*meso*-1,2,3,4,5,6-hexahydroxycyclo-hexane; betitol; bios-II; cyclohexanehexol; cyclohexitol; dambose; hexol; inosite; *i*-inositol; *m*-inositol; meat sugar; mesoinosite; mesoinositol; mouse antialopecia factor; myoinositol; nucite; phaseomannitol; rat antispectacled eye factor; scyllite).

Inositol hexakis(disodium phosphate) *see* Persodium phytate.

Inositol hexanicotinate *see* Inositol nicotinate.

INOSITOL HEXANITRATE ('mesonitrol'; 'nitrositol'; 'tolanate').

Inositolhexaphosphoric acid *see* Phytic acid.

Inositol methyl ether *see* Quebrachitol.

Inositol niacinate *see* Inositol nicotinate.

INOSITOL NICOTINATE* (*meso*-inositol hexanicotinate; inositol niacinate; NSC-49506; WIN-9154).
See also under Bamethan; Clofibrate; Magnesium clofibrate.

'Inostral' *see* Cromoglicate disodium.

'Inoval' *see under* Droperidol.

INPC *see* Propham.

INPEA *see* Nifenalol.

Inprochone* *see* Inproquone.

INPROQUONE* (2,5-bis(1-aziridinyl)-3,6-dipropoxy-*p*-benzoquinone; ethylene iminoquinone; inprochone; E-39; NSC-17261; RP 6870).

INSH *see* Salinazid.

'Insidon' *see* Opipramol.

'Insoral' *see* Phenformin.

'Instrumer' *see* Hydrargaphen.

'Insulatard' *see* Isophane insulin.

Insulin *see also under* Biphasic insulin injection; Dalanated insulin; Isophane insulin; Neutral insulin.

'Insulin actrapid' *see* Neutral insulin injection.

INSULIN DEFALAN (1B-de(L-phenylalanine)-insulin).

INSULIN HUMAN* (8A-L-threonine-10A-L-isoleucine-30B-L-threonineinsulin; human insulin; 'humulin').

'Insulin novo rapitard' *see* Biphasic insulin injection.

'Insulin semilente' *see* Insulin zinc suspension amorphous.

'Insulin ultralente' *see* Insulin zinc suspension crystalline.

INSULIN ZINC SUSPENSION* (lente insulin; 'iletin'; 'lente iletin').

INSULIN ZINC SUSPENSION AMORPHOUS ('insulin semilente').

INSULIN ZINC SUSPENSION CRYSTALLINE ('insulin ultralente').

'Intal' *see* Cromoglicate disodium.

'Intasedol' *see* Secbutabarbital.

'Integrin' *see* Oxypertine.

'Intenkordin' *see* Carbocromen.

'Intensain' *see* Carbocromen.

'Interacton' *see* Cocarboxylase.

'Intercordin' *see* Carbocromen.

INTERFERON* (protein formed by interaction

of animal cells with virus; CI-884).

INTERMEDIN (chromatophore-expanding factor; chromatophore-expanding hormone; melanophore-stimulating hormone; β-melanotropin; MSH; A-732179).

'Intestopan' *see under* Broxyquinoline.

'Intestopan-Q' *see under* Broxyquinoline.

'Intetrix' *see* Tilbroquinol.

'Intex' *see under* Medroxyprogesterone.

'Intrabilix' *see* Adipiodone meglumine.

'Intracaine' *see* Parethoxycaine.

'Intradex' *see* Dextran.

'Intraion' *see under* Potassium aspartate.

'Intranarcon' *see* Thialbarbital.

'Intrathion' *see* Thiometon.

'Intration' *see* Thiometon.

'Intraxium' *see* Penimocycline.

INTRAZOLE (1-(*p*-chlorobenzoyl)-3-(1*H*-tetrazol-3-yl-methyl)indole; BL-R743).

INTRIPTYLINE* (4-(5*H*-dibenzo[*a,d*]cyclohepten-5-ylidene)-*N,N*-dimethyl-2-butynylamine; AY-22124).

'Intropin' *see* Dopamine.

'Inubuse' *see* Naringenin.

Inula camphor *see* Alantolactone.

INULIN (alantin; alant starch; dahlin).

'Invenol' *see* Carbutamide.

'Inversine' *see* Mecamylamine.

'Investin' *see* Doxycycline.

'Inzellon' *see under* Potassium aspartate.

'Inzolen' *see under* Potassium aspartate.

IOBENZAMIC ACID* (*N*-(3-amino-2,4,6-triiodobenzoyl)-*N*-phenyl-β-alanine; 3-[(3-amino-2,4,6-triiodobenzoyl)phenylamino]propionic acid; ST-5066; 'osbil'; 'razebil'; 'tracebyl').

IOBUTOIC ACID* (4-[2,4,6-triiodo-3-(morpholinocarbonyl)phenoxy]butyric acid).

Iocarmate meglumine* *see* Meglumine iocarmate.

IOCARMIC ACID* (adipic acid bis[3-carboxy-2,4,6-triiodo-5-(*N*-methylcarboxamido)anilide]; 5,5'-(adipoyldiimino)bis(2,4,6-triiodo-*N*-methylisophthalamic acid); bis[3-carboxy-2,4,6-triiodo-5-(*N*-methylcarboxamido)anilide] of adipic acid; MP-2032).
See also Meglumine iocarmate.

IOCETAMIC ACID (*N*-acetyl-*N*-(2-carboxypropyl)-2,4,6-triiodo-*m*-phenylenediamine; *N*-acetyl-*N*-(3-amino-2,4,6-triiodophenyl)-2-methyl-β-alanine; 3-[*N*-(3-amino-2,4,6-triiodophenyl)acetamido]-2-methylpropionic acid; MP-620).

IODAMIDE* (5-acetamido-3-acetamidomethyl-2,4,6-triiodobenzoic acid; α,5-diacetamido-2,4,6-triiodo-*m*-toluic acid; B-4130; SH-926).

IODAMIDE MEGLUMINE* (iodamide methylglucamine salt; 'renovue').

IODECIMOL (5,5'-[malonylbis[(2-hydroxyethyl)imino]]bis[*N,N*'-bis[2-hydroxy-1-(hydroxymethyl)ethyl]-2,4,6-triiodoisophthalamide]; iodecol).

Iodecol *see* Iodecimol.

IODETRYL* (ethyl 9,10-diiodooctadecanoate; ethyl diiodostearate; 2-(iodopropylidenedioxy)-

propanol; 'mucantil').

IODINATED GLYCEROL* (mixture of 2-(1-iodoethyl)-1,3-dioxolane-4-methanol and its 2-(2-iodoethyl)- isomer; 2,3-(iodopropylidenedioxy)-propanol; iodinated dimers of glycerol; 'mucantil'; 'organidin').
See also Domiodol.

IODINATED (¹²⁵I) HUMAN SERUM ALBUMIN (radioiodinated human serum albumin).

IODINATED (¹³¹I) HUMAN SERUM ALBUMIN (radioiodinated human serum albumin).

Iodinated (¹³¹I) macroaggregated human albumin *see* Macrosalb (¹³¹I).

IODINATED POPPYSEED OIL (di-, tetra- and hexaiodinated addition products of triolein and trilinolein; iodized oil; iodolipol; oleum iodisatum).

Iodipamide* *see* Adipiodone.

'Iodisan' *see* Prolonium iodide.

Iodized oil* *see* Iodinated poppyseed oil.

Iodoalphionic acid sodium salt *see* Pheniodol sodium.

N-(2-Iodobenzoyl)glycine sodium salt *see* Sodium iodohippurate.

ω-(p-Iodobenzyl)-2-(2-oxopyrrolidin-1-yl) ethamer *see* Tolpovidone.

IODOBRASSID* (ethyl 9,10-diiodobrassidate).

IODOCETYLIC ACID (16-iodohexadecanoic acid).

IODOCETYLIC ACID ¹²³I*** ((16-iodo-¹²³I)-hexadecanoic acid; iodocetylic acid I 123; RA-C-384).

Iodochlorhydroxyquin *see* Clioquinol.

Iodochlorhydroxyquinoline *see* Clioquinol.

Iodochoesterol I 131* *see* Iodocholesterol ¹³¹I.

19-(Iodo-¹³¹I)cholest-5-en-3β-ol *see* Iodocholesterol ¹³¹I.

IODOCHOLESTEROL ¹³¹I*** (19-(iodo-¹³¹I)cholest-5-en-3β-ol; iodochoesterol I 131; CL 19 I; NP-59; 'adrenoscan').

Iododiazoate *see* Sodium diatrizoate.

'Iodoenterol' *see* Clioquinol.

2-(Iodoethyl)-1,3-dioxolane-4-methanol *see* Iodinated glycerol.

2,3-[(2-Iodoethylene)dioxy]-1-propanol *see* Domiodol.

IODOFENPHOS* (O-(2,5-dichloro-4-iodophenyl) O,O-dimethyl phosphorothioate; jodphenphos; 'nuvacron N'; 'nuvanol M').
See also under Dichlorvos.

IODOFORM (triiodomethane).

'Iodoglobin' *see* 3,5-Diiodotyrosine.

Iodogorgoic acid *see* 3,5-Diiodotyrosine.

'Iodogorgon' *see* 3,5-Diiodotyrosine.

Iodogorgonic acid *see* 3,5-Diiodotyrosine.

16-Iodohexadecanoic acid *see* Iodocetylic acid.

(16-Iodo-¹²³I)-hexadecanoic acid *see* Iodocetylic acid ¹²³I.

Iodohippurate sodium* *see* Sodium iodohippurate.

IODOHYDRIN (3-iodo-1,2-propanediol; glycerol α-monoiodohydrin).

p-Iodo-N-isopropyl-α-methylphenethylamine *see* Iofetamine.

Iodolipol (tr) *see* Iodinated poppyseed oil.

Iodomethamate *see* Iodoxyl.

Iodomethanesulfonic acid sodium salt *see* Methiodal sodium.

2-(Iodomethyl)-1,3-dioxolane-4-methanol *see* Domiodol.

N¹-(4-Iodo-3-methylisoxazol-3-yl)sulfanilamide *see* Sulfiodizole.

'Iodopact' *see* Sodium acetrizoate.

Iodopanoic acid* *see* Iopanoic acid.

'Iodopaque' *see* Sodium acetrizoate.

Iodophenylundecanoic acid ethyl ester *see* Iofendylate.

IODOPHTHALEIN SODIUM*** (disodium salt of tetraiodophenolphthalein; phenoltetraiodophthalein; tetiothalein; tetraiodophthalein; tetraiodum).

Iodopovidone *see* Povidone-iodine.

3-Iodo-1,2-propanediol *see* Iodohydrin.

2,3-(Iodopropylidenedioxy)propanol *see* Iodinated glycerol.

3-Iodo-2-propynol 2,4,5-trichlorophenyl ether *see* Haloprogin.

Iodopyracet* *see* Diodone.

IODOPYRIDONE* (sodium 3,5-diiodo-4-oxo-1(4H)-pyridineacetate; 'iopax'; 'pyelosil'; 'uroselectan').

Iodoquinine sulfate *see* Quinine iodosulfate.

Iodoquinoline *see* Chiniofon.

7-Iodo-8-quinolinol-5-sulfonic acid chloroquine salt *see* Cloquinate.

Iodostearic acid ethyl ester(s) *see* Ethyl iodostearate.

3-Iodosulfamethoxole *see* Sulfiodizole.

Iodotetroxide *see* Meglumine iodoxamate.

IODOTHIOURACIL*** (5-iodo-2-thiouracil; iodothiouracil sodium; iothiouracil).

Iodothymol *see* Dithymol diiodide.

'Iodotope-131' *see* Sodium iodide (¹³¹I).

Iodoxamate meglumine* *see* Meglumine iodoxamate.

IODOXAMIC ACID*** (N,N'-(1,16-dioxo-4,7,10,13-tetraoxahexadecane-1,16-diyl)di(3-amino-2,4,6-triiodobenzoic acid); 3,3'-[ethylenebis(oxyethyleneoxyethylenecarbonylimino)]bis(2,4,6-triiodobenzoic acid); 4,7,10,13-tetraoxahexadecane-1,16-dioylbis(3-carboxy-2,4,6-triiodoanilide); BC-17; SQ-21982; 'choloview'; 'endobil'; 'videocolangio').
See also Meglumine iodoxamate.

Iodoxine *see* Diiodohydroxyquin.

IODOXYL* (3,5-diiodo-1-methylchelidamic acid sodium salt; iodomethamate; sodium iodomethamate; D-40).

IOFENDYLATE*** (ethyl 10-(p-iodophenyl)undecanoate; ethyl iodophenylundecylate; iophendylate; neurotrast).

IOFETAMINE ((±)-p-iodo-N-isopropyl-α-methylphenethylamine).

IOFETAMINE ¹²³I** (iofetamine with iodine-123).

IOGLICIC ACID*** (5-acetamido-2,4,6-triiodo-N-[(methylcarbamoyl)methyl]isophthalamic

296

acid; 3-(acetylamino)-2,4,6-triiodo-5-[[[[(methyl-amino)carbonyl]methyl]amino]carbonyl]benzoic acid; SH-H-200-AB).
See also Meglumine ioglicate.
IOGLUCOL*** (*N*-[3-[acetyl(2-hydroxyethyl)-amino]-2,4,6-triiodo-5-[(methylamino)carbonyl]-phenyl]-D-gluconamide; 3′-[*N*-(2-hydroxyethyl)-acetamido]-2′,4′,6′-triiodo-5′-(methylcarbamo-yl)-D-gluconanilide; MP-6026).
IOGLUCOMIDE*** (*N*,*N*′-[2,4,6-triiodo-5-(methylcarbamoyl)-1,3-phenylene]bis[D-glucon-amide]; MP-8000).
IOGLUNIDE*** (*N*-gluconoyl-3-[(2-hydroxy-ethyl)carbamoyl]-5-(*N*-methylacetamido)-2,4,6-triiodoaniline; 3′-[(2-hydroxyethyl)carbamoyl]-2′,4′,6′-triiodo-5′-(*N*-methylacetamido)-D-glu-conanilide).
Ioglycamate meglumine* *see* Meglumine ioglycam-ate.
IOGLYCAMIC ACID*** (diglycolic acid bis(3-carboxy-2,4,6-triiodoanilide); *N*,*N*′-diglycoloyl-di(3-carboxy-2,4,6-triiodoaniline); 3,3′-(diglyco-loyldiimino)bis(2,4,6-triiodobenzoic acid); 3,3′-[oxybis(methylenecarbonylimino)]bis(2,4,6-triio-dobenzoic acid); α,α′-oxydi(3-acetamido-2,4,6-triiodobenzoic acid); BE-419).
See also Meglumine ioglycamate; Sodium iogly-camate.
Ioglycamide *see* Meglumine ioglycamate.
IOHEXOL*** (*N*,*N*′-bis(2,3-dihydroxypropyl)-5-[*N*-(2,3-dihydroxypropyl)acetamido]-2,4,6-triio-doisophthalamide; 'omnipaque').
IOLIDONIC ACID*** (1-[3-(2-carboxybutyl)-2,4,6-triiodophenyl]pyrrolidin-2-one; α-ethyl-2,4,6-triiodo-3-(2-oxopyrrolidin-1-yl)hydrocin-namic acid; 2-ethyl-3-[2,4,6-triiodo-3-(2-oxopyr-rolidin-1-yl)phenyl]propionic acid; 2-[2,4,6-triio-do-3-(2-oxopyrrolidin-1-yl)benzyl]butyric acid).
IOLIXANIC ACID*** (3-[2-(1-carboxyethoxy)-ethoxy]-*N*-ethyl-2,4,6-triiodoacetanilide; 2-[2-[3-(*N*-ethylacetamido)-2,4,6-triiodophenoxy]eth-oxy]propionic acid).
IOMEGLAMIC ACID*** (3′-amino-2′,4′,6′-triio-do-*N*-methylglutaranilic acid; 4-[*N*-(3-amino-2,4,6-triiodophenyl)-*N*-methylcarbamoyl]butyric acid; *N*-(3-amino-2,4,6-triiodophenyl)-*N*-meth-ylglutaramic acid; RG-270; 'falignost').
Iomethin* *see* Iometin.
IOMETIN (4-[[3-(dimethylamino)propyl]amino]-7-iodoquinoline; iomethin; MP-537; NM-113).
IOMETIN (^{125}I)** (iomethin I 125).
IOMETIN (^{131}I)** (iomethin I 131).
IOMORINIC ACID*** (*N*-(2-carboxypropyl)-2,4,6-triiodo-3-(1-morpholinoethylideneamino)-benzamide; 2-methyl-*N*-[2,4,6-triiodo-3-[(1-mor-pholinoethylidene)amino]benzoyl]-β-alanine).
'Ionamine' *see* Phentermine resin.
'Ionaze' *see* Propazolamide.
'Ionol' *see* Butylated hydroxytoluene.
'Ionosteril' *see* Mannitol.
IOPAMIDOL*** ((*S*)-*N*,*N*′-bis[2-hydroxy-1-(hydroxymethyl)ethyl]-2,4,6-triiodo-5-lact-amidoisophthalamide; B-15000; SQ-13396; 'so-

lutrast').
IOPANOIC ACID*** (2-(3-amino-2,4,6-triiodo-benzyl)butyric acid; 3-(3-amino-2,4,6-triiodo-phenyl)-2-ethylpropionic acid; iodopanoic acid; jopanoic acid).
'Iopax' *see* Iodopyridone.
Iophendylate* *see* Iofendylate.
Iophenoic acid*** *see* Iophenoxic acid.
IOPHENOXIC ACID* (2-(3-hydroxy-2,4,6-triio-dobenzyl)butyric acid; iophenoic acid; triio-doethanoic acid).
IOPODIC ACID (3-[(dimethylamino)methylene-amino]-2,4,6-triiodohydrocinnamic acid).
See also Ethyl iopodate; Sodium iopodate.
IOPROMIDE*** (*N*,*N*′-bis(2,3-dihydroxypropyl)-2,4,6-triiodo-5-(2-methoxyacetamido)-*N*-methyl-isophthalamide).
IOPRONIC ACID*** (2-[2-(3-acetamido-2,4,6-triiodophenoxy)ethoxymethyl]butyric acid; B-11420; SQ-21983; 'bilimiron'; 'oraview'; 'vide-bil').
IOPYDOL** (1-(2,3-dihydroxypropyl)-3,5-diiodo-4-pyridone).
IOPYDOL plus IOPYDONE ('hytrast').
IOPYDONE** (3,5-diiodo-4-pyridone).
'Ioquin' *see* Diiodohydroxyquin.
IOSEFAMIC ACID*** (5,5′-sebacoyldiimino-bis[2,4,6-triiodo-*N*-methylisophthalamic acid]; MP-271).
IOSERIC ACID*** (*N*-[2-hydroxy-1-(methylcarb-amoyl)ethyl]-2,4,6-triiodo-5-(2-methoxyacet-amido)isophthalamic acid; 3-[[[1-(hydroxymeth-yl)-2-(methylamino)-2-oxoethyl]amino]carbo-nyl]-2,4,6-triiodo-5-[(methoxyacetyl)amino]-benzoic acid; SH-H-239-AB).
See also Meglumine ioserate.
IOSIMIDE** (*N*,*N*,*N*′,*N*′,*N*″,*N*″-hexakis(2-hydr-oxyethyl)-2,4,6-triiodo-1,3,5-benzenetricarbox-amide).
IOSULAMIDE*** (3,3′-[sulfonylbis[(1-oxo-3,1-propanediyl)imino]]bis[5-(acetyl ethylamino)-2,4,6-triiodobenzoic acid]; 3,3′-[sulfonylbis-(ethylenecarbonylimino)]bis[5-(*N*-ethylacet-amido)-2,4,6-triiodobenzoic acid]).
IOSULAMIDE MEGLUMINE* (iosulamide methylglucamine; WIN-31122).
IOSUMETIC ACID*** (*N*-ethyl-2′,4′,6′-triiodo-3′-(methylamino)succinanilic acid; 4-[ethyl-[2,4,6-triiodo-3-(methylamino)phenyl]amino]-4-oxobutanoic acid).
IOTALAMIC ACID*** (5-acetamido-2,4,6-triio-do-*N*-methylisophthalamic acid; iothalamic acid; jodtalamin; methalamic acid; MI-216).
See also Meglumine iotalamate; Sodium iota-lamate.
IOTASUL*** (5,5′-[thiobis(ethylenecarbonylimi-no)]bis[*N*,*N*′-bis(2,3-dihydroxypropyl)-2,4,6-tri-iodo-*N*,*N*′-dimethylisophthalamide]).
IOTETRIC ACID*** (3,3′-[(1,14-dioxo-3,6,9,12-tetraoxatetradecane-1,14-diyl)diimino]bis[2,4,6-triiodobenzoic acid]; 3,3′-[ethylenebis(oxyethyl-eneoxymethylenecarbonylimino)]bis(2,4,6-triio-dobenzoic acid); ZK-71630).

Iothalamic acid* see Iotalamic acid.
Iothiouracil see Iodothiouracil.
IOTRANIC ACID* (3,3′-[oxybis(ethyleneoxy-ethylenecarbonylimino)]bis(2,4,6-triiodobenzoic acid)).
IOTRIZOIC ACID* (2,4,6-triiodo-3-[2-[2-[2-[2-(2-methoxy)ethoxy]ethoxy]ethoxy]acetamido]-benzoic acid; jotrizoic acid).
Iotrol see Iotrolan.
IOTROLAN* (5,5′-[malonylbis(methylimino)-]bis[N,N′-bis[2,3-dihydoxy-1-(hydroxymethyl)-propyl]-2,4,6-triiodoisophthalamide]; iotrol).
IOTROXIC ACID* (3,3′-[oxybis(ethyleneoxy-methylenecarbonylimino)]bis(2,4,6-triiodobenz-oic acid); 3,3′-[3,6,9-trioxaundecanedioyldiimi-nobis(2,4,6-triiodobenzoic acid)]; SH-213-AB).
See also Meglumine iotroxate.
Ioxaglate meglumine* see Meglumine ioxaglate.
IOXAGLIC ACID* (N-(2-hydroxyethyl)-2,4,6-triiodo-5-[2-[2,4,6-triiodo-3-(N-methylacet-amido)-5-(methylcarbamoyl)benzamido]acet-amido]isophthalamic acid).
See also Meglumine ioxaglate.
IOXITALAMIC ACID* (5-acetamido-N-(2-hydroxyethyl)-2,4,6-triiodoisophthalamic acid; AG-58107; 'vasombrix').
See also Ethanolamine ioxitalamate; Meglumine ioxitalamate.
IOXOTRIZOIC ACID* (3-acetamido-5-glycol-amido-2,4,6-triiodobenzoic acid; SH-21139/H-248-AB).
IOXYNIL* (4-hydroxy-3,5-diiodobenzonitrile; 'ac-tril'; 'certrol'; 'toxynil').
IOXYNIL plus 2,4-DICHLOROPHENOXY-ACETIC ACID ('actril-D').
IOXYNIL OCTANOATE ('totril').
IOZOMIC ACID* (3,3′-[tetramethylenebis-[oxy(2-hydroxytrimethylene)(acetylimino)-]]bis[2,4,6-triiodo-5-(N-methylacetamido)benzo-ic acid]; 'rayodal').
IP-82 see Ibuprofen.
IPA see Riboprine.
IPAZINE* (6-chloro-2-diethylamino-4-isopropyl-amino-s-triazine; 6-chloro-N,N-diethyl-N′-(1-methylethyl)-1,3,5-triazine-2,4-diamine; 'gesa-bel').
IPC see Propham.
Ipecine see Emetine.
IPEXIDINE* (1,1′-[1,4-piperazinediylbis(tri-methyleneiminoimidocarbonyl)]bis[3-hexylurea]; CK-0569).
IPEXIDINE MESILATE (ipexidine dimethanesul-fonate; ipexidine mesylate).
IPM see Isoprocarb.
IPMC see Propoxur.
IPO-62 see Bromfenvinfos.
IPO-63 see Bromfenvinfos-methyl.
IPO-1250 see Benomyl.
Ipodate sodium* see Sodium iopodate.
'Ipoglicone' see Tolbutamide.
'Ipradol' see Hexoprenaline.
IPRAGRATINE* (9-isopropylgranatoline (±)-tropate).

IPRAMIDIL (N,N′-diisopropyl-3,4-furazandi-carboxamide 2-oxide).
IPRATROPIUM BROMIDE* (3-(3-hydroxy-1-oxo-2-phenylpropoxy)-8-methyl-8-(1-methyl-ethyl)-8-azoniabicyclo[3.2.1]octane bromide; 3α-hydroxy-8-isopropyl-1αH,5αH-tropanium bro-mide (±)-tropate; 8-isopropyl-3-(±)-tropoyl-oxy-1αH,5αH-tropanium bromide; N-isopropyl-atropinium bromide; Sch-1000; 'atrovent'; 'itrop').
See also under Fenoterol.
Iprazide (tr) see Iproniazid.
IPRAZOCHROME* (3-hydroxy-3-isopropyl-5,6-indolinedione 5-semicarbazone; N-isoprop-ylnoradrenochrome monosemicarbazone; 'di-vascan').
Iprazone see Isoprazone.
'Iprenol' see Isoprenaline.
IPRIFLAVONE (7-isopropoxyisoflavone; 7-isopropoxy-3-phenylchromone; 7-(1-methyleth-oxy)-3-phenyl-4H-1-benzopyran-4-one; FL-113; 'yambolap').
IPRINDOLE* (5-[3-(dimethylamino)propyl]-6,7,8,9,10,11-hexahydrocyclooct[b]indole; iprindole hydrochloride; pramindole; Wy-3263).
IPROCEMIC ACID* (3-(N-ethylacetamido)-2,4,6-triiodohydrocinnamic acid).
IPROCINODINE* (N-isopropylantibiotic BM-123-γ; isopropylcinodine; N-(1-methylethyl)anti-biotic BM-123-γ; iprocinodine hydrochloride; CL-205925).
IPROCLOZIDE* (1-(p-chlorophenoxyacetyl)-2-isopropylhydrazine; PC-603).
IPROCROLOL* (1-[[4-hydroxy-7-methyl-5-oxo-5H-furo[3,2-g][1]benzopyran-9-yl]oxy]-3-(isopropylamino)-2-propanol; 4-hydroxy-9-[2-hydroxy-3-(isopropylamino)propoxy]-7-methyl-5H-furo[3,2-g][1]benzopyran-5-one).
IPRODIONE (3-(3,5-dichlorophenyl)-N-isoprop-yl-2,4-dioxoimidazolidine-1-carboxamide).
IPROFENIN* (N-(carboxymethyl)-N-[2-[[4-(1-methylethyl)phenyl]amino]-2-oxoethyl]glycine; [[(p-cumenylcarbamoyl)methyl]imino]diacetic acid; 'pipida').
'Iprogen' see Imipramine.
IPROHEPTINE* (N-isopropyl-1,5-dimethyl-hexylamine).
Ipronal (tr) see Proxibarbal.
IPRONIAZID (2-isopropylhydrazide of isonico-tinic acid; iprazide).
IPRONIDAZOLE* (2-isopropyl-1-methyl-5-ni-troimidazole; NSC-109212; Ro 7-1554; 'ipro-pran').
'Ipronin' see Iproniazid.
IPROPLATIN (ab-dichloro-ce-dihydroxy-df-bis(isopropylamine)platinum; JM-9).
'Ipropran' see Ipronidazole.
'Iproveratril' see Verapamil.
IPROXAMINE* (4-[2-(dimethylamino)ethoxy]-5-isopropyl-2-methylphenyl isopropyl carbon-ate; 5-[2-(dimethylamino)ethoxy]carvacryl isopropyl carbonate; iproxamine hydrochloride; Go-2782; W-42782).

IPROZILAMINE*** (1-[4-chloro-2-(isopropyl-amino)-5-(methylthio)pyrimidin-6-yl]-4-methyl-piperazine; 4-chloro-2-(isopropylamino)-6-(4-methylpiperazin-1-yl)-5-(methylthio)pyrimid-ine).

IPSALAZIDE*** (*p*-[(3-carboxy-4-hydroxyphen-yl)azo]hippuric acid; ipsalazide sodium; BX-650A).

'IPTD' *see* Glyprothiazol.

IQUINDAMINE*** (1-[[2-(diethylamino)ethyl]-amino]-3,4-dihydroisoquinoline).

'Irenat' *see* Potassium perchlorate.

'Irgafen' *see* Sulfadimethylbenzoylamide.

'Irgalon' *see* Tetrasodium edetate.

'Irgamide' *see* Sulfadicramide.

'Irgapyrin' *see under* Aminophenazone.

'Irgasan CF3' *see* Halocarban.

'Irgasan DP-30' *see* Triclosan.

'Iricoline' *see* Carbachol.

'Iridocin' *see* Ethionamide.

'Iridozin' *see* Ethionamide.

'Iridus' *see* Naftidrofuryl.

'Irium' *see* Sodium dodecyl sulfate.

'Irmin' *see* Imipramine.

'Iromin' *see* Carbasalate calcium.

Iron.... *see also* Ferr.....

Iron choline citrate *see* Ferrocholinate.

IRON DEXTRAN INJECTION* (dextrafer; iron-dextran complex; 'armidexan'; 'ferridextran'; 'imferdex'; 'imferon').

Iron-dextrin complex *see* Dextriferron.

Ironedetate sodium *see* Sodium feredetate.

Iron-fructose complex *see* Ferric fructose.

Iron-glycine complex *see* Ferroglycine sulfate.

Iron heptonate *see* Gleptoferron.

Iron polymalether *see* Ferropolimaler.

IRON-SERINE COMPLEX ('aktiferrin').

Iron sodium edetate *see* Sodium feredetate.

IRON SORBITEX* (iron sorbitol-citric acid com-plex; ferbitol; Astra-1572; 'jectofer').

Iron-sucrose-polymer complex *see* Polyferose.

'Irrigor' *see* Imolamine.

'Irritren' *see* Lonazolac calcium.

IS-362 *see* Suxethonium chloride.

IS 370 *see* Suxamethonium chloride.

IS-401 *see* Diisopropylamine dichloroacetate.

IS-499 *see* Poldine metilsulfate.

IS-2596 *see* Domoxin.

Isadrin (tr) *see* Isoprenaline.

ISAMFAZONE*** (*N*-methyl-*N*-[[(6-oxo-3-phenylpyridazin-1-yl)methyl]carbonyl]amphet-amine; (−)-*N*-methyl-*N*-(α-methylphenethyl)-6-oxo-3-phenyl-1(6*H*)-pyridazineacetamide).

ISAMOXOLE*** (*N*-butyl-2-methyl-*N*-(4-methyl-oxazol-2-yl)propionamide; compound 90606; LRCL-3950).

Isaphenin (tr) *see* Acetphenolisatin.

Isatidine *see* Retrorsine *N*-oxide.

ISATIN (2,3-indoledione; 2,3-indolinedione).

ISATROPIC ACID (1,2,3,4-tetrahydro-1-phenyl-1,4-naphthalenedicarboxylic acid).

Isatropylditropeine *see* Belladonnin.

ISAXONINE*** (2-(isopropylamino)pyrimidine;

isaxonine phosphate; 'nerfactor').

'Iscador' *see* Viscum album.

'Iscothane' *see* Dinocap.

'I-sedrin' *see* Ephedrine.

ISETHIONIC ACID (2-ethanolsulfonic acid; 2-hydroxyethanesulfonic acid).
See also Isetionate(s).

ISETIONATE(S)** (2-hydroxyethanesulfonate(s); isethionate(s)).

ISF-2001 *see* Tritiozine.

ISF-2073 *see* Dexamethasone linoleate.

ISF-2123 *see* Pildralazine.

ISF-2522 *see* Oxiracetam.

'Iskedyl' *see under* Ajmalicine.

'Ismelin' *see* Guanethidine sulfate.

'Ismicetina' *see* Chloramphenicol.

'Ismipur' *see* Mercaptopurine.

IS-5-MN *see* Isosorbide mononitrate.

'ISMO' *see* Isosorbide mononitrate.

'Isnamide' *see* Sulpiride.

'Iso/80' *see* Isoconazole.

'Isoadanon' *see* Isomethadone.

Isoadrenaline *see* Corbadrine.

ISOALLOXAZINE (benzo[g]pteridine-2,4(3*H*,10*H*)-dione; pyrimido[4,5-*b*]quinoxaline-2,4(3*H*,10*H*)-dione).

Isoalloxazine-adenine dinucleotide *see* Flavin-aden-ine dinucleotide.

Isoamidone *see* Isomethadone.

ISOAMINILE*** (4-(dimethylamino)-2-isoprop-yl-2-phenylvaleronitrile; 2-[2-(dimethylamino)-propyl]-2-isopropyl-2-phenylacetonitrile).

2-(Isoamylamino)-6-methylheptane *see* Octamyl-amine.

N-**Isoamylcadaverine** *see* Isoverine.

Isoamyl *N*-**(2-diethylaminoethyl)-2-phenylglycinate** *see* Camylofin.

N-**Isoamyl-1,5-dimethyl-1-hexylamine** *see* Octamyl-amine.

Isoamylenoxypsoralen *see* Pentosalen.

Isoamylhydrocupreine *see* Euprocin.

Isoamyl nitrite *see* Amyl nitrite.

1-(2-Isoamyloxy-2-phenylethyl)pyrrolidine *see* Ami-xetrine.

N-**[3-Isoamyloxy-2-(3,4,5-trimethoxybenzoyloxy)-propyl]morpholine** *see* Amoproxan.

'Isoamytal' *see* Pentobarbital.

Isoandrosterone *see* 3β-Hydroxy-5α-androstan-17-one.

5-Isoandrosterone *see* 3α-Hydroxy-5β-androstan-17-one.

ISOASCORBIC ACID (D-*erythro*-hex-2-enonic acid γ-lactone; 3-oxohexonic acid lactone; 3-ke-tohexonic acid lactone; araboascorbic acid; ery-corbin; erythorbic acid; glucosaccharonic acid; isovitamin C; saccharosonic acid).

Isobarin (tr) *see* Guanethidine.

ISOBENZAN* (1,3,4,5,6,7,8,8-octachloro-1,3,3a,4,7,7a-hexahydro-4,7-methanoisobenzo-furan; 1,3,4,5,6,7,8,8-octachloro-3a,4,7,7a-tetra-hydro-4,7-methanophthalan; SD-4402; 'telodr-in').

1-Isobenzofuranone *see* Phthalide.

Isobornylamine see 2-Bornanamine.
6-Isobornyl-3,4-xylenol see Xibornol.
ISOBUTAMBEN* (isobutyl *p*-aminobenzoate; 2-methylpropyl 4-aminobenzoate; isobutylcaine; 'benzamelid'; 'cyclocaine'; 'cycloform'; 'cyclogesin').
***p*-Isobutoxybenzoic acid diethylaminodimethylpropyl ester** see Ganglefene.
1-(Isobutoxymethyl)-2-(4-methylpiperazin-1-yl)ethyl 2-phenylbutyrate see Fenetradil.
Isobutyl alcohol see 2-Methyl-1-propanol.
Isobutyl *p*-aminobenzoate see Isobutamben.
4-(Isobutylamino)-2,3-dimethyl-1-phenyl-5-pyrazolin-3-one methanesulfonate see Dibupyrone.
2-(Isobutylamino)ethyl *p*-aminobenzoate see Butethamine.
Isobutylcaine see Isobutamben.
Isobutyl 2-cyanoacrylate see Bucrilate.
Isobutyl 4-(6,7-dimethoxyquinazolin-4-yl)-1-piperazinecarboxylate see Piquizil.
1-Isobutyl-3,4-diphenylpyrazole-4-acetic acid see Bufezolac.
***p*-Isobutylhydratropic acid** see Ibuprofen.
***p*-Isobutylhydratropic acid 2-[4-(α,α,α-trifluoro-*m*-tolyl)piperazin-1-yl]ethyl ester** see Frabuprofen.
***p*-Isobutylhydratropohydroxamic acid** see Ibuproxam.
Isobutylhydrochlorothiazide see Butizide.
Isobutyl methyl 1,4-dihydro-2,6-dimethyl-4-(2-nitrophenyl)-3,5-pyridinedicarboxylate see Nisoldipine.
Isobutylphenazone methanesulfonate see Dibupyrone.
***p*-Isobutylphenylacetic acid** see Ibufenac.
2-(*p*-Isobutylphenyl)butyric acid see Butibufen.
Isobutyl α-phenylcyclohexaneglycolate see Ibuverine.
2-(*p*-Isobutylphenyl)propionic acid see Ibuprofen.
2-(*p*-Isobutylphenyl)propionohydroxamic acid see Ibuproxam.
(−)-(*S*)-4-[*N*-(5-Isobutylpyrimidin-2-yl)sulfamoyl]phenylacetic acid 1-(5-fluoro-2-methoxyphenyl)ethylamide see Gliflumide.
***N*-(5-Isobutyl-1,3,4-thiadiazol-2-yl)-*p*-methoxybenzenesulfonamide** see Glysobuzole.
***N*-Isobutyl(triphenylmethyl)amine** see Isobutyltritylamine.
ISOBUTYLTRITYLAMINE (*N*-isobutyl(triphenylmethyl)amine; ICI-24223; 'molucid').
ISOBUTYRIC ACID (2-methylpropionic acid).
Isobutyric acid diester with 5-(2-*tert*-butylamino-1-hydroxyethyl)resorcinol see Ibuterol.
***O*-Isobutyrylthiamine disulfide** see Sulbutiamine.
Isobuzole* see Glysobuzole.
Isocaine see Pseudococaine.
Isocainide see Lorcainide.
Isocaramidine see Debrisoquine.
ISOCARBOXAZID* (1-benzyl-2-(5-methylisoxazol-3-ylcarbonyl)hydrazine; 5-methyl-3-isoxazolecarboxylic acid 2-benzylhydrazide; BMIH; Ro 5-0831/1; U-10387).
ISOCHLORANIL (3,4,5,6-tetrachloro-*o*-benzoquinone).

ISOCHROMAN (3,4-dihydro-2,1*H*-benzopyran).
ISOCIL* (5-bromo-3-isopropyl-6-methyluracil; 5-bromo-6-methyl-3-(1-methylethyl)-2,4-(1*H*,3*H*)-pyrimidinedione; isoprocil; 'hyvar').
'Isocillin' see Penicillin V.
ISOCITRIC ACID (1-hydroxy-1,2,3-propanetrioic acid).
ISOCONAZOLE* (1-[2,4-dichloro-β-(2,6-dichlorobenzyloxy)phenethyl]imidazole; 1-[2-(2,4-dichlorophenyl)-2-(2,6-dichlorophenylmethoxy)ethyl]-1*H*-imidazole; isoconazole nitrate; R-15454; 'fazol'; 'iso/80'; 'isogyn'; 'travogen'; 'travogyn').
See also under Fluocortin butyl.
'Iso-cornox' see Mecoprop.
1-Isocoumaranone see Phthalide.
ISOCROMIL (2-(*o*-isopropoxyphenyl)-4-oxo-4*H*-1-benzopyran-6-carboxylic acid).
ISOCROTONIC ACID (*cis*-2-butenoic acid).
Isodapamide see Zidapamide.
Isodemeton see Demeton-S.
Isodemeton methyl see Demeton-S-methyl.
'Isodine' see Povidone-iodine.
ISODRIN* (aldrin *endo-endo* isomer; OMS-198).
Isodrin* see Pholedrine.
'Iso-endoxan' see Ifosfamide.
Isoephedrine see Pseudoephedrine.
ISOETARINE* (3,4-dihydroxy-α-(1-isopropylaminopropyl)benzyl alcohol; 1-(3,4-dihydroxyphenyl)-2-isopropylamino-1-butanol; etyprenaline; isoetharine; WIN-3046).
Isoethadione see Paramethadione.
Isoetharine* see Isoetarine.
ISOFEZOLAC* (1,3,4-triphenylpyrazole-5-acetic acid).
'Isoflav' see Proflavine.
ISOFLAVONE (3-phenylchromone).
ISOFLUORANIL (tetrafluorobenzoquinone(s)).
Isofluorphate see Isoflurophate.
ISOFLUPREDONE* (9-fluoro-11β,17,21-trihydroxypregna-1,4-diene-3,20-dione; 9-fluoroprednisolone).
ISOFLUPREDONE ACETATE* (U-6013; 'predef').
ISOFLURANE* (1-chloro-2,2,2-trifluoroethyl difluoromethyl ether; 2-chloro-2-(difluoromethoxy)-1,1,1-trifluoroethane; compound 469; 'forane').
ISOFLUROPHATE* (diisopropyl phosphorofluoridate; diisopropylfluo(ro)phosph(on)ate; diflurophate; dyflos; fluostigmine; DFP; isofluorphate).
Isoformothion see Formothion.
Isofosfamide see Ifosfamide.
'I-so-gel' see Psyllium.
'Isoglaucon' see Clonidine.
ISOGLUTAMINE (4-aminoglutaramic acid).
Isogranatanine see 3-Azabicyclo[3.3.1]nonane.
ISOGUANINE (6-amino-2-hydroxypurine).
Isoguanine riboside see Isoguanosine.
ISOGUANOSINE (isoguanine riboside).
'Isogyn' see Isoconazole.
Isohesperidin see Aurantiin.

cis-**4-Isohexyl-1-methylcyclohexanecarboxylic acid** *see* Loxanast.

2-Isohistamine *see* 2-Imidazoleethylamine.

ISOIDIDE (1,4:3,6-dianhydroiditol). *See also* Isomannide; Isosorbide.

Isoindapamide *see* Zidapamide.

'Isoindokolon' *see* Hexafluoroisopropyl methyl ether.

1,3-Isoindoledione *see* Phthalimide.

ISOINDOLINE (1,3-dihydro-2-benzazole).

1,3-Isoindolinedione *see* Phthalimide.

Isoindolin-1-one *see* Phthalimidine.

'Iso-K' *see* Ketoprofen.

'Isoket' *see* Isosorbide dinitrate.

ISOLEUCINE (2-amino-3-methylvaleric acid).

'Isolevin' *see* Levisoprenaline.

'IsoMack' *see* Isosorbide dinitrate.

ISOMANNIDE (1,4:3,6-dianhydromannitol). *See also* Isoidide; Isosorbide.

Isomeprobamate *see* Carisoprodol.

ISOMETAMIDIUM CHLORIDE* (3-[3-(*m*-amidinophenyl)-2-triazeno]-3-amino-5-ethyl-6-phenylphenanthridinium chloride; anthridonium chloride; antridonium; A-4180; M & B-4180A; 'samorin').

ISOMETHADONE* (6-(dimethylamino)-5-methyl-4,4-diphenyl-3-hexanone; isoamidone; WIN-1783).

Isomethepdrine* *see* Isom_theptene.

ISOMETHEPTENE* (6-methyl-2-(methyl-amino)hept-2-ene; *N*-methylisooctenylamine; *N*,1,5-trimethyl-4-hexenylamine; isomethepdrine; methylaminoisooctane).

ISOMETHIOZINE* (6-*tert*-butyl-4-(isobutylid-eneamino)-3-(methylthio)-1,2,4-triazine-5(4*H*)-one; 'tantizon').

Isomethyl parathion *see* Parathion isomethyl.

ISOMYLAMINE* (2-(diethylamino)ethyl 1-isopentylcyclohexanecarboxylate; isomylamine hydrochloride; NSC-78987; 'neurylan').

'Isomyl nitrite' *see* Amyl nitrite.

ISONIAZID** (isonicotinic acid hydrazide; isoni-cotinoylhydrazine; GINK; INH; tubazid; IN-73; RP 5015).

ISONIAZID plus RIFAMPICIN ('rifinah'; 'rimac-tazid').

Isoniazid 4-aminosalicylate *see* Pasiniazid.

ISONIAZID COBALT COMPLEX ('isonicco').

Isoniazid glucuronolactone *see* Gluconiazone.

ISONIAZID MESILATE (isoniazid mesylate; isoniazid N-(methanesulfonic acid) sodium salt; INHM; 'neotizide'; 'pyridizin').

'Isonicco' *see* Isoniazid cobalt complex.

Isonicophen *see* Aconiazide.

ISONICOTINALDEHYDE (4-pyridinaldehyde; γ-pyridyl aldehyde).

ISONICOTINIC ACID (4-pyridinecarboxylic acid; γ-picolinic acid).

Isonicotinic acid 2-butenylidenehydrazide *see* Croto-niazide.

Isonicotinic acid hydrazide *see* Isoniazid.

Isonicotinic acid (5-nitro-2-furfurylidene)hydrazide *see* Furaniozid.

Isonicotinic thioamide *see* Isonicotinthioamide.

6-[2-[2-(Isonicotinimidoylamino)acetamido]-2-phenylacetamido]penicillanic acid *see* Pirbenicill-in.

N-(Isonicotinoylamino)amphetamine *see* Phenyliso-propylisoniazid.

3-Isonicotinoyl-2-isopropylbenzofuran *see* Inicar-one.

1-Isonicotinoyl-2-(phenylisopropyl)hydrazine *see* Phenylisopropylisoniazid.

1-Isonicotinoyl-2-salicylidenehydrazine *see* Salina-zid.

ISONICOTINTHIOAMIDE (isonicotinic thio-amide; thioisonicotinic acid amide; Th-3624).

Isonipecaine *see* Pethidine.

ISONIPECOTIC ACID (4-piperidinecarboxylic acid).

ISONIXIN** (2-hydroxy-2',6'-nicotinoxylidide; IBH-194; 'nixyn').

ISONORURON* (1,1-dimethyl-3-(octahydro-4,7-methano-1*H*-inden-1-yl)urea mixture with its (inden-2-yl) isomer). *See also under* Brompyrazon; Buturon.

'Isonox' *see under* Methaqualone.

ISO-OMPA (tetraisopropylphosphorodiamidic anhydride; *N*,*N'*,*N''*,*N'''*-tetraisopropylpyrophos-phoramide; tetraisopropylpyrophosphorotetr-amide).

'Isopaque' *see* Sodium metrizoate *and under* Me-glumine metrizoate.

'IsoPC' *see* Propham.

Isopelletierine *see* Pelletierine.

Isopenicillin N *see* (−)-Adicillin.

ISOPENTYLAMINE (3-methylbutylamine).

2-Isopentylaminomethyl-1,4-benzodioxan *see* Penta-moxane.

1-Isopentylcyclohexanecarboxylic acid 2-(diethyl-amino)ethyl ester *see* Isomylamine.

N-Isopentyl-1,5-dimethylhexylamine *see* Octamyl-amine.

Isopentyl hydrocupreine *see* Euprocin.

α-Isopentyloxymethyl-4-morpholineethanol 3,4,5-trimethoxybenzoate *see* Amoproxan.

1-(β-Isopentyloxyphenethyl)pyrrolidine *see* Ami-xetrine.

Isopentyl 2-phenyl-2-[(2-pyrrolidin-1-ylethyl)amino]-acetate *see* Camiverine.

Isopestox (tr) *see* Mipafox.

ISOPHANE INSULIN* (NPH insulin; 'insula-tard').

ISOPHANE INSULIN plus NEUTRAL INSU-LIN ('initard'; 'mixitard').

Isophenethanol *see* Nifenalol.

Isophenylephrine *see* Metaraminol.

Isophosphamide *see* Ifosfamide.

ISOPHTHALAMIC ACID (*m*-carbamoylbenzoic acid; isophthalic acid monoamide).

ISOPHTHALIC ACID (*m*-benzenedicarboxylic acid).

Isophthalic acid monoamide *see* Isophthalamic acid.

ISOPRAZONE* (1-(4-amino-2-methyl-5-phenylpyrrol-3-yl)-2-methyl-1-propanone; ipraz-one; DL-809-IT; L-11809; MDL-809).

ISOPREDNIDENE** (11β,17α,21-trihydroxy-16-methylenepregna-4,6-diene-3,20-dione).

Isopregnenone *see* Dydrogesterone.

ISOPRENALINE*** (3,4-dihydroxy-α-isopropylaminomethylbenzyl alcohol; isopropydrine; isoproterenol; isadrin; isoprenaline bitartrate, chloride or sulfate; isopropylarterenol; A-21; WIN-5162).

'Isoprinosine' *see* Inosine pranobex.

ISOPROCARB* (*o*-isopropylphenyl methylcarbamate; 2-(1-methylethyl)phenyl methylcarbamate; IPM; MIPC; OMS-32; 'carbamat'; 'etrofolan'; 'mipicin').

Isoprocil *see* Isocil.

ISOPROFEN** (2-isopropyl-α-methyl-5-indanacetic acid).

ISOPROPALIN* (4-isopropyl-2,6-dinitro-*N*,*N*-dipropylaniline; 4-(1-methylethyl)-2,6-dinitro-*N*,*N*-dipropylbenzenamine; 'paarlan').

ISOPROPAMIDE IODIDE*** ((3-carbamoyl-3,3-diphenylpropyl)diisopropylmethylammonium iodide; isopropon; R-55; R-79).
See also under Haloperidol; Trifluoperazine.

4-Isopropenyl-1-methylcyclohexene *see* Limonene.

Isoprophenamine *see* Clorprenaline.

ISOPROPICILLIN*** ((1-methyl-1-phenoxyethyl)penicillin).

Isopropon* *see* Isopropamide iodide.

Isopropoxamine *see* Isopropylmethoxamine.

*N*¹-(4-Isopropoxybenzoyl)sulfanilamide *see* Sulfaproxyline.

1-[[α-(2-Isopropoxyethoxy)-*p*-tolyl]oxy]-3-(isopropylamino)-2-propanol *see* Bisoprolol.

7-Isopropoxyisoflavone *see* Ipriflavone.

7-Isopropoxy-9-oxoxanthene-2-carboxylic acid *see* Xanoxic acid.

7-Isopropoxy-3-phenylchromone *see* Ipriflavone.

o-Isopropoxyphenyl methylcarbamate *see* Propoxur.

2-(*o*-Isopropoxyphenyl)-4-oxo-4*H*-1-benzopyran-6-carboxylic acid *see* Isocromil.

Isopropydrine* *see* Isoprenaline.

Isopropyl alcohol *see* 2-Propanol.

Isopropylamine *see* 2-Propylamine.

4-(Isopropylamino)-2,3-dimethyl-1-phenyl-3-pyrazolin-5-one *see* Ramifenazone.

1-(Isopropylamino)-4,4-diphenyl-2-butanol *see* Drobuline.

α-[1-(Isopropylamino)ethyl]-2,5-dimethoxybenzyl alcohol *see* Isopropylmethoxamine.

3-(Isopropylamino)-1-[*p*-[2-[(methoxycarbonyl)-amino]ethyl]phenoxy]-2-propanol *see* Pamatolol.

1-(Isopropylamino)-3-[*p*-(2-methoxyethyl)phenoxy]-2-propanol *see* Metoprolol.

1-(Isopropylamino)-3-(*o*-methoxyphenoxy)-2-propanol *see* Moprolol.

2-(Isopropylamino)-4-(3-methoxypropylamino)-6-(methylthio)-*s*-triazine *see* Methoprotryn.

1-(Isopropylamino)-3-[(2-methylindol-4-yl)oxy]-2-propanol *see* Mepindolol.

α-[(Isopropylamino)methyl]-2-naphthalenemethanol *see* Pronetalol.

α-[(Isopropylamino)methyl]-*p*-nitrobenzyl alcohol

see Nifenalol.

1-(Isopropylamino)-3-(3-methylphenoxy)-2-propanol *see* Toliprolol.

1-(Isopropylamino)-3-[*o*-(methylthio)phenoxy]-2-propanol *see* Tiprenolol.

α-[(Isopropylamino)methyl]vanillyl alcohol *see* Metiprenaline.

1-(Isopropylamino)-3-(1-naphthyloxy)-2-propanol *see* Propranolol.

1-(Isopropylamino)-3-[*o*-(2-*exo*-norbornyl)phenoxy]-2-propanol *see* Bornaprolol.

8-[5-(Isopropylamino)pentylamino]-6-methoxyquinoline *see* Pentaquine.

4-(ISOPROPYLAMINO)PHENAZONE (4-(isopropyl amino)-2,3-dimethyl-1-phenyl-3-pyrazolin-5-one; 'isopyrin').

4-(ISOPROPYLAMINO)PHENAZONE plus PHENYLBUTAZONE ('febuzine isopirin'; 'tomanol').

9-[3-(Isopropylamino)propyl]fluorene-9-carboxamide *see* Indecainide.

2-(Isopropylamino)pyrimidine *see* Isaxonine.

(±)-1-(Isopropylamino)-3-thiazol-2-yloxy-2-propanol *see* Tazolol.

1-(Isopropylamino)-3-(*m*-toloxy)-2-propanol *see* Toliprolol.

N-Isopropylantibiotic BM-123-γ *see* Iprocinodine.

4-Isopropylantipyrine *see* Propyphenazone.

Isopropylarterenol *see* Isoprenaline.

N-Isopropylatropinium bromide *see* Ipratropium bromide.

p-Isopropylbenzaldehyde *see* Cumaldehyde.

p-Isopropylbenzaldehyde thiosemicarbazone *see* Cutizone.

2-Isopropylbenzofuran-3-yl pyrid-4-yl ketone *see* Inicarone.

p-ISOPROPYLBENZOIC ACID (cumic acid).
See also Isopropylcaine.

3-Isopropyl-1*H*-2,1,3-benzothiadiazin-4(3*H*)-one 2,2-dioxide *see* Bentazon.

Isopropyl 2,2-bis(*p*-bromophenyl)glycolate *see* Bromopropylate.

Isopropyl 2,2-bis(*p*-chlorophenyl)glycolate *see* Chloropropylate.

Isopropyl 4-[3-(*tert*-butylamino)-2-hydroxypropoxy]indole-2-carboxylate *see* Carpindolol.

ISOPROPYLCAINE (2-(diethylamino)ethyl *p*-isopropylbenzoate).

Isopropylcarbamic acid ester with 4′-fluoro-4-(4-hydroxypiperid-1-yl)butyrophenone *see* Carperone.

3-[[(Isopropylcarbamoyl)amino]sulfonyl]-4-(*m*-toluidino)pyridine *see* Torasemide.

1-(4-Isopropylcarbamoylbenzyl)-2-methylhydrazine *see* Procarbazine.

1-(Isopropylcarbamoylmethyl)-4-(3,4,5-trimethoxycinnamoyl)piperazine *see* Cinpropazide.

Isopropyl carbanilate *see* Propham.

Isopropyl 2-[*p*-(*p*-chlorobenzoyl)phenoxy]-2-methylpropionate *see* Fenofibrate.

Isopropyl *m*-chlorocarbanilate *see* Chlorpropham.

Isopropylcinodine *see* Iprocinodine.

3-Isopropyl-2,4,6-cycloheptatrien-2-ol-1-one *see* α-

Thujaplicin.

4-Isopropyl-2,4,6-cycloheptatrien-2-ol-1-one *see* β-Thujaplicin.

α-Isopropylcyclohexanemethanol *see* Cimepanol.

Isopropyl 4,4′-dibromobenzilate *see* Bromopropylate.

Isopropyl 4,4′-dichlorobenzilate *see* Chloropropylate.

7-Isopropyl-1,4-dimethylazulene *see* Guaiazulene.

5-Isopropyl-3,8-dimethyl-1-azulenesulfonic acid sodium salt *see* Sodium gualenate.

N-Isopropyl-1,5-dimethylhexylamine *see* Iproheptine.

4-Isopropyl-2,3-dimethyl-1-phenyl-3-pyrazolin-5-one *see* Propyphenazone.

4-Isopropyl-2,6-dinitro-N,N-dipropylaniline *see* Isopropalin.

N-Isopropyl-1,3-dioxo-2-isoindolineethanesulfonamide *see* Taltrimide.

N-Isopropyl-4,4-diphenylcyclohexylamine *see* Pramiverine.

1-Isopropyl-4,4-diphenylpiperidine *see* Prodipine.

9-Isopropylgranatoline (±)-tropate *see* Ipragratine.

16α,17α-Isopropylidenedioxypregn-4-ene-3,20-dione *see* Algestone acetonide.

4,4′-Isopropylidenedithiobis(2,6-di-*tert*-butylphenol) *see* Probucol.

1-Isopropyl-2-imidazolidinethione *see* Mipimazole.

2-Isopropylindol-3-yl pyrid-3-yl ketone *see* Nictindole.

Isopropylmeprobamate *see* Carisoprodol.

ISOPROPYLMETHOXAMINE (α-[1-(isopropylamino)ethyl]-2,5-dimethoxybenzyl alcohol; isopropoxamine; IMA; BW-61-43).

Isopropyl 2-methoxyethyl 1,4-dihydro-2,6-dimethyl-4-(*m*-nitrophenyl)pyridine-3,5-dicarboxylate *see* Nimodipine.

5-Isopropyl-4-methoxyfurobenzopyran-7-one *see* Peucedanin.

Isopropyl 11-methoxy-3,7,11-trimethyl-2,4-dodecadienoate *see* Methoprene.

2-Isopropyl-5-methylbenzoquinone *see* Thymoquinone.

5-Isopropyl 3-methyl 2-cyano-1,4-dihydro-6-methyl-4-(*m*-nitrophenyl)pyridine-3,5-dicarboxylate *see* Nivadipine.

2-Isopropyl-5-methylcyclohexanol *see* Menthol.

2-Isopropyl-3-methyl-4,6-dinitrophenol *see* Dinoprop.

ISOPROPYL METHYL ETHER ('isopryl').

Isopropyl[3-(N-methyl-N-homoveratrylamino)propyl](3,4,5-trimethoxyphenyl)acetonitrile *see* Gallopamil.

N-Isopropyl-α-(2-methylhydrazino)-*p*-toluamide *see* Procarbazine.

2-Isopropyl-5-methylhydroquinone *see* Thymohydroquinone.

2-Isopropyl-α-methyl-5-indanacetic acid *see* Isoprofen.

4-Isopropyl-2-methyl-3-[N-methyl-N-(α-methylphenethyl)aminomethyl]-1-phenyl-3-pyrazolin-5-one *see* Famprofazone.

2-Isopropyl-1-methyl-5-nitroimidazole *see* Ipronidazole.

N-(4-Isopropyl-2-methyl-5-oxo-1-phenyl-3-pyrazolin-3-ylmethyl)-N-methylamphetamine *see* Famprofazone.

2-Isopropyl-5-methylphenol *see* Thymol.

2-[(2-Isopropyl-5-methylphenoxy)methyl]-2-imidazoline *see* Tymazoline.

Isopropyl 1-methyl-4-phenylisonipecotate *see* Properidine.

3-Isopropyl-5-methylphenyl methylcarbamate *see* Promecarb.

1-Isopropyl-7-methyl-4-phenylquinazolin-2(1H)-one *see* Proquazone.

Isopropyl methylphosphonofluoridate *see* Sarin.

1-ISOPROPYL-3-METHYLPYRAZOL-5-YL DIMETHYLCARBAMATE ('isolan'; 'primin').

3-Isopropyl-6-methylsalicylic acid *see* *o*-Thymotic acid.

4-[(Isopropyl)(nicotinamidomethyl)amino]-2,3-dimethyl-1-phenyl-3-pyrazolin-5-one *see* Niprofazone.

4-[(Isopropyl)(nicotinamidomethyl)amino]phenazone *see* Niprofazone.

N-Isopropyl-*p*-nitrophenylethanolamine *see* Nifenalol.

N-Isopropylnoradrenochrome monosemicarbazone *see* Iprazochrome.

1-(2-Isopropyl-3-pentenoyl)urea *see* Apronal.

4-Isopropylphenazone *see* Propyphenazone.

2-(2-Isopropylphenoxymethyl)-2-imidazoline *see* Fenoxazoline.

1-(*p*-Isopropylphenyl)-3,3-dimethylurea *see* Isoproturon.

o-Isopropylphenyl methylcarbamate *see* Isoprocarb.

Isopropylphosphoramidic acid ethyl 3-methyl-4-(methylthio)phenyl ester *see* Fenamiphos.

N-Isopropylphosphoramidothioic acid o-methyl o-(4-methyl-2-nitrophenyl ester *see* Amiprofosmethyl.

10-[(4-Isopropylpiperazin-1-yl)carbonyl]phenothiazine *see* Sopitazine.

4-Isopropylpiperazin-1-yl phenothiazin-10-yl ketone *see* Sopitazine.

'Isopropyl-systral' *see* Mecloxamine.

N¹-(5-Isopropyl-1,3,4-thiadiazol-2-yl)sulfanilamide *see* Glyprothiazol.

Isopropyl 2-thiazol-4-yl-5-benzimidazolecarbamate *see* Cambendazole.

p-(Isopropylthio)-α-(1-octamylaminoethyl)benzyl alcohol *see* Suloctidil.

1-[*p*-(Isopropylthio)phenoxy]-3-(octylamino)-2-propanol *see* Tipropidil.

Isopropyltoluene(s) *see* Cymene(s).

1-Isopropyl-3-[(4-*m*-toluidinopyrid-3-yl)sulfonyl]urea *see* Torasemide.

4-Isopropyl-2-(α,α,α-trifluoro-*m*-tolyl)morpholine *see* Oxaflozane.

N-Isopropyl-4-(3,4,5-trimethoxycinnamoyl)-1-piperazineacetamide *see* Cinpropazide.

3-Isopropyltropolone *see* α-Thujaplicin.

4-Isopropyltropolone *see* β-Thujaplicin.

5-Isopropyltropolone *see* γ-Thujaplicin.

8-Isopropyl-3-(±)-tropoyloxy-1αH,5αH-tropanium

bromide *see* Ipratropium bromide.
Isoprotan (tr) *see* Carisoprodol.
Isoproterenol* *see* Isoprenaline.
Isoprothane *see* Carisoprodol.
ISOPROTURON (1-(*p*-isopropylphenyl)-3,3-di-methylurea).
'Isopryl' *see* Isopropyl methyl ether.
'Isoptin' *see* Verapamil.
'Isopto-flucon' *see* Fluorometholone.
'Isopyrin' *see* Isoniazid *and* 4-(Isopropylamino)-phenazone.
ISOQUERCITRIN (quercetin 3-glucoside).
ISOQUINOLINE (2-benzazine; leucoline).
'Isordil' *see* Isosorbide dinitrate.
'Isorel' *see* Viscum album.
ISORHAMNETIN (3,4',5,7-tetrahydroxy-3'-methoxyflavone).
ISORIBOFLAVIN (6,7-dimethyl-10-(1-D-ribityl)-isoalloxazine; NSC-3100).
ISOSERINE (3-amino-2-hydroxypropionic acid; 3-aminolactic acid).
ISOSORBIDE* (1,4:3,6-dianhydrosorbitol; AT-101; NSC-40725; 'hydronol').
See also Isoidide; Isomannide.
ISOSORBIDE DINITRATE* (sorbide nitrate).
See also under Proscillaridin; Verapamil.
ISOSORBIDE MONONITRATE* (isosorbide 5-nitrate; IS-5-MN; 'elantan'; 'ISMO').
Isosorbide 5-nitrate *see* Isosorbide mononitrate.
ISOSULFAN BLUE* ([4-[α-[*p*-(diethylamino)-phenyl]-2,5-disulfobenzylidene]-2,5-cyclohexadien-1-ylidene]diethylammonium hydroxide inner salt; α-[*p*-(diethylamino)phenyl]-α-[4-(diethylimino)cyclohexa-2,5-dienylidene]toluene-2,5-disulfonic acid sodium salt; anhydro-4,4'-bis(diethylamino)triphenylmethanol-2'',4''-disulfonic acid sodium salt; sulfan blue; blue VRS; food blue 3; patent blue V; P-1888; P-4125; 'disulfine blue').
ISOSULPRIDE* (1-ethyl-2-[[[(5-methoxy-5-sulfamoylphenyl)carbamoyl]methyl]pyrrolidine; 1-ethyl-5'-sulfamoyl-2-pyrrolidineacet-*o*-anisidide).
'Isosumithion' *see* *O,O*-Dimethyl *S*-(*p*-nitro-*m*-tolyl) phosphorothioate.
Isosystox *see* Demeton-S.
'Isoteben' *see* *N*¹-Benzylideneisoniazid.
'Isotense' *see* Syrosingopine.
'Isotensen' *see* Methindethyrium.
'Isothan Q4' *see* 1-Dodecylpyridinium bromide.
'Isothan Q15' *see* 2-Dodecylisoquinolinium bromide.
Isothazine *see* Profenamine.
Isothiazine *see* Profenamine.
4-Isothiocyanato-4'-nitrodiphenylamine *see* Amoscanate.
Isothiocyanatophenyl *p*-nitrophenyl ether *see* Nitroscanate.
Isothiocyanic acid esters *see* Allylisothiocyanate; Amoscanate; Bitoscanate; Nitroscanate.
Isothiourea *see* Pseudothiourea.
ISOTHIPENDYL* (10-[2-(dimethylamino)-propyl]-10*H*-pyrido[3,2-*b*][1,4]benzothiazine; thipendyl; thypendyl; isothipendyl hydrochloride;

D-201).
ISOTIQUIMIDE* ((±)-5,6,7,8-tetrahydro-4-methylquinoline-8-thiocarboxamide; (±)-5,6,7,8-tetrahydro-4-methylthio-8-quinolinecarboxamide; isotiquimide hydrochloride; Wy-24377).
'Isoton 12' *see* Dichlorodifluoromethane.
ISOTRETINOIN* (3,7-dimethyl-9-(2,6,6-trimethyl-1-cyclohexen-1-yl)nona-2,4,6,8-tetraenoic acid; 13-*cis*-retinoic acid; (13*Z*)-15-apo-β-carotene-15-oic acid; Ro 4-3780; 'accutane'; 'roacutan').
'Isotyl AO12' *see* Fenabutene.
Isourea *see* Pseudourea.
Isouretin *see* Formamide oxime.
ISOVALERIC ACID (3-methylbutyric acid).
Isovaleryl-L-valyl-L-valyl-4-amino-3-hydroxy-6-methylheptanoyl-L-alanyl-4-amino-3-hydroxy-6-methylheptanoic acid *see* Pepstatin.
ISOVERINE (tr) (*N*-isoamylcadaverine).
Isovitamin C *see* Isoascorbic acid.
Isoxacillin *see* Oxacillin.
ISOXAPROLOL* (1-(*tert*-butylamino)-3-[*o*-[2-(3-methylisoxazol-5-yl)vinyl]phenoxy]-2-propanol).
ISOXEPAC* (6,11-dihydro-11-oxodibenz[*b,e*]-oxepin-2-acetic acid; HP-549; P-720549).
ISOXICAM (4-hydroxy-2-methyl-*N*-(5-methyl-isoxazol-3-yl)-2*H*-1,2-benzothiazine-3-carboxamide 1,1-dioxide; W-8495; 'pacyl').
'Isoxozol' *see* Danazol.
ISOXSUPRINE* (*p*-hydroxy-*N*-(1-methyl-2-phenoxyethyl)norephedrine; 1-(*p*-hydroxyphenyl)-2-(1-methyl-2-phenoxyethylamino)-1-propanol; phenoxyisopropylnorsuprifen; isoxsuprine hydrochloride; Caa-40; GR-62).
'Isoxyl' *see* Tiocarlide.
Isoyohimbine *see* Rauwolscine.
'Ispaghul' *see* Psyllium.
Ispagula *see* Psyllium.
'Istin' *see* Dantron.
'Istizin' *see* Dantron.
'Istonil' *see* Dimetacrine.
Isuretin *see* Formamide oxime.
ITA-104 *see* Plafibride.
ITA-312 *see* Lozilurea.
ITACONIC ACID (methylenesuccinic acid).
Italchine *see* Mepacrine.
'Italprid' *see* Tiapride.
ITANOXONE* (2-[[(2'-chlorobiphenyl-4-yl)-carbonyl]methyl]acrylic acid; 2-[*p*-(*o*-chlorophenyl)phenacyl]acrylic acid; F-1379).
ITG *see* Tiamiprine.
'Itinerol' *see* Meclozine.
Itobarbital *see* Butalbital.
ITP *see* Inosine triphosphate.
ITRACONAZOLE ((±)-1-*sec*-butyl-4-[*p*-[4-[*p*-[[(2*R*,4*S*)-2-(2,4-dichlorophenyl)-2-(1*H*-1,2,4-triazol-1ylmethyl)-1,3-dioxolan-4-yl]methoxy]-phenyl]piperazin-1-yl]phenyl]-Δ²-1,2,4-triazolin-5-one).
ITRAMIN (aminoethanol nitrate; 2-aminoethyl nitrate; ethanolamine nitrate; 2-nitratoethyl-

304

amine).

ITRAMIN TOSILATE*** (itramin p-toluenesulfonate; itramin tosylate; 'nilatil').

'Itrop' *see* Ipratropium bromide.

'Itrumil' *see* Iodothiouracil.

'Ituran' *see* Nitrofurantoin.

IUDR *see* Idoxuridine.

Iuglone (tr) *see* Juglone.

'Ivalon' *see* Polyvinyl alcohol.

'Ivepirine' *see* Acetylsalicylic acid.

IVERMECTIN*** (mixture of 5-*O*-demethyl-22,23-dihydroavermectin A1a and 5-*O*-demethyl-25-de(1-methylpropyl)-22,23-dihydro-25-(1-methylethyl)avermectin A1a).

'Iversal' *see* Ambazone.

'Ivosit' *see* Dinoseb acetate.

'Ixoten' *see* Trofosfamide.

J

J-51 *see* Diathymosulfone silver.
J-66 *see under* Norethisterone acetate.
J-96 *see* Ethinylestradiol 3-isopropylsulfonate.
'Jacuta' *see* Lindane.
'Jacutin' *see* Lindane.
'Jadit' *see under* Buclosamide.
'Janimine' *see* Imipramine.
'Jatroneural' *see* Trifluoperazine.
'Jatropur' *see* Triamterene.
'Jatrosom' *see under* Tranylcypromine.
JAV-852 *see* Benfosformin.
Javel water *see* Sodium hypochlorite.
JB-11 *see* Trimetrexate.
JB-251 *see* Protokylol.
JB-305 *see* Piperidolate.
JB-323 *see* Pipenzolate bromide.
JB-329 *see* 1-Ethylpiperid-3-yl phenylcyclopentaneglycolate.
JB-340 *see* Mepenzolate bromide.
JB-516 *see* Pheniprazine.
JB-821 *see* Phenylisopropylisoniazid.
JB-835 *see* Phenylisobutylhydrazine.
JB-840 *see* Oxyclipine.
JB-8181 *see* Desipramine.
JD-96 *see* Vinylbital.
JD-177 *see* Aminocaproic acid.
JDL-37 *see* Niflumic acid.
JDL-38 *see* Triflocin.
'Jectofer' *see* Iron sorbitex.
'Jefron' *see* Polyferose.
'Jenotone' *see* Aminopromazine.
'Jestryl' *see* Carbachol.
'Jetrium' *see* Dextromoramide.
JF-1 *see* Nalmefene.
JL-512 *see* Fenadiazole.
JL-998 *see* Dicycloverine.

JL-1078 *see* Dihexyverine.
JM-8 *see* Carboplatin.
JM-9 *see* Iproplatin.
JO-1016 *see* Tixocortol pivalate.
'Jodomiron' *see* Iodamide.
'Jodozoat' *see* Meglumine acetrizoate.
Jodphenphos* *see* Iodofenphos.
Jodtalamin* *see* Iotalamic acid.
'Jomezol' *see* Thiamazole methiodide.
'Jomybel' *see* Josamycin.
'Jonctum' *see* Oxaceprol.
'Jonit' *see* Bitoscanate.
'Jopagnost' *see* Iopanoic acid.
Jopanoic acid* *see* Iopanoic acid.
JOSAMYCIN*** (4-(acetyloxy)-6-[[-3,6-dideoxy-4-*O*-(2,6-dideoxy-3-*C*-methyl-4-*O*-3-methyl-1-oxobutyl)-α-L-*ribo*-hexopyranosyl]-3-(dimethylamino)-β-D-glucopyranosyl]oxy]-10-hydroxy-5-methoxy-9,16-dimethyl-2-oxooxacyclohexadeca-11,13-diene-7-acetaldehyde; 7-(formylmethyl)-4,10-dihydroxy-5-methoxy-9,16-dimethyl-2-oxo-oxacyclohexadeca-11,13-dien-6-yl 3,6-dideoxy-4-*O*-(2,6-dideoxy-3-*C*-methyl-α-L-*ribo*-hexopyranosyl)-3-(dimethylamino)-β-D-glucopyranoside 4'-acetate 4″-isovalerate; leucomycin V 3-acetate 4ᴮ-(3-methylbutanoate; EN-141; 'jomybel'; 'josaxin').
'Josaxin' *see* Josamycin.
Jotrizoic acid* *see* Iotrizoic acid.
JP-428 *see* Fenspiride.
JR-7904 *see* Lidoflazine.
'Jubalon' *see* Carbifene.
'Judolor' *see* Fursultiamine.
JUGLONE (5-hydroxy-1,4-naphthoquinone; iuglone; nucin).
Julin's carbon chloride *see* Hexachlorobenzene.

K

K-III *see* Dinitro-*o*-cresol.
K-IV *see* Dinitro-*o*-cresol.
K-17 *see* Thalidomide.
K-38 *see* Glycyclamide.
K80-KBOT *see under* Tramazoline.
K-206 *see* Tipindole methiodide.
K-315 *see* Tramadol.
K-364 *see* Salinomycin.
K-386 *see* Glycyclamide.
K-509 *see* Endomide.
K-1900 *see* Nimorazole.
K-2004 *see* Taglutimide.
K-2680 *see* Etomidoline.
K-3712 *see* Morclofone.
K-3920 *see* Indobufen.
K-4024 *see* Glipizide.
K-4277 *see* Indoprofen.
K-5407 *see* Nafetolol.
K-9147 *see* Tolciclate.
K-30081 *see* Dipivefrine.
K-748364A *see* Salinomycin.
Kabi-925 *see* Emylcamate.
Kabi-1774 *see* Quadrosilan.
'Kabikinase' *see* Streptokinase.
KAEMPFEROL (3,4',5,7-tetrahydroxyflavone).
Kaempferol 3-galactoside *see* Trifolin.
'Kafocin' *see* Cefaloglycin.
'Kainever' *see* Estazolam.
KAINIC ACID*** (2-carboxy-4-isopropenyl-3-pyrrolidineacetic acid; digenic acid; *xylo*-kainic acid).
KALAFUNGIN** (3,3a,5,11b-tetrahydro-7-hydroxy-5-methyl-2*H*-furo[3,2-*b*]naphtho[2,3-*d*]pyran-2,6,11-trione; kalamycin; NSC-137443; U-19718).
Kalamycin *see* Kalafungin.
'Kalex' *see* Tetrasodium edetate.
'Kalipin' *see* Calcium alginate.
Kallidin I *see* Lysylbradykinin.
Kallidin II *see* Bradykinin.
KALLIDINOGENASE*** (enzyme from mammalian pancreas or urine; callicrein; 'kallikrein').
'Kallikrein' *see* Kallidinogenase.
Kallikrein-trypsin inhibitor *see* Aprotinin.
'Kalma' *see* Tryptophan.
'Kalmin' *see* Phlorizin.
'Kalodil' *see* Diisopropylamine dichloroacetate.
'Kalsetal' *see* Calcium acetylsalicylate.
'Kalymin' *see* Pyridostigmine bromide.
'Kalypnon' *see* Barotal.
'Kalzan' *see* Calcium gluconate.

'Kamaver' *see* Chloramphenicol.
Kamfochlor *see* Campheclor.
'Kamoran' *see* Actaplanin.
Kampfstoff *see* Mustard gas.
'Kamycin' *see* Kanamycin.
'Kamynex' *see* Kanamycin.
'Kanabristol' *see* Kanamycin.
'Kanacillin' *see under* Kanamycin.
'Kanacine' *see* Kanamycin.
KANAMYCIN*** (4,6-diamino-2-hydroxy-1,3-cyclohexene 3,6'-diamino-3,6'-dideoxydi-α-D-glucoside; kanamycin sulfate).
KANAMYCIN plus PENICILLIN ('kanacillin').
Kanamycin B *see* Bekanamycin.
'Kanamytrex' *see* Kanamycin.
'Kanechlor' *see* Polychlorinated biphenyl.
Kanendomycin *see* Bekanamycin.
'Kanesten' *see* Clotrimazole.
'Kannasyn' *see* Kanamycin.
'Kanrenol' *see* Canrenoate potassium.
'Kantrex' *see* Kanamycin.
'Kaon' *see* Potassium gluconate.
'Kappadione' *see* Menadiol sodium phosphate.
'Kappaxan' *see* Kanamycin.
'Kappaxin' *see* Menadione.
'Kaprolsin' *see* Aminocaproic acid.
'Karathane' *see* Dinocap.
'Karbam black' *see* Ferbam.
'Karbam white' *see* Ziram.
Karbation (tr) *see* Metam-sodium.
'Karbatox' *see* Carbaril.
'Karbinone' *see* Naftazone.
Karbofos (tr) *see* Malathion.
'Karbosep' *see* Carbaril.
KARBUTILATE* (1-[*m*-(*tert*-butylcarbamoyloxy)phenyl]-3,3-dimethylurea; 3-[[(dimethylamino)carbonyl]amino]phenyl (1,1-dimethylethyl)carbamate; *m*-(dimethylcarbamoylamino)phenyl *tert*-butylcarbamate; 'tandex').
'Kardiamed' *see* β-Acetyldigoxin.
'Kardylan' *see* Nicofuranose.
'Karion *see* Pimeclone *and* Sorbitol.
'Karmex' *see* Diuron.
'Karsil' *see* 3',4'-Dichloro-2-methylvaleranilide.
KASAL* (sodium aluminium phosphate basic).
KAT-256 *see* Clobutinol.
'Katapyrin' *see* Aminometradine.
'Katin' *see* Sodium menadiol-3-sulfonate.
Katine *see* Cathine.
'Katovit' *see* Prolintane.
'Katril' *see* Dropropizine.

Kautschin *see* Limonene.
Kavahin *see* Methysticin.
Kavain *see* Kawain.
Kava pyrone *see* Kawain.
Kavatin *see* Methysticin.
KAWAIN ((*R*)-5,6-dihydro-4-methoxy-6-(2-phenylethenyl)-2*H*-pyran-2-one; 5,6-dihydro-4-methoxy-6-(2-phenylvinyl)-α-pyrone; 5,6-dihydro-4-methoxy-6-styryl-2-pyrone; 6-hydroxy-3-methoxy-7-phenyl-2,6-heptadienoic acid δ-lactone; gonosan; kavain; kava pyrone; 'kwaform'; 'neuronika').
'Kayexalate' *see* Polystyrenesulfonate sodium.
KB-77 *see* Tramazoline.
KB-95 *see* Benzpiperylone.
KB-227 *see* Tramazoline.
KB-944 *see* Fostedil.
KC-9147 *see* Tolciclate.
KCA *see* Etafenone.
KEBUZONE** (4-(3-oxobutyl)-1,2-diphenyl-3,5-pyrazolidinedione; 4-(2-acetylethyl)-1,2-diphenyl-3,5-pyrazolidinedione; ketophenylbutazone; 'ketazone').
'Kedacillin' *see* Sulbenicillin.
'Kefadol' *see* Cefamandole nafate.
'Kefglycin' *see* Cefaloglycin.
'Keflex' *see* Cefalexin.
'Keflin' *see* Cefalotin.
'Keflodin' *see* Cefaloridine.
'Keflordin' *see* Cefaloridine.
'Keforal' *see* Cefalexin.
'Kefspor' *see* Cefaloridine.
'Kefzol' *see* Cefazolin.
'Keithon' *see* Clofenetamine.
'Kelacid' *see* Alginic acid.
'Kelatin' *see* Penicillamine.
'Kelene' *see* Chloroethane.
'Kelfer' *see* Calcium sodium ferriclate.
'Kelfiprim' *see under* Trimethoprim.
'Kelfizine' *see* Sulfalene.
'Kelgin' *see* Sodium alginate.
'Kelin' *see* Chloroethane.
Kellofylline *see* Visnafylline.
'Kelocyanor' *see* Dicobalt edetate.
'Kelox' *see* Tetroquinone.
'Keltan' *see* Dicofol.
'Kelthane' *see* Dicofol.
'Kemadrin' *see* Procyclidine.
'Kemate' *see* Anilazine.
'Kemicetin' *see* Chloramphenicol.
'Kemithal' *see* Thialbarbital.
'Kenacort' *see* Triamcinolone.
'Kenalog' *see* Triamcinolone acetonide.
Kendall's compound A *see* 11-Dehydrocorticosterone.
Kendall's compound B *see* Corticosterone.
Kendall's compound E *see* Cortisone.
Kendall's dioxy compound B *see* Desoxycortone.
'Kepinol' *see* Co-trimoxazole.
'Kepone' *see* Chlordecone.
'Keracaine' *see* Proxymetacaine.
KERACYANIN** (3-[6-(*O*-6-deoxy-α-L-mannopyranosyl)-β-D-glucopyranosyloxy]-3',4',5,7-tetrahydroxyflavylium chloride).
'Kerb' *see* Propyzamide.
'Kerecid' *see* Idoxuridine.
'Kerlone' *see* Betaxolol.
'Ketaject' *see* Ketamine.
'Ketalar' *see* Ketamine.
KETAMINE** (2-(*o*-chlorophenyl)-2-methylaminocyclohexanone; CI-581; CL-369; CN-52372-2).
KETAMINE plus DROPERIDOL ('ketanest').
'Ketanest' *see under* Ketamine.
KETANSERIN*** (3-[2-[4-(*p*-fluorobenzoyl)piperid-1-yl]ethyl]-2,4(1*H*,3*H*)-quinazolinedione; R-41468).
KETANSERIN TARTRATE (R-49945).
'Ketaset' *see* Ketamine.
'Ketatrium' *see* Ketoprofen.
'Ketavet' *see* Ketamine.
KETAZOCINE*** (2-(cyclopropylmethyl)-2'-hydroxy-5,9-dimethyl-8-oxo-6,7-benzomorphan; 3-(cyclopropylmethyl)-3,4,5,6-tetrahydro-8-hydroxy-6,11-dimethyl-2,6-methano-3-benzazocin-1(2*H*)-one; ketocyclazocine; WIN-34276).
KETAZOLAM*** (11-chloro-8,12b-dihydro-2,8-dimethyl-12b-phenyl-4*H*[1,3]-oxazino[3,2-*d*]-[1,4]benzodiazepine-4,7(6*H*)-dione; U-28774; 'anxon'; 'contamex'; 'solatran'; 'unakalm').
'Ketazone' *see* Kebuzone.
KETENE (carbomethene; ethenone).
'Kethamed' *see* Pemoline.
Kethoxal* *see* Ketoxal.
Kethoxal bis(thiosemicarbazone) *see* Gloxazone.
KETIMIPRAMINE*** (5-[3-(dimethylamino)-propyl]-5,11-dihydro-10*H*-dibenz[*b,f*]azepin-10-one; ketipramine; ketoimipramine; ketimipramine fumarate; G-35359).
Ketipramine* *see* Ketimipramine.
Keto.... *see also* Oxo....
Ketoacetic acid *see* Glyoxylic acid.
KETOBEMIDONE*** (ethyl (*m*-hydroxyphenyl-methylpiperidyl)ketone; 4-(*m*-hydroxyphenyl)-1-methyl-4-propionylpiperidine; 1-[4-(*m*-hydroxy-phenyl)-1-methylpiperid-4-yl]-1-propanone; cetobemidone; A-21; C-5511; C-7115; Ho-10720; WIN-1539).
KETOCAINE*** (2'-(2-diisopropylaminoethoxy)-butyrophenone; A-2358; Rec-7-0518; 'ane-pad').
KETOCAINOL*** (*o*-(2-diisopropylaminoethoxy)-α-propylbenzyl alcohol).
3-Ketocaproic acid *see* 3-Oxohexanoic acid.
KETOCONAZOLE*** ((±)-*cis*-1-acetyl-4-[4-[[2-(2,4-dichlorophenyl)-2-(1*H*-imidazol-1-ylmeth-yl)-1,3-dioxolan-4-yl]methoxy]phenyl]piperazine; (±)-4-(4-acetylpiperazin-1-yl)-α-[2-(2,4-dichlorophenyl)-*r*-2-imidazol-1-ylmethyl-1,3-di-oxolan-*c*-4-yl]anisole; R-41400; 'nizoral').
Ketocyclazocine *see* Ketazocine.
'Ketogestin' *see* 4-Pregnene-3,11,20-trione.
2-Ketoglutaric acid *see* 2-Oxoglutaric acid.
3-Ketohexanoic acid *see* 3-Oxohexanoic acid.
Ketohexazine* *see* Cetohexazine.
3-Ketohexonic acid lactone *see* Isoascorbic acid.

Ketohydroxyestratriene *see* Estrone.
Ketoimipramine *see* Ketimipramine.
α-Ketoisocaproic acid *see* 4-Methyl-2-oxovaleric acid.
Ketole *see* Indole.
Ketomalonic acid *see* Mesoxalic acid.
KETOMYCIN ((*R*)-3-cyclohexenylglyoxylic acid).
Ketophenylbutazone *see* Kebuzone.
KETOPROFEN* (*m*-benzoylhydratropic acid; 2-(3-benzoylphenyl)propionic acid; 3-(1-carboxyethyl)benzophenone; RP-19583; 'ketatrium').
11-Ketoprogesterone *see* 4-Pregnene-3,11,20-trione.
2-Ketopropionaldehyde *see* Methylglyoxal.
2-Ketopropionic acid *see* Pyruvic acid.
KETORFANOL ** (17-(cyclopropylmethyl)-4-hydroxy-morphinan-6-one).
KETOROLAC ** ((±)-5-benzoyl-2,3-dihydro-1*H*-pyrrolizine-1-carboxylic acid).
'Ketoscilium' *see* Fentonium bromide.
'Ketostix' *see* Sodium nitroprusside.
Ketosuccinic acid *see* Oxalacetic acid.
KETOTIFEN ** (4,9-dihydro-4-(1-methylpiperid-4-ylidene)-10*H*-benzo[4,5]cyclohepta[1,2-*b*]thiophen-10-one).
KETOTIFEN FUMARATE* (HC-20511; 'zaditen').
KETOTREXATE ** (*N*-[*p*-[[2-(2-amino-1,4,5,6,7,8-hexahydro-5-methyl-4-oxopteridin-6-yl)ethyl]amino]benzoyl]-L-glutamic acid; tetrahydro-5-methylhomofolic acid; NSC-139490).
4-Ketovaleric acid *see* Levulinic acid.
KETOXAL* (3-ethoxy-1,1-dihydroxy-2-butanone; kethoxal; U-2032).
'Ketrax' *see* Levamisole.
'Keuten' *see* Sodium dibunate.
'Kevopril' *see* Quinupramine.
K-F 224 *see* Naftoxate.
KHELLIN* (5,8-dimethoxy-2-methyl-6,7-furanochromone; 4,9-dimethoxy-7-methyl-5*H*-furo[3,2-*g*][1]benzopyran-5-one; ammicardin).
Khellinin *see* Khelloside.
KHELLOL (7-(hydroxymethyl)-4-methoxybenzopyran-5-one; 2-(hydroxymethyl)-5-methoxy-6,7-furanochromone).
Khellol glucoside *see* Khelloside.
KHELLOSIDE* (7-(hydroxymethyl)-4-methoxy-5*H*-furo-[3,2-*g*][1]benzopyran-5-one glucoside; khellinin; khellol glucoside).
'Khonvan' *see* Fosfestrol.
'Kidira' *see* Dihydroergotamine.
'Kiditard' *see* Quinidine.
'Kidrolase' *see* Asparaginase.
'Kikuthrin' *see* Prothrin.
Killifolin *see* Quillifoline.
'Kilmicen' *see* Tolciclate.
'Kilscour' *see* Arsanilic acid.
'Kilval' *see* Vamidothion.
'Kinalysin' *see* Streptokinase.
Kindekamin *see* Quindecamine.
'Kinevac' *see* Sincalide.
Kinic acid *see* Quinic acid.
KINOPRENE* (*E,E*-2-propynyl 3,7,11-trimethyl-dodeca-2,4-dienoate; 'altodel').

Kinozol (tr) *see* 8-Quinolinol.
'Kinupril' *see* Quinupramine.
'Kiron' *see* Sulfametoxydiazine.
α-Kirondrin *see* Glaucarubin.
'Kitamycin' *see* Kitasamycin.
KITASAMYCIN* (antibiotic from *Str. kitasatoensis*; leucomycin).
'Kitazin P' *see* S-Benzyl O,O-diisopropyl phosphorothioate.
'Kitnos' *see* Etofamide.
KL-255 *see* Bupranolol.
'Klinium' *see* Lidoflazine.
'Klinomycin' *see* Minocycline.
'Klion' *see* Metronidazole.
'Kloben' *see* Neburon.
Klofibrat* *see* Clofibrate.
Kloretazin *see* Chlormethine.
'Klorex' *see* Clorexolone.
Klorfenidim (tr) *see* Monuron.
Klor-IFK *see* Chlorpropham.
Klorinat (tr) *see* Barban.
Klorofos (tr) *see* Metrifonate.
Kloroksifenidim (tr) *see* Chloroxuron.
Klorpromazine *see* Chlorpromazine.
'Klot' *see* Tolonium chloride.
'Klyx' *see* Docusate sodium.
KM-65 *see* Benzonatate.
K-MV *see* Pheneticillin.
Ko-592 *see* Toliprolol.
Ko-1173 *see* Mexiletine.
Ko-1366 *see* Bunitrolol.
Ko-1400 *see* Pargolol.
'Koglucoid' *see* Alseroxylon.
KOJIC ACID (5-hydroxy-2-hydroxymethyl-4-pyrone).
'Kolantyl' *see* Dicycloverine.
'Kollidon' *see* Povidone.
'Kolton' *see* Piprinhydrinate.
'Koluphthisin' *see* Viomycin.
'Kombetin' *see* Strophanthin.
'Kombistrat' *see* Hydroxyzine.
'Kompensan' *see* Dihydroxyaluminium sodium carbonate.
'Komplexic acid' *see* Edetic acid.
'Komplexon' *see* Trisodium edetate.
'Komplexon IV' *see* 1,2-Diaminocyclohexanetetraacetic acid.
'Konakion' *see* Phytomenadione.
'Konsyl' *see* Psyllium.
Korkonium (tr) *see* Dicholine suberate.
'Korlan' *see* Fenclofos.
'K-otrhin' *see* Deltamethrin.
Kr-0151 *see under* Norfenefrine.
'Krasnitin' *see* Asparaginase.
'Krecalvin' *see under* Dichlorvos.
'Kreucosan' *see* Metronidazole.
'Kresatin' *see* m-Cresyl acetate.
'Kronitex' *see* Tricresyl phosphate.
'Kryogenin' *see* Phenicarbazide.
'Kryptocur' *see* Gonadorelin.
'Krysid' *see* Antu.
KS-33 *see* Oxyridazine.
Ksavin (tr) *see* Xantinol nicotinate.

KSW-786 *see* Clofenciclan.
KTS *see* Gloxazone.
'Kufaprim' *see under* Fosfomycin.
'Kumatoks' *see* Warfarin.
'Kumatox' *see* Warfarin.
'Kumoran' *see* Dicoumarol.
KURCHI* (*Holarrhena antidysenterica* bark; conessi bark; telicherry bark).
'Kuron' *see* Fenoprop.
'Kurosal' *see* Fenoprop.
Kutizon (tr) *see* Cutizone.

KW-110 *see* Aceglutamide aluminium.
KW-5338 *see* Domperidone.
'Kwaform' *see* Kawain.
KWD-2019 *see* Terbutaline.
'Kwells' *see* Scopolamine.
KXM *see* Proglumide.
Kyamepromazin *see* Cyamemazine.
'Kynex' *see* Sulfamethoxypyridazine.
KYNURENIC ACID (4-hydroxyquinaldic acid).
KYNURENINE (β-anthranoylalanine).
Kynurine *see* 4-Quinolinol.

L

L-2 *see* Butoctamide hemisuccinate.
L-8 *see* Lypressin.
L-11-6 (tr) *see* Phorate.
L-30 *see* Sulfasomidine.
L-67 *see* Prilocaine.
L-84 *see* Diethylcarbamazine.
L-542 *see* Mercurobutol.
L-554 *see* Tritoqualine.
L-566 *see* Dibemethine.
L-749 *see* Salacetamide.
L-1418 *see* Sultopride.
L-1573 *see* Mercaptamine.
L-1591 *see* Cystamine.
L-1633 *see* Sodium dibunate.
L-1718 *see* Osalmid.
L-2013 *see* Hexapropymate.
L-2197 *see* Benzarone.
L-2214 *see* Benzbromarone.
L-2329 *see* Benziodarone.
L-2642 *see* Etabenzarone.
L-3428 *see* Amiodarone.
L-4296 *see* Pyridarone.
L-5103 *see* Rifampicin.
L-5418 *see* Diftalone.
L-5458 *see* Deflazacort.
L-5818 *see* Coumazoline.
L-6150 *see* Oxdralazine.
L-6257 *see* Oxetorone fumarate.
L-7810 *see* Cicarperone.
L-8027 *see* Nictindole.
L-809 *see* Tianafac.
L-9308 *see* Zetidoline.
L-9394 *see* Butoprozine.
L-11473 *see* Rifapentine.
L-11809 *see* Isoprazone.
L-12181 *see* Premazepam.
L-12507 *see* Teicoplanin.
L-20025 *see* Clorprenaline.
L-64000 *see* Fluazacort.
L-154826 *see* Lisinopril.
L-588357 *see* Metirosine.
L-620388 *see* Cefoxitin.
L-643341 *see* Famotidine.
'L.A.' *see* Psyllium.
LA-1 *see* Nitrazepam.
LA-6 *see* Clonazepam.
LA-012 *see* Quatacaine.
LA-111 *see* Diazepam.
La-271 *see* Bisoxatin.
La-271a *see* Bisoxatin diacetate.
La-391 *see* Sodium picosulfate.

LA-956 *see* Pemoline.
LA-1211 *see* Imolamine.
LA-1221 *see* Butalamine.
LA-6023 *see* Metformin.
Labarraque's solution *see* Sodium hypochlorite.
'Labazene' *see* Valproic acid.
'Labazil' *see* Salacetamide.
LABETALOL*** (3-carboxamido-4-hydroxy-α-
[(1-methyl-3-phenylpropylamino)methyl]benzyl
alcohol; 5-[1-hydroxy-2-(1-methyl-3-phenyl-
propylamino)ethyl]salicylamide; labetalol
hydrochloride; AH-5158A; Sch-15719W; 'trand-
ate').
R,R-Labetalol *see* Dilevalol.
'Laboprin' *see* Lysine acetylsalicylate.
'Labosept' *see* Dequalinium chloride.
'Labotropine' *see* Deanol benzilate.
'Labrafil M-1944CS' *see* Peglicol 5 oleate.
'Labroda' *see* Flopropione.
'Labrodax' *see* Flopropione.
Laburnine *see* Cytisine.
LAC-43 *see* Bupivacaine.
'Lacarnol' *see* Adenosine.
'Lacfer' *see* Lactobacillus acidophilus cultures.
LACHESINE ((2-benzilyloxyethyl)ethyldimethyl-
ammonium chloride; ethyl(2-hydroxyethyl)di-
methylammonium chloride benzilate; E-3).
'Lactaclox' *see under* Ampicillin.
Lactacridine *see* Ethacridine lactate.
β-Lactamase *see* Penicillinase.
LACTIC ACID (2-hydroxypropionic acid).
Lactic acid polyester with glycolic acid *see* Poly-
glactin(s).
Lactic acid 3,3,5-trimethylcyclohexyl ester *see* Cic-
lactate.
Lactoacridine *see* Ethacridine lactate.
LACTOBACILLUS ACIDOPHILUS CUL-
TURES ('enpac'; 'lacfer'; 'lactophil'; 'viacil').
Lactobacillus bulgaricus factor *see* Pantetheine.
Lactobacillus casei factor *see* Folic acid.
Lactobacillus casei fermentation factor *see* Pterop-
terin.
Lactoflavin *see* Riboflavin.
Lactogen *see* Prolactin.
'Lactol' *see* 2-Naphthyl lactate.
Lactonaphthol *see* 2-Naphthyl lactate.
Lactophenin *see* Lactylphenetidin.
Lactophenone *see* 2-Hydroxypropiophenone.
'Lactophenymer' *see* Phenylmercuric lactate.
'Lactophil' *see* Lactobacillus acidophilus cultures.
'Lactotrim' *see* Trimethoprim lactate.

LACTULOSE* (4-*O*-β-D-galactopyranosyl-D-fructose).

LACTYLPHENETIDIN* (*N*-(*p*-ethoxyphenyl)-lactamide; fenolactina; lactophenin).

'Lacumin' *see* Pecazine.

Ladakamycin *see* Azacitidine.

'Ladogal' *see* Glucosulfamide.

'Laetrile' *see* Amygdalin.

'Laevilac' *see* Lactulose.

Laevo.... *see also* Levo.....

'Laevolac' *see* Lactulose.

'Laevostrophan' *see* Strophanthin.

'Lagatrim' *see* Co-trimoxazole.

'Lakarnol' *see* Adenosine.

'Lambrol' *see* Fluenetil.

'Lammacorten' *see* Dexamethasone.

'Lamoryl' *see* Griseofulvin.

Lamoxactam *see* Latamoxef.

'Lampit' *see* Nifurtimox.

'Lamprene' *see* Clofazimine.

'Lamra' *see* Diazepam.

LAMTIDINE* (1-[*m*-[3-[(3-amino-1-methyl-1*H*-1,2,4-triazol-5-yl)amino]propoxy]benzyl]piperidine; 3-amino-1-methyl-1*H*-1,2,4-triazol-5-yl[3-[(α-piperid-1-yl)-*m*-tolyloxy]propyl]amine; AH-22216).

'Lamuran' *see* Ajmalicine.

LANADOXIN (gitaloxigenin monodigitoxoside).

LANATOSIDE A ('adigal'; 'aglunat').

LANATOSIDE C* (digoxigenin 3-acetylglucosyltridigitoxoside; 3β,12,14-trihydroxy-5β-card-20(22)-enolide 3-(acetylglucosyltridigitoxoside)).

'Landamycin' *see* Ribostamycin.

'Landrin' *see under* 3,4,5-Trimethylphenyl methylcarbamate.

'Landromil' *see* Ticlatone.

Lanesta *see* Clorindanol.

'Lanicor' *see* Digoxin.

'Lanimerck' *see* Lanatoside C.

'Lanitop' *see* Metildigoxin.

'Lannate' *see* Methomyl.

'Lanoxalin' *see* Bisoxatin diacetate.

'Lanoxin' *see* Digoxin.

LANTHIONINE (3,3'-thiodialanine; bis(2-amino-2-carboxyethyl)sulfide).

'Lanvis' *see* Tioguanine.

Laokon *see* Oxycodone.

LAPIRIUM CHLORIDE* (1-[*N*-(2-dodecanoyloxyethyl)carbamoylmethyl]pyridinium chloride; 1-[(2-hydroxyethyl)carbamoylmethyl]pyridinium chloride laurate; 1-[*N*-(2-lauroyloxyethyl)-carbamoylmethyl]pyridinium chloride; lapyrium chloride; NSC-33659; 'emcol E-607').

'Lapudrine' *see* Chlorproguanil.

'Lapurol' *see* Urea hydrogen peroxide.

Lapyrium chloride* *see* Lapirium chloride.

Laramycin *see* Zorbamycin.

'Larex' *see* Polynoxylin.

'Largactil' *see* Chlorpromazine.

'Largon' *see* Propiomazine.

'Largophren' *see* Prothipendyl.

Laricic acid *see* Agaric acid.

'Laristin' *see* Histidine.

'Larocaine' *see* Dimethocaine.

'Larocin' *see* Amoxicillin.

'Larodon' *see* Propyphenazone.

'Larodopa' *see* Levodopa.

'Larostidin' *see* Histidine.

'Larotid' *see* Amoxicillin.

'Laroxyl' *see* Amitriptyline.

LARUSAN (tr) (*N*¹-(2-furfurylidene-1-methylethylidene)isoniazid; isonicotinic acid [1-(2-furfurylidene)-1-methylethylidene]hydrazide; 1-furfurylideneacetone 2-isonicotinoylhydrazone).

Larusin *see* Formycin B.

LAS-11871 *see* Thiazolinobutazone.

LASALOCID* (6-[7-ethyl-4-hydroxy-3,5-dimethyl-6-oxo-7-[5-(5-ethyltetrahydro-5-hydroxy-pyran-2-yl)tetrahydro-2-furyl]heptyl]-3-methylsalicylic acid; 6-[7(*R*)-[5(*S*)-ethyl-5-(5(*R*)-ethyltetrahydro-5-hydroxy-6(*S*)-methyl-2*H*-pyran-2(*R*)-yl)tetrahydro-3(*S*)-methyl-2(*S*)-furyl]-4-(*S*)-hydroxy-3(*R*),5(*S*)-dimethyl-6-oxononyl]-2,3-cresotic acid; Ro 2-2985; X-537A; 'avatec').

'Lasan' *see* Dithranol.

'Lasix' *see* Furosemide.

'Lasso' *see* Alachlor.

'Lastanox' *see* Bis(tributyltin) oxide.

LAT *see* Anthiolimine.

LATAMOXEF* (7β-[2-carboxy-2-(4-hydroxyphenyl)acetamido]-7α-methoxy-3-[[(1-methyl-1*H*-tetrazol-5-yl)thio]methyl]-5-dethia-5-oxa-2-cephem-2-carboxylic acid; (6*R*,7*R*)-2-[2-carboxy-2-(4-hydroxyphenyl)acetamido]-7-methoxy-3-[[(1-methyltetrazol-5-yl)thio]methyl]-8-oxo-5-oxa-1-azabicyclo[4.2.0]oct-2-ene-2-carboxylic acid; *N*-[(6*R*,7*R*)-2-carboxy-7-methoxy-3-[[(1-methyl-1*H*-tetrazol-5-yl)thio]methyl]-8-oxo-1-azabicyclo[4.2.0]oct-2-en-7-yl]-2-(*p*-hydroxyphenyl)malonamic acid; lamoxactam; moxalactam disodium; LY-127395; Shionogi 6059-S; 'moxalactam').

'Latepyrine' *see* Aminophenazone ethyl salicylate.

Lateritium wr, antibiotic *see* Fusafungine.

Lathyrus factor *see* 3-Aminopropionitrile.

'Latuss' *see under* Butetamate.

'Laucetin' *see under* Erythromycin estolate.

Laudacon *see* Hydromorphone.

LAUDANOSINE (1,2,3,4-tetrahydro-6,7-dimethoxy-2-methyl-1-veratrylisoquinoline; tetrahydro-*N*-methyl papaverine; veraisoquin).

Laudanum *see* Opium alkaloids.

LAUDEXIUM METILSULFATE* (2,2'-decamethylenebis(1,2,3,4-tetrahydro-6,7-dimethoxy-1-veratrylisoquinolinium methylsulfate); curarexine methylsulfate).

Laughing gas *see* Nitrous oxide.

LAURALKONIUM CHLORIDE* (benzyl[2-(*p*-dodecoylphenoxy)ethyl]dimethylammonium chloride; laurophenonium chloride).

LAURETH 4* (α-dodecyl-ω-hydroxypoly(oxy-1,2-ethanediyl); polyethylene glycol monododecyl ether).

Laureth 9 *see* Polidocanol.

LAURETH 10S* (α-[2-(dodecylthio)ethyl]-ω-hydroxypoly(oxy-1,2-ethanediyl); polyethylene glycol

mono[2-(dodecylthio)ethyl] ether).
LAURIC ACID (dodecanoic acid).
LAURILSULFATE(S)** (dodecyl sulfate(s); lauryl sulfate(s)).
'**Lauritran**' *see* Erythromycin estolate.
LAURIXAMINE** (3-(dodecyloxy)propylamine).
'**Laurobolin**' *see* Nandrolone laurate.
LAUROCAPRAM** (1-dodecylhexahydro-2*H*-azepin-2-one; N-0252; 'azone').
LAUROGUADINE*** (1,3-diguanyl-4-lauryloxybenzene; 1,1'-(4-dodecyloxy-*m*-phenylene)diguanidine; P-7).
LAUROLINIUM ACETATE*** (4-amino-1-dodecylquinaldinium acetate).
LAUROMACROGOL 400*** (mixture of monolauryl ethers of polyoxyethylene glycols having a statistical average of 8 ethylene oxide groups per molecule).
See also Laureth.
'**Lauron**' *see* Aurothioglycanide.
Laurophenonium chloride *see* Lauralkonium chloride.
'**Laurosept**' *see* 1-Dodecylpyridinium bromide.
1-[*N*-(2-Lauroyloxyethyl)carbamoylmethyl]pyridinium chloride *see* Lapirium chloride.
Laurylisoquinolinium bromide *see* 2-Dodecylisoquinolinium bromide.
Laurylpyridinium bromide *see* 1-Dodecylpyridinium bromide.
Lauryl sodium sulfate *see* Sodium dodecyl sulfate.
Lauryl sulfate(s) *see* Laurilsulfate(s).
Lauryl sulfoacetate *see* Dodecyl sulfoacetate.
'**Lautecin**' *see under* Erythromycin estolate.
Lauth's violet *see* Thionine.
'**Lavema**' *see* Acetphenolisatin.
'**Laxanthrene**' *see* Dantron.
'**Laxatin**' *see* Phenisatin.
'**Laxbene**' *see under* Bisacodyl.
'**Laxigen**' *see* Acetphenolisatin.
'**Laxoberal**' *see* Sodium picosulfate.
'**Laxoberon**' *see* Sodium picosulfate.
LB-45 *see under* Pindolol.
LB-46 *see* Pindolol.
LB-125 *see* Cyprodenate.
LB-502 *see* Furosemide.
LC-44 *see* Flupentixol.
LCB-29 *see* Idrocilamide.
LD-335 *see* Propyromazine bromide.
LD-935 *see* Dipiproverine.
LD-2351 *see* Butopiprine.
LD-2480 *see* Piprocurarium iodide.
LD-2630 *see* Difencloxazine.
LD-2988 *see* Folescutol.
LD-3055 *see* Oxypyrronium bromide.
LD-3098 *see* Cirazoline.
LD-3394 *see* Fenozolone.
LD-3598 *see* Spirgetine.
LD-3612 *see* Paraflutizide.
LD-3695 *see* Cyclazodone.
LD-4610 *see* Oxazidione.
LD-4644 *see* Pipebuzone.
LE-29060 *see* Vinblastine.
Lead tetraethyl *see* Tetraethyllead.

'**Lealgin**' *see* Phenoperidine.
'**Leandin**' *see* Cyacetacide.
'**Lebaycid**' *see* Fenthion.
'**Lecibis**' *see* Bephenium hydroxynaphthoate.
Lecithin *see* Phosphatidylcholine.
'**Lectopam**' *see* Bromazepam.
'**Ledacrin**' *see* Nitracrine.
'**Ledclair**' *see* Sodium calcium edetate.
'**Ledercort**' *see* Triamcinolone.
'**Lederfen**' *see* Fenbufen.
'**Lederkyn**' *see* Sulfamethoxypyridazine.
'**Ledermix**' *see under* Demeclocycline.
'**Ledermycin**' *see* Demeclocycline.
'**Lederspan**' *see* Triamcinolone hexacetonide.
'**Ledertepa**' *see* Thiotepa.
'**Ledertrexate**' *see* Methotrexate.
'**Ledopa**' *see* Levodopa.
'**Ledosten**' *see* Diethadione.
LEFETAMINE** ((−)-*N*,*N*-dimethyl-1,2-diphenylethylamine; (−)-*N*,*N*-dimethyl-α-phenylphenethylamine; (−)-*N*,*N*-dimethylstilbylamine; 'spa').
LEFLUNOMIDE*** (α,α,α-trifluoro-5-methyl-4-isoxazolecarboxy-*p*-toluidide; 5-methyl-*N*-[*p*-(trifluoromethyl)phenyl]-4-isoxazolecarboxamide).
'**Legalon**' *see* Silymarin sodium.
'**Legendal**' *see* Lactulose.
'**Legumex extra**' *see* Benazolin.
'**Legurame**' *see* Carbetamide.
'**Leioplegil**' *see* Leiopyrrole.
LEIOPYRROLE*** (1-[*o*-[2-(diethylamino)ethoxy]phenyl]-2-methyl-5-phenylpyrrole; DV-714).
'**Leiormone**' *see* Vasopressin.
LENACIL* (3-cyclohexyl-6,7-dihydro-1*H*-cyclopentapyrimidine-2,4(3*H*,5*H*)-dione).
LENAMPICILLIN** (2,3-dihydroxy-2-butenyl (2*S*,5*R*,6*R*)-6-[(*R*)-2-amino-2-phenylacetamido]-penicillanate cyclic carbonate; ampicillin 2,3-dihydroxy-2-butenyl ester cyclic carbonate).
'**Lendorm**' *see* Brotizolam.
'**Lenetran**' *see* Mephenoxalone.
'**Lenigallol**' *see* Acetpyrogall.
'**Lenigesal**' *see* Dextropropoxyphene theobromin-1-ylacetate.
LENIQUINSIN*** (4-(3,4-dimethoxybenzylideneamino)-6,7-dimethoxyquinoline; 6,7-dimethoxy-4-veratrylideneaminoquinoline; EU-1085; U-1085).
'**Lenopect**' *see* Pipazetate.
'**Lenoxi**' *see* Digitoxin.
'**Lenoxin**' *see* Digoxin.
LENPERONE*** (4'-fluoro-4-[4-(*p*-fluorobenzoyl)piperid-1-yl]butyrophenone; lenperone hydrochloride; AHR-2277).
'**Lente iletin**' *see* Insulin zinc suspension.
Lente insulin *see* Insulin zinc suspension.
'**Lentin**' *see* Carbachol.
'**Lentizol**' *see* Amitriptyline.
'**Lentostamin**' *see* Chlorpheniramine.
Lentysine *see* Eritadenine.
Leo-114 *see* Polyestradiol phosphate.
Leo-275 *see* Estramustine.

Leo-640 *see* Lofepramine.
Leo 1031 *see* Prednimustine.
'Leocentyl' *see* Bendroflumethiazide.
'Leocillin' *see* Penethamate hydriodide.
'Leodrine' *see* Hydroflumethiazide.
'Leofungin' *see* Pecilocin.
'Leopental' *see* Thiopental.
Lepargylic acid *see* Azelaic acid.
'Lepinal' *see* Phenobarbital.
'Lepitoin' *see* Phenytoin.
'Lepivane' *see* Profenamine.
'Leponex' *see* Clozapine.
'Lepsiral' *see* Primidone.
LEPTACLINE* (1-cyclohexylmethylpiperidine; piperidinomethylcyclohexane; leptacline hydrochloride; PMC).
LEPTACLINE CAMSILATE (leptacline camsylate; leptacline DL-camphorsulfonate; SD-210-37).
'Leptanal' *see* Fentanyl.
Leptazol *see* Pentetrazole.
'Lepticur' *see* Tropatepine.
'Leptidrol' *see* Pipradrol.
'Leptilan' *see* Valproic acid.
'Lepton' *see* Leptophos.
LEPTOPHOS* (*O*-(4-bromo-2,5-dichlorophenyl) *O*-methyl phenylphosphonothioate; OMS-1438; 'abar'; 'lepton'; 'phosvel').
'Leptryl' *see* Perimetazine.
'Lergigan' *see* Promethazine.
'Lergine' *see* Tricyclamol chloride.
'Lergitin' *see* Phenbenzamine.
'Lergoban' *see* Diphenylpyraline.
'Lergopenin' *see* Clemizole penicillin.
LERGOTRILE* (2-chloro-6-methylergoline-8β-acetonitrile; 2-chloro-8β-(cyanomethyl)-6-methylergoline).
LERGOTRILE MESILATE (lergotrile methanesulfonate; lergotrile mesylate).
Lergotrile methanesulfonate *see* Lergotrile mesilate.
'Leritin' *see* Anileridine.
'Leron' *see* Guanacline.
'Lertigon' *see* Histamine azoprotein complex.
'Lescopine' *see* Scopolamine methyl bromide.
'Lete' *see* Promazine.
'Lethidrone' *see* Nalorphine.
LETIMIDE* (3-[2-(diethylamino)ethyl]-2*H*-1,3-benzoxazine-2,4(3*H*)-dione; letimide hydrochloride; MA-1443).
LETOSTEINE* (2-[2-[(carboxymethyl)thio]ethyl]-4-thiazolidinecarboxylic acid 2-ethyl ester; 2-[2-[(ethoxycarbonylmethyl)thio]ethyl]thiazolidine-4-carboxylic acid; 'viscotiol').
'Letter' *see* Levothyroxine sodium.
'Letusin' *see* Levopropoxyphene napsilate.
Leucenine *see* Leucenol.
LEUCENOL (DL-2-amino-3-(3-hydroxy-4-oxopyrid-1-yl)propionic acid; α-amino-(3-hydroxy-4-pyridinone)propionic acid; leucenine).
(−)Leucenol *see* Mimosine.
LEUCINE* (2-amino-4-methylvaleric acid; α-aminoisocaproic acid).
LEUCINOCAINE* (*N*,*N*-diethylleucinol ester

of *p*-aminobenzoic acid; leucinocaine mesilate; leucinocaine methanesulfonate; leucinocaine mesylate).
See also under Co-dergocrine.
LEUCINOL (2-amino-4-methyl-1-pentanol).
Leucoalizarin *see* Anthrarobin.
LEUCOCIANIDOL (3,3′,4,4′,5,7-flavanhexol; leucocyanidol; 'resivit').
'Leucocristine' *see* Vincristine.
Leucocyanidol *see* Leucocianidol.
'Leucofen' *see* Chlorphentermine.
LEUCOGEN (tr) (2-[α-(ethoxycarbonyl)benzyl]-thiazolidine-4-carboxylic acid; ethyl 4-carboxy-α-phenyl-2-thiazolidineacetate).
Leucoharmine *see* Harmine.
Leucoline *see* Isoquinoline.
Leucomycin *see* Kitasamycin.
Leucomycin V 3-acetate 4-(3-methylbutanoate) *see* Josamycin.
'Leucomycin N' *see* Azidamfenicol.
Leucovorin* *see* Calcium folinate.
'Leukase' *see* Neomycin.
'Leukeran' *see* Chlorambucil.
'Leukerin' *see* Mercaptopurine.
'Leukomycin' *see* Chloramphenicol.
Leuprolide* *see* Leuprorelin.
LEUPRORELIN* (5-oxo-L-prolyl-L-histidyl-L-trytophyl-L-seryl-L-tyrosyl-D-leucyl-L-leucyl-L-arginyl-*N*-ethyl-L-prolinamide; leuprolide).
'Leupurin' *see* Mercaptopurine.
Leurocristine *see* Vincristine.
Leurosine *see* Vinleurosine.
F-Leurosine *see* Vinformide.
LEVACETYLMETHADOL (levomethadyl acetate).
See also Acetylmethadol.
'Levadenyl' *see* Adenosine triphosphate.
LEVALLORPHAN* (*N*-allyl-3-hydroxymorphinan; naloxiphane; levallorphan acetate; levallorphan tartrate; Ro 1-7059; Ro 1-7700; Ro 1-7929).
See also under Pethidine.
LEVAMFETAMINE* ((−)-α-methylphenethylamine; (−)-amphetamine; levamphetamine).
LEVAMFETAMINE ALGINATE ('levonor').
LEVAMFETAMINE SUCCINATE* ('cydril').
See also Amphetamine; Dexamphetamine.
LEVAMISOLE* ((−)-2,3,5,6-tetrahydro-6-phenylimidazo[2,1-*b*]thiazole; (−)-tetramisole; levamisole hydrochloride; NSC-177023; R-12564; 'decaris'; 'ketrax'; 'nemicide'; 'nilverm GL'; 'tramisol').
See also Dexamisole; Tetramisole.
Levamphetamine* *see* Levamfetamine.
'Levanil' *see* Ectylurea.
'Levanxol' *see* Temazepam.
Levarterenol *see* Norepinephrine.
'Levicor' *see* Metaraminol.
LEVISOPRENALINE* ((−)-isoprenaline; 'isolevin').
'Levium' *see* Diazepam.
'Levius' *see* Acetylsalicylic acid.
LEVLOFEXIDINE* ((−)-(*R*)-2-[1-(2,6-dichlo-

rophenoxy)ethyl]-2-imidazoline).

Levo-BC-2627 *see* Butorphanol.

LEVOBUNOLOL*** ((−)-5-[3-(*tert*-butyl-amino)-2-hydroxy]-3,4-dihydro-1(2*H*)-naphtha-lenone; levobunolol hydrochloride; W-7000A).
See also Bunolol.

LEVOCABASTINE** ((−)-*trans*-1-[*cis*-4-cyano-4-(*p*-fluorophenyl)cyclohexyl]-3-methyl-4-phenylisonipecotic acid).
See also Cabastine; *and under* Cadmium sulfide.

Levocarbinoxamine* *see* Rotoxamine.

LEVODOPA*** ((−)-3-(3,4-dihydroxyphenyl)-L-alanine; (−)dopa).

LEVODOPA plus BENSERAZIDE (Ro 8-0576; 'madopar').

LEVODOPA plus CARBIDOPA ('nacom'; 'sine-met').

'Levo-dromoran' *see* Levorphanol.

LEVOFACETOPERANE*** ((−)-α-phenyl-2-piperidinemethanol acetate; (−)-α-piperid-2-yl-benzyl acetate; acetopherane; levophacetoper-ane; phacetoperan; levofacetoperane hydro-chloride; RP 8228; 'lidepran').

LEVOFURALTADONE*** ((−)-5-morpholi-nomethyl-3-(5-nitrofurfurylideneamino)-2-ox-azolidinone; levofuraltadone hydrochloride; NF-602; NF-902; NSC-527986).

LEVOGLUTAMIDE** (L-glutamine; levoglut-amine).

Levoglutamine* *see* Levoglutamide.

LEVOMENOL*** ((−)-6-methyl-2-(4-methyl-3-cyclohexen-1-yl)-5-hepten-2-ol; (−)-5-(1-hydr-oxy-1,5-dimethylhex-4-en-1-yl)-2-methyl-1-cyclohexene; (−)-α-bisabolol).

Levomepate* *see* Atromepine.

LEVOMEPROMAZINE*** ((−)-10-[3-(dimeth-ylamino)-2-methylpropyl]-2-methoxypheno-thiazine; levopromazine; mepromazine; metho-trimeprazine; levomepromazine maleate; Bayer-1213; CL-36467; CL-39743; RP 7044; SK&F-5116).
See also under Etorphine.

LEVOMETHADONE*** ((−)-(*R*)-6-(dimethyl-amino)-4,4-diphenyl-3-heptanone).

Levomethadyl acetate *see* Levacetylmethadol.

LEVOMETHORPHAN*** (3-methoxy-*N*-meth-ylmorphinan; levomethorphan hydrobromide; Ro 1-5470/6; Ro 1-7788).

LEVOMETIOMEPRAZINE*** ((−)-10-(3-di-methylamino-2-methylpropyl)-2-(methylthio)-phenothiazine; (−)-methiomeprazine).
See also Methiomeprazine.

LEVOMORAMIDE*** ((−)-1-(3-methyl-4-mor-pholino-2,2-diphenylbutyryl)pyrrolidine; (−)-4-(2-methyl-4-oxo-3,3-diphenyl-4-pyrrolidin-1-yl-butyl)morpholine).
See also Dextromoramide; Racemoramide.

Levomycetin (tr) *see* Chloramphenicol.

LEVOMYCIN (tr) (antibiotic from an unidenti-fied streptomyces).

LEVONANTRADOL*** ((−)-(6*S*,6a*R*,9*R*,10a*R*)-5,6,6a,7,8,9,10,10a-octahydro-6-methyl-3-[(*R*)-1-methyl-4-phenylbutoxy]-1,9-phenanthridinediol

1-acetate; levonantradol hydrochloride; CP-50556).

'Levonor' *see* Levamfetamine alginate.

Levonordefrin *see* (−)-Corbadrine.

LEVONORGESTREL*** (D-(−)-13β-ethyl-17β-hydroxy-18,19-dinor-17α-pregn-4-en-20-yn-3-one; dexnorgestrel; 'follistrel'; 'microlut'; 'micro-luton'; 'microval'; 'mikro-30'; 'norgeston').
See also Norgestrel.

LEVONORGESTREL plus ETHINYLESTRADI-OL (SH-71144; SH-71155; SH-B-264 AB; 'edi-wal'; 'eugynon'; 'ovidon'; 'ovran'; 'ovranette'; 'rigevidon'; 'sequilar'; 'stediril-d'; 'terminolut'; 'triagynon'; 'trigynon'; 'trinordiol'; 'triquilar').

'Levopa' *see* Levodopa.

Levophacetoperane* *see* Levofacetoperane.

LEVOPHENACYLMORPHAN*** ((−)-3-hydr-oxy-*N*-phenacylmorphinan; benzorphanol).

Levopromazine* *see* Levomepromazine.

'Levoprome' *see* Levomepromazine.

LEVOPROPICILLIN*** ((−)-6-(2-phenoxybu-tyramido)penicillanic acid; (−)-1-phenoxyprop-ylpenicillin; levopropylcillin; levopropylcillin potassium; potassium levopropylcillin; BRL-284; P-248).

LEVOPROPOXYPHENE*** ((−)-4-(dimethyl-amino)-3-methyl-1,2-diphenyl-2-butanol pro-pionate; *N*,*N*,2-trimethyl-3,4-diphenyl-3-pro-pionoxy-1-butylamine; (−)-propoxyphene).
See also Dextropropoxyphene.

LEVOPROPOXYPHENE DIBUDINATE (levo-propoxyphene 2,6-di-*tert*-butylnaphthalenedi-sulfonate).

LEVOPROPOXYPHENE NAPSILATE* (levo-propoxyphene 2-naphthalenesulfonate hydrate; levopropoxyphene napsylate).

Levopropylcillin *see* Levopropicillin.

LEVOPROPYLHEXEDRINE*** ((−)-*N*,α-di-methylcyclohexaneethylamine).

Levorenin *see* Epinephrine.

LEVORIN** (polyene antibiotic from *Actinomy-ces levoris*).

Levorphan *see* Levorphanol.

LEVORPHANOL*** (3-hydroxy-*N*-methylmor-phinan; levorphan; levorphanol tartrate).

'Levothyl' *see* Methadone.

'Levothym' *see* Oxitriptan.

LEVOTHYROXINE (3-[4-(4-hydroxy-3,5-diiodo-phenoxy)-3,5-diiodophenyl]alanine; 3,3',5,5'-tetraiodothyronine).

LEVOTHYROXINE SODIUM*** (sodium levo-thyroxine; 'euthyrox').

LEVOTHYROXINE SODIUM plus LIOTHY-RONINE SODIUM ('euthyral').

LEVOXADROL*** ((−)-2,2-diphenyl-4-piperid-2-yl-1,3-dioxolane; levoxadrol hydrochloride; CL-912-C; NSC-526063; 'levoxan').

'Levoxan' *see* Levoxadrol.

'Levoxin' *see* Levothyroxine sodium.

'Levsin' *see* Hyoscyamine.

'Levucalcin' *see* Calcium levulinate.

Levulic acid *see* Levulinic acid.

LEVULINIC ACID (4-oxovaleric acid; 4-ketovaleric acid; 3-acetylpropionic acid; levulic acid). *See also* Calcium levulinate; Rare earth levulinates.

LEVULINIC ACID PHENYLHYDRAZONE ('antithermin').

Levulose *see* Fructose.

LEWISITE (dichloro(2-chlorovinyl)arsine).

'**Lexatin**' *see* Bromazepam.

'**Lexinol-cal**' *see* Phosphatidylcholine.

LEXOFENAC* ([*p*-(3-oxo-1-cyclohexen-1-yl)-phenyl]acetic acid).

'**Lexomil**' *see* Bromazepam.

'**Lexotan**' *see* Bromazepam.

'**Lexotanil**' *see* Bromazepam.

'**Ley cornox**' *see* Benazolin.

LF-77 *see* Pifoxime.

LF-178 *see* Fenofibrate.

LG-1 *see* Doxenitoin.

LG-206 *see* Prothipendyl.

LG-278 *see* Xenazoic acid.

LG-11457 *see* Etafenone.

LG-30158 *see* Rociverine.

LH-150 *see* Phenylbutazone megallate.

LH-RH *see* Gonadorelin.

LI-32-468 *see* Spirendolol.

'**Liapten**' *see under* Clofibrate.

LIBECILLIDE* (2-[[(5-carboxy-5-formamido-pentyl)carbamoyl](2-phenylacetamido)methyl]-5,5-dimethyl-4-thiazolidinecarboxylic acid; lisocillide).

'**Libexin**' *see under* Carbocisteine.

'**Libratar**' *see* Chlorbenoxamine.

'**Librax**' *see under* Chlordiazepoxide.

'**Libraxin**' *see under* Chlordiazepoxide.

'**Librium**' *see* Chlordiazepoxide.

'**Licaran**' *see* Feclemine embonate.

'**Licosin**' *see* Camylofin.

LIDAMIDINE* (*N*-(2,6-dimethylphenyl)-*N'*-[imino(methylamino)methyl]urea; 1-(methylamidino)-3-(2,6-xylyl)urea; lidamidine hydrochloride; WHR-1142A).

'**Lidanar**' *see* Mesoridazine.

'**Lidanil**' *see* Mesoridazine.

'**Lidaprim**' *see under* Trimethoprim.

Lidase (tr) *see* Hyaluronidase(s).

'**Liden**' *see* Isomethadone.

'**Lidepran**' *see* Levofacetoperane.

'**Lidex**' *see* Fluocinonide.

LIDIMYCIN (5-(hexahydro-2-oxo-1*H*-thieno[3,4-*d*]imidazol-4-yl)-2-pentenoic acid; lydimycin; streptolydigin; U-15965; 'portamycin').

LIDOCAINE* (2-(diethylamino)-2',6'-acetoxylidide; *N'*-(2,6-dimethylphenyl)-*N,N*-diethylglycinamide; lignocaine; lidocaine hydrochloride; xycaine; LL-30).

Lidocaine benzyl benzoate *see* Denatonium benzoate.

'**Lidocor**' *see* Lidocaine.

LIDOFENIN* (*N*-(carboxymethyl)-*N*-[2-[(2,6-dimethylphenyl)amino]-2-oxoethyl]glycine; [[(2,6-xylylcarbamoyl)methyl]imino]diacetic acid; HIDA; 'hepatoscan').

LIDOFLAZINE* ([4-[4,4-bis(*p*-fluorophenyl)-butyl]piperazin-1-yl]-2',6'-acetoxylidide; JR-7904; McN-JR-7904; R-7904).

Lidol (tr) *see* Pethidine.

'**Lifene**' *see* Phensuximide.

LIFIBRATE (1-methyl-4-piperidinol ester of 2,2-bis(*p*-chlorophenoxy)acetic acid; methylpiperid-4-yl glyoxylate 2-[bis(*p*-chlorophenyl)acetal]; SaH-42-348).

Lignocaine* *see* Lidocaine.

Lignoceric acid *see* Tetracosanoic acid.

Lignosulfonic acid sodium salt *see* Polignate sodium.

'**Likudin**' *see* Griseofulvin.

'**Limbitrol**' *see under* Amitriptyline.

'**Limclair**' *see* Trisodium edetate.

Limettin *see* Citropten.

LIMONENE (4-isopropenyl-1-methylcyclohexene; 1-methyl-4-(1-methylethenyl)cyclohexene; *p*-mentha-1,8-diene; (+)-limonene; cajeputene; cinene; dipentene; kautschin; 'refchole').

'**Limptar**' *see under* Quinine sulfate.

'**Linaris**' *see* Co-trimoxazole.

'**Lincocin**' *see* Lincomycin.

LINCOMYCIN* (methyl 6,8-dideoxy-6-(1-methyl-*trans*-4-propyl-L-2-pyrrolidinecarboxamido)-1-thio-D-*erythro*-α-D-galactooctopyranoside; NSC-70731; U-10149A).

'**Linctussal**' *see* Sodium dibunate.

LINDANE* (γ-1,2,3,4,5,6-hexachlorocyclohexane; gamma benzene hexachloride; benzenehexachlor; benzene hexachloride; benzhexachlor; γ-BHC; geksan; hexachlorane; hexicide). *See also* Mercuran; *and under* DDT.

'**Lindol**' *see* Tricresyl phosphate.

'**Linfolysin**' *see* Chlorambucil.

'**Lingraine**' *see* Ergotamine tartrate.

Link's compound 63 *see* Cyclocoumarol.

'**Linoderm**' *see* Dexamethasone linoleate.

'**Linodil**' *see* Inositol nicotinate.

LINOGLIRIDE* (*N*-(1-methyl-2-pyrrolidinylidene)-*N'*-phenyl-4-morpholinecarboxamidine).

LINOGLIRIDE FUMARATE* (McN-3935).

N-**Linoleamido-***p***-methyl-α-phenylphenethylamine** *see* Moctamide.

LINOLEIC ACID (*cis,cis*-9,12-octadecadienoic acid; linolic acid). *See also* Trilinolein.

LINOLENIC ACID (9,12,15-octadecatrienoic acid).

Linolexamide *see* Clinolamide.

Linolic acid *see* Linoleic acid.

'**Linostil**' *see* Dimetacrine.

'**Lintex**' *see* Niclosamide.

LINURON (1-(3,4-dichlorophenyl)-3-methoxy-3-methylurea; methoxydiuron; 'afalon'; 'lorox').

'**Linyl**' *see* Phentermine resin.

'**Lio-metacen**' *see* Meglumine indometacinate.

'**Lioresal**' *see* Baclofen.

'**Liosol**' *see* Xenbucin.

LIOTHYRONINE* (3-[4-(4-hydroxy-3-iodophenoxy)-3,5-diiodophenyl]alanine; 3,3',5-triiodothyronine; liothyronine sodium; T-3).

LIOTRIX (mixture of levothyroxine sodium and

liothyronine sodium; 'diotroxin'; 'euthroid'; 'thyrolar').
'**Lioxone**' *see* 3-Pyridineacetic acid.
'**Lipan**' *see* Dinitro-*o*-cresol.
'**Lipancreatin**' *see* Pancrelipase.
'**Lipanthyl**' *see* Fenofibrate.
'**Lipantyl**' *see* Fenofibrate.
'**Lipavlon**' *see* Clofibrate.
'**Lipect**' *see* Pholcodine.
'**Lipenan**' *see* Clofibride.
'**Liphadione**' *see* Chlorophacinone.
'**Lipidium**' *see* Nicoclonate.
'**Lipiodol**' *see* Iodinated poppyseed oil.
'**Lipogantrisin**' *see* Acetylsulfafurazole.
'**Lipo-hepin**' *see* Heparin potassium.
α-**Lipoic acid** *see* Thioctic acid.
'**Lipo-Merz**' *see* Etofibrate.
α-**Liponic acid** *see* Thioctic acid.
'**Lipotam**' *see* Trometamol thioctate.
'**Lipotril**' *see* Choline.
'**Lipotrin**' *see* Cyclobutyrol calcium.
'**Liprinal**' *see* Clofibrate.
'**Liprodene**' *see* Pentorex.
'**Liquaemin**' *see* Heparin potassium.
'**Liquamar**' *see* Phenprocoumon.
'**Liquemin**' *see* Heparin potassium.
'**Liquoid**' *see* Sodium polyanetholesulfonate(s).
LIQUORICE ((liquorice extract or juice); glycyrrhiza; succus liquiritiae; 'reglisse'; 'sucsan').
   See also Deglycyrrhizinized liquorice; Glycyrrhizic acid; *and under* Nitrofurantoin.
LIR-1660 *see* Veralipride.
'**Liranol**' *see* Promazine.
Liro antisprout *see* Propham.
'**Lirofeen**' *see* Dioxation.
'**Liromidon**' *see* Phosphamidon.
'**Lironox**' *see* Butyl 2,4-dichlorophenoxyacetate.
'**Lirophen**' *see* Dioxation.
'**Liro-trithion**' *see* Carbofenotion.
'**Lisdonil**' *see* Meladrazine.
'**Liserdol**' *see* Metergoline.
'**Lisergan**' *see* Acepromazine.
LISINOPRIL** (1-[N^2-[(*S*)-1-carboxy-3-phenylpropyl]-L-lysyl]-L-proline; L-154826; MK-521).
'**Lisium**' *see* Chlorhexidine.
'**Liskantin**' *see* Primidone.
'**Liskonium**' *see* Lithium carbonate.
Lisocillide *see* Libecillide.
'**Lisomucil**' *see* Carbocisteine.
'**Lispamol**' *see* Aminopromazine.
'**Lispasmol**' *see* Aminopromazine.
'**Lissolamine**' *see* Cetrimonium bromide.
'**Listeron**' *see* Suxamethonium chloride.
'**Listica**' *see* Oxyfenamate.
'**Listrocol**' *see* Cynarine.
LISURIDE*** (3-(9,10-didehydro-6-methylergolin-8a-yl)-1,1-diethylurea; 3,3-diethyl-1-(6-methylisoergolen-8-yl)urea; 9-(3,3-diethylureido)-4,6,6a,7,8,9-hexahydro-7-methylindolo[4,3-*f*,*g*]quinoline; lysuride; mesorgydine; methylergol carbamide; 'dironyl').
LISURIDE MALEATE (lisuride hydrogen maleate; 'cuvalit'; 'dopergin'; 'lysenil'; 'lysenyl').

'**Litalir**' *see* Hydroxycarbamide.
'**Litec**' *see* Pizotifen maleate.
'**Lithane**' *see* Lithium carbonate.
Lithic acid *see* Uric acid.
'**Lithiofor**' *see* Lithium sulfate.
'**Lithionit**' *see* Lithium sulfate.
LITHIUM ACETATE ('quilonum').
Lithium antimony thiomalate *see* Anthiolimine.
LITHIUM CARBONATE* (CP-15467-61; NSC-16895).
LITHIUM CITRATE* ('lithonate S').
LITHIUM SULFATE ('lithiofor'; 'lithionit').
'**Lithobid**' *see* Lithium carbonate.
LITHOCHOLIC ACID (3-hydroxycholanic acid).
'**Lithonate**' *see* Lithium carbonate.
'**Lithonate S**' *see* Lithium citrate.
'**Lithotabs**' *see* Lithium carbonate.
'**Lito**' *see* Lithium carbonate.
'**Litoduron**' *see* Lithium carbonate.
LITRACEN** (9,10-dihydro-10,10-dimethyl-9-[3-(methylamino)propylidene]anthracene; N-7049).
LIVIDOMYCIN*** (*O*-2-amino-2,3-dideoxy-α-D-ribohexopyranosyl-(1→4)-*O*-[*O*-α-D-mannopyranosyl-(1→4)-*O*-2,6-diamino-2,6-dideoxy-β-L-idopyranosyl-(1→3)-β-D-ribofuranosyl-(1→5)]-2-deoxy-D-streptamine; lividomycin A).
Lividomycin A *see* Lividomycin.
'**Livipas**' *see* Halofenate.
'**Lixophen**' *see* Phenobarbital.
LJ-206 *see* Carbocisteine.
LJ-278 *see* Dimabefylline.
LL-30 *see* Lidocaine.
LL-172 *see under* Phloroglucinol.
LL-705W *see* Neutramycin.
LL-1418 *see* Olmidine.
LL-1530 *see* Nadoxolol.
LL-1558 *see* Tiadenol.
LL-1656 *see* Buflomedil.
LLD factor *see* Cyanocobalamin.
LM-94 *see* Hymecromone.
LM-176 *see* Cobamamide.
LM-192 *see* Viquidil.
LM-203A *see* Biperiden.
LM-208 *see* Quinupramine.
LM-209 *see* Mequitazine.
LM-1404 *see* Lortalamine.
LM-2717 *see* Clobazam.
LM-5008 *see* Indalpine.
'**LMD**' *see* Dextran 40.
'**LMO**' *see* Dextran 40.
LN-107 *see* Broparestrol.
LO-44 *see* Bezafibrate.
'**Lobak**' *see under* Chlormezazone.
'**Lobamine**' *see* Methionine.
LOBELINE*** (2-(β-hydroxyphenethyl)-1-methyl-6-phenacylpiperidine; 2-[6-(β-hydroxyphenethyl)-1-methylpiperid-2-yl]acetophenone; inflatine; lobeline hydrochloride or sulfate).
LOBENDAZOLE*** (ethyl 2-benzimidazolecarbamate; NSC-42044; SK&F-24529).
LOBENZARIT*** (4-chloro-2,2'-iminodibenzoic acid).
'**Lobeton**' *see* Lobeline.

317

'**Locabiosol**' *see* Fusafungine.
'**Locabiotal**' *see* Fusafungine.
'**Locacorten**' *see* Flumetasone pivalate.
'**Locastine**' *see* Amoxecaine.
'**Locoid**' *see* Hydrocortisone butyrate.
'**Locoid C**' *see under* Chlorquinaldol.
'**Locorten**' *see* Flumetasone pivalate.
LODIPERONE* (5-[2-[4-(3,5-dichlorophenyl)-piperazin-1-yl]ethyl]-4-(*p*-fluorophenyl)-4-oxazolin-2-one).
'**Lodosyn**' *see* Carbidopa.
LODOXAMIDE* (2,2′-[(2-chloro-5-cyano-1,3-phenylene)diimino]bis[2-oxoacetic acid]; *N,N′*-(2-chloro-5-cyano-*m*-phenylene)di(oxamic acid)).
LODOXAMIDE ETHYL* (diethyl lodoxamide; lodoxamide diethyl ester; U-42718).
LODOXAMIDE TROMETAMOL (lodoxamide ditrometanol salt; lodoxamide tromethamine; U-42485-E).
Lodoxamide tromethamine* *see* Lodoxamide trometamol.
LOFEMIZOLE* (4-(*p*-chlorophenyl)-5-methylimidazole; lofemizole hydrochloride).
LOFENAL (tr) (2-[*p*-[bis(2-chloroethyl)amino]-phenylacetamido]-3-phenylpropionic acid; *N*-[*p*-[bis(2-chloroethyl)amino]phenylacetyl]-DL-phenylalanine; lophenal).
LOFENDAZAM* (8-chloro-4,5-dihydro-1-phenyl-2*H*-1,5-benzodiazepin-2-one).
'**Lofene**' *see under* Diphenoxylate.
LOFENTANIL* ((−)-methyl *cis*-3-methyl-1-phenethyl-4-(*N*-phenylpropionamido)isonipecotate).
LOFENTANIL OXALATE* (R 34995).
LOFEPRAMINE* (4′-chloro-2-[[3-(10,11-dihydro-5*H*-dibenz-[*b,f*]azepin-5-yl)propyl]methylamino]acetophenone; *N*-(*p*-chlorobenzoylmethyl)-3-(10,11-dihydro-5*H*-dibenz[*b,f*]azepin-5-yl)-*N*-methylpropylamine; 5-[3-[*N*-(*p*-chlorophenacyl)methylamino]propyl]-10,11-dihydro-5*H*-dibenz[*b,f*]azepine; chopramine; lopramine; Leo-640; 'gamanil'; 'gamonil').
'**Lofetensin**' *see* Lofexidine.
LOFEXIDINE* (2-[1-(2,6-dichlorophenoxy)-ethyl]-2-imidazoline; Ba-168; RMI-14042A; 'lofetensin'; 'loxacor').
See also Dexlofexidine; Levlofexidine.
'**Loftyl**' *see* Buflomedil.
'**Logical**' *see* Magnesium valproate.
'**Lomapect**' *see under* Prenoxdiazine.
LOMBAZOLE** ((±)-1-(α-4-biphenylyl-*o*-chlorobenzyl)imidazole; (±)-1-[(biphenyl-4-yl)(2-chlorophenyl)methyl]imidazole; BAY h-6020).
LOMETRALINE* (8-chloro-1,2,3,4-tetrahydro-5-methoxy-*N,N*-dimethyl-1-naphthylamine; lometraline hydrochloride; CP-14368-1).
LOMEVACTONE* (4-(*p*-chlorophenyl)tetrahydro-6-methyl-3-phenyl-2*H*-pyran-2-one; *p*-chloro-β-(2-hydroxypropyl)-α-phenylhydrocinnamic acid δ-lactone).
LOMIFYLLINE* (7-(5-oxohexyl)theophylline).

LOMIFYLLINE plus DIHYDROERGOCRISTINE ('cervilame').
'**Lomodex**' *see* Dextran 40.
LOMOFUNGIN* (methyl 6-formyl-4,7,9-trihydroxy-1-phenazinecarboxylate; lomondomycin; NSC-106995; U-24792).
Lomondomycin *see* Lomofungin.
'**Lomotil**' *see under* Diphenoxylate.
'**Lomudal**' *see* Cromoglicate disodium.
LOMUSTINE* (1-(2-chloroethyl)-3-cyclohexyl-1-nitrosourea; CCNU; NSC-79037; 'CeeNU'; 'CiNU').
'**Lonacol**' *see* Zineb.
LONAPROFEN* (methyl 2-[(1-chloronaphth-2-yl)oxy]propionate).
LONAZOLAC* (3-(*p*-chlorophenyl)-1-phenyl-pyrazole-4-acetic acid).
LONAZOLAC CALCIUM ('irritren').
'**Londomycin**' *see* Metacycline.
'**Longacid**' *see* Butacid.
'**Longacilina**' *see* Benzathine penicillin.
'**Longacor**' *see* Quinidine arabogalactan sulfate.
'**Longamex**' *see* Noscapine.
'**Longanoct**' *see* Butethal.
'**Longasteril**' *see* Dextran.
'**Longasteril 75**' *see* Dextran 75.
'**Longatren**' *see* Azidocillin.
'**Longdigox**' *see* β-Acetyldigoxin.
'**Longestrol**' *see* Broparestrol.
'**Longicid**' *see* Benzathine penicillin.
'**Longifene**' *see* Buclizine.
'**Longopax**' *see under* Amitriptyline.
'**Longoperidol**' *see* Penfluridol.
'**Longum**' *see* Sulfalene.
LONIDAMINE* (1-(2,4-dichlorobenzyl)-1*H*-indazole-3-carboxylic acid; DICA; AF-1980).
'**Lonitan**' *see* Minoxidil.
'**Lonolox**' *see* Minoxidil.
'**Lonovar**' *see* Oxandrolone.
'**Lontanyl**' *see* Testosterone cyclohexanecarboxylate.
'**Lopatol**' *see* Nitroscanate.
LOPERAMIDE* (4-(*p*-chlorophenyl)-4-hydroxy-*N,N*-dimethyl-α,α-diphenyl-1-piperidinebutyramide; 4-[4-(*p*-chlorophenyl)-4-hydroxypiperidino]-*N,N*-dimethyl-2,2-diphenylbutyramide; loperamide hydrochloride; R-18553; 'imodium').
Lophenal (tr) *see* Lofenal.
'**Lopion**' *see* Sodium auroallylthioureidobenzoate.
LOPIRAZEPAM* (7-chloro-5-(*o*-chlorophenyl)-1,3-dihydro-3-hydroxy-2*H*-pyrido[3,2-*e*]-[1,4]diazepin-2-one; D-12524).
'**Lopirin**' *see* Captopril.
Lopramine *see* Lofepramine.
LOPRAZOLAM* (6-(*o*-chlorophenyl)-2,4-dihydro-2-[(4-methylpiperazin-1-yl)methylene]-8-nitro-1*H*-imidazo[1,2-*a*][1,4]benzodiazepin-1-one).
LOPRAZOLAM MESILATE (loprazolam methanesulfonate; HR-458; RU-31158).
Lopremone *see* Protirelin.
'**Lopress**' *see* Hydralazine.
'**Lopressor**' *see* Metoprolol.

LOPRODIOL** (2,2-bis(chloromethyl)-1,3-propanediol).

'Lora' see Chloralodol.

LORAJMINE** (ajmaline 17-(chloroacetate); 17-(chloroacetyl)ajmaline; lorajmine hydrochloride; WIN-11831; 'viaductor').

'Loramet' see Lormetazepam.

'Lorakon' see Benzalkonium chloride.

'Loranil' see Becantone.

LORAPRIDE*** (5-chloro-N^1-[(1-ethylpyrrolidin-2-yl)methyl]-2-methoxysulfanilamide).

LORAZEPAM*** (7-chloro-5-(o-chlorophenyl)-1,3-dihydro-3-hydroxy-2H-1,4-benzodiazepin-2-one; Wy-4036; 'ativan'; 'lorenin'; 'tavor'; 'temesta').

LORBAMATE*** (2-(hydroxymethyl)-2-methylpentyl cyclopropanecarbamate carbamate (ester); Abbott 19957).

LORCAINIDE*** (4'-chloro-N-(1-isopropylpiperid-4-yl)-2-phenylacetanilide; isocainide; socainide; lorcainide hydrochloride; R-15889; RT-15889; 'remivox').

'Lorelco' see Probucol.

'Lorenin' see Lorazepam.

'Lorexane' see Lindane.

'Lorfan' see Levallorphan.

'Loridine' see Cefaloridine.

'Lorinon' see Diazepam.

LORMETAZEPAM*** (7-chloro-5-(o-chlorophenyl)-1,3-dihydro-3-hydroxy-1-methyl-2H-1,4-benzodiazepin-2-one; 1-methyllorazepam; CH-757; Ro 5-5516; Wy-4082; 'loramet'; 'minians'; 'noctamid').

'Lormin' see Chlormadinone acetate.

'Lorol' see Sodium dodecyl sulfate.

'Lorothidol' see Bithionol.

'Lorox' see Linuron.

LORTALAMINE*** ((4aR,10R,10aR)-8-chloro-1,2,3,4,10,10a-hexahydro-2-methyl-4a,10-(iminoethano)-4aH-[1]benzopyrano[3,2-c]pyridin-12-one; 4a-amino-8-chloro-1,2,3,4,4a,10a-hexahydro-2-methyl-10H-benzopyrano[3,2-c]-pyridin-10-ylacetic acid lactam; LM-1404).

'Lorusil' see Aminopromazine.

LORZAFONE*** (2-(2-aminoacetamido)-4'-chloro-2'-(o-chlorobenzoyl)-N-methylacetanilide; glycyl-N-[4-chloro-2-(2-chlorobenzoyl)phenyl]-N-methylglycinamide; lorzafone monohydrate; LY-123508).

'Losalen' see Flumetasone pivalate.

LOSINDOLE*** (6-chloro-3a,4,9,9a-tetrahydro-2-methyl-4-phenylbenz[f]isoindoline).

'Lospoven' see Cefalotin.

Lost see Mustard gas.

N-Lost see Chlormethine.

'Lostinil' see Cyclophosphamide.

LOSULAZINE** (1-[(p-fluorophenyl)sulfonyl]-4-[p-[[7-(trifluoromethyl)-4-quinolyl]amino]benzoyl]piperazine).

'Lotagen' see Methylenedi(m-cresolsulfonic acid) polymer.

LOTIFAZOLE*** (2,2,2-trichloroethyl 4-phenyl-2-thiazolecarbamate).

'Lotone' see Spermine.

'Lotrimin' see Clotrimazole.

LOTUCAINE*** (o-[2-hydroxy-3-(2,2,5,5-tetramethylpyrrolidin-1-yl)propoxy]toluene; 1-[2-hydroxy-3-(o-toloxy)propyl]-2,2,5,5-tetramethylpyrrolidine; 2,2,5,5-tetramethyl-α-(o-toloxymethyl)-1-pyrrolidineethanol; lotucaine hydrochloride; MY-33-7).

Loturin see Harman.

'Lotusate' see Talbutal.

'Loviscol' see Carbocisteine.

'Lovozal' see Fenazaflor.

'Lowila' see Dodecyl sulfoacetate.

Low molecular weight dextran see Dextran 40.

'Loxacor' see Lofexidine.

LOXANAST*** (cis-4-isohexyl-1-methylcyclohexanecarboxylic acid).

'Loxapac' see Loxapine.

LOXAPINE*** (2-chloro-11-(4-methylpiperazin-1-yl)-dibenz[b,f][1,4]oxazepine; oxilapine; CL-62362; S-805; SUM-3170; 'loxapac').

LOXAPINE SUCCINATE (CL-71563; 'daxolin'; 'loxitane').

'Loxitane' see Loxapine succinate.

'Loxon' see Haloxon.

LOXOPROFEN** ((±)-p-[(2-oxocyclopentyl)-methyl]hydratropic acid).

LOXTIDINE** (1-methyl-5-[[3-[(α-piperid-1-yl-m-tolyl)oxy]propyl]amino]-1H-1,2,4-triazole-3-methanol; AH-23844).

LOZILUREA*** (1-(m-chlorobenzyl)-3-ethylurea; ITA-312).

LP-1 (tr) see Chromocarb.

LR-511 see Zoloperone.

LR-19731 see Clodoxopone.

LRCL-3794 see Benoxaprofen.

LRCL-3950 see Isamoxole.

LS-121 see Naftidrofuryl oxalate.

LS-519 see Pirenzepine.

LS-701 see Benzydamine phenylbutazone enolate.

LSD see Lysergide.

LT-1 see Suxamethonium chloride.

LTH see Prolactin.

Lu-2-030 see Gaboxadol.

Lu-3-010 see Talopram.

Lu-5-003 see Talsupram.

Lu-10-171 see Citalopram.

Lu-274 see Cyclomethone.

LU-1631 see Amezinium metilsulfate.

Lu-10022 see Teflutixol.

'Lubergal' see 5-Allyl-5-phenylbarbituric acid.

'Lubomycine' see Erythromycin.

'Lucaine' see Piridocaine.

'Lucamid' see Ethenzamide.

LUCANTHONE*** (1-[[2-(diethylamino)ethyl]-amino]-4-methylthioxanthen-9-one; lucanthone hydrochloride; BW-79T61; MS-752; NSC-14574).

'Lucel' see Chlorquinox.

Lucensomycin see Lucimycin.

'Lucidil' see Benactyzine.

'Lucidryl' see Meclofenoxate.

LUCIMYCIN** (antibiotic from Str. lucensis;

etruscomycin; lucensomycin; antibiotic FI-1163).
'Lucipen' see under Ampicillin.
'Lucofen' see Chlorphentermine.
'Lucopenin' see Meticillin.
'Lucosil' see Sulfamethizole.
'Ludicril' see Meclofenoxate.
'Ludilat' see Bencyclane.
'Ludiomil' see Maprotiline.
'Ludobal' see Quinuronium sulfate.
LUFURADOM** ((±)-N-[(8-fluoro-2,3-dihydro-1-methyl-5-phenyl-1H-1,4-benzodiazepin-2-yl)methyl]-3-furamide).
LU-H-6 see Obidoxime chloride.
'Luliberine' see Gonadorelin.
LUMAZINE (pyrimido[4,5-b]pyrazine-2,4(1H,3H)-dione).
'Lumbrical' see Piperazine.
'Lumetrodiol' see Etynodiol diacetate.
LUMIFLAVIN (7,8,10-trimethylisoalloxazine).
'Luminal' see Phenobarbital.
'Lumirelax' see Methocarbamol.
'Lumota' see Apalcillin.
'Lunaggregate' see Macrosalb (⁹⁹ᵐTc).
'Lunipax' see Flurazepam.
'Luostyl' see Difemerine.
LUPETAZINE (2,5-dimethylpiperazine; dipropylenediamine).
2,6-Lupetidine see Nanofin.
Lupinidine see Sparteine.
LUPROSTIOL*** ((±)-(Z)-7-[(1R*,2S*,3S*,5R*)-2-[[(R*)-3-(m-chlorophenoxy)-2-hydroxypropyl]thio]-3,5-dihydroxycyclopentyl]-5-ḥeptenoic acid; 16-(m-chlorophenoxy)-9,11,15-trihydroxy-ω-tetranor-13-thiaprost-5-enoic acid).
'Lurselle' see Probucol.
'Lutalyse' see Dinoprost trometamol.
'Lutazol' see Salazosulfamide.
Luteinizing hormone releasing factor see Gonadorelin.
Luteohormone see Progesterone.
LUTEOLIN (3',4',5,7-tetrahydroxyflavone).
Luteotropic hormone see Prolactin.
Luteotropin see Prolactin.
'Luteran' see Chlormadinone acetate.
'Lutionex' see Demegestone.
'Lutofollin' see under Estradiol valerate.
'Lutometrodiol' see Etynodiol diacetate.
LUTRELIN** (5-oxo-L-prolyl-L-histidyl-L-tryptophyl-L-seryl-L-tyrosyl-D-tryptophyl-N-methyl-L-leucyl-L-arginyl-N-ethyl-L-prolinamide).
'Lutrexin' see Lututrin.
LUTUTRIN* (uterus-relaxing factor from corpus luteum; 'lutrexin').
'Luvatren' see Moperone.
'Luvistin' see Histapyrrodine.
LX-100-129 see Clozapine.
LY-104208 see Vinzolidine.
LY-108380 see Doxpicomine.
LY-120363 see Flumezapine.
LY-122512 see Anitrazafen.

LY-123508 see Lorzafone.
LY-127123 see Enviradene.
LY-127395 see Latamoxef.
LY-127623 see Metkefamide acetate.
LY-127809 see Pergolide mesilate.
LY-131126 see Butopamine.
LY-150378 see Clofilium phosphate.
LY-150720 see Picenadol.
Lyapolate sodium* see Sodium apolate.
'Lycanol' see Glymidine sodium.
'Lycedan' see Adenosine phosphate.
LYCETAMINE* (L-2,6-diamino-N-hexadecylhexanamide; P-71).
Lycine see Betaine.
'Lycurin' see Ritrosulfan.
Lydasa (tr) see Hyaluronidase(s).
Lydimycin* see Lidimycin.
LYMECYCLINE*** (N²-[(+)-5-amino-5-carboxypentylaminomethyl]tetracycline; tetracycline-L-methylene-lysine; 'tetralysal').
'Lympholysin' see Chlorambucil.
'Lymphoscan' see Antimony trisulfide colloid.
'Lyndiol' see under Lynestrenol.
LYNESTRENOL*** (17α-ethynylestr-4-en-17β-ol; 19-nor-17α-pregn-4-en-20-yn-1-ol; ethinylestrenol; lynoestrenol; NSC-37725). See also under Ethinylestradiol.
LYNESTRENOL plus MESTRANOL ('lyndiol'; 'noracycline'; 'ovariostat'; 'restovar'; 'sistometril').
Lynoestrenol* see Lynestrenol.
'Lyochym' see Chymotrypsin.
'Lyogen' see Fluphenazine.
'Lyomethyl' see under Hydroxocobalamin.
'Lyopect' see Nicocodine.
'Lyorodin' see Fluphenazine.
'Lyorthol' see o-Phenylphenol.
'Lyovac diuril' see Chlorothiazide sodium.
Lyovac sodium edecrin* see Sodium etacrynate.
LYPRESSIN*** (8-lysinevasopressin; L-8).
'Lysanxia' see Prazepam.
'Lyseen' see Pridinol.
'Lysenil' see Lisuride maleate.
'Lysenyl' see Lisuride maleate.
LYSERGAMIDE (lysergic acid amide; ergine).
LYSERGIC ACID (4,6,6a,7,8,9-hexahydro-7-methylindolo[4,3-fg]quinoline-9-carboxylic acid).
Lysergic acid amide see Lysergamide.
Lysergic acid butanolamide see Methylergometrine.
Lysergic acid diethylamide see Lysergide.
Lysergic acid propanolamide see Ergometrine.
LYSERGIDE*** (4,6,6a,7,8,9-hexahydro-7-methylindolo[4,3-fg]quinoline-9-carboxylic acid diethylamide; N,N-diethyllysergamide; lysergic acid diethylamide; LSD).
LYSIDINE (ethyleneethenyldiamine; 2-methyl-2-imidazoline).
Lysin see Plasmin.
LYSINE* (2,6-diaminohexanoic acid; diaminocaproic acid).
LYSINE ACETYLSALICYLATE (lysine soluble aspirin; E-171; 'aspegic'; 'delgesic'; 'endosprin';

'flectadol'; 'laboprin'; 'quinton'; 'solusprin').

Lysine soluble aspirin *see* Lysine acetylsalicylate.

8-Lysinevasopressin *see* Lypressin.

'Lysmucol' *see* Sobrerol.

'Lysocycline' *see* Metacycline.

'Lysodren' *see* Mitotane.

'Lysoform' *see* Formaldehyde.

LYSOSTAPHIN* (enzyme produced by *Staph. staphylolyticus*).

'Lysothiazole' *see* Sulfathiazole aluminium.

'Lyspafen' *see* Difenoxin.

Lysuride* *see* Lisuride.

LYSYLBRADYKININ (kallidin I).

'Lyteca' *see* Paracetamol.

10-(L-Lyxityl)-7,8-dimethylisoalloxazine *see* Lyxoflavin.

LYXOFLAVIN (10-(L-lyxityl)-7,8-dimethylisoalloxazine).

LZ-544 *see* 3,3,3-Tris(*p*-chlorophenyl)propionic acid 4-methylpiperazide.

M

M-1-36 *see* Etilefrine.
M-2H *see* Butoctamide hemisuccinate.
M6/42 *see* Ruvazone.
M-14 *see* Rifamycin.
M-40 (tr) *see* Chlordane.
M-74 (tr) *see* Disulfoton.
M-81 *see* Thiometon.
M-82 (tr) *see* Demephion-S.
M-99 *see* Etorphine.
M-115 *see* Suxethonium chloride.
M-141 *see* Spectinomycin.
M-144 *see* Atrolactamide.
M-183 *see* Acetorphine.
M-285 *see* Cyprenorphine.
M-410 (tr) *see* Chlordane.
M-551 *see* Pheneturide.
M-640 *see* Sulfathiazole aluminium.
M-811 *see* Salverine.
M-1028(Meiji) *see* Haloprogin.
M-4000 *see* Dichlorophenarsine.
M-4365A2 *see* Rosaramicin.
M-4888 *see* Proguanil.
M-5050 *see* Diprenorphine.
M-5276 *see* Gliquidone.
M-5512 *see* Antazoline.
M-5943 *see* Chlorproguanil.
M-7555 *see* Quinapyramine.
M-9500 *see* Tretamine.
M-33536 *see* Dicycloverine.
M-73101 *see* Emorfazone.
MA-540 *see* Quinuclium bromide.
MA-593 *see* Saletamide.
MA-1277 *see* Zolertine.
MA-1291 *see* Quipazine.
MA-1337 *see* Cloperidone.
MA-1443 *see* Letimide.
MA-14012 *see* Picobenzide.
'MAA' *see* Macrosalb (^{99m}Tc).
'Mablin' *see* Busulfan.
MABUTEROL*** (4-amino-α-[(*tert*-butyl-amino)methyl]-3-chloro-5-(trifluoromethyl)-benzyl alcohol).
'Machete' *see* Butoclor.
'Maclicine' *see* Dicloxacillin.
'Macmirror' *see* Nifuratel.
'Macocyn' *see* Oxytetracycline.
Macrisalb (^{131}I) *see* Macrosalb (^{131}I).
Macroaggregated iodinated (^{131}I) human albumin *see* Macrosalb (^{131}I).
'Macrobin' *see* Clostebol acetate.
'Macrocycline' *see under* Erythromycin.

'Macrodantin' *see* Nitrofurantoin.
'Macrodex' *see* Dextran 70.
MACROGOL(S)** (PEG; polyethylene glycols).
Macrogol cetyl ether *see* Cetomacrogol(s).
MACROGOL DI(POLYOXYETHYLENE) FATTY ACID AMIDES (ethomids).
MACROGOL ESTER(S)*** (macrogol monoacid esters of fatty acids).
   See also Macrogol laurate; Macrogol oleate; Macrogol stearate(s).
Macrogol ethers *see* Cetomacrogol; Lauromacrogol; Polysorbate(s); Ricinomacrogol; Tyloxapol.
Macrogol hexadecyl ether *see* Cetomacrogol(s).
MACROGOL LAURATE 600* (polyethylene glycol 600 monolaurate).
MACROGOL OLEATE 600* (polyethylene glycol 600 monooleate).
MACROGOL STEARATE(S) ('cithrol'; 'polymal').
MACROGOL STEARATE 8 (polyoxyethylene 8 stearate; polyoxyl 8 stearate; 'myrj 45').
MACROGOL STEARATE 40 (polyethylene glycol 40 monostearate; polyoxyethylene 40 stearate; polyoxyl 40 stearate; 'myrj 52').
MACROGOL STEARATE 600* (polyethylene glycol 600 monostearate).
MACROGOL STEARATE 1000* (polyethylene glycol 1000 monostearate).
Macrogol (tetramethylbutyl)phenyl ether *see* Octoxinol.
MACROSALB (^{131}I)** (iodinated (^{131}I) macroaggregated human albumin; macrisalb (^{131}I); macroaggregated iodinated (^{131}I) human albumin; 'albumotope'; 'macroscan-131').
MACROSALB (^{99m}Tc)*** (technetium (^{99m}Tc) labeled macroaggregated human serum albumin; technetium Tc 99m albumin aggregated; MAT 99; 'lunaggregate'; 'MAA'; 'macrotec'; 'pulmolite'; 'technescan MAA').
'Macroscan-131' *see* Macrosalb (^{131}I).
'Macrose' *see* Dextran.
'Macrotec' *see* Macrosalb (^{99m}Tc).
MACROZAMIN (methylazoxymethanol primeveroside).
'Madar' *see* Nordazepam.
MADASIATIC ACID (2α,3β,6β-trihydroxyurs-12-en-28-oic acid).
   See also under Asiaticoside.
MADE-1932 *see* Oxitriptan glutamate.
MADECASSIC ACID (2α,3β,6β,23-tetrahydroxy-urs-12-en-28-oic acid).

322

See also under Asiaticoside.
'**Madecassol**' *see* Asiaticoside.
'**Madomicetina**' *see* Chloramphenicol stearate.
'**Madopar**' *see under* Levodopa.
'**Madribon**' *see* Sulfadimethoxine.
'**Madroxin**' *see* Sulfadimethoxine.
MAFENIDE*** (*p*-aminomethylbenzenesulfon-
amide; *p*-sulfamoylbenzylamine; maphenide;
bensulfamide; homosulfamide; homosulfamine;
homosulfanilamide; mafenide acetate; sulfabenz-
amine; sulfbenzamine; NSC-34632).
Mafenide sulfathiourea salt *see* Sulfatolamide.
MAFOSFAMIDE** (($\pm$)-2-[[2-[bis(2-chloro-
ethyl)amino]tetrahydro-2*H*-1,3,2-oxazaphos-
phorin-4-yl]thio]ethananesulfonic acid *P-cis*-
oxide).
MAGALDRATE*** (aluminium magnesium
hydroxide sulfate hydrate; monalium hydrate;
AY-5710; 'dynese'; 'riopan').
'**Magaspirin**' *see* Magnesium acetylsalicylate.
'**Magcyl**' *see* Poloxamer.
Magenta *see* Fuchsine.
'**Magisal**' *see* Magnesium acetylsalicylate.
'**Maglactis**' *see* Magnesium hydroxide.
'**Magmasil**' *see* Magnesium trisilicate.
'**Magmilor**' *see* Nifuratel.
'**Magna-cort**' *see* Hydrocortamate.
'**Magnamycin**' *see* Carbomycin.
'**Magnapen**' *see under* Ampicillin.
'**Magnepurin**' *see* Magnesium mandelate.
Magnesia *see* Magnesium carbonate.
'**Magnesiocard**' *see* Magnesium aspartate.
MAGNESIUM ACETYLSALICYLATE ('apyr-
on'; 'canocyl'; 'fyracyl'; 'magaspirin'; 'magisal';
'magnespirin'; 'magsyn'; 'novactyl'; 'novacyl').
Magnesium aluminosilicate *see* Simaldrate.
Magnesium aluminosilicate hydrate *see* Almasilate
and Simaldrate.
MAGNESIUM ASCORBATE ('magnorbin').
MAGNESIUM ASPARTATE (Wy-2838; 'magne-
siocard').
See also under Potassium aspartate.
MAGNESIUM CARBONATE (Mg subcarbonate;
light Mg carbonate; magnesia; magnesium sub-
carbonate).
MAGNESIUM CLOFIBRATE (bis[2-(*p*-chloro-
phenoxy)-2-methylpropionato]magnesium; UR-
112; 'clomag').
See also Clofibric acid.
**MAGNESIUM CLOFIBRATE plus INOSITOL
NICOTINATE** ('atroplex').
MAGNESIUM DIMECROTATE (dimecrotic
acid magnesium salt; 'hepadial').
Magnesium dioxide *see* Magnesium peroxide.
MAGNESIUM FERULATE (magnesium 4-hydr-
oxy-3-methoxycinnamate; 'fruchol').
MAGNESIUM GLUCONATE ('almora'; 'gyn';
'menesia'; 'relaxin').
**MAGNESIUM GLUTAMATE HYDROBROM-
IDE** ('psicosoma'; 'psychoverlan').
MAGNESIUM HEPARINATE ('cutheparin').
MAGNESIUM HYDROXIDE ('gastrovit'; 'ma-
glactis'; 'polysan').

See also under Pemoline.
MAGNESIUM MANDELATE ('magnepurin').
Magnesium mesosilicate *see* Magnesium trisilicate.
Magnesium 3-(4-methoxy-1-naphthoyl)propionate
see Menbutone.
**MAGNESIUM METHYNOTRITHIOGLYCOL-
ATE** ('eparsulfo').
MAGNESIUM OROTATE ('hippocras').
MAGNESIUM OXOGLURATE (Mg α-ketoglu-
tarate; Mg 2-oxoglutarate; DAN-268; 'proterg-
an').
Magnesium pemoline *see under* Pemoline.
'**Magnesium perhydrol**' *see* Magnesium peroxide.
MAGNESIUM PEROXIDE (magnesium dioxide;
'eraxan'; 'magnesium perhydrol'; 'magnesium
superoxol'; 'sanoma').
**MAGNESIUM PYRIDOXAL 5-PHOSPHATE
GLUTAMATE** ('sedalipid').
**MAGNESIUM SALICYLATE plus SODIUM
SALICYLATE** ('magsalyl'; 'salimagol').
Magnesium subcarbonate *see* Magnesium carbon-
ate.
MAGNESIUM SULFATE (Epsom salts; sel an-
glais; sel de Seidlitz).
Magnesium sulfate choline salicylate compound *see*
Salcolex.
'**Magnesium superoxol**' *see* Magnesium peroxide.
MAGNESIUM TRISILICATE (magnesium meso-
silicate; 'adsorbon'; 'florisil'; 'gastomag'; 'mag-
masil'; 'novabsorb'; 'salisil'; 'trisillac'; 'trisom-
in').
MAGNESIUM VALPROATE ('logical').
'**Magnespirin**' *see* Magnesium acetylsalicylate.
'**Magnipen**' *see* Metampicillin.
'**Magnorbin**' *see* Magnesium ascorbate.
'**Magsalyl**' *see under* Magnesium salicylate.
'**Magsyn**' *see* Magnesium acetylsalicylate.
MAHP *see* Methioprim.
MAITANSINE** (*N*-acetyl-*N*-methyl-L-alanine
[1*S*-(1*R**,2*S**,3*R**,5*R**,6*R**,16*E*,20*S**,21*R**)]-11-
chloro-21-hydroxy-12,20-dimethoxy-2,5,9,16-
tetramethyl-8,23-dioxo-4,24-dioxa-9,22-diaza-
tetracyclo[1.9.3.1^{10,14}0^{3,5}]hexacosa-10,12,
14(26),16,18-pentaen-6-yl ester; maytansine;
NSC-153858).
'**Majeptil**' *see* Thioproperazine.
'**Makarol**' *see* Diethylstilbestrol.
MALACHITE GREEN (acid oxalate, chloride or
sulfate of anhydrobis(2-dimethylaminophenyl)-
phenylmethanol; China green; fast green; green
of bitter almonds; Victoria green; viride mala-
chitum).
Malachite green G *see* Brilliant green.
'**Maladone**' *see* Allomethadione.
'**Malafos**' *see* Malathion.
'**Malakin**' *see* Salicylidene-*p*-phenetidine.
MALAOXON (*S*-[1,2-bis(ethoxycarbonyl)ethyl]
O,*O*-dimethyl phosphorothioate).
'**Malaston**' *see* Malathion.
MALATHION* (*S*-[1,2-bis(ethoxycarbonyl)ethyl]
O,*O*-dimethyl phosphorodithioate; diethyl [(di-
methoxyphosphinothioyl)thio]succinate; diethyl
mercaptosuccinate *S*-ester with *O*,*O*-dimethyl

phosphorodithioate; [(dimethoxyphosphinothio-yl)thio]succinic acid diethyl ester; maldison; carbophos; karbofos; HC-8059; OMS-1; TM-4049).

MALATHION plus PARATHION ('malatox').

'**Malathon**' *see* Malathion.

'**Malatox**' *see under* Malathion.

'**Malazol**' *see* Allomethadione.

'**Malcotran**' *see* Homatropine methyl bromide.

Maldison* *see* Malathion.

MALEAMIC ACID (maleic acid monoamide).

MALEANILIC ACID (*N*-phenylmaleamic acid).

MALEIC ACID (*cis*-butenedioic acid; *cis*-1,2-eth-ylenedicarboxylic acid; toxilic acid).

Maleic acid monoamide *see* Maleamic acid.

Maleic acid polymer with methylvinyl ether, iron salt *see* Ferropolimaler.

Maleic anhydride ethylene polymer *see* Maletamer.

Maleic anhydride-ethylene polymer ammonia reaction product *see* Carbetimer.

MALETAMER* (ethylene-maleic anhydride polymer; maleic anhydride ethylene polymer; malethamer).

Malethamer* *see* Maletamer.

MALEURIC ACID (*N*-carbamoylmaleamic acid; maleylurea).

MALEYLSULFATHIAZOLE* (*p*-(2-thiazolyl-sulfamoyl)phthalanilic acid).

Maleylurea *see* Maleuric acid.

'**Maliasin**' *see* Barbexaclone.

MALIC ACID (hydroxybutanedioic acid; hydr-oxysuccinic acid).

See also Arginine malate.

'**Malidone**' *see* Allomethadione.

'**Malipuran**' *see* Bufexamac.

'**Malix**' *see* Endosulfan.

'**Mallophene**' *see* Phenazopyridine.

'**Mallorol**' *see* Thioridazine.

'**Malloryl**' *see* Thioridazine.

'**Malocide**' *see* Pyrimethamine.

MALONAMIC ACID (malonic acid monoamide).

MALONAMIDE (malondiamide; malonic acid di-amide).

Malondiamide *see* Malonamide.

MALONIC ACID (methanedicarboxylic acid; pro-panedioic acid).

Malonic acid diamide *see* Malonamide.

Malonic acid monoamide *see* Malonamic acid.

Malonic acid mononitrile *see* Cyanoacetic acid.

Malononitrile *see* Cyanoacetic acid.

MALONURIC ACID (*N*-carbamoylmalonamic acid).

5,5'-[Malonylbis[(2-hydroxyethyl)imino]]bis[*N*,*N*'-bis[2-hydroxy-1-(hydroxymethyl)ethyl]-2,4,6-tri-iodoisophthalamide] *see* Iodecimol.

5,5'-[Malonylbis(methylimino)]bis[*N*,*N*'-bis[2,3-di-hydoxy-1-(hydroxymethyl)propyl]-2,4,6-triiodo-isophthalamide] *see* Iotrolan.

N,*N*'-**MALONYLBIS(PROCAINAMIDE)** ('nob-amide').

N,*N*'-**MALONYLBIS(PROCAINE)** ('novdimal').

Malonylurea *see* Barbituric acid.

'**Maloprim**' *see under* Pyrimethamine.

'**Maloran**' *see* Chlorbromuron.

MALOTILATE* (diisopropyl 1,3-dithiole-$\Delta^{2,\alpha}$-malonate; NNK-105).

'**Malproin**' *see* Valproic acid.

Maltonic acid *see* Gluconic acid.

'**Maltrate**' *see* Mannityl hexanitrate.

'**Malysol**' *see* Bemegride.

MAM *see* Cycasin.

Mammotropin *see* Prolactin.

'**Manalox AG**' *see* Glucalox.

'**Manalox AS**' *see* Sucralox.

MANCOZEB* (mixture of maneb and zineb; 'dithane M-45'; 'dithane-ultra'; 'manzate 200').

'**Mandamine**' *see* Methenamine mandelate.

'**Mandecal**' *see* Calcium mandelate.

7-D-Mandelamido-3-[[(1-methyl-1*H*-tetrazol-5-yl)-thio]methyl]-2-cephem-2-carboxylic acid *see* Ce-famandole.

7-Mandelamido-3-[[[1-(sulfomethyl)-1*H*-tetrazol-5-yl]thio]methyl]-2-cephem-2-carboxylic acid *see* Cefonicid.

'**Mandelamine**' *see* Methenamine mandelate.

MANDELIC ACID (2-phenylglycolic acid; α-hydroxyphenylacetic acid; α-hydroxy-α-toluic acid; amygdalic acid; paramandelic acid; racem-ic acid).

See also Ammonium mandelate; Calcium man-delate; Magnesium mandelate; Methenamine mandelate; Sodium mandelate.

'**Mandelix**' *see* Sodium mandelate.

Mandelonitrile gentiobioside *see* Amygdalin.

Mandelyl tropeine *see* Homatropine.

'**Mandicid**' *see* Ammonium mandelate.

'**Mandokef**' *see* Cefamandole nafate.

'**Mandol**' *see* Cefamandole nafate.

'**Mandrax**' *see under* Methaqualone.

'**Manduryl**' *see* Ammonium mandelate.

MANEB* (manganous *N*,*N*'-ethylenebis(carbamo-dithioate); manganous ethylenebis(dithiocarb-amate); MEB; MnEDB; 'dithane M-22'; 'di-thane manganese'; 'manzate').

MANEB plus NICKEL(II) SULFATE ('dithane S31').

See also Mancozeb.

'**Manexin**' *see* Mannityl hexanitrate.

Manganous ethylenebis(carbamodithioate) *see* Maneb.

Manganous ethylenebis(dithiocarbamate) *see* Maneb.

'**Manicole**' *see* Mannityl hexanitrate.

'**Maninil**' *see* Glibenclamide.

'**Manipal**' *see* Dihydrotachysterol.

'**Manite**' *see* Mannityl hexanitrate.

'**Mannex**' *see* Mannityl hexanitrate.

Mannite *see* Mannitol.

MANNITOL (mannite; 'ionosteril'; 'osmitrol'; 'os-mofundin').

D-Mannitol 1,6-di(methanesulfonate) *see* Mannityl dimesilate.

Mannitol hexanitrate* *see* Mannityl hexanitrate.

'**Mannitol myleran**' *see* Mannityl dimesilate.

Mannitol nitrogen mustard *see* Mannomustine.

D-Mannitol 1,2,5,6-tetramethanesulfonate *see* Mannosulfan.

'**Mannitrate**' *see* Mannityl hexanitrate.

MANNITYL DIMESILATE (1,6-bis(methanesulfonyl)mannitol; D-mannitol 1,6-di(methanesulfonate); mannityl dimesylate; dimethanesulfonylmannitol; DSM; CB-2511; NSC-37538; 'mannitol myleran').

MANNITYL HEXANITRATE* (mannitol hexanitrate; hexanitromannitol; nitromannite; nitromannitol).

Mannityl tetramesilate *see* Mannosulfan.

MANNOMUSTINE* (1,6-bis(2-chloroethylamino)-1,6-dideoxy-D-mannitol; mannitol nitrogen mustard; mannomustine dihydrochloride; BCM; NSC-9698).

MANNOMUSTINE HEPARINATE ('heparin-degranol'; 'zitofenton').

MANNOSULFAN* (D-mannitol 1,2,5,6-tetramethanesulfonate; mannityl tetramesilate; tetrakis(methylsulfonyl)mannitol; tetramesylmannitol; tetramethanesulfonylmannitol; R-52; 'zitostop'; 'zytostop').

Mannuronic acid polymers *see* Alginic acid; Sodium polyanhydromannuronic sulfate.

'**Manoxol OT**' *see* Docusate sodium.

MANOZODIL* (4,5,6,7-tetrahydro-2-methyl-5-[(methylamino)methyl]benzothiazole).

'**Mansil**' *see* Oxamniquine.

'**Mansonil**' *see* Niclosamide piperazine salt.

'**Mantadan**' *see* Amantadine.

'**Mantadix**' *see* Amantadine.

Mantheline *see* Methantheline bromide.

'**Mantomide**' *see* Chlorbetamide.

'**Mantropina**' *see* Methenamine mandelate.

'**Manucol**' *see* Sodium alginate.

'**Manuronate**' *see* Sodium polyanhydromannuronic sulfate.

'**Manvene**' *see* Mytatrienediol.

'**Manzate**' *see* Maneb.

'**Manzate 200**' *see* Mancozeb.

MAO *see* Monoamine oxidase.

'**Maolate**' *see* Chlorphenesin carbamate.

'**Mao-rem**' *see* Phenelzine.

MAP *see* Medroxyprogesterone acetate.

MAP (tr) *see* Adenosine phosphate.

Maphenide* *see* Mafenide.

'**Mapiprin**' *see* Piperazine.

MAPO *see* Metepa.

Mappine *see* Bufotenine.

MAPROTILINE* (*N*-methyl-9,10-ethanoanthracene-9(10*H*)-propylamine; 1-[3-(methylamino)propyl]dibenzo[*b*,*e*]bicyclo[2.2.2]octadiene; benzoctarpomine; maprotiline hydrochloride; Ba-34276; 'ludiomil').

'**Maratan**' *see* Bisoxatin diacetate.

'**Marbadal**' *see* Sulfatolamide.

'**Marbagelan**' *see* Gelatin sponge.

'**Marboran**' *see* Metisazone.

'**Marcain**' *see* Bupivacaine.

'**Marcoumar**' *see* Phenprocoumon.

'**Marcumar**' *see* Phenprocoumon.

Maretin *see* Naftalofos.

'**Marevan**' *see* Warfarin.

'**Marezine**' *see* Cyclizine.

'**Margeryl**' *see* Tenylidone.

MARIDOMYCIN* (10-(formylmethyl)-7,13-dihydroxy-8-methoxy-3,12-dimethyl-5-oxo-4,17-dioxabicyclo[14.1.0]heptadec-14-en-9-yl 3,6-dideoxy-4-*O*-(2,6-dideoxy-3-*C*-methyl-α-L-*ribo*-hexopyranosyl)-3-dimethylamino-β-D-glucopyranoside 4″,7′-dipropionate (ester)).

Marihuana *see* Cannabis.

MARIPTILINE* (1a,10b-dihydrodibenzo[*a*,*e*]-cyclopropa[*c*]cyclohepten-6(1*H*)-one *O*-(2-aminoethyl)oxime).

'**Marlate**' *see* Methoxychlor.

'**Marplan**' *see* Isocarboxazid.

'**Marplan bromide**' *see* Clidinium bromide.

'**Marplon**' *see* Isocarboxazid.

'**Marsalid**' *see* Iproniazid.

'**Marsin**' *see* Phenmetrazine.

'**Marvelon**' *see under* Desogestrel.

'**Marvosan**' *see* Paraformaldehyde.

'**Maryosan**' *see* Paraformaldehyde.

'**Masmoran**' *see* Hydroxyzine embonate.

'**Masterid**' *see* Drostanolone.

'**Masteril**' *see* Drostanolone.

'**Masteron**' *see* Drostanolone.

MAT 99 *see* Macrosalb (^{99m}Tc).

'**Matacil**' *see* Aminocarb.

'**Matadan**' *see* Amantadine.

Matecite *see* Pinitol.

Matezite *see* Pinitol.

'**Matromycin**' *see* Oleandomycin.

'**Matulane**' *see* Procarbazine.

'**Maxibolin**' *see* Ethylestrenol.

'**Maxicaine**' *see* Parethoxycaine.

'**Maxidex**' *see* Dexamethasone.

'**Maxifen**' *see* Pivampicillin.

'**Maxilase**' *see* α-Amylase.

'**Maxipen**' *see* Pheneticillin.

'**Maxisporin**' *see* Cefradine.

'**Maxitate**' *see* Mannityl hexanitrate.

'**Maxolon**' *see* Metoclopramide.

'**Maycor**' *see* Isosorbide dinitrate.

'**Mayeptil**' *see* Thioproperazine.

Maytansine* *see* Maitansine.

MAZATICOL* (6,6,9-trimethyl-9-azabicyclo-[3.3.1]non-3β-yl di-2-thien-2-ylglycolate; 6,6,9-trimethylgranatoline dithienylglycolate; mazaticol hydrochloride; PG-501).

MAZIDOX* (azidophosphonic bisdimethylamide; tetramethylphosphorodiamidic azide).

MAZINDOL* (5-(*p*-chlorophenyl)-2,3-dihydro-5-hydroxy-5*H*-imidazo[2,1-*a*]isoindole; 5-(*p*-chlorophenyl)-2,5-dihydro-3*H*-imidazo[2,1-*a*]-isoindol-5-ol; AN-448; SAH-42-548; 'sanorex'; 'teronac').

MAZIPREDONE* (11β,17-dihydroxy-21-(4-methylpiperazin 1-yl)pregna-1,4-diene-3,20-dione; 21-deoxy-21-(4-methylpiperazin-1-yl)prednisolone; 21-(4-methylpiperazin-1-yl)deprodone; mazipredone hydrochloride; Dp; 'depersolon'). *See also under* Miconazole.

M & B-125 *see* Benzylsulfamide.

M & B-693 *see* Sulfapyridine.

M & B-744 *see* Stilbamidine isetionate.
M & B-760 *see* Sulfathiazole.
M & B-782 *see* Propamidine.
M & B-800 *see* Pentamidine.
M & B-1948-A *see* Amphotalide.
M & B-2050-A *see* Pentolonium tartrate.
M & B-2207 *see* Suxamethonium chloride.
M & B-2210 *see* Suxethonium chloride.
M & B-4180A *see* Isometamidium chloride.
M & B-4486 *see* Pempidine.
M & B-5062A *see* Amicarbalide.
M & B-8430 *see* Clorexolone.
M & B-9302 *see* Clorgiline.
M & B-15497 *see* Decoquinate.
M & B-16942A *see* Diacetolol.
M & B-17803 *see* Acebutolol.
M & B-22948 *see* Zaprinast.
M & B-33153 *see* Oxoprostol.
M & B-39565 *see* Mitozolomide.
MBA *see* Chlormethine.
MBAO *see* Chlormethine *N*-oxide.
MBBA *see* Bromebric acid.
MBC *see* Benomyl.
MBLA *see* Melinamide.
MBR-4164-8 *see* Diflumidone.
MBR-4197 *see* Flucrilate.
MBR-4223 *see* Triflumidate.
2-M-4-C *see* 2-(4-Chloro-2-methylphenoxy)acetic acid.
MC-4703 *see* Triflupromazine.
MC-A-600 *see* Benzo[*b*]thien-4-yl methylcarbamate.
4-(MCB) *see* 4-(4-Chloro-2-methylphenoxy)butyric acid.
MCE *see* Metergoline.
MCME *see* (Chloromethyl) methyl ether.
McN-485 *see* Zoxazolamine.
McN-742 *see* Aminorex.
McN-1025 *see* Norbormide.
McN-1075 *see* Fenmetramide.
McN-1107 *see* Clominorex.
McN-1210 *see* Pyrinoline.
McN-1231 *see* Fluminorex.
McN-1564 *see* Flumetramide.
McN-1589 *see* Mixidine.
McN-2259 *see* Tolmetin.
McN-2378 *see* Mefenidil.
McN-2453 *see* Azepindole.
McN-2783-21-98 *see* Zomepirac.
McN-3113 *see* Xilobam.
McN-3377 *see* Fenobam.
McN-3495 *see* Pirogliride tartrate.
McN-3716 *see* Methyl palmoxirate.
McN-3802 *see* Palmoxiric acid.
McN-3802-21-98 *see* Palmoxirate sodium.
McN-3935 *see* Linogliride fumarate.
McN-A-343 *see* [4-(*m*-Chlorophenylcarbamoyl-oxy)-2-butynyl]trimethylammonium chloride.
McN-JR-1625 *see* Haloperidol.
McN-JR-2498 *see* Trifluperidol.
McN-JR-4263-49 *see* Fentanyl.
McN-JR-4584 *see* Benperidol.
McN-JR-4749 *see* Droperidol.

McN-JR-4929 *see* Benzetimide.
McN-JR-6218 *see* Fluspirilene.
McN-JR-6238 *see* Pimozide.
McN-JR-7242-11 *see* Difluanazine.
McN-JR-7904 *see* Lidoflazine.
McN-JR-8299 *see* Tetramisole.
McN-JR-13558-11 *see* Fetoxilate.
McN-JR-15403-11 *see* Difenoxin.
McN-JR-16341 *see* Penfluridol.
McN-R-73-Z *see* Rotoxamine.
McN-R-726-47 *see* Poldine metilsulfate.
McN-R-1162-22 *see* Potassium glucaldrate.
McN-R-1166 *see* Indometacin.
McN-R-1238 *see* Flufenamic acid.
McN-R-1451 *see* Ibuprofen.
McN-X-94 *see* Capuride.
McN-X-181 *see* Valnoctamide.
MCP *see* 2-(4-Chloro-2-methylphenoxy)acetic acid.
MCPA *see* 2-(4-Chloro-2-methylphenoxy)acetic acid.
MCPB *see* 4-(4-Chloro-2-methylphenoxy)butyric acid.
2,4-MCPB *see* 4-(4-Chloro-2-methylphenoxy)butyric acid.
4-(MCPB) *see* 4-(4-Chloro-2-methylphenoxy)butyric acid.
MCPP *see* Mecoprop.
2-MCPP *see* Mecoprop.
MD-2 *see* Hisphen.
MD-154 *see* Etamsylate.
MD-205 *see* Calcium dobesilate.
MD-516 *see* Cinnarizine.
MD-1035 *see under* Cinnarizine.
MD-2028 *see* Fluanisone.
MD-6134 *see* Warfarin-deanol.
MD-6260 *see* Heptaminol theophyllineacetate.
MD-6753 *see* Cinepazet.
MD-6809 *see* Mecinarone.
MD-67350 *see* Cinepazide maleate.
MD-73442 *see* Nilprazole.
MD-77027 *see* Carocainide.
MD-720111 *see* Oxapadol.
MD-780515 *see* Cimoxatone.
MDA *see* 3,4-Methylenedioxyamphetamine.
MDAP (17α-acetoxy-6-dehydro-16-methyleneprogesterone; 6-dehydro-17α-hydroxy-16-methyleneprogesterone acetate; 17α-hydroxy-16-methylenepregna-4,6-diene-3,20-dione acetate; methylenedehydroacetoxyprogesterone; 'superlutin').
MDAP plus MESTRANOL ('antigest').
MDi-193 *see* Cyclothiazide.
MDL-181 *see* Premazepam.
MDL-308 *see* Zetidoline.
MDL-458 *see* Deflazacort.
MDL-473 *see* Rifapentine.
MDL-507 *see* Teicoplanin.
MDL-809 *see* Isoprazone.
MDP *see* Medronate disodium.
Me-3625 *see* Niclofolan.
MEA *see* Mercaptamine.
Meat sugar *see* Inositol.
'Meaverin' *see* Mepivacaine.

MEB *see* Maneb.
MEB-6401 *see* Climbazole.
'Mebacid' *see* Sulfamerazine.
'Mebadin' *see* Dehydroemetine.
Meballymal* *see* Secobarbital.
MEBANAZINE* (α-methylbenzylhydrazine; 1-(1-phenylethyl)hydrazine).
'Mebaral' *see* Methylphenobarbital.
MEBENDAZOLE* (methyl 5-benzoyl-2-benzimidazolecarbamate; R-17635; 'equiverm'; 'mebenvet'; 'pantelmin'; 'sirben'; 'telmin'; 'vermox').
MEBENOSIDE* (methyl 3,5,6-tri-*O*-benzyl-D-glucofuranoside).
'Mebenvet' *see* Mebendazole.
MEBEVERINE (7-(3,4-dimethoxybenzoyloxy)-3-ethyl-1-(*p*-methoxyphenyl)-2-methyl-3-azaheptane; 4-[ethyl(*p*-methoxy-α-methylphenethyl)amino]butyl veratrate; mebeverine hydrochloride; CSAG-144).
MEBEZONIUM IODIDE* (4,4'-methylenebis(cyclohexyltrimethylammonium iodide); (methylenedi-1,4-cyclohexylene)bis(trimethylammonium iodide)).
MEBHYDROLIN* (5-benzyl-1,3,4,5-tetrahydro-2-methyl-2*H*-pyrid[4,3-*b*]indole; diazoline).
MEBHYDROLIN NAPADISILATE (mebhydrolin napadisylate; mebhydrolin 1,5-naphthalenedisulfonate).
'Mebichloramine' *see* Chlormethine.
'Mebinol' *see* Clefamide.
MEBIQUINE (dihydroxy(6-methyl-8-quinolinolato)bismuth; bismuth hydroxide 6-methyl-8-quinolinol compound).
MEBOLAZINE* (17β-hydroxy-2α,17-dimethyl-5α-androstan-3-one azine; dimetazine; 'roxilon').
MEBROFENIN* ([[[(3-bromomesityl)carbamoyl]methyl]imino]diacetic acid).
'Mebroin' *see under* Phenytoin.
Mebromphenhydramine *see* Embramine.
'Mebron' *see* Epirizole.
'Mebryl' *see* Embramine.
Mebubarbital *see* Pentobarbital.
Mebumal* *see* Pentobarbital.
MEBUTAMATE* (2,2-bis(carbamoyloxymethyl)-3-methylpentane; 2-*sec*-butyl-2-methyl-1,3-propanediol dicarbamate; W-583).
MEBUTIZIDE* (6-chloro-3-(1,2-dimethylbutyl)-3,4-dihydro-2*H*-1,2,4-benzothiadiazine-7-sulfonamide 1,1-dioxide).
'Mecadox' *see* Carbadox.
Mecamine (tr) *see* Mecamylamine.
MECAMYLAMINE* (*N*,2,3,3-tetramethylnorbornanamine; 2,2,3-trimethyl-3-(methylamino)-norbornane; methylaminoisobornane; methylaminoisocamphane; mecamine).
MECARBAM* (*S*-[[[(ethoxycarbonyl)amino]methylcarbonyl]methyl] *O,O*-diethyl phosphorodithioate; ethyl [[[(diethoxyphosphinothioyl)thio]acetyl]methyl]carbamate; 'afos'; 'murfotox'; 'murotox'; 'pestan').
MECARBINATE* (ethyl 5-hydroxy-1,2-dimethylindole-3-carboxylate).

MeCCNU *see* Semustine.
MECETRONIUM ETILSULFATE* (ethylhexadecyldimethylammonium ethyl sulfate).
'Mechloral' *see* Chloralodol.
Mechlorethamine* *see* Chlormethine.
'Mechothane' *see* Bethanechol.
MECIADANOL* ((2*R*,3*S*)-3-methoxy-3',4',5,7-flavantetrol).
MECILLINAM* ((2*S*,5*R*,6*R*)-6-[[(hexahydro-1*H*-azepin-1-yl)methylene]amino]penicillanic acid; 6-[*N*,*N*-(1,6-hexamethylene)formamidino]-penicillanic acid; (2*S*,5*R*,6*R*)-6-(perhydroazepin-1-ylmethyleneamino)penicillanic acid; amdinocillin; amidinopenicillin HX; FL-1060; 'selexedin').
See *also* Bacmecillinam; Pivmecillinam.
MECINARONE* (6-[2-(dimethylamino)ethoxy]-4,7-dimethoxy-5-[3-(*p*-methoxyphenyl)-1-oxoprop-2-enyl]benzofuran; 1-[6-[2-(dimethylamino)ethoxy]-4,7-dimethoxybenzofuran-5-yl]-3-(*p*-methoxyphenyl)-2-propen-1-one; MD-6809).
Meclastine* *see* Clemastine.
Meclizine* *see* Meclozine.
'Meclo' *see under* Metronidazole.
MECLOCYCLINE* (7-chloro-6-demethyl-6-deoxy-5-hydroxy-6-methylenetetracycline; GS-2989; NSC-78502).
MECLOFENAMIC ACID* (*N*-(2,6-dichloro-*m*-tolyl)anthranilic acid; 2-[(2,6-dichloro-3-methylphenyl)amino]benzoic acid; 2-carboxy-2',6'-dichloro-3'-methyldiphenylamine; meclofenamate sodium; CI-583; INF-4668; 'meclomen').
See *also* Terofenamate.
MECLOFENOXATE* (2-(dimethylamino)ethyl *p*-chlorophenoxyacetate; centrophenoxine; clofenoxine; ANP-235).
MECLOFENOXATE METHIODIDE (*p*-chlorophenoxyacetylcholine iodide).
'Meclomen' *see* Meclofenamic acid.
MECLONAZEPAM* ((±)-(*S*)-5-(*o*-chlorophenyl)-1,3-dihydro-3-methyl-7-nitro-2*H*-1,4-benzodiazepin-2-one).
Mecloprodine *see* Clemastine.
MECLOQUALONE* (3-(*o*-chlorophenyl)-2-methyl-4-quinazolinone; NSC-142005; W-4744).
MECLORALUREA* (1-methyl-3-(2,2,2-trichloro-1-hydroxyethyl)urea; G-7225; 'heraldium').
MECLORISONE* (9,11β-dichloro-17,21-dihydroxy-16α-methylpregna-1,4-diene-3,20-dione; methyldichlorisone).
Meclorisone butyrate *see* Meclorisone dibutyrate.
MECLORISONE DIBUTYRATE* (meclorisone butyrate; Sch-11572).
'Meclosorb' *see* Meclocycline.
MECLOXAMINE* (2-(*p*-chloro-α-methyl-α-phenylbenzyloxy)-*N*,*N*-dimethylpropylamine; 2-[(*p*-chlorophenyl)-α-methyl-α-phenylmethoxy]propyldimethylamine; methylchlorphenoxamine).
MECLOZINE (1-[α-(*p*-chlorophenyl)benzyl]-4-(*m*-methylbenzyl)piperazine; histametizine; mec-

lizine; parachloramine; UCB-5062).

MECOBALAMIN*** (cobinamide *Co*-methyl derivative hydroxide dihydrogen phosphate (ester), inner salt 3'-ester with 5,6-dimethyl-1-α-D-ribofuranosylbenzimidazole; α-(5,6-dimethylbenzimidazol-2-yl)cobamide methyl; 'algobaz').

'Mecodin' *see* Methadone.

MECONIC ACID (3-hydroxy-4-oxo-1(4*H*)-pyran-2,6-dicarboxylic acid).

MECONIN (6,7-dimethoxyphthalide).

m-**MECONIN** (5,6-dimethoxyphthalide; meconic acid lactone; opianyl).

Meconium *see* Opium alkaloids.

'Mecopar' *see* Mecoprop.

'Mecopex' *see* Mecoprop.

MECOPROP* ((±)-2-(4-chloro-2-methylphenoxy)propionic acid; CMPP; MCPP; 2-MCPP; 'iso-cornox'; 'mecopar'; 'mecopex').

'Mecoral' *see* Chloralodol.

'Mecortolone' *see* Prednisolone trimethyloctanoate.

'Mecostrin' *see* Dimethyltubocurarine chloride.

'Mecothane' *see* Bethanechol.

MECRILATE*** (methyl 2-cyanoacrylate; mecrylate).

Mecrylate* *see* Mecrilate.

MECYSTEINE*** (methyl 2-amino-3-mercaptopropionate; cysteine methyl ester; methyl cysteine; mecysteine hydrochloride).

3'-MeDAB *see* 4-(Dimethylamino)-3'-methylazobenzene.

'Medapan' *see* Heptabarb.

MEDAZEPAM*** (7-chloro-2,3-dihydro-1-methyl-5-phenyl-1*H*-1,4-benzodiazepine; medazepam hydrochloride; Ro 5-4556; 'anxitol'; 'nobrium'; 'rudotel').

See also under Metoclopramide.

MEDAZOMIDE*** (1,4,5,6-tetrahydro-1-methyl-6-oxopyridazine-3-carboxamide; medazonamide; DL-1777).

Medazonamide* *see* Medazomide.

Medemanol *see* Mannityl hexanitrate.

'Medemycin' *see* Midecamycin.

'Mederal' *see* Amoproxan.

Medfalan *see* Medphalan.

'Mediator' *see* Benfluorex.

MEDIBAZINE** (1-(diphenylmethyl)-4-(3,4-methylenedioxyphenyl)piperazine; S-4105).

'Mediben' *see* Dicamba.

MEDIFOXAMINE*** (*N*,*N*-dimethyl-2,2-diphenoxyethylamine; dimethylaminoacetaldehyde diphenylacetal; 'gerdaxyl').

Medigoxin* *see* Metildigoxin.

'Medinal' *see* Barbital.

'Medipectol' *see* Bibenzonium bromide.

Meditrene *see* Chiniofon.

MEDMAIN (5-(dimethylamino)-3-ethyl-2-methylindole; methylethyldimethylaminoindole).

'Medobis' *see* Bismuth 2-allyl-4-pentenoate.

'Medodorm' *see* Chloralodol.

'Medomet' *see* Methyldopa.

'Medomin' *see* Heptabarb.

'Medopaque' *see* Sodium iodohippurate.

MEDORUBICIN*** ((1*S*,3*S*)-3-glycoloyl-1,2,3,4,6,11-hexahydro-3,5,12-trihydroxy-6,11-dioxonaphthacen-1-yl 3-amino-2,3,6-trideoxy-α-L-*lyxo*-hexopyranoside; (7*S*,9*S*)-7-[(3-amino-2,3,6-trideoxy-α-L-*lyxo*-hexopyranosyl)oxy]-9-glycoloyl-7,8,9,10-tetrahydro-6,9,11-trihydroxy-5,12-naphthacenedione).

MEDPHALAN (D-3-[*p*-[bis(2-chloroethyl)amino]phenyl]alanine; D-phenylalanine mustard; D-sarcolysin; medfalan; CB-3026; NSC-35051).

See also Melphalan; Sarcolysin.

'Medrifar' *see* Medrysone.

'Medrin' *see* Embramine teoclate.

'Medrocort' *see* Medrysone.

MEDROGESTONE*** (6,17-dimethylpregna-4,6-diene-3,20-dione; metrogestone; AY-62022; NSC-123018; R-13615).

'Medrol' *see* Methylprednisolone.

MEDRONATE DISODIUM* (disodium dihydrogen methylenebis(phosphonate); disodium dihydrogen methylenediphosphonate; disodium medronate; disodium methylenediphosphonate; MDP; 'amerscan').

'Medrone' *see* Methylprednisolone.

MEDRONIC ACID** (methylenebis(phosphonic acid); methylenediphosphonic acid).

MEDROXALOL*** (5-[2-[[3-(1,3-benzodioxol-5-yl)-1-methylpropyl]amino]-1-hydroxyethyl]-2-hydroxybenzamide; 5-[1-hydroxy-2-[[1-methyl-3-[3,4-(methylenedioxy)phenyl]propyl]amino]ethyl]salicylamide; medroxalol hydrochloride; RMI-81968 A).

MEDROXYPROGESTERONE*** (17α-hydroxy-6α-methylpregn-4-ene-3,20-dione; 17α-hydroxy-6α-methylprogesterone; methypregnone).

MEDROXYPROGESTERONE plus ETHINYLESTRADIOL ('intex'; 'nogest'; 'provest'; 'verafen').

MEDROXYPROGESTERONE ACETATE* (17α-acetoxy-6α-methylprogesterone; depoprogesterone; MAP; NSC-26386).

MEDRYLAMINE*** (2-(*p*-methoxy-α-phenylbenzyloxy)-*N*,*N*-dimethylethylamine; *p*-methoxydiphenhydramine; BS-556).

MEDRYSONE** (11β-hydroxy-6α-methylpregn-4-ene-3,20-dione; 11β-hydroxy-6α-methylprogesterone; hydroxymesterone; HMS; NSC-63278; U-8471).

MEFECLORAZINE*** (1-(*o*-chlorophenyl)-4-(3,4-dimethoxyphenethyl)piperazine; mephechlorazine).

MEFENAMIC ACID** (*N*-(2,3-xylyl)anthranilic acid; *N*-(2,3-dimethylphenyl)anthranilic acid; CI-473; CN-35355; INF-3355).

MEFENIDIL** (5-methyl-2-phenylimidazole-4-acetonitrile; McN-2378).

MEFENOREX** (*N*-(3-chloropropyl)-α-methylphenethylamine; mefenorex hydrochloride; Ro 4-5282).

MEFESERPINE*** (*p*-methoxyphenoxyacetic acid methylreserpate ester; methoxyfenoserpine; methoxyphenoserpine).

'Mefexadyne' *see* Mefexamide.

MEFEXAMIDE* (*N*-[2-(diethylamino)ethyl]-2-
(*p*-methoxyphenoxy)acetamide; ANP-297; NP-
297).

MEFLOQUINE* (DL-*erythro*-α-piperid-2-yl-
2,8-bis(trifluoromethyl)-4-quinolinemethanol;
Ro 21-5998; WR-142490).

Mefosfolan *see* Mephosfolan.

'Mefoxin' *see* Cefoxitin.

MEFRUSIDE* (4-chloro-*N*¹-methyl-*N*¹-(tetra-
hydro-2-methylfuryl)-*m*-benzenedisulfonamide;
BAY-1500; FBA-1500).
See also under Methyldopa.

'Megace' *see* Megestrol acetate.

'Megachlor' *see* Clomocycline.

'Megacillin' *see* Clemizole penicillin.

'Megacillin oral' *see* Penicillin V.

MEGALLATE(S)* (3,4,5-trimethoxybenzoic
acid, esters and salts).

MEGALOMICIN*
(3*R*,4*S*,5*S*,6*R*,7*R*,9*R*,11*R*,12*R*,13*S*,14*R*-4-[(2,6-
dideoxy-3-*C*-methyl-α-L-*ribo*-hexopyranosyl)-
oxy]-14-ethyl-12,13-dihydroxy-3,5,7,9,11,13-
hexamethyl-7-[[2,3,6-trideoxy-3-(dimethylamino)-α-L-*ribo*-hexopyranosyl]oxy]-6-[[3,4,6-
trideoxy-3-(dimethylamino)-β-D-*xylo*-hexopyra-
nosyl]oxy]oxacyclotetradecane-2,10-dione; megalomycin; Sch-13430).

MEGALOMICIN POTASSIUM PHOSPHATE*
(megalomicin compound with potassium dihydrogen phosphate).

Megalomycin *see* Megalomicin.

'Megamycin' *see* Metacycline.

'Megast' *see* Carbenoxolone.

'Megatox' *see* Fluoroacetic acid.

'Megazone' *see* Phenylbutazone megallate.

Megestranol (tr) *see under* Megestrol acetate.

MEGESTROL* (17-hydroxy-6-methylpregna-
4,6-diene-3,20-dione; SC-10363).

MEGESTROL ACETATE* (BDH-1298; NSC-
71423; 'ovarid').

**MEGESTROL ACETATE plus ETHINYLES-
TRADIOL** ('novoquens'; 'oraconal'; 'planovin';
'serial'; 'tri-ervonum'; 'volidan'; 'volplan').

MEGESTROL ACETATE plus MESTRANOL
(megestranol; 'delpregnen').

'Megimide' *see* Bemegride.

MEGLITINIDE* (*N*-(*p*-carboxyphenethyl)-5-
chloro-2-methylbenzamide; *p*-[2-(5-chloro-2-
methylbenzamido)ethyl]benzoic acid; *p*-[2-(5-
chloro-*o*-anisamido)ethyl]benzoic acid).

MEGLUCYCLINE* (2-deoxy-2-(tetracyclinylmethylamino)-β-D-glucopyranose; tetracycline
2-deoxy-2-methylaminoglucose compound).

MEGLUMINE* (1-deoxy-1-methylamino-D-
glucitol; 1-methylamino-1-deoxy-D-glucitol; *N*-
methylglucamine).
See also below and under Adipiodone; Flunixin;
Iodamide; Nitroxinil; Papaverine; Theophylline.

MEGLUMINE ACETRIZOATE (acetrizoic acid
methylglucamine salt; 'angiombrine'; 'fortombrine M'; 'jodozoat'; 'plexombrine'; 'vasurix').

Meglumine amidotrizoate *see* Meglumine diatrizoate.

MEGLUMINE ANTIMONATE (*N*-methylgluc-
amine antimonate; RP 2168; 'glucantime'; 'protostib').

MEGLUMINE DIATRIZOATE (diatrizoic acid
methylglutamine salt; meglumine amidotrizoate;
SH-20932; 'angiografin'; 'cardiografin'; 'gastrografin'; 'hypaque'; 'reno'; 'urografin'; 'urovist').

**MEGLUMINE DIATRIZOATE plus ADIPIOD-
ONE MEGLUMINE** ('sinografin').

**MEGLUMINE DIATRIZOATE plus SODIUM
DIATRIZOATE** ('cystografin'; 'hypaque 76';
'hypaque 90'; 'reno 76'; 'renografin'; 'renovist';
'urografin 76'; 'uropolin'; 'urovison'; 'verografin'; 'visotrast').

MEGLUMINE INDOMETACINATE (meglumine 1-(*p*-chlorobenzoyl)-5-methoxy-2-methyl-3-
indoleacetate; indometacin meglumine; 'lio-metacen').

MEGLUMINE IOCARMATE (iocarmate meglumine; iocarmic acid meglumine salt; DB-
2041; 'dimeray'; 'dimer X').

MEGLUMINE IODOXAMATE (iodoxamate meglumine; iodoxamic acid meglumine salt; iodotetroxide; B-10610; 'cholovue'; 'endobil'; 'endomirabil').

MEGLUMINE IOGLICATE (ioglicic acid methylglucamine salt; 'rayvist').

MEGLUMINE IOGLYCAMATE (ioglycamide;
'biligram'; 'bilipolin'; 'bilivison').

**MEGLUMINE IOGLYCAMATE plus SODIUM
IOGLYCAMATE** ('bilivistan').

MEGLUMINE IOSERATE (ioseric acid meglumine salt; 'myelografin').

MEGLUMINE IOTALAMATE (iotalamic acid
methylglucamine salt; meglumine iothalamate;
'conray'; 'contrix 28').

**MEGLUMINE IOTALAMATE plus SODIUM
IOTALAMATE** ('conray 70'; 'conray FL'; 'vascoray').

MEGLUMINE IOTROXATE (iotroxic acid meglumine salt; 'biliscopin').

MEGLUMINE IOXAGLATE (ioxaglate meglumine; ioxaglic acid methylglucamine salt).

**MEGLUMINE IOXAGLATE plus SODIUM IO-
XAGLATE** ('hexabrix').

MEGLUMINE IOXITALAMATE (ioxitalamic
acid methylglucamine salt; 'telebrix').

**MEGLUMINE IOXITALAMATE plus SODIUM
IOXITALAMATE** ('telebrix 38').
See also under Ethanolamine ioxitalamate.

MEGLUMINE METRIZOATE (metrizoic acid
methylglucamine salt).

**MEGLUMINE METRIZOATE plus CALCIUM
METRIZOATE** ('isopaque'; 'ronpacon').

MEGLUMINE SALICYLATE* (meglumine salicylic acid compound; PFA-186).

MEGLUTOL* (3-hydroxy-3-methylglutaric
acid; CB-337).

'Meguan' *see* Metformin.

'Mekamine' *see* Mecamylamine.

'Meladinin' *see* Methoxsalen.

MELADRAZINE* (2,4-bis(diethylamino)-6-
hydrazino-*s*-triazine; hydramitrazine; Ba-13155;

C-13155; 'lisdonil').

MELAMINE (triamino-s-triazine; azamin; cyanurotriamide).

Melaminsulfone see Sulfamidopyrine sodium.

Melampyrin see Dulcitol.

Melampyrit see Dulcitol.

'Melanex' see Metahexamide.

Melanophore-stimulating hormone see Intermedin.

β-Melanotropin see Intermedin.

'Melantoin' see Methylphenytoin.

Melarsenoxide-BAL see Melarsoprol.

MELARSONYL POTASSIUM*** (2-[p-[(4,6-diamino-s-triazin-2-yl)amino]phenyl]-1,3,2-dithiaarsolane-4,5-dicarboxylic acid dipotassium salt; mel W; RP 9955; 'trimelarsan').

MELARSOPROL*** (2-[p-(4,6-diamino-s-triazin-2-ylamino)phenyl]-1,3,2-dithiaarsolane-4-methanol; 2-[p-(4,6-diamino-s-triazin-4-ylamino)phenyl]-4-hydroxymethyl-1,3-dithia-2-arsenolidine; dimercaprol derivative of p-[(4,6-diamino-s-triazin-2-yl)amino]benzenearsonous acid; mel B; melarsenoxide-BAL; RP 3854; 'arsobal').

MELATONIN (N-acetyl-5-methoxytryptamine; N-acetyl-O-methylserotonin; N-acetylserotonin methyl ether; N-[2-(5-methoxyindol-3-yl)ethyl]-acetamide; NSC-56423).

Mel B see Melarsoprol.

'Melbex' see Mycophenolic acid.

'Meldian' see Chlorpropamide.

MELENGESTROL*** (17-hydroxy-6-methyl-16-methylenepregna-4,6-diene-3,20-dione).

MELENGESTROL ACETATE* (BDH-1921; NSC-70968; 'MGA').

MELETIMIDE*** (DL-2-[1-(p-methylbenzyl)piperid-4-yl]-2-phenylglutarimide; methyldioxatrine; R-5183).

Meletin see Quercetin.

Melfalan see Melphalan.

MELILOTUS OFFICINALIS EXTRACT ('esberiven').
See also Coumarin.

Melin see Rutoside.

MELINAMIDE*** (N-(α-methylbenzyl)linoleamide; MBLA; AC-223).

Melipramine see Imipramine.

'Meliprimin' see Imipramine.

'Melitase' see Chlorpropamide.

'Melitoxin' see Dicoumarol.

MELITRACEN*** (9-[3-(dimethylamino)propylidene]-9,10-dihydro-10,10-dimethylanthracene; N,N,10,10-tetramethyl-Δ$^{9(10H),\gamma}$-anthracenepropylamine; N-7001; U-24973A).
See also under Flupentixol.

Melittin see Bee venom.

MELIZAME*** (5-(m-hydroxyphenoxy)-1H-tetrazole; m-(1H-tetrazol-5-yloxy)phenol; compound 56063).

'Mellaril' see Thioridazine.

'Mellerette' see Thioridazine.

'Melleril' see Thioridazine.

'Meloka' see Ethenzamide.

'Melonex' see Metahexamide.

'Melopat' see Betahistine dimesilate.

'Meloxine' see Methoxsalen.

MELPERONE*** (4'-fluoro-4-(4-methylpiperid-1-yl)butyrophenone; 1-[3-(p-fluorobenzoyl)propyl]-4-methylpiperidine; methylperone; metylperone; flubuperone; FG-5111; 'buronil'; 'eunerpan').

MELPHALAN*** (L-3-[p-[bis(2-chloroethyl)-amino]phenyl]alanine; L-phenylalanine mustard; L-sarcolysin; melfalan; alanine nitrogen mustard; PAM; CB-3025; NSC-8806).
See also Medphalan; Sarcolysin.

'Melprex' see Dodine.

'Melsedin' see Methaqualone.

'Meltrol' see Phenformin.

'Melubrin' see Sulfamidopyrine sodium.

'Melufin' see Dibupyrone.

Mel W see Melarsonyl potassium.

MEMANTINE*** (3,5-dimethyl-1-adamantanamine; dimethylamantadine; D-145; 'akatinol').

MEMOTINE** (3,4-dihydro-1-(p-methoxyphenoxymethyl)isoquinoline; UK-2371).

MENABITAN*** ((±)-8-(1,2-dimethylheptyl)-1,3,4,5-tetrahydro-5,5-dimethyl-2-(2-propynyl)-2H-[1]benzopyrano[4,3-c]pyridin-10-yl α,2-dimethyl-1-piperidinebutyrate; menabitan hydrochloride; SP-204).

'Menacor' see Cloridarol hemisuccinate.

MENADIOL*** (2-methyl-1,4-naphthalenediol).

Menadiol diacetate see Acetomenaphthone.

Menadiol diphosphate see Menadiol sodium phosphate.

Menadiol disulfate see Menadiol sodium sulfate.

MENADIOL POTASSIUM SULFATE (dipotassium salt of 2-methyl-1,4-naphthalenediol bis-(hydrogen sulfate); potassium menadiol disulfate; potassium menaphthosulfate).

MENADIOL SODIUM PHOSPHATE (tetrasodium salt of 2-methyl-1,4-naphthalenediol bis(hydrogen phosphate); menadiol diphosphate; sodium menadiol diphosphate; naftidon; 'kappadione'; 'procoagulo'; 'synkavit').

MENADIOL SODIUM SULFATE*** (disodium salt of 2-methyl-1,4-naphthalenediol bis(hydrogen sulfate); menadiol disulfate; sodium menadiol disulfate).

Menadiol 3-sulfonic acid sodium salt see Sodium menadiol-3-sulfonate.

MENADIONE*** (2-methyl-1,4-naphthoquinone; 2-methyl-1,4-naphthalenedione; menaphthene; menaphthone; menaquinone; vitamin K$_3$).

Menadione carboxymethoxime see Menadoxime.

MENADIONE SODIUM BISULFITE*** (1,2,3,4-tetrahydro-2-methyl-1,4-dioxo-2-naphthalenesulfonic acid sodium salt; vikasol; 'hykinone').

MENADOXIME* (menadione carboxymethoxime ammonium salt; menadione 4-oxime carboxymethyl ether NH$_4$ salt).

Menaphthene see Menadione.

Menaphthone* see Menadione.

Menaquinone see Menadione.

Menaquinone-4 see Farnoquinone.

MENATETRENONE*** (2-methyl-3-(3,7,11,15-

tetramethylhexadecatetraenyl)-1,4-naphthoquin-one).

MENAZON* (*S*-(4,6-diamino-*s*-triazin-2-ylmethyl) *O*,*O*-dimethyl phosphorodithioate; 6-[[(dimethoxyphosphinothioyl)thio]methyl]-1,3,5-triazine-2,4-diamine; azidithion; 'saphi-col'; 'saphizon'; 'sayfos').

MENAZONE (*N'*-[1-(2-furfuryl)ethylidene]isoniazed; 2-furfuryl methyl ketone isonicotinoyl-hydrazone; INF; 'clitizina').

MENBUTONE*** (3-(4-methoxy-1-naphthoyl)-propionic acid; menbutone magnesium; SC-1749).

'**Mendiaxon**' *see* Hymecromone.

'**Mendon**' *see* Clorazepate dipotassium.

'**Menesia**' *see* Magnesium gluconate.

'**Menest**' *see* Conjugated estrogens equine.

'**Menethyl**' *see* Etafedrine.

MENFEGOL*** (α-[*p*-(*p*-menthyl)phenyl]-ω-hydroxypoly(oxyethylene)).

MENGLYTATE*** (menthyl ethoxyacetate; menthyl ethylglycolate).

Menichlopholan *see* Niclofolan.

'**Menifur**' *see under* Metronidazole.

'**Menine**' *see* Methionine.

MENITRAZEPAM*** (5-(1-cyclohexen-1-yl)-1,3-dihydro-1-methyl-7-nitro-2*H*-1,4-benzodiazepin-2-one; CB-4857).

'**Menocil**' *see* Aminorex.

MENOCTONE*** (2-(8-cyclohexyloctyl)-3-hydr-oxy-1,4-naphthoquinone; NSC-103336; WIN-11530).

MENOGARIL**
((2*R**,3*S**,4*R**,5*R**,6*R**,11*R**,13*R**)-4-(dimeth-ylamino)-3,4,5,6,11,12,13,14-octahydro-3,5,8,10,13-pentahydroxy-11-methoxy-6,13-di-methyl-2,6-epoxy-2*H*-naphthaceno[1,2-*b*]oxocin-9,16-dione).

Menotrophine* *see* Human menopausal gonado-trophin.

Menotropins* *see* Human menopausal gonado-trophin.

'**Mensiso**' *see* Sisomicin.

'**Menstridyl**' *see* Chlormadinone acetate.

p-**Mentha-1,8-diene** *see* Limonene.

p-**Mentha-3,6-diene-2,5-dione** *see* Thymoquinone.

p-**Menthan-3-ol** *see* Menthol.

1-*p*-**Menthene-6,8-diol** *see* Sobrerol.

p-**Menth-6-ene-2,8-diol** *see* Sobrerol.

2-*p*-**Menthene 1,4-peroxide** *see* Ascaridole.

MENTHOL (2-isopropyl-5-methylcyclohexanol; *p*-menthan-3-ol; peppermint camphor).

Menthyl ethoxyacetate *see* Menglytate.

Menthyl ethylglycolate *see* Menglytate.

α-[*p*-(*p*-**Menthyl)phenyl]-ω-hydroxypoly(oxyethyl-ene)** *see* Menfegol.

'**Meobal**' *see* 3,4-Xylyl methylcarbamate.

MEOBENTINE*** (1-(*p*-methoxybenzyl)-2,3-di-methylguanidine; betometine; meobentine sulf-ate).

'**Meonine**' *see* Methionine.

MEPACRINE*** (6-chloro-9-[4-(diethylamino)-1-methylbutylamino]-2-methoxyacridine; acrich-ine; acriquine; akrichin; haffkynine; italchine; RP 866; SN-390; 'quinacrine').
See also under Ethosuximide.

Meparfynol *see* Methylpentynol.

MEPARTRICIN*** (methyl partricin; partricin methyl ester; SN-654; SPA-S-160; 'tricandil').

Mepasin *see* Pecazine.

Mepazine *see* Pecazine.

'**Mepedyl**' *see* Piprinhydrinate.

MEPENZOLATE BROMIDE*** (1-methylpip-erid-3-yl benzilate methobromide; 3-hydroxy-1,1-dimethylpiperidinium bromide benzilate; mepenzolone; JB-340).

Mepenzolone* *see* Mepenzolate bromide.

MEPERIDIDE* (4'-fluoro-4-(4-pyrrolidinamido-4-*m*-tolylpiperid-1-yl)butyrophenone; 1-[3-(*p*-fluorobenzoyl)propyl]-4-(pyrrolidin-1-ylcarbon-yl)-4-*m*-tolylpiperidine; methylperidide; R-2963).

Meperidine* *see* Pethidine.

MEPESULFATE (pectin polysulfate; polygalactu-ronic acid methoxylate polysulfate; Ro 2-3053; 'emostat'; 'hemostat'; 'heparoid'; 'stypturon'; 'treburon').

'**Mephanac**' *see* 2-(4-Chloro-2-methylphenoxy)-acetic acid.

MEPHEBARBITAL* (5-methyl-5-phenylbarbitur-ic acid; heptobarbital; 'eudan'; 'rutonal').

Mephechlorazine *see* Mefeclorazine.

'**Mephenamine**' *see* Orphenadrine.

MEPHENESIN*** (3-(*o*-methylphenoxy)-1,2-pro-panediol; 3-(*o*-toloxy)-1,2-propanediol; *o*-cresyl glyceryl ether; cresoxydiol; glykresin; BDH-312; RP 3602).

Mephenetoin* *see* Mephenytoin.

Mephenhydramine *see* Moxastine.

MEPHENOXALONE*** (5-(*o*-methoxyphen-oxymethyl)-2-oxazolidinone; methoxydone; AHR-233; OM-518).

MEPHENTERMINE*** (*N*,α,α-trimethylphen-ethylamine; mephetedrine).

MEPHENYTOIN*** (5-ethyl-3-methyl-5-phenyl-hydantoin; mephenetoin; methoin; methylhy-dantoin; methylphenetoin; phenantoin; trianto-in; NSC-34652).

Mephetedrine *see* Mephentermine.

'**Mephine**' *see* Mephentermine.

Mephobarbital* *see* Methylphenobarbital.

MEPHOSFOLAN* (diethyl (4-methyl-1,3-dithio-lan-2-ylidene)phosphoramidate; mefosfolan; methocarbolane; 'cytrolane').

'**Mephtal**' *see* Methylphenobarbital.

'**Mepiben**' *see* Diphenylpyraline.

Mepicycline *see* Pipacycline.

'**Mepilon**' *see* Pipacycline.

MEPINDOLOL*** (4-[2-hydroxy-3-(isopropyl-amino)propoxy]-2-methylindole; 1-(isopropyl-amino)-3-[(2-methylindol-4-yl)oxy]-2-propanol; methylpindolol; mepindolol hydrochloride; 'cor-indolan').

Mepiperphenidol *see* Piperphenamine.

MEPIPRAZOLE*** (1-(*m*-chlorophenyl)-4-[2-(5-methylpyrazol-3-yl)ethyl]piperazine; mepipraz-ole dihydrochloride; H-4007).

Mepirizole *see* Epirizole.

MEPIROXOL*** (3-pyridinemethanol 1-oxide).

'Mepiserpate' *see* Metoserpate.

MEPITIOSTANE*** (cyclopentanone 2α,3α-epithio-5α-androstan-17β-yl methyl acetal; epitiostanol 1-methoxycyclopentyl ether; S-10364).

MEPIVACAINE*** (1-methyl-2′,6′-pipecoloxylidide; 1-methyl-2-(2,6-xylylcarbamoyl)piperidine; DL-1,2′,6-trimethylpipecolanilide; mepivacaine hydrochloride).
See also Dexivacaine.

MEPIXANOX*** (3-methoxy-4-(piperid-1-ylmethyl)xanthen-9-one).

MEPRAMIDIL (3-[(3,3-diphenylpropyl)amino]propyl 3,4,5-trimethoxybenzoate; PF-26).

'Meprane' *see* Methestrol dipropionate.

MEPREDNISONE*** (17,21-dihydroxy-16β-methylpregna-1,4-diene-3,11,20-trione; 6β-methylprednisolone; NSC-527579; Sch-4358).

MEPROBAMATE*** (2-methyl-2-propyl-1,3-propanediol dicarbamate; 2-methyl-2-propyltrimethylene dicarbamate; meprotan; procalmadiol).
See also under Aceprometazine; Bendroflumethiazide; Methamphetamine.

MEPROBAMATE plus BENACTYZINE ('deprol'; 'idemin').

MEPROBAMATE plus OXYPHENCYLIMINE ('daritran').

MEPROCHOL* ((2-methoxyallyl)trimethylammonium bromide; (2-methoxy-2-propenyl)trimethylammonium bromide).

Mepromazine *see* Levomepromazine.

'Mepronizine' *see under* Aceprometazine.

MEPROPHENIDOL* (3-(*o*-methoxy-*p*-propionylphenoxy)-1,2-propanediol; MPD; DA-1128).

MEPROSCILLARIN*** (3β-[(6-deoxy-4-*O*-methyl-α-L-mannopyranosyl)oxy]-14-hydroxybufa-4,20,22-trienolide; 14-hydroxy-3β-(4-*O*-methyl-α-L-rhamnopyranosyloxy)-14β-bufa-4,20,22-trienolide; 4′-*O*-methylproscillaridin; rambufaside; 'clift').

Meprotan (tr) *see* Meprobamate.

Meprothixol* *see* Meprotixol.

MEPROTIXOL*** (9-[3-(dimethylamino)propyl]-2-methoxythioxanthen-9-ol; meprothixol; N-7020).

MEPRYLCAINE*** (2-methyl-2-(propylamino)-propyl benzoate; 'oracaine').

MEPTAZINOL** (3-ethyl-3-(*m*-hydroxyphenyl)-1-methylhexahydroazepine; 3-ethyl-3-(*m*-hydroxyphenyl)-1-methylhexamethylenamine; *m*-(3-ethylhexahydro-1-methyl-1*H*-azepin-3-yl)phenol; meptazinol hydrochloride; Wy-22811; 'meptid').

'Meptid' *see* Meptazinol.

MEPYRAMINE*** (2-[[2-(dimethylamino)-ethyl](*p*-methoxybenzyl)amino]pyridine; *N*-(*p*-methoxybenzyl)-*N*′,*N*′-dimethyl-*N*-pyrid-2-yl-ethylenediamine; pyranisamine; pyrilamine; mepyramine maleate; PM-273; RP 2786).

Mepyramine bromotheophyllinate *see* Pyrabrom.

Mepyrrotazine *see* Dimelazine.

MEQUIDOX*** (2-(hydroxymethyl)-3-methylquinoxaline 1,4-dioxide; 3-methyl-2-quinoxalinemethanol 1,4-dioxide; GS-7443).

MEQUINOL*** (hydroquinone monomethyl ether; *p*-hydroxyanisole; *p*-methoxyphenol).

Mequinolate* *see* Proquinolate.

MEQUITAZINE*** (3-(phenothiazin-10-ylmethyl)quinuclidine; 10-(quinuclidin-3-ylmethyl)-phenothiazine; LM-209; 'metaplexan'; 'mircol'; 'primalan').

Mer-17 *see* Azacyclonol.

Mer-25 *see* Ethamoxytriphetol.

MER-29 *see* Triparanol.

MER-41 *see* Clomifene.

Meractinomycin *see* Dactinomycin.

MERALEIN SODIUM*** (*o*-(6-hydroxy-5-hydroxymercuri-2,7-diiodo-3-oxo(3*H*)xanthen-9-yl)-benzenesulfonic acid sodium salt; sodium meralein).

'Meralen' *see* Flufenamic acid.

MERALLURIDE*** (1-(3-hydroxymercuri-2-methoxypropyl)-3-succinylurea theophylline derivative).

'Meralop' *see* Cianidanol rutinoside.

'Merapid' *see* Polyoxymethylene glycol.

'Meratonic' *see* Pipradrol.

'Meratran' *see* Pipradrol.

'Merbak' *see* Acetomeroctol.

MERBAPHEN (2-chloro-6-hydroxymercuriphenoxyacetic acid barbital salt; 'novasurol').

'Merbentul' *see* Chlorotrianisene.

'Merbentyl' *see* Dicycloverine.

MERBIURELIDIN (1-(3-hydroxymercuri-2-methoxypropyl)biuret; 'meterox').

MERBROMIN*** (2′,7-dibromo-4-hydroxymercurifluorescein; bromochromium; mercurescein-Na; rhodochromium; 'mercurochrome').

'Mercaleukin' *see* Mercaptopurine.

Mercamine (tr) *see* Mercaptamine.

'Mercaprol' *see* Dimercaprol.

MERCAPTAMINE*** (2-mercaptoethylamine; 2-aminoethanethiol; cysteamine; cysteinamine; decarboxycysteine; MEA; mercamine; thioethanolamine; L-1573; NSC-25116).

Mercaptamine *S*-phosphate *see* Cystafos.

2-Mercaptoacetanilide *S*-gold derivative *see* Aurothioglycanide.

MERCAPTOACETIC ACID (2-mercaptoacetic acid; thioglycolic acid).

β-Mercaptoalanine *see* Cysteine.

Mercaptoarsenol *see* Arsthinol.

Mercaptodimethur *see* Methiocarb.

2-Mercaptoethanesulfonic acid sodium salt *see* Mesna.

2-MERCAPTOETHANOL (2-hydroxyethanethiol; monothioglycol).

2-Mercaptoethylamine *see* Mercaptamine.

***N*-(2-Mercaptoethyl)dimethylamine** *see* Captamine.

(2-Mercaptoethyl)trimethylammonium hydroxide *see* Thiocholine.

MERCAPTOMERIN*** (disodium salt of *N*-[3-(carboxymethylthiomercuri)-2-methoxypropyl]-camphoramic acid).

2-Mercapto-1-methylimidazole *see* Thiamazole.

N-(Mercaptomethyl)phthalimide *S*-(*O,O*-dimethyl-phosphorothioate) *see* Phosmet.

1-(3-Mercapto-2-methylpropanoyl)pyrrolidine-2-carboxylic acid *see* Captopril.

N-(3-Mercapto-2-methylpropionyl)-4-(phenylthio)-L-proline benzoate ester *see* Zofenopril.

1-(3-Mercapto-2-methylpropionyl)-L-proline *see* Captopril.

N-[1-(3-Mercapto-2-methylpropionyl)-L-prolyl]-3-phenyl-L-alanine acetate *see* Alacepril.

Mercaptophas *see under* Demeton-O.

'Mercaptophos' *see* Fenthion.

Mercaptophossystox *see* Demeton-O.

1-(3-Mercaptopropionic acid)-8-D-arginine vaso-pressin *see* Desmopressin.

1-(3-Mercaptopropionic acid)-2-[3-(*p*-ethylphenyl)-L-alanine]-6-(L-2-aminobutyric acid)oxytocin *see* Nacartocin.

1-(3-Mercaptopropionic acid)-2-isoleucine oxytocin *see* 1-Deamino-2-isoleucine oxytocin.

1-(3-Mercaptopropionic acid)oxytocin *see* Demoxy-tocin.

N-(2-Mercaptopropionyl)glycine *see* Tiopronin.

MERCAPTOPURINE*** (6-purinethiol; 6-MP; NSC-755).

MERCAPTOPURINE ARABINOSIDE (9-β-D-arabinofuranosyl(9*H*)purine-6-thiol).

MERCAPTOPURINE RIBONUCLEOSIDE (thioinosine; 6-MP-R; NSC-4911).

4-Mercaptopyrazolo[3,4-*d*]pyrimidine *see* Tisopur-ine.

MERCAPTOSUCCINIC ACID (α-thiomalic acid).
    See also Anthiolimine; Sodium aurothiomalate.

2-Mercaptothiazoline *see* 4-Thiazoline-2-thione.

'Mercaptothion' *see* Malathion.

3-Mercaptovaline *see* Penicillamine.

'Mercate' *see* Isoascorbic acid; Sodium ascorbate.

Mercazolyl (tr) *see* Thiamazole.

'Mercryl' *see* Mercurobutol.

'Mercryl lauryle' *see* Mercurobutol laurate.

MERCUDERAMIDE*** (*o*-carboxyphenoxyacet-ic acid hydroxymercuripropanolamide; *o*-[[2-hydroxy-3-(hydroxymercuri)propyl]carbamoyl]-phenoxyacetic acid).

MERCUFENOL CHLORIDE* (chloro(*o*-hydr-oxyphenyl)mercury; *o*-(chloromercuri)phenol; U-7743).

Mercumallyl-theophylline *see* Mercumatilin sodi-um.

MERCUMATILIN SODIUM*** (mixture of 8-(3-hydroxymercuri-2-methoxypropyl)-3-couma-rincarboxylic acid sodium salt with theophylline; mercumallyl-theophylline).

MERCURAN (tr) (lindane plus ethylmercuric chloride).

Mercurescein-Na *see* Merbromin.

'Mercurex' *see* Meralein sodium.

MERCURIC CHLORIDE (mercury bichloride; mercury perchloride; sublimate).

MERCUROBUTOL*** (4-*tert*-butyl-2-(chloro-mercuri)phenol; (chloromercuri)isobutylphenol;

L-542; 'mercryl').

MERCUROBUTOL LAURATE (mercurobutol dodecanoate; 'mercryl lauryle').

'Mercurochrome' *see* Merbromin.

MERCUROPHYLLINE*** (3-(3-hydroxymercu-ri-2-methoxypropyl)camphoramic acid sodium salt plus theophylline; 'novurit').

Mercurothiolate* *see* Thiomersal.

MERCUROUS CHLORIDE (mercury mono-chloride; mercury subchloride; calomel; precipite blanc).

Mercury bichloride *see* Mercuric chloride.

Mercuryluree* *see* Chlormerodrin.

Mercury monochloride *see* Mercurous chloride.

Mercury perchloride *see* Mercuric chloride.

Mercury subchloride *see* Mercurous chloride.

MERCUSAL (tr) (mersalyl-barbital complex).

'Meregon' *see* Bunaftine citrate.

'Mereprine' *see* Doxylamine.

'Meretran' *see* Pipradrol.

Merfalan *see* Sarcolysin.

'Merfen' *see* Phenylmercuric acetate.

Meridil (tr) *see* Methylphenidate.

'Merinax' *see* Hexapropymate.

MERISOPROL (¹⁹⁷Hg)*** (1-hydroxymercu-ri(¹⁹⁷Hg)-2-propanol; radiomerisoprol).

'Merital' *see* Nomifensine maleate.

'Meritin' *see* Ambucetamide.

Merkaptofos (tr) *see* Demeton-O.

Merkaptofos tiolovyj (tr) *see* Demeton-S.

'Merodicein' *see* Meralein sodium.

'Meroxylan' *see* Crystal violet.

Merpanit (tr) *see* Caramiphen.

Merphalan *see* Sarcolysin.

'Merphenyl' *see* Phenylmercuric acetate.

'Merphos' *see* Tributyl phosphorotrithioite.

'Mersagel' *see* Phenylmercuric nitrate.

MERSALYL** (*o*-[*N*-(3-hydroxymercuri-2-meth-oxypropyl)carbamoyl]phenoxyacetic acid sodi-um salt and/or its theophylline derivative).

Mersalyl-barbital complex *see* Mercusal.

'Mersolite 8' *see* Phenylmercuric acetate.

'Mersolite 19' *see* Phenylmercuric salicylate.

'Mertect' *see* Tiabendazole.

'Merthiolate' *see* Thiomersal.

'Mertricone' *see* Phenylmercuric acetate.

'Mervacycline' *see* Tetracycline bitartrate nucleic acid complex.

'Mervan' *see* Alclofenac.

MESABOLONE*** (17β-hydroxy-5α-androst-1-en-3-one 1-methoxycyclohexyl ether; 17β-(1-methoxycyclohexyloxy)-5α-androst-1-en-3-one).

'Mesalphene' *see* Xenysalate.

'Mesantoin' *see* Mephenytoin.

Mesaton (tr) *see* Phenylephrine.

MESCALINE (3,4,5-trimethoxyphenethylamine; mezcaline).

'Mesconit' *see* Scopolamine methyl nitrate.

'Mescophil' *see* Scopolamine methyl bromide.

Mesdicaine *see* Trimecaine.

MESECLAZONE*** (7-chloro-3,3a-dihydro-2-methyl-2*H*,9*H*-isoxazolo[3,2-*b*][1,3]benzoxazin-9-one; W-2395).

'**Mesentol**' *see* Ethosuximide.

MESFENAL (tr) (diethyl(3-hydroxypropyl)meth-ylammonium methosulfate diphenylacetate; 3-(diethylamino)propyl 2,2-diphenylacetate methyl methosulfate; arpenal methyl methosulfate; mesphenal).

MESIDINE (2,4,6-trimethylaniline).

MESILATE(S)** (methanesulfonate(s); mesylate(s)).

'**Mesitol**' *see* Inositol.

MESITYLENE (1,3,5-trimethylbenzene).

MESNA*** (sodium 2-mercaptoethanesulfonate; UCB-3983; 'mistabron'; 'mucofluid'; 'uromitexan').

Mesocaine (tr) *see* Trimecaine.

MESOCARB*** ((3α-methylphenethyl)-*N*-(phenylcarbamoyl)sydnone imine).

Mesoinosite *see* Inositol.

Mesoinositol *see* Inositol.

'**Meso-lens**' *see* Cellaburate.

Mesomucinase *see* Hyaluronidase(s).

'**Mesonex**' *see* Inositol nicotinate.

'**Mesonitrol**' *see* Inositol hexanitrate.

'**Mesontoin**' *see* Mephenytoin.

'**Mesopin**' *see* Homatropine methyl bromide.

'**Mesopren**' *see* Methylprednisolone.

'**Mesoranil**' *see* Aziprotryne.

Mesorgydine *see* Lisuride.

MESORIDAZINE*** (10-[2-(1-methylpiperid-2-yl)ethyl]-2-(methylsulfinyl)phenothiazine; thioridazine oxide; NC-123; TPS-23).

MESOXALIC ACID (dihydroxymalonic acid; ketomalonic acid; oxomalonic acid).

Mesoxalylurea *see* Alloxan.

'**Mespafin**' *see* Doxycycline.

Mesphenal *see* Mesfenal.

MESPIRENONE** (15α,16α-dihydro-17-hydroxy-7α-mercapto-3-oxo-3'*H*-cyclopropa[15,16]-17α-pregna-1,4,15-triene-21-carboxylic acid γ-lactone acetate).

MESTANOLONE*** (17β-hydroxy-17-methyl-5α-androstan-3-one; 17-methylandrostanolone).

Mestenediol *see* Methandriol.

MESTEROLONE*** (17β-hydroxy-1α-methyl-5α-androstan-3-one; NSC-75054; SH-723).

MESTILBOL* (α,α'-diethyl-4-hydroxy-4-methoxystilbene; 'monomestrol').

'**Mestinon**' *see* Pyridostigmine bromide.

'**Mestoran**' *see* Mesterolone.

MESTRANOL*** (17-ethynyl-3-methoxy-1,3,5(10)-estratrien-17β-ol; 3-methoxy-19-nor-17α-pregna-1,3,5(10)-trien-20-yn-17-ol; ethinylestradiol 3-methyl ether).
    See also under Anagestone acetate; Chlormadinone acetate; Chloro-MDAP; Etynodiol diacetate; Lynestrenol; MDAP; Megestrol acetate; Norethisterone; Noretynodrel.

MESUDIPINE*** (diethyl 1',4'-dihydro-2',6'-dimethyl-2-(methylthio)[3,4'-bipyridine]-3',5'-dicarboxylate).

'**Mesulene**' *see under* Diaveridine.

MESULERGINE*** (*N*'-(1,6-dimethylergolin-8α-yl)-*N*,*N*-dimethylsulfamide; CU-32-085).

MESULFAMIDE*** ((*p*-sulfamoylanilino)methanesulfonic acid).

MESULFEN** (2,7-dimethylthianthrene; dimethyldiphenylene disulfide; mesulphene).

Mesulphene* *see* Mesulfen.

MESUPRINE** (2'-hydroxy-5'-[1-hydroxy-2-(*p*-methoxyphenethylamino)propyl]methanesulfonanilide; 4-hydroxy-α-[1-(*p*-methoxyphenethylamino)ethyl]-5-(methylsulfonamido)benzyl alcohol; mesuprine hydrochloride; MJ-1987).

'**Mesurol**' *see* Methiocarb.

MESUXIMIDE*** (*N*,2-dimethyl-2-phenylsuccinimide; α-methylphensuximide; methsuximide; PM-396).

Mesylate(s)* *see* Mesilate(s).

MESYLCHOLINE (choline mesilate; choline methanesulfonate).

'**Metabolan**' *see under* Xantinol nicotinate.

METABROMSALAN** (3,5-dibromosalicylanilide; NSC-526280).

METABUTOXYCAINE* (2-(diethylamino)ethyl 3-amino-2-butoxybenzoate; metabutoxycaine hydrochloride; 'primacaine').

'**Metacaine**' *see* Tricaine.

Metacaraphen *see* Metcaraphen.

'**Metace**' *see* Chlorotrianisene.

METACETAMOL*** (*m*-acetamidophenol; *N*-acetyl-*m*-aminophenol; 3'-hydroxyacetanilide; BS-749).

Metacin (tr) *see* Oxyphenonium bromide.

METACLAZEPAM*** (7-bromo-5-(*o*-chlorophenyl)-2,3-dihydro-2-(methoxymethyl)-1-methyl-1*H*-1,4-benzodiazepine; brometazepam; metuclazepam).

Metacortandracin *see* Prednisone.

Metacortandralone *see* Prednisolone.

Metacresylacetate *see* *m*-Cresyl acetate.

METACYCLINE** (6-demethyl-6-deoxy-5-hydroxy-6-methylenetetracycline; 5-hydroxy-6-methylenetetracycline; 6-methyleneoxytetracycline; methacycline; methylenecycline; GS-2876).

'**Metadelphene**' *see* Diethyltoluamide.

Metadiazine *see* Pyrimidine.

Metadrenaline *see* Metanephrine.

Metafos (tr) *see* Parathion-methyl.

'**Metagin**' *see* Methyl paraben.

METAGLYCODOL*** (2-(*m*-chlorophenyl)-3-methyl-2,3-butanediol).

METAHEXAMIDE*** (1-(3-amino-4-methylbenzenesulfonyl)-3-cyclohexylurea; glyhexylamide; metahexanamide; S-1600).

Metahexanamide *see* Metahexamide.

'**Metahydrin**' *see* Trichlormethiazide.

'**Metaisosystox**' *see under* Demeton-O-methyl.

'**Metaisosystox(i)**' *see* Demeton-S-methyl.

'**Metaisosystox R**' *see* Oxydemeton-methyl.

'**Metaisosystoxsulfon**' *see* Demeton-S-methylsulfon.

Metaisosystoxsulfoxide *see* Oxydemeton-methyl.

Metakson (tr) *see* Chlorfenson.

β-Metal-binding globulin *see* Transferrin.

'**Metalcaptase**' *see* Penicillamine.

METALLIBURE*** (1-methyl-6-(1-methylallyl)-

2,5-dithiobiurea; 1-(1-methylallylthiocarbamo-
yl)-2-(methylthiocarbamoyl)hydrazine; methallibure; AY-61122; ICI-33828; NSC-69536).
METALLIBURE ZINC COMPLEX ('suisyn-
chron').
METALOL* (4'-(1-hydroxy-2-methylaminoprop-
yl)methanesulfonanilide; metalol hydrochloride;
MJ-1998).
'**Metalutin**' *see* Methylestrenolone.
METAMELFALAN*** (L-3-[*m*-[bis(2-chloro-
ethyl)amino]phenyl]alanine).
Metamelfalan peptide complex *see* Peptichemio.
METAMFAZONE*** (4-amino-6-methyl-2-
phenyl-3-pyridazinone; methamphazone; AGN-
20).
METAMFEPRAMONE** (2-(dimethylamino)-
propiophenone; dimepropion; Mg-559).
'**Metamine**' *see* Trolnitrate.
METAMIZIL (tr) (2-(diethylamino)propyl benzilate; methamizil; methylbenactyzine; methyldiazil).
Metamizole* *see* Dipyrone.
METAMPICILLIN*** (6-[2-(methyleneamino)-2-
phenylacetamido]penicillanic acid; α-(methyleneamino)benzylpenicillin; methyleneampicillin;
'magnipen'; 'pravacillin'; 'suvipen').
METAM-SODIUM* (sodium methylcarbamodithioate; karbation; metham-sodium; VPM;
'carbathion'; 'nematin'; 'SMOC'; 'trimaton'; 'vapam').
'**Metamucil**' *see* Psyllium.
METANDIENONE** (17β-hydroxy-17-methylan-
drosta-1,4-dien-3-one; methandienone; metandrostenolone; methandrostenolone; C-17309;
NSC-42722).
Metandrostenolone *see* Metandienone.
METANEPHRINE (4-hydroxy-3-methoxy-α-
methylaminomethylbenzyl alcohol; 3-*O*-methyl-
adrenaline; 3-*O*-methylepinephrine; metadrenal-
ine).
METANILAMIDE (*m*-aminobenzenesulfon-
amide).
'**Metanite**' *see* Atropine methonitrate.
METANIXIN** (2-(2,6-dimethylanilino)nicotinic
acid; 2-(2,6-xylidino)nicotinic acid).
Metaoxedrine* *see* Phenylephrine.
Metaphos (tr) *see* Parathion-methyl.
Metaphoxide *see* Metepa.
'**Metaplexan**' *see* Mequitazine.
METAPRAMINE** (10,11-dihydro-5-methyl-10-
(methylamino)-5*H*-dibenz[*b,f*]azepine; RP-
19560; 'timaxel').
'**Metaprel**' *see* Orciprenaline.
Metaproterenol* *see* Orciprenaline.
Metaradrine* *see* Metaraminol.
METARAMINOL*** ((−)-α-(1-aminoethyl)-*m*-
hydroxybenzyl alcohol; (−)-2-amino-1-(*m*-hydr-
oxyphenyl)-1-propanol; *m*-hydroxynorephedr-
ine; isophenylephrine; metaradrine; metaraminol
tartrate).
'**Metarsen**' *see* Oxophenarsine.
'**Metasan**' *see* Ziram.
Metasarcolysin *see* *m*-Sarcolysin.

'**Metaspas**' *see* Dihexyverine.
Metasynephrine *see* Phenylephrine.
'**Meta-systemox**' *see under* Demeton-O-methyl.
'**Metasystox**' *see under* Demeton-O-methyl.
'**Metasystox(i)**' *see* Demeton-S-methyl.
'**Metasystox R**' *see* Oxydemeton-methyl.
'**Metatensin**' *see under* Reserpine.
METATEROL*** (*m*-hydroxy-α-[(isopropyl-
amino)methyl]benzyl alcohol).
Metathiazane *see* Tetrahydro-1,3-thiazine.
'**Metathion**' *see* Fenitrothion.
METAXALONE*** (5-(3,5-dimethylpheno-
xymethyl)oxazolidin-2-one; 1-(3,5-xylyloxy-
methyl)oxazolidin-2-one; metaxolone; AHR-
438; 'skelaxin').
Metaxolone* *see* Metaxalone.
METAZAMIDE*** (1-(*p*-methoxyphenyl)-5-
methyl-4-imidazolin-2-one; GPA-878).
Metazepium iodide* *see* Buzepide metiodide.
METAZIDE*** (*N,N*'-methylenebisisoniazid;
methazide).
METAZOCINE*** (1,2,3,4,5,6-hexahydro-8-
hydroxy-3,6,11-trimethyl-2,6-methanobenzazoc-
ine; 2'-hydroxy-2,5,9-trimethyl-6,7-benzomor-
phan).
METAZOXOLON* (3-methyl-5(4*H*)-isoxazolone
4-(*p*-chlorophenyl)hydrazone).
METBUFEN*** (3-(4-biphenylylcarbonyl)-2-
methylpropionic acid).
METCARAPHEN (2-(diethylamino)ethyl *o*-xylyl-
cyclopentanecarboxylate; dimethylcaramiphen;
metacaraphen; G-3012; 'netrin').
METEMBONATE(S)** (4,4'-methylenebis(3-
methoxy-2-naphthoic acid), esters and salts).
METENEPROST*** (7-[3-hydroxy-2-(3-hydroxy-
4,4-dimethyl-1-octenyl)-5-methylenecyclopent-
yl]-5-heptenoic acid; 11α,15-dihydroxy-16,16-
dimethyl-9-methylene-5-*cis*,13-*trans*-prostadie-
noic acid; 9-deoxo-16,16-dimethyl-9-methylene-
dinoprostone).
'**Metenix**' *see* Metolazone.
METENOLONE*** (17β-hydroxy-1-methyl-5α-
androst-1-en-3-one; 1-methyl-1-androstenolone;
methenolone; 'primobolan').
METENOLONE ACETATE (NSC-74226; SH-
567; SQ-16496; 'nibal').
**METENOLONE ACETATE plus CALCIUM
PHOSPHATE** (SH-60931).
METENOLONE ENANTATE (metenolone heptanoate; NSC-64967; SH-601; SQ-16374; 'nibal
injection').
METEPA (1,1',1''-phosphinylidynetris(2-methyl-
aziridine); *N,N',N*''-tris(2-methyl-1-aziridinyl)-
phosphine oxide; metaphoxide; methaphoxide;
methyl aphoxide; MAPO).
Meterazine (tr) *see* Prochlorperazine.
METERGOLINE*** ((+)-*N*-carboxy-9,10-di-
hydro-1-methyllysergamine benzyl ester; 8β-
(benzyloxycarbonylaminomethyl)-1-methyl-10α-
ergoline; MCE; FI-6337; 'liserdol').
METERGOTAMINE** (1-methylergotamine).
METERGOTAMINE TARTRATE (metergotamine bitartrate; MY-25).

'Meterox' see Merbiurelidin.

METESCUFYLLINE*** (7-(2-diethylamino-ethyl)theophylline (7-hydroxy-4-methyl-2-oxo-2H-1-benzopyran-6-yloxy)acetate; etamiphyllin (7-hydroxy-4-methyl-2-oxo-1-benzopyran-6-yloxy)acetate; methescufylline).

METESCULETOL*** ([(7-hydroxy-4-methyl-2-oxo-2H-1-benzopyran-6-yl)oxy]acetic acid).

METETHOHEPTAZINE*** (4-(ethoxycarbonyl)-1,3-dimethyl-4-phenylhexamethylenimine; ethyl hexahydro-1,3-dimethyl-4-phenylazepine-4-carboxylate; Wy-535).

METETOIN*** (5-ethyl-1-methyl-5-phenylhydantoin; methetoin; N-3; NSC-524411).

'Meteverine' see Moxaverine.

Metflorylthiadiazine see Hydroflumethiazide.

METFLURAZON* (4-chloro-5-(dimethylamino)-2-[3-(trifluoromethyl)phenyl]-3(2H)-pyridazinone; H-6706).

METFORMIN** (1,1-dimethylbiguanide; N,N-dimethylguanylguanidine; LA-6023; NNDG; 'deltamin'; 'flumamine'; 'glucophage'; 'haurymellin'; 'meguan'; 'metiguanide').
See also under Chlorpropamide; Glycyclamide.

METFORMIN plus TOLBUTAMIDE ('glucosulfa').

METFORMIN p-CHLOROPHENOXYACETATE ('glucinan'; 'glucirenan').

METFORMIN EMBONATE (metformin 4,4'-methylenebis(3-hydroxy-2-naphthoate); 'stagid').

Methabarbitone see Metharbital.

METHABENZTHIAZURON* (1-benzothiazol-2-yl-1,3-dimethylurea; 'tribunil').

METHACHOLINE CHLORIDE*** ((2-hydroxypropyl)trimethylammonium chloride acetate; acetyl-β-methylcholine; β-methylcholine acetate; methylchol).

'Methacin' see Methocidin.

'Methacolimycin' see Colistimethate sodium.

METHACRYLIC ACID (2-methylacrylic acid; 2-methyl-2-propenoic acid).

Methacycline* see Metacycline.

Methadol see Dimepheptanol.

METHADONE** (6-(dimethylamino)-4,4-diphenyl-3-heptanone; amidone; phenadon; AN-148; Ho-10820; WIN-1766).
See also Levomethadone.

'Methadren' see N-Methylepinephrine.

Methadyl acetate* see Acetylmethadol.

'Methaform' see Chlorbutol.

'Methafrome' see Khellin.

METHAFURYLENE* (N-furfuryl-N',N'-dimethyl-N-pyrid-2-ylethylenediamine; methafurylene hydrochloride, dihydrogen citrate or fumarate; F-151).

Methalamic acid see Iotalamic acid.

METHALLATAL (5-ethyl-5-(2-methylallyl)-2-thiobarbituric acid; V-12; 'mosidal').

METHALLENESTRIL*** (β-ethyl-6-methoxy-α,α-dimethyl-2-naphthalenepropionic acid; 3-(6-methoxy-2-naphthyl)-2,2-dimethylvaleric acid; methallenoestril).

Methallenoestril* see Methallenestril.

Methallibure* see Metallibure.

METHALTHIAZIDE* (3-[(allylthio)methyl]-6-chloro-3,4-dihydro-2-methyl-2H-1,2,4-benzothiadiazine-7-sulfonamide 1,1-dioxide; P-2530).

'Methalutin' see Methylestrenolone.

METHAMIDOPHOS* (O,S-dimethyl phosphoramidothioate; 'monitor'; 'tamaron').

Methaminodiazepoxide see Chlordiazepoxide.

Methamizil (tr) see Metamizil.

Methamphazone* see Metamfazone.

METHAMPHETAMINE*** ((+)-N,α-dimethylphenethylamine; 2-(methylamino)-1-phenylpropane; N-methylamphetamine; phenylmethylaminopropane; desoxyephedrine; methamphetamine hydrochloride).

METHAMPHETAMINE plus MEPROBAMATE ('euphoramin').

Methampyrone see Dipyrone.

Metham-sodium see Metam-sodium.

Methanal see Formaldehyde.

Methandienone* see Metandienone.

METHANDRIOL*** (17α-methyl-4-androstene-3β,17-diol; methyldihydrotestosterone; mestenediol).

Methandrostenolone see Metandienone.

METHANEARSONIC ACID (methylarsinic acid; methylarsonic acid).
See also Disodium methanearsonate.

Methanedicarboxylic acid see Malonic acid.

Methanesulfonic acid, esters and salts see Mesilate(s).

METHANIAZIDE*** (isonicotinic acid 2-sulfomethylhydrazide; N²-sulfomethylisoniazid).

Methanimidamide see Formamidine.

METHANOL (carbinol; methyl alcohol; wood alcohol).

'Methanopyranorin' see Cyclocoumarol.

METHANTHELINE BROMIDE** (diethyl(2-hydroxyethyl)methylammonium bromide 9-xanthenecarboxylate; dixamone bromide; mantheline; MTB-51; SC-2910).

METHAPHENILENE*** (N,N-dimethyl-N'-phenyl-N'-(2-thenyl)ethylenediamine; W-50).

Methaphoxide see Metepa.

Methapyrapone see Metyrapone.

METHAPYRILENE*** (N,N-dimethyl-N'-pyrid-2-yl-N'-then-2-ylethylenediamine; thenylpyramine; AH-2; PM-262; W-33).

METHAQUALONE*** (2-methyl-3-(o-tolyl)-4-quinazolinone; methylquinazolone; B-100; CI-705; CN-38703; QZ 2; R-148; TR-495).

METHAQUALONE plus DIPHENHYDRAMINE ('mandrax'; 'metodril'; 'toquilone compositum').

METHAQUALONE plus ETODROXIZINE MALEATE (UCB-1414M; 'isonox'; 'somnibel').

METHAQUALONE plus PROMAZINE ('eatan').

METHARBITAL*** (5,5-diethyl-1-methylbarbituric acid; endiemal; methabarbital; metharbitone; 'gemonil').

Metharbitone see Metharbital.

336

METHASQUIN (*N*-[*p*-[(2,4-diamino-5-methylqui-nazolin-6-ylmethyl)amino]benzoyl]-L-aspartic acid; NSC-122870; SK-29836).

METHASTYRIDONE*** (2,2-dimethyl-5-styryl-oxazolidin-4-one).

'Methatropine' *see* Homatropine methyl bromide.

Methazide *see* Metazide.

METHAZOLAMIDE*** (5-acetylimino-4-methyl-2-sulfamoyl-1,3,4-thiadiazoline; *N*-(4-methyl-2-sulfamoyl-Δ^2-1,3,4-thiadiazolin-5-ylid-ene)acetamide; CL-8490).

Methazole *see* Chlormethazole.

Methbipyrapone *see* Metyrapone.

METHDILAZINE*** (10-[(1-methylpyrrolidin-3-yl)methyl]phenothiazine; methdilazine hydro-chloride; MJ-5022).

'Methedrine' *see* Methamphetamine.

METHEMOGLOBIN (hemiglobin).

Methenamide *see* Formamide.

METHENAMINE*** (hexamethylenetetramine; 1,3,4,7-tetraazaadamantane; hexamine; amino-form; formamine; hexamethylenamine).

METHENAMINE ANHYDROMETHYLENE-CITRATE (citroformin; citrohexal; citrohex-amine; formamol; hexacitramine).

METHENAMINE BORATE (borohexamine; uro-boramine).

Methenamine bromoform complex *see* Brometen-amine.

Methenamine camphorate *see* Hexacamphamine.

METHENAMINE ETHOBROMIDE (bromethyl-formin).

METHENAMINE HIPPURATE (methenamine hippuric acid complex).

METHENAMINE MANDELATE (hexydaline; 'urocedulamin').

METHENAMINE SALICYLATE (saliformin; 'solurine').

METHENAMINE SULFOSALICYLATE ('hexal'; 'hexalet').

METHENAMINE THIOCYANATE (rhodanhex-amine).

Methenolone* *see* Metenolone.

N,N'**-Methenyl-*o*-phenylenediamine** *see* Benzimid-azole.

METHEPTAZINE*** (methyl 1,2-dimethyl-4-phenylhexamethylenimine-4-carboxylate; methyl hexahydro-1,2-dimethyl-4-phenylazepine-4-carboxylate).

'Methergen' *see* Methylergometrine.

'Methergin' *see* Methylergometrine.

Methescufylline* *see* Metescufylline.

METHESTROL*** (3,4-bis(*p*-hydroxy-*m*-methyl-phenyl)hexane; α,α'-diethyl-4,4'-dihydroxy-3,3'-dimethylbibenzyl; 4,4'-(1,2-diethylene)di-*o*-cres-ol; dimethylhexestrol; methoestrol).

METHESTROL DIPROPIONATE* (3,4-bis(*m*-methyl-*p*-propionoxyphenyl)hexane; prometh-estrol; promethoestrol; 'meprane').

Methetharimide *see* Bemegride.

Methetoin* *see* Metetoin.

Methexenyl *see* Hexobarbital.

Methicillin* *see* Meticillin.

METHIDATHION* (4-[[(dimethoxyphosphino-thioyl)thio]methyl]-2-methoxy-1,3,4-thiadiazol-5-one; *S*-(2-methoxy-5-oxo-1,3,4-thiadiazol-4-ylmethyl) *O,O*-dimethyl phosphorodithioate; 'supracid'; 'ultracid(e)').

Methimazole* *see* Thiamazole.

Methindazate* *see* Metindizate.

METHINDETHYRIUM* (trimethyl[3-[4-[2-(1-methylindol-3-yl)ethyl]pyrid-1-yl]propyl]ammo-nium dibromide; IN-391; 'isotensen').

Methindione *see* Metindione.

METHIOCARB (3,5-dimethyl-4-(methylthio)-phenyl methylcarbamate; 4-(methylthio)-3,5-xyl-yl methylcarbamate; mercaptodimethur; met-mercapturan; MXMC; Bayer-37344; OMS-93; 'draza'; 'mesurol'; 'slug guard').

METHIODAL SODIUM*** (sodium iodometh-anesulfonate; metiodol; sergosin).

METHIOFLURANE (2,2-dichloro-1,1-difluoro-ethyl methyl sulfide).

METHIOMEPRAZINE** (DL-10-[3-(dimethyl-amino)-2-methylpropyl]-2-(methylthio)pheno-thiazine; SK&F-6270).

(−)-Methiomeprazine *see* Levometiomeprazine.

'Methionamine' *see* *N*-Acetylmethionine.

METHIONINE*** ((+)-2-amino-4-(methylthio)-butyric acid).

Methionine acetate *see* *N*-Acetylmethionine.

L-Methionine methylsulfonium salt *see* Vitamin U.

METHIONINE SULFOXIDE (DL-2-amino-4-(methylsulfinyl)butyric acid; NSC-3084).

Methioplegium *see* Trimetaphan camsilate.

METHIOPRIM (2-amino-2-(methylthio)-5-pyr-imidinemethanol; MAHP; NSC-3431).

Methiothepin *see* Metitepine.

METHIOTRIAZAMINE (4,6-diamino-1,2-di-hydro-2,2-dimethyl-1-[*p*-(methylthio)phenyl]-*s*-triazine).

Methioturiate *see* Methitural.

Methisazone* *see* Metisazone.

Methisoprinol *see* Inosine pranobex.

METHITURAL*** (5-(1-methylbutyl)-5-(2-meth-ylthioethyl)-2-thiobarbituric acid; thiomethibu-mal; methioturiate; methiurate; AM-109; Sch-3132).

Methiurate *see* Methitural.

Methixene* *see* Metixene.

Methocamphane methylsulfate *see* Trimethidinium methosulfate.

METHOCARBAMOL*** (3-(*o*-methoxyphen-oxy)-1,2-propanediol 1-carbamate; AHR-85).

Methocarbolane *see* Mephosfolan.

METHOCIDIN*** (hydroxymethylgramicidin; methylolgramicidin).

Methodichlorophen *see* Metodiclorofen.

Methoestrol* *see* Methestrol.

'Methofazine' *see* Sulfametomidine.

METHOHEXITAL*** (α-(±)-5-allyl-1-methyl-5-(1-methyl-2-pentynyl)barbituric acid; enallyny-mal; methohexital sodium; methohexitone).

Methohexitone* *see* Methohexital.

Methoin* *see* Mephenytoin.

'Metholone' *see* Drostanolone.

337

METHOMYL* (methyl *N*-[[(methylamino)carbonyl]oxy]acetimidothioate; methyl *N*-[[(methylamino)carbonyl]oxy]ethanimidothioate; *S*-methyl *N*-(methylcarbamoyloxy)thioacetimidate; 'lannate').

Methophedrine* *see* Methoxyphedrine.

Methophenazine* *see* Metofenazate.

Methopholine* *see* Metofoline.

Methopon *see* Metopon.

METHOPRENE (isopropyl (2*E*,4*E*)-11-methoxy-3,7,11-trimethyl-2,4-dodecadienoate; SR-10; ZR-515; 'altosid').

METHOPROMAZINE*** (10-[3-(dimethylamino)propyl]-2-methoxyphenothiazine; methoxypromazine; methopromazine maleate; FI-5631; RP 4632).

METHOPROTRYN* (2-(isopropylamino)-4-(3-methoxypropylamino)-6-(methylthio)-*s*-triazine; *N*-(3-methoxypropyl)-*N'*-(1-methylethyl)-6-(methylthio)-1,3,5-triazine-2,4-diamine; methoprotryne; 'gesaran').

METHOPROTRYN plus SIMAZINE ('gesaran 207'; 'gesaran 211'; 'gesaran 2079').

Methoprotryne *see* Methoprotryn.

'Methopyranorin' *see* Cyclocoumarol.

Methopyrimazole *see* Epirizole.

'Methorate' *see* Dextromethorphan.

Methorphan *see* Racemethorphan.

Methorphinan *see* Racemorphan.

'Methosarb' *see* Calusterone.

METHOSERPIDINE*** (11-desmethoxy-10-methoxyreserpine; 10-methoxydeserpidine; methoxyserpidine).

METHOSERPIDINE plus BENZTHIAZIDE & POTASSIUM CHLORIDE ('tensimic').

METHOTREXATE*** (*N*-[*p*-[(2,4-diamino-6-pteridin-6-ylmethyl)methylamino]benzoyl]glutamic acid; 4-amino-4-deoxy-*N*[10]-methylfolic acid; methylaminopterin; MTX; CL-14377; NSC-740).

Methotrimeprazine* *see* Levomepromazine.

'Methoxa-dome' *see* Methoxsalen.

Methoxamedrine* *see* Methoxamine.

METHOXAMINE** (2-amino-1-(2,5-dimethoxyphenyl)-1-propanol; α-(1-aminoethyl)-2,5-dimethoxybenzyl alcohol; methoxamedrine; methoxamine hydrochloride).

Methoxiflurane* *see* Methoxyflurane.

METHOXININE (2-amino-4-methoxybutyric acid; oxymethionine).

Methoxiphenadrin* *see* Methoxyphenamine.

'Methoxone' *see* 2-(4-Chloro-2-methylphenoxy)acetic acid.

METHOXSALEN* (δ-lactone of 6-hydroxy-7-methoxy-5-benzofuranacrylic acid; 9-methoxy-7*H*-furo[3,2-*g*][1]benzopyran-7-one; 8-methoxypsoralen; ammoidin; 8-MOP; xanthotoxin).

[[2-(2-Methoxyacetamido)-4-(phenylthio)phenyl]imidocarbonyl]di(carbamic acid) dimethyl ester *see* Febantel.

(2-Methoxyallyl)trimethylammonium bromide *see* Meprochol.

3-Methoxy-15-apo-φ-caroten-15-oic acid *see* Etret-in.

3-Methoxy-8-aza-19-nor-17α-pregna-1,3,5-trien-20-yn-17-ol *see* Estrazinol.

3-Methoxybenzaldehyde *O*-[2-hydroxy-3-[4-(2-methoxyphenyl)piperazin-1-yl]propyl]oxime *see* Peradoxime.

Methoxybenzamide(s) *see* Anisamide(s).

Methoxybenzene *see* Anisole.

***p*-Methoxybenzoic acid** *see* Anisic acid.

1-(6-Methoxybenzothiazol-2-yl)-3-phenylurea *see* Frentizole.

1-[3-(*p*-Methoxybenzoyl)propyl]-4-phenylpiperidine *see* Anisoperidone.

1-(*p*-Methoxybenzoyl)pyrrolidin-2-one *see* Aniracetam.

1-(*p*-Methoxybenzyl)-2,3-dimethylguanidine *see* Meobentine.

***N*-(*p*-Methoxybenzyl)-*N'*,*N'*-dimethyl-*N*-pyrid-2-ylethylenediamine** *see* Mepyramine.

***N*-(*p*-Methoxybenzyl)-*N'*,*N'*-dimethyl-*N*-pyrimid-2-ylethylenediamine** *see* Thonzylamine.

***N*-(*p*-Methoxybenzyl)-*N'*,*N'*-dimethyl-*N*-thiazol-2-ylethylenediamine** *see* Zolamine.

α-(α-Methoxybenzyl)-4-(β-methoxyphenethyl)-1-piperazineethanol *see* Zipeprol.

6-Methoxy-*N*,*N'*-bis(1-methylethyl)-1,3,5-triazine-2,4-diamine *see* Prometon.

3-[(Methoxycarbonyl)amino]phenyl *m*-tolylcarbamate *see* Phenmedipham.

2-(Methoxycarbonyl)-1-methylvinyl dimethyl phosphate *see* Mevinphos.

1-(Methoxycarbonyl)-1-propen-2-yl dimethyl phosphate *see* Mevinphos.

[3-(Methoxycarbonyl)propyl]trimethylammonium chloride *see* Carpronium chloride.

METHOXYCHLOR* (1,1'-(2,2,2-trichloroethylene)bis(4-methoxybenzene); 1,1,1-trichloro-2,2-bis(*p*-methoxyphenyl)ethane; 2,2-di-*p*-anisyl-1,1,1-trichloroethane; dimethoxy-DT; DMDT; methoxy-DDT; 'marlate'; 'metox'). *See also under* DDT.

6'-Methoxycinchonan-9-ol *see* Quinidine; Quinine.

6'-Methoxycinchonidine *see* Quinine.

6'-Methoxycinchonine *see* Quinidine.

***p*-Methoxycinnamic acid 2-ethoxyethyl ester** *see* Cinoxate.

2-Methoxy-*p*-cresol *see* Creosol.

17β-(1-Methoxycyclohexyloxy)-5α-androst-1-en-3-one *see* Mesabolone.

Methoxy-DDT *see* Methoxychlor.

10-Methoxydeserpidine *see* Methoserpidine.

1-(8-Methoxydibenz[*b*,*f*]oxepin-10-yl)-4-methylpiperazine *see* Metoxepin.

10-Methoxy-1,6-dimethylergoline-8β-methanol 5-bromonicotinate *see* Nicergoline.

***o*-Methoxy-*N*,α-dimethylphenethylamine** *see* Methoxyphenamine.

7-Methoxy-α,10-dimethylphenothiazine-2-acetic acid *see* Protizinic acid.

7-Methoxy-2,4-dimethyl-3-quinolyl methyl ketone *see* Acequinoline.

2-Methoxy-*N*,*N*-dimethyl-Δ[9,γ]-xanthenepropylamine *see* Dimeprozan.

p-Methoxydiphenhydramine *see* Medrylamine.

N-(3-Methoxy-3,3-diphenylpropyl)allylamine *see* Alimadol.

Methoxydiuron *see* Linuron.

Methoxydone *see* Mephenoxalone.

3-Methoxyestra-1,3,5(10)-triene-16α,17α-diol *see* Epimestrol.

2-METHOXYETHANOL ('methylcellosolve').

2-[[2-(2-Methoxyethoxy)ethyl]aminomethyl]-1,4-benzodioxan *see* Ambenoxan.

N-[2-(2-Methoxyethoxy)ethyl]-1,4-benzodioxan-2-methylamine *see* Ambenoxan.

[*N*-[5-(2-Methoxyethoxy)pyrimidin-2-yl]benzenesulfonamido]sodium *see* Glymidine sodium.

S-[2-[(2-Methoxyethyl)amino]-1-oxoethyl] *O,O*-dimethyl phosphorodithioate *see* Amidithion.

3,3′-(2-Methoxyethylidene)bis(4-hydroxycoumarin) *see* Coumetarol.

2-(2-Methoxyethyl)pyridine *see* Metyridine.

2-Methoxyethyl (*p*-tolylsulfonyl)carbamate *see* Tosulur.

Methoxyfenoserpine *see* Mefeserpine.

3-Methoxy-3′,4′,5,7-flavantetrol *see* Meciadanol.

METHOXYFLURANE*** (2,2-dichloro-1,1-difluoroethyl methyl ether; 2,2-dichloro-1,1-difluoro-1-methoxyethane; methoxiflurane; ingalan; inhalan; NSC-110432).

4-Methoxy-7*H*-furo[3,2-*g*][1]benzopyran-7-one *see* Bergapten.

9-Methoxy-7*H*-furo[3,2-*g*][1]benzopyran-7-one *see* Methoxsalen.

7-Methoxyharman *see* Harmine.

Methoxyhydrastine *see* Noscapine.

N-[2-(5-Methoxyindol-3-yl)ethyl]acetamide *see* Melatonin.

Methoxymarc *see* Anisuron.

6-Methoxy-3-(*p*-methoxybenzoyl)-2-methylindole-1-acetic acid *see* Duometacin.

5-Methoxy-2-[[(4-methoxy-3,5-dimethylpyrid-2-yl)-methyl]sulfinyl]benzimidazole *see* Omeprazole.

4-Methoxy-2-(5-methoxy-3-methylpyrazol-1-yl)-6-methylpyrimidine *see* Epirizole.

5-Methoxy-1-(4-methoxy-6-methylpyrimidin-2-yl)-3-methylpyrazole *see* Epirizole.

7-Methoxy-8-(*p*-methoxyphenoxy)-2-methylisoquinoline *see* Cularine.

1-Methoxy-3-[4-(2-methoxy-2-phenylethyl)piperazin-1-yl]-1-phenyl-2-propanol *see* Zipeprol.

3-Methoxy-2-methylaminobenzoic acid methyl ester *see* Damascenine.

4′-Methoxy-2-methylaminopropiophenone *see* Methoxyphedrine.

Methoxymethyl 6-(2,2-dimethyl-5-oxo-4-phenylimidazolidin-1-yl)penicillanate *see* Sarpicillin.

10-Methoxy-1,2-(methylenedioxy)-6aα-aporphin-11-ol *see* Bulbocapnine.

8-Methoxy-3,4-methylenedioxy-10-nitrophenanthrene-1-carboxylic acid *see* Aristolochic acid.

3-Methoxy-16-methyl-1,3,5(10)-estratriene-16β,17β-diol *see* Mytatrienediol.

5-Methoxy-2-methyl-6,7-furanochromone *see* Visnagin.

4-Methoxy-7-methyl-5*H*-furo[3,2-*g*]benzopyran-5-

one *see* Visnagin.

Methoxymethyl 6-[4-(*p*-hydroxyphenyl)-2,2-dimethyl-5-oxoimidazolidin-1-yl]penicillanate *see* Sarmoxicillin.

5-Methoxy-2-methylindole-3-acetohydroxamic acid *see* Deboxamet.

3-Methoxy-*N*-methylmorphinan *see* Dextromethorphan; Levomethorphan; Racemethorphan.

(+)-6-Methoxy-α-methyl-2-naphthaleneacetic acid *see* Naproxen.

(−)-6-Methoxy-β-methyl-2-naphthaleneethanol *see* Naproxol.

5-Methoxy-2-methyl-1-nicotinoylindole-3-acetic acid *see* Niometacin.

2-Methoxymethyl-5-nitrofuran *see* Nitrofurfuryl methyl ether.

α-(Methoxymethyl)-2-nitroimidazole-1-ethanol *see* Misonidazole.

[2-(9-Methoxy-7-methyl-5-oxo-5*H*-furo[3,2-*g*]-(1)benzopyran-4-yloxy)ethyl]trimethylammonium theophylline derivative *see* Visnafylline.

α-[*p*-[5-(Methoxymethyl)-2-oxo-3-oxazolidinyl]-phenoxy]-*m*-tolunitrile *see* Cimoxatone.

2-Methoxy-4-methylphenol *see* Creosol.

9-*syn*-Methoxy-3-methyl-9-phenyl-3-azabicyclo-[3.3.1]nonane *see* Anazocine.

9-Methoxy-3-methyl-9-phenylisogranatanine *see* Anazocine.

4β-Methoxy-1-methyl-4α-phenyl-3α,5α-propanopiperidine *see* Anazocine.

4-Methoxy-5-methyl-*o*-phthalaldehyde-3-carboxylic acid *see* Gladiolic acid.

8-Methoxy-10-(4-methylpiperazin-1-yl)dibenz[*b,f*]-oxepin *see* Metoxepin.

4-Methoxy-2′-[2-(1-methylpiperid-2-yl)ethyl]benzanilide *see* Encainide.

2-Methoxy-10-[2-(1-methylpiperid-2-yl)ethyl]phenothiazine *see* Oxyridazine.

*N*¹-(6-Methoxy-2-methylpyrimidin-4-yl)sulfanilamide *see* Sulfametomidine.

2-Methoxy-*N*-[(1-methylpyrrolidin-2-yl)methyl]-5-sulfamoylbenzamide *see* Sulmepride.

2-[2-Methoxy-4-(methylsulfinyl)phenyl]-3*H*-imidazo[4,5-*b*]pyridine *see* Sulmazole.

N-[4-(Methoxymethyl)-1-[2-(2-thienyl)ethyl]-4-piperidyl]propionanilide *see* Sufentanil.

β-Methoxy-*N*-methyl-*m*-trifluoromethylphenethylamine *see* Fludorex.

7-Methoxy-8-methyltropinium bromide benzilate *see* Tropenziline bromide.

3-(4-Methoxy-1-naphthoyl)propionic acid *see* Menbutone.

4-(6-Methoxynaphth-2-yl)-2-butanone *see* Nabumetone.

3-(6-Methoxy-2-naphthyl)-2,2-dimethylvaleric acid *see* Methallenestril.

(+)-2-(6-Methoxynaphth-2-yl)propionic acid *see* Naproxen.

endo-1-[[4-[2-(2-Methoxynicotinamido)ethyl]piperid-1-yl]sulfonyl]-3-(5-norbornen-2-ylmethyl)-urea *see* Gliamilide.

1-Methoxy-3-(2-nitroimidazol-1-yl)-2-propanol *see* Misonidazole.

339

3-(2-Methoxy-4-nitrophenyl)-2-methylquinazolin-4-one *see* Nitromethaqualone.

4-Methoxy-α'-nitro-α-[p-(2-pyrrolidin-1-ylethoxy)phenyl]stilbene *see* Nitromifene.

11β-Methoxy-19-nor-17α-pregna-1,3,5(10)-trien-20-yne-3,17-diol *see* Moxestrol.

3-Methoxy-19-nor-17α-pregna-1,3,5(10)-trien-20-yn-17-ol *see* Mestranol.

2-Methoxyoctaethyleneoxyethyl p-butylaminobenzoate *see* Benzonatate.

S-(5-Methoxy-4-oxo-4H-pyran-2-ylmethyl) O,O-dimethyl phosphorothioate *see* Endothion.

S-(2-Methoxy-5-oxo-1,3,4-thiadiazol-4-ylmethyl) O,O-dimethyl phosphorodithioate *see* Methidathion.

6-Methoxy-6-pentyl-p-benzoquinone *see* Primin.

METHOXYPHEDRINE*** (1-(p-methoxyphenyl)-2-(methylamino)-1-propanone; 4'-methoxy-2-methylaminopropiophenone; methophedrine).

METHOXYPHENAMINE*** (o-methoxy-N,α-dimethylphenethylamine; o-methoxy-N-methyl-amphetamine; methoxiphenadrin; mexyphamine; methoxyphenamine hydrochloride; U-0433).

6-Methoxy-1-phenazinol 5,10-dioxide *see* Myxin.

2-[3-[(m-Methoxyphenethyl)methylamino]propyl]-2-(m-methoxyphenyl)tetradecanenitrile *see* Anipamil.

4-(β-Methoxyphenethyl)-α-phenyl-1-piperazinepropanol *see* Eprozinol.

o-Methoxyphenol *see* Guaiacol.

p-Methoxyphenol *see* Mequinol.

Methoxyphenoserpine *see* Mefeserpine.

1-[3-(2-Methoxyphenothiazin-10-yl)-2-methylpropyl]-4-piperidinol *see* Perimetazine.

p-Methoxyphenoxyacetic acid methylreserpate ester *see* Mefeserpine.

1-[2-[2-(2-(o-Methoxyphenoxy)ethoxy)ethoxy]ethyl]piperidine *see* Guaiapate.

2-(o-Methoxyphenoxy)-2-methyl-1,3-benzodioxan-4-one *see* Guaimesal.

trans-3-[(p-Methoxyphenoxy)methyl]-1-methyl-4-phenylpiperidine *see* Femoxetine.

5-(o-Methoxyphenoxymethyl)-2-oxazolidinone *see* Mephenoxalone.

3-(o-Methoxyphenoxy)-N-methyl-3-phenylpropylamine *see* Nisoxetine.

3-(o-Methoxyphenoxy)-1,2-propanediol *see* Guaifenesin.

N-[2-(m-Methoxyphenoxy)propyl]-m-tolylacetamidine *see* Xylamidine.

2-(o-Methoxyphenoxy)triethylamine *see* Guaiactamine.

2-(p-Methoxy-α-phenylbenzyloxy)-N,N-dimethylethylamine *see* Medrylamine.

6-Methoxy-2-[(phenylcarbamoyl)amino]benzothiazole *see* Frentizole.

2-(o-Methoxyphenyl)-3,3-diphenylacrylic acid *see* Anisacril.

1-(p-Methoxyphenyl)-4,5-dithia-1-cyclopentene-3-thione *see* Anethole trithione.

5-(p-Methoxyphenyl)-1,2-dithiole-3-thione *see* Anethole trithione.

2-(p-Methoxyphenyl)-1,3-indandione *see* Anisindione.

o-Methoxyphenyl 2-(p-isobutylphenyl)propionate *see* Ibuprofen guaiacol ester.

1-(o-Methoxyphenyl)-4-(3-methoxypropyl)piperazine *see* Dimetholizine.

1-(p-Methoxyphenyl)-2-(methylamino)-1-propanone *see* Methoxyphedrine.

1-(p-Methoxyphenyl)-5-methyl-4-imidazolin-2-one *see* Metazamide.

1-[2-[4-[1-(4-Methoxyphenyl)-2-nitro-2-phenylethenyl]phenoxy]ethyl]pyrrolidine *see* Nitromifene.

1-(p-Methoxyphenyl)-2-nitro-1-[p-(2-pyrrolidin-1-ylethoxy)phenyl]ethylene *see* Nitromifene.

1-[2-[p-[α-(p-Methoxyphenyl)-β-nitrostyryl]phenoxy]ethyl]pyrrolidine *see* Nitromifene.

5-(p-Methoxyphenyl)-5-phenyl-3-[3-(4-phenylpiperid-1-yl)propyl]hydantoin *see* Ropitoin.

7-[2-[4-(o-Methoxyphenyl)piperazin-1-yl]ethyl](5H)-1,3-dioxolo[4,5-f]indole *see* Solypertine.

6-[[3-[4-(o-Methoxyphenyl)piperazin-1-yl]propyl]amino]-1,3-dimethyluracil *see* Urapidil.

4'-Methoxy-4-(4-phenylpiperid-1-yl)butyrophenone *see* Anisoperidone.

p-Methoxyphenylpropenetrithione *see* Anethole trithione.

o-Methoxyphenyl salicylate acetate *see* Guacetisal.

(±)-4-(o-Methoxyphenyl)-α-[(3,4,5-trimethoxyphenoxy)methyl]-1-piperazineethanol *see* Enciprazine.

p-Methoxyphenyltrithiopropene *see* Anethole trithione.

3-Methoxy-4-(piperid-1-ylmethyl)xanthen-9-one *see* Mepixanox.

Methoxypromazine *see* Methopromazine.

1-Methoxy-4-propenylbenzene *see* Anethole.

(2-Methoxy-2-propenyl)trimethylammonium bromide *see* Meprochol.

Methoxypropiocin *see* Naproxen.

3-(o-Methoxy-p-propionylphenoxy)-1,2-propanediol *see* Meprophenidol.

17β-Methoxy-3-propoxyestra-1,3,5(10)-triene *see* Promestriene.

N-(3-Methoxypropyl)-N'-(1-methylethyl)-6-(methylthio)-1,3,5-triazine-2,4-diamine *see* Methoprotryn.

2-Methoxy-N-[(1-propylpyrrolidin-2-yl)methyl]-5-sulfamoylbenzamide *see* Prosulpride.

5-Methoxypsoralen *see* Bergapten.

8-Methoxypsoralen *see* Methoxsalen.

N¹-(3-Methoxypyrazin-2-yl)sulfanilamide *see* Sulfalene.

N¹-(6-Methoxypyridazin-3-yl)-N⁴-salicylazosulfanilamide *see* Salazodine.

α-[p-[(6-Methoxypyridazin-3-yl)sulfamoyl]anilino]-2,3-dimethyl-5-oxo-1-phenyl-3-pyrazoline-4-methanesulfonic acid *see* Sulfamazone.

5-[[p-(6-Methoxypyridazin-3-yl)sulfamoyl]phenylazo]salicylic acid *see* Salazodine.

N¹-(6-Methoxypyridazin-3-yl)sulfanilamide *see* Sulfamethoxypyridazine.

N¹-(5-Methoxypyrimidin-2-yl)sulfanilamide *see* Sulfametoxydiazine.

N^1-(6-Methoxypyrimidin-4-yl)sulfanilamide *see* Sulfamonomethoxine.

4-[6-(6-Methoxyquinolin-8-ylamino)hexyl]-α-methyl-1-piperazinepropanol *see* Moxipraquine.

1-(6-Methoxyquinolin-4-yl)-3-(3-vinylpiperid-4-yl)-1-propanone *see* Viquidil.

α-(6-Methoxy-4-quinolyl)-5-vinyl-2-quinuclidine-methanol *see* Quinidine; Quinine.

5-Methoxyresorcinol *see* Flamenol.

Methoxyserpidine *see* Methoserpidine.

5-Methoxy-2-sulfanilamidopyrimidine *see* Sulfametoxydiazine.

N^1-(4-Methoxy-1,2,5-thiadiazol-3-yl)sulfanilamide *see* Sulfametrole.

6-Methoxy-6-(3-thiophenemalonamido)penicillanic acid *see* Temocillin.

N-[6-Methoxythio-5-(trifluoromethyl)-1-naphthoyl]-sarcosine *see* Tolrestat.

Methoxytipepidine methobromide *see* Timepidium bromide.

5-Methoxy-4′-(trifluoromethyl)valerophenone (*E*)-*O*-(2-aminoethyl)oxime *see* Fluvoxamine.

11-Methoxy-3,9,11-trimethyldodeca-2,4-dienethioic acid *S*-ethyl ester *see* Triprene.

11-Methoxy-3,7,11-trimethyl-2,4-dodecadienoic acid isopropyl ester *see* Methoprene.

9-(4-Methoxy-2,3,6-trimethylphenyl)-3,7-dimethyl-2,4,6,8-nonatetraenoic acid *see* Etretin.

5-METHOXYTRYPTAMINE (serotonin methyl ether; mexamine).

6-Methoxyumbelliferone *see* Scopoletin.

Methoxyverapamil *see* Gallopamil.

6-Methoxy-4-[3-(3-vinylpiperid-4-yl)propyl]quinoline *see* Viqualine.

6-Methoxy-α-(5-vinylquinuclidin-2-yl)-4-quinoline-methanol *see* Quinidine; Quinine.

'Methral' *see* Fluperolone.

'Methrazone' *see* Feprazone.

Methscopolamine* *see* Scopolamine methyl bromide.

Methsuximide *see* Mesuximide.

'Methural' *see* 1,3-Bis(hydroxymethyl)urea.

METHYCLOTHIAZIDE*** (6-chloro-3-(chloromethyl)-3,4-dihydro-2-methyl-2*H*-1,2,4-benzothiodiazine-7-sulfonamide 1,1-dioxide; methylchlorothiazide; NSC-11043).

Methyl 4-acetamido-2-ethoxybenzoate *see* Ethopabate.

N-METHYLACETANILIDE (methylantifebrin; 'exalgin').

ar-Methylacetanilide(s) *see* Acetotoluidide(s).

Methylacetopyronone *see* Dehydroacetic acid.

2-Methylacrylic acid *see* Methacrylic acid.

3-Methylacrylic acid *see* Crotonic acid.

α-Methyl-1-adamantanemethylamine *see* Rimantadine.

METHYLADIPHENINE (2-(diethylamino)isopropyl 2,2-diphenylacetate; methyldifacil).

N-Methyladrenaline *see* N-Methylepinephrine.

3-O-Methyladrenaline *see* Metanephrine.

METHYLAL (dimethoxymethane; formal).

Methylalacetamide *see* Formicin.

Methyl alcohol *see* Methanol.

Methyl aldehyde *see* Formaldehyde.

p-[(2-Methylallyl)amino]hydratropic acid *see* Alminoprofen.

1-(1-Methylallylthiocarbamoyl)-2-(methylthiocarbamoyl)hydrazine *see* Metallibure.

1-(Methylamidino)-3-(2,6-xylyl)urea *see* Lidamidine.

METHYLAMINACRIN* (9-amino-4-methylacridine; neomonacrin).

METHYLAMINE (carbinamine).

Methylaminoacetic acid *see* Sarcosine.

Methylaminoantipyrine *see* Noramidopyrine.

4-Methylaminoazophen *see* Noramidopyrine.

N-[(Methylamino)carbonyl]-N-[[(methylamino)carbonyl]oxy]acetamide *see* Caracemide.

N-[[(Methylamino)carbonyl]oxy]acetimidothioic acid methyl ester *see* Methomyl.

N-[[(Methylamino)carbonyl]oxy]ethanimidothioic acid 2-cyanoethyl ester *see* Thiocarboxim.

N-[[(Methylamino)carbonyl]oxy]ethanimidothioic acid methyl ester *see* Methomyl.

1-Methylamino-1-deoxy-D-glucitol *see* Meglumine.

α-(1-Methylaminoethyl)benzyl alcohol *see* Ephedrine; Pseudoephedrine; Racephedrine.

4-[2-(Methylamino)ethyl]-1,2-methylenedioxybenzene *see* Homarylamine.

4-[2-(Methylamino)ethyl]-*o*-phenylene diisobutyrate *see* Ibopamine.

2-[2-(Methylamino)ethyl]pyridine *see* Betahistine.

4-[2-(Methylamino)ethyl]pyrocatechol diisobutyrate *see* Ibopamine.

Methyl 4-amino-3-hydroxybenzoate *see* Orthocaine.

Methylaminoisobornane *see* Mecamylamine.

Methylaminoisocamphane *see* Mecamylamine.

Methylaminoisooctane *see* Isometheptene.

Methyl 2-amino-3-mercaptopropionate *see* Mecysteine.

1-[(Methylamino)methyl]dibenzo[*b,e*]bicyclo-[2.2.2]octadiene *see* Benzoctamine.

α-[(Methylamino)methyl]-9,10-ethanoanthracene-9(10*H*)-ethanol *see* Oxaprotiline.

Methyl α-(aminomethyl)-5-methoxyindole-3-acetate *see* Indorenate.

α-[(Methylamino)methyl]-3-[(trimethylacetyl)oxy]-benzyl alcohol *see* Pivenfrine.

Methylaminonaphthol *see* Vitamin K_5.

6-(Methylamino)-4-oxo-10-propyl-4*H*-pyrano[3,2-*g*]quinoline-2,8-dicarboxylic acid *see* Minocromil.

4-(Methylamino)phenazone *see* Noramidopyrine.

2-(Methylamino)-1-phenylpropane *see* Methamphetamine.

2-(Methylamino)-1-phenyl-1-propanol *see* Ephedrine; Pseudoephedrine; Racephedrine.

2-[3-(Methylamino)-1-phenylpropoxy]anisole *see* Nisoxetine.

Methyl [(*p*-aminophenyl)sulfonyl]carbamate *see* Asulam.

3β-(Methylamino)pregn-5-ene-18,20-diol *see* Paravallarinol.

1-[3-(Methylamino)propyl]dibenzo[*b,e*]bicyclo-[2.2.2]octadiene *see* Maprotiline.

p-(2-Methylaminopropyl)phenol *see* Pholedrine.

Methylaminopterin* *see* Methotrexate.

N-Methylamphetamine *see* Methamphetamine.

o-**Methylamphetamine** *see* Ortetamine.

p-**METHYLAMPHETAMINE** (1-*p*-tolyl-2-propylamine; 'aptrol').

2-Methylamphetamine *see* Ortetamine.

17-Methylandrosta-3,5-diene-3,17β-diol 3-cyclopentyl ether *see* Penmesterol.

1α-Methylandrosta-4,16-dien-3-one *see* Delanterone.

17α-Methyl-5α-androstano[2,3-*c*]furazan-17β-ol *see* Furazabol.

17-Methylandrostanolone *see* Mestanolone.

17α-Methyl-5α-androstano[3,2-*c*]pyrazol-17β-ol *see* Stanozolol.

17α-Methyl-4-androstene-3β,17-diol *see* Methandriol.

17-Methyl-2′*H*-5α-androsteno[3,2-*c*]pyrazol-17β-ol *see* Stanozolol.

N-METHYLANILINE (extraline).

Methylantifebrin *see* N-Methylacetanilide.

Methyl aphoxide *see* Metepa.

METHYLARSINE BIS(DIMETHYLTHIOCARBAMATE) ('urbazid').

Methylarsinic acid *see* Methanearsonic acid.

Methylarsonic acid *see* Methanearsonic acid.

Methylatropine bromide *see* Atropine methobromide.

Methylatropine nitrate *see* Atropine methonitrate.

8-Methylatropinium bromide *see* Atropine methobromide.

8-Methylatropinium nitrate *see* Atropine methonitrate.

8-Methyl-8-azabicyclo[3.2.1]octane *see* Tropane.

3-Methyl-3-azapentamethylene-1,5-bis(1-methylpyrrolidinium) salt(s) *see* Azapyrrolidinium.

3-Methyl-3-azapentane-1,5-bis(dimethylethylammonium bromide) *see* Azamethonium bromide.

Methylazoxymethanol glucoside *see* Cycasin.

Methylazoxymethanol primeveroside *see* Macrozamin.

Methylbenactyzine *see* Metamizil.

METHYLBENACTYZIUM BROMIDE*** (diethyl(2-hydroxyethyl)methylammonium bromide benzilate; benactyzine methobromide; 'finalin'; 'paragone').

Methylbenzene *see* Toluene.

METHYLBENZETHONIUM CHLORIDE*** (benzyldimethyl(octylcresoxyethoxyethyl)ammonium chloride; benzyldimethyl(tetramethylbutyltoloxyethoxyethyl)ammonium chloride).

α-Methyl-5*H*-[1]benzopyrano[2,3-*b*]pyridine-7-acetic acid *see* Pranoprofen.

Methyl benzoquate *see* Nequinate.

2-METHYL-*p*-BENZOQUINONE (toluquinone).

2-(2-Methylbenzo[*b*]thien-3-ylmethyl)-2-imidazoline *see* Metizoline.

Methyl 5-benzoyl-2-benzimidazolecarbamate *see* Mebendazole.

Methylbenztropine *see* Etybenzatropine.

N-(*o*-Methylbenzyl)adenosine *see* Metrifudil.

N¹-[3-[(α-Methylbenzyl)amino]propyl]bleomycinamide *see* Peplomycin.

6-(*o*-Methylbenzylamino)-9-β-D-ribofuranosyl-9*H*-

purine *see* Metrifudil.

α-Methylbenzylhydrazine *see* Mebanazine.

2-(α-Methylbenzyl)hydrazine-1-carboxylic acid ethyl ester *see* Carbenzide.

α-Methylbenzyl 3-hydroxycrotonate dimethyl phosphate *see* Crotoxyphos.

3-(*p*-Methylbenzylideneamino)-4-phenyl-4-thiazoline-2-thione *see* Fezatione.

1-(α-Methylbenzyl)imidazole-5-carboxylic acid esters *see* Etomidate; Metomidate.

N-(α-Methylbenzyl)linoleamide *see* Melinamide.

Methyl 7-benzyloxy-6-butyl-1,4-dihydro-4-oxo-3-quinolinecarboxylate *see* Nequinate.

Methyl 7-benzyloxy-6-butyl-4-hydroxyquinoline-3-carboxylate *see* Nequinate.

2-[1-(*p*-Methylbenzyl)piperid-4-yl]-2-phenylglutarimide *see* Meletimide.

4-Methylbicyclo[2.2.2]oct-2-ene-1-carboxylate(s) *see* Ciclotate(s).

Methylbis-β-chloroethylamine *see* Chlormethine.

Methyl 2-[*p*-[bis(2-chloroethyl)amino]phenylacetamido]-3-imidazol-4-ylpropionate *see* Hisphen.

Methyl N-[*p*-[bis(2-chloroethyl)amino]phenylacetyl]-L-histidinate *see* Hisphen.

Methylbis(2,4-xylyliminomethyl)amine *see* Amitraz.

2-METHYL-2-BUTANOL (*tert*-amyl alcohol; amylene hydrate).

2-Methyl-2-butenoic acid *see* Tiglic acid.

3-Methyl-2-butenoic acid *see* Senecioic acid.

3-METHYL-2-BUTEN-1-OL (prenol).

2-Methyl-2-butenoyltropine *see* Tropigline.

N-(3-Methyl-2-butenyl)adenosine *see* Riboprine.

1-[4-(3-Methyl-1-butenylamino)butyl]guanidine *see* Spherophysine.

4-(3-Methyl-2-butenyl)-1,2-diphenyl-3,5-pyrazolidinedione *see* Feprazone.

3-Methyl-2-butenyl flufenamate *see* Prefenamate.

9-(3-Methyl-2-butenyloxy)-7*H*-furo-[3,2-*g*][1]benzopyran-7-one *see* Pentosalen.

[5-[(3-Methyl-2-butenyl)oxy]-2-[*p*-[(3-methyl-2-butenyl)oxy]cinnamoyl]phenoxy]acetic acid *see* Sofalcone.

3-[(3-Methyl-2-butenyl)thio]-L-alanine *see* Prenisteine.

3-Methyl-2-butenyl N-(α,α,α-trifluoro-*m*-tolyl)anthranilate *see* Prefenamate.

'Methyl butex' *see* Methyl paraben.

1-[2-(3-Methylbutoxy)-2-phenylethyl]pyrrolidine *see* Amixetrine.

Methyl butter yellow *see* 4-(Dimethylamino)-3′-methylazobenzene.

3-Methylbutylamine *see* Isopentylamine.

Methyl 5-butyl-2-benzimidazolecarbamate *see* Parbendazole.

Methyl 1-(butylcarbamoyl)benzimidazole-2-carbamate *see* Benomyl.

5-(1-Methylbutyl)-5-(2-methylthioethyl)-2-thiobarbituric acid *see* Methitural.

5-(1-Methylbutyl)-5-vinylbarbituric acid *see* Vinylbital.

3-Methylbutyric acid *see* Isovaleric acid.

2-Methylbutyric acid 1,2,3,7,8,8a-hexahydro-7-methyl-8-[2-(tetrahydro-4-hydroxy-6-oxo-2*H*-

pyran-2-yl)ethyl]naphth-1-yl ester *see* Mevastatin.
METHYL CARBAMATE (methyl urethan; 'urethylane').
Methylcarbamic acid esters *see* Bendiocarb; Carbofuran; Dioxacarb; Methiocarb; Promecarb; Propoxur; Xylyl methylcarbamate.
2-(Methylcarbamido)benzothiazole *see* Benzthiazuron.
Methylcarbamodithioic acid sodium salt *see* Metam-sodium.
1-(Methylcarbamoyl)-3-[3-(5-nitro-2-furyl)allylideneamino]-2-imidazolinone *see* Nifurizone.
2-Methyl-β-carboline *see* Harman.
3-Methyl-4-carboline *see* Harman.
Methyl-CCNU *see* Semustine.
'Methylcellosolve' *see* 2-Methoxyethanol.
METHYLCELLULOSE*** (cellulose methyl ether).
See also Carmellose.
Methylcephaeline *see* Emetine.
β-Methylchalcone *see* Dypnone.
16α-Methylchlormadinone *see* Clomegestone.
Methyl 2-(4′-chlorobiphenyl-1-yloxy)-2-methylpropionate *see* Methyl clofenapate.
Methyl 3-chloro-3-(*p*-chlorophenyl)propionate *see* Chlorfenprop-methyl.
Methyl 6-chloro-3,4-dihydro-2-methyl-7-sulfamoyl-2*H*-1,2,4-benzothiadiazine-3-carboxylate 1,1-dioxide *see* Carmetizide.
Methyl 9-[3′-(2-chloroethyl)-6,7-didehydro-4β-hydroxy-16-methoxy-1-methyl-2′,4′-dioxo-2β,3β,5α,-12β,19α-spiro[aspidospermine-3,5′-oxazolidin]-15-yl]-5-ethyl-1,4,5,6,7,8,9,10-octahydro-5-hydroxy-2*H*-3,7-methanoazacycloundecino[5,4-*b*]indole-9-carboxylate 4′-acetate *see* Vinzolidine.
Methylchloroform *see* 1,1,1-Trichloroethane.
Methyl 2-[(1-chloronaphth-2-yl)oxy]propionate *see* Lonaprofen.
Methyl 7-[2-[4-(3-chlorophenoxy)-3-hydroxy-1-butenyl]-3,5-dihydroxycyclopentyl]-2,5-heptadienoate *see* Delprostenate.
Methyl 6-(3-chlorophenoxy)-9,11,15-trihydroxy-ω-tetranorprosta-2,5,13-trienoate *see* Delprostenate.
Methyl *N*′-(*p*-chlorophenyl)-*N*,*N*-dimethylcarbamimidate *see* Trimeturon.
Methyl α-[*p*-(*p*-chlorophenyl)phenoxy]isobutyrate *see* Methyl clofenapate.
Methyl 2-[*p*-(*p*-chlorophenyl)phenoxy]-2-methylpropionate *see* Methyl clofenapate.
Methylchlorothiazide *see* Methyclothiazide.
Methyl 7-chloro-6,7,8-trideoxy-6-(*cis*-4-ethyl-L-pipecolamido)-1-thio-L-*threo*-α-D-*galacto*-octopyranoside *see* Pirlimycin.
Methyl 7-chloro-6,7,8-trideoxy-6-(*trans*-1-methyl-4-propyl-L-2-pyrrolidinecarboxamido)-1-thio-L-*threo*-α-D-*galacto*-octopyranoside *see* Clindamycin.
Methyl 7-chloro-6,7,8-trideoxy-6-(4-pentyl-L-2-pyrrolidinecarboxamido)-1-thio-L-*threo*-α-D-*galacto*-octopyranoside *see* Mirincamycin.
Methylchlorphenoxamine *see* Mecloxamine.

Methylchol *see* Methacholine chloride.
3-METHYLCHOLANTHRENE (20-methylcholanthrene; NSC-21970).
20-Methylcholanthrene *see* 3-Methylcholanthrene.
β-METHYLCHOLINE ((2-hydroxypropyl)trimethylammonium ion or salts).
β-Methylcholine acetate *see* Methacholine chloride.
β-Methylcholine carbamate *see* Bethanechol.
β-Methylcholine xylyl ether *see* β-Methylxylocholine.
3-Methylchromen-4-one *see* Methylchromone.
METHYLCHROMONE*** (3-methylchromen-4-one).
Methylchrysazin *see* Chrysophanic acid.
METHYL CLOFENAPATE (methyl 2-(4′-chlorobiphenyl-1-yloxy)-2-methylpropionate; methyl 2-[*p*-(*p*-chlorophenyl)phenoxy]-2-methylpropionate; methyl α-[*p*-(*p*-chlorophenyl)phenoxy]isobutyrate; clofenapate; CDIB; ICI-55695).
2-Methylcrotonic acid *see* Tiglic acid.
3-Methylcrotonic acid *see* Senecioic acid.
Methyl cyanide *see* Acetonitrile.
Methyl 2-cyanoacrylate *see* Mecrilate.
METHYL CYANOFORMATE (cyanoformic acid methyl ester; 'cyclon A').
Methylcyclobarbital *see* Hexobarbital.
β-Methylcyclohexaneacrylic acid *see* Cicrotoic acid.
***p*-(*trans*-2-Methylcyclohexyl)hydratropic acid** *see* Mexoprofen.
Methyl 7-[2-(5-cyclohexyl-3-hydroxy-1-pentynyl)-3,5-dihydroxycyclopentyl]-5-heptenoate *see* Alfaprostol.
5-[*p*-[(1-Methylcyclohexyl)methoxy]benzyl]-2,4-thiazolidinedione *see* Ciglitazone.
2-[4-(*trans*-2-Methylcyclohexyl)phenyl]propionic acid *see* Mexoprofen.
1-(2-Methylcyclohexyl)-3-phenylurea *see* Siduron.
Methyl 5-(cyclohexylthio)-2-benzimidazolecarbamate *see* Dribendazole.
Methyl 5-cyclopropylcarbonyl-2-benzimidazolecarbamate *see* Ciclobendazole.
Methyl cysteine *see* Mecysteine.
3′-MethylDAB *see* 4-(Dimethylamino)-3′-methylazobenzene.
Methyldamascenine *see* Damascenine.
Methyl-demeton *see under* Demeton-O-methyl.
Methyl demeton methyl *see* Demephion-S.
Methyl demeton-*O*-sulfoxide *see* Oxydemetonmethyl.
6-Methyl-Δ⁶-deoxymorphine *see* Methyldesorphine.
METHYLDESORPHINE*** (3-hydroxy-6,*N*-dimethyl-4,5-epoxymorphin-6-ene; 6-methyl-Δ⁶-deoxymorphine; MK-57).
Methyldiazepinone *see* Diazepam.
Methyldiazil (tr) *see* Metamizil.
***N*-Methyl-5*H*-dibenzo[*a*,*d*]cycloheptene-5-propylamine** *see* Protriptyline.
Methyldichlorisone *see* Meclorisone.
Methyl α,4-dichlorobenzenepropanoate *see* Chlorfenprop-methyl.
Methyl 3,4-dichlorocarbanilate *see* Swep.
Methyl 2,10-dichloro-12*H*-dibenzo[*d*,*g*]-[1,3]dioxocin-6-carboxylate *see* Treloxinate.

Methyl 3,6-dichloro-2-methoxybenzoate *see* Dicamba-methyl.

Methyl 6,8-dideoxy-6-(1-methyl-*trans*-4-propyl-L-2-pyrrolidinecarboxamido)-1-thio-D-*erythro*-α-D-galactooctopyranoside *see* Lincomycin.

Methyl 2-(2-diethylaminoacetamido)-*m*-toluate *see* Tolycaine.

Methyl 7-diethylamino-4-hydroxy-6-propyl-3-quinolinecarboxylate *see* Amquinate.

Methyl diethyl carbinol urethan *see* Emylcamate.

Methyldifacil (tr) *see* Methyladiphenine.

S-Methyl-6α,9-difluoro-11β,17-dihydroxy-16α-methyl-3-oxoandrosta-1,4-diene-17β-carbothioate *see* Ticabesone.

β-Methyldigoxin *see* Metildigoxin.

4'''-O-Methyldigoxin *see* Metildigoxin.

METHYLDIHYDROMORPHINE* (3,6-dihydroxy-6,*N*-dimethyl-4,5-epoxymorphinan).

5-Methyldihydromorphinone *see* Metopon.

Methyl 5-(3,6-dihydro-1(2*H*)-pyridyl)-2-oxo-2*H*-[1,2,4]oxadiazolo[2,3-*a*]pyrimidine-7-carbamate *see* Carprazidil.

Methyldihydrotestosterone *see* Methandriol.

Methyl 11,15-dihydroxy-16,16-dimethyl-9-oxoprosta-2,13-dienoate *see* Gemeprost.

Methyl 7-[3,5-dihydroxy-2-(3-hydroxy-3-methyl-1-octenyl)cyclopentyl]-4,5-heptadienoate *see* Prostalene.

Methyl 7-[3,5-dihydroxy-2-(3-hydroxy-4-phenoxy-1-butenyl)cyclopentyl]-4,5-heptadienoate *see* Fenprostalene.

Methyl 11,16-dihydroxy-16-methyl-9-oxoprost-13-enoate *see* Misoprostol.

Methyl 12,13-dimethoxyibogamine-18-carboxylate *see* Conopharyngine.

Methyl 3-(dimethoxyphosphinyloxy)-2-butenoate *see* Mevinphos.

Methyl 2-(dimethylamino)-*N*-[[(methylamino)carbonyl]oxy]-2-oxoethanimidothioate *see* Oxamyl.

Methyl 1,2-dimethyl-4-phenylhexamethylenimine-4-carboxylate *see* Metheptazine.

2-Methyl-3,5-dinitrobenzene *see* Dinitolmide.

2-Methyl-4,6-dinitrophenol *see* Dinitro-*o*-cresol.

15-Methyldinoprost *see* Carboprost.

15-Methyldinoprostone *see* Arbaprostil.

Methyldioxatrine *see* Meletimide.

3-(2-Methyl-1,3-dioxo-2,8-diazaspiro[4.5]decan-8-yl)-4'-fluorobutyrophenone *see* Roxoperone.

N-Methyldiphenethylamine *see* Demelverine.

α-Methyldiphenhydramine *see* Moxastine.

o-Methyldiphenhydramine *see* Orphenadrine.

p-METHYLDIPHENHYDRAMINE (*N,N*-dimethyl-2-(*p*-methylbenzhydroxyloxy)ethylamine; AH-853; 'neobenodine'; 'oxyvermin'; 'toladryl').

3-Methyl-5,5-diphenylhydantoin *see* Methylphenytoin.

5-Methyl-4,4-diphenyl-6-piperid-1-yl-3-hexanone *see* Pipanone.

3-Methyl-1,2-diphenyl-4-pyrrolidin-1-yl-2-butanol acetate *see* Pyrrolifene.

2-Methyl-1,2-dipyrid-3-yl-1-propanone *see* Metyrapone.

1-Methyl-3,3-dithien-2-ylallylamine *see* Thiambut-ene.

(4-Methyl-1,3-dithiolan-2-ylidene)phosphoramidic acid diethyl ester *see* Mephosfolan.

6-Methyl-1,3-dithiolo[4,5-*b*]quinoxalin-2-one *see* Chinomethionat.

N-Methyldithio-1-naphthalenecarbamic acid 2-benzoxazolyl ester *see* Naftoxate.

Methyl dodecahydro-2α,11-dimethoxy-3β-(3,4,5-trimethoxybenzoyloxy)benz[*g*]indolo[2,3-*a*]quinolizine-1β-carboxylate *see* Reserpine.

Methyl dodecahydro-2α,11-dimethoxy-3β-(3,4,5-trimethoxycinnamoyloxy)benz[*g*]indolo[2,3-*a*]quinolizine-1β-carboxylate *see* Rescinnamine.

METHYLDOPA* ((−)-2-amino-3-(3,4-dihydroxyphenyl)-2-methylpropionic acid; 3,4-dihydroxy-α-methylphenylalanine; (−)-3-(3,4-dihydroxyphenyl)-2-methylalanine; alpha methyl dopa; MK-351).
See also under Guanacline.

METHYLDOPA plus CHLOROTHIAZIDE ('aldoclor').

METHYLDOPA plus HYDROCHLOROTHIAZIDE ('aldoril').

METHYLDOPA plus MEFRUSIDE ('sali-presinol').

Methyldopa ethyl ester *see* Methyldopate.

α-Methyldopa-hydrazine *see* Carbidopa.

N-Methyldopamine diisobutyrate *see* Ibopamine.

METHYLDOPATE* (ethyl 2-amino-3-(3,4-dihydroxyphenyl)-2-methylpropionate; methyldopa ethyl ester; methyldopate hydrochloride; 'aldomet ester').

Methyl (3α,16α)-eburnamenine-14-carboxylate *see* Apovincamine.

α-(Methyleneamino)benzylpenicillin *see* Metampicillin.

6-[2-(Methyleneamino)-2-phenylacetamido]penicillanic acid *see* Metampicillin.

Methyleneampicillin *see* Metampicillin.

2,2'-Methylenebiphenyl *see* Fluorene.

2,2'-Methylenebis(4-chlorophenol) *see* Dichlorophen.

2,2'-Methylenebis(6-chlorothymol) *see* Biclotymol.

4,4'-Methylenebis(cyclohexyltrimethylammonium iodide) *see* Mebezonium iodide.

3,3'-Methylenebis(4-hydroxycoumarin) *see* Dicoumarol.

4,4'-Methylenebis(3-hydroxy-2-naphthoic acid), esters and salts *see* Embonate(s).

3,3'-Methylenebis[6-hydroxy-*p*-toluenesulfonic acid] *see* Dicresulene.

N,N'-Methylenebisisoniazid *see* Metazide.

4,4'-Methylenebis(3-methoxy-2-naphthoic acid), esters and salts *see* Metembonate(s).

3,3'-Methylenebis(2-naphthalenesulfonic acid) phenylmercuric salt *see* Hydrargaphen.

Methylenebis(phosphonic acid) *see* Medronic acid.

4,4'-Methylenebis(tetrahydro-1,2,4-thiadiazine 1,1-dioxide) *see* Taurolidine.

2,2'-Methylenebis(3,4,6-trichlorophenol) *see* Hexachlorophene.

METHYLENE BLUE* (3,7-bis(dimethylamino)-phenazathionium chloride; methylthioninium chloride; Swiss blue; CI-922; Schultz-1038).

1α,2α-Methylenechlormadinone *see* Cyproterone.

16-Methylenechlormadinone *see* Chloro-MDAP.

Methylenecitrodisalicylic acid *see* Citrodisalyl.

Methylenecycline* *see* Metacycline.

Methylenedehydroacetoxyprogesterone *see* MDAP.

METHYLENEDI(*m*-CRESOLSULFONIC ACID) POLYMER (*m*-cresolsulfonic acid formaldehyde condensation product; 'albocresil'; 'albothyl'; 'lotagen'; 'negatan'; 'negatol'; 'nelex'; 'vagothyl').

(Methylenedi-1,4-cyclohexylene)bis(trimethylammonium iodide) *see* Mebezonium iodide.

3,4-METHYLENEDIOXYAMPHETAMINE ((3,4-methylenedioxyphenyl)isopropylamine; MDA).

3,4-Methylenedioxybenzaldehyde *see* Piperonal.

1,2-Methylenedioxybenzene *see* 1,3-Benzodioxole.

3,4-Methylenedioxybenzoic acid *see* Piperonylic acid.

1-(3,4-Methylenedioxybenzyl)-4-pyrimid-2-ylpiperazine *see* Piribedil.

3,4-Methylenedioxymandelamidine *see* Olmidine.

1,2-Methylenedioxy-4-[2-(octylsulfinyl)propyl]benzene *see* Sulfoxide.

3,4-Methylenedioxyphenol *see* Sesamol.

2-(3,4-Methylenedioxyphenoxy)-6-(3,4-methylenedioxyphenyl)-*cis*-3,7-dioxabicyclo[3.3.0]octane *see* Sesamolin.

(3,4-Methylenedioxyphenyl)isopropylamine *see* 3,4-Methylenedioxyamphetamine.

1-(3,4-Methylenedioxyphenyl)-3,6,9-trioxaundecane *see* Sesamex.

***o,o*′-Methylenediphenyl ether** *see* Xanthene.

Methylenediphosphonic acid *see* Medronic acid.

3,3′-Methylenedithiobis(2-aminopropionic acid) *see* Djenkolic acid.

3,3′-Methylenedithiodialanine *see* Djenkolic acid.

Methylene oxide *see* Formaldehyde.

2-Methylene-3-oxocyclopentanecarboxylic acid *see* Sarkomycin A.

5-Methylene-2-oxodihydrofuran *see* Protoanemonin.

6-Methyleneoxytetracycline *see* Metacycline.

16-Methyleneprednisolone *see* Prednylidene.

Methylenesuccinic acid *see* Itaconic acid.

2-Methylenetrimethylenebis(methylcarbamate) copolymer with 1-vinyl-2-pyrrolidone *see* Copovithane.

Methyl-18-epi-*O*-methylreserpate *see* Metoserpate.

N-METHYLEPINEPHRINE (α-[(dimethylamino)methyl]-3,4-dihydroxybenzyl alcohol; *N*-methyladrenaline; 'methadren').

3-*O*-Methylepinephrine *see* Metanephrine.

Methyl 18-epireserpate methyl ether *see* Metoserpate.

Methylergobasine *see* Methylergometrine.

'Methylergobrevine' *see* Methylergometrine.

Methylergol carbamide *see* Lisuride.

6-Methylergoline-8α-acetonitrile *see* Delergotrile.

(+)-*N*-(6-Methylergolin-8β-ylmethyl)acetamide *see* Acetergamine.

METHYLERGOMETRINE*** (*N*-[1-(hydroxymethyl)propyl]lysergamide; lysergic acid butanolamide; methylergobasine; methylergonovine; methylergometrine maleate; methylergometrine tartrate).

METHYLERGOMETRINE plus OXYTOCIN (synthetic) ('syntometrin').

Methylergonovine *see* Methylergometrine.

1-Methylergotamine *see* Metergotamine.

METHYLESTRENOLONE (17β-hydroxy-17-methyl-4-norandrost-4-en-3-one; 17β-hydroxy-17-methylestr-4-en-3-one; 17α-methyl-19-nortestosterone; 17α-methylnandrolone; methyloestrenolone; normetandrone; normethandrolone; normethandrone; normethisterone; normethyltestosterone; NSC-10039; 'metalutin'; 'methalutin'; 'orgasteron').

[[(1-Methyl-1,2-ethanediyl)bis(carbamodithioato)](2-)]zinc homopolymer *see* Propineb.

1,1′-[(Methylethanediylidene)dinitrilo]diguanidine *see* Mitoguazone.

N-Methyl-9,10-ethanoanthracene-9(10H)-methylamine *see* Benzoctamine.

N-Methyl-9,10-ethanoanthracene-9(10H)-propylamine *see* Maprotiline.

7-(1-Methylethoxy)-3-phenyl-4H-1-benzopyran-4-one *see* Ipriflavone.

2-(1-Methylethoxy)phenyl methylcarbamate *see* Propoxur.

α-[[(1-Methylethyl)amino]methyl]-γ-phenylbenzenepropanol *see* Drobuline.

N-(1-Methylethyl)antibiotic BM-123-γ *see* Iprocinodine.

3-(1-Methylethyl)-1H-2,1,3-benzothiadiazin-4(3H)-one 2,2-dioxide *see* Bentazon.

1-Methylethyl 4-bromo-α-(4-bromophenyl)-α-hydroxybenzeneacetate *see* Bromopropylate.

1-Methylethyl 4-chloro-α-(4-chlorophenyl)-α-hydroxybenzeneacetate *see* Chloropropylate.

1-Methylethyl 3-chlorophenylcarbamate *see* Chlorpropham.

Methylethyldimethylaminoindole *see* Medmain.

4-(1-Methylethyl)-2,6-dinitro-*N,N*-dipropylbenzenamine *see* Isopropalin.

Methyl 13a-ethyl-2,3,5,6,13a,13b-hexahydro-1H-indolo[3,2,1-*de*]pyrido[3,2,1-*ij*][1,5]naphthyridine-12-carboxylate *see* Apovincamine.

1-Methylethyl [2-(1-methylpropyl)-4,6-dinitrophenyl] carbonate *see* Dinobuton.

***O*-Methyl 2-[(2-ethyl-5-nitroimidazol-1-yl)ethyl]-carbamothioate** *see* Sulnidazole.

1-Methylethyl phenylcarbamate *see* Propham.

2-(1-Methylethyl)phenyl methylcarbamate *see* Isoprocarb.

1-[(1-Methylethyl)sulfonyl]-6-(1-phenyl-1-propenyl)-1H-benzimidazol-2-amine *see* Enviradene.

Methyl 3-ethyl-2,3,3a,4-tetrahydro-1H-indolo[3,2,1-*de*][1,5]naphthyridine-6-carboxylate *see* Vinconate.

1-[4-[(1-Methylethyl)thio]phenoxy]-3-(octylamino)-2-propanol *see* Tipropidil.

Methyletynodiol *see* Metynodiol.

Methylflavone-8-carboxylic acid piperidylethyl ester *see* Flavoxate.

METHYLFLUDROCORTISONE (9α-fluoro-2-methylhydrocortisone; methylfluorocortisol).

α-Methylfluorene-2-acetic acid *see* Cicloprofen.

Methyl 5-(*p*-fluorobenzoyl)-2-benzimidazolecarbamate *see* Flubendazole.

Methylfluorocortisol *see* Methylfludrocortisone.

Methyl 9-fluoro-11β,17-dihydroxy-16β-methyl-3-oxoandrosta-1,4-diene-17β-carbothioate *see* Timobesone.

Methyl 5-[2-(*p*-fluorophenyl)-1,3-dioxolan-2-yl]-2-benzimidazolecarbamate *see* Etibendazole.

Methylflurether *see* Enflurane.

Methyl 6-formyl-4,7,9-trihydroxy-1-phenazinecarboxylate *see* Lomofungin.

5-Methylfurazolidone *see* Furmethoxadone.

Methyl-GAG *see* Mitoguazone.

N-Methylglucamine *see* Meglumine.

Methylglucamine iodipamide *see* Adipiodone meglumine.

N-Methylglycine *see* Sarcosine.

1-(*N*-Methylglycine)-5-L-valine-L-alanine angiotensin II *see* Saralasin.

1-Methylglycocyamidine *see* Creatinine.

Methylglycocyamine *see* Creatine.

Methyl glycol *see* Propylene glycol.

N-[1-[*N*-[*N*-[*N*-[*N*-[*N²*-(*N*-Methylglycyl)-L-arginyl]-L-valyl]-L-tyrosyl]-L-valyl]-L-histidyl]prolyl]-L-alanine *see* Saralasin.

METHYLGLYOXAL (2-oxopropionaldehyde; 2-ketopropionaldehyde; 2-oxopropanal; acetylformaldehyde; pyruvaldehyde; NSC-79019).

Methylglyoxal bisguanylhydrazone *see* Mitoguazone.

4-Methylguaiacol *see* Creosol.

Methylguanidoacetic acid *see* Creatine.

'Methyl guthion' *see* Azinphos-methyl.

O-Methylharmalol *see* Harmaline.

1-(1-Methylheptyl)hydrazine *see* Octamoxin.

Methylhexabital *see* Hexobarbital.

Methyl hexahydro-1,2-dimethyl-4-phenylazepine-4-carboxylate *see* Metheptazine.

Methyl 4-[[3,3a,4,5,6,6a-hexahydro-5-hydroxy-4-(3-hydroxy-1-octenyl)cyclopenta[*b*]pyrrol-2-yl]thio]butyrate *see* Tilsuprost.

Methylhexanamine *see* 1,3-Dimethylamylamine.

Methylhexobarbital *see* Hexobarbital.

1-Methylhexylamine *see* Tuaminoheptane.

Methylhydantoin *see* Mephenytoin.

1-Methylhydantoin-2-imide *see* Creatinine.

'Methylhydrazine' *see* Procarbazine.

Methyl *p*-hydroxybenzoate *see* Methyl paraben.

Methyl 3-hydroxy-*cis*-crotonate dimethyl phosphate *see* Mevinphos.

Methyl 4-hydroxy-6,7-diisopropoxy-3-quinolinecarboxylate *see* Proquinolate.

Methyl 7-[3-hydroxy-2-(3-hydroxy-4,4-dimethyl-1-octenyl)-5-oxocyclopentyl]-2-heptenoate *see* Gemeprost.

Methyl 3-hydroxy-2-(4-hydroxy-4-methyl-1-octenyl)-5-oxocyclopentaneheptanoate *see* Misoprostol.

Methyl 7-[3-hydroxy-2-(4-hydroxy-4-methyl-1-octenyl)-5-oxocyclopentyl]-4-heptenoate *see* Enisoprost.

Methyl 7-[3-hydroxy-2-(3-hydroxy-4-phenoxy-1-butenyl)-5-oxocyclopentyl]-4,5-heptadienoate *see* Enprostil.

Methyl *o*-[2-hydroxy-3-(isopropylamino)propoxy]cinnamate *see* Cinamolol.

Methyl *p*-[2-hydroxy-3-(isopropylamino)propoxy]hydrocinnamate *see* Esmolol.

Methyl [*p*-[2-hydroxy-3-(isopropylamino)propoxy]phenethyl]carbamate *see* Pamatolol.

Methyl 4-[2-hydroxy-3-[(1-methylethyl)amino]propoxy]benzenepropanoate *see* Esmolol.

N-Methylhyoscine methyl sulfate *see* Scopolamine methyl methosulfate.

1-Methyl-2-imidazolethiol *see* Thiamazole.

1-Methyl-2-imidazolethiol ethyl carbonate *see* Carbimazole.

2-Methyl-2-imidazoline *see* Lysidine.

2-[[2-[[(5-Methylimidazol-4-yl)methyl]thio]ethyl]amino]-5-piperonylpyrimidin-4(1*H*)-one *see* Oxmetidine.

[(Methylimino)diethylene]bis(ethyldimethylammonium bromide) *see* Azamethonium bromide.

3-Methylindole *see* Skatole.

1-Methylindole-2,3-dione thiosemicarbazone *see* Metisazone.

Methylisatin thiosemicarbazone *see* Metisazone.

Methyl isodemeton *see* Demeton-S-methyl.

N-Methylisooctenylamine *see* Isometheptene.

2-Methyl-5-isopropylphenol *see* Carvacrol.

Methylisosystox *see* Demeton-S-methyl.

Methylisosystoxsulfon *see* Demeton-S-methylsulfon.

Methylisosystox sulfoxide *see* Oxydemeton-methyl.

N¹-(3-Methylisothiazol-2-yl)sulfanilamide *see* Sulfasomizole.

4-[4-[3-(5-Methylisoxazole-3-carboxamido)ethyl]benzenesulfonyl]-1,1-hexamethylenesemicarbazide *see* Glisoxepide.

5-Methyl-3-isoxazolecarboxylic acid 2-benzylhydrazide *see* Isocarboxazid.

3-Methyl-5(4*H*)-isoxazolone 4-(*p*-chlorophenyl)hydrazone *see* Metazoxolon.

N¹-(5-Methylisoxazol-3-yl)sulfanilamide *see* Sulfamethoxazole.

Methyllorazepam *see* Lormetazepam.

Methyllysergic acid butanolamide *see* Methysergide.

METHYLLYSERGIDE (diethylamide of 1-methyllysergic acid; *N,N*-diethyl-1-methyllysergamide; MLD-41).

Methylmecamylamine *see* Dimecamine.

Methylmelubrin *see* Dipyrone.

'Methylmercadone' *see* Nifuratel.

Methylmercaptoimidazole *see* Thiamazole.

Methylmercaptophos *see* Demeton-O-methyl.

Methylmercaptophos oxide *see* Oxydemeton-methyl.

Methyl methacrylate polymer *see* Polymethyl methacrylate.

Methylmethioninesulfonium chloride (or bromide) *see* Vitamin U.

Methyl 3-methoxy-2-methylaminobenzoate *see* Damascenine.

Methyl 3-methoxy *N*-methylanthranilate *see* Damascenine.

1-Methyl-6-(1-methylallyl)-2,5-dithiobiurea *see* Metallibure.

Methyl *N*-[[(methylamino)carbonyl]oxy]acetimidothioate *see* Methomyl.

Methyl *N*-[[(methylamino)carbonyl]oxy]ethanimidothioate *see* Methomyl.

5-Methyl-10-[2-(methylamino)ethyl]-5*H*-dibenz[*b*,*f*]-azepine *see* Amezepine.

6-Methyl-2-(methylamino)hept-2-ene *see* Isometheptene.

3-Methyl-3-[3-(methylamino)propyl]-1-phenylindoline *see* Daledalin.

3-Methyl-3-[3-(methylamino)propyl]-1-phenyl-2-indolinone *see* Amedalin.

Methyl 1-(α-methylbenzyl)imidazole-5-carboxylate *see* Metomidate.

***S*-Methyl *N*-(methylcarbamoyloxy)thioacetimidate** *see* Methomyl.

(−)-6-Methyl-2-(4-methyl-3-cyclohexen-1-yl)-5-hepten-2-ol *see* Levomenol.

1-Methyl-3-[*p*-[[3-(4-methylcyclohexyl)ureido]sulfonyl]phenethyl]-1-pyrid-2-ylurea *see* Glisamuride.

6-Methyl-5-(2-methylenebutyryl)-2-benzofurancarboxylic acid *see* Furacrinic acid.

***N*-Methyl-3,4-methylenedioxyphenethylamine** *see* Homarylamine.

α-[[(α-Methyl-3,4-methylenedioxyphenethyl)amino]-methyl]protocatechuyl alcohol *see* Protokylol.

1-(α-Methyl-3,4-methylenedioxyphenethyl)-4-(4-methylthiazol-2-yl)piperazine *see* Podilfen.

α-Methyl-β-[3,4-(methylenedioxy)phenyl]-4-morpholineethanol *see* Filenadol.

Methyl *O*-methyl-18-epireserpate *see* Metoserpate.

(1-Methyl)methylergometrine *see* Methysergide.

1-Methyl-4-(1-methylethenyl)cyclohexene *see* Limonene.

2-Methyl-3-(1-methylethyl)-4,6-dinitrophenol *see* Dinoprop.

3-Methyl-5-(1-methylethyl)phenyl methylcarbamate *see* Promecarb.

1-Methyl-3-[2-(5-methylimidazol-4-ylmethylthio)-ethyl]guanidine-2-carbonitrile *see* Cimetidine.

1-Methyl-3-[2-[(5-methylimidazol-4-ylmethyl)thio]-ethyl]-2-thiourea *see* Metiamide.

***N*-Methyl-4′-[(7-methyl-1*H*-imidazo[4,5-*f*]quinolin-9-yl)amino]acetanilide** *see* Acodazole.

1-Methyl-3-[(3-methylindan-1-yl)methyl]pyrrolidine *see* Pyrophendane.

Methyl 6-methyl-2[[(3-methylpyrid-2-yl)methyl]sulfinyl]-5-benzimidazolecarboxylate *see* Picoprazole.

***O*-Methyl [2-(2-methyl-5-nitroimidazol-1-yl)ethyl]-thiocarbamate** *see* Carnidazole.

***O*-Methyl *O*-(4-methyl-2-nitrophenyl) *N*-isopropyl-phosphoramidothioate** *see* Amiprofos-methyl.

1-Methyl 3-[2-methyl-4-oxo-2-(2,4-pentadienyl)-2-cyclopenten-1-yl] chrysanthemumdicarboxylate *see* Pyrethrin II.

(−)-*N*-Methyl-*N*-(α-methylphenethyl)-6-oxo-3-phenyl-1(6*H*)-pyridazineacetamide *see* Isamfazone.

Methyl *cis*-3-methyl-1-phenethyl-4-(*N*-phenylpropionamido)isonipecotate *see* Lofentanil.

Methyl (α-methylphenethyl)prop-2-ynylamine *see* Selegiline.

α-Methyl-*N*-(1-methyl-2-phenoxyethyl)phenethyl-amine *see* Dextrofemine; Racefemine.

***N*-Methyl-2-[(*o*-methyl-α-phenylbenzyl)oxy]ethyl-amine** *see* Tofenacin.

10-Methyl-2-(4-methylpiperazin-1-yl)-3,4-diaza-phenoxazine *see* Pipofezine.

2-Methyl-11-(4-methylpiperazin-1-yl)dibenzo[*b*,*f*]-[1,4]thiazepine *see* Metiapine.

5-Methyl-3-(4-methylpiperazin-1-yl)-5*H*-pyridazi-no[3,4-*b*][1,4]benzoxazine *see* Pipofezine.

D-(+)-1-Methyl-1-(1-methylpiperid-2-yl)ethyl di-phenylacetate *see* Pinolcaine.

Methyl 4-methyl-3-[2-(propylamino)propionamido]-2-thiophenecarboxylate *see* Articaine.

6-Methyl-2-[[(3-methylpyrid-2-yl)methyl]sulfinyl]-5-benzimidazolecarboxylic acid methyl ester *see* Picoprazole.

***N*-Methyl-*N*-(3-methylpyridyl)tropamide** *see* Pimetremide.

Methyl 2-methyl-5-[D-*arabino*-1,2,3,4-tetra(nicoti-noyloxy)butyl]-3-furoate *see* Nicofurate.

1-Methyl-1-[2-(*N*-methyl-α-thien-2-ylmandel-amido)ethyl]pyrrolidinium bromide *see* Dotefonium bromide.

1-Methyl-2-[[*p*-(methylthio)phenoxy]methyl]-5-nitroimidazole *see* Fexnidazole.

2-Methyl-2-(methylthio)propanal *O*-[(methylamino)-carbonyl]oxime *see* Aldicarb.

2-Methyl-2-(methylthio)propionaldehyde *O*-(methyl-carbamoyl)oxime *see* Aldicarb.

Methylmitomycin *see* Porfiromycin.

Methylmorphine *see* Codeine.

4-Methyl-7-(4-morpholinecarboxamido)-3-(2-mor-pholinoethyl)coumarin *see* Morocromen.

1-(3-Methyl-4-morpholino-2,2-diphenylbutyryl)pyr-rolidine *see* Dextromoramide; Levomoramide; Racemoramide.

1-Methyl-2-[[[5-(morpholinomethyl)-2-oxooxazolid-in-3-yl]imino]methyl]-5-nitroimidazole *see* Moxnidazole.

2-Methyl-*N*-(morpholinomethyl)-2-phenylsuccinim-ide *see* Morsuximide.

1-Methyl-3-morpholinopropyl tetrahydro-4-phenyl-2*H*-pyran-4-carboxylate *see* Fedrilate.

7α-Methylnandrolone *see* Trestolone.

17α-Methylnandrolone *see* Methylestrenolone.

α-Methyl-1-naphthaleneacetic acid ester with 1,4-piperazinediethanol *see* Nafiverine.

2-Methyl-1,4-naphthalenediamine dihydrochloride *see* Vitamin K$_6$.

2-Methyl-1,4-naphthalenediol *see* Menadiol.

2-Methyl-1,4-naphthalenedione *see* Menadione.

2-Methyl-1,4-naphthoquinone *see* Menadione.

***N*-Methyl-*N*-naphth-1-yldithiocarbamic acid 2-benzoxazolyl ester** *see* Naftoxate.

***N*-Methyl-*N*-naphth-1-ylfluoroacetamide** *see* *N*-(2-Fluoroacetyl)-*N*-methyl-1-naphthylamine.

O-(2-Methylnaphth-1-ylmethyl)hydroxylamine *see* Nafomine.

3-Methyl-1-[2-(2-naphthyloxy)ethyl]-2-pyrazolin-5-one *see* Nafazatrom.

*N*¹-METHYLNICOTINAMIDE (3-carbamoyl-1-methylpyridinium hydroxide or salts).

4-Methyl-1-(5-nitrofurfurylideneamino)-2-imidazolidinone *see* Nifurimide.

5-Methyl-3-(5-nitro-2-furfurylideneamino)-2-oxazolidinone *see* Furmethoxadone.

2-Methyl-6-[2-(5-nitro-2-furyl)vinyl]-4-pyrimidinol *see* Nifurvidine.

2-Methyl-5-nitroimidazole-1-ethanol *see* Metronidazole.

2-Methyl-5-nitroimidazole-1-ethanol carbamate ester *see* Bamnidazole.

2-Methyl-4-nitroimidazole-1-propanol *see* Ternidazole.

4-[2-(2-Methyl-5-nitroimidazol-1-yl)ethyl]pyridine *see* Panidazole.

[2-(2-Methyl-5-nitroimidazol-1-yl)ethyl]thiocarbamic acid methyl ester *see* Carnidazole.

1-Methyl-5-nitroimidazol-5-ylmethyl carbamate *see* Ronidazole.

3-[[(1-Methyl-5-nitroimidazol-2-yl)methylene]amino]-5-(morpholinomethyl)-2-oxazolidinone *see* Moxnidazole.

1-(1-Methyl-5-nitroimidazol-2-yl)-3-(methylsulfonyl)-2-imidazolinone *see* Satranidazole.

2-[(1-Methyl-5-nitroimidazol-2-ylmethyl)thio]pyridine *see* Pirinidazole.

1-(2-Methyl-5-nitroimidazol-1-yl)-2-propanol *see* Secnidazole.

6-(1-Methyl-4-nitroimidazol-5-ylthio)guanine *see* Tiamiprine.

6-(1-Methyl-4-nitroimidazol-5-ylthio)purine *see* Azathioprine.

4-[2-(1-Methyl-5-nitroimidazol-2-yl)vinyl]pyrimidin-2-ylamine *see* Azanidazole.

2-Methyl-4-nitro-1-(*p*-nitrophenyl)imidazole *see* Nitrefazole.

5-Methyl-5-(*p*-nitrophenylazo)rhodanine *see* Nitrodan.

3-Methyl-5-(4-nitrophenylazo)thiazolidin-4-one-2-thione *see* Nitrodan.

Methylnitrophos (tr) *see* Fenitrothion.

2-Methyl-5-nitro-1-(2-pyrid-4-ylethyl)imidazole *see* Panidazole.

1-Methyl-5-nitro-2-[(pyrid-2-ylthio)methyl]imidazole *see* Pirinidazole.

1-METHYL-1-NITROSOUREA (NSC-23909).

2-Methyl-4′-nitro-3′-(trifluoromethyl)propionanilide *see* Flutamide.

9-Methylnon-6-enoic acid vanillylamide *see* Capsaicin.

2-Methyl-2-nonyl-1,3-dioxolan-4-ylmethyl carbamate *see* Dioxamate.

α-Methylnoradrenaline *see* Corbadrine.

3-*O*-Methylnoradrenaline *see* Normetanephrine.

α-Methylnorepinephrine *see* Corbadrine.

3-*O*-Methylnorepinephrine *see* Normetanephrine.

7α-Methylnoretynodrel *see* Tibolone.

17-Methyl-19-norpregna-4,9-diene-3,20-dione *see* Demegestone.

11β-Methyl-19-nor-17α-pregn-4-en-20-yne-3β,17-diol *see* Metynodiol.

17α-Methyl-Δ⁹-19-norprogesterone *see* Demegestone.

7α-Methyl-19-nortestosterone *see* Trestolone.

17α-Methyl-B-nortestosterone *see* Benorterone.

17α-Methyl-19-nortestosterone *see* Methylestrenolone.

Methyloestrenolone *see* Methylestrenolone.

Methylolchlortetracycline *see* Clomocycline.

Methylolgramicidin *see* Methocidin.

2-[3-(5-Methyl-1,3,4-oxadiazol-2-yl)-3,3-diphenylpropyl]-2-azabicyclo[2.2.2]octane *see* Nufenoxole.

6-Methyl-1,2,3-oxathiazin-4(3*H*)-one 2,2-dioxide *see* Acesulfame.

Methyloxazepam *see* Temazepam.

Methyloxirane polymer with oxirane *see* Poloxamer.

4-[(1-Methyl-3-oxo-1-butenyl)amino]isoxazolidin-3-one *see* Pentizidone.

4-(2-Methyl-4-oxo-3,3-diphenyl-4-pyrrolidin-1-ylbutyl)morpholine *see* Dextromoramide; Levomoramide; Racemoramide.

3-Methyl-1-(5-oxohexyl)-7-propylxanthine *see* Propentofylline.

5-Methyl-2-oxo-4-imidazolidinehexanoic acid *see* Desthiobiotin.

(1-Methyl-4-oxo-2-imidazolidinylidene)phosphoramidic acid *see* Fosfocreatinine.

2-Methyl-4-oxo-2-(2,4-pentadienyl)-2-cyclopenten-1-yl chrysanthemate *see* Pyrethrin I.

5-Methyl-3-oxo-6-phenylmorpholine *see* Fenmetramide.

N-Methyl-*N*-[[(6-oxo-3-phenylpyridazin-1-yl)methyl]carbonyl]amphetamine *see* Isamfazone.

1-Methyl-3-oxo-4-phenylquinuclidinium bromide *see* Quinuclium bromide.

3-Methyl-4-oxo-5-piperidino-Δ²,ᵅ-thiazolidineacetic acid *see* Ozolinone.

3-Methyl-4-oxo-5-piperid-1-yl-Δ²,ᵅ-thiazolidine acetic acid ethyl ester *see* Dexetozoline; Etozolin.

2-Methyl-4-oxo-3-(2-propenyl)-2-cyclopenten-1-yl-2,2-dimethyl-3-(2-methyl-1-propenyl)cyclopropanecarboxylate *see* Allethrin; Bioallethrin.

Methyl 4-[(1-oxopropyl)phenylamino]-1-(2-phenylethyl)-4-piperidinecarboxylate *see* Carfentanil.

1-Methyl-2-oxo-6-(trifluoromethyl)quinoline *see* Flucarbril.

4-METHYL-2-OXOVALERIC ACID (α-keto-isocaproic acid).

METHYL PALMOXIRATE* (methyl (±)-2-tetradecylglycidate; methyl (±)-2-tetradecyloxiranecarboxylate; McN-3716).

METHYL PARABEN (methyl *p*-hydroxybenzoate; 'metagin'; 'methyl butex'; 'methyl parasept'; 'methyl tegasept'; 'nipagin'; 'solbrol').

Methylparafynol* *see* Methylpentynol.

'Methyl parasept' *see* Methyl paraben.

Methyl parathion *see* Parathion-methyl.

Methyl partricin *see* Mepartricin.

3-Methyl-2,4-pentanediol dicarbamate *see* Pentabamate.

4-Methyl-3-penten-2-one (1-phthalazinyl)hydrazone *see* Budralazine.

3-Methyl-3-pentyl carbamate *see* Emylcamate.

METHYLPENTYNOL*** (3-methyl-1-pentyn-3-ol; 1-ethyl-1-methyl-2-propyn-1-ol; methylparafynol; ethynyl methyl carbinol; meparfynol).

Methylpentynol phthalate *see* Ftalofyne.

Methylperidide *see* Meperidide.

Methylperidol *see* Moperone.

Methylperone* *see* Melperone.

10-Methylphenazin-1-one *see* Pyocyanine.

α-Methylphenethylamine *see* Amphetamine; Dexamphetamine; Levamphetamine.

9-[2-(α-Methylphenethylamino)ethyl]acridine *see* Acridorex.

4-[2-(α-Methylphenethylamino)ethyl]morpholine *see* Morforex.

7-[2-(α-Methylphenethylamino)ethyl]theophylline *see* Fenetylline.

2-(α-Methylphenethylamino)-2-phenylacetonitrile *see* Amfetaminil.

3-(α-Methylphenethylamino)propionitrile *see* Fenproporex.

2-[3-(Methylphenethylamino)propyl]-2-phenyltetradecanenitrile *see* Ronipamil.

N-[2-(N-Methylphenethylamino)propyl]propionanilide *see* Diampromide.

N-(α-Methylphenethyl)formamide *see* Formetorex.

α-Methylphenethylhydrazine *see* Pheniprazine.

(3α-Methylphenethyl)-N-(phenylcarbamoyl)sydnone imine *see* Mesocarb.

Methyl 1-phenethyl-4-(N-phenylpropionamido)isonipecotate *see* Carfentanil.

cis-3-Methyl-1-phenethyl-4-(N-phenylpropionamido)isonipecotic acid methyl ester *see* Lofentanil.

3-(α-Methylphenethyl)sydnone imine *see* Feprosidnine.

N-(α-Methylphenethyl)thioxanthene-9-ethylamine *see* Tixadil.

(−)-1-(α-Methylphenethyl)-3-(p-tolylsulfonyl)urea *see* Tosifen.

Methylphenetoin *see* Mephenytoin.

METHYLPHENIDATE*** (methyl α-phenyl-2-piperidineacetate; methylphenidylacetate; meridil; phenidylate; C-4311/b; 'ritalin').

Methylphenidylacetate *see* Methylphenidate.

METHYLPHENOBARBITAL*** (ethyl-1-methyl-5-phenylbarbituric acid; enphenemal; mephobarbital; phemitone).

Methylphenol(s) *see* Cresol(s).

10-Methylphenothiazin-2-ylacetic acid *see* Metiazinic acid.

1-Methyl-1-(1-phenothiazin-2-ylcarbonylethyl)pyrrolidinium bromide *see* Propyromazine bromide.

1-(1-Methyl-2-phenoxyethyl)hydrazine *see* Fenoxypropazine.

(1-Methyl-1-phenoxyethyl)penicillin *see* Isopropicillin.

(α-Methylphenoxymethyl)penicillin *see* Pheneticillin.

3-(o-Methylphenoxy)-1,2-propanediol *see* Mephenesin.

2-Methyl-2-phenoxypropionic acid 2-morpholinoethyl ester *see* Promolate.

5-(3-Methylphenoxy)-2-pyrimidinone *see* Tolimidone.

Methylphensuximide *see* Mesuximide.

2-Methyl-2-phenylacetic acid *see* Hydratropic acid.

1-Methyl-4-phenylazacycloheptane-4-carboxylic acid ethyl ester *see* Ethoheptazine.

5-Methyl-5-phenylbarbituric acid *see* Mephebarbital.

α-Methyl-3-phenyl-7-benzofuranacetic acid *see* Furaprofen.

α-Methyl-2-phenyl-6-benzothiazoleacetic acid *see* Tazeprofen.

3-Methyl-4-phenyl-3-butenoic acid *see* 3-Benzylidenebutyric acid.

Methyl phenyl ether *see* Anisole.

7-[2-(1-Methyl-2-phenylethylamino)ethyl]theophylline *see* Fenetylline.

2-[(1-Methyl-2-phenylethyl)amino]-2-phenylacetonitrile *see* Amfetaminil.

1-Methyl-4-phenylhexamethylenimine-4-carboxylic acid ethyl ester *see* Ethoheptazine.

5-Methyl-2-phenylimidazole-4-acetonitrile *see* Mefenidil.

1-Methyl-4-phenylisonipecotic acid ethyl ester *see* Pethidine.

N-Methyl-N-(2-phenylisopropyl)prop-2-ynylamine *see* Selegiline.

6-[(5-Methyl-3-phenylisoxazol-4-yl)carboxamido]penicillanic acid *see* Oxacillin.

(5-Methyl-3-phenyl-4-isoxazolyl)penicillin *see* Oxacillin.

Methyl phenyl ketone *see* Acetophenone.

3-Methyl-2-phenylmorpholine *see* Phenmetrazine.

2-(3-Methyl-2-phenylmorpholino)ethyl 2-phenylbutyrate *see* Fenbutrazate.

4-(3-Methyl-2-phenylmorpholinomethyl)antipyrine *see* Morazone.

4-(3-Methyl-2-phenylmorpholinomethyl)phenazone *see* Morazone.

5-Methyl-6-phenyl-3-morpholinone *see* Fenmetramide.

(−)-N-(p-Methyl-α-phenylphenethyl)linoleamide *see* Moctamide.

Methyl α-phenyl-2-piperidineacetate *see* Methylphenidate.

5-Methyl-4-phenyl-1-piperid-1-yl-3-hexanol *see* Piperphenidol.

N-Methyl-N-(3-phenylprop-2-enyl)-1-naphthalenemethylamine *see* Naftifine.

N-Methyl-N-(1-phenylprop-2-yl)-2-furfurylamine *see* Furfenorex.

1-(1-Methyl-3-phenylpropyl)hydrazine *see* Phenylisobutylhydrazine.

3-Methyl-5-phenylpyrazole *see* Phemerazole.

3-METHYL-1-PHENYLPYRAZOL-5-YL DIMETHYLCARBAMATE (G-22008; 'pyrolan').

N¹-(3-Methyl-1-phenylpyrazol-5-yl)sulfanilamide *see* Sulfapyrazole.

N¹-(5-Methyl-2-phenylpyrazol-3-yl)sulfanilamide *see* Sulfapyrazole.

349

4-[2-[(4-Methyl-6-phenylpyridazin-3-yl)amino]-ethyl]morpholine *see* Minaprine.

5-Methyl-1-phenylpyridin-2(1*H*)-one *see* Pirfenidone.

N-Methyl-2-phenylsuccinimide *see* Phensuximide.

Methyl 5-(phenylsulfinyl)-2-benzimidazolecarbamate *see* Oxfendazole.

Methyl 5-(phenylthio)-2-benzimidazolecarbamate *see* Fenbendazole.

N-Methyl-3-phenyl-3-(*o*-tolyloxy)propylamine *see* Tomoxetine.

1-Methyl-5-phenyl-7-trifluoromethyl-1*H*-1,5-benzodiazepine-2,4(3*H*,5*H*)-dione *see* Triflubazam.

N-Methyl-3-phenyl-3-[(*p*-trifluoromethyl)phenoxy]-propylamine *see* Fluoxetine.

(±)-*N*-Methyl-3-phenyl-3-[(α,α,α-trifluoro-*p*-tolyl)-oxy]propylamine *see* Fluoxetine.

3-Methyl-2-phenylvaleric acid esters *see* Pentapiperide; Valethamate bromide.

METHYLPHENYTOIN (3-methyl-5,5-diphenyl-hydantoin; 'melantoin').

Methylphosphoramidic acid [2-chloro-4-(1,1-dimethylethyl)phenyl]methyl ester *see* Crufomate.

Methyl phthalate *see* Dimethyl phthalate.

2-Methyl-3-phytyl-1,4-naphthalenediol *see* Phytonadiol.

2-Methyl-3-phytyl-1,4-naphthalenedione *see* Phytomenadione.

2-Methyl-3-phytyl-1,4-naphthoquinone *see* Phytomenadione.

N-Methyl-*N*-(3-picolyl)tropamide *see* Pimetremide.

Methyl pinacolyl phosphonofluoridate *see* Soman.

Methylpindolol *see* Mepindolol.

1-Methyl-2′,6′-pipecoloxylidide *see* Dexivacaine; Mepivacaine.

4-Methyl-1-piperazineacetic acid (5-nitrofurfurylidene)hydrazide *see* Nifurpipone.

4-Methylpiperazine-1-carboxylic acid esters *see* Suriclone; Zopiclone.

1-[2-(4-Methylpiperazin-1-yl)acetyl]-2-(5-nitrofurfurylidene)hydrazine *see* Nifurpipone.

21-(4-Methylpiperazin-1-yl)deprodone *see* Mazipredone.

6-(4-Methylpiperazin-1-yl)dibenz[*b,e*]azepine *see* Perlapine.

2-(4-Methylpiperazin-1-yl)ethyl 2-trifluoromethyl-phenothiazin-10-yl ketone *see* Ftormetazine.

3-(4-Methylpiperazin-1-yliminomethyl)rifamycin SV *see* Rifampicin.

6-(4-Methylpiperazin-1-yl)morphanthridine *see* Perlapine.

10-[3-(4-Methylpiperazin-1-yl)propionyl]-2-trifluoromethylphenothiazine *see* Ftormetazine.

10-[3-(4-Methylpiperazin-1-yl)propyl]phenothiazine *see* Perazine.

1-[10-[3-(4-Methylpiperazin-1-yl)propyl]phenothiazin-2-yl]-1-butanone *see* Butaperazine.

10-[3-(4-Methylpiperazin-1-yl)propyl]-2-propionyl-phenothiazine *see* Propionylperazine.

10-[3-(4-Methylpiperazin-1-yl)propyl]-2-(trifluoromethyl)phenothiazine *see* Trifluoperazine.

2-Methylpiperidine *see* 2-Pipecoline.

2-Methyl-1-piperidinepropanol benzoate *see* Piperocaine.

1-Methyl-4-piperidinol ester of 2,2-bis(*p*-chlorophenoxy)acetic acid *see* Lifibrate.

1-Methylpiperid-3-yl benzilate methobromide *see* Mepenzolate bromide.

1-Methylpiperid-4-yl *p*-butylaminobenzoate *see* Paridocaine.

1-Methylpiperid-3-yl cyclohexylmandelate *see* Oxyclipine.

1-Methylpiperid-4-yl diphenylpropoxyacetate *see* Propiverine.

2-Methyl-3-[*p*-(2-piperid-1-ylethoxy)anilino]phthal-imidine *see* Omidoline.

Methyl *o*-[*p*-(2-piperid-1-ylethoxy)benzoyl]benzoate *see* Pitofenone.

2′-[2-(1-Methylpiperid-2-yl)ethyl]-*p*-anisanilide *see* Encainide.

2-(4-Methylpiperid-1-yl)ethyl 6-ethyl-2,3,6,9-tetra-hydro-3-methyl-2,9-dioxothiazolo[5,4-*f*]quinoline-8-carboxylate *see* Metioxate.

10-[2-(1-Methylpiperid-2-yl)ethyl]-2-(methylsulfinyl)phenothiazine *see* Mesoridazine.

10-[2-(1-Methylpiperid-2-yl)ethyl]-2-methylsulfonyl-phenothiazine *see* Sulforidazine.

10-[2-(1-Methylpiperid-2-yl)ethyl]-2-(methylthio)-phenothiazine *see* Thioridazine.

N-[2-(1-Methylpiperid-2-yl)ethyl]propionanilide *see* Phenampromide.

N-(1-Methyl-2-piperid-1-ylethyl)-*N*-pyrid-2-ylpro-pionamide *see* Propiram.

Methylpiperid-4-yl glyoxylate 2-[bis(*p*-chlorophenyl)acetal] *see* Lifibrate.

5-(1-Methyl-4-piperidylidene)-5*H*-[1]-benzopyra-no[2,3-*b*]pyridine *see* Azanator.

1-Methylpiperid-3-ylidenedithien-2-ylmethane *see* Tipepidine.

9-(*N*-Methyl-4-piperidylidene)thioxanthene *see* Pimethixene.

10-(1-Methylpiperid-3-ylmethyl)phenothiazine *see* Pecazine.

1-Methylpiperid-4-yl 3-methyl-2-phenylvalerate *see* Pentapiperide.

9-(1-Methylpiperid-3-ylmethyl)thioxanthene *see* Metixene.

2-Methyl-3-(β-piperid-1-yl-*p*-phenetidino)phthal-imidine *see* Omidoline.

N-(1-Methylpiperid-4-yl)-*N*-phenylbenzylamine *see* Bamipine.

1-Methylpiperid-3-yl α-phenylcyclohexaneglycolate *see* Oxyclipine.

D-(+)-2-(1-Methylpiperid-2-yl)-2-propanol diphen-ylacetate *see* Pinolcaine.

3-(2-Methylpiperid-1-yl)propyl benzoate *see* Piperocaine.

3-(2-Methylpiperid-1-yl)propyl *p*-(cyclohexyloxy)-benzoate *see* Cyclomethycaine.

2-Methyl-3-piperid-1-ylpyrazine *see* Modaline.

1-Methyl-5-[[3-[(α-piperid-1-yl-*m*-tolyl)oxy]propyl]-amino]-1*H*-1,2,4-triazole-3-methanol *see* Loxtidine.

2-Methyl-3-piperid-1-yl-1-(*p*-tolyl)-1-propanone *see* Tolperisone.

Methylpolysiloxane *see* Dimeticone.

350

7-Methyl 21-potassium 17-hydroxy-3-oxo-17α-pregn-4-ene-7α,21-dicarboxylate *see* Mexrenoate potassium.
METHYLPREDNISOLONE*** (11β,17α,21-trihydroxy-6α-methylpregna-1,4-diene-3,20-dione; 6α-methylprednisolone; NSC-19987).
METHYLPREDNISOLONE ACETATE ('depomedrol'; 'depro-medrone').
METHYLPREDNISOLONE SODIUM PHOS-PHATE* (U-12019E).
METHYLPREDNISOLONE SODIUM SUC-CINATE ('solu-medrol').
6α-Methylprednisolone *see* Methylprednisolone.
6β-Methylprednisolone *see* Meprednisone.
N-**Methylproline choline ester iodide methiodide** *see* Trepirium iodide.
Methylpromazine *see* Alimemazine.
2-METHYL-1-PROPANOL (isobutyl alcohol).
2-METHYL-2-PROPANOL (*tert*-butyl alcohol).
N-**Methyl-*N*-propargylbenzylamine** *see* Pargyline.
p-**(1-Methylpropenyl)phenyl acetate** *see* Fenabutene.
Methylpropiolic acid *see* Tetrolic acid.
2-Methylpropionic acid *see* Isobutyric acid.
17α-Methyl-17-propionylestra-4,9-dien-3-one *see* Promegestone.
Methyl 5-propoxy-2-benzimidazolecarbamate *see* Oxibendazole.
Methyl 6-propoxy-2-benzothiazolecarbamate *see* Tioxidazole.
β-[(2-Methylpropoxy)methyl]-*N*-phenyl-*N*-(phenylmethyl)-1-pyrrolidineethanamine *see* Bepridil.
N-**Methylpropranolol methochloride** *see* Pranolium chloride.
2-Methylpropyl 4-aminobenzoate *see* Isobutamben.
4-Methyl-3-[2-(propylamino)propionamido]-2-thiophenecarboxylic acid methyl ester *see* Articaine.
2′-Methyl-2-(propylamino)propionanilide *see* Prilocaine.
2-Methyl-2-(propylamino)-*o*-propionotoluidide *see* Quatacaine.
2-Methyl-2-(propylamino)propyl benzoate *see* Meprylcaine.
2-(1-Methylpropylamino)-1-(5,6,7,8-tetrahydronaphth-2-yl)ethanol *see* Butidrine.
Methyl propyl carbinol *see* 2-Pentanol.
Methyl propyl carbinol carbamate *see* Hedonal.
6-(1-Methylpropyl)-2,4-dinitrophenol *see* Dinoseb.
2-(1-Methylpropyl)-4,6-dinitrophenyl 3-methyl-2-butenoate *see* Binapacryl.
1-(2-Methylpropyl)-3,4-diphenylpyrazole-4-acetic acid *see* Bufezolac.
METHYL PROPYL ETHER ('metopryl'; 'neothyl').
2-Methyl-2-propyl-1,3-propanediol *see* 2-(Hydroxymethyl)-2-methyl-1-pentanol.
2-Methyl-2-propyl-1,3-propanediol carbamate isopropylcarbamate *see* Carisoprodol.
2-Methyl-2-propyl-1,3-propanediol dicarbamate *see* Meprobamate.
6-METHYL-2-PROPYLPYRIMID-4-YL *N,N*-DIMETHYLCARBAMATE ('pyramat').

m-**(1-Methyl-3-propylpyrrolidin-3-yl)phenol** *see* Profadol.
Methyl 5-(propylthio)benzimidazole-2-carbamate *see* Albendazole.
5-Methyl-5-propyl-2-*p*-tolyl-1,3,2-dioxaborinane *see* Tolboxane.
2-Methyl-2-propyltrimethylene dicarbamate *see* Meprobamate.
N-**Methyl-*N*-(2-propynyl)benzylamine** *see* Pargyline.
1-Methylprop-2-ynyl *m*-chlorocarbanilate *see* Chlorbufam.
1-Methyl-2-propynyl 3-chlorophenylcarbamate *see* Chlorbufam.
[2-Methyl-5-(2-propynyl)furan-3-yl]methyl 2,2-dimethyl-3-(2-methyl-1-propenyl)cyclopropanecarboxylate *see* Prothrin.
2-Methyl-5-prop-2-ynyl-3-furylmethyl chrysanthemate *see* Prothrin.
N-**Methyl-*N*-2-propynyllevamfetamine** *see* Selegiline.
4-Methyl-7-(2-propynyloxy)coumarin *see* Giparmen.
4′-*O*-Methylproscillaridin *see* Meproscillarin.
15-Methylprostaglandin E₂ *see* Arbaprostil.
15-Methylprostaglandin F₂α *see* Carboprost.
5-Methylpyrazinecarboxylic acid 4-oxide *see* Acipimox.
4-Methyl-5-pyrazin-2-yl-3*H*-1,2-dithiole-3-thione *see* Oltipraz.
1-[2-(5-Methylpyrazol-3-yl)ethyl]-4-*m*-tolylpiperazine *see* Tolpiprazole.
2-Methylpyridine *see* 2-Picoline.
4-Methylpyridine *see* 4-Picoline.
1-Methyl-9*H*-pyrido[3,4-*b*]indole *see* Harman.
3-[1-[(4-Methylpyrid-2-yl)carbamoyl]ethyl]benzophenone *see* Piketoprofen.
1-Methyl-5-pyrid-3-ylpyrrolidin-2-one *see* Cotinine.
o-**(1-Methyl-3-pyrid-3-yl-1*H*-1,2,4-triazol-5-yl)-benzyl alcohol** *see* Fepitrizol.
N¹-(4-Methylpyrimidin-2-yl)sulfanilamide *see* Sulfamerazine.
N¹-(5-Methylpyrimidin-2-yl)sulfanilamide *see* Sulfaperin.
1-Methylpyrrolidine-2-carboxylic acid dimethylaminoethyl ester dimethiodide *see* Hygronium.
1-Methyl-3-pyrrolidinemethanol benzilate ester *see* Triclazate.
2-Methyl-2-pyrrolidin-1-yl-*o*-acetotoluidide *see* Aptocaine.
17α-Methyl-3β-pyrrolidin-1-yl-17-aza-D-homo-5-androstene dimethiodide *see* Chandonium iodide.
N-**(1-Methyl-2-pyrrolidinylidene)-*N*′-phenyl-4-morpholinecarboxamidine** *see* Linogliride.
N-**(1-Methylpyrrolidin-2-ylidene)-*N*′-phenyl-1-pyrrolidinecarboxamidine** *see* Pirogliride.
1-(1-Methylpyrrolidin-2-ylidene)-3-(2,6-xylyl)urea *see* Xilobam.
1-Methylpyrrolidin-3-ylmethyl benzilate *see* Triclazate.
1-Methylpyrrolidin-2-ylmethyl bis(*p*-chlorophenoxy)acetate *see* Biclofibrate.
N-**[(1-Methylpyrrolidin-2-yl)methyl]-5-(methylsulfa-**

moyl)-*o*-veratramide *see* Sulverapride.

10-[(1-Methylpyrrolidin-3-yl)methyl]phenothiazine *see* Methdilazine.

1-(2-Methylpyrrolidin-3-ylmethyl)-3-phenylindan *see* Pyrophendane.

N-[(1-Methyl-2-pyrrolidinyl)methyl]-5-sulfamoyl-*o*-anisamide *see* Sulmepride.

1-Methylpyrrolidin-3-yl α-phenyl-α-(2-thienyl)glycolate methobromide *see* Heteronium bromide.

2′-Methyl-2-pyrrolidin-1-ylpropionanilide *see* Aptocaine.

10-[2-(1-Methylpyrrolidin-1-yl)propionyl]phenothiazine bromide *see* Propyromazine bromide.

3-(1-Methylpyrrolidin-2-yl)pyridine *see* Nicotine.

4′-Methyl-2-pyrrolidin-1-ylvalerophenone *see* Pyrovalerone.

Methylquinazolone *see* Methaqualone.

2-Methylquinoline *see* Quinaldine.

5-Methyl-8-quinolinol *see* Tiliquinol.

6-Methyl-8-quinolinol bismuth hydroxide compound *see* Mebiquine.

3-Methylquinoxaline-2-carboxylic acid 2,4-dioxide 2-hydroxyethyl ester *see* Temodox.

3-Methylquinoxaline-2-carboxylic acid hydrazide 1,4-dioxide *see* Drazidox.

6-Methyl-2,3-quinoxalinedithiol cyclic *S*,*S*-dithiocarbonate *see* Chinomethionat.

3-Methyl-2-quinoxalinemethanol 1,4-dioxide *see* Mequidox.

Methyl 3-(2-quinoxalinylmethylene)carbazoate *N*¹,*N*⁴-dioxide *see* Carbadox.

Methylreserpate esters *see* Mefeserpine; Rescimetol; Rescinnamine; Reserpine; Syrosingopine.

5-Methylresorcinol *see* Orcinol.

Methylrosaniline chloride *see* Crystal violet.

3-Methylsalicylamide *see* Cresotamide.

METHYL SALICYLATE (Betula oil; Gaultheria oil; oil of wintergreen; sweet birch oil; teaberry oil; wintergreen oil).

3-Methylsalicylic acid *see* Hydroxytoluic acid.

5-Methylsalicylic acid *see* 2,5-Cresotic acid.

Methyl scopolamine nitrate *see* Scopolamine methyl nitrate.

24-Methyl-9,10-secocholesta-5,7,10(19),22-tetraen-3β-ol *see* Ergocalciferol.

24-Methyl-9,10-secocholesta-5,7,22-trien-3β-ol *see* Dihydrotachysterol.

Methylstanazole *see* Stanozolol.

10-Methylstearic acid *see* Tuberculostearic acid.

Methyl styryl ketone *see* Benzylideneacetone.

2-Methylsulfadiazine *see* Sulfamerazine.

5-Methylsulfadiazine *see* Sulfaperin.

N-(4-Methyl-2-sulfamoyl-Δ²-1,3,4-thiadiazolin-5-ylidene)acetamide *see* Methazolamide.

Methyl sulfanilylcarbamate *see* Asulam.

Methylsulfapyrimidine *see* Sulfamerazine.

Methyl sulfate(s) *see* Metilsulfate(s).

Methylsulfazine (tr) *see* Sulfamerazine.

2-(Methylsulfinylacetyl)pyridine *see* Oxisuran.

Methylsulfinylmethyl 2-pyridyl ketone *see* Oxisuran.

7-(Methylsulfinyl)-9-oxoxanthene-2-carboxylic acid *see* Tixanox.

METHYLSULFONAL (2,2-bis(ethylsulfonyl)butane; bis(ethylsulfonyl)ethylmethylmethane; sulfonethylmethane; ethylsulfonal; 'trional').

4-Methylsulfonyl-2,6-dinitro-*N*,*N*-dipropylaniline *see* Nitralin.

6-[(*R*)-2-[3-(Methylsulfonyl)-2-oxo-1-imidazolidinecarboxamido]-2-phenylacetamido]penicillanic acid *see* Mezlocillin.

(6*R*)-6-[*N*-[3-(Methylsulfonyl)-2-oxoimidazolidin-1-ylcarbonyl]-D-phenylglycylamino]penicillanic acid *see* Mezlocillin.

1-[3-(2-Methylsulfonylphenothiazin-10-yl)propyl]-isonipecotamide *see* Metopimazine.

2-[*p*-(Methylsulfonyl)phenyl]imidazole[1,2-*a*]pyridine *see* Zolimidine.

Methyl sulfoxide *see* Dimethyl sulfoxide.

'Methylsympatol' *see* *p*-Hydroxyephedrine.

'Methylsystox' (tr) *see under* Demeton-O-methyl.

'Methyl tegosept' *see* Methyl paraben.

METHYLTESTOSTERONE*** (17β-hydroxy-17-methylandrost-4-en-3-one; 17-methyltestosterone; NSC-9701).

Methyl 2-tetradecylglycidate *see* Methyl palmoxirate.

Methyl 2-tetradecyloxiranecarboxylate *see* Methyl palmoxirate.

(−)-2-Methyl-3′-(2,3,5,6-tetrahydroimidazo[2,1-*b*]thiazol-6-yl)propionanilide *see* Butamisole.

trans-3-Methyl-2-[2-(1,4,6-tetrahydro-1-methylpyrimid-2-yl)vinyl]thiophene *see* Morantel.

2-Methyl-2-[*p*-(1,2,3,4-tetrahydronaphth-1-yl)phenoxy]propionic acid *see* Nafenopin.

Methyl tetrahydronicotinate *see* Guvacoline.

3-Methyl-7-[2-[*p*-(1,4,5,6-tetrahydropyrimidin-2-yl)-phenyl]acetamido]-2-cephem-2-carboxylic acid *see* Cefrotil.

2-Methyl-3-(3,7,11,15-tetramethylhexadecatetraen-yl)-1,4-naphthoquinone *see* Menatetrenone.

2-Methyl-3-*all*-*trans*-tetraprenyl-1,4-naphthoquinone *see* Farnoquinone.

3-[[(1-Methyl-1*H*-tetrazol-5-yl)thio]methyl]-7-[2-[(trifluoromethyl)thio]acetamido]-2-cephem-2-carboxylic acid *see* Cefazaflur.

Methyl 5-(2-thenoyl)-2-benzimidazolecarbamate *see* Nocodazole.

4′-[(5-Methyl-1,3,4-thiadiazol-2-yl)sulfamoyl]phthalanilic acid *see* Phthalylsulfamethizole.

*N*¹-(5-Methyl-1,3,4-thiadiazol-2-yl)sulfanilamide *see* Sulfamethizole.

3-[[(5-Methyl-1,3,4-thiadiazol-2-yl)thio]methyl]-7-[2-(1*H*-tetrazol-1-yl)acetamido]-2-cephem-2-carboxylic acid *see* Cefazolin.

*N*¹-(4-Methylthiazol-2-yl)sulfanilanide *see* Sulfamethylthiazole.

Methylthiazothion *see* Azinphos-methyl.

α-Methyl-4-(2-thienylcarbonyl)benzeneacetic acid *see* Suprofen.

Methyl 5-(2-thienylcarbonyl)-1*H*-benzimidazole-2-carbamate *see* Nocodazole.

6-Methylthiochroman-7-sulfonamide 1,1-dioxide *see* Meticrane.

3-Methyl-2-thioimidazoline-1-carboxylic acid ethyl ester *see* Carbimazole.

5-(Methylthiomethyl)-3-(5-nitrofurfurylidene-amino)-2-oxazolidinone *see* Nifuratel.

8β-[(Methylthio)methyl]-6-propylergoline *see* Pergolide.

Methylthionine chloride *see* Azure C.

Methylthioninium chloride *see* Methylene blue.

Methyl thiophanate *see* Thiophanate-methyl.

6-(METHYLTHIO)PURINE (NSC-20105).

6-(METHYLTHIO)PURINE RIBOSIDE (6-methylmercaptopurine riboside; NSC-40774).

3-(Methylthio)-5-(4,5,6-trichlorobenzimidazol-2-ylthio)-1,2,4-thiadiazole *see* Subendazole.

METHYLTHIOURACIL* (6-methyl-2-thiouracil; 4-methyl-2-thiouracil; MTU).

4(5)-[4-(3-Methylthioureido)butyl]imidazole *see* Burimamide.

5-Methyl-4-[[[2-(2-thioureido)ethyl]thio]methyl]imidazole *see* Metiamide.

α-Methyl-N-(2-thioxanthen-9-ylethyl)phenethylamine *see* Tixadil.

1-Methyl-4-(thioxanthen-9-ylidene)piperidine *see* Pimethixene.

1-Methyl-3-thioxanthen-9-ylmethylpiperidine *see* Metixene.

4-(Methylthio)-3,5-xylyl methylcarbamate *see* Methiocarb.

α-Methyl-DL-thyroxine ethyl ester *see* Etiroxate.

1-Methyl-5-p-toluoylpyrrole-2-acetic acid *see* Tolmetin.

1-Methyl-2-o-tolylethylamine *see* Ortetamine.

5-Methyl-3-[2-(4-m-tolylpiperazin-1-yl)ethyl]pyrazole *see* Tolpiprazole.

β-Methyl-γ-(p-tolyl)-1-piperidinepropanone *see* Tolperisone.

2-Methyl-3-(o-tolyl)-4-quinazolinone *see* Methaqualone.

(−)-α-Methyl-N-[(p-tolylsulfonyl)carbamoyl]phenethylamine *see* Tosifen.

N-Methyl-N-(m-tolyl)thionocarbamic acid 2-naphthyl ester *see* Tolnaftate.

6-Methyl-1,4,6-triazine-3,5-dione *see* Azathymine.

Methyl 3,5,6-tri-O-benzyl-D-glucofuranoside *see* Mebenoside.

α-Methyl-N-(2,2,2-trichloroethylidene)phenethylamine *see* Amfecloral.

2-Methyl-4-(2,2,2-trichloro-1-hydroxyethoxy)-2-pentanol *see* Chloralodol.

1-Methyl-3-(2,2,2-trichloro-1-hydroxyethyl)urea *see* Mecloralurea.

Methyltrienolone *see* Metribolone.

4,4′-[1-Methyl-2-(2,2,2-trifluoroethyl)ethylene]bis(2-fluorophenol) *see* Pentafluranol.

4,4′-[1-Methyl-2-(2,2,2-trifluoroethyl)ethylene]diphenol *see* Terfluranol.

2-[2-Methyl-3-(trifluoromethyl)anilino]nicotinic acid *see* Flunixin.

2-[[α-Methyl-m-(trifluoromethyl)phenethyl]amino]ethanol benzoate *see* Benfluorex.

α-[[α-Methyl-m-(trifluoromethyl)phenethyl]carbamoyl]-p-acetanisidide *see* Flucetorex.

p-[[[α-Methyl-m-(trifluoromethyl)phenethyl]carbamoyl]methoxy]acetanilide *see* Flucetorex.

2-[[2-Methyl-3-(trifluoromethyl)phenyl]amino]-3-pyridinecarboxylic acid *see* Flunixin.

5-Methyl-N-[p-(trifluoromethyl)phenyl]-4-isoxazolecarboxamide *see* Leflunomide.

N-Methyl-3-[(α,α,α-trifluoro-m-tolyl)oxy]-1-azetidinecarboxamide *see* Fluzinamide.

Methyl 9,11,15-trihydroxy-15-methylprosta-4,5,13-trienoate *see* Prostalene.

Methyl 9,11,15-trihydroxy-16-phenoxy-ω-tetranorprosta-4,5,13-trienoate *see* Fenprostalene.

2-Methyl-N-[2,4,6-triiodo-3-[(1-morpholinoethylidene)amino]benzoyl]-β-alanine *see* Iomorinic acid.

5-Methyl-6-[[(3,4,5-trimethoxyphenyl)amino]methyl]-2,4-quinazolinediamine *see* Trimetrexate.

4-[[2-Methyl-2-(3,4,5-trimethoxyphenyl)-1,3-dioxolan-4-yl]methyl]morpholine *see* Trixolane.

Methyl 11,17α,18α-trimethoxy-3β,20α-yohimban-16β-carboxylate *see* Metoserpate.

2-Methyl-2-(4′,8′,12-trimethyltrideca-3,7,11-trienyl)-6-chromanol *see* Tocotrienol.

'Methyltrithion' *see* Carbofenotion methyl.

α-Methyltropic acid tropine ester *see* Atromepine.

8-Methyltropinium bromide mandelate *see* Homatropine methyl bromide.

8-Methyltropinium bromide 2-propylvalerate *see* Octatropine methylbromide.

8-Methyltropinium bromide xanthene-9-carboxylate *see* Trantelinium bromide.

2-METHYLTRYPTAMINE (indopan; α-methyltryptamine).

N-METHYLTRYPTOPHAN (abrine).

'Methyl tuads' *see* Thiram.

α-Methyltyramine *see* Hydroxyamphetamine.

α-Methyl-m-tyramine *see* Gepefrine.

α-Methyltyrosine *see* Metirosine; Racemetirosine.

4-Methylumbelliferone *see* Hymecromone.

5-Methyluracil *see* Thymine.

Methyl urethan *see* Methyl carbamate.

Methyl vinyl ether polymer with maleic acid, iron salt *see* Ferropolimaler.

METHYL VIOLET* (mixture of hydrochlorides of (chiefly) tetra-, penta- and hexamethylpararosanilines).
See also Crystal violet.

Methyl viologen *see* Paraquat.

β-METHYLXYLOCHOLINE ([2-(2,6-dimethylphenoxy)propyl]trimethylammonium chloride; β-methylcholine xylyl ether; SK&F-6890; β-TM-10).

1-Methyl-2-(2,6-xylylcarbamoyl)piperidine *see* Mepivacaine.

1-Methyl-2-(2,6-xylyloxy)ethylamine *see* Mexiletine.

N-Methyl-N′-2,4-xylyl-N-(N-2,4-xylylformimidoyl)formamidine *see* Amitraz.

1-Methylyohimbane *see* Mimbane.

Methyl yohimbate *see* Yohimbine.

Methynodiol diacetate *see* Metynodiol diacetate.

Methypranol *see* Metipranolol.

Methypregnone* *see* Medroxyprogesterone.

METHYPRYLON* (3,3-diethyl-5-methyl-2,4-piperidinedione; dimerin; Ro 1-6463).

Methyridine* *see* Metyridine.

'Methyrit' *see* Chlorpheniramine.

METHYSERGIDE*** (N-[1-(hydroxymethyl)-propyl]-1-methyl-D-lysergamide; methyllysergic acid butanolamide; (1-methyl)methylergometrine; dimethylergometrine; dimethylergonovine; methysergide maleate; methysergide tartrate; UML-491).

METHYSTICIN (5,6-dihydro-4-methoxy-6-(3,4-methylenedioxystyryl)-2-pyrone; kavahin; kavatin).

Methyzazone* see Metisazone.

METIAMIDE** (1-methyl-3-[2-[(5-methylimidazol-4-ylmethyl)thio]ethyl]-2-thiourea; 5-methyl-4-[[[2-(2-thioureido)ethyl]thio]methyl]imidazole; SK&F-92058).

METIAPINE*** (2-methyl-11-(4-methylpiperazin-1-yl)dibenzo[b,f][1,4]thiazepine).

METIAZINIC ACID*** (2-carboxymethyl-10-methylphenothiazine; 10-methylphenothiazin-2-ylacetic acid; FI-6642; RP 16091; 'soridermal'; 'soripal').

METICILLIN** (6-(2,6-dimethoxybenzamido)penicillanic acid; methicillin; sodium methicillin; dimethoxyphenecillin; dimethoxyphenylpenicillin; penicillin X-1497; BRL-1241; SQ-16123; X-1497).
See also Tameticillin.

Meticlorpindol see Clopidol.

'Meticortelone' see Prednisolone.

'Meticorten' see Prednisone.

METICRANE*** (6-methylthiochroman-7-sulfonamide 1,1-dioxide; thiachromane; SD-17102).

'Metifex' see Ethacridine lactate.

'Metiguanide' see Metformin.

'Metilar' see Paramethasone acetate.

METILDIGOXIN*** (3β-[O-(2,6-dideoxy-4-O-methyl-D-ribo-hexopyranosyl)-(1→4)-O-(2,6-dideoxy-D-ribo-hexopyranosyl)-(1→4)-2,6-dideoxy-D-ribo-hexopyranosyloxy]-12β,14-dihydroxy-5β,14β-card-20(22)-enolide; 3β,12β,14β-trihydroxy-5β-card-20(22)-enolide 3-(4'''-O-methyltridigitoxoside); 4'''-O-methyldigoxin; β-methyldigoxin; medigoxin; 'lanitop').

'Metilenbiotic' see Metacycline.

Metil-merkaptofos (tr) see Demeton-O-methyl.

Metilmerkaptofosoksid (tr) see Oxydemetonmethyl.

Metil-merkaptofos tiolovyj (tr) see Demeton-S-methyl.

METILSULFATE(S)** (methyl sulfate(s)).

Metiltriazotion (tr) see Azinphos-methyl.

METINDIONE (tr) (2-ethyl-2-methylaminoindan-1,3-dione; methindione; metindione hydrochloride).

METINDIZATE*** (2-(hexahydro-1-methylindolin-3-yl)ethyl benzilate; methindazate).

'Metindol' see Indometacin.

Metiodol* see Methiodal sodium.

'Metione' see Methionine.

METIOPRIM*** (2,4-diamino-5-[3,5-dimethoxy-4-(methylthio)benzyl]pyrimidine).

METIOXATE*** (2-(4-methylpiperid-1-yl)ethyl 6-ethyl-2,3,6,9-tetrahydro-3-methyl-2,9-dioxo-thiazolo[5,4-f]quinoline-8-carboxylate; tioxacin 2-(4-methylpiperid-1-yl)ethyl ester).

METIPIROX*** (1-hydroxy-4,6-dimethylpyridin-2(1H)-one).

METIPRANOLOL*** (1-(4-hydroxy-2,3,5-trimethylphenoxy)-3-(isopropylamino)-2-propanol 4-acetate; 4-[2-hydroxy-3-(isopropylamino)propoxy]-2,3,6-trimethylphenyl acetate; methypranol; trimepranol; VUFB-6453; 'disorat').
See also under Butizide.

METIPRENALINE*** (4-hydroxy-α-[(isopropylamino)methyl]-3-methoxybenzyl alcohol; α-[(isopropylamino)methyl]vanillyl alcohol).

METIROSINE*** ((−)-α-methyl-L-tyrosine; metyrosine; H-9/88; L-588357; MK-781).

METIROSINE METHYL ESTER (H-44/68).

METISAZONE*** (1-methylindole-2,3-dione thiosemicarbazone; methylisatin thiosemicarbazone; methisazone; methyzazone; BW-33T57; NSC-69811).

METITEPINE** (1-[10,11-dihydro-8-(methylthio)dibenzo[b,f]thiepin-10-yl]-4-methylpiperazine; 10,11-dihydro-10-(4-methylpiperazin-1-yl)-8-(methylthio)dibenzo[b,f]thiepin; methiothepin).

METIXENE*** (1-methyl-3-thioxanthen-9-ylmethylpiperidine; 9-(1-methylpiperid-3-ylmethyl)thioxanthene; methixene; methixene hydrochloride; NSC-78194; SJ-1977).

METIXENE plus DIPYRONE ('dorsedin').

'Metizol' see Thiamazole.

METIZOLINE*** (3-(2-imidazolin-2-ylmethyl)-2-methylbenzo[b]thiophene; 2-(2-methylbenzo[b]-thien-3-ylmethyl)-2-imidazoline; benazoline; metyzoline; benazoline hydrochloride; EX-10781; 'elsyl'; 'eunasin').

METKEFAMIDE*** (L-tyrosyl-D-alanylglycyl-L-phenylalanyl-N²-methyl-L-methioninamide; metkephamid).

METKEFAMIDE ACETATE (metkefamide monoacetate; LY-127623).

Metkephamid* see Metkefamide.

Metmercapturan see Methiocarb.

METOBROMURON (1-(p-bromophenyl)-3-methoxy-3-methylurea; 'patoron').

METOCHALCONE*** (2',4,4'-trimethoxychalcone; CB-1314; 'neocolan'; 'vesidryl').

METOCINIUM IODIDE** ((2-hydroxyethyl)trimethylammonium iodide benzilate; choline benzilate; choline iodide benzilate).

METOCLOPRAMIDE*** (4-amino-5-chloro-N-(2-diethylaminoethyl)-2-methoxybenzamide; 4-amino-5-chloro-N-(2-diethylaminoethyl)-o-anisamide; metoclopramide dihydrochloride; AHR-3070-C; MK-745).

METOCLOPRAMIDE plus MEDAZEPAM ('randum').

METOCLOPRAMIDE plus PARACETAMOL ('paramax').

METOCLOPRAMIDE plus SORBITOL ('sorbiperan').

Metocurine chloride see Dimethyltubocurarine chloride.

354

METODICLOROFEN (2,4-diamino-5-(3,4-dichlorophenyl)-6-methylpyrimidine; methodichlorophen; metoprine; DDMP; BW-50197; NSC-19494; SK-5265).

'Metodril' see under Methaqualone.

METOFENAZATE*** (2-[4-[3-(2-chlorophenothiazin-10-yl)propyl]piperazin-1-yl]ethyl 3,4,5-trimethoxybenzoate; 2-chloro-10-[3-[4-(2-(3,4,5-trimethoxybenzoyloxy)ethyl)piperazin-1-yl]-propyl]phenothiazine; methophenazine).

METOFOLINE** (1-(p-chlorophenethyl)-1,2,3,4-tetrahydro-6,7-dimethoxy-2-methylisoquinoline; methopholine; ARC-I-K-1; I-K-1; NIH-7672; Ro 4-1778/1).

Metofurone* see Nifurmerone.

METOGEST*** (17β-hydroxy-16,16-dimethyl-estr-4-en-3-one; SC-14207).

METOLAZONE*** (7-chloro-1,2,3,4-tetrahydro-2-methyl-4-oxo-3-o-tolyl-6-quinazolinesulfonamide; SR-720-22; 'metenix'; 'zaroxolyn').

METOMIDATE*** (methyl 1-(α-methylbenzyl)-imidazole-5-carboxylate; R-7315).

METOPIMAZINE*** (10-[3-(4-carbamoylpiperid-1-yl)propyl]-2-methanesulfonylphenothiazine; 1-[3-(2-methylsulfonylphenothiazin-10-yl)-propyl]isonipecotamide; 10-[3-[4-carboxamidopiperid-4-yl)propyl]-2-methylsulfonylphenothiazine; EXP-999; RP 9965).

'Metopirone' see Metyrapone.

METOPON** (4,5-epoxy-3-hydroxy-5,N-dimethyl-6-oxo-morphinan; methopon; 5-methyldihydromorphinone; metopon hydrochloride).

Metoprine* see Metodiclorofen.

METOPROLOL** ((±)-1-isopropylamino-3-[p-(2-methoxyethyl)phenoxy]-2-propanol; metoprolol hydrochloride; metoprolol tartrate; CGP-2175; H-93/26; 'beloc'; 'betabloc'; 'betaloc'; 'lopressor'; 'prelis'; 'seloken').

METOPROLOL plus HYDROCHLOROTHIAZIDE ('selepress').

'Metopryl' see Methyl propyl ether.

'Metopyrone' see Metyrapone.

METOQUIZINE*** (3,5-dimethyl-N-(4,6,6a,7,8,9,10,10a-octahydro-4,7-dimethylindolo[4,3-f,g]quinolin-9-yl)pyrazole-1-carboxamide).

Metorin (tr) see Fluanisone.

METOSERPATE*** (methyl-18-epi-O-methylreserpate; methyl 11,17α,18α-trimethoxy-3β,20α-yohimban-16β-carboxylate; methyl 18-epireserpate methyl ether; methyl O-methyl-18-epireserpate; metoserpate hydrochloride; Su-9064; 'avicalm'; 'mepiserpate'; 'pacitran').

'Metosine' see Fluocinonide.

'Metosyn' see Fluocinonide.

'Metox' see Methoxychlor.

METOXEPIN*** (1-(8-methoxydibenz[b,f]oxepin-10-yl)-4-methylpiperazine; 8-methoxy-10-(4-methylpiperazin-1-yl)dibenz[b,f]oxepin).

'Metoxon' see Chlorpropham.

Metoxuran see Metoxuron.

METOXURON* (1-(3-chloro-4-methoxyphenyl)-3,3-dimethylurea; metoxuran; 'dosanex').

Metoxymarc see Anisuron.

METRAFAZOLINE*** (1,2,3,4-tetrahydro-6-(2-imidazolin-2-ylmethyl)-7-methyl-1,4-ethanonaphthalene; 2-[(1,2,3,4-tetrahydro-7-methyl-1,4-ethanonaphth-6-yl)methyl]-2-imidazoline).

METRALINDOLE*** (2,4,5,6-tetrahydro-9-methoxy-4-methyl-1H-3,4,6a-triazafluoranthene; inkasan).

'Metramas' see Amiton.

'Metramine' see Methenamine.

'Metraspray' see Tetracaine.

METRAZIFONE*** (5,6-bis[p-(dimethylamino)-phenyl]-2-methyl-as-triazin-3(2H)-one).

'Metrazole' see Pentetrazole.

'Metrazone' see Feprazone.

Metriben see Tricamba.

METRIBOLONE*** (17β-hydroxy-17-methylestra-4,9,11-trien-3-one; 17β-hydroxy-17α-methyl-19-norandrosta-4,9,11-trien-3-one; methyltrienolone; R-1881).

METRIBUZIN* (4-amino-6-(1,1-dimethylethyl)-3-(methylthio)-1,2,4-triazin-5(4H)-one; 4-amino-6-tert-butyl-3-(methylthio)-as-triazin-5(4H)-one; BAY-94337; 'sencor').

METRIFONATE*** (dimethyl (2,2,2-trichloro-1-hydroxyethyl)phosphonate; trichlorphon; chlorofos; chlorophos; klorofos; phoschlorin; phosclorine; trichlorfon; trichlorofon; trichlorophone; triclorfon; Bayer-2349; Bayer L-1359; DETF).

METRIFONATE plus ATROPINE ('neguvon').

METRIFONATE plus ATROPINE & PRALIDOXIME ('bubulin').

METRIFONATE plus OXYDEMETON-METHYL ('dipterex-ER').

Metrifonate butyrate see Butonate.

METRIFUDIL*** (N-(o-methylbenzyl)adenosine; 6-(o-methylbenzylamino)-9-β-D-ribofuranosyl-9H-purine; Th-322).

'Metrisone' see Methylprednisolone.

METRIZAMIDE*** (2-[3-acetamido-2,4,6-triiodo-5-(N-methylacetamido)benzamido]-2-deoxy-D-glucose; WIN-39103; 'amipaque').

METRIZOIC ACID* (3-acetamido-2,4,6-triiodo-5-(N-methylacetamido)benzoic acid).
   See also Meglumine metrizoate; Sodium metrizoate.

Metrogestone see Medrogestone.

'Metromin' see Dimetamfetamine.

'Metron' see Parathion methyl and Pheniramine.

'Metronal' see Dixyrazine.

METRONIDAZOLE*** (1-(2-hydroxyethyl)-2-methyl-5-nitroimidazole; 2-methyl-5-nitroimidazole-1-ethanol; trichopol; Bayer-5360; NSC-50364; RP 8823).

METRONIDAZOLE plus CLOTRIMAZOLE ('meclo').

METRONIDAZOLE plus LYSOZYME ('deflamon').

METRONIDAZOLE plus NITROFURANTOIN ('menifur').

METRONIDAZOLE plus SPIRAMYCIN ('rodogyl').

METRONIDAZOLE BENZOATE (benzoylmetronidazole; RP 9712; 'benzoyl-flagyl').

'Metropine' *see* Atropine methonitrate.

'Metrotonin' *see* Dimetamfetamine.

'Metrulen' *see under* Etynodiol diacetate.

'Metubine' *see* Dimethyltubocurarine chloride.

Metuclazepam *see* Metaclazepam.

METUREDEPA*** (ethyl [bis(2,2-dimethylaziridinyl)phosphinyl]carbamate; dimethylurethamide; dimethylurethimine; AB-132; NSC-51325).

'Metycaine' *see* Piperocaine.

Metylperone *see* Melperone.

METYNODIOL*** (17α-ethynyl-3β,17-dihydroxy-11β-methylestr-4-ene; 17α-ethynyl-11β-methyl-19-norandrost-4-ene-3β,17-diol; 17α-ethynyl-11β-methylestr-4-ene-3β,17-diol; 11β-methyl-19-nor-17α-pregn-4-en-20-yne-3β,17-diol; methyletynodiol).

METYNODIOL DIACETATE (methynodiol diacetate; SC-19198).

METYRAPONE*** (2-methyl-1,2-dipyrid-3-yl-1-propanone; methapyrapone; methbipyrapone; metyrapone tartrate; Su-8874; Su-4485).

METYRIDINE** (2-(2-methoxyethyl)pyridine; methyridine).

Metyrosine* *see* Metirosine.

Metyzoline* *see* Metizoline.

MEVALONIC ACID (3,5-dihydroxy-3-methylvaleric acid; hiochic acid; MK-91).

'Mevasine' *see* Mecamylamine.

MEVASTATIN*** ((1*S*,7*S*,8*S*,8a*R*)-1,2,3,7,8,8a-hexahydro-7-methyl-8-[2-[(2*R*,4*R*)-tetrahydro-4-hydroxy-6-oxo-2*H*-pyran-2-yl]ethyl]naphth-1-yl (*S*)-2-methylbutyrate).

MEVINPHOS* (methyl 3-(dimethoxyphosphinyloxy)-2-butenoate; methyl 3-hydroxy-*cis*-crotonate dimethyl phosphate; PD-5; 'phosdrin').

MEXACARBATE* (4-(dimethylamino)-3,5-dimethylphenyl methylcarbamate; 4-(dimethylamino)-3,5-xylyl methylcarbamate; OMS-47; 'zectran').

'Mexaform' *see under* Clioquinol.

MEXAFYLLINE*** (3-(3-cyclohexen-1-ylmethyl)-1,8-dimethylxanthine).

Mexamine *see* 5-Methoxytryptamine.

MEXAZOLAM*** (10-chloro-11b-(*o*-chlorophenyl)-2,3,7,11b-tetrahydro-3-methyloxazolo[3,2-*d*]-[1,4]benzodiazepin-6(5*H*)-one).

MEXENONE** (2-hydroxy-4-methoxy-4'-methylbenzophenone; 'uvistat 2211').

MEXILETINE*** (1-(2-aminopropoxy)-2,6-xylene; 2-(2-aminopropoxy)-*m*-xylene; 1-methyl-2-(2,6-xylyloxy)ethylamine; mexiletine hydrochloride; Ko-1173; 'mexitil').

'Mexitil' *see* Mexiletine.

'Mexocine' *see* Demeclocycline.

MEXOPROFEN*** (*p*-(*trans*-2-methylcyclohexyl)hydratropic acid; 2-[4-(*trans*-2-methylcyclohexyl)phenyl]propionic acid).

MEXRENOATE POTASSIUM*** (17-hydroxy-3-oxo-17α-pregn-4-ene-7,21-dicarboxylic acid 7-methyl ester 21-potassium salt; 7-methyl 21-potassium 17-hydroxy-3-oxo-17α-pregn-4-ene-7α,21-dicarboxylate; potassium mexrenoate; SC-26714).

Mexyphamine *see* Methoxyphenamine.

Mezaton *see* Phenylephrine.

Mezcaline *see* Mescaline.

MEZEPINE*** (5,6-dihydro-5-(3-methylaminopropyl)-11*H*-dibenz[*b*,*e*]azepine).

MEZILAMINE*** (1-[4-chloro-2-(methylamino)-5-(methylthio)pyrimidin-6-yl]-4-methylpiperazine; 4-chloro-2-(methylamino)-6-(4-methylpiperazin-1-yl)-5-(methylthio)pyrimidine).

MEZLOCILLIN*** ((2*S*,5*R*,6*R*)-6-[(*R*)-2-[3-(methylsulfonyl)-2-oxo-1-imidazolidinecarboxamido]-2-phenylacetamido]penicillanic acid; (6*R*)-6-[*N*-[3-(methylsulfonyl)-2-oxoimidazolidin-1-ylcarbonyl]-D-phenylglycylamino]penicillanic acid; mezlocillin sodium; BAY f-1353; 'baypen').

MEZLOCILLIN plus OXACILLIN ('optocillin').

MF-10 *see* Doxepin.

MFQ *see* Morfamquat.

Mg-46 *see* Clofibride.

Mg-482 *see* Silibinin.

Mg-559 *see* Metamfepramone.

Mg-1480 *see* Salinazid.

Mg-1559 *see* Xenbucin.

Mg-2522 *see* Clorindione.

Mg-2555 *see* Bromindione.

Mg-4833 *see* Fencibutirol.

Mg-5454 *see* Guaiapate.

Mg-5771 *see* Butixirate.

Mg-8823 *see* Exaprolol.

Mg-42799 *see* Trospium chloride.

'MGA' *see* Melengestrol acetate.

MGK-264 *see* (Ethylhexyl)norbornenedicarboximide.

M-2H *see* Butoctamide hemisuccinate.

MH-532 *see* Phenprobamate.

MHIP *see* Toliprolol.

2M-4H-M (tr) *see* 4-(4-Chloro-2-methylphenoxy)-butyric acid.

Mi-85 *see* Azapropazone.

MI-216 *see* Iotalamic acid.

MI-217 *see* Ecothiopate iodide.

MI-860 *see under* Anagestone acetate.

MIANSERIN** (1,2,3,4,10,14b-hexahydro-2-methyldibenzo[*c*,*f*]pyrazino[1,2-*a*]azepine; mianserin hydrochloride; GB-94; Org GB-94; 'athymil'; 'bolvidon'; 'norval'; 'tolvin'; 'tolvon').

'Miazide' *see under* Ethambutol.

Miazine *see* Pyrimidine.

MIBOLERONE*** (7α,17-dimethyl-19-nortestosterone; 7α,17-dimethylnandrolone; 17β-hydroxy-7α,17-dimethylestr-4-en-3-one; U-10997).

MIC-135 *see* Colestyramine.

'Micalcic' *see* Salcatonin.

'Micalin' *see* Diethyltoluamide.

'Micalite' *see* Lithium carbonate.

'Micasin' *see* Chlorfenethol.

'Micatin' *see* Miconazole.

MICINICATE*** (nicotinic acid ester with *cis*-3,3,5-trimethylcyclohexyl (±)-mandelate; *cis*-

3,3,5-trimethylcyclohexyl DL-α-(nicotinoyloxy)-phenylacetate; cyclandelate nicotinate; RV-12128).

Mico.... *see also* Myco.....

'Micofur' *see* Nifuroxime.

MICONAZOLE*** (1-[2,4-dichloro-β-(2,4-di-chlorobenzyloxy)phenethyl]imidazole; miconazole nitrate; R-14889).

MICONAZOLE plus HYDROCORTISONE ('daktacort').

MICONAZOLE plus MAZIPREDONE ('mycosolvon').

'Micoren' *see* Prethcamide.

'Microcillin' *see* Carbenicillin.

'Microlut' *see* Levonorgestrel.

'Microluton' *see* Levonorgestrel.

'Micronase' *see* Glibenclamide.

MICRONOMICIN** (*O*-[2-amino-2,3,4,6-tetra-deoxy-6-(methylamino)-α-D-*erythro*-hexopyra-nosyl (1→4)]-*O*-[3-deoxy-4-*C*-methyl-3-(methyl-amino)-β-L-arabinopyranosyl(1→6)]-2-deoxy-D-streptamine).

'Micronor' *see* Norethisterone.

'Micronovum' *see* Norethisterone.

'Micropenin' *see* Oxacillin.

'Microtrim' *see* Co-trimoxazole.

'Microval' *see* Levonorgestrel.

'Mictasol' *see* Methenamine.

'Mictine' *see* Aminometradine.

'Mictonorm' *see* Propiverine.

'Mictral' *see* Nalidixic acid.

MIDAFLUR** (4-amino-2,2,5,5-tetrakis(trifluor-omethyl)-3-imidazoline; 5-imino-2,2,4,4-tetra-kis(trifluoromethyl)imidazolidine; EXP-338).

'Midalgyl' *see under* Proxifezone.

MIDAMALINE** (*N*'-(5-chloro-2-benzimidazol-ylmethyl)-*N*,*N*'-dimethyl-*N*-phenylethylenedi-amine).

'Midamor' *see* Amiloride.

'Midantane' *see* Amantadine.

MIDAZOLAM*** (8-chloro-6-(2-fluorophenyl)-1-methyl-4*H*-imidazo[1,5-*a*][1,4]-benzodiazepine; 'dormicum'; 'hypnovel').

MIDAZOLAM MALEATE* (midazolam (*Z*)-2-butenedioate; Ro 21-3981/001).

'Midecacine' *see* Midecamycin.

MIDECAMYCIN** (7-(formylmethyl)-4,10-di-hydroxy-5-methoxy-9,16-dimethyl-2-oxooxa-cyclohexadeca-11,13-dien-6-yl 3,6-dideoxy-4-*O*-(2,6-dideoxy-3-*C*-methyl-α-L-*ribo*-hexopyranos-yl)-3-dimethylamino-β-D-glucopyranoside 4,4''-dipropionate; mydecamycin; CM-9164; SF-837; 'medemycin'; 'midecacine').

'Midicel' *see* Sulfamethoxypyridazine.

'Midikel' *see* Sulfamethoxypyridazine.

'Midocil' *see* Tolmetin.

MIDODRINE*** ((±)-2-amino-*N*-(β-hydroxy-2,5-dimethoxyphenethyl)acetamide; (±)-2-amino-*N*-[2-(2,5-dimethoxyphenyl)-2-hydroxy-ethyl]acetamide; (±)-1-(2,5-dimethoxyphenyl)-2-glycinamidoethanol; (±)-α-(glycinamido-methyl)-2,5-dimethoxybenzyl alcohol; A-4020 Linz; ST-1085; St.Peter 224; 'alphamine'; 'gu-

tron').

'Midol' *see* Cinnamedrine.

'Midosal' *see* Carbutamide.

'Midoxin' *see* Doxycycline.

'Midronal' *see* Cinnarizine.

'Mielucin' *see* Busulfan.

MIFENTIDINE** (*N*-(*p*-imidazol-4-ylphenyl)-*N*'-isopropylformamidine).

MIFOBATE*** (dimethyl (*p*-chloro-α-hydroxy-benzyl)phosphonate dimethyl phosphate).

'Miglucan' *see* Glibenclamide.

'Migristene' *see* Dimetotiazine mesilate.

MIH *see* Procarbazine.

MIKAMYCIN*** (antibiotic from *Str. mitakaen-sis*; mikamycin B; ostreogrycin B).

Mikamycin B *see* Mikamycin.

'Mikedimide' *see* Bemegride.

'Mikro-30' *see* Levonorgestrel.

MILACEMIDE*** (2-(pentylamino)acetamide; CP-1551-S).

'Milbam' *see* Ziram.

'Milbax' *see under* Chlorfenethol.

'Milcurb' *see* Dimethirimol.

'Mildex' *see* Dinocap.

MILENPERONE*** (5-chloro-1-[3-[4-(*p*-fluoro-benzoyl)piperid-1-yl]propyl]-2-benzimidazolin-one; R-34009).

'Milibis' *see* Glycobiarsol.

'Milid' *see* Proglumide.

MILIPERTINE*** (1-[2-(5,6-dimethoxy-2-meth-ylindol-3-yl)ethyl]-4-(*o*-methoxyphenyl)piperaz-ine; 5,6-dimethoxy-3-[2-[4-(*o*-methoxyphenyl)-piperazin-1-yl]ethyl]-2-methylindole; WIN-18935).

'Milkinol' *see* Docusate sodium.

'Millicaine' *see* Betoxycaine.

'Millicorten' *see* Dexamethasone.

'Milligynon' *see* Norethisterone acetate.

'Millophylline' *see* Etamiphyllin camsilate.

'Milogard' *see* Antu.

'Milontin' *see* Phensuximide.

'Milonton' *see* Phensuximide.

MILOXACIN*** (5,8-dihydro-5-methoxy-8-oxo-1,3-dioxolo[4,5-*g*]quinoline-7-carboxylic acid).

MILRINONE** (1,6-dihydro-2-methyl-6-oxo-[3,4'-bipyridine]-5-carbonitrile; WIN-47203).

'Milstem' *see* Ethirimol.

'Milton' *see* Sodium hypochlorite.

'Miltown' *see* Meprobamate.

'Mil-U-cal' *see* Calcium levulinate.

'Milurit' *see* Allopurinol.

MIMBANE*** (1,2,3,4,4a,5,7,8,13,13b,14,14a-do-decahydro-13-methylbenz[*g*]indolo[2,3-*a*]quino-lizine; 1-methylyohimbane; mimbane hydro-chloride; W-2291A).

MIMOSINE ((−)-2-amino-3-(3-hydroxy-4-oxo-pyrid-1-yl)propionic acid; (−)-α-amino-(3-hydr-oxy-4-pyridinone)propionic acid; 3-hydroxy-4-oxo-1(4*H*)-pyridinealanine).
See also Leucenol.

'Minacide' *see* Promecarb.

'Minanine' *see* Tosylchloramide sodium.

MINAPRINE*** (4-methyl-3-[(2-morpholino-

357

ethyl)amino]-6-phenylpyridazine; 4-[2-[(4-methyl-6-phenylpyridazin-3-yl)amino]ethyl]morpholine; minaprine hydrochloride; Agr-1240; CB-30038; 'cantor').

MINAXOLONE*** (11α-(dimethylamino)-2β-ethoxy-3α-hydroxy-5α-pregnan-20-one; CCI-12933).

'Mincard' *see* Aminometradine.

Mindolic acid *see* Clometacin.

MINDOPERONE*** (4'-fluoro-4-[4-(6-methoxy-2-methylindol-3-yl)piperid-1-yl]butyrophenone; 1-[3-(p-fluorobenzoyl)propyl]-4-(6-methoxy-2-methylindol-3-yl)piperidine).

'Minelcin' *see* Benzilonium bromide.

MINEPENTATE*** (2-[2-(dimethylamino)ethoxy]ethyl 1-phenylcyclopentanecarboxylate; UCB-1549).

'Minians' *see* Lormetazepam.

'Minidiab' *see* Glipizide.

'Minifage' *see* Fenfluramine.

'Minihep' *see* Heparin.

'Minikel' *see* Sulfamethoxypyridazine.

'Minilyn' *see under* Ethinylestradiol.

'Minims' *see* Cyclopentolate.

'Minipress' *see* Prazosin.

'Minirin' *see* Desmopressin diacetate.

'Minocin' *see* Minocycline.

'Minocrin' *see* Aminoacridine.

MINOCROMIL** (6-(methylamino)-4-oxo-10-propyl-4H-pyrano[3,2-g]quinoline-2,8-dicarboxylic acid; minocromil sodium).

MINOCYCLINE*** (6-demethyl-6-deoxy-7-dimethylaminotetracycline).

'Minocyn' *see* Minocycline.

'Minodiab' *see* Glipizide.

'Minomax' *see* Minocycline.

'Minomycin' *see* Minocycline.

'Minoran' *see* Methoserpidine.

'Minovlar' *see under* Norethisterone acetate.

MINOXIDIL*** (2,4-diamino-6-piperid-1-ylpyrimidine 3-oxide; 6-piperid-1-yl-2,4-pyrimidinediamine 3-oxide; 6-piperidino-2,4-pyrimidinediamine 3-oxide; U-10858; 'lonitan'; 'lonolox').

'Minozinan' *see* Levomepromazine.

'Mintacol' *see* Paraoxon.

'Mintezol' *see* Tiabendazole.

'Mintussin' *see* Atropine methobromide.

'Minuric' *see* Benzbromarone.

'Minurin' *see* Desmopressin diacetate.

'Minus' *see* Sodium alginate.

'Minusin' *see* Cathine.

'Minzil' *see* Chlorothiazide.

'Minzol' *see* Tiabendazole.

Mio.... *see also* Myo.....

'Miocarpine' *see* Pilocarpine.

MIOFLAZINE** ((±)-4-[4,4-bis(p-fluorophenyl)butyl]-3-carbamoyl-2',6'-dichloro-1-piperazineacetanilide; 3-(aminocarbonyl)-4-[4,4-bis(4-fluorophenyl)butyl]-N-(2,6-dichlorophenyl)-1-piperazineacetamide; mioflazine hydrochloride; R-51469).

'Miokon' *see* Sodium diprotrizoate.

'Miorelax' *see* Guaifenesin.

'Miostat' *see* Carbachol.

'Mioticol' *see* O,O-Diisopropyl O-p-nitrophenyl phosphate.

'Miotisal' *see* Paraoxon.

MIPAFOX* (N,N'-bis(1-methylethyl)phosphorodiamidic fluoride; bis(isopropylamino)fluorophosphine oxide; N,N'-diisopropylphosphorodiamidic fluoride; isopestox; 'pestox XV').

'Mipax' *see* Dimethyl phthalate.

MIPC *see* Isoprocarb.

'Mipicin' *see* Isoprocarb.

MIPIMAZOLE** (1-isopropyl-2-imidazolidinethione).

'Miracil-D' *see* Lucanthone.

'Miracol' *see* Lucanthone.

'Miradon' *see* Anisindione.

'Mirapront' *see* Phentermine resin.

'Mirbedal' *see* Sulfatolamide.

'Mircol' *see* Mequitazine.

'Miretilan' *see* Endralazine mesilate.

MIREX (1,1a,2,2,3,3a,4,5,5,5a,5b,6-dodecachlorooctahydro-1,3,4-metheno-1H-cyclobuta[cd]pentalene).

'Mirfat' *see* Furosemide.

MIRINCAMYCIN** (mixture of *cis* and *trans* forms of methyl 7-chloro-6,7,8-trideoxy-6-(4-pentyl-L-2-pyrrolidinecarboxamido)-1-thio-L-*threo*-α-D-*galacto*-octopyranoside; mirincamycin hydrochloride; U-24729A).

MIRISTALKONIUM CHLORIDE*** (benzyldimethyltetradecylammonium chloride; myristalkonium chloride).

MIROPROFEN** (2-[p-(imidazo[1,2-a]pyridin-2-yl)phenyl]propionic acid; p-imidazo[1,2-a]pyridin-2-ylhydratropic acid; Y-9213).

'Mirvan' *see* Alclofenac.

'Miscleron' *see* Clofibrate.

'Misedant' *see* Meprobamate.

MISONIDAZOLE*** (1-(2-hydroxy-3-methoxypropyl)-2-nitroimidazole; 1-methoxy-3-(2-nitroimidazol-1-yl)-2-propanol; α-(methoxymethyl)-2-nitroimidazole-1-ethanol; NSC-261037; Ro 7-0582).

MISOPROSTOL*** ((±)-methyl (1R,2R,3R)-3-hydroxy-2-[(E)-(4RS)-4-hydroxy-4-methyl-1-octenyl]-5-oxocyclopentaneheptanoate; (±)-methyl (13E)-11,16-dihydroxy-16-methyl-9-oxoprost-13-enoate; SC-29333).

'Mistabron' *see* Mesna.

Mistletoe *see* Viscum album.

'Misulban' *see* Busulfan.

'Mitaban' *see* Amitraz.

'Mitabol' *see* Mesulfen.

'Mitac' *see* Amitraz.

'Mitarson' *see* Defosfamide.

'Mitenyl' *see under* Dibromsalan.

'Mithracin' *see* Plicamycin.

Mithramycin* *see* Plicamycin.

'Mitigal' *see* Mesulfen.

MITINDOMIDE*** (tricyclo[4.2.2.0^{2,5}]dec-9-ene-3,4,7,8-tetracarboxylic 3,4:7,8-diimide).

MITOBRONITOL*** (1,6-dibromo-1,6-dideoxy-D-mannitol; dibromomannitol; DBM; NSC-

94100; 'myelobromol').

MITOCARCIN** (antibiotic from a streptomyces (Mich. Dept. Publ. Hlth No. 24281)).

'Mitocin-C' *see* Mitomycin.

MITOCLOMINE*** (*N*,*N*-bis(2-chloroethyl)-4-methoxy-3-methyl-1-naphthylamine).

MITOCROMIN* (antibiotic from *Str. viridochromogenes*; B-35251; NSC-77471).

MITOGILLIN*** (antibiotic from *Aspergillus restrictus*; NSC-69529).

MITOGUAZONE*** (1,1'-[(methylethanediylidene)dinitrilo]diguanidine; methylglyoxal bisguanylhydrazone; methyl-GAG; NSC-32946).

MITOLACTOL*** (1,6-dibromo-1,6-dideoxy-D-galactitol; 1,6-dibromo-1,6-dideoxydulcitol; dibromodulcit; NSC-104800; 'dibromdulcitol'; 'elobromo').

MITOMALCIN*** (antibiotic from *Str. malayensis*; NSC-113233; NSC-B-2992).

'Mitomen' *see* Chlormethine *N*-oxide.

MITOMYCIN*** (6-amino-1,1a,2,8,8a,8b-hexahydro-8-hydroxymethyl-8a-methoxy-5-methylazirino[2',3':3,4]pyrrolo[1,2-*a*]indole-4,7-dione carbamate; mitomycin C; NSC-26980; 'amecytine'; 'ametycin'; 'mitocin-C'; 'mutamycin').

Mitomycin C *see* Mitomycin.

MITONAFIDE*** (*N*-[2-(dimethylamino)ethyl]-3-nitronaphthalimide).

MITOPODOZIDE*** (*N'*-ethylpodophyllohydrazide; podophyllic acid 2-ethylhydrazide; NSC-72274; SPI-77; 'proresid').

Mitoquinone *see* Ubiquinone(s).

MITOSPER*** (antibiotic from *Aspergillus glaucus*; NSC-117032).

'Mitostan' *see* Busulfan.

MITOTANE*** (1,1-dichloro-2-(*o*-chlorophenyl)-2-(*p*-chlorophenyl)ethane; o,p'-DDD; o,p'-TDE; chloditan; CB-313; NSC-38721; 'lysodren').

MITOTENAMINE*** (5-bromo-3-[(2-chloroethyl)ethylaminomethyl]benzo(*b*)thiophene; 5-bromo-*N*-(2-chloroethyl)-*N*-ethylbenzo[*b*]thiophene-3-methylamine; AGN-1414).

'Mitox' *see* Chlorbenside.

'Mitoxana' *see* Ifosfamide.

MITOXANTRONE*** (1,4-dihydroxy-5,8-bis[[2-[(2-hydroxyethyl)amino]ethyl]amino]anthraquinone; mitozantrone; mitoxantrone hydrochloride; CL-232315; DHAQ; NSC-279836; NSC-301739).

'Mitoxine' *see* Chlormethine.

Mitozantrone* *see* Mitoxantrone.

MITOZOLOMIDE** (3-(2-chloroethyl)-3,4-dihydro-4-oxoimidazo[5,1-*d*]-*as*-tetrazine-8-carboxamide; CCRG-81010; M&B-39565; RP-46241).

'Mitronal' *see* Cinnarizine.

MIXIDINE*** (2-(3,4-dimethoxyphenethylimino)-1-methylpyrrolidine; McN-1589).

'Mixtard' *see under* Isophane insulin.

'Mixtencillin' *see under* Dihydrostreptomycin.

MIZORIBINE*** (5-hydroxy-1-β-D-ribofuranosylimidazole-4-carboxamide; 5-hydroxyimidazole-4-carboxamide riboside).

MJ-12 *see under* Carbocisteine.

MJ-217 *see* Ecothiopate iodide.

MJ-505 *see* Fenyramidol.

MJ-1986 *see* Indriline.

MJ-1987 *see* Mesuprine.

MJ-1988 *see* Quazodine.

MJ-1992 *see* Soterenol.

MJ-1998 *see* Metalol.

MJ-1999 *see* Sotalol.

MJ-4309-1 *see* Oxybutynin.

MJ-5022 *see* Methdilazine.

MJ-5190 *see* Amidefrine mesilate.

MJ-9022 *see* Buspirone.

MJ-9067 *see* Encainide.

MJ-9184-1 *see* Zinterol.

MJ-10061 *see* Benzbromarone.

MJ-12880 *see* Tipropidil.

MJ-13105 *see* Bucindolol.

MJF-9325 *see* Ifosfamide.

MJF-10938 *see* Xipamide.

MJF-11567-3 *see* Cefadroxil.

MJF-12264 *see* Tegafur.

MK-02 *see* Benzatropine.

MK-7 *see* Homarylamine.

MK-53 *see* Glaucarubin.

MK-56 *see* Pyrazinamide.

MK-57 *see* Methyldesorphine.

MK-65 *see* Cycloserine.

MK-89 *see* Anileridine.

MK-91 *see* Mevalonic acid.

MK-125 *see* Dexamethasone.

MK-128 *see* Ubiquinone(s).

MK-130 *see* Cyclobenzaprine.

MK-135 *see* Benzmalecene.

MK-185 *see* Halofenate.

MK-188 *see* Zeranol.

MK-196 *see* Indacrinone.

MK-208 *see* Famotidine.

MK 231 *see* Sulindac.

MK-240 *see* Protriptyline.

MK-250 *see* Emylcamate.

MK-306 *see* Cefoxitin.

MK-351 *see* Methyldopa.

MK-356 *see* Pivampicillin probenate.

MK-360 *see* Tiabendazole.

MK-366 *see* Norfloxacin.

MK-401 *see* Clorsulon.

MK-421 *see* Enalapril maleate.

MK-422 *see* Enalaprilat.

MK-486 *see* Carbidopa.

MK-521 *see* Lisinopril.

MK-595 *see* Etacrynic acid.

MK-647 *see* Diflunisal.

MK-745 *see* Metoclopramide.

MK-781 *see* Metirosine.

MK-0787 *see* Imipenem.

MK-870 *see* Amiloride.

MK-905 *see* Cambendazole.

MK-915 *see* Flunidazole.

MK-950 *see* Timolol maleate.

MK-955 *see* Fosfomycin.

ML-1024 *see* Etofylline clofibrate.

ML-1034 *see* Celucloral.

359

MLD-41 *see* Methyllysergide.
MnEDB *see* Maneb.
MNFA *see* N-(2-Fluoroacetyl)-N-methyl-1-naphthylamine.
MO-911 *see* Pargyline.
MO-1255 *see* Encyprate.
'**Mobam**' *see* Benzo[b]thien-4-yl methylcarbamate.
'**Moban**' *see* Molindone.
MO-BAY 950 *see* Penicillamine.
MOBECARB* (phenacyl 4-morpholineacetate).
MOBECARB plus PIBECARB ('afragil'; 'ciergin'; 'C-total').
'**Mobenate**' *see* Sodium benzyl succinate.
'**Mobenol**' *see* Tolbutamide.
MOBENZOXAMINE* (4'-fluoro-4-[4-[2-[(p-methoxy-α-phenylbenzyl)oxy]ethyl]piperazin-1-yl]butyrophenone).
'**Mobilan**' *see* Indometacin.
'**Mobilene**' *see* Sodium o-pyrocatechuate.
'**Mobutazon**' *see* Mofebutazone.
'**Mobuzon**' *see* Mofebutazone.
'**Mocap**' *see* Ethoprop.
MOCIMYCIN* (antibiotic from *Str. ramocissimus*; MYC-8003).
MOCIPRAZINE* (α-[[(1-ethynylcyclohexyl)-oxy]methyl]-4-(o-methoxyphenyl)-1-piperazineethanol; 1-(1-ethynylcyclohexyloxy)-3-[4-(o-methoxyphenyl)piperazin-1-yl]-2-propanol).
MOCLOBEMIDE* (p-chloro-N-(2-morpholinoethyl)benzamide; Ro 11-1163).
MOCTAMIDE* (N-linoleamido-p-methyl-α-phenylphenethylamine; (−)-N-(p-methyl-α-phenylphenethyl)linoleamide; N-(1-phenyl-2-p-tolylethyl)linoleamide; AC-485).
'**Modacor**' *see* Oxyfedrine.
MODALINE* (2-methyl-3-piperid-1-ylpyrazine; NSC-89277; W-3207B).
'**Modamide**' *see* Amiloride.
'**Modecate**' *see* Fluphenazine decanoate.
'**Moderil**' *see* Rescinnamine.
'**Modicon**' *see under* Norethisterone.
'**Modirax**' *see* Hexapropymate.
'**Moditen**' *see* Fluphenazine.
'**Modrenal**' *see* Trilostane.
'**Moducren**' *see* Timolol.
'**Modulite**' *see under* Trimebutine.
'**Modumate**' *see* Arginine glutamate.
'**Moduretic**' *see under* Amiloride.
'**Modus**' *see* Papaveroline.
Moenomycin *see* Bambermycin.
MOFEBUTAZONE* (4-butyl-1-phenyl-3,5-pyrazolidinedione; monophenylbutazone).
Mofedione *see* Oxazidione.
'**Mofesal**' *see* Mofebutazone.
MOFLOVERINE* (2-morpholinoethyl 2,4,6-trimethoxybenzoate).
MOFOXIME* (4-[(p-acetylphenoxy)acetyl]morpholine p-oxime; 4-[[p-[1-(hydroxyimino)ethyl]-phenoxy]acetyl]morpholine; 'arphoral').
'**Mogadan**' *see* Nitrazepam.
'**Mogadon**' *see* Nitrazepam.
'**Molcer**' *see* Docusate sodium.
'**Molevac**' *see* Pyrvinium embonate.

MOLINATE* (S-ethyl hexahydro-1H-azepine-1-carbothioate; 'ordram').
MOLINAZONE* (3-morpholino-1,2,3-benzotriazin-4(3H)-one).
MOLINDONE* (3-ethyl-6,7-dihydro-2-methyl-5-(morpholinomethyl)indol-4(5H)-one; EN-1733A).
Molinuron *see* Monolinuron.
'**Molipaxin**' *see* Trazodone.
'**Molofac**' *see* Docusate sodium.
'**Moloid**' *see* Mannityl hexanitrate.
MOLSIDOMINE* (N-carboxy-3-morpholinosydnone imine ethyl ester; N-(ethoxycarbonyl)-3-morpholinosydnone imine; SIN-10; 'corvaton').
'**Molucid**' *see* Isobutyltritylamine.
MOMA *see* Vanilmandelic acid.
MON-0573 *see* Glyphosate.
'**Monacrine**' *see* Aminoacridine.
MONALAZONE DISODIUM* (p-(chlorosulfamoyl)benzoic acid disodium salt).
MONALIDE* (N-(4-chlorophenyl)-2,2-dimethylpentanamide; N-(p-chlorophenyl)-2,2-dimethylvaleramide; chlorvalamide).
'**Monalium hydrate**' *see* Magaldrate.
'**Monase**' *see* Etryptamine.
'**Monaspor**' *see* Cefsulodin.
'**Monatal**' *see under* Chlormezazone.
'**Monazan**' *see* Mofebutazone.
'**Monazone**' *see* Mofebutazone.
MONENSIN* (2-[5-ethyltetrahydro-5-[tetrahydro-3-methyl-5-[tetrahydro-6-hydroxy-6-(hydroxymethyl)-3,5-dimethylpyran-2-yl]-2-furyl]-2-furyl]-9-hydroxy-β-methoxy-α,γ,2,8-tetramethyl-1,6-dioxaspiro[4.5]decane-7-butyric acid; monensin sodium; 'coban'; 'elancoban'; 'romensin').
'**Monistat**' *see* Miconazole.
'**Monitan**' *see* Polysorbate 80.
'**Monitor**' *see* Methamidophos.
MONOAMINE OXIDASE (amine oxidase; amino oxidase; MAO; tyraminase).
'**Mono-attritin**' *see* Ibuprofen.
MONOBENZONE* (p-benzyloxyphenol; hydroquinone monobenzyl ether).
'**Monobutazon**' *see* Mofebutazone.
'**Monocaine**' *see* Butethamine.
Monocalcium tetrasodium bis[pentaaqua-[D-gluconato(4 −)]tetra-μ-hydroxydioxotriferrate(3 −)] *see* Calcium sodium ferriclate.
Monochlorimipramine *see* Clomipramine.
Monochloromethyl ether *see* (Chloromethyl) methyl ether.
Monochlorphenamide *see* Clofenamide.
'**Monocortin**' *see* Paramethasone acetate.
MONOCROTOPHOS* (dimethyl 1-methyl-3-methylamino-3-oxo-1-propenyl phosphate; dimethyl (1-methylcarboxamido-1-propen-2-yl) phosphate; dimethyl (2-methylcarbamoyl-1-methylvinyl) phosphate; 3-hydroxy-N-methyl-cis-crotonamide dimethyl phosphate; 'azodrin'; 'nuvacron').
'**Monoderm**' *see* Fluocinolone acetonide.

'Monodorm' see Butethal.
'Monodral' see Penthienate.
MONOETHANOLAMINE OLEATE*** (2-aminoethanol oleate; ethaminol; ethanolamine oleate).
'Monofen' see Mofebutazone.
Monoglycol salicylate see Glycol salicylate.
'Monolene' see Propylene glycol monostearate.
MONOLINURON* (1-(p-chlorophenyl)-3-methoxy-3-methylurea; molinuron; 'aresin'; 'arezine').
'Monomestrol' see Mestilbol.
MONOMETACRINE*** (9,9-dimethyl-10-(3-methylaminopropyl)acridan).
'Monomex' see Mofebutazone.
'Monomil' see Mofebutazone.
Monooctanoin see Octanoin.
'Monopar' see Stilbazium iodide.
Monophenylbutazone see Mofebutazone.
'Monophosaden' see Adenosine phosphate.
MONOPHOSPHOTHIAMINE*** (phosphothiamine; thiamine monophosphate; thiamine phosphoric ester).
Monophosphothiamine disulfide see Thiamine disulfide phosphate.
Monopotassium clorazepate see Clorazepate monopotassium.
'Monoprine' see Mofebutazone.
MONOSTEARIN (stearic acid monoglyceryl ester).
Monosulfiram see Sulfiram.
Mono-[2,5,7,8-tetramethyl-2-(4,8,12-trimethyldecyl)-6-chromanyl]succinate polyoxyethylene ester see Tocofersolan.
Monothioglycol see 2-Mercaptoethanol.
'Monotrim' see Trimethoprim.
MONOXERUTIN*** (7-O-(2-hydroxyethyl)rutoside; Z-3011; Z-12007; 'venoruton').
Monoxychlorosene see Oxychlorosene.
'Monteban' see Narasin.
MONURON* (1-(p-chlorophenyl)-3,3-dimethylurea; chlorfenidim; CMU; klorfenidim; 'telvar').
MONURON TRICHLOROACETATE ('urox').
8-MOP see Methoxsalen.
'Mopazine' see Methopromazine.
MOPERONE*** (4'-fluoro-4-(4-hydroxy-4-p-tolylpiperid-1-yl)butyrophenone; 1-[3-(p-fluorobenzoyl)propyl]-4-(p-tolyl)-4-piperidinol; mopiperone; methylperidol; R-1658; 'luvatren').
See also under Prozapine.
MOPIDAMOL*** (2,6-bis[bis(2-hydroxyethyl)-amino]-4-piperid-1-ylpyrimido[5,4-d]pyrimidine; 2,2',2'',2'''-[(4-piperid-1-ylpyrimido[5,4-d]pyrimidine-2,6-diyl)nitrilo]tetraethanol; RA-233; 'rapenton').
Mopiperone* see Moperone.
MOPROLOL*** (3-(o-anisyloxy)-1-(isopropylamino)-2-propanol; 1-(isopropylamino)-3-(o-methoxyphenoxy)-2-propanol; D-1601; SD-1601).
MOQUIZONE** (2,3-dihydro-1-(morpholinoacetyl)-3-phenyl-4(1H)-quinazolinone; 1,2,3,4-tetrahydro-1-morpholinoacetyl-3-phenylquin-azolin-4-one; Rec-14/0127).
MORACIZINE*** (ethyl 10-(3-morpholinopropyl)phenothiazine-2-carbamate; ethmozine; moricizine; etmozine; EN-313).
MORANTEL** (trans-3-methyl-2-[2-(1,4,6-tetrahydro-1-methylpyrimid-2-yl)vinyl]thiophene; trans-1,4,5,6-tetrahydro-1-methyl-2-[2-(3-methylthien-2-yl)vinyl]pyrimidine).
MORANTEL TARTRATE (CP-12009-18; 'banminth II'; 'exhelm II'; 'pyrequan').
'Moranyl' see Suramin sodium.
MORAZINE (10-(3-morpholinopropyl)phenothiazine).
MORAZONE*** (2,3-dimethyl-4-(3-methyl-2-phenylmorpholinomethyl)-1-phenyl-3-pyrazolin-5-one; 4-(3-methyl-2-phenylmorpholinomethyl)-antipyrine; 4-(3-methyl-2-phenylmorpholino-methyl)phenazone).
'Morbasin' see Aminothiazole.
'Morbicid' see Formaldehyde.
MORCLOFONE*** (4'-chloro-3,5-dimethoxy-4-(2-morpholinoethoxy)benzophenone; K-3712).
'Morestan' see Chinomethionat.
Morfamoquat see Morfamquat.
MORFAMQUAT* (1,1'-bis[2-(3,5-dimethylmorpholino)-2-oxoethyl]-4,4'-bipyridinium dichloride; 1,1'-bis(3,5-dimethylmorpholinocarbonyl-methyl)-4,4'-bipyridinium dichloride; MFQ; morfamoquat; 'morfoxone').
Morficon see Hydromorphone.
'Morfolep' see Morsuximide.
MORFOREX** (4-[2-(α-methylphenethylamino)-ethyl]morpholine; N-(2-morpholinoethyl)amphetamine).
'Morfoxone' see Morfamquat.
'Morgalin' see Moroxydine.
Moricizine* see Moracizine.
MORIN (2',3,4',5,7-pentahydroxyflavone).
MORINAMIDE** (N-(morpholinomethyl)pyrazinamide; N-morpholinomethylpyrazine-2-carboxamide; morphazinamide; B-2311).
'Mornidine' see Pipamazine.
MORNIFLUMATE*** (2-morpholinoethyl 2-(α,α,α-trifluoro-m-toluidino)nicotinate; 2-(4-morpholinyl)ethyl 2[[3-(trifluoromethyl)phenyl]-amino]-3-pyridinecarboxylate; niflumic acid 2-morpholinoethyl ester; UP-164).
'Morocide' see Binapacryl.
MOROCROMEN*** (4-methyl-7-(4-morpholinecarboxamido)-3-(2-morpholinoethyl)coumarin; TVX-647).
'Moronal' see Nystatin.
'Morosan' see Diazepam.
MOROXYDINE*** (4-morpholinocarboximidoylguanidine; cyclo-3-oxapentamethylenebiguanide; N-(guanidinoformimidoyl)morpholine; N1,N1-anhydrobis(2-hydroxyethyl)biguanide; abitylguanide; biguamor; ABOB; SK&F-8898).
Morphacetinum see Diamorphine.
MORPHANTHRIDINE (11H-dibenz[b,e]azepine; homoacridan).
Morphazinamide see Morinamide.
MORPHERIDINE*** (ethyl ester of 1-(2-mor-

pholinoethyl)-1-phenylisonipecotic acid; morpholinoethylnorpethidine).

Morphethylbutyne* *see* Promolate.

Morphicon *see* Hydromorphone.

MORPHINAN (1,2,3,9,10,10a-hexahydro-10,4a(4*H*)-iminoethanophenanthrene).

MORPHINE (7,8-didehydro-4,5-epoxy-17-methylmorphinan-3,6-diol).

Ψ-Morphine *see* Pseudomorphine.

Morphine benzyl ether *see* Benzylmorphine.

Morphine diacetate *see* Diamorphine.

Morphine dinicotinate *see* Nicomorphine.

Morphine ethyl ether *see* Ethylmorphine.

Morphine 3-methyl ether *see* Codeine.

Morphine morpholinoethyl ether *see* Pholcodine.

MORPHINE NOSCAPINE MECONATE (double salt of morphine and noscapine with meconic acid; 'narcophine'; 'narphin').

MORPHINE N-OXIDE (morphine aminoxide; 'genomorphine').

MORPHOL (3,4-dihydroxyphenanthrene).

'Morpholep' *see* Morsuximide.

MORPHOLINE (tetrahydro-1,4(2*H*)-oxazine; diethylene imidoxide; diethylene oximide).

4-Morpholineacetic acid phenacyl ester *see* Mobecarb.

3-Morpholino-1,2,3-benzotriazin-4(3*H*)-one *see* Molinazone.

4-Morpholinocarboximidoylguanidine *see* Moroxydine.

4-Morpholino-2,2-diphenylbutyric acid ethyl ester *see* Dioxaphetyl butyrate.

1-(4-Morpholino-2,2-diphenylbutyryl)pyrrolidine *see* Desmethylmoramide.

6-Morpholino-4,4-diphenyl-3-heptanone *see* Phenadoxone.

N-(2-Morpholinoethyl)amphetamine *see* Morforex.

2-Morpholinoethyl 2-methyl-2-phenoxypropionate *see* Promolate.

Morpholinoethylmorphine *see* Pholcodine.

1-(2-Morpholinoethyl)-5-nitroimidazole *see* Nimorazole.

Morpholinoethylnorpethidine *see* Morpheridine.

2-Morpholinoethyl 2-phenoxyisobutyrate *see* Promolate.

Morpholinoethylrutoside *see* Ethoxazorutoside.

2-Morpholinoethyl 2-(α,α,α-trifluoro-*m*-toludino)nicotinate *see* Morniflumate.

2-Morpholinoethyl 2,4,6-trimethoxybenzoate *see* Mofloverine.

4-(Morpholinomethyl)esculetin *see* Folescutol.

5-(Morpholinomethyl)furazolidone *see* Furaltadone.

3-(Morpholinomethyl)-1-[(5-nitrofurfurylidene)-amino]hydantoin *see* Nifurfoline.

5-(4-Morpholinomethyl)-3-[(5-nitrofurfurylidene)-amino]-2-oxazolidinone *see* Furaltadone.

2-(Morpholinomethyl)-2-phenyl-1,3-indandione *see* Oxazidione.

N-(Morpholinomethyl)pyrazinamide *see* Morinamide.

10-(3-Morpholinopropionyl)phenothiazine-2-carbamic acid ethyl ester *see* Moracizine.

4-(3-Morpholinopropyl)benzyl phenyl ether *see* Fo-

mocaine.

10-(3-Morpholinopropyl)phenothiazine *see* Morazine.

10-(3-Morpholinopropyl)-2-propionylphenothiazine *see* Propionylmorazine.

2-(4-Morpholinyl)ethyl 2[[3-(trifluoromethyl)phenyl]amino]-3-pyridinecarboxylate *see* Morniflumate.

MORPHOTHEBAINE (apomorphine 10-methyl ether).

MORPHOTHION* (*O,O*-dimethyl *S*-(2-morpholin-4-ylacetyl) phosphorodithioate; *O,O*-dimethyl *S*-(2-morpholino-2-oxoethyl) phosphorodithioate; 'ekatin F'; 'ekatin M'; 'morphotox').

'Morphotox' *see* Morphothion.

MORSUXIMIDE* (2-methyl-*N*-(morpholinomethyl)-2-phenylsuccinimide; S-210; 'morfolep'; 'morpholep'; 'perlepsin').

'Moryl' *see* Carbachol.

'Mosatil' *see* Sodium calcium edetate.

'Mosegor' *see* Pizotifen maleate.

'Mosidal' *see* Methallatal.

'Motilium' *see* Domperidone.

'Motilyn' *see* Dexpanthenol.

'Motipress' *see under* Fluphenazine.

'Motival' *see under* Fluphenazine.

'Motolon' *see* Methaqualone.

MOTRAZEPAM* (1,3-dihydro-1-(methoxymethyl)-7-nitro-5-phenyl-2*H*-1,4-benzodiazepin-2-one).

MOTRETINIDE* ((*all-E*)-*N*-ethyl-9-(4-methoxy-2,3,6-trimethylphenyl)-3,7-dimethyl-2,4,6,8-nonatetraenamide; Ro 11-1430; 'tasmaderm').

'Motrin' *see* Ibuprofen.

'Motylkopielik' *see* Dinoprop.

Mould fibrinolysin *see* Brinase.

'Movellan' *see* Strychnine *N*-oxide.

'Movirene' *see* Dipyrocetyl.

'Mowiol' *see* Polyvinyl alcohol.

'Moxadil' *see* Amoxapine.

MOXADOLEN* (((3*R**, 3a*R**, 4*S**, 7*R**, 7a*S**)-3a,4,7,7a-tetrahydro-3-hydroxy-4,7-methanoisobenzofuran-1(3*H*)-one methylcarbamate ester)).

'Moxalactam' *see* Latamoxef.

Moxalactam disodium* *see* Latamoxef.

MOXAPRINDINE* (*N,N*-diethyl-*N'*-(1-methoxy-2-indanyl)-*N'*-phenyl-1,3-propanediamine; 2-[*N*-[3-(diethylamino)propyl]anilino]-1-methoxyindan).

MOXASTINE* (2-(1,1-diphenylethoxy)-*N,N*-dimethylethylamine; α-methyldiphenhydramine; mephenhydramine; Spofa-325).

MOXAVERINE* (1-benzyl-3-ethyl-6,7-dimethoxyisoquinoline; moxaverine hydrochloride; 'eupaverin'; 'meteverine').

MOXAZOCINE* ((−)-(2*R*,6*S*,11*R*)-3-(cyclopropylmethyl)-1,2,3,4,5,6-hexahydro-11-methoxy-6-methyl-2,6-methano-3-benzazocin-8-ol; 2-(cyclopropylmethyl)-2'-hydroxy-9-methoxy-5-methyl-6,7-benzomorphan; BL-4566).

MOXESTROL* (3,17-dihydroxy-11β-methoxy-19-nor-17α-pregna-1,3,5(10)-trien-20-yne; 17-ethynyl-11β-methoxyestradiol; 11β-methoxy-19-

nor-17α-pregna-1,3,5(10)-trien-20-yne-3,17-diol; R-2858; 'surestryl').

MOXICOUMONE*** (5,7-bis(2-morpholinoethoxy)-4-methylcoumarin; Rec-15/0019).

Moxifensine see Diclofensine.

'Moxile' see Moxicoumone.

MOXIPRAQUINE*** (4-[6-(6-methoxyquinolin-8-ylamino)hexyl]-α-methyl-1-piperazinepropanol; 1-(3-hydroxybutyl)-4-[6-(6-methoxyquinolin-8-ylamino)hexyl]piperazine; moxypraquine; BW-349C59).

'Moxiprim' see under Fosfomycin.

MOXISYLYTE*** ([2-(4-acetoxy-2-isopropyl-5-methylphenoxy)ethyl]dimethylamine; acetoxythymoxamine; thymoxamine).

MOXNIDAZOLE*** (1-methyl-2-[[[5-(morpholinomethyl)-2-oxooxazolidin-3-yl]imino]methyl]-5-nitroimidazole; 3-[[(1-methyl-5-nitroimidazol-2-yl)methylene]amino]-5-(morpholinomethyl)-2-oxazolidinone; SH-240; ZK-25095).

MOXONIDINE*** (4-chloro-5-(2-imidazolin-2-ylamino)-6-methoxy-2-methylpyrimidine).

Moxypraquine see Moxipraquine.

'Mozambin' see Methaqualone.

'Mozol' see Mofebutazone.

6-MP see Mercaptopurine.

MP-11 see Perlapine.

MP-267 see m-Sarcolysin.

MP-271 see Iosefamic acid.

MP-506 see Formylsarcolysin.

MP-537 see Iometin.

MP-620 see Iocetamic acid.

MP-1051 see Simaldrate.

MP-2032 see Iocarmic acid.

MP-4018 see Stannous pyrophosphate.

MP-6026 see Ioglucol.

MP-8000 see Ioglucomide.

MPD see Meprophenidol.

6-MP-R see Mercaptopurine ribonucleoside.

MRD-108 see Pipradrol.

MRD-125 see Phenythilone.

MRL-38 see Hexadiline.

MRL-41 see Clomifene.

MS-53 see Sulfamethoxazole.

MS-222 see Tricaine.

MS-752 see Lucanthone.

MS-1112 see Betamethasone benzoate.

MSD-943 see Sulindac.

MSH see Intermedin.

MTB-51 see Methantheline bromide.

MTS-263 see Tropenziline bromide.

MTU see Methylthiouracil.

MTX see Methotrexate.

'Mucantil' see Iodinated glycerol.

MUCIC ACID (galactaric acid; saccharolactic acid; Schleimsaeure; tetrahydroxyadipic acid).

'Muciclar' see Carbocisteine.

'Mucilose' see Psyllium.

'Mucinol' see Anethole trithione.

'Mucipulgite' see under Attapulgite.

'Mucitux' see Eprazinone.

'Mucodyne' see Carbocisteine.

'Mucofluid' see Mesna.

Mucoitin sodium polysulfate see Heparin.

'Mucojet' see Carbocisteine.

'Mucolysin' see Tiopronin.

'Mucomyst' see Acetylcysteine.

'Muco-panoral' see under Bromhexine.

'Muco-polycid' see Chlormidazole.

Mucopolysaccharide polysulfate see Glycosaminoglycan polysulfate(s).

'Mucopront' see Carbocisteine.

'Mucorex' see Citiolone.

'Mucosolvan' see Ambroxol.

'Mucosolvin' see Acetylcysteine.

'Mudeka' see Amobarbital.

'Mugia' see Dimethyl phthalate.

'Mulfasin' see Methyldopa.

'Mulsculamine' see Spermine.

'Mulsopaque' see Iofendylate.

'Multergan' see Thiazinamium metilsulfate.

'Multezin' see Thiazinamium metilsulfate.

'Multifuge' see Piperazine.

'Multifungin' see 5-Bromo-4'-chlorosalicylamide.

'Multilind' see Nystatin.

'Multimycin' see Colistin.

'Mundiquin' see Quinidine polygalacturonate.

'Mundisal' see Choline salicylate.

'Municaps' see Nicotinoylprocaine.

MURABUTIDE*** (2-acetamido-3-O-[(R)-1-[[(S)-1-[[(R)-3-carbamoyl-1-carboxypropyl]carbamoyl]ethyl]carbamoyl]ethyl]-2-deoxy-D-glucopyranose, butyl ester).

'Muracin' see Methylthiouracil.

MURAMIC ACID (2-amino-3-O-(1-carboxyethyl)-2-deoxy-D-glucose; 3-O-α-carboxyethyl-D-glucosamine).

'Murbetol' see under Propham.

'Murel' see Valethamate bromide.

MUREXINE (choline urocanoate (salt); imidazoleacryloylcholine; urocanoylcholine).

'Murfotox' see Mecarbam.

Muriatic ether see Chloroethane.

MUROCAINIDE*** (1-[4,7-dimethoxy-6-(2-piperid-1-ylethoxy)-5-benzofuranyl]-3-methylurea).

'Murotox' see Mecarbam.

'Murvesco' see Fenson.

'Musaril' see Tetrazepam.

'Muscaran' see Bethanechol.

'Muscatox' see Coumafos.

MUSCIMOL (5-aminomethyl-3-isoxazolol; agarin; pantherin).

Mussel poison see Saxitoxin.

MUSTARD GAS (bis(2-chloroethyl)sulfide; Kampfstoff; Lost; sulfur mustard; yperite; H; HS; 'psoriasin').

Mustard oil see Allyl isothiocyanate.

'Mustargen' see Chlormethine.

Mustine see Chlormethine.

'Mustron' see Chlormethine N-oxide.

'Mutabase' see Diazoxide.

'Mutabon' see under Amitriptyline.

'Mutamycin' see Mitomycin.

'Mutanxion' see under Amitriptyline.

'Mutaspline' see under Amitriptyline.

'Muthesa' see Oxetacaine.

'**Mutox**' *see* Dichlorvos.

MUZOLIMINE* (3-amino-1-[1-(3,4-dichloro-phenyl)ethyl]-2-pyrazolin-5-one; 3-amino-1-(3,4-dichloro-α-methylbenzyl)-2-pyrazolin-5-one; BAY g-2821).

MW-274115 *see* Dichlozoline.

MXMC *see* Methiocarb.

MY-25 *see* Metergotamine tartrate.

MY-33-7 *see* Lotucaine.

MY-41-6 *see* Parsalmide.

My-301 *see* Guaifenesin.

'**Myacyne**' *see* Neomycin.

'**Myagen**' *see* Bolasterone.

'**Myalex**' *see* Fenclozic acid.

'**Myambutol**' *see* Ethambutol.

'**Myanesin**' *see* Mephenesin.

Myarsenol (tr) *see* Sulfarsphenamine.

'**Myasul**' *see* Sulfamethoxypyridazine.

'**Myavan**' *see* Toloxychlorinol.

'**My-B-den**' *see* Adenosine phosphate.

MYC-1080 *see* Stercuronium iodide.

MYC-8003 *see* Mocimycin.

'**Mycal**' *see* Dodecyltriphenylphosphonium bromide.

Mycanden *see* Haloprogin.

'**Mycaptine**' *see* Mercaptopurine.

'**Mycelex**' *see* Clotrimazole.

Mycerin (tr) *see* Neomycin.

'**Mycifradin**' *see* Neomycin.

'**Mycil**' *see* Chlorphenesin.

'**Mycivin**' *see* Lincomycin.

'**Mycobactyl**' *see* Gluconiazone.

'**Mycocten**' *see* Ethyl paraben.

Mycoin C₃ *see* Patulin.

MYCOMYCIN (3,5,7,8-tridecatetraene-10,12-diynoic acid).

MYCOPHENOLIC ACID* (6-(5-carboxy-3-methylpent-2-enyl)-7-hydroxy-5-methoxy-4-methylphthalide; (*E*)-6-(4-hydroxy-6-methoxy-7-methyl-3-oxophthalan-5-yl)-4-methyl-4-hexenoic acid; NSC-129185; 'melbex').

'**Mycophyt**' *see* Natamycin.

'**Mycoplex**' *see* Sulbentine.

'**Myco-polycid**' *see* Chlormidazole.

'**Mycosolvon**' *see under* Miconazole.

'**Mycospor**' *see* Bifonazole.

'**Mycosporin**' *see* Clotrimazole.

'**Mycostatin**' *see* Nystatin.

'**Mycozol**' *see* Chlorbutol.

Mydecamycin *see* Midecamycin.

'**Mydeton**' *see* Tolperisone.

'**Mydocalm**' *see* Tolperisone.

'**Mydriacyl**' *see* Tropicamide.

'**Mydrial**' *see* Tyramine.

'**Mydriatin**' *see* Phenylpropanolamine.

'**Mydrilate**' *see* Cyclopentolate.

'**Mydrin**' *see* Tropicamide.

'**Myelobromol**' *see* Mitobronitol.

'**Myelografin**' *see* Meglumine ioserate.

Myelosan (tr) *see* Busulfan.

'**Myelucin**' *see* Busulfan.

MYFADOL* (1-benzoylmethyl-3-(*m*-hydroxyphenyl)-2,3-dimethylpiperidine; 3-(*m*-hydroxy-phenyl)-2,3-dimethyl-1-phenacylpiperidine; 2-[3-(*m*-hydroxyphenyl)-2,3-dimethylpiperid-1-yl]-acetophenone; TA-306).

'**Mykestron**' *see* Amoxydramine undecenate.

'**Mykomed**' *see* Benzyl benzoate.

'**Mylaxen**' *see* Hexafluronium bromide.

'**Mylecytan**' *see* Busulfan.

'**Mylepsin**' *see* Primidone.

'**Myleran**' *see* Busulfan.

'**Mylol**' *see* Diethyltoluamide.

'**Mylone**' *see* Dazomet.

'**Mynah**' *see under* Ethambutol.

'**Mynocine**' *see* Minocycline.

Myoarsenobenzol *see* Sulfarsphenamine.

'**Myocaine**' *see* Guaifenesin.

'**Myocholine**' *see* Bethanechol.

'**Myochrysin**' *see* Sodium aurothiomalate.

'**Myocrisin**' *see* Sodium aurothiomalate.

'**Myocuran**' *see* Mephenesin.

'**Myodil**' *see* Iofendylate.

'**Myofedrin**' *see* (±)-Oxyfedrine.

Myohematin *see* Cytochrome c.

Myoinositol *see* Inositol.

'**Myolastan**' *see* Tetrazepam.

'**Myolite**' *see* Thallous chloride Tl 201.

'**Myolyseen**' *see* Pridinol.

'**Myordil**' *see* Aminoxytriphene.

'**Myo-relaxin**' *see* Suxamethonium chloride.

'**Myorexon**' *see* Isosorbide dinitrate.

'**Myoscaine**' *see* Guaifenesin.

'**Myoston**' *see* Adenosine phosphate.

'**Myotonine**' *see* Bethanechol.

'**Myprozine**' *see* Natamycin.

MYRALACT* (*N*-(2-hydroxyethyl)tetradecyl-amine lactate; myristylethanolamine lactate; 2-tetradecylaminoethanol lactate).
See also under Cloponone.

'**Myriamycin**' *see* Tetracycline dodecylsulfamate.

MYRICETIN (3,3′,4′,5,5′,7-hexahydroxyflavone; cannabiscetin).

Myricodine *see* Myrophine.

Myristalkonium chloride *see* Miristalkonium chloride.

MYRISTIC ACID (tetradecanoic acid).
See also Myrophine.

MYRISTICIN (1-allyl-3-methoxy-4,5-methylene-dioxybenzene).

Myristylethanolamine lactate *see* Myralact.

MYRISTYLPICOLINIUM CHLORIDE (*N*-tetradecylpicolinium chloride; 'quatrasan').

'**Myrj 45**' *see* Macrogol stearate 8.

'**Myrj 52**' *see* Macrogol stearate 40.

MYROPHINE* (3-benzyloxy-6-hydroxy-*N*-methyl-4,5-epoxymorphin-7-ene tetradecanoate ester; 3-benzyloxy-*N*-methyl-6-myristyloxy-4,5-epoxymorphin-7-ene; benzylmorphine myristyl ester; myricodine).

MYRTECAINE* (2-[2-(6,6-dimethylnorpinen-2-yl)ethoxy]triethylamine; homomyrtenyloxytri-ethylamine).

Myrticolorin *see* Rutoside.

'**Mysoline**' *see* Primidone.

'**Myspamol**' *see* Aminopromazine fumarate.

'**Mysteclin-V**' *see under* Tetracycline.
MYTATRIENEDIOL (3-methoxy-16-methyl-1,3,5(10)-estratriene-16β,17β-diol; SC-6924; 'anvene'; 'manvene').
'**Mytelase**' *see* Ambenonium chloride.
'**Mytolac**' *see* Benzoyl peroxide.

'**Mytolon**' *see* Benzoquinonium chloride.
'**Myxal**' *see* Dodecyltriphenylphosphonium bromide.
MYXIN (6-methoxy-1-phenazinol 5,10-dioxide).
MZ-144 *see* Rimazolium metilsulfate.

N

N-3 *see* Metetoin.
N-5 *see* Tranilast.
N-68 *see* Captodiame.
N-0252 *see* Laurocapram.
N-399 *see* Xenytropium bromide.
N-533 *see* Tolperisone.
N-640 *see* Trantelinium bromide.
N-714 *see* Chlorprothixene.
N-746 *see* Clopenthixol.
N-750 *see* Amitriptyline.
N-1113 *see* Pipoctanone.
N-7001 *see* Melitracen.
N-7009 *see* Flupentixol.
N-7020 *see* Meprotixol.
N-7048 *see* Nortriptyline.
N-7049 *see* Litracen.
NA-66 *see* Pimeclone.
NA-97 *see* Pancuronium bromide.
NA-119 *see* Bromamide.
NA-274 *see* Bromhexine.
NA-872 *see* Ambroxol.
NAB-365 *see* Clenbuterol.
NABAM* (disodium 1,2-ethanediylbis(carbamodi-thioate); disodium ethylenebis(carbamodithioate); sodium *N,N'*-ethylenebis(dithiocarbamate); DSE; 'dithane 1740'; 'dithane A-40'; 'dithane D-14'; 'parzate').
NABAZENIL*** (3-(1,2-dimethylheptyl)-7,8,9,10-tetrahydro-6,6,9-trimethyl-6*H*-dibenzo[*b,d*]pyran-1-yl hexahydro-1*H*-azepine-1-butyrate; SP-175).
NABIDROX* ((±)-(6aα,10aβ)-3-(1,1-dimethyl-heptyl)-6a,7,8,9,10,10a-hexahydro-6,6-dimethyl-6*H*-dibenzo[*b,d*]pyran-1,9-diol; compound 106990).
NABILONE* ((±)-*trans*-3-(1,1-dimethylheptyl)-6,6a,7,8,10,10a-hexahydro-1-hydroxy-6,6-di-methyl-9*H*-dibenzo[*b,d*]pyran-9-one; compound 109514; 'cesamet').
NABITAN** (8-(1,2-dimethylheptyl)-1,3,4,5-tetra-hydro-5,5-dimethyl-2-(2-propynyl)-2*H*-[1]benzo-pyrano[4,3-*c*]pyridin-10-yl 1-piperidinebutyrate; nabitan monohydrochloride; nabutan; nabitan hydrochloride; nabutan hydrochloride; NIB; SP-106).
NABOCTATE*** (7,8,9,10-tetrahydro-6,6,9-tri-methyl-3-(1-methyloctyl)-6-*H*-dibenzo[*b,d*]-pyran-1-yl 4-(diethylamino)butyrate).
NABUMETONE*** (4-(6-methoxynaphth-2-yl)-2-butanone; BRL-14777).
Nabutan *see* Nabitan.

'Nac' *see* Acetylcysteine.
NACARTOCIN*** (1-(3-mercaptopropionic acid)-2-[3-(*p*-ethylphenyl)-L-alanine]-6-(L-2-aminobutyric acid)oxytocin).
'Nacenyl' *see* Chlormadinone acetate.
'Naclex' *see* Hydroflumethiazide.
'Nacom' *see under* Levodopa.
'Nactate' *see* Poldine metilsulfate.
'Nacton' *see* Poldine metilsulfate.
NAD *see* Nadide.
'Nadeine' *see* Dihydrocodeine.
'Nadex' *see* Pirisudanol.
NADIDE*** (3-carbamoyl-1-β-D-ribofuranosyl-pyridinium hydroxide 5'-ester with adenosine 5'-pyrophosphate inner salt; codehydrogenase I; coenzyme I; cozymase; diphosphopyridine nucleotide; DPN; nicotinamide adenine dinucleotide; NAD; NSC-20270).
NADIDE PHOSPHATE (codehydrogenase II; coenzyme II; nicotinamide adenine dinucleotide phosphate; triphosphopyridine nucleotide; TPN).
'Nadisan' *see* Carbutamide.
Nadizan (tr) *see* Carbutamide.
NADOLOL*** (1-[3-(*tert*-butylamino)-2-hydroxy-propoxy]-5,6,7,8-tetrahydro-*cis*-6,7-naphthal-enediol; 1-(*tert*-butylamino)-3-[(5,6,7,8-tetra-hydro-*cis*-6,7-dihydroxynaphth-1-yl)oxy]-2-pro-panol; SQ-11725; 'corgard'; 'solgol').
NADOXOLOL*** (1-[4-amino-2-hydroxy-4-(hydroxyimino)butoxy]naphthalene; 3-hydroxy-4-naphth-1-yloxybutyramidoxime; LL-1530; 'bradyl 250').
NAEPAINE (2-(amylamino)ethyl *p*-aminobenzoate).
NAFARELIN** (5-oxo-L-prolyl-L-histidyl-L-tryptophyl-L-seryl-L-tyrosyl-3-(2-naphthyl)-D-alanyl-L-leucyl-L-arginyl-L-prolylglycinamide).
NAFARIN (tr) (4-hydroxy-3-(1-phenyl-2-propion-ylethyl)coumarin sodium salt; napharin).
NAFAZATROM** (3-methyl-1-[2-(2-naphthyl-oxy)ethyl]-2-pyrazolin-5-one; BAY g-6575).
NAFCAPROIC ACID*** (2-ethyl-2-naphth-1-yl-butyric acid; DA-808).
NAFCILLIN*** (6-(2-ethoxy-1-naphthamido)pe-nicillanic acid; 2-ethoxynaphth-1-yl-penicillin; sodium nafcillin; Wy-3277).
Nafenoic acid *see* Nafenopin.
NAFENOPIN*** (2-methyl-2-[*p*-(1,2,3,4-tetra-hydronaphth-1-yl)phenoxy]propionic acid; nafe-noic acid; CH-13437; Su-13437).

NAFETOLOL*** (5-[3-(*tert*-butylamino)-2-hydroxypropoxy]-1,2,3,4-tetrahydro-8-hydroxy-1,4-ethanonaphthalene; 1-(*tert*-butylamino)-3-[(1,2,3,4-tetrahydro-8-hydroxy-1,4-ethanonaphthalen-5-yl)oxy]-2-propanol; K-5407).

NAFIMIDONE*** (2-imidazol-1-yl-2'-acetonaphthone; 2-(1*H*-imidazol-1-yl)-1-(2-naphthalenyl)-ethanone; nafimidone hydrochloride).

NAFIVERINE*** (1,4-bis[2-(2-naphth-1-ylpropionyloxy)ethyl]piperazine; 1,4-piperazinediethanol α-methyl-1-naphthaleneacetate; naftimepezine; naphthiepazine; DA-914; 'naftidan').

NAFLOCORT** (9-fluoro-1',4'-dihydro-11β,21-dihydroxy-2'β*H*-naphtho[2',3':16,17]pregna-1,4-diene-3,20-dione).

NAFOMINE** (*O*-(2-methylnaphth-1-ylmethyl)-hydroxylamine).

NAFOXADOL** (5-(2-naphthyl)-6,8-dioxa-3-azabicyclo[3.2.1]octane).

NAFOXIDINE*** (1-[2-[*p*-(3,4-dihydro-6-methoxy-2-phenylnaphth-1-yl)phenoxy]ethyl]pyrrolidine; NSC-70735; U-11100A).

'**Nafrine**' *see* Oxymetazoline.

Nafronyl oxalate* *see* Naftidrofuryl oxalate.

NAFTALOFOS*** (*N*-hydroxynaphthylimide diethyl phosphate; diethyl *N*-hydroxynaphthylimido phosphate; *N*-hydroxynaphthalimide diethyl phosphate; diethyl naphthyloximido phosphate; naphthalophos; maretin; phthalophos; Bayer-9002; E-9002; ENT-25567; S-940).

Naftamon (tr) *see* Bephenium hydroxynaphthoate.

NAFTAZONE*** (1,2-naphthoquinone 2-semicarbazone; β-naphthoquinone semicarbazone).

'**Naftidan**' *see* Nafiverine.

Naftidon (tr) *see* Menadiol sodium phosphate.

NAFTIDROFURYL*** (2-(diethylamino)ethyl tetrahydro-α-(1-naphthylmethyl)-2-furanpropionate; naphthydrofuryl; 'dusodril'; 'iridus').

NAFTIDROFURYL OXALATE (nafronyl oxalate; EU-1806; LS-121; 'praxilene').

NAFTIFINE*** ((*E*)-*N*-cinnamyl-*N*-methyl-1-naphthalenemethylamine; (*E*)-*N*-methyl-*N*-(3-phenylprop-2-enyl)-1-naphthalenemethylamine; naftifungin; SN-105-843).

Naftifungin *see* Naftifine.

Naftimepezine *see* Nafiverine.

Naftipramide *see* Naftypramide.

Naftizin (tr) *see* Naphazoline.

'**Naftopen**' *see* Nafcillin.

NAFTOXATE** (2-benzoxazolyl *N*-methyldithio-1-naphthalenecarbamate; K-F 224).

NAFTYPRAMIDE*** (α-[2-(dimethylamino)-ethyl]-α-isopropyl-1-naphthaleneacetamide; naftipramide; naphthypramide; DA-992).

'**Naganin**' *see* Suramin sodium.

'**Naganol**' *see* Suramin sodium.

NA-III *see* Etifelmine.

'**Nalador**' *see* Sulprostone.

NALBUPHINE*** (17-cyclobutylmethyl-4,5a-epoxymorphinan-3,6a,14-triol; 12-cyclobutylmethyl-7,7a,8,9-tetrahydro-3,7a-dihydroxy-6*H*-8,9c-iminoethanophenanthro[4,5-*bcd*]furan-5-(4a*H*)-ol; nalbuphine hydrochloride; EN-2234-

A).

'**Nalcrom**' *see* Cromoglicate disodium.

NALED* (1,2-dibromo-2,2-dichloroethyl dimethyl phosphate; bromchlophos; 'alvora'; 'bromex'; 'dibrom'; 'ortho dibrom').

'**Nalfon**' *see* Fenoprofen.

'**Nalgesic**' *see* Fenoprofen calcium.

Nalidixan* *see* Nalidixic acid.

NALIDIXIC ACID*** (1-ethyl-1,4-dihydro-7-methyl-4-oxo-1,8-naphthyridine-3-carboxylic acid; nalidixan; nalidixin; nalidixate sodium; NSC-82174; WIN-18320).
See also Sodium nalidixate.

Nalidixin *see* Nalidixic acid.

'**Nalline**' *see* Nalorphine.

NALMEFENE*** (17-(cyclopropylmethyl)-4,5α-epoxy-6-methylenemorphinan-3,14-diol; nalmetrene; JF-1).

Nalmetrene *see* Nalmefene.

NALMEXONE*** (7,8-dihydro-14-hydroxy-*N*-(3-methyl-2-butenyl)normorphinone; 7,7a,8,9-tetrahydro-3,7a-dihydroxy-12-(3-methyl-2-butenyl)-6*H*-8,9c-iminoethanophenanthro[4,5-*bcd*]furan-5(4a*H*)-one; EN-1620A).

NALORPHINE*** (*N*-allylnormorphine; allorphine; antorfin; antorphine; nalorphine hydrobromide; NANM).
See also under Nicomorphine.

Nalorphine diacetate *see* Diacetylnalorphine.

NALORPHINE DINICOTINATE ('nimelan').

Naloxiphane* *see* Levallorphan.

NALOXONE*** (17-allyl-4,5α-epoxy-3,14-dihydroxymorphinan-6-one; (−)-12-allyl-7,7a,8,9-tetrahydro-3,7a-dihydroxy-4a*H*-8,9c-iminoethanophenanthro[4,5-*bcd*]furan-5(6*H*)-one; L-*N*-allyl-14-hydroxynordihydromorphinone; N-allylnoroxymorphone; naloxone hydrochloride; EN-15304).

'**Nalpen**' *see* Azidocillin.

NALTREXONE*** ((−)-17-(cyclopropylmethyl)-4,5α-epoxy-3,14-dihydroxymorphinan-6-one; naltrexone hydrochloride; EN-1639A).

NALTROPINE (*N*-allylnoratropine).

'**Namestin**' *see* Clonidine.

Namol xenyrate *see* Namoxyrate.

NAMOXYRATE*** (2-(dimethylamino)ethyl 2-(*p*-biphenylyl)butyrate; namol xenyrate; W-1760A).

'**Nanbacin**' *see* Xibornol.

'**Nandoral**' *see* Ethylestrenol.

'**Nandrolin**' *see* Nandrolone phenpropionate.

NANDROLONE*** (17β-hydroxyestr-4-en-3-one; 19-nortestosterone; norandrostenolone; nortestosterone; SC-4341; 'nortestonate').

Nandrolone adamantane-1-carboxylate *see* Bolmantalate.

NANDROLONE CIPIONATE (nandrolone 17-(3-cyclopentanepropionate); nandrolone cypionate; 'depo-nortestosterone').

NANDROLONE CYCLOHEXANECARBOXYLATE (nandrolone hexahydrobenzoate; NSC-3351; 'durabol'; 'nor-durandron'; 'norlongandron').

**NANDROLONE CYCLOHEXANEPROPION-
ATE** (nandrolone 17-cyclohexylpropionate; 'retarbolin'; 'sanabolic').

Nandrolone cyclopentanepropionate *see* Nandrolone cipionate.

NANDROLONE CYCLOTATE* (nandrolone 4-
methylbicyclo[2.2.2]oct-2-2-ene-1-carboxylate;
RS-3268R).

Nandrolone cypionate *see* Nandrolone cipionate.

NANDROLONE DECANOATE* ('deca-durabolin'; 'retabolil').

Nandrolone dodecanoate *see* Nandrolone laurate.

Nandrolone hexahydrobenzoate *see* Nandrolone
cyclohexanecarboxylate.

**NANDROLONE (p-HEXYLOXY)HYDROCIN-
NAMATE** (nandrolone 3-(p-hexyloxyphenyl)-
propionate; PNS; 'anadur').

Nandrolone hydrocinnamate *see* Nandrolone phenpropionate.

NANDROLONE LAURATE (nandrolone dodecanoate; 'clinibolin'; 'laurobolin').

**Nandrolone 4-methylbicyclo[2.2.2]oct-2-2-ene-1-
carboxylate** *see* Nandrolone cyclotate.

NANDROLONE PHENPROPIONATE* (nandrolone hydrocinnamate; nandrolone 17-(3-
phenylpropionate); NSC-23162; 'durabolin';
'nandrolin'; 'nerobolil').

**NANDROLONE PHENPROPIONATE plus
DESOXYCORTONE PHENPROPIONATE**
('docabolin').

Naniopin* *see* Nanofin.

'Nankor' *see* Fenclofos.

NANM *see* Nalorphine.

NANOFIN*** (2,6-dimethylpiperidine; 2,6-lupe-
tidine; naniopin; nanophyn).

Nanophyn *see* Nanofin.

NANTRADOL*** ((±)-5,6,6a,7,8,9,10,10a-octa-
hydro-6-methyl-3-(1-methyl-4-phenylbutoxy)-
1,9-phenanthridinediol 1-acetate; nantradol
hydrochloride; CP-44001).
See also Levonantradol.

'Naotin' *see* Sodium nicotinate.

'NAPA' *see* Accecainide.

NAPACTADINE*** (*N*,*N'*-dimethyl-2-naphthal-
eneacetamidine; napactadine hydrochloride;
DL-588).

NAPADISILATE(S)** (naphthalene-1,5-disulfon-
ic acid, esters and salts; napadisylate(s)).

Napadisylate(s)* *see* Napadisilate(s).

'Napafen' *see* Paracetamol.

'Napaltan' *see* Mafenide.

Napharin (tr) *see* Nafarin.

NAPHAZOLINE*** (2-(1-naphthylmethyl)-2-imi-
dazoline; naftizin; naphthazoline; naphthyzine;
naphazoline hydrochloride).

Naphthacaine *see* Naphthocaine.

Naphthalenecarboxylic acid(s) *see* Naphthoic
acid(s).

NAPHTHALENE 1,5-DIISOCYANATE ('desmo-
dure-15').

1,8-Naphthalenediol-3,6-disulfonic acid *see* Chromotropic acid.

Naphthalene-1,5-disulfonic acid, esters and salts *see*
Napadisilate(s).

2-Naphthalenesulfonic acid, esters and salts *see*
Napsilate(s).

Naphthalophos* *see* Naftalofos.

'Naphthamine' *see* Methenamine.

Naphthazoline *see* Naphazoline.

Naphthiepazine *see* Nafiverine.

'Naphthiomate-T' *see* Tolnaftate.

NAPHTHIONIC ACID (4-amino-1-naphthalene-
sulfonic acid; 1-naphthylamine-4-sulfonic acid).

NAPHTHOCAINE (2-(diethylamino)ethyl 4-
amino-1-naphthoate; naphthacaine; naphthocaine hydrochloride).

NAPHTHOIC ACID(S) (naphthalenecarboxylic
acid(s)).

1-NAPHTHOL (α-naphthol).

2-NAPHTHOL (β-naphthol).

NAPHTHONONE*** (2-(2-hydroxynaphth-1-yl)-
cyclohexanone; 1-(2-oxocyclohexyl)-2-naphth-
ol).

β-Naphthoquinone semicarbazone *see* Naftazone.

1,2-Naphthoquinone 2-semicarbazone *see* Naftazone.

Naphthydrofuryl *see* Naftidrofuryl.

1-NAPHTHYLAMINE (α-naphthylamine).

2-NAPHTHYLAMINE (β-naphthylamine).

Naphthylamine blue *see* Trypan blue.

1-Naphthylamine-4-sulfonic acid *see* Naphthionic
acid.

2-[(Naphth-1-ylamino)carbonyl]benzoic acid *see*
Naptalam.

1-(Naphth-1-ylazo)-2-naphthol-3,6-disulfonic acid
see Bordeaux B.

2-NAPHTHYL BENZOATE (benzonaphthol).

5-(2-Naphthyl)-6,8-dioxa-3-azabicyclo[3.2.1]octane
see Nafoxadol.

1-(2-Naphthyl)-2-isopropylaminoethanol *see* Pronetalol.

2-NAPHTHYL LACTATE (lactonaphthol; 'lactol').

1-Naphthyl methylcarbamate *see* Carbaril.

2-(1-Naphthylmethyl)-2-imidazoline *see* Naphazoline.

**N-[[[1-(2-Naphthylmethyl)piperidin-4-yl]amino]carb-
onyl]benzamide** *see* Panuramine.

2-Naphthyl N-methyl-N-(m-tolyl) thionocarbamate
see Tolnaftate.

2-(1-Naphthyloxy)propionamidoxime *see* Napro-
doxime.

1-NAPHTHYL SALICYLATE (alphol).

2-NAPHTHYL SALICYLATE (betol; salinaphthol).

α-Naphthylthiourea *see* Antu.

1-Naphth-1-yl-2-thiourea *see* Antu.

Naphthypramide *see* Naftypramide.

Naphthyzine (tr) *see* Naphazoline.

'Naphuride' *see* Suramin sodium.

'Napoton' *see* Chlordiazepoxide.

Napriline (tr) *see* Propranolol.

'Naproc' *see* Procaine-penicillin.

NAPRODOXIME*** (2-(1-naphthyloxy)propion-
amidoxime).

NAPROPAMIDE (*N*,*N*-diethyl-2-(naphth-1-yloxy)propionamide; 1-[1-(diethylcarbamoyl)eth-oxy]naphthalene; 'devrinol').

'Naprosine' *see* Naproxen.

'Naprosyn' *see* Naproxen.

NAPROXEN* ((+)-6-methoxy-α-methyl-2-naphthaleneacetic acid; (+)-2-(6-methoxy-naphth-2-yl)propionic acid; methoxypropiocin; naproxen sodium; CG-3117; RS-3540; RS-3650).

NAPROXOL* ((−)-6-methoxy-β-methyl-2-naphthaleneethanol; RS-4034).

NAPSILATE(S)* (2-naphthalenesulfonic acid, esters and salts; napsylate(s)).

Napsylate(s)* *see* Napsilate(s).

NAPTALAM* (1-(2-carboxybenzamido)naphthal-ene; 2-[(naphth-1-ylamino)carbonyl]benzoic acid; NPA; 'alanap').

'Naqua' *see* Trichlormethiazide.

'Naquival' *see under* Reserpine.

'Naramycin' *see* Cicloheximide.

NARANOL* (8,9,10,11,11a,12-hexahydro-8,10-dimethyl-7a*H*-naphtho[1',2':5,6]pyrano[3,2-*c*]-pyridin-7a-ol; naranol hydrochloride; W-5494A).

NARASIN* (α-ethyl-6-[5-[2-(5-ethyltetrahydro-5-hydroxy-6-methyl-2*H*-pyran-2-yl)-15-hydroxy-2,10,12-trimethyl-1,6,8-trioxadispiro[4.1.5.3]pen-tadec-13-en-9-yl]-2-hydroxy-1,3-dimethyl-4-oxo-heptyl]tetrahydro-3,5-dimethyl-2*H*-pyran-2-acetic acid; compound 79891; 'monteban').

'Narcan' *see* Naloxone.

'Narcanti' *see* Naloxone.

'Narcaricin' *see* Benzbromarone.

Narcobarbital *see* Enibomal.

'Narcodorm' *see* Enibomal.

'Narcogen' *see* Trichloroethylene.

'Narcolo' *see* Dextromoramide.

'Narcompren' *see* Noscapine.

'Narcon' *see* Naloxone.

'Narconumal' *see* Enallylpropymal.

'Narcophine' *see* Morphine noscapine meconate.

Narcosine *see* Noscapine.

'Narcotal' *see* Enibomal.

'Narcotile' *see* Chloroethane.

DL-Narcotine *see* Gnoscapine.

L-Narcotine *see* Noscapine.

'Narcovene' *see* Enibomal.

'Narcozep' *see* Flunitrazepam.

'Narcylene' *see* Acetylene.

'Nardelzine' *see* Phenelzine.

'Nardil' *see* Phenelzine.

'Naridan' *see* Oxyphencyclimine.

NARINGENIN (4',5,7-trihydroxyflavanone; asahi-na; naringetol; pelargidanon; salipurpol).

Naringenin 7-rhamnoglucoside *see* Aurantiin.

Naringenin 7-rutoside *see* Aurantiin.

Naringetol *see* Naringenin.

Naringin *see* Aurantiin.

Naringoside *see* Aurantiin.

'Narkogen' *see* Buthalital.

'Narkolan' *see* Bromethol.

'Narkotal' *see* Enibomal.

'Narkotan' *see* Halothane.

'Narkothion' *see* Thiobutabarbital.

'Narphen' *see* Phenazocine.

'Narphin' *see* Morphine noscapine meconate.

'Nasan' *see* Tetryzoline.

'Nasivin' *see* Oxymetazoline.

NAT-324 *see* Quindecamine acetate.

NAT-327 *see* Trimoxamine.

NAT-333 *see* Fenspiride.

'Nataba' *see* Sodium *p*-aminobenzoate.

NATAMYCIN* (22-[(3-amino-3,6-dideoxy-β-D-mannopyranosyl)oxy]-1,3,26-trihydroxy-12-methyl-10-oxo-6,11,28-trioxatricyclo-[2.2.3.1.0^{5,7}]octacosa-8,14,16,18,20-pentaene-25-carboxylic acid; A-5283; CL-12625).

'Natirene' *see* Clofenamide.

'Natirose' *see* Glyceryl trinitrate.

'Natisedine' *see* Quinidine 5-ethyl-5-phenylbarbi-turate.

'Natorexic' *see* Amfepramone.

'Natrilix' *see* Indapamide.

'Natrionex' *see* Acetazolamide.

Natrog (tr) *see* Sodium 2,3,4-trihydroxyglutarate.

'Natulan' *see* Procarbazine.

'Natulanar' *see* Procarbazine.

'Naturetin' *see* Bendroflumethiazide.

'Naturine' *see* Bendroflumethiazide.

'Natusan' *see* Benzalkonium chloride.

'Nausidol' *see* Pipamazine.

'Nautamine' *see* Diphenhydramine theophyllinate.

'Nautisan' *see* Chlorbutol.

'Navadel' *see* Dioxation.

'Navane' *see* Tiotixene.

'Navicalm' *see* Meclozine.

'Navidrex' *see* Cyclopenthiazide.

'Navidrix' *see* Cyclopenthiazide.

'Naxogin' *see* Nimorazole.

NB-68 *see* Dacuronium bromide.

NB-106-689 *see* Fluperlapine.

'NB/C' *see* Cianidanol.

'N.B.L.' *see* Metandienone.

NC-123 *see* Mesoridazine.

NC-150 *see* Phenazopyridine.

NC-1264 *see* Tonzonium bromide.

NC-1968 *see* Fungimycin.

NC-2983 *see* Chlorflurazole.

NC-5016 *see* Fenazaflor.

NC-6897 *see* Bendiocarb.

NC-7197 *see* Esproquine.

ND-50 *see* Octopamine.

ND-1966 *see* Aminoglutethimide.

NDC 0082-4155 *see* Daunorubicin.

NDGA *see* Nordihydroguaiaretic acid.

NDR-263 *see* Oxyclipine.

NDR-304 *see* Ethyl dibunate.

NDR-5061A *see* Alfetamine.

NDR-5523A *see* Trimoxamine.

NDR-5998A *see* Fenspiride.

'N.E.A.' *see* Norethisterone acetate.

NEALBARBITAL* (5-allyl-5-(2,2-dimethyl-propyl)barbituric acid; 5-allyl-5-neopentylbarbi-turic acid; neallymal).

Neallymal* *see* Nealbarbital.

'Neazolin' *see* Sulfafurazole.

'**Nebcin**' *see* Tobramycin.

NEBIDRAZINE*** (4-amino-3-(2,6-dichloro-benzylidenehydrazino)-1,2,4-triazine; 4-amino-3-[2-[(2,6-dichlorophenyl)methylene]hydrazino]-4*H*-1,2,4-triazole; 2,6-dichlorobenzaldehyde (4-amino-4*H*-1,2,4-triazol-3-yl)hydrazone; FLA-136).

NEBRAMYCIN** (antibiotic complex from *Str. tenebrarius*; tenemycin; A-12253A).

Nebramycin factor 6 *see* Tobramycin.

'**Nebs**' *see* Paracetamol.

NEBULARINE (4-(β-D-ribofuranosyl)-9*H*-purine; purine riboside).

Neburea *see* Neburon.

NEBURON* (1-butyl-3-(3,4-dichlorophenyl)-1-methylurea; neburea; 'kloben').

'**Necatorina**' *see* Carbon tetrachloride.

'**Nectadon**' *see* Noscapine.

'**Nedeltran**' *see* Alimemazine.

NEDOCROMIL** (9-ethyl-6,9-dihydro-4,6-di-oxo-10-propyl-4*H*-pyrano[3,2-*g*]quinoline-2,8-dicarboxylic acid; nedocromil sodium; FPL-59002 KP).

NEFAZODONE** (1-[3-[4-(*m*-chlorophenyl)pip-erazin-1-yl]propyl]-3-ethyl-4-(2-phenoxyethyl)-Δ²-1,2,4-triazolin-5-one).

NEFOPAM*** (3,4,5,6-tetrahydro-5-methyl-1-phenyl-1*H*-2,5-benzoxazocine; nefopam hydrochloride; Riker-738; 'acupan'; 'ajan').

'**Nefrix**' *see* Hydrochlorothiazide.

'**Nefrocarnit**' *see* Carnitine.

'**Nefrolan**' *see* Clorexolone.

'**Negasunt**' *see* Coumafos.

'**Negatan**' *see* Methylenedi(*m*-cresolsulfonic acid) polymer.

'**Negatol**' *see* Methylenedi(*m*-cresolsulfonic acid) polymer.

'**Neggram**' *see* Nalidixic acid.

'**Negram**' *see* Nalidixic acid.

'**Neguvon**' *see under* Metrifonate.

'**Nehydrin**' *see* Dihydroergocristine.

'**Neipertec 99m**' *see* Sodium pertechnetate Tc 99m.

'**Neirotrast**' *see* Iofendylate.

'**Nektrohan**' *see* Allopurinol.

'**Nelex**' *see* Methylenedi(*m*-cresolsulfonic acid) polymer.

'**Nema**' *see* Tetrachloroethylene.

'**Nemacide**' *see* Dichlofenthion.

'**Nemacur P**' *see* Fenamiphos.

'**Nemafax**' *see* Thiophanate.

'**Nemafos**' *see* Thionazin.

'**Nemaphos**' *see* Thionazin.

'**Nematin**' *see* Metam-sodium.

'**Nematolyt**' *see* Papain.

'**Nemazine**' *see* Phenothiazine.

'**Nemazon**' *see* 1,2-Dibromo-3-chloropropane.

'**Nembutal**' *see* Pentobarbital.

'**Nemex**' *see* Bephenium hydroxynaphthoate.

'**Nemicide**' *see* Levamisole.

NEMOTIN (4-hydroxy-5,6-undecadiene-8,10-di-ynoic acid γ-lactone).

'**Nemural**' *see* Arecoline-acetarsol.

Nendrin *see* Endrin.

'**Neo-absentol**' *see* Ethadione.

'**Neo-alfasol**' *see* Algestone acetofenide.

'**Neoamfo**' *see* Amphotericin B.

'**Neoantimosan**' *see* Stibophen.

NEOARSPHENAMINE*** (sodium 3,3'-di-amino-4,4'-dihydroxyarsenobenzene-*N*-formal-dehydesulfoxylate; arsphenamine methylenesulf-oxylic acid sodium salt; novarsenol; 'neosalvar-san').

'**Neo-arsycodile**' *see* Disodium methanearsonate.

'**Neoatromidin**' *see* Clofibrate.

'**Neobenodine**' *see p*-Methyldiphenhydramine.

'**Neobicin salicyl**' *see* Salinazid.

'**Neocalcin**' *see* Calcium levulinate.

Neocarzinostatin *see* Zinostatin.

'**Neo-cebicure**' *see* Isoascorbic acid.

'**Neo-cebitate**' *see* Sodium isoascorbate.

'**Neocide**' *see* DDT.

'**Neocidol**' *see* Dimpylate.

NEOCINCHOPHEN** (ethyl 6-methyl-2-phenyl-cinchoninate).

'**Neo-citrullamon**' *see* Phenytoin valerate.

'**Neo-cobefrin**' *see* (−)-Corbadrine.

'**Neocolan**' *see* Metochalcone.

'**Neocon**' *see under* Norethisterone.

'**Neoconserviet**' *see* Propham.

'**Neocortef**' *see* Hydrocortisone.

'**Neocycline**' *see* Tetracycline.

'**Neodecyllin**' *see* Neomycin undecenate.

'**Neo-dema**' *see* Chlorothiazide.

'**Neo-diacid**' *see* Bromisoval.

Neodicumarin (tr) *see* Ethyl biscoumacetate.

'**Neodistol**' *see* Bithionoloxide.

'**Neodorm**' *see* Pentobarbital.

'**Neodrast**' *see* Oxyphenisatine.

'**Neodrol**' *see* Androstanolone.

Neodymium and praesodymium levulinates *see* Rare earth levulinates.

NEODYMIUM PYROCATECHOLDISULFON-ATE COMPLEX ('phlogodym').

NEODYMIUM 3-SULFOISONICOTINATE ('thrombodym').

'**Neodyne**' *see* Ethyl dibunate.

Neoeserine *see* Neostigmine bromide.

'**Neofemergen**' *see* Ergometrine.

'**Neogel**' *see* Carbenoxolone.

'**Neogest**' *see* Norgestrel.

'**Neo-gilurytmal**' *see* Prajmalium bitartrate.

'**Neogynon**' *see under* Norgestrel.

'**Neohetramine**' *see* Thonzylamine.

'**Neo-hibernex**' *see* Promazine.

'**Neo-hollaxans**' *see* Phenisatin.

'**Neo-hydrazid**' *see* Cyacetacide.

'**Neohydrin**' *see* Chlormerodrin.

'**Neo-iopax**' *see* Iodoxyl.

Neoisocodeine *see* Pseudocodeine.

'**Neo-istafene**' *see* Meclozine.

'**Neoisuprel**' *see* Isoetarine.

'**Neokompensan**' *see* Povidone.

'**Neolamin**' *see* Thiamine disulfide.

'**Neolin**' *see* Benzathine penicillin.

'**Neolutin**' *see* Hydroxyprogesterone caproate.

'**Neomercazole**' *see* Carbimazole.

370

'Neo-methidin' *see* Methionine.

Neomonacrin *see* Methylaminacrin.

NEOMYCIN** (antibiotic from *Str. fradiae*; colimycin; framycin; mycerin; neomycin sulfate). *See also under* Clostebol acetate.

NEOMYCIN plus BACITRACIN ('bimixin'; 'bykomycin').

NEOMYCIN plus OXYTETRACYCLINE ('neotarchocin'; 'neoterramycin').

NEOMYCIN plus SULFAMETHIZOLE (By-123; 'uro-beniktol'; 'uro-nebacetin').

NEOMYCIN UNDECENATE (neomycin undecylenate; 'neodecyllin').

Neomycin undecylenate* *see* Neomycin undecenate.

Neomycin B *see* Framycetin.

'Neomyson G' *see* Thiamphenicol glycinate.

'Neo-naclex' *see* Bendroflumethiazide.

'Neonal' *see* Butethal.

'Neoniagar' *see* Mebutizide.

'Neoniazide' *see* Gluconiazone.

Neonicotine *see* Anabasine.

Neo-oxedrine *see* Phenylephrine.

'Neo-oxypate' *see* Pyrvinium embonate.

'Neopenil' *see* Penethamate hydriodide.

NEOPENTANE (2,2-dimethylpropane; tetramethylmethane).

1,1',1'',1'''-(Neopentanetetryltetraoxy)tetrakis(2,2,2-trichloroethanol) *see* Petrichloral.

'Neo-penyl' *see* Clemizole penicillin.

'Neophylline' *see under* Diprophylline.

Neopinamine *see* Tetramethrin.

NEOPINE (8,14-didehydro-4,5α-epoxy-3-methoxy-17-methylmorphinan-6α-ol; β-codeine; hydroxycodeine).

'Neoplatin' *see* Cisplatin.

'Neoprontosil' *see* Azosulfamide.

'Neopsicaine' *see* Pseudococaine.

NEOPTERIN (2-amino-4-hydroxy-6-(1,2,3-trihydroxypropyl)pteridine).

'Neo-pynamin' *see* Tetramethrin.

Neopyrithiamine *see* Pyrithiamine.

Neoquate *see* Nequinate.

'Neoron' *see* Bromopropylate.

'Neorontyl' *see* Bendroflumethiazide.

'Neosalvarsan' *see* Neoarsphenamine.

'Neo-scabicidol' *see* Lindane.

'Neo-schiwadex' *see* Dextran.

'Neosedyl' *see* Thalidomide.

'Neoserpine' *see* Methoserpidine.

'Neosoralen' *see* Trioxysalen.

'Neostam' *see* Stibamine glucoside.

NEOSTANOX* (hexakis(1-methyl-2-phenylpropyl)distannoxane; 'torque'; 'vendex').

'Neostibosan' *see* Ethylstibamine.

NEOSTIGMINE BROMIDE** ((*m*-hydroxyphenyl)trimethylammonium bromide dimethylcarbamate; neoeserine; synstigmine).

'Neoston' *see* Alclofenac.

'Neosubsidal' *see* Dextran.

'Neosulfine' *see* Mesulfen.

'Neosynephrine' *see* Phenylephrine.

'Neotarchocin' *see under* Neomycin.

'Neoterramycin' *see under* Neomycin.

NEOTETRAZOLIUM (*p,p'*-biphenylene-2,2'-bis(3,5-diphenyltetrazolium chloride)).

'Neothiate' *see* O-(*m*-Chlorophenyl) O,O-dimethyl phosphorothioate.

'Neothyl' *see* Methyl propyl ether.

'Neo-thyreostat' *see* Carbimazole.

'Neotizide' *see* Isoniazid mesilate.

'Neotri' *see under* Triamterene.

NEOTROPIN (6-butoxy-3-(2,6-diaminopyrid-3-ylazo)pyridine; 2',6'-diamino-2-butoxy-3,3'-azopyridine; 'niazo').

'Neo-urofort' *see* Chlorazanil.

'Neoviacept' *see under* Chloroquine diphosphate.

'Neozine' *see* Levomepromazine.

Nephocarp *see* Carbofenotion.

'Nephramid' *see* Acetazolamide.

'Nephril' *see* Polythiazide.

'Nephrin' *see* Cystine.

'Nephrotest' *see* Sodium *p*-aminohippurate.

'Nepresol' *see* Dihydralazine.

'Neptal' *see* Mercuderamide.

'Neptall' *see* Acebutolol.

NEPTAMUSTINE*** (1-(2-chloroethyl)-3-(2,2-dimethylpropyl)-1-nitrosourea; 1-(2-chloroethyl)-3-neopentyl-1-nitrosourea; pentamustine).

'Neptazane' *see* Methazolamide.

NEQUINATE** (methyl 7-benzyloxy-6-butyl-1,4-dihydro-4-oxo-3-quinolinecarboxylate; methyl 7-benzyloxy-6-butyl-4-hydroxyquinoline-3-carboxylate; methyl benzoquate; neoquate; AY-20385; ICI-55052).

'Neratox' *see* Warfarin.

'Neraval' *see* Methitural.

'Neravan' *see* Secbutabarbital.

NEREISTOXIN (4-(dimethylamino)-1,2-dithiolane).

'Nerfactor' *see* Isaxonine.

'Nerial' *see* Peruvoside.

Neriine *see* Conessine.

'Nerisone' *see* Diflucortolone valerate.

'Nerobol' *see* Metandienone.

'Neroboletta' *see* Metandienone.

'Nerobolil' *see* Nandrolone phenpropionate.

'Nervacton' *see* Benactyzine.

'Nervanaid B' *see* Tetrasodium edetate.

Nervic acid *see* 15-Tetracosenoic acid.

Nervonic acid *see* 15-Tetracosenoic acid.

'Nesacaine' *see* Chloroprocaine.

'Nesdonal' *see* Thiopental sodium.

'Nesivine' *see* Oxymetazoline.

'Nesontil' *see* Oxazepam.

'Netamine' *see* Etafedrine.

Nethalide *see* Pronetalol.

'Nethamine' *see* Etafedrine.

'Netilar' *see* Paramethasone acetate.

'Netillin' *see* Netilmicin.

NETILMICIN*** (O-3-deoxy-4-C-methyl-3-(methylamino)-β-L-arabinopyranosyl-(1→4)-O-(2,6-diamino-2,3,4,6-tetradeoxy-α-D-*glycero*-hex-4-enopyranosyl-(1→6))-2-deoxy-N^3-ethyl-L-streptamine; N^1-ethylsisomicin; netilmicin sulfate; Sch-20569; 'certomycin'; 'netillin'; 'netro-

mycin').
'Netrin' *see* Metcaraphen.
'Netromycin' *see* Netilmicin.
'Netrosylla' *see* Etisazole.
Neuberg ester *see* Fructose 6-phosphate.
'Neulactil' *see* Periciazine.
'Neuleptil' *see* Periciazine.
'Neupentedrin' *see* Oxedrine.
'Neuracen' *see* Beclamide.
'Neuractil' *see* Levomepromazine.
'Neuraxin' *see* Methocarbamol.
'Neuridal' *see under* Paracetamol.
'Neuridine' *see* Spermine.
NEURINE (trimethylvinylammonium hydroxide).
'Neuriplege' *see* Chlorproethazine.
'Neurocil' *see* Levomepromazine.
'Neurolepsin' *see* Lithium carbonate.
'Neuroleptone' *see* Benactyzine.
'Neurolytril' *see* Diazepam.
'Neuronika' *see* Kawain.
'Neuroplegil' *see* Promazine.
'Neurosterone' *see* Cyclopregnol.
Neurotrast (tr) *see* Iofendylate.
'Neurotropan' *see* Choline citrate.
'Neurylan' *see* Isomylamine.
NEUTRAL INSULIN INJECTION* (porcine insulin solution buffered to pH 7; 'actrapid'; 'insulin actrapid'; 'nuso'; 'velosulin').
See also under Isophane insulin.
NEUTRAMYCIN*** (antibiotic from *Str. rimosus*; AE-705-W; LL-705W).
'Neutrapen' *see* Penicillinase.
'Neutrazyme' *see* Sodium dodecyl sulfate.
'Neuvitan' *see* Octotiamine.
'Nevax' *see* Docusate sodium.
'Nevenal' *see* Nealbarbital.
'Nevigramon' *see* Nalidixic acid.
'Nevimycin' *see* Chloramphenicol.
'Nevitron' *see* Bentiamine *and* Prosultiamine.
'New cacodyle' *see* Disodium methanearsonate.
'New urotropin' *see* Methenamine anhydromethylenecitrate.
'Nexagan' *see* Bromofos-ethyl.
'Nexarato' *see* Warfarin.
NEXERIDINE*** (1-[2-(dimethylamino)-1-methylethyl]-2-phenylcyclohexanol acetate ester; nexeridine hydrochloride).
'Nexion' *see* Bromofos.
'Nezeril' *see* Oxymetazoline.
NF-35 *see* Thiophanate.
NF-44 *see* Thiophanate-methyl.
NF-67 *see* Nidroxyzone.
NF-71 *see* Nifurmerone.
NF-84 *see* Nifuraldezone.
NF-161 *see* Nifursemizone.
NF-246 *see* Nifuradene.
NF-260 *see* Furaltadone.
NF-602 *see* Levofuraltadone.
NF-902 *see* Levofuraltadone.
NF-963 *see* Furazolium chloride.
NF-1010 *see* Nifurdazil.
NF-1088 *see* Nifurquinazol.
NF-1120 *see* Nifurimide.

NF-1425 *see* Furazolium tartrate.
NIA-10242 *see* Carbofuran.
Niacin *see* Nicotinic acid.
Niacinamide *see* Nicotinamide.
'Niacol' *see* Nicotinyl alcohol.
'Niagar' *see* Hydrochlorothiazide.
'Niagara-1240' *see* Ethion.
'Niagara blue' *see* Trypan blue.
'Niagaramite' *see* 2-(*p-tert*-Butylphenoxy)isopropyl 2-chloroethyl sulfite.
'Niagestin' *see* Megestrol.
NIALAMIDE*** (isonicotinic acid 2-[(2-benzyl-carbamoyl)ethyl]hydrazide; *N'*-(2-benzylcarba-moylethyl)isoniazid; BEIH).
'Nialate' *see* Ethion.
'Niallate' *see* Ethion.
'Niamid' *see* Nialamide.
NIAPRAZINE*** (*N*-[3-[4-(*p*-fluorophenyl)pip-erazin-1-yl]-1-methylpropyl]nicotinamide; CERM 1709).
'Niazo' *see* Neotropin.
NIB *see* Nabitan.
'Nibal' *see* Metenolone acetate.
'Nibal injection' *see* Metenolone enantate.
'Nibiol' *see* Nitroxoline.
'Nibrisin' *see* Co-trimazine.
NIBROXANE*** (5-bromo-2-methyl-5-nitro-*m*-dioxane; compound 85287).
NIBUFIN (tr) (dibutyl *p*-nitrophenyl phosphate).
NICAFENINE*** (*N*-(7-chloro-4-quinolyl)anthra-nilic acid ester with *N*-(2-hydroxyethyl)nicotin-amide).
NICAINOPROL*** ((±)-1,2,3,4-tetrahydro-8-[2-hydroxy-3-(isopropylamino)propoxy]-1-nicoti-noylquinoline).
NICAMETATE*** (2-(diethylamino)ethyl nico-tinate; nicametate citrate).
'Nicamin' *see* Ethanolamine nicotinate.
'Nicarb' *see* Nicarbazin.
NICARBAZIN* (equimolecular complex of 4,4'-dinitrocarbanilic acid and 4,6-dimethyl-2-pyr-imidinol; 'nicarb'; 'nicoxin'; 'nicrazin').
NICARDIPINE*** (2-(benzylmethylamino)ethyl methyl 1,4-dihydro-2,6-dimethyl-4-(3-nitrophen-yl)-3,5-pyridinedicarboxylate; nicardipine hydrochloride; RS-69216; YC-93).
'Nicascorbin' *see* Ascorbic acid nicotinamide com-plex.
'Nicastubin' *see* Ascorbic acid nicotinamide com-plex.
'Nicene' *see* Nitroxoline.
NICERGOLINE*** (8β-(5-bromonicotinoyl-oxymethyl)-10-methoxy-1,6-dimethylergoline; 8β-(hydroxymethyl)-10-methoxy-1,6-dimethyl-ergoline 5-bromonicotinate; 10-methoxy-1,6-di-methylergoline-8β-methanol 5-bromonicotinate; FI-6714; 'sermion'; 'varson').
NICERITROL*** (pentaerythrityl tetranicotinate; 'cardiolipol'; 'pericyt'; 'perycit').
Nicethamide* *see* Nikethamide.
NICEVERINE*** (1-(3,4-dihydroxybenzyl)-6,7-dimethoxyisoquinoline dinicotinate; 4-[(6,7-di-methoxyisoquinolin-1-yl)methyl]pyrocatechol

372

dinicotinate; 6,7-dimethoxy-1-protocatechuyl-isoquinoline dinicotinate; dimethylpapaveroline dinicotinate; RC-167).

Nichlorfos *see* Phosnichlor.

'Nicholin' *see* Citicoline.

Niclofen *see* Nitrofen.

NICLOFOLAN*** (5,5'-dichloro-2,2'-dihydroxy-3,3'-dinitrobiphenyl; 5,5'-dichloro-3,3'-dinitro-2,2'-biphenol; 4,4'-dichloro-6,6'-dinitro-*o,o*-biphenol; menichlopholan; Bayer 9015; Me-3625; 'bilevon'; 'distolon').

NICLOSAMIDE*** (5-chloro-*N*-(2-chloro-4-nitrophenyl)salicylamide; 2',5-dichloro-2-hydroxy-4'-nitrobenzanilide; 2',5-dichloro-4'-nitrosalicyl-anilide; fenasal; phenasal; Bayer-2353; RP 10768).

Niclosamide ethanolamine salt *see* Clonitralide.

NICLOSAMIDE PIPERAZINE SALT ('manso-nil').

NICOBOXIL*** (2-butoxyethyl nicotinate).

NICOBOXIL plus NONIVAMIDE ('finalgon').

NICOCLONATE*** (*p*-chloro-α-isopropylbenzyl nicotinate; 'lipidium').

NICOCODINE*** (6-nicotinoylcodeine; 'lyo-pect').

NICOCORTONIDE*** (11β,14,17,21-tetrahydro-xypregn-4-ene-3,20-dione cyclic 14,17-acetal with crotonaldehyde, 21-isonicotinate).

'Nicodan' *see* Sodium nicotinate.

NICODICODINE** (7,8-dihydro-*O*³-methyl-*O*⁶-nicotinoylmorphine; dihydrocodeine 6-nicotin-ate; 6-nicotinoyldihydrocodeine).

Nicofezon (tr) *see* Nifenazone.

NICOFIBRATE** (pyrid-3-ylmethyl 2-(*p*-chloro-phenoxy)-2-methylpropionate; clofenpyride; clo-finol).

NICOFURANOSE*** (fructofuranose tetranico-tinate; fructose nicotinate; fructose tetranicotin-ate; nicofurazone; nicotinoylfructose; tetranico-tinoylfructofuranose; ES-304; 'cardilan').

NICOFURATE*** (methyl 2-methyl-5-[D-*arabi-no*-1,2,3,4-tetra(nicotinoyloxy)butyl]-3-furoate; 5-(D-*arabino*-1,2,3,4-tetrahydroxybutyl)-2-methyl-3-furoic acid methyl ester tetranicotin-ate).

Nicofurazone *see* Nicofuranose.

NICOGRELATE** ((±)-(*E*)-3-imidazol-1-yl-1-pentylallyl nicotinate).

'Nicolane' *see* Noscapine.

Nicomethanol* *see* Nicotinyl alcohol.

NICOMOL*** (2-hydroxy-1,1,3,3-cyclohexane-tetramethanol tetranicotinate).

NICOMORPHINE*** (3,6-dinicotinoylmorphine; morphine dinicotinate; nicomorphine hydro-chloride; 'vilan').

NICOMORPHINE plus NALORPHINE DINI-COTINATE ('vendal neu').

NICOPHOLINE*** (4-nicotinoylmorpholine).

'Nicoprazine' *see* Morinamide.

'Nicopyron' *see* Nifenazone.

NICORANDIL** (*N*-(2-hydroxyethyl)nicotin-amide nitrate; 2-nicotinamidoethyl nitrate; SG-75).

'Nicorine' *see* Nikethamide.

'Nicorol' *see* Furosemide.

NICOSIN (tr) (*p*-[bis(2-chloroethyl)amino]-*N*-ni-cotinoylphenylalanine ethyl ester; ethyl 3-[*p*-[bis(2-chloroethyl)amino]phenyl]-2-nicotinoyl-aminopropionate; nicozin; *N*-sarcolysylnicotin-amide).

'Nicosode' *see* Sodium nicotinate.

'Nicosterol' *see* Sorbinicate.

Nicotafuryl* *see* Thurfyl nicotinate.

NICOTHIAZONE*** (nicotinaldehyde thiosemi-carbazone; G-469).

NICOTINALDEHYDE (3-pyridinaldehyde; β-pyridyl aldehyde).

Nicotinaldehyde thiosemicarbazone *see* Nicothiaz-one.

NICOTINAMIDE*** (3-pyridinecarboxamide; vi-tamin B₃; amide PP; niacinamide; PP-factor).

Nicotinamide adenine dinucleotide *see* Nadide.

2-Nicotinamidoethyl clofibrate *see* Picafibrate.

2-Nicotinamidoethyl nitrate *see* Nicorandil.

NICOTINE (3-(1-methylpyrrolidin-2-yl)pyridine).

NICOTINIC ACID*** (3-pyridinecarboxylic acid; vitamin PP; niacin; β-picolinic acid; PP-factor). *See also under* Aluminium clofibrate; Pentifyll-ine.

NICOTINIC ACID plus PENTOSAN POLY-SULFATE ('compuron').

Nicotinic acid salts *see* Ethanolamine nicotinate; Sodium nicotinate.

Nicotinic acid *N*-methylbetaine *see* Trigonelline.

Nicotinic acid *N*-oxide *see* Oxiniacic acid.

Nicotinic alcohol *see* Nicotinyl alcohol.

Nicotinohydroxamic acid *see* Nicoxamat.

p-**Nicotinoylaminobenzoic acid 2-diethylaminoethyl ester** *see* Nicotinoylprocaine.

N-**Nicotinoylamphetamine** *see* Phenatin.

6-Nicotinoylcodeine *see* Nicocodine.

6-Nicotinoyldihydrocodeine *see* Nicodicodine.

Nicotinoylfructose *see* Nicofuranose.

Nicotinoylglycine *see* Nicotinuric acid.

4-Nicotinoylmorpholine *see* Nicopholine.

2-(Nicotinoyloxy)ethyl clofibrate *see* Etofibrate.

NICOTINOYLPROCAINE (2-(diethylamino)-ethyl *p*-nicotinoylaminobenzoate; 'municaps'; 'sklerovitol').

NICOTINURIC ACID (nicotinoylglycine).

NICOTINYL ALCOHOL* (3-pyridinemethanol; β-pyridyl carbinol; nicomethanol; nicotinic alco-hol; nicotinyl alcohol tartrate; NSC-526046; Nu-2121; Ro 1-5155). *See also* Eniclobrate; Nicofibrate *and under* Clo-fibrate.

Nicoumalone* *see* Acenocoumarol.

NICOXAMAT*** (nicotinohydroxamic acid).

'Nicoxin' *see* Nicarbazin.

Nicozin (tr) *see* Nicosin.

'Nicrazin' *see* Nicarbazin.

NICTINDOLE*** (2-isopropylindol-3-yl pyrid-3-yl ketone; L-8027).

'Nidanthel' *see* Nitrodan.

'Nidantin' *see* Oxolinic acid.

'Nidaton' *see* Isoniazid.

373

NIDROXYZONE* (5-nitro-2-furaldehyde 2-(2-hydroxyethyl)semicarbazone; nitrofuroxizone; furaloxon; F-26; NF-67).

'Nierofu' see Nitrofurantoin.

NIFEDIPINE* (dimethyl 1,4-dihydro-2,6-dimethyl-4-(2-nitrophenyl)pyridine-3,5-dicarboxylate; BAY a-1040; 'adalate'; 'corinfar').

NIFENALOL* (α-[(isopropylamino)methyl]-*p*-nitrobenzyl alcohol; *N*-isopropyl-*p*-nitrophenylethanolamine; isophenethanol; INPEA).

NIFENAZONE* (2,3-dimethyl-4-nicotinamido-1-phenyl-3-pyrazolin-5-one; *N*-antipyrinylnicotinamide; nicofezon).

'Niflucid' see Niflumic acid.

NIFLUMIC ACID* (2-(α,α,α-trifluoro-*m*-toluidino)nicotinic acid; 2-[3-(trifluoromethyl)anilino]nicotinic acid; JDL-37; R-368c; UP-83). *See also* Morniflumate; Talniflumate.

'Nifluril' see Niflumic acid.

'Nifos' see Tetraethyl pyrophosphate.

Niftolid (tr) see Flutamide.

'Nifucin' see Nitrofural.

'Nifulidone' see Furazolidone.

NIFUNGIN* (antibiotic from *Aspergillus giganteus*).

NIFURADENE* (1-(5-nitrofurfurylideneamino)-2-imidazolidinone; oxafuradene; NF-246; NSC-6470).

Nifuralazin* see Furalazine.

NIFURALDEZONE* (5-nitro-2-furaldehyde semioxamazone; NF-84; NSC-3184; 'aldefur').

NIFURALIDE* (1-(2-allylamino-1,3-thiazol-4-yl)-6-(5-nitro-2-furyl)-1-oxo-2,3-diaza-3,5-hexadiene; 2-(allylamino)-4-thiazolecarboxylic acid 3-(5-nitro-2-furyl)allylidene)hydrazide; CB-12025).

Nifuramizone* see Nifurethazone.

'Nifuran' see Furazolidone.

'Nifurantin' see Nitrofurantoin.

NIFURATEL* (5-(methylthiomethyl)-3-(5-nitrofurfurylideneamino)-2-oxazolidinone; SAP-113).

NIFURATRONE* (*N*-(2-hydroxyethyl)-α-(5-nitro-2-furyl)nitrone).

Nifurazolidone* see Furazolidone.

NIFURDAZIL* (1-(2-hydroxyethyl)-3-(5-nitrofurfurylideneamino)-2-imidazolidinone; edrofuradene; NF-1010).

NIFURETHAZONE* (5-nitro-2-furaldehyde (dimethylaminoethyl)semicarbazone; nifuramizone).

Nifurhydrazone* see Nihydrazone.

NIFURIMIDE (4-methyl-1-(5-nitrofurfurylideneamino)-2-imidazolidinone; NF-1120).

NIFURIZONE (1-(methylcarbamoyl)-3-[3-(5-nitro-2-furyl)allylideneamino]-2-imidazolinone; CB-11380).

NIFURMAZOLE* (3-(hydroxymethyl)-1-[3-(5-nitro-2-furyl)allylideneamino]hydantoin; CB-10615).

NIFURMERONE* (chloromethyl 5-nitro-2-furyl ketone; metofurone; NF-71).

NIFUROQUINE* (4-(5-nitro-2-furyl)quinaldic acid 1-oxide; 'abimasten').

NIFUROXAZIDE* (*p*-hydroxy-*N²*-(5-nitro-2-furfurylidene)benzohydrazide; NSC-27109; RC-27109).

NIFUROXIME* (5-nitro-2-furaldehyde oxime).

NIFURPIPONE* (4-methyl-1-piperazineacetic acid (5-nitrofurfurylidene)hydrazide; 1-[2-(4-methylpiperazin-1-yl)acetyl]-2-(5-nitrofurfurylidene)hydrazine; 5-nitro-2-furaldehyde [(4-methylpiperazin-1-yl)acetyl]hydrazone; NP; 'Rec-15/0122'; 'recofur').

NIFURPIRINOL* (2-(hydroxymethyl)-6-[2-(5-nitro-2-furyl)vinyl]pyridine; 6-[2-(5-nitro-2-furanyl)ethenyl]-2-pyridinemethanol; 6-[2-(5-nitro-2-furyl)vinyl]-2-pyridinemethanol; P-7138; 'furanace').

NIFURPRAZINE* (3-amino-6-[2-(5-nitrofuryl)vinyl]pyridazine; furenapyridazine; furenazine; HB-115).

NIFURQUINAZOL* (4-[bis(2-hydroxyethyl)amino]-2-(5-nitrofur-2-yl)quinazoline; 2,2'-[2-(5-nitrofur-2-yl)quinazolin-4-ylimino]diethanol; NF-1088).

NIFURSEMIZONE* (5-nitro-2-furaldehyde 2-ethylsemicarbazone; etafurazone; NF-161).

NIFURSOL (1-(3,5-dinitrosalicoyl)-2-(5-nitrofurfurylidene)hydrazine; 3,5-dinitrosalicylic acid 2-(5-nitrofurfurylidene)hydrazide; RT-6912; 'salfuride').

NIFURTHIAZOLE* (2-(2-formylhydrazino)-4-(5-nitro-2-furyl)thiazole; AS-17665; NSC-525334).

Nifurthiline* see Thiofuradene.

NIFURTIMOX* (4-(5-nitrofurfurylideneamino)-3-methylthiomorpholine 1,1-dioxide; tetrahydro-3-methyl-4-(5-nitrofurfurylideneamino)-1,4-thiazine 1,1-dioxide; Bayer 2502; 'lampit').

NIFURTOINOL* (3-(hydroxymethyl)-1-[(5-nitrofurfurylidene)amino]hydantoin; 1-(5-nitro-2-furfurylideneamino)-3-hydantoinmethanol; hydroxymethylnitrofurantoin; 'urfadyne'; 'uridurine').

NIFURVIDINE (2-methyl-6-[2-(5-nitro-2-furyl)vinyl]-4-pyrimidinol).

NIFURZIDE* (1-[3-(5-nitro-2-furyl)allylidene]-2-(5-nitro-2-thenoyl)hydrazine; 5-nitro-2-thiophenecarboxylic acid [3-(5-nitro-2-furyl)allylidene]hydrazide; 'ricridene').

Nigelline see Damascenine.

'Nigrin' see Rufocromomycin.

NIH-2933 see Dimepheptanol.

NIH-7519 see Phenazocine.

NIH-7574 see Benzethidine.

NIH-7607 see Etonitazene.

NIH-7667 see Noracymethadol.

NIH-7672 see Metofoline.

NIH-8805 see Buprenorphine.

NIHYDRAZONE* (acetic acid 5-nitrofurfurylidenehydrazide; 5-nitro-2-furaldehyde acetylhydrazone; nifurhydrazone).

NIKETHAMIDE*** (*N,N*-diethylnicotinamide; nicethamide; betapyrimidum; cordiamin).
'Nikkol HCO50' *see* Ricinomacrogol.
'Nikoban' *see* Lobeline.
'Nilatil' *see* Itramin tosilate.
NILEPROST*** (δ-cyano-3,3a,4,5,6,6a-hexahydro-5-hydroxy-4-(3-hydroxy-4-methyl-1-octenyl)-2-*H*-cyclopenta[*b*]furan-Δ²δ-valeric acid).
'Nilergex' *see* Isothipendyl.
NILESTRIOL*** (3-cyclopentyloxy-16α,17-dihydroxy-19-nor-17α-pregna-1,3,5(10)-trien-20-yne; 3-cyclopentyloxy-19-nor-17α-pregna-1,3,5(10)-trien-20-yne-16α,17-diol; nylestriol).
'Nilevar' *see* Norethandrolone.
'Nilodin' *see* Lucanthone.
NILPRAZOLE*** (1-(2-benzoylethyl)-2-[[4-[(isopropylcarbamoyl)methyl]piperazin-1-yl]methyl]benzimidazole; 4-[[1-(2-benzoylethyl)-benzimidazol-2-yl]methyl]-*N*-isopropyl-1-piperazineacetamide; MD-73442).
'Nilstat' *see* Nystatin.
NILUDIPINE*** (bis(2-propoxyethyl) 1,4-dihydro-2,6-dimethyl-4-(3-nitrophenyl)pyridine-3,5-dicarboxylate; BAY a-7168).
NILVADIPINE** (5-isopropyl 3-methyl 2-cyano-1,4-dihydro-6-methyl-4-(*m*-nitrophenyl)pyridine-3,5-dicarboxylate).
'Nilverm' *see* Tetramisole.
'Nilverm GL' *see* Levamisole.
'Nimaol' *see* Octamoxin.
NIMAZONE** (3-(*p*-chlorophenyl)-1-cyanomethyl-4-iminoimidazolidin-2-one; 3-(*p*-chlorophenyl)-4-imino-2-oxo-1-imidazolidineacetonitrile; WIN-25347).
'Nimelan' *see* Nalorphine dinicotinate.
NIMESULIDE*** (4'-nitro-2'-phenoxymethanesulfonanilide; R-805).
NIMETAZEPAM*** (1,3-dihydro-1-methyl-7-nitro-5-phenyl-2*H*-1,4-benzodiazepin-2-one; ID-530; S-1530).
NIMIDANE*** (4-chloro-*N*-1,3-dithietan-2-ylidene-2-methylaniline; cyclic methylene (4-chloro-*o*-tolyl)dithioimidocarbonate; CL-84633; ENT-29106; 'abequito').
NIMODIPINE*** (isopropyl 2-methoxyethyl 1,4-dihydro-2,6-dimethyl-4-(*m*-nitrophenyl)pyridine-3,5-dicarboxylate; BAY e-9736).
NIMORAZOLE*** (1-(2-morpholinoethyl)-5-nitroimidazole; 4-[2-(5-nitroimidazol-1-yl)ethyl]-morpholine; nitrimidazine; K-1900; 'acterol'; 'naxogin'; 'nulogyl').
NIMUSTINE*** (3-[(4-amino-2-methylpyrimidin-5-yl)methyl]-1-(2-chloroethyl)-1-nitrosourea; ACNU).
NINHYDRIN (1,2,3-indantrione hydrate).
NIN PD-3 *see* Prolactin.
'Nioform' *see* Clioquinol.
NIOMETACIN*** (5-methoxy-2-methyl-1-nicotinoylindole-3-acetic acid).
'Nipabenzyl' *see* Benzyl paraben.
'Nipagen E' *see* Ethyl paraben.
'Nipagin' *see* Methyl paraben.
'Nipantiox 1-F' *see* Butylated hydroxyanisole.

'Nipaphenyl' *see* Phenyl paraben.
'Nipasol' *see* Butyl paraben.
'Nipasol P' *see* Propyl paraben.
'Nipaxon' *see* Noscapine.
NIPECOTIC ACID (3-piperidinecarboxylic acid).
'Niperyt' *see* Pentaerythrityl tetranitrate.
'Nipodal' *see* Prochlorperazine.
NIPRADILOL** (8-[2-hydroxy-3-(isopropylamino)propoxy]-3-chromanol 3-nitrate; nipradolol).
Nipradolol *see* Nipradilol.
'Nipride' *see* Sodium nitroprusside.
NIPROFAZONE*** (*N*-[(antipyrinylisopropylamino)methyl]nicotinamide; 4-[(isopropyl)(nicotinamidomethyl)amino]phenazone; 4-[(isopropyl)(nicotinamidomethyl)amino]-2,3-dimethyl-1-phenyl-3-pyrazolin-5-one; RA-101).
'Niran' *see* Parathion.
'Niren' *see* Polychlorinated biphenyl.
NIRIDAZOLE*** (1-(5-nitrothiazol-2-yl)imidazolidin-2-one; nitrothiamidazol; Ba-32644; NSC-136947; 'ambilhar').
'Nirvanil' *see* Valnoctamide.
'Nirvegil' *see* Carfimate.
'Nirvotin' *see* Carfimate.
'Nirvotinal' *see* Carfimate.
NISBUTEROL*** ((±)-α-[(*tert*-butylamino)methyl]-3,4-dihydroxybenzyl alcohol 3-acetate 4-*p*-anisate; colterol 3-acetate 4-*p*-anisate).
NISBUTEROL MESILATE (nisbuterol methanesulfonate (salt); nisbuterol mesylate; WIN-34886).
'Nisentil' *see* Alphaprodine.
'Nisidan' *see* Opipramol.
'Nisidana' *see* Opipramol.
NISOBAMATE*** (2-*sec*-butyl-2-methyl-1,3-propanediol carbamate isopropylcarbamate; 2-hydroxymethyl-2,3-dimethylpentyl carbamate isopropylcarbamate; W-1015).
NISOLDIPINE*** (isobutyl methyl 1,4-dihydro-2,6-dimethyl-4-(2-nitrophenyl)-3,5-pyridinedicarboxylate; BAY k-5552).
NISOXETINE*** (3-(*o*-methoxyphenoxy)-*N*-methyl-3-phenylpropylamine; 2-[3-(methylamino)-1-phenylpropoxy]anisole; compound 89218).
'Nissol' *see* *N*-(2-Fluoroacetyl)-*N*-methyl-1-naphthylamine.
NISTERIME** (2α-chloro-17β-hydroxy-5α-androstan-3-one *O*-(*p*-nitrophenyl)oxime).
NISTERIME ACETATE* (17β-acetoxy-2α-chloro-5α-androstan-3-one 3-*O*-(*p*-nitrophenyl)oxime; nisterime 17β-acetate; ORF-9326).
'Nisulfazole' *see* Nitrosulfathiazole.
NITARSONE*** (*p*-nitrobenzenearsonic acid; NSC-5085; 'hep-a-stat'; 'histostat').
NITAZOXANIDE*** (*N*-(5-nitrothiazol-2-yl)salicylamide acetate (ester)).
Nithiamide* *see* Aminitrozole.
NITHIAZIDE (1-ethyl-3-(5-nitrothiazol-2-yl)urea; 'hepzide').
'Nitoman' *see* Tetrabenazine.
NITRACRINE*** (9-[[3-(dimethylamino)propyl]-

375

amino]-1-nitroacridine; C-283; 'ledacrin').
'**Nitradisc**' *see* Glyceryl trinitrate.
'**Nitrados**' *see* Nitrazepam.
NITRAFUDAM*** (5-(*o*-nitrophenyl)-2-furamidine; 5-(2-nitrophenyl)-2-furancarboximidamide; nitrofudam hydrochloride; F-853).
NITRALAMINE* (2-(*o*-chloro-α-nitromethylbenzylthio)ethylamine; nitralamine hydrochloride; SC-12350).
'**Nitralettae**' *see* Trolnitrate.
NITRALIN* (4-methylsulfonyl-2,6-dinitro-*N*,*N*-dipropylaniline; 'planavin').
NITRAMISOLE*** ((±)-2,3,5,6-tetrahydro-6-(*m*-nitrophenyl)imidazo[2,1-*b*]thiazole; nitramisole hydrochloride; R-29860).
'**Nitramyl**' *see* Amyl nitrite.
'**Nitrangin**' *see* Glyceryl trinitrate.
'**Nitranitol**' *see* Mannityl hexanitrate.
Nitranol (tr) *see* Trolnitrate.
2-Nitratoethylamine *see* Itramin.
NITRAZEPAM*** (1,3-dihydro-7-nitro-5-phenyl-2*H*-1,4-benzodiazepin-2-one; LA-1; NSC-58775; Ro 4-5360; Ro 5-3059).
See also Potassium nitrazepate.
NITREFAZOLE*** (2-methyl-4-nitro-1-(*p*-nitrophenyl)imidazole; EMD-15700; 'altimol').
NITRENDIPINE*** (ethyl methyl 1,4-dihydro-2,6-dimethyl-4-(3-nitrophenyl)-3,5-pyridinedicarboxylate; BAY e-5009).
'**Nitretamin**' *see* Trolnitrate.
NITRICHOLINE PERCHLORATE*** (choline nitrate ester perchlorate; nitrocholine).
'**Nitricide**' *see* Fenson.
2-Nitrilo-*N*-*tert*-butylphenoxypropanolamine *see* Bunitrolol.
NITRILOTRIACETIC ACID (*N*,*N*-bis(carboxymethyl)glycine; triglycine; triglycollamic acid).
See also Sodium nitrilotriacetate.
Nitrilotriethanol *see* Triethanolamine.
2,2′,2″-Nitrilotriethanol trinitrate *see* Trolnitrate.
Nitrimidazine *see* Nimorazole.
'**Nitrisken**' *see* Isosorbide dinitrate.
NITRITOCOBALAMIN (vitamin B$_{12c}$).
3-Nitro *see* Roxarsone.
p-(*p*-**Nitroanilino)phenyl isothiocyanate** *see* Amoscanate.
p-**Nitrobenzenearsonic acid** *see* Nitarsone.
NITROCAPHANE (2-(2-amino-2-carboxyethyl)-*N*,*N*-bis(2-chloroethyl)-4-nitrophenethylamine; 2-[2-(2-amino-4-carboxyethyl)-4-nitrophenyl]-2′,2 dichlorotriethylamine; 3-[2-[2-[bis(2-chloroethyl)amino]ethyl]-4-nitrophenyl]alanine; AT-1258).
NITROCEFIN* ((7*R*)-3-[(*E*)-2,4-dinitrostyryl]-7-(thien-2-ylacetamido)-2-cephem-2-carboxylic acid; nitrocefin sodium; compound 87/312).
Nitrocellulose *see* Pyroxylin.
Nitrochloroform *see* Chloropicrin.
Nitrocholine *see* Nitricholine perchlorate.
NITROCLOFENE*** (4,6′-dichloro-4′,6-dinitro-2,2′-methylenediphenol).
NITROCYCLINE*** (6-demethyl-6-deoxy-7-nitrotetracycline).

NITRODAN** (3-methyl-5-(4-nitrophenylazo)-thiazolidin-4-one-2-thione; 5-methyl-5-(*p*-nitrophenylazo)rhodanine; CTR-6110).
'**Nitroderm TTS**' *see* Glyceryl trinitrate.
'**Nitrodex**' *see* Pentaerythrityl tetranitrate.
'**Nitroduran**' *see* Nitrodan *and* Trolnitrate.
'**Nitroerythrite**' *see* Erythrityl tetranitrate.
Nitroerythrol *see* Erythrityl tetranitrate.
'**Nitrofar**' *see* Dinitro-*o*-cresol.
NITROFEN* (2,4-dichloro-1-(*p*-nitrophenoxy)-benzene; 2,4-dichloro-4′-nitrodiphenyl ether; niclofen; TOK E25).
'**Nitrofungin**' *see* 2-Chloro-4-nitrophenol.
'**Nitrofuracin**' *see* Nitrofurantoin.
Nitrofuradoxadone* *see* Furmethoxadone.
NITROFURAL** (5-nitro-2-furaldehyde semicarbazone; furacilin; nitrofurazone; NSC-2100).
Nitrofuralazin *see* Furalazine.
5-Nitro-2-furaldehyde acetylhydrazone *see* Nihydrazone.
5-Nitro-2-furaldehyde (dimethylaminoethyl)semicarbazone *see* Nifurethazone.
5-Nitro-2-furaldehyde 2-ethylsemicarbazone *see* Nifursemizone.
5-Nitro-2-furaldehyde 2-(2-hydroxyethyl)semicarbazone *see* Nidroxyzone.
5-Nitro-2-furaldehyde isonicotinoylhydrazone *see* Furaniozid.
5-Nitro-2-furaldehyde [(4-methylpiperazin-1-yl)acetyl]hydrazone *see* Nifurpipone.
5-Nitro-2-furaldehyde oxime *see* Nifuroxime.
5-Nitro-2-furaldehyde semicarbazone *see* Nitrofural.
5-Nitro-2-furaldehyde semioxamazone *see* Nifuraldezone.
NITROFURANTOIN*** (1-(5-nitro-2-furfurylideneamino)hydantoin; furadoine; furadonin; F-30; NSC-2107).
See also under Metronidazole.
NITROFURANTOIN plus LIQUORICE ('ceduran').
NITROFURANTOIN plus SULFADIAZINE ('sulfa-urolong').
6-[2-(5-Nitro-2-furanyl)ethenyl]-2-pyridinemethanol *see* Nifurpirinol.
Nitrofurazone *see* Nitrofural.
1-(5-Nitro-2-furfurylideneamino)guanidine *see* Furaguanidine.
1-(5-Nitro-2-furfurylideneamino)hydantoin *see* Nitrofurantoin.
1-(5-Nitro-2-furfurylideneamino)-3-hydantoinmethanol *see* Nifurtoinol.
1-(5-Nitrofurfurylideneamino)imidazolidine-2-thione *see* Thiofuradene.
1-(5-Nitrofurfurylideneamino)-2-imidazolidinone *see* Nifuradene.
4-(5-Nitrofurfurylideneamino)-3-methylthiomorpholine 1,1-dioxide *see* Nifurtimox.
3-(5-Nitrofurfurylideneamino)-2-oxazolidinone *see* Furazolidone.
Nitrofurfurylideneisoniazid *see* Furaniozid.
NITROFURFURYL METHYL ETHER (5-nitro-2-furfuryl methyl ether; 2-methoxymethyl-5-ni-

trofuran; F-1; 'furamicid'; 'furaspore'; 'furbenal').

Nitrofuroxizone* *see* Nidroxyzone.

1-[(5-Nitro-2-furyl)acrylideneamino]-1,3,4-triazole *see* Furacrylin.

1-[3-(5-Nitro-2-furyl)allylideneamino]hydantoin *see* Furazidin.

1-[3-(5-Nitro-2-furyl)allylidene]-2-(5-nitro-2-thenoyl)hydrazine *see* Nifurzide.

4-(5-Nitro-2-furyl)quinaldic acid 1-oxide *see* Nifuroquine.

2,2'-[2-(5-Nitrofur-2-yl)quinazolin-4-ylimino]diethanol *see* Nifurquinazol.

6-[2-(5-Nitro-2-furyl)vinyl]-2-pyridinemethanol *see* Nifurpirinol.

Nitrogen dioxide *see* Nitrogen peroxide.

Nitrogen monoxide *see* Nitrous oxide.

Nitrogen mustard *see* Chlormethine.

NITROGEN PEROXIDE (nitrogen dioxide; nitrogen tetroxide).

Nitrogen protoxide *see* Nitrous oxide.

Nitrogen tetroxide *see* Nitrogen peroxide.

NITROGEN TRICHLORIDE ('agene').

'Nitro-gesanit' *see* Glyceryl trinitrate.

Nitroglycerin *see* Glyceryl trinitrate.

Nitroglycerol *see* Glyceryl trinitrate.

'Nitrogranulogen' *see* Chlormethine.

NITROGUANIL (1-amidino-3-(p-nitrophenyl)-urea; T-72; WR-25979).

4-[2-(5-Nitroimidazol-1-yl)ethyl]morpholine *see* Nimorazole.

'Nitrolande' *see* Glyceryl trinitrate.

Nitrolime *see* Calcium carbimide.

'Nitroman' *see* Mannityl hexanitrate.

Nitromannite *see* Mannityl hexanitrate.

Nitromannitol *see* Mannityl hexanitrate.

NITROMETHAQUALONE (3-(2-methoxy-4-nitrophenyl)-2-methylquinazolin-4-one; 'parnox').

NITROMIDE* (3,5-dinitrobenzamide; NSC-60719).

NITROMIFENE* (1-[2-[p-[α-(p-methoxyphenyl)-β-nitrostyryl]phenoxy]ethyl]pyrrolidine; 4-methoxy-α'-nitro-α-[p-(2-pyrrolidin-1-ylethoxy)phenyl]stilbene; 1-(p-methoxyphenyl)-2-nitro-1-[p-(2-pyrrolidin-1-ylethoxy)phenyl]ethylene; 1-[2-[4-[1-(4-methoxyphenyl)-2-nitro-2-phenylethenyl]phenoxy]ethyl]pyrrolidine; CI-628; CN-55945).

'Nitromin' *see* Chlormethine N-oxide.

'Nitrong' *see* Glyceryl trinitrate.

2-Nitro-1-(p-nitrophenoxy)-4-(trifluoromethyl)benzene *see* Fluorodifen.

Nitropentaerythrite *see* Pentaerythrityl tetranitrate.

Nitropenton *see* Pentaerythrityl tetranitrate.

4'-Nitro-2'-phenoxymethanesulfonanilide *see* Nimesulide.

p-(p-Nitrophenoxy)phenyl isothiocyanate *see* Nitroscanate.

p-NITROPHENYL DIBUTYLPHOSPHINATE (nivufin; nivuphin).

5-(2-Nitrophenyl)-2-furamidine *see* Nitrafudam.

1-[5-(p-Nitrophenyl)-2-furfurylideneamino]hydantoin *see* Dantrolene.

1-(p-NITROPHENYL)-3-(PYRID-3-YLMETHYL)UREA ('vacor').

4-[(p-Nitrophenyl)sulfamoyl]acetanilide *see* Sulfanitran.

2-(p-Nitrophenylsulfonamido)thiazole *see* Nitrosulfathiazole.

Nitroprusside sodium *see* Sodium nitroprusside.

3-Nitro-N-(2-pyrrolidin-1-ylethyl)naphthalimide *see* Pinafide.

5-Nitro-8-quinolinol *see* Nitroxoline.

NITROSCANATE* (p-(p-nitrophenoxy)phenyl isothiocyanate; p-isothiocyanatophenyl p-nitrophenyl ether; CGA-23654; GS-23654; 'lopatol').

'Nitrositol' *see* Inositol hexanitrate.

N-Nitrosodiethylamine *see* Diethylnitrosamine.

N-Nitrosodimethylamine *see* Dimethylnitrosamine.

Nitrostigmine* *see* Parathion.

NITROSULFATHIAZOLE* (p-nitro-N-(2-thiazolyl)benzenesulfonamide; 2-(p-nitrophenylsulfonamido)thiazole).

'Nitro-tabletten' *see* Trolnitrate.

Nitrothiamidazol *see* Niridazole.

p-Nitro-N-(2-thiazolyl)benzenesulfonamide *see* Nitrosulfathiazole.

1-(5-Nitrothiazol-2-yl)imidazolidin-2-one *see* Niridazole.

N-(5-Nitrothiazol-2-yl)salicylamide acetate (ester) *see* Nitazoxanide.

N-(5-Nitrothiazol-2-yl)-2-thiophenecarboxamide *see* Tenonitrozole.

5-Nitro-2-thiophenecarboxylic acid [3-(5-nitro-2-furyl)allylidene]hydrazide *see* Nifurzide.

1-(2-Nitro-p-tolylazo)-2-naphthol *see* Toluidine red.

4'-Nitro-3'-(trifluoromethyl)isobutyranilide *see* Flutamide.

NITROUS OXIDE (dinitrogen monoxide; hyponitrous acid anhydride; nitrogen monoxide; nitrogen protoxide; laughing gas).

NITROUS OXIDE plus OXYGEN ('entonox'; 'eutonal').

NITROVIN* (1,5-bis(5-nitro-2-furyl)-1,4-pentadien-3-one amidinohydrazone; 'payzone').

p-[2-(5-Nitro-1-vinylimidazol-2-yl)vinyl]benzoic acid *see* Stirimazole.

'Nitrox' *see* Parathion methyl.

Nitroxanthic acid *see* Picric acid.

NITROXINIL* (4-cyano-2-iodo-6-nitrophenol; 4-hydroxy-3-iodo-5-nitrobenzonitrile; nitroxynil; 'dovenix').

NITROXINIL MEGLUMINE (methylglucamine salt of nitroxinil; 'trodax').

NITROXOLINE** (8-hydroxy-4-nitroquinoline; 5-nitro-8-quinolinol; 5-NOK; A-82).

Nitroxynil* *see* Nitroxinil.

'Nitrumon' *see* Carmustine.

NIUIF-1 (tr) *see* Ethylmercuric phosphate.

NIUIF-100 *see* Parathion.

NIVACORTOL* (2'-(p-fluorophenyl)-2'H-17α-pregna-2,4-dien-20-yno[3,2-c]pyrazol-17-ol; nivazol; WIN-27914).

Nivadipine *see* Nilvadipine.

Nivaline *see* Galantamine.

'Nivaquine B' *see* Chloroquine sulfate.

'Nivaquine C' *see* Sontoquine.
Nivazol* *see* Nivacortol.
'Nivelona' *see* Diphemanil metilsulfate.
'Nivembin' *see under* Chloroquine sulfate.
NIVIMEDONE*** (5,6-dimethyl-2-nitroindan-1,3-dione).
NIVIMEDONE SODIUM* (5,6-dimethyl-2-aci-nitro-1,3-indandione sodium salt monohydrate; BRL-10833).
'Nivitin' *see* Sorbitol.
'Nivoman' *see* Triflupromazine.
Nivufin (tr) *see* *p*-Nitrophenyl dibutylphosphinate.
Nivuphin (tr) *see* *p*-Nitrophenyl dibutylphosphin-ate.
NIXYLIC ACID*** (2-(2,3-dimethylanilino)nico-tinic acid; 2-(2,3-xylidino)nicotinic acid; UP-74).
'Nixyn' *see* Isonixin.
NIZATIDINE*** (*N*-[2-[[[2-[(dimethylamino)-methyl]thiazol-4-yl]methyl]thio]ethyl]-*N'*-methyl-2-nitro-1,1-ethenediamine).
'Nizin' *see* Zinc sulfanilate.
NIZOFENONE*** (2'-chloro-2-[2-[(diethyl-amino)methyl]imidazol-1-yl]-5-nitrobenzophen-one).
'Nizoral' *see* Ketoconazole.
NK-631 *see* Peplomycin.
NK-1006 *see* Bekanamycin.
N-Lost *see* Chlormethine.
NM-113 *see* Iometin.
NNDG *see* Metformin.
NNK-105 *see* Malotilate.
'Noan' *see* Diazepam.
'Nobacid' *see* Salsalate.
'Nobacter' *see* Triclocarban.
'Nobamide' *see* *N*,*N'*-Malonylbis(procainamide).
'Nobecutane' *see* Thiram.
'Nobedon' *see* Paracetamol.
'Nobedorm' *see* Methaqualone.
'Nobrium' *see* Medazepam.
Nocardia lurida, antibiotic *see* Ristocetin.
'Nocertone' *see* Oxetorone fumarate.
NOCLOPROST** ((*Z*)-7-[(1*R*,2*R*,3*R*,5*R*)-5-chloro-3-hydroxy-2-[(*E*)-(3*R*)-3-hydroxy-4,4-dimethyl-1-octenyl]cyclopentyl]-5-heptenoic acid).
NOCODAZOLE*** (methyl 5-(2-thenoyl)-2-benzimidazolecarbamate; methyl 5-(2-thienyl-carbonyl)-1*H*-benzimidazole-2-carbamate; on-codazole; NSC-238159; R-17934).
'Noctal' *see* Propallylonal.
'Noctamid' *see* Lormetazepam.
'Noctan' *see* Methyprylon.
'Noctazepam' *see* Oxazepam.
'Noctenal' *see* Propallylonal.
'Noctinal' *see* Secbutabarbital.
'Nocturette' *see under* Valepotriate.
'Nocu' *see* Diazepam.
'Nodapton' *see* Glycopyrronium bromide.
NOFECAINIDE*** (3-[2-hydroxy-3-(isopropyl-amino)propoxy]-2-phenylphthalimidine).
'Noflamol' *see* Polychlorinated biphenyl.
'Nogacit' *see* Nalidixic acid.
NOGALAMYCIN*** (antibiotic from *Str. noga-*

later; NSC-70845; U-15167).
'Nogest' *see under* Medroxyprogesterone.
'Nogos' *see* Dichlorvos.
5-NOK *see* Nitroxoline.
'Nokhel' *see* Amikhelline.
'No-kotin' *see* Lobeline.
'Nolamine' *see* Phenindamine.
'Noleptan' *see* Fominoben.
NOLINIUM BROMIDE*** (2-(3,4-dichloroanili-no)quinolizinium bromide; diclonium bromide; EU-2972).
'Nolotil' *see* Noramidopyrine methanesulfonate magnesium.
'Noltran' *see* Dicapthon.
'Noludar' *see* Methyprylon.
'Nolvadex' *see* Tamoxifen citrate.
'Nolvasan' *see* Chlorhexidine.
NOMEGESTROL*** (17-hydroxy-6-methyl-19-norpregna-4,6-diene-3,20-dione).
NOMELIDINE*** ((*Z*)-3-[1-(*p*-bromophenyl)-3-(methylamino)propenyl]pyridine).
'Nomersan' *see* Thiram.
'Nometan' *see* Piperazine.
'Nometine' *see* Pipamazine.
NOMIFENSINE*** (8-amino-1,2,3,4-tetrahydro-2-methyl-4-phenylisoquinoline).
NOMIFENSINE MALEATE* (HOE-36984; HOE-984; 'alival'; 'merital'; 'psicronizer').
NONABINE** (7-(1,2-dimethylheptyl)-2,2-di-methyl-4-pyrid-4-yl-2*H*-1-benzopyran-5-ol; BRL-4664).
Nonachlazine *see* Azaclorzine.
Nonaethylene glycol methyl *p*-butylaminobenzoate *see* Benzonatate.
Nonaethylene glycol monododecyl ether *see* Polido-canol.
3,5,7,9,11,13,15,26,27-Nonahydroxy-2-(1-hydroxy-hexyl)-16-methyl-16,18,20,22,24-octacosapen-taenoic acid 1,27-lactone *see* Filipin.
NONANOIC ACID (nonylic acid; 1-octanecarb-oxylic acid; pelargonic acid).
Nonanoic acid vanillylamide *see* Nonivamide.
NONAPERONE*** (4-(3-azabicyclo[3.2.2]non-3-yl)-4'-fluorobutyrophenone; 3-[3-(*p*-fluorobenz-oyl)propyl]-3-azabicyclo[3.2.2]nonane).
NONAPYRIMINE*** (4-nonylamino-7*H*-pyr-rolo[2,3-*d*]pyrimidine).
Nonasodium phytate *see* Sodium phytate.
'Nonframin' *see* Tinoridine.
'Nonidet' *see* Tyloxapol.
'Nonipol' *see* Nonoxinol(s).
NONIVAMIDE*** (*N*-(4-hydroxy-3-methoxy-benzyl)nonamide; nonanoic acid vanillylamide; nonylic acid vanillamide; *N*-vanillylnonamide; HH-50).
See also under Nicoboxil.
'Non-ovlon' *see under* Norethisterone acetate.
2,5,8,11,14,17,20,23,26-Nonoxaoctacosan-28-ol *p*-butylaminobenzoate *see* Benzonatate.
NONOXINOL(S)*** (α-(*p*-nonylphenyl)-ω-hydr-oxypoly(oxyethylenes)); polyethylene glycol *p*-nonylphenyl ether(s); polyoxyethylene nonyl-phenyl ether(s); nonoxynol(s); nonylphenoxypo-

378

lyethoxyethanol(s)).

NONOXINOL 4* (2-[2-[2-[2-(*p*-nonylphenoxy)ethoxy]ethoxy]ethoxy]ethanol; α-(*p*-nonylphenyl)-ω-hydroxytetra(oxyethylene)).

NONOXINOL 9* (α-(*p*-nonylphenyl)-ω-hydroxynona(oxyethylene); 'conceptrol'; 'delfen'; 'ortho-delfen'; 'orthoform').

NONOXINOL 15* (44-(*p*-nonylphenoxy)-3,6,9,12,15,18,21,24,27,30,33,36,39,42-tetradecaoxatetratetracontan-1-ol; α-(*p*-nonylphenyl)-ω-hydroxypentadeca(oxyethylene)).

NONOXINOL 30* (89-(*p*-nonylphenoxy)-3,6,9,12,15,18,21,24,27,30,33,36,39,42,45,48,51,54,57,60,63,66,69,72,75,78,81,84,87-nonacosaoxanonaoctacontan-1-ol; α-(*p*-nonylphenyl-ω-hydroxytriaconta(oxyethylene)).

Nonoxynol(s)* *see* Nonoxinol(s).

Non-staining scarlet *see* Aminoazotoluene.

4-Nonylamino-7*H*-pyrrolo[2,3-*d*]pyrimidine *see* Nonapyrimine.

Nonylic acid *see* Nonanoic acid.

Nonylic acid vanillamide *see* Nonivamide.

Nonylphenoxypolyethoxyethanol(s) *see* Nonoxinol(s).

α-(*p*-Nonylphenyl)-ω-hydroxypoly(oxyethylene(s)) *see* Nonoxinol(s).

'Nootropyl' *see* Piracetam.

'Nopenol' *see* Procaine-penicillin.

'Nopoxamine' *see* Myrtecaine.

NOPRYLSULFAMIDE (*N*⁴-(3-phenyl-1,3-disulfopropyl)sulfathiazole disodium salt; thiasolucin; 'soluthiazole').

'Noracycline' *see under* Lynestrenol.

NORACYMETHADOL* (α-3-acetoxy-6-(methylamino)-4,4-diphenylheptane; noracymethadol hydrochloride; NIH-7667).

'Noradin' *see* Methamphetamine.

NORADNAMINE (5-(aminomethyl)-2,3,7,8-tetrahydroxydibenzo[*a*,*e*]cycloheptatriene).

Noradrenaline* *see* Norepinephrine.

Noradrenaline-theophylline *see* Theodrenaline.

NORADRENALONE (2-amino-3′,4′-dihydroxyacetophenone).

'Noral' *see under* Norgestrel.

Noramidazophen *see* Dipyrone.

NORAMIDOPYRINE (2,3-dimethyl-4-(methylamino)-1-phenyl-3-pyrazolin-5-one; 4-(methylamino)phenazone; methylaminoantipyrine; 4-methylaminoazophen).

NORAMIDOPYRINE METHANESULFONATE MAGNESIUM ('nolotil').

Noramidopyrine methanesulfonate sodium** *see* Dipyrone.

19-Norandrostane *see* Estrane.

Norandrostenolone *see* Nandrolone.

'Norbiline' *see* Prozapine.

'Norbiogest' *see under* Norethisterone.

NORBIOTIN (hexahydro-2-oxo(1*H*)thieno-[3,4]imidazole-4-butyric acid).

Norbolethone* *see* Norboletone.

NORBOLETONE* (13-ethyl-17-hydroxy-18,19-dinor-17α-pregn-4-en-3-one; norbolethone; Wy-3475).

'Norboral' *see* Carbutamide.

NORBORMIDE* (5-(α-hydroxy-α-pyrid-2-ylbenzyl)-7-(α-pyrid-2-ylbenzylidene)norborn-5-ene-2,3-dicarboxamide; 3a,4,7,7a-tetrahydro-5-(hydroxyphenyl-2-pyridinylmethyl)-7-(phenyl-2-pyridinylmethylene)-4,7-methano-1*H*-isoindole-3(2*H*)-dione; McN-1025; 'raticate'; 'shoxin').

NORBORNANAMINE (norcamphanamine).

NORBORNANE (bicyclo[2.2.1]heptane; 1,4-endomethylenecyclohexane; norcamphane).

3-(*N*-Norbornane-2,3-dicarboximido)glutarimide *see* Taglutimide.

NORBORNENE (bicyclo[2.2.1]hept-2-ene; 1,4-endomethylene-2-cyclohexene; norcamphene).

***cis*-*exo*-5-Norbornene-2,3-dicarboximide** *see* Noreximide.

5-NORBORNENE-2,3-DICARBOXYLIC ACID (3,6-endomethylene-1,2,3,6-tetrahydrophthalic acid; 1,4-endomethylene-Δ⁵-cyclohexene-2,3-dicarboxylic acid).
See also Dimethyl carbate.

α-(5-Norbornen-2-yl)-α-phenyl-1-piperidinepropanol *see* Biperiden.

NORBUDRINE* (2-cyclobutylamino-1-(3,4-dihydroxyphenyl)ethanol; α-cyclobutylaminomethyl-3,4-dihydroxybenzyl alcohol; *N*-cyclobutylnoradrenaline; norbutrine; RD-9338).

Norbutrine* *see* Norbudrine.

Norcaine *see* Benzocaine.

Norcamphanamine *see* Norbornanamine.

Norcamphane *see* Norbornane.

Norcamphene *see* Norbornene.

NORCAPERATIC ACID (α-tetradecylcitric acid).

NORCLOSTEBOL* (4-chloro-17β-hydroxyestr-4-en-3-one; 4-chloro-19-nortestosterone; 4-chloronandrolone; SK&F-6611).

NORCLOSTEBOL ACETATE (CP-73).

NORCODEINE* (4,5-epoxy-6-hydroxy-3-methoxymorphin-7-ene; *N*-desmethylcodeine).

'Norcuron' *see* Vecuronium bromide.

Norcycline *see* Sancycline.

NORDAZEPAM* (7-chloro-1,3-dihydro-5-phenyl-2*H*-1,4-benzodiazepin-2-one; demethyldiazepam; nordiazepam; A-101; 'madar'; 'stilny').

Nordefrin *see* Corbadrine.

'Norden' *see* Octopamine.

Nordiazepam *see* Nordazepam.

Nordiazepam oxide *see* Demoxepam.

NORDIHYDROGUAIARETIC ACID (2,3-bis(3,4-dihydroxybenzyl)butane; 1,4-bis(3,4-dihydroxyphenyl)-2,3-dimethylbutane; dihydronorguaiaretic acid; NDGA; NSC-4291).

NORDINONE* (11α-hydroxy-17,17-dimethyl-18-norandrosta-4,13-dien-3-one).

Nordopan (tr) *see* Uramustine.

'Nor-durandron' *see* Nandrolone cyclohexanecarboxylate.

Norea *see* Noruron.

'Norephedrine' *see* Phenylpropanolamine.

Norephedrine-theophylline *see* Cafedrine.

NOREPINEPHRINE* ((−)-α-(aminomethyl)-3,4-dihydroxybenzyl alcohol; noradrenaline; arterenol; levarterenol; sympathin; urosympathin).

NORETHANDROLONE*** (17α-ethyl-17β-hydroxyestr-4-en-3-one; 17α-ethyl-17-hydroxy-19-norandrost-4-en-3-one; 17-ethyl-19-nortestosterone; 17-hydroxy-19-norpregn-4-en-3-one).

Norethindrone *see* Norethisterone.

NORETHISTERONE*** (17-ethynyl-17β-hydroxy-19-norandrost-4-en-3-one; 17-ethynyl-17β-hydroxyestr-4-en-3-one; 17α-ethynyl-19-nortestosterone; 17β-hydroxy-19-norpregn-4-en-20-yn-3-one; anhydrohydroxynorprogesterone; ethinylnortestosterone; norethindrone; norethyndron; norpregneninolone; NSC-9564).

NORETHISTERONE plus ETHINYLESTRADIOL ('brevinor'; 'modicon'; 'neocon'; 'norimin'; 'ovysmen').

NORETHISTERONE plus MESTRANOL ('conlumin'; 'enidrel'; 'norbiogest'; 'norinyl'; 'ortho-novin'; 'ortho-novum'; 'ortho 1557-O'; 'regovar'; 'sophia').

NORETHISTERONE ACETATE (SH-420; 'milligynon'; 'N.E.A.'; 'norlutate'; 'orlutate').

NORETHISTERONE ACETATE plus ETHINYLESTRADIOL (J-66; ORF-1557-BA; SH-420; 'anovlar'; 'gynophase'; 'gynovlar'; 'minovlar'; 'non-ovlon'; 'norlestrin'; 'orlest'; 'orlestrin').

NORETHISTERONE ENANTATE (norethisterone heptanoate; 'noristerat').

Norethyndron *see* Norethisterone.

Norethynodrel* *see* Noretynodrel.

NORETYNODREL*** (17α-ethynyl-17-hydroxy-5(10)-estren-3-one; 17-hydroxy-19-nor-17α-pregn-5(10)-en-20-yn-3-one; norethynodrel; NSC-15432; SC-4642).

NORETYNODREL plus MESTRANOL ('conovid'; 'enavid'; 'enovid'; 'feminor sequential'; 'infecundin').

'Nor-evipal' *see* Norhexobarbital.

NOREXIMIDE*** (*cis-exo*-5-norbornene-2,3-dicarboximide).

'Norfemac' *see* Bufexamac.

'Norfen' *see* Octopamine.

NORFENEFRINE*** (2-amino-1-(3-hydroxyphenyl)ethanol; α-aminomethyl-*m*-hydroxybenzyl alcohol; 2-(*m*-hydroxyphenyl)ethanolamine; normethoxedrine; norphenylephrine; *m*-norsynephrine).

NORFENEFRINE plus PHOLEDRINE (Kr-0151; 'adyston').

See also under Octodrine camsilate.

'Norflex' *see* Orphenadrine citrate.

NORFLOXACIN*** (1-ethyl-6-fluoro-1,4-dihydro-4-oxo-7-piperazin-1-ylquinoline-3-carboxylic acid; AM-715; MK-366; 'noroxin'; 'utinor').

NORFLURANE*** (1,1,1,2-tetrafluoroethane).

'Norgamem' *see* Timonacic.

'Norgesic' *see under* Orphenadrine citrate.

NORGESTERONE** (17β-hydroxy-17α-vinyl-5(10)-estren-3-one).

NORGESTIMATE*** ((+)-13-ethyl-17-hydroxy-18,19-dinor-17α-pregn-4-en-20-yn-3-one oxime acetate; 13β-ethyl-3-(hydroxyimino)-18,19-di-

nor-17-pregn-4-en-20-yn-17β-yl acetate; dexnorgestrel acetime; norgestrel oxime acetate; D-138; ORF-10131).

NORGESTOMET*** (17-acetoxy-11β-methyl-19-norpregn-4-ene-3,20-dione; 17-acetoxy-11β-methyl-19-norprogesterone; 17-hydroxy-11β-methyl-19-norpregn-4-ene-3,20-dione acetate; SC-21099).

'Norgeston' *see* Levonorgestrel.

NORGESTREL*** ((±)-13β-ethyl-17-hydroxy-18,19-dinor-17α-pregn-4-en-20-yn-3-one; 13β-ethyl-17α-ethynyl-17-hydroxygon-4-en-3-one; Wy-3707).

NORGESTREL plus ETHINYLESTRADIOL ('duoluton'; 'follinett'; 'neogynon'; 'noral'; 'ovral'; 'stediril').

See also Levonorgestrel *and under* Estradiol valerate.

Norgestrel oxime acetate *see* Norgestimate.

NORGESTRIENONE*** (17-hydroxy-19-nor-17α-pregna-4,9,11-trien-20-yn-3-one; 17α-ethynyl-17-hydroxyestra-4,9,11-trien-3-one; ethinyltrienolone; gestrienone; A-301; R 2010).

NORGESTRIENONE plus ETHINYLESTRADIOL (R-178; 'rapitest').

Norgine *see* Alginic acid.

'Norglycin' *see* Tolazamide.

NORHEXOBARBITAL (5-cyclohexen-1-yl-5-methylbarbituric acid).

Norhomoepinephrine *see* Corbadrine.

Norhydroxyprogesterone *see* Gestonorone.

'Noriday' *see* Norethisterone.

'Norimin' *see under* Norethisterone.

Norimipramine *see* Desipramine.

'Norinyl' *see under* Norethisterone.

'Norisodrine' *see* Isoprenaline.

'Noristerat' *see* Norethisterone enantate.

'Noritren' *see* Nortriptyline.

Norlaudanosoline *see* Tetrahydropapaveroline.

'Norlax' *see* Docusate sodium.

'Norlestrin' *see under* Norethisterone acetate.

NORLETIMOL*** (*o*-(*N*-benzylformimidoyl)-phenol; α-(benzylimino)-*o*-cresol; 2-(benzyliminomethyl)phenol).

NORLEUCINE (2-aminohexanoic acid; α-aminocaproic acid; caprine; glycoleucine).

NORLEUSACTIDE** (D-ser¹-nle⁴-(val-NH₂)-β¹⁻²⁵-corticotrophin; pentacosactide; DW-75).

NORLEVORPHANOL*** ((−)-3-hydroxymorphinan).

'Norlongandron' *see* Nandrolone cyclohexanecarboxylate.

'Norlutate' *see* Norethisterone acetate.

'Norlutin' *see* Norethisterone.

'Norluton' *see* Norethisterone.

'Normabrain' *see* Piracetam.

'Normatens' *see* Pempidine.

'Normatensyl' *see under* Hydracarbazine.

'Normenon' *see* Chlormadinone acetate.

Normetadrenaline *see* Normetanephrine.

Normetandrone *see* Methylestrenolone.

NORMETANEPHRINE (α-aminomethyl-4-hydroxy-3-methoxybenzyl alcohol; 3-*O*-methylnoradrenaline; 3-*O*-methylnorepinephrine; normetadrenaline).

NORMETHADONE*** (6-(dimethylamino)-4,4-diphenyl-3-hexanone; Ho-10582).

Normethandrolone *see* Methylestrenolone.

Normethandrone *see* Methylestrenolone.

Normethisterone *see* Methylestrenolone.

Normethoxedrine *see* Norfenefrine.

Normethyltestosterone *see* Methylestrenolone.

'**Normison**' *see* Temazepam.

'**Normoc**' *see* Bromazepam.

'**Normolipem**' *see* Clofibric acid.

'**Normolipol**' *see* Clofibrate.

NORMORPHINE*** (*N*-desmethylmorphine; 4,5-epoxy-3,6-dihydroxymorphin-7-ene).

'**Normoson**' *see* Ethchlorvynol.

'**Normospas**' *see* Atromepine.

'**Normud**' *see* Zimeldine.

'**Norobritten**' *see* Ampicillin.

'**Noroclox**' *see* Cloxacillin.

Noroxedrine *see* Octopamine.

'**Noroxin**' *see* Norfloxacin.

'**Norpace**' *see* Disopyramide phosphate.

NORPETHIDINE (ethyl 4-phenylisonipecotate).

'**Norphen**' *see* Octopamine.

Norphenylephrine *see* Norfenefrine.

Norpholedrine *see* Hydroxyamphetamine.

Norphytane *see* Pristane.

NORPIPANONE*** (4,4-diphenyl-6-piperid-1-yl-3-hexanone; Ho-10495; 'hexalgon').

'**Norpramine**' *see* Desipramine.

19-NORPREGNANE (17β-ethylestrane).

19-NOR-17α-PREGNANE (17α-ethylestrane).

19-NORPREGNATRIEN-20-ONE (17-acetylestratriene).

19-Nor-17α-pregn-4-ene-3,17-diol 3-propionate *see* Propetandrol.

Norpregneninolone *see* Norethisterone.

19-Nor-17α-pregn-4-en-17-ol *see* Ethylestrenol.

19-Nor-17α-pregn-5-en-17-ol *see* Bolenol.

19-Nor-17α-pregn-5-en-20-yl-17-ol *see* Cingestol.

19-Nor-17α-pregn-4-en-20-yne-3β,17-diol *see* Etynodiol.

19-Nor-17α-pregn-5(10)-en-20-yn-17-ol *see* Tigestol.

19-Nor-17α-pregn-4-en-20-yn-1-ol *see* Lynestrenol.

(+)-**Norpseudoephedrine** *see* Cathine.

NORPSEUDOTROPINE (8-desmethylpseudotropine; 2,3-dihydro-3β-hydroxynortropidine).

NORPSEUDOTROPINE BENZOATE (nortropacocaine).

'**Norsulfasol**' *see* Sulfathiazole.

Norsulfazole (tr) *see* Sulfathiazole.

'**Norsympathol**' *see* Octopamine.

m-**Norsynephrine** *see* Norfenefrine.

p-**Norsynephrine** *see* Octopamine.

'**Nortase**' *see* Rizolipase.

'**Nortensin**' *see under* Reserpine.

'**Nortestonate**' *see* Nandrolone.

Nortestosterone *see* Nandrolone.

19-Nortestosterone *see* Nandrolone.

NORTETRAZEPAM*** (7-chloro-5-cyclohexen-1-yl-1,3-dihydro-2*H*-1,4-benzodiazepin-2-one;

CB-4260).

NORTHIADENE (6,11-dihydro-11-[3-(methylamino)propylidene]dibenzo[*b,e*]thiepin; desmethylprothiadene; northiadene hydrochloride).

'**Nortran**' *see* Ethofumesate.

'**Nortrilen**' *see* Nortriptyline.

NORTRIPTYLINE*** (10,11-dihydro-5-(3-methylaminopropylidene)-5*H*-dibenzo[*a,d*]cycloheptene; 10,11-dihydro-*N*-methyl-5*H*-dibenzo[*a,d*]cycloheptene-Δ$^{5,\gamma}$-propylamine; desitriptyline; desmethylamitriptyline; nortriptyline hydrochloride; N-7048).

See also under Fluphenazine.

Nortropacocaine *see* Norpseudotropine benzoate.

NORTROPANE (8-azabicyclo[3.2.1]octane; 2,3-dihydronortropidine).

3α-Nortropanol *see* Nortropine.

2-Nortropene *see* Nortropidine.

NORTROPIDINE (2-nortropene).

NORTROPINE (2,3-dihydro-3α-hydroxynortropidine; 8-desmethyltropine; 3α-nortropanol).

NORURON* (1,1-dimethyl-3-(octahydro-4,7-methano-1*H*-inden-5-yl)urea; 1-(3a,4,5,6,7,7a-hexahydro-4,7-methanoindan-5-yl)-3,3-dimethylurea; norea; 'herban').

'**Norval**' *see* Mianserin.

NORVALINE (2-aminopentanoic acid; 2-aminovaleric acid).

'**Norvedan**' *see* Fentiazac.

NORVINISTERONE*** (17β-hydroxy-17α-vinyl-19-norandrost-4-en-3-one; 17β-hydroxy-17α-vinylestr-4-en-3-one; 17α-vinylnortestosterone).

'**Noscapal**' *see* Noscapine.

'**Noscapect**' *see* Noscapine.

NOSCAPINE*** (1-(6,7-dimethoxy-3-phthalidyl)-1,2,3,4-tetrahydro-8-methoxy-2-methyl-6,7-methylenedioxyisoquinoline; 5-(6,7-dimethoxyphthalidyl)-5,6,7,8-tetrahydro-4-methoxy-6-methyl-1,3-dioxolo[4,5-*g*]isoquinoline; methoxyhydrastine; narcosine; L-narcotine; opian; opianine; NSC-5366).

See also Clofedanol noscapine succinate; Morphine noscapine meconate.

NOSCAPINE plus GUAIFENESIN ('tuscalman').

NOSCAPINE EMBONATE (noscapine pamoate; 'teletux').

DL-Noscapine *see* Gnoscapine.

'**Noscosed**' *see* Chlorpheniramine.

NOSIHEPTIDE*** (antibiotic from *Str. actuosus* 40037; RP 9671; 'primofax').

'**No-spa**' *see* Drotaverine.

Nospanum (tr) *see* Drotaverine.

'**Nostal**' *see* Propallylonal.

'**Nostral**' *see* Propallylonal.

'**Nostyn**' *see* Ectylurea.

'**Notec**' *see* Chloral hydrate.

'**Notensil**' *see* Acepromazine.

'**Nothiazine**' *see* Pecazine.

'**Nourical**' *see* Calcium gluconate.

'**Nourilax N**' *see* Bisacodyl.

'**Nourycid**' *see* Lindane.

'**Novabsorb**' *see* Magnesium trisilicate.

'**Novacrysin**' *see* Sodium aurotiosulfate.

'Novactyl' *see* Magnesium acetylsalicylate.
'Novacyl' *see* Magnesium acetylsalicylate.
'Novadral' *see* Norfenefrine.
'Novafed' *see* Pseudoephedrine.
'Novahistex' *see under* Phenylephrine.
'Novain' *see* Carnitine.
'Novaldin' *see* Dipyrone.
'Novalgetol' *see* Dipyrone.
'Novalgin' *see* Dipyrone.
Novamidazophen *see* Dipyrone.
'Novamidon' *see* Aminophenazone.
'Novamin' *see* Dimenhydrinate.
Novaminsulfon *see* Dipyrone.
'Novarscodyle' *see* Disodium methanearsonate.
Novarsenol (tr) *see* Neoarsphenamine.
'Novartrine' *see* Morazone.
'Novaspirin' *see* Citrodisalyl.
'Novastat' *see* Aklomide.
'Novasurol' *see* Merbaphen.
'Novatoxyl' *see* Tryparsamide.
'Novatrine' *see* Homatropine methyl bromide.
Novatropine *see* Homatropine methyl bromide.
Novaurantium *see* Orange G.
'Novdimal' *see* N,N'-Malonylbis(procaine).
'Novedrin' *see* Etafedrine.
NOVEMBICHIN (tr) (2-chloro-N,N-bis(2-chloro-ethyl)-1-propylamine; embichin 7; novoembichin).
'Noveril' *see* Dibenzepin.
'Novesin' *see* Oxybuprocaine.
'Novestrin' *see* Methallenestril.
'Novex' *see* Fenticlor.
'Novicodin' *see* Dihydrocodeine.
'Novidium' *see* Homidium chloride.
'Noviform' *see* Bibrocathol.
'Novivermol' *see* Piperazine.
NOVOBIOCIN*** (7-(carbamoyltetrahydro-3-hydroxy-5-methoxy-6,6-dimethylpyran-2-yloxy)-4-hydroxy-3-[4-hydroxy-3-(3-methylbut-2-enyl)-benzamido]-8-methyl-2H-chromen-2-one; crystallinic acid; novobiocin calcium; novobiocin sodium; streptonivicin; PA-93).
  See also under Tetracycline.
'Novocaine' *see* Procaine.
'Novocebrin' *see* Tinofedrine.
'Novocell' *see* Oxidized cellulose.
Novocillin (tr) *see* Procaine-penicillin.
'Novocodon' *see* Thebacon.
'Novodrin' *see* Isoprenaline.
Novoembichin *see* Novembichin.
'Novoform' *see* Bibrocathol.
'Novofosfan' *see* Toldimfos.
'Novofur' *see* Furazolium chloride.
'Novohydrin' *see* Ambuside.
'Novolaudon' *see* Hydromorphone.
'Novon' *see* Erbon.
'Novonal' *see* Valdetamide.
'Novophone' *see* Dapsone.
'Novoquens' *see under* Megestrol acetate.
'Novoscabian' *see* Benzyl benzoate.
'Novoscabin' *see* Benzyl benzoate.
'Novoseptale' *see* Sulfamethylthiazole.
'Novosparol' *see* Bietamiverine.

'Novospasmin' *see* Camylofin.
'Novostat' *see under* Aklomide.
'Novoter' *see* Fluocinonide.
'Novotrone' *see* Aldesulfone sodium.
'Novrad' *see* Levopropoxyphene napsilate.
'Novurit' *see* Mercurophylline.
'Novutox' *see* Procaine.
'Noxfish' *see* Rotenone.
NOXIPTILINE*** (10,11-dihydro-5H-dibenzo-[a,d]cyclohepten-5-one O-[2-(dimethylamino)-ethyl]oxime; 3-[[2-(dimethylamino)ethyl]oxy-imino]-1,2:4,5-dibenzocyclohepta-1,4-diene; di-benzoxine; noxiptyline; noxiptiline hydrochloride; BAY-1521; 'agedal'; 'elronon').
Noxiptyline* *see* Noxiptiline.
'Noxiron' *see* Glutethimide.
'Noxiurotan' *see* Piperazine.
'Noxybel' *see* Methaqualone.
N-oxyd-lost *see* Chlormethine N-oxide.
'Noxyflex' *see under* Noxytiolin.
'Noxyflex-S' *see* Noxytiolin.
'Noxyron' *see* Glutethimide.
Noxythiolin* *see* Noxytiolin.
NOXYTIOLIN*** (1-(hydroxymethyl)-3-methyl-2-thiourea; noxythiolin; 'noxyflex-S').
NOXYTIOLIN plus TETRACAINE ('noxyflex').
'Nozinan' *see* Levomepromazine.
NP *see* Nifurpipone.
NP-13 *see* Bemegride.
NP-59 *see* Iodocholesterol ^{131}I.
NP-113 *see* Inosine pranobex.
NP-297 *see* Mefexamide.
NPA *see* Naptalam.
NPAP *see* Prajmalium bitartrate.
NPH insulin *see* Isophane insulin.
NPT-10381 *see* Inosine pranobex.
NRDC-104 *see* Resmethrin.
NRDC-106 *see* Pyresmethrin.
NRDC-107 *see* Bioresmethrin.
NRDC-119 *see* Cismethrin.
NRDC-143 *see* Permethrin.
NRDC-149 *see* Cypermethrin.
NRDC-161 *see* Deltamethrin.
NSC-185 *see* Cicloheximide.
NSC-660 *see* Diacetyl monoxime.
NSC-676 *see* Benzoyl peroxide.
NSC-739 *see* Aminopterin sodium.
NSC-740 *see* Methotrexate.
NSC-741 *see* Hydrocortisone acetate.
NSC-742 *see* Azaserine.
NSC-746 *see* Urethan.
NSC-749 *see* Azaguanine.
NSC-750 *see* Busulfan.
NSC-751 *see* Ethionine.
NSC-752 *see* Tioguanine.
NSC-753 *see* Purine.
NSC-755 *see* Mercaptopurine.
NSC-757 *see* Colchicine.
NSC-758 *see* Glucosamine.
NSC-762 *see* Chlormethine.
NSC-763 *see* Dimethyl sulfoxide.
NSC-1026 *see* Cycloleucine.
NSC-1390 *see* Allopurinol.

NSC-1771 *see* Thiram.
NSC-1800/24 *see* Carubicin.
NSC-1879 *see* Phenazopyridine.
NSC-1895 *see* Guanazole.
NSC-2100 *see* Nitrofural.
NSC-2101 *see* Roxarsone.
NSC-2105 *see* Propham.
NSC-2107 *see* Nitrofurantoin.
NSC-2619 *see* Sulfabenz.
NSC-2834 *see* Paroxypropione.
NSC-3053 *see* Dactinomycin.
NSC-3055 *see* Puromycin.
NSC-3056 *see* Puromycin aminonucleoside.
NSC-3061 *see* Pyrimethamine.
NSC-3063 *see* Deoxypyridoxine.
NSC-3070 *see* Diethylstilbestrol.
NSC-3073 *see* Folic acid.
NSC-3084 *see* Methionine sulfoxide.
NSC-3085 *see* Desthiobiotin.
NSC-3086 *see* Pantoyltaurine.
NSC-3087 *see* Oxophenarsine.
NSC-3088 *see* Chlorambucil.
NSC-3096 *see* Demecolcine.
NSC-3097 *see* Arsphenamine.
NSC-3099 *see* Galactoflavin.
NSC-3100 *see* Isoriboflavin.
NSC-3184 *see* Nifuraldezone.
NSC-3351 *see* Nandrolone cyclohexanecarboxyl-ate.
NSC-3364 *see* Filipin.
NSC-3425 *see* Azauracil.
NSC-3426 *see* Azathymine.
NSC-3431 *see* Methioprim.
NSC-3590 *see* Calcium folinate.
NSC-3951 *see* Benzoxiquine.
NSC-4112 *see* Fenticlor.
NSC-4291 *see* Nordihydroguaiaretic acid.
NSC-4911 *see* Mercaptopurine ribonucleoside.
NSC-5085 *see* Nitarsone.
NSC-5109 *see* Dinsed.
NSC-5366 *see* Noscapine.
NSC-5547 *see* Dimantine.
NSC-5648 *see* Tonzonium bromide.
NSC-6091 *see* Dapsone.
NSC-6135 *see* Cholic acid.
NSC-6365 *see* Trometamol.
NSC-6386 *see* Bialamicol.
NSC-6396 *see* Thiotepa.
NSC-6470 *see* Nifuradene.
NSC-6738 *see* Dichlorvos.
NSC-7214 *see* Etoxazene.
NSC-7365 *see* DON.
NSC-7571 *see* Aminoacridine.
NSC-7760 *see* Pralidoxime iodide.
NSC-7778 *see* Oxybenzone.
NSC-8746 *see* Cysteine.
NSC-8798 *see* Cholesterol.
NSC-8806 *see* Melphalan.
NSC-9120 *see* Prednisolone.
NSC-9166 *see* Testosterone propionate.
NSC-9168 *see* Fumagillin.
NSC-9169 *see* Oxytetracycline.
NSC-9170 *see* N-Deacetylthiocolchicine.

NSC-9324 *see* Allobarbital.
NSC-9564 *see* Norethisterone.
NSC-9565 *see* Ethisterone.
NSC-9566 *see* Estradiol benzoate.
NSC-9698 *see* Mannomustine.
NSC-9700 *see* Testosterone.
NSC-9701 *see* Methyltestosterone.
NSC-9702 *see* 11-Dehydrocorticosterone.
NSC-9703 *see* Cortisone.
NSC-9704 *see* Progesterone.
NSC-9705 *see* Corticosterone.
NSC-9706 *see* Tretamine.
NSC-9717 *see* Tepa.
NSC-9894 *see* Hexestrol.
NSC-10023 *see* Prednisone.
NSC-10039 *see* Methylestrenolone.
NSC-10107 *see* Chlormethine N-oxide.
NSC-10108 *see* Chlorotrianisene.
NSC-10270 *see* Ambomycin.
NSC-10285 *see* Cinnopentazone.
NSC-10481 *see* Fosfestrol.
NSC-10483 *see* Hydrocortisone.
NSC-10973 *see* Ethinylestradiol.
NSC-11043 *see* Methyclothiazide.
NSC-11319 *see* Desoxycortone.
NSC-12165 *see* Fluoxymesterone.
NSC-12169 *see* Estriol.
NSC-12198 *see* Drostanolone.
NSC-13252 *see* Chlortetracycline.
NSC-13875 *see* Altretamine.
NSC-14083 *see* Streptomycin.
NSC-14210 *see* Sarcolysin.
NSC-14279 *see* Pyrabrom.
NSC-14347 *see* Sarkomycin A.
NSC-14574 *see* Lucanthone.
NSC-15197 *see* Thallous chloride.
NSC-15432 *see* Noretynodrel.
NSC-15780 *see* Amygdalin.
NSC-15796 *see* Becantone.
NSC-16895 *see* Lithium carbonate.
NSC-17261 *see* Inproquone.
NSC-17590 *see* Estradiol valerate.
NSC-17592 *see* Hydroxyprogesterone caproate.
NSC-17777 *see* Fenyramidol.
NSC-17789 *see* Benzindopyrine.
NSC-18268 *see* Cactinomycin.
NSC-18317 *see* Cortodoxone.
NSC-19043 *see* Oxycodone.
NSC-19477 *see* Hexafluronium bromide.
NSC-19494 *see* Metodiclorofen.
NSC-19892 *see* Hydrogen peroxide.
NSC-19893 *see* Fluorouracil.
NSC-19962 *see* Carbestrol.
NSC-19987 *see* Methylprednisolone.
NSC-20105 *see* 6-(Methylthio)purine.
NSC-20246 *see* Clamoxyquine.
NSC-20264 *see* Adenosine phosphate.
NSC-20270 *see* Nadide.
NSC-20293 *see* Estradiol.
NSC-20526 *see* Tribromsalan.
NSC-20527 *see* Dibromsalan.
NSC-21626 *see* Propiolactone.
NSC-21970 *see* 3-Methylcholanthrene.

NSC-22877 *see* AET.
NSC-23162 *see* Nandrolone phenpropionate.
NSC-23516 *see* Risocaine.
NSC-23759 *see* Testolactone.
NSC-23909 *see* 1-Methyl-1-nitrosourea.
NSC-24559 *see* Plicamycin.
NSC-24567 *see* Vindesine.
NSC-24818 *see* Podophyllotoxin.
NSC-24819 *see* β-Peltatin.
NSC-24970 *see* Bromchlorenone.
NSC-25116 *see* Mercaptamine.
NSC-25141 *see* Buclizine.
NSC-25154 *see* Pipobroman.
NSC-25159 *see* Pemoline.
NSC-25413 *see* Fenamole.
NSC-25614 *see* Ftalofyne.
NSC-25855 *see* Timonacic.
NSC-26154 *see* Aminocaproic acid.
NSC-26198 *see* Oxymetholone.
NSC-26271 *see* Cyclophosphamide.
NSC-26386 *see* Medroxyprogesterone acetate.
NSC-26812 *see* Apholate.
NSC-26980 *see* Mitomycin.
NSC-27109 *see* Nifuroxazide.
NSC-27178 *see* Capuride.
NSC-27381 *see* *m*-Sarcolysin.
NSC-27640 *see* Floxuridine.
NSC-28120 *see* Amidapsone.
NSC-29215 *see* Triaziquone.
NSC-29422 *see* Thioguanosine.
NSC-29485 *see* Elmustine.
NSC-29863 *see* Guanethidine sulfate.
NSC-30152 *see* Dimethadione.
NSC-30211 *see* Trichlormethine.
NSC-30223 *see* Buramate.
NSC-31083 *see* Actinobolin.
NSC-32065 *see* Hydroxycarbamide.
NSC-32074 *see* Azauridine.
NSC-32363 *see* Valnoctamide.
NSC-32942 *see* Cetalkonium chloride.
NSC-32946 *see* Mitoguazone.
NSC-33077 *see* Carbocloral.
NSC-33659 *see* Lapirium chloride.
NSC-33669 *see* Emetine.
NSC-34249 *see* Calcium trisodium pentetate.
NSC-34443 *see* Papaverine.
NSC-34462 *see* Uramustine.
NSC-34521 *see* Dexamethasone.
NSC-34533 *see* Griseofulvin.
NSC-34632 *see* Mafenide.
NSC-34652 *see* Mephenytoin.
NSC-35051 *see* Medphalan.
NSC-35770 *see* Clomifene.
NSC-37024 *see* Formylmelphalan.
NSC-37095 *see* Uredepa.
NSC-37096 *see* Benzodepa.
NSC-37538 *see* Mannityl dimesilate.
NSC-37725 *see* Lynestrenol.
NSC-37917 *see under* Streptozocin.
NSC-38297 *see* Broxuridine.
NSC-38721 *see* Mitotane.
NSC-38887 *see* Tiamiprine.
NSC-39068 *see* D-Dihydroxybusulfan.

NSC-39069 *see* Treosulfan.
NSC-39084 *see* Azathioprine.
NSC-39147 *see* Hydroxycycloheximide.
NSC-39274 *see* Formylsarcolysin.
NSC-39415 *see* Domiphen bromide.
NSC-39470 *see* Betamethasone.
NSC-39661 *see* Idoxuridine.
NSC-39690 *see* Proadifen.
NSC-40144 *see* Fenamisal.
NSC-40725 *see* Isosorbide.
NSC-40774 *see* 6-(Methylthio)purine riboside.
NSC-40902 *see* Phencyclidine.
NSC-42044 *see* Lobendazole.
NSC-42722 *see* Metandienone.
NSC-43183 *see* Fenyripol.
NSC-43193 *see* Stanozolol.
NSC-43748 *see* Pargyline.
NSC-44175 *see* 2,5-Dihydroxy-3,6-diphenyl-*p*-benzoquinone.
NSC-44629 *see* Dopan.
NSC-44827 *see* Descinolone.
NSC-44827 *see* Descinolone acetonide.
NSC-45383 *see* Rufocromomycin.
NSC-45388 *see* Dacarbazine.
NSC-45463 *see* Captamine.
NSC-45624 *see* Sodium thiosulfate.
NSC-46077 *see* Demoxepam.
NSC-47438 *see* Fluorometholone acetate.
NSC-47547 *see* 1-(2-Chloroethyl)-1-nitrosourea.
NSC-47774 *see* Piposulfan.
NSC-49000 *see* 5α-Androstane.
NSC-49171 *see* Salsalate.
NSC-49506 *see* Inositol nicotinate.
NSC-49842 *see* Vinblastine.
NSC-50364 *see* Metronidazole.
NSC-51001 *see* Carbomycin.
NSC-51097 *see* Duazomycin.
NSC-51325 *see* Meturedepa.
NSC-51812 *see* Sancycline.
NSC-52644 *see* Pyrrocaine.
NSC-52947 *see* Pactamycin.
NSC-53397 *see* Ambomycin.
NSC-54702 *see* Flumetasone.
NSC-55202 *see* Roseolic acid.
NSC-55975 *see* Epimestrol.
NSC-56228 *see* Doxycycline.
NSC-56308 *see* Epipropidine.
NSC-56410 *see* Porfiromycin.
NSC-56423 *see* Melatonin.
NSC-56654 *see* Azotomycin.
NSC-56769 *see* Dioxybenzone.
NSC-56808 *see* Quinaldine blue.
NSC-57199 *see* *o*-Sarcolysin.
NSC-58514 *see* Chromomycin A$_3$.
NSC-58775 *see* Nitrazepam.
NSC-59687 *see* Acetphenolisatin.
NSC-59727 *see* Sparsomycin.
NSC-59989 *see* Clorofene.
NSC-60584 *see* Sulisobenzone.
NSC-60719 *see* Nitromide.
NSC-61586 *see* Phleomycin.
NSC-61815 *see* Diatrizoic acid.
NSC-62164 *see* Bretylium tosilate.

NSC-62786 *see* Epinephrine.
NSC-62939 *see* Trimetozine.
NSC-63278 *see* Medrysone.
NSC-63878 *see* Cytarabine.
NSC-63963 *see* Etryptamine.
NSC-64013 *see* Ethosuximide.
NSC-64087 *see* Clopenthixol.
NSC-64198 *see* Diazoxide.
NSC-64375 *see* Benzquinamide.
NSC-64393 *see* Spiramycin.
NSC-64540 *see* Pyroxamine.
NSC-64826 *see* Azatepa.
NSC-64967 *see* Metenolone enantate.
NSC-65411 *see* Flugestone acetate.
NSC-66233 *see* Bolasterone.
NSC-66847 *see* Thalidomide.
NSC-66952 *see* Aminorex.
NSC-67068 *see* Oxandrolone.
NSC-67239 *see* Azaribine.
NSC-67574 *see* Vincristine.
NSC-67934 *see* Glyceraldehyde.
NSC-68982 *see* Guanabenz acetate.
NSC-69200 *see* Chlortalidone.
NSC-69529 *see* Mitogillin.
NSC-69536 *see* Metallibure.
NSC-69811 *see* Metisazone.
NSC-69856 *see* Zinostatin.
NSC-69948 *see* Trestolone acetate.
NSC-70600 *see* Acetophenazine.
NSC-70731 *see* Lincomycin.
NSC-70735 *see* Nafoxidine.
NSC-70762 *see* Tolazamide.
NSC-70845 *see* Nogalamycin.
NSC-70933 *see* Cycliramine.
NSC-70968 *see* Melengestrol acetate.
NSC-71047 *see* Trioxysalen.
NSC-71423 *see* Megestrol acetate.
NSC-71755 *see* Carfenazine.
NSC-71795 *see* Ellipticine.
NSC-71901 *see* Vistatolon.
NSC-71964 *see* Chlorphenacyl.
NSC-72005 *see* Triclocarban.
NSC-72274 *see* Mitopodozide.
NSC-73205 *see* Dipyrone.
NSC-73713 *see* Dexamphetamine.
NSC-74226 *see* Metenolone acetate.
NSC-75054 *see* Mesterolone.
NSC-76239 *see* Oxipurinol.
NSC-76455-D *see* Peliomycin.
NSC-77120 *see* Sulfanitran.
NSC-77213 *see* Procarbazine.
NSC-77370 *see* Fenclonine.
NSC-77471 *see* Mitocromin.
NSC-77518 *see* Diazepam.
NSC-77622 *see under* Estradiol valerate.
NSC-77625 *see* Triamterene.
NSC-77747 *see* Triclofenol piperazine.
NSC-77830 *see* Cycloguanil embonate.
NSC-78194 *see* Metixene.
NSC-78502 *see* Meclocycline.
NSC-78559 *see* Flurazepam.
NSC-78714 *see* Clotixamide.
NSC-78987 *see* Isomylamine.

NSC-79019 *see* Methylglyoxal.
NSC-79037 *see* Lomustine.
NSC-79249 *see* Homofolic acid.
NSC-79389 *see* Clofibrate.
NSC-80998 *see* Cortivazol.
NSC-81430 *see* Cyproterone acetate.
NSC-82116 *see* Gloxazone.
NSC-82151 *see* Daunorubicin.
NSC-82174 *see* Nalidixic acid.
NSC-82260 *see* Benzathine tenuazonate.
NSC-82261 *see* Gentamicin.
NSC-82699 *see* Flufenamic acid.
NSC-83142 *see* Daunorubicin.
NSC-83265 *see* Tritylthioalanine.
NSC-83653 *see* Amantadine.
NSC-83799 *see* Simtrazene.
NSC-84054 *see* Gestonorone caproate.
NSC-84223 *see* Oxybate sodium.
NSC-84973 *see* Cyprolidol.
NSC-85680 *see* Zedalan.
NSC-85791 *see* Etacrynic acid.
NSC-85998 *see* Streptozocin.
NSC-88536 *see* Calusterone.
NSC-89199 *see* Estramustine.
NSC-89277 *see* Modaline.
NSC-91523 *see* Propranolol.
NSC-92336 *see* Dydrogesterone.
NSC-92338 *see* Chlormadinone acetate.
NSC-92339 *see* Fluocinolone acetonide.
NSC-93158 *see* Asperlin.
NSC-94100 *see* Mitobronitol.
NSC-94219 *see* Candicidin.
NSC-95072 *see* Ormetoprim.
NSC-95147 *see* Silandrone.
NSC-95441 *see* Semustine.
NSC-97925 *see* Glutamine.
NSC-100071 *see* Haloprogin.
NSC-100638 *see* Amfonelic acid.
NSC-100880 *see* Camptothecin.
NSC-101791 *see* Fluocinonide.
NSC-102498 *see* Carbamoylcysteine.
NSC-102627 *see* Improsulfan.
NSC-102629 *see* Flazalone.
NSC-102816 *see* Azacitidine.
NSC-102824 *see* Azapropazone.
NSC-103336 *see* Menoctone.
NSC-104469 *see* Phenesterin.
NSC-104800 *see* Mitolactol.
NSC-105546 *see* Riboprine.
NSC-106563 *see* Betanidine.
NSC-106564 *see* Butacetin.
NSC-106565 *see* Butaxamine.
NSC-106566 *see* Erythrityl tetranitrate.
NSC-106568 *see* Trimethoprim.
NSC-106569 *see* Thenium closilate.
NSC-106570 *see* Rolodine.
NSC-106571 *see* Bunamidine.
NSC-106572 *see* Tolpyrramide.
NSC-106959 *see* Carbifene.
NSC-106960 *see* Glyhexamide.
NSC-106962 *see* Sodium iopodate.
NSC-106995 *see* Lomofungin.
NSC-107041 *see* Scopafungin.

NSC-107079 *see* Chymopapain.
NSC-107412 *see* Coumamycin.
NSC-107429 *see* Cyclazocine.
NSC-107430 *see* Pentazocine.
NSC-107431 *see* Sodium metrizoate.
NSC-107433 *see* Teclozan.
NSC-107434 *see* Sodium tyropanoate.
NSC-107528 *see* Sulfadiasulfone sodium.
NSC-107529 *see* Pararosaniline embonate.
NSC-107654 *see* Pyrrolnitrin.
NSC-107677 *see* Dimetindene.
NSC-107678 *see* Angiotensinamide.
NSC-107680 *see* Flumetasone pivalate.
NSC-108034 *see* Oxyfenamate.
NSC-108160 *see* Doxepin.
NSC-108161 *see* Polythiazide.
NSC-108163 *see* Guanoclor.
NSC-108164 *see* Epitizide.
NSC-108165 *see* Tiotixene.
NSC-108166 *see* Troleandomycin.
NSC-109212 *see* Ipronidazole.
NSC-109229 *see* Asparaginase.
NSC-109724 *see* Ifosfamide.
NSC-110364 *see* Oxolinic acid.
NSC-110430 *see* Carbocromen.
NSC-110432 *see* Methoxyflurane.
NSC-110433 *see* Sulfalene.
NSC-111071 *see* Carbenicillin.
NSC-111180 *see* Acetylcysteine.
NSC-112259 *see* Estradiol mustard.
NSC-112682 *see* Enpromate.
NSC-112846 *see* Quinaspar.
NSC-112931 *see* Tetroquinone.
NSC-113233 *see* Mitomalcin.
NSC-113916 *see* Rifampicin.
NSC-114460 *see* Chlorozotocin tetraacetate.
NSC-114649 *see* Flavoxate.
NSC-114650 *see* Dimefline.
NSC-114901 *see* Desipramine.
NSC-115748 *see* Chlordiazepoxide.
NSC-115944 *see* Enflurane.
NSC-116785 *see* Phenester.
NSC-117032 *see* Mitosper.
NSC-119875 *see* Cisplatin.
NSC-120949 *see* Poly I:C.
NSC-122758 *see* Tretinoin.
NSC-122819 *see* Teniposide.
NSC-122870 *see* Methasquin.
NSC-123018 *see* Medrogestone.
NSC-123127 *see* Doxorubicin.
NSC-125066 *see* Bleomycin.
NSC-125717 *see* Cinanserin.
NSC-129185 *see* Mycophenolic acid.
NSC-129220 *see* Ancitabine acetate.
NSC-129224 *see* Adiphenine.
NSC-129943 *see* Razoxane.
NSC-130044 *see* Thiethylperazine.
NSC-130678 *see* Buthiopurine.
NSC-132313 *see* Dianhydrogalactitol.
NSC-133099 *see* Rifamide.
NSC-133100 *see* Rifamycin.
NSC-134087 *see* Prednimustine.
NSC-134434 *see* Hycanthone.

NSC-134679 *see* Carboquone.
NSC-136947 *see* Niridazole.
NSC-137443 *see* Kalafungin.
NSC-139490 *see* Ketotrexate.
NSC-139593 *see* Sulfasomizole.
NSC-140117 *see* Improsulfan tosilate.
NSC-140781 *see* Daunosaminyldaunorubicin.
NSC-141046 *see* Clofazimine.
NSC-141540 *see* Etoposide.
NSC-142005 *see* Mecloqualone.
NSC-143095 *see* Pirazofurin.
NSC-143114 *see* Daunorubicin semicarbazone.
NSC-143491 *see* Daunorubicin oxime.
NSC-143647 *see* Alanosine.
NSC-143969 *see* Tilorone.
NSC-145668 *see* Ancitabine.
NSC-148958 *see* Tegafur.
NSC-153858 *see* Maitansine.
NSC-156303 *see* Amsacrine.
NSC-157658 *see* Denatonium benzoate.
NSC-158565 *see* Clorindanol.
NSC-163501 *see* Acivicin.
NSC-164011 *see* Zorubicin.
NSC-169774 *see* Bromocriptine.
NSC-172755 *see* Butocin.
NSC-177023 *see* Levamisole.
NSC-178248 *see* Chlorozotocin.
NSC-180024 *see* Carubicin.
NSC-182986 *see* Diaziquone.
NSC-192965 *see* Spirogermanium.
NSC-194684 *see* Epitiostanol.
NSC-208642 *see* Filipin.
NSC-224131 *see* Sparfosic acid.
NSC-233898 *see* Oxidopamine.
NSC-238159 *see* Nocodazole.
NSC-241240 *see* Carboplatin.
NSC-249008 *see* Trimetrexate.
NSC-249992 *see* Amsacrine.
NSC-253272 *see* Caracemide.
NSC-261037 *see* Misonidazole.
NSC-264127 *see* Elliptinium acetate.
NSC-279836 *see* Mitoxantrone.
NSC-286193 *see* Tiazofurine.
NSC-287513 *see* Ametantrone diacetate.
NSC-296961 *see* Amifostine.
NSC-301739 *see* Mitoxantrone.
NSC-305884 *see* Acodazole.
NSC-311056 *see* Spiroplatin.
NSC-312887 *see* Fludarabine phosphate.
NSC-337766 *see* Bisantrene.
NSC-400018 *see* Paraxanthine.
NSC-400978 *see* Iludin M.
NSC-400979 *see* Iludin S.
NSC-402815 *see* Penicillin G.
NSC-404421 *see* Vidarabine.
NSC-405124 *see* Symclosene.
NSC-406087 *see* Etamivan.
NSC-408735 *see* Diaveridine.
NSC-409962 *see* Carmustine.
NSC-515776 *see* Dipyridamole.
NSC-524411 *see* Metetoin.
NSC-525334 *see* Nifurthiazole.
NSC-525816 *see* Sodium tenuazonate.

NSC-526046 *see* Nicotinyl alcohol.
NSC-526062 *see* Dexoxadrol.
NSC-526063 *see* Levoxadrol.
NSC-526280 *see* Metabromsalan.
NSC-527579 *see* Meprednisone.
NSC-527604 *see* Deferoxamine.
NSC-527986 *see* Levofuraltadone.
NSC-528004 *see* Vinleurosine.
NSC-528880 *see* Pimetine.
NSC-528986 *see* Ampicillin.
NSC-529860 *see* Deazaaminopterin.
NSC-529861 *see* Chlorasquin.
NSC-B-2992 *see* Mitomalcin.
NSD-1055 *see* Brocresine.
NTA-194 *see* Tiaramide.
NTD-2 *see* Cartap.
'N-toin' *see* Nitrofurantoin.
NU-445 *see* Sulfafurazole diolamine.
Nu-903 *see* Pyrithyldione.
Nu-1196 *see* Alphaprodine.
Nu-1504 *see* Phenindamine.
Nu-1510 *see* Dihyprylone.
NU-1779 *see* Betaprodine.
NU-1932 *see* Betameprodine.
Nu-2121 *see* Nicotinyl alcohol.
Nu-2206 *see* Racemorphan.
Nu-2222 *see* Trimetaphan camsilate.
'Nucidol' *see* Dimpylate.
Nucin *see* Juglone.
Nucite *see* Inositol.
NUCLOTIXENE*** (3-[(2-chlorothioxanthen-9-
   ylidene)methyl]quinuclidine; 2-chloro-9-(quinuc-
   lidin-3-ylmethylene)thioxanthene).
'Nuctalon' *see* Estazolam.
NUFENOXOLE*** (2-[3-(5-methyl-1,3,4-oxadiaz-
   ol-2-yl)-3,3-diphenylpropyl]-2-azabicyclo-

[2.2.2]octane; SC-27166).
'Nulans' *see* Oxazepam succinate.
'Nullapon' *see* Tetrasodium edetate.
'Nulogyl' *see* Nimorazole.
'Nulsa' *see* Proglumide.
'Numorphan' *see* Oxymorphone.
'Numotac' *see* Isoetarine.
'Nuncital' *see* Emylcamate.
'Nupa-sal' *see* Salinazid.
'Nupercaine' *see* Cinchocaine.
'Nuprin' *see* Sulfamoxole.
'Nuran' *see* Cyproheptadine.
'Nuredal' *see* Nialamide.
'Nurofen' *see* Ibuprofen.
'Nuso' *see* Neutral insulin injection.
'Nutinal' *see* Benactyzine.
'Nuvacron' *see* Monocrotophos.
'Nuvacron N' *see* Iodofenphos.
'Nuvan' *see* Dichlorvos.
'Nuvanol M' *see* Iodofenphos.
'Nuvan staykill' *see under* Dichlorvos.
'Nuvan top' *see under* Dichlorvos.
'Nycoline' *see* Macrogol(s).
'Nydrane' *see* Beclamide.
Nylestriol* *see* Nilestriol.
Nylidrin* *see* Buphenine.
'Nylmerate' *see* Phenylmercuric borate.
'Nyloxin' *see* Cobra venom.
'Nystadermal' *see under* Triamcinolone acetonide.
'Nystan' *see* Nystatin.
NYSTATIN*** (antibiotic from *Str. noursei*; fun-
   gicidin).
   See also under Oxytetracycline; Triamcinolone
   acetonide.
'Nyxolan' *see* 8-Quinolinol sulfate aluminium.

O

'Obesin' see Propylhexedrine.

'Obesitex' see Amfepramone.

OBIDOXIME CHLORIDE** (1,1′-oxydimethyl-enebis(4-formylpyridinium chloride) dioxime; 1,1′-[oxybis(methylene)]bis[4-(hydroxyimino)-methyl]pyridinium dichloride; bis[(4-hydroxy-iminomethyl)pyridinium-1-methyl] ether di-chloride; HS-3; LU-H-6; 'toxogonin').

'Obiturin' see Fluorescein disodium.

'Obracine' see Tobramycin.

'Obsidan' see Propranolol.

'Obston' see Docusate sodium.

OC-340 see Vinconate.

OCAPHANE (2-(2-amino-2-carboxyethyl)-N,N-bis(2-chloroethyl)phenethylamine; 2-[2-(2-amino-2-carboxyethyl)phenyl]-2′,2″-dichlorotri-ethylamine; 3-[o-[2-[bis(2-chloroethyl)amino]-ethyl]phenyl]alanine; AT-581).

'Ocestrol' see Benzestrol.

Ocotea glaziovii, alkaloid see Glaziovine.

OCRASE*** (fibrinolytic enzyme from *Aspergillus ochraceus*).

OCRILATE*** (octyl 2-cyanoacrylate; ocrylate).

Ocrylate* see Ocrilate.

OCTABENZONE*** (2-hydroxy-4-(octyloxy)-benzophenone; UV-531).

OCTACAINE** (3-(diethylamino)butyranilide).

Octachlor see Chlordane.

1,2,4,5,6,7,8,8-Octachlorohexahydro-4,7-meth-anoindene see Chlordane.

1,3,4,5,6,7,8,8-Octachloro-1,3,3a,4,7,7a-hexahydro-4,7-methanoisobenzofuran see Isobenzan.

1,3,4,5,6,7,8,8-Octachloro-3a,4,7,7a-tetrahydro-4,7-methanophthalan see Isobenzan.

'Octacide 264' see (Ethylhexyl)norbornenedicarb-oximide.

Octacosactrin* see Tosactide.

cis,cis-9,12-Octadecadienoic acid see Linoleic acid.

Octadecafluorodecahydronaphthalene see Perflu-nafene.

Octadecanoic acid see Stearic acid.

1-OCTADECANOL (octadecyl alcohol; stearyl al-cohol; stearylic alcohol; 'stenol').

cis,cis,cis-Octadeca-6,9,12-trienoic acid see Gam-olenic acid.

9,12,15-Octadecatrienoic acid see Linolenic acid.

cis-6-Octadecenoic acid see Petroselinic acid.

trans-6-Octadecenoic acid see Petroselaidic acid.

cis-9-Octadecenoic acid see Oleic acid.

trans-9-Octadecenoic acid see Elaidic acid.

trans-11-Octadecenoic acid see Vaccenic acid.

9-Octadecenylamine hydrofluoride see Dectaflur.

Octadecyl alcohol see 1-Octadecanol.

3-Octadecyloxy-1,2-propanediol see Batilol.

Octadine (tr) see Guanethidine.

'Octaflex' see Octafonium chloride.

OCTAFLUOROCYCLOBUTANE (perfluoro-cyclobutane; CF-138C; FC-318; 'freon C-138′).

OCTAFONIUM CHLORIDE*** (benzyldi-ethyl[2-[4-(1,1,3,3-tetramethylbutyl)phenoxy]-ethyl]ammonium chloride; octaphonium; phen-octide).

Octahydroazocine see Heptamethylenimine.

1-(Octahydroazocin-2-ylmethyl)guanidine see Guanazodine.

2,3,4,4a,8,9,13b,14-Octahydro-1H-benzo[6,7]cyclo-hepta[1,2,3-*de*]pyrido[2,1-*a*]isoquinoline see Tacl-amine.

Octahydro-5,8-dihydroxy-4,6,9,10-tetramethyl-6-vinyl-3a,9-propano-3aH-cyclopentacycloocten-1(4H)-one esters see Pleuromulin; Tiamulin.

Octahydro 5β,8aβ-dimethyl-3-methylenenaph-tho[2,3-*b*]furan-2(3H)-one see Alantolactone.

1,3,3a,5,6,11,12,12a-Octahydro-8-hydroxy-1H-benzo[*a*]cyclopenta[*f*]quinolizinium bromide see Quindonium bromide.

2,3,5,6,12,13,13a,13b-Octahydro-1H-indolo[3,2,1-*de*]pyrido[3,2,1-*ij*][1,5]naphthyridin-12-ol see Vin-deburnol.

4,6,6a,7,8,9,10,10a-Octahydroindolo[4,3-*fg*]quinol-ine see Ergoline.

(+)-2,3,4,4aβ,8,9,13bα,14-Octahydro-3α-isopropyl-1H-benzo[6,7]cyclohepta[1,2,3-*de*]pyrido[2,1-*a*]-isoquinolin-3-ol see Dexclamol.

1,2,3,4,6,7,7a,11*c*-Octahydro-9-methoxy-2-methyl-benzofuro[4,3,2-*efg*]benzazocin-6-ol see Galant-amine.

1,2,3,4,4a,5,6,10b-Octahydro-9-methoxy-10b-meth-ylphenanthridine see Tofetridine.

5,6,6a,7,8,9,10,10a-Octahydro-6-methyl-3-(1-methyl-4-phenylbutoxy)-1,9-phenanthridinediol-1-acetate see Levonantradol; Nantradol.

Octahydro-1-(3,4,5-trimethoxybenzoyl)azocine see Trocimine.

Octahydro-1-(3,4,5-trimethoxycinnamoyl)azocine see Cinoctramide.

4,6,8,10,12,14,16,27-Octahydroxy-3-(1-hydroxy-hexyl)-17,28-dimethyloxacyclooctacosa-17,19,21,23,25-pentaen-2-one see Filipin.

'Octa-klor' see Chlordane.

'Octalene' see Aldrin.

'Octalox' see Dieldrin.

Octamethyl (tr) *see* Schradan.
Octamethyldiphosphoramide *see* Schradan.
Octamethylpyrophosphoramide *see* Schradan.
OCTAMOXIN*** (2-hydrazinooctane; 1-(1-methylheptyl)hydrazine; D-15-14).
OCTAMYLAMINE*** (*N*-isopentyl-1,5-dimethylhexylamine; *N*-(1,5-dimethylhexyl)isopentylamine; *N*-isoamyl-1,5-dimethyl-1-hexylamine; 2-(isoamylamino)-6-methylheptane; octisamyl).
1-Octanecarboxylic acid *see* Nonanoic acid.
1,8-Octanedicarboxylic acid *see* Sebacic acid.
Octanedioic acid *see* Suberic acid.
'Octanil' *see* Isometheptene.
OCTANOIC ACID** (1-heptanecarboxylic acid; caprylic acid).
OCTANOIN (glyceryl 1-octanoate; monooctanoin; 'capmul 8210').
1-OCTANOL (octyl alcohol; caprylic alcohol).
2-OCTANOL (hexyl methyl carbinol).
'Octaphen' *see* Octafonium chloride.
Octaphonium* *see* Octafonium chloride.
OCTAPINOL*** (4-(2-propylpentyl)-1-piperidineethanol).
'Octapressin' *see* Felypressin.
Octasodium tetrakis(gluconato)bis(salicylato) μ-di-acetodialuminate III dihydrate *see* Sodium glucaspaldrate.
OCTASTINE*** (1-[2-[(*p*-chloro-α-methyl-α-phenylbenzyl)oxy]ethyl]octahydroazocine).
Octatensin (tr) *see* Guanethidine.
OCTATROPINE METHYLBROMIDE*** (8-methyl-*O*-(2-propylvaleryl)tropinium bromide; 8-methyltropinium bromide 2-propylvalerate; anisotropine methylbromide; octatropone bromide).
Octatropone bromide* *see* Octatropine methylbromide.
OCTAVERINE*** (6,7-dimethoxy-1-(3,4,5-triethoxyphenyl)isoquinoline).
OCTAZAMIDE*** (5-benzoylhexahydro-1*H*-furo[3,4-*c*]pyrrole; ICI-US 457).
OCTENIDINE*** (1,1'-decamethylenebis[1,4-dihydro-4-(octylimino)pyridine]; octenidine hydrochloride; WIN-41464).
Octestrol *see* Benzestrol.
OCTICIZER* (2-ethylhexyl diphenyl phosphate; 'santicizer 141').
'Octin' *see* Isometheptene.
Octisamyl *see* Octamylamine.
Octoclothepin *see* Clorotepine.
OCTOCRILENE*** (2-ethylhexyl 2-cyano-3,3-diphenylacrylate; octocrylene; 'uvinul N-539').
Octocrylene* *see* Octocrilene.
OCTODRINE*** (2-amino-6-methylheptane; 1,5-dimethylhexylamine; SK&F-51; 'heptamine').
OCTODRINE CAMSILATE (octodrine camphorsulfonate; octodrine camsylate).
OCTODRINE CAMSILATE plus NORFENEFRINE & ADENOSINE ('ordinal').
Octoestrol *see* Benzestrol.
'Octofene' *see* Clofoctol.
'Octofollin' *see* Benzestrol.
'Octon' *see* Isometheptene.

OCTOPAMINE*** (α-aminomethyl-*p*-hydroxybenzyl alcohol; β,4-dihydroxyphenethylamine; 2-(*p*-hydroxyphenyl)ethanolamine; noroxedrine; *p*-norsynephrine; ND-50; WV-569; 'norden'; 'norfen'; 'norphen'; 'norsympathol').
'Octopirox' *see* Piroctone olamine.
OCTOTIAMINE*** (8-[2-[*N*-(4-amino-2-methylpyrimidin-5-ylmethylformamido)-1-(2-hydroxyethyl)propenyl]dithio]-6-mercaptooctanoic acid methyl ester acetate; 3-(3-acetylthio-7-methoxycarbonylheptyldithio)-4-[*N*-(4-amino-2-methylpyrimid-5-ylmethyl)formamido]pent-3-en-1-ol; thiamine acetylthiooctyl disulfide; TATD).
OCTOXINOL*** (α-[*p*-(1,1,3,3-tetramethylbutyl)-phenyl]-ω-hydroxypoly(oxyethylene); polyethylene glycol *p*-isooctylphenyl ether; macrogol (tetramethylbutyl)phenyl ether; octylphenoxypolyethoxyethanol; octoxynol; 'antarox A'; 'igepal CA'; 'triton X').
Octoxynol* *see* Octoxinol.
OCTRIPHENATE (trimethyloctadecylammonium pentachlorophenate; 'hyamine 3528').
OCTRIPTYLINE*** (1a,10b-dihydro-6-[3-(methylamino)propylidene]dibenzo[*a,e*]cyclopropa[*c*]-cycloheptene; 1a,10b-dihydro-*N*-methyldibenzo-[*a,e*]cyclopropa[*c*]cyclohepten-Δ$^{6(1H),γ}$-propylamine; octriptyline phosphate; SC-27123).
OCTRIZOLE*** (2-(2*H*-benzotriazol-2-yl)-4-(1,1,3,3-tetramethylbutyl)phenol; 'cyasorb 5411').
Octyl alcohol *see* 1-Octanol.
Octylatropinium bromide *see* Atropine octyl bromide.
N-Octylbicycloheptenedicarboximide *see* (Ethylhexyl)norbornenedicarboximide.
Octyl 2-cyanoacrylate *see* Ocrilate.
tert-Octylguanidine *see* Guanoctine.
Octylphenoxypolyethoxyethanol *see* Octoxinol.
4'-Octyl-3-piperid-1-ylpropiophenone *see* Pipoctanone.
Octyl sulfate *see* Sodium etasulfate.
5-[2-(Octylsulfinyl)propyl]-1,3-benzodioxole *see* Sulfoxide.
S-Octyl thiobenzoate *see* Tioctilate.
Ocytocin *see* Oxytocin.
ODA-914 *see* Demoxytocin.
'Oddibil' *see* Fumaria officinalis extract.
O-Dimethoate *see* Omethoate.
'Odiston' *see* Diatrizoic acid.
'Odylen' *see* Mesulfen.
'Oedemase' *see* Furosemide.
Oenanthaldehyde *see* Heptyl aldehyde.
Oenanthic acid *see* Enanthic acid.
Oestr.... *see* Estr.....
'Off' *see* Diethyltoluamide.
OFLOXACIN** ((±)-9-fluoro-2,3-dihydro-3-methyl-10-(4-methylpiperazin-1-yl)-7-oxo-7*H*-pyrido[1,2,3-*de*]-1,4-benzoxazine-6-carboxylic acid; DL-8280; HOE-280).
OFTASCEINE*** (2',7'-bis[[bis(carboxymethyl)-amino]methyl]fluorescein).
'Ogen' *see* Piperazine estrone sulfate.
'Ogostal' *see* Capreomycin.

'**Ogyline**' *see* Norgestrienone.
'**Ohton**' *see* Dimethylthiambutene.
Oil of wintergreen *see* Methyl salicylate.
OIL SCARLET (1-(*p*-phenylazophenylazo)-2-naphthol; cerasine red; Sudan III).
'**OKO**' *see* Dichlorvos.
Okt.... *see also* Oct.....
Oktadin *see* Guanethidine.
Oktametil (tr) *see* Schradan.
OL-1 *see* Tioxolone.
OL-110 *see* Tioxolone.
OLAFLUR*** (2,2'-[[3-(2-hydroxyethyl)octadecylaminopropyl]imino]diethanol dihydrofluoride; SK&F-38095).
Olamine* *see* Ethanolamine.
OLAQUINDOX** (*N*-(2-hydroxyethyl)-3-methyl-2-quinoxalinecarboxamide 1,4-dioxide; BAY Va-9391).
'**Oleanbel**' *see* Troleandomycin.
OLEANDOMYCIN*** (antibiotic from *Str. antibioticus*; (2*R*,3*S*,4*R*,5*S*,6*S*,8*R*,10*R*,11*S*,12*R*,13*R*)-3-(2,6-dideoxy-3-*O*-methyl-α-L-*arabino*-hexopyranosyloxy)-8,8-epoxymethano-11-hydroxy-2,4,6,10,12,13-hexamethyl-9-oxo-5-[3,4,6-trideoxy-3-(dimethylamino)-β-D-*xylo*-hexopyranosyloxy]-tridecan-13-olide).
See also Diproleandomycin; Troleandomycin; *and under* Chloramphenicol; Tetracycline.
OLEANDOPEN (oleandomycin salt of penicillin G).
'**Oleasorbate(s)**' *see* Polysorbate(s).
OLEIC ACID (*cis*-9-octadecenoic acid).
See also Calcium oleate.
Oleocid (tr) *see* Sodium morrhuate.
'**Oleothorb**' *see* Polysorbate 80.
Oleovitamin A *see* Retinol.
Oleovitamin D$_2$ *see* Ergocalciferol.
Oleovitamin D$_3$ *see* Colecalciferol.
'**Oletetrin**' *see under* Tetracycline.
OLETIMOL** (*o*-(*N*-benzylacetimidoyl)phenol; 2-[1-(benzylimino)ethyl]phenol).
Oleum iodisatum *see* Iodinated poppyseed oil.
OLIVOMYCIN*** (antibiotic from *Actinomyces olivoreticuli*).
OLMIDINE** (2-hydroxy-2-(3,4-methylenedioxyphenyl)acetamidine; α-hydroxypiperonylformamidine; 3,4-methylenedioxymandelamidine; LL-1418).
'**Olquadil**' *see* Cloxazolam.
OLTIPRAZ*** (4-methyl-5-pyrazin-2-yl-3*H*-1,2-dithiole-3-thione; RP-35972).
'**Olympax**' *see* Difencloxazine.
'**Olynth**' *see* Xylometazoline.
OM-518 *see* Mephenoxalone.
OM-977 *see* Etaminile.
'**Omadine**' *see* Pyrithione.
'**Omadine disulfide**' *see* Dipyrithione.
'**Omadine zinc**' *see* Pyrithione zinc.
Omain (tr) *see* Demecolcine.
'**Omca**' *see* Fluphenazine.
OMDS *see* Dipyrithione.
'**Omega**' *see* Adrenochrome.

OMEPRAZOLE*** (5-methoxy-2-[[(4-methoxy-3,5-dimethylpyrid-2-yl)methyl]sulfinyl]benzimidazole; H-168/68).
'**Omeril**' *see* Mebhydrolin napadisilate.
OMETHOATE* (*O,O*-dimethyl *S*-[2-(methylamino)-2-oxoethyl] phosphorothioate; *O,O*-dimethyl *S*-(methylcarbamoylmethyl) phosphorothioate; O-dimethoate; dimethoxon; 'folimat').
OMIDOLINE** (2-methyl-3-(β-piperid-1-yl-*p*-phenetidino)phthalimidine; 2-methyl-3-[*p*-(2-piperid-1-ylethoxy)anilino]phthalimidine; tamidoline).
'**Omifin**' *see* Clomifene.
'**Omite**' *see* Propargite.
'**Omnes**' *see* Nifuratel.
'**Omnifen**' *see* Clomifene.
'**Omnipaque**' *see* Iohexol.
'**Omni-passin**' *see* Dithiazanine iodide.
'**Omnipen**' *see* Ampicillin.
OMOCONAZOLE*** (1-[2,4-dichloro-β-[2-(*p*-chlorophenoxy)ethoxy]-α-methylstyryl]imidazole).
OMONASTEINE*** (tetrahydro-2*H*-1,3-thiazine-4-carboxylic acid).
OMPA *see* Schradan.
OMS-1 *see* Malathion.
OMS-32 *see* Isoprocarb.
OMS-33 *see* Propoxur.
OMS-43 *see* Fenitrothion.
OMS-47 *see* Mexacarbate.
OMS-93 *see* Methiocarb.
OMS-198 *see* Isodrin.
OMS-479 *see* Dimetilan.
OMS-597 *see* 3,4,5-Trimethylphenyl methylcarbamate.
OMS-708 *see* Benzo[*b*]thien-4-yl methylcarbamate.
OMS-736 *see* Temefos.
OMS-971 *see* Chlorpyrifos.
OMS-1394 *see* Bendiocarb.
OMS-1438 *see* Leptophos.
OMS-1800 *see* Cismethrin.
OMS-1821 *see* Permethrin.
OMS-1998 *see* Deltamethrin.
OMS-2000 *see* Fenvalerate.
'**Omsat**' *see* Co-trimoxazole.
OMU *see* Cycluron.
'**Omyl**' *see under* DDT.
Oncodazole *see* Nocodazole.
'**Oncotiotepa**' *see* Thiotepa.
'**Oncovertin**' *see* Dextran.
'**Oncovin**' *see* Vincristine.
'**Ondasil**' *see* Glutethimide.
'**Ondena**' *see* Daunorubicin.
'**Ondogyne**' *see* Cyclofenil.
'**Ondonid**' *see* Cyclofenil.
'**One-alpha**' *see* Alfacalcidol.
'**Onix-BTC**' *see* Benzalkonium chloride.
'**Onkotin**' *see* Dextran.
'**Onkovertin**' *see* Dextran.
ONO-802 *see* Gemeprost.
Ononein *see* Formonetin.
'**Onservan**' *see* Procyclidine.
ONTIANIL** (4'-chloro-2,6-dioxocyclohexane-

carbothioanilide).

'Ontosein' see Orgotein.

OOSPONOL (8-hydroxyisocoumarin-4-yl hydroxymethyl ketone).

'Opalene' see Trimetozine.

OPC-1085 see Carteolol.

OPC-1427 see Bometolol.

OPC-2009 see Procaterol.

'Operidene' see Phenoperidine.

'Opertil' see Oxypertine.

OPHIDINE (N-(β-alanyl)-2-methylhistidine).

'Ophtalmokalixan' see Kanamycin.

'Ophtamidine' see Hexamidine.

'Ophthaine' see Proxymetacaine.

Ophthalin see Retinol.

'Ophthalmadine' see under Idoxuridine.

'Ophthetic' see Proxymetacaine.

'Ophthochlor' see Chloramphenicol.

'Ophthocortin' see Medrysone.

'Ophticor' see Cortisone.

'Ophtorenin' see Bupranolol.

Opial see Opium alkaloids.

Opian see Noscapine.

'Opianyl' see m-Meconin.

OPIANIC ACID (5,6-dimethoxyphthalaldehydic acid).

Opianic acid isonicotinoylhydrazone see Opiniazide.

Opianine see Noscapine.

'Opilon' see Moxisylyte.

OPINIAZIDE*** (5,6-dimethoxyphthalaldehydic acid isonicotinoylhydrazone; 2-carboxy-3,4-dimethoxybenzaldehyde isonicotinoylhydrazone; carboxyveratrylideneisoniazid; carboxyverazid; opianic acid isonicotinoylhydrazone; saluzid). See also Streptomycin opiniazide salt.

'Opino' see Buphenine.

OPIPRAMOL*** (4-[3-(5H-dibenz(b,f)azepin-5-yl)propyl]-1-piperazineethanol; 5-[3-[3-(2-hydroxyethyl)piperazin-1-yl]propyl]dibenz[b,f]azepine; G-33040; RP 8307).

'Opiran' see Pimozide.

OPIUM ALKALOIDS (laudanum; meconium; opial; papaveretum; tetrapon). See also Codeine; Meconin; Morphine; Noscapine; Papaverine; Paregoric; Thebaine.

'Opren' see Benoxaprofen.

Opromazine see Chlorpromazine sulfoxide.

'Optamine' see Co-dergocrine.

'Optanox' see Vinylbital.

'Opticillin' see Mezlocillin.

'Opticortenol' see Dexamethasone pivalate.

'Opticortenol-S' see under Dexamethasone pivalate.

'Opticrom' see Cromoglicate disodium.

'Optiform' see Formaldehyde.

'Optimax' see under Tryptophan.

'Optimil' see Methaqualone.

'Optimine' see Azatadine.

'Optimycin' see Metacycline.

'Optocillin' see under Mezlocillin.

'Opturem' see Ibuprofen.

'Orabet' see Tolbutamide.

'Orabetic' see Carbutamide.

'Orabilex' see Bunamiodyl.

'Orabilix' see Bunamiodyl.

'Orabolin' see Ethylstrenol.

'Oracaine' see Meprylcaine.

'Oracef' see Cefalexin.

'Oracefal' see Cefadroxil.

'Oracon' see under Dimethisterone.

'Oraconal' see under Megestrol acetate.

'Oradash' see Methionine.

'Oradexon' see Dexamethasone.

'Oradian' see Chlorhexamide.

'Oragest' see Medroxyprogesterone.

'Oragrafin-Na' see Sodium iopodate.

'Oragulant' see Diphenadione.

'Oralcer' see under Clioquinol.

'Oralcon' see Diclofenamide.

'Oraldene' see Hexetidine.

'Oralin' see Tolbutamide.

'Oralopen' see Pheneticillin.

'Oral turinabol' see 4-Chloro-17β-hydroxy-17-methyl-1,4-androstadien-3-one.

'Oramyl' see α-Amylase.

'Oranabol' see Oxymesterone.

ORANGE G* (chiefly the di-Na salt of 1-phenylazo-2-naphthol-6,8-disulfonic acid; novaurantium).

ORANGE RN (1-phenylazo-2-naphthol-6-sulfonic acid sodium salt).

'Oranil' see Carbutamide.

'Oranixon' see Mephenesin.

'Orap' see Pimozide.

'Orasulin' see Carbutamide.

'Oratestryl' see Fluoxymesterone.

'Oratrol' see Diclofenamide.

'Oraview' see Iopronic acid.

ORAZAMIDE*** (5-aminoimidazole-4-carboxamide orotate; AICA; 'aicamine').

'Orbenin' see Cloxacillin.

'Orbicin' see Dibekacin.

'Orbinamon' see Tiotixene.

'Orbisect' see Phosmet.

Orcin see Orcinol.

ORCINOL (3,5-dihydroxytoluene; 5-methylresorcinol; orcin).

Orcinol dimethyl ether see Elemicin.

ORCIPRENALINE*** (3,5-dihydroxy-α-isopropylaminomethylbenzyl alcohol; metaproterenol; orciprenaline sulfate; Th-152).

ORCIPRENALINE plus OXAZEPAM ('tranquoalupent'). See also under Bromhexine.

ORCONAZOLE*** ((±)-1-[p-chloro-β-[(2,6-dichlorobenzyl)oxy]phenethyl]imidazole; (±)-1-[2-(4-chlorophenyl)-2-[(2,6-dichlorophenyl)methoxy]ethyl]-1H-imidazole; orconazole nitrate; R-15556).

'Ordimel' see Acetohexamide.

'Ordinal' see under Octodrine camsilate.

'Ordinator' see Fenozolone.

'Ordram' see Molinate.

'Orencil' see Benzhydrylamine penicillinate.

'Oresol' see Guaifenesin.

'Oreson' see Guaifenesin.

391

ORESTRATE** (17β-cyclohexen-1-yloxyestra-1,3,5(10)-trien-3-ol propionate; estradiol 17-cyclohexen-1-yl ether 3-propionate).
'Oretic' *see* Hydrochlorothiazide.
OREXIN (3-phenyl-3,4-dihydroquinazoline; cedrarin; phenzoline).
ORF-1557-BA *see under* Norethisterone acetate.
ORF-8063 *see* Triflubazam.
ORF-9326 *see* Nisterime acetate.
ORF-10131 *see* Norgestimate.
ORF-15927 *see* Rioprostil.
Orferon (tr) *see* Ferroglycine sulfate.
'Orfiril' *see* Valproic acid.
Org-817 *see* Epimestrol.
Org-2969 *see* Desogestrel.
Org-6001 *see* Amafolone.
Org-6216 *see* Rimexolone.
'Orgabolin' *see* Ethylestrenol.
'Orgametil' *see* Lynestrenol.
'Orgametril' *see* Lynestrenol.
'Organidin' *see* Iodinated glycerol.
'Organoderm' *see* Malathion.
'Orga-phenkapton' *see* Phenkapton.
'Orgasteron' *see* Methylestrenolone.
Org GB-94 *see* Mianserin.
Org.NA97 *see* Pancuronium bromide.
Org.NC-45 *see* Vecuronium bromide.
Org.OD-14 *see* Tibolone.
ORGOTEIN** (soluble metalloproteins from liver, red blood cells and other mammalian tissues; ormetein; superoxide dismutase; 'ontosein'; 'palosein'; 'peroxinorm').
'Oricillin' *see* Propicillin.
'Orientomycin' *see* Cycloserine.
'Orimeten' *see* Aminoglutethimide.
'Orinase' *see* Tolbutamide.
'Oriodide-131' *see* Sodium iodide (^{131}I).
'Orion' *see* Triamcinolone.
'Orisul' *see* Sulfaphenazole.
'Orisulf' *see* Sulfaphenazole.
'Orlest' *see under* Norethisterone acetate.
'Orlestrin' *see under* Norethisterone acetate.
'Orlutate' *see* Norethisterone acetate.
Ormetein *see* Orgotein.
ORMETOPRIM*** (2,4-diamino-4-(6-methylveratryl)pyrimidine; 2,4-diamino-5-(3,4-dimethoxy-6-methylbenzyl)pyrimidine; NSC-95072; Ro 5-9754).
ORMETOPRIM plus SULFADIMETHOXINE ('rofenaid').
'Ornicetil' *see* Ornithine oxoglurate.
Ornid (tr) *see* Bretylium tosilate.
ORNIDAZOLE*** (1-(3-chloro-2-hydroxypropyl)-2-methyl-5-nitroimidazole; α-(chloromethyl)-2-methyl-5-nitroimidazole-1-ethanol; Ro 7-0207; 'tiberal').
ORNIPRESSIN*** (8-ornithine vasopressin; orpressin; 'POR 8').
ORNITHINE (2,5-diaminopentanoic acid; 2,5-diaminovaleric acid).
ORNITHINE ASPARTATE ('hepa-merz').
ORNITHINE CARBAMYL TRANSFERASE ('preortan').

ORNITHINE OXOGLURATE (ornithine 2-oxo-glutarate; 'ornicetil').
Ornithine 2-oxoglutarate *see* Ornithine oxoglurate.
8-Ornithine vasopressin *see* Ornipressin.
'Ornitrol' *see* Azacosterol.
'Oronol' *see* Aurothioglucose.
OROTIC ACID** (1,2,3,6-tetrahydro-2,6-dioxo-4-pyrimidinecarboxylic acid; 6-uracilcarboxylic acid; animal galactose factor; animal glucose factor; whey factor).
See also Choline orotate; Magnesium orotate; Orazamide.
ORPANOXIN*** (5-(*p*-chlorophenyl)-2-furanhydracrylic acid; F-776).
Orphenadrine* *see* Orphenadrine.
ORPHENADRINE*** (*N,N*-dimethyl-2-(*o*-methyl-α-phenylbenzyloxy)ethylamine; *o*-methyldiphenhydramine; benhexol; orphenadine; orphenadrine hydrochloride; BS-5930).
ORPHENADRINE CITRATE ('norflex').
ORPHENADRINE CITRATE plus PARACETAMOL ('norgesic'; 'strilexin').
'Orphol' *see* Co-dergocrine.
'Orpidan' *see* Chlorazanil.
'Orpizin' *see* Chlorazanil.
Orpressin *see* Ornipressin.
'Orstanorm' *see* Dihydroergotamine.
'Ortal' *see* Hexethal.
ORTETAMINE*** (2,α-dimethylphenethylamine; 1-methyl-2-*o*-tolylethylamine; 2-methylamphetamine; *o*-methylamphetamine).
ORTHANILAMIDE (*o*-aminobenzenesulfonamide).
'Orthene' *see* Acephate.
'Orthesin' *see* Benzocaine.
'Orthiodine' *see* Sodium iodohippurate.
'Orthiourea' *see* Sodium auroallylthioureidobenzoate.
'Ortho 1557-O' *see under* Norethisterone.
ORTHOCAINE* (methyl 3-amino-4-hydroxybenzoate; 'aminobenz'; 'orthoform').
'Orthocide-406' *see* Captan.
'Orthocol' *see* Sulfogaiacol.
'Ortho crabgrass killer' *see* Disodium methanearsonate.
'Orthodelfen' *see* Nonoxinol 9.
Orthodiazine *see* Pyridazine.
'Ortho dibrom' *see* Naled.
'Orthoform' *see* Nonoxinol 9 *and* Orthocaine.
'Ortho-gynest' *see* Estriol.
'Orthoiodine' *see* Sodium iodohippurate.
'Ortho-klor' *see* Chlordane.
'Ortho-mite' *see* 2-(*p-tert*-Butylphenoxy)isopropyl 2-chloroethyl sulfite.
'Orthonal' *see* Methaqualone.
'Orthonovin' *see under* Norethisterone.
'Ortho-novum' *see under* Norethisterone.
'Orthoparaquat' *see* Paraquat.
'Ortho-phaltan' *see* Folpet.
Orthophosphoric acid *see* Phosphoric acid.
ORTHOPROCAINAMIDE (*o*-amino-*N*-(2-diethylaminoethyl)benzamide).
Orthosarcolysin *see* *o*-Sarcolysin.

'**Orthoxenol**' *see* o-Phenylphenol.
'**Orthoxine**' *see* Methoxyphenamine.
'**Ortin**' *see* Trolnitrate.
'**Ortizon**' *see* Urea hydrogen peroxide.
'**Ortodrine**' *see* Methoxyphenamine.
'**Orudis**' *see* Ketoprofen.
'**Orval**' *see* Sulbutiamine.
ORYZALIN* (3,5-dinitro-N^4,N^4-dipropylsulfanil-amide; 4-(dipropylamino)-3,5-dinitrobenzenesulfonamide; 'ryzelan').
'**Osadrin**' *see under* Aminophenazone.
OSALMID* (N-(p-hydroxyphenyl)salicylamide; 4'-hydroxysalicylanilide; oxafenamide; L-1718).
Osarsol (tr) *see* Acetarsol.
'**Osbil**' *see* Iobenzamic acid.
'**Oscine**' *see* Scopolamine.
OSMADIZONE* ([2-(phenylsulfinyl)ethyl]malonic acid mono(1,2-diphenylhydrazide)).
'**Osmitrol**' *see* Mannitol.
'**Osmofundin**' *see* Mannitol.
'**Osmosin**' *see* Indometacin.
'**Ospolot**' *see* Sultiame.
'**Ossiamina**' *see* Chlormethine N-oxide.
'**Ossiclorin**' *see* Chlormethine N-oxide.
'**Ossitetra**' *see* Oxytetracycline.
'**Ossopan**' *see under* Hydroxyapatite.
'**Ostamer**' *see* Polyurethane foam.
'**Ostensin**' *see* Trimethidinium methosulfate.
OSTREOGRYCIN* (antibiotic from *Str. ostreogriseus*).
Ostreogrycin B *see* Mikamycin.
'**Ostrocilline**' *see* Benzathine penicillin V.
OSTRUTHIN (6-geranyl-7-hydroxycoumarin).
Osyritin *see* Rutoside.
'**Osyrol**' *see* Canrenoate potassium *and* Spironolactone.
OTILONIUM BROMIDE* (diethyl(2-hydroxyethyl)methylammonium bromide p-[o-(octyloxy)benzamido]benzoate; 'spasmomen').
OTIMERATE SODIUM (ethyl(hydrogen 2-mercapto-5-benzoxazolecarboxylato)mercury sodium salt).
'**Otokalixan**' *see* Kanamycin.
'**Otowaxol**' *see* Docusate sodium.
'**Otrhomin**' *see* Methenamine thiocyanate.
'**Otrivine**' *see* Phenmazoline *and* Xylometazoline.
'**Otrun**' *see* Deanol aceglumate.
OTS-68 *see* Oxytocin synthetic.
Ouabagenin L-rhamnoside *see* Ouabain.
OUABAIN (1β,3β,5,11α,14,19-hexahydroxy-5β-card-20(22)-enolide 3-L-rhamnoside; ouabagenin L-rhamnoside; acoantherin; gratus strophanthin; strophanthin g).
'**Ovaban**' *see* Megestrol acetate.
'**Ovanon**' *see under* Ethinylestradiol.
'**Ovarelin**' *see* Gonadorelin acetate.
'**Ovaribran**' *see under* Conjugated estrogens.
'**Ovarid**' *see* Megestrol acetate.
'**Ovariostat**' *see under* Lynestrenol.
'**Ovatran**' *see* Chlorfenson.
'**Ovestin**' *see* Estriol.
Ovex *see* Chlorfenson.
'**Ovidon**' *see under* Levonorgestrel.

'**Oviol**' *see under* Desogestrel.
'**Ovitrol**' *see* Fenticlor.
Ovochlor *see* Chlorfenson.
'**Ovocyclin P**' *see* Estradiol dipropionate.
Ovoflavin *see* Riboflavin.
'**Ovol**' *see* Dicycloverine.
'**Ovoresta**' *see under* Ethinylestradiol.
'**Ovosiston**' *see under* Chlormadinone acetate.
'**Ovotran**' *see* Chlorfenson.
'**Ovral**' *see under* Norgestrel.
'**Ovran**' *see under* Levonorgestrel.
'**Ovranette**' *see under* Levonorgestrel.
'**Ovrette**' *see* Norgestrel.
'**Ovulen**' *see under* Etynodiol diacetate.
'**Ovysmen**' *see under* Norethisterone.
'**Owadofos**' *see* Fenitrothion.
m-(1-Oxa-4-azaspiro[4.6]undec-2-yl)phenol *see* Ciclafrine.
'**Oxabel**' *see* Oxacillin.
endo-endo-7-Oxabicyclo[2.2.1]heptane-2,3-dicarboxylic acid disodium salt *see* Endothal sodium.
OXABOLONE CIPIONATE* (17β-(3-cyclopentylpropionoxy)-4-hydroxyestr-4-en-3-one; 4,17β-dihydroxyestr-4-en-3-one 17-cyclopentanepropionate; FI-5852; 'steranabol depot').
OXABREXINE* (ethyl [[4,6-dibromo-α-(cyclohexylmethylamino)-o-tolyl]oxy]acetate).
OXACEPROL* ((−)-1-acetyl-4-hydroxy-L-proline; N-acetylhydroxyproline; 'jonctum').
OXACILLIN (6-[(5-methyl-3-phenylisoxazol-4-yl)carboxamido]penicillanic acid; (5-methyl-3-phenyl-4-isoxazolyl)penicillin; isoxacillin; oxacillin; penicillin P-12; oxacillin sodium; P-12; SQ-16423).
See also under Ampicillin; Mezlocillin.
Oxacyclobutane *see* Oxetane.
o-(1,3,4-Oxadiazol-2-yl)phenol *see* Fenadiazole.
'**Oxadilene**' *see under* Butalamine.
OXADIMEDINE* (N-benzoxazol-2-yl-N-benzyl-N',N'-dimethylethylenediamine; 2-[benzyl(2-dimethylaminoethyl)amino]benzoxazole).
Oxadrol* *see* Dioxadrol.
7-Oxa-3,6-endomethylenehexahydrophthalic acid disodium salt *see* Endothal sodium.
Oxafenamide *see* Osalmid.
OXAFLOZANE* (4-isopropyl-2-(α,α,α-trifluoro-m-tolyl)morpholine; CERM-1766).
OXAFLUMAZINE* (10-[3-[4-(2-m-dioxanylethyl)piperazin-1-yl]propyl]-2-(trifluoromethyl)-phenothiazine).
OXAFLUMAZINE DISUCCINATE (SD-270-31).
Oxafuradene *see* Nifuradene.
Oxagestone *see* Oxogestone phenpropionate.
OXAGRELATE* (ethyl 3,4-dihydro-1-(hydroxymethyl)-5,7-dimethyl-4-oxo-6-phthalazinecarboxylate).
17α-Oxa-D-homoandrosta-1,4-diene-3,17-dione *see* Testolactone.
'**Oxaine**' *see* Oxetacaine.
OXALACETIC ACID (ketosuccinic acid; oxosuccinic acid).
Oxalaldehyde *see* Glyoxal.
Oxalamide *see* Oxamide.

OXALIC ACID (ethanedioic acid).
Oxalic acid diamide *see* Oxamide.
Oxalic acid monoamide *see* Oxamic acid.
'Oxalid' *see* Oxyphenbutazone.
OXALINAST* (($\pm$)-(6,7,8,8a-tetrahydro-2-oxo-3-acenaphthenyl)oxamic acid).
[Oxalylbis(iminoethylene)]bis[(o-chlorobenzyl)diethylammonium chloride] *see* Ambenonium chloride.
1,3-Oxalylurea *see* Parabanic acid.
OXAMARIN* (6,7-bis(2-diethylaminoethoxy)-4-methylcoumarin; ethoxarine; SK&F-17035-A).
OXAMETACIN* (1-(p-chlorobenzoyl)-5-methoxy-2-methylindole-3-acetohydroxamic acid; indometacin hydroxylamide; indoxamic acid; ABC 8/3; 'flogar').
OXAMIC ACID (aminoglyoxylic acid; aminooxoacetic acid; oxalic acid monoamide).
Oxamic acid hydrazide *see* Semioxamazide.
OXAMIDE (ethane diamide; oxalamide; oxalic acid diamide).
Oxammonium *see* Hydroxylamine.
OXAMNIQUINE* (1,2,3,4-tetrahydro-2-[(isopropylamino)methyl]-7-nitro-6-quinolinemethanol; 1,2,3,4-tetrahydro-6-hydroxymethyl-2-isopropylaminomethyl-7-nitroquinoline; UK-4271; 'mansil'; 'vansil').
Oxamphetamine* *see* Hydroxyamphetamine.
'Oxamycin' *see* Cycloserine.
OXAMYL* (methyl 2-(dimethylamino)-N-[[(methylamino)carbonyl]oxy]-2-oxoethanimidothioate; 'vydate').
OXANAMIDE* (2,3-epoxy-2-ethyl-3-propylpropionic acid; 2-ethyl-3-propylglycidamide).
OXANDROLONE* (17β-hydroxy-17-methyl-2-oxa-5α-androstan-3-one; dodecahydro-3-hydroxy-6-(hydroxymethyl)-3,3a,6-trimethyl(11H)-benz[e]indene-7-acetic acid delta lactone; NSC-67068; SC-11585).
'Oxanid' *see* Oxazepam.
OXANTEL ((E)-m-[2-(1,4,5,6-tetrahydro-1-methylpyrimidin-2-yl)vinyl]phenol; *trans*-3-hydroxy-β-(1,4,5,6-tetrahydro-1-methylpyrimid-2-yl)styrene; CP-14445).
OXANTEL EMBONATE (oxantel pamoate; CP-14445-16; 'telopar').
Oxantel pamoate *see* Oxantel embonate.
OXAPADOL* (4,5-dihydro-1-phenyl-1,4-epoxy-1H,3H-[1,4]oxazepino[4,3-a]benzimidazole; MD-720111).
3-Oxapentane-1,5-diol *see* Diethylene glycol.
OXAPIUM IODIDE* (1-(2-cyclohexyl-2-phenyl-1,3-dioxolan-4-ylmethyl)-1-methylpiperidinium iodide; ciclonium iodide; cyclonium iodide; SH-100; 'esperan').
OXAPRAZINE* (10-[3-[4-(2-m-dioxan-2-ylethyl)-piperazin-1-yl]propyl]phenothiazine; SD-270-07).
OXAPROPANIUM IODIDE* ((1,3-dioxolan-4-ylmethyl)trimethylammonium iodide; formal of (dihydroxypropyl)trimethylammonium iodide; F-2249).
OXAPROTILINE* (α-[(methylamino)methyl]-9,10-ethanoanthracene-9(10H)-ethanol; Ba-49802B).
OXAPROZIN* (4,5-diphenyl-2-oxazolepropionic acid; Wy-21743).
OXARBAZOLE* (9-benzoyl-1,2,3,4-tetrahydro-6-methoxycarbazole-3-carboxylic acid; WIN-34284).
Oxarutin* *see* Ethoxazorutoside.
'Oxastaph' *see* Oxacillin.
OXATOMIDE* (1-[3-[4-(diphenylmethyl)piperazin-1-yl]propyl]-2-benzimidazolinone; 1-(diphenylmethyl)-4-[3-(2-oxobenzimidazolin-1-yl)-propyl]piperazine; R 35443; 'tilset'; 'tinset').
6-Oxa-1,11-undecamethylenebis(trimethylammonium chloride) *see* Oxydipentonium chloride.
Oxazacillin* *see* Oxacillin.
OXAZAFONE* (2'-benzoyl-4'-chloro-2-[(2-hydroxyethyl)methylamino]-N-methylacetanilide; 5-chloro-2-[[2-(2-hydroxyethyl)methylamino]-N-methylacetamido]benzophenone).
OXAZEPAM* (7-chloro-1,3-dihydro-3-hydroxy-5-phenyl-2H-1,4-benzodiazepin-2-one; CB-8092; Wy-3498; Z-10-TR).
See also under Conjugated estrogens; Orciprenaline; Scopolamine butyl bromide.
Oxazepam dipropylacetate *see* Oxazepam valproate.
Oxazepam hemisuccinate *see* Oxazepam succinate.
Oxazepam pivalate *see* Pivoxazepam.
Oxazepam 2-propylvalerate *see* Oxazepam valproate.
OXAZEPAM SUCCINATE (oxazepam hemisuccinate; Wy-4426; 'nulans').
Oxazepam trimethylacetate *see* Pivoxazepam.
OXAZEPAM VALPROATE (oxazepam 2-propylvalerate; oxazepam dipropylacetate; SAS-554).
OXAZIDIONE* (2-(morpholinomethyl)-2-phenyl-1,3-indandione; mofedione; LD-4610; 'amplidione').
Oxazimedrine* *see* Phenmetrazine.
OXAZOLAM* (10-chloro-2,3,7,11β-tetrahydro-2-methyl-11b-phenyloxazolo[3,2-d][1,4]benzodiazepin-6(5H)-one; CS-370; 'serenal'; 'tranquit').
OXAZOLE (furo[b]monazole).
'Oxazolidin' *see* Oxyphenbutazone.
OXAZOLIDINE (tetrahydrooxazole).
OXAZOLINE (dihydrooxazole).
OXAZORONE* (7-hydroxy-4-morpholinomethylcoumarin).
OX BILE (fel tauri; 'anabile'; 'desibyl'; 'felkreon'; 'glissitol').
OXCARBAZEPINE* (10,11-dihydro-10-oxo-5H-dibenz[b,f]azepine-5-carboxamide).
OXDRALAZINE* (2,2'-[[(6-hydrazinopyridazin-3-yl)imino]diethanol; 3-[bis(2-hydroxyethyl)amino]-6-hydrazinopyridazine; 2-[6-[bis(2-hydroxyethyl)amino]pyridazin-3-yl]hydrazine; DL-150; L-6150).
OXEDRINE* (p-hydroxy-α-(methylaminomethyl)-benzyl alcohol; synephrine; aetaphen; pentedrine; vasoton; 'symcortol'; 'sympathol'; 'sympatol').

OXEDRINE ASCORBATE ('corva-C').

OXELADIN* (2-[2-(diethylamino)ethoxy]ethyl ester of 2-ethyl-2-phenylbutyric acid).

OXENDOLONE* (16β-ethyl-17β-hydroxyestr-4-en-3-one; TSAA-291).

OXEPINAC* (6,11-dihydro-11-oxodibenz[*b,e*]-oxepin-3-acetic acid).

OXERUTINS* (mixture of 5 different *O*-(2-hydroxyethyl)rutosides with not less than 45% of troxerutin; 'paroven').

OXETACAINE* (2,2'-(2-hydroxyethylimino)-bis-[*N*-(α,α-dimethylphenethyl)-*N*-methylacetamide]; *N,N*-bis[*N*-methyl-*N*-(phenyl-*tert*-butyl)-acetamido]-2-hydroxyethylamine; oxethazaine; Wy-806).

OXETACILLIN* (6-[4-(*p*-hydroxyphenyl)-2,2-dimethyl-5-oxoimidazolidin-1-yl]penicillanic acid).
See also Sarmoxicillin.

OXETANE (oxacyclobutane; oxethane; trimethylene oxide).

2-Oxetanone *see* Propiolactone.

Oxethane *see* Oxetane.

Oxethazaine* *see* Oxetacaine.

OXETORONE* (6-[3-(dimethylamino)propylidene](12*H*)benzofuro[3,2-*c*][1]benzoxepine; *N,N*-dimethylbenzofuro[3,2-*c*][1]benzoxepin-Δ$^{6(12H),\gamma}$-propylamine).

OXETORONE FUMARATE* (L-6257; 'nocertone').

Oxfenamide *see* Oxiramide.

OXFENDAZOLE* (methyl 5-(phenylsulfinyl)-2-benzimidazolecarbamate; RS-8858).

OXFENICINE* (L-2-(*p*-hydroxyphenyl)glycine; UK-25842).

Oxiamin *see* Inosine.

OXIBETAINE* ((carboxymethyl)(2-hydroxyethyl)dimethylammonium hydroxide inner salt).

OXIBETAINE* ((carboxymethyl)(2-hydroxyethyl)dimethylammonium hydroxide inner salt).

Oxibuprocaine* *see* Oxybuprocaine.

Oxibutynin* *see* Oxybutynin.

Oxichlorochin* *see* Hydroxychloroquine.

Oxiclipine* *see* Oxyclipine.

OXICONAZOLE* (2',4'-dichloro-2-imidazol-1-ylacetophenone *O*-(2,4-dichlorobenzyl)oxime; oxiconazole nitrate; Ro 13-8996).

Oxiconum *see* Oxycodone.

OXIDIZED CELLULOSE* (oxidized cellulosic acid; cellulosic acid; oxycellulose; 'hemo-pak'; 'novocell'; 'oxycel'; 'sorbacel').

OXIDIZED REGENERATED CELLULOSE* ('surgicel'; 'tabotamp').

OXIDOPAMINE* (5-(2-aminoethyl)-1,2,4-benzenetriol; 6-hydroxydopamine; 2,4,5-trihydroxyphenethylamine; H-88/32; NSC-233898; '6-HD').

OXIDRONIC ACID ((hydroxymethylene)diphosphonic acid; HDP; HMDP).

Oxifenamate* *see* Oxyfenamate.

OXIFENTOREX* (*N*-benzyl-*N*,α-dimethyl-

phenethylamine *N*-oxide; benzphetamine oxide).

OXIFUNGIN (1,2-dihydro-3-(phenoxymethyl)-pyrido[3,4-*e*]-1,2,4-triazine; oxifungin hydrochloride; EU-3421).

Oxilapine *see* Loxapine.

OXILORPHAN ((−)-17-(cyclopropylmethyl)-3,4-dihydroxymorphinan; (−)-17-(cyclopropylmethyl)morphinan-3,14-diol).

Oximetazoline* *see* Oxymetazoline.

Oxin *see* 8-Quinolinol.

OXINDOLE (2-indolinone; 2-(3*H*)-indolone).

Oxine *see* 8-Quinolinol.

OXINE-COPPER* (bis(8-quinolinato-*N*²,*O*⁸)copper; 8-quinolinol copper compound; oxine-Cu).

OXINIACIC ACID* (nicotinic acid *N*-oxide).

'Oxinofen' *see* Oxycinchophen.

Oxipendyl* *see* Oxypendyl.

OXIPEROMIDE (1-[1-(2-phenoxyethyl)piperid-4-yl]benzimidazol-2-one;1,3-dihydro-1-(1-(2-phenoxyethyl)piperid-4-yl)-2*H*-benzimidazol-2-one; R-4714).

Oxipertin *see* Oxypertine.

Oxiprocaine* *see* Hydroxyprocaine.

OXIPURINOL* (4,6-dihydroxypyrazolo[3,4-*d*]-pyrimidine; 1*H*-pyrazolo[3,4-*d*]pyrimidine-4,6-diol; oxypurinol; BW-55-5; NSC-76239).

Oxipyrronium* *see* Oxypyrronium bromide.

Oxiquinazine *see* Dipyrone.

OXIRACETAM* (4-hydroxy-2-oxo-1-pyrrolidineacetamide; 4-hydroxypiracetam; ISF-2522).

OXIRAMIDE* (2,6-dimethyl-1-[4-(2-phenoxy-2-phenylacetamido)butyl]piperidine; *N*-[4-(2,6-dimethylpiperid-1-yl)butyl]-2-phenoxy-2-phenylacetamide; oxfenamide; CI-661).

Oxirane *see* Ethylene oxide.

Oxiranecarboxylic acid *see* Glycidic acid.

Oxisone* *see* Oxysonium iodide.

OXISOPRED* (11β,17,21-trihydroxy-*B*-homo-*A*-norpregn-1-ene-3,6,20-dione).

'Oxistan' *see* Tin oxide.

OXISURAN* (2-(methylsulfinylacetyl)pyridine; methylsulfinylmethyl 2-pyridyl ketone; W-6495).

OXITEFONIUM BROMIDE* (diethyl(2-hydroxyethyl)methylammonium bromide α-phenyl-2-thiopheneglycolate; F-70).

OXITRIPTAN* (5-hydroxy-L-tryptophan; 5-HTP; Ro 0783/B; 'levothym'; 'pretonine').

OXITRIPTAN ETHYL ESTER (Ro 3-5940).

OXITRIPTAN GLUTAMATE (MADE-1932).

OXITRIPTYLINE* (2-(10,11-dihydro-5*H*-dibenzo[*a,d*]cyclohepten-5-yloxy)-*N,N*-dimethylacetamide; 5-[(dimethylcarbamoyl)methoxy]-10,11-dihydro-5*H*-dibenzo[*a,d*]cycloheptene; oxytriptyline).

OXITROPIUM BROMIDE* ((8*r*)-6β,7β-epoxy-8-ethyl-3α-hydroxy-1α*H*,5α*H*-tropanium bromide (−)-tropate; (3*s*,6*R*,7*S*,8*r*)-8-ethyl-3-[(*S*)-tropoyloxy]-6,7-epoxytropanium bromide; BA-253; 'tersigat'; 'ventilat').

OXMETIDINE* (2-[[2-[[(5-methylimidazol-4-yl)methyl]thio]ethyl]amino]-5-piperonylpyrimidin-4(1*H*)-one; SK&F-92994).

Oxo.... *see also* Keto.....

Oxoacetic acid *see* Glyoxylic acid.

'Oxo-ate' *see* Amiodoxyl benzoate.

'Oxo-ate-B' *see* Calciodoxyl benzoate.

4-Oxo-4*H***-1-benzopyran-2-carboxylic acid** *see* Chromocarb.

4-Oxo-4*H***-1-benzopyran-2-carboxylic acid 5,5′-diether (1,3) with glycerol** *see* Cromoglicic acid.

2-Oxo-2*H***-1,3-benzoxazine-3(4***H***)-acetamide** *see* Caroxazone.

γ-Oxo[1,1′-biphenyl]-4-butanoic acid *see* Fenbufen.

2-OXO-3-BORNANECARBOXYLIC ACID (camphocarbonic acid; camphocarboxylic acid; 3-camphorcarboxylic acid).

2-Oxobornane-10-sulfonic acid *see* Camphorsulfonic acid.

4-(3-Oxobutyl)-1,2-diphenyl-3,5-pyrazolidinedione *see* Kebuzone.

π-Oxocamphor *see* 1,7-Dimethyl-2-oxo-7-norbornanecarboxaldehyde.

8-Oxocamphor *see* 1,7-Dimethyl-2-oxo-7-norbornanecarboxaldehyde.

18-Oxocorticosterone *see* Aldosterone.

[*p*-(3-Oxo-1-cyclohexen-1-yl)phenyl]acetic acid *see* Lexofenac.

***p*-(3-Oxocyclohexyl)hydratropic acid oxime** *see* Ximoprofen.

1-(2-Oxocyclohexylmethyl)piperidine *see* Pimeclone.

1-(2-Oxocyclohexyl)-2-naphthol *see* Naphthonone.

***p*-[(Oxocyclopentyl)methyl]hydratropic acid** *see* Loxoprofen.

γ-Oxo-2-dibenzofuranbutyric acid *see* Furobufen.

14-Oxo-*cis*-eburnane *see* Vinburnine.

γ-Oxo-8-fluoranthrenebutyric acid *see* Florantyrone.

9-Oxofluoren-2-ylglyoxal bisulfite compound *see* Florenal.

OXOGESTONE*** (20β-hydroxy-19-norpregn-4-en-3-one).

Oxogestone hydrocinnamate *see* Oxogestone phenpropionate.

OXOGESTONE PHENPROPIONATE* (oxagestone; oxogestone hydrocinnamate).

OXOGLURATE(S)** (2-oxoglutarate(s); 2-oxoglutaric acid, esters and salts).
See also under Arginine; Magnesium; Ornithine.

2-OXOGLUTARIC ACID (2-ketoglutaric acid).

3-Oxo-L-gulofuranolactone *see* Ascorbic acid.

2-Oxohexamethylenimine *see* Caprolactam.

3-OXOHEXANOIC ACID (butyrylacetic acid; 3-ketocaproic acid; 3-ketohexanoic acid).

3-Oxohexonic acid lactone *see* Isoascorbic acid.

1-(5-Oxohexyl)theobromine *see* Pentoxifylline.

7-(5-Oxohexyl)theophylline *see* Lomifylline.

6-[D-2-(2-Oxoimidazolidine-1-carboxamido)-2-phenylacetamido]penicillanic acid *see* Azlocillin.

***p*-(1-Oxoisoindolin-2-yl)hydratropic acid** *see* Dexindoprofen; Indoprofen.

2-[*p*-(1-Oxoisoindolin-2-yl)phenyl]butyric acid *see* Indobufen.

OXOLAMINE*** (5-[2-(diethylamino)ethyl]-3-phenyl-1,2,4-oxadiazole; 'perebron').

OXOLAMINE BENZILATE (oxolamine diphenylglycolate).

OXOLAMINE BENZILATE plus TETRACYCLINE ('proxybron').

OXOLAMINE CITRATE (AF-438; SK&F-9976).

OXOLIN (tr) (1,2,3,4-tetrahydro-1,2,3,4-tetraoxonaphthalene dihydrate).

OXOLINIC ACID*** (5-ethyl-5,8-dihydro-8-oxo-1,3-dioxolo[4,5-*g*]quinoline-7-carboxylic acid; oxolonic acid; NSC-110364; W-4565).

Oxolonic acid *see* Oxolinic acid.

Oxomalonic acid *see* Mesoxalic acid.

OXOMEMAZINE*** (10-(3-dimethylamino-2-methylpropyl)phenothiazine 5,5-dioxide; alimemazine *S,S*-dioxide; RP 6847).

Oxomethane *see* Formaldehyde.

OXONAZINE*** (4,6-diamino-2-(diallylamino)-*s*-triazine N^2-oxide; diallylmelamine *N*-oxide).

'Oxone' *see* Sodium peroxide.

OXOPHENARSINE*** (2-amino-4-arsenosophenol; *m*-amino-*p*-hydroxyphenylarsenoxide; arsphenoxide; oxyphenarsine; Ehrlich 5; NSC-3087).

Oxophenylarsine *see* Arsenosobenzene.

[(4-Oxo-2-phenyl-4*H***-1-benzopyran-5,7-diyl)dioxy]diacetic acid** *see* Flavodic acid.

5-Oxo-*N*-(*trans*-2-phenylcyclopropyl)-2-pyrrolidinecarboxamide *see* Rolicyprine.

4-(3-Oxo-3-phenylpropyl)-1,2-diphenyl-3,5-pyrazolidinedione *see* Benzopyrazone.

2-Oxo-5-phenyl-*N*-propyloxazolidine-3-carboxamide *see* Profexalone.

2-(2-Oxopiperid-3-yl)-1,2-benzisothiazolin-3-one 1,1-dioxide *see* Supidimide.

11-Oxoprogesterone *see* 4-Pregnene-3,11,20-trione.

5-Oxoproline *see* Pidolic acid.

5-Oxo-L-prolyl-L-glutaminyl-L-aspartyl-L-tyrosyl-L-threonylglycyl-L-tryptophyl-L-methionyl-L-aspartyl-L-phenylalaninamide 4-(hydrogen sulfate) ester *see* Ceruletide.

5-Oxo-L-prolyl-L-histidyl-L-prolinamide *see* Protirelin.

5-Oxo-L-prolyl-L-histidyl-L-tryptophyl-L-seryl-L-tyrosyl-(*O-tert*-butyl-D-seryl)-L-leucyl-L-arginyl-*N*-ethyl-L-prolinamide *see* Buserelin.

5-Oxo-L-prolyl-L-histidyl-L-tryptophyl-L-seryl-L-tyrosylglycyl-L-leucyl-L-arginyl-*N*-ethyl-L-prolinamide *see* Fertirelin.

5-Oxo-L-prolyl-L-histidyl-L-tryptophyl-L-seryl-L-tyrosylglycyl-L-leucyl-L-arginyl-L-prolylglycinamide *see* Gonadorelin.

5-Oxo-L-prolyl-L-histidyl-L-tryptophyl-L-seryl-L-tyrosyl-D-tryptophyl-*N*-methyl-L-leucyl-L-arginyl-*N*-ethyl-L-prolinamide *see* Lutrelin.

5-Oxo-L-prolyl-L-histidyl-L-tryptophyl-L-seryl-L-tyrosyl-D-leucyl-L-leucyl-L-arginyl-*N*-ethyl-L-prolinamide *see* Leuprorelin.

5-Oxo-L-prolyl-L-histidyl-L-tryptophyl-L-seryl-L-tyrosyl-3-(2-naphthyl)-D-alanyl-L-leucyl-L-arginyl-L-prolylglycinamide *see* Nafarelin.

5-Oxo-L-prolyl-L-tryptophyl-L-prolyl-L-arginyl-L-prolyl-L-glutaminyl-L-isoleucyl-L-prolyl-L-proline *see* Teprotide.

2-Oxopropanal *see* Methylglyoxal.

2-Oxopropionaldehyde *see* Methylglyoxal.

2-Oxopropionic acid *see* Pyruvic acid.

4-[(1-Oxopropyl)phenylamino]-1-(2-phenylethyl)-4-piperidinecarboxylic acid methyl ester *see* Carfentanil.

OXOPROSTOL*** ((±)-*trans*-2-(7-hydroxyheptyl)-3-(3-oxo-4-phenoxybutyl)cyclopentanone; *trans*-1-hydroxy-16-phenoxy-ω-tetranorprostane-9,15-dione; M & B-33153).

N-[1-Oxo-5(1*H*)-(purin-6-ylthio)pentyl]glycine ethyl ester *see* Butocin.

11-Oxo-11*H*-pyrido[2,1-*b*]quinazoline-2-carboxylic acid *see* Doqualast.

2-Oxo-1-pyrrolidineacetamide *see* Piracetam.

2-Oxo-1-pyrrolidineacetic acid 3,3,5-trimethylcyclohexyl ester *see* Piraxelate.

5-Oxopyrrolidine-2-carboxylic acid *see* Pidolic acid.

1-(2-Oxopyrrolidino)-4-pyrrolidino-2-butyne *see* Oxotremorine.

2-(2-Oxopyrrolidin-1-yl)acetamide *see* Piracetam.

Oxosuccinic acid *see* Oxalacetic acid.

8-Oxo-5-thia-1-azabicyclo[4.2.0]oct-2-ene-2-carboxylic acid *see* 2-Cephem-2-carboxylic acid.

2-[2-[4-Oxo-3-(*o*-tolyl)quinazolin-2-yl]vinyl]pyridine *see* Piriqualone.

OXOTREMORINE ((1-(2-oxopyrrolidino)-4-pyrrolidino-2-butyne)).

2-Oxo-1,7,7-trimethylbicyclo[2.2.1]heptane *see* Camphor.

4-Oxovaleric acid *see* Levulinic acid.

22-Oxovinblastine *see* Vincristine.

Oxpentifylline* *see* Pentoxifylline.

OXPHENERIDINE*** (ethyl 1-(β-hydroxyphenethyl)-4-phenylpiperidine-4-carboxylate; ethyl 1-(2-hydroxy-2-phenylethyl)-4-phenylisonipecotate).

OXPRENOLOL*** (1-(*o*-allyloxyphenoxy)-3-isopropylaminopropan-2-ol; oxprenolol hydrochloride; Ba-39089; 'coretal'; 'trasicor').

OXPRENOLOL plus CHLORTALIDONE ('trasitensin').

OXPRENOLOL plus CHLORTALIDONE & HYDRALAZINE ('trepress').

OXPRENOLOL plus CYCLOPENTHIAZIDE ('trasidrex').

OXPRENOLOL plus DIHYDRALAZINE ('trasipresol').

'Oxsoralen' *see* Methoxsalen.

'Oxstan' *see* Tin oxide.

Oxtrimethylline* *see* Choline theophyllinate.

Oxtriphylline* *see* Choline theophyllinate.

'Oxucide' *see* Piperazine.

'Oxurasin' *see* Piperazine.

'Oxyamine' *see* Chlormethine *N*-oxide.

OXYBATE SODIUM* (sodium 4-hydroxybutyrate; sodium oxybate; gamma-OH; NSC-84223; Wy-3478; 'fisiogamma'; 'somsanit').

OXYBENZONE*** (2-hydroxy-4-methoxybenzophenone; NSC-7778).

'Oxy-biciron' *see under* Tramazoline.

β,β'-Oxybis(*p*-acetophenetidide) *see* Diamfenetide.

4,4'-Oxybis(2-chloroacetophenone) *see* Clofenoxyde.

1,1'-Oxybisethene *see* Vinyl ether.

Oxybis(*p*-ethoxyacetanilide) *see* Diamfenetide.

3,3'-[Oxybis(ethyleneoxyethylenecarbonylimino)-]bis(2,4,6-triiodobenzoic acid *see* Iotranic acid.

3,3'-[Oxybis(ethyleneoxymethylenecarbonylimino)-]bis(2,4,6-triiodobenzoic acid) *see* Iotroxic acid.

1,1'-[Oxybis(methylene)]bis[4-(hydroxyimino)methyl]pyridinium dichloride *see* Obidoxime chloride.

3,3'-[Oxybis(methylenecarbonylimino)]bis(2,4,6-triiodobenzoic acid) *see* Ioglycamic acid.

[Oxybis(pentamethylene)]bis(trimethylammonium chloride) *see* Oxydipentonium chloride.

Oxybisphenacetin *see* Diamfenetide.

OXYBUPROCAINE*** (2-(diethylamino)ethyl 4-amino-3-butoxybenzoate; benoxinate; oxibuprocaine; 'cebesine'; 'conjuncain'; 'dorsacaine'; 'novesin').

OXYBUTYNIN*** (4-(diethylamino)-2-butynyl α-phenylcyclohexaneglycolate; oxibutynin; oxybutinin chloride; oxybutynin hydrochloride; MJ-4309-1).

'Oxycaine' *see* Hydroxyprocaine.

Oxycarboxin *see* Carboxin dioxide.

'Oxycel' *see* Oxidized cellulose.

Oxycellulose *see* Oxidized cellulose.

Oxychinolin *see* 8-Quinolinol.

Oxychloroquine *see* Hydroxychloroquine.

OXYCHLOROSENE* (complex of hypochlorous acid with phenylsulfonates of aliphatic hydrocarbons; monoxychlorosene; 'chlorpactin').

OXYCINCHOPHEN** (3-hydroxy-2-phenylcinchoninic acid; 3-hydroxycinchophen; HPC).

OXYCLIPINE*** ((±)-1-methylpiperid-3-yl α-phenylcyclohexaneglycolate; (±)-1-methylpiperid-3-yl cyclohexylmandelate; oxiclipine; propenzolate; oxyclipine hydrochloride; JB-840; NDR-263).

OXYCLOZANIDE*** (3,3',5,5',6-pentachloro-2,2'-dihydroxybenzanilide; ICI-46683).

OXYCODONE*** (4,5-epoxy-14-hydroxy-3-methoxy-*N*-methyl-6-oxomorphinan; 14-hydroxydihydrocodeinone; dihydrohydroxycodeinone; laokon; oxiconum; oxycodone pectinate; tecodin; tekodin; thecodine; NSC-19043).

OXYDEMETON-METHYL* (*S*-[2-(ethylsulfinyl)ethyl] *O*,*O*-dimethyl phosphorothioate; demeton-*S*-methylsulfoxide; methyl demeton-*O*-sulfoxide; metaisosystoxsulfoxide; methylisosystox sulfoxide; methylmercaptophos oxide; metilmerkaptofosoksid; 'metaisosystox R'; 'metasystox R').

See also under Metrifonate.

α,α'-Oxydi(3-acetamido-2,4,6-triiodobenzoic acid) *see* Ioglycamic acid.

Oxydiacetic acid *see* Diglycolic acid.

Oxydibenzamidine *see* Phenamidine.

1,1'-Oxydimethylenebis(4-formylpyridinium chloride) dioxime *see* Obidoxime chloride.

Oxydimethylquinazine *see* Phenazone.

Oxydimorphine *see* Pseudomorphine.

OXYDIPENTONIUM CHLORIDE*** (6-oxa-1,11-undecamethylenebis(trimethylammonium chloride); [oxybis(pentamethylene)]bis(trimethylammonium chloride); UCB-5067).

OXYDISULFOTON* (*O,O*-diethyl *S*-[2-(ethylsul-finyl)ethyl] phosphorodithioate; 'disyston-S').

Oxyethyltheophylline *see* Etofylline.

OXYFEDRINE*** ((−)-3-(β-hydroxy-α-methyl-phenethylamino)-3′-methoxypropiophenone; 3-(1-hydroxy-1-phenylisopropylamino)-3′-meth-oxypropiophenone; (−)-oxyfedrine; D-563).

(−)-Oxyfedrine *see* Oxyfedrine.

(±)-OXYFEDRINE ('myofedrin').

OXYFENAMATE*** (β-ethyl-β-hydroxyphen-ethyl carbamate; 2-hydroxy-2-phenylbutyl carb-amate; 2-phenyl-1,2-butanediol 1-carbamate; hydroxyphenamate; oxifenamate; AL-0361; NSC-108034; P-301).

Oxyflavyl *see* Efloxate.

'Oxy-kesso-tetra' *see* Oxytetracycline.

'Oxylan' *see* Diphenan.

'Oxyleine' *see* 8-Quinolinol.

Oxylidine *see* Benzoclidine.

'Oxylone' *see* Fluorometholone.

OXYMESTERONE*** (4,17β-dihydroxy-17-methylandrost-4-en-3-one).

OXYMETAZOLINE*** (6-*tert*-butyl-3-(2-imi-dazolin-2-ylmethyl)-2,4-dimethylphenol; 2-(4-*tert*-butyl-3-hydroxy-2,6-dimethylbenzyl)-2-imi-dazoline; oximetazoline; oxymetazoline hydro-chloride; H-990; Sch-9384).

OXYMETHEBANOL (dihydro-14-hydroxy-6β-thebainol 4-methyl ether; RAM-327).

Oxymethionine *see* Methoxinine.

OXYMETHOLONE*** (17β-hydroxy-2-hydr-oxymethylene-17-methyl-5α-androstan-3-one; HMD; CI-406; NSC-26198).

Oxymethylene *see* Formaldehyde.

OXYMORPHONE*** (7,8-dihydro-14-hydroxy-morphinone; 4,5-epoxy-3,14-dihydroxy-*N*-methyl-6-oxomorphinan; hydroxydihydromor-phinone).

Oxyneurine *see* Betaine.

'Oxypate' *see* Piperazine.

OXYPENDYL*** (4-[3-(10*H*-pyrido[3,2-*b*]-[1,4]benzothiazin-10-yl)propyl]piperazin-1-yleth-anol; oxipendyl).

OXYPERTINE*** (5,6-dimethoxy-2-methyl-3-[2-(4-phenylpiperazin-1-yl)ethyl]indole; oxipertin; WIN-18501-2).

Oxyphenarsine *see* Oxophenarsine.

OXYPHENBUTAZONE*** (4-butyl-1-(*p*-hydr-oxyphenyl)-2-phenyl-3,5-pyrazolidinedione; *p*-hydroxyphenylbutazone; G-27202).

OXYPHENBUTAZONE plus PARACETAMOL ('dolo-tanderil').

OXYPHENBUTAZONE plus PREDNISOLONE ('realin').

OXYPHENBUTAZONE plus PROPETAMIDE ('binartrina').

See also Fenyramidol oxyphenbutazone *and under* Ampicillin.

OXYPHENCYCLIMINE*** (1,4,5,6-tetrahydro-1-methyl-2-pyrimidinemethanol α-phenylcyclo-hexaneglycolate ester; oxyphencyclimine hydro-chloride; SI-1236).

See also under Meprobamate.

Oxyphenhydrazone *see* Carsalam.

OXYPHENISATINE*** (3,3-bis(*p*-hydroxyphen-yl)-2-indolinone; 2,3-bis(*p*-hydroxyphenyl)ox-indole).

Oxyphenisatine acetate* *see* Acetphenolisatin.

Oxyphenisatine dehydrocholate *see* Cofisatin.

'Oxyphenon duplex' *see* Oxyphenonium bromide.

OXYPHENONIUM BROMIDE*** (diethyl(2-hydroxyethyl)methylammonium bromide α-phenylcyclohexaneglycolate; metacin; Ba-5473; C-5473).

See also under Clioquinol.

'Oxyphylline' *see* Etofylline.

Oxypolyethoxydodecane *see* Polidocanol.

Oxyprocaine *see* Hydroxyprocaine.

OXYPROTHEPINE (10,11-dihydro-10-[4-(3-hydroxypropyl)piperazin-1-yl]-8-(methylthio)di-benzo[*b*,*f*]thiepin).

OXYPROTHEPINE DECANOATE (VUFB-9977).

Oxypurinol* *see* Oxipurinol.

OXYPYRRONIUM BROMIDE*** (2-hydroxy-methyl-1,1-dimethylpyrrolidinium bromide α-phenylcyclohexaneglycolate; oxipyrronium; BRL-556; LD-3055).

Oxyquinoline* *see* 8-Quinolinol.

OXYQUINOTHEINE (quinine hydroxycaffeine derivative).

OXYRIDAZINE*** (2-methoxy-10-[2-(1-methyl-piperid-2-yl)ethyl]phenothiazine; KS-33).

OXYSONIUM IODIDE*** ((2-hydroxyethyl)di-methylsulfonium iodide α-phenylcyclohexane-glycolate ester; oxisone).

OXYTETRACYCLINE*** (5-hydroxytetracycl-ine; oxytetracycline hydrochloride; NSC-9169).

OXYTETRACYCLINE plus NYSTATIN ('terras-tain').

See also under Bromhexine; Hydrocortisone; Neomycin; Tramazoline.

OXYTOCIN*** (alphahypophamine; α-hypoph-amine; ocytocin).

OXYTOCIN SYNTHETIC (OTS-68; 'syntoci-non').

See also Argiprestocin; Demoxytocin; Nacartoc-in; Vasotocin; *and under* Methylergometrine.

Oxytriptyline *see* Oxitriptyline.

'Oxyvermin' *see p*-Methyldiphenhydramine.

'Oxyzin' *see* Piperazine.

'Oy' *see* Carbutamide.

OZOLINONE** ((*Z*)-3-methyl-4-oxo-5-piperidi-no-Δ$^{2,\alpha}$-thiazolidineacetic acid; 3-methyl-4-oxo-5-piperid-1-ylthiazolidinylidene-2-acetic acid; Goedecke 3282).

See also Etozolin.

'Ozothine' *see* Turpentine oil oxidation product.

P

P-2-S *see* Pralidoxime mesilate.
P-4 *see* Dipiproverine.
P-7 *see* Lauroguadine.
P-12 *see* Oxacillin.
P-23 *see* Pyricarbate.
P-25 *see* Cloxacillin.
P-26 *see* Aliflurane.
P-50 *see* Ampicillin.
P-71 *see* Lycetamine.
P-113 *see* Saralasin acetate.
P-165 *see* Azaserine.
P-201-1 *see* Caroverine.
P-204 *see* Polyvinylpyridine *N*-oxide.
P-248 *see* Levopropicillin.
P-253 *see* Diphenylpyraline.
P-301 *see* Oxyfenamate.
P-391 *see* Pecazine.
P-463 *see* Fenamole.
P-501 *see* Glucosulfone.
P-607 *see* Chlorpropamide.
P-652 *see* Fomocaine.
P-683 *see* Puromycin.
P-725 *see* Perazine.
P-841 *see* Barbexaclone.
P-845 *see* Phenobarbital-norpseudoephedrine.
P-1003 *see* Guanoxan.
P-1011 *see* Dicloxacillin.
P-1029 *see* Guanoclor.
P-1048 *see* Pecazine sulfoxide.
P-1134 *see* Pinacidil.
P-1306 *see* Glyparamide.
P-1393 *see* Benzthiazide.
P-1496 *see* Zeranol.
P-1560 *see* Taleranol.
P-1742 *see* Fluperolone.
P-1779 *see* Altizide.
P-1888 *see* Isosulfan blue.
P-2105 *see* Epitizide.
P-2525 *see* Polythiazide.
P-2530 *see* Methalthiazide.
P-2647 *see* Benzquinamide.
P-3693A *see* Doxepin.
P-3896 *see* Guanisoquine.
P-4125 *see* Isosulfan blue.
P-4385B *see* Clotixamide.
P-4599 *see* Cidoxepin.
P-4657B *see* Tiotixene.
P-5227 *see* Pinoxepin.
P-7138 *see* Nifurpirinol.
P-9295 *see* Azamethonium bromide.
P-17922 *see* Sulfaphenazole.

P-720549 *see* Isoxepac.
P-762494A *see* Fluradoline.
PA-93 *see* Novobiocin.
PA-94 *see* Cycloserine.
PA-106 *see* Anisomycin.
PA-144 *see* Plicamycin.
PA-248 *see* Propicillin.
PAA-155 *see* Indolmycin.
PAA-701 *see* Bialamicol.
PAA-3854 *see* Clamoxyquine.
'Paarlan' *see* Isopropalin.
PAB *see* *p*-Aminobenzoic acid.
PABA *see* *p*-Aminobenzoic acid.
Pabacidum *see* *p*-Aminobenzoic acid.
'Pabialgin' *see under* Aminophenazone.
PABS *see* Sulfanilamide.
'PAC' *see* Calcium aminosalicylate *and* Parathion.
'Pacatal' *see* Pecazine.
'Pacatol' *see* Pecazine.
'Pacetyn' *see* Ectylurea.
'Pacilan' *see* Calcium carbamoylaspartate.
'Pacinox' *see* Capuride.
'Pacisyn' *see* Nitrazepam.
'Pacitran' *see* Metoserpate.
'Pacitron' *see* Tryptophan.
PACRINOLOL*** ((−)-*p*-[3-[(3,4-dimethoxy-phenethyl)amino]-2-hydroxypropoxy]-β-methyl-cinnamonitrile; (−)-3-[4-[3-[[2-(3,4-dimethoxy-phenyl)ethyl]amino]-2-hydroxypropoxy]phenyl]-3-methylacrylonitrile; crinolol).
PACTAMYCIN (antibiotic from *Str. pactum*; NSC-52947).
'Pacyl' *see* Isoxicam.
'Padan' *see* Cartap.
PADIMATE*** (mixture of pentyl, isopentyl and 2-methylbutyl *p*-(dimethylamino)benzoates; pentyl *p*-dimethylaminobenzoate; 'escalol'; 'es-culol'; 'spectraban').
PADIMATE A* (pentyl *p*-dimethylaminobenzo-ate).
PADIMATE O* (2-ethylhexyl *p*-(dimethylamino)-benzoate).
PADIMATE O plus OXYBENZONE ('solabar').
'Padisal' *see* Thiazinamium metilsulfate.
'Padophene' *see* Phenothiazine.
'Padreatin' *see* Kallidinogenase.
'Padrin' *see* Prifinium bromide.
'Padutin' *see* Kallidinogenase.
Paecillomyces varioti banier var. antibioticus, anti-biotic *see* Pecilocin.
'Paediathrocin' *see* Erythromycin ethylsuccinate.

Paeonol *see* Peonol.
PAFENOLOL*** (($\pm$)-1-[*p*-[2-hydroxy-3-(isopropylamino)propoxy]phenethyl]-3-isopropylurea).
'Pagitane' *see* Cycrimine.
PAH *see* *p*-Aminohippuric acid.
PALA *see* Sparfosic acid.
'Palacos' *see* Polymethyl methacrylate.
'Palaprin' *see* Aloxiprin.
'Palatinol M' *see* Dimethyl phthalate.
'Palerol' *see* Tropenziline bromide.
'Palfium' *see* Dextromoramide.
'Palitrex' *see* Cefalexin.
Pallethrine *see* Allethrin.
'Pallidin' *see* Sulfaperin.
PALMIDROL*** (*N*-(2-hydroxyethyl)palmitamide; 'impulsin').
PALMITAMIDE (hexadecanamide).
PALMITIC ACID (hexadecanoic acid; cetylic acid).
PALMOXIRATE SODIUM* (sodium ($\pm$)-2-tetradecyloxiranecarboxylate dihydrate; sodium ($\pm$)-2-tetradecylglycidate dihydrate; sodium palmoxirate; McN-3802-21-98).
PALMOXIRIC ACID*** (($\pm$)-2-tetradecylglycidic acid; ($\pm$)-2-tetradecyloxiranecarboxylic acid; McN-3802).
See also Methyl palmoxirate; Palmoxirate sodium.
'Palohex' *see* Inositol nicotinate.
'Palosein' *see* Orgotein.
'Paloxin' *see* Aloxiprin.
'Palphium' *see* Dextromoramide.
'Paludrine' *see* Proguanil.
'Palusil' *see* Proguanil.
PAM *see* Melphalan *and* Pralidoxime.
PAM-780 *see* Amopyroquine.
Pamachin *see* Pamaquine.
'Pamacyl' *see* Aminosalicylic acid.
Pamaquin *see* Pamaquine.
PAMAQUINE*** (8-[[4-(diethylamino)-1-methylbutyl]amino]-6-methoxyquinoline salt of 4,4'-methylenebis(3-hydroxy-2-naphthoic acid); pamaquine embonate; pamaquine naphthoate; pamaquine pamoate; gametocidum; pamachin; pamaquin; plasmochin; plasmoquine; plasmoquinum; SN-971).
Pamaquine embonate* *see* Pamaquine.
Pamaquine naphthoate* *see* Pamaquine.
Pamaquine pamoate* *see* Pamaquine.
PAMATOLOL*** (($\pm$)-3-(isopropylamino)-1-[*p*-[2-[(methoxycarbonyl)amino]ethyl]phenoxy]-2-propanol; methyl ($\pm$)-[*p*-[2-hydroxy-3-(isopropylamino)propoxy]phenethyl]carbamate; pamatolol sulfate; H-104/08).
PAMBA *see* *p*-Aminomethylbenzoic acid.
'Pameion' *see* Papaverine.
'Pamelor' *see* Nortriptyline.
'Pamine' *see* Scopolamine methyl bromide.
PAM-MR-807-23A *see* Cycloguanil embonate.
PAM-MR-1165 *see* Acedapsone.
'PAMN' *see* Prampine methonitrate.
Pamoate(s)* *see* Embonate(s).

'Pamocil' *see* Amoxicillin.
'Panabolide' *see under* Ginseng.
'Panacaine' *see* Fomocaine.
'Panacur' *see* Fenbendazole.
'Panadol' *see* Paracetamol.
'Panalba' *see under* Tetracycline.
'Panangin' *see under* Potassium aspartate.
'Panaquine' *see* Pamaquine.
Panax ginseng *see* Ginseng.
Panax quinquefolium root *see* Ginseng.
'Panbesy' *see* Phentermine.
'Pancal' *see* Calcium pantothenate.
'Panclar' *see* Deanol phosphate.
'Pancodone' *see* Oxycodone.
'Pancreabil' *see* Fenocinol.
PANCREATIC DORNASE* (pancreatic desoxyribonuclease; 'dornavac').
PANCRELIPASE* ('accelerase'; 'cotazym'; 'lipancreatin'; 'viokase').
PANCREOZYMIN* (polypeptide hormone from duodenal mucosa; cholecystokinin; 'cecekin').
PANCURONIUM BROMIDE*** (($3\alpha,17\beta$-dihydroxy-5α-androstan-$2\beta,16\beta$-ylene)bis(1-methylpiperidinium bromide) 3,17-diacetate; $2\beta,16\beta$-dipiperid-1-yl-5α-androstane-$3\alpha,17\beta$-diol diacetate dimethobromide; NA-97; Org.NA97).
'Pandiona' *see* Oxycodone.
'Pandryl P' *see* Difeterol.
'Panectyl' *see* Alimemazine.
'Panergon' *see* Papaverine.
'Panets' *see* Paracetamol.
'Pangametin' *see* Pangamic acid.
PANGAMIC ACID (6-(dimethylamino)acetylgluconic acid; 'calgam'; 'pangametin'; 'sopangamine'; 'vitamin B$_{15}$').
'Pangesic' *see under* Paracetamol.
'Panhepin' *see* Heparin potassium.
PANIDAZOLE*** (2-methyl-5-nitro-1-(2-pyrid-4-ylethyl)imidazole; 4-[2-(2-methyl-5-nitroimidazol-1-yl)ethyl]pyridine).
'Panimit' *see* Bupranolol.
'Panimycin' *see* Dibekacin.
'Panitrin' *see* Papaverine nitrate.
'Panjopaque' *see* Iopanoic acid.
'Panklar' *see* Deanol phosphate.
'Panolid' *see* Etybenzatropine.
'Panoral' *see* Cefaclor.
'Panoxyl' *see* Benzoyl peroxide.
'Panparnit' *see* Caramiphen.
'Panpuron' *see* Pipethanate ethobromide.
Pantaphene (tr) *see* Caramiphen.
'Pantelmin' *see* Mebendazole.
PANTETHEINE (2-pantothenylaminoethanethiol; *N*-pantothenylmercaptamine; *Lactobacillus bulgaricus* factor; LBF thiol form).
PANTETHINE (bis[2-(pantothenylamino)ethyl]disulfide; LBF disulfide form).
PANTHENOL*** (2,4-dihydroxy-*N*-(3-hydroxypropyl)-3,3-dimethylbutyramide; pantothenyl alcohol; pantothenylol).
See also Dexpanthenol.
Pantherin *see* Muscimol.
'Panthesine' *see* Leucinocaine.

'Panthoderm' *see* Panthenol.
'Pantocaine' *see* Tetracaine.
Pantocide (tr) *see* Halazone.
'Pantofenicol' *see* Cloramfenicol pantotenate complex.
PANTOIC ACID (2,4-dihydroxy-3,3-dimethylbutyric acid).
  See also Pantolactone; Sodium dipantoylferrate.
PANTOLACTONE (pantoic acid γ-lactone; pantoyl lactone).
'Pantomicina' *see* Erythromycin.
'Pantomycin' *see* Erythromycin ethylsuccinate.
PANTONINE (2-amino-4-hydroxy-3,3-dimethylbutyric acid).
'Pantopaque' *see* Iofendylate.
'Pantosept' *see* Halazone.
'Pantothaxin' *see* Calcium pantothenate.
PANTOTHENIC ACID (*N*-(2,4-dihydroxy-3,3-dimethylbutyryl)-β-alanine; vitamin B₅; chick antidermatitis factor).
  See also Calcium pantothenate; Cloramfenicol pantotenate complex.
Pantothenol* *see* Dexpanthenol.
Pantothenyl alcohol *see* Panthenol.
Pantothenylaminoethanethiol *see* Pantetheine.
Pantothenylmercaptamine *see* Pantetheine.
Pantothenylol *see* Panthenol.
'Pantovernil' *see* Cloramfenicol pantotenate complex.
'Panto-viocin' *see under* Viomycin.
Pantoyl lactone *see* Pantolactone.
PANTOYLTAURINE (2-[(2,4-dihydroxy-3,3-dimethylbutyryl)amino]ethanesulfonic acid; thiopanic acid; NSC-3086).
'Pantrop' *see under* Amitriptyline.
PANURAMINE*** (1-benzoyl-3-[1-(2-naphthylmethyl)piperid-4-yl]urea; *N*-[[[1-(2-naphthylmethyl)piperidin-4-yl]amino]carbonyl]benzamide; panuramine hydrochloride; Wy-26002).
'Panwarfin' *see* Warfarin.
'Panzalone' *see* Pregnenolone succinate.
PAPAIN (enzyme mixture from *Carica papaya*; papayotin; vegetable pepsin).
  See also Chymopapain *and under* Phenylbutazone.
'Papase' *see* Papain.
Papaveretum *see* Opium alkaloids.
PAPAVERINE (1-(3,4-dimethoxybenzyl)-6,7-dimethoxyisoquinoline; 4-(6,7-dimethoxyisoquinolin-1-ylmethyl)pyrocatechol; 6,7-dimethoxy-1-veratrylisoquinoline; NSC-34443).
  See also under Butalamine; Co-dergocrine.
PAPAVERINE ADENYLATE (papaverine monophosadenine; CERM-3209).
PAPAVERINE CROMESILATE (papaverine dihydroxycoumarinylmethanesulfonate; 'permaverine').
PAPAVERINE MANDELATE (papaverine phenylglycolate; 'endoverine').
Papaverine monophosadenine *see* Papaverine adenylate.
PAPAVERINE NITRATE ('panitrin').
Papaverine phenylglycolate *see* Papaverine mandelate.
PAPAVEROLINE*** (1-(3,4-dihydroxybenzyl)-6,7-dihydroxyisoquinoline; 1-(3,4-dihydroxybenzyl)-6,7-isoquinolinediol; 4-(6,7-dihydroxyisoquinolin-1-ylmethyl)pyrocatechol; demethylpapaverine; 'modus').
PAPAVEROLINE MEGLUMINE (papaveroline *N*-methylglucamine compound; 'udieci').
Papayotin *see* Papain.
'Papetherine' *see* Ethaverine.
'Papital' *see* Pecazine.
PARABANIC ACID (imidazolidinetrione; 1,3-oxalylurea).
PARABENS* (*p*-hydroxybenzoic acid esters; 'butex'; 'parasept').
  See also Benzyl paraben; Butyl paraben; Ethyl paraben; Methyl paraben; Phenyl paraben; Propyl paraben.
Parabenzylphenylcarbamate *see* Diphenan.
'Parabis' *see* Dichlorophen.
Parabromdylamine* *see* Brompheniramine.
Paracarbinoxamine *see* Carbinoxamine.
Paracetaldehyde *see* Paraldehyde.
PARACETAMOL*** (4'-hydroxyacetanilide; *p*-acetamidophenol; *N*-acetyl-*p*-aminophenol; acetaminophen; acetomenophen).
PARACETAMOL plus ASCORBIC ACID ('efferalgan').
PARACETAMOL plus DEXTROMETHORPHAN ('neuridal').
PARACETAMOL plus PENTAZOCINE ('fortagesic'; 'pangesic').
PARACETAMOL plus PHENYLBUTAZONE ('parazolidine').
  See also Benorilate; Diacemate *and under* Acecarbromal; Acetylsalicylic acid; Chlormezanone; Dextropropoxyphene; Metoclopramide; Orphenadrine citrate.
Paracetamol diethylglycinate *see* Propacetamol.
Paracetophentidine *see* Phenacetin.
Parachloramine *see* Meclozine.
Parachlorocide *see* DDT.
'Paracodin' *see* Dihydrocodeine.
'Paractol' *see under* Algeldrate.
Paradiazine *see* Pyrazine.
'Paradione' *see* Paramethadione.
'Paradrine' *see* Hydroxyamphetamine.
'Paraflex' *see* Chlorzoxazone.
PARAFLUTIZIDE*** (6-chloro-3-(*p*-fluorobenzyl)-3,4-dihydro-2*H*-1,2,4-benzothiadiazine-7-sulfonamide 1,1-dioxide; LD-3612).
  See also under Spirgetine.
Paraform *see* Paraformaldehyde.
PARAFORMALDEHYDE* (polymerized formaldehyde; paraform; pentamethanal; trioxymethylene).
'Paragone' *see* Methylbenactyzium bromide.
'Parahexyl' *see* Pyrahexyl.
Paralaudin *see* Diacetyldihydromorphine.
PARALDEHYDE (polymerized acetaldehyde; paracetaldehyde).
Paralytic shellfish poison *see* Saxitoxin.
Paramandelic acid *see* Mandelic acid.

'**Paramax**' *see under* Metoclopramide.

Parametazon *see* Paramethasone.

PARAMETHADIONE*** (5-ethyl-3,5-dimethyl-2,4-oxazolidinedione; isoethadione).

PARAMETHASONE*** (6α-fluoro-11β,17,21-trihydroxy-16α-methylpregna-1,4-diene-3,20-dione; 6α-fluoro-16α-methylprednisolone; parametazon; paramezone).

PARAMETHASONE ACETATE* (paramethasone 21-acetate).

Paramezone *see* Paramethasone.

'**Paramidine**' *see* Bucolome.

'**Paramol**' *see* Paracetamol.

PARAMORPHAN (dihydromorphine).

Paramorphine *see* Thebaine.

'**Paramoth**' *see* p-Dichlorobenzene.

PARAMYON (tr) (3,4-diphenylhexamethylenebis-(trimethylammonium iodide)).

'**Paranausine**' *see* Dimenhydrinate.

Paranyline* *see* Renytoline.

PARAOXON (diethyl (p-nitrophenyl) phosphate; fosfakol; phosphacol; E-600; 'eticol'; 'mintacol'; 'miotisal').

PARAPENZOLATE BROMIDE*** (4-hydroxy-1,1-dimethylpiperidinium bromide benzilate; Sch-3444).

'**Paraphos**' *see* Parathion.

PARAPROPAMOL** (4'-hydroxypropionanilide; p-propionamidophenol; 'solvodol').

PARAQUAT* (1,1'-dimethyl-4,4'-bipyridinium dichloride; 1,1'-dimethyl-4,4'-dipyridylium dichloride; methyl viologen; 'dextrone X'; 'gramoxone'; 'orthoparaquat'; 'pathclear'; 'preeglone'; 'weedol').

PARAQUAT METILSULFATE (paraquat bis-(methyl sulfate); 'aerial grammoxone').

PARAROSANILINE (tris(p-aminophenyl)methanol).

PARAROSANILINE EMBONATE*** (bis[tris(p-aminophenyl)methylium] 4,4'-methylenebis(3-hydroxy-2-naphthoate); pararosaniline pamoate; CI-403-A; CN-15573-23A; NSC-107529; PS-1286).

Pararosaniline pamoate* *see* Pararosaniline embonate.

'**Parasan**' *see* Benactyzine.

'**Parasept**' *see* Parabens.

PARASORBIC ACID (5-hydroxy-2-hexenoic acid lactone; δ-hexenolactone; hexenolide; sorbic oil).

Parasoxon (tr) *see* Diethyl 3-methylpyrazol-5-yl phosphate.

'**Parastimal**' *see* Meprochol.

'**Parasympatol**' *see* Oxedrine.

'**Parathesin**' *see* Benzocaine.

Parathiazan *see* Thiomorpholine.

PARATHIAZINE** (10-(2-pyrrolidin-1-ylethyl)-phenothiazine; pyrathiazine; RP 4270).

PARATHIAZINE DIOXIDE (U-5641).

PARATHION* (O,O-diethyl O-(p-nitrophenyl) phosphorothioate; nitrostigmine; parathion ethyl; phosphostigmine; PAC; thiophos-3422; 'T-47').

See also under Malathion.

Parathion ethyl* *see* Parathion.

PARATHION ISOMETHYL (O,S-dimethyl O-(p-nitrophenyl) phosphorothioate; isomethyl parathion; HC-8061).

PARATHION-METHYL* (O,O-dimethyl O-(p-nitrophenyl) phosphorothioate; metafos; metaphos; methyl parathion; Bayer-45515; HC-8056).

'**Parathorm**' *see* Parathyroid hormone.

'**Parathormone**' *see* Parathyroid hormone.

PARATHYROID HORMONE ('parathorm'; 'parathormone').

PARAVALLARINE (20-hydroxy-3β-(methylamino)-5-pregnene-18-carboxylic acid lactone).

PARAVALLARINOL (18,20-dihydroxy-3β-(methylamino)pregn-5-ene; 3β-(methylamino)-pregn-5-ene-18,20-diol).

PARAXANTHINE (1,7-dimethylxanthine; urotheobromine; NSC-400018).

PARAXAZONE*** (4-(carbamoylmethyl)-2,3-dihydro-3-oxo-1,4-benzoxazine; 2,3-dihydro-3-oxo-4H-1,4-benzoxazine-4-acetamide).

'**Paraxin**' *see* Chloramphenicol.

'**Parazine**' *see* Piperazine.

'**Parazolidine**' *see under* Paracetamol.

Parazoxon (tr) *see* Diethyl 3-methylpyrazol-5-yl phosphate.

PARBENDAZOLE*** (methyl 5-butyl-2-benzimidazolecarbamate; SK&F-29044).

PARCONAZOLE*** (cis-1-[[2-(2,4-dichlorophenyl)-4-[(2-propynyloxy)methyl]-1,3-dioxolan-2-yl]methyl]imidazole; parconazole hydrochloride; R-39500).

'**Paredrine**' *see* Hydroxyamphetamine.

PAREGORIC (camphorated opium tincture).

'**Parenabol**' *see* Boldenone undecenoate.

'**Parenogen**' *see* Fibrinogen.

'**Parenzyme**' *see* Trypsin.

'**Parenzymol**' *see* Trypsin.

'**Parephylline**' *see* Etamiphyllin.

PAREPTIDE*** (N-[D-1-[(carbamoylmethyl)-carbamoyl]-3-methylbutyl]-N-methyl-L-2-pyrrolidinecarboxamide; L-prolyl-N-methyl-D-leucylglycinamide; pareptide sulfate; AY-24856).

'**Parest**' *see* Methaqualone.

PARETHOXYCAINE*** (2-(diethylamino)ethyl p-ethoxybenzoate).

'**Parfenac**' *see* Bufexamac.

Parfezin (tr) *see* Profenamine.

'**Parfuran**' *see* Nitrofurantoin.

PARGEVERINE*** (2-(dimethylamino)ethyl diphenyl(2-propynyloxy)acetate; propinox; R-164; 'sertal').

PARGOLOL*** (1-(tert-butylamino)-3-[o-(2-propynyloxy)phenoxy]-2-propanol; Ko-1400).

PARGYLINE*** (N-benzyl-N-methyl-2-propynylamine; N-methyl-N-(2-propynyl)benzylamine; N-methyl-N-propargylbenzylamine; A-19120; MO-911; NSC-43748).

'**Parid**' *see* Piperazine.

PARIDOCAINE*** (1-methylpiperid-4-yl p-butylaminobenzoate).

Parietic acid *see* Rhein.

'Parinase' see Glypinamide.
PARINOL* (α,α-bis(p-chlorophenyl)-3-pyridine-methanol; p-chloro-α-(p-chlorophenyl)-α-pyrid-3-ylbenzyl alcohol; p,p′-dichloro-α-pyrid-3-yl-benzhydrol; EL-241).
'Parisolon' see Prednisolone.
'Paritol' see Sodium polyanhydromannuronic sulfate.
'Parkemed' see Mefenamic acid.
'Parkinane' see Trihexyphenidyl.
'Parkopan' see Trihexyphenidyl.
'Parks-12' see Pridinol.
'Parlodel' see Bromocriptine mesilate.
Parmaceti see Cetaceum.
'Parmacetyl' see Cetaceum.
'Parmetol' see Chlorocresol.
'Parnate' see Tranylcypromine.
'Parnon' see Parinol.
'Parnox' see Nitromethaqualone.
PAROMOMYCIN*** (O-(2,6-diamino-2,6-dide-oxy-β-L-idopyranosyl)-(1→3)-O-(β-D-ribofura-nosyl)-(1→5)-O-[(2-amino-2-deoxy-α-D-gluco-pyranosyl)-(1→4)]-2-deoxystreptamine; amino-sidin; amminosidine; catenulin; estomycin; hydr-oxymycin; C-1488; FI-5853).
'Paroven' see Oxerutins.
PAROXETINE*** ((−)-trans-4-(p-fluorophenyl)-3-[[3,4-(methylenedioxy)phenoxy]methyl]pip-eridine; (−)-trans-5-[[4-(p-fluorophenyl)piperid-3-yl]methoxy]-1,3-benzodioxole; paroxetine hydrochloride; BRL-29060A).
PAROXYPROPIONE*** (4′-hydroxypropio-phenone; p-hydroxypropiophenone; p-propion-ylphenol; proxyfenone; POP; B-360; H-365; NSC-2834).
'Parpanit' see Caramiphen.
'Parpon' see Benactyzine.
PARSALMIDE*** (5-amino-N-butyl-2-prop-2-ynyloxybenzamide; MY-41-6).
'Parsetic' see Procaine.
'Parsidol' see Profenamine.
'Parsotil' see Profenamine.
'Parstelazine' see under Tranylcypromine.
'Parstelin' see under Tranylcypromine.
'Partel' see Dithiazanine iodide.
'Partergin' see Methylergometrine.
'Parterol' see Dihydrotachysterol.
PARTRICIN** (antibiotic from Str. aureofaciens; SPA-S-132).
Partricin methyl ester see Mepartricin.
'Partusisten' see Fenoterol.
PARVAQUONE*** (2-cyclohexyl-3-hydroxy-1,4-naphthoquinone).
'Parvolex' see Acetylcysteine.
'Parzate' see Nabam; Zineb.
'Parzone' see Dihydrocodeine.
PAS see Aminosalicylic acid.
PASA see Aminosalicylic acid.
'Pasaden' see Homofenazine.
'Pasadox' see Benzoyl peroxide.
'Pasalin' see Difenamizole.
Pascain (tr) see Hydroxyprocaine.
'Pascorbic' see under Aminosalicylic acid.

'Pasdrazide' see Aminosalicylic acid hydrazide.
PASINIAZID** (isoniazid 4-aminosalicylate; R-106; RD-328).
'Pasit' see Glyprothiazol.
PASK see Aminosalicylic acid.
'Paskalium' see Potassium 4-aminosalicylate.
'Paskate' see Potassium 4-aminosalicylate.
'Pasomycin' see Dihydrostreptomycin aminosalic-ylate.
'Paspertin' see Metoclopramide.
Passiflorin see Harman.
PAT see Antimonyl potassium tartrate and Fen-amole.
PATENT BLUE (anhydro-4,4′-bis(diethylamino)-5″-hydroxytriphenylmethanol-2″,4″-disulfonic acid sodium salt; 'alphazurine 2G').
Patent blue V see Isosulfan blue.
'Pathclear' see Paraquat.
'Pathilon' see Tridihexethyl iodide.
'Pathocil' see Dicloxacillin.
'Pathomycin' see Sisomicin.
'Patoron' see Metobromuron.
'Patrovina' see Adiphenine.
PATULIN (4-hydroxy-4H-furo[3,2-c]pyran-2(6H)-one; clavacin; clavatin; claviformin; expansin; mycoin C₃; penicidin).
PAULOMYCIN** (antibiotic from Streptomyces paulus, variant).
'Pavabid' see Papaverine.
'Paveril' see Dimoxyline.
'Paveroid' see Ethaverine.
'Pavolex' see Acetylcysteine.
'Pavulon' see Pancuronium bromide.
PAXAMATE*** (4-biphenylyl methylcarbamate).
'Paxanol' see Deanol tartrate.
'Paxeladine' see Oxeladin.
'Paxipam' see Halazepam.
'Paxistil' see Hydroxyzine embonate.
'Paxital' see Secbutabarbital and Pecazine.
'Payzone' see Nitrovin.
'Pazidet' see Tyloxapol.
PAZOXIDE** (6,7-dichloro-3-(3-cyclopenten-1-yl)-2H-1,2,4-benzothiadiazine 1,1-dioxide; Sch-12149).
PB-89 see Fominoben.
PB-106 see Pipethanate ethobromide.
PC-1 see Fenipentol.
PC-603 see Iproclozide.
PC-904 see Apalcillin.
PC-1421 see Piperacetazine.
PCA see Chloridazon.
PCB see Polychlorinated biphenyl.
PCBS see Fenson.
PCI see Fenson.
PCMX see Chloroxylenol.
PCNB see Quintozene.
PCPBS see Fenson.
PCPCBS see Chlorfenson.
PCT see Polychlorinated terphenyl.
PD-5 see Mevinphos.
PD-93 see Piromidic acid.
PDB see Prifinium bromide.
PDDB see Domiphen bromide.

403

PDLA *see* Foscolic acid.

PDS *see* Polydioxanone.

PDX *see* Polidexide sulfate.

PEBC *see* Pebulate.

PEBULATE* (*S*-propyl butylethylcarbamothioate; PEBC; 'tillam').

PECAZINE** (10-(1-methylpiperid-3-ylmethyl)-phenothiazine; mepasin; mepazine; pecazine acetate; pecazine hydrochloride; P-391; W-1224).

PECAZINE SULFOXIDE (P-1048).

PECILOCIN** (1-[(2*E*,4*E*,6*Z*,8*R*)-8-hydroxy-6-methyldodeca-2,4,6-trienoyl]-2-pyrrolidone; antibiotic from *Paecillomyces varioti banier* var. *antibioticus*).

PECOCYCLINE** (*N*-(tetracyclinylmethyl)nipecotic acid).

'Pectamol' *see* Oxeladin.

'Pectan' *see* 8-Quinolinol sulfate.

Pectin polysulfate *see* Mepesulfate.

'Pectobloc' *see* Pindolol.

'Pedaform' *see* Formaldehyde.

'Pedameth' *see* Methionine.

PEDG *see* Phenformin.

'Pediamycin' *see* Erythromycin ethylsuccinate.

'Pediathrocin' *see* Erythromycin ethylsuccinate.

'Pedilaxin' *see* Acetphenolisatin.

Pedinex *see* Dinex.

'Pedyol' *see* Cetylpyridinium o-thymotate.

PEFLOXACIN** (1-ethyl-6-fluoro-1,4-dihydro-7-(4-methylpiperazin-1-yl)-4-oxo-3-quinoline-carboxylic acid; perfloxacin; RB-1589).

PEG *see* Macrogol(s).

'Peganone' *see* Ethotoin.

PEGLICOL 5 OLEATE* (mixture of partial mixed esters of glycerol and polyethylene glycols of mol. wt. 200-400, with average number of ethylene glycol units = 5; glycerides oleiques polyoxyethylenes; 'labrafil M-1944CS').

PEGOTERATE** (condensation polymer between terephthalic acid and ethylene glycol; poly(oxy-1,2-ethanediyloxycarbonyl-1,4-phenylenecarbonyl); poly(oxyethyleneoxyterephthaloyl); terephthalic acid ethylene glycol polymer; 'aviester').

PEGOXOL 7 STEARATE* (mixture of mono- and distearic esters of ethylene glycol and of polyoxyethylene glycol (average mol. wt. 450) with average number of ethylene glycol units = 7; 'tefose 63').

'Pehanorm' *see* Trometamol.

Pelargidanon *see* Naringenin.

Pelargonic acid *see* Nonanoic acid.

Pelentan *see* Ethyl biscoumacetate.

PELIOMYCIN** (antibiotic from *Str. luteogriseus*; NSC-76455-D).

PELLETIERINE (1-piperid-2-yl-2-propanone; 2-acetonylpiperidine; isopelletierine; pelletierine tannate; punicine).

'Pellidol' *see* Diacetazotol.

'Pelpica' *see* Promethazine.

PELS *see* Erythromycin estolate.

β-PELTATIN (5,6,7,8-tetrahydro-9-hydroxy-7-(hydroxymethyl)-5-(3,4,5-trimethoxyphenyl)-naphtho[2,3-*d*]-1,3-dioxole-6-carboxylic acid γ-lactone; NSC-24819).

PEMERID** (4-[3-(dimethylamino)propoxy]-1,2,2,6,6-pentamethylpiperidine; W-2394A).

PEMOLINE** (2-amino-5-phenyl-2-oxazolin-4-one; 2-imino-5-phenyl-4-oxazolidinone; phenylisohydantoin; azoxodone; fenoxazol; phenoxazole; LA-956; NSC-25159; PW/135).

PEMOLINE plus MAGNESIUM HYDROXIDE (magnesium pemoline; A-30400; A-31528; 'cylert').

PEMPIDINE** (1,2,2,6,6-pentamethylpiperidine; pempidine tartrate; pempidine *p*-toluenesulfonate; pempidine tosilate; piriline; M & B-4486; Th-2131).

See also under Hydracarbazine.

'Penadur' *see* Benzathine penicillin.

'Penagen' *see* Penicillin V.

PENAMECILLIN** (acetoxymethyl ester of penicillin G; acetate ester of hydroxymethyl ester of benzylpenicillin; acetoxymethyl 6-phenylacetamidopenicillanate; Wy-20788).

'Penamox' *see* Amoxicillin.

'Penbristol' *see* Ampicillin.

'Penbritin' *see* Ampicillin.

'Penbrock' *see* Ampicillin.

Penbutalol *see* Penbutolol.

PENBUTOLOL** ((−)-1-*tert*-butylamino-3-(*o*-cyclopentylphenoxy)-2-propanol; penbutalol; penbutolol sulfate; HOE-893D; HOE-39-893d; 'betapressin').

PENDECAMAINE** ((carboxymethyl)dimethyl(3-palmitamidopropyl)ammonium hydroxide inner salt; *N*,*N*-dimethyl(3-palmitamidopropyl)-aminoacetic acid; 'tego-betaine').

Pendepon *see* Benzathine penicillin.

'Pendex' *see* Penicillin G.

'Pen-di-ben' *see* Benzathine penicillin.

PENDIMETHALIN (*N*-(1-ethylpropyl)-3,4-dimethyl-2,6-dinitroaniline).

'Pendine' *see* Pentolonium tartrate.

'Pendiomid' *see* Azamethonium bromide.

'Penditan' *see* Benzathine penicillin.

'Penduran' *see* Benzathine penicillin.

'Penemve' *see* Pheneticillin.

'Penetek' *see* Pentaerythritol.

PENETHAMATE HYDRIODIDE* (2-diethylaminoethyl ester hydriodide of penicillin G).

'Penetracyne' *see* Penimepicycline.

'Penetradol' *see* Phenylbutazone.

'Penfene' *see* Campheclor.

PENFLURIDOL** (1-[4,4-bis(*p*-fluorophenyl)-butyl]-4-(4-chloro-α,α,α-trifluoro-*m*-tolyl)-4-piperidinol; 4-(4-chloro-α,α,α-trifluoro-*m*-tolyl)-1-[4,4-bis(*p*-fluorophenyl)butyl]-4-piperidinol; McN-JR-16341; R-16341; 'longoperidol'; 'semap').

PENFLUTIZIDE** (3,4-dihydro-3-pentyl-6-(trifluoromethyl)-2*H*-1,2,4-benzothiadiazine-7-sulfonamide 1,1-dioxide).

PENGITOXIN** (pentaacetylgitoxin).

'Penglobe' *see* Bacampicillin.

404

Penicidin *see* Patulin.
PENICILLAMINE* (3,3-dimethylcysteine; D-3-mercaptovaline; D-(−)-penicillamine; MO-BAY 950).
PENICILLANIC ACID (3,3-dimethyl-7-oxo-4-thia-1-azabicyclo[3.2.0]heptane-2-carboxylic acid).
Penicillanic acid 4,4-dioxide *see* Sulbactam.
Penicillanoyloxymethyl 6-[(D-2-phenylglycyl)-amino]penicillanate S,S-dioxide *see* Sultamicillin.
Penicillin 152 *see* Pheneticillin.
PENICILLINASE* (enzyme obtained by fermentation from cultures of *Bac. cereus*; β-lactamase).
Penicillin B *see* Pheneticillin.
Penicillin benzatin* *see* Benzathine penicillin.
PENICILLIN F (2-pentenylpenicillin; amylpenicillin; gigantic acid; penicillin I).
PENICILLIN G (6-phenylacetamidopenicillanic acid; benzylpenicillin; specilline; NSC-402815). *See also* Oleandopen; Penethamate; *and under* Benethamine; Benzathine; Benzhydrylamine; Clemizole; Ephenamine; Hydrabamine penicillin; Hydroxyprocaine; Kanamycin; Procaine.
Penicillin G acetoxymethyl ester *see* Penamecillin.
PENICILLIN G, PURIFIED (BRL-3000; 'purapen G').
Penicillin I *see* Penicillin F.
PENICILLIN K (heptylpenicillin).
Penicillin MV *see* Pheneticillin.
Penicillin N *see* Adicillin.
Penicillin O *see* Almecillin.
Penicillin P-12 *see* Oxacillin.
Penicillinphenyrazine* *see* Phenyracillin.
Penicillin-procaine *see* Procaine-penicillin.
PENICILLIN S (γ-chlorocrotylmercaptomethylpenicillin).
PENICILLIN T (*p*-aminobenzylpenicillin).
PENICILLIN V (6-(2-phenoxyacetamido)penicillanic acid; phenomycillin; phenoxymethylpenicillin; fenoxypen).
Penicillin V pipacycline salt *see* Penimepicycline.
PENICILLIN X (*p*-hydroxybenzylpenicillin).
Penicillin X-1497 *see* Meticillin.
2-(Penicillin-6-ylaminomethyl)tetracycline *see* Penimocycline.
Penicinate *see* Hetacillin.
'Penicline' *see* Ampicillin.
'Penidryl' *see* Benzhydrylamine penicillinate.
'Penidural' *see* Benzathine penicillin.
'Penidure' *see* Benzathine penicillin.
PENIMEPICYCLINE* (phenoxymethylpenicillinate of [4-(2-hydroxyethyl)piperazin-1-ylmethyl]tetracycline; penicillin V pipacycline salt; pipacycline phenoxymethylpenicillinate).
PENIMOCYCLINE* (2-(penicillin-6-ylaminomethyl)tetracycline; 6-(tetracyclin-2-ylmethylamino)penicillin G; 'intraxium').
PENIROLOL* (*o*-[2-hydroxy-3-(*tert*-pentylamino)propoxy]benzonitrile; 1-(2-cyanophenoxy)-3-(*tert*-pentylamino)-2-propanol).
'Penistaph' *see* Meticillin.
'Penitardon' *see* Buphenine.

PENMESTEROL* (3-cyclopentyloxy-17-methylandrosta-3,5-dien-17β-ol; 17-methylandrosta-3,5-diene-3,17β-diol 3-cyclopentyl ether; RP-12222).
PENOCTONIUM BROMIDE* (diethyl(2-hydroxyethyl)octylammonium bromide dicyclopentylacetate; (2-dicyclopentylacetoxyethyl)diethyloctylammonium bromide; Ug-767).
'Pen-oral' *see* Penicillin V.
'Penorsin' *see* Ampicillin.
'Penplenum' *see* Hetacillin.
PENPROSTENE* ((±)-(Z)-7-[(1R*,2R*)-2-[(E)-3R*-5-ethoxy-3-hydroxy-4,4-dimethyl-1-pentenyl]-5-oxo-3-cyclopenten-1-yl]-5-heptenoic acid).
'Pensanate' *see* Pipethanate.
'Penspek' *see* Fenbenicillin.
'Penstabil' *see* Ampicillin.
'Penstapho' *see* Oxacillin.
'Penstapho N' *see* Cloxacillin.
'Pensyn' *see* Ampicillin.
Pentaacetylgitoxin *see* Pengitoxin.
PENTABAMATE* (3-methyl-2,4-pentanediol dicarbamate).
'Pentac' *see* Dienochlor.
Pentacemin* *see* Pentetic acid.
Pentachlorin *see* DDT.
3,3′,5,5′,6-Pentachloro-2,2′-dihydroxybenzanilide *see* Oxyclozanide.
Pentachloronitrobenzene *see* Quintozene.
Pentacine (tr) *see* Calcium trisodium pentetate.
Pentacosactride* *see* Norleusactide.
PENTACYNIUM CHLORIDE* (*N*-(5-cyano-5,5-diphenylpentyl)-*N,N,N*′-trimethylethyl-1-ammonium-2-morpholinium chloride; 4-[2-[(5-cyano-5,5-diphenylpentyl)methylamino]ethyl]-4lmethylmorpholinium chloride methochloride; BW-139C55).
PENTAERYTHRITOL (2,2-bis(hydroxymethyl)-1,3-propanediol; tetrahydroxyneopentane; tetramethylolmethane). *See also* Feneritrol; Niceritrol; Pentaerythrityl tetranitrate; Pentrinitrol; Petrichloral.
Pentaerythritol tetranitrate *see* Pentaerythrityl tetranitrate.
Pentaerythrityl tetranicotinate *see* Niceritrol.
PENTAERYTHRITYL TETRANITRATE (pentanitrol; erinit; nitropentaerythrite; nitropenton; pentaerythritol tetranitrate; penthrit; PETN). *See also under* Butidrine.
Pentaerythrityl trinitrate *see* Pentrinitrol.
'Pentafen' *see* Caramiphen.
PENTAFLURANOL* ((1R,2S)-3,3′-difluoro-4,4′-[1-methyl-2-(2,2,2-trifluoroethyl)ethylene]-diphenol; 4,4′-[(1R,2S)-1-methyl-2-(2,2,2-trifluoroethyl)ethylene]bis(2-fluorophenol); 1,1,1-trifluoro-3,4-bis(3-fluoro-4-hydroxyphenyl)pentane; BX-430).
Pentaformylgitoxin *see* Gitoformate.
PENTAGASTRIN* (*N-tert*-butyloxycarbonyl-β-alanyl-L-tryptophyl-L-methionyl-L-aspartyl-L-phenylalanine amide; gastrin-like pentapep-

tide; AY-6608; ICI-50123).

PENTAGESTRONE*** (3-(cyclopentyloxy)-17-hydroxypregna-3,5-dien-20-one; 3,17-dihydroxy-pregna-3,5-dien-20-one-3-cyclopentyl ether).

PENTAGESTRONE ACETATE* (pentagestrone 17-acetate).

'Pentagin' see Pentazocine.

'Pentagit' see Pengitoxin.

3,3′,4′,5,7-Pentahydroxyflavan see Cianidanol.

3,3′,4′,5,7-Pentahydroxyflavanone see Taxifolin.

2′,3,4′,5,7-Pentahydroxyflavone see Morin.

3,3′,4′,5,7-Pentahydroxyflavone see Quercetin.

Pentahydroxyhexanoic acid see Gluconic acid.

5,6,21,23,25-Pentahydroxy-27-methoxy-2,4,11,16,20,22,24,26-octamethyl-2,7-(epoxypent-deca[1,11,13]trienimino)benzofuro[4,5-e]pyr-ido[1,2-a]benzimidazole-1,15(2H)-dione 25 acet-ate see Rifaximin.

2,2,4,4,6-Pentakis(1-aziridinyl)-2,2,4,4,6,8-hexa-hydro-6-morpholino-1,3,5,2,4,6,-triazatriphos-phorine see Fotretamine.

3,3′,4′,5,7-Pentakis(benzyloxy)flavone see Benz-quercin.

Pentakis(N-sulfomethyl)polymyxin B see Sulfomyx-in.

PENTALAMIDE*** (o-pentyloxybenzamide; O-pentylsalicylamide; salicylamide pentyl ether).

Pentamethanal see Paraformaldehyde.

Pentamethazene see Azamethonium bromide.

Pentamethazol see Pentetrazole.

PENTAMETHONIUM BROMIDE*** (penta-methylenebis(trimethylammonium bromide); C 5).

4′,5,6,7,8-Pentamethoxyflavone see Tangeretin.

Pentamethylenebis(1-methylpyrrolidinium bitar-trate) see Pentolonium tartrate.

Pentamethylenebis(trimethylammonium bromide) see Pentamethonium bromide.

Pentamethylenediamine see Cadaverine.

Pentamethylenedioxydibenzamidine see Pentamid-ine.

β,β-Pentamethylene-γ-hydroxybutyric acid see Hexacyclonic acid.

Pentamethylene-1,5-tetrazole see Pentetrazole.

N,N,2,3,3-Pentamethyl-2-norbornanamine see Di-mecamine.

Pentamethylpiperidine see Pempidine.

PENTAMIDINE*** (4,4-pentamethylenedioxydi-benzamidine; pentamidine di(ethanol-2-sulfon-ate); pentamidine diisethionate; pentamidine isetionate; M&B-800; RP-2512).

Pentamine (tr) see Azamethonium bromide.

PENTAMOXANE*** (2-isopentylaminomethyl-1,4-benzodioxan).

Pentamustine* see Neptamustine.

1-Pentanecarboxylic acid see Hexanoic acid.

Pentanedial see Glutaral.

1,5-Pentanediamine see Cadaverine.

1,5-Pentanedicarboxylic acid see Pimelic acid.

Pentanedioic acid see Glutaric acid.

2,4-Pentanedione see Acetylacetone.

Pentanitrol* see Pentaerythrityl tetranitrate.

PENTANOCHLOR* (3′-chloro-2,4′-dimethylva-leranilide; N-(3-chloro-4-methylphenyl)-2-meth-ylpentanamide; N-(3-chloro-4-methylphenyl)-2-methylvaleramide; 'solan').

Pentanoic acid see Valeric acid.

2-PENTANOL (methyl propyl carbinol).

Pentaphene see Caramiphen.

PENTAPIPERIDE*** (1-methylpiperid-4-yl 3-methyl-2-phenylvalerate; C-4675).

Pentapiperide methylsulfate* see Pentapiperium metilsulfate.

Pentapiperium methylsulfate* see Pentapiperium metilsulfate.

PENTAPIPERIUM METILSULFATE*** (4-hydroxy-1,1-dimethylpiperidinium methylsulfate 3-methyl-2-phenylvalerate ester; pentapiperide methylsulfate; pentapiperium methylsulfate; AY-5810; 'crillin'; 'crylene'; 'perium'; 'quilene').

Pentapyrrolidinium see Pentolonium tartrate.

PENTAQUINE*** (8-[5-(isopropylamino)pentyl-amino]-6-methoxyquinoline; SN-13276).

'Pentastib' see p-Aminobenzenestibonic acid.

PENTAZOCINE*** (1,2,3,4,5,6-hexahydro-6,11-dimethyl-3-(3-methyl-2-butenyl)-2,6-methano-3-benzazocin-8-ol; 2′-hydroxy-5,9-dimethyl-2-(3-methyl-2-butenyl)-6,7-benzomorphan; pentazo-cine hydrochloride; NSC-107430; WIN-20228). See also under Paracetamol.

Pentazol(e) see Pentetrazole.

Pentedrine see Oxedrine.

'Pentek' see Pentaerythritol.

2-Pentenylpenicillin see Penicillin F.

Pentetate calcium trisodium* see Calcium trisodi-um pentetate.

PENTETATE INDIUM DISODIUM In 111* (disodium [N,N-bis[2-[bis(carboxymethyl)-amino]ethyl]glycinato(5−)]indate(2−)-¹¹¹In; in-dium disodium pentetate).

PENTETATE INDIUM TRISODIUM In 111* (trisodium [N,N-bis[2-[bis(carboxymethyl)-amino]ethyl]glycinato(5−)]indate(3−)-¹¹¹In; in-dium trisodium pentetate).

PENTETIC ACID* (N,N-bis[2-[bis(carboxymeth-yl)amino]ethyl]glycine; carboxymethyliminobis-(ethylenenitrilodiacetic acid); diethylenetriam-inepentaacetic acid; pentacemin; DTPA; pentha-nil). See also Pentetate (etc.).

PENTETRAZOLE*** (6,7,8,9-tetrahydro-5H-tetrazoloazepine; pentamethylene-1,5-tetrazole; tetrazolo[1,5]perhydroazepine; tetrahydroazepo-tetrazole; corazol; leptazol; pentamethazol; pent-azol(e); pentylenetetrazole).

'Penthamil' see Calcium trisodium pentetate.

Penthanil see Pentetic acid.

PENTHIENATE* (2-diethylaminoethyl ester methobromide of α-cyclopentyl-2-thiophenegly-colic acid; WIN-4369; 'monodral').

Penthiobarbital* see Thiopental sodium.

'Penthrane' see Methoxyflurane.

PENTHRICHLORAL*** ((5,5-bis(hydroxymeth-yl)-2-(trichloromethyl)-1,3-dioxane; 5,5-di-(hydroxymethyl)-2-(trichloromethyl)-1,3-diox-ane; 2-(trichloromethyl)-1,3-dioxane-5,5-dimethanol).

Penthrit *see* Pentaerythrityl tetranitrate.

Penticidum *see* DDT.

'Penticort' *see* Amcinonide.

PENTIFYLLINE** (1-hexyl-3,7-dimethylxanthine; 1-hexyltheobromine; SK-7).

PENTIFYLLINE plus NICOTINIC ACID ('cosaldon').

'Pentilium' *see* Pentolonium tartrate.

PENTISOMICIN*** (*O*-3-deoxy-4-*C*-methyl-3-(methylamino)-β-L-arabinopyranosyl-(1→1)-*O*-[2,6-diamino-2,3,4,6-tetradeoxy-α-D-glycerohex-4-enopyranosyl-(1→3)]-4,6-diamino-4,5,6-trideoxy-D-myo-inositol; Sch-22591).

PENTIZIDONE*** ((*R*)-4-[(1-methyl-3-oxo-1-butenyl)amino]isoxazolidin-3-one; pentizidone sodium).

PENTOBARBITAL*** (5-ethyl-5-(1-methylbutyl)barbituric acid; ethaminal; mebubarbital; mebumal; pentobarbital calcium; pentobarbital sodium; pentobarbital soluble).

'Pentofuryl' *see* Nifuroxazide.

Pentolinium* *see* Pentolonium tartrate.

PENTOLONIUM TARTRATE*** (1,1'-pentamethylenebis(1-methylpyrrolidinium bitartrate); pentolinium; pyrroplegium; pentapyrrolidinium; pentolonium hydrogen tartrate; M & B-2050-A).

PENTOMONE*** (6,6aα,12,12aα,13aα,14-hexahydro-4,8-dimethoxy-6,6-dimethyl-5a*αH*,13*H*-[1]benzopyrano[3,2-*b*]xanthen-13-one; compound 113935).

PENTOREX*** (α,α,β-trimethylphenethylamine; pentorex tartrate; RD-354).

PENTOSALEN* (9-(3-methyl-2-butenyloxy)-7*H*-furo-[3,2-*g*][1]benzopyran-7-one; isoamylenoxypsoralen; ammidin; imperatorin).

PENTOSAN POLYSULFATE (pentosan polysulfate sodium; CB-8016; PZ-68; SP-54; 'fibrase'; 'tavan').
See also under Nicotinic acid; Xantinol nicotinate.

'Pentostam' *see* Sodium stibogluconate.

PENTOSTATIN*** ((*R*)-3-(2-deoxy-β-D-*erythro*-pentofuranosyl)-3,6,7,8-tetrahydroimidazo[4,5-*d*][1,3]diazepin-8-ol; 2'-deoxycoformycin; CI-825; DCF).

'Pentothal' *see* Thiopental sodium.

Pentothiobarbital *see* Thiopental sodium.

'Pentovis' *see* Quinestradol.

PENTOXIFYLLINE*** (3,7-dimethyl-1-(5-oxohexyl)xanthine; 1-(5-oxohexyl)theobromine; oxpentifylline; BL-191; 'elorgan'; 'torental'; 'trental').

Pentoxil (tr) *see* Pentoxyl.

PENTOXYL (tr) (5-(hydroxymethyl)-6-methyluracil; pentoxil).

PENTOXYVERINE*** (2-[2-(diethylamino)ethoxy]ethyl 1-phenylcyclopentanecarboxylate; carbetapentane; pentoxyverine citrate; UCB-2543).

'Pentrane' *see* Methoxyflurane.

'Pentrexyl' *see* Ampicillin.

PENTRINITROL** (pentaerythrityl trinitrate; W-2197).

'Pentritol' *see* Pentaerythrityl tetranitrate.

'Pentrofane' *see* Desipramine.

2-(Pentylamino)acetamide *see* Milacemide.

Pentyl carbamate *see* Hedonal.

6-Pentyl-*m*-cresol *see* Amylmetacresol.

Pentyl *p*-dimethylaminobenzoate *see* Padimate.

Pentylenetetrazole *see* Pentetrazole.

***o*-Pentyloxybenzamide** *see* Pentalamide.

Pentyl phenyl ketone *see* Hexanophenone.

2-Pentyl-6-phenyl-1*H*-pyrazolo[1,2-*a*]cinnoline-1,3(2*H*)-dione *see* Cinnopentazone.

***O*-Pentylsalicylamide** *see* Pentalamide.

Pentymal* *see* Amobarbital.

PEONOL (2'-hydroxy-4'-methoxyacetophenone; resacetophenone 4-methyl ether; paeonol).

PEPLOMYCIN*** (*N*¹-[3-[(α-methylbenzyl)-amino]propyl]bleomycinamide; peplomycin sulfate; NK-631).

Peppermint camphor *see* Menthol.

PEPSTATIN*** (isovaleryl-L-valyl-L-valyl-4-amino-3-hydroxy-6-methylheptanoyl-L-alanyl-4-amino-3-hydroxy-6-methylheptanoic acid).

'Peptavlon' *see* Pentagastrin.

PEPTICHEMIO (complex of peptides of L-3-[*m*-[bis(2-chloroethyl)amino]phenyl]alanine with amino acids; metamelfalan peptide complex).

PEPTIDE 67-82 (alanylglycylisoleucinylvalylserine; 'solvosterol').

'Peracon' *see* Isoaminile.

PERADOXIME*** (*m*-anisaldehyde *O*-[2-hydroxy-3-[4-(*o*-methoxyphenyl)piperazin-1-yl]propyl]oxime; 3-methoxybenzaldehyde *O*-[2-hydroxy-3-[4-(2-methoxyphenyl)piperazin-1-yl]propyl]oxime).

PERAFENSINE*** (1-phenyl-3-piperazin-1-yl-isoquinoline).

'Peralga' *see* Barbipyrine.

PERALOPRIDE*** (1-(4-amino-5-chloro-2-methoxybenzoyl)-4-[3,4-(methylenedioxy)benzyl]piperazine; 1-(4-amino-5-chloro-*o*-anisoyl)-4-piperonylpiperazine).

'Perandren' *see* Testosterone isobutyrate.

PERAQUINSIN** (6,7-dimethoxy-2-[2-[4-(*o*-methoxyphenyl)piperazin-1-yl]ethyl]-4(3*H*)-quinazolinone; 1-(6,7-dimethoxy-4(3*H*)-oxoquinazolin-2-yl)-4-(*o*-methoxyphenyl)piperazine).

PERASTINE** (1-[2-(diphenylmethoxy)ethyl]piperidine).

PERATHIEPINE (10,11-dihydro-10-(4-methylpiperazin-1-yl)dibenzo[*b*,*f*]thiepin).

PERATIZOLE*** (1-[4-(2,4-dimethylthiazol-5-yl)butyl]-4-(4-methylthiazol-2-yl)piperazine; EMD-19698).

PERAZINE* (10-[3-(4-methylpiperazin-1-yl)propyl]phenothiazine; P-725; 'taxilan').

'Percarbamid' *see* Urea hydrogen peroxide.

Perchlorethylene *see* Tetrachloroethylene.

Perchlorobenzene *see* Hexachlorobenzene.

Perchloroethane *see* Hexachloroethane.

'Perclene' *see* Tetrachloroethylene.

'Perclusone' *see* Clofezone.

'Percorten' *see* Desoxycortone.

'Percutol' see Glyceryl trinitrate.
'Perdilatal' see Buphenine.
'Perebron' see Oxolamine.
'Perfanazin' see Perphenazine.
'Perfekthion' see Dimethoate.
Perfenazine see Perphenazine.
Perfloxacin* see Pefloxacin.
PERFLUAMINE** (heneicosafluorotripropyl-amine; tris(heptafluoropropyl)amine).
PERFLUAMINE plus PERFLUNAMINE ('fluos-ol DA').
PERFLUNAFENE*** (octadecafluorodecahydro-naphthalene).
Perfluorocyclobutane see Octafluorocyclobutane.
'Pergalen' see Sodium apolate.
PERGOLIDE*** (8β-[(methylthio)methyl]-6-pro-pylergoline).
PERGOLIDE MESILATE (pergolide mesylate; pergolide methanesulfonate; LY-127809).
Pergolide mesylate* see Pergolide mesilate.
'Pergonal' see Human menopausal gonadotrophin.
PERHEXILINE*** (2-(2,2-dicyclohexylethyl)pip-eridine; perhexilene maleate; WSM-3978G; 'pe-xid').
'Perhydrit' see Urea hydrogen peroxide.
Perhydroazepine see Hexamethylenimine.
6-(Perhydroazepin-1-ylmethyleneamino)penicillanic acid see Mecillinam.
Perhydroazocine see Heptamethylenimine.
'Perhydrol' see Hydrogen peroxide.
'Periactin' see Cyproheptadine.
'Periactinol' see Cyproheptadine.
'Pericel' see Flavodic acid sodium salt.
'Perichlor' see Petrichloral.
PERICIAZINE** (2-cyano-10-[3-(4-hydroxypip-erid-1-yl)propyl]phenothiazine; 10-[2-(4-hydr-oxypiperid-1-yl)propyl]phenothiazine-1-carboni-trile; pericyazine; propericiazine; RP 8909; SK&F-20716).
'Periclor' see Petrichloral.
Pericyazine* see Periciazine.
'Pericyt' see Niceritrol.
'Peridamol' see Dipyridamole.
'Perilax' see Bisacodyl.
PERIMETAZINE*** (10-[3-(4-hydroxypiperid-1-yl)-2-methylpropyl]-2-methoxyphenothiazine; 1-[3-(2-methoxyphenothiazin-10-yl)-2-methyl-propyl]-4-piperidinol; AN-1317; RP 9159).
Perimycin see Fungimycin.
'Perin' see Piperazine calcium edetate.
'Peripherin' see under Etofylline.
Periphermium see Diacetazotol.
PERISOXAL** (3-(1-hydroxy-2-piperid-1-yl-ethyl)-5-phenylisoxazole; α-(5-phenylisoxazol-3-yl)-1-piperidineethanol; S-31252).
'Peristim' see Casanthranol.
'Periston' see Povidone.
PERITHIADENE (6,11-dihydro-11-(1-methylpip-erid-4-ylidene)dibenzo[b,e]thiepin; perithiadene hydrochloride).
'Peritol' see Cyproheptadine.
'Peritonan' see Chlorocresol.
'Perium' see Pentapiperium metilsulfate.

'Perivar' see Sparteine.
'Perklone' see Tetrachloroethylene.
PERLAPINE*** (6-(4-methylpiperazin-1-yl)mor-phanthridine; 6-(4-methylpiperazin-1-yl)dibenz-[b,e]azepine; AW-142333; HF-2333; MP-11).
'Perlepsin' see Morsuximide.
'Perlinganit' see Glyceryl trinitrate.
'Perlutex' see Medroxyprogesterone acetate.
'Permapen' see Benzathine penicillin.
'Permasect' see Permethrin.
'Permaverine' see Papaverine cromesilate.
'Permethol' see Metescufylline.
PERMETHRIN** ((±)-cis-trans-(3-phen-oxyphenyl)methyl 3-(2,2-dichlorovinyl)-2,2-di-methylcyclopropane carboxylate; 3-phen-oxybenzyl 3-(2,2-dichlorovinyl)-2,2-dimethyl-cyclopropanecarboxylate; FMC-33297; NRDC-143; OMS-1821; PP-557; S-3151; WL-43479; WL-43497; 'ambush'; 'permasect'; 'pounce'; 'stockade'; 'stomoxin'; 'strong-ciclon').
'Permitil' see Fluphenazine.
'Permonid' see Desomorphine.
'Pernazene' see Tymazoline.
'Perneuron' see Mefexamide.
'Pernocton' see Butallylonal.
'Pernoston' see Butallylonal.
'Perocan' see Isoaminile.
'Peroidin' see Potassium perchlorate.
'Perolysen' see Pempidine.
'Peronine' see Benzylmorphine.
'Peroxinorm' see Orgotein.
'Perparin' see Ethaverine.
'Perphenan' see Perphenazine.
PERPHENAZINE*** (2-chloro-10-[3-[4-(2-hydr-oxyethyl)piperazin-1-yl]propyl]phenothiazine; chlorperphenazine; chlorpiprazine; chlorpiproz-ine; etaperazine; ethaperazine; perfenazine; Sch-3940).
See also under Amitriptyline; Fentonium bro-mide.
PERPHENAZINE ENANTATE (perphenazine enanthate; perphenazine heptanoate; 'decen-tan').
Perphenazine-prednisolone succinate see Prednaz-ate.
'Persantin' see Dipyridamole.
'Persantinal' see under Clofibrate.
'Persedon' see Pyrithyldione.
PERSILIC ACID*** (2,5-dihydroxy-p-benzenedi-sulfonic acid).
'Persistol Hol/193' see Tretamine.
PERSODIUM PHYTATE (myo-inositol hexa-kis(disodium phosphate); phytate persodium).
See also Sodium phytate.
'Perspex' see Polymethyl methacrylate.
Perstoff see Diphosgene.
'Persumbran' see under Dipyridamole.
Pertechnate sodium see Sodium pertechnate Tc 99m.
'Pertestis' see Testosterone cipionate.
'Perthane' see 1,1-Dichloro-2,2-bis(p-ethylphenyl)-ethane.
Perthipendyl see Oxypendyl.
'Pertofran' see Desipramine.

'Pertofrina' *see* Desipramine.
'Pertscan 99m' *see* Sodium pertechnetate Tc 99m.
'Peruol' *see* Benzyl benzoate.
Peruscabin *see* Benzyl benzoate.
PERUSITIN (cannogenic acid L-thevetoside).
PERUVOSIDE (cannogenin L-thevetoside).
'Pervetral' *see* Oxypendyl.
'Pervincamine' *see* Vincamine.
'Pervit' *see* Tetrachloroethylene.
'Pervitin' *see* Methamphetamine.
'Pervium' *see under* Xantinol nicotinate.
'Perycit' *see* Niceritrol.
'Peson' *see* Sodium apolate.
'Pestan' *see* Mecarbam.
'Pestocid' *see* Niclosamide.
'Pestox III' *see* Schradan.
'Pestox XIV' *see* Dimefox.
'Pestox XV' *see* Mipafox.
Pethanol *see* Pethidine.
PETHIDINE*** (ethyl 1-methyl-4-phenylisonipe-cotate; ethyl 1-methyl-4-phenylpiperidine-4-carboxylate; meperidine; isonipecaine; lidol; pethanol; piridosal).
PETHIDINE plus LEVALLORPHAN ('pethilor-fan').
'Pethilorfan' *see under* Pethidine.
'Petidon' *see* Trimethadione.
'Petinutin' *see* Mesuximide.
PETN *see* Pentaerythrityl tetranitrate.
'Petnidan' *see* Ethosuximide.
PETRICHLORAL*** (1,1',1'',1'''-(neopentanetetr-yltetraoxy)tetrakis(2,2,2-trichloroethanol); pentaerythritol-chloral).
PETROSELAIDIC ACID (*trans*-6-octadecenoic acid).
PETROSELINIC ACID (*cis*-6-octadecenoic acid).
'Petylyl' *see* Desipramine.
PEUCEDANIN (5-isopropyl-4-methoxy-7*H*-furo[3,2-*g*][1]benzopyran-7-one; 5-isopropyl-4-methoxyfuro-2,3,6,7-coumarin; peutsedanin).
Peutsedanin (tr) *see* Peucedanin.
'Pevaryl' *see* Econazole.
'Pe-ve-gel' *see* Polyvinyl alcohol.
'Pevisone' *see under* Triamcinolone acetonide.
PEXANTEL*** (1-(cyclohexylcarbonyl)-4-methyl-piperazine; cyclohexyl 4-methylpiperazin-1-yl ketone).
'Pexid' *see* Perhexiline.
'Pezavin' *see* Tetrachloroethylene.
'Pezetamid' *see* Pyrazinamide.
PF-26 *see* Mepramidil.
PFA-186 *see* Meglumine salicylate.
PFT *see* Bentiromide.
PFU *see* Phenformin.
PG.... *see also under* Prostaglandin (etc)..
PG-430 *see* Febuverine.
PG-501 *see* Mazaticol.
PGA *see* Polyglycolic acid.
Ph 60-40 *see* Diflubenzuron.
Ph-218 *see* Edogestrone.
Ph-1503 *see* Hexachlorophene phosphate.
'Phacetoperan* *see* Levofacetoperane.
'Phaldrone' *see* Chloral hydrate.

'Phaltan' *see* Folpet.
Phanchinon* *see* Phanquinone.
'Phanodorn' *see* Cyclobarbital.
PHANQUINONE*** (4,7-phenanthroline-5,6-di-one; 4,7-phenanthroline-5,6-quinone; phanchi-non; phanquone; fankinon; C-11925).
See also under Clioquinol.
Phanquone* *see* Phanquinone.
'Phanurane' *see* Canrenone.
'Pharcetil' *see* Acetylcysteine.
'Pharmaethyl 114' *see* Cryofluorane.
'Pharmodex' *see* Dextran.
'Pharmotal' *see* Thiopental sodium.
Pharnoquinone *see* Farnoquinone.
'Phasal' *see* Lithium carbonate.
Phaseolosaxin *see* Phytohemagglutinin.
Phaseomannitol *see* Inositol.
PHB *see* Cetaben sodium *and* Phenylmercuric bor-ate.
Phebutazine *see* Febuverine.
PHEDRAZINE (2-(3,4,5-trimethoxybenzyl)-2-imi-dazoline).
PHEMERAZOLE (tr) (3-methyl-5-phenylpyraz-ole).
'Phemeride' *see* Benzethonium chloride.
'Phe-mer-nite' *see* Phenylmercuric nitrate.
'Phemerol' *see* Benzethonium chloride.
Phemitone *see* Methylphenobarbital.
Phen.... *see also* Fen.....
PHENACAINE*** (*N*,*N'*-bis(*p*-ethoxyphenyl)-acetamidine; *N*,*N'*-di-*p*-phenethylacetamidine; phenetidylphenacetin; phenacaine hydrochlor-ide).
Phenacal* *see* Phenacemide.
Phenacarbamide *see* Fencarbamide.
PHENACEMIDE*** (1-(2-phenylacetyl)urea; phenacal; phenacetylurea).
PHENACETIN*** (4'-ethoxyacetanilide; *N*-(*p*-ethoxyphenyl)acetamide; *p*-acetophenetidide; *p*-ethoxyacetanilide; acetophenetidin; acetpara-phenalide; paracetophentidine).
See also Phenapyrine.
Phenacetin acetylsalicylate *see* Etersalate.
Phenacetylurea *see* Phenacemide.
'Phenacide' *see* Camphechlor.
Phenacon (tr) *see* Fenaclon.
PHENACRIDAN CHLORIDE* (9-(*p*-hexyloxy-phenyl)-10-methylacridinium chloride; 'acriz-ane').
PHENACTROPINIUM CHLORIDE*** (homa-tropine phenacyl chloride; *N*-phenacylhomatro-pinium chloride).
Phenacyl chloride *see* 2-Chloroacetophenone.
Phenacylhomatropinium chloride *see* Phenactropi-nium chloride.
Phenacyl 4-morpholineacetate *see* Mobecarb.
Phenacyl pivalate *see* Pibecarb.
Phenadon *see* Methadone.
PHENADOXONE*** (6-morpholino-4,4-diphen-yl-3-heptanone; phenodoxone; CB-11; Ho-10600).
PHENAGLYCODOL*** (2-(*p*-chlorophenyl)-3-methyl-2,3-butanediol).

Phenalzine *see* Phenelzine.

PHENAMAZOLINE* (2-anilinomethyl-2-imidazoline; 'otrivine').

PHENAMET (tr) (ethyl ester of *N*-[*p*-[bis(2-chloroethyl)amino]phenylacetyl]methionine; ethyl 2-[*p*-[bis(2-chloroethyl)amino]phenylacetamido]-4-(methylthio)butyrate; fenamet).

PHENAMIDINE (bis(*p*-amidinophenyl)ether; 4,4'-diamidinodiphenyl ether; 4,4'-oxydibenzamidine).

Phenamine (tr) *see* Phenocoll.

Phenamine *see* Amphetamine.

Phenamizole *see* Amiphenazole.

PHENAMPROMIDE* (*N*-[2-(1-methylpiperid-2-yl)ethyl]propionanilide).

PHENANTHRIDINE (benzo[*c*]quinoline).

4,7-Phenanthroline-5,6-dione *see* Phanquinone.

4,7-Phenanthroline-5,6-quinone *see* Phanquinone.

Phenantoin *see* Mephenytoin.

PHENAPHAN (tr) (*N*-acetyl-*p*-[bis(2-chloroethyl)-amino]phenylalanine ethyl ester; ethyl 2-acetamido-3-[*p*-[bis(2-chloroethyl)amino]phenyl]propionate; fenafan).

'Phenaphen' *see* Paracetamol.

PHENARSAZINE CHLORIDE (5-aza-10-arsenaanthracene chloride; 10-chloro-5,10-dihydroarsacridine; diphenylaminechlorarsine; adamsite; phenazarsine; DM).

PHENARSONE SULFOXYLATE (compound of 4-hydroxy-*m*-arsanilic acid with sodium formaldehydesulfoxylate; 3-amino-4-hydroxybenzenearsonic acid *N*-methanal sulfoxylate; 'aldarsone').

Phenasal (tr) *see* Niclosamide.

PHENASTEZIN (tr) (ethyl *p*-[2-[*p*-(bis(2-chloroethyl)amino)phenyl]acetamido]benzoate; fenastezin).

PHENATIN (tr) (*N*-nicotinoylamphetamine; *N*-(2-phenylisopropyl)nicotinamide; fenatin).

'Phenatol' *see* Phenetole.

'Phenatox' *see* Campheclor.

Phenazacillin *see* Hetacillin.

Phenazarsine *see* Phenarsazine chloride.

Phenazidinium *see* Fazadinium bromide.

PHENAZINE (dibenzopyrazine; azophenylene; dibenzoparadiazine).

PHENAZOCINE* (1,2,3,4,5,6-hexahydro-6,11-dimethyl-3-phenethyl-2,6-methano-3-benzazocin-8-ol; 2'-hydroxy-5,9-dimethyl-2-phenethyl-6,7-benzomorphan; phenethylazocine; fenethylazocine; phenazocine hydrochloride; NIH-7519; SK&F-6574).

'Phenazodine' *see* Phenazopyridine.

'Phenazol' *see* Pentetrazole.

Phenazoline *see* Antazoline.

PHENAZONE* (2,3-dimethyl-1-phenyl-3-pyrazolin-5-one; antipyrine; analgesine; azophen; dimethyloxychinizin; oxydimethylquinazine; phenyldimethylpyrazolone).

PHENAZONE MANDELATE ('tussol').

PHENAZONE SALICYLACETATE ('pyrosal').

PHENAZONE SALICYLATE ('capellin'; 'salazolon'; 'saliphenazone'; 'salipyrazolon'; 'salipyr-in').

PHENAZONE SODIUM SULFONATE ('phesin').

PHENAZOPYRIDINE* (2,6-diamino-3-phenylazopyridine; phenazopyridine hydrochloride; NC-150; NSC-1879; W-1655).

Phenbenicillin* *see* Fenbenicillin.

PHENBENZAMINE* (*N*-benzyl-*N'*,*N'*-dimethyl-*N*-phenylethylenediamine; PM-245; RP 2339).

PHENBENZAMINE ETHOBROMIDE ([2-(*N*-benzylanilino)ethyl]ethyldimethylammonium bromide; 'dispasmol').

PHENBUTAZONE SODIUM GLYCERATE* (4-butyl-3-hydroxy-1,2-diphenyl-3-pyrazolin-5-one sodium salt compound (1:1) with glycerol; G-26872).

Phenbutrazate *see* Fenbutrazate.

Phencapton *see* Phenkapton.

Phencarbamide *see* Fencarbamide.

Phencarol (tr) *see* Quifenadine.

Phenchlorphos *see* Fenclofos.

PHENCYCLIDINE* (1-phenyl-1-piperid-1-yl-cyclohexane; 1-(1-phenylcyclohexyl)piperidine; CI-395; CN-2525-3-2; GP-121; NSC-40902).

PHENDIMETRAZINE* ((±)-3,4-dimethyl-2-phenylmorpholine; phendimetrazine tartrate).

PHENDIMETRAZINE EMBONATE (phendimetrazine pamoate; 'fringanor').

Phendioxin *see* Dibenzo-*p*-dioxin.

Phenecyclamine *see* Feclemine.

'Phenegic' *see* Phenothiazine.

PHENELZINE* (β-phenethylhydrazine; 1-(2-phenylethyl)hydrazine; fenizin; phenalzine; W-1544).

Phenemal* *see* Phenobarbital.

(Phenenyltrisoxyethylene)tris(trimethylammonium iodide) *see* Gallamine triethiodide.

'Phenergan' *see* Promethazine.

PHENERIDINE* (ethyl 1-phenethyl-4-phenyl-isonipecotate).

PHENESTER (2-[*p*-[bis(2-chloroethyl)amino]-phenyl]ethyl acetate; NSC-116785).

PHENESTERIN (tr) (chlorphenacyl cholesteryl ester; cholesteryl *p*-[bis(2-chloroethyl)amino]-phenylacetate; fenesterin; phenestrin; NSC-104469).

Phenestrin *see* Phenesterin.

Phenetamine *see* Feclemine.

Phenetazine *see* Fenethazine.

'Phenethamid' *see* 2-Phenylbutyramide.

Phenethanol *see* Phenethyl alcohol.

Phenethanolamine *see* Phenylethanolamine.

Phenethazine *see* Fenethazine.

Phenethicillin* *see* Pheneticillin.

PHENETHYL ALCOHOL* (2-phenylethanol; benzyl carbinol; phenethanol; phenethylol).

PHENETHYLAMINE (2-phenylethylamine; benzeneethanamine).

4-[2-[[6-(Phenethylamino)hexyl]amino]ethyl]pyrocatechol *see* Dopexamine.

2-(Phenethylamino)-4-phenylthiazole *see* Fanetizole.

N-Phenethylanthranilic acid *see* Enfenamic acid.

Phenethylazocine* *see* Phenazocine.
Phenethylbiguanide *see* Phenformin.
Phenethyldiguanide *see* Phenformin.
Phenethylene *see* Styrene.
Phenethylhydrazine *see* Phenelzine.
Phenethylol *see* Phenethyl alcohol.
8-Phenethyl-1-oxa-3,8-diazaspiro[4.5]decan-2-one *see* Fenspiride.
α-(p-Phenethylphenyl)imidazole-1-ethanol *see* Denzimol.
1-Phenethyl-4-phenylisonipecotic acid ethyl ester *see* Pheneridine.
1-Phenethyl-4-(N-phenylpropionamido)isonipecotic acid methyl ester *see* Carfentanil.
Phenethyl(4-phenylthiazol-2-yl)amine *see* Fanetizole.
3-[2-(1-Phenethylpiperid-4-yl)ethyl]indole *see* Indopine.
N-(1-Phenethylpiperid-4-yl)propionanilide *see* Fentanyl.
1-Phenethyl-4-(N-propionylanilino)piperidine *see* Fentanyl.
1-Phenethyl-4-(2-propynyl)-4-piperidinol propionate *see* Propinetidine.
PHENETICILLIN*** (6-(2-phenoxypropionamido)penicillanic acid; (α-methylphenoxymethyl)penicillin; 1-phenoxyethylpenicillin; phenethicillin; penicillin 152; penicillin B; penicillin MV; BL-P152; BRL-152; K-MV).
'Phenetidin' *see* Phenacetin.
p-PHENETIDINE (p-ethoxyaniline).
2-p-Phenetidino-N-propylpropionamide *see* Propetamide.
Phenetidylphenacetin *see* Phenacaine.
PHENETOLE (ethoxybenzene).
Phenetolurea *see* Phenetylurea.
'Phenetsal' *see* Acetaminosalol.
PHENETURIDE*** (1-(2-phenylbutyryl)urea; 1-(α-ethyl-α-phenylacetyl)urea; ethylphenacemide; phenylethylacetylurea; phetylurea; M-551; S-46; 'benuride').
4-(p-Phenetylazo)-m-phenylenediamine *see* Etoxazene.
PHENETYLSUCCINIMIDE (N-(p-ethoxyphenyl)succinimide).
PHENETYLUREA (1-(p-ethoxyphenyl)urea; phenetolurea; 'dulcin'; 'sucrol'; 'valzin').
Phenfluoramine* *see* Fenfluramine.
PHENFORMIN** (phenethylbiguanide; phenethyldiguanide; DBI; PEDG; PFU; W-32).
PHENFORMIN plus TOLBUTAMIDE ('tolbutaphen').
See also under Carbutimide; Glibenclamide.
PHENGLUTARIMIDE*** (2-[2-(diethylamino)ethyl]-2-phenylglutarimide; phenglutarimide hydrochloride).
'Phenhydan' *see* Phenytoin.
Phenic acid *see* Phenol.
PHENICARBAZIDE*** (phenylsemicarbazide).
Phenidiemal* *see* Phetharbital.
PHENIDIUM CHLORIDE (8-amino-6-(p-aminophenyl)-5-methylphenanthridinium chloride).
Phenidylate *see* Methylphenidate.

'Phenigam' *see* 4-Amino-3-phenylbutyric acid.
Phenigama (tr) *see* 4-Amino-3-phenylbutyric acid.
PHENINDAMINE*** (2,3,4,9-tetrahydro-2-methyl-9-phenyl-1H-indeno[2,1-c]pyridine; 1,2,3,4-tetrahydro-2-methyl-9-phenyl-2-azafluorene; 1,2,3,4-tetrahydro-2-methyl-9-phenyl-2-pyridindene; phenindamine tartrate; Nu-1504; PM-254).
'Phenindan' *see* Phenindione.
PHENINDIONE*** (2-phenyl-1,3-indandione; phenyllin; PID).
PHENIODOL SODIUM*** (sodium 3-(4-hydroxy-3,5-diiodophenyl)-2-phenylpropionate; sodium 3,5-diiodo-α-phenylphloretate; iodoalphionic acid sodium salt; bilitrast; feniodol).
'Phenipan' *see under* Broxyquinoline.
PHENIPRAZINE** (α-methylphenethylhydrazine; 1-phenyl-2-hydrazinopropane; phenylisopropylhydrazine; PIH; HM-11; JB-516).
PHENIRAMINE*** (2-[α-[2-(dimethylamino)ethyl]benzyl]pyridine; N,N-dimethyl-3-phenyl-3-pyrid-2-ylpropylamine; histapyridamine; prophenpyridamine; pheniramine maleate; Ho-11513; PM-241).
PHENIRAMINE p-AMINOSALICYLATE (pheniramine 4-aminosalicylate; 'avil'; 'daneral').
PHENISATIN* (3,3-bis(p-acetoxyphenyl)-1-acetyloxindole; triacetyldihydroxydiphenylisatin).
Phenisobromolate *see* Bromopropylate.
PHENISONONE (3',4'-dihydroxy-2-isopropylaminopropiophenone; phenisonone hydrobromide; bronchodilator-1313).
'Phenitol' *see* Phenylmercuric nitrate.
Phenitron *see* Fenitron.
'Phenixin' *see* Carbon tetrachloride.
PHENKAPTON* (S-[(2,5-dichlorophenylthio)methyl] O,O-diethyl phosphorodithioate; phencapton; przedziorkofos).
PHENMEDIPHAM* (3-[(methoxycarbonyl)amino]phenyl m-tolylcarbamate; fenmedifam; SN-38584; 'betanal').
'Phenmerzyl' *see* Phenylmercuric nitrate.
Phenmethylol *see* Benzyl alcohol.
Phenmetralin* *see* Phenmetrazine.
Phenmetramide *see* Fenmetramide.
PHENMETRAZINE*** (3-methyl-2-phenylmorpholine; oxazimedrine; phenmetralin; dexphenmetrazine; A-66).
PHENMETRAZINE TEOCLATE (phenmetrazine theoclate; R-382; 'filon').
PHENMETRAZINE TEOCLATE plus FENBUTRAZATE ('cafilon').
Phenobamate *see* Febarbamate.
PHENOBARBITAL*** (5-ethyl-5-phenylbarbituric acid; phenemal; phenobarbitone; phenobarbitone sodium).
See also under Bromisoval; Diniprofylline; Phenytoin.
PHENOBARBITAL-NORPSEUDOEPHEDRINE (P-845; 'fali-lepsin').
Phenobarbital-propylhexedrine *see* Barbexaclone.
Phenobarbitone* *see* Phenobarbital.

PHENOBENZURON* (1-benzoyl-1-(3,4-dichlorophenyl)-3,3-dimethylurea).

PHENOBUTIODIL* (2-(2,4,6-triiodophenoxy)-butyric acid; Th-4114).

'Phenoclor' see Polychlorinated biphenyl.

PHENOCOLL (N-(aminoacetyl)-p-phenetidine; glycine-p-phenetidine; phenamine).

Phenocoll salicylate see Salocoll.

Phenoctide see Octafonium chloride.

'Phenoctyl' see Propiomazine.

Phenodianisyl* see Guanicaine.

'Phenodin' see Hematin.

Phenododecinium bromide* see Domiphen bromide.

Phenodoxone see Phenadoxone.

PHENOL (carbolic acid; phenic acid).

PHENOLPHTHALEIN* (3,3-bis(p-hydroxyphenyl)phthalide; purgenum).

PHENOLPHTHALOL (o-[bis(p-hydroxyphenyl)methyl]benzyl alcohol; dihydroxyphenylmethenylbenzyl alcohol; 'egmol').

Phenol red see Phenolsulfonphthalein.

Phenol rubrum see Phenolsulfonphthalein.

PHENOLSULFAZOLE (N-thiazol-2-yl-p-phenolsulfonamide; phenosulfazole; 'darvisul'; 'virazene').

2-PHENOLSULFONIC ACID (sozolic acid).

PHENOLSULFONPHTHALEIN* (3,3-bis(p-hydroxyphenyl)-2,1-benzoxathiole 1,1-dioxide; phenol red; phenol rubrum; PSP).

Phenoltetraiodophthalein see Iodophthalein sodium.

Phenomerbor see Phenylmercuric borate.

Phenomitur see Barbexaclone.

PHENOMORPHAN* (3-hydroxy-N-(2-phenylethyl)morphinan).

Phenomycillin* see Penicillin V.

PHENOPERIDINE* (ethyl 1-(3-hydroxy-3-phenylpropyl)-4-phenylpiperidine-4-carboxylate; ethyl 1-(3-hydroxy-3-phenylpropyl)-4-phenylisonipecotate; fenoperidine; R-1406).

'Phenopromin' see Amphetamine.

Phenopropazine see Profenamine.

'Phenopropyl' see Alverine.

Phenopryldiasulfone sodium* see Solasulfone.

'Phenopyrazone' see 1,2-Diphenyl-3,5-pyrazolidinedione.

'Phenosal' see Acetaminosalol.

'Phenosuccin' see Phenetylsuccinimide.

Phenosulfazole see Phenolsulfazole.

PHENOTHIAZINE* (phenthiazine; dibenzoparathiazine; thiodiphenylamine).

(3H)PHENOTHIAZIN-3-ONE (phenothiazone).

Phenothiazinylethylenediamine see Diethazine.

1-(Phenothiazin-10-ylmethylcarbonyl)-4-piperonylpiperazine see Fenoverine.

3-(Phenothiazin-10-ylmethyl)quinuclidine see Mequitazine.

Phenothiazin-10-yl 4-piperonylpiperazin-1-ylmethyl ketone see Fenoverine.

Phenothazone see Phenothiazin-3-one.

'Phenovis' see Phenothiazine.

'Phenoxadrine' see Phenyltoloxamine.

'Phenoxalid' see Aconiazide.

Phenoxan see Fendiline.

Phenoxazole see Pemoline.

'Phenoxene' see Chlorphenoxamine.

'Phenoxethol' see 2-Phenoxyethanol.

'Phenoxetol' see 2-Phenoxyethanol.

'Phenoxin' see Carbon tetrachloride.

'Phenoxine' see Chlorphenoxamine.

6-(2-Phenoxyacetamido)penicillanic acid see Penicillin V.

PHENOXYACETIC ACID (O-phenylglycolic acid).

PHENOXYBENZAMINE* (N-(2-chloroethyl)-N-(1-methyl-2-phenoxyethyl)benzylamine; bensylyt; SK&F-688-A).

3-Phenoxybenzyl 3-(2,2-dichlorovinyl)-2,2-dimethylcyclopropanecarboxylate see Permethrin.

Phenoxybenzylpenicillin see Fenbenicillin.

6-(2-Phenoxybutyramido)penicillanic acid see Propicillin.

6-[2-(Phenoxycarbonyl)-2-phenylacetamido]penicillanic acid see Carfecillin.

2-PHENOXYETHANOL (ethylene glycol monophenyl ether).

2-Phenoxyethyl 1-(3-cyano-3,3-diphenylpropyl)-4-phenylisonipecotate see Fetoxilate.

2-Phenoxyethyl difenoxilate see Fetoxilate.

1-Phenoxyethylpenicillin see Pheneticillin.

1-[1-(2-Phenoxyethyl)piperid-4-yl]benzimidazolin-2-one see Oxiperomide.

(±)-m-Phenoxyhydratropic acid see Fenoprofen.

Phenoxyisopropylnorsuprifen see Isoxsuprine.

m-Phenoxymandelonitrile esters see Cypermethrin; Cypothrin; Deltamethrin; Fenvalerate.

Phenoxymethylpenicillin* see Penicillin V.

4-[3-(4-Phenoxymethylphenyl)propyl]morpholine see Fomocaine.

6-(2-Phenoxy-2-phenylacetamido)penicillanic acid see Fenbenicillin.

2-(3-Phenoxyphenyl)propionic acid see Fenoprofen.

Phenoxypropazine* see Fenoxypropazine.

6-(2-Phenoxypropionamido)penicillanic acid see Pheneticillin.

1-(3-Phenoxypropyl)guanidine see Guanoxyfen.

(1-Phenoxypropyl)penicillin see Propicillin.

(−)-1-Phenoxypropylpenicillin see Levopropicillin.

4-Phenoxy-3-pyrrolidin-1-yl-5-sulfamoylbenzoic acid see Piretanide.

16-Phenoxy-ω-tetranordinoprostone methylsulfonamide see Sulprostone.

16-Phenoxy-17,18,19,20-tetranorprostaglandin E$_2$ methylsulfonamide see Sulprostone.

'Phenphene' see Camphechlor.

Phenpiazine see Quinoxaline.

Phenpiperazole see Zolertine.

PHENPROBAMATE* (3-phenylpropyl carbamate; proformiphen; MH-532).

Phenprocoumarol see Phenprocoumon.

PHENPROCOUMON* (3-(α-ethylbenzyl)-4-hydroxycoumarin; 4-hydroxy-3-(1-phenylpropyl)coumarin; phenprocoumarol; phenylpropylhydroxycoumarin).

Phenpromethadrine* see Phenpromethamine.

412

PHENPROMETHAMINE***(*N*,β-dimethyl-phenethylamine; phenpromethadrine; phenyl-propylmethylamine).

Phenpropamine* *see* Alverine.

PHENSUXIMIDE* (*N*-methyl-2-phenylsuccin-imide; α-phenylsuccinimide; PM-334).

Phentanyl *see* Fentanyl.

PHENTERMINE* (α,α-dimethylphenethyl-amine; 2-benzyl-2-propylamine; β-aminoiso-propylbenzene; (2-amino-2-methylpropyl)benz-ene; 1,1-dimethyl-2-phenylethylamine; β-phenyl-*tert*-butylamine; phentermine hydrochloride; ter-butylamine).

PHENTERMINE RESIN* (complex of phenter-mine with an ion-exchange resin).

Phenthiazine* *see* Phenothiazine.

PHENTHOATE* (*S*-[α-(ethoxycarbonyl)benzyl] *O*,*O*-dimethyl phosphorodithioate; ethyl 2-[(di-methoxyphosphinothioyl)thio]-2-phenylacetate; dimenthenthoate; 'cidial'; 'elsan'; 'tanone').

PHENTHOATE OXON (*S*-[α-(ethoxycarbonyl)-benzyl] *O*,*O*-dimethyl phosphorothioate).

PHENTOLAMINE* (2-[(*N*-(*m*-hydroxyphenyl)-*p*-toluidino)methyl]-2-imidazoline; phentolamine mesilate; phentolamine methanesulfonate; C-7337).

PHENTRIAZOPHOS* (3-[(diethoxyphosphino-thioyl)oxy]-1-phenyl-1*H*-1,2,4-triazole; *O*,*O*-di-ethyl *O*-(1-phenyl-1*H*-1,2,4-triazol-3-yl) phos-phorothioate; 'hostathion').

PHENTYDRONE (tetrahydro-9-fluorenone).

'Phenurin' *see* Nitrofurantoin.

'Phenurone' *see* Phenacemide.

'Phenychol' *see* 1-Phenyl-1-propanol.

Phenygam (tr) *see* 4-Amino-3-phenylbutyric acid.

N-**Phenylacetamide** *see* Acetanilide.

7-Phenylacetamidocephalosporanic acid *see* Cefalo-ram.

6-Phenylacetamidopenicillanic acid *see* Penicillin G.

6-Phenylacetamidopenicillanic acid acetoxymethyl ester *see* Penamecillin.

Phenyl acetylsalicylate *see* Acetylsalol.

1-(2-Phenylacetyl)urea *see* Phenacemide.

Phenylacrylic acid *see* Cinnamic acid.

PHENYLALANINE (2-amino-3-phenylpropionic acid; α-amino-β-phenylpropionic acid; α-amino-hydrocinnamic acid).

Phenylalanine-lysine vasopressin *see* Felypressin.

D-Phenylalanine mustard *see* Medphalan.

DL-Phenylalanine mustard *see* Sarcolysin.

L-Phenylalanine mustard *see* Melphalan.

Phenylallyl alcohol *see* Cinnamyl alcohol.

Phenylamine *see* Aniline.

Phenyl 4-aminosalicylate *see* Fenamisal.

Phenylamyl camphorate *see* Fenipentol camphor-ate.

Phenylarsenoxide *see* Arsenosobenzene.

Phenylazobenzene *see* Azobenzene.

Phenylazo-2-naphthol-6,8-disulfonic acid disodium salt *see* Orange G.

1-Phenylazo-2-naphthol-6-sulfonic acid sodium salt *see* Orange RN.

1-(*p*-Phenylazophenylazo)-2-naphthol *see* Oil scar-let.

4-Phenylazo-*m*-phenylenediamine *see* Chrysoidine.

Phenylazothionoformic acid phenylhydrazide *see* Di-thizone.

N-**Phenylbarbital** *see* Phetharbital.

N-**Phenylbenzamide** *see* Benzanilide.

Phenylbenzene *see* Biphenyl.

2-Phenylbenzimidazole *see* Phenzidole.

2-Phenyl-1,2-benzisoselenazolin-3-one *see* Ebselen.

2-(3-Phenylbenzofuran-7-yl)propionic acid *see* Fu-raprofen.

α-**Phenylbenzylamine** *see* Benzhydrylamine.

8-(*p*-Phenylbenzyl)atropinium bromide *see* Xenytro-pium bromide.

2-Phenylbicyclo[2.2.1]heptane-2-carboxylic acid *see* 2-Phenylnorbornane-2-carboxylic acid.

2-Phenylbutanamide *see* 2-Phenylbutyramide.

2-Phenyl-1,2-butanediol 1-carbamate *see* Oxyfen-amate.

1-Phenyl-1-butanone *see* Butyrophenone.

PHENYLBUTAZONE* (4-butyl-1,2-diphenyl-3,5-pyrazolidinedione; butadion; diphenylbutaz-one; fenbutazona; G-13871).

PHENYLBUTAZONE plus PAPAIN ('penetrad-ol').

PHENYLBUTAZONE plus PREDNISOLONE ('delta-elmedal').

PHENYLBUTAZONE plus PREDNISONE ('del-ta-butazolidine').

See also Benzydamine phenylbutazone enolate; Clofezone; Phenbutazone sodium glycerate; Pro-xifezone; Thiazolinobutazone; *and under* Aminophenazone; Paracetamol.

PHENYLBUTAZONE MEGALLATE (phenyl-butazone 3,4,5-trimethoxybenzoate; phenyl-butazone trimethylgallate; LH-150; 'ditrone'; 'megazone').

Phenylbutazone piperazine *see* Pyrazinobutazone.

Phenylbutazone trimethoxybenzoate *see* Phenyl-butazone megallate.

4-Phenyl-3-buten-2-one *see* Benzylideneacetone.

β-**Phenyl-*tert*-butylamine** *see* Phentermine.

2-PHENYLBUTYRAMIDE (2-ethyl-2-phenyl-acetamide; 2-phenylbutanamide; phenylethyl-acetamide; Th-4128; 'hyposterol'; 'phenetha-mid'; 'redusterol').

2-PHENYLBUTYRIC ACID (2-ethyl-2-phenyl-acetic acid).

See also Butamirate; Butetamate; Cetamifen; Febuverine; Fenbutrazate; Feneritrol; Fenetra-dil.

1-(2-Phenylbutyryl)urea *see* Pheneturide.

Phenylcarbamide *see* Carbanilamide.

4-(Phenylcarbamoyl)butyric acid *see* Glutaranilic acid.

Phenyl carbinol *see* Benzyl alcohol.

'Phenyl cellosolve' *see* 2-Phenoxyethanol.

2-Phenylchroman *see* Flavan.

2-Phenyl-4-chromanone *see* Flavanone.

2-Phenylchromone *see* Flavone.

3-Phenylchromone *see* Isoflavone.

2-Phenylcinchoninic acid *see* Cinchophen.

α-**Phenyl-*o*-cresol** *see* *o*-Benzylphenol.

Phenyl cyanide *see* Benzonitrile.

α-Phenylcyclohexaneacetic acid diethylaminoethyl ester *see* Drofenine.

α-PHENYLCYCLOHEXANEGLYCOLIC ACID (cyclohexylmandelic acid).
See also Ibuverine; Oxybutynin; Oxyclipine; Oxyphencyclimine; Oxyphenonium bromide; Oxypyrronium bromide.

trans-4-Phenylcyclohexylamine 2-(*p*-biphenylyl)butyrate *see* Butixirate.

1-(1-Phenylcyclohexyl)piperidine *see* Phencyclidine.

1-(1-Phenylcyclohexyl)pyrrolidine *see* Rolicyclidine.

1-Phenylcyclopentanecarboxylic acid esters *see* Caramiphen; Minepentate; Pentoxyverine; Tropentane.

2-Phenylcyclopentylamine *see* Cypenamine.

trans-2-Phenylcyclopropylamine *see* Tranylcypromine.

Phenyldiallylacetic acid *see* 2-Allyl-2-phenyl-4-pentenoic acid.

Phenyl 5,6-dichloro-2-(trifluoromethyl)-1*H*-benzimidazole-1-carboxylate *see* Fenazaflor.

3-Phenyl-3,4-dihydroquinazoline *see* Orexin.

Phenyldimethylpyrazolone *see* Phenazone.

N^4-(3-Phenyl-1,3-disulfopropyl)sulfathiazole disodium salt *see* Noprylsulfamide.

1,1′-*o*-Phenylenebis[3-(ethoxycarbonyl)-2-thiourea] *see* Thiophanate.

p-Phenylene bis(isothiocyanate) *see* Bitoscanate.

1,1-*o*-Phenylenebis[(3-methoxycarbonyl)-2-thiourea] *see* Thiophanate-methyl.

4,4′-(*p*-Phenylene)bis(methyleneamino)di(isoxazolidin-3-one) *see* Terizidone.

N^4,$N^{4'}$-(*p*-Phenylene)bis(methylene)di(cycloserine) *see* Terizidone.

4,4′-[*m*-Phenylenebis(oxyethylene)]bis[hexahydro-1-hydroxy-7-(hydroxymethyl)pyrrolizinium chloride] *see* Diplacin.

Phenylenebis(oxypropylene)bis(ethyldimethylammonium iodide) *see* Dipropamine.

4,4′-*o*-Phenylenebis(3-thioallophanic acid) diethyl ester *see* Thiophanate.

4,4′-*o*-Phenylenebis(3-thioallophanic acid) dimethyl ester *see* Thiophanate-methyl.

α,β-Phenylenebutyrolactone *see* Phthalide.

Phenylene diisothiocyanate *see* Bitoscanate.

N,N'-(*p*-Phenylenedimethylene)bis[2,2-dichloro-N-(2-ethoxyethyl)acetamide] *see* Teclozan.

Phenylenedioxybis[ethylhydroxy(hydroxymethyl)hexahydropyrrolopyrrole] *see* Diplacin.

PHENYLEPHRINE*** ((−)-*m*-hydroxy-α-(methylaminomethyl)benzyl alcohol; metaoxedrine; mesaton; metasynephrine; mezaton; neooxedrine; phenylephrine hydrochloride; *m*-synephrine).

PHENYLEPHRINE plus DIMETINDENE ('vibrocil').

PHENYLEPHRINE plus DIPHENYLPYRALINE ('novahistex').

PHENYLEPHRINE plus ZINC SULFATE ('zincfrin').

2-Phenylethanol *see* Phenethyl alcohol.

PHENYLETHANOLAMINE (α-(aminomethyl)-benzyl alcohol; phenethanolamine).

Phenylethylacetamide *see* 2-Phenylbutyramide.

Phenylethylacetylurea *see* Pheneturide.

2-Phenylethylamine *see* Phenethylamine.

1-Phenylethyl 3-(dimethoxyphosphinyloxy)-2-butenoate *see* Crotoxyphos.

1-(1-Phenylethyl)hydrazine *see* Mebanazine.

Phenylethylmalonic acid monoethyl ester diethylaminoethylamide *see* Fenalamide.

N-[2-[4-(2-Phenylethyl)phenyl]-2-hydroxyethyl]imidazole *see* Denzimol.

N-Phenylformamide *see* Formanilide.

Phenylformic acid *see* Benzoic acid.

N-Phenylformoguanamine *see* Amanozine.

N-Phenylglutaramic acid *see* Glutaranilic acid.

N-Phenylglycinamide-*p*-arsonic acid sodium salt *see* Tryparsamide.

O-Phenylglycolic acid *see* Phenoxyacetic acid.

2-Phenylglycolic acid *see* Mandelic acid.

6-(α-D-Phenylglycylamino)penicillanic acid *see* Ampicillin.

Phenylglyoxylnitrile oxime O,O-diethyl phosphorothioate *see* Phoxim.

2-Phenylhydracrylic acid *see* Tropic acid.

1-Phenyl-2-hydrazinopropane *see* Pheniprazine.

Phenyl 3α-hydroxy-8-azabicyclo[3.2.1]octane-8-carboxylate carbazate (ester) *see* Tropabazate.

Phenyl *p*-hydroxybenzoate *see* Phenyl paraben.

'Phenylin' *see* Phenindione.

2-Phenyl-1,3-indandione *see* Phenindione.

PHENYLISOBUTYLHYDRAZINE (1-(1-methyl-3-phenylpropyl)hydrazine; JB-835).

Phenylisohydantoin *see* Pemoline.

β-Phenylisopropylamine *see* Amphetamine.

Phenylisopropylhydrazine *see* Pheniprazine.

PHENYLISOPROPYLISONIAZID (N-(isonicotinoylamino)amphetamine; 1-isonicotinoyl-2-(phenylisopropyl)hydrazine; JB-821).

Phenylisopropylmethylpropinylamine *see* Selegiline.

N-(2-Phenylisopropyl)nicotinamide *see* Phenatin.

N-(2-Phenylisopropyl)nicotinthioamide *see* Thiophenatin.

3-(2-Phenylisopropyl)-N-(phenylcarbamino)sydnone imine *see* Sydnocarb.

3-(2-Phenylisopropyl)sydnone imine *see* Sydnofen.

α-(5-Phenylisoxazol-3-yl)-1-piperidineethanol *see* Perisoxal.

Phenyllin (tr) *see* Phenindione.

N-Phenylmaleamic acid *see* Maleanilic acid.

6-(Phenylmalonamido)penicillanic acid *see* Carbenicillin.

α-Phenylmandelic acid *see* Benzilic acid.

6-Phenylmercaptoacetamidopenicillanic acid *see* Tifencillin.

PHENYLMERCURIC ACETATE ('merfen'; 'merphenyl'; 'mersolite 8'; 'mertricone'; 'sanmicron'; 'volpar').

PHENYLMERCURIC BORATE*** (PHB; phenomerbor; 'aderman'; 'exomycol'; 'hydromerfene'; 'nylmerate').
See also under Dexamethasone pivalate; Hexachlorophene.

414

PHENYLMERCURIC LACTATE ('lactophen-ymer').

PHENYLMERCURIC NITRATE ('aero-ped'; 'calped'; 'epido'; 'mersagel'; 'phe-mer-nite'; 'phenitol'; 'phenmerzyl'; 'phenymer'; 'scleromer-fen'; 'spidox').

PHENYLMERCURIC SALICYLATE ('mersolite 19').

Phenylmethylaminopropane *see* Methamphetamine.

Phenylmethylaminopropanol *see* Ephedrine.

Phenylmethylimidazoline *see* Tolazoline.

2-PHENYLNORBORNANE-2-CARBOXYLIC ACID (2-phenylbicyclo[2.2.1]heptane-2-carb-oxylic acid).
See also Bornaprine.

PHENYL PARABEN (phenyl *p*-hydroxybenzoate; 'nipaphenyl').

Phenyl-PAS *see* Fenamisal.

1-Phenyl-1-pentanol *see* Fenipentol.

Phenylpentyl camphorate *see* Fenipentol camphor-ate.

α-Phenylphenacylamine *see* Desylamine.

α-Phenylphenethylamine *see* Stilbylamine.

o-PHENYLPHENOL (2-hydroxybiphenyl; 'do-wicide'; 'lyorthol'; 'orthoxenol'; 'rotoline').

2-Phenyl-2-(phenylisopropylamino)acetonitrile *see* Amfetaminil.

Phenylphosphonothioic acid esters *see* Cyanofen-phos; Ethyl *p*-nitrophenyl phenylphosphono-thioate; Leptophos; Quintiofos.

N-Phenylphthalamic acid *see* Phthalanilic acid.

1-[2-[Phenyl(2-picolyl)amino]ethyl]piperidine *see* Picoperine.

1-Phenyl-3-piperazin-1-ylisoquinoline *see* Perafens-ine.

3-(4-Phenylpiperazin-1-yl)-1,2-propanediol *see* Dro-propizine.

α-PHENYL-1-PIPERIDINEACETIC ACID (2-phenyl-2-piperid-1-ylacetic acid).
See also Bietamiverine; Dipiproverine; Piprocu-marium.

α-PHENYL-2-PIPERIDINEACETIC ACID (2-phenyl-2-piperid-2-ylacetic acid).
See also Butopiprine.

(−)-α-Phenyl-2-piperidinemethanol acetate *see* Le-vofacetoperane.

1-Phenyl-1-piperid-1-ylcyclohexane *see* Phencyclid-ine.

5-Phenyl-5-piperid-2-ylmethylbarbituric acid *see* Prazitone.

3-Phenyl-3-piperid-1-ylpropionic acid butyl ester *see* Butaverine.

N-Phenyl-2-piperid-1-yl-N-pyrid-2-ylmethylethyl-amine *see* Picoperine.

1-Phenyl-3-piperid-1-ylpyrrolidin-2-one *see* Felipyr-ine.

Phenylprenazone *see* Feprazone.

1-PHENYL-1-PROPANOL (α-ethylbenzyl alco-hol; 'felicur'; 'phenychol').

PHENYLPROPANOLAMINE* (2-amino-1-phenyl-1-propanol; (±)-α-(1-aminoethyl)benzyl alcohol; (±)-norephedrine; apoephedrine).

Phenylpropenoic acid *see* Cinnamic acid.

3-Phenyl-2-propen-1-ol *see* Cinnamyl alcohol.

2-Phenyl-2-prop-2-enyl-4-pentenoic acid *see* 2-Allyl-2-phenyl-4-pentenoic acid.

2-Phenylpropionic acid *see* Hydratropic acid.

3-Phenylpropionic acid *see* Hydrocinnamic acid.

3-Phenylpropyl carbamate *see* Phenprobamate.

Phenylpropylhydroxycoumarin *see* Phenprocou-mon.

Phenyl propyl ketone *see* Butyrophenone.

Phenylpropylmethylamine *see* Phenpromethamine.

1-Phenyl-2-propynyl carbamate *see* Carfimate.

N¹-(2-Phenylpyrazol-3-yl)sulfanilamide *see* Sulfa-phenazole.

5-Phenylpyrimido[4,5-d]pyrimidine-2,4,7-triamine *see* Ampyrimine.

Phenylpyrrolidinopentane *see* Prolintane.

2-Phenyl-N-(2-pyrrolidin-1-ylethyl)glycine isopentyl ester *see* Camiverine.

N-Phenyl-N-(2-pyrrolid-1-ylethyl)benzylamine *see* Histapyrrodine.

N-Phenylsalicylamide *see* Salicylanilide.

Phenyl salicylate *see* Salol.

3-Phenylsalicylic acid diethylaminoethyl ester *see* Xenysalate.

Phenyl-sec-butylnorsuprifen *see* Buphenine.

Phenylsemicarbazide *see* Phenicarbazide.

Phenyl styryl ketone *see* Chalcone.

N-Phenylsuccinamic acid *see* Succinanilic acid.

L-2-Phenyl-N-[N-[N-[N-[N-[N-(N²-succinamoyl-L-arginyl)-L-valyl]-L-tyrosyl]-L-valyl]-L-histidyl]-L-prolyl]glycine *see* Arfalasin.

6-[(Phenylsulfaminoacetyl)amino]penicillanic acid *see* Suncillin.

N¹-Phenylsulfanilamide *see* Sulfabenz.

Phenylsulfapyrazole *see* Sulfaphenazole.

5-(Phenylsulfinyl)-2-benzimidazolecarbamic acid methyl ester *see* Oxfendazole.

[2-(Phenylsulfinyl)ethyl]malonic acid mono(1,2-di-phenylhydrazide) *see* Osmadizone.

6-(2-Phenyl-2-sulfoacetamido)penicillanic acid *see* Sulbenicillin.

6-[2-Phenyl-D-(sulfoamino)acetamido]penicillanic acid *see* Suncillin.

4-Phenyl-1-(tetrahydrofurfuryloxyethyl)isonipecotic acid ethyl ester *see* Furethidine.

6-[2-Phenyl-2-[2-[p-(1,4,5,6-tetrahydropyrimidin-2-yl)phenyl]acetamido]acetamido]penicillanic acid *see* Rotamicillin.

1-Phenyl-1-(2-tetrazol-5-ylethyl)piperazine *see* Zolertine.

4-Phenyl-2-thiazolecarbamic acid 2,2,2-trichloro-ethyl ester *see* Lotifazole.

5-Phenyl-5-(2-thienyl)hydantoin *see* Thyphenytoin.

Phenylthilone *see* Phenythilone.

6-(Phenylthioacetamido)penicillanic acid *see* Tifen-cillin.

5-(Phenylthio)-2-benzimidazolecarbamic acid methyl ester *see* Fenbendazole.

Phenylthiomethyl penicillin *see* Tifencillin.

α-Phenyl-2-thiopheneglycolic acid ester with di-ethyl(2-hydroxyethyl)methylammonium bromide *see* Oxitefonium bromide.

PHENYLTOLOXAMINE*** (N,N-dimethyl-2-

(α-phenyl-*o*-toloxy)ethylamine; phenyltoloxamine citrate; PRN; C-5581).

2-(α-Phenyl-*o*-toloxy)triethylamine *see* Etoloxamine.

2-Phenyl-4-(trichloromethyl)-Δ²-1,3,4-oxadiazolin-5-one *see* Clotioxone.

1-Phenyl-1-[3-(trifluoromethyl)phenyl]-1-propanol *see* Flumecinol.

Phenylurea *see* Carbanilamide.

2-Phenylvaleric acid diethylaminoethyl ester *see* Propivane.

Phenyl vinyl ketone *see* Acrylophenone.

'Phenymer' *see* Phenylmercuric nitrate.

'Pheny-pas-tebamin' *see* Fenamisal.

PHENYRACILLIN*** (2,5-diphenylpiperazine 1,4-bis[(6-phenylacetamido)penicillinate]; 2,5-diphenylpiperazine salt of penicillin G; penicillinphenyrazine).

'Phenyral' *see* 5-Allyl-5-phenylbarbituric acid.

Phenyramidol* *see* Fenyramidol.

PHENYTHILONE*** (2-ethyl-2-phenylthiamorpholine-3,5-dione; 5-ethyl-6-phenylmetathiazine-2,4-dione; 2-ethyltetrahydro-2-phenyl-1,4-thiazine-3,5-dione; phenylthilone; MRD-125).

PHENYTOIN*** (5,5-diphenylhydantoin; phenytoin sodium; difenin; diphenin).

PHENYTOIN plus DIAZEPAM (A-124).

PHENYTOIN plus METHYLPHENOBARBITAL ('mebroin').

PHENYTOIN plus PHENOBARBITAL ('garoin').

PHENYTOIN VALERATE ('neo-citrullamon').

PHENZIDOLE (2-phenylbenzimidazole).

Phenzoline *see* Orexin.

Phepracet (tr) *see* Fepracet.

'Phesin' *see* Phenazone sodium sulfonate.

Phetenylate *see* Thyphenytoin.

Phethanol (tr) *see* Etilefrine.

PHETHARBITAL*** (5,5-diethyl-1-phenylbarbituric acid; phenidiemal; *N*-phenylbarbital).

Phethenylate* *see* Thyphenytoin.

Phetylurea *see* Pheneturide.

PhGABA *see* 4-Amino-3-phenylbutyric acid.

'Phiangin' *see* Paraformaldehyde.

'Phiniphos' *see* Toldimfos.

'Phisohex' *see* Chlorhexidine.

'Ph isomed' *see* Chlorhexidine.

'Phlebolan' *see* Dimethyl sulfoxide.

PHLEOMYCIN (antibiotic from *Str. verticillus*; NSC-61586).

'Phlogodym' *see* Neodymium pyrocatecholdisulfonate complex.

'Phlogosam' *see* Samarium sulfosalicylate.

PHLORETIC ACID (*p*-hydroxyhydrocinnamic acid).

Phloretic acid tranexamate ester *see* Cetraxate.

PHLORETIN (2′,4′,6′-trihydroxy-3-(*p*-hydroxyphenyl)propiophenone; asebogenol).

Phloretin 2′-β-glucoside *see* Phlorizin.

Phlorhizin *see* Phlorizin.

Phloridzin *see* Phlorizin.

Phlorimycin (tr) *see* Viomycin.

PHLORIZIN (phloretin 2′-β-glucoside; asebotin;

phlorhizin; phloridzin; phlorizoside; 'kalmin').

Phlorizoside *see* Phlorizin.

PHLOROGLUCINOL (1,3,5-trihydroxybenzene; 'dilospan').

PHLOROGLUCINOL plus 1,3,5-TRIMETHOXYBENZENE (phloroglucinol trimethylphloroglucinol mixture; LL-172; 'dilexan'; 'spasfon').

Phloropropiophenone *see* Flopropione.

PHNB (tr) *see* Quintozene.

'Phobex' *see* Benactyzine.

'Phoebex' *see* Benactyzine.

'Phoenixin' *see* Carbon tetrachloride.

PHOLCODINE*** (3-(2-morpholinoethyl) ether of morphine; pholcodine citrate; pholcodine tartrate; homocodeine; morpholinoethylmorphine).

PHOLEDRINE*** (*p*-(2-methylaminopropyl)-phenol; isodrin; promethin).
See also under Norfenefrine.

PHORATE* (*O,O*-diethyl *S*-(ethylthiomethyl) phosphorodithioate; timet; L-11-6; 'thimet').

PHOSACETIM* (*O,O*-bis(*p*-chlorophenyl)(1-iminoethyl)phosphoramidothioate).

'Phosaden' *see* Adenosine phosphate.

PHOSALONE* (*S*-[(6-chloro-2-oxobenzoxazol-3(2*H*)-yl)methyl] *O,O*-diethyl phosphorodithioate; 6-chloro-3(2*H*)-[[(diethoxyphosphinothioyl)thio]methyl]benzoxazol-2-one; RP 11974; 'zolone').

Phosarbin *see* Pyrophos.

Phoschlorin *see* Metrifonate.

Phosclorine *see* Metrifonate.

Phoscolic acid *see* Foscolic acid.

'Phosdrin' *see* Mevinphos.

Phosethoprop *see* Ethoprop.

PHOSFOLAN* (2-(diethoxyphosphinylimino)-1,3-dithiolane; diethyl 1,3-dithiolan-2-ylidenephosphoramidate; carbolane; fosfolan; 'cyolane').

PHOSGENE (COCl$_2$; carbonyl chloride; chloroformyl chloride; collongite).

PHOSMET* (*S*-[(1,3-dihydro-1,3-dioxo-2*H*-isoindol-2-yl)methyl] *O,O*-dimethyl phosphorodithioate; 2-[[(dimethoxyphosphinothioyl)thio]methyl]phthalimide; *O,O*-dimethyl *S*-(phthalimidomethyl) phosphorodithioate; *N*-(mercaptomethyl)phthalimide *S*-(*O,O*-dimethylphosphorothioate); ftalofos; phthalofos; 'imidan'; 'orbisect'; 'prolate'; 'rycovet-nupor').

PHOSNICHLOR* (*O*-(4-chloro-3-nitrophenyl) *O,O*-dimethyl phosphorothioate; nichlorfos).

'Phosodyl' *see* Toldimfos.

Phosphacol (tr) *see* Paraoxon.

Phosphagen *see* Creatinephosphoric acid.

Phosphamide (tr) *see* Dimethoate.

PHOSPHAMIDON* (2-chloro-1-diethylaminocroton-3-yl dimethyl phosphate; [2-chloro-2-(diethylcarbamoyl)-1-methylvinyl] dimethyl phosphate; (2-chloro-3-diethylamino-1-methyl-3-oxo-1-propenyl) dimethyl phosphate; 2-chloro-*N,N*-diethyl-3-hydroxycrotonamide dimethyl phosphate; 'dimecron'; 'liromidon').

PHOSPHANILIC ACID (*p*-aminobenzenephosphonic acid).

PHOSPHATIDYLCHOLINE (lecithin; 'lexinol-cal').

'Phosphemol' see Parathion.

2,2′-Phosphinicodilactic acid see Foscolic acid.

1,1′,1″-Phosphinylidynetris(2-methylaziridine) see Metepa.

Phosphocreatine see Creatinephosphoric acid.

Phosphocreatinine see Fosfocreatinine.

'Phosphocycline' see Tetracycline phosphate complex.

'Phosphoestrol' see Fosfestrol.

'Phospholine' see Ecothiopate iodide.

Phosphonoacetic acid disodium salt monohydrate see Fosfonet sodium.

N-Phosphonoacetyl-L-aspartic acid see Sparfosic acid.

N-(Phosphonoamidino)sarcosine see Creatinephosphoric acid.

2-Phosphonobenzoic acid see Fosfosal.

Phosphonodithioimidocarbonic acid ethylene dibenzyl P,P,P′,P′-tetraethyl ester see Zilantel.

Phosphonoformic acid trisodium salt see Foscarnet sodium.

N-(Phosphonomethyl)glycine see Glyphosate.

Phosphonomycin see Fosfomycin.

Phosphoramide(s) see Phosphoramidic acid; Phosphoric triamide; Phosphorodiamidic acid.

PHOSPHORAMIDIC ACID (phosphoramide; phosphoric acid amide; phosphoric acid monoamide).

PHOSPHORIC ACID (orthophosphoric acid).

Phosphoric acid amide see Phosphoramidic acid.

Phosphoric acid diamide see Phosphorodiamidic acid.

Phosphoric acid monoamide see Phosphoramidic acid.

Phosphoric acid triamide see Phosphoric triamide.

Phosphoric acid triethylenimide see Tepa.

PHOSPHORIC TRIAMIDE (phosphoramide; phosphoric acid triamide).

PHOSPHORODIAMIDIC ACID (phosphoramide; phosphoric acid diamide).

Phosphorodiamidic anhydride see Pyrophosphoramide.

PHOSPHORODIAMIDIC FLUORIDE (phosphorofluoridic diamide).

PHOSPHORODITHIOIC ACID (dithiophosphoric acid).

Phosphorofluoridic diamide see Phosphorodiamidic fluoride.

PHOSPHOROTHIOIC ACID (thiophosphoric acid).

PHOSPHOROTHIOIC TRIAMIDE (thiophosphoramide; triaminophosphine sulfide).

Phosphorylcreatine see Creatinephosphoric acid.

Phosphoryldimethylaminoethanol see Deanol phosphate.

Phosphostigmine* see Parathion.

Phosphothiamine see Monophosphothiamine.

'Phosphotope' see Sodium phosphate (^{32}P).

'Phosvel' see Leptophos.

'Photodyn' see Hematoporphyrin.

PHOXIM* (O-(α-cyanobenzylimino) O,O-diethyl phosphorothioate; α-[[(diethoxyphosphinothioyl)oxy]imino]benzeneacetonitrile; O,O-diethyl O-(α-nitrilobenzylimino)phosphorothioate; phenylglyoxylnitrile oxime O,O-diethyl phosphorothioate; Bayer 9053; 'baythion'; 'sebacil'; 'valexon').

'Phrenotropin' see Prothipendyl.

PHTHALALDEHYDIC ACID (benzaldehyde-2-carboxylic acid; o-formylbenzoic acid).

'Phthalamaquin' see Quinetalate.

PHTHALAMIC ACID (o-carbamoylbenzoic acid; phthalic acid monoamide). See also Ammonium phthalamate.

PHTHALAMIDE (phthalic acid diamide).

Phthalamudine see Chlortalidone.

PHTHALAN (1,3-dihydroisobenzofuran).

PHTHALANILIC ACID (N-phenylphthalamic acid).

PHTHALAZINE (2,3-benzo[d]pyridazine).

Phthalazino[2,3-b]phthalazine-5,12(7H,14H)-dione see Diftalone.

3-Phthalazin-1-ylcarbazic acid ethyl ester see Todralazine.

Phthalazole see Phthalylsulfathiazole.

PHTHALHYDRAZIDE (2,3-dihydro-1,4-phthalazinedione; phthalic acid hydrazide).

PHTHALIC ACID (o-benzenedicarboxylic acid). See also Dibutyl phthalate; Dimethyl phthalate.

Phthalic acid amides see Phthalamic acid; Phthalamide.

Phthalic acid hydrazide see Phthalhydrazide.

Phthalic acid imide see Phthalimide.

PHTHALIDE (1-(3H)-isobenzofuranone; 1-isocoumaranone; α,β-phenylenebutyrolactone; S-3).

Phthalidyl 6-(D(−)-α-aminophenylacetamido)penicillinate see Talampicillin.

Phthalidylampicillin see Talampicillin.

Phthalidyl niflumate see Talniflumate.

Phthalidyl salicylate acetate see Talosalate.

PHTHALIMIDE (1,3-isoindoledione; 1,3-isoindolinedione; phthalic acid imide).

PHTHALIMIDINE (isoindolin-1-one).

3-(N-Phthalimido)glutarimide see Thalidomide.

Phthalofos see Phosmet.

Phthalofyne* see Ftalofyne.

Phthalophos see Naftalofos.

Phthalthrin see Tetramethrin.

PHTHALYLSULFACETAMIDE* (4′-(acetylsulfamoyl)phthalanilic acid; ftalicetimida).

PHTHALYLSULFAMETHIZOLE* (4′-[(5-methyl-1,3,4-thiadiazol-2-yl)sulfamoyl]phthalanilic acid).

PHTHALYLSULFATHIAZOLE* (4′-(2-thiazolylsulfamoyl)phthalanilic acid; phthalazole; phthalylsulfonazole).

Phthalylsulfonazole see Phthalylsulfathiazole.

PHTHIOCOL (2-hydroxy-3-methyl-1,4-naphthoquinone).

Phthivazid see Ftivazide.

Phycite see Erythritol.

Phycitol see Erythritol.

'Phygon' see Dichlone.
'Phyllocontin' see Aminophylline.
'Phyllocormin-N' see Etofylline.
α-Phyllohydroquinone see Phytonadiol.
PHYLLOKININ (bradykinyl-isoleucyl-tyrosine O-sulfate).
Phylloquinone see Phytomenadione.
'Phyllotemp' see Aminophylline.
'Physeptone' see Methadone.
'Physiolax' see Docusate sodium.
'Physiomycin' see Metacycline.
'Physoscorbate' see Physostigmine ascorbate.
PHYSOSTIGMINE (2,3,3a,8a-tetrahydro-5-hydroxy-1,3a,8-trimethylpyrrolo[2,3-b]indole methylcarbamate ester; eserine; physostigmine salicyclate; physostigmine sulfate).
PHYSOSTIGMINE ASCORBATE ('physoscorbate').
PHYSOSTIGMINE N-OXIDE (eseridine; 'geneserine').
'Physostol' see Physostigmine.
PHYTANIC ACID (3,7,11,15-tetramethylhexadecanoic acid; tetramethylpalmitic acid).
Phytate persodium* see Persodium phytate.
Phytate sodium* see Sodium phytate.
PHYTIC ACID (cyclohexanehexol hexaphosphate; inositolhexaphosphoric acid; fytic acid). See also Persodium phytate; Sodium phytate.
'Phytin' see Calcium magnesium phytate.
'Phytobiase' see Calcium magnesium phytate.
Phytocalcine see Calcium magnesium phytate.
PHYTOHEMAGGLUTININ (phaseolosaxin; 'difco-M').
PHYTOL (3,7,11,15-tetramethyl-2-hexadecen-1-ol).
Phytomelin see Rutoside.
PHYTOMENADIONE*** (2-methyl-3-phytyl-1,4-naphthalenedione; 2-methyl-3-phytyl-1,4-naphthoquinone; phylloquinone; phytonadione; vitamin K₁; antihemorrhagic vitamin).
PHYTONADIOL (2-methyl-3-phytyl-1,4-naphthalenediol; vitamin K₁ hydroquinone; dihydrovitamin K₁; α-phyllohydroquinone).
PHYTONADIOL SODIUM DIPHOSPHATE*** (phytonadiol 1,4-di(sodium hydrogen phosphate)).
Phytonadione* see Phytomenadione.
'Phytosol' see Trichloronat.
α-Phytosterol see β-Sitosterol.
'Piafolina' see Morinamide.
'Piarine' see Promazine.
Pi-A-T see Piperazine diantimonyl tartrate.
'Piavermit' see Piperazine.
Piazine see Pyrazine.
'Piazol' see Morinamide.
'Piazolina' see Morinamide.
PIBECARB*** (phenacyl pivalate). See also under Mobecarb.
PIBERALINE*** (1-benzyl-4-(pyrid-2-ylcarbonyl)piperazine; 1-benzyl-4-picolinylpiperazine; Egyt-475).
PICAFIBRATE*** (2-(p-chlorophenoxy)-2-methylpropionic acid ester with N-(2-hydroxyethyl)-

nicotinamide; 2-nicotinamidoethyl clofibrate).
PICARTAMIDE** ((±)-tetrahydro-N-methyl-2-(pyrid-2-yl)thio-2-thiophenecarboxamide).
PICENADOL*** ((±)-trans-m-(1,3-dimethyl-4-propylpiperid-4-yl)phenol; LY-150720).
'Picfume' see Chloropicrin.
PICILOREX*** (3-(p-chlorophenyl)-5-cyclopropyl-2-methylpyrrolidine).
PICILOREX SUCCINATE (UP-507-04).
PICLONIDINE*** ((±)-2-[2,6-dichloro-N-(tetrahydro-2H-pyran-2-yl)anilino]-2-imidazoline).
PICLOPASTINE*** (1-(p-chloro-α-pyrid-2-ylbenzyl)-4-[2-(2-hydroxyethoxy)ethyl]piperazine; 2-[2-[4-(p-chloro-α-pyrid-2-ylbenzyl)piperazin-1-yl]ethoxy]ethanol).
PICLORAM* (4-amino-3,5,6-trichloropicolinic acid; 4-amino-3,5,6-trichloropyridine-2-carboxylic acid; 'tordon').
PICLOXYDINE*** (1,4-bis[N¹-[N¹-(p-chlorophenyl)amidino]amidino]piperazine; 1,1'-(p-chlorophenylguanidinoformimidoyl)bispiperazine; 1,1'-(piperazinediyl(1,4)dicarbonimidoyl)-bis[3-(p-chlorophenyl)guanidine]).
PICOBENZIDE*** (3,5-dimethyl-N-(pyrid-4-ylmethyl)benzamide; MA-14012).
PICODRALAZINE*** (1-hydrazino-4-pyrid-4-ylmethylphthalazine).
PICOLAMINE*** (3-(aminomethyl)pyridine; pyrid-3-ylmethylamine).
'Picolax' see Sodium picosulfate.
PICOLINALDEHYDE (2-formylpyridine; 2-pyridinaldehyde).
2-Picolinaldoxime methiodide see Pralidoxime iodide.
2-PICOLINE (2-methylpyridine).
4-PICOLINE (4-methylpyridine).
PICOLINIC ACID (2-pyridinecarboxylic acid).
β-Picolinic acid see Nicotinic acid.
γ-Picolinic acid see Isonicotinic acid.
4,4'-(2-Picolylidene)bis(phenylsulfuric acid)disodium salt see Sodium picosulfate.
PICONOL*** (2-pyridinemethanol).
Picoperidamine see Picoperine.
PICOPERINE*** (1-[2-(N-pyrid-2-ylmethylanilino)ethyl]piperidine; 1-[2-[phenyl(2-picolyl)-amino]ethyl]piperidine; N-phenyl-N-(2-picolyl)-2-piperid-1-ylethylamine; picoperine hydrochloride; TAT-3; 'coben').
PICOPRAZOLE*** (methyl 6-methyl-2[[(3-methylpyrid-2-yl)methyl]sulfinyl]-5-benzimidazolecarboxylate; H-149/94).
Picosulfol see Sodium picosulfate.
PICOTRIN** (5-(triphenylmethyl)-2-pyridinecarboxylic acid; 5-tritylpicolinic acid).
PICOTRIN DIOLAMINE* (picotrin compound (1:1) with 2,2'-iminodiethanol; Sch-19741).
PICRIC ACID (carbazotic acid; nitroxanthic acid; picronitric acid; trinitrophenol; 'trinophenon').
Picronitric acid see Picric acid.
PICROTOXIN (cocculin).
PICUMAST*** (7-[3-[4-(p-chlorobenzyl)piperazin-1-yl]propoxy]-3,4-dimethylcoumarin; BM-15100).

PID *see* Diphenadione *and* Phenindione.

PIDOLIC ACID** (5-oxoproline; 5-oxopyrrolidine-2-carboxylic acid; 2-pyrrolidone-5-carboxylic acid; glutamic acid lactam; glutimic acid; glutiminic acid; pyroglutamic acid).
See also Arginine pidolate; Calcium pidolate; Deanol pidolate.

Pidorubicin *see* Epirubicin.

'Pielik' *see* 2,4-Dichlorophenoxyacetic acid.

Pierrel-TQ 86 *see* Azipramine.

PIFARNINE*** (1-piperonyl-4-(3,7,11-trimethyl-2,6,10-dodecatrienyl)piperazine; 1-[(1,3-benzodioxol-5-yl)methyl]-4-(3,7,11-trimethyl-2,6,10-dodecatrienyl)piperazine; 1-farnesyl-4-piperonylpiperazine; U-27).

PIFENATE*** (ethyl α,α-diphenyl-2-piperidinepropionate; AGN-197).

PIFEXOLE*** (4-[5-(*o*-chlorophenyl)-1,2,4-oxadiazol-3-yl]pyridine; 5-(*o*-chlorophenyl)-3-pyrid-4-yl-1,2,4-oxadiazole; RI-64).

PIFLUTIXOL*** (1-[3-[6-fluoro-2-(trifluoromethyl)thioxanthen-9-ylidene]propyl]-4-piperidineethanol; 6-fluoro-9-[3-[4-(2-hydroxyethyl)piperid-1-yl]propylidene]-2-(trifluoromethyl)thioxanthene).

PIFOXIME*** (1-[(*p*-acetylphenoxy)acetyl]piperidine *p*-oxime; 1-[[*p*-1-(hydroxyimino)ethyl]phenoxy]acetyl]piperidine; LF-77; 'flamanil').

'Pigmentigen 8-MOP' *see* Methoxsalen.

PIH *see* Pheniprazine.

PIKETOPROFEN*** (*m*-benzoyl-*N*-(4-methylpyrid-2-yl)hydratropamide; 3-[1-[(4-methylpyrid-2-yl)carbamoyl]ethyl]benzophenone).

Piknolepsin (tr) *see* Ethosuximide.

PILDRALAZINE*** ((±)-1-[(6-hydrazinopyridazin-3-yl)methylamino]-2-propanol; (±)-3-hydrazino-6-[(2-hydroxypropyl)methylamino]pyridazine; propildazine; ISF-2123).

PILOCARPINE (5-[(4-ethyl-2,3,4,5-tetrahydrofuran-5-on-3-yl)methyl]-1-methylimidazole).
See also under Dipivefrine.

'Pilocarpol' *see* Pilocarpine.

'Piloptic' *see* Proxymetacaine.

'Pimadine' *see* Piminodine.

'Pimafucin' *see* Natamycin.

'Pimaricin' *see* Natamycin.

PIMECLONE*** (1-(2-oxocyclohexylmethyl)piperidine; 2-(piperid-1-ylmethyl)cyclohexanone; NA-66; 'karion'; 'spiractin').

PIMEFYLLINE*** (7-[2-[(pyrid-3-ylmethyl)amino]ethyl]theophylline).

PIMEFYLLINE NICOTINATE (ES-902; 'teonicon').

PIMELIC ACID (heptanedioic acid; 1,5-pentanedicarboxylic acid).

PIMETACIN*** (1-(*p*-chlorobenzoyl)-5-methoxy-2-methyl-3-indoleacetic acid 3-pyridylmethyl thioester; indometacin 3-pyridylmethyl thioester; pyrid-3-ylmethanethiol ester with indometacin).

PIMETHIXENE*** (1-methyl-4-(thioxanthen-9-ylidene)piperidine; 9-(*N*-methyl-4-piperidylidene)thioxanthene; BP-400).

PIMETINE*** (4-benzyl-1-(2-dimethylamino-ethyl)piperidine; IN-379; NSC-528880).

PIMETREMIDE*** (*N*-methyl-*N*-(3-methylpyridyl)tropamide; *N*-methyl-*N*-(3-picolyl)tropamide; pimeverine; pimetremide hydrobromide).

Pimeverine* *see* Pimetremide.

PIMINODINE*** (1-(3-anilinopropyl)-4-phenyl isonipecotic acid ethyl ester; 4-(ethoxycarbonyl)-1-(3-phenylaminopropyl)-4-phenylpiperidine; piminodine esylate; piminodine ethanesulfonate).

PIMOBENDAN*** (4,5-dihydro-6-[2-(*p*-methoxyphenyl)benzimidazol-5-yl]-5-methyl-3(2*H*)-pyridazinone).

PIMOZIDE*** (1-[4,4-bis(*p*-fluorophenyl)butyl]-4-(2-oxobenzimidazolin-1-yl)piperidine; 1-[1-[4,4-bis(*p*-fluorophenyl)butyl]piperid-4-yl]-2-benzimidazolinone; McN-JR-6238; R-6238).

PINACIDIL*** ((±)-2-cyano-1-pyrid-4-yl-3-(1,2,2-trimethylpropyl)guanidine; P-1134).

Pinacoloxymethylphosphoryl fluoride *see* Soman.

PINACOLYL ALCOHOL (3,3-dimethyl-2-butanol).

Pinacolyl methylphosphonofluoridate *see* Soman.

PINADOLINE** (1-[(8-chlorodibenz[*b*,*f*][1,4]oxazepin-10(11*H*)-yl)carbonyl]-2-(5-chlorovaleryl)-hydrazine).

PINAFIDE*** (3-nitro-*N*-(2-pyrrolidin-1-ylethyl)naphthalimide).

PINAVERIUM BROMIDE*** (4-(2-bromo-4,5-dimethoxybenzyl)-4-[2-[2-(6,6-dimethylbicyclo[3.1.1]hept-2-yl)ethoxy]ethyl]morpholinium bromide; 4-(6-bromoveratryl)-4-[2-[2-(6,6-dimethyl-2-norpinyl)ethoxy]ethyl]morpholinium bromide; 'dicetel').

PINAZEPAM*** (7-chloro-1,3-dihydro-5-phenyl-1-prop-2-ynyl-2*H*-1,4-benzodiazepin-2-one; Z-905; 'domar').

PINCAINIDE*** (2,3,4,5,6,7-hexahydro-1*H*-azepine-1-aceto-2′,6′-xylidide).

'Pindex' *see* Metacycline.

'Pindione' *see* Phenindamine.

PINDOLOL*** (4-[2-hydroxy-3-(isopropylamino)propoxy]indole; indol-4-yloxy-3-isopropylamino-2-propanol; prinodolol; LB-46; 'pectobloc'; 'visken').

PINDOLOL plus CLOPAMIDE ('viskaldix').

PINDOLOL plus ISOSORBIDE DINITRATE (LB-45; 'viskenit').

PINDONE* (2-(2,2-dimethyl-1-oxopropyl)-1*H*-indene-1,3(2*H*)-dione; 2-pivaloyl-1,3-indandione; 2-(2,2,2-trimethylacetyl)-1,3-indandione; pivalylindandione; pivaldione; 'pival'; 'pivalyl valone'; 'pivalyn').

PINENE (2,6,6-trimethylbicyclo[3.1.1]-2-heptene; α-pinene).

'Pinetox' *see* Campheclor.

Pinite *see* Pinitol.

PINITOL (matecite; matezite; pinite; sennite).

PINOLCAINE*** (D-(+)-2-(1-hydroxy-1-methylethyl)-1-methylpiperidine diphenylacetate (ester); D-(+)-1-methyl-1-(1-methylpiperid-2-yl)ethyl diphenylacetate; D-(+)-2-(1-methylpiperid-2-yl)-2-propanol diphenylacetate).

PINOXEPIN*** (*cis*-4-[3-(2-chlorodibenz[*b,e*]oxepin-11-(6*H*)-ylidene)propyl]-1-piperazineethanol; pinoxepin dihydrochloride; pinoxepin hydrochloride; P-5227).

'Piostacin' *see* Pristinamycin.

'Pioxol' *see* Pemoline.

PIPACYCLINE*** ([4-(2-hydroxyethyl)diethylenediaminomethyl]tetracycline; *N*-[4-(2-hydroxyethyl)piperazin-1-yl-methyl]tetracycline; mepicycline; piperazinoethyltetracycline). *See also* Penimepicycline.

Pipacycline phenoxymethylpenicillinate *see* Penimepicycline.

'Pipadone' *see* Dipipanone.

'Pipadox' *see* Piperazine.

PIPAMAZINE*** (10-[3-(4-carbamoylpiperid-1-yl)propyl]-2-chlorophenothiazine; RP 9153).

PIPAMPERONE*** (4-(4-carboxamido-4-piperid-1-ylpiperid-1-yl)-4'-fluorobutyrophenone; 1'-[3-(*p*-fluorobenzoyl)propyl][1,4'-bipiperidine]-4'-carboxamide; 1-[3-(*p*-fluorobenzoyl)propyl]-4-piperid-1-ylisonipecotamide; floropipamide; R-3345).

'Pipanol' *see* Trihexyphenidyl.

PIPANONE (5-methyl-4,4-diphenyl-6-piperid-1-yl-3-hexanone; pipanone hydrochloride; BW-29C48; 'pipidone').

PIPAZETATE*** (2-(2-piperid-1-ylethoxy)ethyl 10*H*-pyrido[3,2-*b*][1,4]benzothiazine 10-carboxylate; pipazethate; thiophenylpyridylamine; D-254; SK&F-70230-A; SQ-15874).

Pipazethate* *see* Pipazetate.

PIPEBUZONE*** (4-butyl-4-((4-methylpiperazin-1-yl)methyl)-1,2-diphenyl-3,5-pyrazolidinedione; LD-4644; 'elarzone').

PIPECOLIC ACID (2-piperidinecarboxylic acid; hexahydropicolinic acid; homoproline; dihydrobaikiaine).

2-PIPECOLINE (2-methylpiperidine).

PIPECOLINIC ACID (1-piperidinecarboxylic acid).

Pipecurium bromide *see* Pipecuronium bromide.

PIPECURONIUM BROMIDE*** (4,4'-(3α,17β-dihydroxy-5α-androstan-2β,16β-ylene)bis[1,1-dimethylpiperazinium] dibromide diacetate (ester) dihydrate; 2β,16β-bis(4,4-dimethyl-1-piperazino)-3α,17β-diacetoxyandrostane dibromide; pipecurium bromide; RGH-1106; 'arduan').

'Pipedac' *see* Pipemidic acid.

'Pipedase' *see* Pipemidic acid.

'Pipemid' *see* Pipemidic acid.

PIPEMIDIC ACID*** (8-ethyl-5,8-dihydro-5-oxo-2-piperazin-1-ylpyrido[2,3-*d*]pyrimidine-6-carboxylic acid; RB-1489; 'deblaston'; 'pipedac'; 'pipedase'; 'pipemid'; 'pipram'; 'urotractin').

PIPENDYL METHANE (1-ethyl-4-piperidylidene-1,1'-dithienylmethane; Sch-2747; 'prantaldithienyl').

'Pipenin' *see* Piperazine.

PIPENZOLATE BROMIDE*** (1-ethyl-3-hydroxy-1-methylpiperidinium bromide benzilate; 1-ethylpiperid-3-yl benzilate methobromide; JB-323; 'piptal').

PIPERACETAZINE*** (2-acetyl-10-[3-[4-(2-hydroxyethyl)piperid-1-yl]propyl]phenothiazine; 10-[3-[4-(2-hydroxyethyl)piperid-1-yl]propyl]-phenothiazin-2-yl methyl ketone; PC-1421).

PIPERACILLIN*** ((2*S*,5*R*,6*R*)-6-[(*R*)-2-(4-ethyl-2,3-dioxo-1-piperazinecarboxamido)-2-phenylacetamido]penicillanic acid; piperacillin sodium; CL-227193; T-1220; 'pipril').

PIPERAMIDE*** (1-acetamidophenyl-4-(3-dimethylaminopropyl)piperazine; 4'-[4-[3-(dimethylamino)propyl]piperazin-1-yl]acetamide; piperamide maleate; CL-54131).

Piperamine *see* Bamipine.

'Piperate' *see* Piperazine.

Piperazidine *see* Piperazine.

PIPERAZINE (diethylenediamine; hexahydropyrazine; piperazidine; piperazine adipate, citrate gluconate, phosphate or tartrate; piperazine hexahydrate).

Piperazine bis(theophyllin-7-ylacetate) *see* Acefylline piperazine.

Piperazine calcium edathamil *see* Piperazine calcium edetate.

PIPERAZINE CALCIUM EDETATE*** (chelate of piperazine with edetic acid and calcium; piperazine calcium edathamil; piperazine edetate).

PIPERAZINE DIANTIMONYL TARTRATE (Pi-A-T; 'bilharcid').

1,4-Piperazinediethanol di(2-phenylbutyrate) ester *see* Febuverine.

1,4-Piperazinediethanol α-methyl-1-naphthaleneacetate *see* Nafiverine.

Piperazine-1,4-diphosphoric acid tetraethylenimide *see* Dipin.

Piperazine di(2,4,5-trichlorophenoxide) *see* Triclofenol piperazine.

1,4-Piperazinediylbis[bis(1-aziridinyl)phosphine oxide] *see* Dipin.

1,4-Piperazinediylbis[bis(1-aziridinyl)phosphine sulfide] *see* Thiodipin.

N,N'-[1,4-Piperazinediylbis(2,2,2-trichloroethylidene)]bisformamide *see* Triforine.

1,1'-[1,4-Piperazinediylbis(trimethyleneiminoimidocarbonyl)]bis[3-hexylurea] *see* Ipexidine.

1,1'-(Piperazinediyl(1,4)dicarbonimidoyl)bis[3-(*p*-chlorophenyl)guanidine] *see* Picloxydine.

Piperazine edetate *see* Piperazine calcium edetate.

PIPERAZINE ESTRONE SULFATE (estropiprate; 'harmogen'; 'ogen'; 'sulestrex').

Piperazine theophyllin-7-ylacetate *see* Acefylline piperazine.

Piperazinoethyltetracycline *see* Pipacycline.

2-Piperazin-1-ylquinoline *see* Quipazine.

PIPERIDINE (hexahydropyridine).

1-Piperidinecarboxylic acid *see* Pipecolinic acid.

2-Piperidinecarboxylic acid *see* Pipecolic acid.

3-Piperidinecarboxylic acid *see* Nipecotic acid.

4-Piperidinecarboxylic acid *see* Isonipecotic acid.

2,6-Piperidinedione *see* Glutarimide.

2-Piperidineethanol anthranilate *see* Piridocaine.

1-Piperidineethanol benzilate *see* Pipethanate.

Piperidinomethylcyclohexane *see* Leptacline.

6-Piperidino-2,4-pyrimidinediamine 3-oxide *see* Minoxidil.

Piperidione *see* Dihyprylone.

PIPERIDOLATE*** (1-ethylpiperid-3-yl diphenylacetate; JB-305; 'dactil').

Piperidyl amidone *see* Dipipanone.

(−)-α-Piperid-2-ylbenzyl acetate *see* Levofacetoperane.

α-Piperid-2-yl-2,8-bis(trifluoromethyl)-4-quinolinemethanol *see* mefloquine.

o-[p-(2-Piperid-1-ylethoxy)benzoyl]benzoic acid methyl ester *see* Pitofenone.

2-Piperid-1-ylethyl α-acetoxy-α-benzylhydrocinnamate *see* Fenperate.

2-Piperid-2-ylethyl o-aminobenzoate *see* Piridocaine.

2-Piperid-1-ylethyl benzilate *see* Pipethanate.

2-Piperid-1-ylethyl α-benzyl-α-hydroxyhydrocinnamate acetate *see* Fenperate.

2-Piperid-1-ylethyl [bicyclohexyl]-1-carboxylate *see* Dihexyverine.

2-Piperid-1-ylethyl 2,2-diphenylacetate *see* Anicaine.

2-Piperid-1-ylethyl 2,2-diphenylcyclopropanecarboxylate *see* Pituxate.

3-(2-Piperid-4-ylethyl)indole *see* Indalpine.

2-Piperid-1-ylethyl 8-methylflavonecarboxylate *see* Flavoxate.

2-Piperid-1-ylethyl 3-methyl-4-oxo-2-phenyl-4H-1-benzopyran-8-carboxylate *see* Flavoxate.

2-Piperid-1-ylethyl phenylpiperidylacetate *see* Dipiproverine.

2-Piperid-1-ylethyl p-propoxyphenyl ketone *see* Propipocaine.

2-Piperid-1-ylmethyl-1,4-benzodioxan *see* Piperoxan.

N-(Piperid-2-ylmethyl)-2,5-bis(2,2,2-trifluoroethoxy)benzamide *see* Flecainide.

(Piperid-1-ylmethyl)cyclohexane *see* Leptacline.

2-(Piperid-1-ylmethyl)cyclohexanone *see* Pimeclone.

1-Piperid-2-yl-2-propanone *see* Pelletierine.

β-Piperid-1-yl-4-propoxypropiophenone *see* Propipocaine.

3-Piperid-1-ylpropyl m-anisate *see* Pribecaine.

3-Piperid-1-ylpropyl 1,2-dicarbanilate *see* Diperodon.

3-Piperid-1-ylpropyl m-methoxybenzoate *see* Pribecaine.

6-Piperid-1-yl-2,4-pyrimidinediamine 3-oxide *see* Minoxidil.

2,2′,2″,2‴-[(4-Piperid-1-ylpyrimido[5,4-d]pyrimidine-2,6-diyl)nitrilo]tetraethanol *see* Mopidamol.

Piperilate *see* Pipethanate.

Piperilone *see* Piperylone.

PIPEROCAINE*** (3-(2-methylpiperid-1-yl)propyl benzoate; piperocaine hydrochloride).

PIPERONAL (3,4-methylenedioxybenzaldehyde).

PIPERONAL BIS[2-(2-BUTOXYETHOXY)-ETHYL]ACETAL (5-[bis[2-(2-butoxyethoxy)ethoxy]methyl]-1,3-benzodioxole; 'tropital').

'Piperonyl' *see* Pipamperone.

PIPERONYL BUTOXIDE* (α-[2-(2-butoxyethoxy)ethoxy]-4,5-methylenedioxy-2-propyltoluene; 5-[[2-(2-butoxyethoxy)ethoxy]methyl]-6-propyl-1,3-benzodioxole; 'butacide').

PIPERONYLIC ACID (3,4-methylenedioxybenzoic acid).

Piperonylic acid 2-(2-butoxyethoxy)ethyl ester *see* Bucarpolate.

10-[(4-Piperonylpiperazin-1-yl)acetyl]phenothiazine *see* Fenoverine.

2-(4-Piperonylpiperazin-1-yl)pyrimidine *see* Piribedil.

1-Piperonyl-4-pyrimid-2-ylpiperazine *see* Piribedil.

1-Piperonyl-4-(3,7,11-trimethyl-2,6,10-dodecatrienyl)piperazine *see* Pifarnine.

PIPEROXAN*** (2-piperid-1-ylmethyl-1,4-benzodioxan; benzodioxane; F-933).

PIPERPHENAMINE* (1-(3-hydroxy-5-methyl-4-phenylhexyl)-1-methylpiperidinium bromide; mepiperphenidol; piperphenidol methobromide).

PIPERPHENIDOL* (5-methyl-4-phenyl-1-piperid-1-yl-3-hexanol; piperphenidol hydrochloride).

Piperphenidol methobromide *see* Piperphenamine.

PIPERYLONE** (4-ethyl-1-(1-methylpiperid-4-yl)-3-phenyl-3-pyrazolin-5-one; piperilone; PR-66).

PIPETHANATE*** (2-piperid-1-ylethyl benzilate; 1-piperidineethanol benzilate; piperilate; pipethanate hydrochloride; DPX-8).

PIPETHANATE ETHOBROMIDE (1-ethyl-1-(2-hydroxyethyl)piperidinium bromide benzilate; PB-106).

'Pipida' *see* Iprofenin.

'Pipidone' *see* Pipanone.

'Pipizan' *see* Piperazine.

PIPOBROMAN** (1,4-bis(3-bromopropionyl)-piperazine; di(bromopropionyl)piperazine; A-8103; NSC-25154).

PIPOCTANONE*** (4′-octyl-3-piperid-1-ylpropiophenone; pipoctanone hydrochloride; N-1113).

PIPOFEZINE*** (5-methyl-3-(4-methylpiperazin-1-yl)-5H-pyridazino[3,4-b][1,4]benzoxazine; 10-methyl-2-(4-methylpiperazin-1-yl)-3,4-diazaphenoxazine; azafen; azaphen).

'Piportil' *see* Pipotiazine.

PIPOSULFAN*** (1,4-dihydracryloylpiperazine dimethanesulfonate; 1,4-bis(3-hydroxypropionyl)piperazine dimesilate; A-20968; NSC-47774).

Pipothiazine* *see* Pipotiazine.

PIPOTIAZINE*** (1-[3-[2-(dimethylsulfamoyl)-phenothiazin-10-yl]propyl]-4-(2-hydroxyethyl)-piperidine; 10-[4-[3-(2-hydroxyethyl)piperid-1-yl]propyl]-N,N-dimethylphenothiazine 2-sulfonamide; pipothiazine; RP 19366; 'piportil').

PIPOTIAZINE PALMITATE* (2-[1-[3-[[2-[(dimethylamino)sulfonyl]-10H-phenothiazin-10-yl] propyl]piperidin-4-yl]ethyl]hexadecanoate; FI-6927; IL-19552; RP-19552).

PIPOTIAZINE UNDECENATE (RP-19551).

PIPOXIZINE*** (4-(diphenylmethylene)-1-[2-[2-(2-hydroxyethoxy)ethoxy]ethyl]piperidine; 2-[2-[2-[4-(diphenylmethylene)piperid-1-yl]ethoxy]-

ethoxy]ethanol; C-325; UCB-c325).

PIPOXOLAN** (5,5-diphenyl-2-(2-piperid-1-yl-ethyl)-1,3-dioxolan-4-one; pipoxolan hydro-chloride; BR-18; 'rowapraxin').

PIPRADIMADOL*** (1-(2-chlorophenethyl)-*N*-cyclohexyl-4-hydroxy-*N*,α,α-trimethyl-4-pip-eridineacetamide).

PIPRADROL*** (α,α-diphenyl-2-piperidinemeth-anol; pipradrol hydrochloride; piridrol; MRD-108).

'Pipram' *see* Pipemidic acid.

PIPRAMADOL*** ((±)-1-(2-chlorophenethyl)-*N*-cyclohexyl-4-hydroxy-*N*,α-dimethyl-4-pip-eridineacetamide).

PIPRATECOL*** (3,4-dihydroxy-α-[4-(*o*-meth-oxyphenyl)piperazin-1-ylmethyl]benzyl alcohol; 1-[2-(3,4-dihydroxyphenyl)-2-hydroxyethyl]-4-(*o*-methoxyphenyl)piperazine; α-(3,4-dihydroxy-phenyl)-4-(2-methoxyphenyl)-1-piperazineeth-anol; SE-711).
See also under Ajmalicine.

Piprazine *see* Piribedil.

'Pipril' *see* Piperacillin.

PIPRINHYDRINATE*** (4-(diphenylmethoxy)-1-methylpiperidine 8-chlorotheophyllinate (salt)).

PIPROCURARIUM IODIDE*** (1-(α-carboxy-benzyl)-1-methylpiperidinium iodide ester with diethyl(hydroxyethoxyethyl)methylammonium iodide; 2-[2-(diethylamino)ethoxy]ethyl α-phenyl-1-piperidineacetate dimethiodide; LD-2480).

PIPROFUROL** (α-(*p*-hydroxyphenethyl)-4,7-di-methoxy-6-(2-piperid-1-ylethoxy)-5-benzofuran-methanol).

PIPROZOLIN*** (ethyl 3-ethyl-4-oxo-5-piperid-1-yl-Δ²,α-thiazolidine acetate; Go-919; W-3699).

'Piptal' *see* Pipenzolate bromide.

PIQUIZIL*** (isobutyl 4-(6,7-dimethoxyquin-azolin-4-yl)-1-piperazinecarboxylate; piquizil hydrochloride; CP-12521-1).

PIRANDAMINE*** (1-[2-(dimethylamino)ethyl]-1,3,4,9-tetrahydro-1-methylindeno[2,1-*c*]pyran; 1,3,4,9-tetrahydro-*N*,*N*,1-trimethylindeno[2,1-*c*]-pyran-1-ethylamine; AY-23713).

PIRAXELATE*** (3,3,5-trimethylcyclohexyl 2-oxo-1-pyrrolidineacetate).

Pirazapon *see* Ripazepam.

Pirazocillin *see* Prazocillin.

PIRAZOFURIN** (4-hydroxy-5-β-D-ribofura-nosyl-1*H*-pyrazole-3-carboxamide; 4-hydroxy-pyrazole-3-carboxamide 5-riboside; pyrazofurin; NSC-143095).

PIRAZOLAC*** (4-(*p*-chlorophenyl)-1-(*p*-fluoro-phenyl)pyrazole-3-acetic acid; ZK-76004).

PIRBENICILLIN*** (6-[2-[2-(isonicotinimidoyl-amino)acetamido]-2-phenylacetamido]penicil-lanic acid; pirbenicillin sodium; CP-33994-2).

PIRBUTEROL*** (α⁶-[(*tert*-butylamino)methyl]-3-hydroxy-2,6-pyridinedimethanol; 2-*tert*-butyl-amino-1-(5-hydroxy-6-hydroxymethylpyrid-2-yl)ethanol; pirbuterol dihydrochloride; CP-24314-1; 'exirel').

PIRBUTEROL ACETATE* (pirbuterol acetate salt; CP-24314-14).

PIRDONIUM BROMIDE*** (1,1-dimethyl-2-[(*p*-methyl-α-phenylbenzyloxy)methyl]piperidinium bromide).

'Pirem' *see* Carbuterol.

PIRENOXINE*** (1-hydroxy-5-oxo-5*H*-pyrido-[3,2-*a*]phenoxazine-3-carboxylic acid; pirfen-oxone; 'catalin').

PIRENPERONE*** (3-[2-[4-(*p*-fluorobenzoyl)-piperid-1-yl]ethyl]-2-methyl-4*H*-pyrido[1,2-*a*]-pyrimidin-4-one; R-47465).

PIRENZEPINE** (5,11-dihydro-11-[(4-methyl-piperazin-1-yl)acetyl]-6*H*-pyrido[2,3-*b*][1,4]ben-zodiazepin-6-one; pirenzepine dihydrochloride; CL-2; LS-519; 'gastrozepin'; 'tabe').

PIREPOLOL*** ((±)-6-[[2-[[3-(*p*-butoxyphen-oxy)-2-hydroxypropyl]amino]ethyl]amino]-1,3-dimethyluracil).

PIRETANIDE*** (3-(aminosulfonyl)-4-phenoxy-5-(1-pyrrolidinyl)benzoic acid; 4-phenoxy-3-pyr-rolidin-1-yl-5-sulfamoylbenzoic acid; HOE-118; S-734118; 'arelix').

'Pirevan' *see* Quinuronium sulfate.

'Pirexyl' *see* Benproperine.

PIRFENIDONE*** (5-methyl-1-phenylpyridin-2(1*H*)-one; AMR-69).

Pirfenoxone *see* Pirenoxine.

Pirglutargine *see* Arginine pidolate.

PIRIBEDIL*** (1-(3,4-methylenedioxybenzyl)-4-pyrimid-2-ylpiperazine; 1-piperonyl-4-pyrimid-2-ylpiperazine; 2-(4-piperonylpiperazin-1-yl)pyr-imidine; piribendyl; piprazine; pyrimidylpip-eronylpiperazine; ET-495; EU-4200; TF-871; 'trivastal').

Piribendyl* *see* Piribedil.

Piribenzil *see* Bevonium metilsulfate.

PIRIDICILLIN** (6-[2-[6-[*p*-bis(2-hydroxyethyl)-sulfamoyl]phenyl]-1,2-dihydro-2-oxonicotin-amido]-2-(*p*-hydroxyphenyl)acetamido]penicil-lanic acid; piridicillin sodium; CI-867).

PIRIDOCAINE*** (2-piperidineethanol anthra-nilate; 2-piperid-2-ylethyl *o*-aminobenzoate; piri-docaine hydrochloride).

'Piridol' *see* Aminophenazone.

'Piridolan' *see* Piritramide.

Piridosal *see* Pethidine.

PIRIDOXILATE*** (2-[(5-hydroxy-4-hydroxy-methyl-6-methylpyrid-3-yl)methoxy]glycolic acid compound with [4,5-bis(hydroxymethyl)-2-methylpyrid-3-yloxy]glycolic acid (1:1); 'glyo 6').

Piridrol (tr) *see* Pipradrol.

PIRIFIBRATE*** (6-(hydroxymethyl)pyrid-2-ylmethyl 2-(*p*-chlorophenoxy)-2-methylpropion-ate; 2,6-pyridinedimethanol monoester with clo-fibric acid).

Piriline (tr) *see* Pempidine.

PIRIMICARB* (2-(dimethylamino)-5,6-dimethylpyrimidin-4-yl dimethylcarbamate; 'pirimor').

PIRIMIPHOS ETHYL* (*O*-[2-(diethylamino)-6-methylpyrimidin-4-yl] *O*,*O*-diethyl phosphorothioate).

PIRIMIPHOS METHYL* (*O*-[2-(diethylamino)-6-methylpyrimidin-4-yl] *O*,*O*-dimethyl phosphorothioate; pyrimidine phosphoran; 'actellic').

'Pirimor' *see* Pirimicarb.

PIRINIDAZOLE* (1-methyl-5-nitro-2-[(pyrid-2-ylthio)methyl]imidazole; 2-[(1-methyl-5-nitroimidazol-2-ylmethyl)thio]pyridine).

Pirinitramide* *see* Piritramide.

PIRINIXIC ACID* ([[4-chloro-6-(2,3-dimethylanilino)pyrimidin-2-yl]thio]acetic acid; [[4-chloro-6-(2,3-xylidino)pyrimidin-2-yl]thio]acetic acid; Wy-14643).

PIRINIXIL* (4-chloro-6-(2,3-dimethylanilino)-2-[[[(2-hydroxyethyl)carbamoyl]methyl]thio]pyrimidine; 2-[[4-chloro-6-(2,3-xylidino)pyrimidin-2-yl]thio]-*N*-(2-hydroxyethyl)acetamide; BR-931).

PIRIPROST* ((4*R*,5*R*)-1,4,5,6-tetrahydro-5-hydroxy-4-[(*E*)-(3*S*)-3-hydroxy-1-octenyl]-1-phenylcyclopenta[*b*]pyrrole-2-valeric acid).

PIRIQUALONE* (2-[2-[4-oxo-3-(*o*-tolyl)quinazolin-2-yl]vinyl]pyridine; 2-(2-pyrid-2-ylvinyl)-3-(*o*-tolyl)quinazolin-4(3*H*)-one).

'Pirisal' *see* Morazone.

'Pirissal' *see* Aminophenazone gentisate.

PIRISUDANOL* (2-(dimethylamino)ethyl [5-hydroxy-4-(hydroxymethyl)-6-methylpyrid-3-yl]methyl succinate; deanol pyrisuccinate; deanol 3-hydroxy-4-(hydroxymethyl)-2-methylpyrid-5-ylmethyl succinate; deanol pyridoxine succinate; deanol pyrisuccinate; 3-pyridoxyl deanol succinate; pyrisuccideanol; 'nadex'; 'stivan').

PIRITRAMIDE* (1'-(3-cyano-3,3-diphenylpropyl)-[1,4'-bipiperidine]-4'-carboxamide; pirinitramide; R-3365).

'Pirium' *see* Piritramide.

PIRLIMYCIN* (methyl 7-chloro-6,7,8-trideoxy-6-(*cis*-4-ethyl-L-pipecolamido)-1-thio-L-*threo*-α-D-*galacto*-octopyranoside; pirlimycin hydrochloride; U-57930).

PIRLIMYCIN ADENYLATE (U-63440).

PIRLINDOLE* (2,3,3a,4,5,6-hexahydro-8-methyl-1*H*-pyrazino[3,2,1-*jk*]carbazole; pirlindole hydrochloride).

PIRMENOL* ((±)-*cis*-α-[3-(2,6-dimethyl-1-piperidinyl)propyl]-α-phenyl-2-pyridinemethanol; (±)-*cis*-2,6-dimethyl-α-phenyl-α-2-pyridyl-1-piperidinebutanol; pirmenol hydrochloride; pirmenol monohydrochloride; CI-845).

PIRNABIN* (7,8,9,10-tetrahydro-3,6,6,9-tetramethyl-6*H*-dibenzo[*b,d*]pyran-1-ol acetate; pirnabine; SP-304).

Pirnabine* *see* Pirnabin.

'Pirocrid' *see* Protizinic acid.

PIROCTONE* (1-hydroxy-4-methyl-6-(2,4,4-trimethylpentyl)-2(1*H*)-pyridone).

PIROCTONE OLAMINE* (piroctone compound with 2-aminoethanol (1:1); 'octopirox').

'Pirocyl' *see* Quinuronium sulfate.

'Pirodal' *see* Piromidic acid.

PIROGLIRIDE* (*N*-(1-methylpyrrolidin-2-ylidene)-*N*'-phenyl-1-pyrrolidinecarboxamidine).

PIROGLIRIDE TARTRATE* (McN-3495).

'Pirogram' *see* Piromidic acid.

PIROHEPTINE* (3-(10,11-dihydro-5*H*-dibenzo[*a,d*]cyclohepten-5-ylidene)-1-ethyl-2-methylpyrrolidine; piroheptine hydrochloride; 'trimol').

PIROLATE* (ethyl 1,4-dihydro-7,8-dimethoxy-4-oxopyrimido[4,5-*b*]quinoline-2-carboxylate; CP-32387).

PIROLAZAMIDE* (hexahydro-α,α-diphenylpyrrolo[1,2-*a*]pyrazine-2(1*H*)-butyramide; SC-26438).

PIROMIDIC ACID* (8-ethyl-5,8-dihydro-5-oxo-2-pyrrolidin-1-ylpyrido[2,3-*d*]pyrimidine-6-carboxylic acid; PD-93; 'pirodal'; 'pirogram'; 'septural').

'Pirothesin' *see* Aptocaine.

PIROXICAM* (4-hydroxy-2-methyl-*N*-pyrid-2-yl-2*H*-1,2-benzothiazine-3-carboxamide 1,1-dioxide; CP-16171; 'feldene').

PIROXICILLIN* ((2*S*,5*R*,6*R*)-6-[(*R*)-2-(*p*-hydroxyphenyl)-2-[3-[4-hydroxy-2-(*p*-sulfamoylanilino)pyrimidin-5-yl]ureido]acetamido]penicillanic acid).

PIROZADIL* (2,6-pyridinediyldimethylene bis(3,4,5-trimethoxybenzoate)).

PIRPROFEN* (1-[4-(1-carboxyethyl)-2-chlorophenyl]-3-pyrroline; 3-chloro-4-(3-pyrrolin-1-yl)hydratropic acid; 2-[3-chloro-4-(3-pyrrolin-1-yl)phenyl]propionic acid; Su-21524; 'rangasil'; 'rengasil').

PIRQUINOZOL* (2-(hydroxymethyl)pyrazolo[1,5-*c*]quinazolin-5(6*H*)-one; SQ-13847).

PIRRALKONIUM BROMIDE* (bis[3-(2,5-dimethylpyrrolidin-1-yl)propyl]hexadecylmethylammonium bromide).

Pirroksan (tr) *see* Pirroxan.

'Pistocaine' *see* Polidocanol.

Pitayine *see* Quinidine.

PITENODIL* (1-[2-(dimethylcarbamoyloxy)-ethyl]-4-[3-(2-thenoyl)propyl]piperazine; 2-[4-[3-(2-thenoyl)propyl]piperazin-1-yl]ethyl dimethylcarbamate).

'Pitocin' *see* Oxytocin.

PITOFENONE* (methyl *o*-[*p*-(2-piperid-1-ylethoxy)benzoyl]benzoate).

'Pitressin' *see* Vasopressin.

'Pitressin tannate' *see* Argipressin tannate.

PITUXATE* (2-piperid-1-ylethyl 2,2-diphenylcyclopropanecarboxylate).

'Pival' *see* Pindone.

Pivaldione *see* Pindone.

PIVALIC ACID* (2,2-dimethylpropionic acid; trimethylacetic acid).
  See also Clocortolone pivalate; Flumetasone pivalate; Fluocortolone pivalate; Pibecarb; Pivenfrine; Prednisolone pivalate.

Pivalic acid benzylhydrazide *see* Pivhydrazine.

'Pivalone' *see* Tixocortol pivalate.

2-Pivaloyl-1,3-indandione *see* Pindone.

Pivaloyloxymethyl penicillanate 1,1-dioxide *see* Sulbactam pivoxil.

Pivaloyloxymethyl (2S,5R,6R)-6-(perhydroazepin-1-ylmethyleneamino)penicillanate see Pivmecillinam.

Pivaloyloxymethyl 6-(α-D-phenylglycylamino)penicillanate see Pivampicillin.

Pivalylindandione see Pindone.

'Pivalyl valone' see Pindone.

'Pivalyn' see Pindone.

PIVAMPICILLIN*** (hydroxymethyl 6-D(−)-(α-aminophenylacetamido)penicillinate pivalate; pivaloyloxymethyl (6R)-6-(α-D-phenylglycylamino)penicillanate; ampicillin hydroxymethyl ester pivalate (ester); pivampicillin hydrochloride; 'berocillin'; 'maxifen'; 'pivatil'; 'pondocillin').

Pivampicillin p-(dipropylsulfamoyl)benzoate see Pivampicillin probenate.

PIVAMPICILLIN PROBENATE* (pivampicillin p-(dipropylsulfamoyl)benzoate; pivampicillin probenecid ester; pivampicillin probenicidate; MK-356).

'Pivatil' see Pivampicillin.

Pivazide see Pivhydrazine.

PIVENFRINE*** ((±)-3-[1-hydroxy-2-(methylamino)ethyl]phenyl pivalate; (±)-α-[(methylamino)methyl]-3-[(trimethylacetyl)oxy]benzyl alcohol).

PIVHYDRAZINE* (1-benzyl-2-(trimethylacetyl)-hydrazine; 1-benzyl-2-pivaloylhydrazine; pivalic acid benzylhydrazide; betamezid; pivazide; Ro 4-1634; 'tersavid').

PIVMECILLINAM*** (pivaloyloxymethyl (2S,5R,6R)-6-(perhydroazepin-1-ylmethyleneamino)penicillanate; mecillinam hydroxymethyl ester pivalate (ester); FL-1039; 'selexid').

PIVOXAZEPAM*** (oxazepam pivalate ester; oxazepam trimethylacetate).

Pivsulbactam* see Sulbactam pivoxil.

PIZOTIFEN*** (4-(9,10-dihydro-4H-benzo-[4,5]cyclohepta[1,2-b]thien-4-ylidene)-1-methylpiperidine; 9,10-dihydro-4-(1-methylpiperid-4-ylidene)-4H-benzo[4,5]cyclohepta[1,2-b]thiophene; pizotyline; BC-105).

PIZOTIFEN MALEATE ('litec'; 'mosegor'; 'sandomigran'; 'sanomigran').

Pizotyline* see Pizotifen.

'Placidyl' see Ethchlorvynol.

PLAFIBRIDE*** (1-[2-(p-chlorophenoxy)-2-methylpropionyl]-3-(morpholinomethyl)urea; N-[2-(p-chlorophenoxy)isobutyryl]-N'-(morpholinomethyl)urea; ITA-104).

'Planavin' see Nitralin.

'Planoform' see Butylcaine.

'Planor' see under Etynodiol diacetate.

'Planovin' see under Megestrol acetate.

Plantago ovata see Psyllium; Sodium psylliate.

'Plantavax' see Carboxin dioxide.

'Planum' see Temazepam.

'Plaquenil' see Hydroxychloroquine.

'Plasdone' see Povidone.

'Plasil' see Metoclopramide.

'Plasin' see Proguanil.

'Plasmafusin' see Dextran.

PLASMIN* (fibrinolysin; lysin; serum tryptase).

PLASMINOGEN* (plasma trypsinogen; profibrinolysin).

Plasmochin see Pamaquine.

PLASMOCID (tr) (8-[[3-(diethylamino)propyl]-amino]-6-methoxyquinoline; plasmocid dihydrochloride; plasmocid diphosphate; plasmocid methylenebis(salicylate); F-710; SN-3115; 'antimalarine'; 'plasmozid'; 'rhodoquine').

'Plasmodex' see Dextran.

Plasmokinase see Streptokinase.

Plasmoquine see Pamaquine.

Plasmoquinum see Pamaquine.

'Plasmosan' see Povidone.

'Plasmozid' see Plasmocid.

'Plastenan' see Acexamic acid.

'Platinex' see Cisplatin.

'Platinol' see Cisplatin.

cis-Platinum (II) diaminodichloride see Cisplatin.

PLATYNECINE (2,3,5,6,7,7aα-hexahydro-7β-hydroxy-1H-pyrrolizine-1β-methanol).

PLAUNOTOL*** ((2Z,6E)-2-[(3E)-4,8-dimethyl-3,7-nonadienyl]-6-methyl-2,6-octadiene-1,8-diol).

PLAURACIN** (antibiotic complex from Actinoplanes auranticolor; CP-38754).

'Plavolex' see Dextran.

'Plecton' see Cicloxilic acid.

'Plegicil' see Acepromazine.

'Plegicin' see Acepromazine.

'Plegicyl' see Acepromazine.

'Plegine' see Phendimetrazine.

'Pleiatensin' see under Bietaserpine.

'Plenastril' see Oxymetholone.

'Plenosol' see Viscum album.

'Pleocide' see Aminitrozole.

'Plesmet' see Ferroglycine sulfate.

'Plethorit-C' see Hydralazine.

'Plethoryl' see under Tiratricol.

PLEUROMULIN*** (glycolic acid 8-ester with octahydro-5,8-dihydroxy-4,6,9,10-tetramethyl-6-vinyl-3a,9-propano-3aH-cyclopentacycloocten-1(4H)-one).

'Plexiglas' see Polymethyl methacrylate.

'Plexochrom' see Trisodium edetate.

'Plexofer' see Sodium feredetate.

'Plexombrine' see Meglumine acetrizoate.

PLICAMYCIN** (antibiotic from Str. argillaceus, Str. plicatis and Str. tanashiensis; mithramycin; A-2371; NSC-24559; PA-144; 'mithracin').

'Plictran' see Cyhexatin.

'Plitican' see Alizapride.

'Plitrexyl' see Ampicillin.

PLUMBAGIN (5-hydroxy-2-methyl-1,4-naphthoquinone).

'Plurine' see Hydroflumethiazide.

'Pluronic' see Poloxamer.

'Pluryl' see Bendroflumethiazide.

PLV-2 see Felypressin.

PM-241 see Pheniramine.

PM-245 see Phenbenzamine.

PM-254 see Phenindamine.

PM-255 *see* Diphenhydramine.
PM-262 *see* Methapyrilene.
PM-265 *see* Antazoline.
PM-273 *see* Mepyramine.
PM-284 *see* Promethazine.
PM-297 *see* Glaziovine.
PM-334 *see* Phensuximide.
PM-396 *see* Mesuximide.
PM-671 *see* Ethosuximide.
PM-1807 *see* Fenimide.
PM-1952 *see* Fenacetinol.
PM-3944 *see* Flucetorex.
PM-185184 *see* Secnidazole.
PMC *see* Leptacline.
PMP *see* Tolperisone.
PMS *see* Serum gonadotrophin.
PMSG *see* Serum gonadotrophin.
'Pneumorel' *see* Fenspiride.
PNIA-17370 *see* Resmethrin.
PNS *see* Nandrolone (p-hexyloxy)hydrocinnamate.
PODILFEN*** (1-(α-methyl-3,4-methylenedioxyphenethyl)-4-(4-methylthiazol-2-yl)piperazine).
Podophyllic acid ethylhydrazide *see* Mitopodozide.
PODOPHYLLOTOXIN (5,8,8a,9-tetrahydro-9-hydroxy-5-(3,4,5-trimethoxyphenyl)furo-[3',4':6,7]naphtho[2,3-*d*]-1,3-dioxol-6(5a*H*)-one; 1,2,3,4-tetrahydro-1-hydroxy-2-(hydroxymethyl)-6,7-methylenedioxy)-4-(3,4,5-trimethoxyphenyl)naphthalene-3-carboxylic acid lactone; NSC-24818).
PODOPHYLLOTOXIN BENZYLIDENE GLUCOSIDE (SPG-827).
POISONOAK EXTRACT* (extract of *Toxicodendron quercifolium*; 'anergex').
'Pol 35' *see under* Co-dergocrine.
'Pol 65' *see* Carbocisteine.
POLACRILIN*** (divinylbenzene-methacrylic acid polymer; polacrilin potassium; 'amberlite IRP-88').
'Polamidone' *see* Methadone.
'Polaramine' *see* Dexchlorpheniramine.
'Polaronil' *see* Dexchlorpheniramine.
'Polase' *see under* Potassium aspartate.
'Polawax' *see* Polysorbate 80.
POLDINE METILSULFATE** (2-(hydroxymethyl)-1,1-dimethylpyrrolidinium methylsulfate benzilate; IS-499; McN-R-726-47).
'Poldone' *see* Poldine metilsulfate.
'Polfamycine' *see* Tetracycline.
'Polfos' *see* Bromfenvinfos-methyl.
POLI 67 *see* Tetridamine.
'Polibutin' *see* Trimebutine.
POLICAPRAM** (poly[imino(1-oxo-1,6-hexanediyl)]; poly(iminocarbonylpentamethylene); caprolactam polymer; 'aviamide-6').
POLIDEXIDE SULFATE*** (dextran 2-(diethylamino)ethyl 2-[(2-diethylaminoethyl)diethylammonio]ethyl ether sulfate epichlorohydrin crosslinked; PDX; 'secholex').
POLIDOCANOL*** (polyethylene glycol monododecyl ether (av. polymer n = 9); α-dodecyl-ω-hydroxypoly(oxy-1,2-ethanediyl); hydroxypoly-ethoxydodecane; nonaethylene glycol monododecyl ether; oxypolyethoxydodecane; polyethylene glycol monododecyl ether; polyoxyethylene lauryl ether; laureth 9; 'aethoxysklerol'; 'aetoxisclerol'; 'ethoxysclerol'; 'pistocaine').
POLIGEENAN*** (3,6-anhydro-4-*O*-β-D-galactopyranosyl-α-D-galactopyranose 2,4'-bis(potassium/sodium sulfate)(1→3')polysaccharide; polygalactosulfate; carrageenin depolymerization product; carrageenan degradation product; *Euchema spinosum* degradation product; C-16; 'ebimar').
POLIGNATE SODIUM* (lignosulfonic acid sodium salt; sodium lignosulfate; AHR-2438B).
POLIHEXANIDE*** (poly(iminoimidocarbonyliminoimidocarbonyliminohexamethylene monohydrochloride); poly(1-hexamethylenebiguanide hydrochloride); polyhexanide).
Poliklorkamfen (tr) *see* Campheclor.
'Polimucil' *see under* Carbocisteine.
'Polinalin' *see* Aminophenazone.
POLISAPONIN*** (total steroid saponins from *Dioscorea polystachya*).
'Polistine' *see* Carbinoxamine.
POLITEF** (poly(tetrafluoroethylene); polytef; ftoroplast; PTFE; 'fluon'; 'teflon').
'Poliuron' *see* Bendroflumethiazide.
'Polival' *see* Tiabendazole.
'Polmiror' *see* Nifuratel.
'Polocaine' *see* Phenacaine.
'Pologols' *see* Macrogol(s).
POLOXALENE*** (polymer containing 67% polyoxypropylene; SK&F-18666).
Poloxalkol *see* Poloxamer.
POLOXAMER** (α-hydro-ω-hydroxypoly(oxyethylene)poly(oxypropylene) poly(oxyethylene) block copolymer(s); methyloxirane polymer(s) with oxirane; poloxalkol; polyethylene-polypropylene glycol; polyoxyethylene polyoxypropylene copolymer; 'magcyl'; 'pluronic'; 'polykol').
POLOXYL LANOLIN* (polyoxyethylene condensation products of anhydrous lanolin; 'aqualose').
Polyanetholesulfonate *see* Sodium polyanetholesulfonate(s).
POLYBENZARSOL*** (mixture of polymers from reaction of formaldehyde with 4-hydroxybenzenearsonic acid; poly(methylene-4-hydroxy-benzenearsonic acid)).
'Polybrene' *see* Hexadimethrine bromide.
Poly(butyl vinyl ether) *see* Polyvinox.
POLYCARBOPHIL*** (polyacrylic acid crosslinked with divinyl glycol; polycarbophil calcium; AHR-3260B; WL-140; 'quival').
Polycarbophil calcium *see* Polycarbophil.
Poly(carboxymethyl)ether of cellulose *see* Carmellose.
Polychlorcamphene (tr) *see* Campheclor.
POLYCHLORINATED BIPHENYL (chlorinated biphenyl; PCB; 'aroclor'; 'chlorhextol'; 'clophen'; 'dykanol'; 'inerteen'; 'kanechlor'; 'niren'; 'noflamol'; 'phenoclor'; 'pyranol'; 'therminol').
POLYCHLORINATED TERPHENYL (PCT;

'aroclor').

Polychrome *see* Esculin.

'Polycid' *see* Xantocillin.

'Polycillin' *see* Ampicillin.

POLYDEXTROSE* (D-glucose polymer reaction product with citric acid and sorbitol; CP-31081).

Poly(1,2-dicarboxy-3-hexadecyltetramethylene) *see* Surfomer.

Polydimethylsiloxane *see* Dimeticone.

POLYDIOXANONE* (poly[oxy(1-oxo-1,2-ethanediyl)oxy-1,2-ethanediyl]; poly(oxycarbonylmethyleneoxyethylene); PDS).

POLYESTRADIOL PHOSPHATE*** (polyester of estradiol and phosphoric acid; estradiol polyphosphate; polyoestradiol; SEP; Leo-114; 'estradurin').

POLYETADENE*** (1,2:3,4-diepoxybutane ethylenimine polymer; 1,2:3,4-diepoxybutane aziridine polymer; erythritol anhydride polyethylenimine polymer; polyethadene).

Polyethadene* *see* Polyetadene.

Polyethoxyquinoline *see* Ethoxyquin.

Polyethylene glycol *p*-isooctylphenyl ether *see* Octoxinol.

Polyethylene glycol mono[2-(dodecylthio)ethyl] ether *see* Laureth 10S.

Polyethylene glycol *p*-nonylphenyl ether(s) *see* Nonoxinol(s).

Polyethylene glycols *see* Macrogol(s).

Polyethylene polyamine polymer with (chloromethyl)oxirane *see* Colestipol.

Polyethylene-polypropylene glycol *see* Poloxamer.

POLY(ETHYLENETHIURAM DISULFIDE) ('polyram').

POLYFEROSE* (iron-sucrose-polymer complex; 'jefron').

Polygalactosulfate *see* Poligeenan.

Polygalacturonic acid methoxylate polysulfate *see* Mepesulfate.

POLYGELINE** (polymer of urea and polypeptides from denatured gelatin; repolymerized gelatin; 'haemaccel').

POLYGLACTIN(S)* (1,4-dioxane-2,5-dione polymer with 3,6-dimethyl-1,4-dioxane-2,5-dione; lactic acid polyester with glycolic acid; poly[(oxycarbonylmethylene)$_m$ co-oxycarbonylethylidene)$_n$]; XLG; 'vicryl').

Polyglucin (tr) *see* Dextran.

Polyglukina (tr) *see* Dextran.

POLYGLYCOLIC ACID*** (poly(oxycarbonylmethylene); PGA; 'dexon').

'Polygris' *see* Griseofulvin.

Poly(1-hexamethylenebiguanide hydrochloride) *see* Polihexanide.

Polyhexanide* *see* Polihexanide.

Polyhydroxyaluminium monocarbonate hexitol complex sodium *see* Alexitol sodium.

POLY I:C (polyinosinic acid polycytidylic acid complex; poly I:poly C; In:Cn; NSC-120949).

Poly(iminocarbonylpentamethylene) *see* Policapram.

Poly(iminoimidocarbonyliminoimidocarbonyliminohexamethylene monohydrochloride) *see* Polihexanide.

Poly[imino(1-oxo-1,6-hexanediyl)] *see* Policapram.

Polyinosinic acid polycytidylic acid complex *see* Poly I:C.

'Polykol' *see* Poloxamer.

'Polymal' *see* Macrogol stearate(s).

Polymannuronic acid *see* Alginic acid.

Poly[methi[bis(hydroxymethyl)]ureylene]amer *see* Polynoxylin.

Poly(methylene-4-hydroxy-benzenearsonic acid) *see* Polybenzarsol.

POLY(1-METHYLENEPIPERAZINE) ('viruseen').

POLYMETHYL METHACRYLATE (methyl methacrylate polymer).

'Polymox' *see* Amoxicillin.

POLYMYXIN B*** (antibiotic from *Bac. polymyxa*; 'aerosporin'; 'bacillosporin').

Polymyxin E *see* Colistin.

POLYMYXIN METHYLENESULFONIC ACID ('aremyxin').

POLYNOXYLIN*** (polymer of methylenebis-(hydroxymethyl)urea; poly[methi[bis(hydroxymethyl)]ureylene]amer; polyoxymethyleneurea).

Polyoestradiol *see* Polyestradiol phosphate.

Poly(2-oxopyrrolidin-1-ylethylene) *see* Povidone.

Poly(oxycarbonylmethylene) *see* Polyglycolic acid.

Poly[(oxycarbonylmethylene)$_m$ co-(oxycarbonylethylidene)$_n$] *see* Polyglactin(s).

Poly(oxycarbonylmethyleneoxyethylene) *see* Polydioxanone.

Poly(oxy-1,2-ethanediyloxycarbonyl-1,4-phenylenecarbonyl) *see* Pegoterate.

Polyoxyethylene lauryl ether *see* Polidocanol.

Polyoxyethylene nonylphenyl ether(s) *see* Nonoxinol(s).

Poly(oxyethyleneoxyterephthaloyl) *see* Pegoterate.

Polyoxyethylene polyoxypropylene copolymer *see* Poloxamer.

POLYOXYETHYLENE 20 SORBITAN (tris-(polyethyleneglycol 300) sorbitan ethers).

Polyoxyl 8 stearate *see* Macrogol stearate 8.

Polyoxyl 40 stearate *see* Macrogol stearate 40.

POLYOXYMETHYLENE GLYCOL (mixture of polymers of di- and trioxymethylene glycols; 'merapid').

Polyoxymethyleneurea *see* Polynoxylin.

Poly[oxy(1-oxo-1,2-ethanediyl)oxy-1,2-ethanediyl] *see* Polydioxanone.

Poly I:poly C *see* Poly I:C.

Polyporic acid *see* 2,5-Dihydroxy-3,6-diphenyl-*p*-benzoquinone.

Polyporin *see* 2,5-Dihydroxy-3,6-diphenyl-*p*-benzoquinone.

'Polypress' *see under* Prazosin.

Polypropylene glycol monooctadecyl ether *see* PPG-15 stearyl ether.

'Polyram' *see* Poly(ethylenethiuram disulfide).

'Polyran' *see* Dextran sulfate.

'Polysan' *see* Magnesium hydroxide.

Polysilane* *see* Dimeticone.

Polysiloxane *see* Dimeticone.

POLYSORBATE(S) (sorbimacrogol(s); sorethytan(s)).

POLYSORBATE 20* (polyoxyethylene 20 sorbitan monolaurate; sorbimacrogol laurate 300; sorethytan 20 monolaurate; 'emasol').

POLYSORBATE 40* (polyoxyethylene 20 sorbitan monopalmitate; sorbimacrogol palmitate 300).

POLYSORBATE 60* (polyoxyethylene 20 sorbitan monostearate; sorbimacrogol stearate 300).

POLYSORBATE 65* (polyoxyethylene 20 sorbitan tristearate; sorbimacrogol tristearate 300).

POLYSORBATE 80* (polyoxyethylene 20 sorbitan monooleate; sorbimacrogol oleate 300; sorethytan 20 monooleate; 'monitan'; 'oleothorb'; 'polawax'; 'rybadet'; 'sorbester').

POLYSORBATE 85* (polyoxyethylene 20 sorbitan trioleate; sorbimacrogol trioleate 300).

POLYSTYRENESULFONATE POTASSIUM (potassium polystyrenesulfonate; 'campanol').

POLYSTYRENESULFONATE SODIUM (sodium polystyrenesulfonate; 'kayexalate').

Polytef* see Politef.

Poly(tetrafluoroethylene) see Politef.

POLYTHIAZIDE* (6-chloro-3,4-dihydro-2-methyl-3-[[(2,2,2-trifluoroethyl)thio]methyl]-2*H*-1,2,4-benzothiadiazine-7-sulfonamide 1,1-dioxide; NSC-108161; P-2525).
See also under Prazosin.

POLYURETHANE FOAM* ('ostamer').

Polyvidone** see Povidone.

POLYVINOX* (butyl vinyl ether polymer; poly(butyl vinyl ether); Shostakovsky balsam; vinilin; vinylene).

POLYVINYL ALCOHOL (ethenol homopolymer; PVA).

POLYVINYLPYRIDINE *N*-OXIDE (PVNO; Bayer-3504; P-204).

Polyvinylpyrrolidone see Povidone.

'Polyviol' see Polyvinyl alcohol.

'Pomarsol' see Thiram.

'Pomasol' see Thiram.

'Ponalar' see Mefenamic acid.

'Ponalid' see Etybenzatropine.

'Ponderal' see Fenfluramine.

'Ponderax' see Fenfluramine.

'Ponderex' see Fenfluramine.

'Pondinil' see Mefenorex.

'Pondocillin' see Pivampicillin.

'Pondomin' see Fenfluramine.

'Ponecil' see Ampicillin.

PONFIBRATE* (ethyl *trans*-2,10-dichloro-12-methyl-12*H*-dibenzo[*d*,*g*][1,3]dioxocin-6-carboxylate).

'Ponoxylan' see Polynoxylin.

'Ponsital' see Imiclopazine.

'Ponstan' see Mefenamic acid.

'Ponstel' see Mefenamic acid.

'Ponstyl' see Mefenamic acid.

'Pontal' see Mefenamic acid.

'Pontalin' see Chlorbetamide.

'Pontocaine' see Tetracaine.

POP see Paroxypropione.

Populin see Salicin benzoate.

'Poquil' see Pyrvinium chloride.

'POR 8' see Ornipressin.

'Porcam' see Cambendazole.

PORFIROMYCIN* (6-amino-1,1a,2,8,8a,8b-hexahydro-8-(hydroxymethyl)-8a-methoxy-1,5-dimethylazirino[2',3':3,4]pyrrolo[1,2-*a*]indole-4,7-dione carbamate; methylmitomycin; NSC-56410; U-14743).

'Porfyron' see Hematoporphyrin.

'Portamycin' see Lidimycin.

'Posedrine' see Beclamide.

'Positol' see under β-Sitosterol.

POSKINE* (3-[2-phenyl-2-(propionyloxymethyl)acetoxy]-6,7-epoxytropane; propionylhyoscine; propionylscopolamine; poskine hydrobromide).

'Postafene' see Meclozine.

'Postonal' see Macrogol(s).

'Potaba' see Potassium *p*-aminobenzoate.

POTASSIUM *p*-AMINOBENZOATE ('potaba').

POTASSIUM 4-AMINOSALICYLATE ('paskalium'; 'paskate').

Potassium ascorbate flavonoid complex see Galascorbin.

POTASSIUM ASPARTATE (Wy-2837).

POTASSIUM ASPARTATE plus MAGNESIUM ASPARTATE (Wy-2657; 'cardilan'; 'conditio'; 'elozell'; 'intraion'; 'inzellon'; 'inzolen'; 'panangin'; 'polase'; 'spartase'; 'tromcardin'; 'trophicard').

Potassium bitartrate see Potassium hydrogen tartrate.

Potassium canrenoate* see Canrenoate potassium.

Potassium 7-chloro-2,3-dihydro-2-oxo-5-phenyl-1*H*-1,4-benzodiazepine-3-carboxylate see Clorazepate monopotassium.

Potassium clorazepate see Clorazepate dipotassium; Clorazepate monopotassium.

Potassium dichloroisocyanurate see Troclosene potassium.

Potassium 6,7-dihydro-17-hydroxy-3-oxo-3'*H*-cyclopropa[6,7]-17α-pregna-4,6-diene-21-carboxylate see Prorenoate potassium.

Potassium 2,3-dihydro-7-nitro-5-phenyl-1*H*-1,4-benzodiazepin-2-one-3-carboxylate see Potassium nitrazepate.

Potassium dihydroxy gluconatoaluminate see Potassium glucaldrate.

POTASSIUM DIIODOPHENOLSULFONATE (potassium 2,6-diiodo-1-phenol-4-sulfonate; potassium soziodolate).

POTASSIUM GLUCALDRATE* (potassium dihydroxy gluconatoaluminate; glucaldrate potassium; McN-R-1162-22; 'aciquel').

POTASSIUM GLUCONATE ('kaon').

Potassium guaiacol sulfonate see Sulfogaiacol.

POTASSIUM HYDROGEN TARTRATE (potassium bitartrate; cream of tartar).

Potassium menadiol disulfate see Menadiol potassium sulfate.

Potassium menaphthosulfate* *see* Menadiol potassium sulfate.

Potassium mexrenoate *see* Mexrenoate potassium.

POTASSIUM NITRAZEPATE*** (potassium 2,3-dihydro-7-nitro-5-phenyl-1*H*-1,4-benzodiazepin-2-one-3-carboxylate).

POTASSIUM PERCHLORATE ('astrumal'; 'irenat'; 'peroidin'; 'thyrochlorate').

Potassium polystyrenesulfonate *see* Polystyrenesulfonate potassium.

Potassium prorenoate *see* Prorenoate potassium.

POTASSIUM SODIUM TARTRATE (Rochelle salt; Seignette salt).

Potassium soziodolate *see* Potassium diiodophenolsulfonate.

Potassium thiophencillin* *see* Tifencillin.

Potassium troclosene *see* Troclosene potassium.

'Poteseptyl' *see under* Trimethoprim.

'Pounce' *see* Permethrin.

'Povan' *see* Pyrvinium embonate.

POVIDONE* (poly(2-oxopyrrolidin-1-ylethylene); poly(1-vinyl-2-pyrrolidinone); polyvinylpyrrolidone; polyvidone; PVP; RP-143).
    See also Povidone-iodine; Tolpovidone *and under* Sodium acetrizoate.

POVIDONE-IODINE* (complex of povidone with iodine; iodopovidone; 'betadine'; 'betaisodona'; 'bevidine'; 'disadine'; 'isodine'; 'traumasept').

'Poviol' *see* Polyvinyl alcohol.

PP-036 *see* Cloramfenicol pantotenate complex.

PP-557 *see* Permethrin.

PP-563 *see* Cyhalothrin.

PP-4420 *see* Hexamethonium bromide.

PP factor *see* Nicotinamide; Nicotinic acid.

PPG-15 STEARYL ETHER* (polypropylene glycol monooctadecyl ether; 'arlamol E').

'Pq-tus' *see under* Bromhexine.

PR-66 *see* Piperylone.

PR-741-976A *see* Somantadine.

PR-0818-156-A *see* Verilopam.

PR-870-714A *see* Veradoline.

PR-3847 *see* Teroxalene.

PRACTOLOL** (1-(*p*-acetamidophenoxy)-3-isopropylamino-2-propanol; 4'-[2-hydroxy-3-(isopropylamino)propoxy]acetanilide; AY-21011; ICI-50172; 'dalzic'; 'eraldin').
    See also under Clofibrate.

'Praenitrona' *see* Trolnitrate.

'Praequine' *see* Pamaquine.

'Pragmacort' *see under* Prednisone.

'Pragman' *see* Tolpropamine.

'Pragmazone' *see* Trazodone.

PRAJMALIUM BITARTRATE*** (*N*-propylajmalinium hydrogen tartrate; NPAP; 'neo-gilurytmal').

PRALIDOXIME CHLORIDE* (2-formyl-1-methylpyridinium chloride oxime; 2-[(hydroxyimino)methyl]-1-methylpyridinium chloride; 2-PAM chloride; 'protopam chloride').

PRALIDOXIME IODIDE*** (2-formyl-1-methylpyridinium iodide oxime; 2-[(hydroxyimino)-methyl]-1-methylpyridinium iodide; 2-pyridinal-

oxime methiodide; 2-PAM iodide; 2-picolinaldoxime methiodide; NSC-7760; 'protopam iodide').
    See also under Metrifonate.

PRALIDOXIME MESILATE (pralidoxime mesylate; pralidoxime methanesulfonate; P2S; P-2-S; RP 7676; 'contrathion').

Pralidoxime methanesulfonate *see* Pralidoxime mesilate.

Pralidoxime methyl ether *see* Obidoxime chloride.

PRALIDOXIME PHENACYL CHLORIDE (FAOP).

'Pramidex' *see* Tolbutamide.

Pramindole *see* Iprindole.

'Praminil' *see* Imipramine.

PRAMIRACETAM*** (*N*-[2-(diisopropylamino)-ethyl]-2-oxo-1-pyrrolidineacetamide).

PRAMIVERINE*** (*N*-isopropyl-4,4-diphenyl-cyclohexylamine; EMD-9806; Hsp-2986; 'sintaverin'; 'sistalgin').

PRAMOCAINE*** (*p*-butoxyphenyl 3-morpholinopropyl ether; pramoxine; pramocaine hydrochloride).

'Pramolan' *see* Opipramol.

Pramoxine* *see* Pramocaine.

PRAMPINE*** (atropine propionate ester; *O*-propionylatropine).

PRAMPINE METHONITRATE ('PAMN').

PRANOLIUM CHLORIDE*** ((2-hydroxy-3-naphth-1-yloxypropyl)isopropyldimethylammonium chloride; 2-hydroxy-*N*,*N*-dimethyl-*N*-(1-methylethyl)-3-(1-naphthalenyloxy)-1-propanaminium chloride; *N*-methylpropranolol methochloride; dimethylpropranolol; SC-27761).

PRANOLIUM IODIDE (*N*-methylpropranolol methiodide; UM-272).

PRANOPROFEN*** (α-methyl-5*H*-[1]benzopyrano[2,3-*b*]pyridine-7-acetic acid).

PRANOSAL*** (2,5-dimethyl-1-pyrrolidinepropanol salicylate (ester)).

'Pranosine' *see* Inosine pranobex.

'Prantal' *see* Diphemanil metilsulfate.

'Prantal-dithienyl' *see* Pipendyl methane.

PRASTERONE*** (3β-hydroxyandrost-5-en-17-one; 5,6-dehydroisoandrosterone; dehydroandrosterone; dehydroepiandrosterone; DHA; 'chetovis'; 'diandrone'; 'hormoformin'; 'pricosterone').

PRASTERONE ENANTATE (prasterone heptanoate).

PRASTERONE ENANTATE plus ESTRADIOL VALERATE (SH-70833).

PRATOL (7-hydroxy-4'-methoxyflavone).

'Pravacillin' *see* Metampicillin.

'Pravidel' *see* Bromocriptine mesilate.

'Pravocaine' *see* Propoxycaine.

PRAXADINE*** (pyrazole-1-carboxamidine).

'Praxilene' *see* Naftidrofuryl oxalate.

'Praxinor' *see under* Cafedrine.

'Praxiten' *see* Oxazepam.

PRAZEPAM*** (7-chloro-1-cyclopropylmethyl-1,3-dihydro-5-phenyl-2*H*-1,4-benzodiazepin-2-one; W-4020).

PRAZEPINE** (5-[3-(dimethylamino)propyl]-5,6-

dihydro-11*H*-dibenz[*b,e*]azepine; *N*-[3-(dimethyl-amino)propyl]-5,6-dihydromorphanthridine; propazepine).
'Prazil' *see* Chlorpromazine.
'Prazine' *see* Promazine.
'Prazinil' *see* Carpipramine.
PRAZIQUANTEL* (2-(cyclohexylcarbonyl)-1,3,4,6,7,11b-hexahydro-2*H*-pyrazino[2,1-*a*]-isoquinolin-4-one; EMBAY 8440; 'biltricide'; 'cesol'; 'droncit').
PRAZITONE* (5-phenyl-5-piperid-2-ylmethyl-barbituric acid; prazitone hydrochloride; AGN-511).
PRAZOCILLIN* (6-[[1-(2,6-dichlorophenyl)-4-methylpyrazol-5-yl]carboxamido]penicillanic acid; pirazocillin; pyrazocillin; F-75).
PRAZOSIN* (4-amino-2-[4-(2-furoyl)piperazin-1-yl]-6,7-dimethoxyquinazoline; 1-(4-amino-6,7-dimethoxyquinazolin-2-yl)-4-(2-furoyl)piperaz-ine; furazosin; prazosin hydrochloride; CP-12299-1; 'adversuten'; 'hypovase'; 'minipress'; 'sinetens').
PRAZOSIN plus POLYTHIAZIDE ('polypress'; 'redupront').
'Prebane' *see* Terbutryn.
Prebediolone *see* Pregnenolone.
Precipite blanc *see* Mercurous chloride.
Preconsol (tr) *see* 8-Quinolinol.
'Predef' *see* Isoflupredone acetate.
'Predenema' *see* Prednisolone sodium *m*-sulfoben-zoate.
Prednacinolone acetonide *see* Desonide.
PREDNAZATE* (compound of prednisolone 21-hydrogen succinate with perphenazine; per-phenazine-prednisolone succinate; Sch-6620).
PREDNAZOLINE* (prednisolone 21-dihydro-gen phosphate compound with 2-(2-isopropyl-phenoxymethyl)-2-imidazoline; fenoxazoline prednisolone compound; 'deturgylone').
'Prednelan' *see* Prednisolone acetate.
'Prednesol' *see* Prednisolone sodium phosphate.
PREDNICARBATE* (prednisolone 17-(ethyl carbonate) 21-propionate).
PREDNIMUSTINE* (prednisolone 21-[4-[*p*-[bis(2-chloroethyl)amino]phenyl]butyrate]; Leo 1031; NSC-134087).
PREDNISOLAMATE* (prednisolone 21-(*N,N*-diethylglycine ester); prednisolone 21-diethyl-aminoacetate; prednisolamate hydrochloride).
PREDNISOLONE* (11β,17α,21-trihydro-xypregna-1,4-diene-3,20-dione; dehydrocortisol; delta-F; deltahydrocortisone; metacortandral-one; NSC-9120).
See also under Oxyphenbutazone; Phenylbutaz-one.
Prednisolone acetamidocaproate *see* Prednisolone acexamate.
PREDNISOLONE ACETATE ('econopred'; 'infl-anefran'; 'prednelan').
PREDNISOLONE ACETATE plus CINCHOCA-INE ('anumedin').
PREDNISOLONE ACEXAMATE (prednisolone acetamidocaproate).

Prednisolone 21-[4-[*p*-[bis(2-chloroethyl)amino]-phenyl]butyrate] *see* Prednimustine.
Prednisolone *tert*-butylacetate *see* Prednisolone te-butate.
Prednisolone 21-diethylaminoacetate *see* Predniso-lamate.
Prednisolone 21-(*N,N*-diethylglycine ester) *see* Pre-dnisolamate.
Prednisolone 21-dihydrogen phosphate compound with fenoxazoline *see* Prednazoline.
Prednisolone 17-(ethyl carbonate) 21-propionate *see* Prednicarbate.
PREDNISOLONE PALMITATE ('erythran').
PREDNISOLONE PIVALATE (prednisolone tri-methylacetate; 'ultracortenol').
PREDNISOLONE SODIUM PHOSPHATE (prednisolone 21-phosphoric acid disodium salt; 'codelsol'; 'hydeltrasol'; 'inflamase'; 'prednesol'; 'predsol').
PREDNISOLONE SODIUM SUCCINATE ('so-ludacortin').
PREDNISOLONE SODIUM *m*-SULFOBENZO-ATE (R-812; 'predenema'; 'solucort'; 'so-lupred').
PREDNISOLONE STEAGLATE* (stearate ester of prednisolone 21-glycolate; 'glistelone'; 'sintisone').
PREDNISOLONE TEBUTATE* (prednisolone *tert*-butylacetate; 'codelcortone-TBA'; 'hydeltra-TBA').
Prednisolone trimethylacetate *see* Prednisolone pi-valate.
PREDNISOLONE TRIMETHYLOCTANOATE ('mecortolone').
Prednisolone valerate *see* Prednival.
PREDNISONE* (17α,21-dihydroxypregna-1,4-diene-3,11,20-trione; delta-E; deltacortisone; me-tacortandracin; NSC-10023).
PREDNISONE plus TRIAMCINOLONE ('prag-macort').
See also under Chloramphenicol; Phenylbutaz-one.
PREDNIVAL* (prednisolone 17-valerate; W-4869).
PREDNYLIDENE* (11β,17,21-trihydroxy-16-methylenepregna-1,4-diene-3,20-dione; 16-meth-yleneprednisolone; ST-104).
'Predsol' *see* Prednisolone sodium phosphate.
'Preeglone' *see* Paraquat.
'Prefar' *see* Bensulide.
PREFENAMATE* (3-methyl-2-butenyl flufen-amate; 3-methyl-2-butenyl *N*-(α,α,α-trifluoro-*m*-tolyl)anthranilate; prenyl flufenamate).
'Prefil' *see* Guar gum.
'Prefix' *see* Chlorthiamid.
'Preforan' *see* Fluorodifen.
'Prefox' *see* Ethiolate.
PREGNA-4,6-DIENE-3,20-DIONE (6-dehydro-progesterone).
9β,10α-Pregna-4,6-diene-3,20-dione *see* Dydro-gesterone.
17α-Pregna-2,4-dien-20-yno[2,3-*d*]isoxazol-17-ol *see* Danazol.

429

Pregnancy urine extract *see* Chorionic gonadotrophin.

Pregnane *see* 5β-Pregnane.

5α-PREGNANE (17β-ethyl-5α-androstane; 17β-ethyletioallocholane; allopregnane).

5β-PREGNANE (17β-ethyl-5β-androstane; 17β-ethyletiocholane; pregnane).

Pregnane-3,11,17,20,21-pentol *see* Cortol; β-Cortol.

PREGNAN-20-ONE (17-acetylandrostane).

Pregnant mare serum gonadotrophin *see* Serum gonadotrophin.

PREGN-20-ENE (17β-vinylandrostane).

4-Pregnene-3,20-dione *see* Progesterone.

9β,10α-Pregn-4-ene-3,20-dione *see* Retroprogesterone.

4-PREGNENE-3,11,20-TRIONE (11-ketoprogesterone; 11-oxoprogesterone; Bio-66; U-1258; 'ketogestin').

Pregneninolone *see* Ethisterone.

Pregneninonol *see* Ethisterone.

PREGNENOLONE*** (3β-hydroxypregn-5-en-20-one; prebediolone).

PREGNENOLONE ACETATE (acetoxypregnenolone).

PREGNENOLONE SUCCINATE* (pregnenolone hydrogen succinate; 'panzalone').

'Pregnesin' *see* Chorionic gonadotrophin.

Pregnin (tr) *see* Ethisterone.

Pregnocin *see* Hydroxydione sodium succinate.

'Pregnon 28' *see under* Ethinylestradiol.

'Pregnyl' *see* Chorionic gonadotrophin.

PREGN-20-YNE (17-ethynylandrostane).

'Pregova' *see* Human menopausal gonadotrophin.

'Prelis' *see* Metoprolol.

'Preludin' *see* Phenmetrazine.

'Premar' *see* Ritodrine.

'Premarin' *see* Conjugated estrogens equine.

PREMAZEPAM*** (3,7-dihydro-6,7-dimethyl-5-phenylpyrrolo[3,4-*e*]-1,4-diazepin-2(1*H*)-one; 1,2,3,7-tetrahydro-6,7-dimethyl-5-phenylpyrrolo[3,4-*e*]-1,4-diazepin-2-one; DL-181-IT; L-12181; MDL-181).

'Premerge' *see* Dinoseb trolamine.

'Preminex' *see* Mebutamate.

'Prempak' *see under* Conjugated estrogens.

PRENALTEROL*** ((−)-(*S*)-1-(*p*-hydroxyphenoxy)-3-(isopropylamino)-2-propanol; CGP-7760; H-80/62; H-133/22; 'hyprenan'; 'tonoplus'; 'varbian').

Prenazone *see* Feprazone.

PRENISTEINE*** (3-[(3-methyl-2-butenyl)thio]-L-alanine).

Prenol *see* 3-Methyl-2-buten-1-ol.

PRENOVERINE*** ((±)-2'-(diphenylmethoxy)-*N*,1-dimethyl-2-phenoxydiethylamine).

PRENOXDIAZINE (3-(2,2-diphenylethyl)-5-(2-piperid-1-ylethyl)-1,2,4-oxadiazole). *See also under* Carbocisteine.

PRENOXDIAZINE plus DIPHENHYDRAMINE ('lomapect').

PRENOXDIAZINE HIBENZATE (prenoxdiazine benzhydrate; prenoxdiazine o-(p-hydroxybenzo-yl)benzoate).

'Prensols' *see* Hexylresorcinol.

'Prent' *see* Acebutolol.

'Prentif' *see* Hexylresorcinol.

PRENYLAMINE*** (*N*-(3,3-diphenylpropyl)-α-methylphenethylamine; *N*-(3,3-diphenylpropyl)-amphetamine; prenylamine lactate; B-436).

4-Prenyl-1,2-diphenyl-3,5-pyrazolidinedione *see* Feprazone.

Prenyl flufenamate *see* Prefenamate.

'Preortan' *see* Ornithine carbamyl transferase.

'Pre-par' *see* Ritodrine.

'Preparin' *see* Ethaverine.

'Prequine' *see* Pamaquine.

'Presamine' *see* Imipramine.

'Pre-sate' *see* Chlorphentermine.

'Presid' *see* Hydroxindasol.

'Presidal' *see* Pentacynium chloride.

'Presidon' *see* Pyrithyldione.

'Presinol' *see* Methyldopa.

'Presomen' *see* Conjugated estrogens equine.

'Pressamina' *see* Dimetofrine.

'Pressedrine' *see* Phenylpropanolamine.

'Pressimune' *see* Antilymphocyte immunoglobulin (horse).

'Pressionorm' *see* Gepefrine.

'Pressomin' *see* Methoxamine.

'Pressonex' *see* Metaraminol.

'Pressoton' *see* Etilefrine.

'Prestim' *see under* Timolol maleate.

'Prestonal' *see* Prodeconium bromide.

'Presuren' *see* Hydroxydione sodium succinate.

'Presyn' *see* Allethrin.

PRETAMAZIUM IODIDE*** (4-(4-biphenylyl)-3-ethyl-2-(*p*-pyrrolidin-1-ylstyryl)thiazolium iodide).

PRETHCAMIDE* (crotetamide plus cropropamide; G-5668; 'micoren'; 'respirot').

PRETIADIL*** (6,11-dihydro-6-methyl-11[3-[methyl(α-methylphenethyl)amino]propyl]dibenzo[1,2,5]thiadiazepine 5,5-dioxide; *N*-[3-(6,11-dihydro-6-methyl-5,5-dioxidodibenzo-[1,2,5]thiadiazepin-11-yl)propyl]-*N*,α-dimethylphenethylamine).

'Pretonine' *see* Oxitriptan.

'Prevenol' *see* Bithionol.

'Preventa' *see under* Anagestone acetate.

'Preventol-G-D' *see* Dichlorophen.

'Prevepen' *see* Propicillin.

'Previcur' *see* Propamocarb.

PRF-36 *see* Setazindol.

PR-G 138-CL *see* Ciclosidomine.

'Priadel' *see* Lithium carbonate.

'Priamide' *see* Isopropamide iodide.

PRIBECAINE*** (3-piperid-1-ylpropyl *m*-anisate; 3-piperid-1-ylpropyl *m*-methoxybenzoate).

'Pricosterone' *see* Prasterone.

'Pridazol' *see* Tolazoline.

PRIDEFINE*** (3-(diphenylmethylene)-1-ethylpyrrolidine; pridefine hydrochloride; AHR-1118).

PRIDINOL*** (1,1-diphenyl-3-piperidino-1-propanol; pridinol mesilate; pridinol methanesulfonate; C-238).

PRIFINIUM BROMIDE* (3-(diphenylmethyl-ene)-1,1-diethyl-2-methylpyrrolidinium bromide; PDB; prodifenium bromide; 'padrin'; 'riabal').

PRIFUROLINE* (4-(2-benzofuranyl)-2-(dimethylamino)-1-pyrroline).

PRILOCAINE* (2-(propylamino)-*o*-propiono-toluidide; 2'-methyl-2-(propylamino)propion-anilide; *N*-[2-(propylamino)propionyl]-*o*-toluid-ine; propitocaine; prilocaine hydrochloride; As-tra-1512; L-67).

'Primacaine' see Metabutoxycaine.

Primaclone see Primidone.

'Primalan' see Mequitazine.

'Primamycin' see Hamycin.

PRIMAPERONE (4'-fluoro-4-piperid-1-ylbuty-rophenone; 1-[3-(*p*-fluorobenzoyl)propyl]pip-eridine).

PRIMAQUINE* (8-(4-amino-1-methylbutyl-amino)-6-methoxyquinoline; SN-13272).
See also under Amodiaquine.

PRIMIDOLOL* (1-[2-[[2-hydroxy-3-(2-methyl-phenoxy)propyl]amino]ethyl]-5-methyl-2,4-pyr-imidinedione; 1-[2-[[2-hydroxy-3-(*o*-toloxy)prop-yl]amino]ethyl]thymine; UK-11443).

PRIMIDONE* (5-ethyldihydro-5-phenyl-4,6(1*H*,5*H*)-pyrimidinedione; desoxyphenobar-bital; hexamidin; primaclone).

PRIMIN (6-methoxy-6-pentyl-*p*-benzoquinone; primula antigen).

'Primin' see 1-Isopropyl-3-methylpyrazol-5-yl di-methylcarbamate.

'Primobolan' see Metenolone.

'Primofax' see Nosiheptide.

'Primolut depot' see Hydroxyprogesterone capro-ate.

'Primolut N' see Norethisterone.

'Primperan' see Metoclopramide.

PRIMULETIN (5-hydroxyflavone).

PRIMYCIN ([5-[19-(α-D-arabinofuranosyloxy)-35-butyl-10,12,14,16,18,22,26,30,34-nonahydr-oxy-3,5,21,33-tetramethyl-36-oxooxacyclohexa-triaconta-4,20-dien-2-yl]-4-hydroxyhexyl]gua-nidine; 'debrycen').

'Prinadol' see Phenazocine.

'Prinalgin' see Alclofenac.

'Principen' see Ampicillin.

Prinodolol* see Pindolol.

'Priodax' see 3f1Pheniodal sodium.

'Prioderm' see Malathion.

'Priscol' see Tolazoline.

'Priscoline' see Tolazoline.

'Prisilidene' see Alphaprodine.

PRISTANE (2,6,10,14-tetramethylpentadecane; norphytane).

PRISTINAMYCIN* (antibiotic from *Str. pristi-na spiralis*; RP 7293).

'Privine' see Naphazoline.

PRIZIDILOL* (1-(*tert*-butylamino)-3-[*o*-(6-hydrazinopyridazin-3-yl)phenoxy]-2-propanol; prizidilol hydrochloride; SK&F-92657).

PRN see Phenyltoloxamine.

'Pro-actidil' see Triprolidine.

PROADIFEN* (2-(diethylamino)ethyl diphenyl-valerate; 2-(diethylamino)ethyl diphenylpropyl-acetate; proadifen hydrochloride; NSC-39690; RP 5171; SK&F-525-A).

Proazamine see Promethazine.

'Proban' see Cythioate.

PROBARBITAL SODIUM* (sodium derivative of 5-ethyl-5-isopropylbarbituric acid; ethypropy-mal).

'Probe' see Chlormethazole.

'Probecid' see Probenecid.

PROBENECID* (*p*-(dipropylsulfamoyl)benzoic acid; etamid; ethamid).
See also Pivampicillin probenate.

'Probenid' see Probenecid.

Probicromil see Ambicromil.

'Probilin' see Piprozolin.

'Probon' see Rimazolium metilsulfate.

PROBUCOL* (acetone bis(3,5-di-*tert*-butyl-4-hydroxyphenyl)mercaptole; 4,4'-isopropylidene-dithiobis(2,6-di-*tert*-butylphenol); ditiobisfenol; DH-581; 'biphenabid'; 'lorelco'; 'lurselle').

'Probunafon' see Levopropoxyphene dibudinate.

'Procacillin' see Procaine-penicillin.

PROCAINAMIDE* (*p*-amino-*N*-[2-(diethyl-amino)ethyl]benzamide; procaine amide; pro-cainamide hydrochloride).

PROCAINAMIDE plus QUINIDINE ('rhyth-mochin').

PROCAINE* (2-(diethylamino)ethyl *p*-amino-benzoate; H-3).

PROCAINE plus vitamin mixture ('aslavital').

Procaine amide see Procainamide.

PROCAINE-CAFFEINE COMPLEX ('impletol').

Procaine 8-chlorotheophyllinate see Procaine teo-clate.

PROCAINE-PENICILLIN (compound of 2 mol. procaine with 1 mol. penicillin G; novocillin; penicillin-procaine).
See also under Dihydrostreptomycin.

PROCAINE TEOCLATE (procaine 8-chlorotheo-phyllinate; procaine theoclate; 'francaine').

'Procalm' see Benactyzine.

Procalmadiol see Meprobamate.

PROCARBAZINE* (*N*-isopropyl-α-(2-methyl-hydrazino)-*p*-toluamide; 1-(4-isopropylcarbamo-ylbenzyl)-2-methylhydrazine; ibenzmethyzin; MIH; procarbazine hydrochloride; NSC-77213; Ro 4-6467).

PROCATEROL* (1-(8-hydroxy-2-oxoquinolin-5-yl)-2-isopropylamino-1-butanol; (±)-(*R,S*)-8-hydroxy-5-[1-hydroxy-2-[(1-methylethyl)amino]-butyl]-2(1*H*)-quinolinone; (±)-*erythro*-8-hydr-oxy-5-[1-hydroxy-2-(isopropylamino)butyl]car-bostyril; procaterol hydrochloride; CI-888; OPC-2009).

Procetofene* see Fenofibrate.

PROCHLORAZ (*N*-propyl-*N*-[2-(2,4,6-trichloro-phenoxy)ethyl]-1*H*-imidazole-1-carboxamide; BTS-40542).

Prochlorpemazine see Prochlorperazine.

PROCHLORPERAZINE* (2-chloro-10-[3-(4-methylpiperazin-1-yl)-propyl]phenothiazine;

chlormeprazine; chlorperazine; meterazine; prochlorpemazine; prochlorperazine maleate; RP 6140; SK&F-4657).

PROCINOLOL*** (1-(*o*-cyclopropylphenoxy)-3-isopropylamino-2-propanol; SD-2124-01).

PROCINONIDE*** (6α,9-difluoro-11β-hydroxy-16α,17-[(1-methylethylidene)bis(oxy)]-21-(1-oxopropoxy)pregna-1,4-diene-3,20-dione; fluocinolone acetonide 21-propionate; RS-2362).

'Proclival' *see* Bufeniode.

PROCLONOL*** (α,α-bis(*p*-chlorophenyl)cyclopropanemethanol; 2,2'-dichloro-α-cyclopropylbenzhydrol; R-8284).

'Procoagulo' *see* Menadiol sodium phosphate.

PROCODAZOLE*** (2-benzimidazolepropionic acid).

'Procol' *see* Phenylpropanolamine.

'Procortan' *see* Corticotrophin.

'Procortolon' *see* Triamcinolone.

'Procorum' *see* Gallopamil.

PROCROMIL* (6,7,8,9-tetrahydro-4-oxo-10-propylbenzo[*g*]chromene-2-carboxylic acid; 6,7,8,9-tetrahydro-4-oxo-10-propyl-4*H*-naphtho[2,3-*b*]pyran-2-carboxylic acid).

'Procto-glyvenol' *see* Tribenoside.

PROCYCLIDINE*** (α-cyclohexyl-α-phenyl-1-pyrrolidinepropanol; procyclidine hydrochloride).

Procyclidine methochloride *see* Tricyclamol chloride.

PROCYMATE** (1-cyclohexylpropyl carbamate).

'Procytox' *see* Cyclophosphamide.

PRODECONIUM BROMIDE*** (dipropyl ester of [decamethylenebis(oxymethylene)]bis[(carboxymethyl)dimethylammonium bromide]; 3,14-dioxahexadecamethylene-1,16-bis[(carbopropoxymethyl)dimethylammonium bromide]; dioxahexadekanium bromide; G-25178).

'Prodectin' *see* Pyricarbate.

'Prodermide' *see* Sodium dodecyl sulfate.

'Pro-diaban' *see* Glisoxepide.

'Prodiaben' *see* Chlorpropamide.

Prodifenium bromide *see* Prifinium bromide.

PRODILIDINE*** (1,2-dimethyl-3-phenyl-3-pyrrolidyl propionate; prodilidine hydrochloride; A-1981-12; CI-427).

PRODIPINE** (1-isopropyl-4,4-diphenylpiperidine).

PRODOLIC ACID*** (1,3,4,9-tetrahydro-1-propylpyrano[3,4-*b*]indole-1-acetic acid; AY-23289).

'Prodox' *see* Hydroxyprogesterone acetate.

'Prodoxol' *see* Oxolinic acid.

'Produral' *see* Procaine-penicillin.

PROFADOL*** (3-(*m*-hydroxyphenyl)-1-methyl-3-propylpyrrolidine; *m*-(1-methyl-3-propylpyrrolidin-3-yl)phenol; profadol hydrochloride; A-2205; CI-572).

'Profasi' *see* Chorionic gonadotrophin.

PROFENAMINE*** (10-[2-(diethylamino)propyl]phenothiazine; ethopropazine; prophenamine; isothazine; isothiazine; parfezin; phenopropazine; profenamine hydrochloride; RP 3356; SC-2538).

'Profenid' *see* Ketoprofen.

'Profenil' *see* Alverine.

'Profenone' *see* Paroxypropione.

PROFEXALONE*** (2-oxo-5-phenyl-*N*-propyloxazolidine-3-carboxamide).

Profibrinolysin *see* Plasminogen.

PROFLAVINE** (3,6-diaminoacridine).

PROFLAZEPAM** (7-chloro-1-(2,3-dihydroxypropyl)-5-(*o*-fluorophenyl)-1,3-dihydro-2*H*-1,4-benzodiazepin-2-one).

Proformiphen *see* Phenprobamate.

PROGABIDE*** (4-[[(4-chlorophenyl)(5-fluoro-2-hydroxyphenyl)methylidene]amino]butyramide; 4-[[α-(*p*-chlorophenyl)-5-fluorosalicylidene]amino]butyramide; halogabide; SL-76002).

'Pro-gen' *see* Arsanilic acid.

'Progeril' *see under* Co-dergocrine.

'Progeryl' *see under* Co-dergocrine.

'Progesic' *see* Fenoprofen calcium.

PROGESTERONE*** (4-pregnene-3,20-dione; corpus luteum hormone; luteohormone; NSC-9704).

Progesterone hydroxycaproate *see* Progesterone hydroxyhexanoate.

PROGESTERONE HYDROXYHEXANOATE (progesterone hydroxycaproate). *See also under* Estradiol valerate.

9β,10α-Progesterone *see* Retroprogesterone.

'Proglicem' *see* Diazoxide.

PROGLUMETACIN*** (3-[4-[2-[[1-(*p*-chlorobenzoyl)-5-methoxy-2-methyl-indol-3-yl]acetoxy]ethyl]piperazin-1-yl]propyl 4-benzamido-*N*,*N*-dipropylglutaramate; 3-[4-(2-hydroxyethyl)piperazin-1-yl]propyl DL-4-benzamido-*N*,*N*-dipropylglutaramate 1-(*p*-chlorobenzoyl)-5-methoxy-2-methylindole-3-acetate).

PROGLUMETACIN DIMALEATE (protacin; CR-604; 'protaxil').

PROGLUMIDE*** (DL-4-benzamido-*N*,*N*-dipropylglutaramic acid; (±)-5-(benzoylamino)-5-(dimethylamino)-5-oxopentanoic acid; xilamide; CR-242; KXM; W-5219).

PROGLUMIDE plus SCOPOLAMINE BUTYL BROMIDE (CR-242-B; 'buscalide').

'Proguanide' *see* Proguanil.

PROGUANIL*** (1-(*p*-chlorophenyl)-5-isopropylbiguanide; chloroguanide; bigumal; chlorguanide; chloriguane; chloroguanil; diguanyl; proguanil hydrochloride; M-4888; RP 3359; SN-12837).

Proguanil metabolite *see* Cycloguanil.

'Progylut' *see under* Estradiol valerate.

'Progynon-DP' *see* Estradiol dipropionate.

'Progynova' *see* Estradiol valerate.

'Prohalone' *see* Haloprogesterone.

Proheptadiene *see* Amitriptyline.

PROHEPTATRIENE (5-[3-(dimethylamino)propylidene]dibenzocycloheptene).

PROHEPTAZINE*** (1,3-dimethyl-4-phenyl-4-propionoxyazacycloheptane; hexahydro-1,3-dimethyl-4-phenylazepin-4-ol propionate ester; Wy-757).

'Prokarbol' *see* Dinitro-*o*-cresol.

432

Proketazine *see* Carfenazine.

Proketofen *see* Fenofibrate.

PROLACTIN (galactin; lactogen; luteotropic hormone; luteotropin; mammotropin; LTH; IIH P-S10; NIN PD-3).

'Proladone' *see* Oxycodone.

'Proladyl' *see* Pyrrobutamine.

'Prolan' *see* Chorionic gonadotrophin.

'Prolate' *see* Phosmet.

'Prolergic' *see* Cycliramine.

PROLIGESTONE* (14,17-dihydroxypregn-4-ene-3,20-dione cyclic acetal with propionaldehyde; 14,17-dihydroxyprogesterone cyclic acetal with propionaldehyde; 'delvosteron').

'Proligne' *see* Amfepentorex.

PROLINE (2-pyrrolidinecarboxylic acid).

PROLINTANE* (1 (α-propylphenethyl)pyrrolidine; 1-phenyl-2-pyrrolidinopentane; phenylpyrrolidinopentane; prolintane hydrochloride; SP-732).

'Prolixan 300' *see* Azapropazone.

'Prolixene' *see* Fluphenazine.

'Prolixin' *see* Fluphenazine.

'Proloid' *see* Thyroglobulin.

'Prolongine' *see* Probenecid.

PROLONIUM IODIDE* (2-hydroxytrimethylene-1,3-bis(trimethylammonium iodide); 1,3-bis-(dimethylamino)-2-propanol dimethiodide; hydroxytrimethonium iodide; propiodal).

'Proluton C' *see* Ethisterone.

'Proluton depot' *see* Hydroxyprogesterone caproate.

L-Prolyl-N-methyl-D-leucylglycinamide *see* Pareptide.

'Proma' *see* Promazine.

'Promactil' *see* Chlorpromazine.

'Promantine' *see* Promazine.

'Promanyl' *see* Promazine.

'Promapar' *see* Chlorpromazine.

'Promaquid' *see* Dimetotiazine mesilate.

PROMAZINE ** (10-[3-(dimethylamino)propyl]-phenothiazine; promazine hydrochloride; propazin; A-145; RP 3276; Wy-1094).
See also under Methaqualone.

'Promazol' *see* Chlorpromazine.

PROMECARB* (3-isopropyl-5-methylphenyl methylcarbamate; 3-methyl-5-(1-methylethyl)-phenyl methylcarbamate; 'carbamult'; 'minacide').

'Promecon' *see* Benzquinamide.

Promedol (tr) *see* Trimeperidine.

PROMEGESTONE* (17α-methyl-17-propionylestra-4,9-dien-3-one; 'surgestone').

PROMELASE ** (*Aspergillus melleus* alkaline proteinase).

Promeran (tr) *see* Chlormerodrin.

PROMESTRIENE ** (estradiol 17β-methyl ether 3-propyl ether; 17β-methoxy-3-propoxyestra-1,3,5(10)-triene; 'colpotrophin'; 'delipoderm').

PROMETHAZINE* (10-[2-(dimethylamino)-propyl]phenothiazine; difasin; difazin; diphasin; diphazin; diprazin; proazamine; promethazine hydrochloride; PM-284; RP-3389; RP 3277; RP 4460).

Promethazine 8-chlorotheophyllinate *see* Promethazine teoclate.

PROMETHAZINE S,S-DIOXIDE (9,9-dioxopromethazine; 'prothanon').

PROMETHAZINE HYDROXYETHYL CHLORIDE ((2-hydroxyethyl)dimethyl-[1-(10-phenothiazinylmethyl)ethyl]ammonium chloride; N-hydroxyethylpromethazine; 'aprobit').

Promethazine methyl methosulfate *see* Thiazinamium metilsulfate.

PROMETHAZINE TEOCLATE* (promethazine 8-chlorotheophyllinate; promethazine theoclate; 'avomine').

Promethestrol *see* Methestrol dipropionate.

Promethin (tr) *see* Pholedrine.

Promethoestrol *see* Methestrol dipropionate.

PROMETON* (4,6-bis(isopropylamino)-2-methoxy-s-triazine; 6-methoxy-N,N'-bis(1-methylethyl)-1,3,5-triazine-2,4-diamine).

PROMETRYN* (N,N'-bis(1-methylethyl)-6-(methylthio)-1,3,5-triazine-2,4-diamine; 4,6-bis-(isopropylamino)-2-(methylthio)-s-triazine; 'caparol'; 'gesagard').

'Promiben' *see* Imipramine.

'Promilene' *see* Promazine.

'Prominal' *see* Methylphenobarbital.

'Prominthic' *see* Metyridine.

'Promizole' *see* Thiazosulfone.

PROMOLATE* (2-morpholinoethyl 2-methyl-2-phenoxypropionate; 2-morpholinoethyl 2-phenoxyisobutyrate; morphethylbutyne).

'Promone E' *see* Medroxyprogesterone acetate.

PROMOXOLANE* (2,2-diisopropyl-1,3-dioxolane-4-methanol; diisopropylmethanoldioxolane).

'Promwill' *see* Promazine.

'Pronarcon' *see* Enibomal.

'Prondol' *see* Iprindole.

'Pronestyl' *see* Procainamide.

PRONETALOL* (α-[(isopropylamino)methyl]-2-naphthalenemethanol; pronethalol; nethalide; pronetalol hydrochloride; AY-6204; ICI-38174).

Pronethalol* *see* Pronetalol.

'Prontosil' *see* Sulfachrysoidine; Sulfamidochrysoidine.

'Prontosil album' *see* Sulfanilamide.

'Prontosil soluble' *see* Azosulfamide.

'Prontylin' *see under* Aminophenazone.

PROPACETAMOL ** (N,N-diethylglycine ester with 4'-hydroxyacetanilide; paracetamol diethylglycinate).

PROPACHLOR* (2-chloro-N-(1-methylethyl)-N-phenylacetamide; 2-chloro-N-isopropylacetanilide; 'ramrod').

'Propaderm' *see* Beclometasone dipropionate.

'Propadrine' *see* Phenylpropanolamine.

'Propaesin' *see* Risocaine.

PROPAFENONE* (2'-[2-hydroxy-3-(propylamino)propoxy]-3-phenylpropiophenone; fenoprain; propafenone hydrochloride; SA-79; WZ-884; 'baxarytmon'; 'rhythmonorm'; 'rytmonorm').

433

'**Propagin**' *see* Propyl paraben.
PROPALLYLONAL* (5-(2-bromoallyl)-5-isopropylbarbituric acid; bromoaprobarbital).
PROPAMIDINE*** (*p,p'*-(trimethylenedioxy)dibenzamidine; 4,4'-diamidinodiphenoxypropane; propamidine di(ethanol-2-sulfonate); propamidine diisethionate; propamidine isetionate; M & B-782).
PROPAMOCARB* (propyl [3-(dimethylamino)-propyl]carbamate; propamocarb hydrochloride; 'previcur').
Propanal *see* Propionaldehyde.
1,3-PROPANEDIAMINE (propylenediamine).
Propanedioic acid *see* Malonic acid.
1,2-Propanediol *see* Propylene glycol.
1,3-Propanediol bis[2-(*p*-chlorophenoxy)isobutyrate] *see* Simfibrate.
2,3-Propanedithiol-1-sulfonic acid sodium salt *see* Unithiol.
Propane nitrile *see* Propionitrile.
1,2,3-Propanetricarboxylic acid *see* Tricarballylic acid.
1,2,3-Propanetriol *see* Glycerol.
Propanid (tr) *see* Propanil.
PROPANIDID*** (*N,N*-diethyl-2-[2-methoxy-4-[(propoxycarbonyl)methyl]phenoxy]acetamide; propyl 4-[(diethylcarbamoyl)methoxy]-3-methoxyphenylacetate; B-1420; Bayer 1420; FBA-1420; Th-2180; WH-5668).
PROPANIL* (*N*-(3,4-dichlorophenyl)propionamide; 3',4'-dichloropropionanilide; DPA; propanid; 'rogue'; 'stam F-34'; 'surcopur').
PROPANOCAINE*** (α-[2-(diethylamino)ethyl]-benzyl benzoate; 3-(diethylamino)-1-phenylpropyl benzoate).
1-PROPANOL (propyl alcohol).
2-PROPANOL (isopropyl alcohol).
Propanolide *see* Propiolactone.
2-Propanone *see* Acetone.
3,5-Propanopiperidine *see* 3-Azabicyclo[3.3.1]nonane.
PROPANTHELINE BROMIDE*** (2-diisopropylaminoethyl ester methobromide of 9-xanthenecarboxylic acid; (2-hydroxyethyl)diisopropylmethylammonium bromide xanthene-9-carboxylate; SC-3171).
'**Propaphenin**' *see* Chlorpromazine.
Proparacaine *see* Proxymetacaine.
PROPARGITE* (2-(*p-tert*-butylphenoxy)cyclohexyl 2-propynyl sulfite; 2-[4-(1,1-dimethylethyl)phenoxy]cyclohexyl 2-propynyl sulfite; 'omite').
Propargylamine *see* 2-Propynylamine.
Propargylcyclohexanol carbamate *see* Hexapropymate.
'**Proparthrin**' *see* Prothrin.
PROPATYLNITRATE*** (2-ethyl-2-(hydroxymethyl)-1,3-propanediol trinitrate; 1,1,1-tris-(hydroxymethyl)propane trinitrate; 1,1,1-tris-(nitratomethyl)propane; ettriol nitrate; ETTN; WIN-9317).
'**Propavan**' *see* Propiomazine.
'**Propaxoline**' *see* Proxazole.

Propazepine *see* Prazepine.
Propazin (tr) *see* Promazine.
PROPAZINE* (2-chloro-4,6-bis(isopropylamino)-*s*-triazine; 6-chloro-*N,N'*-bis(1-methylethyl)-1,3,5-triazine-2,4-diamine; 'gesamil').
PROPAZOLAMIDE*** (5-propionamido-1,3,4-thiadiazole-2-sulfonamide).
'**Propazone**' *see* Dimethadione.
Propenal *see* Acrolein.
Propene nitrile *see* Acrylonitrile.
PROPENIDAZOLE*** (ethyl *trans*-α-acetyl-1-methyl-5-nitroimidazole-2-acrylate).
Propenoic acid *see* Acrylic acid.
2-Propen-1-ol *see* Allyl alcohol.
PROPENTOFYLLINE*** (3-methyl-1-(5-oxohexyl)-7-propylxanthine; HWA-285).
2-Propenylacrylic acid *see* Sorbic acid.
2-Propenylamine *see* Allylamine.
p-**Propenylanisole** *see* Anethole.
p-**(1-Propenyl)phenol** *see* Anol.
Propenzolate* *see* Oxyclipine.
Propericiazine* *see* Periciazine.
PROPERIDINE*** (isopropyl 1-methyl-4-phenylisonipecotate; properidine hydrochloride; 'gevelina').
'**Propesin**' *see* Risocaine.
PROPETAMIDE*** (2-(*p*-ethoxyanilino)-*N*-propylpropionamide; 2-*p*-phenetidino-*N*-propylpropionamide; *N*-[1-(propylcarbamoyl)ethyl]-*p*-phenetidine; etampromide).
See also under Oxyphenbutazone.
PROPETANDROL*** (17α-ethylestr-4-ene-3,17-diol 3-propionate; 19-nor-17α-pregn-4-ene-3,17-diol 3-propionate; 3-propionyloxy-19-nor-17α-pregn-4-en-17-ol; SC-7294).
Propethon* *see* Tridihexethyl iodide.
PROPHAM* (isopropyl carbanilate; 1-methylethyl phenylcarbamate; carbanilic acid (phenylcarbamic acid), esters; anti-sprout; IFK; INPC; IPC; B-22; Liro antisprout; NSC-2105; 'conservasept'; 'Denka antisprout'; 'Duphar antisprout'; 'isoPC'; 'neoconserviet'; 'septon'; 'Servo antisprout'; 'tuberlite').
PROPHAM plus ENDOTHAL SODIUM ('murbetol').
'**Prophenal**' *see* 5-Allyl-5-phenylbarbituric acid.
Prophenamine* *see* Profenamine.
Prophenpyridamine *see* Pheniramine.
Prophos *see* Ethoprop.
PROPICILLIN** (6-(2-phenoxybutyramido)penicillanic acid; (1-phenoxypropyl)penicillin; propicillin potassium; PA-248).
See also Levopropicillin.
'**Propicol**' *see* *O,O*-Diisopropyl *O-p*-nitrophenyl phosphate.
PROPIKACIN** (*O*-3-amino-3-deoxy-α-D-glucopyranosyl(1→4)-*O*-[2,6-diamino-2,6-dideoxy-α-D-glucopyranosyl(1→6)]-2-deoxy-*N*³-[2-hydroxy-1-(hydroxymethyl)ethyl]-L-streptamine; UK-31214).
Propildazine *see* Pildralazine.
PROPINAL (*N,N*-diethyl-2-(3-methoxy-4-propylphenoxy)acetamide).

PROPINEB* ([[(1-methyl-1,2-ethanediyl)bis(carb-amodithioato)](2-)]zinc homopolymer; zineb methyl derivative polymer; 'antracol').

PROPINETIDINE*** (1-phenethyl-4-(2-propyn-yl)-4-piperidinol propionate).

Propinox *see* Pargeverine.

'Propiocin' *see* Erythromycin propionate.

Propiodal *see* Prolonium iodide.

PROPIOLACTONE*** (β-propiolactone; hydr-acrylic acid β-lactone; 2-oxetanone; β-propiono-lactone; propanolide; NSC-21626).

PROPIOLIC ACID (acetylenecarboxylic acid).

PROPIOMAZINE*** (10-[2-(dimethylamino)-propyl]-2-propionylphenothiazine; 1-[10-[2-(di-methylamino)propyl]phenothiazin-2-yl]-1-pro-panone; propiomazine maleate; CB-1678; Wy-1359).

PROPIONALDEHYDE (propanal).

p-**Propionamidophenol** *see* Parapropamol.

3-(Propionamidosulfonyl)-4-[*m*-(trifluoromethyl)ani-lino]pyridine *see* Galosemide.

5-Propionamido-1,3,4-thiadiazole-2-sulfonamide *see* Propazolamide.

PROPIONITRILE (propane nitrile; cyanoethane; ethyl cyanide).

Propionolactone *see* Propiolactone.

O-**Propionylatropine** *see* Prampine.

Propionylhyoscine *see* Poskine.

PROPIONYLMORAZINE (10-(3-morpholino-propyl)-2-propionylphenothiazine).

3-Propionyloxy-19-nor-17α-pregn-4-en-17-ol *see* Propetandrol.

PROPIONYLPERAZINE (10-[3-(4-methylpip-erazin-1-yl)propyl]-2-propionylphenothiazine).

p-**Propionylphenol** *see* Paroxypropione.

4-Propionyl-1-piperazinecarboxylic acid ester with (±)-6-(7-chloro-1,8-naphthyridin-2-yl)-2,3,6,7-tetrahydro-7-hydroxy-5*H*-*p*-dithiino[2,3-*c*]pyrrol-5-one *see* Suproclone.

PROPIONYLPROMAZINE (10-[3-(dimethyl-amino)propyl]-2-propionylphenothiazine; dipro-piomazine; propiopromazine; 'combelen'; 'tran-vet').

Propionylscopolamine *see* Poskine.

PROPIOPHENONE (1-phenyl-1-propanone; ethyl phenyl ketone).

Propiopromazine *see* Propionylpromazine.

PROPIPOCAINE*** (β-piperid-1-yl-4-propoxy-propiophenone; 2-piperid-1-ylethyl *p*-propoxy-phenyl ketone; 'falicaine').

PROPIRAM*** (*N*-(1-methyl-2-piperid-1-yl-ethyl)-*N*-pyrid-2-ylpropionamide; FBA-4503).

PROPIRAM FUMARATE* (BAY-4503; 'algeril').

PROPISERGIDE*** (9,10-didehydro-*N*-[(*S*)-2-hydroxy-1-methylethyl]-1,6-dimethylergoline-8β-carboxamide).

'Propitan' *see* Pipamperone.

Propitocaine *see* Prilocaine.

PROPIVANE (2-(diethylamino)ethyl 2-phenylva-lerate; propivane hydrochloride; RP 177; 'pro-spasmine').

PROPIVERINE*** (1-methylpiperid-4-yl diphen-ylpropoxyacetate; 'mictonorm').

PROPIZEPINE*** (6-[2-(dimethylamino)-2-methylethyl]-6,11-dihydro-5*H*-pyrido[2,3-*b*]-benzodiazepin-5-one; UP-106).

PROPOCTAMINE (N^1,N^3-bis(2-ethylhexyl)-2-methyl-1,2,3-propanetriamine).

PROPOFOL*** (2,6-diisopropylphenol; disoprof-ol; ICI-35868).

'Proponal' *see* 5,5-Dipropylbarbituric acid.

'Proponesin' *see* Tolpronine.

'Propoquin' *see* Amopyroquine.

PROPOXATE*** (propyl DL-1-(1-phenylethyl)-imidazole-5-carboxylate; propyl DL-1-(α-meth-ylbenzyl)imidazole-5-carboxylate; R-7464).

PROPOXUR* (*o*-isopropoxyphenyl methylcarb-amate; 2-(1-methylethoxy)phenyl methylcarb-amate; aprocarb; IPMC; Bayer-39007; OMS-33; Z-100; 'apacarb'; 'baygon'; 'blattanex'; 'bolfo'; 'unden').

o-**PROPOXYBENZAMIDE** (salicylamide propyl ether; *O*-propylsalicylamide).

5-Propoxy-2-benzimidazolecarbamic acid methyl ester *see* Oxibendazole.

6-Propoxy-2-benzothiazolecarbamic acid methyl ester *see* Tioxidazole.

PROPOXYCAINE*** (2-(diethylamino)ethyl 4-amino-2-propoxybenzoate; WIN-3459).

(+)-Propoxyphene *see* Dextropropoxyphene.

(−)-Propoxyphene *see* Levopropoxyphene.

Propoxyphene napsylate *see* Dextropropoxyphene napsilate.

PROPRANOLOL*** (1-[2-hydroxy-3-(isopropyl-amino)propoxy]naphthalene; 1-(isopropyl-amino)-3-(1-naphthyloxy)-2-propanol; propras-ylyte; anaprilin; napriline; propranolol hydro-chloride; AY-64043; ICI-45520; NSC-91523). *See also* Dexpropranolol *and under* Bendroflu-methiazide.

'Propranur' *see* Propranolol.

Proprasylyte* *see* Propranolol.

Propylacetic acid *see* Valeric acid.

N-**Propylajmalinium hydrogen tartrate** *see* Prajma-lium bitartrate.

Propyl alcohol *see* 1-Propanol.

1-PROPYLAMINE (propylamine).

2-PROPYLAMINE (isopropylamine).

Propyl *p*-aminobenzoate *see* Risocaine.

2-(Propylamino)-*o*-propionotoluidide *see* Prilocaine.

Propylbarbital *see* 5,5-Dipropylbarbituric acid.

Propyl 1,3-bis(clofibrate) *see* Simfibrate.

'Propyl butex' *see* Propyl paraben.

S-**Propyl butylethylcarbamothioate** *see* Pebulate.

Propylcaine *see* Risocaine.

N-**[1-(Propylcarbamoyl)ethyl]-*p*-phenetidine** *see* Propetamide.

Propyl 3-diacetylamino-2,4,6-triiodobenzoate *see* Propyl docetrizoate.

Propyl diatrizoate *see* Propyl docetrizoate.

Propyl 4-[(diethylcarbamoyl)methoxy]-3-methoxy-phenylacetate *see* Propanidid.

Propyl 3,5-diiodo-5-oxo-1-piperidineacetate *see* Propyliodone.

Propyl [3-(dimethylamino)propyl]carbamate *see* Propamocarb.

S-Propyl dipropylcarbamothioate *see* Vernolate.

PROPYL DOCETRIZOATE*** (propyl 3-diacetylamino-2,4,6-triiodobenzoate; propyldiatrizoate).

4,4'-Propylenedi(2,6-piperazinedione) *see* Razoxane.

PROPYLENE GLYCOL* (1,2-propanediol; methyl glycol).

PROPYLENE GLYCOL MONOSTEARATE (1,2-propanediol monostearate; 'monolene'; 'prostearin').

PROPYLHEXEDRINE*** (($\pm$)-1-cyclohexyl-*N*-methyl-2-propylamine; ($\pm$)-*N*,α-dimethylcyclohexaneethylamine; desoxyhexahydroephedrine; hexahydrodesoxyephedrine; E-111).
See also Levopropylhexedrine.

Propylhexedrine-phenobarbital *see* Barbexaclone.

Propyl *p*-hydroxybenzoate *see* Propyl paraben.

PROPYLIODONE*** (propyl 3,5-diiodo-5-oxo-1-piperidineacetate).

Propylisonicotinthioamide *see* Protionamide.

Propyl DL-1-(α-methylbenzyl)imidazole-5-carboxylate *see* Propoxate.

19-Propylnorvinol *see* Etorphine.

'Propylon' *see* Isoprenaline.

Propylorvinol *see* Etorphine.

PROPYL PARABEN (propyl *p*-hydroxybenzoate).

2-Propylpentanoic acid *see* Valproic acid.

4-(2-Propylpentyl)-1-piperidineethanol *see* Octapinol.

Propylphenazone *see* Propyphenazone.

1-(α-Propylphenethyl)pyrrolidine *see* Prolintane.

Propyl DL-1-(1-phenylethyl)imidazole-5-carboxylate *see* Propoxate.

($-$)-1-Propyl-2',6'-pipecoloxylidide *see* Ropivacaine.

2-Propylpiperidine *see* Coniine.

***N*-[(1-Propyl-2-pyrrolidinyl)methyl]-5-sulfamoyl-*o*-anisamide** *see* Prosulpride.

***O*-Propylsalicylamide** *see* *o*-Propoxybenzamide.

2-Propyl-5-thiazolecarboxylic acid *see* Tizoprolic acid.

5-(Propylthio)benzimidazole-2-carbamic acid methyl ester *see* Albendazole.

2-Propylthioisonicotinamide *see* Protionamide.

3-[4-[4-[*o*-(Propylthio)phenyl]piperazin-1-yl]butyl]-2,4(1*H*,3*H*)-quinazolinedione *see* Tioperidone.

PROPYLTHIOURACIL*** (6-propyl-2-thiouracil; 4-propyl-2-thiouracil).

***N*-Propyl-*N*-[2-(2,4,6-trichlorophenoxy)ethyl]-1*H*-imidazole-1-carboxamide** *see* Prochloraz.

2-Propylvaleramide *see* Valpromide.

2-Propylvaleric acid *see* Valproic acid.

2-Propylvaleric acid-sodium 2-propylvalerate *see* Valproate semisodium.

3-Propylxanthine *see* Enprofylline.

'Propymal' *see* Valproic acid.

2-PROPYNYLAMINE (propargylamine).

1-(2-Propynyl)cyclohexyl carbamate *see* Hexapropymate.

***E,E*-2-Propynyl 3,7,11-trimethyldodeca-2,4-dienoate** *see* Kinoprene.

PROPYPERONE*** (4-[4-(ethylcarbonyl)-4-piperid-1-ylpiperid-1-yl]-4'-fluorobutyrophenone; 4'-fluoro-4-(4-piperid-1-yl-4-propionylpiperid-1-yl)butyrophenone; 1'-[3-(*p*-fluorobenzoyl)propyl]-4'-propionyl-1,4'-bipiperidine; floropipetone; R-4082).

PROPYPHENAZONE*** (4-isopropyl-2,3-dimethyl-1-phenyl-3-pyrazolin-5-one; 4-isopropylantipyrine; 4-isopropylphenazone; propylphenazone).
See also under Famprofazone.

PROPYROMAZINE BROMIDE*** (1-methyl-1-(1-phenothiazin-2-ylcarbonylethyl)pyrrolidinium bromide; 10-[2-(1-methylpyrrolidin-1-yl)-propionyl]phenothiazine bromide; LD-335; SD-10419).

'Propytal' *see* 5,5-Dipropylbarbituric acid.

PROPYZAMIDE* (3,5-dichloro-*N*-(1,1-dimethyl-2-propynyl)benzamide; 'kerb').

Proquamezine* *see* Aminopromazine.

PROQUAZONE*** (1-isopropyl-7-methyl-4-phenylquinazolin-2(1*H*)-one; RU 43-715n; 'biarison').

PROQUINOLATE*** (methyl 4-hydroxy-6,7-diisopropoxy-3-quinolinecarboxylate; mequinolate; EU-1063; U-1063).

PRORENOATE POTASSIUM*** (potassium 6,7-dihydro-17-hydroxy-3-oxo-3'*H*-cyclopropa[6,7]-17α-pregna-4,6-diene-21-carboxylate; potassium prorenoate; SC-23992).

'Proresid' *see* Mitopodozide.

PROROXAN** (1-(1,4-benzodioxan-6-yl)-3-(3-phenylpyrrolidin-1-yl)-1-propanone; 1-(2,3-dihydro-1,4-benzodioxin-6-yl)-3-(3-phenylpyrrolidin-1-yl)-1-propanone; pirroksan; proroxan hydrochloride; pyrroxan; AY-24269).

'Prosalol S-9' *see* Bornelone.

'Proscabin' *see* Benzyl benzoate.

PROSCILLARIDIN*** (3,14-dihydroxybufa-4,20,22-trienolide 3-rhamnoside; 14-hydroxy-3β-rhamnosyloxybufa-4,20,22-trienolide; scillarenin 3β-rhamnoside; proscillaridin A; A-32686; PSC-801; TV-274B).

PROSCILLARIDIN plus ETOFYLLINE ('teostellarid').

PROSCILLARIDIN plus ISOSORBIDE DINITRATE (TV-274C).

PROSCILLARIDIN plus THEOPHYLLINE (BS-272; 'teocaradrin').

'Proscomide' *see* Scopolamine methyl bromide.

'Proscopine' *see* Poskine.

'Proserine' *see* Neostigmine bromide.

'Prospasmine' *see* Propivane.

Prospidin (tr) *see* Prospidium chloride.

PROSPIDIUM CHLORIDE*** (3,12-bis(3-chloro-2-hydroxypropyl)-3,12-diaza-6,9-diazoniadispiro[5.2.5.2]hexadecane dichloride; *N*,*N*^{3}-bis(3-chloro-2-hydroxypropyl)-*N*,*N*^{2}-dispirotripiperazine dichloride; prospidin).

Prostacyclin *see* Epoprostenol.

PROSTAGLANDIN A$_1$ (15α-hydroxy-9-oxo-10,13-*trans*-prostadienoic acid).

PROSTAGLANDIN B$_2$ (15-hydroxy-9-oxo-5-*cis*-

8(12),13-*trans*-prostatrienoic acid).

Prostaglandin E₁ *see* Alprostadil.

Prostaglandin E₂ *see* Dinoprostone.

Prostaglandin F₂ₐ *see* Dinoprost.

Prostaglandin I₂ *see* Epoprostenol.

Prostaglandin X *see* Epoprostenol.

PROSTALENE* (methyl 7-[3,5-dihydroxy-2-(3-hydroxy-3-methyl-1-octenyl)cyclopentyl]-4,5-heptadienoate; methyl (13*E*)-(9*S*,11*R*,15*R*)-9,11,15-trihydroxy-15-methylprosta-4,5,13-trienoate; RS-9390; 'synchrocept').

'Prostaphlin' *see* Oxacillin.

'Prostasal' *see* β-Sitosterol.

'Prostearin' *see* Propylene glycol monostearate.

'Prostigmine' *see* Neostigmine bromide.

'Prostin E₂' *see* Dinoprostone.

'Prostin F2 alpha' *see* Dinoprost.

'Prostin 15 M' *see* Carboprost.

'Prostin VR' *see* Alprostadil.

PROSULPRIDE* (2-methoxy-*N*-[(1-propylpyrrolidin-2-yl)methyl]-5-sulfamoylbenzamide; *N*-[(1-propyl-2-pyrrolidinyl)methyl]-5-sulfamoyl-*o*-anisamide).

Prosulthiamine* *see* Prosultiamine.

PROSULTIAMINE* (*N*-(4-amino-2-methylpyrimidin-5-ylmethyl)-*N*-[4-hydroxy-1-methyl-2-(propyldithio)-1-butenyl]formamide; dithiopropylthiamine; prosulthiamine; thiamine propyl disulfide; DTP; TPD; 'alinamin'; 'nevriton').

'Prosymasul' *see* Sulfasymazine.

'Prosympal' *see* 2-[(Diethylamino)methyl]-1,4-benzodioxan.

'Protacil' *see* Promazine.

Protacin *see* Proglumetacin dimaleate.

'Protactyl' *see* Promazine.

'Protagent' *see* Povidone.

PROTAMINE ZINC INSULIN ('durasuline').
See also Isophane insulin.

'Pro-tan' *see* Promazine.

'Protanal' *see* Sodium alginate.

'Protasin' *see* Proscillaridin.

'Protaxil' *see* Proglumetacin dimaleate.

'Proteina' *see* Androstanolone.

'Protergan' *see* Magnesium oxoglurate.

PROTERGURIDE (1,1-diethyl-3-(6-propylergolin-8α-yl)urea).

'Prothanon' *see* Promethazine S,S-dioxide.

'Prothazin' *see* Promethazine.

PROTHEOBROMINE* (1-(2-hydroxypropyl)theobromine).

'Prothiaden' *see* Dosulepin.

'Prothidium' *see* Pyritidium bromide.

'Prothidryl' *see under* Dosulepin.

'Prothil' *see* Medrogestone.

PROTHIOFOS* (*O*-(2,4-dichlorophenyl) *O*-ethyl *S*-propyl phosphorodithioate; 'tokuthion').

Prothionamide* *see* Protionamide.

PROTHIPENDYL* (10-[3-(dimethylamino)propyl]-1-azaphenothiazine; 10-[3-(dimethylamino)propyl]-10*H*-pyrido[3,2-*b*][1,4]benzothiazine; prothipendyl hydrochloride; D-206; LG-206).

PROTHIXENE* (9-[3-(dimethylamino)propylidene]thioxanthene; *N*,*N*-dimethylthioxanthene-Δ⁹,ᵞ-propylamine).

PROTHOATE* (*O*,*O*-diethyl *S*-[2-[(1-methylethyl)amino]-2-oxoethyl] phosphorodithioate; *O*,*O*-diethyl *S*-(isopropylcarbamoylmethyl) phosphorodithioate; trimethoate; 'aafac'; 'FAC'; 'fostion').

PROTHRIN ([2-methyl-5-(2-propynyl)furan-3-yl]methyl 2,2-dimethyl-3-(2-methyl-1-propenyl)-cyclopropanecarboxylate; 2-methyl-5-prop-2-ynyl-3-furylmethyl chrysanthemate; D-1201; 'kikuthrin'; 'proparthrin').

'Prothromadin' *see* Warfarin.

PROTIOFATE* (dipropyl 3,4-dihydroxy-2,5-thiophenedicarboxylate).

PROTIONAMIDE* (2-propylisonicotinthioamide; 2-propylthioisonicotinamide; prothionamide; RP 9778; Th-1321).

PROTIRELIN (5-oxo-L-prolyl-L-histidyl-L-prolinamide; lopremone; thyrotrophin releasing hormone synthetic; TRH synthetic; Abbott 38579; 'antepan'; 'thypinone'; 'thyroliberin'; 'TRH-Roche').
See also under Gonadorelin.

PROTIZINIC ACID* (2-(1-carboxyethyl)-7-methoxy-10-methylphenothiazine; 7-methoxy-α,10-dimethylphenothiazine-2-acetic acid; R-17190; RP 17190; 'pirocrid').

PROTOANEMONIN (4-hydroxy-2,4-pentadienoic acid γ-lactone; γ-hydroxyvinylacrylic acid γ-lactone; 5-methylene-2-oxodihydrofuran).

PROTOCATECHUIC ACID (3,4-dihydroxybenzoic acid).

PROTOCATECHUYL ALCOHOL (3,4-dihydroxybenzyl alcohol).

Protogen A *see* Thioctic acid.

Protoheme *see* Heme.

PROTOKYLOL* (3,4-dihydroxy-α-[(α-methyl-3,4-methylenedioxyphenethylamino)methyl]-benzyl alcohol; α-[[(α-methyl-3,4-methylenedioxyphenethyl)amino]methyl]protocatechuyl alcohol; protokylol hydrochloride; JB-251).

'Protopam chloride' *see* Pralidoxime chloride.

'Protopam iodide' *see* Pralidoxime iodide.

'Protostib' *see* Meglumine antimonate.

'Prototapen' *see under* Ampicillin.

PROTRIPTYLINE* (*N*-methyl-5*H*-dibenzo[*a*,*d*]cycloheptene-5-propylamine; 5-[3-(methylamino)propyl]dibenzo[*a*,*d*]cycloheptene; amimethyline; protriptyline hydrochloride; MK-240).

'Provamycin' *see* Spiramycin.

'Provasan' *see* Nicametate.

'Provera' *see* Medroxyprogesterone acetate.

'Provest' *see under* Medroxyprogesterone.

'Proviron' *see* Mesterolone.

Provitamin D₃ *see* 7-Dehydrocholesterol.

PROXAZOLE* (5-[2-(diethylamino)ethyl]-3-(1-phenylpropyl)-1,2,4-oxadiazole; 5-[2-(diethylamino)ethyl]-3-(α-ethylbenzyl)-1,2,4-oxadiazole; proxazole citrate; AF-634).

'Proxen' *see* Naproxen.

PROXIBARBAL* (5-allyl-5-(2-hydroxypropyl)-

barbituric acid; 5-(2-hydroxypropyl)-5-(2-propenyl)-2,4,6(1H,3H,5H)-pyrimidinetrione; ipronal; 'axeen'; 'D,H'; 'vasalgin').

PROXIBUTENE*** (3-[(dimethylamino)methyl]-1,2-diphenyl-3-buten-2-ol propionate; Ba-40088).

See also Dexproxibutene.

PROXICROMIL*** (6,7,8,9-tetrahydro-5-hydroxy-4-oxo-10-propylbenzo[g]chromene-2-carboxylic acid; 6,7,8,9-tetrahydro-5-hydroxy-4-oxo-10-propyl-4H-naphtho[2,3-b]pyran-2-carboxylic acid).

PROXIFEZONE** (dextropropoxyphene compound with phenylbutazone).

PROXIFEZONE plus CRESOTAMIDE ('midalgyl').

PROXORPHAN*** ((−)-(4aR,5R,10bS)-13-(cyclopropylmethyl)-4,4a,5,6-tetrahydro-3H-5,10b-(iminoethano)-1H-naphtho[1,2-c]pyran-9-ol).

PROXORPHAN TARTRATE* (BL-5572M).

'Proxybron' see under Oxolamine benzilate.

Proxyfenone see Paroxypropione.

PROXYMETACAINE*** (2-(diethylamino)ethyl 3-amino-4-propoxybenzoate; proparacaine; proxymetacaine hydrochloride).

PROXYPHYLLINE*** (7-(2-hydroxypropyl)-theophylline).

PROZAPINE*** (1-(3,3-diphenylpropyl)cyclohexamethylenimine; 1,1-diphenyl-3-hexamethyleniminopropane; 1-(3,3-diphenylpropyl)hexahydroazepine; 1-(3,3-diphenylpropyl)hexamethylenimine; hexadiphane).

PROZAPINE plus MOPERONE ('sedalium').

'Prozine' see Promazine.

Prunetol see Genistein.

'Pruralgin' see Quinisocaine.

'Pruridol' see Benzyl benzoate.

PRUSSIAN BLUE (ferric cyanoferrate; ferric ferrocyanide).

'Pryleugan' see Imipramine.

PRYNACHLOR* (2-chloro-N-(1-methyl-2-propynyl)acetanilide; chloretin).

Przedziorkofos see Phenkapton.

P2S see Pralidoxime mesilate.

P-2-S see Pralidoxime mesilate.

PS-1286 see Pararosaniline embonate.

PS-2383 see Trimetozine.

PSC-801 see Proscillaridin.

PSEUDOATROPINE (atrolactic acid tropine ester; tropine α-methylmandelate).

Pseudobrucine see Ajmaline.

'Pseudocef' see Cefsulodin.

Pseudocholestane see Coprostane.

PSEUDOCOCAINE (D-3β-(benzoyloxy)-2α-(methoxycarbonyl)tropane; isocaine; isococaine).

PSEUDOCODEINE (6,7-didehydro-4,5α-epoxy-3-methoxy-17-methylmorphinan-8β-ol; neo-isocodeine).

PSEUDOCUMIDINE (2,4,5-trimethylaniline).

Pseudodigitonin see Gitalin crystalline.

Pseudodigitoxin see Gitoxin.

PSEUDOEPHEDRINE*** ((+)-(1S,2R)-2-(methylamino)-1-phenyl-1-propanol; α-[1-(methylamino)ethyl]benzyl alcohol; isoephedrine; pseudoephedrine hydrochloride; pseudoephedrine sulfate).

PSEUDOEPHEDRINE plus CHLORPHENIRAMINE MALEATE ('deconamine'; 'demazin').

PSEUDOEPHEDRINE plus TRIPROLIDINE ('actagen'; 'actifed'; 'triphed').

(3H)PSEUDOINDOL-3-ONE (Ψ-indolone).

PSEUDOINDOXYL (2,3-dihydro-3-oxoindole; 3-indolinone).

PSEUDOMECONIN (4,5-dimethoxyphthalide).

PSEUDOMONIC ACID** ((E)-(2S,3R,4R,5S)-5-[(2S,3S,4S,5S)-2,3-epoxy-5-hydroxy-4-methylhexyl]tetrahydro-3,4-dihydroxy-β-methyl-2H-pyran-2-crotonic acid, ester with 9-hydroxynonanoic acid; 9-[(2E)-4-[(2S,3R,4R,5S)-5-[(2S,3S,4S,5S)-2,3-epoxy-5-hydroxy-4-methylhexyl]tetrahydro-3,4-dihydroxypyran-2-yl]-3-methylbut-2-enoyloxy]nonanoic acid; BRL-4910A).

'Pseudomonil' see Cefsulodin.

PSEUDOMORPHINE (2,2'-bimorphine; 2,2'-dehydrodimorphine; Ψ-morphine; oxydimorphine).

Pseudostilbestrol see 3,4-Bis(p-hydroxyphenyl)-2-hexene.

PSEUDOTHIOUREA (carbamimidothioic acid; isothiourea).

PSEUDOTROPINE (3β-tropanol).

PSEUDOTROPINE BENZOATE (syn-benzoyltropine; tropacocaine).

PSEUDOUREA (carbamimidic acid; isourea).

'Psicaine' see Pseudococaine.

'Psichoperidol' see Trifluperidol.

'Psicofuranine' see Angustmycin C.

'Psiconal' see Pseudococaine.

'Psicosoma' see Magnesium glutamate hydrobromide.

'Psicronizer' see Nomifensine maleate.

PSILOCIN (4-hydroxy-N,N-dimethyltryptamine).

Psilocin phosphate ester see Psilocybine.

PSILOCYBINE*** (3-[2-(dimethylamino)ethyl]-indol-4-yl hydrogen phosphate; psilocin phosphate ester; CY-39).

'Psocorten' see under Flumetasone pivalate.

'Psoil' see under Tioxolone.

'Psoradexan' see under Dithranol.

'Psoradrate' see Dithranol.

PSORALEN (7H-furo[3,2-g][1]benzopyran-7-one).

'Psoralon-MOP' see Methoxsalen.

'Psoriacide' see Dithranol.

'Psoriasin' see Mustard gas.

PSP see Phenolsulfonphthalein and Saxitoxin.

'Psychamine' see Phenmetrazine.

Psychoforine (tr) see Imipramine.

'Psychopax' see Diazepam.

'Psychosan' see Azacyclonol.

'Psychostyl' see Nortriptyline.

'Psychoverlan' see Magnesium glutamate hydrobromide.

PSYLLIUM (ispagula; mucilage of *Plantago ovata*

seeds; *Plantago ovata* coating).
See also Sodium psylliate.
'Psymod' *see* Piperacetazine.
'Psyquil' *see* Triflupromazine.
'Psyton' *see under* Clobazam.
PT-9 *see* Betahistine.
PTERIDINE (pyrimido[4,5-*b*]pyrazine; azinepurine; benzotetrazine).
PTEROIC ACID (*p*-[(2-amino-4-hydroxy-6-pteridylmethyl)amino]benzoic acid).
PTEROPTERIN (pteroyl-γ-glutamyl-γ-glutamylglutamic acid; pteroyltriglutamic acid; *Lactobacillus casei* fermentation factor; PTGA).
Pteroylglutamic acid *see* Folic acid.
Pteroyl-γ-glutamyl-γ-glutamylglutamic acid *see* Pteropterin.
Pteroyltriglutamic acid *see* Pteropterin.
PTFE *see* Politef.
PTG *see* Teniposide.
PTGA *see* Pteropterin.
PU-239 *see* Benzilonium bromide.
Puddmetin *see* Genkwanin.
'Pularin' *see* Heparin.
'Pulmadil' *see* Rimiterol.
'Pulmaxil N' *see* Penethamate hydriodide.
'Pulmicort' *see* Budesonide.
'Pulmidol' *see* Propyl docetrizoate.
'Pulmidur' *see* Theophylline.
'Pulmo 500' *see* Penethamate hydriodide.
'Pulmolite' *see* Macrosalb (^{99m}Tc).
'Pulsoton' *see* Hydroxyamphetamine.
PUMITEPA* (*P,P*-bis(1-aziridinyl)-*N*-[2-(dimethylamino)-7-methylpurin-6-yl]phosphinic amide).
Punicine *see* Pelletierine.
'Puralin' *see* Thiram.
'Purantix' *see* Clocortolone pivalate.
'Purapen' *see* Azidocillin.
'Purapen G' *see* Penicillin G, purified.
'Purazol' *see* Sulfapyridine.
Purgenum *see* Phenolphthalein.
PURINE (7*H*-imidazo[4,5-*d*]pyrimidine; NSC-753).
2,6(1*H*,3*H*)-Purinedione *see* Xanthine.
Purine riboside *see* Nebularine.
6-Purinethiol *see* Mercaptopurine.
'Puri-nethol' *see* Mercaptopurine.
2,6,8(1*H*,3*H*,9*H*)-Purinetrione *see* Uric acid.
6(1*H*)-Purinone *see* Hypoxanthine.
5-(Purin-6-ylthio)valeric acid *see* Buthiopurine.
***N*-[5-(Purin-6-ylthio)valeryl]glycine ethyl ester** *see* Butocin.
'Purodigin' *see* Digitoxin.
PUROMYCIN* (3'-(L-α-amino-*p*-methoxyhydrocinnamamido)-3'-deoxy-*N,N*-dimethyladenosine; 6-dimethylamino-9-[3'-deoxy-3'-(*p*-methoxy-L-phenylalanylamino)-β(or α)-ribosyl]purine; puromycin hydrochloride; CL-13900; CL-16536; NSC-3055; P-683).
PUROMYCIN AMINONUCLEOSIDE (9-(3-amino-3-deoxy-β-D-ribofuranosyl)-6-dimethylaminopurine; 3'-amino-3'-deoxy-*N,N*-dimethyladenosine; aminonucleoside; ARDMA; NSC-

3056).
'Purophylline' *see* Proxyphylline.
'Purostrophan' *see* Ouabain.
Purpurea glycoside C *see* Deslanoside.
'Purpurid' *see* Digitoxin.
PUTRESCINE (1,4-butanediamine; tetramethylenediamine).
PVA *see* Polyvinyl alcohol.
PVNO *see* Polyvinylpyridine *N*-oxide.
PVP *see* Povidone.
'PVP-macrose' *see* Povidone.
PVTD *see* Dextran.
PW/135 *see* Pemoline.
PX-917 *see* Tricresyl phosphate.
'Pyasan' *see* Cefalexin.
'Pycaril' *see* Benzyl nicotinate.
'Pyelectan' *see* Iodoxyl.
'Pyelokon-R' *see* Sodium acetrizoate.
'Pyelombrine' *see* Sodium diatrizoate.
'Pyelombrine M' *see* Diodone meglumine.
'Pyelosil' *see* Iodopyridone.
Pyknolepsin (tr) *see* Ethosuximide.
'Pylostropin' *see* Atropine methonitrate.
'Pylumbrin' *see* Diodone.
'Pyoclox' *see under* Carbenicillin.
PYOCYANINE (1-hydroxy-5-methylphenazinium hydroxide inner salt; 10-methylphenazin-1-one; cyanomycin).
'Pyoktanin' *see* Crystal violet.
'Pyopen' *see* Carbenicillin.
'Pyostacin' *see* Pristinamycin.
'Pyrabital' *see* Barbipyrine.
PYRABROM* (8-bromotheophylline compound with mepyramine; NSC-14279; SMP-68-40).
Pyracrimycin A *see* Desdanine.
'Pyradone' *see* Aminophenazone.
'Pyra-elmedal' *see under* Aminophenazone.
PYRAHEXYL (3-hexyl-7,8,9,10-tetrahydro-6,6,9-trimethyl-6*H*-dibenzo[*b,d*]pyran-1-ol).
Pyraldin (tr) *see* Quinapyramine.
'Pyramat' *see* 6-Methyl-2-propylpyrimid-4-yl *N,N*-dimethylcarbamate.
'Pyramem' *see* Piracetam.
'Pyramidon' *see* Aminophenazone.
'Pyramin' *see* Chloridazon.
'Pyraminal' *see* Aminophenazone.
'Pyramon' *see* Aminophenazone.
Pyranisamine *see* Mepyramine.
'Pyranol' *see* Polychlorinated biphenyl.
PYRANTEL* (1,4,5,6-tetrahydro-1-methyl-2-(2-thien-2-ylvinyl)pyrimidine; 1,4,5,6-tetrahydro-1-methyl-2-[*trans*-2-(thien-2-yl)vinyl]pyrimidine; pyrantel tartrate; CP-10423-18).
PYRANTEL EMBONATE (pyrantel compound (1:1) with 4,4'-methylenebis(3-hydroxy-2-naphthoic acid); pyrantel pamoate; CP-10423-16).
Pyrantel pamoate *see* Pyrantel embonate.
'Pyrantin' *see* Phenetylsuccinimide.
'Pyrasanone' *see* Pyrazinobutazone.
Pyrathiazine* *see* Parathiazine.
'Pyrathyn' *see* Methapyrilene.
Pyrazapon *see* Ripazepam.
PYRAZINAMIDE* (pyrazine-2-carboxamide;

pyrazinoic acid amide; D-50; MK-56).

PYRAZINE (1,4-diazine; paradiazine; piazine).

Pyrazine-2-carboxamide *see* Pyrazinamide.

Pyrazinecarboxylic acid *see* Pyrazinoic acid.

PYRAZINOBUTAZONE (phenylbutazone piperazine; DB-139; 'carudol'; 'pyrasanone'; 'ranoroc').

PYRAZINOIC ACID (pyrazinecarboxylic acid).

Pyrazinoic acid amide *see* Pyrazinamide.

*N*¹-**Pyrazin-2-ylsulfanilamide** *see* Sulfapyrazine.

Pyrazocillin *see* Prazocillin.

Pyrazofurin* *see* Pirazofurin.

'**Pyrazogin**' *see* Sulfamidopyrine sodium.

PYRAZOLE (1,2-diazole).

Pyrazole-1-carboxamidine *see* Praxadine.

PYRAZOLIDINE (tetrahydropyrazole).

PYRAZOLIDINONE (pyrazolidone).

Pyrazolidone *see* Pyrazolidinone.

PYRAZOLINE (dihydropyrazole).

2-PYRAZOLIN-5-ONE (5-pyrazolone).

3-PYRAZOLIN-5-ONE (3-pyrazolone).

3-Pyrazolone *see* 3-Pyrazolin-5-one.

5-Pyrazolone *see* 2-Pyrazolin-5-one.

PYRAZOLOPYRIMIDINE (tetraazaindene).

1*H*-Pyrazolo[3,4-*d*]pyrimidine-4,6-diol *see* Oxipurinol.

1*H*-Pyrazolo[3,4-*d*]pyrimidine-4-thiol *see* Tisopurine.

1*H*-Pyrazolo[3,4-*d*]pyrimidin-4-ol *see* Allopurinol.

Pyrazon* *see* Chloridazon.

PYRAZOPHOS* (ethyl 2-[(diethoxyphosphinothioyl)oxy]-5-methylpyrazolo[1,5-*a*]pyrimidine-6-carboxylate; 'afugan'; 'curamil').

'**Pyrbenine**' *see* Benzilonium bromide.

Pyrbenzindole *see* Benzindopyrine.

'**Pyrcon**' *see* Pyrvinium embonate.

Pyrene (chemical name for a 4 ring system).

'**Pyrene**' *see* Carbon tetrachloride.

'**Pyrequan**' *see* Morantel tartrate.

PYRESMETHRIN* (*trans*-(+)-5-benzylfuran-3-ylmethyl 3-(3-methoxy-2-methyl-3-oxo-1-propenyl)-2,2-dimethylcyclopropanecarboxylate; NRDC-106; RU-12061).

'**Pyrethia**' *see* Promethazine.

PYRETHRIC ACID (2,2-dimethyl-3-[2-(methoxycarbonyl)-1-propenyl]cyclopropanecarboxylic acid; chrysanthemumdicarboxylic acid monomethyl ester).

See also Cinerin II; Pyrethrin II.

PYRETHRIN I (pyrethrolone ester of chrysanthemic acid; 2-methyl-4-oxo-2-(2,4-pentadienyl)-2-cyclopenten-1-yl chrysanthemate).

PYRETHRIN II (pyrethrolone ester of chrysanthemumdicarboxylic acid methyl ester; 1-methyl 3-[2-methyl-4-oxo-2-(2,4-pentadienyl)-2-cyclopenten-1-yl] chrysanthemumdicarboxylate; pyretholone ester of pyrethric acid).

PYRETHROLONE (4-hydroxy-3-methyl-2-(2,4-pentadienyl)-2-cyclopenten-1-one).

'**Pyrgasol**' *see* Lauralkonium chloride.

'**Pyribenzamine**' *see* Tripelennamine.

PYRICARBATE* (2,6-bis(hydroxymethyl)pyridyl bis(methylcarbamate); 2,6-pyridinedimethanol bis(methylcarbamate); 2,6-pyridinediyldimethylene bis(methylcarbamate); pyridinol carbamate; P-23; 'anginin'; 'angioxin'; 'aterofal'; 'colesterinex'; 'duvaline'; 'prodectin'; 'sospitan'; 'vasoverin').

'**Pyrictal**' *see* Phetharbital.

'**Pyridacil**' *see* Phenazopyridine.

PYRIDARONE** (2-pyrid-4-ylbenzofuran; L-4296).

PYRIDAZINE (1,2-diazine; orthodiazine).

2-Pyridinaldehydes *see* Isonicotinaldehyde; Nicotinaldehyde; Picolinaldehyde.

2-Pyridinaldoxime methochloride *see* Pralidoxime chloride.

2-Pyridinaloxime methiodide *see* Pralidoxime iodide.

2-PYRIDINDENE (2-azafluorene).

5*H*-PYRID[4,3-*b*]INDOLE (γ-carboline).

9*H*-PYRID[3,4-*b*]INDOLE (β-carboline).

3-PYRIDINEACETIC ACID (2-pyrid-3-ylacetic acid; 'lioxone').

2-Pyridinecarboxylic acid *see* Picolinic acid.

3-Pyridinecarboxylic acid *see* Nicotinic acid.

4-Pyridinecarboxylic acid *see* Isonicotinic acid.

2,3-Pyridinedicarboxylic acid *see* Quinolinic acid.

2,6-Pyridinedimethanol bis(methylcarbamate) *see* Pyricarbate.

2,6-Pyridinedimethanol monoester with clofibric acid *see* Pirifibrate.

2,6-Pyridinediyldimethylene bis(methylcarbamate) *see* Pyricarbate.

2,6-Pyridinediyldimethylene bis(3,4,5-trimethoxybenzoate) *see* Pirozadil.

2-Pyridinemethanol *see* Piconol.

3-Pyridinemethanol *see* Nicotinyl alcohol.

3-Pyridinemethanol 1-oxide *see* Mepiroxol.

Pyridine-2-thione 1-oxide sodium derivative *see* Pyrithione sodium.

PYRIDINITRIL* (2,6-dichloro-4-phenyl-3,5-pyridinedicarbonitrile).

See also under Captafol.

Pyridinol carbamate *see* Pyricarbate.

3-Pyridinol tartrate *see* Hydroxypyridine tartrate.

'**Pyridium**' *see* Phenazopyridine.

'**Pyridizin**' *see* Isoniazid mesilate.

10*H*-PYRIDO[3,2-*b*][1,4]BENZOTHIAZINE (1-azaphenothiazine; 9-thia-1,10-diazanthracene; thiophenylpyridylamine).

10*H*-Pyrido[3,2-*b*][1,4]benzothiazine-10-carboxylic acid 2-(2-piperid-1-ylethoxy)ethyl ester *see* Pipazetate.

4-[3-(Pyrido[3,2-*b*][1,4]benzothiazin-10-yl)propyl]-piperazin-1-ylethanol *see* Oxypendyl.

PYRIDOFYLLINE* (pyridoxine salt of 7-(2-hydroxyethyl)theophylline hydrogen sulfate ester; etofylline pyridoxol salt hydrogen sulfate ester; pyridoxol theophylline ethoxysulfate).

4*H*-PYRIDO[1,2-*a*]PYRIMIDINE (homopyrimidazole).

'**Pyridoscorbine**' *see* Ascorbic acid pyridoxine complex.

PYRIDOSTIGMINE BROMIDE* (3-hydroxy-1-methylpyridinium bromide dimethylcarbam-

440

ate).

PYRIDOXAL (4-formyl-3-hydroxy-(5-hydroxy-methyl)-2-methylpyridine; 3-hydroxy-5-(hydroxymethyl)-2-methylisonicotinaldehyde; pyridoxal hydrochloride).

PYRIDOXAL 5-PHOSPHATE (codecarboxylase).
See also Magnesium pyridoxal 5-phosphate glutamate.

PYRIDOXAMINE (4-(aminomethyl)-5-hydroxy-6-methyl-3-pyridinemethanol; pyridoxamine dihydrochloride).

PYRIDOXIC ACID (3-hydroxy-5-(hydroxymeth-yl)-2-methylisonicotinic acid).

PYRIDOXINE*** (3-hydroxy-4,5-di(hydroxy-methyl)-2-methylpyridine; 3-hydroxy-2-methyl-4,5-pyridinedimethanol; 3-hydroxy-4,5-bis-(hydroxymethyl)-α-picoline; adermine; pyridox-ol; vitamin B$_6$; pyridoxine hydrochloride).
See also under Ascorbic acid; Tryptophan.

Pyridoxine-amphetamine condensation product *see* Pyridoxiphen.

PYRIDOXINE ASPARTATE ('aspardoxine').

Pyridoxine 2-(p-chlorophenoxy)-2-methylpropionate *see* Pyridoxine clofibrate.

PYRIDOXINE CLOFIBRATE (pyridoxine 2-(p-chlorophenoxy)-2-methylpropionate; 'claresan').

Pyridoxine 5-disulfide *see* Pyritinol.

Pyridoxine 3-ether with glycolic acid *see* 2-[(5-Hydroxy-4-hydroxymethyl-6-methylpyrid-3-yl)-methoxy]glycolic acid.

PYRIDOXIPHEN (tr) (amphetamine-pyridoxine condensation product).

Pyridoxol *see* Pyridoxine.

3-Pyridoxyl deanol succinate *see* Pirisudanol.

β-Pyridyl aldehyde *see* Nicotinaldehyde.

γ-Pyridyl aldehyde *see* Isonicotinaldehyde.

α-[(2-Pyridylamino)methyl]benzyl alcohol *see* Fenyramidol.

Pyridylazopyridine *see* Azopyridine.

2-Pyrid-4-ylbenzofuran *see* Pyridarone.

N-Pyrid-2-ylbiphenylacetamide *see* Diphenpyr-amide.

β-Pyridyl carbinol *see* Nicotinyl alcohol.

α-(2-Pyrid-4-ylcyclopropyl)benzhydrol *see* Cyprolidol.

Pyrid-3-ylmethanethiol ester with indometacin *see* Pimetacin.

Pyrid-3-ylmethylamine *see* Picolamine.

7-[2-[(Pyrid-3-ylmethyl)amino]ethyl]theophylline *see* Pimefylline.

4-(Pyrid-5-ylmethylaminomethyl)pyridine *see* Gapicomine.

1-[2-(*N*-Pyrid-2-ylmethylanilino)ethyl]piperidine *see* Picoperine.

Pyrid-3-ylmethyl 2-(p-chlorophenoxy)-2-methylpro-pionate *see* Nicofibrate.

Pyrid-3-ylmethyl 2-[[α-(p-chlorophenyl)-p-tolyl]-oxy]-2-methylbutyrate *see* Eniclobrate.

4,4′-(Pyrid-2-ylmethylene)diphenol bis(dihydrogen phosphate) tetrasodium salt *see* Sodium picofosfate.

4,4′-(Pyrid-2-ylmethylene)diphenol bis(hydrogen sulfate) disodium salt *see* Sodium picosulfate.

4,4′-Pyrid-2-ylmethylenediphenol diacetate *see* Bis-acodyl.

2-[(Pyrid-2-ylmethyl)sulfinyl]benzimidazole *see* Timoprazole.

3-(Pyrid-1-ylmethyl)-7-(thien-2-ylacetamido)-2-cephem-2-carboxylic acid betaine *see* Cefaloridine.

2-[(Pyrid-4-ylmethyl)thio]ethanol *see* Ristianol.

1-(3-Pyrid-2-yloxypropyl)-4-(o-tolyl)piperazine *see* Toprilidine.

2-Pyrid-3-ylpiperidine *see* Anabasine.

-Pyrid-2-yl-3-pyrrolidin-1-yl-1-p-tolyl-1-propene *see* Triprolidine.

5-[p-(2-Pyridylsulfamoyl)phenylazo]salicylic acid *see* Salazosulfapyridine.

N^1-Pyrid-2-ylsulfanilamide *see* Sulfapyridine.

Pyrid-3-yl tartrate *see* Hydroxypyridine tartrate.

7-[2-(Pyrid-4-ylthio)acetamido]cephalosporanic acid *see* Cefapirin.

2-(2-Pyrid-2-ylvinyl)-3-(o-tolyl)quinazolin-4(3*H*)-one *see* Piriqualone.

Pyrilamine *see* Mepyramine.

'Pyrilax' *see* Bisacodyl.

'Pyrilene' *see* Pempidine.

'Pyrilgin' *see* Dipyrone.

PYRIMETHAMINE*** (5-(4-chlorophenyl)-6-ethyl-2,4-pyrimidinediamine; 2,4-diamino-5-(p-chlorophenyl)-6-ethylpyrimidine; chloridine; BW-50-63; NSC-3061; RP 4753).

PYRIMETHAMINE plus DAPSONE ('maloprim').

PYRIMETHAMINE plus SULFADOXINE ('fansidar').

PYRIMIDINE (1,3-diazine; metadiazine; miazine).

2,4(1*H*,3*H*)-Pyrimidinedione *see* Uracil.

Pyrimidine phosphoran *see* Pirimiphos methyl.

2,4,5,6(1*H*,3*H*)-Pyrimidinetetrone *see* Alloxan.

2,4,6(1*H*,3*H*,5*H*)-Pyrimidinetrione *see* Barbituric acid.

PYRIMIDINONE (pyrimidone).

α-[(Pyrimidin-2-ylamino)methyl]benzyl alcohol *see* Fenyripol.

8-[4-[4-(Pyrimidin-2-yl)piperazin-1-yl]butyl]-8-azaspiro[4.5]decane-7,9-dione *see* Buspirone.

Pyrimidone *see* Pyrimidinone.

Pyrimido[4,5-*b*]pyrazine *see* Pteridine.

Pyrimido[4,5-*b*]pyrazine-2,4(1*H*,3*H*)-dione *see* Lumazine.

PYRIMIDO[5,4-*d*]PYRIMIDINE (1,3,5,7-tetra-azanaphthalene).

Pyrimido[4,5-*b*]quinoxaline-2,4(3*H*,10*H*)-dione *see* Isoalloxazine.

Pyrimidylpiperonylpiperazine *see* Piribedil.

Pyrimidyl-quinaldin *see* Quinapyramine.

N^1-Pyrimid-2-ylsulfanilamide *see* Sulfadiazine.

PYRIMITATE*** (*O*-[2-(dimethylamino)-6-meth-ylpyrimidin-4-yl] *O,O*-diethyl phosphorothioate; pyrimithate; ICI-29661; 'diothyl').

Pyrimithate* *see* Pyrimitate.

PYRINOLINE*** (3-(dipyrid-2-ylmethylene)-α,α-dipyrid-2-yl-1,4-cyclopentadiene-1-methanol; α,α,6,6-tetrapyrid-2-ylmethano-1,4-cyclopentadienemethanol; McN-1210).

'Pyripyridium' *see* Phenazopyridine.

'Pyrisept' *see* Cetylpyridinium bromide.

Pyrisuccideanol *see* Pirisudanol.

PYRITHIAMINE (1-(4-amino-2-methylpyrimid-in-5-ylmethyl)-3-(2-hydroxyethyl)-2-methylpyridinium bromide; neopyrithiamine).

Pyrithidium* *see* Pyritidium bromide.

PYRITHIONE (1-hydroxy-2(1*H*)-pyridinethione; 2-pyridinethiol 1-oxide; 'omadine').

PYRITHIONE SODIUM (pyrithione sodium salt; B-907; 'fonderma').

PYRITHIONE ZINC* (bis(1-hydroxy-2(1*H*)-pyridinethionato) zinc; zinc bis(pyridine-2-thiol 1-oxide); zinc pyridinethione; zinc pyrithione).

Pyrithioxine* *see* Pyritinol.

PYRITHYLDIONE* (3,3-diethyl-1,2,3,4-tetra-hydropyridine-2,4-dione; 3,3-diethyl-2,4(1*H*,3*H*)-pyridinedione; didropyridine; di-hydropyridinium; tetridin; Nu-903; 'benedorm'; 'persedon'; 'presidon').

PYRITIDIUM BROMIDE* (3-amino-8-[(2-amino-6-methylpyrimidin-4-yl)amino]-6-(*p*-aminophenyl)-5-methylphenanthridinium bromide 1'-methobromide; pyrithidium; pyrithidium bromide; RD-2801; 'prothidium').

PYRITINOL* (bis(3-hydroxy-4-(hydroxymeth-yl)-2-methylpyrid-5-ylmethyl) disulfide; 3,3'-di-thiodimethylenebis(5-hydroxy-6-methyl-4-pyr-idinemethanol); pyrithioxine; pyridoxine 5-di-sulfide; pyritinol hydrochloride).

'Pyrizidin' *see* Isoniazid.

Pyroboric acid *see* Tetraboric acid.

'Pyrocat' *see* Dipyrocetyl.

Pyrocatechin *see* Pyrocatechol.

PYROCATECHOL (*o*-dihydroxybenzene; pyroca-techin).

Pyrocatechol-3,5-disulfonic acid salts *see* Neody-mium pyrocatecholdisulfonate complex; Sodium pyrocatecholdisulfonate; Stibophen.

o-**PYROCATECHUIC ACID** (2,3-dihydroxybenz-oic acid; pyrocatechol-3-carboxylic acid).
See also Sodium *o*-pyrocatechuate.

'Pyrodin' *see* Aminophenazone.

Pyrogallic acid *see* Gallic acid; Pyrogallol.

PYROGALLOL (1,2,3-trihydroxybenzene; pyro-gallic acid).

Pyrogallol-5-carboxylic acid *see* Gallic acid.

Pyrogallol monoacetate *see* Gallacetophenone.

Pyrogallol triacetate *see* Acetpyrogall.

Pyrogallol 1,2,3-tris(diethylaminoethyl ether) tri-ethiodide *see* Gallamine triethiodide.

'Pyrogastrone' *see* Carbenoxolone.

Pyroglutamic acid *see* Pidolic acid.

L-Pyroglutamyl-L-histidyl-L-tryptophyl-L-seryl-L-tyrosylglycyl-L-leucyl-L-arginyl-L-prolylglycin-amide *see* Gonadorelin.

'Pyrolan' *see* 3-Methyl-1-phenylpyrazol-5-yl di-methylcarbamate.

Pyrolaxon (tr) *see* Gallamine triethiodide.

Pyromucic acid *see* 2-Furoic acid.

Pyromucic aldehyde *see* 2-Furaldehyde.

'Pyronil' *see* Pyrobutamine.

PYROPHENDANE* (1-methyl-3-[(3-methylin-dan-1-yl)methyl]pyrrolidine; 1-(2-methylpyrro-lidin-3-ylmethyl)-3-phenylindan).

PYROPHOS (tr) (tetraethyl thiopyrophosphate; tetraethyl monothiopyrophosphate; ethyl pyro-phosphorothionate; fosarbin; phosarbin; A-2).

PYROPHOSPHORAMIDE (phosphorodiamidic anhydride; pyrophosphorotetramide).

Pyrophosphoric acid tetraethyl ester *see* Tetraethyl pyrophosphate.

Pyrophosphorotetramide *see* Pyrophosphoramide.

Pyroracemic acid *see* Pyruvic acid.

'Pyrosal' *see* Phenazone salicylacetate.

'Pyrostib' *see* Stibophen.

PYROVALERONE* (4'-methyl-2-pyrrolidin-1-ylvalerophenone; 2-pyrrolidin-1-yl-1-*p*-tolyl-1-pentanone; pyrovalerone hydrochloride; F-1983).

PYROXAMINE* (3-(*p*-chloro-α-phenylbenzyl-oxy)-1-methylpyrrolidine; pyroxamine maleate; AHR-224; NSC-64540).

PYROXYLIN* (fulmicoton; cellulose nitrate; nitrocellulose; soluble guncotton).

'Pyrozone' *see* Hydrogen peroxide.

PYRROBUTAMINE* (1-[4-(*p*-chlorophenyl)-3-phenylbut-2-enyl]pyrrolidine; pyrrobutamine di-phosphate).

PYRROCAINE* (2-pyrrolidin-1-yl-2',6'-acet-oxylidide; 1-pyrrolidineaceto-2',6'-xylidide; EN-1010; NSC-52644).

Pyrrolamidole *see* Dextromoramide.

'Pyrrolazote' *see* Parathiazine.

1-Pyrrolidineaceto-2',6'-xylidide *see* Pyrrocaine.

2-Pyrrolidinecarboxylic acid *see* Proline.

2,5-Pyrrolidinedione *see* Succinimide.

1-Pyrrolidineethanol 4-butoxy-3,5-dimethoxybenzo-ate *see* Burodiline.

2-PYRROLIDINONE (2-pyrrolidone; pyrrolid-one; 4-aminobutyric acid lactam).

2-Pyrrolidin-1-yl-2',6'-acetoxylidide *see* Pyrrocaine.

1-(Pyrrolidin-1-ylcarbonylmethyl)-4-(3,4,5-trimeth-oxycinnamoyl)piperazine *see* Cinepazide.

2-Pyrrolidin-1-ylethyl 4-butoxy-3,5-dimethoxyben-zoate *see* Burodiline.

10-(2-Pyrrolidin-1-ylethyl)phenothiazine *see* Para-thiazine.

2-Pyrrolidin-1-ylethyl *N*-[7-(trifluoromethyl)-4-qui-nolyl]anthranilate *see* Florifenine.

***N*-(Pyrrolidin-1-ylmethyl)tetracycline** *see* Rolitetra-cycline.

***N*-(2-Pyrrolidin-1-ylpropionyl)-*o*-toluidine** *see* Ap-tocaine.

3-Pyrrolidin-1-ylpropyl 2,4,6-trimethoxyphenyl ket-one *see* Buflomedil.

2-Pyrrolidin-1-yl-1-*p*-tolyl-1-pentanone *see* Pyrova-lerone.

***trans*-2-(3-Pyrrolidin-1-yl-1-*p*-tolylpropenyl)pyrid-ine** *see* Triprolidine.

6-(3-Pyrrolidin-1-yl-1-*p*-tolylpropenyl)-2-pyridine-acrylic acid *see* Acrivastine.

Pyrrolidone *see* 2-Pyrrolidinone.

2-Pyrrolidone-5-carboxylic acid *see* Pidolic acid.

PYRROLIFENE* ((+)-α-benzyl-β-methyl-α-phenyl-1-pyrrolidinepropanol acetate; (+)-3-methyl-1,2-diphenyl-4-pyrrolidin-1-yl-2-butanol acetate; pyrroliphene; pyrroliphene hydrochloride).

trans-**3-(1-Pyrrolin-2-yl)acrylamide** *see* Desdanine.

Pyrroliphene* *see* Pyrrolifene.

PYRROLNITRIN*** (3-chloro-3-(3-chloro-2-nitrophenyl)pyrrole; FR-005759; NSC-107654).

Pyrroplegium* *see* Pentolonium tartrate.

Pyrrovinyquinium chloride *see* Pyrvinium chloride.

Pyrroxan (tr) *see* Proroxan.

Pyruvaldehyde *see* Methylglyoxal.

Pyruvate oxidation factor *see* Thioctic acid.

PYRUVIC ACID (2-oxopropionic acid; 2-ketopropionic acid; acetylformic acid; Brenztraubensaure; pyroracemic acid).

Pyruvic acid *o*-ethoxybenzylhydrazone *see* Ruvazone.

PYRVINIUM CHLORIDE*** (6-(dimethylamino)-2-[2-(2,5-dimethyl-1-phenyl-3-pyrrolyl)-vinyl]-1-methylquinolinium chloride; pyrrovinyquinium chloride; viprynium chloride; Chemotherapy Centre Cpd. No. 715).

PYRVINIUM EMBONATE (pyrvinium 4,4′-methylenebis(3-hydroxynaphthalene-2-carboxylate); pyrvinium pamoate; viprynium pamoate).

PYTAMINE** (2-[α-(2-dimethylaminoethoxy)-2,6-diethylbenzyl]pyridine; pytamine hydrochloride; BS-7161-D).

PZ-68 *see* Pentosan polysulfate.

PZ-1511 *see* Carpipramine.

'PZC' *see* Perphenazine.

Q

Q-137 *see* 1,1-Dichloro-2,2-bis(*p*-ethylphenyl)ethane.
Q-275 *see* Ubiquinone(s).
QB-1 *see* Cloquinozine.
QBH *see* Benquinox.
'Qidamp' *see* Ampicillin.
'Qidmycin' *see* Erythromycin stearate.
'Qidtet' *see* Tetracycline.
Qinghaosu *see* Artemisin.
QM-6008 *see* Bentazepam.
'Quaalude' *see* Methaqualone.
'Quadrol' *see* Edetol.
QUADROSILAN** (*cis*-2,2,4,6,6,8-hexamethyl-4,8-diphenylcyclotetrasiloxane; Kabi-1774).
'Quam' *see under* Trimethoprim.
'Quamonium' *see* Cetrimonium bromide.
'Quantalan' *see* Colestyramine.
'Quantril' *see* Benzquinamide.
'Quarzan' *see* Clidinium bromide.
'Quat' *see* Bromhexine.
QUATACAINE*** (2,2'-dimethyl-2-(propyl-amino)propionanilide; 2-methyl-2-(propyl-amino)-*o*-propionotoluidide; quatacaine hydrochloride; LA-012).
QUATERON (tr) ([3-[(*p*-butoxybenzoyl)oxy]-2,3-dimethylpropyl]triethylammonium iodide; 3-(diethylamino)-1,2-dimethylpropyl *p*-butoxybenzoate ethiodide; triethyl(3-hydroxy-2,3-dimethyl-propyl)ammonium iodide *p*-butoxybenzoate).
'Quatommon' *see* Benzalkonium chloride.
'Quatrasan' *see* Myristylpicolinium chloride.
QUAZEPAM*** (7-chloro-5-(*o*-fluorophenyl)-1,3-dihydro-1-(2,2,2-trifluoroethyl)-2*H*-1,4-benzodiazepine-2-thione; Sch-16134).
QUAZODINE*** (4-ethyl-6,7-dimethoxyquin-azoline; MJ-1988).
Quebrachine *see* Yohimbine.
QUEBRACHITOL (inositol methyl ether).
Quebrachol *see* β-Sitosterol.
'Queleton' *see* Fenthion.
'Quellada' *see* Lindane.
'Quemid' *see* Colestyramine.
QUERCETAGETIN (3,3',4',5,6,7-hexahydroxy-flavone).
QUERCETIN (3,3',4',5,7-pentahydroxyflavone; flavin; meletin; quercetol; sophoretin; 'quert-ine').
Quercetin 3-galactoside *see* Hyperin.
Quercetin 3-glucoside *see* Isoquercitrin.
Quercetin pentabenzyl ether *see* Benzquercin.
Quercetin rhamnoglucoside *see* Rutoside.

Quercetin 3-rhamnoside *see* Quercitrin.
Quercetin 3-rutinoside *see* Rutoside.
Quercetol *see* Quercetin.
Quercimelin *see* Quercitrin.
QUERCITOL (1,2,3,4,5-cyclohexanepentol).
QUERCITRIN (quercetin 3-rhamnoside; querci-melin; quercitrinic acid).
Quercitrinic acid *see* Quercitrin.
'Quertine' *see* Quercetin.
'Questran' *see* Colestyramine.
'Quiactin' *see* Oxanamide.
'Quick' *see* Chlorophacinone.
'Quick-kill' *see* Thallium sulfate.
'Quide' *see* Piperacetazine.
'Quiescin' *see* Reserpine.
'Quietal' *see* Propallylonal.
'Quietidine' *see* Diphenazine.
QUIFENADINE*** (α,α-diphenyl-3-quinuclidine-methanol; 3-quinuclidyl diphenyl carbinol; fen-carol; phencarol).
'Quilan' *see* Benfluralin.
'Quilene' *see* Pentapiperium metilsulfate.
'Quilil' *see* Phenprobamate.
QUILLIFOLINE*** (2-(*p*-chlorophenyl)-1,3,4,6,7,11b-hexahydro-9,10-dimethoxy-2*H*-benzo[*a*]quinolizine; chillifolin; killifolin).
'Quilonum' *see* Lithium acetate.
'Quimar' *see* Chymotrypsin.
'Quimbo' *see* Potassium diiodophenolsulfonate.
'Quimbosan' *see* Potassium diiodophenolsulfonate.
'Quimocycline' *see* Prazosin.
'Quimotrase' *see* Chymotrypsin.
Quin.... *see also* Chin.....
QUINACAINOL** (2-*tert*-butyl-α-(2-piperid-4-yl-ethyl)-4-quinolinemethanol).
QUINACETOPHENONE (2,5-dihydroxyaceto-phenone).
QUINACILLIN** (6-(3-carboxy-2-quinoxaline-carboxamido)penicillanic acid; 3-carboxyquin-oxalin-2-yl-penicillin).
'Quinacrine' *see* Mepacrine.
'Quinadome' *see* Diiodohydroxyquin.
'Quinaglute' *see* Quinidine gluconate.
Quinalbarbitone* *see* Secobarbital.
QUINALDIC ACID (2-quinolinecarboxylic acid).
QUINALDINE (2-methylquinoline).
QUINALDINE BLUE*** (1-ethyl-2-[3-(1-ethyl-2(1*H*)-quinolylidene)propenyl]quinolinium chloride; NSC-56808; 'vernitest').
QUINALPHOS* (2-[(diethoxyphosphinothioyl)-oxy]quinoxaline; *O,O*-diethyl *O*-quinoxalin-2-yl

phosphorothioate; diethchinalphion; 'bayrusil').

'Quinambicide' *see* Clioquinol.

'Quinamin' *see* Quinine sulfate.

QUINAPHTHOL (quinine bis(2-naphthol-1-sulfonate); chinaphthol).

QUINAPYRAMINE* (4-amino-6-[(2-amino-1,6-dimethylpyrimid-4-yl)amino]-1,2-dimethylquinolinium dichloride or disulfate; pyraldin; pyrimidyl-quinaldin; M-7555; 'antrycide').

QUINASPAR (*N*-[*p*-[(2,4-diaminoquinazolin-6-yl-methyl)amino]benzoyl]aspartic acid; NSC-112846; SK-29728).

QUINAZOLINE (benzo[*a*]pyrimidine).

QUINAZOLINONE (quinazolone).

Quinazolone *see* Quinazolinone.

QUINAZOSIN*** (2-(4-allylpiperazin-1-yl)-4-amino-6,7-dimethoxyquinazoline; quinazosin dihydrochloride; quinazosin hydrochloride; CP-11332-1).

QUINBOLONE*** (17β-cyclopenten-1-yloxyandrosta-1,4-dien-3-one).

QUINCARBATE** (ethyl 10-chloro-3-ethoxymethyl-2,3,6,9-tetrahydro-9-oxo-*p*-dioxino[2,3-*g*]quinoline-8-carboxylate; DU-23187).

QUINDECAMINE** (4,4'-(decamethylenediimino)diquinaldine; chindecamine; kindekamin).

QUINDECAMINE ACETATE* (quindecamine diacetate; NAT-324; 'quindemin').

'Quindemin' *see* Quindecamine acetate.

QUINDONIUM BROMIDE*** (1,3,3a,5,6,11,12,12a-octahydro-8-hydroxy-1*H*-benzo[*a*]cyclopenta[*f*]quinolizinium bromide; W-3366A).

QUINDOXIN*** (quinoxaline 1,4-dioxide; ICI-8173; RD-2579; 'grofas').

'Quinercyl' *see* Chloroquine digentisate.

QUINESTRADOL*** (3-cyclopentyloxyestratriene-16α,17β-diol; estriol 3-cyclopentyl ether).

QUINESTROL*** (3-cyclopentyloxy-17α-ethynylestra-1,3,5(10)-trien-17β-ol; 3-cyclopentyloxy-19-nor-17α-pregna-1,3,5(10)-trien-20-yn-17β-ol; ethinylestradiol 3-cyclopentyl ether; W-3566).

QUINETALATE*** (compound of 4-[(2-dimethylaminoethyl)amino]-6-methoxyquinoline with 6-diethylcarbamoyl-3-cyclohexene-1-carboxylic acid; quinetolate).

QUINETHAZONE*** (7-chloro-2-ethyl-1,2,3,4-tetrahydro-4-oxo-6-quinazolinesulfonamide; 7-chloro-2-ethyl-1,2,3,4-tetrahydro-6-sulfamoylquinazolin-4(3*H*)-one; chinethazone; CL-36010).

Quinetolate* *see* Quinetalate.

QUINETUM (mixture of quinine, cinchonine and cinchonidine).

See also Totaquine.

QUINFAMIDE*** (1-(dichloracetyl)-1,2,3,4-tetrahydro-6-quinolinyl 2-furoate; WIN-40014).

Quingamine (tr) *see* Chloroquine diphosphate.

QUINGESTANOL*** (3-cyclopentyloxy-19-nor-17α-pregna-3,5-dien-20-yn-17-ol).

See also under Ethinylestradiol.

QUINGESTANOL ACETATE (W-4540).

QUINGESTRONE*** (3-cyclopentyloxypregna-3,5-dien-20-one; W-3399).

QUINIC ACID (1,3,4,5-tetrahydroxycyclohexanecarboxylic acid; kinic acid).

See also Piperazine quinate; Urea quinate.

'Quinicardine' *see* Quinidine.

'Quinidate' *see* Quinidine.

QUINIDINE ((9*S*)-6'-methoxycinchonan-9-ol; (+)-6-methoxy-α-(5-vinylquinuclidin-2-yl)-4-quinolinemethanol; α-(6-methoxy-4-quinolyl)-5-vinyl-2-quinuclidinemethanol; 6'-methoxycinchonine; conquinine; pitayine; β-quinine).

See also under Procainamide.

α-Quinidine *see* Cinchonidine.

QUINIDINE ARABOGALACTAN SULFATE ('longacor').

QUINIDINE 5-ETHYL-5-PHENYLBARBITURATE (quinidine phenobarbital salt; 'natisedine'; 'sedoquin').

QUINIDINE GLUCONATE ('dura-tab'; 'gluquinate'; 'quinaglute').

QUINIDINE POLYGALACTURONATE ('cardioquin'; 'mundiquin').

QUININE ((8α,9*R*)-6'-methoxycinchonan-9-ol; (−)-6-methoxy-α-(5-vinylquinuclidin-2-yl)-4-quinolinemethanol; α-(6-methoxy-4-quinolyl)-5-vinyl-2-quinuclidinemethanol; 6'-methoxycinchonidine).

β-Quinine *see* Quinidine.

Quinine bis(2-naphthol-1-sulfonate) *see* Quinaphthol.

QUININE BISULFATE (neutral quinine sulfate; quinine acid sulfate).

QUININE CARBONATE (diquinine carbonate).

QUININE CARBOPHENETIDINE (quininecarboxylic acid p-ethoxyanilide; quinine carboxylic acid phenetidide).

Quinine chloral derivative *see* Quinochloral.

QUININE DIHYDROCHLORIDE (quinine acid hydrochloride).

QUININE ETHYL CARBONATE (aecachinum; 'euchinin'; 'euquinine').

QUININE HYDROCHLORIDE (basic quinine-HCl; quinine monohydrochloride; SN-359).

Quinine hydroxycaffeine derivative *see* Oxyquinotheine.

QUININE IODOBISMUTHATE (biioquinol).

QUININE IODOSULFATE (iodoquinine sulfate).

QUININE SULFATE (basic quinine sulfate).

QUININE SULFATE plus AMINOPHYLLINE ('limptar').

Quiniodochlor *see* Clioquinol.

Quiniofon *see* Chiniofon.

QUINISOCAINE*** (2-butyl-1-(2-dimethylaminoethoxy)isoquinoline; dimethisoquin; quinisocaine hydrochloride; SK&F-538-A).

Quinium *see* Totaquine.

QUINIZARINE (1,4-dihydroxyanthraquinone).

Quinocaine *see* Cinchocaine.

QUINOCHLORAL (compound of quinine and chloral; 'chinoral').

QUINOCIDE*** (8-(4-aminopentylamino)-6-methoxyquinoline; chinocide; CN-155; WIN-10448).

'Quin-o-creme' *see* Clioquinol.

'**Quinoderm**' *see under* 8-Quinolinol sulfate.

Quinoform *see* Clioquinol.

Quinol *see* Hydroquinone.

QUINOLIN-2-AMIC ACID (2-carbamoylnicotinic acid; quinolinic acid monoamide).

QUINOLINE (benzo[*b*]pyridine).

2-Quinolinecarboxylic acid *see* Quinaldic acid.

4-Quinolinecarboxylic acid *see* Cinchoninic acid.

2,3-Quinolinedicarboxylic acid *see* Acridinic acid.

QUINOLINIC ACID (2,3-pyridinedicarboxylic acid).

Quinolinic acid monoamide *see* Quinolin-2-amic acid.

2-Quinolinol *see* Carbostyril.

4-QUINOLINOL (4-hydroxyquinoline; kynurine).

8-QUINOLINOL (8-hydroxyquinoline; oxyquinoline; kinozol; oxin; oxine; oxychinolin; preconsol).
See also Benzoxiquine; Oxine-copper.

8-QUINOLINOL SULFATE (8-hydroxyquinoline sulfate and/or its potassium salt; 'chinosol'; 'cryptonol'; 'idril'; 'pectan'; 'quinosol'; 'solquinol'; 'sunoxol'; 'superol').

8-QUINOLINOL SULFATE plus BENZOYL PEROXIDE ('quinoderm').

8-QUINOLINOL SULFATE ALUMINIUM ('aloxyn'; 'nyxolan').

'**Quinolor**' *see* Halquinols.

α-(4-Quinolyl)-5-vinyl-2-quinuclidinemethanol *see* Cinchonidine; Cinchonine.

Quinomethionate *see* Chinomethionat.

Quinophan *see* Cinchophen.

'**Quinophenol**' *see* 8-Quinolinol.

Quinopyrine *see* Chinopyrine.

'**Quinora**' *see* Quinidine.

'**Quinosol**' *see* 8-Quinolinol sulfate.

QUINOXALINE (benzo[*a*]pyrazine; 1,4-benzodiazine; benzoparadiazine; phenpiazine).

Quinoxaline-3-carboxylic acid penicillin derivative *see* Quinacillin.

Quinoxaline-2,3-dimethanol 1,4-dioxide *see* Dioxidine.

Quinoxaline-2,3-dimethanol 1,4-dioxide diacetate *see* Quinoxidine.

Quinoxaline 1,4-dioxide *see* Quindoxin.

3-(2-Quinoxalinylmethylene)carbazic acid N^1,N^4-dioxide methyl ester *see* Carbadox.

N^1-**Quinoxalin-2-ylsulfanilamide** *see* Sulfaquinoxaline.

QUINOXIDINE (tr) (quinoxaline-2,3-dimethanol

1,4-dioxide diacetate; dioxidine diacetate (ester)).

QUINPRENALINE* (5-[1-hydroxy-2-(isopropylamino)ethyl]-8-quinolinol; 8-hydroxy-α-[(isopropylamino)methyl]-5-quinolinemethanol; quinterenol; quinterenol sulfate; CP-10308-8).

Quinterenol* *see* Quinprenaline.

QUINTIOFOS* (*O*-ethyl *O*-quinolin-8-yl phenylphosphonothioate; Bayer-9037; 'bacdip').

'**Quinton**' *see* Lysine acetylsalicylate.

QUINTOZENE* (pentachloronitrobenzene; PCNB; PHNB; 'botrilex'; 'brassicol'; 'terraclor'; 'tilcarex'; 'tritisan').

QUINUCLIDINE (1-azabicyclo[2.2.2]octane; 1,4-ethylenepiperidine).

3-Quinuclidinyl acetate *see* Aceclidine.

3-QUINUCLIDINYL BENZILATE (Ro 2-3308).

3-Quinuclidinyl benzoate *see* Benzoclidine.

10-(Quinuclidin-3-ylmethyl)phenothiazine *see* Mequitazine.

3-Quinuclidyl diphenyl carbinol *see* Quifenadine.

QUINUCLIUM BROMIDE* (1-methyl-3-oxo-4-phenyl-1-azoniabicyclo[2.2.2]octane bromide; 1-methyl-3-oxo-4-phenylquinuclidinium bromide; MA-540).

QUINUPRAMINE* (3-(10,11-dihydro-5*H*-dibenz[*b*,*f*]azepin-5-yl)quinuclidine; 10,11-dihydro-5-quinuclidin-3-yl-5*H*-dibenz[*b*,*f*]azepine; LM-208; 'kevopril'; 'kinupril').

QUINUREA (mixed crystals of quinine and urea).

Quinuronium methyl sulfate *see* Quinuronium sulfate.

QUINURONIUM SULFATE (6,6′-ureylenebis(1-methylquinolinium sulfate); dimethylquinolinyl methyl sulfate urea; diquinolylurea bismethosulfate; quinuronium methyl sulfate; SN-5870).

QUIPAZINE* (2-piperazin-1-ylquinoline; quipazine maleate; MA-1291).

'**Quipenyl**' *see* Pamaquine.

QUISULTAZINE (*N*,*N*-dimethyl-10-quinuclidin-3-ylphenothiazine-2-sulfonamide; quisultidine).

Quisultidine *see* Quisultazine.

'**Quitaxon**' *see* Doxepin.

'**Quival**' *see* Polycarbophil.

'**Quixalin**' *see* Halquinols.

'**Quotane**' *see* Quinisocaine.

QX-572 *see* Carcainum chloride.

QZ 2 *see* Methaqualone.

R

R-14 *see* Fenpipramide.
R-47 *see* Trichlormethine.
R-48 *see* Chlornaphazine.
R-52 *see* Mannosulfan.
R-55 *see* Isopropamide iodide.
R-79 *see* Isopropamide iodide.
R-88 *see* 2-(*p-tert*-Butylphenoxy)isopropyl 2-chloroethyl sulfite.
R-100 *see* Ambutonium bromide.
R-106 *see* Pasiniazid.
R-113 *see* 1,1,2-Trichloro-1,2,2-trifluoroethane.
R-148 *see* Methaqualone.
R-164 *see* Pargeverine.
R-178 *see under* Norgestrienone.
R-239 *see* 5-(2-Bromoallyl)-5-(1-methylbutyl)bar-bituric acid.
R-246 *see* Tretamine.
R-261-P *see* *N*-Deacetylthiocolchicine.
R-368c *see* Niflumic acid.
R-381 *see* Fenbutrazate.
R-382 *see* Phenmetrazine teoclate.
R-516 *see* Cinnarizine.
R-548 *see* Tricetamide.
R-610 *see* Racemoramide.
R-661 *see* Buzepide metiodide.
R-720-11 *see* Fenetylline.
R-760 *see* Flazalone.
R-798 *see* Rimiterol.
R-802 *see* Flumequine.
R-803 *see* Furaprofen.
R-805 *see* Nimesulide.
R-807 *see* Diflumidone.
R-812 *see* Prednisolone sodium *m*-sulfobenzoate.
R-818 *see* Flecainide acetate.
R-875 *see* Dextromoramide.
R-1132 *see* Diphenoxylate.
R-1303 *see* Carbofenotion.
R-1406 *see* Phenoperidine.
R-1575 *see* Cinnarizine.
R-1625 *see* Haloperidol.
R-1647 *see* Anisoperidone.
R-1658 *see* Moperone.
R-1707 *see* Glafenine.
R-1881 *see* Metribolone.
R-1929 *see* Azaperone.
R 2010 *see* Norgestrienone.
R-2028 *see* Fluanisone.
R-2055 *see* Calcium methyl polygalacturonate sul-fonate(s).
R-2113 *see* Desoximetasone.
R-2159 *see* Anisopirol.

R-2167 *see* Fluanisone.
R-2323 *see* Gestrinone.
R-2453 *see* Demegestone.
R-2498 *see* Trifluperidol.
R-2580 *see* Trenbolone.
R-2858 *see* Moxestrol.
R-2962 *see* Amiperone.
R-2963 *see* Meperidide.
R-3201 *see* Haloperidide.
R-3248 *see* Aceperone.
R-3345 *see* Pipamperone.
R-3365 *see* Piritramide.
R-3588 *see* Etamiphyllin.
R-3939 *see* Clometacin.
R-4082 *see* Propyperone.
R-4263 *see* Fentanyl.
R-4318 *see* Floctafenine.
R-4444 *see* Duometacin.
R-4584 *see* Benperidol.
R-4714 *see* Oxiperomide.
R-4749 *see* Droperidol.
R-4845 *see* Bezitramide.
R-4929 *see* Benzetimide.
R-5046 *see* Cinperene.
R-5147 *see* Spiperone.
R-5183 *see* Meletimide.
R-5188 *see* Spiroxatrine.
R-5385 *see* Acoxatrine.
R-5908 *see* Spiramide.
R-6109 *see* Spirilene.
R-6218 *see* Fluspirilene.
R-6238 *see* Pimozide.
R-6348 *see* Antazonite.
R-7158 *see* Roxoperone.
R-7242 *see* Difluanazine.
R-7315 *see* Metomidate.
R-7405 *see* Etomidate.
R-7464 *see* Propoxate.
R-7904 *see* Lidoflazine.
R-8025 *see* Antienite.
R-8141 *see* Antienite.
R-8193 *see* Antafenite.
R-8284 *see* Proclonol.
R-8299 *see* Tetramisole.
R-9298 *see* Clofluperol.
R-10100 *see* Etonam nitrate.
R-10948 *see* Diamocaine cyclamate.
R-11333 *see* Bromperidol.
R-12563 *see* Dexamisole.
R-12564 *see* Levamisole.
R-13423 *see* Dicloxacillin.

R-13558 *see* Fetoxilate.
R-13615 *see* Medrogestone.
R-14827 *see* Econazole.
R-14889 *see* Miconazole.
R-14950 *see* Flunarizine.
R-15403 *see* Difenoxin.
R-15454 *see* Isoconazole.
R-15497 *see* Gemazocine.
R-15556 *see* Orconazole.
R-15889 *see* Lorcainide.
R-16341 *see* Penfluridol.
R-16470 *see* Dexetimide.
R-16659 *see* Etomidate.
R-17147 *see* Ciclobendazole.
R-17190 *see* Protizinic acid.
R-17635 *see* Mebendazole.
R-17889 *see* Flubendazole.
R-17934 *see* Nocodazole.
R-18553 *see* Loperamide.
R-18910 *see* Fluperamide.
R-19317 *see* Rodocaine.
R-22700 *see* Rodocaine.
R-23050 *see* Salantel.
R-23633 *see* Fludazonium chloride.
R-25061 *see* Suprofen.
R-25160 *see* Cliprofen.
R-25540 *see* Imafen.
R-25831 *see* Carnidazole.
R-26333 *see* Deximafen.
R-26412 *see* Sulnidazole.
R-26490 *see* Etomidate.
R-27500 *see* Sepazonium chloride.
R-28096 *see* Carnidazole.
R-28930 *see* Fluspiperone.
R-29764 *see* Clopimozide.
R-29860 *see* Nitramisole.
R-30730 *see* Sufentanil.
R-31520 *see* Closantel.
R-33204 *see* Declenperone.
R-33799 *see* Carfentanil citrate.
R-33800 *see* Sufentanil citrate.
R-33812 *see* Domperidone.
R-34000 *see* Doconazole.
R-34009 *see* Milenperone.
R-34301 *see* Halopemide.
R-34803 *see* Etibendazole.
R 34995 *see* Lofentanil oxalate.
R 35443 *see* Oxatomide.
R-38198 *see* Buterizine.
R-39209 *see* Alfentanil.
R-39500 *see* Parconazole.
R-41400 *see* Ketoconazole.
R-41468 *see* Ketanserin.
R 42470 *see* Terconazole.
R-43512 *see* Astemizole.
R-45486 *see* Flumeridone.
R 46541 *see* Bromperidol decanoate.
R-47465 *see* Pirenperone.
R-49945 *see* Ketanserin tartrate.
R-51469 *see* Mioflazine.
R-51619 *see* Cisapride.
R-67408 *see* Fenclofenac.
RA-8 *see* Dipyridamole.

RA-101 *see* Niprofazone.
RA-233 *see* Mopidamol.
'Rabon' *see* Stirofos.
RA-C-384 *see* Iodocetylic acid [123]I.
'Racedrine' *see* Racephedrine.
RACEFEMINE*** (($\pm$)-α-methyl-N-(1-methyl-2-phenoxyethyl)phenethylamine; ($\pm$)-3,5-dimethyl-1,6-diphenyl-1-oxa-4-azahexane; CB-3697).
See also Dextrofemine.
RACEFENICOL*** (($\pm$)-*threo*-2,2-dichloro-N-(β-hydroxy-α-hydroxymethyl-p-methylsulfonylphenethyl)acetamide; ($\pm$)-*threo*-N-(2,2-dichloroacetyl)-β-hydroxy-α-hydroxymethyl-p-methylsulfonylphenethylamine; racephenicol; SW-5063; WIN-5063; 'dexawin').
Racemelfalan *see* Sarcolysin.
RACEMETHORPHAN*** (($\pm$)-3-methoxy-N-methylmorphinan; methorphan; racemethorphan hydrobromide; Ro 1-5470).
See also Dextromethorphan; Levomethorphan.
RACEMETIROSINE*** (($\pm$)-α-methyl-DL-tyrosine).
See also Metirosine.
Racemic acid *see* Mandelic acid.
RACEMORAMIDE*** (($\pm$)-1-(3-methyl-4-morpholino-2,2-diphenylbutyryl)pyrrolidine; ($\pm$)-4-(2-methyl-4-oxo-3,3-diphenyl-4-pyrrolidin-1-yl-butyl)morpholine; racemoramide bitartrate; R-610).
See also Dextromoramide; Levomoramide.
RACEMORPHAN*** (($\pm$)-3-hydroxy-N-methylmorphinan; methorphinan; racemorphan bitartrate; Nu-2206; Ro 1-5431).
See also Dextrorphan; Levorphanol.
RACEPHEDRINE* (($\pm$)-α-[1-(methylamino)ethyl]benzyl alcohol; ($\pm$)-2-(methylamino)-1-phenyl-1-propanol; racephedrine hydrochloride).
Racephenicol* *see* Racefenicol.
RACEPINEFRINE*** (($\pm$)-3,4-dihydroxy-α-[(methylamino)methyl]benzyl alcohol).
'Rachineocaine' *see* Procaine.
'Rachromate' *see* Sodium chromate (^{51}Cr).
'Racobalamin-57' *see* Cyanocobalamin ([57]Co).
'Racumin' *see* Coumatetralyl.
'Racuza' *see* Dicamba-methyl.
'Radanil' *see* Benznidazole.
'Radapon' *see* Dalapon.
'Radedorm' *see* Nitrazepam.
'Radepur' *see* Chlordiazepoxide.
'Radeverm' *see* Niclosamide.
'Radikill' *see* Cyanazine.
Radioaurum* *see* Gold ([198]Au) colloidal.
'Radiocaps-131' *see* Sodium iodide (^{131}I).
Radiocesium chloride *see* Cesium([131]Cs) chloride.
Radiocyanocobalamin *see* Cyanocobalamin ([57]Co); Cyanocobalamin ([58]Co); Cyanocobalamin (^{60}Co).
Radiocycobemin* *see* Cyanocobalamin (^{60}Co).
Radioethiodized oil *see* Ethiodized (^{131}I) oil.
Radiogallium citrate *see* Gallium (^{67}Ga) citrate.
Radiogold, colloidal *see* Gold ([198]Au) colloidal.

'**Radiographol**' *see* Methiodal sodium.
Radioiodinated human serum albumin *see* Iodinated (^{125}I) human serum albumin; Iodinated (^{131}I) human serum albumin.
Radiomerisoprol *see* Merisoprol (^{197}Hg).
'**Radiomiro**' *see* Iodamide.
'**Radiopol**' *see* Iodinated poppyseed oil.
'**Radioselectan**' *see* Adipiodone meglumine.
Radioselenomethionine *see* Selenomethionine (^{75}Se).
Radiostrontium nitrate *see* Strontium nitrate Sr 85.
Radiothallium chloride *see* Thallous chloride Tl 201.
Radiotolpovidone *see* Tolpovidone(^{131}I).
Radioxenon *see* Xenon (^{133}Xe).
Radium emanation *see* Radon.
RADON (radium emanation; 'alphatron').
RAFOXANIDE*** (3'-chloro-4'-(*p*-chlorophenoxy)-3,5-diiodosalicylanilide; afoxanide; 'flukanide'; 'ranide').
'**Ralabol**' *see* Zeranol.
'**Ralgro**' *see* Zeranol.
RAM-327 *see* Oxymethebanol.
Rambufaside *see* Meproscillarin.
RAMIFENAZONE** (4-(isopropylamino)-2,3-dimethyl-1-phenyl-3-pyrazolin-5-one).
RAMNODIGIN*** (14-hydroxy-3β-[(2,3,6-trideoxy-α-L-*erythro*-hexopyranosyl)oxy]-5β-card-20(22)-enolide).
'**Ramocillin**' *see* Procaine-penicillin.
'**Ramrod**' *see* Propachlor.
'**Randolectil**' *see* Butaperazine.
'**Randonos**' *see* Chorionic gonadotrophin.
'**Randox**' *see* Allidochlor.
'**Randum**' *see under* Metoclopramide.
'**Ranestol**' *see* Triclofenol piperazine.
'**Rangasil**' *see* Pirprofen.
'**Ranide**' *see* Rafoxanide.
RANIMYCIN*** (antibiotic from *Str. lincolnensis*; U-25873).
RANITIDINE*** (*N*-[2-[[5-[(dimethylamino)-methyl]furfuryl]thio]ethyl]-*N*'-methyl-2-nitro-1,1-ethenediamine; ranitidine hydrochloride; AH-19065; 'raticina'; 'sostril'; 'ulcex'; 'zantac'; 'zantic').
'**Ranocaine**' *see* Propoxycaine.
'**Ranoroc**' *see* Pyrazinobutazone.
'**Rantudil**' *see* Acemetacin.
'**Raovin**' *see* Tolpovidone(^{131}I).
'**Rapacodin**' *see* Dihydrocodeine.
'**Rapenton**' *see* Mopidamol.
'**Rapidol**' *see* Paracetamol.
'**Rapidosept**' *see* 2,4-Dichlorobenzyl alcohol.
'**Rapifen**' *see* Alfentanil.
'**Rapitest**' *see under* Norgestrienone.
RARE EARTH LEVULINATES (neodymium and praesodymium levulinates; 'helmodym-88').
'**Rasprin**' *see* Calcium acetylsalicylate.
'**Rastinon**' *see* Tolbutamide.
'**Rathimed N**' *see* Metronidazole.
RATHYRONINE*** (DL-3-[4-(4-hydroxy-3-iodophenoxy)-3,5-diiodophenyl]alanine; 3,3',5-triiodothyronine; 'trionine').

See also Detrothyronine; Liothyronine.
'**Raticate**' *see* Norbormide.
'**Raticina**' *see* Ranitidine.
'**Ratilan**' *see* Coumachlor.
'**Ratindan 1**' *see* Diphenadione.
'**Ratindan 3**' *see* Chlorophacinone.
'**Ratofarin**' *see* Warfarin.
RATTLESNAKE VENOM ('crotalin'; 'dicrotalin'; 'epileptasid').
'**Rattrack**' *see* Antu.
Raubasine *see* Ajmalicine.
'**Raunormine**' *see* Deserpidine.
'**Raurine**' *see* Reserpine.
'**Rau-sed**' *see* Reserpine.
'**Rausedan**' *see* Reserpine.
'**Rautensin**' *see* Alseroxylon.
'**Rauwilid**' *see* Reserpine.
'**Rauwiloid**' *see* Alseroxylon.
RAUWOLFIA ALKALOIDS (*R. serpentina* and/or *R. vomitoria*; RS-51).
See also Ajmalicine; Ajmaline; Alseroxylon; Deserpidine; Rauwolscine; Rescinnamine; Reserpine.
Rauwolfine *see* Ajmaline.
RAUWOLSCINE (17α-hydroxy-20α-yohimban-16β-carboxylic acid methyl ester; corynanthidine; isoyohimbine; α-yohimbine).
Raviac *see* Chlorophacinone.
'**Ravocaine**' *see* Propoxycaine.
'**Raybanol**' *see* Sodium benzyl succinate.
'**Rayodal**' *see* Iozomic acid.
'**Rayomiro**' *see* Iodamide.
'**Raythesin**' *see* Risocaine.
'**Rayvist**' *see* Meglumine ioglicate.
'**Razebil**' *see* Iobenzamic acid.
RAZINODIL*** (3,4,5-trimethoxybenzoic acid ester with 3-(2-hydroxy-3-morpholinopropyl)-6,7,8-trimethoxy-1,2,3-benzotriazin-4(3*H*)-one).
RAZOXANE*** ((±)-1,2-bis(3,5-dioxopiperazin-1-yl)propane; (±)-4,4'-propylenedi(2,6-piperazinedione); ICI-59118; ICRF-159; NSC-129943; 'razoxin').
'**Razoxin**' *see* Razoxane.
RB-1466 *see* Silymarin.
RB-1489 *see* Pipemidic acid.
RB-1589 *see* Pefloxacin.
RC 61-91 *see* Ifenprodil tartrate.
RC-167 *see* Niceverine.
RC-172 *see* Aldioxa.
RC-173 *see* Alcloxa.
RC-27109 *see* Nifuroxazide.
RCH-314 *see* Benhepazone.
RCM-258 *see* Fepentolic acid.
RD-292 *see* Fenpentadiol.
RD-328 *see* Pasiniazid.
RD-354 *see* Pentorex.
RD-406 *see* Cyprodenate.
RD-2579 *see* Quindoxin.
RD-2801 *see* Pyritidium bromide.
RD-3803 *see* Diloxanide.
RD-9338 *see* Norbudrine.
RD-11654 *see* Ibufenac.
RD-13621 *see* Ibuprofen.

RD-17435 *see* Fluprofen.
RD-20000 *see* Deprodone propionate.
'Reacid' *see* Cyacetacide.
'Reactivan' *see* Fencamfamin.
'Realin' *see under* Oxyphenbutazone.
'Reapam' *see* Prazepam.
'Reasec' *see under* Diphenoxylate.
'Reazide' *see* Cyacetacide.
'Rebugen' *see* Ibuprofen.
Rec-7-0040 *see* Flavoxate.
Rec-7-0052 *see* Flavamine.
Rec-7-0267 *see* Dimefline.
Rec-7-0518 *see* Ketocaine.
Rec-14/0127 *see* Moquizone.
Rec-15/0019 *see* Moxicoumone.
Rec-15/0122 *see* Nifurpipone.
Rec-15/0691 *see* Tibezonium iodide.
Rec 15/1476 *see* Fenticonazole.
Rec 15-1533 *see* Denzimol.
'Recanescine' *see* Deserpidine.
'Recetan' *see* Butidrine.
'Recofur' *see* Nifurpipone.
'Recolip' *see* Clofibrate.
'Recordil' *see* Efloxate.
'Recrein' *see* Deanol.
'Rectidon' *see* 5-(2-Bromoallyl)-5-(1-methylbutyl)-barbituric acid.
'Rectodelt' *see* Prednisone.
'Recton' *see* 5-(2-Bromoallyl)-5-(1-methylbutyl)-barbituric acid.
'Rectormone' *see* Testosterone propionate.
'Rectovalone' *see* Tixocortol pivalate.
'Rectules' *see* Chloral hydrate.
'Redden' *see* Tiopropamine.
'Redeptin' *see* Fluspirilene.
Redergam (tr) *see* Co-dergocrine.
'Redergine' *see* Co-dergocrine.
'Redimyl' *see* Glutethimide.
'Redomex' *see* Amitriptyline.
'Redouline' *see* Reserpiline.
Red tetrazolium *see* 2,3,5-Triphenyltetrazolium chloride.
REDUCTIC ACID (2,3-dihydroxy-2-cyclopenten-1-one).
'Reducyl' *see* Phentermine.
'Redul' *see* Glymidine.
'Redupront' *see under* Prazosin.
'Redusterol' *see* 2-Phenylbutyramide.
Ref-185 *see* Cortivazol.
'Refchole' *see* Limonene.
'Reflux' *see* Methenamine mandelate.
'Refobacin' *see* Gentamicin.
'Refosporin' *see* Cefazedone.
'Refugal' *see* Clofedanol.
'Refungine' *see* Sulbentine.
'Refusal' *see* Disulfiram.
'Regadrin' *see* Clofibrate.
'Regasprin' *see* Calcium acetylsalicylate.
'Regelan' *see* Clofibrate.
'Regenon' *see* Amfepramone.
'Regitin' *see* Phentolamine.
'Reglan' *see* Metoclopramide.
'Reglisse' *see* Liquorice.

'Reglone' *see* Diquat.
'Regonol' *see* Pyridostigmine bromide.
'Regovar' *see under* Norethisterone.
'Regreton' *see under* Reserpine.
'Regulton' *see* Amezinium metilsulfate.
'Regutol' *see* Docusate sodium.
Reichstein's substance H *see* Corticosterone.
Reichstein's substance Q *see* Desoxycortone.
Reichstein's substance S *see* Cortodoxone.
Reichstein's substance Fa *see* Cortisone.
'Rektidon' *see* Paraldehyde.
'Rela' *see* Carisoprodol.
'Relane' *see* Dexoxadrol.
'Relanium' *see* Diazepam.
'Relanol' *see* Parapenzolate bromide.
RELAXIN ((the hormone); 'cervilaxin'; 'releasin').
'Relaxin' *see* Magnesium gluconate.
'Releasin' *see* Relaxin.
'Relefact LH-RH' *see* Gonadorelin.
'Relefact LH-RH/TRH' *see under* Gonadorelin.
RELOMYCIN*** (antibiotic from *Str. hygroscopicus*; AM-684-beta).
'Relovis' *see under* Ethinylestradiol.
'Reltine' *see* Piperphenidol.
'Remanex' *see under* Hexachlorophene.
'Remedacen' *see* Dihydrocodeine.
'Remeflin' *see* Dimefline.
'Remestan' *see* Temazepam.
'Remid' *see* Allopurinol.
'Remiderm' *see under* Triamcinolone.
'Remivox' *see* Lorcainide.
'Remnos' *see* Nitrazepam.
'Remotic' *see under* Triamcinolone.
REMOXIPRIDE*** ((−)-(*S*)-3-bromo-*N*-[(1-ethylpyrrolidin-2-yl)methyl]-2,6-dimethoxybenzamide).
'Remsed' *see* Promethazine.
'Renacidin' *see* Citric acid.
Renactide *see* Giractide.
'Renafur' *see* Nifuradene.
'Renamid' *see* Acetazolamide.
RENANOLONE** (3α-hydroxy-5β-pregnane-11,20-dione).
'Renascin' *see* α-Tocopherol nicotinate.
'Renese' *see* Polythiazide.
'Rengasil' *see* Pirprofen.
'Reno' *see* Meglumine diatrizoate.
'Reno 76' *see under* Meglumine diatrizoate.
'Renografin' *see under* Meglumine diatrizoate.
'Renolon' *see* Calcium acetylsalicylate.
'Renoquid' *see* Sulfacitine.
'Renovist' *see under* Meglumine diatrizoate.
'Renovue' *see* Iodamide meglumine.
RENYTOLINE*** (9-(*p*-amidinobenzylidene)-fluorene; α-fluoren-9-ylidene-*p*-toluamidine; paranyline; paranyline hydrochloride; renytoline hydrochloride).
Reoisodex (tr) *see* Dextran 40.
Reopoliglukin (tr) *see* Dextran 40.
'Reorganin' *see* Guaifenesin.
'Reoxyl' *see* Hexobendine.
'Reparil' *see* Escin.
'Repeltin' *see* Alimemazine.

'Repetabs' see Chlorpheniramine.
'Repocal' see Pentobarbital.
'Repodral' see Stibophen.
'Repoise' see Butaperazine.
Repolymerized gelatin see Polygeline.
'Reprodal' see Stibophen.
REPROMICIN*** (16-ethyl-4-hydroxy-5,9,13,15-tetramethyl-2,10-dioxo-6-[[3,4,6-trideoxy-3-(dimethylamino)-β-D-xylo-hexopyranosyl]oxy]oxacyclohexadeca-11,13-diene-7-acetaldehyde; 12,13-deepoxy-12,13-didehydro-4'-deoxycirramycin A$_1$; Sch-16524).
REPROTEROL*** (7-[3-[(β,3,5-trihydroxyphenethyl)amino]propyl]theophylline; 7-[3-[2-(3,5-dihydroxyphenyl)-2-hydroxyethylamino]propyl]-theophylline; reproterol hydrochloride; D-1959; W-2946M; 'bronchodil'; 'bronchospasmin').
'Reptilase' see Batroxobin.
RESACETOPHENONE (2',4'-dihydroxyacetophenone).
Resacetophenone 4-methyl ether see Peonol.
'Resactin A' see Hydroxycycloheximide.
'Resantin' see Fenpipramide.
RESCIMETOL*** (methyl reserpate (E)-4-hydroxy-3-methoxycinnamate (ester); ferulic acid ester with methyl reserpate; CD-3400).
RESCINNAMINE*** (methyl reserpate 3,4,5-trimethoxycinnamate ester; methyl dodecahydro-2α,11-dimethoxy-3β-(3,4,5-trimethoxycinnamoyloxy)benz[g]indolo[2,3-a]quinolizine-1β-carboxylate; reserpinine).
'Rescisan' see Rescinnamine.
'Rescuvolin' see Calcium folinate.
'Resercen' see Reserpine.
Reserpene see Reserpine.
RESERPIC ACID (18β-hydroxy-11,17α-dimethoxy-3β,20α-yohimban-16β-carboxylic acid; reserpinic acid; reserpinolic acid).
See also Mefeserpine; Methyl reserpate; Rescimetol; Rescinnamine; Reserpine; Syrosingopine.
RESERPILINE (alkaloid from Rauwolfia spp; 'redouline').
RESERPINE*** (methyl reserpate 3,4,5-trimethoxybenzoate (ester); methyl dodecahydro-2α,11-dimethoxy-3β-(3,4,5-trimethoxybenzoyloxy)-benz[g]indolo[2,3-a]quinolizine-1β-carboxylate; reserpene).
RESERPINE plus BENDROFLUMETHIAZIDE ('abicol'; 'tensionorme').
RESERPINE plus CHLORTALIDONE ('darebon'; 'regreton').
RESERPINE plus CLOPAMIDE & DIHYDROERGOCRISTINE (DCR-515; 'brinerdine'; 'briserin').
RESERPINE plus FUROSEMIDE ('nortensin'; 'tenserlix'; 'terbolan').
RESERPINE plus TRICHLORMETHIAZIDE ('metatensin'; 'naquival').
RESERPINE plus XIPAMIDE ('durotan').
Reserpinic acid see Reserpic acid.
Reserpinine see Rescinnamine.
Reserpinolic acid see Reserpic acid.
'Reserpoid' see Reserpine.

'Resertene' see Methoserpidine.
'Resil' see Guaifenesin.
'Resimatil' see Primidone.
'Resistab' see Thonzylamine.
'Resistoflex' see Polyvinyl alcohol.
'Resistomycin' see Kanamycin.
'Resistopen' see Oxacillin.
'Resitan' see Valethamate bromide.
'Resitox' see Coumafos.
'Resivit' see Leucocianidol.
RESMETHRIN* (cis,trans-(±)-5-benzylfuran-3-ylmethyl 2,2-dimethyl-3-(2-methyl-1-propenyl)-cyclopropanecarboxylate; cis,trans-(±)-5-benzyl-3-furylmethyl chrysanthemate, cis,trans-(±)-; bencifurolin; benzylfuroline; NRDC-104; PNIA-17370; SBP-1382; 'chryson'; 'synthrin').
'Resochin' see Chloroquine.
'Resochin S' see Chloroquine silicate.
'Resoquine' see Chloroquine.
RESORANTEL*** (4'-bromo-2,6-dihydroxybenzanilide; 4'-bromo-γ-resorcylanilide; Hoe-296V; 'terenol').
RESORCINOL (m-dihydroxybenzene).
RESORCINOL ACETATE (resorcinol monoacetate; 'euresol').
Resorcinolphthalein see Fluorescein.
α-RESORCYLIC ACID (3,5-dihydroxybenzoic acid).
β-RESORCYLIC ACID (2,4-dihydroxybenzoic acid).
γ-RESORCYLIC ACID (2,6-dihydroxybenzoic acid).
'Resorptol' see 16-Acetylgitoxin.
'Resotren' see under Cloquinate.
'Respectol' see Dibromsalicil.
'Respenyl' see Guaifenesin.
'Respigon' see Bufogenin.
'Respilene' see Zipeprol.
'Respilyt' see Noscapine.
'Respiride' see Fenspiride.
'Respirot' see Prethcamide.
'Resteclin' see under Tetracycline.
'Restovar' see under Lynestrenol.
'Resyl' see Guaifenesin.
'Retabolil' see Nandrolone decanoate.
'Retamin' see Buclizine.
RETAMINE (hydroxyisosparteine).
'Retandrol' see Testosterone phenylpropionate.
'Retarbolin' see Nandrolone cyclohexanepropionate.
'Retardin' see under Diphenoxylate.
'Retcin' see Erythromycin.
'Retenema' see Betamethasone valerate.
'Retentin' see Carinamide.
'Reticus' see Desonide.
'Retin-A' see Tretinoin.
RETINAL* (3,7-dimethyl-9-(2,6,6-trimethyl-1-cyclohexen-1-yl)nona-(all-trans)-2,4,6,8-tetraenal; 15-apo-β-caroten-15-al; vitamin A aldehyde; axerophthal; retinene).
Retinene see Retinal.
Retinic acid see Glycyrrhizic acid.
all-trans-Retinoic acid see Tretinoin.

13-*cis*-Retinoic acid *see* Isotretinoin.

RETINOL*** (3,7-dimethyl-9-(2,6,6-trimethyl-1-cyclohexen-1-yl)nona-2,4,6,8-tetraen-1-ol; axerophthol; vitamin A; vitamin A$_1$; vitamin A alcohol; antiinfective vitamin; antixerophthalmic vitamin; biosterol; oleovitamin A; ophthalin).

RETINOL ACETATE (vitamin A acetate).

'Retrangor' *see* Benziodarone.

'Retroid' *see* Trengestone.

'Retromyopen' *see under* Dihydrostreptomycin.

Retroprogestagen *see* 16α-Ethylthio-6-dehydro-retroprogesterone.

RETROPROGESTERONE (9β,10α-pregn-4-ene-3,20-dione; 9β,10α-progesterone; 19-retroprogesterone).

RETRORSINE *N*-OXIDE (isatidine).

'Reublonil' *see* Benzpiperylone.

'Reuprosal' *see o*-Propoxybenzamide.

'Revasa' *see* Aminoquinuride.

REVENAST** (2,3-diphenyl-1-[3-(4-pyrid-2-ylpiperazin-1-yl)propyl]-3-pyrazolin-5-one).

'Reverin' *see* Rolitetracycline.

'Revertina' *see* Mecamylamine.

'Revivan' *see* Dopamine.

'Revivon' *see* Diprenorphine.

'Revonal' *see* Methaqualone.

'Revoxyl' *see* Dibemethine.

'Rexitine' *see* Guanabenz.

'Rexitine plus' *see under* Guanabenz.

'Rezifilm' *see* Thiram.

RF-46-790 *see* Fluproquazone.

RG-270 *see* Iomeglamic acid.

RG-833 *see* Betamethasone.

RGH-1106 *see* Pipecuronium bromide.

RGH-4405 *see* Vinpocetine.

RGH-4406 *see* Vincanol.

RH-565 *see* Uredofos.

RH-32565 *see* Uredofos.

Rhabarberone *see* Aloe-emodin.

'Rhaetocaine' *see* Benzocaine.

RHAMNETIN (3,3′,4′,5-tetrahydroxy-7-methoxyflavone; β-rhamnocitrin).

β-Rhamnocitrin *see* Rhamnetin.

Rhamnol *see* β-Sitosterol.

6-(β-L-Rhamnosido)-D-glucose *see* Rutinose.

Rhamnoxanthin *see* Frangulin A.

RHAPONTIZIN (2,3,3′-trihydroxy-4′-methoxy-stilbene 2-glucoside).

RHC-2592 *see* Tiaramide.

RHC-G233 *see* Bucainide maleate.

Rheic acid *see* Rhein.

RHEIN (4,5-dihydroxyanthraquinone-2-carboxylic acid; chrysazin-3-carboxylic acid; cassic acid; parietic acid; rheic acid; rhubarb yellow).

'Rhenocaine' *see* Hydroxytetracaine.

'Rheomacrodex' *see* Dextran 40.

'Rheosolon' *see* Phenylbutazone.

'Rheotran' *see* Dextran 40.

Rhetinic acid *see* Enoxolone.

'Rheumacyl' *see* Glycol salicylate.

'Rheumasit' *see under* Dexamethasone.

Rheum emodin *see* Emodin.

'Rheumon' *see* Etofenamate.

'Rheumox' *see* Azapropazone.

'Rhinathiol' *see* Carbocisteine.

'Rhinogutt' *see* Tramazoline.

'Rhinopront' *see* Tetryzoline.

'Rhinoptil' *see* Cafaminol.

'Rhinosan' *see* Oxymetazoline.

'Rhinospray' *see* Tramazoline.

'Rhizoctol' *see under* Benquinox.

Rhizopus arrhizus, lipase *see* Rizolipase.

Rhodallin *see* Allylthiourea.

Rhodanhexamine *see* Methenamine thiocyanate.

Rhodanic acid *see* Rhodanine; Thiocyanic acid.

RHODANINE (thiazolidin-4-one-2-thione; 2-thioxo-4-thiazolidinone; rhodanic acid).

'Rhodiacid' *see* Ziram.

'Rhodiatox' *see* Parathion.

Rhodochromium *see* Merbromin.

RHODOPSIN (visual purple).

'Rhodoquine' *see* Plasmocid.

'Rhodovet' *see* Methenamine thiocyanate.

'Rhodoviol' *see* Polyvinyl alcohol.

'Rhomex' *see* Piperazine.

'Rhonal' *see* Acetylsalicylic acid.

'Rhothane' *see* DDD.

Rhubarb yellow *see* Rhein.

'Rhythmochin' *see under* Procainamide.

'Rhythmodan' *see* Disopyramide.

'Rhythmodul' *see* Disopyramide.

'Rhythmonorm' *see* Propafenone.

RI-64 *see* Pifexole.

'Riabal' *see* Prifinium bromide.

RIBAMINOL*** (ribonucleic acid compound with 2-diethylaminoethanol; 2-(diethylamino)-ethanol ribonucleate; 2-hydroxytriethylamine ribonucleate; ICN-542).

RIBAVIRIN** (1-β-D-ribofuranosyl-1,2,4-triazole-3-carboxamide; 1,2,4-triazole-3-carboxamide riboside; tribavirin; ICN-1229; 'vilona'; 'viramid'; 'virazole').

Riboazauracil *see* Azaribine.

RIBOFLAVIN*** (7,8-dimethyl-10-(1-ribityl)isoalloxazine; lactoflavin; ovoflavin; riboflavine; vitamin B$_2$; vitamin G).

Riboflavin 5′-adenosine diphosphate *see* Flavin-adenine dinucleotide.

Riboflavin 5′-phosphate sodium salt *see* Flavin mononucleotide.

3-(β-D-Ribofuranosyl)maleimide *see* Showdomycin.

4-(β-D-Ribofuranosyl)-9*H*-purine *see* Nebularine.

***N*-(9-β-D-Ribofuranosyl-9*H*-purin-6-yl)butyramide cyclic 3′,5′-(hydrogen phosphate) 2′-butyrate** *see* Bucladesine.

7-β-D-Ribofuranosyl-7*H*-pyrrolo[2,3-*d*]pyrimidin-4-amine *see* Tubercidin.

2-β-D-Ribofuranosyl-4-thiazolecarboxamide *see* Tiazofurine.

2-β-D-Ribofuranosyl-*as*-triazine-3,5-(2*H*,4*H*)dione *see* Azauridine.

2-β-D-Ribofuranosyl-*as*-triazine-3,5-(2*H*,4*H*)dione 2′,3′,5′-triacetate *see* Azaribine.

1-β-D-Ribofuranosyl-1,2,4-triazole-3-carboxamide *see* Ribavirin.

'Ribomycin' *see* Ribostamycin.

RIBOPRINE*** (*N*-(3-methyl-2-butenyl)adenosine; IPA; NSC-105546).

RIBOSTAMYCIN*** (*O*-[2,6-diamino-2,6-dideoxy-α-D-glucopyranosyl-(1→4)]-*O*-[β-D-ribofuranosyl-(1→5)]-2-deoxystreptamine; SF-733; 'ibistacin'; 'landamycin'; 'ribomycin'; 'vistamycin').

'Ribrain' *see* Betahistine dimesilate.

Ricainide *see* Indecainide.

RICINOLEIC ACID (12-hydroxy-9-octadecenoic acid).
See also Sodium ricinoleate; Zinc ricinoleate.

RICINOMACROGOL* (castor oil polyoxyethylene ether; 'nikkol HCO50').

'Ricridene' *see* Nifurzide.

'Ridaura' *see* Auranofin.

'Ridazole' *see* Ronidazole.

RIDAZOLOL** ((±)-4-chloro-5-[[2-[[3-(*o*-chlorophenoxy)-2-hydroxypropyl]amino]ethyl]amino]-3(2*H*)-pyridazone).

'Ridinol' *see* Pridinol.

'Rido rato' *see* Warfarin.

'Ridzol' *see* Ronidazole.

'Riedemil' *see* Calusterone.

'Rifa' *see* Rifampicin.

'Rifadin' *see* Rifampicin.

RIFAMIDE** (N,N-diethylrifamycin B amide; rifamycin B diethylamide; NSC-133099).

RIFAMPICIN*** (3-(4-methylpiperazin-1-yliminomethyl)rifamycin SV; rifampin; AMP; Ba-41166/E; L-5103; NSC-113916).
See also under Isoniazid; Trimethoprim.

Rifampin* *see* Rifampicin.

RIFAMYCIN*** (5,6,9,17,19,21-hexahydroxy-23-methoxy-2,4,12,16,18,20,22-heptamethyl-2,7-(epoxypentadeca(1,11,13)trienimino)-naphtho-[2,1-*b*]furan-1,11(2*H*)-dione 21-acetate; rifamycin SV; rifomycin; rifamycin sodium; M-14; NSC-133100).

Rifamycin SV *see* Rifamycin.

RIFAPENTINE*** (3-[*N*-(4-cyclopentylpiperazin-1-yl)formimidoyl]rifamycin; DL-473-IT; L-11473; MDL-473).

'Rifaprim' *see under* Trimethoprim.

Rifaxidin *see* Rifaximin.

RIFAXIMIN*** ((2*S*,16*Z*,18*E*,20*S*,21*S*,22*R*,23*R*,24*R*,25*S*,26*S*,27*S*,28*E*)-5,6,21,23,25-pentahydroxy-27-methoxy-2,4,11,16,20,22,24,26-octamethyl-2,7-(epoxypentadeca[1,11,13]trienimino)-benzofuro[4,5-*e*]pyrido[1,2-*a*]benzimidazole-1,15(2*H*)-dione 25 acetate; rifaxidin).

'Rifinah' *see under* Isoniazid.

'Rifloc' *see* Isosorbide dinitrate.

'Rifocine' *see* Rifamycin.

'Rifocin-M' *see* Rifamide.

'Rifocyne' *see* Rifamycin.

'Rifoldin' *see* Rifampicin.

Rifomycin *see* Rifamycin.

'Rigedal' *see* Isosorbide dinitrate.

'Rigevidon' *see under* Levonorgestrel.

'Rigikin' *see* Levodopa.

'Rigitrem' *see* Levodopa.

Riker 52G *see* Aprotinin.

Riker 548 *see* Tricetamide.

Riker-594 *see* Sultiame.

Riker-595 *see* Butaperazine.

Riker-601 *see* Triaziquone.

Riker-738 *see* Nefopam.

'Rimactane' *see* Rifampicin.

'Rimactazid' *see under* Isoniazid.

'Rimadyl' *see* Carprofen.

RIMANTADINE*** (α-methyl-1-adamantanemethylamine; rimantadine hydrochloride; EXP-126).

'Rimaon' *see* Ethacridine lactate.

RIMAZOLIUM METILSULFATE*** (3-(ethoxycarbonyl)-6,7,8,9-tetrahydro-1,6-dimethyl-4-oxo-4*H*-pyrido[1,2-*a*]pyrimidinium methyl sulfate; 3-(ethoxycarbonyl)-6,7,8,9-tetrahydro-1,6-dimethyl-4-oxohomopyrimidazole methyl sulfate; MZ-144; 'probon').

'Rimetin' *see* Metoclopramide.

RIMEXOLONE*** (11β-hydroxy-16α,17α-dimethyl-17-propionylandrosta-1,4-dien-3-one; 11β-hydroxy-16α,17α,21-trimethylpregna-1,4-diene-3,20-dione; trimexolone; Org-6216).

'Rimidol' *see* Naphazoline.

'Rimifon' *see* Isoniazid.

Riminophenazine *see* Clofazimine.

RIMITEROL*** (*erythro*-3,4-dihydroxy-α-piperid-2-ylbenzyl alcohol; α-(3,4-dihydroxyphenyl)-2-piperidinemethanol; rimiterol hydrobromide; R-798; WG-253; 'pulmadil').

'Rimso-50' *see* Dimethyl sulfoxide.

'Rinderon' *see* Betamethasone.

'Rinoglin' *see under* Cromoglicate disodium.

'Rintal' *see* Febantel.

RIODIPINE** (dimethyl 4-[*o*-(difluoromethoxy)-phenyl]-1,4-dihydro-2,6-dimethyl-3,5-pyridinedicarboxylate).

'Riogon' *see* Chorionic gonadotrophin.

'Riomitsin' *see* Oxytetracycline.

'Riomycin' *see* Fluvomycin.

'Riopan' *see* Magaldrate.

RIOPROSTIL*** ((2*R*,3*R*,4*R*)-4-hydroxy-2-(7-hydroxyheptyl)-3-[(*E*)-(4*RS*)-(4-hydroxy-4-methyl-1-octenyl)]cyclopentanone; (11α,13*E*)-1,11,16-trihydroxy-16-methylprost-13-en-9-one; BAY o-6893; ORF-15927; TR-4698).

RIPAZEPAM*** (1-ethyl-4,6-dihydro-3-methyl-8-phenylpyrazolo[4,3-*e*][1,4]diazepin-5(1*H*)-one; pirazapon; pyrazapon; CI-683).

'Ripcord' *see* Cypermethrin.

'Ripercol' *see* Tetramisole.

'Risatarun' *see* Deanol aceglumate.

'Riself' *see* Mephenoxalone.

'Riseptin' *see* Dichlorobenzododecinium chloride.

'Risicordin' *see under* Hydrochlorothiazide.

RISOCAINE** (propyl *p*-aminobenzoate; propylcaine; NSC-23516; 'propaesin'; 'raythesin').

'Risolid' *see* Chlordiazepoxide.

'Risordan' *see* Isosorbide dinitrate.

RISTIANOL** (2-[(pyrid-4-ylmethyl)thio]ethanol; ristianol phosphate; CP-48867-09).

RISTOCETIN*** (antibiotic from *Nocardia lurida*; ristocetins A and B).

'Riston' *see* Ristocetin.

RIT-1140 *see* Apicycline.

'Ritalin' *see* Methylphenidate.

RITANSERIN** (6-[2-[4-[bis(*p*-fluorophenyl)-methylene]piperid-1-yl]ethyl]-7-methyl-5*H*-thiazolo[3,2-*a*]pyrimidin-5-one).

'Ritmodan' *see* Disopyramide.

'Ritmoforine' *see* Disopyramide.

RITODRINE*** (*p*-hydroxy-α-[1-(*p*-hydroxyphenethylamino)ethyl]benzyl alcohol; 2-(*p*-hydroxyphenethylamino)-1-(*p*-hydroxyphenyl)-propan-1-ol; ritodrine hydrochloride; Du-21220; 'premar'; 'pre-par'; 'yutopan').

RITROPIRRONIUM BROMIDE*** (*erythro*-3-hydroxy-1,1-dimethylpyrrolidinium bromide α-cyclopentylmandelate).

RITROSULFAN*** (1,4-dideoxy-1,4-bis[(2-hydroxyethyl)amino]erythritol 1,4-dimethanesulfonate; 1,4-dideoxy-1,4-bis[(2-mesyloxyethyl)-amino]erythritol; dimesyldideoxyerythritol; 'lycurin').

'Rivanol' *see* Ethacridine lactate.

'Rivon' *see* Pempidine.

'Rivotril' *see* Clonazepam.

'Rixapen' *see* Clometocillin.

RIZOLIPASE*** (lipase from *Rhizopus arrhizus* var. *delmar*; 'nortase').

RMI-9918 *see* Terfenadine.

RMI-14042A *see* Lofexidine.

RMI-16238 *see* Eterobarb.

RMI-16289 *see* Enclomifene.

RMI-16312 *see* Zuclomifene.

RMI-81968 A *see* Medroxalol.

Ro 1-5155 *see* Nicotinyl alcohol.

Ro 1-5431 *see* Racemorphan.

Ro 1-5470 *see* Racemethorphan.

Ro 1-5470/5 *see* Dextromethorphan.

Ro 1-5470/6 *see* Levomethorphan.

Ro 1-5479 *see* Dextromethorphan.

Ro 1-6463 *see* Methyprylon.

Ro 1-6794 *see* Dextrorphan.

Ro 1-7059 *see* Levallorphan.

Ro 1-7700 *see* Levallorphan.

Ro 1-7788 *see* Levomethorphan.

Ro 1-7929 *see* Levallorphan.

Ro 1-7977 *see* Succimer.

Ro 1-8300 *see* Betacarotene.

Ro 1-9334 *see* Dehydroemetine.

Ro 1-9569 *see* Tetrabenazine.

Ro 2-2222 *see* Trimetaphan camsilate.

Ro 2-2453 *see* Dimazole.

Ro 2-2985 *see* Lasalocid.

Ro 2-3053 *see* Mepesulfate.

Ro 2-3198 *see* Edrophonium chloride.

Ro 2-3248 *see* Azapetine.

Ro 2-3308 *see* 3-Quinuclidinyl benzilate.

Ro 2-3773 *see* Clidinium bromide.

Ro 2-7113 *see* Allylprodine.

Ro 2-9757 *see* Fluorouracil.

Ro 2-9915 *see* Flucytosine.

Ro 3-4787 *see* Bufuralol.

Ro 3-5940 *see* Oxitriptan ethyl ester.

Ro 3-7008 *see* Alafosfalin.

Ro 4-0403 *see* Chlorprothixene.

Ro 4-1544-6 *see* Sodium stibocaptate.

Ro 4-1575 *see* Amitriptyline.

Ro 4-1634 *see* Pivhydrazine.

Po 4-1778/1 *see* Metofoline.

Ro 4-2130 *see* Sulfamethoxazole.

Ro 4-3780 *see* Isotretinoin.

Ro 4-3816 *see* Alcuronium chloride.

Ro 4-4393 *see* Sulfadoxine.

Ro 4-4602 *see* Benserazide.

Ro 4-5282 *see* Mefenorex.

Ro 4-5360 *see* Nitrazepam.

Ro 4-6467 *see* Procarbazine.

Ro 4-6711 *see* Cyclorphan.

Ro 4-8347 *see* Trengestone.

Ro 5-0690 *see* Chlordiazepoxide.

Ro 5-0810/1 *see* Triclobisonium chloride.

Ro 5-0831/1 *see* Isocarboxazid.

Ro 5-2092 *see* Demoxepam.

Ro 5-2807 *see* Diazepam.

Ro 5-3027 *see* Delorazepam.

Ro 5-3059 *see* Nitrazepam.

Ro 5-3307/B1 *see* Debrisoquine.

Ro 5-3350 *see* Bromazepam.

Ro 5-4023 *see* Clonazepam.

Ro 5-4200 *see* Flunitrazepam.

Ro 5-4556 *see* Medazepam.

Ro 5-5516 *see* Lormetazepam.

Ro 5-6846 *see* Trimethoprim.

Ro 5-6901 *see* Flurazepam.

Ro 5-9110/1 *see* Dorastine.

Ro 5-9754 *see* Ormetoprim.

Ro 6-2580/11 *see* Co-trimoxazole.

Ro 6-3129 *see* 16α-Ethylthio-6-dehydroretroprogesterone.

Ro 6-4563 *see* Glibornuride.

Ro 7-0207 *see* Ornidazole.

Ro 7-0582 *see* Misonidazole.

Ro 7-1051 *see* Benznidazole.

Ro 7-1554 *see* Ipronidazole.

Ro 7-4488/1 *see* Cuprimyxin.

Ro 8-0576 *see under* Levodopa.

Ro 8-4650 *see* Diclofensine.

Ro 10-1670 *see* Etretin.

Ro 10-6338 *see* Bumetanide.

Ro 10-7453 *see under* Bromazepam.

Ro 10-7614 *see* Diflucortolone valerate.

Ro 10-9359 *see* Etretinate.

Ro 11-1163 *see* Moclobemide.

Ro 11-1430 *see* Motretinide.

Ro 11-1781 *see* Tiapamil.

Ro 11-2465 *see* Cianopramine.

Ro 11-7891 *see* Bentiromide.

Ro 13-5057 *see* Aniracetam.

Ro 13-8996 *see* Oxiconazole.

Ro 13-9904 *see* Ceftriaxone.

Ro-15-1788 *see* Flumazepil.

Ro 20-5720 *see* Carprofen.

Ro 21-3981/001 *see* Midazolam maleate.

Ro 21-5535 *see* Calcitriol.

Ro 21-5998 *see* Mefloquine.

Ro-21-6937 *see* Trimoprostil.

Ro 21-8837 *see* Estramustine.

Ro 21-9738 *see* Doxifluridine.
Ro-31-1411 *see* Flusoxolol.
Ro 0783/B *see* Oxitriptan.
'Roacutan' *see* Isotretinoin.
'Robalate' *see* Aluminium glycinate.
'Robamox' *see* Amoxicillin.
'Robaxin' *see* Methocarbamol.
'Robengatope I-131' *see* Rose bengal (^{131}I) sodium.
ROBENIDINE*** (1,3-bis(*p*-chlorobenzylidene-amino)guanidine; robenzidine; 'robenz').
'Robenz' *see* Robenidine.
Robenzidine *see* Robenidine.
'Robimycin' *see* Erythromycin.
Robinson ester *see* Glucose 6-phosphate.
'Robinul' *see* Glycopyrronium bromide.
'Robitussin' *see* Guaifenesin.
'Rocaltrol' *see* Calcitriol.
'Rocephin' *see* Ceftriaxone.
Rochelle salt *see* Potassium sodium tartrate.
'Ro-cillin' *see* Pheneticillin.
ROCIVERINE*** (2-(diethylamino)-1-methyl-ethyl *cis*-1-hydroxy[bicyclohexyl]-2-carboxylate; LG-30158; 'rilaten').
'Rocmaline' *see* Arginine malate.
'Rocornal' *see* Trapidil.
'Rodameb' *see* Difetarsone.
'Rodavan' *see* Chlorphenoxamine teoclate.
'Rodilone' *see* Acedapsone.
'Rodiuran' *see* Hydroflumethiazide.
RODOCAINE** (*trans*-*N*-(6-chloro-2-methyl-phenyl)-3-(1*H*-1-octahydropyrindin-1-yl)pro-pionamide; *trans*-6'-chloro-2,3,4,4a,5,6,7,7a-octahydro-1*H*-1-pyrindine-1-propiono-*o*-toluid-ide; *trans*-1-[2-[*N*-(6-chloro-*o*-tolyl)carbox-amido]ethyl]octahydro-1*H*-1-pyrindine; rodoca-ine hydrochloride; R-19317; R-22700).
'Rodogyl' *see under* Metronidazole.
ROFELODINE*** ((±)-2,6,7,8-tetrahydro-7-phenylpyrrolo[1,2-*a*]pyrimidin-4(3*H*)-one).
'Rofenaid' *see under* Ormetoprim.
'Rofenid' *see* Ketoprofen.
ROFLURANE*** (bromotrifluoroethyl methyl ether; DA-893).
'Rogitine' *see* Phentolamine.
'Rogor' *see* Dimethoate.
'Rogue' *see* Propanil.
'Rohypnol' *see* Flunitrazepam.
'Roipnol' *see* Flunitrazepam.
'Rolaids' *see* Dihydroxyaluminium sodium carbon-ate.
'Rolazote' *see* Parathiazine.
ROLETAMIDE*** (3',4',5'-trimethoxy-3-(3-pyr-rolin-1-yl)acrylophenone; CL-59112).
ROLGAMIDINE*** (*trans*-*N*-(diaminomethyl-ene)-2-(2,5-dimethyl-3-pyrrolin-1-yl)acetamide; rolgamidine hydrochloride; Wy-25021).
ROLICYCLIDINE*** (1-(1-phenylcyclohexyl)-pyrrolidine).
Rolicypram* *see* Rolicyprine.
ROLICYPRINE*** ((+)-5-oxo-*N*-(*trans*-2-phenylcyclopropyl)-2-pyrrolidinecarboxamide; rolicypram; EX-4883).
ROLIPRAM*** (4-[3-(cyclopentyloxy)-4-meth-

oxyphenyl]-2-pyrrolidinone; ZK-62711).
ROLITETRACYCLINE*** (*N*-(pyrrolidin-1-yl-methyl)tetracycline; rolitetracycline nitrate; SQ-15659).
ROLODINE** (4-(benzylamino)-2-methyl-7*H*-pyrrolo[2,3-*d*]pyrimidine; BW-58-271; NSC-106570).
'Romensin' *see* Monensin.
'Romergan' *see* Promethazine.
'Rometin' *see* Clioquinol.
'Romicil' *see* Oleandomycin.
ROMIFENONE** (2'-hydroxy-3-morpholinopro-piophenone; *o*-hydroxyphenyl-2-morpholino-ethyl ketone).
'Romilar' *see* Dextromethorphan.
'Romosol' *see* Aurothioglucose.
'Romotal' *see* Tacrine.
'Romparkin' *see* Trihexyphenidyl.
'Rompun' *see* Xylazine.
'Romthiazine' *see* Promazine.
'Romtiazin' *see* Promazine.
'Rondimen' *see* Mefenorex.
'Rondomycin' *see* Metacycline.
'Ro-neet' *see* Cycloate.
'Roniacol' *see* Nicotinyl alcohol.
'Ronicol' *see* Nicotinyl alcohol.
RONIDAZOLE** (1-methyl-5-nitroimidazol-5-ylmethyl carbamate).
RONIPAMIL** ((±)-2-[3-(methylphenethyl-amino)propyl]-2-phenyltetradecanenitrile).
Ronnel* *see* Fenclofos.
'Ronpacon' *see under* Meglumine metrizoate.
'Ronton' *see* Ethosuximide.
'Rontyl' *see* Hydroflumethiazide.
'Ronyl' *see* Pemoline.
'Rophene' *see* Adiphenine.
'Rophynal' *see* Flunitrazepam.
ROPITOIN*** (5-(*p*-methoxyphenyl)-5-phenyl-3-[3-(4-phenylpiperid-1-yl)propyl]hydantoin; 5-(4-methoxyphenyl)-5-phenyl-3-[3-(4-phenyl-1-pip-eridinyl)propyl]-2,4-imidazolidinedione; ropitoin hydrochloride; TR-2985).
ROPIVACAINE** ((−)-1-propyl-2',6'-pipecol-oxylidide; (−)-*N*-(2,6-dimethylphenyl)-1-propyl-piperidine-2-carboxamide).
ROPIZINE** (1-(diphenylmethyl)-4-[[(6-methyl-pyrid-2-yl)methylene]amino]piperazine; SC-13501).
Roquessine *see* Conessine.
'Rorasul' *see* Salazosulfapyridine.
Rosamicin* *see* Rosaramicin.
ROSAPROSTOL*** (2-hexyl-5-hydroxycyclo-pentaneheptanoic acid (mixture of (1*RS*,2*SR*,5*RS*) and (1*RS*,2*SR*,5*SR*) forms)).
ROSARAMICIN*** (12,13-epoxy-6-(formylmeth-yl)-3-hydroxy-4,8,12,14-tetramethyl-9-oxo-5-[3,4,6-trideoxy-3-(dimethylamino)-β-D-*xylo*-hexopyranosyloxy]heptadec-10-en-15-olide; 3-ethyl-7-hydroxy-2,8,12,16-tetramethyl-5,13-di-oxo-9-[[3,4,6-trideoxy-3-(dimethylamino)-β-D-*xylo*-hexopyranosyl]oxy]-4,17-dioxabicyclo-[14.1.0]heptadec-14-ene-10-acetaldehyde; rosa-micin; M-4365A2; Sch-14947).

ROSARAMICIN BUTYRATE (rosaramicin 2'-butanoate; rosamicin butyrate; Sch-18667).

ROSARAMICIN PROPIONATE (rosaramicin 2'-propanoate; rosamicin propionate; Sch-17894).

ROSARAMICIN SODIUM PHOSPHATE (rosaramicin compound (1:1) with sodium dihydrogen phosphate).

ROSARAMICIN STEARATE (rosaramicin octadecanoate (salt); rosamicin stearate).

'**Roscal**' *see* Dixyrazine.

ROSE BENGAL (4,5,6,7-tetrachloro-2',4',5',7'-tetraiodofluorescein).

ROSE BENGAL (^{131}I) SODIUM* (disodium rose bengal labelled with radioiodine; 'robengatope I-131').

Rosein *see* Fuchsine.

ROSEOLIC ACID (4-(bis(*p*-hydroxyphenyl)methylene)-2,5-cyclohexadien-1-one; *p*-roseolic acid; NSC-55202).

ROSOXACIN* (1-ethyl-1,4-dihydro-4-oxo-7-pyrid-4-yl-3-quinolinecarboxylic acid; 4-(3-carboxy-1-ethyl-1,4-dihydro-4-oxoquinolin-7-yl)pyridine; acrosoxacin; WIN-35213; 'eradacin'; 'winuron').

'**Rospin**' *see* Chloropropylate.

ROTAMICILLIN* ((2*S*,5*R*,6*R*)-6-[(*R*)-2-phenyl-2-[2-[*p*-(1,4,5,6-tetrahydropyrimidin-2-yl)phenyl]acetamido]acetamido]penicillanic acid).

ROTENONE ((2*R*(2α,6aα,12aα))-1,2,12,12a-tetrahydro-2-isopropenyl-8,9-dimethoxy[1]benzopyrano[3,4-*b*]furo[2,3-*h*][1]benzopyran-6-one; 1,2,12,12a-tetrahydro-8,9-dimethoxy-2-(1-methylethenyl)[1]benzopyrano[3,4-*b*]furo[2,3-*h*]-[1]benzopyran-6-one; tubatoxin; 'noxfish').

'**Rotersept**' *see* Chlorhexidine.

'**Rotoline**' *see* *o*-Phenylphenol.

ROTOXAMINE* (2-[*p*-chloro-α-(2-dimethylaminoethoxy)benzyl]pyridine; levocarbinoxamine; McN-R-73-Z).
See also Carbinoxamine.

ROTOXAMINE TARTRATE* (rotoxamine D-tartrate; 'twiston').

'**Rovamycin**' *see* Spiramycin.

'**Rovan**' *see* Fenclofos.

'**Rowapraxin**' *see* Pipoxolan.

'**Rowmate**' *see* Dichlormate.

'**Roxanthin red 10**' *see* Canthaxanthin.

ROXARSONE* (4-hydroxy-3-nitrobenzenearsonic acid; 3-nitro; NSC-2101).

ROXIBOLONE* (11β,17β-dihydroxy-17-methyl-3-oxoandrosta-1,4-diene-2-carboxylic acid).

'**Roxilon**' *see* Mebolazine.

'**Roxion**' *see* Dimethoate.

ROXOLONIUM METILSULFATE*
((3β,20β)-2-[[(3-hydroxy-11,29-dioxoolean-12-en-29-yl)oxy]methyl]-1,1-dimethylpyrrolidinium methylsulfate; 2-(hydroxymethyl)-1,1-dimethylpyrrolidinium methylsulfate 3β-hydroxy-11-oxoolean-12-en-30-oate).

ROXOPERONE* (4'-fluoro-3-(2-methyl-1,3-dioxo-2,8-diazaspiro[4.5]dec-8-yl)butyrophenone;

8-[3-(*p*-fluorobenzoyl)propyl]-2-methyl-2,8-diazaspiro[4.5]decane-1,3-dione; 3-(2-methyl-1,3-dioxo-2,8-diazaspiro[4.5]decan-8-yl)-4'-fluorobutyrophenone; FR-33; R-7158).

'**Roxstan**' *see* Levothyroxine sodium.

RP 40 (tr) *see* Sulfasolucin.

RP 46 (tr) *see* Benzylsulfamide.

RP-50 (tr) *see* Dimethyl carbate.

RP 177 *see* Propivane.

RP 245 *see* Thiopental sodium.

RP 866 *see* Mepacrine.

RP 2090 *see* Sulfathiazole.

RP 2168 *see* Meglumine antimonate.

RP 2254 *see* Glyprothiazol.

RP 2255 *see* Sulfathiourea.

RP 2259 *see* Glybuthiazol.

RP 2275 *see* Sulfaguanidine.

RP 2339 *see* Phenbenzamine.

RP-2512 *see* Pentamidine.

RP-2535 *see* Hexamidine.

RP 2591 *see* Dichlorophenarsine.

RP-2632 *see* Sulfamerazine.

RP 2786 *see* Mepyramine.

RP 2831 *see* Heptaminol.

RP 2856 *see* Amoxecaine.

RP 2921 *see* Aminothiazole.

RP 2987 *see* Diethazine.

RP 3015 *see* Fenethazine.

RP 3038 *see* Sontoquine.

RP 3203 *see* Diodone.

RP 3227 *see* Tetrabromsalicil.

RP 3276 *see* Promazine.

RP 3277 *see* Promethazine.

RP 3356 *see* Profenamine.

RP 3359 *see* Proguanil.

RP 3377 *see* Chloroquine.

RP-3389 *see* Promethazine.

RP-3554 *see* Thiazinamium metilsulfate.

RP 3580 *see* Diethazine ethiodide.

RP 3602 *see* Mephenesin.

RP 3668 *see* Solasulfone.

RP 3697 *see* Gallamine triethiodide.

RP 3799 *see* Diethylcarbamazine.

RP 3828 *see* Aminopromazine.

RP 3854 *see* Melarsoprol.

RP-4207 *see* Thioacetazone.

RP 4270 *see* Parathiazine.

RP 4460 *see* Promethazine.

RP 4560 *see* Chlorpromazine.

RP 4632 *see* Methopromazine.

RP 4753 *see* Pyrimethamine.

RP-4763 *see* Difetarsone.

RP 4891 *see* Suramin pentamidine salt.

RP 4909 *see* Chlorproethazine.

RP 5015 *see* Isoniazid.

RP 5171 *see* Proadifen.

RP-5278 *see* Rufocromomycin.

RP 5337 *see* Spiramycin.

RP 6140 *see* Prochlorperazine.

RP 6484 *see* Etymemazine.

RP 6549 *see* Alimemazine.

RP 6847 *see* Oxomemazine.

RP 6870 *see* Inproquone.

RP 7044 *see* Levomepromazine.
RP 7162 *see* Trimipramine.
RP 7204 *see* Cyamemazine.
RP 7293 *see* Pristinamycin.
RP-7405 *see* Etomidate.
RP 7452 *see* Ethanolamine acetylleucinate.
RP 7522 *see* Sulfamethoxypyridazine.
RP 7676 *see* Pralidoxime mesilate.
RP 7843 *see* Thioproperazine.
RP 7891 *see* Glybuzole.
RP 8228 *see* Levofacetoperane.
RP 8307 *see* Opipramol.
RP 8357 *see* Triamcinolone diacetate.
RP 8595 *see* Dimetridazole.
RP 8599 *see* Dimetotiazine.
RP 8823 *see* Metronidazole.
RP 8909 *see* Periciazine.
RP 9153 *see* Pipamazine.
RP 9159 *see* Perimetazine.
RP 9671 *see* Nosiheptide.
RP 9712 *see* Metronidazole benzoate.
RP 9715 *see* Cyclobenzaprine.
RP 9778 *see* Protionamide.
RP 9921 *see* Aprotinin.
RP 9955 *see* Melarsonyl potassium.
RP 9965 *see* Metopimazine.
RP 10284 *see* Sultiame.
RP 10768 *see* Niclosamide.
RP 11589 *see* Acetylsulfalene.
RP 11614 *see* Canrenone.
RP 11974 *see* Phosalone.
RP-12222 *see* Penmesterol.
RP 13057 *see* Daunorubicin.
RP 13607 *see* Clotioxone.
RP-13907 *see* Flopropione.
RP 14539 *see* Secnidazole.
RP 16091 *see* Metiazinic acid.
RP 17190 *see* Protizinic acid.
RP 19366 *see* Pipotiazine.
RP-19551 *see* Pipotiazine undecenate.
RP-19552 *see* Pipotiazine palmitate.
RP-19560 *see* Metapramine.
RP-19583 *see* Ketoprofen.
RP-20578 *see* Bamnidazole.
RP-21679 *see* Carpipramine.
RP-22050 *see* Zorubicin.
RP 22410 *see* Glisoxepide.
RP-27267 *see* Zopiclone.
RP-31264 *see* Suriclone.
RP-35972 *see* Oltipraz.
RP-46241 *see* Mitozolomide.
RR-32705 *see* Rutamycin.
RS-51 *see* Rauwolfia alkaloids.
R&S 218-M *see* Alletorphine.
RS-410 FAPG *see* Fluocinonide.
RS-1301 *see* Delmadinone acetate.
RS-1320 *see* Flunisolide acetate.
RS-1401 AT *see* Fluocinolone acetonide.
RS-2177 *see* Flumetasone.
RS-2208 *see* Amadinone acetate.
RS-2252 *see* Fluclorolone acetonide.
RS-2362 *see* Procinonide.
RS-2386 *see* Ciprocinonide.

RS-3268R *see* Nandrolone cyclotate.
RS-3540 *see* Naproxen.
RS-3650 *see* Naproxen.
RS-3694R *see* Cormetasone acetate.
RS-3999 *see* Flunisolide.
RS-4034 *see* Naproxol.
RS-4464 *see* Triclonide.
RS-4691 *see* Cloprednol.
R&S 5205-M *see* Homprenorphine.
RS-6245 *see* Tazolol.
RS-6818 *see* Xanoxic acid.
RS-7337 *see* Tixanox.
RS-8858 *see* Oxfendazole.
RS-9390 *see* Prostalene.
RS-35887 *see* Butoconazole.
RS-35909 *see* Ticabesone propionate.
RS-40584 *see* Flumoxonide.
RS-40974-00 *see* Tiopinac.
RS-44872 *see* Sulconazole.
RS-69216 *see* Nicardipine.
RS-84043 *see* Fenprostalene.
RT *see* 2,3,5-Triphenyltetrazolium chloride.
RT-6912 *see* Nifursol.
RT-15889 *see* Lorcainide.
RU 43-715n *see* Proquazone.
RU-2323 *see* Gestrinone.
RU-3292 *see* Disopyramide.
RU-4723 *see* Clobazam.
RU-12061 *see* Pyresmethrin.
RU-12063 *see* Cismethrin.
RU-15060 *see* Tiaprofenic acid.
RU-15750 *see* Floctafenine.
RU-19100 *see* Halofuginone.
RU-19583 *see* Calcium clofibrate.
RU-20201 *see* Taziprinone.
RU-24756 *see* Cefotaxime.
RU-31158 *see* Loprazolam mesilate.
'Ruberon' *see* Ethylmercuric phosphate.
'Rubidazone' *see* Zorubicin.
Rubidomycin *see* Daunorubicin.
Rubin *see* Fuchsine.
'Rubratope-57' *see* Cyanocobalamin (^{57}Co).
'Rubratope-60' *see* Cyanocobalamin (^{60}Co).
'Rubrocol' *see* Rubrophen.
RUBROPHEN (dihydroxytrimethoxyfuchsone; 'rubrocol').
'Rucedal' *see* Deglycyrrhizinized liquorice.
'Rudotel' *see* Medazepam.
'Ruelene' *see* Crufomate.
RUFOCROMOMYCIN*** (5-amino-6-(7-amino-5,8-dihydro-6-methoxy-5,8-dioxoquinolin-2-yl)-4-(2-hydroxy-3,4-dimethoxyphenyl)-3-methylpicolinic acid; antibiotic from *Str. rufochromogenes* or *Str. flocculus*; streptonigrin; bruneomycin; NSC-45383; RP-5278; 'nigrin').
'Rumarid' *see* Calcium acetylsalicylate.
'Rumatral' *see* Aloxiprin.
'Rumicin' *see* Chrysophanic acid.
RUSSELL'S VIPER VENOM ('rusven'; 'stypven').
'Rusven' *see* Russell's viper venom.
RUTAMYCIN*** (antibiotic from *Str. rutgersensis*; A-272; RR-32705).

457

Rutgers-612 *see* Ethohexadiol.
Rutin *see* Rutoside.
RUTINOSE (6-(β-L-rhamnosido)-D-glucose).
'Rutonal' *see* Mephebarbital.
RUTOSIDE*** (3,3′,4′,5,7-pentahydroxyflavone 3-rhamnoglucoside; quercetin 3-rutinoside; quercetin rhamnoglucoside; eldrin; globularia-cintrin; melin; myrticolorin; osyritin; phytomelin; rutin; sophorin; violaquercitrin).
RUVAZONE*** (*o*-ethoxybenzoic acid (1-carboxyethylidene)hydrazide; pyruvic acid *o*-ethoxy-benzylhydrazone; M6/42; 'ethoxydrazone'; 'etossidrazone').
RV-12128 *see* Micinicate.
RV-12165 *see* Delorazepam.
RX-6029-M *see* Buprenorphine.

RX-67408 *see* Fenclofenac.
RX-781094 *see* Idazoxan.
RYANODINE (alkaloid from *Ryania speciosa*; ryanodol pyrrole-2-carboxylate).
Ryanodol pyrrole-2-carboxylate *see* Ryanodine.
'Rybadet' *see* Polysorbate 80.
'Rycopel' *see* Cypermethrin.
'Rycovet fly repellent' *see* Crotoxyphos.
'Rycovet-nupor' *see* Phosmet.
'Rycovet widespec' *see* Oxibendazole.
'Rydar' *see* Dioxadrol.
'Rynacrom' *see* Cromoglicate disodium.
'Ryomycin' *see* Oxytetracycline.
'Rytmonorm' *see* Propafenone.
'Ryzelan' *see* Oryzalin.

S

S-3 *see* Phthalide.
S-7 *see* Fenticlor.
S-25 *see* Batroxobin.
S-46 *see* Pheneturide.
S-51 *see* Diphenhydramine.
S-62 *see* Chlorphentermine.
S-78 *see* Valethamate bromide.
S-115 *see* Sodium nicotinate.
S-167 *see* Deanol hemisuccinate.
S-210 *see* Morsuximide.
S-222 *see* Ditazole.
S-314 *see* Fusafungine.
S-596 *see* Arotinolol.
S-602-1 *see under* Ethinylestradiol.
S-640-P *see* Cefatrizine.
S-768 *see* Fenfluramine.
S-780 *see* Benfluorex.
S-805 *see* Loxapine.
S-940 *see* Naftalofos.
S-992 *see* Benfluorex.
S-1210 *see* Bietaserpine.
S-1320 *see* Budesonide.
S-1520 *see* Indapamide.
S-1530 *see* Nimetazepam.
S-1540 *see* Bitolterol.
S-1600 *see* Metahexamide.
S-1694 *see* Amineptine.
S-2395 *see* Tertatolol.
S-2620 *see* Almitrine dimesilate.
S-2957 *see* Chlorthiophos.
S-3151 *see* Permethrin.
S-3850 *see under* Chlormadinone acetate.
S-4004 *see* Trimetazidine.
S4084 *see* Cyanophos.
S-4087 *see* Cyanofenphos.
S-4105 *see* Medibazine.
S-5602 *see* Fenvalerate.
S-8440 *see* Betamethasone dipropionate.
S-9700 *see* Dextropropoxyphene napsilate.
S-10275 *see* Epitiostanol.
S-10364 *see* Mepitiostane.
S-31252 *see* Perisoxal.
S-55009 *see* Dichlozoline.
S-730740B *see* Tizolemide.
S-734118 *see* Piretanide.
SA *see* Ubiquinone(s).
SA-1 *see* Etafenone.
SA-79 *see* Propafenone.
Sa-267 *see* Diponium bromide.
SA-504 *see* Timepidium bromide.
SACCHARIC ACID (D-glucaric acid; D-glucosac-

charic acid).
Saccharic acid 1,4:6,3-dilactone acetate *see* Aceglatone.
SACCHARIC ACID 1,4-LACTONE (1,4-glucosaccharolactone; saccharolactone).
SACCHARIN (1,2-benzothiazol-3(2*H*)-one; 2,3-dihydro-3-oxobenzisosulfonazole; *o*-benzoic sulfimide; *o*-benzosulfimide; garantose; saccharinol; saccharin sodium; saccharoid; saccharol).
SACCHARIN AMMONIUM SALT ('daramin'; 'sucramin').
Saccharinol *see* Saccharin.
Saccharoid *see* Saccharin.
Saccharol *see* Saccharin.
Saccharolactic acid *see* Mucic acid.
Saccharolactone *see* Saccharic acid 1,4-lactone.
Saccharose *see* Sucrose.
Saccharosonic acid *see* Isoascorbic acid.
Saccharum amylaceum *see* Glucose.
'Sadamine' *see* Xantinol nicotinate.
'S-adchnon' *see* Adrenochrome guanylhydrazone mesilate.
'Sadophos' *see* Malathion.
'Safapryn' *see under* Acetylsalicylic acid.
'Saffan' *see under* Alfadolone acetate.
'Safprin' *see under* Acetylsalicylic acid.
Safrol *see* Safrole.
SAFROLE (4-allyl-1,4-methylenedioxybenzene; allylcatechol methylene ether; allylpyrocatechol methylene ether; safrol).
'Sagimid' *see* Niclosamide.
SaH-42-348 *see* Lifibrate.
SAH-42-548 *see* Mazindol.
SALABROSE (tetraglucosan).
SALACETAMIDE*** (*N*-acetylsalicylamide; L-749).
'Salacetol' *see* Salicyl acetol.
SALAFIBRATE*** (glyceryl 2-(acetylsalicylate) 1,3-di(clofibrate); 2-hydroxy-1-(hydroxymethyl)-ethyl acetylsalicylate diclofibrate; 2-hydroxy-1-(hydroxymethyl)ethyl salicylate 2-acetate bis[2-(*p*-chlorophenoxy)-2-methylpropionate]).
'Salantal' *see* Salicyl acetol.
SALANTEL*** (3'-chloro-4'-(*p*-chlorobenzoyl)-3,5-diiodosalicylanilide; 2,4'-dichloro-4-(2-hydroxy-3,5-diiodobenzamido)benzophenone; R-23050).
SALAZODINE*** (*N*¹-(6-methoxypyridazin-3-yl)-*N*⁴-salicylazosulfanilamide; 5-[[*p*-(6-methoxy-pyridazin-3-yl)sulfamoyl]phenylazo]salicylic acid; salazosulfamethoxypyridazine; salicylazo-

sulfamethoxypyridazine).

'Salazolon' *see* Phenazone salicylate.

'Salazopyrin' *see* Salazosulfapyridine.

SALAZOSULFADIMIDINE* (5-[*p*-(4,6-di-methylpyrimidin-2-ylsulfamoyl)phenylazo]sali-cylic acid; *N*⁴-salicylazosulfadimidine).

Salazosulfamethoxypyridazine *see* Salazodine.

SALAZOSULFAMIDE* (5-(*p*-sulfamoylphen-ylazo)salicylic acid).

SALAZOSULFAPYRIDINE** (4-hydroxy-4'-(pyrid-2-ylsulfamoyl)azobenzene-3-carboxylic acid; 4-(2-pyridylaminosulfonyl)-3'-carboxy-4'-hydroxyazobenzene; 5-[*p*-(2-pyridylsulfamoyl)-phenylazo]salicylic acid; *N*⁴-salicylazosulfapyrid-ine; sulfasalazine).

SALAZOSULFATHIAZOLE* (5-[*p*-(2-thiazo-lylsulfamoyl)phenylazo]salicylic acid; salicyl-azosulfathiazole).

'Salazothiazole' *see* Salazosulfathiazole.

SALBUTAMOL* (α¹-[(*tert*-butylamino)-methyl]-4-hydroxy-*m*-xylene-α,α'-diol; α-[(*tert*-butylamino)methyl]-4-hydroxy-3-(hydroxymeth-yl)benzyl alcohol; α'-[(1,1-dimethylethyl)-aminomethyl]-4-hydroxy-1,3-benzenedimethan-ol; albuterol; salbutamol sulfate; AH-3365; Sch-13949W; 'broncovaleas'; 'salbutan'; 'sultanol'; 'ventolin').

'Salbutan' *see* Salbutamol.

SALCATONIN* (Cys-Ser-Asn-Leu-Ser-Thr-Cys-Val-Leu-Gly-Lys-Leu-Ser-Gln-Glu-Leu-His-Lys-Leu-Gln-Thr-Tyr-Pro-Arg-Thr-Asn-Thr-Gly-Ser-Gly-Thr-Pro-NH₂; component of natu-ral salmon calcitonin; synthetic salmon salcaton-in; SCT-1; 'calsynar'; 'micalcic').
See also Elcatonin.

SALCATONIN HYDRATED POLYACETATE (SMC-20-051).

'Salco' *see* Clofenamide.

SALCOLEX* (choline salicylate compound with magnesium sulfate (2:1) tetrahydrate).

'Salcostat' *see* Dinitolmide.

SALETAMIDE* (*N*-[2-(diethylamino)ethyl]sa-licylamide; salethamide; saletamide maleate; MA-593).

Salethamide* *see* Saletamide.

'Sal-ethyl' *see* Ethyl salicylate.

'Sal-ethyl carbonate' *see* Carbethyl salicylate.

SALFLUVERINE* (α,α,α-trifluoro-*m*-salicylo-toluidide; α,α,α-trifluoro-*N*-salicyloyl-*m*-toluid-ine).

'Salfuride' *see* Nifursol.

Salicain *see* Salicyl alcohol.

'Salicaine' *see* Hydroxytetracaine.

'Salicel' *see* Salicylamide.

Saliceral *see* Glyceryl salicylate.

SALICIL (2,2'-dihydroxybenzil; bis(2-hydroxy-phenyl)glyoxal; salicyl).

SALICIN (salicyl alcohol β-D-glucopyranoside; salicoside; saligenin glucoside).

SALICIN BENZOATE (benzosalicin; populin).

'Salicitrin' *see* Citrodisalyl.

Salicoside *see* Salicin.

Salicyl *see* Salicil.

SALICYL ACETOL (salicylate ester of 1-hydr-oxy-2-propanone; acetol salicylate; hydroxyacet-one salicylate).

Salicylacetone *see* Salicylideneacetone.

SALICYL ALCOHOL (*o*-hydroxybenzyl alcohol; saligenin; saligenol; salicain).
See also Salicin.

SALICYLALDEHYDE (*o*-hydroxybenzaldehyde).

SALICYLAMIDE* (*o*-hydroxybenzamide).

Salicylamide-2-ethoxyethyl ether *see* Etosalamide.

Salicylamide ethyl ether *see* Ethenzamide.

Salicylamide pentyl ether *see* Pentalamide.

Salicylamide propyl ether *see o*-Hydroxybenz-amide.

SALICYLANILIDE (*N*-phenylsalicylamide).

Salicylanilide methylcarbamate *see* Anilamate.

Salicylazosulfadimidine *see* Salazosulfadimidine.

Salicylazosulfamethoxypyridazine *see* Salazodine.

Salicylazosulfapyridine *see* Salazosulfapyridine.

Salicylazosulfathiazole *see* Salazosulfathiazole.

N-**Salicylglycine** *see* Salicyluric acid.

SALICYLIC ACID (*o*-hydroxybenzoic acid).

Salicylic acid acetate *see* Acetylsalicylic acid.

Salicylic acid bimolecular ester *see* Salsalate.

Salicylic acid 2-diethylaminoethyl ester *see* Detano-sal.

Salicylic acid dihydrogen phosphate *see* Fosfosal.

Salicylic acid ester with 2,5-dimethyl-1-pyrrolidine-propanol *see* Pranosal.

Salicylic acid ester with 3-hydroxy-1-propanesulfon-ic acid *see* Sulprosal.

'Salicylide' *see* Salicylaldehyde.

SALICYLIDENEACETONE (4-(*o*-hydroxyphen-yl)-3-buten-2-one; salicylacetone).

Salicylideneisoniazid *see* Salinazid.

SALICYLIDENE-*p*-PHENETIDINE (*p*-(*o*-hydr-oxybenzylideneimino)phenetole).

'Salicylix' *see* Sodium sulfosalicylate.

Salicylosalicylic acid *see* Salsalate.

Salicyl salicylate *see* Salsalate.

Salicylsulfonic acid *see* Sulfosalicylic acid.

SALICYLURIC ACID (*N*-salicylglycine).

'Salifebrin' *see* Salicylanilide.

Saliformin *see* Methenamine salicylate.

'Salifungin' *see* 5-Bromo-4'-chlorosalicylamide.

Saligenin *see* Salicyl alcohol.

Saligenin glucoside *see* Salicin.

Saligenol *see* Salicyl alcohol.

'Salimagol' *see under* Magnesium salicylate.

Salinaphthol *see* 2-Naphthyl salicylate.

SALINAZID* (1-isonicotinoyl-2-salicylidene-hydrazine; isonicotinic acid salicylidenehydraz-ide; *N*'-salicylideneisoniazid; salicylideneisonia-zid; saliniazid; HP-213; Mg-1480).

Saliniazid* *see* Salinazid.

'Salinidol' *see* Salicylanilide.

SALINOMYCIN* ((αR,2R,5S,6R)-α-ethyl-6-[(1S,2S,3S,5R)-5-[(2S,5S,7R,9S,10S,12R,15R)-2-[(2R,5R,6S)-5-ethyltetrahydro-5-hydroxy-6-methyl-2*H*-pyran-2-yl]-15-hydroxy-2,10,12-tri-methyl-1,6,8-trioxadispiro[4.1.5.3]pentadec-13-en-9-yl]-2-hydroxy-1,3-dimethyl-4oxoheptyl]-tetra-hydro-5-methyl-2-*H*-pyran-2-acetic acid; AHR-

3096; K-364; K-748364A).

'Saliphenazone' *see* Phenazone salicylate.
'Saliphenin' *see* Salicylidene-*p*-phenetidine.
'Salipran' *see* Benorilate.
'Sali-prent' *see under* Acebutolol.
'Sali-presinol' *see under* Methyldopa.
Salipurpol *see* Naringenin.
'Salipyrazolon' *see* Phenazone salicylate.
'Salipyrin' *see* Phenazone salicylate.
'Salisan' *see* Chlorothiazide.
'Salisil' *see* Magnesium trisilicate.
'Salizid' *see* Salinazid.
SALMEFAMOL* (4-hydroxy-α-[(*p*-methoxy-α-methylphenethylamino)methyl]-*m*-xylene-α,α'-diol; 1-[4-hydroxy-3-(hydroxymethyl)phenyl]-2-(4-methoxy-α-methylphenethylamino)ethanol; AH-3923).
'Salmidochol' *see* Osalmid.
Salnabrom *see* Theobromine sodium salicylate.
SALOCOLL (salicylate of *N*-aminoacetyl-*p*-phenetidine; phenocoll salicylate).
SALOL (phenyl salicylate; salphenyl).
'Salophen' *see* Acetaminosalol.
'Salostan' *see* Tin oxide.
Salphenyl *see* Salol.
'Salpix' *see under* Sodium acetrizoate.
SALPROTOSIDE* (ethyl 3-*O*-propylglucofuranoside 5,6-disalicylate).
SALSALATE* (salicylic acid bimolecular ester; *O*-(2-hydroxybenzoyl)salicylic acid; salicyl salicylate; salicylosalicylic acid; disalicylic acid; salysal; NSC-49171; 'dinuclan'; 'diplosal'; 'disalcid'; 'disalyl'; 'nobacid').
Salsalate acetate *see* Acetylsalicylsalicylic acid.
SALSOLIDINE (1,2,3,4-tetrahydro-6,7-dimethoxy-1-methylisoquinoline).
SALSOLINE (1,2,3,4-tetrahydro-6-hydroxy-7-methoxy-1-methylisoquinoline).
'Saltucin' *see* Butizide.
'Salures' *see* Bendroflumethiazide.
'Saluretil' *see* Chlorothiazide.
'Saluric' *see* Chlorothiazide.
'Saluron' *see* Hydroflumethiazide.
Saluzid (tr) *see* Opiniazide.
Salvarsan *see* Arsphenamine.
SALVERINE* (2-[2-(diethylamino)ethoxy]benzanilide; salicylanilide diethylaminoethyl ether; M-811).
'Salvicyclin' *see* Dequalinium acetate.
'Salyrgan' *see* Mersalyl.
Salysal *see* Salsalate.
'Salzen' *see* Clofenamide.
'Salzone' *see* Paracetamol.
SAM *see* Adenosylmethionine.
SAMARIUM SULFOSALICYLATE (complex of samarium with sulfosalicylic acid).
'SAMH' *see* Methamphetamine.
'Samorin' *see* Isometamidium chloride.
'Samyr' *see* Adenosylmethionine.
'Sanabolic' *see* Nandrolone cyclohexanepropionate.
'Sanamethason' *see* Dexamethasone.
'Sanamycin' *see* Cactinomycin.

'Sanasil' *see* Sulfadoxine.
'Sanasthmyl' *see* Beclometasone dipropionate.
'Sanatrichom' *see* Metronidazole.
SANCYCLINE* (6-demethyl-6-deoxytetracycline; norcycline; GS-2147; NSC-51812).
'Sandimmun' *see* Ciclosporin.
'Sandocycline' *see under* Broxyquinoline.
'Sandolanid' *see* β-Acetyldigoxin
'Sandomigran' *see* Pizotifen maleate.
'Sandopart' *see* Demoxytocin.
'Sandoptal' *see* Butalbital.
'Sandoscill' *see* Proscillaridin.
'Sandosten' *see* Thenalidine.
'Sandril' *see* Reserpine.
'Sandrix' *see* Scopolamine methyl methosulfate.
'Sanegyt' *see* Guanazodine.
'Sanicyl' *see* Salicylanilide.
'Sanigal' *see* Sulfiram.
'Sanmicron' *see* Phenylmercuric acetate.
'Sanocrysin' *see* Sodium aurotiosulfate.
'Sanoma' *see* Magnesium peroxide.
'Sanomigran' *see* Pizotifen maleate.
'Sanopron' *see* Chlorpromazine.
'Sanoquin' *see* Chloroquine.
'Sanorex' *see* Mazindol.
'Sanotensin' *see* Guanethidine.
'Sanoxit' *see* Benzoyl peroxide.
'Sansalid' *see* Uredofos.
'Sansert' *see* Methysergide.
SANTAL (3',4',5-trihydroxy-7-methoxyisoflavone).
Santheose *see* Theobromine.
'Santicizer 141' *see* Octicizer.
'Santochin' *see* Sontoquine.
Santolactone *see* Santonin.
SANTONIN (lactone of 7-(1-carboxypropyl)-5,6,7,8-tetrahydro-8-hydroxy-1,4a-dimethyl-2(4a*H*)-naphthalenone; santolactone).
'Santophen-1' *see* Clorofene.
'Santoquin' *see* Ethoxyquin.
SAP-113 *see* Nifuratel.
'Sapecron' *see* Clofenvinfos.
'Saphi-col' *see* Menazon.
'Saphizon' *see* Menazon.
SARALASIN (1-(*N*-methylglycine)-5-L-valine-L-alanine angiotensin *II*; *N*-[1-[*N*-[*N*-[*N*-[*N*-[*N*²-(*N*-methylglycyl)-L-arginyl]-L-valyl]-L-tyrosyl]-L-valyl]-L-histidyl]prolyl]-L-alanine).
SARALASIN ACETATE* (saralasin acetate salt hydrate; P-113; 'sarenin').
Sarcine *see* Hypoxanthine.
'Sarcochlorin' *see* Sarcolysin.
'Sarcoclorin' *see* Sarcolysin.
SARCOLYSIN* (DL-3-[*p*-[bis(2-chloroethyl)-amino]phenyl]alanine; DL-phenylalanine mustard; merfalan; merphalan; racemelfalan; sarkolysin; CB-3007; NSC-14210).
D-Sarcolysin *see* Medphalan.
L-Sarcolysin *see* Melphalan.
m-SARCOLYSIN (DL-3-[*m*-[bis(2-chloroethyl)-amino]phenyl]alanine; metasarcolysin; MP-267; NSC-27381).
o-SARCOLYSIN (DL-3-[*o*-[bis(2-chloroethyl)-

amino]phenyl]alanine; orthosarcolysin; CB-1729; NSC-57199).

N-Sarcolysylnicotinamide *see* Nicosin.

Sarcomycin *see* Sarkomycin A.

SARCOSINE (methylaminoacetic acid; *N*-methylglycine).

'**Saren**' *see* Ibuprofen-lysine.

'**Sarenin**' *see* Saralasin acetate.

'**Sargenor**' *see* Arginine aspartate.

SARIN (isopropyl methylphosphonofluoridate; GB).

Sarkin *see* Hypoxanthine.

Sarkolysin *see* Sarcolysin.

SARKOMYCIN A (2-methylene-3-oxocyclopentanecarboxylic acid; sarcomycin; NSC-14347).

SARMOXICILLIN*** (methoxymethyl (2*S*,5*R*,6*R*)-6-[4-(*p*-hydroxyphenyl)-2,2-dimethyl-5-oxoimidazolidin-1-yl]penicillanic acid; oxetacillin methoxymethyl ester; BL-P1780).

'**Sarodormin**' *see* Glutethimide.

'**Sarolex**' *see* Dimpylate.

'**Saroten**' *see* Amitriptyline.

'**Sarotex**' *see* Amitriptyline.

SARPICILLIN** (methoxymethyl (2*S*,5*R*,6*R*)-6-(2,2-dimethyl-5-oxo-4-phenylimidazolidin-1-yl)-penicillanate; hetacillin methoxymethyl ester; BL-P1761).

SAS-554 *see* Oxazepam valproate.

'**Sasil**' *see* Sodium aluminium silicate.

'**Sastridex**' *see* Flufenamic acid.

'**Satietyl**' *see* (±)-Amphetamine *p*-chlorophenoxyacetate.

SATRANIDAZOLE*** (1-(1-methyl-5-nitroimidazol-2-yl)-3-(methylsulfonyl)-2-imidazolinone).

'**Saturn**' *see* Benthiocarb.

'**Sauran**' *see* Citicoline.

SAXITOXIN (clam poison; mussel poison; paralytic shellfish poison; PSP).

'**Sayfos**' *see* Menazon.

Sb-58 *see* Sodium stibocaptate.

Sb-5833 *see* Camazepam.

SB-7505 *see* Ibopamine.

SBP-1382 *see* Resmethrin.

SC-1627 *see* Fenethazine.

SC-1674 *see* Florantyrone.

SC-1749 *see* Menbutone.

SC-2538 *see* Profenamine.

SC-2910 *see* Methantheline bromide.

SC-3171 *see* Propantheline bromide.

SC-4341 *see* Nandrolone.

SC-4642 *see* Noretynodrel.

SC-6924 *see* Mytatrienediol.

SC-7031 *see* Disopyramide.

SC-7105 *see* Thiopropazate.

SC-7294 *see* Propetandrol.

SC-7525 *see* Bolandiol.

SC-8470 *see* Ethisterone acetate.

SC-9376 *see* Canrenone.

SC-9420 *see* Spironolactone.

SC-9880 *see* Flugestone acetate.

SC-10363 *see* Megestrol.

SC-11585 *see* Oxandrolone.

SC-11800 *see* Etynodiol diacetate.

SC-11952 *see* 22,25-Diazacholestanol.

SC-12222 *see* Etynodiol acetate.

SC-12350 *see* Nitralamine.

SC-12937 *see* Azacosterol.

SC-13504 *see* Ropizine.

SC-13957 *see* Disopyramide phosphate.

SC-14207 *see* Metogest.

SC-14266 *see* Canrenoate potassium.

SC-16148 *see* Silandrone.

SC-18862 *see* Aspartame.

SC-19198 *see* Metynodiol diacetate.

SC-21099 *see* Norgestomet.

SC-23992 *see* Prorenoate potassium.

SC-26100 *see* Difenoximide.

SC-26438 *see* Pirolazamide.

SC-26714 *see* Mexrenoate potassium.

SC-27123 *see* Octriptyline.

SC-27166 *see* Nufenoxole.

SC-27761 *see* Pranolium chloride.

SC-29333 *see* Misoprostol.

SC-31828 *see* Disobutamide.

SC-37681 *see* Gemeprost.

'**Scabinol**' *see* Benzyl benzoate.

'**Scabintan**' *see* Chloroxylenol.

'**Scandicaine**' *see* Mepivacaine.

SCARLET RED* (1-(4-*o*-tolylazo-*o*-tolylazo)-2-naphthol; Biebrich scarlet R medicinal; Sudan IV; 'fat Ponceau R').

SCC *see* Carbamoylcysteine.

SCE-129 *see* Cefsulodin.

SCE-963 *see* Cefotiam.

SCE-1365 *see* Cefmenoxime.

Sch-1000 *see* Ipratropium bromide.

Sch-1366D *see* Domazoline.

Sch-2544 *see* Cycliramine.

Sch-2747 *see* Pipendyl methane.

Sch-3132 *see* Methitural.

Sch-3444 *see* Parapenzolate bromide.

Sch-3940 *see* Perphenazine.

Sch-4358 *see* Meprednisone.

Sch-4831 *see* Betamethasone.

Sch-5706 *see* Fenalamide.

Sch-6620 *see* Prednazate.

Sch-6673 *see* Acetophenazine.

Sch-6783 *see* Diazoxide.

Sch-7056 *see* Acrisorcin.

Sch-9384 *see* Oxymetazoline.

Sch-9724 *see* Gentamicin.

Sch-10144 *see* Tolnaftate.

Sch-10159 *see* Triclofos.

Sch-10304 *see* Clonixin.

Sch-10595 *see* Bupicomide.

Sch-10649 *see* Azatadine.

Sch-11460 *see* Betamethasone dipropionate.

Sch-11527 *see* Cefaloridine.

Sch-11572 *see* Meclorisone dibutyrate.

Sch-11973 *see* Tosifen.

Sch-12041 *see* Halazepam.

Sch-12149 *see* Pazoxide.

Sch-12169 *see* Closiramine aceturate.

Sch-12650 *see* Dazadrol.

Sch-12679 *see* Trepipam maleate.

Sch-12707 *see* Clonixeril.

Sch-13430 *see* Megalomicin.
Sch-13475 *see* Sisomicin.
Sch-13521 *see* Flutamide.
Sch-13949W *see* Salbutamol.
Sch-14342 *see* Betamicin.
Sch-14714 *see* Flunixin meglumine.
Sch-14947 *see* Rosaramicin.
Sch-15280 *see* Azanator maleate.
Sch-15427 *see* Carmantadine.
Sch-15507 *see* Dopamantine.
Sch-15698 *see* Fletazepam.
Sch-15719W *see* Labetalol.
Sch-16134 *see* Quazepam.
Sch-16524 *see* Repromicin.
Sch-17894 *see* Rosaramicin propionate.
Sch-18020W *see* Beclometasone dipropionate.
Sch-18667 *see* Rosaramicin butyrate.
Sch-19741 *see* Picotrin diolamine.
Sch-19927 *see* Dilevalol.
Sch-20569 *see* Netilmicin.
Sch-21480 *see* Tioxidazole.
Sch-22219 *see* Alclometasone dipropionate.
Sch-22591 *see* Pentisomicin.
Sch-28316Z *see* Indenolol.
Scha-306 *see* Cinnopentazone.
'Scherisolon' *see* Prednisolone.
'Scherofluron' *see* Fludrocortisone.
'Scherosone' *see* Cortisone.
'Scherosone-F' *see* Hydrocortisone.
'Schiwadex' *see* Dextran.
'Schiwadex 60' *see* Dextran 60.
Schleimsaeure *see* Mucic acid.
SCHRADAN* (bis(*N*,*N*,*N'*,*N'*-tetramethylphos-phorodiamidic) anhydride; octamethyl; octa-methyldiphosphoramide; octamethylpyrophos-phoramide; oktametil; OMPA; shradan; A-15; E-3314; 'pestox III'; 'sytam').
Schultz-1038 *see* Methylene blue.
Schultz-1041 *see* Tolonium chloride.
SCILLAREN A (14β-hydroxy-3β-(rhamnoglucos-yloxy)bufa-4,20,22-trienolide; 3β,14β-dihydr-oxybufa-4,20,22-trienolide 3-rhamnoglucoside; glucoproscillaridin A).
Scillarenin 3β-rhamnoside *see* Proscillaridin.
'Scleromerfen' *see* Phenylmercuric nitrate.
'Scobenol' *see* Benzyl benzoate.
'Scolaban' *see* Bunamidine.
SCOPAFUNGIN* (antibiotic from *Str. hygrosco-picus*; NSC-107041; U-29479).
Scopine tropate *see* Scopolamine.
'Scopodex' *see* Scopolamine *N*-oxide.
SCOPOLAMINE (L-epoxytropine tropate; L-atroscine; L-hyoscine; atrochin; atroquin; scop-ine tropate; scopolamine hydrobromide).
See also under Dimenhydrinate.
SCOPOLAMINE BUTYL BROMIDE (butylsco-polamine; hyoscine N-butyl bromide; SK&F-1637).
SCOPOLAMINE BUTYL BROMIDE plus OXA-ZEPAM (Bwy20; 'buscopax').
SCOPOLAMINE METHYL BROMIDE (epoxy-methamine bromide; hyoscine *N*-methyl bro-mide; methscopolamine; U-0382).

SCOPOLAMINE METHYL METHOSULFATE (*N*-methylhyoscine methyl sulfate; CERM-1290; DD-234).
SCOPOLAMINE METHYL NITRATE (hyoscine N-methyl nitrate; methyl scopolamine nitrate). *See also under* Amobarbital.
SCOPOLAMINE *N*-OXIDE (hyoscine amine oxide).
'Scopolate' *see* Scopolamine methyl bromide.
SCOPOLETIN (7-hydroxy-6-methoxycouma-rin; 6-methoxyumbelliferone; chrysatropic acid).
'Scopolin' *see* Scopolamine methyl nitrate.
'Scopos' *see* Scopolamine.
'Scopovyl' *see* Scopolamine methyl nitrate.
'Scopyl' *see* Scopolamine methyl nitrate.
'Scorprin' *see* Co-trimazine.
'Scotine' *see* Cotinine fumarate.
SCS *see* Serotonin creatinine sulfate.
SCT-1 *see* Salcatonin.
'SCTZ' *see* Clomethiazole edisilate.
'Scuroform' *see* Butylcaine.
Scyllite *see* Inositol.
SD-25 *see* Dicarfen.
SD-149-01 *see* Feneritrol.
SD-206-03 *see* Cimemoxin.
SD-210-37 *see* Leptacline camsilate.
SD-270-07 *see* Oxaprazine.
SD-270-31 *see* Oxaflumazine disuccinate.
SD-271-12 *see* Clobenzorex.
SD-709 *see* Dimetacrine.
SD-1223-01 *see* Trazitiline.
SD-1601 *see* Moprolol.
SD-1750 *see* Dichlorvos.
SD-2101-18 *see* Acrocinonide.
SD-2124-01 *see* Procinolol.
SD-3447 *see* Stirofos.
SD-4402 *see* Isobenzan.
SD-7859 *see* Clofenvinfos.
SD-8447 *see* Stirofos.
SD-8530 *see under* 3,4,5-Trimethylphenyl methyl-carbamate.
SD-8747 *see* Stirofos.
SD-10419 *see* Propyromazine bromide.
SD-14112 *see* Sulclamide.
SD-15418 *see* Cyanazine.
SD-15803 *see* Vincofos.
SD-17102 *see* Meticrane.
SD-27115 *see* Furfenorex cyclamate.
SD-124817 *see* Tropatepine.
'SDC' *see* Solway purple.
SDDS *see* Sulfamoyldapsone.
Sdt-91 *see* Stibophen.
Sdt-1041 *see* Thioacetazone.
SE-711 *see* Pipratecol.
SE-780 *see* Benfluorex.
SE-1513 *see* Benfluorex mesilate.
SE-1520 *see* Indapamide.
Se-1702 *see* Gliclazide.
SE-2620 *see* Almitrine dimesilate.
SE-4601 *see* Diosmin.
Se-5007 *see* Sulbutiamine.
SE-5023 *see under* Ajmalicine.

'Sea-legs' *see* Piprinhydrinate.
SEBACIC ACID (decanedioic acid; 1,8-octanedi-
carboxylic acid).
'Sebacil' *see* Phoxim.
'Sebaclen' *see* Xenysalate.
5,5'-(Sebacoyldiimino)bis(2,4,6-triiodo-*N*-methyl-
isophthalamic acid) *see* Iosefamic acid.
'Sebatrol' *see* Flutamide.
'Sebizon' *see* Sulfacetamide.
SECBUMETON* (2-(*sec*-butylamino)-4-ethyl-
amino-6-methoxy-*s*-triazine; *N*-ethyl-6-methoxy-
N'-(1-methylpropyl)-1,3,5-triazine-2,4-diamine;
GS-14254; 'etazine').
SECBUTABARBITAL*** (5-*sec*-butyl-5-ethyl-
barbituric acid; 5-ethyl-5-(1-methylpropyl)barbi-
turic acid; butabarbital; secbutobarbitone; secumal).
Secbutobarbitone* *see* Secbutabarbital.
'Secholex' *see* Polidexide sulfate.
SECLAZONE*** (7-chloro-3,3a-dihydro-2*H*,9*H*-
isoxazolo-[3,2-*b*][1,3]benzoxazin-9-one; W-
2354).
SECNIDAZOLE** (α,2-dimethyl-5-nitroimidaz-
ole-1-ethanol; 1-(2-hydroxypropyl)-2-methyl-5-
nitroimidazole; 1-(2-methyl-5-nitroimidazol-1-
yl)-2-propanol; PM-185184; RP 14539; Th-
20578; 'flagentyl').
SECOBARBITAL*** (5-allyl-5-(1-methylbutyl)-
barbituric acid; meballymal; quinalbarbitone; secobarbital sodium).
See also under Brallobarbital.
9,10-Secocholesta-5,7,10(19)-triene-1α,3β-diol *see*
Alfacalcidol.
9,10-Secocholesta-5,7,10(19)-triene-3β,25-diol *see*
Calcifediol.
9,10-Secocholesta-5,7,10(19)-triene-1α,3β,25-triol
see Calcitriol.
9,10-Secocholesta-5,7,10(19)-trien-3-ol *see* Colecalciferol.
9,10-Secoergosta-5,7,10(19),22-tetraen-3β-ol *see*
Ergocalciferol.
9,10-Secoergosta-5,7,22-trien-3β-ol *see* Dihydrotachysterol.
'Seconal' *see* Secobarbital.
'Secotil' *see* Chlorpromazine sulfoxide.
SECOVERINE*** (1-cyclohexyl-4-[ethyl(*p*-meth-
oxy-α-methylphenethyl)amino]-1-butanone; *N*-
[3-(cyclohexylcarbonyl)propyl]-*N*-ethyl-*p*-meth-
oxyamphetamine).
SECRETIN*** (hormone from duodenal mucosa;
synthetic secretin; HOE-069).
'Secrosteron' *see* Dimethisterone.
SECT *see* Cetotiamine.
'Sectral' *see* Acebutolol.
Secumal* *see* Secbutabarbital.
SECURININE*** ((6*S*,11a*R*,11b*S*)-9,10,11,11a-
tetrahydro-8*H*-6,11b-methanofuro[2,3-*c*]pyr-
ido[1,2-*a*]azepin-2-(6*H*)-one).
'Securopen' *see* Azlocillin.
'Sedafamen' *see* Phendimetrazine.
'Sedaform' *see* Chlorbutol.
'Sedalande' *see* Fluanisone.
'Sedalipid' *see* Magnesium pyridoxal 5-phosphate

glutamate.
'Sedalium' *see under* Prozapine.
'Sedamyl' *see* Acecarbromal.
'Sedapam' *see* Diazepam.
'Sedathil' *see* Sulfathiadiazole.
'Sedilan' *see* Dihyprylone.
'Sediston' *see* Promazine.
'Sedobex' *see* Bibenzonium bromide.
'Sedocalene' *see under* Hydroxyzine embonate.
'Sedolatan' *see* Prenylamine.
'Sedometil' *see* Methyldopa.
'Sedomuth' *see under* Camylofin.
'Sedoquin' *see* Quinidine 5-ethyl-5-phenylbarbitur-
ate.
'Sedormid' *see* Apronal.
'Sedothyron' *see* Thiobarbital.
'Sedotussin' *see* Pentoxyverine.
'Sedulon' *see* Dihyprylone.
'Seduxen' *see* Diazepam.
'Seedrin' *see* Aldrin.
'Sefacin' *see* Cefaloridine.
'Sefril' *see* Cefradine.
'Seglor' *see* Dihydroergotamine.
'Segolan' *see* Co-dergocrine.
'Segontin' *see* Prenylamine.
Seignette salt *see* Potassium sodium tartrate.
'Seki' *see* Cloperastine.
'Sekundal' *see under* Carbromal.
Selacholic acid *see* 15-Tetracosenoic acid.
'Selacryn' *see* Tienilic acid.
Sel anglais *see* Magnesium sulfate.
Sel de Seidlitz *see* Magnesium sulfate.
'Selectol' *see* Celiprolol.
'Selectomycin' *see* Spiramycin.
SELEGILINE*** ((*R*)-(−)-*N*,α-dimethyl-*N*-prop-
2-ynylphenethylamine; *N*-methyl-*N*-2-propynyl-
levamfetamine; *N*-methyl-*N*-(2-phenylisoprop-
yl)prop-2-ynylamine; phenylisopropylmethyl-
propinylamine; deprenyl; E-250; 'deprenaline';
'eldepryl').
Selenocysteamine *see* Selenomercaptamine.
SELENOMERCAPTAMINE (2-aminoethane-
selenol; selenocysteamine).
SELENOMETHIONINE (2-amino-4-(methylse-
lenyl)butyric acid).
SELENOMETHIONINE (⁷⁵Se)*** (methionine
selenium analogue; radioselenomethionine;
'sethotope').
'Selepress' *see under* Metoprolol.
'Selexedin' *see* Mecillinam.
'Selexid' *see* Pivmecillinam.
'Seloken' *see* Metoprolol.
'Selvigon' *see* Pipazetate.
'Semap' *see* Penfluridol.
'Sembrina' *see* Methyldopa.
'Semcox' *see* Hydromorphone.
'Semdoxan' *see* Cyclophosphamide.
'Semesan' *see* 2-Chloro-4-(hydroxymercuri)phenol.
SEMICARBAZIDE (aminourea; carbamic acid
hydrazide).
'Semicillin' *see* Ampicillin.
SEMIOXAMAZIDE (oxamic acid hydrazide).
Semisodium valproate* *see* Valproate semisodium.

'Semopen' see Pheneticillin.
'Semophen' see Pheneticillin.
SEMUSTINE*** (1-(2-chloroethyl)-3-(4-methyl-cyclohexyl)-1-nitrosourea; MeCCNU; methyl-CCNU; NSC-95441).
'Sencor' see Metribuzin.
'Sendoxan' see Cyclophosphamide.
SENECIOIC ACID (3,3-dimethylacrylic acid; 3-methyl-2-butenoic acid; 3-methylcrotonic acid).
Senecioic acid 2-sec-butyl-4,6-dinitrophenyl ester see Binapacryl.
SENECIOYLCHOLINE (β,β-dimethylacryloyl-choline; SCh).
N^1-Senecioylsulfanilamide see Sulfadicramide.
Sennite see Pinitol.
'Sensaval' see Nortriptyline.
'Sensit' see Fendiline.
'Sensor' see Fibrinogen (^{125}I).
SEP see Polyestradiol phosphate.
'Sepazon' see Cloxazolam.
SEPAZONIUM CHLORIDE*** (1-[2,4-dichloro-β-[(2,4-dichlorobenzyl)oxy]phenethyl]-3-phen-ethylimidazolium chloride; R-27500).
Seperidol* see Clofluperol.
'Sephadex' see Cross-linked dextran.
'Septiolan' see Bensulfene.
Septiphene see Clorofene.
'Septisol' see Hexachlorophene.
'Septivon' see Triclocarban.
'Septon' see Propham.
'Septopal' see under Gentamicin.
'Septra' see Co-trimoxazole.
'Septran' see Co-trimoxazole.
'Septrin' see Co-trimoxazole.
'Septural' see Piromidic acid.
'Septuryl' see Co-trimazine.
'Sequamycin' see Spiramycin.
'Sequens' see under Chlormadinone acetate.
'Sequestrene' see Trisodium edetate.
'Sequilar' see under Levonorgestrel.
SERACTIDE** (ala^{26}-gly^{27}-ser^{31}-α$^{1-39}$-cortico-trophin; 25-L-aspartic acid-26-L-alanine-27-glycine-30-L-glutamine-30-L-serineα$^{1-39}$-cortico-trophin (pig)).
SERACTIDE ACETATE* (seractide acetate salt).
'Seral' see Methylpentynol.
'Serax' see Oxazepam.
Serazide see Benserazide.
'Serbose' see Glyhexamide.
'Serc' see Betahistine.
'Serenace' see Haloperidol.
'Serenal' see Oxazolam.
'Serenase' see Haloperidol.
'Serenesil' see Ethchlorvynol.
'Serenid' see Oxazepam.
'Serenium' see Etoxazene.
'Serentil' see Mesoridazine.
'Seren vita' see Chlordiazepoxide.
'Serepax' see Oxazepam.
'Seresta' see Oxazepam.
'Seretin' see Carbon tetrachloride.
SERFIBRATE*** (2-acetamido-4-mercaptobutyr-ic acid clofibrate ester; N-acetylhomocysteine

clofibrate).
'Sergetyl' see Etymemazine.
Sergosin (tr) see Methiodal sodium.
'Serial' see under Megestrol acetate.
Seric gonadotrophin see Serum gonadotrophin.
SERINE* (2-amino-3-hydroxypropionic acid; 2-aminohydracrylic acid; β-hydroxyalanine).
L-Serine diazoacetate see Azaserine.
1-D-Serine-17-L-lysine-18-L-lysinamide-α$^{1-18}$-corti-cotrophin see Codactide.
DL-Serine 2-(2,3,4-trihydroxybenzyl)hydrazide see Benserazide.
'Sermaka' see Fludroxycortide.
SERMETACIN*** (N-[[-1-(p-chlorobenzoyl)-5-methoxy-2-methylindol-3-yl]acetyl]-L-serine; in-dometacin serine salt; SH-G-318-AB).
'Sermion' see Nicergoline.
'Sernyl' see Phencyclidine.
'Seromycin' see Cycloserine.
'Serophene' see Clomifene.
SEROTONIN (5-hydroxytryptamine; 3-(2-amino-ethyl)-5-indolol; DS substance; enteramine; 5-HT; thrombocytin; thrombotonin).
Serotonin benzyl analogue see Benanserin.
SEROTONIN CREATININE SULFATE (SCS; 'antemovis').
Serotonin methyl ether see 5-Methoxytryptamine.
'Serpasil' see Reserpine.
SERPENTINE (dehydroraubasine; dehydro-δ-yo-himbine; methyl serpentinate).
'Serpiloid' see Reserpine.
SERRAPEPTASE** (proteolytic enzyme from Serratia sp. E15; serratiopeptidase; TSP; 'dan-zen').
SERRATAMIC ACID (N-(3-hydroxydecanoyl)-serine).
Serratia sp. E15, proteolytic enzyme see Serrapept-ase.
Serratiopeptidase see Serrapeptase.
'Sertal' see Pargeverine.
'Sertan' see Primidone.
SERTRALINE*** ((1S,4S)-4-(3,4-dichlorophen-yl)-1,2,3,4-tetrahydro-N-methyl-1-naphthyl-amine; (1S,4S)-4-(3,4-dichlorophenyl)-1,2,3,4-tetrahydronaphth-1-yl(methyl)amine; sertraline hydrochloride; CP-51974).
SERUM GONADOTROPHIN*** (pregnant mare serum gonadotrophin containing chiefly FSH activity; equine gonadotrophin; PMS; PMSG; seric gonadotrophin).
'Servo antisprout' see Propham.
1-Seryl-2-(2,3,4-trihydroxybenzyl)hydrazine see Benserazide.
'SES' see Disul.
SESAMEX (1-[(2-ethoxyethoxy)ethoxy]-2-(3,4-methylenedioxyphenyl)ethane; 5-[1-[2-(2-ethoxy-ethoxy)ethoxy]ethyl]1,2-benzodioxole; 1-(3,4-methylenedioxyphenyl)-3,6,9-trioxaundecane).
SESAMIN (2,6-bis(3,4-methylenedioxyphenyl)-3,7-dioxabicyclo[3.3.0]octane; 5,5'-(tetrahydro-1H,3H-furo[3,4-c]furan-1,4-diyl)bis(1,3-benzodi-oxole); tetrahydro-1,4-bis[(3,4-methylenedioxy)-phenyl]-1H,3H-furo[3,4-c]furan; (±)-sesamin;

fagarol).
SESAMOL (3,4-methylenedioxyphenol).
SESAMOLIN (2-(3,4-methylenedioxyphenoxy)-6-(3,4-methylenedioxyphenyl)-*cis*-3,7-dioxabi-cyclo[3.3.0]octane).
'Sesden' *see* Timepidium bromide.
'Sesoxane' *see* Sesamex.
'Sestron' *see* Alverine.
SETASTINE** (1-[2-[(*p*-chloro-α-methyl-α-phenylbenzyl)oxy]ethyl]hexahydro-1*H*-azepine).
SETAZINDOL*** (4′-chloro-2-[(methylamino)-methyl]benzhydrol; *p*-chloro-α-[2-(methylamino-methyl)phenyl]benzyl alcohol; PRF-36).
'Sethadil' *see* Sulfaethidole.
'Sethotope' *see* Selenomethionine (⁷⁵Se).
'Sethyl' *see* Homatropine methyl bromide.
SETOPERONE** (6-[2-[4-(*p*-fluorobenzoyl)pip-erid-1-yl]ethyl]-2,3-dihydro-7-methyl-5*H*-thiaz-olo[3,2-*a*]pyrimidin-5-one).
'Setrol' *see* Oxyphencyclimine.
'Sevin' *see* Carbaril.
'Sevinal' *see* Fluphenazine.
'Sevinol' *see* Fluphenazine.
SEVOFLURANE*** (fluoromethyl 2,2,2-tri-fluoro-1-(trifluoromethyl)ethyl ether).
'Sexovid' *see* Cyclofenil.
SF-733 *see* Ribostamycin.
SF-837 *see* Midecamycin.
SF-979 *see under* Atenolol.
SFERICASE*** (alkaline proteinase of *Bacillus sphaericus*).
SG-75 *see* Nicorandil.
Sgd-101/75 *see* Indanidine.
Sgd-24774 *see* Beclobrate.
Sgd-33374 *see* Eniclobrate.
Sgd-Scha-1059 *see* Binedaline.
SH-100 *see* Oxapium iodide.
SH-213-AB *see* Iotroxic acid.
SH-240 *see* Moxnidazole.
SH-263 *see* Droxacin.
SH-420 *see* Norethisterone acetate.
SH-420 *see under* Norethisterone acetate.
SH-567 *see* Metenolone acetate.
SH-582 *see* Gestonorone caproate.
SH-601 *see* Metenolone enantate.
SH-613 *see* Sulfametoxydiazine.
SH-617-L *see* Ethyl iopodate.
SH-714 *see* Cyproterone acetate.
SH-717 *see* Glymidine sodium.
SH-723 *see* Mesterolone.
SH-741 *see* Clomegestone acetate.
SH-742 *see* Fluocortolone.
SH-770 *see* Fluocortolone caproate.
SH-818 *see* Clocortolone acetate.
SH-863 *see* Clocortolone pivalate.
SH-881 *see* Cyproterone.
SH-926 *see* Iodamide.
SH-968 *see* Diflucortolone pivalate.
SH-1040 *see* Gestaclone.
SH-1051 *see* Glicetanile.
SH-20932 *see* Meglumine diatrizoate.
SH-21139/H-248-AB *see* Ioxotrizoic acid.
SH-31168 *see* Gliflumide.

SH-60931 *see under* Metenolone acetate.
SH-70833 *see under* Prasterone enantate.
SH-71144 *see under* Levonorgestrel.
SH-71155 *see under* Levonorgestrel.
SH-80881 *see* Cyproterone.
SH-B-209-AB *see under* Cyproterone acetate.
SH-B-264 AB *see under* Levonorgestrel.
SHB-286 *see* Sulprostone.
SH B-331 *see* Gestodene.
SHCH-58 (tr) *see* Cutizone.
SHCH-85 (tr)*see* Amithizone.
SHCH-87 (tr) *see* Thioacetazone.
SHCH-431 (tr) *see* Subathizone.
SHE 199 *see* Etoformin.
'Shellsol A' *see* Benzoylprop-ethyl.
SH-G-318-AB *see* Sermetacin.
SH-H-200-AB *see* Ioglicic acid.
SH-H-239-AB *see* Ioseric acid.
SHIKIMIC ACID (3,4,5-trihydroxycyclohexene-1-carboxylic acid).
Shionogi 6059-S *see* Latamoxef.
'Shirlan' *see* Salicylanilide.
SH K-203 *see* Fluocortin butyl.
Shostakovsky balsam *see* Polyvinox.
SHOWDOMYCIN (3-(β-D-ribofuranosyl)male-imide).
'Shoxin' *see* Norbormide.
Shradan *see* Schradan.
'S-hydril' *see* Sodium thiosulfate.
SI-1236 *see* Oxyphencyclimine.
'Sialan' *see* Endosulfan.
'Sibelium' *see* Flunarizine.
SICCANIN** ((13a*S*)-1,2,3,4,4aβ,5,6,6a,11bβ,13bβ-decahydro-4,4,6aβ,9-tetramethyl-13*H*-benzo[*a*]furo[2,3,4-*mn*]xanthen-11-ol).
Siderophilin *see* Transferrin.
Sidnocarb (tr) *see* Sydnocarb.
SIDURON* (1-(2-methylcyclohexyl)-3-phenyl-urea; 'tupersan').
'Sifacycline' *see* Tetracycline cyclamate.
'Sigadoxin' *see* Doxycycline.
'Sigamopen' *see* Amoxicillin.
'Sigaprin' *see* Co-trimoxazole.
'Sigasalur' *see* Furosemide.
'Sigmacef' *see* Cefalexin.
'Sigmaform' *see* Bismuth tribromophenate.
'Sigmamycin' *see under* Tetracycline.
'Sigmodal' *see* 5-(2-Bromoallyl)-5-(1-methylbutyl)-barbituric acid.
'Sigmuth' *see* Bismuth sodium neutral tartrate.
'Signemycin' *see under* Tetracycline.
SILANDRONE*** (17β-(trimethylsiloxy)androst-4-en-3-one; NSC-95147; SC-16148).
'Silastic' *see* Silicone rubber.
SILIBININ*** (3,5,7-trihydroxy-2-[2-(4-hydroxy-3-methylphenyl)-3-(hydroxymethyl)-1,4-benzo-dioxan-6-yl]-4-chromanone; silybin; Mg-482).
Silica *see* Silicon dioxide.
Silicic acid *see* Silicon dioxide.
SILICON DIOXIDE (silica; silicic acid).
Silicone *see* Dimeticone.
SILICONE RUBBER ('silastic').

SILICRISTIN*** (2-[2,3-dihydro-7-hydroxy-2-(4-hydroxy-3-methoxyphenyl)-3-(hydroxymethyl)-benzofuran-5-yl]-3,5,7-trihydroxy-4-chroman-one; silychristin).

SILIDIANIN*** ((+)-2,3α,3aα,7a-tetrahydro-7aα-hydroxy-8-(4-hydroxy-3-methoxyphenyl)-4-(3α,5,7-trihydroxy-4-oxo-2β-chromanyl)-3,6-methanobenzofuran-7(6aH)-one; silydianin).

Silidone *see* Dimeticone.

'Silital' *see* Halquinols.

'Silliver' *see* Silymarin.

Silodrate* *see* Simaldrate.

'Silomat' *see* Clobutinol.

'Silphostrol' *see* Fosfestrol.

'Silpromin' *see* Xantinol nicotinate.

'Silubin' *see* Buformin.

'Silvadene' *see* Sulfadiazine silver.

'Silvederma' *see* Sulfadiazine silver.

Silver fusidate *see* Fusidate silver.

Silver sulfadiazine *see* Sulfadiazine silver.

Silver sulfone *see* Diathymosulfone silver.

Silvex *see* Fenoprop.

Silybin *see* Silibinin.

Silychristin *see* Silicristin.

Silydianin *see* Silidianin.

SILYMARIN (mixture of silibinin, silicristin and silidianin; product of *Silybum marinum*; RB-1466; 'carsil'; 'silliver').

SILYMARIN SODIUM ('legalon').

SIMALDRATE** ($Al_2Mg_2O_{11}Si_3.nH_2O$; magnesium aluminosilicate hydrate; silodrate; MP-1051).
   See also Almasilate.

'Simaran' *see* Scopolamine methyl methosulfate.

'Simatin' *see* Ethosuximide.

SIMAZINE* (2-chloro-4,6-bis(ethylamino)-s-triazine; 6-chloro-N,N'-diethyl-1,3,5-triazine-2,4-diamine; symazin; CDT; 'amizine'; 'gesatop'; 'tofazine 50W').
   See also under Methoprotryn.

'Simesphylline' *see* Etamiphyllin.

SIMETHICONE* (dimeticone plus silica gel).

SIMETRIDE** (1,4-bis(2-methoxy-4-propylphenoxyacetyl)piperazine).

SIMETRYNE* (4,6-bis(ethylamino)-2-(methylthio)-s-triazine; N,N'-diethyl-6-(methylthio)-1,3,5-triazine-2,4-diamine).

SIMFIBRATE*** (1,3-propanediol bis[2-(p-chlorophenoxy)isobutyrate]; clofibric acid diester with 1,3-propanediol; clofibric acid trimethylene diester; propyl 1,3-bis(clofibrate); trimethylenebis(clofibrate); diclofibrate; CLY-503; 'cholesolvin').

'Simpalon' *see* Oxedrine.

'Simpatol' *see* Oxedrine.

'Simplotan' *see* Tinidazole.

SIMTRAZENE*** (1,4-dimethyl-1,4-diphenyl-2-tetrazene; centrazene; CL-26193; NSC-83799).

SIN-10 *see* Molsidomine.

'Sinalost' *see* Trichlormethine.

'Sinapause' *see* Estriol succinate.

'Sinaspril' *see* Calcium acetylsalicylate.

'Sinaxar' *see* Styramate.

'Sinbar' *see* Terbacil.

SINCALIDE*** (1-de(5-oxo-L-proline)-2-de-L-glutamine-5-L-methioninecaerulein; L-aspartyl-L-tyrosyl-L-methionylglycyl-L-tryptophyl-L-methionyl-L-aspartylphenyl-L-alaninamide hydrogen sulfate (ester); SQ-19844; 'kinevac').

'Sincomen' *see* Canrenoate potassium *and* Spironolactone.

'Sinderesin' *see* Iproclozide.

'Sindiatil' *see* Buformin.

'Sinecod' *see* Butamirate citrate *and* Noscapine.

'Sinedyston' *see under* Co-dergocrine.

SINEFUNGIN*** (6,9-diamino-1-(6-amino-9H-purin-9-yl)-1,5,6,7,8,9-hexadeoxy-β-D-*ribo*-decofuranuronic acid; compound 57926).

'Sinemet' *see under* Levodopa.

'Sinequan' *see* Doxepin.

'Sinesalin' *see* Bendroflumethiazide.

Sinestrol (tr) *see* Hexestrol.

'Sinetens' *see* Prazosin.

SINH *see* Streptoniazid.

Sinkol (tr) *see* Dextran.

'Sinnamin' *see* Azapropazone.

Sinocurarine *see* Gallamine triethiodide.

'Sinogan' *see* Levomepromazine.

'Sinografin' *see under* Meglumine diatrizoate.

'Sinomin' *see* Sulfamethoxazole.

'Sinomin acetyl' *see* Acetylsulfamethoxazole.

'Sinophenine' *see* Promazine.

'Sinovir' *see* Cyproterone acetate.

'Sinox' *see* Dinitro-o-cresol.

'Sinquan' *see* Doxepin.

'Sintaverin' *see* Pramiverine.

'Sinteroid' *see under* Clofibrate.

'Sintespasmil' *see* Camylofin.

'Sinthrome' *see* Acenocoumarol.

'Sintisone' *see* Prednisolone steaglate.

Sinto.... *see also* Syntho.....

'Sintodian' *see* Droperidol.

'Sintrom' *see* Acenocoumarol.

SINTROPIUM BROMIDE*** ((8r)-3α-hydroxy-8-isopropyl-1αH,5αH-tropanium bromide 2-propylvalerate; valproic acid ester with 3α-hydroxy-8-isopropyl-1αH,5αH-tropanium bromide).

'Sintyal' *see* Methylpentynol.

'Siogen' *see* Chlorquinaldol.

'Sionon' *see* Sorbitol.

'Siosteran' *see* Chlorquinaldol.

'Siqualone' *see* Fluphenazine.

'Siquil' *see* Triflupromazine.

'Siquoline' *see* Fluphenazine.

'Sirben' *see* Mebendazole.

'Sirmate' *see* Dichlormate.

'Sisolline' *see* Sisomicin.

SISOMICIN*** (O-2,6-diamino-2,3,4,6-tetradeoxy-α,D-glycerohex-4-enopyranosyl-(1→4)-O-[3-deoxy-4-C-methyl-3-(methylamino)-β,L-arabinopyranosyl)-(1→6)]-2-deoxy-D-streptamine; sissomicin; Sch-13475; 'baymicin'; 'extramycin'; 'mensiso'; 'pathomycin'; 'sisolline'; 'sisomin'; 'sisomycin').

'Sisomin' *see* Sisomicin.

'Sisomycin' *see* Sisomicin.

467

'Sisotox' *see* Dexamethasone sodium *m*-sulfobenzoate.

Sissomicin* *see* Sisomicin.

'Sistalgin' *see* Pramiverine.

'Sistilin' *see* Calcium methyl polygalacturonate sulfonate.

'Sistometril' *see under* Lynestrenol.

'Sistyline' *see* Calcium methyl polygalacturonate sulfonate.

'Sisuril' *see* Hydroflumethiazide.

SITOFIBRATE*** (stigmast-5-en-3β-ol 2-(*p*-chlorophenoxy)-2-methylpropionate; stigmastenol clofibrate).

SITOGLUSIDE*** (3β-(β-D-glucopyranosyloxy)-stigmast-5-ene; AW-10; BSSG; EU-4906; WA-184).

Sitosterin *see* β-Sitosterol.

β-SITOSTEROL (24β-ethyl-Δ⁵-cholesten-3β-ol; 22,23-dihydrostigmasterol; α-dihydrofucosterol; α-phytosterol; stigmast-5-en-3β-ol; cinchol; cupreol; quebrachol; rhamnol; sitosterin; 'harzol'; 'prostasal'; 'triastonal').

β-SITOSTEROL plus β-DIHYDROSITOSTEROL ('cytellin'; 'positol').

'Sixtysix-20' *see* Prednazate.

SJ-1977 *see* Metixene.

SK-7 *see* Pentifylline.

'SK-65' *see* Dextropropoxyphene.

SK-74 *see* Clofedanol.

SK-100 *see* Trichlormethine.

SK-101 *see* Chlormethine.

SK-331-A *see* Xantinol nicotinate.

SK-1133 *see* Tretamine.

SK-3818 *see* Tepa.

SK-5265 *see* Metodiclorofen.

SK-18615 *see* Thioguanosine.

SK-29728 *see* Quinaspar.

SK-29836 *see* Methasquin.

SK-29861 *see* Chlorasquin.

'SK-APAP' *see* Paracetamol.

SKATOLE (3-methylindole).

'Skelaxin' *see* Metaxalone.

'SK-estrogens' *see* Conjugated estrogens equine.

'Sketofax' *see* Dimethyl phthalate.

SK&F-51 *see* Octodrine.

SK&F-385 *see* Tranylcypromine.

SK&F-478 *see* Difenidol.

SK&F-478-J *see* Difenidol embonate.

SK&F-525-A *see* Proadifen.

SK&F-538-A *see* Quinisocaine.

SK&F-688-A *see* Phenoxybenzamine.

SK&F-1340 *see* Dimefadane.

SK&F-1637 *see* Scopolamine butyl bromide.

SK&F-1700-A *see* Buphenine.

SK&F-1717 *see* Anethole trithione.

SK&F-1995 *see* Dicloralurea.

SK&F-2208 *see* Hetaflur.

SK&F-2599 *see* Doxenitoin.

SK&F-2601-A *see* Chlorpromazine.

SK&F-3050 *see* Cortodoxone.

SK&F-4648A *see* Triflupromazine.

SK&F-4657 *see* Prochlorperazine.

SK&F-5116 *see* Levomepromazine.

SK&F-5137 *see* Dextromoramide.

SK&F-5345-A *see* Trifluomeprazine.

SK&F-6270 *see* Methiomeprazine.

SK&F-6539 *see* Flurotyl.

SK&F-6574 *see* Phenazocine.

SK&F-6611 *see* Norclostebol.

SK&F-6890 *see* β-Methylxylocholine.

SK&F-7690 *see* Benorterone.

SK&F-7988 *see* Virginiamycin.

SK&F-8318 *see* Xenazoic acid.

SK&F-8542 *see* Triamterene.

SK&F-8898 *see* Moroxydine.

SK&F-9976 *see* Oxolamine citrate.

SK&F-12866 *see* Cloretate.

SK&F-13338 *see* Ampyrimine.

SK&F-13364-A *see* Tyromedan.

SK&F-14287 *see* Idoxuridine.

SK&F-14336 *see* Clomacran.

SK&F-15601A *see* Toliodium chloride.

SK&F-16046 *see* Anisacril.

SK&F-17035-A *see* Oxamarin.

SK&F-18666 *see* Poloxalene.

SK&F-20716 *see* Periciazine.

SK&F-22908 *see* Flutiazin.

SK&F-24529 *see* Lobendazole.

SK&F-28175 *see* Fluotracen.

SK&F-29044 *see* Parbendazole.

SK&F-30310 *see* Oxibendazole.

SK&F-33134-A *see* Amiodarone.

SK&F-38094 *see* Dectaflur.

SK&F-38095 *see* Olaflur.

SK&F-39162 *see* Auranofin.

SK&F-39186 *see* Amicloral.

SK&F-40383 *see* Carbuterol.

SK&F-41558 *see* Cefazolin.

SK&F-53705A *see* Sulfonterol.

SK&F-59962 *see* Cefazaflur.

SK&F-60771 *see* Cefatrizine.

SK&F-61636 *see* Bromoxanide.

SK&F-62698 *see* Tienilic acid.

SK&F-62979 *see* Albendazole.

SK&F-69634 *see* Clopipazan mesilate.

SK&F-70230-A *see* Pipazetate.

SK&F-72517 *see* Elfazepam.

SK&F-82526-J *see* Fenoldopam mesilate.

SK&F-92058 *see* Metiamide.

SK&F-92334 *see* Cimetidine.

SK&F-92657 *see* Prizidilol.

SK&F-92676-A3 *see* Impromidine.

SK&F-92994 *see* Oxmetidine.

SK&F-100168 *see* Ibopamine.

SK&F-100916J *see* Aclatonium napadisilate.

SK&F D-39162 *see* Auranofin.

SK&F-D-39304 *see* Cefradine.

SK&F-D-75073 *see* Cefonicid.

'Skleromexe' *see* Clofibrate.

'Skleronorm' *see* Etiroxate.

'Sklerovitol' *see* Nicotinoylprocaine.

'Sk-lygen' *see* Chlordiazepoxide.

'Skopal' *see* Scopolamine methyl nitrate.

'Skopolate' *see* Scopolamine methyl nitrate.

'Skopyl' *see* Scopolamine methyl nitrate.

SL-501 *see* Clofedanol.

SL-573 *see* Ciproquazone.
SL-6057 *see* Clobenztropine.
SL-6058 *see* Clobenztropine methobromide.
SL-73033 *see* Antrafenine.
SL-75177-10 *see* Cicloprolol.
SL-75212 *see* Betaxolol.
SL-76002 *see* Progabide.
SL-77499 *see* Alfuzosin.
SLAFRAMINE ((1*S*,6*S*,8a*S*)-1-acetoxy-6-amino-octahydroindolizine; 6-aminooctahydro-1-hydroxyindolizine acetate).
'Slam' *see* Azothoate.
'Slimin' *see under* Hydrochlorothiazide.
'Slug guard' *see* Methiocarb.
SM-14 *see* Dimetofrine.
SM-1652 *see* Cefpiramide.
SMC-20-051 *see* Salcatonin hydrated polyacetate.
'SMOC' *see* Metam-sodium.
SMP-68-40 *see* Pyrabrom.
SMP-78 acid S *see* Ambruticin.
SN-44 *see* Dalanated insulin.
SN-46 *see* Dinex.
SN-105-843 *see* Naftifine.
SN-107 *see* Cefuroxime.
SN-166 *see* Glucosulfone.
SN-263 *see* Sodium amylosulfate.
SN-359 *see* Quinine hydrochloride.
SN-390 *see* Mepacrine.
SN-654 *see* Mepartricin.
SN-971 *see* Pamaquine.
SN-3115 *see* Plasmocid.
SN-5870 *see* Quinuronium sulfate.
SN-6771 *see* Bialamicol.
SN-6911 *see* Sontoquine.
SN-7618 *see* Chloroquine.
SN-8137 *see* Hydroxychloroquine.
SN-10751 *see* Amodiaquine.
SN-11841 *see* Amsacrine.
SN-12837 *see* Proguanil.
SN-13272 *see* Primaquine.
SN-13276 *see* Pentaquine.
SN-38584 *see* Phenmedipham.
'Snip' *see* Dimetilan.
'Snophenicol' *see* Chloramphenicol.
'S.N.P' *see* Parathion.
SNR-1804 *see* Clamidoxic acid.
'Sobelin' *see* Clindamycin.
'Sobiodopa' *see* Levodopa.
'Sobrepin' *see* Sobrerol.
SOBREROL (5-(1-hydroxy-1-methylethyl)-2-methyl-2-cyclohexen-1-ol; 5-hydroxy-α,α,4-trimethyl-3-cyclohexene-1-methanol; 4-(α-hydroxyisopropyl)-1-methylcyclohexen-6-ol; *p*-menth-6-ene-2,8-diol; 1-*p*-menthene-6,8-diol; 6,8-carvomenthenediol; 'lysmucol'; 'sobrepin').
See also under Carbocisteine.
'Sobril' *see* Oxazepam.
Socainide *see* Lorcainide.
'Soclidan' *see* Nicametate.
'Sodar' *see* Disodium methanearsonate.
Sodium 6-acetamidohexanoate *see* Sodium acexamate.
Sodium 5-acetamido-2,4,6-triiodo-*N*-methylisoph-

thalamate *see* Sodium iotalamate.
SODIUM ACETRIZOATE* (sodium 3-acetamido-2,4,6-triiodobenzoate; triiotrast).
SODIUM ACETRIZOATE plus POVIDONE ('salpix').
Sodium (*N*-acetyl-2-sulfamoyl)-4,4'-diaminodiphenylsulfone *see* Sulfadiasulfone sodium.
SODIUM ACEXAMATE (sodium acetamido-caproate; sodium 6-acetamidohexanoate; 'celuton').
SODIUM ALGINATE (sodium polymannuronate; 'algin'; 'kelgin'; 'manucol'; 'minus'; 'protanal').
Sodium aluminium phosphate basic *see* Kasal.
SODIUM ALUMINIUM SILICATE (zeolith A; 'sasil').
Sodium amidotrizoate* *see* Sodium diatrizoate.
Sodium *p*-aminobenzenestibonate *see* Stibamine.
SODIUM *p*-AMINOBENZOATE ('nataba').
SODIUM *p*-AMINOHIPPURATE (*p*-aminohippurate; 'nephrotest').
SODIUM AMYLOSULFATE* (sodium salt of sulfonated amylopectin from *Solanum tuberosum* (potato) tubers; amylosulfate; SN-263; 'depepsen').
Sodium anazolene *see* Anazolene sodium.
SODIUM ANHYDROMETHYLENECITRATE ('citarin'; 'goutin'; 'transren').
Sodium anoxynaphthonate* *see* Anazolene sodium.
Sodium antimony dimercaptosuccinate *see* Sodium stibocaptate.
SODIUM ANTIMONYL GLUCONATE* (sodium salt of a trivalent antimony derivative of gluconic acid; TSAG).
See also Sodium stibogluconate.
Sodium antimosan *see* Stibophen.
SODIUM APOLATE* (sodium ethensulfonate polymer; sodium ethylenesulfonate polymer; lyapolate sodium; apolate).
SODIUM ASCORBATE* (sodium derivative of 3-oxo-L-gulofuranolactone).
SODIUM AUROALLYLTHIOUREIDOBENZOATE (sodium salt of *S*-gold derivative of *m*-[[(allylimino)mercaptomethyl]amino]benzoic acid; aurothiosinamine-*m*-benzoic acid; gold sodium allylthioureidobenzoate; C-2924; 'lopion'; 'orthiourea').
SODIUM AUROTHIOMALATE* (*S*-gold derivative of thiomalic acid disodium salt; *S*-gold derivative of mercaptosuccinic acid; aurothiomalate; disodium aurothiomalate; gold sodium thiomalate).
Sodium aurothiosulfate *see* Sodium aurotiosulfate.
SODIUM AUROTIOSULFATE* (sodium dithiosulfatoaurate; aurothiosulfate; gold sodium thiosulfate; sodium aurothiosulfate).
SODIUM BENZYL SUCCINATE (succinic acid monobenzyl ester sodium salt).
Sodium biborate *see* Borax.
Sodium bis(acetato)tetrakis[gluconato(2-)]bis[salicylato(2-)] dialuminate dihydrate *see* Sodium glucaspaldrate.
Sodium bis(2,4-dihydroxy-3,3-dimethylbutyryl)fer-

rate *see* Sodium dipantoylferrate.

Sodium bithionolate* *see* Sodium bitionolate.

SODIUM BITIONOLATE*** (disodium 2,2'-thiobis(4,6-dichlorophenoxide); bithionolate sodium; sodium bithionolate).
See also Bithionol.

SODIUM CALCIUM EDETATE*** (calcium chelate of disodium salt of ethylenediaminetetraacetic acid; calcitetramate disodium; calcium disodium edetate; edetate disodium calcium).

SODIUM CAPOBENATE (sodium 6-(3,4,5-trimethoxybenzamido)hexanoate; TMBAC; 'capben').

Sodium N-(carbamoylmethyl)arsanilate *see* Tryparsamide.

Sodium carboxymethylcellulose *see* Carmellose.

Sodium 21-(3-carboxypropionyloxy)pregnane-3,20-dione *see* Hydroxydione sodium succinate.

Sodium cellulose glycolate *see* Carmellose.

SODIUM 4-(4-CHLORO-2-METHYLPHENOXY)BUTYRATE ('tropotox').

SODIUM CHROMATE (^{51}Cr)*** (sodium radiochromate; 'chromitope sodium'; 'rachromate').

Sodium cloxacillin* *see* Cloxacillin.

Sodium cromoglycate *see* Cromoglicate disodium.

Sodium cuproallylthioureidobenzoate *see* Allocupreide sodium.

SODIUM CYCLAMATE*** (sodium salt of N-cyclohexylsulfamic acid; cyclamate).

Sodium cyclohexanehexol hexaphosphate *see* Sodium phytate.

Sodium N-cyclohexylsulfamate *see* Sodium cyclamate.

Sodium dehydrocholate *see* Dehydrocholic acid.

SODIUM DIATRIZOATE* (sodium 3,5-diacetamido-2,4,6-triiodobenzoate; sodium amidotrizoate; amidotrizoate; iododiazoate).
See also Diatrizoic acid *and under* Meglumine diatrizoate.

SODIUM DIBUNATE*** (sodium salt of 2,6-di-*tert*-butylnaphthalene-1(or 3)-sulfonic acid; dibunate; L-1633).

Sodium dichloroisocyanurate *see* Troclosene sodium.

Sodium dicloxacillin* *see* Dicloxacillin.

Sodium diethyldithiocarbamate *see* Dithiocarb.

Sodium 3,3'-diglycolyldiiminobis(2,4,6-triiodobenzoate) *see* Sodium ioglycamate.

SODIUM DIHEXYL SULFOSUCCINATE (bis(1-methylamyl) ester Na salt of succinic acid; dihexyl sodium sulfosuccinate; 'alphasol MA').

Sodium 2,5-dihydroxybenzoate *see* Sodium gentisate.

Sodium dihydroxygluconatoaluminate *see* Sodium glucaldrate.

Sodium 3,5-diiodo-4-oxo-1(4H)-pyridineacetate *see* Iodopyridone.

Sodium 3,5-diiodo-α-phenylphloretate *see* Pheniodol sodium.

Sodium dimercaptopropanesulfonate *see* Unithiol.

Sodium 3-[[(dimethylamino)methylene]amino]-2,4,6-triiodohydrocinnamate *see* Sodium iopodate.

Sodium 3-[3-[[(dimethylamino)methylene]amino]-

2,4,6-triiodophenyl]propionate *see* Sodium iopodate.

Sodium [p-(dimethylamino)phenyl]diazenesulfonate *see* Fenaminosulf.

Sodium 4-(dimethylamino)-o-toluenephosphinite *see* Toldimfos.

Sodium dioctyl sulfosuccinate *see* Docusate sodium.

Sodium dioxide *see* Sodium peroxide.

SODIUM DIPANTOYLFERRATE (ferrous sodium pantoate; sodium bis(2,4-dihydroxy-3,3-dimethylbutyryl)ferrate; 'ferronascin').

SODIUM DIPROTRIZOATE*** (3,5-dipropionamido-2,4,6-triiodobenzoic acid Na salt; 'miokon').

Sodium dithiosulfatoaurate *see* Sodium aurotiosulfate.

Sodium ditolyldiazobis-8-amino-1-naphthol-3,6-disulfonate *see* Trypan blue.

Sodium dodecanoylmethylaminoacetate *see* Sodium N-lauroylsarcosinate.

SODIUM DODECYL SULFATE (dodecyl sodium sulfate; lauryl sodium sulfate).

Sodium edetate *see* Disodium edetate; Tetrasodium edetate; Trisodium edetate.

SODIUM ETACRYNATE (sodium salt of etacrynic acid; ethacrynate sodium; 'lyovac sodium edecrin').

SODIUM ETASULFATE*** (2-ethyl-1-hexanol sulfate sodium salt; 2-ethylhexyl sodium sulfate; ethasulfate sodium; sodium ethasulfate; octyl sulfate; sodium octyl sulfate; 'tergemist'; 'tergitol 8').

Sodium ethacrynate *see* Sodium etacrynate.

Sodium ethasulfate* *see* Sodium etasulfate.

Sodium ethensulfonate polymer *see* Sodium apolate.

Sodium ethylenebis(dithiocarbamate) *see* Nabam.

Sodium ethylenesulfonate polymer *see* Sodium apolate.

Sodium p-(ethylmercurithio)benzenesulfonate *see* Sodium timerfonate.

Sodium (ethylmercurithio)salicylate *see* Thiomersal.

SODIUM FEREDETATE*** (iron chelate of sodium edetate; ferritetraceminnatrium; ironedetate sodium; iron sodium edetate; sodium iron edetate).

SODIUM GENTISATE*** (sodium 2,5-dihydroxybenzoate; sodium 5-hydroxysalicylate).

SODIUM GLUCALDRATE* (sodium dihydroxygluconatoaluminate; glucaldrate).

SODIUM GLUCASPALDRATE*** (octasodium tetrakis(gluconato)bis(salicylato) μ-diacetodialuminate III dihydrate; sodium bis(acetato)tetrakis[gluconato(2−)]bis[salicylato(2−)] dialuminate dihydrate; glucaspaldrate).

Sodium glucoheptonate *see* Gluceptate sodium.

SODIUM GLUTAMATE (monosodium glutamate; 'accent'; 'glutavene').

Sodium 4-glycylamidobenzenearsonate *see* Tryparsamide.

SODIUM GUALENATE*** (5-isopropyl-3,8-dimethyl-1-azulenesulfonic acid sodium salt; guaiazulene soluble).

SODIUM HEPTADECYL SULFATE (3,9-di-

470

ethyl-6-tridecanol sodium sulfate; 'tergitol 7').

SODIUM HEXACYCLONATE*** (sodium salt of β,β-pentamethylene-γ-hydroxybutyric acid; sodium 4-hydroxy-3,3-pentamethylenebutyrate; sodium hydroxymethylcyclohexaneacetate; hexacyclonate).

Sodium *o*-(3-hexyloxy-2-hydroxypropoxy)benzoate *see* Exiproben.

Sodium hydrogen bis(2-propylvalerate) *see* Valproate semisodium.

Sodium 4-hydroxybutyrate *see* Oxybate sodium.

Sodium 3-(4-hydroxy-3,5-diiodophenyl)-2-phenyl-propionate *see* Pheniodol sodium.

Sodium hydroxymethylcyclohexaneacetate *see* Sodium hexacyclonate.

Sodium 4-hydroxy-3,3-pentamethylenebutyrate *see* Sodium hexacyclonate.

Sodium 5-hydroxysalicylate *see* Sodium gentisate.

SODIUM HYPOCHLORITE (Javel water; Labarraque's solution).

Sodium inositol hexaphosphate *see* Sodium phytate.

SODIUM IODIDE (^{125}I)*** (sodium radioiodide (^{125}I)).

SODIUM IODIDE (^{131}I)*** (sodium radioiodide (^{131}I); 'iodotope-131'; 'oriodide-131'; 'radiocaps-131'; 'theriode-131'; 'tracervial-131').

Sodium iodipamide *see* Adipiodone sodium.

SODIUM IODOHIPPURATE (*N*-(2-iodobenzoyl)glycine sodium salt; iodohippurate sodium; sodium *o*-iodohippurate; 'hippodine'; 'hippuran'; 'medopaque'; 'orthiodine').

SODIUM IODOHIPPURATE (^{123}I) (iodohippurate sodium I 123).

SODIUM IODOHIPPURATE (^{125}I) (iodohippurate sodium I 125; 'hippuran I-125'; 'hipputope I-125').

SODIUM IODOHIPPURATE (^{131}I)*** (sodium radioiodohippurate; iodohippurate sodium I 131; 'hippuran I 131'; 'hipputope').

Sodium iodomethamate *see* Iodoxyl.

Sodium iodomethanesulfonate *see* Methiodal sodium.

SODIUM IOGLYCAMATE (sodium 3,3'-diglycolyldiiminobis(2,4,6-triiodobenzoate)). *See also under* Meglumine ioglycamate.

SODIUM IOPODATE*** (sodium 3-[3-[[(dimethylamino)methylene]amino]-2,4,6-triiodophenyl]-propionate; sodium 3-[[(dimethylamino)methylene]amino]-2,4,6-triiodohydrocinnamate; ipodate sodium; sodium ipodate; NSC-106962; SQ-15761).

SODIUM IOTALAMATE (sodium 5-acetamido-2,4,6-triiodo-*N*-methylisophthalamate; sodium iothalamate).

SODIUM IOTALAMATE (^{125}I)*** (sodium radioiotalamate; 'glofil-125').

SODIUM IOTALAMATE (^{131}I)*** (sodium radioiotalamate).

Sodium iothalamate *see* Sodium iotalamate.

Sodium ipodate* *see* Sodium iopodate.

Sodium iron edetate *see* Sodium feredetate.

SODIUM ISOASCORBATE ('neo-cebitate').

Sodium 5-isopropyl-3,8-dimethyl-1-azulenesulfonate *see* Sodium gualenate.

SODIUM *N*-LAUROYLSARCOSINATE (sodium dodecanoylmethylaminoacetate; 'gardol').

Sodium levothyroxine *see* Levothyroxine sodium.

Sodium lignosulfate *see* Polignate sodium.

SODIUM MANDELATE ('mandelix').

Sodium menadiol diphosphate *see* Menadiol sodium phosphate.

Sodium menadiol disulfate *see* Menadiol sodium sulfate.

SODIUM MENADIOL-3-SULFONATE (menadiol 3-sulfonic acid sodium salt; 'katin').

Sodium 2-mercaptoethanesulfonate *see* Mesna.

Sodium metharsinite *see* Disodium methanearsonate.

Sodium methicillin* *see* Meticillin.

Sodium methylcarbamodithioate *see* Metam-sodium.

SODIUM METRIZOATE*** (sodium salt of 3-acetamido-2,4,6-triiodo-5-(*N*-methylacetamido)-benzoic acid; NSC-107431; 'isopaque').

Sodium monomethylarsonate *see* Disodium methanearsonate.

SODIUM MORRHUATE*** (sodium salts of fatty acids of cod-liver oil; oleocid).

SODIUM NICOTINATE (S-115; 'naotin'; 'nicodan'; 'nicosode').

SODIUM NITRILOTRIACETATE (sodium triglycollamate; 'trilon A').

Sodium nitroprussiate *see* Sodium nitroprusside.

SODIUM NITROPRUSSIDE (nitroprusside sodium; sodium nitroprussiate; sodium nitrosoferricyanide; sodium nitrosopentacyanoferrate-III; 'ketostix'; 'nipride').

Sodium nitrosoferricyanide *see* Sodium nitroprusside.

Sodium nitrosopentacyanoferrate-III *see* Sodium nitroprusside.

Sodium oxybate* *see* Oxybate sodium.

Sodium palmoxirate *see* Palmoxirate sodium.

Sodium β,β-pentamethylene-γ-hydroxybutyrate *see* Sodium hexacyclonate.

SODIUM PERBORATE ('bocasan'; 'dexol').

SODIUM PEROXIDE (sodium dioxide; sodium superoxide; 'oxone'; 'solozone').

SODIUM PERTECHNETATE Tc 99m (pertechnetate sodium; 'neipertec 99m'; 'pertscan 99m').

Sodium phenone acetate *see* Guaiacetin.

SODIUM PHOSPHATE (^{32}P)*** (mixture of sodium dihydrogen phosphate and disodium hydrogen phosphate containing ^{32}P; sodium radiophosphate; 'phosphotope').

Sodium phosphate triamcinolone acetonide *see* Triamcinolone acetonide sodium phosphate.

Sodium phosphonoformate *see* Foscarnet sodium.

SODIUM PHYTATE* (*myo*-inositol hexakis(dihydrogen phosphate) nonasodium salt; nonasodium phytate; phytate sodium; sodium cyclohexanehexol hexaphosphate; sodium inositol hexaphosphate; SQ-9343). *See also* Persodium phytate.

SODIUM PICOFOSFATE*** (4,4'-(pyrid-2-yl-methylene)diphenol bis(dihydrogen phosphate)

471

tetrasodium salt).

SODIUM PICOSULFATE* (4,4′-(pyrid-2-yl-methylene)diphenol bis(hydrogen sulfate) disodium salt; disodium 4,4′-pyrid-2-ylmethyl-enedi(phenyl sulfate); 4,4′-(2-picolylidene)bis-(phenylsulfuric acid)disodium salt; picosulfol; DA-1773; La-391).

SODIUM POLYANETHOLESULFONATE(S) (polyanetholesulfonate; 'liquoid').

SODIUM POLYANHYDROMANNURONIC SULFATE ('hepoid'; 'manuronate'; 'paritol'; 'thrombocid').

Sodium polyhydroxyaluminium monocarbonate hexitol complex *see* Alexitol sodium.

Sodium polymannuronate *see* Sodium alginate.

Sodium polystyrenesulfonate* *see* Polystyrenesulfonate sodium.

SODIUM PSYLLIATE (Na salts of fatty acids of *Plantago ovata* seeds; 'sylnasol').

Sodium pyrocatechol acetate *see* Guaiacetin.

SODIUM PYROCATECHOL-3,5-DISULFONATE (sodium-1,2-dihydroxybenzene-3,5-disul-fonate; sodium 4,5-dihydroxy-*m*-benzenedisul-fonate; 'tiferron'; 'tiron').

SODIUM *o*-PYROCATECHUATE (sodium pyrocatechol-3-carboxylate; 'mobilene').

Sodium radiochromate* *see* Sodium chromate (^{51}Cr).

Sodium radioiodide (^{125}I) *see* Sodium iodide (^{125}I).

Sodium radioiodide (^{131}I) *see* Sodium iodide (^{131}I).

Sodium radioiotalamate *see* Sodium iotalamate (^{125}I); Sodium iotalamate (^{131}I).

Sodium radiophosphate *see* Sodium phosphate (^{32}P).

SODIUM RICINOLEATE ('colidosan'; 'soricin').

SODIUM STIBOCAPTATE* (hexasodium salt of *S*,*S*-diester of cyclic thioantimonate (III) of 2,3-dimercaptosuccinic acid; antimony (III) sodium *meso*-2,3-dimercaptosuccinate; stibocaptate; TwSb; Ro 4-1544-6; Sb-58).

SODIUM STIBOGLUCONATE* (sodium salt of a pentavalent antimony derivative of gluconic acid; solusurmin).
See also Sodium antimonyl gluconate.

Sodium sulfaminochloride *see* Tosylchloramide sodium.

SODIUM SULFATE (anhydrous sodium sulfate; Glauber salt).

SODIUM SULFOSALICYLATE (sodium 5-sul-fosalicylate; 'arcylate'; 'salicylix').

Sodium superoxide *see* Sodium peroxide.

Sodium tartrobismuthate *see* Bismuth sodium neutral tartrate.

SODIUM TENUAZONATE (sodium derivative of 3-acetyl-5-*sec*-butyl-4-hydroxy-3-pyrrolin-2-one; NSC-525816).

Sodium tetraborate *see* Borax.

SODIUM TETRADECYL SULFATE* (7-ethyl-2-methyl-4-undecanol sodium sulfate; STS).

Sodium 1,2,3,4-tetrahydro-2-methyl-1,4-dioxo-2-naphthalenesulfonate *see* Menadione sodium bisulfite.

SODIUM THEOPHYLLIN-7-YLACETATE (7-carboxymethyltheophylline sodium salt; glycol-yltheophylline sodium; 'aminodal').

Sodium thimerfonate* *see* Sodium timerfonate.

SODIUM THIOSULFATE (hypo; hyposulfite; NSC-45624).

SODIUM TIMERFONATE* (ethyl[(*p*-sulfo-phenyl)thio]mercury sodium salt; sodium *p*-(eth-ylmercurithio)benzenesulfonate; sodium thimer-fonate; thimerfonate sodium; timerfon).

Sodium triclofos* *see* Triclofos.

Sodium triglycollamate *see* Sodium nitrilotriacetate.

SODIUM 2,3,4-TRIHYDROXYGLUTARATE (natrog).

Sodium 6-(3,4,5-trimethoxybenzamido)hexanoate *see* Sodium capobenate.

Sodium troclosene* *see* Troclosene sodium.

SODIUM TYROPANOATE* (3-butyramido-α-ethyl-2,4,6-triiodohydrocinnamic acid sodium salt; tyropanoate; NSC-107434; WIN-8851-2).

'Sodothiol' *see* Sodium thiosulfate.

SOFALCONE ([5-[(3-methyl-2-butenyl)oxy]-2-[*p*-[(3-methyl-2-butenyl)oxy]cinnamoyl]phen-oxy]acetic acid).

'Soffecine' *see* Docusate sodium.

'Soframycin' *see* Framycetin.

'Sofro' *see* Pemoline.

'Softenon' *see* Thalidomide.

'Softil' *see* Docusate sodium.

'Sokaral' *see* Dexamethasone.

'Solabar' *see under* Padimate O.

'Solacen' *see* Tybamate.

'Solamine' *see* Benzethonium chloride.

'Solan' *see* Pentanochlor.

Solapsone* *see* Solasulfone.

SOLASULFONE (tetrasodium salt of 1,1′-[sul-fonylbis(*p*-phenylimino)]bis(3-phenyl-1,3-pro-panedisulfonic acid); tetrasodium salt of 4,4′-bis(1,3-disulfo-3-phenylpropylamino)diphenyl sulfone; phenopryldiasulfone sodium; solapsone; solusulfone; RP 3668).

'Solatene' *see* Betacarotene.

'Solatran' *see* Ketazolam.

'Solaxin' *see* Chlorzoxazone.

'Solbase' *see* Macrogol(s).

'Solbrol' *see* Methyl paraben.

'Solbrol P' *see* Propyl paraben.

'Soldactone' *see* Canrenoate potassium.

'Solestril' *see* Proscillaridin.

'Solestrin' *see* Estrone.

'Solestro' *see* Estradiol benzoate.

'Solevar' *see* Propetandrol.

'Solex' *see* Dichlozoline.

'Solferino' *see* Fuchsine.

'Solfocrisol' *see* Sodium aurotiosulfate.

'Solganal-B' *see* Aurothioglucose.

'Solgeretic' *see under* Bendroflumethiazide.

'Solgol' *see* Nadolol.

Solid green *see* Brilliant green.

'Solimidine' *see* Zolimidine.

'Soliphylline' *see* Choline theophyllinate.

'Solis' *see* Diazepam.

'**Solitacin**' *see under* Indometacin.
'**Solium**' *see* Febarbamate.
'**Solnicol**' *see* Chloramphenicol hemisuccinate sodium.
'**Solozone**' *see* Sodium peroxide.
'**Solprin**' *see* Calcium acetylsalicylate.
'**Solquinol**' *see* 8-Quinolinol sulfate.
'**Solubacter**' *see* Triclocarban.
Soluble guncotton *see* Pyroxylin.
'**Solucort**' *see* Prednisolone sodium *m*-sulfobenzoate.
'**Solucortef**' *see* Hydrocortisone sodium succinate.
'**Soludacortin**' *see* Prednisolone sodium succinate.
'**Soludiazine**' *see* Sulfadiazine-meglumine.
'**Solufontamide**' *see* Sulfathiourea.
'**Solugastril**' *see under* Algeldrate.
'**Solu-medrol**' *see* Methylprednisolone sodium succinate.
'**Soluphylline**' *see* Etamiphyllin.
'**Solupred**' *see* Prednisolone sodium *m*-sulfobenzoate.
'**Soluran**' *see* Clofenamide.
'**Solurine**' *see* Methenamine salicylate.
'**Solurol**' *see* Suxibuzone.
'**Solusediv**' *see* Fluanisone.
'**Soluseptacin**' *see* Sulfasolucin.
'**Soluseptacine**' *see* Sulfasolucin.
'**Soluseptazine**' *see* Sulfasolucin.
'**Solusprin**' *see* Lysine acetylsalicylate.
'**Solustibosan**' *see* Sodium stibogluconate.
Solusulfone (tr) *see* Solasulfone.
Solusurmin (tr) *see* Sodium stibogluconate.
'**Solutedarol**' *see* Triamcinolone diacetate.
'**Soluthiazole**' *see* Noprylsulfamide.
'**Solutrast**' *see* Iopamidol.
'**Solvar**' *see* Polyvinyl alcohol.
'**Solvat**' *see* Benzyl thiocyanate.
'**Solvent P**' *see* 2-Phenoxyethanol.
'**Solvezink**' *see* Zinc sulfate.
'**Solvodol**' *see* Parapropamol.
'**Solvosterol**' *see* Peptide 67-82.
'**Solvostrept A**' *see* Streptoduocin.
'**Solvotricin**' *see* Tyrothricin.
SOLWAY PURPLE (1-hydroxy-4-toluidinoanthraquinone-*m*-sulfonic acid; 'SDC'; 'supracen violet').
SOLYPERTINE*** (1-[2-(1,3-dioxolo[4,5-*f*]indol-7-yl)ethyl]-4-(*o*-methoxyphenyl)piperazine; 7-[2-[4-(*o*-methoxyphenyl)piperazin-1-yl]ethyl](5*H*)-1,3-dioxolo[4,5-*f*]indole).
SOLYPERTINE TARTRATE* (solypertine hydrogen tartrate; WIN-18413-2).
'**Solyusurmin**' *see* Sodium stibogluconate.
'**Soma**' *see* Carisoprodol.
'**Somagest**' *see* Amixetrine.
SOMAN (1,2,2-trimethylpropyl methylphosphonofluoridate; 3,3-dimethylbut-2-yl methylphosphorofluoridate; methyl pinacolyl phosphonofluoridate; pinacoloxymethylphosphoryl fluoride; pinacolyl methylphosphonofluoridate).
SOMANTADINE** (α,α-dimethyl-1-adamantaneethylamine; α,α-dimethyltricyclo[3.3.1.1³,⁷]decane-1-ethanamine; somantadine hydrochloride;

PR-741-976A).
SOMATOMEDIN (growth hormone releasing hormone; sulfation factor; GHRH).
SOMATOSTATIN*** (L-alanylglycyl-L-cysteinyl-L-lysyl-L-asparaginyl-L-phenylalanyl-L-phenylalanyl-L-tryptophyl-L-lysyl-L-threonyl-L-phenylalanyl-L-threonyl-L-seryl-L-cysteine cyclic (3→14) disulfide; growth hormone release inhibiting factor; somatotrophin release inhibiting factor; SRIF; AY-24873; AY-24910).
Somatotrophin *see* Growth hormone.
Somatotropin *see* Growth hormone.
Somatropin* *see* Human growth hormone.
'**Somatyl**' *see* Betaine aspartate.
'**Somazina**' *see* Citicoline.
'**Somben**' *see* Carbromal.
'**Sombrevin**' *see* Propanidid.
'**Sombulex**' *see* Hexobarbital.
'**Somilan**' *see* Chloral betaine.
'**Somilar**' *see* Chloral betaine.
'**Sominat**' *see* Dichloralphenazone.
'**Somnased**' *see* Nitrazepam.
'**Somnibel**' *see under* Methaqualone.
'**Somnipront**' *see* Dimethyl sulfoxide.
'**Somnite**' *see* Nitrazepam.
'**Somnofac**' *see* Methaqualone.
'**Somnolens**' *see* Phenobarbital.
'**Somnos**' *see* Chloral hydrate.
'**Somsanit**' *see* Oxybate sodium.
'**Sonapax**' *see* Thioridazine.
'**Sonbutal**' *see* Butallylonal.
'**Soneryl**' *see* Butethal.
'**Sonin**' *see* Pimethixine.
'**Soni-slow**' *see* Isosorbide dinitrate.
Sontochin *see* Sontoquine.
SONTOQUINE* (7-chloro-4-(4-diethylamino-1-methylbutylamino)-3-methylquinoline; sontochin; RP 3038; SN-6911).
'**Sopangamine**' *see* Pangamic acid.
'**Sophia**' *see under* Norethisterone.
Sophoretin *see* Quercetin.
Sophorin *see* Rutoside.
Sophorine *see* Cytisine.
SOPITAZINE*** (10-[(4-isopropylpiperazin-1-yl)carbonyl]phenothiazine; 4-isopropylpiperazin-1-yl phenothiazin-10-yl ketone).
'**Sopor**' *see* Methaqualone.
'**Soprintin**' *see* Acepromazine.
SOPROMIDINE*** ((−)-1-[(R)-2-imidazol-4-yl-1-methylethyl]-3-[2-[[(5-methylimidazol-4-yl)-methyl]thio]ethyl]guanidine).
'**Soprontin**' *see* Acepromazine.
SOQUINOLOL*** (5-[3-(*tert*-butylamino)-2-hydroxypropoxy]-3,4-dihydro-2(1*H*)-isoquinolinecarboxaldehyde).
'**Soraxa**' *see* Warfarin.
'**Sorbacel**' *see* Oxidized cellulose.
'**Sorbangil**' *see* Isosorbide dinitrate.
'**Sorbester**' *see* Polysorbate 80.
SORBIC ACID (2,4-hexadienoic acid; 2-propenylacrylic acid).
Sorbic oil *see* Parasorbic acid.
Sorbide nitrate *see* Isosorbide dinitrate.

473

'**Sorbidilat**' *see* Isosorbide dinitrate.
Sorbimacrogol(s)* *see* Polysorbate(s).
SORBINICATE*** (D-glucitol hexanicotinate; sorbitol hexanicotinate; 'nicosterol').
SORBINIL* ((*S*)-6-fluoro-2,3-dihydrospiro[4*H*-1-benzopyran-4,4'-imidazolidine]-2',5'-dione; (*S*)-6-fluorospiro[chroman-4,4'-imidazolidine]-2',5'-dione; CP-45634).
'**Sorbiperan**' *see under* Metoclopramide.
'**Sorbisolo**' *see* Isosorbide dinitrate.
Sorbitan esters *see below and under* Polysorbate(s).
SORBITAN LAURATE*** (monoesters of lauric acid and sorbitan).
SORBITAN OLEATE*** (monoesters of oleic acid and sorbitan).
SORBITAN PALMITATE*** (monoesters of palmitic acid and sorbitan).
SORBITAN SESQUIOLEATE*** (mixture of monoesters and diesters of oleic acid and sorbitan).
SORBITAN STEARATE*** (monoesters of stearic acid sorbitan).
SORBITAN TRIOLEATE*** (triesters of oleic acid and sorbitan).
SORBITAN TRISTEARATE*** (triesters of stearic acid and sorbitan).
SORBITOL (D-sorbitol; D-glucitol; L-gulitol; glucohexitol).
See also Glusoferron; Iron sorbitex; Sorbitan(s).
Sorbitol hexanicotinate *see* Sorbinicate.
Sorbitol polymers *see* Sorbitan(s).
'**Sorbitrate**' *see* Isosorbide dinitrate.
'**Sorbo**' *see* Sorbitol.
'**Sorbol**' *see* Sorbitol.
'**Sordinol**' *see* Clopenthixol.
Sorethytan(s)* *see* Polysorbate(s).
'**Sorexa**' *see* Warfarin.
'**Sorgoa**' *see* Tolnaftate.
'**Soricin**' *see* Sodium ricinoleate.
'**Soridermal**' *see* Metiazinic acid.
'**Soripal**' *see* Metiazinic acid.
'**Sorlate(s)**' *see* Polysorbate(s).
'**Sormodren**' *see* Bornaprine.
'**Sorot**' *see* Dequalinium chloride.
'**Sorquad**' *see* Isosorbide dinitrate.
'**Sorquetan**' *see* Tinidazole.
'**Sosegon**' *see* Pentazocine.
'**Sosenyl**' *see* Pentazocine.
'**Sosol**' *see* Sulfafurazole.
'**Sospitan**' *see* Pyricarbate.
'**Sostril**' *see* Ranitidine.
'**Sotacor**' *see* Sotalol.
'**Sotalex**' *see* Sotalol.
SOTALOL*** (4'-[1-hydroxy-2-(isopropylamino)-ethyl]methanesulfonanilide; MJ-1999).
SOTERENOL** (2'-hydroxy-5'-(1-hydroxy-2-isopropylaminoethyl)methanesulfonanilide; 4-hydroxy-α-[(isopropylamino)methyl]-3-(methanesulfonamido)benzyl alcohol; MJ-1992).
'**Sotorni**' *see* Levopropoxyphene dibudinate.
'**Sotradecol**' *see* Sodium tetradecyl sulfate.
'**Souframine**' *see* Phenothiazine.
'**Sovelin**' *see under* Bromhexine.

'**Soventol**' *see* Bamipine.
Sovkain (tr) *see* Cinchocaine.
'**Soxidyl**' *see* Tiocarlide.
'**Soxisol**' *see* Sulfafurazole.
'**Soxomide**' *see* Sulfafurazole.
Soziodolic acid *see* 2,6-Diiodo-1-phenol-4-sulfonic acid.
Sozolic acid *see* 2-Phenolsulfonic acid.
SP-54 *see* Pentosan polysulfate.
SP-104 *see* Dronabinol.
SP-106 *see* Nabitan.
SP-119 *see* Tinabinol.
SP-175 *see* Nabazenil.
SP-204 *see* Menabitan.
SP-304 *see* Pirnabin.
SP-732 *see* Prolintane.
'**Spa**' *see* Lefetamine.
'**α-Spa**' *see* (+)-*N*,*N*-Dimethyl-α-phenylphenethylamine.
SPAGLUMIC ACID*** (*N*-(*N*-acetyl-L-β-aspartyl)-L-glutamic acid).
SPARFOSATE SODIUM* (sparfosic acid disodium salt; CI-882).
SPARFOSIC ACID*** (*N*-(phosphonoacetyl)-L-aspartic acid; PALA; NSC-224131).
'**Sparine**' *see* Promazine.
'**Sparsamycin A**' *see* Tubercidin.
SPARSOMYCIN*** (antibiotic from *Str. sparsogenes*; NSC-59727; U-19183).
'**Spartase**' *see under* Potassium aspartate.
SPARTEINE*** (dodecahydro-7,14-methano-2*H*,6*H*-dipyrido[1,2-*a*:1',2'-*e*][1,5]diazocine; lupinidine; sparteine sulfate).
SPARTEINE ADENYLATE (adenylic acid sparteine salt; 'spartopan').
'**Spartepur**' *see* Sparteine.
'**Spartocin**' *see* Sparteine.
'**Spartopan**' *see* Sparteine adenylate.
'**Spartrix**' *see* Carnidazole.
SPA-S-132 *see* Partricin.
SPA-S-160 *see* Mepartricin.
'**Spasfon**' *see under* Phloroglucinol.
'**Spasmacol**' *see* Alverine.
'**Spasmadryl**' *see* Aprofene.
'**Spasmalgan**' *see* Denaverine.
'**Spasmamide**' *see* Fenalamide.
'**Spasmatol**' *see under* Drofenine.
'**Spasmaverine**' *see* Alverine.
'**Spasmentral**' *see* Benzetimide.
'**Spasmex**' *see* Trospium chloride.
'**Spasmocalm**' *see* Diethyl benzyl(2-diethylaminoethyl)malonate.
'**Spasmocyclone**' *see* Cyclandelate.
'**Spasmodex**' *see* Dihexyverine.
'**Spasmolysin**' *see* Proxyphylline.
'**Spasmo-lyt**' *see* Trospium chloride.
Spasmolytin (tr) *see* Adiphenine.
'**Spasmomen**' *see* Otilonium bromide.
'**Spasmonal**' *see* Dipiproverine.
'**Spasmoparid**' *see* Bietamiverine.
'**Spasmoparine**' *see* Bietamiverine.
'**Spasmopriv**' *see* Fenoverine.
'**Spasuret**' *see* Flavoxate.

'Spazmokalm' see Diethyl benzyl(2-diethylamino-ethyl)malonate.
'Spazoc' see Isometheptene.
SPC-297D see Azidocillin.
'Speciadopa' see Levodopa.
Specilline G see Penicillin G.
'Spectacillin' see Epicillin.
'Spectan' see Spectinomycin.
SPECTINOMYCIN*** (decahydro-4a,7,9-tri-hydroxy-2-methyl-6,8-bis(methylamino)pyrano-[2,3-b][1,4]benzodioxin-4-one; antibiotic from Str. spectabilis; actinospectinomycin; M-141; U-18409E).
'Spectraban' see Padimate.
'Spectra-sorb UV 9' see Oxybenzone.
'Spectra-sorb UV 24' see Dioxybenzone.
'Spectra-sorb UV 284' see Sulisobenzone.
'Spectra-sorb UV 531' see Octabenzone.
'Spectrobact' see Troleandomycin.
'Spectrocide' see Dimpylate.
'Speda' see Vinylbital.
'Speed' see Methamphetamine.
'Spenitol' see Moroxydine.
'Spergon' see Chloranil.
Spermaceti see Cetaceum.
SPERMIDINE (N-(3-aminopropyl)-1,4-butanedi-amine; N-(3-aminopropyl)putrescine).
SPERMINE (N,N'-bis(3-aminopropyl)-1,4-but-anediamine; N,N'-bis(3-aminopropyl)putrescine; di(aminopropyl)tetramethylenediamine; sper-mocrine).
Spermocrine (tr) see Spermine.
'Spermol' see Spermine.
SPG-827 see Podophyllotoxin benzylidene gluco-side.
Sphaerophysin see Spherophysine.
'Spheromycin' see Novobiocin.
SPHEROPHYSINE (tr) (1-[4-(3-methyl-1-buten-ylamino)butyl]guanidine; sphaerophysin).
SPHINGINE (2-amino-1-octadecanol).
SPHINGOSINE (2-amino-4-octadecene-1,3-diol).
SPICLOMAZINE*** (8-[3-(2-chlorophenothiaz-in-10-yl)propyl]-1-thia-4,8-diazaspiro[4.5]decan-3-one; clospirazine; APY-606; 'disepron').
'Spidox' see Phenylmercuric nitrate.
SPINACEAMINE (4,5,6,7-tetrahydroimidazo[5,4-c]pyridine).
Spinacene see Squalene.
'Spinocaine' see Procaine.
SPIPERONE*** (4'-fluoro-4-[spiro(5-oxo-3-phenylimidazolidin-4,4'-piperidin)-1'-yl]butyro-phenone; 8-[3-(p-fluorobenzoyl)propyl]-1-phenyl-1,3,8-triazaspiro[4.5]decan-4-one; spiro-peridol; R-5147; 'spiropitan').
'Spiractin' see Pimeclone.
SPIRAMIDE*** (8-[3-(p-fluorophenoxy)propyl]-1-phenyl-1,3,8-triazaspiro[4.5]decan-4-one; flur-oxyspiramine; R-5908).
SPIRAMYCIN*** (antibiotic from Str. ambofa-ciens; IL-5902; NSC-64393; RP 5337).
See also under Metronidazole.
SPIRAZIDINE (tr) (3,12-bis(2-chloroethyl)-3,6,9,12-tetrazadispiro[5.5]hexadecane).

SPIRAZINE** (2,4-diamino-5-(p-chlorophenyl)-9-methyl-1,3,5-triazaspiro[5.5]undeca-1,3-diene).
SPIRENDOLOL*** ((±)-4'-[3-(tert-butylamino)-2-hydroxypropoxy]spiro[cyclohexane-1,2'-in-dan]-1'-one; LI-32-468).
SPIRGETINE*** ([2-(6-azaspiro[2.5]oct-6-yl)-ethyl]guanidine; N-(2-guanidinoethyl)aza-6-spi-ro[2.5]-octane; LD-3598).
SPIRGETINE plus PARAFLUTIZIDE ('divi-max').
SPIRILENE** (8-[4-(p-fluorophenyl)-3-pentenyl]-1-phenyl-1,3,8-triazaspiro[4.5]decan-4-one; R-6109).
'Spiro-32' see Spirogermanium.
'Spiroctan' see Spironolactone.
Spirodiflamine see Fluspirilene.
'Spiroform' see Acetylsalol.
'Spirogen' see Ammonium phthalamate.
SPIROGERMANIUM*** (8,8-diethyl-N,N-di-methyl-2-aza-8-germaspiro[4.5]decane-2-propan-amine; 2-[3-(dimethylamino)propyl]-8,8-diethyl-2-aza-8-germaspiro[4.5]decane; 3-(8,8-diethyl-2-aza-8-germaspiro[4.5]dec-2-yl)propyldimethyl-amine; spirogermanium hydrochloride; NSC-192965; 'spiro-32').
Spirolactone see Spironolactone.
SPIROMUSTINE*** (3-[2-[bis(2-chloroethyl)-amino]ethyl]-1,3-diazaspiro[4.5]decane-2,4-di-one).
SPIRONOLACTONE*** (3-[7α-(acetylthio)-17β-hydroxy-3-oxoandrost-4-en-17α-yl]propionic acid γ-lactone; 17-hydroxy-7-mercapto-3-oxo-17α-pregn-4-ene-21-carboxylic acid γ-lactone 7-acetate; spirolactone; SC-9420).
See also under Altizide; Butizide; Hydrochloro-thiazide; Hydroflumethiazide.
'Spironothiazid' see Hydrochlorothiazide.
'Spiropent' see Clenbuterol.
Spiroperidol see Spiperone.
'Spiropitan' see Spiperone.
SPIROPLATIN*** (cis-[1,1-cyclohexanebis(meth-ylamine)](sulfato)platinum; cis-(cyclohexylidene-dimethylenediamine-N,N')(sulfato)platinum; NSC-311056; TNO-6).
SPIRORENONE*** (17-hydroxy-6β,7β:15β,16β-dimethylene-3-oxo-17α-pregna-1,4-diene-21-carboxylic acid γ-lactone; 3',4',6,7,8,9,11,12,13,14,15,16,20,21-tetradecahydro-10,13-dimethylspiro[17H-dicyclopropa[6,7:15,16]-cyclopenta[a]phenanthrene-17,2'(5'H)-furan]-3(10H),5'-dione).
'Spirosal' see Glycol salicylate.
SPIROXASONE*** (7α-acetylthio-20-spirox-4-en-3-one; 7α-(acetylthio)-4',5'-dihydrospiro[an-drost-4-ene-17,2'(3'H)-furan]-3-one; 4',5'-di-hydro-7α-mercaptospiro[androst-4-ene-17,2'(3'H)-furan]-3-one acetate; 2',3'α-tetra-hydrofuran-2'-spiro-17-(7-acetylthio-4-androst-en)-3-one).
SPIROXATRINE*** (8-(1,4-benzodioxan-2-yl-methyl)-1-phenyl-1,3,8-triazaspiro[4.5]decan-4-one; R-5188).
SPIROXEPIN*** (N,N-dimethylspiro[dibenz-

475

[*b,e*]oxepin-11(6*H*),2'-[1,3]dioxolane]-4'-methyl-amine).
'**Spizef**' *see* Cefotiam.
Spofa-325 *see* Moxastine.
'**Spofadiazin**' *see* Sulfamethoxypyridazine.
'**Spondyril**' *see* Phenylbutazone.
Spongoadenosine *see* Vidarabine.
'**Spontin**' *see* Ristocetin.
'**Sporostacin**' *see* Clodantoin.
Spreading factor *see* Hyaluronidase(s).
SQ-1089 *see* Hydroxycarbamide.
SQ-1489 *see* Thiram.
SQ-2128 *see* Etoxazene.
SQ-9343 *see* Sodium phytate.
SQ-9453 *see* Dimethyl sulfoxide.
SQ-9538 *see* Testolactone.
SQ-9993 *see* Estradiol undecylate.
SQ-10269 *see* Carbifene.
SQ-10496 *see* Tiazesim.
SQ-10643 *see* Cinanserin.
SQ-11302 *see* Epicillin.
SQ-11436 *see* Cefradine.
SQ-11725 *see* Nadolol.
SQ-13050 *see* Econazole.
SQ-13396 *see* Iopamidol.
SQ-13847 *see* Pirquinozol.
SQ-14055 *see* Tiamulin.
SQ-14225 *see* Captopril.
SQ-15010 *see* Algestone acetofenide.
SQ-15102 *see* Amcinafal.
SQ-15112 *see* Amcinafide.
SQ-15659 *see* Rolitetracycline.
SQ-15761 *see* Sodium iopodate.
SQ-15860 *see* Glyhexamide.
SQ-15874 *see* Pipazetate.
SQ-16123 *see* Meticillin.
SQ-16150 *see* Estradiol enantate.
SQ-16360 *see* Fusidate sodium.
SQ-16374 *see* Metenolone enantate.
SQ-16401 *see* Halquinols.
SQ-16423 *see* Oxacillin.
SQ-16496 *see* Metenolone acetate.
SQ-18566 *see* Halcinonide.
SQ-19844 *see* Sincalide.
SQ-20009 *see* Etazolate.
SQ-20824 *see* Cicloprofen.
SQ-20881 *see* Teprotide.
SQ-21982 *see* Iodoxamic acid.
SQ-21983 *see* Iopronic acid.
SQ-22947 *see* Tiamulin fumarate.
SQ-26776 *see* Aztreonam.
SQ-65396 *see* Cartazolate.
SQUALENE (2,6,10,15,19,23-hexamethyl-2,6,10,14,18,22-tetracosahexaene; spinacene).
SR-10 *see* Methoprene.
SR-406 *see* Captan.
SR-720-22 *see* Metolazone.
SR-1368 *see* Timegadine.
SRG-95213 *see* Diazoxide.
SRIF *see* Somatostatin.
'**Srilane**' *see* Idrocilamide.
SS-578 *see* Diiodohydroxyquin.
ST-25 *see* Batroxobin.

ST-37 *see* Hexylresorcinol.
ST-52 *see* Fosfestrol.
ST-104 *see* Prednylidene.
ST-155 *see* Clonidine.
ST-375 *see* Tolonidine.
ST 567-BR *see* Alinidine.
ST-600 *see* Flutonidine.
ST-1085 *see* Midodrine.
ST-1191 *see* Etoperidone.
ST-1396 *see* Celiprolol.
ST-1411 *see* Dimepregnen.
ST-1512 *see* Hexoprenaline.
ST-5066 *see* Iobenzamic acid.
ST-7090 *see* Hexobendine.
ST-8005 *see* Sulfametrole.
ST-9067 *see* Azintamide.
STA-307 *see* Tiomesterone.
'**Stabilene**' *see* Ethyl biscoumacetate.
'**Stabinol**' *see* Glysobuzole.
'**Stadacaine**' *see* Leucinocaine.
'**Stadol**' *see* Butorphanol.
'**Stafac**' *see* Virginiamycin.
'**Staff**' *see* Etoperidone.
'**Stafylopenin**' *see* Meticillin.
'**Stagid**' *see* Metformin embonate.
'**Stagural**' *see* Norfenefrine.
'**Stakane**' *see* Antrafenine.
STALLIMYCIN** (*N*″-(2-amidinoethyl)-4-form-amido-1,1',1″-trimethyl-*N*,4':*N*′,4″-ter(pyrrole-2-carboxamide); distamycin A; stallimycin hydrochloride; FI-6426; 'herperal').
'**Stam F-34**' *see* Propanil.
'**Stamicin**' *see* Nystatin.
'**Stampen**' *see* Dicloxacillin.
STAMPYRINE (tr) (2,3-dimethyl-1-phenyl-4-stearamido-3-pyrazolin-5-one; *N*-antipyrinyl-stearamide; 4-stearamidophenazone).
'**Stamycin**' *see* Nystatin.
'**Stanaprol**' *see* Androstanolone.
Stanazolol* *see* Stanozolol.
'**Stangyl**' *see* Trimipramine.
'**Stanilo**' *see* Spectinomycin.
'**Stannacne**' *see* Tin oxide.
STANNOUS PYROPHOSPHATE* (diphosphoric acid ditin (2+) salt; ditin (2+) pyrophosphate; tin pyrophosphate; MP-4018).
'**Stannoxyl**' *see* Tin oxide.
Stanolone* *see* Androstanolone.
'**Stanoprol**' *see* Androstanolone.
STANOZOLOL** (17α-methyl-5α-androstano-[3,2-*c*]pyrazol-17β-ol; 17-methyl-2'*H*-5α-androsteno[3,2-*c*]pyrazol-17β-ol; stanazolol; androstanazole; methylstanazole; NSC-43193; WIN-14833).
'**Stapenor**' *see* Oxacillin.
'**Staphcillin**' *see* Meticillin.
'**Staphobristol**' *see* Cloxacillin.
'**Staphylex**' *see* Flucloxacillin.
Staphylococcus staphylolyticus, enzyme *see* Lysostaphin.
'**Staphylomycin**' *see* Virginiamycin.
'**Staporos**' *see* Calcitonin.
'**Stapyocine**' *see* Pristinamycin.

Starch epichlorohydrin reaction products *see* Amilomer; Eldexomer.

Starch sugar *see* Glucose.

'Staticin' *see* Carinamide.

'Staticum' *see* Glipentide.

Statolon* *see* Vistatolon.

'Statran' *see* Emylcamate.

'Staurodorm' *see* Flurazepam.

'Staxidin' *see* Virginiamycin.

StC-1106 *see* Fluprednidene acetate.

StC-1400 *see* Fludrocortisone.

STEAGLATE(S)** (*O*-stearoylglycolate(s)).
   See also Prednisolone steaglate.

4-Stearamidophenazone *see* Stampyrine.

STEARIC ACID (octadecanoic acid).
   See also Monostearin; Propylene glycol monostearate; Stearin.

STEARIN (stearic acid glyceryl triester).

O-**Stearoylglycolate(s)** *see* Steaglate(s).

Stearyl alcohol *see* 1-Octadecanol.

Stearylic alcohol *see* 1-Octadecanol.

STEARYLSULFAMIDE*** (*N*-sulfanilylstearamide).

'Stediril' *see under* Norgestrel.

'Stediril-d' *see under* Levonorgestrel.

STEFFIMYCIN*** (antibiotic from *Str. steffisburgensis*; U-20661).

'Stelabid' *see under* Trifluoperazine.

'Stelazine' *see* Trifluoperazine.

'Stellamycin' *see* Streptoduocin.

'Stellarid' *see* Proscillaridin.

'Stellidine' *see* Histidine.

'Stemetil' *see* Prochlorperazine.

'Stemex' *see* Paramethasone acetate.

STENBOLONE*** (17β-hydroxy-2-methyl-5α-androst-1-en-3-one).

'Stenediol' *see* Methandriol.

'Stenol' *see* 1-Octadecanol.

'Stenoptin' *see under* Verapamil.

'Stenorol' *see* Halofuginone.

'Stenosine' *see* Disodium methanearsonate.

STEPA *see* Thiotepa.

'Stepin' *see* Tioxolone.

STEPRONIN*** (*N*-(2-mercaptopropionyl)glycine 2-thiophenecarboxylate (ester); 2-(2-thenoylthio)propionylglycine; tiopronin 2-thiophenecarboxylate; tiofacic; 'broncoplus').

'Steranabol' *see* Clostebol acetate.

'Steranabol depot' *see* Oxabolone cipionate.

'Sterane' *see* Prednisolone.

'Sterax' *see* Desonide.

Stercorin *see* Coprosterol.

STERCURONIUM IODIDE*** ((cona-4,6-dienin-3β-yl)ethyldimethylammonium iodide; MYC-1080).

'Stereocidin' *see* Bekanamycin.

'Sterilon' *see* Chlorhexidine.

'Sterinol' *see* Benzododecinium chloride.

'Sterinor' *see* Co-tetroxazine.

'Sterisil' *see* Hexetidine.

'Sterisol' *see* Hexedine.

'Sterlifix' *see* Triclosan.

'Sterogenol' *see* Cetylpyridinium bromide.

'Sterolibrin' *see under* Chloro-MDAP.

'Sterolone' *see* Prednisolone.

'Sterosan' *see* Chlorquinaldol.

'Steroxin' *see* Chlorquinaldol.

'Ster-zac' *see* Triclosan.

'Stesolid' *see* Diazepam.

STEVALADIL*** (3β-(dimethylamino)-5α-pregnane-18,20α-diol diacetate ester).

STH *see* Growth hormone.

STIBAMINE* (sodium *p*-aminobenzenestibonate).

STIBAMINE GLUCOSIDE*** (*N*-glucoside of sodium *p*-aminobenzenestibonate; 'neostam').

'Stibanate' *see* Sodium stibogluconate.

'Stibanose' *see* Sodium stibogluconate.

'Stibatin' *see* Sodium stibogluconate.

'Stibinol' *see* Sodium stibogluconate.

Stibocaptate *see* Sodium stibocaptate.

STIBOCAPTIC ACID (cyclic thioantimonate (III) *S*,*S*-diester of succimer; antimony 2,3-dimercaptosuccinate).

STIBOPHEN* (antimony (III) sodium bispyrocatechol-2,4-disulfonate; Sdt-91).

STIBOPHEN POTASSIUM (antimony (III) potassium bispyrocatechol-2,4-disulfonate; Heyden-611).

Stibosamine** *see* Ethylstibamine.

'Stiburea' *see* Urea stibamine.

Stickstofflost *see* Chlormethine.

'Stiedex' *see under* Desoximetasone.

Stigmastadienol *see* Stigmasterol.

Stigmast-5-en-3β-ol *see* β-Sitosterol.

Stigmast-5-en-3β-ol 2-(*p*-chlorophenoxy)-2-methylpropionate *see* Sitofibrate.

Stigmastenol clofibrate *see* Sitofibrate.

STIGMASTEROL (24-ethyl-3β-hydroxy-5,22-cholestadiene; stigmastadienol; antistiffness factor).
   See also β-Sitosterol.

'Stigmenene' *see* Benzpyrinium bromide.

'Stigminene' *see* Benzpyrinium bromide.

Stilbamidine isethionate* *see* Stilbamidine isetionate.

STILBAMIDINE ISETIONATE*** (4,4′-stilbenedicarboxamidine bis(2-hydroxyethanesulfonate); stilbamidine isethionate; stilbamidine di(ethanol-2-sulfonate); M & B-744).

'Stilbarol' *see* Diethylstilbestrol.

STILBAZIUM IODIDE*** (1-ethyl-2,6-bis(*p*-pyrrolidin-1-ylstyryl)pyridinium iodide; stilbazium; BW-61-32).

2-STILBAZOLE (2-styrylpyridine).

4-STILBAZOLE (4-styrylpyridine).

Stilbazum* *see* Stilbazium iodide.

STILBENE (1,2-diphenylethene; 1,2-diphenylethylene; styrylbenzene; toluylene).

4,4′-Stilbenedicarboxamidine bis(2-hydroxyethanesulfonate) *see* Stilbamidine isetionate.

'Stilbenol' *see* Diethylstilbestrol.

Stilbestrol *see* Diethylstilbestrol.

Stilbestrol dipalmitate *see* Stilpalmitate.

Stilbestrol diphosphate *see* Fosfestrol.

Stilboestrol* *see* Diethylstilbestrol.

STILBYLAMINE (α-aminodiphenylethane; 1,2-diphenylethylamine; α-phenylphenethylamine).

'Stillomycin' *see* Puromycin.

'Stilny' *see* Nordazepam.

STILONIUM IODIDE*** (triethyl 2-[(*E*)-(*p*-styrylphenoxy)ethyl]ammonium iodide; *p*-[2-(diethylamino)ethoxy]stilbene ethiodide; (*E*)-*N*,*N*,*N*-triethyl-2-[4-(2-phenylethenyl)phenoxy]ethanaminium iodide).

STILPALMITATE* (stilbestrol dipalmitate).

'Stilphostrol' *see* Fosfestrol.

'Stimol' *see* Citrulline malate.

'Stimovul' *see* Epimestrol.

'Stimsen' *see* Tozalinone.

'Stimulest' *see* Deanol tartrate.

'Stimulexin' *see* Doxapram.

'Stinerval' *see* Phenelzine.

STIRIMAZOLE*** (2-(4-carboxystyryl)-5-nitro-1-vinylimidazole; *p*-[2-(5-nitro-1-vinylimidazol-2-yl)vinyl]benzoic acid).

STIRIPENTOL*** (1-(1,3-benzodioxol-5-yl)-4,4-dimethyl-1-penten-3-ol; 4,4-dimethyl-1-[(3,4-methylenedioxy)phenyl]-1-penten-3-ol; 5-(3-hydroxy-4,4-dimethyl-1-pentenyl)-1,3-benzodioxole; α-(1-hydroxy-2,2-dimethylpropyl)-3,4-(methylenedioxy)styrene; BCX-2600).

STIROCAINIDE*** ((*E*)-2-benzylidenecycloheptanone (*E*)-*O*-[2-(diisopropylamino)ethyl]oxime; 2-benzylidene-1-[[2-(diisopropylamino)ethoxy]imino]cycloheptane).

STIROCAINIDE FUMARATE (stirocainide hydrogen fumarate; Th-494).

STIROFOS* ([2-chloro-1-(2,4,5-trichlorophenyl)-vinyl] dimethyl phosphate; tetrachlorfenvinfos; CVMP; SD-3447; SD-8447; SD-8747; 'gardona'; 'rabon').

'Stivan' *see* Pirisudanol.

'Stockade' *see* Permethrin.

'Stomacaine' *see* Oxetacaine.

'Stomalene' *see* Guaiazulene.

'Stomoxin' *see* Permethrin.

'Stop-scald' *see* Ethoxyquin.

'Stovaine' *see* Amylocaine.

'Stovarsol' *see* Acetarsol.

'Stoxil' *see* Idoxuridine.

'STP' *see* 2,5-Dimethoxy-4-methylamphetamine.

St.Peter 224 *see* Midodrine.

'Straminol' *see* Dodecarbonium chloride.

STRAMONIUM (*Datura stramonium* and/or *Datura tatula*).

'Stranoval' *see under* Betamethasone valerate.

'Stratene' *see* Cetiedil.

'Strazide' *see* Streptoniazid.

'Strepantin' *see* Streptomycin pantothenate.

'Strepsils' *see* Amylmetacresol.

STREPTAMINE (1,3-diamino-2,4,5,6-tetrahydroxycyclohexane).

'Streptase' *see* Streptokinase.

STREPTIDINE (1,3-diguanidino-2,4,5,6-tetrahydroxycyclohexane).

Streptococcal deoxyribonuclease *see* Streptodornase.

Streptococcal fibrinolysin *see* Streptokinase.

STREPTODORNASE*** (streptococcal deoxyribonuclease).

STREPTODORNASE plus STREPTOKINASE ('bistreptase'; 'distreptaze'; 'dornokinase'; 'varidase').

STREPTODUOCIN* (equal parts of streptomycin and dihydrostreptomycin as sulfates and/or pantothenates).

'Streptohydrazid' *see* Streptoniazid.

STREPTOKINASE*** (plasmokinase; streptococcal fibrinolysin; 'awelysin'; 'kabikinase'; 'kinalysin'; 'streptase').
See also under Streptodornase.

Streptolydigin *see* Lidimycin.

Streptomyces paulus, antibiotic *see* Paulomycin.

Streptomyces tendae, α-amylase-inhibiting polypeptide *see* Tendamistat.

Streptomycilidene isonicotinoylhydrazone *see* Streptoniazid.

STREPTOMYCIN*** (2,4-diguanidino-3,5,6-trihydroxycyclohexyl-5-deoxy-2-*O*-(2-deoxy-2-methylamino-α-L-glucopyranosyl)-3-formyl-β-L-*lyxo*-pentafuranoside; streptomycin A; streptomycin hydrochloride, phosphate or sulfate; NSC-14083).

STREPTOMYCIN OPINIAZIDE SALT (streptomycin isoniazidveratrylidenecarboxylate; streptosaluzid).

STREPTOMYCIN PANTOTHENATE ('strepantin'; 'streptothenate').
See also Dihydrostreptomycin; Streptoduocin; Streptoniazid.

Streptomycylideneisoniazid sulfate *see* Streptoniazid.

STREPTONIAZID*** (isonicotinic acid streptomycilidenehydrazide; compound of isoniazid with streptomycin sulfate; streptomycilidene isonicotinoylhydrazone; streptomycylideneisoniazid sulfate; streptonicozid; streptotubazid; SINH).

Streptonicozid* *see* Streptoniazid.

Streptonigrin* *see* Rufocromomycin.

Streptonivicin *see* Novobiocin.

Streptosaluzid (tr) *see* Streptomycin opiniazide salt.

'Streptothenate' *see* Streptomycin pantothenate.

Streptotubazid (tr) *see* Streptoniazid.

Streptovaricin *see* Streptovarycin.

STREPTOVARYCIN*** (antibiotic mixture from *Str. variabilis*; streptovaricin; B-44-P; U-7750).

'Streptovitacin A' *see* Hydroxycycloheximide.

STREPTOZOCIN*** (1-D-glucos-2-yl-3-methyl-3-nitrosourea; 2-deoxy-2-(3-methyl-3-nitrosoureido)-D-glucopyranose; streptozotocin; NSC-85998; U-9889; 'zanosar').

STREPTOZOCIN plus ZEDALAN (NSC-37917).

Streptozotocin *see* Streptozocin.

'Stresnil' *see* Azaperone.

'Stresson' *see* Bunitrolol.

'Streunex' *see* Lindane.

'Striadyne' *see* Adenosine triphosphate.

'Striatran' *see* Emylcamate.

'Strilaxin' *see under* Orphenadrine citrate.

STRINOLINE*** (*as*-triazino[5,6-*c*]quinoline).

'Strodival' *see* Ouabain.
'Stromba' *see* Stanozolol.
'Strong-ciclon' *see* Permethrin.
'Strongid' *see* Pyrantel embonate.
STRONTIUM NITRATE Sr 85* (radiostrontium nitrate; 'strotope').
Strophanthidin cymaroside diglucoside *see* Strophanthoside.
Strophanthidin cymaroside glucoside *see* Strophanthin.
STROPHANTHIDOL D-CYMAROSIDE (cymarol).
STROPHANTHIDOL L-RHAMNOSIDE (convallatoxol).
STROPHANTHIN (3β,5,14-trihydroxy-19-oxo-5β-card-20(22)-enolide 3-D-cymaro-D-glucoside; strophanthidin cymaroside glucoside; strophanthin k; cymarin; C-197).
Strophanthin g *see* Ouabain.
Strophanthin k *see* Strophanthin.
Strophanthin D-glucoside *see* Strophanthoside.
STROPHANTHOSIDE (strophanthidin cymaroside diglucoside; strophanthin D-glucoside; strophanthoside k).
'Strophoside' *see* Strophanthoside.
'Strotope' *see* Strontium nitrate Sr 85.
'Structum' *see* Chondroitin sulfate.
'Stryadine' *see* Adenosine triphosphate.
Strychnine amine oxide *see* Strychnine *N*-oxide.
STRYCHNINE *N*-OXIDE (strychnine amine oxide; Z-203).
STS *see* Sodium tetradecyl sulfate.
'Stugeron' *see* Cinnarizine.
'Stylomycin' *see* Puromycin.
STYPHNIC ACID (2,4,6-trinitroresorcinol).
'Styptanon' *see* Estriol succinate.
'Styptopur' *see* *p*-Aminomethylbenzoic acid.
'Stypturon' *see* Mepesulfate.
'Stypven' *see* Russell's viper venom.
STYRAMATE* (2-hydroxy-2-phenylethyl carbamate; β-hydroxyphenethyl carbamate).
STYRENE (ethenylbenzene; vinylbenzene; phenethylene; cinnamene; styrol; styrolene).
Styrol *see* Styrene.
Styrolene *see* Styrene.
'Styron' *see* Sodium feredetate.
Styrone *see* Cinnamyl alcohol.
Styrylbenzene *see* Stilbene.
Styrylpyridine *see* Stilbazole.
Su-3088 *see* Chlorisondamine chloride.
Su-3118 *see* Syrosingopine.
Su-4485 *see* Metyrapone.
Su-5864 *see* Guanethidine sulfate.
Su-6518 *see* Dimetindene.
Su-8341 *see* Cyclopenthiazide.
Su-8874 *see* Metyrapone.
Su-9064 *see* Metoserpate.
SU-10568 *see* Clortermine.
Su-13437 *see* Nafenopin.
Su-18137 *see* Ciproquinate.
Su-21524 *see* Pirprofen.
'Suavedol' *see* Glaziovine.
'Suavitil' *see* Benactyzine.

'Subamycin' *see* Tetracycline.
SUBATHIZONE* (*p*-ethylsulfonylbenzaldehyde thiosemicarbazone; sulzon; SHCH-431; Tb III/1347).
'Subcutin' *see* Benzocaine.
Subecholine *see* Dicholine suberate.
SUBENDAZOLE* (3-(methylthio)-5-(4,5,6-trichlorobenzimidazol-2-ylthio)-1,2,4-thiadiazole; 4,5,7-trichloro-2-[3-(methylthio)-1,2,4-thiadiazol-2-ylthio]benzimidazole; CB-12592).
SUBERIC ACID (1,6-hexanedicarboxylic acid; octanedioic acid).
Suberoylbis(choline) *see* Dicholine suberate.
Suberyldicholine *see* Dicholine suberate.
Sublimate *see* Mercuric chloride.
'Sublimaze' *see* Fentanyl.
'Subose' *see* Glyhexamide.
'Subtosan' *see* Povidone.
'Sucaryl-calcium' *see* Calcium cyclamate.
Succicurarium *see* Suxamethonium chloride.
SUCCIMER* (meso-2,3-dimercaptosuccinic acid; *R**,*S**-2,3-dimercaptosuccinic acid; DIMSA; DMS; DMSA; DTS; Ro 1-7977). *See also* Stibocaptic acid.
SUCCINAMIC ACID (succinic acid monoamide).
1-Succinamic acid-5-L-valine-8-(L-2-phenylglycine)-angiotensin II *see* Arfalasin.
SUCCINAMIDE (succinic acid diamide).
SUCCINANILIC ACID (*N*-phenylsuccinamic acid).
SUCCINCHLORIMIDE (*N*-chlorosuccinimide).
SUCCINIC ACID (butanedioic acid; amber acid). *See also* Cadmium succinate; Daminozide; Diadonium iodide; Dibutyl succinate.
Succinic acid bis[2-(*N*-adamant-1-yl-*N*-methyl-amino)ethyl] ester dimethiodide *see* Diadonium iodide.
Succinic acid diamide *see* Succinamide.
Succinic acid imide *see* Succinimide.
Succinic acid monoamide *see* Succinamic acid.
SUCCINIMIDE (butanimide; 2,5-dioxopyrrolidine; 2,5-pyrrolidinedione; succinic acid imide).
SUCCINONITRILE (butanedinitrile; *sym* dicyanoethane; ethylene dicyanide; 'deprelin'; 'dinile').
'Succinutin' *see* Ethosuximide.
Succinylcholine *see* Suxamethonium chloride.
Succinyldapsone *see* Succisulfone.
Succinyldicholine *see* Suxamethonium chloride.
2,2'-Succinyldioxybis(ethylenedimethylethylammonium chloride) *see* Suxethonium chloride.
2,2'-Succinyldioxybis(ethylenetrimethylammonium chloride) *see* Suxamethonium chloride.
SUCCINYLDISULFOCHOLINE (succinylbis ester of dimethyl(2-hydroxyethyl)sulfonium chloride; succinylsulfacholine).
SUCCINYLSALICYLIC ACID (bis(*o*-carboxyphenyl) salicylate; 'diasprin').
Succinylsulfacholine *see* Succinyldisulfocholine.
N⁴-Succinylsulfanilamide *see* Sulfasuccinamide.
SUCCINYLSULFATHIAZOLE* (*N*⁴-succinyl-*N*¹-thiazol-2-ylsulfanilamide; 4'-(thiazol-2-ylsulfamoyl)succinanilic acid).

N^4-**Succinyl-**N^1-**thiazol-2-ylsulfanilamide** *see* Succinylsulfathiazole.

SUCCISULFONE* (4-amino-4'-succinylaminodiphenyl sulfone; 4'-sulfanilylsuccinanilic acid; succinyldapsone; F-1500).

SUCCISULFONE DIETHANOLAMINE SALT ('exosulfonyl').

'Succitimal' *see* Phensuximide.

Succus liquiritiae *see* Liquorice.

SUCLOFENIDE* (3-chloro-4-(phenylsuccinimido)benzenesulfonamide; N-(2-chloro-4-sulfamoylphenyl)-2-phenylsuccinimide; GS-385; 'sulfalepsine').

SUCRALFATE* (sucrose octakis(hydrogen sulfate) aluminium complex; aluminium sucrose hydrogen sulfate basic salt; 'antepsin'; 'ulcerban'; 'ulcerimin'; 'ulcogant'; 'ulsanic').

SUCRALOX* (polymerized complex of sucrose and aluminium hydroxide; 'manalox AS').

'Sucramin' *see* Saccharin ammonium salt.

Sucre de gelatine *see* Glycine.

'Sucrets' *see* Hexylresorcinol.

'Sucrol' *see* Phenetylurea.

SUCROSE (α-D-glucopyranosyl-β-D-fructofuranoside; saccharose).

Sucrose aluminium hydroxide complex *see* Sucralox.

Sucrose octakis(hydrogen sulfate) aluminium complex *see* Sucralfate.

'Sucsan' *see* Liquorice.

'Sudafed' *see* Pseudoephedrine.

Sudan III *see* Oil scarlet.

Sudan IV *see* Scarlet red.

'Sudermo' *see* Mesulfen.

SUDEXANOX* (S-(7-carboxy-4-hexyl-9-oxoxanthen-2-yl)-S-methylsulfoximine).

SUDOXICAM* (4-hydroxy-2-methyl-N-thiazol-2-yl-2H-1,2-benzothiazine-3-carboxamide 1,1-dioxide; CP-15973).

SUFENTANIL* (4-[N-(ethylcarbonyl)anilino]-4-(methoxymethyl)-1-(2-thien-2-ylethyl)piperidine; N-[4-(methoxymethyl)-1-[2-(2-thienyl)ethyl]-4-piperidyl]propionanilide; fentathienyl; sulfentanyl; R-30730).

SUFENTANIL CITRATE (R-33800).

'Sufortanon' *see* Penicillamine.

SUFOSFAMIDE* (2-[[3-(2-chloroethyl)tetrahydro-2H-1,3,2-oxazaphosphorin-2-yl]amino]-ethanol methanesulfonate (ester) P-oxide; 3-(2-chloroethyl)tetrahydro-2-[(2-hydroxyethyl)-amino]-2H-1,3,2-oxazaphosphorine methanesulfonate 2-oxide; Asta 5122; 'cytimun').

'Suicalm' *see* Azaperone.

'Suinox' *see* Secobarbital.

'Suisynchron' *see* Metallibure zinc complex.

'Suladrin' *see* Sulfafurazole diolamine.

SULAZEPAM* (7-chloro-1,3-dihydro-1-methyl-5-phenyl-2H-1,4-benzodiazepine-2-thione; W-3676).

SULBACTAM* (penicillanic acid 4,4-dioxide; sulbactam sodium; CP-45899).

SULBACTAM PIVOXIL* ((2,2-dimethyl-1-oxopropoxy)methyl penicillanate 4,4-dioxide; pivaloyloxymethyl penicillanate 1,1-dioxide; pivalate

ester of hydroxymethyl ester of penicillanic acid 4,4-dioxide; pivsulbactam; sulbactam hydroxymethyl ester pivalate; CP-47904).

SULBENICILLIN* (6-(2-phenyl-2-sulfoacetamido)penicillanic acid; α-sulfobenzylpenicillin; sulfocillin; 'kedacillin').

SULBENOX* ((4,5,6,7-tetrahydro-6-oxobenzo-[b]thien-4-yl)urea; CL-206576).

SULBENTINE* (3,5-dibenzyltetrahydro-2H-1,3,5-thiadiazine-2-thione; dibenzthion; D-47).

SULBUTIAMINE* (N,N'-[dithiobis[2-(2-hydroxyethyl)-1-methylvinylene]]bis[N-[(4-amino-2-methyl-5-pyrimidinyl)methyl]formamide] diisobutyrate(ester); N,N'-[dithiobis[(2-isobutyryloxyethyl)-1-methylvinylene]bis[N-(4-amino-2-methylpyrimidin-5-yl)methyl]formamide]; O-isobutyrylthiamine disulfide; thiamine disulfide diisobutyrate; bisbutiamine; diisobutyrylthiamine; Se-5007; 'arcalion'; 'orval'; 'vitaverm').

Sulcimide *see* Sulcymide.

SULCLAMIDE* (5-carboxamido-2-chlorobenzenesulfonamide; 4-chloro-3-sulfamoylbenzamide; SD-14112).

'Sulcolon' *see* Salazosulfapyridine.

SULCONAZOLE* (($\pm$)-1-[2,4-dichloro-β-[(p-chlorobenzyl)thio]phenethyl]imidazole; sulconazole nitrate; RS-44872).

SULCYMIDE (tr) (p-aminobenzenesulfocyanamide; N'-cyanosulfanilamide; sulcimide; sulfanilcyanamide).

'Suleo' *see* DDT.

Sulergine *see* Disulergine.

'Sulestrex' *see* Piperazine estrone sulfate.

SULFABENZ* (N^1-phenylsulfanilamide; sulphanilanilide; NSC-2619; 'sulfa-vet').

SULFABENZAMIDE* (N^1-benzoylsulfanilamide; N-sulfanilylbenzamide; 'sulfabenzide').

Sulfabenzamine *see* Mafenide.

'Sulfabenzide' *see* Sulfabenzamide.

Sulfabenzoylamide *see* Sulfadimethylbenzoylamide.

'Sulfabid' *see* Sulfaphenazole.

Sulfabutin *see* Busulfan.

SULFACARBAMIDE* (N^1-carbamoylsulfanilamide; sulfaurea; sulfanilylurea; urosulfan).

Sulfacarboxythiazole *see* Sulfacarizole.

SULFACARIZOLE (N^1-(carboxythiazolyl)sulfanilamide; sulfacarboxythiazole).

SULFACECOLE (2-ethoxy-4'-[(5-methylisoxazol-3-yl)sulfamoyl]acetanilide; N^4-(2-ethoxyacetyl)-N^1-(5-methylisoxazol-3-yl)sulfanilamide).

SULFACETAMIDE* (N^1-acetylsulfanilamide; N-sulfanilylacetamide; acetosulfaminum; acetsulfanilamide; sulfacetamide sodium).

Sulfachloropyrazine *see* Sulfaclozine.

SULFACHLORPYRIDAZINE* (N^1-(6-chloropyridazin-3-yl)sulfanilamide; Ba-10370).

SULFACHRYSOIDINE* (3,5-diamino-2-(p-sulfamoylphenylazo)benzoic acid; N^4-(2,4-diamino-6-carboxyphenylazo)sulfanilamide; carboxysulfamidochrysoidine).

SULFACITINE (N^1-(1-ethyl-1,2-dihydro-2-oxopyrimidin-4-yl)sulfanilamide; 1-ethyl-N-sulfanilylcytosine; sulfacytine; CI-636; 'renoquid').

SULFACLOMIDE** (N^1-(5-chloro-2,6-dimethyl-pyrimidin-4-yl)sulfanilamide).
SULFACLORAZOLE*** (N^1-[1-(m-chlorophen-yl)-3-methylpyrazol-5-yl]sulfanilamide).
SULFACLOZINE*** (N^1-(6-chloropyrazinyl)sulfanilamide; sulfachloropyrazine; Esb-3; 'sulfatyl').
Sulfacombin* see Sulfadiazine.
'Sulfactol' see Sodium thiosulfate.
Sulfacytine* see Sulfacitine.
Sulfadiamine see Acedapsone.
SULFADIASULFONE SODIUM*** ((N^1-acetyl-6-sulfanilylmetanilamido) sodium; sodium (N-acetyl-2-sulfamoyl)-4,4'-diaminodiphenylsulfone; N-(6-sulfanilylmetanilyl)acetamide monosodium salt; acetosulfone sodium; CI-100; IA-307; NSC-107528).
SULFADIAZINE*** (N^1-pyrimid-2-ylsulfanilamide; sulfacombin; sulfapyrimidine; sulfazine; WR-7577).
See also Co-trimazine; Co-tetroxazine *and under* Bromhexine; Nitrofurantoin.
SULFADIAZINE-MEGLUMINE (sulfadiazine methylglucamine derivative; 'soludiazine').
SULFADIAZINE SILVER (silver sulfadiazine; 'flammazin'; 'silvadene'; 'silvederma').
SULFADICRAMIDE*** (N^1-(3,3-dimethylacryloyl)sulfanilamide; N^1-senecioylsulfanilamide).
SULFADIMETHOXINE*** (N^1-(2,6-dimethoxy-4-pyrimidyl)sulfanilamide; sulfadimethoxypyrimidine).
See also under Diaveridine; Ormetoprim.
Sulfadimethoxypyrimidine see Sulfadimethoxine; Sulfamoprine.
SULFADIMETHYLBENZOYLAMIDE (N^1-(3,4-dimethylbenzoyl)sulfanilamide; sulfabenzoylamide; G-867; 'irgafen').
Sulfadimethyloxazole see Sulfamoxole.
Sulfadimethylpyrimidine see Sulfadimidine.
Sulfadimetine (tr) see Sulfasomidine.
Sulfadimezine see Sulfadimidine.
SULFADIMIDINE*** (N^1-(4,6-dimethylpyrimid-2-yl)sulfanilamide; dimethylsulfadiazine; dimethylsulfapyrimidine; sulfadimethylpyrimidine; sulfadimezine; sulfamethazine; sulfamethiazine; sulfamidine; sulfodimezine).
See also under Trimethoprim.
'Sulfadione' see Dapsone.
SULFADOXINE*** (N^1-(5,6-dimethoxypyrimidin-4-yl)sulfanilamide; sulformethoxine; sulformetoxine; sulforthodimethoxine; sulforthomidine; Ro 4-4393; WR-4873; 'fanasil'; 'fanzil'; 'sanasil').
See also under Pyrimethamine; Trimethoprim.
SULFAETHIDOLE*** (N^1-(5-ethyl-1,3,4-thiadiazol-2-yl)sulfanilamide; etazol; ethazole; VK-55).
SULFAETHIDOLE plus SULFAMETHIZOLE ('harnosal').
SULFAETHOXYPYRIDAZINE (N^1-(6-ethoxy-pyridazin-3-yl)sulfanilamide).
SULFAFURAZOLE** (N^1-(3,4-dimethylisoxazol-5-yl)sulfanilamide; sulfisoxazole).

Sulfafurazole diethanolamine see Sulfafurazole diolamine.
SULFAFURAZOLE DIOLAMINE (2,2'-iminodiethanol salt of sulfafurazole; sulfisoxazole diolamine; sulfafurazole diethanolamine; NU-445; 'suladrin').
SULFAGUANIDINE*** (N^1-amidinosulfanilamide; sulfamidinum; sulgin; RP 2275).
SULFAGUANOLE** (N^1-[(4,5-dimethyloxazol-2-yl)amidino]sulfanilamide; 'enterocura').
Sulfaisodimerazine see Sulfasomidine.
Sulfaisodimidine see Sulfasomidine.
Sulfaisopropylthiadiazole see Glyprothiazol.
'Sulfalar' see Sulfafurazole.
SULFALENE** (N^1-(3-methoxypyrazin-2-yl)sulfanilamide; sulfametopyrazine; sulfamethoxypyrazine; sulfapyrazinmetoxin; NSC-110433; WR-4629).
See also under Trimethoprim.
'Sulfalepsine' see Suclofenide.
'Sulfalex' see Sulfamethoxypyridazine.
SULFALOXATE CALCIUM (sulfaloxic acid calcium salt; 'enteromide').
SULFALOXIC ACID*** (4'-[[(hydroxymethyl)-carbamoyl]sulfamoyl]phthalanilic acid; 2-[4-(hydroxymethylureidosulfonyl)phenylcarbamoyl]benzoic acid).
SULFAMAZONE** (α-[p-[(6-methoxypyridazin-3-yl)sulfamoyl]anilino]-2,3-dimethyl-5-oxo-1-phenyl-3-pyrazoline-4-methanesulfonic acid).
SULFAMERAZINE*** (N^1-(4-methylpyrimidin-2-yl)sulfanilamide; 2-methylsulfadiazine; methylsulfapyrimidine; methylsulfazine; sulfamethylpyrimidine; sulfamonomethyldiazine; RP-2632).
SULFAMERAZINE plus SULFATOLAMIDE ('supronal').
Sulfameter* see Sulfametoxydiazine.
Sulfamethazine see Sulfadimidine.
Sulfamethiazine see Sulfadimidine.
Sulfamethiazole see Sulfamethizole.
SULFAMETHIN (tr) (polymerized condensation product of diaminodiaphenylsulfone with p-dimethylaminobenzaldehyde).
'Sulfamethin' see Sulfasomidine.
SULFAMETHIZOLE*** (N^1-(5-methyl-1,3,4-thiadiazol-2-yl)sulfanilamide; sulfamethiazole; sulfamethylthiadiazole; sulfathiodiazole; VK-53).
See also under Neomycin; Sulfaethidole.
SULFAMETHOXAZOLE*** (N^1-(5-methylisoxazol-3-yl)sulfanilamide; sulfisomezole; MS-53; Ro 4-2130).
See also Co-trimoxazole.
Sulfamethoxine see Sulfametoxydiazine.
Sulfamethoxydiazine* see Sulfametoxydiazine.
'Sulfamethoxydin' see Sulfametoxydiazine.
Sulfamethoxypyrazine see Sulfalene.
SULFAMETHOXYPYRIDAZINE*** (N^1-(6-methoxypyridazin-3-yl)sulfanilamide; CL-13494; RP 7522).
Sulfamethoxypyrimidine see Sulfametoxydiazine.
Sulfa-5-methyldiazine see Sulfaperin.
Sulfamethylphenylpyrazole see Sulfapyrazole.

Sulfamethylpyrimidine *see* Sulfamerazine.
Sulfamethylthiadiazole *see* Sulfamethizole.
SULFAMETHYLTHIAZOLE (N^1-(4-methyl-thiazol-2-yl)sulfanilanide).
Sulfametin *see* Sulfametoxydiazine.
SULFAMETOMIDINE* (N^1-(6-methoxy-2-methylpyrimidin-4-yl)sulfanilamide).
Sulfametopyrazine* *see* Sulfalene.
SULFAMETOXYDIAZINE* (N^1-(5-methoxy-pyrimidin-2-yl)sulfanilamide; 5-methoxy-2-sulfanilamidopyrimidine; sulfameter; sulfamethoxydiazine; sulfamethoxypyrimidine; sulfametin; AHR-857; Bayer-5400; DJ-1550; SH-613).
SULFAMETROLE (N^1-(4-methoxy-1,2,5-thiadiazol-3-yl)sulfanilamide; ST-8005).
See also under Trimethoprim.
Sulfamidine *see* Sulfadimidine.
Sulfamidinum *see* Sulfaguanidine.
SULFAMIDOCHRYSOIDINE (N^4-(2,4-diamino-phenylazo)sulfanilamide).
SULFAMIDOPYRINE SODIUM (Na salt of 2,3-dimethyl-4-(methanesulfonylamino)-1-phenyl-3-pyrazolin-5-one; 4-aminoantipyrine sodium N^4-methanesulfonate; amizole; melaminsulfone; sulfamipyrine).
Sulfaminum *see* Sulfanilamide.
Sulfamipyrine *see* Sulfamidopyrine sodium.
SULFAMONOMETHOXINE* (N^1-(6-methoxypyrimidin-4-yl)sulfanilamide; DS-36; ICI-32525).
Sulfamonomethyldiazine *see* Sulfamerazine.
SULFAMOPRINE* (N^1-(4,6-dimethoxypyrimidin-2-yl)sulfanilamide; sulfadimethoxypyrimidine).
SULFAMOXOLE* (N^1-(4,5-dimethyloxazol-2-yl)sulfanilamide; sulfadimethyloxazole).
See also Co-trifamole.
(*p*-Sulfamoylanilino)methanesulfonic acid *see* Mesulfamide.
***p*-Sulfamoylbenzoic acid** *see* Carzenide.
***p*-Sulfamoylbenzylamine** *see* Mafenide.
***p*-Sulfamoylcarbanilic acid 2-hydroxyethyl ester** *see* Sulocarbilate.
SULFAMOYLDAPSONE (4,4'-diamino-2-sulfamoyldiphenyl sulfone; 2-sulfamoyldiaminodiphenyl sulfone; SDDS).
2-Sulfamoyldiaminodiphenyl sulfone *see* Sulfamoyldapsone.
5-(*p*-Sulfamoylphenylazo)salicylic acid *see* Salazosulfamide.
***N*-(*p*-Sulfamoylphenyl)-1,4-butane sultam** *see* Sultiame.
4'-Sulfamoylsuccinanilic acid *see* Sulfasuccinamide.
'Sulfamylon' *see* Mafenide.
Sulfamyxin *see* Sulfomyxin.
Sulfan blue* *see* Isosulfan blue.
SULFANILAMIDE* (*p*-aminobenzenesulfonamide; sulfaminum; PABS; F-1162).
SULFANILAMIDE SULFOSALICYLATE (sulfanilamide N^4-(5-sulfosalicylate); 'amindan').
Sulfanilanilide *see* Sulfabenz.
Sulfanilcyanamide *see* Sulcymide.

SULFANILIC ACID (*p*-aminobenzenesulfonic acid).
See also Zinc sulfanilate.
***N*-Sulfanilylacetamide** *see* Sulfacetamide.
3-Sulfanilyl-3-azabicyclo[3.2.2]nonane *see* Azabon.
***N*-Sulfanilylbenzamide** *see* Sulfabenzamide.
***N*-(6-Sulfanilylmetanilyl)acetamide** *see* Sulfadiasulfone sodium.
***N*-(*p*-Sulfanilylphenyl)glycine** *see* Acediasulfone sodium.
(*p*-Sulfanilylphenyl)urea *see* Amidapsone.
***N*-Sulfanilylstearamide** *see* Stearylsulfamide.
4'-Sulfanilylsuccinanilic acid *see* Succisulfone.
1-Sulfanilyl-2-thiourea *see* Sulfathiourea.
Sulfanilylurea *see* Sulfacarbamide.
SULFANITRAN* (N^1-acetyl-N^1-(*p*-nitrophenyl)sulfanilamide; 4-[(*p*-nitrophenyl)sulfamoyl]-acetanilide; NSC-77120; 'unistat').
See also under Aklomide.
SULFAPERIN* (N^1-(5-methylpyrimidin-2-yl)-sulfanilamide; 5-methylsulfadiazine; sulfa-5-methyldiazine; BT-325).
See also under Trimethoprim.
'Sulfa-perlongit' *see* Sulfaethidole.
SULFAPHENAZOLE* (N^1-(2-phenylpyrazol-3-yl)sulfanilamide; phenylsulfapyrazole; sulfaphenylpyrazole; P-17922).
Sulfaphenylpyrazole *see* Sulfaphenazole.
SULFAPROXYLINE* (N^1-(4-isopropoxybenzoyl)sulfanilamide; G-13289).
'Sulfapyelon' *see* Sulfamethizole.
SULFAPYRAZINE (N^1-pyrazin-2-ylsulfanilamide; sulfapyrazine sodium).
Sulfapyrazinmetoxin *see* Sulfalene.
SULFAPYRAZOLE* (N^1-(3-methyl-1-phenyl-pyrazol-5-yl)sulfanilamide; N^1-(5-methyl-2-phenylpyrazol-3-yl)sulfanilamide; sulfazamet; sulfamethylphenylpyrazole; Ba-18605).
SULFAPYRIDINE* (N^1-pyrid-2-ylsulfanilamide; sulfidine; M & B-693).
Sulfapyrimidine *see* Sulfadiazine.
SULFAQUINOXALINE* (N^1-quinoxalin-2-yl-sulfanilamide; 'embazin'; 'sulquin').
'Sulfarlem' *see* Anethole trithione.
'Sulfarsan' *see* Sulfarsphenamine.
Sulfarsenobenzene *see* Sulfarsphenamine.
'Sulfarsenol' *see* Sulfarsphenamine.
SULFARSPHENAMINE* (3,3'-bis(sulfomethylamino)-*p*-arsenophenol disodium salt; myarsenol; myoarsenobenzene; sulfarsenobenzene; thioarsphenamine).
Sulfasalazine* *see* Salazosulfapyridine.
SULFASOLUCIN* (disodium salt of N^4-(1,3-disulfo-3-phenylpropyl)sulfanilamide; sulfasolutin; RP 40).
Sulfasolutin *see* Sulfasolucin.
SULFASOMIDINE* (N^1-(2,6-dimethylpyrimid-4-yl)sulfanilamide; sulfisomidine; sulfadimetine; sulfaisodimerazine; sulfaisodimidine; L-30).
SULFASOMIZOLE* (N^1-(3-methylisothiazol-2-yl)sulfanilamide; E-438; NSC-139593; Th-2132).
SULFASUCCINAMIDE* (N^4-succinylsulfanil-

amide; 4'-sulfamoylsuccinanilic acid).

SULFASYMAZINE*** (N^1-(4,6-diethyl-*s*-triazin-2-yl)sulfanilamide).

Sulfated glyptide *see* Sulglicotide.

Sulfatertiobutylthiadiazole *see* Glybuthiazol.

SULFATHIADIAZOLE (N^1-(1,3,4-thiadiazol-2-yl)sulfanilamide).

SULFATHIAZOLE*** (N^1-thiazol-2-ylsulfanilamide; norsulfazole; M & B-760; RP 2090).

SULFATHIAZOLE ALUMINIUM (M-640; 'lysothiazole').

Sulfathiocarbamide* *see* Sulfathiourea.

Sulfathiodiazole *see* Sulfamethizole.

SULFATHIOUREA*** (N^1-thiocarbamylsulfanilamide; 1-sulfanilyl-2-thiourea; sulfathiocarbamide; RP 2255).
See also Sulfatolamide.

Sulfation factor *see* Somatomedin.

SULFATOLAMIDE*** (1-sulfanilyl-2-thiourea derivative of α-amino-*p*-toluenesulfonamide; mafenide sulfathiourea salt).

SULFATROXAZOLE*** (N^1-(4,5-dimethylisoxazol-3-yl)sulfanilamide).

SULFATROZOLE*** (N^1-(4-ethoxy-1,2,5-thiadiazol-3-yl)sulfanilamide).

'Sulfatyl' *see* Sulfaclozine.

Sulfaurea* *see* Sulfacarbamide.

'Sulfa-urolong' *see under* Nitrofurantoin.

'Sulfa-vet' *see* Sulfabenz.

Sulfazamet* *see* Sulfapyrazole.

'Sulfazin' *see* Sulfafurazole.

Sulfazine (tr) *see* Sulfadiazine.

'Sulfazole' *see* Sulfamethylthiazole.

Sulfbenzamine *see* Mafenide.

Sulfentanyl *see* Sufentanil.

'Sulfenthal' *see* Phenolsulfonphthalein.

SULFESTOL ('teepol').

'Sulfetrone' *see* Solasulfone.

Sulfidine (tr) *see* Sulfapyridine.

'Sulfile' *see* Timonacic arginine.

SULFINALOL** (4-hydroxy-α-[[[3-(*p*-methoxyphenyl)-1-methylpropyl]amino]methyl]-3-(methylsulfinyl)benzyl alcohol; sulfinalol hydrochloride; WIN-40808-7).

SULFINPYRAZONE*** (1,2-diphenyl-4-(2-phenylsulfinylethyl)-3,5-pyrazolidinedione; sulfoxyphenylpyrazolidine; G-28315).

2,2'-Sulfinylbis[4,6-dichlorophenol] *see* Bithionoloxide.

SULFIODIZOLE* (N^1-(4-iodo-3-methylisoxazol-3-yl)sulfanilamide; 3-iodosulfamethoxole).

SULFIRAM*** (bis(diethylthiocarbamyl) sulfide; monosulfiram; tetraethylthiuram monosulfide; 'sanigal'; 'tetmosol').

'Sulfirgamide' *see* Sulfadicramide.

Sulfisomezole *see* Sulfamethoxazole.

Sulfisomidine*** *see* Sulfasomidine.

Sulfisoxazole* *see* Sulfafurazole.

3-Sulfoalanine *see* Cysteic acid.

[α-(Sulfoamino)benzyl]penicillin *see* Suncillin.

o-**SULFOBENZHEPARIDE** (*N*-desulfo-*N*-(2-sulfobenzoyl)heparin).

3-(*o*-Sulfobenzoylimido)-2-piperidinone *see* Supi-

dimide.

N^1-(*m*-**Sulfobenzylideneisoniazid)** *see* Sulfoniazid.

α-**Sulfobenzylpenicillin** *see* Sulbenicillin.

SULFOBROMPHTHALEIN* (3,4,5,6-tetrabromo-3,3-bis(4-hydroxy-3-sulfophenyl)phthalide; tetrabromophenolphthalein disodium sulfonate; bromosulfonphthalein; bromphthalein; bromsulfophthalein; BSP).

Sulfocillin *see* Sulbenicillin.

Sulfocyanic acid *see* Thiocyanic acid.

Sulfodiamine (tr) *see* Acedapsone.

p,*p*'-**Sulfodianiline** *see* Dapsone.

Sulfodimezine (tr) *see* Sulfadimidine.

N-(2-**Sulfoethyl)-L-glutamine** *see* Glutaurine.

SULFOGAIACOL*** (potassium 4-hydroxy-3-methoxyphenyl sulfonate; potassium guaiacol sulfonate; thiocol).
See also under Butetamate.

'Sulfogal' *see* Anethole trithione.

Sulfoglycopeptide *see* Sulglicotide.

SULFOLANE (tetrahydrothiophene 1:1-dioxide; thiophan sulfone).

'Sulfo-merthiolate' *see* Sodium timerfonate.

N^2-**Sulfomethylisoniazid** *see* Methaniazide.

SULFOMYXIN*** (pentakis(*N*-sulfomethyl)polymyxin B; sulfamyxin; sulfomyxin sodium; GS-6742).

'Sulfonazine-SN' *see* Solasulfone.

p-**Sulfondichloramidobenzoic acid** *see* Halazone.

Sulfone *N*-acetate *see* Acetyldapsone.

Sulfone-mere *see* Dapsone.

'Sulfonet' *see* Sulfathiazole.

SULFONIAZID* (isonicotinoylhydrazone of benzaldehyde-*m*-sulfonic acid; N^1-(*m*-sulfobenzylideneisoniazid); G-605).

'Sulfonphthal' *see* Phenolsulfonphthalein.

SULFONTEROL** (α-[(*tert*-butylamino)methyl]-4-hydroxy-3-(methylsulfonylmethyl)benzyl alcohol; SK&F-53705A).

4',4'''-Sulfonylbis(acetanilide) *see* Acedapsone.

4',4''-Sulfonylbis(cyclopentanetridecananilide) *see* Chaulmosulfone.

3,3'-[Sulfonylbis(ethylenecarbonylimino)]bis[5-(*N*-ethylacetamido)-2,4,6-triiodobenzoic acid] *see* Iosulamide.

3,3'-[Sulfonylbis[(1-oxo-3,1-propanediyl)imino]-]bis[5-(acetyl ethylamino)-2,4,6-triiodobenzoic acid *see* Iosulamide.

6,6'-[Sulfonylbis(*p*-phenyleneazo)]dithymol *see* Diathymosulfone.

p,*p*'-**Sulfonyldiacetanilide** *see* Acedapsone.

1-*p*-Sulfophenylazo-2-naphthol-6-sulfonic acid disodium salt *see* Sunset yellow FCF.

8-(3-Sulfopropyl)atropinium hydroxide inner salt *see* Sultroponium.

SULFORIDAZINE*** (10-[2-(1-methylpiperid-2-yl)ethyl]-2-methylsulfonylphenothiazine; thioridazine dioxide; TPN-12).

Sulformethoxine* *see* Sulfadoxine.

Sulformetoxine *see* Sulfadoxine.

Sulforthodimethoxine *see* Sulfadoxine.

Sulforthomidine *see* Sulfadoxine.

SULFOSALICYLIC ACID (3-carboxy-4-

hydroxybenzenesulfonic acid; 5-sulfosalicylic acid; salicylsulfonic acid).

See also Samarium sulfosalicylate; Sodium sulfosalicylate; Sulfanilamide sulfosalicylate.

Sulfosuccinic acid bis(2-ethylhexyl)ester sodium salt *see* Docusate sodium.

SULFOTEP* (tetraethyl dithiopyrophosphate; tetraethyl thiodiphosphate; dithio; dithion; dithione; dithiophos; dithio-TEPP; sulfotepp; TEDTP; 'bladafum'; 'bladan 393').

Sulfotepp *see* Sulfotep.

'Sulfothiorine' *see* Sodium thiosulfate.

'Sulfotrim' *see* Co-trimoxazole.

SULFOXIDE (1,2-methylenedioxy-4-[2-(octylsulfinyl)propyl]benzene; 5-[2-(octylsulfinyl)propyl]-1,3-benzodioxole).

'Sulfoxol' *see* Sulfafurazole.

Sulfoxone *see* Aldesulfone sodium.

Sulfoxyphenylpyrazolidine *see* Sulfinpyrazone.

'Sulfralem' *see* Anethole trithione.

'Sulfune' *see* Sulfamoxole.

'Sulfuno' *see* Sulfamoxole.

Sulfuric oxyfluoride *see* Sulfuryl fluoride.

Sulfur mustard *see* Mustard gas.

SULFURYL FLUORIDE (sulfuric oxyfluoride; 'vikane').

Sulgin (tr) *see* Sulfaguanidine.

SULGLICOTIDE** (sulfuric polyester of a glycopeptide from pig duodenum; sulglycotide; glyptide sulfate; sulfated glyptide; sulfoglycopeptide; GLPS; 'gliptide').

Sulglycotide* *see* Sulglicotide.

Sulimarin *see* Sulmarin.

SULINDAC** ((*Z*)-5-fluoro-2-methyl-1-[*p*-(methylsulfinyl)benzylidene]indene-3-acetic acid; MK 231; MSD-943; 'arthrocine'; 'clinoril'; 'imbaral').

SULISATIN** (3,3-bis(*p*-hydroxyphenyl)-7-methyl-2-indolinone bis(hydrogen sulfate)).

SULISOBENZONE*** (5-benzoyl-4-hydroxy-2-methoxybenzenesulfonic acid; BSA; NSC-60584).

'Sulla' *see* Sulfametoxydiazine.

SULMARIN** (6,7-dihydroxy-4-methylcoumarin bis(hydrogen sulfate); sulimarin).

SULMAZOLE** (2-[2-methoxy-4-(methylsulfinyl)phenyl]-3*H*-imidazo[4,5-*b*]pyridine; AR-L 115-BS; 'vardax').

SULMEPRIDE*** (2-methoxy-*N*-[(1-methylpyrrolidin-2-yl)methyl]-5-sulfamoylbenzamide; *N*-[(1-methyl-2-pyrrolidinyl)methyl]-5-sulfamoyl-*o*-anisamide).

'Sulmetine' *see* Magnesium sulfate.

Sulmetozine *see* Tritiozine.

'Sulmycin' *see* Gentamicin.

SULNIDAZOLE*** (*O*-methyl 2-[(2-ethyl-5-nitroimidazol-1-yl)ethyl]carbamothioate; R-26412).

SULOCARBILATE*** (2-hydroxyethyl ester of *p*-sulfamoylcarbanilic acid; *N*⁴-(carbo-2-hydroxyethoxy)sulfanilamide; W-1548-1).

SULOCTIDIL** (*p*-(isopropylthio)-α-(1-octamylaminoethyl)benzyl alcohol; β-hydroxy-*p*-(isopropylthio)-α-methyl-*N*-octylphenethyl-

amine; 'fluversin'; 'sulocton').

'Sulocton' *see* Suloctidil.

SULODEXIDE*** (glucurono-2-amino-2-deoxyglucoglucan sulfate; glucuronylglucosaminoglycan sulfate; 'vessel').

SULOSEMIDE*** (2-(furfurylamino)-4-phenoxy-5-sulfamoylbenzenesulfonic acid).

SULOXIFEN** (*N*-(2-diethylaminoethyl)-*S*,*S*-diphenylsulfoximide).

SULOXIFEN OXALATE* (Go-1733; W-6439A).

Sulph.... *see* Sulf.....

Sul-phenytame *see* Sultiame.

SULPIRIDE*** (*N*-(1-ethylpyrrolidin-2-ylmethyl)-2-methoxy-5-sulfamoylbenzamide; *N*-(1-ethylpyrrolidin-2-ylmethyl)-5-sulfamoyl-*o*-anisamide; FK-880).

'Sulprim' *see* Co-trimoxazole.

SULPROSAL** (salicylic acid ester with 3-hydroxy-1-propanesulfonic acid).

SULPROSTONE*** ((*Z*)-7-[(1*R*,2*R*,3*R*)-3-hydroxy-2-[(*E*)-(3*R*)-3-hydroxy-4-phenoxy-1-butenyl]-5-oxocyclopentyl]-*N*-(methylsulfonyl)-5-heptenamide; 16-phenoxy-17,18,19,20-tetranorprostaglandin E_2 methylsulfonamide; 16-phenoxy-ω-tetranordinoprostone methylsulfonamide; CP-34089; SHB-286; ZK-57671; 'nalador').

Sulpyrin *see* Dipyrone.

'Sulquin' *see* Sulfaquinoxaline.

'Sulredox' *see* Penicillamine.

'Sul-spansion' *see* Sulfaethidole.

'Sul-spantab' *see* Sulfaethidole.

SULTAMICILLIN*** ([2*S*-[2α(2*R**,5*S**),5α,6β(*S**)]]-[[(3,3-dimethyl-7-oxo-4-thia-1-azabicyclo[3.2.0]hept-2-yl)carbonyl]oxy]methyl 6-[(aminophenylacetyl)amino]-3,3-dimethyl-7-oxo-4-thia-1-azabicyclo[3.2.0]heptane-2-carboxylate *S*,*S*-dioxide; hydroxymethyl (2*S*,5*R*,6*R*)-6-[(*R*)-(2-amino-2-phenylacetamido)]-3,3-dimethyl-7-oxo-4-thia-1-azabicyclo-[3.2.0]heptane-2-carboxylate (2*S*,5*R*)-3,3-dimethyl-7-oxo-4-thia-1-azabicyclo[3.2.0]heptane-2-carboxylate (ester) *S*,*S*-dioxide; ampicillin ester with hydroxymethyl ester of penicillanic acid *S*,*S*-dioxide; hydroxymethyl 6-(α-aminophenylacetamido)penicillanate penicillanate (ester) *S*,*S*-dioxide; penicillanoyloxymethyl (6*R*)-6-[(D-2-phenylglycyl)amino]penicillanate *S*,*S*-dioxide; CP-49952).

'Sultanol' *see* Salbutamol.

Sulthiame* *see* Sultiame.

SULTIAME** (*p*-(tetrahydro-2*H*-1,2-thiazin-2-yl)benzenesulfonamide *S*,*S*-dioxide; *N*-(*p*-sulfamoylphenyl)-1,4-butane sultam; sulthiame; sulphenytame; Riker-594; RP 10284).

'Sultirene' *see* Sulfamethoxypyridazine.

SULTOPRIDE*** (*N*-(1-ethylpyrrolidin-2-ylmethyl)-5-(ethylsulfonyl)-2-methoxybenzamide; *N*-(1-ethylpyrrolidin-2-ylmethyl)-5-(ethylsulfonyl)-*o*-anisamide; L-1418; 'barnetil').

SULTOSILIC ACID*** (2,5-dihydroxybenzenesulfonic acid 5-*p*-toluenesulfonate).

SULTROPONIUM*** (8-(3-sulfopropyl)atropinium hydroxide inner salt; A-118).

SULVERAPRIDE*** (2,3-dimethoxy-*N*-[(1-methylpyrrolidin-2-yl)methyl]-5-(methylsulfamoyl)-benzamide; *N*-[(1-methylpyrrolidin-2-yl)methyl]-5-(methylsulfamoyl)-*o*-veratramide).

'**Sulzol**' *see* Sulfathiazole.

Sulzon (tr) *see* Subathizone.

SUM-3170 *see* Loxapine.

SUMETIZIDE** (6-chloro-3,4-dihydro-3-succinimidomethyl-2*H*-1,2,4-benzothiadiazine-7-sulfonamide 1,1-dioxide).

'**Sumetrolim**' *see* Co-trimoxazole.

'**Sumial**' *see* Propranolol.

'**Sumicidin**' *see* Fenvalerate.

'**Sumicombi**' *see under* Fenitrothion.

'**Sumifive**' *see* Fenvalerate.

'**Sumioxon**' *see* Fenitrooxon.

'**Sumithion**' *see* Fenitrothion.

'**Sumitox**' *see* Malathion.

'**Summetrin**' *see* Papain.

'**Summopenil**' *see under* Ampicillin.

'**Sumox**' *see* Amoxicillin.

'**Sumycin**' *see* Tetracycline phosphate complex.

SUNCILLIN*** (6-[2-phenyl-D-(sulfoamino)acetamido]penicillanic acid; 6-[(phenylsulfaminoacetyl)amino]penicillanic acid; [α-(sulfoamino)-benzyl]penicillin; B-14030; BL-P1462).

'**Sundare**' *see* Cinoxate.

'**Sungard**' *see* Sulisobenzone.

'**Sun-nitt**' *see* Bis(tributyltin) oxide.

'**Sunoxol**' *see* 8-Quinolinol sulfate.

SUNSET YELLOW FCF (1-*p*-sulfophenylazo-2-naphthol-6-sulfonic acid disodium salt; FD&C 6).

'**Supacox**' *see* Amprolium.

'**Supanate**' *see* Flopropione.

'**Supavan**' *see* Alverine.

'**Superinone**' *see* Tyloxapol.

'**Superlutin**' *see* MDAP.

'**Superol**' *see* 8-Quinolinol sulfate.

Superoxide dismutase *see* Orgotein.

'**Superoxol**' *see* Hydrogen peroxide.

Superpalite *see* Diphosgene.

SUPIDIMIDE*** (2-(2-oxopiperid-3-yl)-1,2-benzisothiazolin-3-one 1,1-dioxide; 3-(*o*-sulfobenzoylimido)-2-piperidinone; CG-3033).

'**Suplexedil**' *see* Fenoxedil.

'**Supona**' *see* Clofenvinfos.

'**Supotran**' *see* Chlormezanone.

'**Suppangin**' *see* Bismuth valproate.

'**Supponeryl**' *see* Butethal.

'**Supracen violet**' *see* Solway purple.

'**Supracid**' *see* Methidathion.

'**Supral**' *see* Pecilocin.

'**Supramid**' *see* Sulfametoxydiazine.

'**Suprifen**' *see* *p*-Hydroxyephedrine.

'**Suprifen-Psb**' *see* Buphenine.

'**Suprilent**' *see* Isoxsuprine.

'**Suprimal**' *see* Dimenhydrinate *and* Meclozine.

'**Supristol**' *see* Co-trifamole.

SUPROCLONE*** (4-propionyl-1-piperazinecarboxylic acid ester with (±)-6-(7-chloro-1,8-naphthyridin-2-yl)-2,3,6,7-tetrahydro-7-hydroxy-5*H*-*p*-dithiino[2,3-*c*]pyrrol-5-one).

SUPROFEN*** (*p*-2-thenoylhydratropic acid; 2-(*p*-2-thenoylphenyl)propionic acid; α-methyl-4-(2-thienylcarbonyl)benzeneacetic acid; sutoprofen; R-25061; 'suprol').

'**Suprol**' *see* Suprofen.

'**Supronal**' *see under* Sulfamerazine.

'**Suractin**' *see* Ampicillin.

'**Suralgon**' *see* Fenproporex.

Suramin *see* Suramin sodium.

SURAMIN PENTAMIDINE SALT (RP 4891).

SURAMIN SODIUM*** (hexasodium salt of 8,8'-[ureylenebis[*m*-phenylenecarbonylimino(4-methyl-*m*-phenylene)carbonylimino]]-di(1,3,5-naphthalenetrisulfonic acid); hexasodium salt of symmetrical urea deriv. of 8-[3-(*m*-aminobenzoyl)amino]-*p*-methylbenzoylamino-1,3,5-naphthalenetrisulfonic acid; suramin; Bayer-205; F-309).

'**Surcopur**' *see* Propanil.

'**Surecide**' *see* Cyanofenphos.

'**Surem**' *see* Nitrazepam.

'**Sureptil**' *see under* Cinnarizine.

'**Surestryl**' *see* Moxestrol.

'**Surexin**' *see* Pyrinoline.

'**Surfacaine**' *see* Cyclomethycaine.

'**Surfak**' *see* Docusate calcium.

'**Surfathesin**' *see* Cyclomethycaine.

'**Surfen**' *see* Aminoquinuride.

SURFOMER*** (poly(1,2-dicarboxy-3-hexadecyltetramethylene); AOMA).

'**Surgam**' *see* Tiaprofenic acid.

'**Surgestone**' *see* Promegestone.

'**Surgex**' *see* Nialamide.

'**Surgicel**' *see* Oxidized regenerated cellulose.

'**Surgi-cen**' *see* Hexachlorophene.

'**Surheme**' *see* Butalamine.

SURICLONE*** (4-methyl-1-piperazinecarboxylic acid ester with (±)-6-(7-chloro-1,8-naphthyridin-2-yl)-2,3,6,7-tetrahydro-7-hydroxy-5*H*-*p*-dithiino[2,3-*c*]pyrrol-5-one; RP-31264).

'**Surital**' *see* Thiamylal.

'**Surmontil**' *see* Trimipramine.

'**Surofene**' *see* Hexachlorophene.

Surpalite *see* Diphosgene.

'**Surplix**' *see* Imipramine.

'**Surrectan**' *see* AET.

'**Sursum**' *see* Iproclozide.

'**Survector**' *see* Amineptine.

'**Susadrin**' *see* Glyceryl trinitrate.

'**Sutan**' *see* Butylate.

SUTILAINS*** (proteolytic enzymes from *Bac. subtilis*; BAX-1515; 'travase').

Sutoprofen* *see* Suprofen.

'**Suversin**' *see* Mecamylamine.

'**Suvipen**' *see* Metampicillin.

'**Suvren**' *see* Captodiame.

SUXAMETHONIUM CHLORIDE** ((2-hydroxyethyl)trimethylammonium chloride succinate 2,2'-succinyldioxybis(ethylenetrimethylammonium chloride); diacetylcholine; ditilin; succicurarium; succinylcholine; succinyldicholine; IS 370; LT-1; M & B-2207).

SUXEMERID*** (bis(1,2,2,6,6-pentamethylpiperid-4-yl) succinate; suxemerid sulfate; W-2180).

SUXETHONIUM CHLORIDE*** (ethyl(2-hydroxyethyl)dimethylammonium chloride succinate; 2,2′-succinyldioxybis(ethylenedimethylethylammonium chloride); IS-362; M-115; M & B-2210).

SUXIBUZONE*** (4-butyl-4-(hydroxymethyl)-1,2-diphenyl-3,5-pyrazolidinedione hydrogen succinate; 'calibene'; 'flamilon'; 'solurol').

'**Suxilep**' *see* Ethosuximide.

'**Suxinutin**' *see* Ethosuximide.

'**Suxiphen**' *see* Sodium benzyl succinate.

SV-108 *see* Diflunisal.

SW-5063 *see* Racefenicol.

Sweet birch oil *see* Methyl salicylate.

SWEP* (methyl 3,4-dichlorocarbanilate).

Swiss blue *see* Methylene blue.

'**Sycotrol**' *see* Pipethanate.

SYD-230 *see* Clioxanide.

SYDNOCARB (tr) (3-(1-methyl-2-phenylethyl)-1-(*N*-phenylcarbamoylimino)sydnone; 3-(2-phenylisopropyl)-*N*-(phenylcarbamino)sydnone imine; sidnocarb).

SYDNOFEN (tr) (3-(2-phenylisopropyl)sydnone imine; sydnophen).

Sydnofen *N*-phenylcarbamoyl derivative *see* Sydnocarb.

Sydnophen (tr) *see* Sydnofen.

'**Sylnasol**' *see* Sodium psylliate.

'**Symasul**' *see* Sulfasymazine.

Symazin *see* Simazine.

SYMCLOSENE*** (trichloro-*s*-triazine-2,4,6-(1*H*,3*H*,5*H*)-trione; trichloroisocyanuric acid; ACL-85; NSC-405124).

'**Symcortol**' *see* Oxedrine.

SYMETINE** (4,4′-ethylenedioxybis(*N*-hexyl-*N*-methylbenzylamine); symetine hydrochloride).

'**Symmetrel**' *see* Amantadine.

'**Symoron**' *see* Methadone.

Sympathin *see* Norepinephrine.

'**Sympathol**' *see* Oxedrine.

Sympatholytin (tr) *see* Dibenamine.

'**Sympathomim**' *see* Phenylephrine.

'**Sympatol**' *see* Oxedrine.

Sympectothion *see* Thioneine.

'**Sympocaine**' *see* Ambucaine.

'**Symprocaine**' *see* Procaine.

'**Synacthar**' *see* Tetracosactide.

'**Synacthen**' *see* Tetracosactide.

'**Synacthen-depot**' *see* Tetracosactide zinc phosphate complex.

'**Synadrin**' *see* Prenylamine.

'**Synalar**' *see* Fluocinolone acetonide.

'**Synandone**' *see* Fluocinolone acetonide.

'**Synanthin**' *see* Inulin.

'**Synapause**' *see* Estriol succinate.

'**Synaplege**' *see* Pempidine.

'**Synasteron**' *see* Oxymetholone.

'**Synaxsyn**' *see* Naproxen.

'**Syncarpine**' *see* Pilocarpine.

'**Synchrocept**' *see* Prostalene.

'**Syncillin**' *see* Azidocillin *and* Pheneticillin.

'**Syncl**' *see* Cefalexin.

'**Syncortyl**' *see* Desoxycortone.

'**Syncro-mate**' *see* Flugestone acetate.

'**Synedil**' *see* Sulpiride.

'**Synemol**' *see* Fluocinolone acetonide.

Synephrine* *see* Oxedrine.

m-**Synephrine** *see* Phenylephrine.

'**Syneptine**' *see* Kitasamycin.

'**Synergomycin**' *see under* Erythromycin.

Synestrol (tr) *see* Hexestrol.

'**Synflex**' *see* Naproxen.

'**Synhexyl**' *see* Pyrahexyl.

'**Synkavit**' *see* Menadiol sodium phosphate.

'**Synkonin**' *see* Hydrocodone.

'**Synmiol**' *see* Idoxuridine.

Synnematin B *see* Adicillin.

Synstigmine *see* Neostigmine bromide.

'**Syntaris**' *see* Flunisolide.

'**Syntarpen 201**' *see* Cloxacillin.

'**Syntes-12A**' *see* Tetrasodium edetate.

'**Syntestan**' *see* Cloprednol.

'**Syntetrin**' *see* Rolitetracycline.

'**Syntexan**' *see* Dimethyl sulfoxide.

'**Synthenate**' *see* Oxedrine.

'**Synthepen**' *see* Propicillin.

Synthetic secretin *see* Secretin.

'**Synthila**' *see* Dianisylhexene.

Synthomycin (tr) *see* DL-chloramphenicol.

'**Synthrin**' *see* Resmethrin.

'**Synthroid**' *see* Levothyroxine sodium.

'**Synticillin**' *see* Meticillin.

'**Syntocinon**' *see* Oxytocin synthetic.

'**Syntomen**' *see* Ethambutol.

'**Syntometrin**' *see under* Methylergometrine.

'**Syntopressin**' *see* Lypressin.

'**Syntropan**' *see* Amprotropine.

'**Syracort**' *see* Fluocortolone.

'**Syraprim**' *see* Trimethoprim.

SYRINGIC ACID (4-hydroxy-3,5-dimethoxybenzoic acid).

SYROSINGOPINE*** (ester of syrigic acid ethyl carbonate with methyl reserpate; 18-[4-(ethoxycarbonyl)-3,5-dimethoxybenzoyl]reserpic acid methyl ester; Su-3118).

'**Sysmeton**' *see* Thiometon.

'**Systogene**' *see* Tyramine.

'**Systox**' *see under* Demeton-O.

'**Systral**' *see* Chlorphenoxamine.

'**Sytam**' *see* Schradan.

'**Sytron**' *see* Sodium feredetate.

T

2,4,5-T *see* 2,4,5-Trichlorophenoxyacetic acid.
T-3 *see* Liothyronine.
T-4 *see* Thyroxine.
T-47 *see* Parathion.
T-72 *see* Nitroguanil.
T-113 *see* Butonate.
T-712 *see* Amfepramone.
T-1220 *see* Piperacillin.
T-1551 *see* Cefoperazone.
T-1824 *see* Evans blue.
TA-306 *see* Myfadol.
'Tabalgin' *see* Paracetamol.
'Tabard' *see* Diethyltoluamide.
'Tabe' *see* Pirenzepine.
'Tabotamp' *see* Oxidized regenerated cellulose.
TABUN (dimethylamido ethoxy phosphoryl cyanide; ethyl dimethylphosphoramidocyanidate).
'Tabutrex' *see* Dibutyl succinate.
'Tacaryl' *see* Methdilazine.
'Tacazyl' *see* Methdilazine.
'Tace' *see* Chlorotrianisene.
'Tachmalcor' *see* Detajmium bitartrate.
'Tachmalin' *see* Ajmaline.
'Tacholiquin' *see* Tyloxapol.
'Tachydrol' *see* Dihydrotachysterol.
'Tachystin' *see* Dihydrotachysterol.
'Tachystol' *see* Dihydrotachysterol.
'Tacitin' *see* Benzoctamine.
TACLAMINE*** (2,3,4,4a,8,9,13b,14-octahydro-1*H*-benzo[6,7]cyclohepta[1,2,3-*de*]pyrido[2,1-*a*]-isoquinoline; taclamine hydrochloride; AY-22214).
TACRINE*** (9-amino-1,2,3,4-tetrahydroacridine; hydroaminacridine; hydroaminacrine; tetrahydroaminacrin; tacrine hydrochloride; THA).
'Tadip' *see under* Guanacline.
'Tagamet' *see* Cimetidine.
TAGLUTIMIDE*** (*N*-(2,6-dioxopiperid-3-yl)-2,3-norbornanedicarboximide; 3-(*N*-norbornane-2,3-dicarboximido)glutarimide; K-2004).
TAI-284 *see* Clidanac.
'Taketron' *see* Prosultiamine.
'Taktic' *see* Amitraz.
'Takus' *see* Ceruletide.
TALAMPICILLIN** ((D(−)-6-(2-amino-2-phenylacetamido)penicillanic acid ester with 3-hydroxyphthalide; 1,3-dihydro-3-oxo-1-isobenzofuranyl [2*S*-[2α,5α,6β(*S*)]]-6-[(aminophenylacetyl)amino]penicillanate; phthalidyl 6-(D(−)-α-aminophenylacetamido)penicillinate; ampicillin phthalidyl ester; phthalidylampicillin; talampicillin hydrochloride; BRL-8988; CP-271B).
'Talanton' *see* Carbutamide.
TALASTINE*** (4-benzyl-2-(2-dimethylamino-ethyl)-1(2*H*)-phthalazinone).
'Talatrol' *see* Trometamol.
Talbumal* *see* Talbutal.
TALBUTAL*** (5-allyl-5-(1-methylpropyl)barbituric acid; 5-allyl-5-*sec*-butylbarbituric acid; talbumal).
'Talcit' *see* Hydrotalcite.
'Talcord' *see* Thiocarboxim.
TALERANOL*** ((3*S*,7*S*)-3,4,5,6,7,8,9,10,11,12-decahydro-7,14,16-trihydroxy-3-methyl-1*H*-2-benzoxacyclotetradecin-1-one; P-1560).
'Talesco' *see* Secobarbital.
'Talidan' *see* Tralonide.
'Talin' *see* Thaumatin.
TALINOLOL*** ((±)-1-[*p*-(3-*tert*-butylamino-2-hydroxypropoxy)phenyl]-3-cyclohexylurea; (±)-1-*tert*-butylamino-3-[*p*-(3-cyclohexylureido)-phenoxy]-2-propanol; 'cordanum').
TALISOMYCIN*** (*N*¹-[4-amino-5-[[3-[(4-aminobutyl)amino]propyl]carbamoyl]pentyl]-13-[(4-amino-4,6-dideoxy-α-L-talopyranosyl)oxy]-19-demethyl-12-hydroxybleomycinamide; antibiotic from *Streptoalloteichus hindustanus*; tallysomycin A; BU-2231A).
'Talisulfazol' *see* Phthalylsulfathiazole.
Tallysomycin A *see* Talisomycin.
TALMETACIN*** ((±)-1-(*p*-chlorobenzoyl)-5-methoxy-2-methylindole-3-acetic acid ester with 3-hydroxyphthalide; 3-hydroxyphthalide indometacin ester).
TALMETOPRIM*** (*N*-[4-amino-5-(3,4,5-trimethoxybenzyl)pyrimidin-2-yl]phthalimide).
TALNIFLUMATE*** (1,3-dihydro-3-oxo-1-isobenzofuranyl 2-[[3-(trifluoromethyl)phenyl]-amino]-3-pyridinecarboxylate; phthalidyl 2-(α,α,α-trifluoro-*m*-toluidino)nicotinate; phthalidyl niflumate; BA-7602-06).
'Talofen' *see* Promazine.
TALOPRAM*** (3,3-dimethyl-1-(3-methylamino-propyl)-1-phenylphthalan; *N*,3,3-trimethyl-1-phenyl-1-phthalanpropylamine; AY-21554; Lu-3-010).
TALOSALATE*** (phthalidyl salicylate acetate; ester of acetylsalicylic acid with 3-hydroxy-phthalide; BA-7604-02).
TALOXIMINE*** (4-[2-(dimethylamino)ethoxy]-1(2*H*)-phthalazinone oxime).
'Talpen' *see* Talampicillin.

'Talsis' *see* Bisoxatin diacetate.

TALSUPRAM*** (1,3-dihydro-*N*,3,3-trimethyl-1-phenylbenzo[*c*]thiophene-1-propylamine; 1-(3-aminopropyl)-1,3-dihydro-*N*,3,3-trimethyl-1-phenylbenzo[*c*]thiophene; 3,3-dimethyl-1-(3-methylaminopropyl)-1-phenylthiophthalan; Lu-5-003).

TALTIBRIDE** (2-chloro-*N*,*N*-dimethyl-5-[3-methyl-2-(phenylimino)-4-thiazolin-4-yl]benzenesulfonamide).

TALTRIMIDE*** (*N*-isopropyl-1,3-dioxo-2-isoindolineethanesulfonamide).

'Talucard' *see* Proscillaridin.

'Talusin' *see* Proscillaridin.

'Talwin' *see* Pentazocine.

TAM *see* Tosyl-L-arginine methyl ester.

'Tamaron' *see* Methamidophos.

'Tambocor' *see* Flecainide acetate.

TAME *see* Tosyl-L-arginine methyl ester.

TAMETICILLIN*** (2-(diethylamino)ethyl (2*S*,5*R*,6*R*)-6-(2,6-dimethoxybenzamido)penicillanate; meticillin 2-diethylaminoethyl ester; DAN-523).

TAMETRALINE*** ((1*R*,4*S*)-1,2,3,4-tetrahydro-*N*-methyl-4-phenyl-1-naphthylamine).

Tamidoline *see* Omidoline.

TAMITINOL*** (4-[(ethylamino)methyl]-2-methyl-5-[(methylthio)methyl]-3-pyridinol).

'Tamoplex' *see* Tamoxifen.

TAMOXIFEN*** (*trans*-1-[*p*-[2-(dimethylamino)-ethoxy]phenyl]-1,2-diphenylbut-1-ene; *trans*-α-[*p*-[2-(dimethylamino)ethoxy]phenyl]-α'-ethylstilbene; 2-[*p*-(1,2-diphenyl-1-butenyl)phenoxy]-*N*,*N*-dimethylethylamine; 'tamoplex').

TAMOXIFEN CITRATE* (ICI-46474; 'nolvadex').

'Tanacaine' *see* Quatacaine.

Tanaceton *see* Absinthol.

'Tanakan' *see* Chloroquine *and* Ginkgo biloba extract.

'Tandacote' *see* Oxyphenbutazone.

'Tandak' *see* Delmadinone.

TANDAMINE** (1-[2-(dimethylamino)ethyl]-9-ethyl-1,3,4,9-tetrahydro-1-methylthiopyrano[3,4-*b*]indole; 9-ethyl-1,3,4,9-tetrahydro-*N*,*N*,1-trimethylthiopyrano[3,4-*b*]indole-1-ethanamine; tandamine hydrochloride; AY-23946).

'Tanderil' *see* Oxyphenbutazone.

'Tandex' *see* Karbutilate.

'Tanganil' *see* Ethanolamine acetylleucinate.

TANGERETIN (4',5,6,7,8-pentamethoxyflavone).

'Tannalbin' *see* Albumin tannate.

Tannalbumin *see* Albumin tannate.

'Tannex' *see* Indometacin.

Tannic acid *see* Tannin(s).

TANNIN(S) (gallotannic acid; tannic acid).

'Tanone' *see* Phenthoate.

'Tantizon' *see* Isomethiozine.

'Tantum' *see* Benzydamine.

'Tantum biotic' *see under* Benzydamine.

'Tao' *see* Troleandomycin.

'Taoryl' *see* Caramiphen edisilate.

'Tapazole' *see* Thiamazole.

'Taractan' *see* Chlorprothixene.

'Tarasan' *see* Chlorprothixene.

'Tardamid' *see* Sulfamoxole.

'Tardocillin' *see* Benzathine penicillin.

'Tardokrein' *see* Kallidinogenase.

'Tardolyt' *see* Aristolochic acid.

'Tardomycocel' *see* Benzathine penicillin.

'Tarodyl' *see* Glycopyrronium bromide.

'Tarodyn' *see* Glycopyrronium bromide.

'Tarpane' *see* Clobenzepam.

'Tarquinor' *see* Halquinols.

Tartar emetic *see* Antimonyl potassium tartrate.

TARTARIC ACID (2,3-dihydroxysuccinic acid).

TARTRAZINE (chiefly the trisodium salt of 5-hydroxy-1-(*p*-sulfophenyl)-4-(*p*-sulfophenylazo)-pyrazole-3-carboxylic acid; hydrazine yellow).

TARTRONIC ACID (hydroxymalonic acid).

Tartronylurea *see* Dialuric acid.

'Tarugan' *see* Morazone.

'Task' *see* Dichlorvos.

'Taskel' *see* Malathion.

'Tasmaderm' *see* Motretinide.

'Tasnon' *see* Piperazine.

'Tasto' *see* Aloglutamol.

TAT-3 *see* Picoperine.

TATBA *see* Triamcinolone hexacetonide.

TATD *see* Octotiamine.

'Tathion' *see* Glutathione.

'Tauglicolcillin' *see* Ampicillin guaiacolsulfonate.

'Tauredon' *see* Sodium aurothiomalate.

TAURINE (2-aminoethanesulfonic acid).

TAUROCHOLIC ACID (cholic acid taurine conjugate; cholaic acid; cholyltaurine).

TAUROCYAMINE (guanidotaurine).

'Tauroflex' *see* Taurultam.

TAUROLIDINE*** (4,4'-methylenebis(tetrahydro-1,2,4-thiadiazine 1,1-dioxide); taurolin; 'drainasept').

Taurolin *see* Taurolidine.

TAUROMUSTINE** (1-(2-chloroethyl)-3-[2-(dimethylsulfamoyl)ethyl]-1-nitrosourea).

TAURULTAM*** (tetrahydro-1,2,4-thiadiazine 1,1-dioxide; 'tauroflex').

'Tavan' *see* Pentosan polysulfate.

'Tavegil' *see* Clemastine fumarate.

'Ta-verm' *see* Piperazine.

'Tavist' *see* Clemastine fumarate.

'Tavor' *see* Lorazepam.

TAXIFOLIN (3,3',4',5,7-pentahydroxyflavanone; 2,3-dihydroquercetin; distylin).

'Taxilan' *see* Perazine.

TAZASUBRATE** ((±)-α-[(6-ethoxybenzothiazol-2-yl)thio]hydratropic acid).

TAZEPROFEN** ((±)-α-methyl-2-phenyl-6-benzothiazoleacetic acid).

TAZIPRINONE*** ((±)-*N*-[(4*R**,4a*R**,9b*S**)-1,2,3,4,4a,9b-hexahydro-8,9b-dimethyl-3-oxo-4-dibenzofuranyl]-4-methyl-1-piperazinepropionamide; taziprinone dihydrochloride; taziprinone hydrochloride; RU-20201).

TAZOLOL** ((±)-2-[2-hydroxy-3-(isopropylamino)propoxy]thiazole; (±)-1-(isopropylamino)-3-thiazol-2-yloxy-2-propanol; RS-6245).

TbI/698 *see* Thioacetazone.
Tb III/1347 *see* Subathizone.
2,3,6-TBA* *see* Trichlorobenzoic acid.
TBF-43 *see* Acetiromate.
TBI *see* Triamcinolone benetonide.
TBP *see* Bithionol.
'T.B.T.O' *see* Bis(tributyltin) oxide.
TCAP *see* Cetrimonium pentachlorophenate.
'TCC' *see* Triclocarban.
TCDD *see* 2,3,7,8-Tetrachlorodibenzo-*p*-dioxin.
TCDS *see* Tetradifon.
TCNB *see* Tecnazene.
TCP *see* Tricresyl phosphate.
TDE *see* DDD.
o,p'-**TDE*** *see* Mitotane.
TDI *see* Toluene diisocyanate.
TE-114 *see* Tiemonium iodide.
TEA *see* Tetrylammonium bromide.
Teaberry oil *see* Methyl salicylate.
Tear gas *see* 2-Chloroacetophenone.
'Tebalon' *see* Thioacetazone.
'Tebamin' *see* Fenamisal.
'Tebanyl' *see* Fenamisal.
TEBATIZOLE*** (1-(4-*tert*-butyl-2-thiazolyl)-4-methylpiperazine).
'Tebeform' *see* Protionamide.
'Tebonin' *see* Ginkgo biloba extract.
'Tebrazid' *see* Pyrazinamide.
TEBROFEN (tr) (3,3',5,5'-tetrabromo-2,2',4,4'-tetrahydroxybiphenyl; tebrophen).
Tebrophen (tr) *see* Tebrofen.
TEBUQUINE*** (3-[(*tert*-butylamino)methyl]-4'-chloro-5-[(7-chloro-4-quinolyl)amino]-2-biphenylol; 4'-chloro-5-[(7-chloro-4-quinolyl)amino]-3-[[(1,1-dimethylethyl)amino]methyl][1,1'-biphenyl]-2-ol; CI-897; WR-228258).
TEBUTATE(S)** (*tert*-butylacetic acid esters and salts).
TEC *see* Triethyl(2-hydroxyethyl)ammonium chloride.
'Tecesal' *see* Calcium thiosulfate.
'Technescan MAA' *see* Macrosalb (^{99m}Tc).
Technetium (^{99m}Tc) labeled macroaggregated human serum albumin *see* Macrosalb (^{99m}Tc).
Technetium Tc 99m albumin aggregated* *see* Macrosalb (^{99m}Tc).
TECLOTHIAZIDE*** (6-chloro-3,4-dihydro-3-(trichloromethyl)-2*H*-1,2,4-benzothiadiazine-7-sulfonamide 1,1-dioxide; teclothiazide potassium).
TECLOZAN** (*N,N'*-(*p*-phenylenedimethylene)-bis[2,2-dichloro-*N*-(2-ethoxyethyl)acetamide]; NSC-107433; WIN-13146; WIN-AM-13146).
TECNAZENE* (1,2,4,5-tetrachloro-3-nitrobenzene; TCNB; 'folosan'; 'fumite TCNB'; 'fusarex').
'Tecodin' *see* Codeine methyl bromide.
Tecodin (tr) *see* Oxycodone.
'Tecquinol' *see* Hydroquinone.
'Tecto' *see* Tiabendazole.
TECTORIGENIN (4',5,7-trihydroxy-6-methoxy-isoflavone).
'Tedarol' *see* Triamcinolone diacetate.
'Tedegyl' *see* Thiodiglycol.

'Tedion' *see* Tetradifon.
'Tedralan' *see under* Theophylline.
TEDTP *see* Sulfotep.
'Teejel' *see under* Choline salicylate.
'Teepol' *see* Sulfestol.
TEF (tr) *see* Tepa.
TEFAZOLINE*** (5,6,7,8-tetrahydro-1-(2-imidazolin-2-ylmethyl)naphthalene; 2-(5,6,7,8-tetrahydronaphth-1-ylmethyl)-2-imidazoline; tenaphthoxaline; tefazoline nitrate; 'tenaphtho').
TEFENPERATE*** (2-(2,2,6,6-tetramethylpiperid-1-yl)ethyl *o*-chloro-α-(*o*-chlorobenzyl)-α-hydroxyhydrocinnamate acetate (ester)).
'Teflon' *see* Politef.
TEFLUDAZINE*** (*trans*-4-[3-(*p*-fluorophenyl)-6-(trifluoromethyl)-1-indanyl]-1-piperazineethanol).
TEFLURANE*** (2-bromo-1,1,1,2-tetrafluoroethane; tetraflurane; A-16900; Abbott 16900; DA-708).
TEFLUTIXOL*** (4-[3-[6-fluoro-2-(trifluoromethyl)thioxanthen-9-yl]propyl]-1-piperazineethanol; 6-fluoro-9-[3-[4-(2-hydroxyethyl)piperazin-1-yl]propyl]2-(trifluoromethyl)thioxanthene; Lu-10022).
'Tefose 63' *see* Pegoxol 7 stearate.
TEGAFUR*** (5-fluoro-1-(tetrahydro-2-furyl)-uracil; 5-fluoro-1-(2-furanidyl)uracil; 5-fluoro-1-(tetrahydro-2-furanyl)-2,4-(1*H,3H*)-pyrimidinedione; fluorafur; ftorafur; FT-207; MJF-12264; NSC-148958; 'futraful').
'Tego-betaine' *see* Pendecamaine.
'Tegopen' *see* Cloxacillin.
'Tego 103S' *see* Dodicin.
'Tegotin' *see* Vitamin T-complex.
'Tegretol' *see* Carbamazepine.
'Tegunor' *see under* Choline salicylate.
TEH *see* Heptaminol theophyllineacetate.
Teichman's crystals *see* Hemin.
Teichomycin A$_2$ *see* Teicoplanin.
TEICOPLANIN*** (antibiotic from *Actinoplanes teichomyceticus*; teichomycin A$_2$; A/8 327; DL-507-IT; L-12507; MDL-507).
Tekodin (tr) *see* Oxycodone.
TEL *see* Tetraethyllead.
'Telazol' *see under* Tiletamine.
'Teldane' *see* Terfenadine.
'Teldrin' *see* Chlorpheniramine.
'Telebrix' *see* Meglumine ioxitalamate.
'Telebrix 38' *see under* Meglumine ioxitalamate.
TELENZEPINE** (4,9-dihydro-3-methyl-4-[(4-methylpiperazin-1-yl)acetyl]-10*H*-thieno[3,4-*b*]-[1,5]benzodiazepin-10-one).
'Telepaque' *see* Iopanoic acid.
Telepathine *see* Harmine.
'Teletrast' *see* Iopanoic acid.
'Teletux' *see* Noscapine embonate.
Telicherry bark *see* Kurchi.
'Telmid' *see* Dithiazanine iodide.
'Telmin' *see* Mebendazole.
'Telodrin' *see* Isobenzan.
'Telodron' *see* Chlorpheniramine.
'Telon' *see* Benzpiperylone.

'**Telopar**' *see* Oxantel embonate.
'**Telvar**' *see* Monuron.
TEM *see* Tretamine.
'**Temagin**' *see* Acetylsalicylic acid.
'**Temanyl**' *see* Alimemazine.
'**Temaril**' *see* Alimemazine.
'**Temaryl**' *see* Alimemazine.
'**Temasept I**' *see under* Dibromsalan.
'**Temasept IV**' *see* Tribromsalan.
TEMAZEPAM*** (7-chloro-1,3-dihydro-3-hydr-oxy-1-methyl-5-phenyl-2*H*-1,4-benzodiazepin-2-one; methyloxazepam; A-102; ER-115; Wy-3917; 'euhypnos'; 'levanxol'; 'normison'; 'pla-num'; 'remestan').
Temazepam dimethylcarbamate *see* Camazepam.
Temechin (tr) *see* 2,2,6,6-Tetramethylquinuclidine methiodide.
TEMEFOS** (*O,O*'-thiodi(*p*-phenylene) *O,O,O',O*'-tetramethyl bis(phosphorothioate); *O,O,O',O*'-tetramethyl *O,O*'-(thiodi-4,1-phenyl-ene)phosphorothioate; temephos; OMS-736; 'abate'; 'abathion'; 'bithion').
Temephos* *see* Temefos.
Temequin (tr) *see* 2,2,6,6-Tetramethylquinuclidine methiodide.
'**Temesta**' *see* Lorazepam.
'**Temetex**' *see* Diflucortolone valerate.
'**Temetil**' *see* Prochlorperazine.
'**Temgesic**' *see* Buprenorphine.
'**Temick**' *see* Aldicarb.
'**Temik**' *see* Aldicarb.
'**Temina**' *see* Vitamin T-complex.
TEMOCILLIN*** (*N*-[(2*S*,5*R*,6*S*)-2-carboxy-6-methoxy-3,3-dimethyl-7-oxo-4-thia-1-azabi-cyclo[3.2.0]hept-2-yl]-3-thiophenemalonamic acid; 6-methoxy-6-(3-thiophenemalonamido)-penicillanic acid; 6-[2-carboxy-2-(3-thienyl)acet-amido]-6-methoxypenicillanic acid; temocillin sodium; BRL-17421).
TEMODOX** (2-hydroxyethyl 3-methylquinoxal-ine-2-carboxylate 2,4-dioxide; CP-22341).
'**Temparin**' *see* Dicoumarol.
'**Tempidon**' *see* 2,2,6,6-Tetramethylpiperid-4-one tosilate.
'**Temposil**' *see* Calcium carbimide citrate.
'**Tempra**' *see* Paracetamol.
'**Tenac**' *see* Dichlorvos.
'**Tenaphtho**' *see* Tefazoline.
Tenaphthoxaline *see* Tefazoline.
'**Tenavoid**' *see under* Bendroflumethiazide.
'**Tencilan**' *see* Clorazepate dipotassium.
TENDAMISTAT*** (α-amylase-inhibiting poly-peptide from *Streptomyces tendae*; HOE-467).
'**Tendor**' *see* Debrisoquine.
Tenemycin *see* Nebramycin.
'**Teneretic**' *see under* Atenolol.
'**Tenfidil**' *see* Thenyldiamine.
'**Teniathane**' *see* Dichlorophen.
'**Teniatol**' *see* Dichlorophen.
TENILSETAM** ((±)-3-(2-thienyl)-2-piperazin-one).
TENIPOSIDE*** (4'-demethylepipodophyllotox-in 9-(4,6-*O*-2-thenylidene-β-D-glucopyranoside);

5*R*-(5α,5aβ,8aα,9β(*R**))-5,8,8a,9-tetrahydro-5-(4-hydroxy-3,5-dimethoxyphenyl)-9-[[4,6-*O*-(2-thienylmethylene)-β-D-glucopyranosyl]oxy]furo-[3',4':6,7]naphtho[2,3-*d*]-1,3-dioxol-6(5a*H*)-one; PTG; NSC-122819; VM-26).
'**Tenoban**' *see* Arecoline-acetarsol.
TENOCYCLIDINE*** (1-(1-thien-2-ylcyclohex-yl)piperidine).
TENONITROZOLE*** (*N*-(5-nitrothiazol-2-yl)-2-thiophenecarboxamide).
'**Tenoran**' *see* Chloroxuron.
'**Tenoretic**' *see under* Atenolol.
'**Tenormal**' *see* Pempidine.
'**Tenormine**' *see* Atenolol.
'**Tenox-BHA**' *see* Butylated hydroxyanisole.
TENOXICAM*** (4-hydroxy-2-methyl-*N*-pyrid-2-yl-2*H*-thieno[2,3-*e*]-1,2-thiazine-3-carbox-amide 1,1-dioxide).
'**Tenserlix**' *see under* Reserpine.
'**Tenserpina**' *see* Methoserpidine.
'**Tensicor**' *see* Diisopropylamine dichloroacetate.
'**Tensigradyl**' *see under* Guabenxan.
'**Tensilest**' *see* Pentolonium tartrate.
'**Tensilon**' *see* Edrophonium chloride.
'**Tensimic**' *see under* Methoserpidine.
'**Tensionorme**' *see under* Reserpine.
'**Tensobon**' *see* Captopril.
'**Tensofin**' *see* Fluphenazine.
'**Tensopam**' *see* Diazepam.
'**Tentone**' *see* Methopromazine.
'**Tenuate**' *see* Amfepramone.
TENUAZONIC ACID (3-acetyl-5-*sec*-butyl-4-hydroxy-3-pyrrolin-2-one; α-acetyl-5-*sec*-butyl-tetramic acid).
See also Benzathine tenuazonate; Sodium tenu-azonate.
TENYLIDONE*** (2,6-bis(2-thenylidene)cyclo-hexanone; 'margeryl').
'**Teocaradrin**' *see under* Proscillaridin.
'**Teocholine**' *see* Choline theophyllinate.
TEOCLATE(S)** (8-chlorotheophyllinate(s); theoclate(s)).
'**Teokolin**' *see* Choline theophyllinate.
'**Teonicon**' *see* Pimefylline nicotinate.
TEOPRANITOL** (1,4:3,6-dianhydro-2-deoxy-2-[[3-(1,2,3,6-tetrahydro-1,3-dimethyl-2,6-dioxo-purin-7-yl)propyl]amino]-L-iditol 5-nitrate).
TEOPROLOL*** (7-[3-[[2-hydroxy-3-[(2-methyl-indol-4-yl)oxy]propyl]amino]butyl]theophylline).
'**Teoquil**' *see* Hedaquinium chloride.
'**Teostellarid**' *see under* Proscillaridin.
TEPA* (tris(1-aziridinyl)phosphine oxide; phos-phoric acid triethylenimide; triethylenephos-phoramide; trisethylenimino phosphate; aph-oxide; TEF; ENT-24915; NSC-9717; SK-3818).
Tepa-132 *see* Hexamethyltepa.
'**Tepanil**' *see* Amfepramone.
'**Teperin**' *see* Amitriptyline.
'**Tepilta**' *see* Oxetacaine.
TEPP* *see* Tetraethyl pyrophosphate.
TEPRENONE** (6,10,14,18-tetramethyl-5,9,13,17-nonadecatetraen-2-one (mixture of (5*E*,9*E*,13*E*) and (5*Z*,9*E*,13*E*) isomers)).

TEPROSILATE(S)** (1,2,3,6-tetrahydro-1,3-dimethyl-2,6-dioxopurine-7-propanesulfonic acid, esters and salts).

TEPROTIDE*** (2-L-tryptophan-3-de-L-leucine-4-de-L-proline-8-L-glutaminebradykinin potentiator B; 5-oxo-L-prolyl-L-tryptophyl-L-prolyl-L-arginyl-L-prolyl-L-glutaminyl-L-isoleucyl-L-prolyl-L-proline; SQ-20881).

Tequinol see Actinoquinol.

'Tequinophil' see under Clioquinol.

'Teralen' see Alimemazine.

'Teralithe' see Lithium carbonate.

'Teramine' see Benzethonium chloride.

TERAZOSIN*** (1-(4-amino-6,7-dimethoxyquinazolin-2-yl)-4-(tetrahydro-2-furoyl)piperazine; 6,7-dimethoxy-2-[4-(tetrahydrofuran-2-carbonyl)piperazin-1-yl]quinazolin-4-ylamine; terazosin hydrochloride).

TERBACIL* (3-tert-butyl-5-chloro-6-methyluracil; 5-chloro-3-(1,1-dimethylethyl)-6-methyl-2,4(1H,3H)-pyrimidinedione; 'sinbar').

'Terbasmin' see Terbutaline.

'Terbolan' see under Reserpine.

TERBUCARB** (2,6-bis(1,1-dimethylethyl)-4-methylphenyl methylcarbamate; 2,6-di-tert-butyl-4-methylphenyl methylcarbamate; terbutol; 'azak').

TERBUCROMIL*** (6,8-di-tert-butyl-4-oxo-4H-1-benzopyran-2-carboxylic acid).

TERBUFIBROL*** (p-[3-(p-tert-butylphenoxy)-2-hydroxypropoxy]benzoic acid; 1-(p-tert-butylphenoxy)-3-(p-carboxyphenoxy)-2-propanol).

TERBUFICIN** (2,2-bis(3,5-di-tert-butyl-4-hydroxyphenyl)acetic acid).

TERBUMETON* (2-(tert-butylamino)-4-ethylamino-6-methoxy-s-triazine; N-(1,1-dimethylethyl)-N'-ethyl-6-methoxy-1,3,5-triazine-2,4-diamine; terbuthylaton; 'caragard').

TERBUPROL*** (1-tert-butoxy-3-methoxy-2-propanol).

TERBUTALINE*** (2-(tert-butylamino)-1-(3,5-dihydroxyphenyl)ethanol; α-[(tert-butylamino)methyl]-3,5-dihydroxybenzyl alcohol; terbutaline sulfate; KWD-2019; 'brethine'; 'bricanyl'; 'filair'; 'terbasmin').

Terbuthylaton see Terbumeton.

TERBUTHYLAZINE*** (2-(tert-butylamino)-6-chloro-4-(ethylamino)-s-triazine; 6-chloro-N-(1,1-dimethylethyl)-N'-ethyl-1,3,5-triazine-2,4-diamine; GS-15329).

Terbutol see Terbucarb.

TERBUTRYN* (2-tert-butylamino-4-ethylamino-6-(methylthio)-s-triazine; N-(1,1-dimethylethyl)-N'-ethyl-6-(methylthio)-1,3,5-triazine-2,4-diamine; terbutryne; 'igran'; 'prebane').

Terbutryne see Terbutryn.

Terbutylamine see Phentermine.

'Tercian' see Cyamemazine.

TERCIPRAZINE*** ((±)-α-[[(1-ethynylcyclohexyl)oxy]methyl]-4-(α,α,α-trifluoro-m-tolyl)-1-piperazineethanol).

TERCONAZOLE*** (cis-1-[p-[[2-(2,4-dichlorophenyl)-2-(1H-1,2,4-triazol-1-ylmethyl)-1,3-dioxolan-4-yl]methoxy]phenyl]-4-isopropylpiperazine; triaconazole; R 42470).

Terebinth oil see Turpentine oil.

'Terenol' see Resorantel.

TEREPHTHALAMIC ACID (p-carbamoylbenzoic acid; terephthalic acid monoamide).

TEREPHTHALIC ACID (p-benzenedicarboxylic acid).

Terephthalic acid ethylene glycol polymer see Pegoterate.

TERFENADINE*** (α-(p-tert-butylphenyl)-4-(hydroxydiphenylmethyl)-1-piperidinebutanol; p-tert-butyl-α-[3-[4-(hydroxydiphenylmethyl)-piperid-1-yl]propyl]benzyl alcohol; α-[4-(1,1-dimethylethyl)phenyl]-4-(hydroxydiphenylmethyl)-1-piperidinebutanol; RMI-9918; 'teldane'; 'triludan').

TERFLURANOL*** (4,4'-[(1R,2S)-1-methyl-2-(2,2,2-trifluoroethyl)ethylene]diphenol; BX-428).

'Terfluzine' see Trifluoperazine.

'Tergemist' see Sodium etasulfate.

'Tergitol 4' see Sodium tetradecyl sulfate.

'Tergitol 7' see Sodium heptadecyl sulfate.

'Tergitol 8' see Sodium etasulfate.

TERGURIDE** (1,1-diethyl-3-(6-methylergolin-8α-yl)urea).

'Teriam' see Triamterene.

'Teridax' see Iophenoxic acid.

'Terion' see Fominoben.

'Terivalidin' see Terizidone.

TERIZIDONE*** (N^4,$N^{4'}$-(p-phenylene)bis(methylene)di(cycloserine); 4,4'-(p-phenylene)bis-(methyleneamino)di(isoxazolidin-3-one)).

TERLIPRESSIN*** (N-[N-(N-glycylglycyl)glycyl]-8-lysinevasopressin; glypressin; triglycyllysine vasopressin; triglycylvasopressin; TGLVP; 'glycylpressin').

'Termidor' see Paracetamol.

'Termil' see Chlorothalonil.

'Terminolut' see under Levonorgestrel.

Termitin see Vitamin T-complex.

TERNIDAZOLE*** (1-(3-hydroxypropyl)-2-methyl-4-nitroimidazole; 2-methyl-4-nitroimidazole-1-propanol).

TERODILINE*** (N-tert-butyl-1-methyl-3,3-diphenylpropylamine; terodiline hydrochloride).

TEROFENAMATE*** (ethoxymethyl N-(2,6-dichloro-m-tolyl)anthranilate; ethoxymethyl meclofenamate; etoclofene; A-3).

'Terolut' see Dydrogesterone.

'Teronac' see Mazindol.

'Teropterin' see Pteropterin.

TEROXALENE*** (1-(3-chloro-p-tolyl)-4-[6-(p-tert-pentylphenoxy)hexyl]piperazine; teroxalene hydrochloride; A-16612; PR-3847).

TEROXIRONE*** ((RS,RS,SR)-1,3,5-tris(2,3-epoxypropyl)-s-triazine-2,4,6-(1H,3H,5H)-trione).

'Terraclor' see Quintozene.

'Terra-cortril' see under Hydrocortisone.

'Terracur P' see Fensulfothion.

'Terrafungine' see Oxytetracycline.

'Terramycin' see Oxytetracycline.

'Terrastain' see under Oxytetracycline.

'Terra-sytam' *see* Dimefox.
'Terravenos' *see* Oxytetracycline.
'Terrazole' *see* Etmt.
'Tersan' *see* Thiram.
'Tersan SP' *see* Chloroneb.
'Tersavid' *see* Pivhydrazine.
'Tersigat' *see* Oxitropium bromide.
TERTATOLOL*** ((±)-1-(*tert*-butylamino)-3-(thiochroman-8-yloxy)-2-propanol; (±)-8-[3-(*tert*-butylamino)-2-hydroxypropoxy]thiochroman; S-2395).
'Tertensif' *see* Indapamide.
'Tertran' *see* Iprindole.
'Tertroxin' *see* Liothyronine.
'Terulcon' *see* Carbenoxolone.
TESICAM** (4'-chloro-1,2,3,4-tetrahydro-1,3-dioxo-4-isoquinolinecarboxanilide; CP-13608).
TESIMIDE*** (4-benzylidene-5,6,7,8-tetrahydro-1,3(2*H*,4*H*)-isoquinolinedione).
'Teslac' *see* Testolactone.
TESPA *see* Thiotepa.
'Tespamin' *see* Thiotepa.
'Tessalon' *see* Benzonatate.
Testenat (tr) *see* Testosterone.
'Testodrin prolongatum' *see* Testosterone cipionate.
TESTOLACTONE***
  (1,2,3,4,4a,4b,5,6,7,9,10,10a-dodecahydro-2-hydroxy-2,4b-dimethyl-7-oxo-1-phenanthrenepropionic acid δ-lactone; 17α-oxa-D-homo-androsta-1,4-diene-3,17-dione; Δ¹-testolactone; NSC-23759; SQ-9538; 'teslac').
Δ¹-Testolactone *see* Testolactone.
TESTOSTERONE*** (17β-hydroxyandrost-4-en-3-one; testenat; NSC-9700).
Testosterone caprate *see* Testosterone decanoate.
TESTOSTERONE CIPIONATE (testosterone cyclopentanepropionate; testosterone cypionate; 'depoviron'; 'pertestis'; 'testodrin prolongatum').
TESTOSTERONE CYCLOHEXANECARB-OXYLATE ('lontanyl').
Testosterone cyclopentanepropionate *see* Testosterone cipionate.
Testosterone cypionate *see* Testosterone cipionate.
TESTOSTERONE DECANOATE (testosterone caprate).
TESTOSTERONE ENANTATE (testosterone heptanoate; 'atlatest'; 'delatestryl'; 'testoviron-depot').
  See also under Estradiol valerate.
Testosterone heptanoate *see* Testosterone enantate.
TESTOSTERONE 3-*p*-(HEXYLOXY)HYDRO-CINNAMATE (testosterone 3-(*p*-hexyloxyphenyl)propionate; 'andradurin').
TESTOSTERONE ISOBUTYRATE ('perandren').
  See also under Estradiol benzoate.
Testosterone isocaproate *see* Testosterone 4-methylvalerate.
TESTOSTERONE KETOLAURATE*** (testosterone 3-oxododecanoate; 'androdurin').
TESTOSTERONE 4-METHYLVALERATE (testosterone isocaproate).

TESTOSTERONE NICOTINATE ('bolfortan').
Testosterone 3-oxododecanoate *see* Testosterone ketolaurate.
TESTOSTERONE PHENYLPROPIONATE (TPP; 'retandrol').
TESTOSTERONE PROPIONATE (TP; NSC-9166; 'rectormone').
Testosterone trichlorohydroxyethyl ether *see* Cloxotestosterone.
TESTOSTERONE UNDECANOATE ('andriol').
TESTOSTERONE UNDECENATE ('deposteron').
'Testoviron-depot' *see* Testosterone enantate.
TET (tr) *see* Tretamine.
TETA *see* Trientine.
Tetamon (tr) *see* Tetrylammonium bromide.
Tetiothalein *see* Iodophthalein sodium.
'Tetmosol' *see* Sulfiram.
'Tetra' *see* Tetrachloroethylene.
β-Tetra *see* 1,2,3,4-Tetrahydro-2-naphthylamine.
1,3,4,7-Tetraazaadamantane *see* Methenamine.
Tetraazaindene *see* Pyrazolopyrimidine.
'Tetrabamate' *see under* Febarbamate.
TETRABARBITAL*** (5-ethyl-5-(1-ethylbutyl)-barbituric acid; tetramal).
TETRABENAZINE*** (1,3,4,6,7,11b-hexahydro-3-isobutyl-9,10-dimethoxy-2*H*-benzo[*a*]quinolizin-2-one; Ro 1-9569).
TETRABORIC ACID (pyroboric acid).
  See also Borax.
3,3',5,5'-Tetrabromo-2,2'-biphenyldiol mono(dihydrogen phosphate) *see* Bromofenofos.
3,4,5,6-Tetrabromo-3,3-bis(4-hydroxy-3-sulfophenyl)phthalide *see* Sulfobromphthalein.
3,3',5,5'-Tetrabromo-2,2'-dihydroxybenzil *see* Tetrabromsalicil.
Tetrabromophenolphthalein disodium sulfonate *see* Sulfobromphthalein.
Tetrabromosalicil *see* Tetrabromsalicil.
3,3',5,5'-Tetrabromo-2,2',4,4'-tetrahydroxybiphenyl *see* Tebrofen.
TETRABROMSALICIL (3,3',5,5'-tetrabromo-2,2'-dihydroxybenzil; tetrabromosalicil; RP 3227).
TETRAC (3,3',5,5'-tetraiodothyroacetic acid).
TETRACAINE*** (2-(dimethylamino)ethyl *p*-butylaminobenzoate; amethocaine; dicaine).
'Tetracap' *see* Tetrachloroethylene.
Tetra(carboxymethyl)ethylenediamine *see* Edetic acid.
Tetracemin *see* Edetic acid.
Tetrachlorfenvinfos *see* Stirofos.
2,4,5,6-Tetrachloro-1,3-benzenedicarbonitrile *see* Chlorothalonil.
2,3,5,6-Tetrachlorobenzene-1,4-dicarboxylic acid *see* Chlorthal.
Tetrachlorobenzoquinone(s) *see* Chloranil; Isochloranil.
2,3,7,8-TETRACHLORODIBENZO-*p*-DIOXIN (dioxine; TCDD).
1,3,4,5-Tetrachloro-2,6-dicyanobenzene *see* Chlorothalonil.
TETRACHLORODIFLUOROETHANE ('freon

112′; 'frigen 112′).

1,1,2,2-TETRACHLORO-1,2-DIFLUOROETH-ANE (difluorotetrachloroethane; 'freon 113′).

Tetrachlorodihydroxydiphenyl sulfide *see* Bithionol.

4,5,6,7-Tetrachloro-2-[2-(dimethylamino)ethyl]-2-methylisoindolinium chloride methochloride *see* Chlorisondamine chloride.

1,3,4,5-Tetrachloro-2,6-dinitrilobenzene *see* Chlorothalonil.

2,4,4′,5-Tetrachlorodiphenyl sulfide *see* Tetrasul.

2,4,4′,5-Tetrachlorodiphenyl sulfone *see* Tetradifon.

TETRACHLOROETHANE (1,1,2,2-tetrachloroethane; acetylene tetrachloride).

TETRACHLOROETHYLENE (1,1,2,2-tetra-chloroethylene; carbon dichloride; perchlorethylene).

N-[(1,1,2,2′-Tetrachloroethyl)thio]-4-cyclohexenedi-carboximide *see* Captafol.

N-(Tetrachloroethylthio)-Δ⁴-tetrahydrophthalimide *see* Captafol.

2,3,5,6-Tetrachloro-4-hydroxyanisole *see* Drosophilin A.

Tetrachloroisophthalonitrile *see* Chlorothalonil.

Tetrachloromethane *see* Carbon tetrachloride.

2,3,5,6-Tetrachloro-4-methoxyphenol *see* Drosophilin A.

1,2,4,5-Tetrachloro-3-nitrobenzene *see* Tecnazene.

5,6,7,8-Tetrachloroquinoxaline *see* Chlorquinox.

2,3,5,6-Tetrachloroterephthalic acid *see* Chlorthal.

4,5,6,7-Tetrachloro-2′,4′,5′,7′-tetraiodofluorescein *see* Rose bengal.

TETRACOSACTIDE*** (corticotrophin (1-24) tetracosapeptide; cosyntropin; tetracosactrin; Ba-30920; 'cortrosyn'; 'synacthar'; 'synacthen').

TETRACOSACTIDE ZINC PHOSPHATE COMPLEX (zinc tetracosactide; Ba-42915; 'synacthen-depot').

Tetracosactrin* *see* Tetracosactide.

TETRACOSANOIC ACID (lignoceric acid).

15-TETRACOSENOIC ACID (nervic acid; nervonic acid; selacholic acid).

TETRACYCLINE*** (4-(dimethylamino)-1,4,4a,5,5a,6,11,12a-octahydro-3,6,10,12,12a-pentahydroxy-6-methyl-1,11-dioxonaphthacene-2-carboxamide; deschlorbiomycin; tetracycline hydrochloride; tsiklomitsin).

See also under Benzydamine; Broxyquinoline; Clioquinol; Diiodohydroxyquin; Erythromycin; Erythromycin estolate; Oxolamine benzilate; Prazosin.

TETRACYCLINE plus AMPHOTERICIN B ('mysteclin-V').

TETRACYCLINE plus ASCORBIC ACID ('resteclin').

TETRACYCLINE plus BROMELAINS ('tetranase'; 'traumanase-cyclin').

TETRACYCLINE plus CHLORTETRACYCLINE and DEMECLOCYCLINE ('deteclo'; 'triple tetracycline').

TETRACYCLINE plus NOVOBIOCIN ('panalba').

TETRACYCLINE plus OLEANDOMYCIN ('oletetrin'; 'sigmamycin'; 'signemycin'; 'tetraolean').

TETRACYCLINE plus yeasts ('florocycline').

TETRACYCLINE BITARTRATE NUCLEIC ACID COMPLEX ('mervacycline').

Tetracycline colistin compound *see* Colimecycline.

TETRACYCLINE CYCLAMATE (tetracycline cyclohexylsulfamate; 'sifacycline').

Tetracycline cyclohexylsulfamate *see* Tetracycline cyclamate.

Tetracycline 2-deoxy-2-methylaminoglucose compound *see* Meglucycline.

TETRACYCLINE DIHYDRONOVOBIOCIN SODIUM PHYTATE (dihydronovobiocin tetracycline compound; 'vulcacycline').

TETRACYCLINE DODECYLSULFAMATE ('myriamycin').

TETRACYCLINE GLUCOSAMINE ('glutrex').

Tetracycline-L-methylene-lysine *see* Lymecycline.

TETRACYCLINE PHOSPHATE COMPLEX* (tetracycline addition product with sodium hexametaphosphate; 'alfaciclina'; 'bristaciclina A'; 'hexacycline'; 'phosphocycline'; 'sumycin'; 'tetrex'; 'tevacycline'; 'ultracycline').

α-Tetracyclinyl-4-(2-hydroxyethyl)-1-piperazine-acetic acid *see* Apicycline.

6-(Tetracyclin-2-ylmethylamino)penicillin G *see* Penimocycline.

N-(Tetracyclinylmethyl)nipecotic acid *see* Pecocycline.

3′,4′,6,7,8,9,11,12,13,14,15,16,20,21-Tetradeca-hydro-10,13-dimethylspiro[17*H*-dicyclopropa-[6,7:15,16]cyclopenta[*a*]phenanthrene-17,2′(5′*H*)-furan]-3(10*H*),5′-dione *see* Spirorenone.

Tetradecanoic acid *see* Myristic acid.

2-Tetradecylaminoethanol lactate *see* Myralact.

α-Tetradecylcitric acid *see* Norcaperatic acid.

(±)-2-Tetradecylglycidic acid *see* Palmoxiric acid.

(±)-2-Tetradecyloxiranecarboxylic acid *see* Palmoxiric acid.

Tetradecyltrimethylammonium bromide *see* Cetrimide.

TETRADIFON* (*p*-chlorophenyl 2,4,5-trichlorophenyl sulfone; 2,4,4′,5-tetrachlorodiphenyl sulfone; 1,2,4-trichloro-5-(*p*-chlorophenylsulfonyl)-benzene; chlorodifon; TCDS; 'akaritox'; 'duphar'; 'tedion').

TETRADONIUM BROMIDE*** (trimethyltetradecylammonium bromide; trimethylmyristylammonium bromide).

Tetraethylammonium bromide *see* Tetrylammonium bromide.

Tetraethyl diphosphate *see* Tetraethyl pyrophosphate.

Tetraethyl dithiopyrophosphate *see* Sulfotep.

Tetraethylenimide piperazine diphosphate *see* Dipin.

TETRAETHYLLEAD (lead tetraethyl; TEL; 'ethyl').

Tetraethyl [(2-methoxy-*p*-phenylene)bis[imino(thio-carbonyl)]]diphosphoramidate *see* Imcarbofos.

Tetraethyl methylene diphosphorodithioate *see* Ethion.

Tetraethyl monothiopyrophosphate *see* Pyrophos.

N,*N*,*N*′,*N*′-Tetraethyl-5-norbornene-*trans*-2,3-di-carboxamide *see* Endomide.

TETRAETHYL PYROPHOSPHATE (tetraethyl diphosphate; ethyl pyrophosphate; tetrastigmine; TEP; TEPP; 'nifos'; 'tetron'; 'vapotone').

Tetraethyl thiodiphosphate *see* Sulfotep.

Tetraethyl thiopyrophosphate *see* Pyrophos.

Tetraethylthiuram disulfide *see* Disulfiram.

Tetraethylthiuram monosulfide *see* Sulfiram.

TETRAFENPHOS (*O*,*O*′-thiodi(*p*-phenylene) phosphorothioate).

Tetrafluorobenzoquinone(s) *see* Fluoranil; Isofluoranil.

1,1,1,2-Tetrafluoroethane *see* Norflurane.

Tetrafluoroethylene polymer *see* Politef.

Tetraflurane *see* Teflurane.

'Tetraform' *see* Carbon tetrachloride.

TETRAGASTRIN (gastrin-like tetrapeptide).

Tetraglucosan *see* Salabrose.

'Tetrahelmin' *see* Tetrachloroethylene.

Tetrahydroaminacrin *see* Tacrine.

Tetrahydroazepotetrazole *see* Pentetrazole.

3,4,5,6-Tetrahydro-2,3′-bipyridine *see* Anabaseine.

Tetrahydro-1,4-bis[(3,4-methylenedioxy)phenyl]-1*H*,3*H*-furo[3,4-*c*]furan *see* Sesamin.

TETRAHYDROCANNABINOL(S) (3-amyltetrahydro-6,9,9-trimethyl-6*H*-dibenzo[*b*,*d*]pyran-1-ol; tetrahydro-6,6,9-trimethyl-3-pentyl-6*H*-dibenzo[*b*,*d*]pyran-1-ol).

Δ¹-Tetrahydrocannabinol *see* Dronabinol.

Δ⁶-Tetrahydrocannabinol *see* Δ⁸-Tetrahydrocannabinol.

Δ⁸-TETRAHYDROCANNABINOL (Δ⁶-tetrahydrocannabinol).

Δ⁹-Tetrahydrocannabinol *see* Dronabinol.

Tetrahydro-β-carboline *see* Tryptoline.

Tetrahydro-1*H*-1,4-diazepine-1,4(5*H*)-dipropanol *see* Biopropazepan.

Tetrahydro-1*H*-1,4-diazepine-1,4(5*H*)-dipropanol 3,4,5-trimethoxybenzoate diester *see* Dilazep.

2,3,4,5-Tetrahydro-1*H*-(1,4)diazepino[1,2-*a*]indole *see* Azepindole.

2,3,4,5-Tetrahydro-1*H*-1,4-diazepino[1,2-*a*]indole *see* Azepindole.

5,6,13,13a-Tetrahydro-8*H*-dibenzo[*a*,*g*]quinolizine *see* Berbine.

5,5a,13,13a-Tetrahydro-5,13-dihydroxy-8*H*,16*H*-7a,15a-epidithio-7*H*,15*H*-bisoxepino[3′,4′:4,5]pyrrolo[1,2-*a*:1′,2′-*d*]pyrazine-7,15-dione 5-acetate *see* Aranotin.

7,7a,8,9-Tetrahydro-3,7a-dihydroxy-12-(3-methyl-2-butenyl)-6*H*-8,9*c*-iminoethanophenanthro[4,5-*bcd*]furan-5(4a*H*)-one *see* Nalmexone.

5,10,11,11a-Tetrahydro-9,11-dihydroxy-8-methyl-5-oxo-1*H*-pyrrolo[2,1-*c*][1,4]benzodiazepine-*trans*-2-acrylamide *see* Antramycin.

1,2,3,4-Tetrahydro-6,7-dihydroxy-1-protocatechuylisoquinoline *see* Tetrahydropapaveroline.

3,4,5,6-Tetrahydro-3,4-dihydroxyspiro(benzofuran-2(3*H*),2′-oxirane)-6-methanol 6-acetate 3,4-diisovalerate *see* Didrovaltrate.

1,4a,5,7a-Tetrahydro-1,6-dihydroxyspiro[cyclopenta[*c*]pyran-7(6*H*),2′-oxirane]-4-methanol 6-acetate 1,4-diisovalerate *see* Didrovaltrate.

4-[2-(1,2,4,5-Tetrahydro-7,8-dimethoxy-3*H*-3-benz-

azepin-3-yl)ethyl]benzenamine *see* Verilopam.

5,6,6a,7-Tetrahydro-1,10-dimethoxy-6-methyl-4*H*-dibenzo[*de*,*g*]quinoline-2,9-diol *see* Boldine.

1,2,12,12a-Tetrahydro-8,9-dimethoxy-2-(1-methylethenyl)[1]benzopyrano[3,4-*b*]furo[2,3-*h*][1]benzopyran-6-one *see* Rotenone.

1,2,3,4-Tetrahydro-6,7-dimethoxy-1-methylisoquinoline *see* Salsolidine.

6,7,8,9-Tetrahydro-2,12-dimethoxy-7-methyl-6-phenethyl-5*H*-dibenz[*d*,*f*]azonin-1-ol *see* Asocainol.

2,3,4,5-Tetrahydro-7,8-dimethoxy-3-methyl-1-phenyl-1*H*-3-benzazepine *see* Trepipam.

1,2,3,4-Tetrahydro-6,7-dimethoxy-2-methyl-1-veratrylisoquinoline *see* Laudanosine.

2,3,4,9-Tetrahydro-*N*,*N*-dimethyl-1*H*-carbazol-3-amine *see* Ciclindole.

1,2,3,6-Tetrahydro-1,3-dimethyl-2,6-dioxopurine-7-ethanesulfonic acid, esters and salts *see* Tofesilate(s).

1,2,3,6-Tetrahydro-1,3-dimethyl-2,6-dioxopurine-7-propanesulfonic acid, esters and salts *see* Teprosilate(s).

1,2,3,7-Tetrahydro-6,7-dimethyl-5-phenylpyrrolo[3,4-*e*]-1,4-diazepin-2-one *see* Premazepam.

7,8,9,10-Tetrahydro-1,9-dimethyl-6*H*-pyrido[4,3-*b*]thieno[3,2-*e*]indole *see* Tienocarbine.

Tetrahydro-3,5-dimethyl-2*H*-1,3,5-thiadiazine-2-thione *see* Dazomet.

Tetrahydro-*p*-dioxin *see* 1,4-Dioxane.

1,2,3,6-Tetrahydro-2,6-dioxo-4-pyrimidinecarboxylic acid *see* Orotic acid.

Tetrahydro-9-fluorenone *see* Phentydrone.

2′,3′α-Tetrahydrofuran-2′-spiro-17-(7-acetylthio-4-androsten)-3-one *see* Spiroxasone.

2-Tetrahydrofurfuryl-1*H*-benzo[*c*]pyrazolo[1,2-*a*]cinnoline-1,3(2*H*)-dione *see* Cinnofuradione.

Tetrahydrofurfuryl (2-carbamoylphenoxy)acetate *see* Fenamifuril.

5,5′-(Tetrahydro-1*H*,3*H*-furo[3,4-*c*]furan-1,4-diyl)-bis(1,3-benzodioxole) *see* Sesamin.

Tetrahydrofuryl esters *see* Thurfyl etc.

Tetrahydroglyoxaline *see* Imidazolidine.

5,8,8a,9-Tetrahydro-5-(4-hydroxy-3,5-dimethoxyphenyl)-9-[[4,6-*o*-(2-thienylmethylene) β-*D*-glucopyranosyl]oxy]furo[3′,4′:6,7]naphtho[2,3-*d*]-1,3-dioxol-6(5a*H*)-one *see* Teniposide.

2,3α,3aα,7a-Tetrahydro-7aα-hydroxy-8-(4-hydroxy-3-methoxyphenyl)-4-(3α,5,7-trihydroxy-4-oxo-2β-chromanyl)-3,6-methanobenzofuran-7(6α*H*)-one *see* Silidianin.

1,2,3,4-Tetrahydro-1-hydroxy-2-(hydroxymethyl)-6,7-(methylenedioxy)-4-(3,4,5-trimethoxyphenyl)-naphthalene-3-carboxylic acid lactone *see* Podophyllotoxin.

Tetrahydro-2-[3-hydroxy-5-(hydroxymethyl)-2-methylpyrid-4-yl]-2*H*-1,3-thiazine-4-carboxylic acid *see* Tiapirinol.

5,6,7,8-Tetrahydro-9-hydroxy-7-(hydroxymethyl)-5-(3,4,5-trimethoxyphenyl)naphtho[2,3-*d*]-1,3-dioxole-6-carboxylic acid γ-lactone *see* β-Peltatin.

1,4,5,6-Tetrahydro-5-hydroxy-4-(3-hydroxy-1-octenyl)-1-phenylcyclopenta[*b*]pyrrole-2-valeric acid *see* Piriprost.

2,3,3a,9a-Tetrahydro-3-hydroxy-6-imino-6*H*-furo-**
[2′,3′:4,5]oxazolo[3,2-*a*]pyrimidine-2-methanol *see*
Ancitabine.
1,2,3,4-Tetrahydro-8-[2-hydroxy-3-(isopropyl-
amino)propoxy]-1-nicotinoylquinoline *see*
Nicainoprol.
3a,4,7,7a-Tetrahydro-3-hydroxy-4,7-methanoiso-
benzofuran-1(3*H*)-one methylcarbamate** *see* Moxadolen.
1,2,3,4-Tetrahydro-6-hydroxy-7-methoxy-1-methyl-
isoquinoline *see* Salsoline.
6,7,8,14-Tetrahydro-7α-(1-hydroxy-1-methylbutyl)-
6,14-*endo*-ethenooripavine *see* Etorphine.
6,7,8,14-Tetrahydro-7a-(1-hydroxy-1-methylbutyl)-
6,14-*endo*-ethenooripavine 3-acetate *see* Acetorphine.
3,3a,5,11b-Tetrahydro-7-hydroxy-5-methyl-2*H*-**
furo[3,2-*b*]naphtho[2,3-*d*]pyran-2,6,11-trione *see*
Kalafungin.
1,2,3,4-Tetrahydro-6-hydroxymethyl-2-isopropyl-
aminomethyl-7-nitroquinoline *see* Oxamniquine.
3,4,5,6-Tetrahydro-*N*-(hydroxymethyl)phthalimide
chrysanthemate (ester) *see* Tetramethrin.
6,7,8,9-Tetrahydro-5-hydroxy-4-oxo-10-propylben-
zo[*g*]chromene-2-carboxylic acid *see* Proxicromil.
6,7,8,9-Tetrahydro-5-hydroxy-4-oxo-10-propyl-4*H*-**
naphtho[2,3-*b*]pyran-2-carboxylic acid *see* Proxicromil.
3a,4,7,7a-Tetrahydro-5-(hydroxyphenyl-2-pyridin-
ylmethyl)-7-(phenyl-2-pyridinylmethylene)-4,7-
methano-1*H*-isoindole-3(2*H*)-dione** *see* Norbormide.
5,8,8a,9-Tetrahydro-9-hydroxy-5-(3,4,5-trimethoxy-
phenyl)furo[3′,4′:6,7]naphtho[2,3-*d*]-1,3-dioxol-
6(5*H*)-one** *see* Podophyllotoxin.
3a,5,5a,9b-Tetrahydro-4-hydroxy-3,5a,9-trimethyl-
naphtho[1,2-*b*]furan-2,8(3*H*,4*H*)-dione** *see* Artemisin.
2,3,3a,8a-Tetrahydro-5-hydroxy-1,3a,8-trimethyl-
pyrrolo[2,3-*b*]indole methylcarbamate *see* Physostigmine.
1,2,3,4-Tetrahydro-6-(2-imidazolin-2-ylmethyl)-7-
methyl-1,4-ethanonaphthalene *see* Metrafazoline.
5,6,7,8-Tetrahydro-1-(2-imidazolin-2-ylmethyl)-
naphthalene *see* Tefazoline.
4,5,6,7-Tetrahydroimidazo[5,4-*c*]pyridine *see* Spinaceamine.
1,2,12,12a-Tetrahydro-2-isopropenyl-8,9-dimeth-
oxy[1]benzopyrano[3,4-*b*]furo[2,3-*h*][1]benzopyr-
an-6-one *see* Rotenone.
1,2,3,4-Tetrahydro-2-[(isopropylamino)methyl]-7-ni-
tro-6-quinolinemethanol *see* Oxamniquine.
4,5,6,7-Tetrahydroisoxazolo[5,4-*c*]pyridin-3-ol *see*
Gaboxadol.
2,3,6,7-Tetrahydro-2-(mesitylimino)-9,10-dimeth-
oxy-3-methyl-4*H*-pyrimido[6,1-*a*]isoquinolin-4-**
one *see* Trequinsin.
9,10,11,11a-Tetrahydro-8*H*-6,11b-methanofuro[2,3-**
c*]pyrido[1,2-*a*]azepin-2-(6H*)-one** *see* Securinine.
6,7,7a,8-Tetrahydro-11-methoxy-7-methyl-5*H*-**
benzo[*g*]-1,3-benzodioxolo[6,4,5-*de*]quinolin-12-ol
see Bulbocapnine.
1,2,3,4-Tetrahydro-6-methoxy-1-methyl-9*H*-pyr-**

id[3,4-*b*]indole *see* Glomerulotrophin.
2,4,5,6-Tetrahydro-9-methoxy-4-methyl-1*H*-3,4,6a-**
triazafluoranthene *see* Metralindole.
cis-2,3,4,5-Tetrahydro-3-(methylamino)-1-benz-**
oxepin-5-ol *see* Exepanol.
2,3,7,8-Tetrahydro-3-(methylamino)-1*H*-quino[1,8-**
***ab*]benzazepine** *see* Ciclopramine.
5,6,6a,7-Tetrahydro-6-methyl-4*H*-dibenzo[*de*,*g*]qui-**
noline *see* Aporphine.
6-(5,6,7,8-Tetrahydro-6-methyl-1,3-dioxolo[4,5-*g*]-
isoquinolin-5-yl)furo[3,4-*e*]-1,3-benzodioxol-
8(6*H*)-one** *see* Bicuculline.
1,2,3,4-Tetrahydro-2-methyl-1,4-dioxo-2-naphthal-
enesulfonic acid sodium salt *see* Menadione sodium bisulfite.
2-[(1,2,3,4-Tetrahydro-7-methyl-1,4-ethanonaphth-
6-yl)methyl]-2-imidazoline *see* Metrafazoline.
Tetrahydro-5-methylhomofolic acid *see* Ketotrexate.
4,5,6,7-Tetrahydro-2-methyl-3-methylamino-2*H*-in-**
dazole *see* Tetridamine.
4,5,6,7-Tetrahydro-2-methyl-5-[(methylamino)meth-
yl]benzothiazole *see* Manozodil.
trans-1,4,5,6-Tetrahydro-1-methyl-2-[2-(3-methyl-**
thien-2-yl)vinyl]pyrimidine *see* Morantel.
1,2,5,6-Tetrahydro-1-methylnicotinic acid *see* Arecaidine.
Tetrahydro-3-methyl-4-(5-nitrofurfurylideneamino)-
1,4-thiazine 1,1-dioxide *see* Nifurtimox.
1,4,5,6-Tetrahydro-1-methyl-6-oxopyridazine-3-
carboxamide *see* Medazomide.
Tetrahydro-*N*-methyl papaverine *see* Laudanosine.
1,2,3,4-Tetrahydro-2-methyl-9-phenyl-2-azafluorene
see Phenindamine.
3,4,5,6-Tetrahydro-5-methyl-1-phenyl-1*H*-2,5-benz-**
oxazocine *see* Nefopam.
2,3,4,9-Tetrahydro-2-methyl-9-phenyl-1*H*-inde-**
no[2,1-*c*]pyridine *see* Phenindamine.
1,2,3,4-Tetrahydro-*N*-methyl-4-phenyl-1-naphthyl-
amine *see* Tametraline.
1,2,3,4-Tetrahydro-2-methyl-9-phenyl-2-pyridindene
see Phenindamine.
2,3,5,6-Tetrahydro-6-[3-[(2-methylpropionyl)-
amino]phenyl]imidazo[2,1-*b*]thiazole *see* Butamisole.
5,6,7,8-Tetrahydro-α-[(1-methylpropylamino)-
methyl]-2-naphthalenemethanol *see* Butidrine.
(±)-1,3,4,14b-Tetrahydro-2-methyl-2*H*,10*H*-pyr-**
azino[1,2-*a*]pyrrolo[2,1-*c*][1,4]benzodiazepine *see*
Aptazapine.
Tetrahydro-*N*-methyl-2-(pyrid-2-yl)thio-2-thio-
phenecarboxamide *see* Picartamide.
1,3,4,6-Tetrahydro-1-methyl-2-pyrimidinemethanol
α-phenylcyclohexaneglycolate *see* Oxyphencyclimine.
m-[2-(1,4,5,6-Tetrahydro-1-methylpyrimidin-2-yl)-**
vinyl]phenol *see* Oxantel.
5,6,7,8-Tetrahydro-3-methylquinoline-8-thiocarbox-
amide *see* Tiquinamide.
5,6,7,8-Tetrahydro-4-methylquinoline-8-thiocarbox-
amide *see* Isotiquimide.
1,4,5,6-Tetrahydro-1-methyl-2-[*trans*-2-(thien-2-yl)-
vinyl]pyrimidine *see* Pyrantel.

5,6,7,8-Tetrahydro-4-methylthio-8-quinolinecarbox-amide *see* Isotiquimide.

1,2,3,4-Tetrahydro-1-morpholinoacetyl-3-phenylqui-nazolin-4-one *see* Moquizone.

1,2,3,4-TETRAHYDRONAPHTHALENE (tetral-in).

1,2,3,4-TETRAHYDRO-2-NAPHTHYLAMINE (2-aminotetralin; β-tetra).

2-(5,6,7,8-Tetrahydro-1-naphthylamino)-2-imidazol-ine *see* Tramazoline.

1-(1,2,3,4-Tetrahydronaphth-1-yl)imidazole-5-carb-oxylic acid ethyl ester *see* Etonam.

2-(1,2,3,4-Tetrahydro-1-naphthyl)-2-imidazoline *see* Tetryzoline.

Tetrahydro-α-(1-naphthylmethyl)furan-2-propionic acid diethylaminoethyl ester *see* Naftidrofuryl.

2-(5,6,7,8-Tetrahydronaphth-1-ylmethyl)-2-imid-azoline *see* Tefazoline.

Tetrahydronicotinic acid *see* Guvacine.

(±)-2,3,5,6-Tetrahydro-6-(*m*-nitrophenyl)imid-azo[2,1-*b*]thiazole *see* Nitramisole.

Tetrahydronorcholenic acid lactone *see* Gitoxigenin.

1,2,3,4-Tetrahydronorharman *see* Tryptoline.

Tetrahydro-1,4-oxazine *see* Morpholine.

Tetrahydrooxazole *see* Oxazolidine.

(6,7,8,8a-Tetrahydro-2-oxo-3-acenaphthenyl)oxam-ic acid *see* Oxalinast.

(4,5,6,7-Tetrahydro-6-oxobenzo[*b*]thien-4-yl)urea *see* Sulbenox.

6,7,8,9-Tetrahydro-4-oxo-10-propylbenzo[*g*]chrom-ene-2-carboxylic acid *see* Procromil.

6,7,8,9-Tetrahydro-4-oxo-10-propyl-4*H*-naphtho-[2,3-*b*]pyran-2-carboxylic acid *see* Procromil.

cis-Tetrahydro-2-oxothieno[3,4-*d*]imidazoline-4-va-leric acid *see* Biotin.

N-(Tetrahydro-2-oxothien-3-yl)acetamide *see* Ci-tiolone.

TETRAHYDROPAPAVEROLINE (1-(3,4-di-hydroxybenzyl)-1,2,3,4-tetrahydro-6,7-dihydr-oxyisoquinoline; 1,2,3,4-tetrahydro-6,7-dihydr-oxy-1-protocatechuylisoquinoline; norlaudano-soline).

1,2,3,6-Tetrahydro-1,2,2,6,6-pentamethylpyridine *see* Dropempine.

3,6,7,8-Tetrahydro-3-(β-D-*erythro*-pentofuranosyl)-imidazo[4,5-*d*][1,3]diazepin-8-ol *see* Coformycin.

Tetrahydrophenobarbital *see* Cyclobarbital.

Tetrahydro-6-(phenoxymethyl)-2*H*-1,3-oxazine-2-thione *see* Tifemoxone.

2,3,5,6-Tetrahydro-5-phenyl-1*H*-imidazo[1,2-*a*]imi-dazole *see* Deximafen; Imafen.

2,3,5,6-Tetrahydro-6-phenylimidazo[2,1-*b*]thiazole *see* Dexamisole; Levamisole; Tetramisole.

1,2,3,4-Tetrahydro-1-phenyl-1,4-naphthalenedicarb-oxylic acid *see* Isatropic acid.

Tetrahydro-4-phenyl-2*H*-pyran-4-carboxylic acid 1-methyl-3-morpholinopropyl ester *see* Fedrilate.

2,6,7,8-Tetrahydro-7-phenylpyrrolo[1,2-*a*]pyrimidin-4(3*H*)-one *see* Rofelodine.

1,3,4,9-Tetrahydro-1-propylpyrano[3,4-*b*]indole-1-acetic acid *see* Prodolic acid.

Tetrahydroprotoberberine *see* Berbine.

Tetrahydropyrazole *see* Pyrazolidine.

1,2,3,4-Tetrahydro-9*H*-pyrido[3,4-*b*]indole *see* Tryptoline.

3,4,5,6-Tetrahydro-2-pyrid-3-ylpyridine *see* Anaba-seine.

Tetrahydroserpentine *see* Ajmalicine.

3a,4,7,7a-Tetrahydro-2-[(1,1,2,2-tetrachloroethyl)-thio]-1*H*-isoindole-1,3-(2*H*)-dione *see* Captafol.

7,8,9,10-Tetrahydro-3,6,6,9-tetramethyl-6*H*-diben-zo[*b*,*d*]pyran-1-ol acetate *see* Pirnabin.

1,2,3,4-Tetrahydro-1,2,3,4-tetraoxonaphthalene di-hydrate *see* Oxolin.

6,7,8,9-Tetrahydro-5*H*-tetrazoloazepine *see* Pen-tetrazole.

Tetrahydrᴏ-1,2,4-thiadiazine 1,1-dioxide *see* Tau-rultam.

TETRAHYDRO-1,3-THIAZINE (metathiazane).

Tetrahydro-1,4-thiazine *see* Thiomorpholine.

Tetrahydro-2*H*-1,3-thiazine-4-carboxylic acid *see* Omonasteine.

p-(Tetrahydro-2*H*-1,2-thiazin-2-yl)benzenesulfon-amide *S*,*S*-dioxide *see* Sultiame.

Tetrahydrothiophene 1:1-dioxide *see* Sulfolane.

1,2,3,4-Tetrahydrothiopyrano[4,3-*b*]indole-8-carb-oxylic acid 2-dimethylaminoethyl ester *see* Ti-pindole.

5,6,7,8-Tetrahydro-3-[2-(4-*o*-tolylpiperazin-1-yl)-ethyl]-*s*-triazolo[4,3-*a*]pyridine *see* Dapiprazole.

5,6,7,8-Tetrahydro-6-(4-*o*-tolylpiperazin-1-yl)-2-naphthol *see* Tolnapersine.

3a,4,7,7a-Tetrahydro-2-[(trichloromethyl)thio]-1*H*-isoindole-1,3(2*H*)-dione *see* Captan.

1,2,3,4-Tetrahydro-1-(3,4,5-trimethoxybenzyl)-6,7-isoquinolinediol *see* Tretoquinol.

Tetrahydro-4-(3,4,5-trimethoxythiobenzoyl)-1,4-oxazine *see* Tritiozine.

1,3,4,9-Tetrahydro-*N*,*N*,1-trimethylindeno[2,1-*c*]-pyran-1-ethylamine *see* Pirandamine.

7,8,9,10-Tetrahydro-6,6,9-trimethyl-3-(1-methyloct-yl)-6-*H*-dibenzo[*b*,*d*]pyran-1-yl 4-(diethylamino)-butyrate *see* Naboctate.

Tetrahydro-6,6,9-trimethyl-3-pentyl-6*H*-dibenzo-[*b*,*d*]pyran-1-ol *see* Tetrahydrocannabinol(s).

6a,7,8,10a-Tetrahydro-6,6,9-trimethyl-3-pentyl-6*H*-dibenzo[*b*,*d*]pyran-1-ol *see* Dronabinol.

Tetrahydroxyadipic acid *see* Mucic acid.

2,3,7,8-Tetrahydroxy[1]benzopyrano[5,4,3-*cde*]-[1]benzopyran-5,10-dione *see* Ellagic acid.

Tetrahydroxy-*p*-benzoquinone *see* Tetroquinone.

5-(D-*arabino*-1,2,3,4-Tetrahydroxybutyl)-2-methyl-3-furoic acid methyl ester tetranicotinate *see* Ni-cofurate.

1,3,4,5-Tetrahydroxycyclohexanecarboxylic acid *see* Quinic acid.

3′,4′,5,7-Tetrahydroxyflavanone *see* Eriodictyol.

2′,3,5,7-Tetrahydroxyflavone *see* Datiscetin.

3′,4′,5,7-Tetrahydroxyflavone *see* Luteolin.

3,4′,5,7-Tetrahydroxyflavone *see* Kaempferol.

3,3′,4′,5-Tetrahydroxy-7-methoxyflavone *see* Rhamnetin.

3,4′,5,7-Tetrahydroxy-3′-methoxyflavone *see* Isorhamnetin.

2,3,7,8-Tetrahydroxy-5-methylaminomethyldibenzo-[*a*,*e*]cycloheptatriene *see* Adnamine.

Tetrahydroxyneopentane *see* Pentaerythritol.

11β,16α,17,21-Tetrahydroxypregna-1,4-diene-3,20-dione cyclic acetal with acetone *see* Desonide.

11β,16α,17,21-Tetrahydroxypregna-1,4-diene-3,20-dione cyclic 16,17-acetal with butyraldehyde *see* Budesonide.

3,17,20,21-Tetrahydroxypregnan-11-one *see* Cortolone; β-Cortolone.

11β,14,17,21-Tetrahydroxypregn-4-ene-3,20-dione cyclic 14,17-acetal with crotonaldehyde, 21-isonicotinate *see* Nicocortonide.

Tetrahydroxyquinone *see* Tetroquinone.

2α,3β,6β,23-tetrahydroxyurs-12-en-28-oic acid *see* Madecassic acid.

Tetrahydrozolin* *see* Tetryzoline.

Tetraiodophthalein *see* Iodophthalein sodium.

3,3′,5,5′-Tetraiodothyroacetic acid *see* Tetrac.

3,3′,5,5′-Tetraiodothyronine *see* Ddextrothyroxine; Levothyroxine; Thyroxine.

Tetraiodum *see* Iodophthalein sodium.

Tetraisopropylphosphorodiamidic anhydride *see* Iso-OMPA.

N,N′,N″,N‴-Tetraisopropylpyrophosphoramide *see* Iso-OMPA.

Tetraisopropylpyrophosphorotetramide *see* Iso-OMPA.

Tetrakis(methylsulfonyl)mannitol *see* Mannosulfan.

'Tetralex' *see* Tetrachloroethylene.

Tetralin *see* 1,2,3,4-Tetrahydronaphthalene.

Tetrallobarbital *see* Butalbital.

'Tetralysal' *see* Lymecycline.

'Tetram' *see* Amiton.

Tetramal* *see* Tetrabarbital.

Tetrameprozine *see* Aminopromazine.

Tetramesylmannitol *see* Mannosulfan.

'Tetramet-125' *see* Thyroxine I 125.

Tetramethanesulfonylmannitol *see* Mannosulfan.

1,2,9,10-Tetramethoxy-6aα-aporphine *see* Glaucine.

6′,7′,10,11-Tetramethoxyemetan *see* Emetine.

TETRAMETHRIN* (1-cyclohexene-1,2-dicarboximidomethyl 2,2-dimethyl-3-(2-methylpropenyl)-cyclopropanecarboxylate; hexahydro-1,3-dioxo-2*H*-isoindol-2-ylmethyl chrysanthemate; 3,4,5,6-tetrahydro-*N*-(hydroxymethyl)phthalimide chrysanthemate (ester); chrysanthemic acid ester with *N*-hydroxymethyl-1-cyclohexene-1,2-dicarboximide; neopinamine; phthalthrin; 'neo-pynamin').

N,N,10,10-Tetramethyl-Δ⁹⁽¹⁰ᴴ⁾,γ-anthracenepropylamine *see* Melitracen.

N,N,N′,N′-Tetramethylazoformamide *see* Diamide.

3,7,12,16-Tetramethyl-1,18-bis(2,6,6-trimethyl-1-cyclohexen-1-yl)-1,3,5,7,9,11,13,15,17-octadecanonaene *see* Betacarotene.

(1,1,3,3-Tetramethylbutyl)guanidine *see* Guanoctine.

2-[2-[2-[*p*-(1,1,3,3-Tetramethylbutyl)phenoxy]ethoxy]ethoxy]ethanesulfonic acid *see* Entsufon.

α-[*p*-(1,1,3,3-Tetramethylbutyl)phenyl]-ω-hydroxypoly(oxyethylene) *see* Octoxinol.

p-(1,1,3,3-Tetramethylbutyl)phenyl polyoxyethylene derivative *see* Tyloxapol.

2,2,9,9-Tetramethyl-1,10-decanediol *see* Gemcadiol.

3,3′-[Tetramethylenebis[oxy(2-hydroxytrimethylene)(acetylimino)]]bis[2,4,6-triiodo-5-(*N*-methylacetamido)benzoic acid] *see* Iozomic acid.

1,1′-Tetramethylenebis(1,2,3,4-tetrahydro-6,7-dimethoxyisoquinoline) *see* Bisobrin.

Tetramethylenediamine *see* Putrescine.

Tetramethylene dimesilate *see* Busulfan.

1-Tetramethylene-3-*p*-toluenesulfonylurea *see* Tolpyrramide.

3,7,11,15-Tetramethylhexadecanoic acid *see* Phytanic acid.

3,7,11,15-Tetramethyl-2-hexadecen-1-ol *see* Phytol.

Tetramethylmethane *see* Neopentane.

6,10,14,18-Tetramethyl-5,9,13,17-nonadecatetraen-2-one *see* Teprenone.

N,2,3,3-Tetramethylnorbornanamine *see* Mecamylamine.

Tetramethylolmethane *see* Pentaerythritol.

Tetramethylpalmitic acid *see* Phytanic acid.

2,6,10,14-Tetramethylpentadecane *see* Pristane.

N,N,N-α-Tetramethyl-10*H*-phenothiazine-10-ethanamium methyl sulfate *see* Thiazinamium metilsulfate.

Tetramethylphosphorodiamidic azide *see* Mazidox.

Tetramethylphosphorodiamidic fluoride *see* Dimefox.

1,2,2,6-Tetramethyl-4-piperidinol mandelate *see* Eucatropine.

2,2,6,6-TETRAMETHYLPIPERID-4-ONE TOSILATE (tetramethyl-4-oxopiperidine *p*-toluenesulfonate; 'tempidon').

2-(2,2,6,6-Tetramethylpiperid-1-yl)ethyl *o*-chloro-α-(*o*-chlorobenzyl)-α-hydroxyhydrocinnamate acetate (ester) *see* Tefenperate.

2,2,6,6-TETRAMETHYLQUINUCLIDINE METHIODIDE (imequin; temechin; temequin).

O,O,O′,O′-Tetramethyl O,O′-(thiodi-4,1-phenylene)phosphorothioate *see* Temefos.

Tetramethylthioperoxycarbonic diamide *see* Thiram.

Tetramethylthiuram disulfide *see* Thiram.

2,2,5,5-Tetramethyl-α-(*o*-toloxymethyl)-1-pyrrolidineethanol *see* Lotucaine.

2,5,7,8-Tetramethyl-2-(4,8,12-trimethyldecyl)-6-chromanol *see* α-Tocopherol.

Tetramethyltrimethylenehexamethylenebis(ammonium bromide)polymer *see* Hexadimethrine bromide.

2,5,7,8-Tetramethyl-2-(4,8,12-trimethyltridecyl)-6-chromanyl (*p*-chlorophenoxy)acetate *see* Tocofenoxate.

TETRAMISOLE*** ((±)-2,3,5,6-tetrahydro-6-phenylimidazo[2,1-*b*]thiazole; tetramizole; McN-JR-8299; R-8299; 'citarin'; 'nilverm').
See also Dexamisole; Levamisole.

Tetramizole *see* Tetramisole.

Tetramon *see* Tetrylammonium bromide.

'Tetran' *see* Oxytetracycline.

'Tetranase' *see under* Tetracycline.

Tetranicotinoylfructofuranose *see* Nicofuranose.

'Tetranitrin' *see* Erythrityl tetranitrate.

1,2,3,4-TETRANITROCARBAZOLE (Ho-2374;

497

'holfidal').

'**Tetranitrol**' *see* Erythrityl tetranitrate.

Tetranium *see* Tetrylammonium bromide.

'**Tetraolean**' *see under* Tetracycline.

4,7,10,13-Tetraoxahexadecane-1,16-dioylbis(3-carboxy-2,4,6-triiodoanilide) *see* Iodoxamic acid.

Tetrapon *see* Opium alkaloids.

α,α,6,6-Tetrapyrid-2-ylmethano-1,4-cyclopentadienemethanol *see* Pyrinoline.

TETRASODIUM EDETATE (edetate sodium; ethylenediaminetetraacetic acid tetrasodium salt).

Tetrastigmine* *see* Tetraethyl pyrophosphate.

TETRASUL* (2,4,4′,5-tetrachlorodiphenyl sulfide; 1,2,4-trichloro-5-[(*p*-chlorophenyl)thio]benzene; 'animert').

Tetrathion (tr) *see* Thiram.

'**Tetraverin**' *see* Rolitetracycline.

Tetraynoic acid *see* Eicosa-5,8,11,14-tetraynoic acid.

1-TETRAZENE (NH:NNHNH$_2$).

2-TETRAZENE (NH$_2$N:NNH$_2$).

TETRAZEPAM** (7-chloro-5-cyclohexen-1-yl-1,3-dihydro-1-methyl-2*H*-1,4-benzodiazepin-2-one; CB-4261; 'musaril'; 'myolastan').

TETRAZOLIUM BLUE (3,3′-dianisolebis-4,4′-(3,5-diphenyltetrazolium chloride); 3,3′-(3,3′-dimethoxy-4,4′-biphenylene)bis-(2,5-diphenyl-2*H*-tetrazolium chloride); blue tetrazolium; ditetrazolium chloride; BT).

Tetrazolium red *see* 2,3,5-Triphenyltetrazolium chloride.

Tetrazolo[1,5]perhydroazepine *see* Pentetrazole.

7-[2-(1*H*-Tetrazol-1-yl)acetamido]-3-[(1,3,4-thiadiazol-2-ylthio)methyl]-2-cephem-2-carboxylic acid *see* Ceftezole.

m-**(1*H*-Tetrazol-5-yloxy)phenol** *see* Melizame.

3-Tetrazol-5-ylthioxanthen-9-one 10,10-dioxide *see* Doxantrazole.

'**Tetrex**' *see* Tetracycline phosphate complex.

TETRIDAMINE*** (4,5,6,7-tetrahydro-2-methyl-3-methylamino-2*H*-indazole; tetrydamine; POLI 67).

Tetridin (tr) *see* Pyrithyldione.

'**Tetrim**' *see* Rolitetracycline.

'**Tetrine**' *see* Tetrasodium edetate.

TETRIPROFEN*** (1-[*p*-(1-carboxyethyl)phenyl]cyclohexene; *p*-(1-cyclohexen-1-yl)hydratropic acid; 2-[*p*-(cyclohexen-1-yl)phenyl]propionic acid).

'**Tetriv**' *see* Rolitetracycline.

TETROLIC ACID (2-butynoic acid; methylpropiolic acid).

'**Tetron**' *see* Tetraethyl pyrophosphate.

'**Tetronal**' *see* Dimethylsulfonal.

TETROQUINONE*** (tetrahydroxy-*p*-benzoquinone; tetrahydroxyquinone; HPEK; THQ; NSC-112931).

TETROXOPRIM*** (2,4-diamino-5-[3,5-dimethoxy-4-(2-methoxyethoxy)benzyl]pyrimidine; 5-[[3,5-dimethoxy-4-(2-methoxyethoxy)phenyl]methyl]-2,4-pyrimidinediamine; HL-781). *See also* Co-tetroxazine.

Tetrydamine* *see* Tetridamine.

TETRYLAMMONIUM BROMIDE*** (tetraethylammonium bromide; tetamon; tetramon; tetranium; TEA; TMD-10).

TETRYZOLINE*** (2-(1,2,3,4-tetrahydro-1-naphthyl)-2-imidazoline; tetrahydrozolin).

'**Tetucur**' *see* Ferropolimaler.

Teturam (tr) *see* Disulfiram.

'**Tevacycline**' *see* Tetracycline phosphate complex.

'**Texofor A.I.P**' *see* Cetomacrogol 1000.

TF-871 *see* Piribedil.

TFT *see* Trifluridine.

TGLVP *see* Terlipressin.

TGR *see* Thioguanosine.

Th-152 *see* Orciprenaline.

Th-322 *see* Metrifudil.

Th-494 *see* Stirocainide fumarate.

Th-1064 *see* Dimorpholamine.

Th-1165a *see* Fenoterol.

Th-1314 *see* Ethionamide.

Th-1321 *see* Protionamide.

Th-1325 *see* Hydracarbazine.

Th-1395 *see* Glybuthiazol.

Th-1405 *see* Ethionamide sulfoxide.

Th-2131 *see* Pempidine.

Th-2132 *see* Sulfasomizole.

Th-2180 *see* Propanidid.

Th-2516 *see under* Hydracarbazine.

Th-3624 *see* Isonicotinthioamide.

Th-4082 *see* Hydratropic acid.

Th-4114 *see* Phenobutiodil.

Th-4128 *see* 2-Phenylbutyramide.

Th-6040 *see* Diflubenzuron.

Th-20578 *see* Secnidazole.

THA *see* Tacrine.

'**Thalamonal**' *see under* Droperidol.

'**Thalamyd**' *see* Phthalylsulfacetamide.

THALIDOMIDE*** (*N*-(2,6-dioxopiperid-3-yl)-phthalimide; 3-(*N*-phthalimido)glutarimide; E-217; K-17; NSC-66847).

'**Thalisobumal**' *see* Buthalital sodium.

'**Thalisul**' *see* Phthalylsulfacetamide.

THALLIUM SULFATE ('celiopaste'; 'quick-kill'; 'zelio').

THALLOUS CHLORIDE (thallium chloride; NSC-15197).

THALLOUS CHLORIDE Tl 201* (radiothallium chloride; 'myolite').

'**THAM**' *see* Trometamol.

'**Thapsin**' *see* Calycopterin.

THAUMATIN* (mixture of 2 polypeptides from a tropical fruit; *Thaumatococcus daniellii* polypeptides; 'talin').

Thaumatococcus daniellii polypeptide mixture *see* Thaumatin.

'**Thawpit**' *see* Carbon tetrachloride.

THDT *see* Dilazep.

'**Thean**' *see* Proxyphylline.

'**Thebacetyl**' *see* Thebacon.

THEBACON** (6-acetoxy-4,5-epoxy-3-methoxy-*N*-methylmorphinan-6-ene; acetyldihydrocodeinone; dihydrocodeinone enol acetate; hydrocodone enol acetate; 'acedicon'; 'acetylcodone').

THEBAINE (codeinone (enol) methyl ether; paramorphine).

'Thebes' *see* Protheobromine.

Thecodine (tr) *see* Oxycodone.

Theelin *see* Estrone.

Theelol *see* Estriol.

'Thefanil' *see* Thenyldiamine.

Thein *see* Caffeine.

'Thekodin' *see* Codeine methyl bromide.

'Thelmesan' *see* Dimantine.

'Thelmin' *see* Piperazine.

'Themalon' *see* Thiambutene.

'Themisone' *see* Atrolactamide.

THENALIDINE*** (1-methyl-4-[*N*-(2-thenyl)anilino]piperidine; thenophenopiperidine; thenopiperidine; thenalidine tartrate; AS-716).

'Thenfadil' *see* Thenyldiamine.

THENIUM CLOSILATE*** (dimethyl(2-phenoxyethyl)-2-thenylammonium *p*-chlorobenzenesulfonate; BW-611C65; NSC-106569).

Thenoic acid(s) *see* Thiophenecarboxylic acid(s).

Thenophenopiperidine *see* Thenalidine.

Thenopiperidine *see* Thenalidine.

5-(2-Thenoyl)-2-benzimidazolecarbamic acid methyl ester *see* Nocodazole.

p-**2-Thenoylhydratropic acid** *see* Suprofen.

2-(*p*-2-Thenoylphenyl)propionic acid *see* Suprofen.

2-[4-[3-(2-Thenoyl)propyl]piperazin-1-yl]ethyl dimethylcarbamate *see* Pitenodil.

2-(2-Thenoylthio)propionylglycine *see* Stepronin.

THENYLDIAMINE*** (*N*,*N*-dimethyl-*N'*-pyrid-2-yl-*N'*-then-3-ylethylenediamine; 2-[[2-(dimethylamino)ethyl]-3-thenylamino]pyridine; dethylandiamine; WIN-2848; 'tenfidil'; 'thefanil'; 'thenfadil').

Thenylpyramine *see* Methapyrilene.

THEOBROMINE (3,7-dimethylxanthine; santheose).

Theobromineacetic acid *see* Theobromin-1-ylacetic acid.

THEOBROMINE CALCIUM SALICYLATE (calcium theobromsal).

THEOBROMINE SODIUM SALICYLATE (salnabrom; theobromsal).

THEOBROMIN-1-YLACETIC ACID (1-carboxymethyltheobromine; theobromineacetic acid).

See also Dextropropoxyphene theobromin-1-ylacetate.

Theobromsal *see* Theobromine sodium salicylate.

Theoclate(s)* *see* Teoclate(s).

'Theocor' *see* Protheobromine.

THEODRENALINE*** (7-[2[2-(3,4-dihydroxyphenyl)-2-hydroxyethylamino]ethyl]theophylline; 7-[2-(3,4,β-trihydroxyphenethylamino)-ethyl]theophylline; noradrenaline-theophylline; L-theodrenaline hydrochloride).

See also under Cafedrine.

Theofibrate* *see* Etofylline clofibrate.

'Theofrenon' *see under* Theophylline.

'Theo-heptylon' *see* Heptaminol theophyllineacetate.

'Theolair' *see* Theophylline.

'Theon' *see* Proxyphylline.

Theophyllamine* *see* Aminophylline.

THEOPHYLLINE (1,3-dimethylxanthine).

See also under Carbocisteine; Proscillaridin.

THEOPHYLLINE plus PROXYPHYLLINE ('theofrenon').

THEOPHYLLINE plus RACEPHEDRINE ('tedralan').

Theophyllineacetic acid *see* Theophyllin-7-ylacetic acid.

Theophylline-aminoisobutanol *see* Bufylline.

Theophylline cholinate *see* Choline theophyllinate.

Theophylline-diethylenediamine *see* Theophyllinepiperazine.

THEOPHYLLINE EPHEDRINE*** (compound of theophylline with (−)-ephedrine).

See also under Etophylline.

Theophylline-ethylenediamine *see* Aminophylline.

Theophylline-isobutanolamine *see* Bufylline.

THEOPHYLLINE-MEGLUMINE* (theophylline-methylglucamine).

Theophylline-methylglucamine *see* Theophyllinemeglumine.

THEOPHYLLINE-PIPERAZINE (theophyllinediethylenediamine).

Theophylline piperazine acetate *see* Acefylline piperazine.

THEOPHYLLINE PIPERAZINE *p*-AMINOBENZOATE ('antalby').

Theophylline-piperazine ethanoate *see* Acefylline piperazine.

THEOPHYLLINE SODIUM GLYCINATE (1 mol. theophylline with 2 mol. Na aminoacetate).

THEOPHYLLIN-7-YLACETIC ACID (7-(carboxymethyl)theophylline; theophyllineacetic acid).

See also Acefylline clofibrol; Heptaminol theophyllineacetate; Sodium theophyllin-7-ylacetate.

2-Theophyllin-7-ylethyl 2-(*p*-chlorophenoxy)-2-methylpropionate *see* Etofylline clofibrate.

'Theosalvose' *see* Theobromine.

'Theoxylline' *see* Choline theophyllinate.

'Thephorin' *see* Phendimetrazine *and* Phenindamin.

'Therabloat' *see* Poloxalene.

'Theralene' *see* Alimemazine.

'Theraleptique' *see* Dimorpholamine.

'Theraplix' *see* Glybuzole.

'Theraptique' *see* Dimorpholamine.

'Theratuss' *see* Pipazetate.

'Theriode-131' *see* Sodium iodide (^{131}I).

'Therminol' *see* Polychlorinated biphenyl.

'Thermogene' *see* Capsaicin.

'Theuralon' *see* Diethylthiambutene.

'Thevetigenin' *see* Digitoxigenin.

THFES(HM) *see* Zeranol.

Thiabendazole* *see* Tiabendazole.

Thiabenzonium *see* Tibezonium iodide.

Thiabutizide *see* Butizide.

THIACETARSAMIDE SODIUM*** (disodium salt of *S*,*S*-diester of *p*-carbamoyldithiobenzenearsonous acid with mercaptoacetic acid; disodium salt of *p*-[bis(carboxymethylmercapto)arsino]benzamide; 'arsenamide').

Thiacetazone* *see* Thioacetazone.

Thiachroman *see* Thiochroman.

Thiachromane *see* Meticrane.

Thiacyclobutane *see* Thietane.

Thiadenol *see* Tiadenol.

9-Thia-1,10-diazathracene *see* 10*H*-Pyrido[3,2-*b*]-[1,4]benzothiazine.

*N*¹**-(1,3,4-Thiadiazol-2-yl)sulfanilamide** *see* Sulfathiadiazole.

'Thiadipon' *see* Bentazepam.

THIALBARBITAL*** (5-allyl-5-(2-cyclohexen-1-yl)-2-thiobarbituric acid; thialbarbitone; thiohexallymal).

Thialbarbitone* *see* Thialbarbital.

Thialbutone* *see* Buthalital sodium.

Thialisobumal *see* Buthalital sodium.

THIAMAZOLE*** (2-mercapto-1-methylimidazole; 1-methyl-2-imidazolethiol; methimazole; mercazolyl; methylmercaptoimidazole; thymidazole; timidazol).

THIAMAZOLE METHIODIDE ('jomezol').

THIAMBUTENE* (3-amino-1,1-dithien-2-ylbut-1-ene; 1-methyl-3,3-dithien-2-ylallylamine).

THIAMBUTOSINE*** (4-butoxy-4'-dimethylamino-2-thiocarbanilide; 1-(*p*-butoxyphenyl)-3-(*p*-dimethylaminophenyl)-2-thiourea; C-15095 E; Ciba 1906).

Thiamethonium *see* Tiametonium iodide.

'Thiameton' *see* Tiametonium iodide.

THIAMINE*** (3-[(4-amino-2-methyl-5-pyrimidyl)methyl]-5-(2-hydroxyethyl)-4-methylthiazolium chloride; vitamin B₁; aneurine).

Thiamine acetylthiooctyl disulfide *see* Octotiamine.

Thiamine allyl disulfide *see* Allithiamine.

THIAMINE DISULFIDE (*N,N*'-[dithiobis[2-(2-hydroxyethyl)]-1-methylvinylene]bis[*N*-[(4-amino-2-methyl-5-pyrimidinyl)methyl]formamide]; 'neolamin').

Thiamine disulfide benzoate *see* Bisbentiamine.

Thiamine disulfide diisobutyrate *see* Sulbutiamine.

THIAMINE DISULFIDE PHOSPHATE (monophosphothiamine disulfide; 'biotinin'; 'vitamogen').

Thiamine monophosphate *see* Monophosphothiamine.

Thiamine phosphoric ester *see* Monophosphothiamine.

Thiamine propyl disulfide *see* Prosultiamine.

Thiamine pyrophosphate *see* Cocarboxylase.

Thiamine tetrahydrofurfuryl disulfide *see* Fursultiamine.

Thiamiprine* *see* Tiamiprine.

Thiamizide* *see* Tiamizide.

Thiamorpholine *see* Thiomorpholine.

THIAMPHENICOL*** (D(+)-*threo*-2,2-dichloro-*N*-(β-hydroxy-α-hydroxymethyl-*p*-methylsulfonylphenethyl)acetamide; D(+)-*threo*-2-dichloroacetamido-1-(*p*-methylsulfonylphenyl)-1,3-propanediol; dextrosulfenidol; thiophenicol; CB-8053; WIN-5063-2; 'glitisol'; 'thiocymetin').

THIAMPHENICOL GLYCINATE (thiamphenicol aminoacetate; 'neomyson G'; 'urfamicina'; 'urfamycin').

THIAMYLAL* (5-allyl-5-(1-methylbutyl)-2-thiobarbituric acid; 5-allyl-5-isoamyl-2-thiobarbituric acid; thiamylal sodium).

Thianide (tr) *see* Ethionamide.

'Thiantoin' *see* Thyphenytoin.

Thiasine *see* Thioneine.

Thiasolucin *see* Noprylsulfamide.

'Thiaver' *see* Epitizide.

Thiaxanthene *see* Thioxanthene.

1,4-Thiazan *see* Thiomorpholine.

Thiazenone *see* Tiazesim.

Thiazesium* *see* Tiazesim.

THIAZINAMIUM CHLORIDE* (trimethyl(1-methyl-2-phenothiazin-10-yl)ethylammonium chloride; *N,N,N*,α-tetramethyl-10*H*-phenothiazine-10-ethanamium chloride; Wy-460E).

THIAZINAMIUM METILSULFATE*** (*N,N,N*-α-tetramethyl-10*H*-phenothiazine-10-ethanamium methyl sulfate; trimethyl(1-methyl-2-phenothiazin-10-ylethyl)ammonium methyl sulfate; promethazine methyl methosulfate; thiazinamon; RP-3554; 'multergan'; 'multezin'; 'padisal').

Thiazinamon *see* Thiazinamium metilsulfate.

Thiazolidine-4-carboxylic acid *see* Timonacic.

Thiazolidine-2,4-dicarboxylic acid *see* Tidiacic.

Thiazolidin-4-one-2-thione *see* Rhodanine.

4-THIAZOLINE-2-THIONE (2-mercaptothiazoline; 'thyroidan').

THIAZOLINOBUTAZONE (phenylbutazone compound (salt) with 2-amino-2-thiazoline; LAS-11871; 'fordonal').

Thiazolsulfone *see* Thiazosulfone.

2-Thiazol-4-ylbenzimidazole *see* Tiabendazole.

2-Thiazol-4-yl-5-benzimidazolecarbamic acid isopropyl ester *see* Cambendazole.

N-**Thiazol-2-yl-*p*-phenolsulfonamide** *see* Phenolsulfazole.

p-**(2-Thiazolylsulfamoyl)maleamic acid** *see* Maleylsulfathiazole.

5-[*p*-(2-Thiazolylsulfamoyl)phenylazo]salicylic acid *see* Salazosulfathiazole.

4'-(2-Thiazolylsulfamoyl)phthalanilic acid *see* Phthalylsulfathiazole.

4'-(Thiazol-2-ylsulfamoyl)succinanilic acid *see* Succinylsulfathiazole.

*N*¹**-Thiazol-2-ylsulfanilamide** *see* Sulfathiazole.

Thiazon *see* Dazomet.

THIAZOSULFONE*** (*p*-aminophenyl 2-aminothiazol-5-yl sulfone; thiazolsulfone).

Thiazothielite *see* Antienite.

Thiazothienol *see* Antazonite.

2-Thiazylamine *see* Aminothiazole.

THIBENZAZOLINE (benzimidazole-1,3-dimethanol-2-thione; 1,3-bis(hydroxymethyl)benzimidazole-2-thione).

'Thibenzole' *see* Tiabendazole.

'Thibetine' *see* Trolnitrate.

Thidoxol *see* Tioxolone.

THIENAMYCIN (3-[[(2-aminoethyl)thio]-6-(1-hydroxyethyl)-7-oxo-1-azabicyclo[3.2.0]hept-2-ene-2-carboxylic acid).

7-(2-Thienylacetamido)cephalosporanic acid *see* Cefalotin.

N-[7-(2-Thienylacetamido)ceph-3-em-3-ylmethyl-pyridinium]-4-carboxylate *see* Cefaloridine.

7-[2-(2-Thienyl)acetamido]-3-[(*s*-triazol-3-ylthio)-methyl]-2-cephem-2-carboxylic acid *see* Cefetrizole.

Thienylcarbenicillin *see* Ticarcillin.

5-(2-Thienylcarbonyl)-1*H*-benzimidazole-2-carbamic acid methyl ester *see* Nocodazole.

α-Thien-3-ylcyclohexaneacetic acid 2-hexamethyl-eniminoethyl ester *see* Cetiedil.

1-(1-Thien-2-ylcyclohexyl)piperidine *see* Tenocyclidine.

6-(Thienylmalonamido)penicillanic acid *see* Ticarcillin.

3-(2-Thienyl)-2-piperazinone *see* Tenilsetam.

THIETANE (thiacyclobutane; thiethane; trimethylene sulfide).

'Thiethamyl' *see* Thiamylal.

Thiethane *see* Thietane.

THIETHYLPERAZINE*** (2-(ethylthio)-10-[3-(4-methylpiperazin-1-yl)propyl]phenothiazine; thietylperazine; tietylperazine; thiethylperazine maleate; GS-95; NSC-130044).

Thietylperazine *see* Thiethylperazine.

Thifenamil* *see* Tifenamil.

'Thifor' *see* Endosulfan.

THIHEXINOL METHYLBROMIDE*** (*trans*-[4-(hydroxydi-2-thienylmethyl)cyclohexyl]trimethylammonium bromide).

'Thilatazin' *see* Perphenazine.

'Thiloadren' *see under* Dipivefrine.

'Thilorbin' *see* Fluorescein.

Thimerfonate sodium* *see* Sodium timerfonate.

Thimerosal* *see* Thiomersal.

'Thimet' *see* Phorate.

Thimethaphan *see* Trimetaphan camsilate.

'Thimolone' *see* Phenythilone.

'Thimul' *see* Endosulfan.

THIOACETAZONE*** (4'-formylacetanilide thiosemicarbazone; *p*-acetamidobenzaldehyde thiosemicarbazone; thiacetazone; amithiozone; tibon; RP-4207; Sdt-1041; SHCH-87; TbI/698).

Thioamobarbital *see* Thioethamyl.

Thioarsphenamine *see* Sulfarsphenamine.

Thiobaral (tr) *see* Thiobarbital.

THIOBARBITAL (5,5-diethyl-2-thiobarbituric acid; thiobaral).

Thiobenzoic acid esters *see* Tibenzate; Tioctilate.

'Thiobilin' *see under* Tidiacic.

2,2'-Thiobis(4-chlorophenol) *see* Fenticlor.

2,2-Thiobis(4,6-dichlorophenoxide) *see* Bithionol.

5,5'-[Thiobis(ethylenecarbonylimino)]bis[*N*,*N'*-bis(2,3-dihydroxypropyl)-2,4,6-triiodo-*N*,*N'*-dimethylisophthalamide] *see* Iotasul.

THIOBUTABARBITAL (5-*sec*-butyl-5-ethyl-2-thiobarbituric acid; 5-ethyl-5-(1-methylpropyl)-2-thiobarbituric acid).

Thiobutazine *see* Butizide.

Thiobutone *see* Buthalital sodium.

THIOCAINE (2-(diethylamino)ethyl *p*-aminothiolobenzoate).

Thiocarbamide *see* Thiourea.

N[1]-Thiocarbamylsulfanilamide *see* Sulfathiourea.

THIOCARBANILIDE (1,3-diphenyl-2-thiourea).

THIOCARBOXIM* (2-cyanoethyl *N*-[[(methylamino)carbonyl]oxy]ethanimidothioate; 2-cyanoethyl *N*-(methylcarbamoyloxy)acetimidothioate; *N*-[[(methylamino)carbonyl]oxy]ethanimidothioic acid 2-cyanoethyl ester; 'talcord').

Thiocarlide* *see* Tiocarlide.

THIOCHOLINE ((2-mercaptoethyl)trimethylammonium hydroxide or salts).

Thiocholine acetate *see* Acetylthiocholine.

THIOCHROMAN (3,4-dihydro-1,2*H*-benzothiopyran; thiachroman).

'Thiochrysine' *see* Sodium aurotiosulfate.

Thiocol *see* Sulfogaiacol.

THIOCOLCHICOSIDE** (4-acetamido-15-glucopyranosyloxy-13,14-dimethoxy-8-methylthio-7-oxotricyclo[10.4.0.0^{5,11}]hexadeca-1(12),5,8,10,13,15-hexaene; 2,10-di(demethoxy)-2-glucosyloxy-10-methylthiocolchicine).

'Thiocolciran' *see* *N*-Deacetylthiocolchicine.

'Thiocron' *see* Amidithion.

'Thioctacid' *see* Thioctic acid.

THIOCTIC ACID (1,2-dithiolane-3-pentanoic acid; 5-(1,2-dithiolan-3-yl)valeric acid; 6,8-thioctic acid; α-lipoic acid; α-liponic acid; acetate-replacing factor; protogen A; pyruvate oxidation factor).
See also Trometamol thioctate.

'Thioctidase' *see* Thioctic acid.

'Thiocuran' *see* Co-trimoxazole.

THIOCYANIC ACID (rhodanic acid; sulfocyanic acid).

'Thiocymetin' *see* Thiamphenicol.

'Thiodan' *see* Endosulfan.

Thiodemeton *see* Disulfoton.

3,3'-Thiodialanine *see* Lanthionine.

Thiodiethylenebis(ethyldimethylammonium iodide) *see* Tiametonium iodide.

THIODIGLYCOL*** (bis(2-hydroxyethyl) sulfide; 'tedegyl').

Thiodiphenylamine *see* Phenothiazine.

O,*O'*-Thiodi(*p*-phenylene) phosphorothioate *see* Tetrafenphos.

O,*O'*-Thiodi(*p*-phenylene) *O*,*O*,*O'*,*O'*-tetramethyl bis(phosphorothioate) *see* Temefos.

THIODIPIN (tr) (1,4-bis[*N*,*N'*-bis(ethylene)diamidothiophosphoryl]piperazine; *N*,*N'*-diethylenebis(*N*,*N'*-diethylenephosphorothioic diamide); 1,4-piperazinediylbis[bis(1-aziridinyl)phosphine sulfide]).

2,2'-Thiodipyridine 1,1'-dioxide *see* Dipyrithione.

'Thiodrol' *see* Epitiostanol.

THIOETHAMYL (5-ethyl-5-(3-methylbutyl)-2-thiobarbituric acid; 5-ethyl-5-isoamyl-2-thiobarbituric acid; 5-ethyl-5-isopentyl-2-thiobarbituric acid; thioamobarbital; V-7; 'venesetic').

Thioethanolamine *see* Mercaptamine.

THIOFURADENE*** (1-(5-nitrofurfurylideneamino)imidazolidine-2-thione; nifurthiline; 'furidin').

Thiofuran *see* Thiophene.

Thiofurfuran *see* Thiophene.

'Thiogenal' *see* Methitural.

(1-Thio-D-glucopyranosato)gold see Aurothioglucose.

(1-Thio-β-D-glucopyranosato)(triethylphosphine)-gold 2,3,4,6-tetraacetate see Auranofin.

Thioglucose S-gold derivative see Aurothioglucose.

Thioglycolic acid see Mercaptoacetic acid.

Thioguanine* see Tioguanine.

6-Thioguanine see Tioguanine.

6-Thioguanine riboside see Thioguanosine.

THIOGUANOSINE (2-amino-9-β-D-ribofuranosylpurine-6-thiol; 6-thioguanine riboside; tioguanine riboside; TGR; NSC-29422; SK-18615).

Thiohexallymal* see Thialbarbital.

THIOHEXAMIDE*** (1-cyclohexyl-3-(p-methylthiobenzenesulfonyl)urea).

THIOHEXETHAL (5-ethyl-5-hexyl-2-thiobarbituric acid).

Thiohistidine trimethylbetaine see Thioneine.

Thioinosine see Mercaptopurine ribonucleoside.

'Thiola' see Tiopronin.

Thiole see Thiophene.

Thiolhistidine-betaine see Thioneine.

Thiolosystox see Demeton-S.

Thiolpropionamidoacetic acid see Tiopronin.

Thiomalic acid see Mercaptosuccinic acid.

Thiomebumal* see Thiopental sodium.

'Thiomedon' see N-Acetylmethionine.

'Thiomerin' see Mercaptomerin.

THIOMERSAL** (sodium o-(ethylmercurithio)-benzoate; mercurothiolate; thimerosal; sodium (ethylmercurithio)salicylate; thiomersalate).

Thiomersalate see Thiomersal.

THIOMERSAL TANNATE ('amertan').

Thiomesterone* see Tiomesterone.

Thiomethibumal* see Methitural.

THIOMETON* (S-[2-(ethylthio)ethyl] O,O-dimethyl phosphorodithioate; dithiomethon; dithiometon; M-81; 'aasystem'; 'dimeate'; 'ekatin'; 'intrathion'; 'intration'; 'sysmeton').

Thiometon ethyl see Disulfoton.

THIOMORPHOLINE (tetrahydro-1,4-thiazine; 1,4-thiazan; parathiazan; thiamorpholine).

'Thiomucase' see Chondroitinase.

THIONAZIN* (O,O-diethyl O-1,4-diazinyl phosphorothioate; O,O-diethyl O-pyrazinyl phosphorothioate; 'cynem'; 'nemafos'; 'nemaphos'; 'zinophos').

THIONEINE ((S)-α-carboxy-2,3-dihydro-N,N,N-trimethyl-2-thioxo-1H-imidazole-4-ethanamium hydroxide inner salt; 1-carboxy-[2-(2-mercaptoimidazol-4(or-5)-yl)ethyl]trimethylammonium hydroxide inner salt; methyl ester betaine of 2-mercapto-N,N-dimethylhistidine; ergothioneine; ergothionone; sympectothion; thiasine; thiohistidine trimethylbetaine; thiolhistidine-betaine; thiozone).

'Thionembutal' see Thiopental sodium.

'Thionex' see Endosulfan.

THIONINE (7-amino-3-imino(3H)phenothiazine; Lauth's violet).

THIONOL (7-hydroxyphenothiazin-3-one).

N-Thiononicotinoylamphetamine see Thiophenatin.

Thionosystox see Demeton-O.

Thiopanic acid see Pantoyltaurine.

'Thioparamizone' see Thioacetazone.

THIOPENTAL SODIUM*** (sodium derivative of 5-ethyl-5-(1-methylbutyl)-2-thiobarbituric acid; penthiobarbital; pentothiobarbital; thiomebumal; thiopentemal; thiopentone; RP 245; V-5).

Thiopentemal* see Thiopental sodium.

Thiopentone* see Thiopental sodium.

Thioperazine see Thioproperazine.

THIOPHANATE* (1,2-bis(3-ethoxycarbonyl-2-thioureido)benzene; diethyl 4,4'-o-phenylenebis(3-thioallophanate); diethyl [1,2-phenylenebis(iminocarbonothioyl)]bis(carbamate); 1,1'-o-phenylenebis[3-(ethoxycarbonyl)-2-thiourea]; NF-35; 'cercobin'; 'nemafax'; 'topsin').

THIOPHANATE-METHYL* (dimethyl 4,4'-(o-phenylene)bis(3-thioallophanate); dimethyl [1,2-phenylenebis(iminocarbonothioyl)]bis(carbamate); 1,2-bis(3-methoxycarbonyl-2-thioureido)-benzene; 1,1-o-phenylenebis[(3-methoxycarbonyl)-2-thiourea]; methyl thiophanate; NF-44; 'topsin M').

Thiophan sulfone see Sulfolane.

THIOPHENATIN (tr) (N-(2-phenylisopropyl)nicotinthioamide; N-thiononicotinoylamphetamine; tiofenatin).

THIOPHENE (divinylene sulfide; thiofuran; thiofurfuran; thiole; thiotetrole).

THIOPHENECARBOXYLIC ACID(S) (thenoic acid(s)).

6-(Thiophenemalonamido)penicillanic acid see Ticarcillin.

Thiophenicol see Thiamphenicol.

THIOPHENOBARBITAL (5-ethyl-5-phenyl-2-thiobarbituric acid).

Thiophenylpyridylamine see Pipazetate and 10H-Pyrido[3,2-b][1,4]benzothiazine.

Thiophos-3422 see Parathion.

Thiophosphamide (tr) see Thiotepa.

Thiophosphoramide see Phosphorothioic triamide. See also Phosphoramidothioic acid; Phosphoramidodithioic acid.

Thiophosphoric acid see Phosphorothioic acid.

Thioproline see Timonacic.

THIOPROPAZATE*** (10-[3-[4-(2-acetoxyethyl)piperazin-1-yl]propyl]-2-chlorophenothiazine; thiopropazate dihydrochloride; SC-7105).

THIOPROPERAZINE*** (N,N-dimethyl-10-[3-(4-methylpiperazin-1-yl)propyl]-2-phenothiazinesulfonamide; thioperazine; thioproperazine mesilate; thioproperazine methanesulfonate; RP 7843).

Thiopurinol see Tisopurine.

THIOQUINOX* (1,3-dithiolo[4,5-b]quinoxaline-2-thione; chinothionat; 'eradex').

THIORIDAZINE*** (10-[2-(1-methylpiperid-2-yl)ethyl]-2-(methylthio)phenothiazine; thioridazine hydrochloride; TP-21). See also under Co-dergocrine.

Thioridazine dioxide see Sulforidazine.

Thioridazine oxide see Mesoridazine.

Thiosalan* see Tiosalan.

502

'Thiosan' *see* Thiram.
'Thioseconal' *see* Thiamylal.
Thiosinamine *see* Allylthiourea.
'Thiospasmin' *see* Hexasonium iodide.
'Thiosporin' *see* Sulfomyxin.
Thiosulfates *see* Calcium thiosulfate; Sodium thiosulfate.
'Thiosulfil' *see* Sulfamethizole.
'Thiosystox' *see* Disulfoton.
THIOTEPA*** (*N,N',N'''*-triethylenephosphorothioic triamide; triethylenethiophosphoramide; triethylenimine thiophosphoramide; tris(1-aziridinyl)phosphine sulfide; tris(ethylenimino)thiophosphate; STEPA; TESPA; thiophosphamide; tiofosfamide; tio-TEF; TSPA; NSC-6396).
THIOTETRABARBITAL*** (5-ethyl-5-(1-ethylbutyl)-2-thiobarbituric acid; thiotetramal).
Thiotetramal* *see* Thiotetrabarbital.
Thiotetrole *see* Thiophene.
'Thio-theo' *see under* Carbocisteine.
6-THIOTHEOPHYLLINE (1,3-dimethyl-6-thioxanthine; 1,3-dimethylpurin-2-one-6-thione).
Thiothixene* *see* Tiotixene.
'Thiothyr' *see* Thiobarbital.
[Thio[*o*-[3-(*p*-tolylsulfonyl)ureido]phenyl]carbamoyl]phosphoramidic acid diethyl ester *see* Uredofos.
'Thiotox' *see* Endosulfan.
'Thiotyr' *see* Thiobarbital.
THIOURACIL (2-thiouracil).
THIOUREA (thiocarbamide; 2-thiourea).
4-(Thiovanilloyl)morpholine *see* Vanitiolide.
THIOXANTHENE (thiaxanthene).
'Thioxidrene' *see* Citiolone.
Thioxolone* *see* Tioxolone.
2-Thioxo-4-thiazolidinone *see* Rhodanine.
Thiozone *see* Thioneine.
THIP *see* Gaboxadol.
Thipendyl *see* Isothipendyl.
Thiphen *see* Tifenamil.
Thiphenamil* *see* Tifenamil.
Thiphencillin *see* Tifencillin.
THIRAM** (bis(dimethylthiocarbamoyl) disulfide; tetramethylthiuram disulfide; tetramethylthioperoxycarbonic diamide; tetrathion; TMTDS; NSC-1771; SQ-1489).
See also under Benomyl.
'Thitrol' *see* 4-(4-Chloro-2-methylphenoxy)butyric acid.
'Thiurad' *see* Thiram.
'Thiuramyl' *see* Thiram.
'Thiuranide' *see* Disulfiram.
'Thiuretic' *see* Hydrochlorothiazide.
THN *see* Tryptoline.
'Thomasin' *see* Etilefrine.
'Thombran' *see* Trazodone.
'Thonzide' *see* Tonzonium bromide.
Thonzonium* *see* Tonzonium bromide.
THONZYLAMINE*** (*N*-(*p*-methoxybenzyl)-*N',N'*-dimethyl-*N*-pyrimid-2-ylethylenediamine; histazylamine; thonzylamine hydrochloride).
Thonzylamine hexadecyl bromide *see* Tonzonium bromide.

'Thoragol' *see* Bibenzonium bromide.
'Thorazine' *see* Chlorpromazine.
THORIUM DIOXIDE SOL ('thorotrast').
'Thorotrast' *see* Thorium dioxide sol.
'Thoxan' *see* Etoxadrol.
Thozalinone* *see* Tozalinone.
THPP *see* Diponium bromide.
THQ *see* Tetroquinone.
THR *see* Troxerutin.
THREITOL (*threo*-1,2,3,4-butanetetrol).
D-Threitol 1,4-dimethanesulfonate *see* D-Dihydroxybusulfan.
D-Threityl dimesilate *see* D-Dihydroxybusulfan.
L-Threityl dimesilate *see* Treosulfan.
THREONINE* (2-amino-3-hydroxybutyric acid).
8A-L-Threonine-10A-L-isoleucine-30B-L-threonineinsulin *see* Insulin human.
'Thrombocid' *see* Sodium polyanhydromannuronic sulfate.
Thrombocytin *see* Serotonin.
'Thrombodym' *see* Neodymium 3-sulfoisonicotinate.
'Thromboliquin' *see* Heparin.
'Thrombolysin' *see* Fibrinolysin (human).
'Thrombophob' *see* Heparin.
'Thrombossoine-heparin' *see* Diarbarone.
Thrombotonin *see* Serotonin.
'Thrombovar' *see* Sodium tetradecyl sulfate.
'Thrombo-vetren' *see* Heparin.
THS-839 *see* Denatonium benzoate.
3-Thujanone *see* Absinthol.
α-THUJAPLICIN (3-isopropyl-2,4,6-cycloheptatrien-2-ol-1-one; 3-isopropyltropolone).
β-THUJAPLICIN (4-isopropyl-2,4,6-cycloheptatrien-2-ol-1-one; 4-isopropyltropolone; hinokitiol).
γ-THUJAPLICIN (5-isopropyltropolone).
Thujone *see* Absinthol.
THURFYL NICOTINATE* (tetrahydrofuryl ester of nicotinic acid; nicotafuryl; 'trafuril').
Thuyon *see* Absinthol.
'Thybon' *see* Liothyronine.
'Thylamid' *see* Tricetamide.
'Thylate' *see* Thiram.
'Thylin' *see* Nifenazone.
'Thyloquinone' *see* Menadione.
'Thymergix' *see* Pyrovalerone.
Thymic acid *see* Thymol.
Thymidazole (tr) *see* Thiamazole.
THYMIDINE (thymine deoxyriboside).
THYMIDYLIC ACID (thymidine phosphate).
THYMINE (2,4-dihydroxy-5-methylpyrimidine; 5-methyluracil).
Thymine deoxyriboside *see* Thymidine.
THYMOHYDROQUINONE (*p*-cymene-2,5-diol; 2-isopropyl-5-methylhydroquinone).
THYMOL (3-*p*-cymenol; 1-hydroxy-2-isopropyl-5-methylbenzene; 2-isopropyl-5-methylphenol; thymic acid; *m*-thymol).
m-Thymol *see* Thymol.
Thymolated silver sulfone *see* Diathymosulfone silver.
THYMOPENTIN*** (*N*-[*N*-[*N*-(*N²*-L-arginyl-L-

503

lysyl]-L-α-aspartyl]-L-valyl]-L-tyrosine; TP-5; 'immunox').

THYMOQUINONE (*p*-cymene-2,5-dione; 2-isopropyl-5-methylbenzoquinone; *p*-mentha-3,6-diene-2,5-dione).

THYMOSTIMULIN* (polypeptide immunostimulant from thymus of mammalian species).

THYMOSTIMULIN (bovine) (TP-1).

Thymosulfone *see* Diathymosulfone.

o-**THYMOTIC ACID** (3-hydroxy-2-*p*-cymenecarboxylic acid; 3-isopropyl-6-methylsalicylic acid; thymotinic acid).
See also Cetylpyridinium *o*-thymotate.

Thymotinic acid *see o*-Thymotic acid.

Thymoxamine* *see* Moxisylyte.

Thymus polypeptide *see* Thymostimulin.

2-(Thymyloxymethyl)-2-imidazoline *see* Tymazoline.

'**Thyodan**' *see* Endosulfan.

'**Thyonex**' *see* Endosulfan.

Thypendyl *see* Isothipendyl.

THYPHENYTOIN (5-phenyl-5-(2-thienyl)hydantoin; phetenylate; phethenylate; thyphenytoin sodium; 'thiantoin').

'**Thypinone**' *see* Protirelin.

'**Thyractin**' *see* Thyroglobulin.

'**Thyreocordon**' *see* Thibenzazoline.

'**Thyreosedine**' *see* Thiobarbital.

'**Thyreostat II**' *see* Propylthiouracil.

THYROACETIC ACID (2-[4-(4-hydroxyphenoxy)phenyl]acetic acid).

Thyrocalcitonin *see* Calcitonin.

'**Thyrochlorate**' *see* Potassium perchlorate.

'**Thyrodex**' *see* Dextrothyroxine.

THYROGLOBULIN* (pig thyroid fraction containing not less than 0.7% total iodine; 'proloid'; 'thyractin').

'**Thyroidan**' *see* 4-Thiazoline-2-thione.

'**Thyrolar**' *see* Liotrix.

'**Thyroliberin**' *see* Protirelin.

Thyromedan* *see* Tyromedan.

THYRONAMINE (β-(4-hydroxyphenoxy)phenethylamine).

THYRONINE (3-[4-(4-hydroxyphenoxy)phenyl]alanine).

THYROPROPIC ACID* (4-(4-hydroxy-3-iodophenoxy)-3,5-diiodohydrocinnamic acid; 3-[4-(4-hydroxy-3-iodophenoxy)-3,5-diiodophenyl]propionic acid; triiodothyropropionic acid; triprop; 'triopron').

'**Thyrosan**' *see* Aminothiazole.

Thyrotrophic hormone *see* Thyrotrophin.

THYROTROPHIN* (thyrotrophic hormone; thyrotropin; TSH; TTH).

Thyrotrophin releasing hormone synthetic *see* Protirelin.

Thyrotropin *see* Thyrotrophin.

Thyroxin *see* Thyroxine.

THYROXINE (3-[4-(4-hydroxy-3,5-diiodophenoxy)-3,5-diiodophenyl]alanine; 3,3',5,5'-tetraiodothyronine; thyroxin; T4).
See also Dextrothyroxine; Levothyroxine.

THYROXINE I 125 ('tetramet-125').

'**Thyrtropar**' *see* Thyrotrophin.

TIABENDAZOLE* (2-thiazol-4-ylbenzimidazole; thiabendazole; G-491; MK-360).

TIADENOL* (1,10-bis(2-hydroxyethylthio)decane; 2,2'-(decamethylenedithio)diethanol; 1,16-dihydroxy-3,14-dithiahexadecane; thiadenol; LL-1558; 'fonlipol').

Tiadenol bis(clofibrate) *see* Tiafibrate.

'**Tiadilon**' *see* Tidiacic arginine.

TIAFIBRATE* (clofibric acid diester with 2,2'-(decamethylenedithio)diethanol; 2,2'-(decamethylenedithio)diethanol bis(clofibrate)).

TIAMENIDINE* (2-(2-chloro-4-methylthien-3-ylamino)-2-imidazoline; tiamenidine hydrochloride; HOE-440; HOE-42-440).

Tiameton* *see* Tiametonium iodide.

TIAMETONIUM IODIDE* (thiodiethylenebis-(ethyldimethylammonium iodide); tiameton; thiamethonium).

TIAMIPRINE* (2-amino-6-(1-methyl-4-nitroimidazol-5-ylthio)purine; 6-(1-methyl-4-nitroimidazol-5-ylthio)guanine; imidazolylthioguanine; thiamiprine; ITG; BW-57-323; NSC-38887; 'guaneran').

TIAMIZIDE (4-chloro-*N*-methyl-3-(methylsulfamoyl)benzamide; diapamide; thiamizide; CI-456; CN-36337; D-1593).

TIAMULIN* ([[2-(diethylamino)ethyl]thio]acetic acid 8-ester with octahydro-5,8-dihydroxy-4,6,9,10-tetramethyl-6-vinyl-3a,9-propano-3a*H*-cyclopentacycloocten-1(4*H*)-one; 6-ethenyldecahydro-5-hydroxy-4,6,9,10-tetramethyl-1-oxo-3a,9-propano-3a*H*-cyclopentacycloocten-8-yl [[2-(diethylamino)ethyl]thio]acetate; HFU-81723; SQ-14055; 'dynalin'; 'dynamutilin').

TIAMULIN FUMARATE* (SQ-22947; 'tiamutin').

'**Tiamutin**' *see* Tiamulin fumarate.

TIANAFAC (5-chloro-3-methylbenzo[*b*]thiophene-2-acetic acid; L-8109).

TIANEPTINE* (7-[[3-chloro-6,11-dihydro-6-methyldibenzo[*c,f*][1,2]-thiazepin-11-yl]amino]-heptanoic acid *S,S*-dioxide).

TIAPAMIL* (*N*-(3,4-dimethoxyphenethyl)-2-(3,4-dimethoxyphenyl)-*N*-methyl-1,3-dithiane-2-propylamine 1,1,3,3-tetraoxide; dimeditiapramine; verocainine; Ro 11-1781).

TIAPIRINOL* (tetrahydro-2-[3-hydroxy-5-(hydroxymethyl)-2-methylpyrid-4-yl]-2*H*-1,3-thiazine-4-carboxylic acid).

'**Tiapridal**' *see* Tiapride.

TIAPRIDE* (*N*-[2-(diethylamino)ethyl]-2-methoxy-5-(methylsulfonyl)benzamide; *N*-[2-(diethylamino)ethyl]-5-(methylsulfonyl)-*o*-anisamide; tiapride hydrochloride; FLO-1347; 'italprid'; 'tiapridal'; 'tiapridex').

'**Tiapridex**' *see* Tiapride.

TIAPROFENIC ACID* (5-benzoyl-α-methyl-2-thiopheneacetic acid; 5-benzoyl-2-(1-carboxyethyl)thiophene; 2-(5-benzoylthien-2-yl)propionic acid; RU-15060; 'surgam').

TIAPROST* ((±)-(*Z*)-7-[(1*R**,2*R**,3*R**,5*S**)-3,5-dihydroxy-2-[(*E*)-(3*R**S**)-3-hydroxy-4-(3-

thienyloxy)-1-butenyl]cyclopentyl]-5-heptenoic acid).

TIARAMIDE* (4-[(5-chloro-2-oxobenzothiazol-in-3-yl)acetyl]-1-piperazineethanol; FK-1160; NTA-194; RHC-2592).

TIAZESIM* (5-[2-(dimethylamino)ethyl]-2,3-di-hydro-2-phenyl-1,5-benzothiazepin-4(5H)-one; thiazenone; thiazesium; SQ-10496; 'altinil').

TIAZOFURINE* (2-β-D-ribofuranosyl-4-thiaz-olecarboxamide; CI-909; NSC-286193).

Tiazon (tr) see Dazomet.

TIAZURIL (2-[4-[(p-chlorophenyl)thio]-3,5-xyl-yl]-as-triazine-3,5(2H,4H)-dione; CP-25673).

TIBALOSIN* ((±)-erythro-2,3-dihydro-α-[1-[(4-phenylbutyl)amino]ethyl]benzo[b]thiophene-5-methanol).

Tibamide see Tybamate.

TIBENZATE (S-benzyl thiobenzoate).

'Tiberal' see Ornidazole.

TIBEZONIUM IODIDE* (diethylmethyl[2-[[4-[p-(phenylthio)phenyl]3H-1,5-benzodiazepin-2-yl]thio]ethyl]ammonium iodide; thiabenzonium; Rec-15/0691).

'Tibiocorten' see Triamcinolone benetonide.

'Tibirox' see Co-tetroxazine.

TIBOLONE* (17α-ethynyl-17-hydroxy-7α-methyl-5(10)-estren-3-one; 17-hydroxy-7α-methyl-19-nor-17α-pregn-5(10)-en-20-yn-3-one; 7α-methylnoretynodrel; Org.OD-14).

Tibon (tr) see Thioacetazone.

TIBRIC ACID (1-[(3-carboxy-4-chlorophenyl)-sulfonyl]-3,5-dimethylpiperidine; 2-chloro-5-[(3,5-dimethylpiperidino)sulfonyl]benzoic acid; CP-18524).

TIBROFAN* (4,4′,5-tribromo-2-thiophenecarb-oxanilide).

'Tibutol' see Ethambutol.

TICABESONE* (S-methyl-6α,9-difluoro-11β,17-dihydroxy-16α-methyl-3-oxoandrosta-1,4-diene-17β-carbothioate).

TICABESONE PROPIONATE* (ticabesone 17-propionate; RS-35909).

'Ticar' see Ticarcillin.

TICARBODINE (α,α,α-trifluoro-2,6-dimethyl-1-piperidinethiocarboxy-m-toluidide; EL-974).

TICARCILLIN (N-(2-carboxy-3,3-dimethyl-7-oxo-4-thia-1-azabicyclo[3.2.0]hept-6-yl)-3-thio-phenemalonamic acid; 6-(α-carboxy-α-thien-3-ylacetamido)penicillanic acid; 6-(thienylmalon-amido)penicillanic acid; 6-(thiophenemalon-amido)penicillanic acid; (α-carboxy-3-thenyl)-penicillin; thienylcarbenicillin; ticarcillin disodi-um; BRL-2288; 'aerugipen'; 'ticar'; 'triacilline').

TICARCILLIN CRESYL SODIUM* (ticarcillin p-tolyl ester monosodium salt; BRL-12594).

'Ticelgesic' see Paracetamol.

TICLATONE* (6-chloro-1,2-benzisothiazolin-3-one; FER-1443; 'landromil').

'Ticlid' see Ticlopidine.

'Ticlodix' see Ticlopidine.

'Ticlodone' see Ticlopidine.

TICLOPIDINE* (5-(o-chlorobenzyl)-4,5,6,7-tetrahydrothieno[3,2-c]pyridine; ticlopidine

hydrochloride; 'ticlid'; 'ticlodix'; 'ticlodone'; 'tiklid').

Ticrynafen* see Tienilic acid.

'Tidemol' see Buformin.

TIDIACIC* (thiazolidine-2,4-dicarboxylic acid).

TIDIACIC plus SORBITOL ('thiobilin').

TIDIACIC ARGININE (arginine 2,4-thiazolidine-dicarboxylate; tidiacic arginine salt; 'tiadilon').

TIEMONIUM IODIDE* (4-(3-hydroxy-3-phenyl-3-thien-2-ylpropyl)-4-methylmorpholi-nium iodide; TE-114; 'visceralgine').

TIENILIC ACID* (2-[2,3-dichloro-4-(2-theno-yl)phenoxy]acetic acid; ticrynafen; ANP-3624; SK&F-62698; 'diflurex'; 'selacryn').

TIENOCARBINE (7,8,9,10-tetrahydro-1,9-di-methyl-6H-pyrido[4,3-b]thieno[3,2-e]indole).

TIENOPRAMINE* (4-[3-(dimethylamino)prop-yl]-4H-thieno[3,2-b][1]benzazepine).

Tietylperazine* see Thiethylperazine.

TIFEMOXONE* (tetrahydro-6-(phenoxymeth-yl)-2H-1,3-oxazine-2-thione).

Tifen (tr) see Tifenamil.

TIFENAMIL* (S-2-diethylaminoethyl diphenyl-thioacetate; thifenamil; thiphenamil; thiphen; ti-fen; tiphen; B-23).

TIFENCILLIN* (6-(phenylthioacetamido)peni-cillanic acid; phenylthiomethyl penicillin; potas-sium thiophencillin; thiphencillin; tifencillin potas-sium).

'Tiferron' see Sodium pyrocatechol-3,5-disulfon-ate.

TIFLAMIZOLE* (4,5-bis(p-fluorophenyl)-2-[(1,1,2,2-tetrafluoroethyl)sulfonyl]imidazole).

TIFLOREX* ((+)-N-ethyl-α-methyl-m-[(tri-fluoromethyl)thio]phenethylamine.

TIFLUADOM* ((±)-N-[[5-(o-fluorophenyl)-2,3-dihydro-1-methyl-1H-1,4-benzodiazepin-2-yl]methyl]-3-thiophenecarboxamide).

TIFORMIN* (4-guanidinobutyramide; tyform-in; tiformin hydrochloride; HL-523).

'Tifosyl' see Thiotepa.

'Tigan' see Trimethobenzamide.

'Tigason' see Etretinate.

TIGESTOL* (17α-ethynyl-5(10)-estren-17-ol; 19-nor-17α-pregn-5(10)-en-20-yn-17-ol).

TIGLIC ACID (2,3-dimethylacrylic acid; 2-methyl-2-butenoic acid; 2-methylcrotonic acid; crotonolic acid).

TIGLOIDINE* (tiglylpseudotropine).

Tiglylpseudotropine see Tigloidine.

Tiglyltropine see Tropigline.

'Tiglyssin' see Tigloidine.

'Tiguvon' see Fenthion.

'Tik-20' see Fenitrothion.

'Tiklid' see Ticlopidine.

TILACTASE (β-D-galactosidase; E.C.3.2.1.23).

'Tilase' see Hyaluronidase.

'Tilaze' see Hyaluronidase.

TILBROQUINOL (7-bromo-5-methyl-8-quino-linol; 'intetrix').

'Tilcarex' see Quintozene.

'Tildiem' see Diltiazem.

TILETAMINE* (2-[1-(ethylamino)-2-oxocyclo-

505

hexyl]thiophene; 2-(ethylamino)-2-thien-2-yl-cyclohexanone; tiletamine hydrochloride; CI-634; CL-399; CN-54521-2).

TILETAMINE plus ZOLAZEPAM (CI-744; 'telazol').

Tilidate* *see* Tilidine.

TILIDINE** (ethyl 2-(dimethylamino)-2-phenyl-3-cyclohexene-1-carboxylate; tilidate; tilidine hydrochloride; Go-1261; W-5759A; 'valoron').

TILIDINE plus NALOXONE ('valoron N').
See also Dextilidine.

TILIQUINOL*** (5-methyl-8-quinolinol).

'Tillam' *see* Pebulate.

TILORONE*** (2,7-bis(2-diethylaminoethoxy)-fluoren-9-one; bis(DEAE)fluorenone; NSC-143969).

TILOZEPINE*** (7-chloro-4-(4-methylpiperazin-1-yl)-10*H*-thieno[3,2-*c*][1]benzazepine).

'Tilset' *see* Oxatomide.

TILSUPROST** (methyl ($\pm$)-4-[[(3a*R**,4*R**, 5*R**,6a*S**)-3,3a,4,5,6,6a-hexahydro-5-hydroxy-4-[(*E*)-(3*S**)-3-hydroxy-1-octenyl]cyclopenta[*b*]-pyrrol-2-yl]thio]butyrate).

'Timacor' *see* Timolol maleate.

'Timaxel' *see* Metapramine.

TIMEFURONE** (4,9-dimethoxy-7-[(methylthio)methyl]-5*H*-furo[3,2-*g*][1]benzopyran-5-one).

TIMEGADINE*** (1-cyclohexyl-2-(2-methylquinolin-4-yl)-3-thiazol-2-ylguanidine; SR-1368).

TIMEPIDIUM BROMIDE*** (3-(diethien-2-yl-methylene)-5-methoxy-1,1-dimethylpiperidinium bromide; methoxytipepidine methobromide; trimepidium; SA-504; 'sesden').

Timerfon* *see* Sodium timerfonate.

Timet (tr) *see* Phorate.

Timidazol (tr) *see* Thiamazole.

TIMIPERONE*** (4'-fluoro-4-[4-(2-thioxobenz-imidazolin-1-yl)piperid-1-yl]butyrophenone; 1-[3-(*p*-fluorobenzoyl)propyl]-4-(2-thioxobenzimi-dazolin-1-yl)piperidine).

TIMOBESONE** (*S*-methyl 9-fluoro-11β,17-di-hydroxy-16β-methyl-3-oxoandrosta-1,4-diene-17β-carbothioate).

'Timodyne' *see* Mefexamide.

TIMOFIBRATE*** (3-[2-(*p*-chlorophenoxy)-2-methylpropionyl]-4-thiazolidinecarboxylic acid).

TIMOLOL*** ((−)-3-(3-*tert*-butylamino-2-hydr-oxypropoxy)-4-morpholino-1,2,5-thiadiazole; (−)-1-(*tert*-butylamino)-3-(4-morpholino-1,2,5-thiadiazol-3-yloxy)-2-propanol; 'moducren').

TIMOLOL MALEATE* (MK-950; 'betim'; 'blocadren'; 'timacor'; 'timoptic'; 'timoptol').

TIMOLOL MALEATE plus BENDROFLU-METHIAZIDE ('prestim').

TIMONACIC*** (thiazolidine-4-carboxylic acid; thioproline; NSC-25855; 'hepaldine'; 'hepareg-ene'; 'norgamem').

TIMONACIC ARGININE (arginine 4-thiazolid-inecarboxylate; ATC; 'sulfile').

'Timonil' *see* Carbamazepine.

TIMOPRAZOLE*** (2-[(pyrid-2-ylmethyl)sulfin-yl]benzimidazole).

'Timoptic' *see* Timolol maleate.

'Timoptol' *see* Timolol maleate.

'Timostenil' *see* Caroxazone.

Timosulfone *see* Diathymosulfone.

TINABINOL*** (8-(1,2-dimethylheptyl)-1,2,3,5-tetrahydro-5,5-dimethylthiopyrano[2,3-*c*]-[1]benzopyran-10-ol; SP-119).

'Tinactin' *see* Tolnaftate.

'Tinaderm' *see under* Butylated hydroxytoluene.

'Tinagel' *see* Benzoyl peroxide.

'Tin anti-slime' *see* Bis(tributyltin) oxide.

TINAZOLINE** (3-(2-imidazolin-2-ylthio)ind-ole).

'Tindal' *see* Acetophenazine.

TINIDAZOLE*** (ethyl 2-(2-methyl-5-nitroimid-azol-1-yl)ethyl sulfone; 1-(2-ethylsulfonylethyl)-2-methyl-5-nitroimidazole; CP-12574; 'fasigyn'; 'simplotan'; 'sorquetan').

TINISULPRIDE*** (5-[(1,1-dimethyl-2-propyn-yl)sulfamoyl]-*N*-[(1-ethylpyrrolidin-2-yl)methyl]-*o*-anisamide).

TINOFEDRINE*** ((+)-(*R*)-α-[(*S*)-1-[1-(3,3-di-thien-3-ylallyl)amino]ethyl]benzyl alcohol; D-8955; 'novocebrin').

TINORIDINE*** (2-amino-6-benzyl-3-ethoxy-carbonyl-4,5,6,7-tetrahydrothieno[2,3-*c*]pyrid-ine; ethyl 2-amino-6-benzyl-4,5,6,7-tetrahydro-thieno[2,3-*c*]pyridine-3-carboxylate; Y-3642; 'nonframin').

'Tinox' *see* Demephion-S.

TIN OXIDE (colloidal tin oxide with tin; 'oxistan'; 'oxstan'; 'salostan'; 'stannacne'; 'stannoxyl'; 'vistannyl').

Tin pyrophosphate *see* Stannous pyrophosphate.

'Tinset' *see* Oxatomide.

'Tintorane' *see* Warfarin.

'Tinuvin 326' *see* Bumetrizole.

'Tinuvin P' *see* Drometrizole.

'Tiobicina' *see* Thioacetazone.

TIOCARLIDE*** (4,4'-bis(isopentyloxy)thiocarb-anilide; 4,4'-diisoamyloxythiocarbanilide; thio-carlide; DATC).

TIOCLOMAROL** (3-[5-chloro-α-(*p*-chloro-β-hydroxyphenethyl)-2-thenyl]-4-hydroxycoumar-in; 'apegmone').

TIOCONAZOLE*** (1-[2-[(2-chloro-3-thienyl)-methoxy]-2-(2,4-dichlorophenyl)ethyl]-1*H*-imi-dazole; 1-[2,4-dichloro-β-[(2-chloro-3-thienyl)-oxy]phenethyl]imidazole; UK-20349).

TIOCTILATE*** (*S*-octyl thiobenzoate).

'Tiodan' *see* Endosulfan.

TIODAZOSIN*** (1-(4-amino-6,7-dimethoxy-2-quinazolinyl)-4-[[5-(methylthio)-1,3,4-oxadiazol-2-yl]carbonyl]piperazine; BL-5111).

TIODONIUM CHLORIDE*** ((*p*-chlorophenyl)-2-thienyliodonium chloride; DL-164).

Tiofacic *see* Stepronin.

Tiofenatin *see* Thiophenatin.

'Tiofos' *see* Parathion.

Tiofosfamide *see* Thiotepa.

'Tiofosyl' *see* Thiotepa.

TIOGUANINE*** (2-amino-6-mercaptopurine; 2-aminopurine-6-thiol; 6-thioguanine; thioguan-

506

ine; BW-50-71; NSC-752).

Tioguanine riboside *see* Thioguanosine.

TIOMERGINE* (9,10-didehydro-6-methyl-8β-[(pyrid-2-ylthio)methyl]ergoline).

TIOMESTERONE* (1α,7α-bis(acetylthio)-17β-hydroxy-17-methylandrost-4-en-3-one; 1α,7α-diacetylthio-17β-hydroxy-17-methylandrost-4-en-3-one; thiomesterone; STA-307).

'Tionidel' *see* Ethylmorphine.

TIOPERIDONE (3-[4-[4-[*o*-(propylthio)phenyl]-piperazin-1-yl]butyl]-2,4(1*H*,3*H*)-quinazolinedione; tioperidone hydrochloride; CI-787).

TIOPINAC* (6,11-dihydro-11-oxodibenzo-[*b,e*]thiepin-3-acetic acid; RS-40974-00).

TIOPRONIN* (*N*-(2-mercaptopropionyl)glycine; thiolpropionamidoacetic acid; TPAA; 'mucolysin'; 'thiola').

Tiopronin 2-thiophenecarboxylate *see* Stepronin.

TIOPROPAMINE* (3,3-diphenyl-3'-(phenylthio)dipropylamine; 'redden').

TIOSALAN* (3,4',5-tribromo-2-mercaptobenzanilide; thiosalan).

Tiosinamine *see* Allylthiourea.

Tio-TEF (tr) *see* Thiotepa.

TIOTIDINE* (2-cyano-1-[2-[[[2-[(diaminomethylene)amino]thiazol-4-yl]methyl]thio]ethyl]-3-methylguanidine; ICI-125211).

TIOTIXENE* (*N,N*-dimethyl-9-[3-(4-methylpiperazin-1-yl)propylidene]thioxanthene-2-sulfonamide; thiothixene; CP-12252-1; NSC-108165; P-4657B).

'Tiotrifar' *see* Anethole trithione.

TIOXACIN* (6-ethyl-2,3,6,9-tetrahydro-3-methyl-2,6-dioxothiazolo[5,4-*f*]quinoline-8-carboxylic acid).

Tioxacin 2-(4-methylpiperid-1-yl)ethyl ester *see* Metioxate.

TIOXAPROFEN* (2-[[4,5-bis(*p*-chlorophenyl)-2-oxazolyl]thio]propionic acid).

TIOXIDAZOLE* (methyl 6-propoxy-2-benzothiazolecarbamate; Sch-21480).

TIOXOLONE* (4-hydroxy-1,3-benzoxathiol-2-one; thidoxol; thioxolone; HBT; OL-1; OL-110).

TIOXOLONE plus HYDROCORTISONE ('psoil').

TIPEPIDINE* (3-(dithien-2-ylmethylene)-1-methylpiperidine; bithiodine; tipepidine citrate; tipepidine hibenzate; AT-327).

TIPETROPIUM BROMIDE* (3α-[(6,11-dihydro)dibenzo[*b,e*]thiepin-11-yl]oxy-8*r*-propyl-1α*H*,5α*H*-tropanium bromide).

Tiphen (tr) *see* Tifenamil.

TIPINDOLE* (2-(dimethylamino)ethyl 1,3,4,5-tetrahydrothiopyrano[4,3-*b*]indole-8-carboxylate).

TIPINDOLE METHIODIDE (K-206).

TIPRENOLOL* (1-(isopropylamino)-3-[*o*-(methylthio)phenoxy]-2-propanol; tiprenolol hydrochloride; DU-21445).

TIPRINAST (3,4-dihydro-6-isobutyl-5-methyl-4-oxothieno[2,3-*d*]pyrimidine-2-carboxylic acid).

TIPROPIDIL* (1-[*p*-(isopropylthio)phenoxy]-3-(octylamino)-2-propanol; 1-[4-[(1-methylethyl)-thio]phenoxy]-3-(octylamino)-2-propanol; tipropidil hydrochloride; MJ-12880).

TIPROSTANIDE* ((1*S*,2*R*,3*R*)-3-hydroxy-2-[(2-hydroxy-2-methylheptyl)thio]-5-oxocyclopentaneheptanoic acid ester with 4'-hydroxybenzanilide; (±)-*p*-benzamidophenyl 7-[(1*S*,2*R*,3*R*)-3-hydroxy-2-[(2-hydroxy-2-methylheptyl)thio]-5-oxocyclopentyl]heptanoate; (±)-*p*-benzamidophenyl 11,15-dihydroxy-15-methyl-9-oxo-13-thiaprostanoate).

TIQUINAMIDE* (5,6,7,8-tetrahydro-3-methylquinoline-8-thiocarboxamide; tiquinamide hydrochloride; Wy-24081).

TIQUIZIUM BROMIDE* (*trans*-3-(di-2-thienylmethylene)octahydro-5-methyl-2*H*-quinolizinium bromide).

TIRATRICOL* ([4-(4-hydroxy-3-iodophenoxy)-3,5-diiodophenyl]acetic acid; 3,3',5-triiodothyroacetic acid; triac; 'triacana').

TIRATRICOL plus CYCLOVALONE ('plethoryl').

'Tirian' *see* Proguanil.

'Tiron' *see* Sodium pyrocatechol-3,5-disulfonate.

TIROPRAMIDE* (DL-α-benzamido-*p*-[2-(diethylamino)ethoxy]-*N,N*-dipropylhydrocinnamamide; CR-605).

'Tisercin' *see* Levomepromazine.

'Tisercinetta' *see* Levomepromazine.

TISOCROMIDE* (*N*-[3-(dimethylamino)-1,3-dimethylbutyl]-6,7-dimethoxy-2,1-benzoxathian-3-carboxamide 1,1-dioxide).

'Tisomycin' *see* Cycloserine.

TISOPURINE* (4-mercaptopyrazolo[3,4-*d*]pyrimidine; 1*H*-pyrazolo[3,4-*d*]pyrimidine-4-thiol; thiopurinol).

TISOQUONE* (4-ethyl-3,4-dihydro-4-phenyl-1(2*H*)-isoquinolinethione; 4-ethyl-3,4-dihydro-4-phenylthioisocarbostyril).

'Tissucol' *see* Fibrin adhesive.

'Titriplex' *see* Disodium edetate.

Tiuram *see* Disulfiram.

'Tiuramyl' *see* Thiram.

TIVANIDAZOLE* ((*E*)-2-ethyl-5-[1-methyl-2-(1-methyl-5-nitroimidazol-2-yl)vinyl]-1,3,4-thiadiazole).

TIXADIL* (α-methyl-*N*-(2-thioxanthen-9-yl-ethyl)phenethylamine; *N*-(α-methylphenethyl)-thioxanthene-9-ethylamine; BS-7561).

TIXANOX* (7-(methylsulfinyl)-9-oxoxanthene-2-carboxylic acid; RS-7337).

'Tixantone' *see* Lucanthone.

TIXOCORTOL* (11β,17-dihydroxy-21-mercaptopregn-4-ene-3,20-dione).

TIXOCORTOL PIVALATE (tixocortol 21-pivalate; tixocortol 21-trimethylacetate; JO-1016; 'pivalone'; 'rectovalone').

TIZABRIN* ((1*R*,3*S*,5*R*)-2,2,5-trimethyl-3-thiomorpholinecarboxylic acid 1-oxide).

TIZANIDINE* (5-chloro-4-(2-imidazolin-2-ylamino)-2,1,3-benzothiadiazole; tizanidine hydrochloride; DS-103-282).

TIZOLEMIDE* (4-(4-chloro-3-sulfamoylphenyl)-4-hydroxy-3-methyl-2-(methylimino)thiazolidine; 2-chloro-5-[4-hydroxy-3-methyl-2-(meth-ylimino)thiazolidin-4-yl]benzenesulfonamide; tizolemide hydrochloride; HOE-740; S-730740B).

TIZOPROLIC ACID* (2-propyl-5-thiazole-carboxylic acid).

TM-10 *see* Xylocholine.

β-TM-10 *see* β-Methylxylocholine.

TM-4049 *see* Malathion.

TMB-4 *see* Trimedoxime bromide.

TMBAC *see* Sodium capobenate.

TMD-10 *see* Tetrylammonium bromide.

TMP *see* Trioxysalen.

TMQ *see* Trimetrexate.

TMT *see* (+)-Atromepine.

TMTDS *see* Thiram.

TNO-6 *see* Spiroplatin.

'**Tobanum**' *see* Cloranolol.

'**Tobradistin**' *see* Tobramycin.

TOBRAMYCIN* (antibiotic from *Str. tenebra-rius*; *O*-3-amino-3-deoxy-α-D-glucopyranosyl-(1→4)-*O*-[2,6-diamino-2,3,6-trideoxy-α-D-*ribo*-hexopyranosyl-(1→6)]-2-deoxystreptamine; ne-bramycin factor 6; tobramycin sulfate; 'garneb-cin'; 'nebcin'; 'obracine'; 'tobradistin').

TOBUTEROL* (5-[2-(*tert*-butylamino)-1-hyd-roxyethyl]-*m*-phenylene di-*p*-toluate; 5-[2-(*tert*-butylamino)-1-hydroxyethyl]resorcinol diester with *p*-toluic acid).

TOCAINIDE* (2-amino-2',6'-propionoxylidide; 2-amino-2',6'-dimethylpropionanilide; 2-amino-*N*-(2,6-dimethylphenyl)propanamide; alanino-2',6'-xylidide; tocainide hydrochloride; W-36095; 'tonocard'; 'xylotocan').

TOCAMPHYL* (diethanolamine salt of mono-D-camphoric ester of *p*,α-dimethylbenzyl alco-hol).

'**Toce**' *see* Diethadione.

'**Toclase**' *see* Pentoxyverine.

TOCOFENOXATE* (*all-rac*-2,5,7,8-tetrameth-yl-2-(4,8,12-trimethyltridecyl)-6-chromanyl (*p*-chlorophenoxy)acetate).

Tocoferol* *see* α-Tocopherol.

TOCOFERSOLAN* (mono-[2,5,7,8-tetrameth-yl-2-(4,8,12-trimethyldecyl)-6-chromanyl]suc-cinate polyoxyethylene ether; tocopherol succin-ate polyoxyethylene ether; tocophersolan; TPGS).

TOCOFIBRATE* (tocopheryl clofibrate).

α-TOCOPHEROL (2,5,7,8-tetramethyl-2-(4,8,12-trimethyldecyl)-6-chromanol; 5,7,8-trimethyltoc-ol; tocoferol; vitamin E; antisterility vitamin; α-tocopherol acetate, phosphate or succinate).

α-TOCOPHEROL NICOTINATE ('renascin').

Tocopherol succinate polyoxyethylene ether *see* To-cofersolan.

TOCOPHERONIC ACID (2-(5-carboxy-3-hydr-oxy-3-methylpentyl)-3,5,6-trimethylbenzoquin-one lactone).

Tocophersolan* *see* Tocofersolan.

Tocopheryl clofibrate *see* Tocofibrate.

α-TOCOPHERYLQUINONE ('eutrophyl').

'**Tocosamine**' *see* Sparteine.

'**Tocosine**' *see* Tyramine.

TOCOTRIENOL (2-methyl-2-(4',8',12-trimethyl-trideca-3,7,11-trienyl)-6-chromanol).

TOCP *see* Tri-*o*-cresyl phosphate.

'**Tod'l**' *see* Hexachlorophene.

TODRALAZINE* (ethyl 3-phthalazin-1-ylcarb-azate; ethyl 2-phthalazin-1-ylhydrazinecarboxyl-ate; ecarazine; todrazoline; BT-621; CEPH).

Todrazoline *see* Todralazine.

'**Tofacin**' *see* Tofenacin.

'**Tofazine 50W**' *see* Simazine.

TOFENACIN* (*N*-methyl-2-[(*o*-methyl-α-phenylbenzyl)oxy]ethylamine; *N*-demethylor-phenadrine; tofenacin hydrochloride).

TOFESILATE(S)** (1,2,3,6-tetrahydro-1,3-di-methyl-2,6-dioxopurine-7-ethanesulfonic acid, esters and salts).

TOFETRIDINE** ((−)-1,2,3,4,4a,5,6,10b-octa-hydro-9-methoxy-10b-methylphenanthridine).

TOFISOPAM* (1-(3,4-dimethoxyphenyl)-5-ethyl-7,8-dimethoxy-4-methyl-5*H*-2,3-benzodia-zepine; 'grandaxin').

'**Tofranil**' *see* Imipramine.

'**Togamycin**' *see* Spectinomycin.

Togholamine *see* Triacanthine.

'**Togiren**' *see* Erythromycin estolate.

'**Toilax**' *see* Bisacodyl.

TOK E25 *see* Nitrofen.

'**Tokunol M**' *see* Amiprofos-methyl.

'**Tokuthion**' *see* Prothiofos.

'**Toladryl**' *see* *p*-Methyldiphenhydramine.

Tolamidol *see* Tolamolol.

TOLAMOLOL* (1-[2-(4-carbamoylphenoxy)-ethylamino]-3-(2-methylphenoxy)-2-propanol; *p*-[2-[[2-hydroxy-3-(*o*-toloxy)propyl]amino]eth-oxy]benzamide; tolamidol; tolamolol hydro-chloride; UK-6558-01).

'**Tolanate**' *see* Inositol hexanitrate.

TOLAZAMIDE* (1-(hexahydro-1*H*-azepin-1-yl)-3-(*p*-toluenesulfonyl)urea; 1,1-hexamethyl-ene-4-(*p*-toluenesulfonyl)semicarbazide; NSC-70762; U-17835).

TOLAZOLINE* (2-benzyl-2-imidazoline; phenylmethylimidazoline; benzazolin; benzolin; tolazoline hydrochloride).

'**Tolazul**' *see* Tolonium chloride.

'**Tolbet**' *see* Tolbutamide.

TOLBOXANE* (5-methyl-5-propyl-2-*p*-tolyl-1,3,2-dioxaborinane; *p*-tolylboric acid ester with 2-(hydroxymethyl)-2-methyl-1-pentanol).

TOLBUTAMIDE* (1-butyl-3-*p*-toluenesulfon-ylurea; 1-butyl-3-tosylurea; butamid; tolbutyl-urea; D-860; HLS-831; U-2043).

See also under Metformin; Phenformin.

'**Tolbutaphen**' *see under* Phenformin.

Tolbutylurea *see* Tolbutamide.

TOLCICLATE* (*m*,*N*-dimethylthiocarbanilic acid *O*-(1,2,3,4-tetrahydro-1,4-methanonaphth-6-yl) ester; KC-9147; 'fungifos'; 'kilmicen').

Tolclotide* *see* Disulfamide.

TOLDIMFOS* (4-(dimethylamino)-*o*-tolyl-phosphinic acid; toldimfos sodium; 'foston'; 'no-vofosfan'; 'phiniphos'; 'phosodyl'; 'tonofosfan';

'tonophosphan').

'Tolectin' *see* Tolmetin.

TOLFAMIDE* (*N*-(diaminophosphinyl)-*o*-toluamide).

TOLFENAMIC ACID* (*N*-(3-chloro-*o*-tolyl)-anthranilic acid; 'clotam').

Tolhexamide *see* Glycyclamide.

o-**TOLIDINE** (3,3'-dimethylbenzidine).

TOLIMIDONE (5-(3-methylphenoxy)-2-pyrimidinone; 5-(*m*-tolyloxy)-2(1*H*)-pyrimidinone; CP-26154).

'Tolinase' *see* Tolazamide.

TOLINDATE* (*O*-indan-5-yl *m*,*N*-dimethyl-thiocarbanilate; 'dalnate').

TOLIODIUM CHLORIDE* (bis(4-methyl-phenyl)iodonium chloride; di-*p*-tolyliodonium chloride; SK&F-15601A).

TOLIPROLOL* (1-(isopropylamino)-3-(3-methylphenoxy)-2-propanol; 1-(isopropyl-amino)-3-(*m*-toloxy)-2-propanol; ICI-45673; Ko-592; MHIP; 'doberol').

TOLMESOXIDE* (4,5-dimethoxy-2-(methyl-sulfinyl)toluene).

TOLMETIN* (1-methyl-5-*p*-toluoylpyrrole-2-acetic acid; tolmetin sodium; McN-2259; 'mido-cil'; 'tolectin').

'Tolnaftal' *see* Tolnaftate.

TOLNAFTATE* (2-naphthyl *N*-methyl-*N*-(*m*-tolyl) thionocarbamate; Sch-10144).

TOLNAPERSINE (5,6,7,8-tetrahydro-6-(4-*o*-tolylpiperazin-1-yl)-2-naphthol).

'Tolnate' *see* Prothipendyl.

TOLNIDAMINE* (1-(4-chloro-2-methylbenz-yl)-1*H*-indazole-3-carboxylic acid).

Tolocinium* *see* Toloconium metilsulfate.

TOLOCONIUM CHLORIDE (trimethyl(1-*p*-tol-yldodecyl)ammonium chloride; 'desogen').

TOLOCONIUM METILSULFATE* (trimeth-yl(1-*p*-tolyldodecyl)ammonium methyl sulfate; tolocinium; tolytrimonium).

TOLONIDINE* (2-(2-chloro-*p*-toluidino)-2-imidazoline; ST-375; 'euctan').

TOLONIUM CHLORIDE* (3-amino-7-(di-methylamino)-2-methylphenazthionium chlor-ide; dimethyltoluthionine chloride; toluidine blue; CI-925; Schultz-1041).

TOLOXATONE (5-(hydroxymethyl)-3-(3-meth-ylphenyl)oxazolidin-2-one; 5-(hydroxymethyl)-3-*m*-tolyloxazolidin-2-one).

Toloxichloral* *see* Toloxychlorinol.

TOLOXYCHLORINOL* (1,1'-(3-*o*-toloxy-propylenedioxy)bis(2,2,2-trichloroethanol); 1,3-bis(2,2,2-trichloro-1-hydroxyethoxy)-3-*o*-toloxy-propane; toloxichloral).

3-(*o*-Toloxy)-1,2-propanediol *see* Mephenesin.

1,1'-(3-*o*-Toloxypropylenedioxy)bis(2,2,2-trichloro-ethanol) *see* Toloxychlorinol.

TOLPADOL* (*N*,*N*'-(1,2-di-4-pyridylethylene)-bis[*o*-toluamide]).

TOLPENTAMIDE* (1-cyclopentyl-3-*p*-toluene-sulfonylurea; BH-135).

TOLPERISONE* (2,4'-dimethyl-3-piperid-1-yl-propiophenone; 2-methyl-3-piperid-1-yl-1-(*p*-tol-yl)-1-propanone; β-methyl-γ-(*p*-tolyl)-1-piperid-inepropanone; N-533; PMP; 'mydeton'; 'mydo-calm').

TOLPIPRAZOLE* (5-methyl-3-[2-(4-*m*-tolyl-piperazin-1-yl)ethyl]pyrazole; 1-[2-(5-methylpyr-azol-3-yl)ethyl]-4-*m*-tolylpiperazine; H-4170).

TOLPOVIDONE (ω-(*p*-iodobenzyl)-2-(2-oxopyr-rolidin-1-yl) ethamer).

TOLPOVIDONE (¹³¹I)* (tolpovidone labeled with radioiodine; radiotolpovidone; 'raovin').

TOLPRONINE* (3,6-dihydro-α-(*o*-toloxymeth-yl)-1(2*H*)-pyridinethanol; tolpronine hydro-chloride).

TOLPROPAMINE* (*N*,*N*-dimethyl-3-phenyl-3-*p*-tolyl-1-propylamine).

TOLPYRRAMIDE* (1-tetramethylene-3-*p*-to-luenesulfonylurea; *N*-(*p*-toluenesulfonyl)-1-pyr-rolidinecarboxamide; *N*-tosylpyrrolidinecarbox-amide; NSC-106572).

TOLQUINZOLE* (2-ethyl-1,3,4,6,7,11b-hexa-hydro-10-methyl-2*H*-benzo[*a*]quinolizin-2-ol).

TOLRESTAT (*N*-[6-methoxythio-5-(trifluoro-methyl)-1-naphthoyl]sarcosine).

'Tolseron' *see* Guaifenesin.

TOLUAMIDE(S) (toluic acid amide(s); *ar*-methyl-benzamide(s)).

TOLUENE (methylbenzene).

TOLUENE DIISOCYANATE (2,3-diisocyanato-toluene; toluylene diisocyanate; TDI; 'desmodur T').

p-**(α-Toluenesulfonamido)benzoic acid** *see* Carin-amide.

p-**Toluenesulfonic acid, esters and salts** *see* Tosil-ate(s).

N-**(*p*-Toluenesulfonyl)-1-pyrrolidinecarboxamide** *see* Tolpyrramide.

TOLUFAZEPAM (7-chloro-5-(*o*-chlorophen-yl)-1,3-dihydro-1-[2-(*p*-tolylsulfonyl)ethyl]-2*H*-1,4-benzodiazepin-2-one).

Toluidine blue *see* Tolonium chloride.

TOLUIDINE RED (1-(2-nitro-*p*-tolylazo)-2-naphthol; CI-69).

'Toluina' *see* Tolbutamide.

Toluquinone *see* 2-Methyl-*p*-benzoquinone.

Toluylene *see* Stilbene.

Toluylene diisocyanate *see* Toluene diisocyanate.

'Tolvin' *see* Mianserin.

'Tolvon' *see* Mianserin.

TOLYCAINE* (*N*-[2-(diethylamino)acetyl]-6-(methoxycarbonyl)-*o*-toluidine; methyl 2-(2-di-ethylaminoacetamido)-*m*-toluate; tolycaine hydrochloride).

m-**Tolyl acetate** *see* *m*-Cresyl acetate.

1-*p*-Tolyl-3-azabicyclo[3.1.0]hexane *see* Bicifadine.

4-(*o*-Tolylazo)-*o*-diacetotoluidide *see* Diacetazotol.

1-(4-*o*-Tolylazo-*o*-tolylazo)-2-naphthol *see* Scarlet red.

p-**Tolylboric acid ester with 2-(hydroxymethyl)-2-methyl-1-pentanol** *see* Tolboxane.

m-**Tolylcarbamic acid 3-[(methoxycarbonyl)amino]-phenyl ester** *see* Phenmedipham.

m-**TOLYL METHYLCARBAMATE** ('tsumac-ide').

509

p-Tolyl methyl carbinol *see* p,α-Dimethylbenzyl alcohol.

5-(m-Tolyloxy)-2(1H)-pyrimidinone *see* Tolimidone.

Tolyl phosphate *see* Tricresyl phosphate.

2-[3-[4-(o-Tolyl)piperazin-1-yl]propoxy]pyridine *see* Toprilidine.

1-p-Tolyl-2-propylamine *see* p-Methylamphetamine.

p-Tolylsulfonylcarbamic acid 2-methoxyethyl ester *see* Tosulur.

Tolytrimonium *see* Toloconium metilsulfate.

'Tomanol' *see under* 4-(Isopropylamino)phenazone.

Tomarin *see* Coumafuryl.

'Tomatotone' *see* 2-(p-Chlorophenoxy)acetic acid.

'Tomil' *see* Promazine.

'Tomorin' *see* Coumachlor.

TOMOXETINE** ((−)-N-methyl-3-phenyl-3-(o-tolyloxy)propylamine).

'Tonarsin' *see* Disodium methanearsonate.

TONAZOCINE*** ((±)-1-[(2R*,6S*,11S*)-1,2,3,4,5,6-hexahydro-8-hydroxy-3,6,11-trimethyl-2,6-methano-3-benzazocin-11-yl]-3-octanone; 2'-hydroxy-2,5,9-trimethyl-9-(3-oxooctyl)-6,7-benzomorphan).

TONAZOCINE MESILATE (tonazocine methanesulfonate; tonazocine mesylate).

'Toness' *see* Proxazole.

'Tonibral' *see* Deanol hemisuccinate.

'Tonifor' *see* Vincamine.

Tonka bean camphor *see* Coumarin.

'Tonocard' *see* Tocainide.

'Tonofosfan' *see* Toldimfos.

'Tonoftal' *see* Tolnaftate.

'Tonolyt' *see* Carisoprodol.

'Tonophosphan' *see* Toldimfos.

'Tonoplus' *see* Prenalterol.

'Tonopres' *see* Dihydroergotamine.

'Tonsillol' *see* Dequalinium chloride.

'Tonuron' *see* Chlorothiazide.

TONZONIUM BROMIDE*** (hexadecyl[2-[(p-methoxybenzyl)-2-pyrimidinylamino]ethyl]dimethyl ammonium bromide; thonzonium bromide; thonzylamine cetyl bromide; thonzylamine hexadecyl bromide; NC-1264; NSC-5648).

'Topcaine' *see* Benzocaine.

'Topicorte' *see* Desoximetasone.

'Topilan' *see* Chloroprednisone acetate.

'Topilar' *see* Fluclorolone acetonide.

'Topisolone' *see* Desoximetasone.

'Topocaine' *see* Cyclomethycaine.

TOPRILIDINE*** (1-(3-pyrid-2-yloxypropyl)-4-(o-tolyl)piperazine; 2-[3-[4-(o-tolyl)piperazin-1-yl]propoxy]pyridine; HOE-757).

'Topsin' *see* Thiophanate.

'Topsin M' *see* Thiophanate-methyl.

'Topsym' *see* Fluocinonide.

'Topsyne' *see* Fluocinonide.

TOPTERONE*** (17β-hydroxy-17-propylandrost-4-en-3-one; WIN-17665).

'Toquilone' *see* Methaqualone.

'Toquilone compositum' *see under* Methaqualone.

TOQUIZINE** (N-(4-ethyl-4,6,6a,7,8,9,10,10a-octahydro-7-methylindolo[4,3-fg]quinolin-9-yl)-3,5-dimethylpyrazole-1-carboxamide).

'Torak' *see* Dialifos.

'Torantil' *see* Diamine oxidase.

'Torantyl' *see* Diamine oxidase.

TORASEMIDE*** (1-isopropyl-3-[(4-m-toluidinopyrid-3-yl)sulfonyl]urea; 3-[[(isopropylcarbamoyl)amino]sulfonyl]-4-(m-toluidino)pyridine).

'Tordon' *see* Picloram.

'Torecan' *see* Thiethylperazine.

'Torelle' *see* Fospirate.

'Torental' *see* Pentoxifylline.

'Toresten' *see* Thiethylperazine.

'Toriseptin' *see* Sulfamethylthiazole.

'Tornalate' *see* Bitolterol mesilate.

'Torque' *see* Neostanox.

'Torrat' *see under* Butizide.

Torutilen *see* Vitamin T-complex.

'Toryn' *see* Caramiphen edisilate.

TOSACTIDE*** (human α[1-28] corticotrophin; ACTH human synthetic; octacosactrin; 'homactid'; 'humachtid').

TOSIFEN*** ((−)-α-methyl-N-[(p-tolylsulfonyl)carbamoyl]phenethylamine; (−)-1-(α-methylphenethyl)-3-(p-tolylsulfonyl)urea; Sch-11973).

TOSILATE(S)** (p-toluenesulfonic acid, esters and salts).

'Tosmilen' *see* Demecarium bromide.

TOSULUR** (2-methoxyethyl (p-tolylsulfonyl)carbamate).

TOSYL-L-ARGININE METHYL ESTER (methyl ester of p-toluenesulfonyl-L-arginine; TAM; TAME).

Tosylate(s) *see* Tosilate(s).

TOSYLCHLORAMIDE SODIUM*** (sodium derivative of N-chloro-p-toluenesulfonamide trihydrate; chloramide; chloramine-T; sodium sulfaminochloride).

N-Tosylpyrrolidinecarboxamide *see* Tolpyrramide.

'Totacef' *see* Cefazolin.

TOTAQUINE (quinium; mixture of cinchona alkaloids).
See also Quinetum.

'Totocillin' *see under* Ampicillin.

'Totokaine' *see* Butamin.

'Totril' *see* Ioxynil octanoate.

'Tovene' *see* Diosmin.

'Tox-47' *see* Parathion.

'Toxakil' *see* Campheclor.

'Toxaphene' *see* Campheclor.

'Toxichlor' *see* Chlordane.

Toxicodendron quercifolium *see* Poisonoak extract.

'Toxiferene' *see* Alcuronium chloride.

Toxilic acid *see* Maleic acid.

'Toxinal' *see* Oxytetracycline.

'Toxivers' *see* Piperazine.

'Toxogonin' *see* Obidoxime chloride.

TOXOPYRIMIDINE (4-amino-2-methyl-5-pyrimidinemethanol; 4-amino-5-hydroxymethyl-2-methylpyrimidine).

'Toxynil' *see* Ioxynil.

TOYOCAMYCIN (4-amino-5-cyano-7-(β-D-ribofuranosyl)pyrrolo[2,3-*d*]pyrimidine; 4-amino-7-β-D-ribofuranosyl-7*H*-pyrrolo[2,3-*d*]pyrimidine-5-carbonitrile; uramycin B; antibiotic 1037; E-212; 'vengicide').

'Toyomycin' *see* Chromomycin.

TOZALINONE*** (2-(dimethylamino)-5-phenyl-2-oxazolin-4-one; thozalinone; CL-39808; 'stimsen').

TP *see* Testosterone propionate.

2,4,5-TP *see* Fenoprop.

TP-1 *see* Thymostimulin (bovine).

TP-5 *see* Thymopentin.

TP-21 *see* Thioridazine.

TPAA *see* Tiopronin.

TPB *see* Bithionol.

TPD *see* Prosultiamine.

TPGS *see* Tocofersolan.

TPN *see* Nadide phosphate *and* Chlorothalonil.

TPN-12 *see* Sulforidazine.

TPP *see* Testosterone phenylpropionate.

TPS-23 *see* Mesoridazine.

TPTC *see* Fentin chloride.

TPTH *see* Fentin hydroxide.

TPTZ *see* 2,3,5-Triphenyltetrazolium chloride.

TQ-86 *see* Azipramine.

TR-495 *see* Methaqualone.

TR-2378 *see* Broperamole.

TR-2985 *see* Ropitoin.

TR-4698 *see* Rioprostil.

TR-5109 *see* Conorfone.

TR-5379M *see* Xorphanol mesilate.

TRACAZOLATE*** (ethyl 4-(butylamino)-1-ethyl-6-methyl-1*H*-pyrazolo[3,4-*b*]pyridine-5-carboxylate; ICI-136753).

'Tracebyl' *see* Iobenzamic acid.

'Tracervial-131' *see* Sodium iodide (^{131}I).

'Tracrium' *see* Atracurium besilate.

'Tradenal' *see* Proscillaridin.

'Tradone' *see* Pemoline.

'Trafuril' *see* Thurfyl nicotinate.

'Tral' *see* Hexocyclium metilsulfate.

'Tralgon' *see* Paracetamol.

TRALONIDE*** (9,11-dichloro-6,21-difluoro-16,17-dihydroxypregna-1,4-diene-3,20-dione 16,17-acetonide; 'talidan').

'Tramacin' *see* Triamcinolone acetonide.

TRAMADOL** (($\pm$)-*trans*-1-(*m*-anisyl)-2-[(dimethylamino)methyl]cyclohexanol; ($\pm$)-*trans*-2-[(dimethylamino)methyl]-1-(*m*-methoxyphenyl)-cyclohexanol; CG-315; K-315; U-26225A; 'tramal').

'Tramal' *see* Tramadol.

TRAMAZOLINE*** (2-(5,6,7,8-tetrahydro-1-naphthylamino)-2-imidazoline; tramazoline hydrochloride; KB-77; KB-227).

TRAMAZOLINE plus OXYTETRACYCLINE (K80-KBOT; 'oxy-biciron').

'Tramisol' *see* Levamisole.

'Tranapal' *see* Thiopental sodium.

'Trancalgyl' *see* Ethenzamide.

'Trancin' *see* Fluphenazine.

'Tranco-gesic' *see under* Chlormezazone.

'Trancopal' *see* Chlormezanone.

'Trancote' *see* Chlormezanone.

'Trandate' *see* Labetalol.

TRANEXAMIC ACID*** (*trans*-4-aminomethyl-cyclohexanecarboxylic acid; AMCA; AMCHA; CL-65336).
See also Cetraxate.

'Tranid' *see* 5-Chloro-6-oxo-2-norbornanecarbonitrile *o*-(methylcarbamoyl)oxime.

TRANILAST*** (*N*-(3,4-dimethoxycinnamoyl)-anthranilic acid; N-5).

'Tranpoise' *see* Mephenoxalone.

'Tran-Q' *see* Hydroxyzine.

'Tranquilin' *see* Benactyzine.

'Tranquisan' *see* Perphenazine.

'Tranquit' *see* Oxazolam.

'Tranquo-alupent' *see under* Orciprenaline.

'Tranquo-tablinen' *see* Diazepam.

Transamine (tr) *see* Tranylcypromine.

'Transannon' *see* Conjugated estrogens equine.

'Transbilix' *see* Adipiodone meglumine.

'Transbronchin' *see* Carbocisteine.

TRANSCAINIDE** (($\pm$)-*trans*-4-(dimethyl-amino)-1-(2-hydroxycyclohexyl)-2′,6′-isonipecot-oxylidide; ($\pm$)-*trans*-4-(dimethylamino)-*N*-(2,6-dimethylphenyl)-1-(2-hydroxycyclohexyl)-4-piperidinecarboxamide).

Transclomifene* *see* Zuclomifene.

Transclomiphene *see* Zuclomifene.

'Transcycline' *see* Rolitetracycline.

TRANSFERRIN (β-metal-binding globulin; siderophilin).

'Transoddi' *see* Cinametic acid.

'Transren' *see* Sodium anhydromethylenecitrate.

TRANTELINIUM BROMIDE*** (8-methyltropinium bromide xanthene-9-carboxylate; N-640; 'gastrixone').

'Tranvet' *see* Propionylpromazine.

'Tranxene' *see* Clorazepate dipotassium.

'Tranxilene' *see* Clorazepate dipotassium.

'Tranxilium' *see* Clorazepate dipotassium.

TRANYLCYPROMINE*** (DL-*trans*-2-phenyl-cyclopropylamine; transamine; tranylcypromine sulfate; SK&F-385).

TRANYLCYPROMINE plus TRIFLUOPERAZ-INE ('jatrosom'; 'parstelazine'; 'parstelin').

'Tranzine' *see* Chlorpromazine.

'Trapanal' *see* Thiopental sodium.

TRAPIDIL*** (7-(diethylamino)-5-methyl-*s*-tri-azolo[1,5-*a*]pyrimidine; trapymin; AR-12008; 'rocornal').

Trapymin *see* Trapidil.

'Trascolan' *see* Aprotinin.

'Trasentin' *see* Adiphenine.

'Trasentine-A' *see* Drofenine.

'Trasentin-6H' *see* Drofenine.

'Traserit' *see* Apicycline.

'Trasicor' *see* Oxprenolol.

'Trasidrex' *see under* Oxprenolol.

'Trasipresol' *see under* Oxprenolol.

'Trasitensin' *see under* Oxprenolol.

'Trasylol' *see* Aprotinin.

Traubenzucker *see* Glucose.

'Traumanase' *see* Bromelains.

'**Traumanase-cyclin**' *see under* Tetracycline.
'**Traumasept**' *see* Povidone-iodine.
'**Trausabun**' *see* Melitracen.
'**Travase**' *see* Sutilains.
'**Travocort**' *see* Diflucortolone valerate.
'**Travogen**' *see* Isoconazole.
'**Travogyn**' *see* Isoconazole.
TRAXANOX** (9-chloro-7-(1*H*-tetrazol-5-yl)-5*H*-[1]benzopyrano[2,3-*b*]pyridin-5-one).
TRAZITILINE** (1-(9,10-dihydro-9,10-ethano-anthryl)-4-methylpiperazine; 9,10-dihydro-9-(4-methylpiperazin-1-yl)-9,10-ethanoanthracene; SD-1223-01).
TRAZODONE** (2-[3-[4-(*m*-chlorophenyl)pip-erazin-1-yl]propyl]-*s*-triazolo[4,3-*a*]pyridin-3(2*H*)-one; trazodone hydrochloride; AF-1161; 'desyrel'; 'molipaxin'; 'pragmazone'; 'thombran'; 'trittico').
TRAZOLOPRIDE** (*N*-(1-benzylpiperid-4-yl)-6-methoxy-1*H*-benzotriazole-5-carboxamide).
TREBENZOMINE** ((±)-3-(dimethylamino)-2,3-dihydro-2-methylbenzopyran; (±)-*N*,*N*,2-trimethyl-3-chromanamine; trebenzomine hydrochloride; CI-686).
'**Treburon**' *see* Mepesulfate.
'**Trecalmo**' *see* Clotiazepam.
'**Trecator**' *see* Ethionamide.
'**Tredum**' *see* Fenpentadiol.
'**Treflan**' *see* Trifluralin.
'**Treloc**' *see under* Hydrochlorothiazide.
TRELOXINATE** (methyl 2,10-dichloro-12*H*-dibenzo[*d,g*]-[1,3]dioxocin-6-carboxylate).
'**Tremaril**' *see* Metixene.
'**Tremblex**' *see* Dexetimide.
'**Tremerad**' *see* Clioxanide.
'**Tremin**' *see* Trihexyphenidyl.
'**Tremonil**' *see* Metixene.
TREMORINE (1,4-dipyrrolidin-1-yl-2-butyne).
TRENBOLONE** (17β-hydroxy-19-norandros-ta-4,9,11-trien-3-one; 17β-hydroxyestra-4,9,11-trien-3-one; trienbolone; trienolone; R-2580).
TRENBOLONE ACETATE* ('finajet'; 'finaplex').
TRENBOLONE CYCLOHEXYLMETHYL-CARBONATE ('hexabolan').
TRENGESTONE** (6-chloro-1,6-didehydrore-troprogesterone; 6-chloro-9β,10α-pregna-1,4,6-triene-3,20-dione; Ro 4-8347; 'retroid').
'**Trenimon**' *see* Triaziquone.
TRENIZINE** ((±)-α-(*p-tert*-butylphenyl)-4-(diphenylmethyl)-1-piperazinebutanol).
'**Trentadil**' *see* Bamifylline.
'**Trental**' *see* Pentoxifylline.
TREOSULFAN** (L-*threo*-1,2,3,4-butanetetrol 1,4-bis(methanesulfonate) ester; L-dihydroxybu-sulfan; L-threityl dimesilate; NSC-39069).
TREPIBUTONE** (3-(2,4,5-triethoxybenzoyl)-propionic acid; AA-149).
TREPIPAM** ((+)-2,3,4,5-tetrahydro-7,8-di-methoxy-3-methyl-1-phenyl-1*H*-3-benzazepine; trimopam).
TREPIPAM MALEATE (trepipam hydrogen ma-leate; Sch-12679).
TREPIRIUM IODIDE** (2-carboxy-1,1-dimeth-ylpyrrolidinium iodide ester with choline iodide; choline iodide 1,1-dimethylpyrrolidinium iodide 2-carboxylate; *N*-methylproline choline ester iodide methiodide).
'**Trepress**' *see under* Oxprenolol.
TREPTILAMINE** (2-[(α-tricyclo[2.2.1.0²,⁶]-hept-3-ylidenebenzyl)oxy]triethylamine).
TREQUINSIN** (2,3,6,7-tetrahydro-2-(mesityl-imino)-9,10-dimethoxy-3-methyl-4*H*-pyrimi-do[6,1-*a*]isoquinolin-4-one).
'**Tresanil**' *see* Tritiozine.
'**Trescatyl**' *see* Ethionamide.
'**Trescillin**' *see* Propicillin.
'**Tresochin**' *see* Chloroquine diphosphate.
'**Trest**' *see* Metixene.
TRESTOLONE** (17β-hydroxy-7α-methylestr-4-en-3-one; 7α-methyl-19-nortestosterone; 7α-methylnandrolone).
TRESTOLONE ACETATE* (NSC-69948; U-15614).
TRETAMINE** (2,4,6-tris(1-aziridinyl)-*s*-triaz-ine; triethylenimino-*s*-triazine; triethanomel-amine; triethylenemelamine; TEM; TET; Ho-1/93; M-9500; NSC-9706; R-246; SK-1133).
TRETHINIUM TOSILATE** (2-ethyl-1,2,3,4-tetrahydro-2-methylisoquinolinium *p*-toluene-sulfonate).
TRETHOCANIC ACID** (3-hydroxy-3,7,11-tri-methyldodecanoic acid).
TRETINOIN** (*all-trans*-3,7-dimethyl-9-(2,6,6-trimethyl-1-cyclohexen-1-yl)nona-2,4,6,8-tetra-enoic acid; *all-trans*-retinoic acid; 15-apo-β-caro-ten-15-oic acid; vitamin A acid; NSC-122758; 'aberel'; 'airol'; 'dermairol'; 'eudyna'; 'retin-A').
Tretinoin *p*-hydroxyanilide *see* Fenretinide.
TRETOQUINOL** ((−)-1,2,3,4-tetrahydro-1-(3,4,5-trimethoxybenzyl)-6,7-isoquinolinediol; trimethoquinol; trimetoquinol; tretoquinol hydrochloride; AQ-110; AQL-208; 'expansolin'; 'inolin').
'**Trevintix**' *see* Protionamide.
'**TRH-Roche**' *see* Protirelin.
TRH synthetic *see* Protirelin.
Tri *see* Trichloroethylene.
'**Tri-6**' *see* Lindane.
'**Tri-abrodil**' *see* Sodium acetrizoate.
Triac *see* Tiratricol.
'**Triacana**' *see* Tiratricol.
TRIACANTHINE (togholamine).
TRIACETIC ACID (3,5-diketocaproic acid; 3,5-dioxohexanoic acid).
TRIACETIN** (glyceryl triacetate).
1,8,9-Triacetoxyanthracene *see* Dithranol triacet-ate.
2′,3′,5′-Tri-*O*-acetyl-6-azauridine *see* Azaribine.
Triacetyldihydroxydiphenylisatin *see* Phenisatin.
Triacetyloleandomycin *see* Troleandomycin.
'**Triacilline**' *see* Ticarcillin.
Triaconazole* *see* Terconazole.
'**Triadenyl**' *see* Adenosine triphosphate.
TRIADIMEFON (1-[2-*tert*-butyl-1-(*p*-chlorophen-yl)-2-oxoethyl]-1*H*-1,2,4-triazole; 1-(4-chloro-phenoxy)-3,3-dimethyl-1-(1*H*-1,2,4-triazol-1-yl)-

2-butanone; 'bayleton').

TRIADIMENOL (1-[2-*tert*-butyl-1-(*p*-chlorophenoxy)-2-hydroxyethyl]-1*H*-1,2,4-triazole; β-(4-chlorophenoxy)-α-(1,1-dimethylethyl)-1*H*-1,2,4-triazole-1-ethanol; 'bayfidan'; 'baytan').

TRIAFUNGIN** (3-benzylpyrido[3,4-*e*]-1,2,4-triazine; EU-3325).

'Triagynon' *see under* Levonorgestrel.

TRIALLATE* (*S*-(2,3,3-trichloro-2-propenyl) bis(1-methylethyl)carbamothioate; *S*-(2,3,3-trichloroallyl) diisopropylcarbamothioate; 'avadex BW'; 'fargo').

TRIAMCINOLONE** 9α-fluoro-11β,16α,17,21-tetrahydroxypregna-1,4-diene-3,20-dione; 9α-fluoro-16α-hydroxyprednisolone; fluoxiprednisolone; fluoxyprednisolone; CL-19823).

TRIAMCINOLONE plus HALQUINOLS ('remiderm'; 'remotic').

TRIAMCINOLONE ACETONIDE* (9α-fluoro-11β,21-dihydroxy-16α,17α-isopropylidenedioxypregna-1,4-diene-3,20-dione; triamcinolone cyclic 16,17-acetal with acetone).

TRIAMCINOLONE ACETONIDE plus ECONAZOLE ('epipevisone'; 'pevisone').

TRIAMCINOLONE ACETONIDE plus NEOMYCIN ('cidermex').

TRIAMCINOLONE ACETONIDE plus NYSTATIN ('nystadermal').

Triamcinolone acetonide 21-(2-benzofurancarboxylate) *see* Triamcinolone furetonide.

Triamcinolone acetonide dimethylbutyrate *see* Triamcinolone hexacetonide.

Triamcinolone acetonide 21-ester with *N*-benzoyl-2-methyl-β-alanine *see* Triamcinolone benetonide.

TRIAMCINOLONE ACETONIDE SODIUM PHOSPHATE* (triamcinolone acetonide 21-disodium phosphate; CL-53381; CL-61965; CL-106359; 'aristosol').

TRIAMCINOLONE BENETONIDE*** (triamcinolone acetonide 21-ester with N-benzoyl-2-methyl-β-alanine; TBI; 'tibiocorten').

Triamcinolone cyclic 16,17-acetal with acetone *see* Triamcinolone acetonide.

Triamcinolone cyclic 16,17-acetal with acetophenone *see* Amcinafide.

Triamcinolone cyclic 16,17-acetal with acrolein *see* Acrocinonide.

Triamcinolone cyclic 16,17-acetal with cyclopentanone, 21-acetate *see* Amcinonide.

Triamcinolone cyclic 16,17-acetal with 3-pentanone *see* Amcinafal.

TRIAMCINOLONE DIACETATE* (triamcinolone 16,21-diacetate; RP 8357; 'aristocort'; 'solutedarol'; 'tedarol').

TRIAMCINOLONE FURETONIDE*** (triamcinolone acetonide 21-(2-benzofurancarboxylate)).

TRIAMCINOLONE HEXACETONIDE*** (triamcinolone acetonide 21-(2,3-dimethylbutyrate); TATBA; CL-34433; 'aristospan'; 'hexatrione'; 'lederspan').

'Triamelin' *see* Tretamine.

2,4,7-Triamino-6-(2-furyl)pteridine *see* Furterene.

2,4,7-Triamino-6-phenylpteridine *see* Triamterene.

1,4,7-Triamino-5-phenylpyrimido[4,5-*d*]pyrimidine *see* Ampyrimine.

Triaminophosphine sulfide *see* Phosphorothioic triamide.

Triamino-*s*-triazine *see* Melamine.

TRIAMIPHOS* (5-amino-1-(bisdimethylaminophosphoryl)-3-phenyl-1,2,4-triazole; *P*-(5-amino-3-phenyl-1,2,4-triazol-1-yl)-*N,N,N',N'*-phosphonic diamide; 'wepsyn').

TRIAMPYZINE*** (2-(dimethylamino)-3,5,6-trimethylpyrazine; triampyzine sulfate; W-3976B).

TRIAMTERENE*** (2,4,7-triamino-6-phenylpteridine; NSC-77625; SK&F-8542).
See also under Bemetizide;Benzthiazide; Cyclothiazide; Hydrochlorothiazide.

TRIAMTERENE plus XIPAMIDE ('neotri').

'Triamteril' *see* Triamterene.

'Triamteryl' *see* Triamterene.

'Triamthiazid' *see under* Hydrochlorothiazide.

Triantoin *see* Mephenytoin.

TRIARIMOL* (α-(2,4-dichlorophenyl)-α-phenyl-5-pyrimidinemethanol; EL-273).

'Triastonal' *see* β-Sitosterol.

'Triavil' *see under* Amitriptyline.

2,5,8-Triazaeicosane-1-carboxylic acid *see* Dodicin.

TRIAZENE (HN:NNH$_2$).

s-TRIAZINE (1,3,5-triazine).

as-Triazine-3,5-dione *see* Azauracil.

s-Triazine-2,4-dione-6-carboxylic acid *see* 5-Azaorotic acid.

s-Triazinetriol *see* Cyanuric acid.

as-Triazino[5,6-*c*]quinoline *see* Strinoline.

TRIAZIQUONE*** (2,3,5-triethylenimino-1,4-benzoquinone; 2,3,5-tris(1-aziridinyl)-*p*-benzoquinone; 2,3,5-trisethylenimino-1,4-benzoquinone; A-163; Bayer-3231; NSC-29215; Riker-601).

TRIAZOLAM** (8-chloro-6-(*o*-chlorophenyl)-1-methyl-4*H*-*s*-triazolo[4,3-*a*][1,4]benzodiazepine; U-33030; 'halcion').

1*H*-1,2,4-Triazol-3-amine *see* Amitrole.

1,2,4-Triazole-3-carboxamide riboside *see* Ribavirin.

v-Triazolo[3,4-*d*]pyrimidine *see* 8-Azapurine.

Triazotion (tr) *see* Azinphos-ethyl.

'Triazure' *see* Azaribine.

'Triazurol' *see* Chlorazanil.

'Trib' *see* Co-trimoxazole.

Tribavarin* *see* Ribavirin.

TRIBENOSIDE*** (ethyl 3,5,6-tri-*O*-benzyl-D-glucurofuranoside; benzylglucofuranoside; glucofuranoside; Ba-21401; 'glyvenol'; 'procto-glyvenol').

'Tribrissen' *see under* Trimethoprim.

Tribromoethanol *see* Bromethol.

3,4',5-Tribromo-6-hydroxybenzanilide *see* Tribromsalan.

3,4',5-Tribromo-2-mercaptobenzanilide *see* Tiosalan.

Tribromomethane *see* Bromoform.

3,4',5-Tribromosalicylanilide *see* Tribromsalan.

4,4',5-Tribromo-2-thiophenecarboxanilide *see* Ti-

513

brofan.

TRIBROMSALAN*** (3,4′,5-tribromo-6-hydroxybenzanilide; 3,4′,5-tribromosalicylanilide; ET-394; NSC-20526).
See also under Dibromsalan.

'Tribunil' see Methabenzthiazuron.

'Triburon' see Triclobisonium chloride.

TRIBUTYL PHOSPHOROTRITHIOATE (DEF).

TRIBUTYL PHOSPHOROTRITHIOITE ('folex'; 'merphos').

TRIBUZONE** (4-(4,4-dimethyl-3-oxopentyl)-1,2-diphenylpyrazolidine-3,5-dione; 4-[2-(2,2-dimethylpropionyl)ethyl]-1,2-diphenyl-3,5-pyrazolidinedione; 1,2-diphenyl-4-(2-pivaloylethyl)-3,5-pyrazolidinedione; 1,2-diphenyl-4-(4,4,4-trimethyl-3-oxobutyryl)-3,5-pyrazolidinedione; trimetazone; trimethazone; 'benetazone').

TRICAINE (3-aminobenzoic acid ethyl ester methanesulfonate; ethyl *m*-aminobenzoate mesilate; MS-222; 'finquel'; 'metacaine').

TRICAMBA* (2,3,5-trichloro-6-methoxybenzoic acid; metriben; 'banvel T').

'Tricandil' see Mepartricin.

TRICARBALLYLIC ACID (1,2,3-propanetricarboxylic acid; β-carboxyglutaric acid).

Tricarbocyanine-II see Indocyanine green.

TRICETAMIDE* (*N*,*N*-diethyl-α-(3,4,5-trimethoxybenzamido)acetamide; *N*′,*N*′-diethyl-*N*-(3,4,5-trimethoxybenzoyl)glycinamide; *N*-(diethylcarbamoylmethyl)-3,4,5-trimethoxybenzamide; trimethobenzoylglycine; trimethoxybenzoylglycine diethylamide; R-548; Riker 548; 'thylamid'; 'trimeglamide').

'Trichex' see Metronidazole.

'Trichlofos' see Triclofos.

Trichloramate see Carbocloral.

Trichlorfon see Metrifonate.

TRICHLORMETHIAZIDE*** (6-chloro-3-(dichloromethyl)-3,4-dihydro-1,2,4-benzothiadiazine-7-sulfonamide 1,1-dioxide; hydrotrichlorothiazide; trichloromethiazide; trichloromethylhydrochlorothiazide).
See also under Reserpine.

TRICHLORMETHINE*** (2,2′,2″-trichlorotriethylamine; tris(2-chloroethyl)amine; trimustine; tris-*N*-lost; HN3; NSC-30211; R-47; SK-100; TS-160).

Trichlormethylfos see Chlorpyrifos-methyl.

Trichloroacetaldehyde monohydrate see Chloral hydrate.

Trichloroacetonitrile see Chlorocyanohydrin.

S-**(2,3,3-Trichloroallyl) diisopropylcarbamothioate** see Triallate.

TRICHLOROBENZOIC ACID (2,3,6-TBA; 'trysben').
See also Dimethylamine trichlorobenzoate.

1,1,1-Trichloro-2,2-bis(*p*-chlorophenyl)ethane see DDT.

1,1,1-Trichloro-2,2-bis(*p*-chlorophenyl)ethanol see Dicofol.

1,1,1-TRICHLORO-2,2-BIS(*p*-FLUOROPHENYL)ETHANE (DFDT; 'gix').

1,1,1-Trichloro-2,2-bis(*p*-methoxyphenyl)ethane see Methoxychlor.

2,2,3-Trichloro-1,1-butanediol see Butylchloral hydrate.

Trichlorobutylidene glycol see Butylchloral hydrate.

3,4,4′-Trichlorocarbanilide see Triclocarban.

2,2,2-Trichloro-1-(*o*-chlorophenyl)-1-*p*-chlorophenyl)ethane see o,p′-DDT.

1,2,4-Trichloro-5-(*p*-chlorophenylsulfonyl)benzene see Tetradifon.

1,2,4-Trichloro-5-[(*p*-chlorophenyl)thio]benzene see Tetrasul.

3,5,6-Trichloro-2-[(diethoxyphosphinothioyl)oxy]-pyridine see Chlorpyrifos.

3′,4′,7-Trichloro-2,3-dihydro-5-hydroxy-1-benzothiepin-4-carboxanilide 1,1-dioxide see Enolicam.

1,1,1-TRICHLOROETHANE (methylchloroform; 'chlorothene'; 'drano liquid').

1,1,2-TRICHLOROETHANE (vinyl trichloride).

Trichloroethene see Trichloroethylene.

Trichloroethyl carbamate see Trichlorourethan.

Trichloroethyl dihydrogen phosphate see Triclofos.

TRICHLOROETHYLENE*** (1,1,2-trichloroethylene; trichloroethene; ethinyl trichloride; tri).

1,1′-(2,2,2-Trichloroethylene)bis(4-chlorobenzene) see DDT.

1,1′-(2,2,2-Trichloroethylene)bis(4-methoxybenzene) see Methoxychlor.

1,2-*O*-(2,2,2-Trichloroethylidene)-α-D-glucofuranose see Chloralose.

2,2,2-Trichloroethyl 4-phenyl-2-thiazolecarbamate see Lotifazole.

Trichloroethyl phosphate see Triclofos.

9,11β,21-Trichloro-6α-fluoro-16α,17-dihydroxypregna-1,4-diene-3,20-dione cyclic acetal with acetone see Triclonide.

TRICHLOROFLUOROMETHANE (FC-11; fluorocarbon 11).

Trichlorofon see Metrifonate.

N-**(2,2,2-Trichloro-1-formamidoethyl)aniline** see Chloraniformethan.

2,2,2-Trichloro-4′-hydroxyacetanilide see Triclacetamol.

β,β,β-Trichloro-α-hydroxy-*p*-acetophenetidide see Cloracetadol.

2,4,4′-Trichloro-2′-hydroxydiphenyl ether see Triclosan.

p-**(2,2,2-Trichloro-1-hydroxyethoxy)acetanilide** see Cloracetadol.

17β-(2,2,2-Trichloro-1-hydroxyethoxy)androst-4-en-3-one see Cloxotestosterone.

17β-(2,2,2-Trichloro-1-hydroxyethoxy)estra-1,3,5(10)-trien-3-ol see Cloxestradiol.

7-[2-(2,2,2-Trichloro-1-hydroxyethoxy)ethyl]theophylline see Triclofylline.

N-**(2,2,2-Trichloro-1-hydroxyethyl)carbamic acid ethyl ester** see Carbocloral.

(2,2,2-Trichloro-1-hydroxyethyl) estradiol ether see Cloxestradiol.

6-*O*-(2,2,2-Trichloro-1-hydroxyethyl)-α,D-glucopyranose 1→4 polymer with α-D-glucopyranose see Amicloral.

514

(2,2,2-Trichloro-1-hydroxyethyl)phosphonic acid dimethyl ester *see* Metrifonate.

(2,2,2-Trichloro-1-hydroxyethyl) testosterone ether *see* Cloxotestosterone.

2,4,4'-Trichloro-α-(imidazol-1-ylmethyl)-α,α'-ditolyl ether *see* Econazole.

2,4,5-Trichloro-1-(3-iodo-2-propyn-1-yl-oxy)benzene *see* Haloprogin.

Trichloroisocyanuric acid *see* Symclosene.

Trichloromethane *see* Chloroform.

Trichloromethiazide *see* Trichlormethiazide.

2,3,5-Trichloro-6-methoxybenzoic acid *see* Tricamba.

Trichloromethyl chloroformate *see* Diphosgene.

2-(Trichloromethyl)-1,3-dioxane-5,5-dimethanol *see* Penthrichloral.

Trichloromethylhydrochlorothiazide *see* Trichlormethiazide.

1,1,1-Trichloro-2-methyl-2-propanol *see* Chlorbutol.

N-(Trichloromethylthio)-4-cyclohexene-1,2-dicarboximide *see* Captan.

2-(Trichloromethylthio)-1H-isoindole-1,3-(2H)-dione *see* Folpet.

N-(Trichloromethylthio)phthalimide *see* Folpet.

N-(Trichloromethylthio)tetrahydrophthalimide *see* Captan.

4,5,7-Trichloro-2-[3-(methylthio)-1,2,4-thiadiazol-2-ylthio]benzimidazole *see* Subendazole.

TRICHLORONAT* (O-ethyl O-(2,4,5-trichlorophenyl) ethylphosphonothioate; fenophosphon; 'agrisil'; 'apritox'; 'phytosol').

Trichloronitromethane *see* Chloropicrin.

TRICHLOROPHEN (tr) (4-chloro-2,6-bis(5-chloro-2-hydroxybenzyl)phenol; trichlosal; G-610).

2,4,5-Trichlorophenolate(s) *see* Triclofenate(s).

2,4,5-Trichlorophenol piperazine compound *see* Triclofenol piperazine.

2,4,5-TRICHLOROPHENOXYACETIC ACID (2,4,5-T; 'weedar T'; 'weedone special').
See also Chlorinated phenoxyacetic acid.

2-(2,4,5-Trichlorophenoxy)ethyl 2,2-dichloropropionate *see* Erbon.

2-(2,4,5-Trichlorophenoxy)propionic acid *see* Fenoprop.

2,4,5-Trichlorophenyl γ-iodopropargyl ether *see* Haloprogin.

2,4,5-Trichlorophenyl 3-iodo-2-propynyl ether *see* Haloprogin.

Trichlorophone *see* Metrifonate.

Trichlorophos *see* Triclofos.

S-(2,3,3-Trichloro-2-propenyl) bis(1-methylethyl)-carbamothioate *see* Triallate.

Trichlorotriethylamine *see* Trichlormethine.

1,1,2-TRICHLORO-1,2,2-TRIFLUOROETHANE (R-113; 'arcton-63'; 'freon 113'; 'frigen-113'; 'genetron-113').

TRICHLOROURETHAN (trichloroethyl carbamate; 'voluntal').

Trichlorphon* *see* Metrifonate.

'Trichloryl' *see* Triclofos.

Trichlosal *see* Trichlorophen.

'Trichocid' *see* Aminitrozole.

'Tricho cordes' *see* Metronidazole.

'Trichofuron' *see* Furazolidone.

'Tricho-gynaedron' *see* Metronidazole.

'Trichojel' *see* Aminoacridine.

'Trichomol' *see* Metronidazole.

'Trichomon' *see* DDT.

'Trichomonacid' *see* Metronidazole.

TRICHOMONACIDE (tr) (4-[4-(diethylamino)-1-methylbutylamino]-6-methoxy-2-(4-nitrostyryl)-quinoline).

'Trichomycin' *see* Hachimycin.

'Trichonat' *see* Hachimycin.

Trichopol (tr) *see* Metronidazole.

'Trichorad' *see* Aminitrozole.

'Trichoral' *see* Aminitrozole.

'Trichosept' *see* Hachimycin.

TRICIN (4',5,7-trihydroxy-3',5'-dimethoxyflavone).

TRICIRIBINE* (3-amino-1,5-dihydro-5-methyl-1-β-D-ribofuranosyl-1,4,5,6,8-penta-azaacenaphthylene).

TRICLABENDAZOLE* (5-chloro-6-(2,3-dichlorophenoxy)-2-(methylthio)benzimidazole).

TRICLACETAMOL* (2,2,2-trichloro-4'-hydroxyacetanilide).

TRICLAZATE* (1-methyl-3-pyrrolidinemethanol benzilate ester; 1-methylpyrrolidin-3-yl-methyl benzilate).

'Tricleryl' *see* Triclofos.

TRICLOBISONIUM CHLORIDE* (hexamethylene-1,6-bis[dimethyl[1-methyl-3-(2,2,6-trimethylcyclohexyl)propyl]ammonium chloride]; Ro 5-0810/1).

TRICLOCARBAN* (3,4,4'-trichlorocarbanilide; NSC-72005).

TRICLODAZOL* (5,5-diphenyl-3-(2,2,2-trichloro-1-hydroxyethyl)-4-imidazolidinone).

TRICLOFENATE(S)* (2,4,5-trichlorophenolate(s)).

TRICLOFENOL PIPERAZINE* (piperazine compound (1:2) with 2,4,5-trichlorophenol; piperazine di(2,4,5-trichlorophenoxide); CI-416; CN-5834-5931B; IN-29-5931; NSC-77747).

TRICLOFOS* (trichloroethyl dihydrogen phosphate; trichloroethyl phosphate; sodium triclofos; trichlorophos; Sch-10159; 'trichlofos'; 'tricleryl'; 'tricloryl'; 'triclos').

TRICLOFYLLINE* (7-[2-(2,2-trichloro-1-hydroxyethoxy)ethyl]theophylline).

TRICLONIDE* (9,11β,21-trichloro-6α-fluoro-16α,17-dihydroxypregna-1,4-diene-3,20-dione cyclic acetal with acetone; RS-4464).

Triclorfon *see* Metrifonate.

'Tricloryl' *see* Triclofos.

'Triclos' *see* Triclofos.

TRICLOSAN* (5-chloro-2-(2,4-dichlorophenoxy)phenol; 2,4,4'-trichloro-2'-hydroxydiphenyl ether; cloxifenol; CH-3565; GP-41353; 'cidal'; 'irgasan DP-30'; 'sterlifix'; 'ster-zac').

'Triclose' *see* Azanidazole.

'Tricofuron' *see* Furazolidone.

'Tricoloid' *see* Tricyclamol chloride.

'**Tricoperidol**' *see* Trifluperidol.
'**Tricornox**' *see* Benazolin.
'**Tricoryl**' *see* Trolnitrate.
TRICOSACTIDE*** (23-L-tyrosinamide-α$^{1-23}$-corticotrophin).
TRICRESOL (mixture of *o*-, *m*- and *p*-cresols).
TRICRESYL PHOSPHATE (mixture of tris(*o*-, *m*- and *p*-cresyl) esters of phosphoric acid; tolyl phosphate; triorthocresyl phosphate; tritolyl phosphate; PX-917; TCP; 'celluflex'; 'kronitex'; 'lindol').
TRI-*o*-CRESYL PHOSPHATE (TOCP).
'**Tricuran**' *see* Gallamine triethiodide.
Tricyanic acid *see* Cyanuric acid.
TRICYCLAMOL CHLORIDE*** ((±)-1-(3-cyclohexyl-3-hydroxy-3-phenylpropyl)-1-methylpyrrolidinium chloride; procyclidine methochloride).
Tricyclo[3.3.1.1^{3,7}]decane *see* Adamantane.
Tricyclo[4.2.2.0^{2,5}]dec-9-ene-3,4,7,8-tetracarboxylic 3,4:7,8-diimide *see* Mitindomide.
1-Tricyclo[3.3.1.1^{3,7}]dec-1-yl-2-azetidinecarboxylic acid *see* Carmantadine.
2-[(α-Tricyclo[2.2.1.0^{2,6}]-hept-3-ylidenebenzyl)oxy]-triethylamine *see* Treptilamine.
Tricyclohexylhydroxystannane *see* Cyhexatin.
Tricyclohexylhydroxytin *see* Cyhexatin.
3,5,7,8-Tridecatetraene-10,12-diynoic acid *see* Mycomycin.
TRIDEMORPH* (2,6-dimethyl-4-tridecylmorpholine; 'calixin').
'**Tridesilon**' *see* Desonide.
'**Tridesonit**' *see* Desonide.
Tridihexethide *see* Tridihexethyl chloride.
TRIDIHEXETHYL CHLORIDE* ((3-cyclohexyl-3-hydroxy-3-phenylpropyl)trimethylammonium chloride; tridihexethide).
TRIDIHEXETHYL IODIDE*** ((3-cyclohexyl-3-hydroxy-3-phenylpropyl)trimethylammonium iodide; propethon; tridihexide).
Tridihexide *see* Tridihexethyl iodide.
'**Tridione**' *see* Trimethadione.
'**Trieffortil**' *see* Etilefrine.
Trienbolone *see* Trenbolone.
Trienolone *see* Trenbolone.
TRIENTINE*** (triethylenetetramine; 2,2'-ethylenediiminobis(ethylamine); trientine dihydrochloride; TETA).
'**Tri-ervonum**' *see under* Megestrol acetate.
TRIETAZINE* (2-chloro-4-diethylamino-6-ethylamino-*s*-triazine; 6-chloro-*N*,*N'*,*N'*-triethyl-1,3,5-triazine-2,4-diamine).
TRIETHANOLAMINE (2,2',2''-nitrilotriethanol; trolamine).
Triethanolamine trinitrate *see* Trolnitrate.
Triethanomelamine *see* Tretamine.
3-(2,4,5-Triethoxybenzoyl)propionic acid *see* Trepibutone.
Triethylaminoethanol chloride *see* Triethyl(2-hydroxyethyl)ammonium chloride.
Triethylcholine *see* Triethyl(2-hydroxyethyl)ammonium chloride.
TRIETHYLENE GLYCOL (3,6-dioxaoctane-1,8-diol; triglycol).
Triethylene glycol diglycidyl ether *see* Etoglucid.
Triethylenemelamine *see* Tretamine.
Triethylenephosphoramide *see* Tepa.
N,*N'*,*N''*-**Triethylenephosphorothioic triamide** *see* Thiotepa.
Triethylenetetramine *see* Trientine.
Triethylenethiophosphoramide *see* Thiotepa.
Triethylenimine thiophosphoramide *see* Thiotepa.
2,3,5-Triethylenimino-1,4-benzoquinone *see* Triaziquone.
Triethylenimino-*s*-triazine *see* Tretamine.
Triethyl(3-hydroxy-2,3-dimethylpropyl)ammonium iodide *p*-butoxybenzoate *see* Quateron.
Triethyl(2-hydroxyethyl)ammonium bromide dicyclopentylacetate *see* Diponium bromide.
TRIETHYL(2-HYDROXYETHYL)AMMONIUM CHLORIDE (choline triethyl analog; triethylaminoethanol chloride; triethylcholine; TEC).
Triethyl(2-hydroxyethyl)ammonium *p*-toluenesulfonate 3,4,5-trimethoxybenzoate *see* Troxonium tosilate.
N,*N'*,*N'*-**Triethyl-*N*-(2-hydroxyethyl)ethylenediamine *p*-aminobenzoate** *see* Amoxecaine.
Triethyl(2-phenothiazin-10-ylethyl)ammonium iodide *see* Diethazine ethiodide.
(*E*)-*N*,*N*,*N*-**Triethyl-2-[4-(2-phenylethenyl)phenoxy]ethanaminium iodide** *see* Stilonium iodide.
S-**(Triethylphosphoranediylaurio)-1-thio-β-D-glucopyranose 2,3,4,6-tetraacetate** *see* Auranofin.
Triethyl 2-[(*E*)-(*p*-styrylphenoxy)ethyl]ammonium iodide *see* Stilonium iodide.
Triethyl[2-(trimethoxybenzoyloxy)ethyl]ammonium *p*-toluenesulfonate *see* Troxonium tosilate.
TRIFENMORPH* (*N*-(triphenylmethyl)morpholine; tritylmorpholine; triphenmorph; WL-8008; 'frescon').
TRIFEZOLAC*** (1,3,5-triphenylpyrazole-4-acetic acid).
TRIFLOCIN** (*N*-(3-carboxypyridin-4-yl)-α,α,α-trifluoro-*m*-toluidine; 4-(α,α,α-trifluoro-*m*-toluidino)nicotinic acid; 4-(3-trifluoromethylanilino)-nicotinic acid; CL-65562; JDL-38).
TRIFLUBAZAM*** (1-methyl-5-phenyl-7-trifluoromethyl-1*H*-1,5-benzodiazepine-2,4(3*H*,5*H*)-dione; ORF-8063; WE-352).
TRIFLUMIDATE*** (3-[*N*-carboxy-*N*-(trifluoromethylsulfonyl)amino]benzophenone ethyl ester; ethyl *m*-benzoyl-*N*-(trifluoromethylsulfonyl)-carbanilate; BA-4223; MBR-4223).
TRIFLUOMEPRAZINE*** (10-[3-(dimethylamino)-2-methylpropyl]-2-trifluoromethylphenothiazine; triflutrimeprazine; SK&F-5345-A).
TRIFLUOPERAZINE*** (10-[3-(4-methylpiperazin-1-yl)propyl]-2-(trifluoromethyl)phenothiazine; trifluoromethylperazine; trifluperazine; trifluoperazine hydrochloride; triftazine).
TRIFLUOPERAZINE plus ISOPROPAMIDE IODIDE ('stelabid').
See also under Tranylcypromine.
1,1,1-Trifluoro-3,4-bis(3-fluoro-4-hydroxyphenyl)-pentane *see* Pentafluranol.

α,α,α-Trifluoro-2,4-cresotic acid acetate *see* Triflusal.

α,α,α-Trifluoro-2,4-cresotic acid dihydrogen phosphate *see* Flufosal.

α,α,α-Trifluoro-2,6-dimethyl-1-piperidinethiocarboxy-*m*-toluidide *see* Ticarbodine.

α,α,α-Trifluoro-2,6-dinitro-*N,N*-dipropyl-*p*-toluidine *see* Trifluralin.

Trifluoroethyl vinyl ether *see* Fluroxene.

Trifluoromethane *see* Fluoroform.

(±)-α,α,α-Trifluoro-*p*-[3-(methylamino)-1-phenylpropoxy]toluene *see* Fluoxetine.

2-[3-(Trifluoromethyl)anilino]nicotinic acid *see* Niflumic acid.

4-(3-Trifluoromethylanilino)nicotinic acid *see* Triflocin.

6-(Trifluoromethyl)-2*H*-1,2,4-benzothiadiazine-7-sulfonamide 1,1-dioxide *see* Flumethiazide.

1-[2-[4'-(Trifluoromethyl)biphenyl-4-yloxy]ethyl]-pyrrolidine *see* Boxidine.

2,2,2-Trifluoro-1-methylethyl 2-cyanoacrylate *see* Flucrilate.

Trifluoromethylhydrothiazide *see* Hydroflumethiazide.

α,α,α-Trifluoro-5-methyl-4-isoxazolecarboxy-*p*-toluidide *see* Leflunomide.

α,α,α-Trifluoro-2-methyl-4'-nitro-*m*-propionotoluamide *see* Flutamide.

Trifluoromethylperazine *see* Trifluoperazine.

8-(Trifluoromethyl)phenothiazine-1-carboxylic acid *see* Flutiazin.

4-[3-[2-(Trifluoromethyl)phenothiazin-2-yl]propyl]-1-piperazineethanol *see* Fluphenazine.

2-[[1-[3-[2-(Trifluoromethyl)phenothiazin-10-yl]propyl]piperid-4-yl]oxy]ethanol *see* Flupimazine.

6,6,9-Trifluoro-16α-methylprednisolone *see* Cormetasone.

Trifluoromethylpromazine *see* Triflupromazine.

N-(8-Trifluoromethylquinolin-4-yl)anthranilic acid 2,3-dihydroxypropyl ester *see* Floctafenine.

N-[7-(Trifluoromethyl)quinolin-4-yl]anthranilic acid 2-pyrrolidin-1-ylethyl ester *see* Florifenine.

N-[7-(Trifluoromethyl)quinol-4-yl]anthranilic acid 2-[4-(α,α,α-trifluoro-*m*-tolyl)piperazin-1-yl]ethyl ester *see* Antrafenine.

Trifluoromethylthiazide *see* Flumethiazide.

4-[3-(6-Trifluoromethyl-4*H*-thieno[2,3-*b*][1,4]benzothiazin-4-yl)propyl]-1-piperazineethanol *see* Flutizenol.

α,α,α-Trifluoro-*m*-morpholin-2-yltoluene *see* Flumexadol.

α',α',α'-Trifluoro-4'-nitroisobutyro-*m*-toluidide *see* Flutamide.

α,α,α-Trifluoro-3-nitro-4-(*p*-nitrophenoxy)toluene *see* Fluorodifen.

α,α,α-Trifluoro-*m*-salicylotoluidide *see* Salfluverine.

α,α,α-Trifluoro-*N*-salicyloyl-*m*-toluidine *see* Salfluverine.

α,α,α-Trifluorothymidine *see* Trifluridine.

2-(α,α,α-Trifluoro-*m*-toluidino)nicotinic acid *see* Niflumic acid.

4-(α,α,α-Trifluoro-*m*-toluidino)nicotinic acid *see* Triflocin.

N-[[4-(α,α,α-Trifluoro-*m*-toluidino)pyrid-3-yl]sulfonyl]propionamide *see* Galosemide.

N-(α,α,α-Trifluoro-*m*-tolyl)anthranilic acid *see* Flufenamic acid.

2-(α,α,α-Trifluoro-*p*-tolyl)-1,3-indandione *see* Fluindarol.

2-(α,α,α-Trifluoro-*m*-tolyl)morpholine *see* Flumexadol.

6-(α,α,α-Trifluoro-*p*-tolyl)-3-morpholinone *see* Flumetramide.

2-[4-(α,α,α-Trifluoro-*m*-tolyl)piperazin-1-yl]ethyl (±)-*p*-isobutylhydratropate *see* Frabuprofen.

2-[4-(α,α,α-Trifluoro-*m*-tolyl)piperazin-1-yl]ethyl *N*-[7-(trifluoromethyl)-4-quinolyl]anthranilate *see* Antrafenine.

[2-[4-(α,α,α-Trifluoro-*m*-tolyl)piperazin-1-yl]ethyl]-urea *see* Fluprazine.

6,6,9-Trifluoro-11β,17,21-trihydroxy-16α-methylpregna-1,4-diene-3,20-dione *see* Cormetasone.

2-(α³,α³,α³-trifluoro-2,3-xylidino)nicotinic acid *see* Flunixin.

Trifluperazine *see* Trifluoperazine.

TRIFLUPERIDOL* (4'-fluoro-4-[hydroxy-4-(α,α,α-trifluoro-*m*-tolyl)piperid-1-yl]butyrophenone; 4'-fluoro-4-[hydroxy-4-(*m*-trifluoromethylphenyl)piperid-1-yl]butyrophenone; 1-[3-(*p*-fluorobenzoyl)propyl]-4-(*m*-trifluoromethylphenyl)-4-piperidinol; flumoperon; McN-JR-2498; R-2498).

TRIFLUPROMAZINE* (10-[3-(dimethylamino)propyl]-2-(trifluoromethyl)phenothiazine; fluopromazine; trifluoromethylpromazine; triflupromazine hydrochloride; MC-4703; SK&F-4648A).

TRIFLURALIN* (α,α,α-trifluoro-2,6-dinitro-*N,N*-dipropyl-*p*-toluidine; 'treflan').

TRIFLURIDINE* (2'-deoxy-5-(trifluoromethyl)uridine; α,α,α-trifluorothymidine; F₃TDR; TFT; 'viroptic').

TRIFLUSAL* (2-acetoxy-4-(trifluoromethyl)benzoic acid; α,α,α-trifluoro-2,4-cresotic acid acetate).

Triflutrimeprazine *see* Trifluomeprazine.

TRIFOLIN (kaempferol 3-galactoside).

TRIFORINE (*N,N'*-[1,4-piperazinediylbis(2,2,2-trichloroethylidene)]bisformamide; biformylchlorazin; formchlorazin).

'Triformol' *see* Paraformaldehyde.

Triftazine (tr) *see* Trifluoperazine.

'Trigemine' *see* Butylchloralamidopyrine.

'Trigeminin' *see* Butylchloralamidopyrine.

'Trigenolline' *see* Trigonelline.

'Triglobe' *see* Co-trimazine.

Triglycine *see* Nitrilotriacetic acid.

Triglycol *see* Triethylene glycol.

Triglycollamic acid *see* Nitrilotriacetic acid.

Triglycyllysine vasopressin *see* Terlipressin.

Triglycylvasopressin *see* Terlipressin.

TRIGONELLINE (nicotinic acid *N*-methylbetaine; caffearin; 'coffearine'; 'gynesin'; 'trigenolline').

'Trigonyl' *see* Co-trimoxazole.

'Trigot' *see* Co-dergocrine.

'Trigynon' *see under* Levonorgestrel.

TRIHEXYPHENIDYL* (α-cyclohexyl-α-phenyl-1-piperidinepropanol; benzhexol; hexyphenidyl; trihexyphenidyl hydrochloride).

2',3',4'-Trihydroxyacetophenone *see* Gallacetophenone.

1,8,9-Trihydroxyanthracene *see* Dithranol.

1,2,3-Trihydroxybenzene *see* Pyrogallol.

1,3,5-Trihydroxybenzene *see* Phloroglucinol.

3,4,5-Trihydroxybenzoic acid *see* Gallic acid.

3β,12,14-Trihydroxy-5β-card-20(22)-enolide 3-(acetylglucosyltridigitoxoside) *see* Lanatoside C.

3β,12,14-Trihydroxy-5β-card-20(22)-enolide 3-(4'''-acetyltridigitoxoside) *see* β-Acetyldigoxin.

3β,12β,14β-Trihydroxy-5β-card-20(22)-enolide 3-(4'''-O-methyltridigitoxoside) *see* Metildigoxin.

3β,12,14-Trihydroxy-5β-card-20(22)-enolide 3-tridigitoxoside *see* Digoxin.

3,6,7-Trihydroxycholanic acid *see* Hyocholic acid.

3,7,12-Trihydroxycholanic acid *see* Cholic acid.

Trihydroxycyanidine *see* Cyanuric acid.

3,4,5-Trihydroxycyclohexene-1-carboxylic acid *see* Shikimic acid.

4',5,7-Trihydroxy-3',5'-dimethoxyflavone *see* Tricin.

3,4,5-Trihydroxy-2,2-dimethyl-6-chromanacrylic acid δ-lactone 4-acetate 3-(2-methylbutyrate) *see* Visnadine.

11β,17,21-Trihydroxy-6,16α-dimethyl-2'-phenyl-2'H-pregna-2,4,6-trieno[3,2-c]pyrazol-20-one 21-acetate *see* Cortivazol.

11β,17,21-Trihydroxy-6,16α-dimethyl-2'-phenyl-2'H-pregna-2,4,6-trieno[3,2-c]pyrazol-20-one 21-(m-sulfobenzoate) *see* Cortisuzol.

Trihydroxyestrin *see* Estriol.

Trihydroxyethylrutin *see* Troxerutin.

3',4',7-Trihydroxyflavanone *see* Butin.

4',5,7-Trihydroxyflavanone *see* Naringenin.

3,5,7-Trihydroxyflavone *see* Galangin.

4',5,7-Trihydroxyflavone *see* Apigenin.

11β,17,21-Trihydroxy-B-homo-A-norpregn-1-ene-3,6,20-dione *see* Oxisopred.

3,5,7-Trihydroxy-2-[2-(4-hydroxy-3-methylphenyl)-3-(hydroxymethyl)-1,4-benzodioxan-6-yl]-4-chromanone *see* Silibinin.

2',4',6'-Trihydroxy-3-(p-hydroxyphenyl)propiophenone *see* Phloretin.

4',5,7-Trihydroxyisoflavone *see* Genistein.

3',5,7-Trihydroxy-4'-methoxyflavanone *see* Hesperetin.

4',5,7-Trihydroxy-3'-methoxyflavone *see* Homoeriodictyol.

3',5,7-Trihydroxy-4'-methoxyflavone 7-[6-O-(6-deoxy-α-L-mannopyranosyl)-β-D-glucopyranoside] *see* Diosmin.

3',5,7-Trihydroxy-4'-methoxyflavone rutinoside *see* Diosmin.

3',4',5-Trihydroxy-7-methoxyisoflavone *see* Santal.

4',5,7-Trihydroxy-6-methoxyisoflavone *see* Tectorigenin.

2,3,3'-Trihydroxy-4'-methoxystilbene 2-glucoside *see* Rhapontizin.

1,3,8-Trihydroxy-6-methylanthraquinone *see* Emodin.

1,6,8-Trihydroxy-3-methylanthraquinone 6-(D-apicofuranoside) *see* Frangulin B.

1,3,8-Trihydroxy-6-methylanthraquinone L-rhamnoside *see* Frangulin A.

11β,17,21-Trihydroxy-16-methylenepregna-1,4-diene-3,20-dione *see* Prednylidene.

11β,17α,21-Trihydroxy-16-methylenepregna-4,6-diene-3,20-dione *see* Isoprednidene.

3,5,6-Trihydroxy-1-methylindole *see* Adrenolutin.

11β,17α,21-Trihydroxy-6α-methylpregna-1,4-diene-3,20-dione *see* Methylprednisolone.

9α,11α,15-Trihydroxy-15-methylprosta-5-cis-13-trans-dien-1-oic acid *see* Carboprost.

9,11,15-Trihydroxy-15-methylprosta-4,5,13-trienoic acid methyl ester *see* Prostalene.

1,11,16-Trihydroxy-16-methylprost-13-en-9-one *see* Rioprostil.

3α,11α,16β-Trihydroxy-29-nor-8α,9β,13α,14β-dammara-17(20),24-dien-21-oic acid 16-acetate *see* Fusidic acid.

3β,5,14-Trihydroxy-19-oxo-5β-bufa-20,22-dienolide 3-(3-methylcrotonate) *see* Acrihellin.

3β,5,14-Trihydroxy-19-oxo-5β-card-20(22)-enolide 3-D-cymaro-D-glucoside *see* Strophanthin.

2,4,5-Trihydroxyphenethylamine *see* Oxidopamine.

7-[2-(3,4,β-Trihydroxyphenethylamino)ethyl]theophylline *see* Theodrenaline.

7-[3-[(β,3,5-Trihydroxyphenethyl)amino]propyl]-theophylline *see* Reproterol.

9,11,15-Trihydroxy-16-phenoxy-ω-tetranorprosta-4,5,13-trienoic acid methyl ester *see* Fenprostalene.

2,4,5-Trihydroxyphenylalanine *see* 6-Hydroxydopa.

11β,17α,21-Trihydroxypregna-1,4-diene-3,20-dione *see* Prednisolone.

11β,17α,21-Trihydroxypregn-4-ene-3,20-dione *see* Hydrocortisone.

2',4',6'-Trihydroxypropiophenone *see* Flopropione.

9α,11α,15-Trihydroxy-5-cis-13-trans-prostadienoic acid *see* Dinoprost.

2,4,6-Trihydroxy-s-triazine *see* Cyanuric acid.

9α,11α,15α-Trihydroxy-16-[3-(trifluoromethyl)phenoxy]-17,18,19,20-tetranor-5-cis-13-trans-prostadienoic acid *see* Fluprostenol.

cis-3α,11α,16β-Trihydroxy-4α,8,14-trimethyl-18-nor-5α,8α,9β,13α,14β-cholesta-17(20),24-dien-21-oic acid 16-acetate *see* Fusidic acid.

2α,3β,6β-Trihydroxyurs-12-en-28-oic acid *see* Madasiatic acid.

2α,3β,23-Trihydroxyurs-12-en-28-oic acid *see* Asiatic acid.

Triiodoethanoic acid *see* Iophenoxic acid.

Triiodomethane *see* Iodoform.

2,4,6-Triiodo-3-[2-[2-[2-[2-(2-methoxy)ethoxy]ethoxy]ethoxy]acetamido]benzoic acid *see* Iotrizoic acid.

N,N'-[2,4,6-Triiodo-5-(methylcarbamoyl)-1,3-phenylene]bis[D-gluconamide] *see* Ioglucomide.

4-[2,4,6-Triiodo-3-(morpholinocarbonyl)phenoxy]butyric acid *see* Iobutoic acid.

2-[2,4,6-Triiodo-3-(2-oxopyrrolidin-1-yl)benzyl]butyric acid *see* Iolidonic acid.

2-(2,4,6-Triiodophenoxy)butyric acid *see* Phenobutiodil.

3,3′,5-Triiodothyroacetic acid *see* Tiratricol.

3,3′,5-Triiodothyronine *see* Detrothyronine; Liothyronine; Rathyronine.

Triiodothyropropionic acid *see* Thyropropic acid.

'Triiodyl' *see* Sodium acetrizoate.

Triiotrast (tr) *see* Sodium acetrizoate.

3,7,12-Triketocholanic acid *see* Dehydrocholic acid.

'Trilafan' *see* Perphenazine.

'Trilafon' *see* Perphenazine.

'Trilene' *see* Trichloroethylene.

TRILETIDE** (*N*-[*N*-(*N*-acetyl-3-phenyl-L-alanyl)-3-phenyl-L-alanyl]-L-histidine methyl ester).

TRILINOLEIN (glyceryl trilinoleate; linoleic acid triglyceride).

'Trillekamin' *see* Trichlormethine.

'Trilombrine' *see* Iophenoxic acid.

'Trilon' *see* Trisodium edetate.

'Trilon A' *see* Sodium nitrilotriacetate.

TRILOSTANE** (4α,5-epoxy-17β-hydroxy-3-oxo-5α-androstane-2α-carbonitrile; WIN-24540; 'modrenal').

'Triludan' *see* Terfenadine.

'Trimanyl' *see* Trimethoprim.

'Trimaton' *see* Metam-sodium.

TRIMAZOSIN** (2-hydroxy-2-methylpropyl 4-(4-amino-6,7,8-trimethoxyquinazolin-2-yl)piperazine-1-carboxylate; trimazosin hydrochloride; CP-19106-1).

TRIMEBUTINE*** (2-(dimethylamino)-2-phenylbutyl 3,4,5-trimethoxybenzoate; β-(dimethylamino)-β-ethylphenethyl alcohol 3,4,5-trimethoxybenzoate; 'polibutin').

TRIMEBUTINE plus SORBITOL ('modulite').

TRIMEBUTINE MALEATE ('debridat').

TRIMECAINE** (2-(diethylamino)acetomeside; 2-diethylamino-2′,4′,6′-trimethylacetanilide; *N*-(α-diethylaminoacetyl)mesidine; mesdicaine; mesocaine).

'Trimedone' *see* Trimethadione.

TRIMEDOXIME BROMIDE*** (1,3-bis(4-formylpyridinium)propane dibromide dioxime; 1,3-bis(4-hydroxyiminomethylpyridinium)propane dibromide; 1,1′-trimethylenebis(4-formylpyridinium bromide) dioxime; dipyroxime; C-434; TMB-4).

'Trimeglamide' *see* Tricetamide.

'Trimelarsan' *see* Melarsonyl potassium.

TRIMEPERIDINE*** (1,2,5-trimethyl-4-phenyl-4-piperidinol propionate; 1,2,5-trimethyl-4-phenyl-4-propionoxypiperidine; dimethylmeperidine; promedol).

Trimepidium *see* Timepidium bromide.

Trimepranol (tr) *see* Metipranolol.

Trimeprazine* *see* Alimemazine.

Trimeprimine* *see* Trimipramine.

Trimeproprimine *see* Trimipramine.

TRIMETAMIDE*** (*N*-(2-amino-6-methylpyrid-3-ylmethyl)-3,4,5-trimethoxybenzamide; trimethamide).

TRIMETAPHAN CAMSILATE*** (1,3-dibenzyldecahydro-2-oxoimidazo[4,5-c]thieno[1,2-a]-thiolium 10-camphorsulfonate; methioplegium; thimethaphan; Nu-2222; Ro 2-2222).

TRIMETAZIDINE*** (1-(2,3,4-trimethoxybenzyl)piperazine; S-4004; 'vastarel').

Trimetazone *see* Tribuzone.

TRIMETHADIONE*** (3,5,5-trimethyloxazolidine-2,4-dione; troxidone; trimethin; trimetin).

Trimethamide *see* Trimetamide.

Trimethazone *see* Tribuzone.

TRIMETHIDINIUM METHOSULFATE*** ((+)-3-[3-(dimethylamino)propyl]-1,3,8,8-tetramethyl-3-azabicyclo[3.2.1]octane methyl sulfate methosulfate; methocamphane methylsulfate; Wy-1395).

Trimethin (tr) *see* Trimethadione.

Trimethoate *see* Prothoate.

TRIMETHOBENZAMIDE*** (4-[2-(dimethylamino)ethoxy]-*N*-(3,4,5-trimethoxybenzoyl)-benzylamine; *N*-[*p*-(2-dimethylaminoethoxy)-benzyl]-3,4,5-trimethoxybenzamide; trimethobenzamide hydrochloride).

Trimethobenzoylglycine *see* Tricetamide.

TRIMETHOPRIM*** (2,4-diamino-5-(3,4,5-trimethoxybenzyl)pyrimidine; BW-56-72; NSC-106568; Ro 5-6846; WR-5949).

See also Co-trifamole; Co-trimazine; Co-trimoxazole.

TRIMETHOPRIM plus RIFAMPICIN ('rifaprim').

TRIMETHOPRIM plus SULFADIAZINE ('tribrissen').

TRIMETHOPRIM plus SULFADIMIDINE ('poteseptyl').

TRIMETHOPRIM plus SULFADOXINE ('borgal'; 'trivetrin').

TRIMETHOPRIM plus SULFALENE ('kelfiprim').

TRIMETHOPRIM plus SULFAMERAZINE ('berlocombin').

TRIMETHOPRIM plus SULFAPERIN ('trimlen').

TRIMETHOPRIM plus SULFAMETROLE (cosoltrim; 'lidaprim'; 'quam').

TRIMETHOPRIM LACTATE ('lactotrim').

Trimethoquinol *see* Tretoquinol.

6-(3,4,5-Trimethoxybenzamido)caproic acid *see* Capobenic acid.

6-(3,4,5-Trimethoxybenzamido)hexanoic acid *see* Capobenic acid.

1,3,5-TRIMETHOXYBENZENE (trimethylphloroglucinol).

See also under Phloroglucinol.

3,4,5-Trimethoxybenzoic acid 3-[(3,3-diphenylpropyl)amino]propyl ester *see* Mepramidil.

3,4,5-Trimethoxybenzoic acid, esters and salts *see* Megallate(s).

2,4,6-Trimethoxybenzoic acid 2-morpholinoethyl ester *see* Mofloverine.

Trimethoxybenzoyl-6-aminocaproic acid *see* Capobenic acid.

Trimethoxybenzoylglycine diethylamide *see* Tricetamide.

4-(3,4,5-Trimethoxybenzoyl)morpholine *see* Trimetozine.

1-[3-(2,4,6-Trimethoxybenzoyl)propyl]pyrrolidine *see* Buflomedil.

2-(3,4,5-Trimethoxybenzyl)-2-imidazoline *see* Phedrazine.

1-(2,3,4-Trimethoxybenzyl)piperazine *see* Trimetazidine.

2′,4,4′-Trimethoxychalcone *see* Metochalcone.

3,4,5-Trimethoxycinnamamide *see* Cintramide.

3,4,5-Trimethoxycinnamic acid ester with 3-(2-hydroxy-3-morpholinopropyl)-4-methyl-7-(4-morpholinecarboxamido)coumarin *see* Cinecromen.

4-(3,4,5-Trimethoxycinnamoyl)-1-piperazineacetic acid *see* Cinepazic acid.

4-(3,4,5-Trimethoxycinnamoyl)-1-piperazineacetic acid ethyl ester *see* Cinepazet.

7′,10,11-Trimethoxyemetan-6′-ol *see* Cephaeline.

3,4,5-Trimethoxyphenethylamine *see* Mescaline.

3,4,5-Trimethoxy-*N*-(1-phenoxymethyl-2-pyrrolidin-1-ylethyl)benzamide *see* Fepromide.

4-[[2-(3,4,5-Trimethoxyphenyl)-2-methyl-1,3-dioxolan-4-yl]methyl]morpholine *see* Trixolane.

3,4,5-Trimethoxy-*N*-piperid-3-ylbenzamide *see* Troxipide.

2,4,5-Trimethoxy-1-propenylbenzene *see* Asarone.

2′,4′,6′-Trimethoxy-4-pyrrolidin-1-ylbutyrophenone *see* Buflomedil.

3′,4′,5′-Trimethoxy-3-(3-pyrrolin-1-yl)acrylophenone *see* Roletamide.

4-(3,4,5-Trimethoxythiobenzoyl)morpholine *see* Tritiozine.

2′,4′,6′-Trimethylacetanilide *see* Acetomesidide.

Trimethylacetic acid *see* Pivalic acid.

2-(2,2,2-Trimethylacetyl)-1,3-indandione *see* Pindone.

4,4,17-Trimethylandrosta-2,5-dieno[2,3-*d*]isoxazol-17β-ol *see* Azastene.

2,4,5-Trimethylaniline *see* Pseudocumidine.

2,4,6-Trimethylaniline *see* Mesidine.

6,6,9-Trimethyl-9-azabicyclo[3.3.1]non-3β-yl di-2-thien-2-ylglycolate *see* Mazaticol.

1,3,5-Trimethylbenzene *see* Mesitylene.

2,6,6-Trimethylbicyclo[3.1.1]-2-heptene *see* Pinene.

2-(1,7,7-Trimethylbicyclo[2.2.1]hept-2-yl)-3,4-xylenol *see* Xibornol.

*N,N,*2-Trimethyl-3-chromanamine *see* Trebenzomine.

3,3,5-Trimethylcyclohexyl lactate *see* Ciclactate.

3,3,5-Trimethylcyclohexyl mandelate *see* Cyclandelate.

trans-3,3,5-Trimethylcyclohexyl nicotinate *see* Ciclonicate.

cis-3,3,5-Trimethylcyclohexyl DL-α-(nicotinoyloxy)phenylacetate *see* Micinicate.

3,3,5-Trimethylcyclohexyl 2-oxo-1-pyrrolidineacetate *see* Piraxelate.

3,3,5-Trimethylcyclohexyl salicylate *see* Homosalate.

Trimethyldeoxyprostaglandin E₂ *see* Trimoprostil.

*N,N,*1-Trimethyl-3,3-dithien-2-ylallylamine *see* Dimethylthiambutene.

3,7,11-Trimethyldodeca-2,4-dienoic acid, esters *see* Hydroprene; Kinoprene; Methoprene.

3,7,11-Trimethyl-2,6,10-dodecatrien-1-ol *see* Farnesol.

Trimethylene *see* Cyclopropane.

Trimethylenebis(clofibrate) *see* Simfibrate.

1,1′-Trimethylenebis(4-formylpyridinium bromide) dioxime *see* Trimedoxime bromide.

4,4′-(Trimethylenedioxy)bis(3-bromobenzamidine) *see* Dibrompropamidine.

p,p′-(Trimethylenedioxy)dibenzamidine *see* Propamidine.

Trimethylene oxide *see* Oxetane.

Trimethylene sulfide *see* Thietane.

2,5,9-Trimethyl-7*H*-furo[3,2-*g*][1]benzopyran-7-one *see* Trioxysalen.

Trimethylglycine hydroxide inner salt *see* Betaine.

Trimethylglycocoll anhydride *see* Betaine.

6,6,9-Trimethylgranatoline dithienylglycolate *see* Mazaticol.

(3,5,5-Trimethylhexanoyl)ferrocene *see* Diciferron.

*N,*1,5-Trimethyl-4-hexenylamine *see* Isometheptene.

7,8,10-Trimethylisoalloxazine *see* Lumiflavin.

2,2,3-Trimethyl-3-(methylamino)norbornane *see* Mecamylamine.

2,4,6-Trimethyl-*N*-(1-methylhexyl)benzylamine *see* Trimexiline.

Trimethyl[3-[4-[2-(1-methylindol-3-yl)ethyl]pyrid-1-yl]propyl]ammonium dibromide *see* Methindethyrium.

Trimethyl(1-methyl-2-phenothiazin-10-ylethyl)ammonium methyl sulfate *see* Thiazinamium metilsulfate.

Trimethylmyristylammonium bromide *see* Tetradonium bromide.

1,7,7-Trimethylnorbornane *see* Bornane.

Trimethyloctadecylammonium pentachlorophenate *see* Octriphenate.

Trimethylolaminomethane *see* Trometamol.

Trimethylolmelamine *see* Hexamethylolmelamine.

1,3,3-Trimethyl-2-oxabicyclo[2.2.2]octane *see* Cineole.

3,5,5-Trimethyloxazolidine-2,4-dione *see* Trimethadione.

6,6,9-Trimethyl-3-pentylbenzo[*c*]chromen-1-ol *see* Cannabinol.

6,6,9-Trimethyl-3-pentyl-6*H*-dibenzo[*b,d*]pyran-1-ol *see* Cannabinol.

α,α,β-Trimethylphenethylamine *see* Pentorex.

*N,*α,α-Trimethylphenethylamine *see* Mephentermine.

*N,N,*α-Trimethylphenethylamine *see* Dimetamfetamine.

3,4,α-Trimethylphenethylamine *see* Xylopropamine.

3,4,5-TRIMETHYLPHENYL METHYLCARBAMATE (3,4,5-hemimellitinol *N*-methylcarbamate ester; OMS-597).

3,4,5-TRIMETHYLPHENYL METHYLCARBAMATE plus its 2,3,5-isomer (methylcarbamates of 3,4,5-hemimellitinol and isopseudocumenol; SD-8530; 'landrin').

*N,*3,3-Trimethyl-1-phenyl-1-phthalanpropylamine

520

see Talopram.

1,2,5-Trimethyl-4-phenyl-4-piperidinol propionate *see* Trimeperidine.

1,2,5-Trimethyl-4-phenyl-4-propionoxypiperidine *see* Trimeperidine.

Trimethylphloroglucinol *see* 1,3,5-Trimethoxybenzene.

1,2′,6-Trimethylpipecolanilide *see* Mepivacaine.

1,2,2-Trimethylpropyl methylphosphonofluoridate *see* Soman.

4,5′,8-Trimethylpsoralen *see* Trioxysalen.

17β-(Trimethylsiloxy)androst-4-en-3-one *see* Silandrone.

2-(TRIMETHYLSILYL)ETHYL ACETATE (acetylsilicocholine).

5,9,13-Trimethyltetradeca-4,8,12-trienoic acid 3,7-dimethylocta-2,6-dienyl ester *see* Gefarnate.

Trimethyltetradecylammonium bromide *see* Tetradonium bromide.

2,2,5-Trimethyl-3-thiomorpholinecarboxylic acid 1-oxide *see* Tizabrin.

Trimethylthionine chloride *see* Azure B.

5,7,8-Trimethyltocol *see* α-Tocopherol.

Trimethyl(1-p-tolyldodecyl)ammonium chloride *see* Toloconium chloride.

Trimethyl(1-p-tolyldodecyl)ammonium methyl sulfate *see* Toloconium metilsulfate.

Trimethylvinylammonium hydroxide *see* Neurine.

1,3,7-Trimethylxanthine *see* Caffeine.

Trimetin (tr) *see* Trimethadione.

'Trimeton' *see* Pheniramine.

Trimetoquinol *see* Tretoquinol.

TRIMETOZINE* (4-(3,4,5-trimethoxybenzoyl)-morpholine; A-22370; NSC-62939; PS-2383).

TRIMETREXATE* (2,4-diamino-5-methyl-6-[[(3,4,5-trimethoxyanilino)methyl]quinazoline; 5-methyl-6-[[(3,4,5-trimethoxyphenyl)amino]methyl]-2,4-quinazolinediamine; CI-898; JB-11; NSC-249008; TMQ).

TRIMETURON* (1-(p-chlorophenyl)-3,3-dimethylpseudourea O-methyl derivative; methyl N′-(p-chlorophenyl)-N,N-dimethylcarbamimidate).

TRIMEXILINE* ((±)-2,4,6-trimethyl-N-(1-methylhexyl)benzylamine).

Trimexolone *see* Rimexolone.

TRIMIPRAMINE* (5-[3-(dimethylamino)-2-methylpropyl]-10,11-dihydro-5H-dibenz[b,f]-azepine; trimeprimine; trimeproprimine; trimipramine maleate; trimipramine mesilate; IL-6001; RP 7162).

'Trimitan' *see* Trichlormethine.

'Trimlen' *see under* Trimethoprim.

'Trimol' *see* Piroheptine.

'Trimolets' *see* Phenylpropanolamine.

'Trimon' *see* Stibophen.

Trimopam* *see* Trepipam.

'Trimopan' *see* Trimethoprim.

TRIMOPROSTIL* ((Z)-7-[(1R,2R,3R)-2-[(E)-(3R)-3-hydroxy-4,4-dimethyl-1-octenyl]-3-methyl-5-oxocyclopentyl]-5-heptenoic acid; (5Z,11α,13E,15R)-15-hydroxy-11,16,16-trimethyl-9-oxoprosta-5,13-dien-1-oic acid; 11-deoxy-11,16,16-trimethyldinoprostone; trimethylde-oxyprostaglandin E₂; Ro-21-6937).

'Trimovate' *see under* Clobetasone butyrate.

'Trimox' *see* Amoxicillin.

TRIMOXAMINE* (α-allyl-3,4,5-trimethoxy-N-methylphenethylamine; trimoxamine hydrochloride; NAT-327; NDR-5523A).

Trimustine* *see* Trichlormethine.

'Trimysten' *see* Clotrimazole.

Trinitrine *see* Glyceryl trinitrate.

Trinitroglycerin *see* Glyceryl trinitrate.

Trinitrophenol *see* Picric acid.

2,4,6-Trinitroresorcinol *see* Styphnic acid.

'Trinophenon' *see* Picric acid.

'Trinordiol' *see under* Levonorgestrel.

'Triocil' *see* Hexetidine.

'Triodan' *see* Iopanoic acid.

'Triognost' *see* Sodium acetrizoate.

'Triomet' *see* Liothyronine.

'Triomiro' *see* Iodamide.

'Trional' *see* Methylsulfonal.

'Trionine' *see* Rathyronine.

'Triopac' *see* Sodium acetrizoate.

'Triopaed' *see* Pholcodine.

'Triopron' *see* Thyropropic acid.

Triorthocresyl phosphate *see* Tricresyl phosphate.

'Triosil' *see* Sodium metrizoate.

'Triosol' *see* Sodium metrizoate.

'Triostam' *see* Sodium antimonyl gluconate.

'Triostib' *see* Sodium antimonyl gluconate.

'Triothyrone' *see* Liothyronine.

'Trioxasin' *see* Trimetozine.

3,6,9-TRIOXAUNDECANE (bis(2-ethoxyethyl) ether).

3,3′-(3,6,9-Trioxaundecanedioyldiimino)bis(2,4,6-triiodobenzoic acid) *see* Iotroxic acid.

3,6,9-Trioxaundecanoate(s) *see* Troxundate(s).

'Trioxazine' *see* Trimetozine.

TRIOXIFENE* (3,4-dihydro-2-(p-methoxy-phenyl)-1-naphthyl p-[[2-(1-pyrrolidinyl)ethoxy]-phenyl ketone; [3,4-dihydro-2-(4-methoxyphen-yl)-1-naphthalenyl]-4-[2-(1-pyrrolidinyl)ethoxy)-phenyl]methanone).

TRIOXIFENE MESILATE (trioxifene mesylate; compound 133314).

Trioxifene mesylate* *see* Trioxifene mesilate.

3,7,12-Trioxo-5β-cholan-24-oic acid *see* Dehydrocholic acid.

Trioxsalen* *see* Trioxysalen.

Trioxymethylene *see* Paraformaldehyde.

TRIOXYSALEN* (2,5,9-trimethyl-7H-furo[3,2-g][1]benzopyran-7-one; 6-hydroxy-β,2,7-trimethyl-5-benzofuranacrylic acid δ-lactone; 4,5′,8-trimethylpsoralen; trioxsalen; NSC-71047; TMP).

TRIPAMIDE* (4-chloro-N-(endo-hexahydro-4,7-methanoisoindolin-2-yl)-3-sulfamoylbenz-amide; N-(4-aza-endo-tricyclo[5.2.1.0²·⁶]decan-4-yl)-4-chloro-3-sulfamoylbenzamide; E-614).

TRIPARANOL* (2-(p-chlorophenyl)-1-[p-[2-(di-ethylamino)ethoxy]phenyl]-1-p-tolylethanol; MER-29).

'Tripavlon' *see* Clofibrate.

TRIPELENNAMINE* (N-benzyl-N′,N′-

dimethyl-*N*-pyrid-2-ylethylenediamine; diamino-
benzpyrylum).
'Triperidol' *see* Trifluperidol.
'Tripervan' *see* Vincamine.
'Triphed' *see under* Pseudoephedrine.
Triphenmorph *see* Trifenmorph.
Triphenyl carbinol *see* Tritanol.
Triphenylhydroxytin *see* Fentin hydroxide.
Triphenylmethanol *see* Tritanol.
(Triphenylmethyl)amine *see* Tritylamine.
N-(Triphenylmethyl)morpholine *see* Trifenmorph.
3-(Triphenylmethylthio)-L-alanine *see* Tritylthio-
alanine.
1,3,4-Triphenylpyrazole-5-acetic acid *see* Isofezo-
lac.
1,3,5-Triphenylpyrazole-4-acetic acid *see* Trifezo-
lac.
2,3,5-TRIPHENYLTETRAZOLIUM CHLOR-
IDE (red tetrazolium; RT; tetrazolium red;
TPTZ; TTC; 'uroscreen'; 'vita-stain').
Triphenyltin *see* Fentin.
Triphosadenine *see* Adenosine triphosphate.
Triphosphopyridine nucleotide *see* Nadide phos-
phate.
'Triple tetracycline' *see under* Tetracycline.
Tripotassium dicitratobismuthate *see* Bismuth sub-
citrate.
'Tripoton' *see* Pheniramine.
TRIPRENE* ((*E*,*E*)-*S*-ethyl 11-methoxy-3,9,11-
trimethyldodeca-2,4-dienethioate; 'altorick').
TRIPROLIDINE*** (*trans*-1-pyrid-2-yl-3-pyr-
rolidin-1-yl-1-*p*-tolyl-1-propene; *trans*-2-(3-pyr-
rolidin-1-yl-1-*p*-tolylpropenyl)pyridine; BW-
295C51).
See also under Pseudoephedrine.
Triprop *see* Thyropropic acid.
Tripropylacetamide *see* Valdipromide.
'Triptafen' *see under* Amitriptyline.
'Triptide' *see* Glutathione.
'Triptil' *see* Protriptyline.
'Triquilar' *see under* Levonorgestrel.
'Triraupin' *see* Rescinnamine.
Tris *see* Trometamol.
'Trisaminol' *see* Trometamol.
Tris(*p*-aminophenyl)methanol *see* Pararosaniline.
2,3,5-Tris(1-aziridinyl)-*p*-benzoquinone *see* Triazi-
quone.
Tris(1-aziridinyl)phosphine oxide *see* Tepa.
Tris(1-aziridinyl)phosphine sulfide *see* Thiotepa.
Tris(1-aziridinyl)-*s*-triazine *see* Tretamine.
Tris(2-chloroethyl)amine *see* Trichlormethine.
3,3,3-TRIS(*p*-CHLOROPHENYL)PROPIONIC
ACID 4-METHYLPIPERAZIDE (LZ-544; 'hetolin').
1,2,3-Tris[2-(diethylamino)ethoxy]benzene triethiodide *see* Gallamine triethiodide.
Tris[di(hydroxymethyl)amino]triazine *see* Hexamethylolmelamine.
N,*N*′,*N*‴-Tris[[4-(dimethylamino)-1,4,4a,5,5a,6,11,
12a-octahydro-3,5,6,10,12,12a-hexahydroxy-
6-methyl-1,11-dioxo-2-naphthacenecarbox-
amido]methyl]polymyxin E *see* Colimecycline.

2,4,6-Tris(dimethylamino)-*s*-triazine *see* Altret-
amine.
p,*p*′,*p*″-Tris(dimethylamino)triphenylmethane chlor-
ide *see* Crystal violet.
Tris(2,2-dimethylaziridin-1-yl)phosphine oxide *see*
Hexamethyltepa.
S,*S*′,*S*″-Tris(dimethylcarbamodithioato)iron *see*
Ferbam.
'Trisedyl' *see* Trifluperidol.
1,3,5-Tris(2,3-epoxypropyl)-*s*-triazine-2,4,6-
(1*H*,3*H*,5*H*)-trione *see* Teroxirone.
Tris(ethylenimino) phosphate *see* Tepa.
Tris(ethylenimino) thiophosphate *see* Thiotepa.
Tris(heptafluoropropyl)amine *see* Perfluamine.
3′,4′,7-Tris(2-hydroxyethyl)rutin *see* Troxerutin.
Tris(hydroxyethyl)rutoside *see* Troxerutin.
Tris(hydroxymethyl)aminomethane gluconate alu-
minate *see* Aloglutamol.
1,1,1-Tris(hydroxymethyl)methylamine *see* Trom-
etamol.
1,1,1-Tris(hydroxymethyl)propane trinitrate *see*
Propatylnitrate.
'Trisilate' *see under* Choline salicylate.
'Trisillac' *see* Magnesium trisilicate.
'Trisix' *see* Lindane.
Tris-*N*-lost *see* Trichlormethine.
2,3,3-Tris(*p*-methoxyphenyl)-*N*,*N*-dimethylallyl-
amine *see* Aminoxytriphene.
N,*N*′,*N*″-Tris(2-methyl-1-aziridinyl)phosphine oxide
see Metepa.
1,1,1-Tris(nitratomethyl)propane *see* Propatylnitrate.
Trisodium 4-anilino-8-hydroxy-1,1′-azonaphthalene-
3,5′,6-trisulfonate *see* Anazolene sodium.
Trisodium [*N*,*N*-bis[2-[bis(carboxymethyl)amino]-
ethyl]glycinato(5-)]indate(3-)-¹¹¹In *see* Pentetate
indium trisodium In 111.
TRISODIUM EDETATE (trisodium salt of ethylenediaminetetraacetic acid; edetate trisodium;
sodium edetate; 'chelaton'; 'complexon'; 'kom-
plexon'; 'limclair'; 'plexochrom'; 'sequestrene';
'trilon'; 'versene').
Trisodium phosphonoformate *see* Foscarnet sodi-
um.
'Trisomin' *see* Magnesium trisilicate.
'Trisophene' *see* Hexachlorophene.
'Trisoralen' *see* Trioxysalen.
Tris(polyethyleneglycol 300) sorbitan ethers *see*
Polyoxyethylene 20 sorbitan.
'Trisweet' *see* Aspartame.
TRITANOL (triphenyl carbinol; triphenylmethan-
ol).
'Tritheon' *see* Aminitrozole.
'Trithio' *see* Anethole trithione.
Trithio-(*p*-methoxyphenyl)propene *see* Anethole tri-
thione.
'Trithion' *see* Carbofenotion.
Trithiozine *see* Tritiozine.
TRITIOZINE*** (tetrahydro-4-(3,4,5-trimethoxy-
thiobenzoyl)-1,4-oxazine; 4-(3,4,5-trimethoxy-
thiobenzoyl)morpholine; sulmetozine; trithioz-
ine; ISF-2001; 'tresanil').
'Tritisan' *see* Quintozene.

Tritolyl phosphate *see* Tricresyl phosphate.
'Triton(s)' *see* Tyloxapol.
'Triton X' *See* Octoxinol.
TRITOQUALINE*** (7-amino-4,5,6-triethoxy-(5,6,7,8-tetrahydro-4-methoxy-6-methyl-1,3-dioxolo[4,5-*g*]isoquinolin-5-yl)phthalide; 1-(3-amino-4,5,6-triethoxyphthalid-3-yl)-1,2,3,4-tetrahydro-8-methoxy-2-methyl-6,7-methylenedioxyisoquinoline; L-554).
'Tritox' *see under* DDT.
'Trittico' *see* Trazodone.
TRITYLAMINE ((triphenylmethyl)amine).
Tritylmorpholine *see* Trifenmorph.
5-Tritylpicolinic acid *see* Picotrin.
TRITYLTHIOALANINE (3-(triphenylmethyl-thio)-L-alanine; NSC-83265).
'Triumbren' *see* Acetrizoic acid.
'Triurol' *see* Sodium acetrizoate.
'Trivastal' *see* Piribedil.
'Trivetrin' *see under* Trimethoprim.
'Trix' *see under* DDT.
TRIXOLANE** (4-[[2-methyl-2-(3,4,5-trimethoxyphenyl)-1,3-dioxolan-4-yl]methyl]morpholine).
'Trizma' *see* Trometamol.
TRIZOXIME*** (5-benzyl-4,5-dihydro-4-oxo-1*H*-1,2,5-benzotriazepine-3-carboxamidoxime).
TROCIMINE** (octahydro-1-(3,4,5-trimethoxybenzoyl)azocine).
'Trocinate' *see* Tifenamil.
TROCLOSENE* (3,5-dichloro-*s*-triazine-2,4,6(1*H*,3*H*,5*H*)-trione; dichloroisocyanuric acid).
TROCLOSENE POTASSIUM*** (potassium dichloroisocyanurate; potassium troclosene; ACL-59).
TROCLOSENE SODIUM (sodium dichloroisocyanurate; sodium troclosene; ACL-60; 'halane').
'Trodax' *see* Nitroxinil meglumine.
'Trofodermin' *see under* Clostebol acetate.
'Troformone' *see* Methandriol.
TROFOSFAMIDE*** (3-(2-chloroethyl)-2-[bis(2-chloroethyl)amino]tetrahydro-2*H*-1,3,2-oxazaphosphorine 2-oxide; A-4828; Asta-4828; Z-4828; 'ixoten').
'Trofozim' *see* Cobamamide.
Trolamine* *see* Triethanolamine.
TROLEANDOMYCIN*** (triacetyloleandomycin; acetyloleandomycin; NSC-108166; Wy-651; 'aovin'; 'cyclamycin'; 'evramicina'; 'evramycin'; 'oleanbel'; 'spectrobact'; 'tao').
'Trolene' *see* Fenclofos.
TROLNITRATE*** (2,2′,2″-nitrilotriethanol trinitrate; di[tris(2-nitratoethyl]ammonium hydrogen phosphate); triethanolamine trinitrate; aminotrate phosphate; nitranol; trolnitrate phosphate).
'Trolone' *see* Sultiame.
'Trolovol' *see* Penicillamine.
'Tromal' *see* Butacetin.
TROMANTADINE*** (*N*-adamant-1-yl-2-(2-dimethylaminoethoxy)acetamide; tromantadine hydrochloride; D-41; 'viru-merz').

'Tromasedan' *see* Bendazol.
'Trombo-vetren' *see* Heparin.
'Tromcardin' *see under* Potassium aspartate.
TROMETAMOL*** (2-amino-2-(hydroxymethyl)-1,3-propanediol; 1,1,1-tris(hydroxymethyl)-methylamine; trimethylolaminomethane; tromethamine; tris; NSC-6365).
See also under Dinoprost; Lodoxamide.
Trometamol gluconate aluminate *see* Aloglutamol.
TROMETAMOL THIOCTATE ('lipotam').
Tromethamine* *see* Trometamol.
'Tromexan' *see* Ethyl biscoumacetate.
'Tronothane' *see* Pramocaine.
TROPABAZATE*** (phenyl 3α-hydroxy-8-azabicyclo[3.2.1]octane-8-carboxylate carbazate (ester)).
TROPACIN (tr) (tropine diphenylacetate; tropazine).
Tropacocaine *see* Pseudotropine benzoate.
TROPANE (8-methyl-8-azabicyclo[3.2.1]octane).
3α-Tropanol *see* Tropine.
3β-Tropanol *see* Pseudotropine.
DL-Tropanyl 2-hydroxy-1-phenylpropionate *see* Atropine.
(−)-3α-Tropanyl 2-methyl-2-phenylhydracrylate *see* Atromepine.
TROPAPRIDE*** (*N*-(8-benzyl-1α*H*,5α*H*-nortropan-3β-yl)-*o*-veratramide; *N*-(8-benzyl-1α*H*,5α*H*-nortropan-3β-yl)-2,3-dimethoxybenzamide).
TROPATEPINE*** (3-dibenzo[*b*,*e*]thiepin-11(6*H*)-ylidene-1α*H*,5α*H*-tropane; SD-124817; 'lepticur').
Tropazine (tr) *see* Tropacin.
TROPENTANE (tr) (tropine phenylcyclopentanecarboxylate).
TROPENZILINE BROMIDE*** (7-methoxy-8-methyltropinium bromide benzilate; tropenzilium; MTS-263; 'palerol').
Tropenzilium *see* Tropenziline bromide.
'Tropesin' *see* Indometacin tropine ester.
Tropethydryline *see* Etybenzatropine.
'Trophenium' *see* Phenactropinium chloride.
'Trophicard' *see under* Potassium aspartate.
'Trophicardyl' *see* Inosine.
'Trophodermin' *see under* Clostebol acetate.
'Trophozym' *see* Cobamamide.
TROPIC ACID (3-hydroxy-2-phenylpropionic acid; 2-phenylhydracrylic acid).
(±)-Tropic acid 9-isopropylgranatoline ester *see* Ipragratine.
TROPICAMIDE*** (*N*-ethyl-2-phenyl-*N*-(pyrid-4-ylmethyl)hydracrylamide; bistropamide).
TROPIGLINE*** (2,3-dimethylacrylic acid tropine ester; 2-methyl-2-butenoyltropine; tiglyltropine).
Tropin *see* Atropine methobromide.
TROPINE (3-hydroxytropane; 3α-tropanol).
Tropine benzhydryl ether *see* Benzatropine.
Tropine-2-carboxylic acid *see* Ecgonine.
Tropine esters *see* Atromepine; Atropine; Belladonnin; Cyheptopine; Homatropine; Hyoscyamine; Pseudoatropine; Tropacin; Tropentane;

Tropigline; Tropodifene.

Tropine indometacinate *see* Indometacin tropine ester.

'**Tropino**' *see* Atropine oxide.

TROPIRINE* (3α-[(5*H*-benzo[4,5]cyclohepta[1,2-*b*]pyridyl)-5-oxy]tropane; 5-(3α-tropyloxy)-5*H*-benzo[4,5]cyclohepta[1,2-*b*]pyridine; tropirine maleate; BS-7723).

'**Tropital**' *see* Piperonal bis[2-(2-butoxyethoxy)-ethyl]acetal.

'**Tropium**' *see* Chlordiazepoxide.

TROPODIFENE* (tropine 3-(*p*-hydroxyphenyl)-2-phenylpropionate (ester) acetate (ester)).

TROPOLONE (2-hydroxy-2,4,6-cycloheptatrien-1-one).

'**Tropotox**' *see* Sodium 4-(4-chloro-2-methylphenoxy)butyrate.

Tropyl isatropate *see* Belladonnin.

5-(3α-Tropyloxy)-5*H*-benzo[4,5]cyclohepta[1,2-*b*]-pyridine *see* Tropirine.

'**Trosinone**' *see* Ethisterone.

TROSPIUM CHLORIDE* (3α-hydroxyspiro-[1α*H*,5α*H*-nortropane-8,1′-pyrrolidinium]chloride benzilate; azoniaspiro(3α-benziloyloxynortropane-8,1′-pyrrolidine) chloride; 8α-benziloyloxy-6,10-ethano-5-azoniaspiro[4.5]decane chloride; 8α-hydroxy-6,10-ethano-5-azoniaspiro-[4.5]decane chloride benzilate; AS XVII; Mg-42799; 'spasmex'; 'spasmo-lyt').

TROXERUTIN* (3′,4′,7-tris(2-hydroxyethyl)-rutin; tris(hydroxyethyl)rutoside; trihydroxyethylrutin; vitamin P₄; THR; Z-6000; Z-12001).
See also Oxerutins *and under* Carbazochrome; Coumarin; Dihydroergotamine.

Troxidone* *see* Trimethadione.

TROXIPIDE ((±)-3,4,5-trimethoxy-*N*-piperid-3-ylbenzamide).

Troxone* *see* Troxonium tosilate.

TROXONIUM TOSILATE* (triethyl[2-(trimethoxybenzoyloxy)ethyl]ammonium *p*-toluenesulfonate; triethyl(2-hydroxyethyl)ammonium *p*-toluenesulfonate 3,4,5-trimethoxybenzoate; troxone; FWH-399).

TROXUNDATE(S) ([2-(2-ethoxyethoxy)ethoxy]acetate(s); 3,6,9-trioxaundecanoate(s)).

Troxypyrrole* *see* Troxypyrrolium tosilate.

TROXYPYRROLIUM TOSILATE* (1-ethyl-1-(2-hydroxyethyl)pyrrolidinium *p*-toluenesulfonate 3,4,5-trimethoxybenzoate; 1-ethyl-1-[2-(3,4,5-trimethoxybenzoyloxy)ethyl]pyrrolidinium *p*-toluenesulfonate; troxypyrrole).

'**Truxal**' *see* Chlorprothixene.

TRUXICURIUM IODIDE* (diethyl(3-hydroxypropyl)methylammonium iodide 2,4-diphenyl-1,3-cyclobutanedicarboxylate).

TRUXILLIC ACID (2,4-diphenyl-1,3-cyclobutanedicarboxylic acid).
See also Truxicurium; Truxipicurium iodide.

TRUXIPICURIUM IODIDE* (1-ethyl-1-(3-hydroxypropyl)piperidinium iodide 2,4-diphenyl-1,3-cyclobutanedicarboxylate).

'**Trypadine**' *see* Dimidium bromide.

TRYPAN BLUE (sodium ditolyldiazobis-8-amino-1-naphthol-3,6-disulfonate; benzamine blue; Congo blue; naphthylamine blue; 'benzo blue'; 'diamine blue'; 'dianil blue'; 'niagara blue').

TRYPARSAMIDE* (monosodium salt of *N*-(carbamoylmethyl)arsanilic acid; 4-glycylamidobenzenearsonic acid sodium salt; *N*-phenylglycinamide-*p*-arsonic acid sodium salt; glyphenarsine).

'**Tryparsone**' *see* Tryparsamide.

'**Trypchymase**' *see* Chymotrypsin.

'**Tryponarsyl**' *see* Tryparsamide.

'**Trypothane**' *see* Tryparsamide.

TRYPSIN ('parenzyme'; 'parenzymol'; 'tryptar'; 'trypure').
See also under Chymotrypsin.

TRYPTAMINE (3-(2-aminoethyl)indole; 3-indoleethylamine).

'**Tryptanol**' *see* Amitriptyline.

'**Tryptar**' *see* Trypsin.

'**Tryptizol**' *see* Amitriptyline.

TRYPTOLINE (1,2,3,4-tetrahydro-9*H*-pyrido[3,4-*b*]indole; tetrahydro-β-carboline; 1,2,3,4-tetrahydronorharman; THN).

TRYPTOPHAN* (2-amino-3-indolepropionic acid; L-tryptophan; 'kalma'; 'pacitron').

TRYPTOPHAN plus PYRIDOXINE ('optimax').

2-L-Tryptophan-3-de-L-leucine-4-de-L-proline-8-L-glutaminebradykinin potentiator B *see* Teprotide.

TRYPTOPHOL (3-(2-hydroxyethyl)indole; indole-3-ethanol).

'**Trypure**' *see* Trypsin.

'**Trysben**' *see* Trichlorobenzoic acid.

'**Trysben 200**' *see* Dimethylamine trichlorobenzoate.

TS-160 *see* Trichlormethine.

TSAA-291 *see* Oxendolone.

TSAG *see* Sodium antimonyl gluconate.

TSH *see* Thyrotrophin.

Tsiklomitsin (tr) *see* Tetracycline.

TSP *see* Serrapeptase.

TSPA *see* Thiotepa.

'**Tsumacide**' *see* *m*-Tolyl methylcarbamate.

TTC *see* 2,3,5-Triphenyltetrazolium chloride.

TTD *see* Disulfiram.

TTFD *see* Fursultiamine.

TTH *see* Thyrotrophin.

'**Tuad**' *see* Thiram.

'**Tuamine**' *see* Tuaminoheptane.

TUAMINOHEPTANE* (2-aminoheptane; 2-heptylamine; 1-methylhexylamine; tuaminoheptane sulfate; 'heptamine').

'**Tuasal 100**' *see* Tribromsalan.

'**Tuazole**' *see* Methaqualone.

'**Tuazolone**' *see* Methaqualone.

Tubatoxin *see* Rotenone.

Tubazid (tr) *see* Isoniazid.

Tuberactinomycin B *see* Viomycin.

Tuberactinomycin N *see* Enviomycin.

'**Tubercazone**' *see* Thioacetazone.

TUBERCIDIN (4-amino-7-β-D-ribofuranosyl-7*H*-pyrrolo[2,3-*d*]pyrimidine; 7-deazaadenosine; 7-β-D-ribofuranosyl-7*H*-pyrrolo[2,3-*d*]pyrimidin-4-

amine; 'sparsamycin A').

TUBERCULOSTEARIC ACID (10-methylstearic acid).

'Tuberlite' *see* Propham.

'Tubocin' *see* Rifampicin.

TUBOCURARINE CHLORIDE*** ((+)-tubocurarine chloride; *Chondrodendrum tomentosum* extract; curare).

Tubocurarine dimethyl ether *see* Dimethyltubocurarine chloride.

TUBULOZOLE** (ethyl (±)-*cis*-*p*-[[[2-(2,4-dichlorophenyl)-2-(imidazol-1-ylmethyl)-1,3-dioxolan-4-yl]methyl]thio]carbanilate).

'Tuclase' *see* Pentoxyverine.

TUCLAZEPAM*** (7-chloro-5-(*o*-chlorophenyl)-2,3-dihydro-1-methyl-1*H*-1,4-benzodiazepine-2-methanol).

'Tugon' *see* Metrifonate.

'Tulisan' *see* Thiram.

TULOBUTEROL*** (α-[(*tert*-butylamino)methyl]-*o*-chlorobenzyl alcohol; tulobuterol hydrochloride; C-78).

'Tumovan' *see* Prothipendyl.

'Tunic' *see* Chlormethazole.

'Tupen' *see under* Ampicillin.

'Tupersan' *see* Siduron.

'Turfa' *see under* Hydrochlorothiazide.

'Turinabol' *see* Clostebol acetate.

'Turinal' *see* Allylestrenol.

'Turisynchron' *see* Metallibure.

'Turloc' *see* Meturedepa.

TURPENTINE OIL (rectified turpentine oil; terebinth oil).

TURPENTINE OIL OXIDATION PRODUCT ('ozothine').

'Tuscalman' *see under* Noscapine.

'Tuscapine' *see* Noscapine.

'Tussafug' *see* Benproperine embonate.

'Tussal' *see* Methadone.

'Tussefane' *see* Fedrilate.

'Tussilan' *see* Dextromethorphan.

'Tussilax' *see* Diphepanol.

'Tussilex' *see* Dropropizine.

'Tussils' *see* Noscapine.

'Tussinol' *see* Oxeladin.

'Tussol' *see* Phenazone mandelate.

'Tussucal' *see* Diphepanol.

'Tussukal' *see* Diphepanol.

'Tutocaine' *see* Butamin.

TV-274B *see* Proscillaridin.

TV-274C *see under* Proscillaridin.

TV-485 *see* Etofenamate.

TVX-647 *see* Morocromen.

TVX-916 *see* Flufenamic acid.

TVX-1322 *see* Acemetacin.

'Tween(s)' *see* Polysorbate(s).

'Twiston' *see* Rotoxamine tartrate.

TwSb *see* Sodium stibocaptate.

TYBAMATE*** (2-methyl-2-propyltrimethylene butylcarbamate carbamate; tibamide; W-713).

'Tybatran' *see* Tybamate.

'Tyclarosol' *see* Tetrasodium edetate.

'Tydantil' *see* Nifuratel.

'Tyformin*' *see* Tiformin.

'Tylagel' *see* Tolpropamine.

'Tylan' *see* Tylosin.

'Tylcalsin' *see* Calcium acetylsalicylate.

'Tylciprine' *see* Tranylcypromine.

'Tylemal*' *see* Carbubarb.

'Tylenol' *see* Paracetamol.

'Tylinal' *see* Amfepramone.

TYLOSIN*** (antibiotic from *Str. fradiae*; tylosin phosphate; tylosin tartrate).

TYLOXAPOL*** (polymer of *p*-(1,1,3,3-tetramethylbutyl) phenol with ethylene glycol and formaldehyde; ethoxylated *tert*-octylphenol formaldehydepolymer).

TYMAZOLINE* (2-[(2-isopropyl-5-methylphenoxy)methyl]-2-imidazoline; 2-thymyloxymethyl-2-imidazoline; 'pernazene').

Tyraminase *see* Monoamine oxidase.

TYRAMINE (4-hydroxyphenethylamine; *p*-(2-aminoethyl)phenol; 2-(*p*-hydroxyphenyl)ethylamine; *p*-tyramine; tyrosamine).

m-**TYRAMINE** (3-hydroxyphenethylamine).

o-**TYRAMINE** (2-hydroxyphenethylamine).

p-**Tyramine** *see* Tyramine.

'Tyranton' *see* Diacetone alcohol.

'Tyrimide' *see* Isopropamide iodide.

Tyrocidin plus gramicidin *see* Tyrothricin.

TYROMEDAN*** (2-(diethylamino)ethyl 2-[3,5-diiodo-4-(3-iodo-4-methoxyphenoxy)phenyl]-acetate; thyromedan; SK&F-13364-A).

Tyropanoate *see* Sodium tyropanoate.

Tyrosamine *see* Tyramine.

23-L-Tyrosinamide-α¹⁻²³-corticotrophin *see* Tricosactide.

TYROSINE* (α-amino-*p*-hydroxyhydrocinnamic acid; 2-amino-3-(*p*-hydroxyphenyl)propionic acid; 3-(*p*-hydroxyphenyl)alanine; α-tyrosine).

α-**Tyrosine** *see* Tyrosine.

β-**TYROSINE** (β-amino-*p*-hydroxyhydrocinnamic acid; 3-amino-3-(*p*-hydroxyphenylpropionic acid; 3-(*p*-hydroxyphenyl)-β-alanine).

L-Tyrosyl-D-alanylglycyl-L-phenylalanyl-*N*²-methyl-L-methioninamide *see* Metkefamide.

TYROTHRICIN*** (antibiotic from *Bacillus brevis*; mixture of gramicidin and tyrocidin).

'Tyzanol' *see* Tetryzoline.

'Tyzine' *see* Tetryzoline.

U

U-27 *see* Pifarnine.
U-0229 *see* Fenpipramide.
U-0382 *see* Scopolamine methyl bromide.
U-0433 *see* Methoxyphenamine.
U-935 *see* Amiquinsin.
U-1063 *see* Proquinolate.
U-1085 *see* Leniquinsin.
U-1093 *see* Buquinolate.
U-1258 *see* 4-Pregnene-3,11,20-trione.
U-1363 *see* Diphenadione.
U-2032 *see* Ketoxal.
U-2043 *see* Tolbutamide.
U-4527 *see* Cicloheximide.
U-5641 *see* Parathiazine dioxide.
U-5897 *see* Chlorohydrin.
U-5956 *see* Filipin.
U-6013 *see* Isoflupredone acetate.
U-6987 *see* Carbutamide.
U-7720 *see* Diallylmelamine.
U-7743 *see* Mercufenol chloride.
U-7750 *see* Streptovarycin.
U-8344 *see* Uramustine.
U-8471 *see* Medrysone.
U-9361 *see* Hydroxycycloheximide.
U-9889 *see* Streptozocin.
U-10136 *see* Alprostadil.
U-10149A *see* Lincomycin.
U-10387 *see* Isocarboxazid.
U-10858 *see* Minoxidil.
U-10974 *see* Flumetasone.
U-10997 *see* Mibolerone.
U-11100A *see* Nafoxidine.
U-12019E *see* Methylprednisolone sodium phosphate.
U-12062 *see* Dinoprostone.
U-12241 *see* Cirolemycin.
U-12504 *see* Glypinamide.
U-12898 *see* Bluensomycin.
U-13933 *see* Asperlin.
U-14583 *see* Dinoprost.
U-14583E *see* Dinoprost trometamol.
U-14624 *see* Dithiocarb.
U-14743 *see* Porfiromycin.
U-15167 *see* Nogalamycin.
U-15614 *see* Trestolone acetate.
U-15965 *see* Lidimycin.
U-17312E *see* Etryptamine.
U-17323 *see* Fluorometholone acetate.
U-17835 *see* Tolazamide.
U-18409E *see* Spectinomycin.
U-18496 *see* Azacitidine.

U-18573 *see* Ibuprofen.
U-18573G *see* Ibuprofen aluminum.
U-19183 *see* Sparsomycin.
U-19646 *see* Chlorphenesin carbamate.
U-19718 *see* Kalafungin.
U-19763 *see* Bolasterone.
U-19920A *see* Cytarabine.
U-20661 *see* Steffimycin.
U-21251 *see* Clindamycin.
U-22020 *see* Indoxole.
U-22550 *see* Calusterone.
U-22559A *see* Dexoxadrol.
U-24729A *see* Mirincamycin.
U-24792 *see* Lomofungin.
U-24973A *see* Melitracen.
U-25179E *see* Clindamycin palmitate.
U-25873 *see* Ranimycin.
U-26225A *see* Tramadol.
U-26452 *see* Glibenclamide.
U-26597A *see* Colestipol.
U-26921E *see* Carboprost trometamol.
U-27182 *see* Flurbiprofen.
U-28009 *see* Denofungin.
U-28288D *see* Guanadrel.
U-28508 *see* Clindamycin.
U-28774 *see* Ketazolam.
U-29479 *see* Scopafungin.
U-30604 *see* Zorbamycin.
U-31889 *see* Alprazolam.
U-31920 *see* Uldazepam.
U-32070 *see* Calcifediol.
U-32921 *see* Carboprost.
U-33030 *see* Triazolam.
U-34865 *see* Diflorasone diacetate.
U-36059 *see* Amitraz.
U-36384 *see* Carboprost methyl.
U-42126 *see* Acivicin.
U-42485-E *see* Lodoxamide trometamol.
U-42718 *see* Lodoxamide ethyl.
U-42842 *see* Arbaprostil.
U-47931E *see* Bromadoline maleate.
U-53217 *see* Epoprostenol.
U-57930 *see* Pirlimycin.
U-63287 *see* Ciglitazone.
U-63440 *see* Pirlimycin adenylate.
UBIDECARENONE*** (2-(3,7,11,15,19,23,27,31,35,39-decamethyl-2,6,10,14,18,22,26,30,34,38-tetracontadecaenyl)-5,6-dimethoxy-3-methyl-*p*-benzoquinone; coenzyme Q_{10}; ubiquinone 10; 'neuquinone').
UBIQUINONE(S) (coenzyme Q; mitoquinone;

MK-128; Q-275; SA).
Ubiquinone 10 *see* Ubidecarenone.
UBISINDINE*** (2-[2-(diethylamino)ethyl]-3-phenylphthalimidine).
'**Ubretid**' *see* Distigmine bromide.
UCB-1402 *see* Decloxizine.
UCB-1414 *see* Etodroxizine.
UCB-1414M *see under* Methaqualone.
UCB-1474 *see* Chlorbenoxamine.
UCB-1545 *see* Feclemine.
UCB-1549 *see* Minepentate.
UCB-1967 *see* Dropropizine.
UCB-2073 *see* Etoxeridine.
UCB-2543 *see* Pentoxyverine.
UCB-3412 *see* Dixyrazine.
UCB-3928 *see* Fedrilate.
UCB-3983 *see* Mesna.
UCB-4445 *see* Buclizine.
UCB-4492 *see* Hydroxyzine.
UCB-5033 *see* Brallobarbital.
UCB-5062 *see* Meclozine.
UCB-5067 *see* Oxydipentonium chloride.
UCB-6215 *see* Piracetam.
UCB-79171 *see* Ibuprofen.
UCB-B-192 *see* Dazolicine.
UCB-c325 *see* Pipoxizine.
'**Ucenol LS**' *see* Sodium dodecyl sulfate.
'**Udieci**' *see* Papaveroline meglumine.
'**Udolac**' *see* Dapsone.
UDP *see* Uridine diphosphate.
UFENAMATE** (butyl *N*-(α,α,α-trifluoro-*m*-tolyl)anthranilate; butyl flufenamate).
Ug-767 *see* Penoctonium bromide.
'**Ugurol**' *see* Tranexamic acid.
'**Ujoviridin**' *see* Indocyanine green.
UK-738 *see* Etybenzatropine.
UK-2054 *see* Famotine.
UK-2371 *see* Memotine.
UK-3540 *see* Amedalin.
UK-3557 *see* Daledalin.
UK-3557-15 *see* Daledalin tosilate.
UK-4271 *see* Oxamniquine.
UK-6558-01 *see* Tolamolol.
UK-11443 *see* Primidolol.
UK-14275 *see* Buquineran.
UK-18892 *see* Butikacin.
UK-20349 *see* Tioconazole.
UK-25842 *see* Oxfenicine.
UK-31214 *see* Propikacin.
UK-31557 *see* Carbazeran.
UK-33274 *see* Doxazosin.
UK-37248 *see* Dazoxiben.
'**Ukapen**' *see* Ampicillin.
'**Ukidan**' *see* Urokinase.
'**Ulbretid**' *see* Distigmine bromide.
'**Ulcedal**' *see* Deglycyrrhizinized liquorice.
'**Ulcerban**' *see* Sucralfate.
'**Ulcerfen**' *see* Cimetidine.
'**Ulcerimin**' *see* Sucralfate.
'**Ulcesium**' *see* Fentonium bromide.
'**Ulcex**' *see* Ranitidine.
'**Ulcoban**' *see* Benzilonium bromide.
'**Ulcogant**' *see* Sucralfate.

'**Ulcostidine**' *see* Histidine.
ULDAZEPAM** (2-(allyloxyamino)-7-chloro-5-(*o*-chlorophenyl)-3*H*-1,4-benzodiazepine; U-31920).
Ulexine *see* Cytisine.
'**Ulix**' *see* Scopolamine methyl methosulfate.
'**Ulo**' *see* Clofedanol.
'**Ulpepsan**' *see* Aluminium glycinate.
'**Ulsanic**' *see* Sucralfate.
'**Ultandren**' *see* Fluoxymesterone.
'**Ultrabil**' *see* Adipiodone.
'**Ultrabiotic**' *see* Penimepicycline.
'**Ultracain**' *see* Articaine.
'**Ultracid(e)**' *see* Methidathion.
'**Ultracillin**' *see* Ciclacillin.
'**Ultracit**' *see* Hydrotalcite.
'**Ultracortenol**' *see* Prednisolone pivalate.
'**Ultracur**' *see under* Fluocortolone pivalate.
'**Ultracycline**' *see* Tetracycline phosphate complex.
'**Ultralan**' *see* Fluocortolone caproate.
'**Ultrapen**' *see* Propicillin.
'**Ultraphen**' *see* Clorofene.
Ultraquinine *see* Cupreine.
'**Ultraren**' *see* Iodoxyl.
'**Ultraseptyl**' *see* Sulfamethylthiazole.
'**Ultrax**' *see* Sulfametoxydiazine.
'**Ultrazeozon**' *see* Esculetin.
UM-272 *see* Pranolium iodide.
UM-952 *see* Buprenorphine.
UMBELLIFERONE (7-hydroxycoumarin).
'**Umbrium**' *see* Diazepam.
UML-491 *see* Methysergide.
UMP *see* Uridylic acid.
'**Unakalm**' *see* Ketazolam.
UNDECANOIC ACID (hendecanoic acid; undecylic acid).
UNDECENOIC ACID (hendec-10-enoic acid; undecylenic acid).
Undecylenic acid *see* Undecenoic acid.
Undecylic acid *see* Undecanoic acid.
'**Unden**' *see* Propoxur.
'**Unephral**' *see* Mercuderamide.
'**Unidigin**' *see* Digitoxin.
'**Unidone**' *see* Anisindione.
'**Unidox**' *see* Doxycycline.
'**Unilobine**' *see* Lobeline.
'**Union-nox**' *see* Cyclobarbital.
'**Unipen**' *see* Nafcillin.
'**Uniprin**' *see* Calcium acetylsalicylate.
'**Unisal**' *see* Diflunisal.
'**Unistat**' *see* Sulfanitran.
UNITHIOL (tr) (2,3-propanedithiol-1-sulfonic acid sodium salt; dimercaptopropane sodium sulfonate; sodium dimercaptopropanesulfonate; unitiol; DMPS).
'**Unitocin**' *see* Sparteine.
'**Unitop**' *see* Cuprimyxin.
'**Unospaston**' *see* Diponium bromide.
'**Unosulf**' *see* Sulfamethoxypyridazine.
'**Unstetic**' *see* Nalidixic acid.
UP-74 *see* Nixylic acid.
UP-83 *see* Niflumic acid.
UP-106 *see* Propizepine.

UP-107 *see* Bepiastine.

UP-164 *see* Morniflumate.

UP-507-04 *see* Picilorex succinate.

UP-33901 *see* Cibenzoline.

UR-112 *see* Magnesium clofibrate.

UR-389 *see* Brovanexine.

UR-661 *see* Glipentide.

'**Urab**' *see* Fenuron trichloroacetate.

URACIL (2,4-dihydroxypyrimidine; 2,4(1*H*,3*H*)-pyrimidinedione).

6-Uracilcarboxylic acid *see* Orotic acid.

Uracil-chlorethamine *see* Uramustine.

Uracil mustard *see* Uramustine.

Uracil riboside *see* Uridine.

Uracylic acid *see* Uridylic acid.

Uradal *see* Carbromal.

'**Ural**' *see* Carbocloral.

'**Uraline**' *see* Carbocloral.

'**Uralium**' *see* Carbocloral.

'**Uralysol**' *see* Methenamine.

'**Uramid**' *see* Sulfacarbamide.

URAMIL (5-aminobarbituric acid).

Uramine *see* Guanidine.

URAMUSTINE*** (5-[bis(2-chloroethyl)amino]-uracil; desmethyldopan; nordopan; uracil-chlor-ethamine; uracil mustard; NSC-34462; U-8344).

Uramycin B *see* Toyocamycin.

Uranin *see* Fluorescein disodium.

'**Urantoin**' *see* Nitrofurantoin.

URAPIDIL*** (6-[[3-[4-(*o*-methoxyphenyl)pip-erazin-1-yl]propyl]amino]-1,3-dimethyluracil; 1-[3-[(1,3-dimethyl-2,4-dioxopyrimidin-6-yl)-amino]propyl]-4-(*o*-methoxyphenyl)piperazine; B-66256; 'ebrantil').

'**Uraseptine**' *see* Methenamine.

'**Urazine**' *see* Methenamine salicylate.

'**Urbadan**' *see* Clobazam.

'**Urbanyl**' *see* Clobazam.

'**Urbason**' *see* Methylprednisolone.

'**Urbazid**' *see* Methylarsine bis(dimethylthiocarb-amate).

UREA (carbamide; carbonyldiamide).
See also Polygeline *and under* Dithranol; Hydro-cortisone.

UREA HYDROGEN PEROXIDE ('hydroperit'; 'hyperol'; 'lapurol'; 'ortizon'; 'percarbamid'; 'perhydrit').

UREA QUINATE (diurea tetrahydroxycyclohex-anecarboxylate; 'urol').

UREA STIBAMINE (*p*-ureidobenzenestibonic acid ammonium salt; carbostibamide).

'**Urecholine**' *see* Bethanechol.

UREDEPA*** (ethyl bis(1-aziridinyl)phosphinyl-carbamate; AB-100; NSC-37095).

UREDOFOS*** (diethyl [[[2-[[[[(4-methylphenyl)-sulfonyl]amino]carbonyl]amino]phenyl]amino]-thioxomethyl]phosphoramidate; diethyl [thio[*o*-[3-(*p*-tolylsulfonyl)ureido]phenyl]carbamoyl]-phosphoramidate; RH-565; RH-32565; 'sansa-lid').

UREFIBRATE*** (glyoxyloylurea *aldehydo*-[bis(*p*-chlorophenyl) acetal]).

'**Uregit**' *see* Etacrynic acid.

'**Uregyt**' *see* Etacrynic acid.

Ureidobenzene *see* Carbanilamide.

p-**Ureidobenzenearsonic acid** *see* Carbarsone.

p-**Ureidobenzenestibonic acid ammonium salt** *see* Urea stibamine.

Ureidoformamide *see* Biuret.

5-Ureidohydantoin *see* Allantoin.

5-Ureidonorvaline *see* Citrulline.

Ureidosuccinic acid *see* *N*-Carbamoylaspartic acid.

'**Urelim**' *see* Etebenecid.

'**Urese**' *see* Benzthiazide.

URETHAN (ethyl carbamate; urethane; ethyl urethan; NSC-746).

Urethane*** *see* Urethan.

'**Urethylane**' *see* Methyl carbamate.

'**Urex**' *see* Methenamine hippurate.

6,6′-Ureylenebis(1-methylquinolinium sulfate) *see* Quinuronium sulfate.

8,8′-[Ureylenebis[*m*-phenylenecarbonylimino(4-methyl-*m*-phenylene)carbonylimino]]di(1,3,5-naphthalenetrisulfonic acid) *see* Suramin sodium.

'**Urfadyne**' *see* Nifurtoinol.

'**Urfamicina**' *see* Thiamphenicol glycinate.

'**Urfamycin**' *see* Thiamphenicol glycinate.

'**Urgilan**' *see* Proscillaridin.

'**Urgo**' *see* Benzalkonium chloride.

URIC ACID (2,6,8(1*H*,3*H*,9*H*)-purinetrione; lithic acid).

URIC ACID OXIDASE (CB-8129; 'uricosydase').

'**Uricida**' *see* Piperazine.

'**Uricosid**' *see* Probenecid.

'**Uricosydase**' *see* Uric acid oxidase.

'**Uricovac**' *see* Benzbromarone.

URIDINE (uracil riboside).

URIDINE DIPHOSPHATE (UDP).

Uridine monophosphate *see* Uridylic acid.

URIDINE TRIPHOSPHATE (uridine triphos-phoric acid; UTP; 'uteplex').

'**Uridione**' *see* 5-Bromo-2-phenyl-1,3-indandione.

'**Uridognost**' *see* Iodoxyl.

'**Uridurine**' *see* Nifurtoinol.

URIDYLIC ACID (uridine monophosphoric acid; uridine monophosphate; uracylic acid; UMP).

'**Urisol**' *see* Methenamine.

'**Urispas**' *see* Flavoxate.

'**Uritone**' *see* Methenamine.

'**Uro-beniktol**' *see under* Neomycin.

'**Urobenyl**' *see* Allopurinol.

Uroboramine *see* Methenamine borate.

UROCANIC ACID (4-imidazoleacrylic acid).

Urocanoylcholine *see* Murexine.

'**Urocedulamin**' *see* Methenamine mandelate.

'**Urodil**' *see* Nitrofurantoin.

'**Urodixin**' *see* Nalidixic acid.

UROFOLLITROPHIN* (menopausal gonado-trophin extracted from human urine but possess-ing no LH activity).

'**Urofort**' *see* Amanozine.

'**Urogenine**' *see* Methenamine.

'**Urografin**' *see* Meglumine diatrizoate.

UROKINASE*** (plasminogen activator from hu-man sources).

'**Urokolin**' *see* Acetrizoic acid.

'Urokon' *see* Sodium acetrizoate.
'Urol' *see* Urea quinate.
'Urolocide' *see* Dodecarbonium chloride.
'Urolong' *see* Nitrofurantoin.
'Urolucosil' *see* Sulfamethizole.
'Uromandelin' *see* Methenamine mandelate.
'Urombrine' *see* Iodamide.
'Uromiro' *see* Iodamide.
'Uromitexan' *see* Mesna.
'Uronamin' *see* Methenamine mandelate.
'Uro-nebacetin' *see under* Neomycin.
'Uropac' *see* Iodoxyl.
'Uropax' *see* Oxolinic acid.
'Uropen' *see* Hetacillin.
'Uropolin' *see under* Meglumine diatrizoate.
'Uropurgol' *see* Methenamine anhydromethylene-citrate.
'Uropuryl' *see* Methenamine anhydromethylene-citrate.
'Uroscreen' *see* 2,3,5-Triphenyltetrazolium chloride.
'Uroselectan' *see* Iodopyridone.
'Uroselectan-B' *see* Iodoxyl.
'Urosept' *see* Nitrofurantoin.
'Urosin' *see* Allopurinol.
Urosulfan (tr) *see* Sulfacarbamide.
Urosympathin *see* Norepinephrine.
'Uro-tablinen' *see* Nitrofurantoin.
Urotheobromine *see* Paraxanthine.
'Urotractan' *see* Methenamine hippurate.
'Urotractin' *see* Pipemidic acid.
'Urotrast' *see* Dimethiodal sodium.
'Urotrate' *see* Oxolinic acid.
'Urotropin' *see* Methenamine.
'Urovison' *see under* Meglumine diatrizoate.
'Urovist' *see* Meglumine diatrizoate.
'Urox' *see* Monuron trichloroacetate.
Uroxin *see* Alloxantin.
Ursin *see* Hydroquinone β-D-glucopyranoside.

Ursocholanic acid *see* Cholanic acid.
'Ursocyclin' *see* Oxytetracycline.
URSODEOXYCHOLIC ACID*** (3α,7β-dihydroxy-5β-cholan-24-oic acid; 3,7-dihydroxycholanic acid; 'cholit-ursan'; 'delursan'; 'destolit'; 'de-ursil'; 'ursofalk'; 'ursolvan').
'Ursofalk' *see* Ursodeoxycholic acid.
'Ursolvan' *see* Ursodeoxycholic acid.
'Urumbrin' *see* Iodoxyl.
'Urupan' *see* Dexpanthenol.
'Uskan' *see* Oxazepam.
Usnein *see* Usnic acid.
USNIC ACID (2,6-diacetyl-7,9-dihydroxy-8,9a-dimethyldibenzofuran-1,3-dione; usnein; usninic acid).
USNIC ACID SODIUM SALT (binan; BIN-7).
'Uspulun' *see* 2-Chloro-4-(hydroxymercuri)phenol.
'Ustimon' *see* Hexobendine.
'Ustinex PA' *see* Amitrole.
'Uteplex' *see* Uridine triphosphate.
'Utibid' *see* Oxolinic acid.
'Uticillin' *see* Carfecillin.
'Uticillin V' *see* Penicillin V.
'Uticort' *see* Betamethasone benzoate.
'Utinor' *see* Norfloxacin.
UTP *see* Uridine triphosphate.
'Utropine' *see* Methenamine.
'Uv-284' *see* Sulisobenzone.
UV-531 *see* Octabenzone.
'Uval' *see* Sulisobenzone.
'Uvasol' *see* Hydroquinone β-D-glucopyranoside.
'Uviban' *see* Actinoquinol.
'Uvilon' *see* Piperazine.
'Uvinul M-40' *see* Oxybenzone.
'Uvinul MS-40' *see* Sulisobenzone.
'Uvinul N-35' *see* Etocrilene.
'Uvinul N-539' *see* Octocrilene.
'Uvistat 2211' *see* Mexenone.

V

V-5 *see* Thiopental sodium.
V-7 *see* Thioethamyl.
V-12 *see* Methallatal.
'Vaben' *see* Oxazepam.
VACCENIC ACID (*trans*-11-octadecenoic acid).
'Vacor' *see* 1-(*p*-Nitrophenyl)-3-(pyrid-3-ylmethyl)-urea.
'Vadephen' *see* Tetramisole.
'Vadilex' *see* Ifenprodil tartrate.
'Vaditon' *see* Aminophenazone ascorbate.
'Vaelo' *see* Diazepam.
'Vagestrol' *see* Diethylstilbestrol.
'Vagimid' *see* Metronidazole.
'Vagopax' *see* Parapenzolate bromide.
'Vagophemanil' *see* Diphemanil metilsulfate.
'Vagoprol' *see* Ibrotamide.
'Vagosin' *see* Tricyclamol chloride.
'Vagospasmyl' *see* Adiphenine.
'Vagothyl' *see* Methylenedi(*m*-cresolsulfonic acid) polymer.
'Vagran' *see* Propizepine.
'Val-679' *see* Flunisolide.
'Val-779' *see* Flurazepam.
'Valadol' *see* Paracetamol.
'Valamin' *see* Ethinamate.
'Valbazan' *see* Albendazole.
'Valbil' *see* Febuprol.
VALCONAZOLE* ((±)-2-(2,4-dichlorophen-oxy)-1-imidazol-1-yl-4,4-dimethyl-3-pentanone; 1-[2-(2,4-dichlorophenoxy)-4,4-dimethyl-3-oxo-pentyl]imidazole; BAY f-8751).
VALDETAMIDE (2,2-diethyl-4-pentenoic amide; allyldiethylacetamide; 'epinoval'; 'novo-nal').
VALDETAMIDE plus DIPHENHYDRAMINE ('betadorm N').
VALDIPROMIDE* (2,2-dipropylvaleramide; tripropylacetamide).
VALEPOTRIATE (mixture of acevaltrate, didro-valtrate and valtrate; 'valmane').
VALEPOTRIATE plus DIPHENHYDRAMINE ('nocturette').
VALERIC ACID (1-butanecarboxylic acid; penta-noic acid; propylacetic acid; valerianic acid).
VALETHAMATE BROMIDE (diethyl(2-hydroxy-ethyl)methylammonium bromide 3-methyl-2-phenylvalerate; S-78).
'Valexon' *see* Phoxim.
'Valibran' *see* Medibazine.
VALINE (α-aminoisovaleric acid; 2-amino-3-methylbutyric acid).

'Valisone' *see* Betamethasone valerate.
'Valium' *see* Diazepam.
'Valladan' *see* Benactyzine.
'Valledrine' *see* Alimemazine.
'Vallergan' *see* Alimemazine.
'Vallestril' *see* Methallenestril.
'Valmane' *see* Valepotriate.
Valmethamide *see* Valnoctamide.
'Valmid' *see* Ethinamate.
'Valmidate' *see* Ethinamate.
'Valmorin' *see* Chlorthenoxazine.
VALNOCTAMIDE* (2-ethyl-3-methylvaler-amide; valmethamide; McN-X-181; NSC-32363).
VALOFANE* (3-(allyltetrahydro-5-methyl-2-oxo-3-furoyl)urea).
'Valoron' *see* Tilidine.
VALPERINOL* ((2*R**,4*R**,4a*S**,5*R**, 7*S**,7a*R**,8*R**)-hexahydro-4-methoxy-8-methyl-7a-(piperid-1-ylmethyl)-2,5-methano-cyclopenta-*m*-dioxin-7-ol).
VALPROATE PIVOXIL (hydroxymethyl 2-propylvalerate pivalate).
VALPROATE SEMISODIUM (sodium hydro-gen bis(2-propylvalerate); 2-propylvaleric acid-sodium 2-propylvalerate; semisodium valpro-ate).
VALPROIC ACID* (2-propylvaleric acid; 2-propylpentanoic acid; dipropylacetic acid; valproate sodium; Abbott 44089; Abbott 44090; 'convulex'; 'depakene'; 'epilim'; 'ergenyl'; 'labaz-ene'; 'leptilan'; 'malproin'; 'orfiril'; 'propymal'). *See also* Bismuth valproate; Oxazepam valpro-ate.
Valproic acid ester with 3α-hydroxy-8-isopropyl-1α*H*,5α*H*-tropanium bromide *see* Sintropium bromide.
VALPROMIDE* (2-propylvaleramide; diprop-ylacetamide; 'depamide').
'Valsyn' *see* Furaltadone.
'Valtomicina' *see* Pipacycline.
'Valtorin' *see* Chlorthenoxazine.
VALTRATE (1,7a-dihydro-1,6-dihydroxyspiro-[cyclopenta[*c*]pyran-7(6*H*),2′-oxirane]-4-metha-nol 4-acetate 1,6-diisovalerate; 3α,4-dihydro-3,4-dihydroxyspiro[benzofuran-2(3*H*),2′-oxirane]-6-methanol 6-acetate 3,4-diisovalerate). *See also* Valepotriate.
'Valyl' *see* N,N-Diethylvaleramide.
'Valzin' *see* Phenetylurea.
'VAM' *see* Vinycombinum.

VAMIDOTHION* (O,O-dimethyl S-[2-[[1-methyl-2-(methylamino)-2-oxoethyl]thio]ethyl] phosphorothioate; O,O-dimethyl S-[[2-[1-(methylaminocarboxy)ethyl]thio]ethyl]phosphorothioate; O,O-dimethyl S-[[2-[1-(methylcarbamoyl)-ethyl]thio]ethyl] phosphorothioate; 'kilval').

'**Vanabol**' *see* Metandienone.
'**Vanay**' *see* Triacetin.
'**Vanceril**' *see* Beclometasone dipropionate.
'**Vancide-89**' *see* Captan.
'**Vancide-BN**' *see* Sodium bitionolate.
'**Vancide Z**' *see under* Ziram.
'**Vancocin**' *see* Vancomycin.
VANCOMYCIN* (antibiotic from *Str. orientalis*).
'**Vandid**' *see* Etamivan.
'**Van Dyke 264**' *see* (Ethylhexyl)norbornenedicarboximide.
'**Vanectyl**' *see* Alimemazine.
VANEPRIM* (($\pm$)-α-[[4-amino-5-(3,4,5-trimethoxybenzyl)pyrimidin-2-yl]amino]-3-ethoxy-4-hydroxy-α-toluenesulfonic acid).
'**Vanidene**' *see* Cyclovalone.
'**Vanillal**' *see* Homovanillin.
Vanillaldehyde *see* Vanillin.
VANILLAMIDE (4-hydroxy-3-methoxybenzamide; vanillic acid amide).
VANILLIC ACID (4-hydroxy-3-methoxybenzoic acid).
Vanillic acid diethylamide *see* Etamivan.
Vanillic aldehyde *see* Vanillin.
Vanillideneisoniazid *see* Ftivazide.
VANILLIN (4-hydroxy-3-methoxybenzaldehyde; protocatechualdehyde 3-methylether; vanillaldehyde; vanillic aldehyde).
Vanillin isonicotinoylhydrazone *see* Ftivazide.
Vanillylacetone *see* Zingerone.
N^4,N^4-**Vanillylidenebissulfanilamide** *see* Vanyldisulfamide.
N-**Vanillylnonamide** *see* Nonivamide.
VANILMANDELIC ACID (4-hydroxy-3-methoxymandelic acid; 4-hydroxy-3-methoxyphenylglycolic acid; MOMA; VMA).
'**Vanilone**' *see* Cyclovalone.
VANITIOLIDE* (4-(thiovanilloyl)morpholine).
'**Vanizide**' *see* Ftivazide.
'**Vanobid**' *see* Candicidin.
'**Vanquin**' *see* Pyrvinium embonate.
'**Vansil**' *see* Oxamniquine.
'**Vantal**' *see under* DDT.
'**Vantoc**' *see* Cetrimonium bromide.
VANYLDISULFAMIDE* (N^4,N^4-vanillylidenebissulfanilamide).
'**Vanzide**' *see* Ftivazide.
'**Vanzoate**' *see* Benzyl benzoate.
'**Vapam**' *see* Metam-sodium.
'**Vapona**' *see* Dichlorvos.
'**Vaporole**' *see* Amyl nitrite.
'**Vaporpac**' *see* Octodrine.
'**Vapotone**' *see* Tetraethyl pyrophosphate.
'**Varbian**' *see* Prenalterol.
'**Vardax**' *see* Sulmazole.
'**Varemoid**' *see* Troxerutin.

'**Variagil**' *see* Alimemazine.
'**Varicocid**' *see* Sodium morrhuate.
'**Varidase**' *see under* Streptodornase.
'**Variotin**' *see* Pecilocin.
'**Varnoline**' *see under* Desogestrel.
'**Varophen**' *see* Promazine.
'**Varsaclox**' *see under* Cloxacillin.
'**Varson**' *see* Nicergoline.
'**Vasalgin**' *see* Proxibarbal.
'**Vasangor**' *see* Propatylnitrate.
'**Vasazol**' *see* Pentetrazole.
'**Vascardin**' *see* Isosorbide dinitrate.
'**Vascoray**' *see under* Meglumine iotalamate.
'**Vascoril**' *see* Cinepazet maleate.
'**Vasculat**' *see* Bamethan.
'**Vasculit**' *see* Bamethan.
'**Vascunicol**' *see under* Bamethan.
'**Vasoatherolip**' *see under* Aluminium clofibrate.
'**Vasobral**' *see* Dihydroergocryptine mesilate.
'**Vasobrix**' *see under* Ethanolamine ioxitalamate.
'**Vasoc**' *see* Benzarone.
'**Vasocordrin**' *see* Oxedrine.
'**Vasodilian**' *see* Isoxsuprine.
'**Vasodistal**' *see* Cinepazide maleate.
'**Vasolan**' *see* Verapamil.
'**Vasombrix**' *see* Ioxitalamic acid.
'**Vasomotal**' *see* Betahistine.
'**Vasopentol**' *see* Burodiline.
'**Vasophemanil**' *see* Diphemanil metilsulfate.
VASOPRESSIN* (antidiuretic hormone; beta-hypophamine; β-hypophamine; vasopressin injection).
See also Argipressin; Desmopressin; Felypressin; Lypressin; Terlipressin.
'**Vasorbate**' *see* Isosorbide dinitrate.
'**Vasosuprine**' *see* Isoxsuprine.
Vasotocin *see* Argiprestocin.
Vasoton (tr) *see* Oxedrine.
'**Vasotran**' *see* Isoxsuprine.
'**Vasoverin**' *see* Pyricarbate.
'**Vasoxine**' *see* Methoxamine.
'**Vasoxyl**' *see* Methoxamine.
'**Vaspit**' *see* Fluocortin butyl.
'**Vastarel**' *see* Trimetazidine.
'**Vasurix**' *see* Meglumine acetrizoate.
'**Vasylox**' *see* Methoxamine.
'**Vatensol**' *see* Guanoclor.
'**Vatsol OT**' *see* Docusate sodium.
V-C 9-104 *see* Ethoprop.
V-C-13 *see* Dichlofenthion.
'**Vebonol**' *see* Boldenone undecanoate.
'**Vectarion**' *see* Almitrine.
'**Vectran**' *see* Minocycline.
'**Vectren**' *see* Tiamizide.
VECURONIUM BROMIDE* (1-[[($2\beta,3\alpha,16\beta,17\beta$)-3,17-bis(acetoxy)-2-piperidin-1-yl]-5α-androstan-16-yl]-1-methylpiperidinium bromide; 3α-17β-dihydroxy-2β,16β-dipiperidino-5α-androstane 3,17-diacetate 16β-methobromide; 2β,16β-dipiperid-1-yl-5α-androstane-3α,17β-diol 3,17-diacetate 16β-methobromide; Org-NC-45; 'norcuron').
'**Vegaben**' *see* Chloramben.

Vegetable pepsin *see* Papain.
'**Vegolysin**' *see* Hexamethonium bromide.
'**Veinamitol**' *see* Troxerutin.
'**Veinartan**' *see* Metescufylline.
'**Velacycline**' *see* Rolitetracycline.
'**Velardon**' *see* Papain.
'**Velban**' *see* Vinblastine.
'**Velbe**' *see* Vinblastine.
'**Veldopa**' *see* Levodopa.
'**Velmol**' *see* Docusate sodium.
'**Velonarcon**' *see* Ketamine.
'**Velosef**' *see* Cefradine.
'**Velosulin**' *see* Neutral insulin injection.
'**Velsicol 1068**' *see* Chlordane.
'**Venacil**' *see* Ancrod.
'**Venactone**' *see* Canrenoate potassium.
'**Venalot**' *see under* Coumarin.
'**Vendal neu**' *see under* Nicomorphine.
'**Vendarcin**' *see* Oxytetracycline.
'**Vendex**' *see* Neostanox.
'**Venelbin**' *see under* Dihydroergotamine.
'**Venesetic**' *see* Thioethamyl.
'**Vengicide**' *see* Toyocamycin.
'**Venobarbital**' *see* Thiobutabarbital.
'**Venomin**' *see* Viper venom.
Venoms *see under names of animals.*
'**Venopan**' *see* Enibomal.
'**Venoruton**' *see* Monoxerutin.
'**Venostasin**' *see* Escin.
'**Venotex**' *see* Sodium morrhuate.
'**Ventaire**' *see* Protokylol.
'**Ventilat**' *see* Oxitropium bromide.
'**Ventipulmin**' *see* Clenbuterol.
'**Ventolin**' *see* Salbutamol.
'**Ventox**' *see* Acrylonitrile.
'**Venzar**' *see* Lenacil.
'**Venzonate**' *see* Benzyl benzoate.
'**Vepesid**' *see* Etoposide.
'**Veracillin**' *see* Dicloxacillin.
VERADOLINE* (($\pm$)-2-(*p*-aminophenethyl)-
    1,2,3,4-tetrahydro-6,7-dimethoxy-1-methyliso-
    quinoline; ($\pm$)-4-[2-(3,4-dihydro-6,7-dimethoxy-
    1-methyl-2(1*H*)-isoquinolinyl)ethyl]benzen-
    amine; veradoline hydrochloride; PR-870-714A).
'**Veradyne**' *see* Carsalam.
'**Verafem**' *see under* Medroxyprogesterone.
Veraisoquin *see* Laudanosine.
VERALIPRIDE* (*N*-[(1-allylpyrrolidin-2-yl)-
    methyl]-2,3-dimethoxy-5-sulfamoylbenzamide;
    N-[(1-allylpyrrolidin-2-yl)methyl]-5-sulfamoyl-*o*-
    veratramide; LIR-1660; 'agreal').
'**Veramex**' *see* Verapamil.
'**Veramix**' *see* Medroxyprogesterone acetate.
'**Veramon**' *see* Barbipyrine.
VERAPAMIL* (5-[(3,4-dimethoxyphenethyl)-
    methylamino]-2-(3,4-dimethoxyphenyl)-2-
    isopropylvaleronitrile; 2-(3,4-dimethoxyphenyl)-
    2-isopropyl-2-[3-(*N*-methylhomoveratrylamino)-
    propyl]acetonitrile; CP-16533-1; D-365).
VERAPAMIL plus DIAZEPAM ('elthon').
VERAPAMIL plus ISOSORBIDE DINITRATE
    ('stenoptin').
VERATRALDEHYDE (3,4-dimethoxybenzalde-

hyde).
VERATRYL ALCOHOL (3,4-dimethoxybenzyl
    alcohol).
VERATRYLAMINE (3,4-dimethoxybenzyl-
    amine).
Veratrylideneisoniazid *see* Verazide.
VERAZIDE* (1-isonicotinoyl-2-veratrylidene-
    hydrazine; veratraldehyde isonicotinoylhydraz-
    one; *N'*-veratrylideneisoniazid).
'**Verazinc**' *see* Zinc sulfate.
'**Vercidon**' *see* Dithiazanine iodide.
'**Vercyte**' *see* Pipobroman.
'**Verecolene**' *see* Fencibutirol.
'**Vergentan**' *see* Alizapride.
'**Vergonil**' *see* Hydroflumethiazide.
'**Vericyline**' *see* Ampicillin.
'**Veriloid**' *see* Alkavervir.
VERILOPAM* (3-(4-aminophenethyl)-2,3,4,5-
    tetrahydro-7,8-dimethoxy-1*H*-3-benzazepine; 4-
    [2-(1,2,4,5-tetrahydro-7,8-dimethoxy-3*H*-3-benz-
    azepin-3-yl)ethyl]benzenamine; verilopam
    hydrochloride; PR-0818-156-A).
'**Verina**' *see* Buphenine *and* Ethaverine.
'**Verindal ultra**' *see* Lindane.
'**Veripaque**' *see* Oxyphenisatine.
'**Veritan**' *see* Clofenciclan.
'**Vermexane**' *see* Lindane.
'**Vermicompren**' *see* Piperazine.
'**Vermi-drageletten**' *see* Ascaridole.
'**Vermisol**' *see* Piperazine.
'**Vermitin**' *see* Niclosamide.
'**Vermizene**' *see* Piperazine.
'**Vermizym**' *see* Papain.
'**Vermox**' *see* Mebendazole.
'**Vernam**' *see* Vernolate.
Vernine *see* Guanosine.
'**Vernitest**' *see* Quinaldine blue.
VERNOLATE (*S*-propyl dipropylcarbamothioate;
    'vernam').
Verocainine *see* Tiapamil.
'**Verodigen**' *see* Gitalin amorphous.
VEROFYLLINE* (($\pm$)-3,7-dihydro-1,8-di-
    methyl-3-(2-methylbutyl)-1*H*-purine-2,6-dione;
    ($\pm$)-1,8-dimethyl-3-(2-methylbutyl)xanthine;
    CK-0383).
'**Verografin**' *see under* Meglumine diatrizoate.
'**Veronal**' *see* Barbital.
'**Veronigen**' *see* Barbital.
'**Verophen**' *see* Promazine.
'**Veropyrin**' *see* Barbipyrine.
'**Verospiron**' *see* Spironolactone.
'**Veroxil**' *see* Piperazine.
'**Versacort**' *see* Bendacort.
'**Versamine**' *see* Mecamylamine.
'**Versapen**' *see* Hetacillin.
'**Versene**' *see* Trisodium edetate.
'**Versenic acid**' *see* Edetic acid.
'**Versidyne**' *see* Metofoline.
'**Verstran**' *see* Prazepam.
'**Versulin**' *see* Apigenin.
'**Versus**' *see* Bendazac.
'**Vertigon**' *see* Prochlorperazine.
'**Veryl**' *see under* Amobarbital.

'Vesadol' *see under* Buzepide metiodide.
'Vesalium' *see under* Haloperidol.
'Vesalvine' *see* Methenamine.
'Vesamin' *see* Sodium acetrizoate.
'Vesidryl' *see* Metochalcone.
'Vesipaque' *see* Phenobutiodil.
'Vesipin' *see* Acetylsalol.
'Vesipyrin' *see* Acetylsalol.
'Vesparax' *see under* Brallobarbital.
'Vespazin' *see* Fluphenazine.
'Vesperone' *see* Brallobarbital.
'Vespral' *see* Triflupromazine.
'Vesprin' *see* Triflupromazine.
'Vessel' *see* Sulodexide.
'Vesulong' *see* Sulfapyrazole.
'Vetalar' *see* Ketamine.
'Vetalog' *see* Triamcinolone acetonide.
'Vetame' *see* Triflupromazine.
'Vetanabol' *see* Metandienone.
'Vetomazin' *see* Methopromazine.
VETRABUTINE*** (3,4-dimethoxy-*N,N*-di-
methyl-α-(3-phenylpropyl)benzylamine; *N,N*-di-
methyl-α-(3-phenylpropyl)veratrylamine).
'Vetranquil' *see* Acepromazine.
Vetrazin (tr) *see* 3,4-Dimethoxybenzylhydrazine.
'Vetren' *see* Heparin.
'Vetsovate' *see* Betamethasone valerate.
'Viaben' *see* Bromopride.
'Viacil' *see* Lactobacillus acidophilus cultures.
'Viadril' *see* Hydroxydione sodium succinate.
'Viaductor' *see* Lorajmine.
'Vialin' *see* Mephentermine.
'Vianin' *see* Crystal violet.
'Vianol' *see* Butylated hydroxytoluene.
'Viarespan' *see* Fenspiride.
'Viarex' *see* Beclometasone dipropionate.
'Vibatex S' *see* Polyvinyl alcohol.
'Vibazine' *see* Buclizine.
'Vibeline' *see* Visnadine.
'Vibramycin' *see* Doxycycline hyclate.
'Vibratussal' *see under* Doxycycline.
'Vibravenos' *see* Doxycycline.
'Vibrocil' *see under* Phenylephrine.
VICANTRIL** ((±)-10-chloro-1,2,3,3a,4,5-hexa-
hydro-6*H*-indolo[3,2,1-*de*][1,5]naphthyridin-6-
one).
'Viccillin' *see* Ampicillin.
'Viceton' *see* Chloramphenicol.
'Vicryl' *see* Polyglactin(s).
'Victan' *see* Ethyl loflazepate.
Victoria green *see* Malachite green.
VIDARABINE*** (9-β-D-arabinofuranosyladen-
ine; adenine arabinofuranoside; ara-A; spongo-
adenosine; vidarabine phosphate; vidarabine so-
dium phosphate; CI-673; CI-808; NSC-404421;
'vira-A').
'Videbil' *see* Iopronic acid.
'Videocolangio' *see* Iodoxamic acid.
'Vidipon' *see* Cloforex.
'Vidopen' *see* Ampicillin.
'Vigilor' *see* Fipexide.
'Vikane' *see* Sulfuryl fluoride.
Vikasol (tr) *see* Menadione sodium bisulfite.

'Vilan' *see* Nicomorphine.
'Vilexin' *see* Fenyramidol.
'Vilona' *see* Ribavirin.
VILOXAZINE** (2-(*o*-ethoxyphenoxymethyl)-
morpholine; 2-(2-ethoxyphenoxymethyl)tetra-
hydro-1,4-oxazine; viloxazine hydrochloride;
ICI-58834; 'vivalan'; 'vivarint').
VIMINOL*** (1-(*o*-chlorobenzyl)-α-[(di-*sec*-but-
ylamino)methyl]pyrrole-2-methanol; 1-[α-*N*-(*o*-
chlorobenzyl)pyrryl]-2-di-*sec*-butylaminoethan-
ol; diviminol; Z-424).
VIMINOL *p*-HYDROXYBENZOATE ('dividol').
'Vinactane' *see* Viomycin.
'Vinactine' *see* Viomycin.
'Vinamar' *see* Ethyl vinyl ether.
'Vinarol' *see* Polyvinyl alcohol.
VINBARBITAL*** (5-ethyl-5-(1-methyl-1-buten-
yl)barbituric acid sodium derivative; butenemal;
vinbarbitone).
Vinbarbitone* *see* Vinbarbital.
VINBLASTINE*** (alkaloid from *Vinca rosea*;
vinblastine sulfate; vincaleucoblastine; vincaleu-
koblastine; vincoblastine; VLB; LE-29060; NSC-
49842).
VINBURNINE*** (16-ethyl-14-oxopyridocantin-
one; 14-oxo-*cis*-eburnane; eburnamonine; vin-
camone; 'cervoxan').
'Vinca 10' *see* Vincamine.
'Vincadar' *see* Vincamine.
Vincaleucoblastine *see* Vinblastine.
Vincaleukoblastine *see* Vinblastine.
VINCAMINE*** (alkaloid from *Vinca minor*;
14,15-dihydro-14β-hydroxy(3α,16α)-eburnamen-
ine-14-carboxylic acid methyl ester; 13α-ethyl-
2,3,5,6,12,13,13a,13b-octahydro-12-hydroxy-
1*H*-indolo[3,2,1-*de*]pyrido[3,2,1-*ij*][1,5]naphthyr-
idine-12-carboxylic acid methyl ester).
Vincamone *see* Vinburnine.
VINCANOL** (RGH-4406).
Vincantenate *see* Vinconate.
'Vincapront' *see* Vincamine.
'Vincimax' *see* Vincamine.
VINCLOZOLIN (3-(3,5-dichlorophenyl)-5-
methyl-5-vinyloxazolidine-2,4-dione).
Vincoblastine *see* Vinblastine.
VINCOFOS*** (2,2-dichlorovinyl methyl octyl
phosphate; SD-15803).
VINCONATE*** ((±)-methyl 3-ethyl-2,3,3a,4-
tetrahydro-1*H*-indolo[3,2,1-*de*][1,5]naphthyrid-
ine-6-carboxylate; vincantenate; vintenate; OC-
340).
VINCRISTINE*** (alkaloid from *Vinca rosea*; 22-
oxovinblastine; leurocristine; vincristine sulfate;
NSC-67574).
VINDEBURNOL*** ((±)-(12*R**,13a*R**,13b*S**)-
2,3,5,6,12,13,13a,13b-octahydro-1*H*-indo-
lo[3,2,1-*de*]pyrido[3,2,1-*ij*][1,5]naphthyridine-12-
ol; (±)-20,21-dinor-16α-eburnamine).
VINDESINE*** (3-carbamoyl-4-deacetyl-3-de-
(methoxycarbonyl)vincaleukoblastine; compound 112531; NSC-24567; 'eldisine').
VINEPIDINE** ((4'*S*)-4'-deoxyleurocristine).
'Vinesthene' *see* Vinyl ether.

533

'Vinesthesin' *see* Vinyl ether.

'Vinethene' *see* Vinyl ether.

VINFORMIDE*** (*N*-demethyl-*N*-formylleurosine; F-leurosine).

VINGLYCINATE*** (deacetylvinblastine 4-(*N*,*N*-dimethylglycinate) (ester); vinglycinate sesquisulfate; vinglycinate sulfate).

'Vinicristine' *see* Vinleurosine.

Vinilin (tr) *see* Polyvinox.

'Vinisil' *see* Povidone.

VINLEUROSINE*** (alkaloid from *Vinca rosea*; leurosine; vinleurosine sulfate; NSC-528004; 'vinicristine').

'Vinol' *see* Polyvinyl alcohol.

VINPOCETINE*** (ethyl apovincamin-22-oate; RGH-4405; 'cavinton').

VINPOLINE*** (2-hydroxypropyl 14-deoxyvincaminate).

VINROSIDINE*** (alkaloid from *Vinca rosea*; vinrosidine sulfate).

Vintenate *see* Vinconate.

VINTIAMOL*** (*N*-(4-amino-2-methylpyrimid-5-ylmethyl)-*N*-[2-(2-benzoylvinylthio)-4-hydroxy-1-methyl-1-butenyl]formamide).

VINTRIPTOL** ([23(*S*)]-4-deacetyl-3-[(1-carboxy-2-indol-3-ylethyl)carbamoyl]-3-de(methoxycarbonyl)vincaleukoblastine, ethyl ester).

VINYCOMBINUM* (75% ethyl ether with 25% vinyl ether; 'ethydan'; 'VAM').

'Vinydan' *see* Vinyl ether.

17β-Vinylandrostane *see* Pregn-20-ene.

Vinylbenzene *see* Styrene.

VINYLBITAL*** (5-(1-methylbutyl)-5-vinylbarbituric acid; butyvinal; vinylbitone; vinymal; JD-96).

Vinylbitone* *see* Vinylbital.

Vinyl cyanide *see* Acrylonitrile.

Vinylene (tr) *see* Polyvinox.

VINYL ETHER (1,1'-oxybisethene; divinyl ether; divinyl oxide; ethenyloxyethene).
See also Vinycombinum.

Vinylformic acid *see* Acrylic acid.

Vinylidene chloride *see* 1,1-Dichloroethylene.

17α-Vinylnortestosterone *see* Norvinisterone.

'Vinylofos' *see* Dichlorvos.

5-Vinyl-2-oxazolidinethione *see* Goitrin.

1-Vinyl-2-pyrrolidone, polymers *see* Copovithane; Povidone.

α-(5-Vinylquinuclidin-2-yl)-4-quinolinemethanol *see* Cinchonidine;Cinchonine.

Vinyl trichloride *see* 1,1,2-Trichloroethane.

Vinymal* *see* Vinylbital.

'Vinyzene' *see* Bromchlorenone.

VINZOLIDINE*** (methyl (3*R*,5*S*,7*R*,9*S*)-9-[3'-(2-chloroethyl)-6,7-didehydro-4β-hydroxy-16-methoxy-1-methyl-2',4'-dioxo-2β,3β,5α,12β,19α-spiro[aspidospermidine-3,5'-oxazolidin]-15-yl]-5-ethyl-1,4,5,6,7,8,9,10-octahydro-5-hydroxy-2*H*-3,7-methanoazacycloundecino[5,4-*b*]indole-9-carboxylate 4'-acetate (ester); vinzolidine sulfate; LY-104208).

'Viocid' *see* Crystal violet.

'Viocin' *see* Viomycin.

'Vioform' *see* Clioquinol.

'Viokase' *see* Pancrelipase.

Violaquercitrin *see* Rutoside.

VIOLARIN (tr) (antibiotic from *Actinomyces violaceus*; antibiotic 452-7).

'Violen' *see* Fenclofos.

VIOMYCIN** (antibiotic from *Str. puniceus* or *Str. floridae*; florimycin; phlorimycin; tuberactinomycin B; viomycin sulfate).

VIOMYCIN plus DEXPANTHENOL ('pantoviocin').

VIOMYCIN PANTOTHENATE ('viothenat').

'Vionactan' *see* Viomycin.

Viosterol *see* Ergocalciferol.

'Viothenat' *see* Viomycin pantothenate.

'Vio-thene' *see* Oxyphencyclimine.

'Viozene' *see* Fenclofos.

'Vipericin' *see* Viper venom.

VIPER VENOM ('venomin'; 'vipericin').
See also Russell's viper venom.

Viprynium chloride* *see* Pyrvinium chloride.

Viprynium embonate *see* Pyrvinium embonate.

Viprynium pamoate *see* Pyrvinium embonate.

VIQUALINE*** (6-methoxy-4-[3-[(3*R*,4*R*)-3-vinylpiperid-4-yl]propyl]quinoline).

VIQUIDIL*** (1-(6-methoxyquinolin-4-yl)-3-(3-vinylpiperid-4-yl)-1-propanone; LM-192; 'desclidium').

'Vira-A' *see* Vidarabine.

'Viramid' *see* Ribavirin.

'Virazene' *see* Phenolsulfazole.

'Virazole' *see* Ribavirin.

'Viregyt' *see* Amantadine.

'Virex' *see* Testosterone.

'Virexen' *see* Idoxuridine.

Virgimycin* *see* Virginiamycin.

VIRGINIAMYCIN*** (antibiotic from *Str. virginiae*; virgimycin; virginiamycin M_1 plus virginiamycin S; SK&F-7988; 'stafac'; 'staphylomycin'; 'staxidin').

Viride malachitum *see* Malachite green.

Viride nitens *see* Brilliant green.

VIRIDOFULVIN*** (antibiotic from *Str. viridogriseus*; viridogrisein).

Viridogrisein *see* Viridofulvin.

'Virobis' *see* Moroxydine.

'Virofral' *see* Amantadine.

'Viroptic' *see* Trifluridine.

VIROXIME** (2-amino-6-benzoyl-1-(isopropylsulfonyl)benzimidazole oxime,mixture of *E* (enviroxime) and *Z* (zinviroxime) isomers; 2-amino-1-(isopropylsulfonyl)-6-benzimidazole phenyl ketone oxime).

'Virugon' *see* Moroxydine.

'Viru-Merz' *see* Tromantadine.

'Virunguent' *see* Idoxuridine.

'Viruseen' *see* Poly(1-methylenepiperazine).

'Virustat' *see* Moroxydine.

'Viruxan' *see* Inosine pranobex.

'Visammin' *see* Khellin.

'Visceralgine' *see* Tiemonium iodide.

'Visclair' *see* Mecysteine.

'Viscotiol' *see* Letosteine.

VISCUM ALBUM (mistletoe; 'helixor'; 'iscador'; 'isorel'; 'plenosol').

'Visergil' *see under* Co-dergocrine.

'Vi-siblin' *see* Psyllium.

'Visine' *see* Tetryzoline.

'Viskaldix' *see under* Pindolol.

'Visken' *see* Pindolol.

'Viskenit' *see under* Pindolol.

VISNADINE*** (3,4,5-trihydroxy-2,2-dimethyl-6-chromanacrylic acid δ-lactone 4-acetate 3-(2-methylbutyrate); 4'-acetoxy-3',4'-dihydro-3'-(2-methylbutyryloxy)seselin; 10-acetoxy-9,10-dihydro-8,8-dimethyl-9-(α-methylbutyryloxy)-benzodipyran-2-one).

VISNAFYLLINE*** ([2-(9-methoxy-7-methyl-5-oxo-5*H*-furo[3,2-g][1]benzopyran-4-yloxy)ethyl]-trimethylammonium theophylline derivative; kellofylline).

Visnagidin *see* Visnagin.

VISNAGIN (5-methoxy-2-methyl-6,7-furanochromone; 4-methoxy-7-methyl-5*H*-furo[3,2-g]-benzopyran-5-one; desmethoxykhellin; visnagidin).

'Visotrast' *see under* Meglumine diatrizoate.

'Vistalbalon' *see* Naphazoline.

'Vistamycin' *see* Ribostamycin.

'Vi-stannyl' *see* Tin oxide.

'Vistaril' *see* Hydroxyzine.

VISTATOLON*** (antiviral antibiotic from *Penicillium stoloniferum*; statolon; NSC-71901).

'Vistimon' *see* Mesterolone.

Visual purple *see* Rhodopsin.

'Vitacarpine' *see* Pilocarpine.

Vitamin A *see* Retinol.

Vitamin A$_1$ *see* Retinol.

Vitamin A$_2$ *see* 3-Dehydroretinol.

Vitamin A acid *see* Tretinoin.

Vitamin A alcohol *see* Retinol.

Vitamin A aldehyde *see* Retinal.

Vitamin B"c *see* Folic acid.

Vitamin B$_t$ *see* Carnitine.

Vitamin B$_w$ *see* Biotin.

Vitamin B$_1$ *see* Thiamine.

Vitamin B$_2$ *see* Riboflavin.

Vitamin B$_3$ *see* Nicotinamide.

Vitamin B$_4$ *see* Adenine.

Vitamin B$_5$ *see* Pantothenic acid.

Vitamin B$_6$ *see* Pyridoxine.

Vitamin B$_{12}$ *see* Cyanocobalamin.

Vitamin B$_{12}$"a *see* Hydroxocobalamin.

Vitamin B$_{12b}$ *see* Aquocobalamin.

Vitamin B$_{12}$"c *see* Nitritocobalamin.

'Vitamin B$_{15}$' *see* Pangamic acid.

'Vitamin B-17' *see* Amygdalin.

Vitamin C *see* Ascorbic acid.

Vitamin C$_2$ *see references under* Vitamin(s) P.

Vitamin D$_2$ *see* Ergocalciferol.

Vitamin D$_3$ *see* Colecalciferol.

Vitamin D$_4$ *see* 25-Hydroxycolecalciferol.

Vitamin E *see* α-Tocopherol.

Vitamin G *see* Riboflavin.

Vitamin H *see* Biotin.

Vitamin H$_1$ *see* p-Aminobenzoic acid.

Vitamin K$_1$ *see* Phytomenadione.

Vitamin K$_1$ hydroquinone *see* Phytonadiol.

Vitamin K$_2$ *see* Farnoquinone.

Vitamin K$_3$ *see* Menadione.

Vitamin K$_4$ *see* Acetomenaphthone.

VITAMIN K$_5$ (4-amino-2-methyl-1-naphthol hydrochloride; methylaminonaphthol).

VITAMIN K$_6$ (2-methyl-1,4-naphthalenediamine dihydrochloride).

VITAMIN K$_7$ (4-amino-3-methyl-1-naphthol).

Vitamin M *see* Folic acid.

Vitamin(s) P *see* Eriodictyol; Hesperidin; Rutoside.

Vitamin P$_4$ *see* Troxerutin.

Vitamin PP *see* Nicotinamide; Nicotinic acid.

VITAMIN T-COMPLEX (Goetsch's vitamin; termitin; torutilen; 'tegotin'; 'temina').

VITAMIN U ((3-amino-3-carboxypropyl)dimethylulfonium salt; L-methionine methylsulfonium salt; *S*-methylmethionine sulfonium chloride; methylmethioninesulfonium chloride (or bromide); antiulcer vitamin).

Vitamogen' *see* Thiamine disulfide phosphate.

Vita-stain' *see* 2,3,5-Triphenyltetrazolium chloride.

'Vitavax' *see* Carboxin.

'Vitaverm' *see* Sulbutiamine.

'Vitax F-15' *see* Fluoroacetic acid.

'Vivacalcium' *see* Calcium glutamate.

'Vivalan' *see* Viloxazine.

'Vivarint' *see* Viloxazine.

'Vivicil' *see* Fluvomycin.

'Vivol' *see* Diazepam.

VK-53 *see* Sulfamethizole.

VK-55 *see* Sulfaethidole.

VK-57 *see* Glyprothiazol.

VLB *see* Vinblastine.

VM-26 *see* Teniposide.

VMA *see* Vanilmandelic acid.

'Vnuran' *see under* Demeton-O.

'Vogalene' *see* Metopimazine.

VOLAZOCINE*** (3-(cyclopropylmethyl)-1,2,3,4,5,6-hexahydro-*cis*-6,11-dimethyl-2,6-methano-3-benzazocine; 3-cyclopropylmethyl-*cis*-6,11-dimethyl-2,6-methano-6,7-benzomorphan; WIN-23200).

'Volenyl' *see under* Chlormadinone acetate.

'Volex' *see* Hetastarch.

'Volidan' *see under* Megestrol acetate.

'Volital' *see* Pemoline.

'Volon A' *see* Triamcinolone acetonide.

'Volpar' *see* Phenylmercuric acetate.

'Volplan' *see under* Megestrol acetate.

'Voltaren' *see* Diclofenac.

'Voltarol' *see* Diclofenac.

'Voluntal' *see* Trichlorourethan.

'Vomex A' *see* Dimenhydrinate.

'Vonedrine' *see* Phenpromethamine.

'Vontac' *see* Methiomeprazine.

'Vontrol' *see* Difenidol.

'Voranil' *see* Clortermine.

'Voren' *see* Dexamethasone isonicotinate.

'Voronit' *see* Fuberidazole.

'Voveran' *see under* Cafedrine.

'**Voxifral**' *see* Dequalinium chloride.
'**Voxsan**' *see* Sodium hypochlorite.
VP-16-213 *see* Etoposide.
VPM *see* Metam-sodium.
'**Vucine**' *see* Ethacridine lactate.
VUFB-6453 *see* Metipranolol.
VUFB-6683 *see* Acetergamine.

VUFB-9977 *see* Oxyprothepine decanoate.
'**Vulcacycline**' *see* Tetracycline dihydronovobiocin sodium phytate.
'**Vulcamycin**' *see* Novobiocin.
'**Vulkamycin**' *see* Novobiocin.
'**Vulklor**' *see* Chloranil.
'**Vydate**' *see* Oxamyl.

W

W-32 *see* Phenformin.
W-33 *see* Methapyrilene.
W-37 *see* Buformin.
W-50 *see* Methaphenilene.
W-108/HF-1854 *see* Clozapine.
W-108/HF-2159 *see* Clotiapine.
W-583 *see* Mebutamate.
W-713 *see* Tybamate.
W-1015 *see* Nisobamate.
W-1191-2 *see* Amanozine.
W-1224 *see* Pecazine.
W-1372 *see* Beloxamide.
W-1544 *see* Phenelzine.
W-1548-1 *see* Sulocarbilate.
W-1655 *see* Phenazopyridine.
W-1760A *see* Namoxyrate.
W-1803 *see* Benzolamide.
W-1929 *see* Colistimethate sodium.
W-2180 *see* Suxemerid.
W-2197 *see* Pentrinitrol.
W-2291A *see* Mimbane.
W-2354 *see* Seclazone.
W-2394A *see* Pemerid.
W-2395 *see* Meseclazone.
W-2900A *see* Etozolin.
W-2946M *see* Reproterol.
W-3207B *see* Modaline.
W-3366A *see* Quindonium bromide.
W-3395 *see* Algestone acetonide.
W-3399 *see* Quingestrone.
W-3566 *see* Quinestrol.
W-3580B *see* Ampyzine.
W-3623 *see* Cyprazepam.
W-3676 *see* Sulazepam.
W-3699 *see* Piprozolin.
W-3746 *see* Cetofenicol.
W-3976B *see* Triampyzine.
W-4020 *see* Prazepam.
W-4425 *see* Almadrate sulfate.
W-4454A *see* Estrazinol.
W-4540 *see* Quingestanol acetate.
W-4565 *see* Oxolinic acid.
W-4600 *see* Algeldrate.
W-4701 *see* Hexedine.
W-4744 *see* Mecloqualone.
W-4869 *see* Prednival.
W-5219 *see* Proglumide.
W-5494A *see* Naranol.
W-5759A *see* Tilidine.
W-6309 *see* Difluprednate.
W-6412A *see* Bunolol.

W-6439A *see* Suloxifen oxalate.
W-6495 *see* Oxisuran.
W-6693 *see* Atrazine.
W-7000A *see* Levobunolol.
W-7320 *see* Alclofenac.
W-7618 *see* Chloroquine.
W-7783 *see* Ambruticin.
W-8495 *see* Isoxicam.
W-19053 *see* Etidocaine.
W-36095 *see* Tocainide.
W-42782 *see* Iproxamine.
W-43026A *see* Ciclafrine.
WA-184 *see* Sitogluside.
WA-335 *see* Danitracen.
'Warbex' *see* Famphur.
WARFARIN** (3-(α-acetonylbenzyl)-4-hydroxy-coumarin; 4-hydroxy-3-(3-oxo-1-phenylbutyl)-2*H*-1-benzopyran-2-one; coumafene; warfarin sodium; zookumarin).
WARFARIN-DEANOL ([3-(α-acetonylbenzyl)-4-hydroxycoumarin]dimethylaminoethanol; MD-6134; WDMA).
'Warfex' *see* Warfarin.
WDMA *see* Warfarin-deanol.
WE-352 *see* Triflubazam.
WE-941 *see* Brotizolam.
WE 973-BS *see* Ciclotizolam.
'Weedar' *see* 2,4-Dichlorophenoxyacetic acid.
'Weedar T' *see* 2,4,5-Trichlorophenoxyacetic acid.
'Weedazol' *see* Amitrole.
'Weedex' *see* 2-(4-Chloro-2-methylphenoxy)acetic acid.
'Weedol' *see* Paraquat.
'Weedone aero concentrate' *see* Butyl 2,4-dichloro-phenoxyacetate.
'Weedone crabgrass killer' *see* Disodium methane-arsonate.
'Weedone special' *see* 2,4,5-Trichlorophenoxyacetic acid.
'Wehdryl' *see* Diphenhydramine.
'Wellbutrin' *see* Amfebutamone.
Wellcome.... *see also* BW.....
Wellcome 248U *see* Aciclovir.
'Wellcoprim' *see* Trimethoprim.
'Welldorm' *see* Dichloralphenazone.
'Wepsyn' *see* Triamiphos.
WG-253 *see* Rimiterol.
WG-537 *see* Flumedroxone.
Wh-3363 *see* Fencarbamide.
WH-5668 *see* Propanidid.
Whey factor *see* Orotic acid.

'Whipicide' *see* Ftalofyne.
'Whitsyn T' *see* Dinitolmide.
WHR-539 *see* Fenclorac.
WHR-1142A *see* Lidamidine.
'Wilpo' *see* Phentermine.
'Wilprufen' *see* Cefoperazone.
WIN-244 *see* Chloroquine.
WIN-771 *see* Hydroxypethidine.
WIN-1011 *see* Glycobiarsol.
WIN-1344 *see* Gamfexine.
WIN-1539 *see* Ketobemidone.
WIN-1766 *see* Methadone.
WIN-1783 *see* Isomethadone.
WIN-2747 *see* Benzoquinonium chloride.
WIN-2848 *see* Thenyldiamine.
WIN-3046 *see* Isoetarine.
WIN-3459 *see* Propoxycaine.
WIN-3706 *see* Ambucaine.
WIN-4369 *see* Penthienate.
WIN-5047 *see* Chlorbetamide.
WIN-5063 *see* Racefenicol.
WIN-5063-2 *see* Thiamphenicol.
WIN-5162 *see* Isoprenaline.
WIN-5494-1 *see* Aminoxytriphene.
WIN-5563-3 *see* Colterol mesilate.
WIN-5606 *see* Benactyzine.
WIN-8077 *see* Ambenonium chloride.
WIN-8851-2 *see* Sodium tyropanoate.
WIN-9154 *see* Inositol nicotinate.
WIN-9317 *see* Propatylnitrate.
WIN-10448 *see* Quinocide.
WIN-11318 *see* Bupivacaine.
WIN-11450 *see* Benorilate.
WIN-11464 *see* Fludorex.
WIN-11530 *see* Menoctone.
WIN-11831 *see* Lorajmine.
WIN-12267 *see* Dichlormezanone.
WIN-13146 *see* Teclozan.
WIN-13820 *see* Becantone.
WIN-14833 *see* Stanozolol.
WIN-17625 *see* Azastene.
WIN-17665 *see* Topterone.
WIN-17757 *see* Danazol.
WIN-18320 *see* Nalidixic acid.
WIN-18413-2 *see* Solypertine tartrate.
WIN-18501-2 *see* Oxypertine.
WIN-18935 *see* Milipertine.
WIN-19356 *see* Clorindanol.
WIN-19578 *see* Cyanoketone.
WIN-20228 *see* Pentazocine.
WIN-20740 *see* Cyclazocine.
WIN-21904 *see* Alexidine.
WIN-23200 *see* Volazocine.
WIN-24540 *see* Trilostane.
WIN-24933 *see* Hycanthone.
WIN-25347 *see* Nimazone.
WIN-25978 *see* Amfonelic acid.
WIN-27147-2 *see* Ciclindole.
WIN-27914 *see* Nivacortol.
WIN-29194-6 *see* Carbantel lauryl sulfate.
WIN-31122 *see* Iosulamide meglumine.
WIN-31665 *see* Alpertine.
WIN-32784 *see* Bitolterol mesilate.

WIN-34276 *see* Ketazocine.
WIN-34284 *see* Oxarbazole.
WIN-34886 *see* Nisbuterol mesilate.
WIN-35150 *see* Flucindole.
WIN-35213 *see* Rosoxacin.
WIN-35833 *see* Ciprofibrate.
WIN-38020 *see* Arildone.
WIN-38770 *see* Azarole.
WIN-39103 *see* Metrizamide.
WIN-40014 *see* Quinfamide.
WIN-40350 *see* Hydroxyapatite.
WIN-40680 *see* Amrinone.
WIN-40808-7 *see* Sulfinalol.
WIN-41464 *see* Octenidine.
WIN-47203 *see* Milrinone.
'Winadryl' *see* Diphenhydramine.
WIN-AM-13146 *see* Teclozan.
'Win-kinase' *see* Urokinase.
'Winobanin' *see* Danazol.
'Winstrol' *see* Stanozolol.
Wintergreen oil *see* Methyl salicylate.
Wintersteiner's compound F *see* Cortisone.
'Wintomylon' *see* Nalidixic acid.
'Winuron' *see* Rosoxacin.
'Wirnesin' *see* Proscillaridin.
WL-140 *see* Polycarbophil.
WL-287 *see* Euprocin.
WL-291 *see* Zolamine.
WL-8008 *see* Trifenmorph.
WL-17731 *see* Benzoylprop-ethyl.
WL-19805 *see* Cyanazine.
WL-43467 *see* Cypermethrin.
WL-43479 *see* Permethrin.
WL-43497 *see* Permethrin.
WL-43775 *see* Fenvalerate.
WL-63611 *see* Cyanatryn.
'Wofatox' *see* Parathion methyl.
'Wofaverdin' *see* Indocyanine green.
'Wofazurin' *see* Anazolene sodium.
Wood alcohol *see* Methanol.
Woolley's antiserotonin *see* Benanserin.
'Worm guard' *see* Parbendazole.
'Wormin' *see* 1-Bromo-2-naphthol.
WR-2721 *see* Amifostine.
WR-4629 *see* Sulfalene.
WR-4873 *see* Sulfadoxine.
WR-5949 *see* Trimethoprim.
WR-7577 *see* Sulfadiazine.
WR-25979 *see* Nitroguanil.
WR-38839 *see* Clociguanil.
WR-142490 *see* Mefloquine.
WR-171669 *see* Halofantrine.
WR-228258 *see* Tebuquine.
Wrightine *see* Conessine.
WSM-3978G *see* Perhexiline.
WV-569 *see* Octopamine.
WX-2412 *see* Fungimycin.
WX-2426 *see* Chlorphentermine.
Wy-401 *see* Ethoheptazine.
Wy-460E *see* Thiazinamium chloride.
Wy-535 *see* Metethoheptazine.
Wy-651 *see* Troleandomycin.
Wy-757 *see* Proheptazine.

Wy-806 *see* Oxetacaine.
Wy-1094 *see* Promazine.
Wy-1359 *see* Propiomazine.
Wy-1395 *see* Trimethidinium methosulfate.
Wy-2039 *see* Etoxeridine.
Wy-2445 *see* Carfenazine.
Wy-2657 *see under* Potassium aspartate.
Wy-2837 *see* Potassium aspartate.
Wy-2838 *see* Magnesium aspartate.
Wy-3263 *see* Iprindole.
Wy-3277 *see* Nafcillin.
Wy-3467 *see* Diazepam.
Wy-3475 *see* Norboletone.
Wy-3478 *see* Oxybate sodium.
Wy-3498 *see* Oxazepam.
Wy-3707 *see* Norgestrel.
Wy-3917 *see* Temazepam.
Wy-4036 *see* Lorazepam.
Wy-4082 *see* Lormetazepam.
Wy-4426 *see* Oxazepam succinate.
Wy-4508 *see* Ciclacillin.
Wy-5103 *see* Ampicillin.
Wy-5733 *see* Atolide.

Wy-8138 *see* Bisoxatin diacetate.
Wy-8678 *see* Guanabenz acetate.
Wy-14643 *see* Pirinixic acid.
Wy-15705 *see* Ciramadol.
Wy-16225 *see* Dezocine.
Wy-20788 *see* Penamecillin.
Wy-21743 *see* Oxaprozin.
Wy-21894 *see* Fentiazac.
Wy-21901 *see* Indoramin.
Wy-22811 *see* Meptazinol.
Wy-23409 *see* Ciclazindol.
Wy-24081 *see* Tiquinamide.
Wy-24377 *see* Isotiquimide.
Wy-25021 *see* Rolgamidine.
Wy-26002 *see* Panuramine.
'Wyamin' *see* Mephentermine.
'Wycil' *see* Ciclacillin.
'Wydane' *see* Chlordane.
'Wydase' *see* Hyaluronidase.
'Wylaxin' *see* Bisoxatin.
'Wyovin' *see* Dicycloverine.
'Wypicil' *see* Ciclacillin.
WZ-884 *see* Propafenone.

X

X-23 *see* Azintamide.
X-40 *see* Exiproben.
X-60 *see* Denaverine.
X-537A *see* Lasalocid.
X-1497 *see* Meticillin.
XA-2 *see* Chlormethine *N*-oxide.
'Xalyl' *see* *N*,*N*-Diethylvaleramide.
XAMOTEROL*** ((±)-*N*-[2-[[2-hydroxy-3-(*p*-hydroxyphenoxy)propyl]amino]ethyl]morpholine-4-carboxamide).
XAMOTEROL FUMARATE* (ICI-118587).
'Xanax' *see* Alprazolam.
XANOXIC ACID*** (7-isopropoxy-9-oxoxanthene-2-carboxylic acid; xanoxate sodium; RS-6818).
Xanthacridine *see* Acriflavinium chloride.
9-XANTHENE (diphenylmethane oxide; *o*,*o'*-methylenediphenyl ether).
9-Xanthenecarboxylic acid esters *see* Methantheline bromide; Trantelinium bromide; Propantheline bromide.
9*H*-Xanthen-9-one *see* Xanthone.
XANTHINE (2,6(1*H*,3*H*)-purinedione).
Xanthine riboside *see* Xanthosine.
Xanthinol niacinate* *see* Xantinol nicotinate.
Xanthinol nicotinate* *see* Xantinol nicotinate.
XANTHIOL*** (4-[3-(2-chlorothioxanthen-9-yl)propyl]-1-piperazinepropanol).
Xanthocillin* *see* Xantocillin.
Xanthogen *see* Dixanthogen.
XANTHONE (9*H*-xanthen-9-one; dibenzo-γ-pyrone; diphenylene ketone oxide; 'genicide').
Xanthophyll dipalmitate *see* Xantofyl palmitate.
XANTHOPTERIN (2-amino-4,6-dihydroxypteridine).
XANTHOSINE (xanthine riboside).
Xanthotoxin *see* Methoxsalen.
XANTHURENIC ACID (4,8-dihydroxyquinaldic acid).
XANTIFIBRATE** (7-[2-hydroxy-3-[(2-hydroxyethyl)methylamino]propyl]theophylline compound with 2-(*p*-chlorophenoxy)-2-methylpropionic acid (1:1); xantinol clofibrate).
Xantinol clofibrate *see* Xantifibrate.
XANTINOL NICOTINATE*** (7-[2-hydroxy-3-[(2-hydroxyethyl)methylamino]propyl]theophylline compound with nicotinic acid; xanthinol niacinate; xanthinol nicotinate; ksavin; SK-331-A).
XANTINOL NICOTINATE plus B-GROUP VITAMINS ('metabolan').
XANTINOL NICOTINATE plus PENTOSAN POLYSULFATE ('pervium').
'Xantociclina' *see* Guamecycline.
XANTOCILLIN*** (antibiotic from *Penicillium notatum*; 1,4-bis(*p*-hydroxyphenyl)-2,3-diisocyanato-1,4-butadiene; xanthocillin; 'polycid').
XANTOFYL PALMITATE*** ((3*R*,3'*R*,6'*R*)-β,ε-carotene-3,3'-diol dipalmitate; helenien; xanthophyl dipalmitate; 'adaptinol').
'Xavin' *see* Xantinol nicotinate.
Xenalamine* *see* Xenazoic acid.
Xenalazone *see* Xenygloxal.
Xenaldial *see* Xenygloxal.
'Xenalvis' *see* Xenygloxal.
XENAZOIC ACID*** (*p*-(α-ethoxy-*p*-phenylphenacylamino)benzoic acid; xenalamine; CV-58903; LG-278; SK&F-8318).
XENBUCIN** (α-ethyl-4-biphenylacetic acid; 2-(*p*-biphenylyl)butyric acid; 4-biphenylylethylacetic acid; α-(*p*-xenyl)butyric acid; xenbuficin; Mg-1559; 'liosol').
See also Butixirate; Namoxyrate.
Xenbuficin *see* Xenbucin.
'Xeneisol 133' *see* Xenon (¹³³Xe).
XENIPENTONE*** ((*E*)-4-biphenyl-4-yl-3-penten-2-one).
XENON (¹³³Xe)*** (radioxenon; 'xeneisol 133').
'Xenovis' *see* Xenazoic acid.
XENTHIORATE*** (*S*-[2-(diethylamino)ethyl] 2-[4-biphenyl]thiobutyrate).
XENYGLOXAL*** (*p*,*p'*-biphenylenebisglyoxal; 4,4'-biphenylyldiglyoxyl aldehyde; xenalazone; xenaldial).
XENYHEXENIC ACID*** (2-(*p*-biphenylyl)-4-hexenoic acid; diphenhexenic acid; CV-57533).
Xenylacetic acid *see* Biphenylylacetic acid.
α-(*p*-Xenyl)butyric acid *see* Xenbucin.
XENYSALATE*** (2-(diethylamino)ethyl 3-phenylsalicylate; 2-(diethylamino)ethyl 2-hydroxybiphenyl-3-carboxylate; biphenamine).
XENYTROPIUM BROMIDE*** (atropine *p*-biphenylylmethyl bromide; 8-(*p*-biphenylylmethyl)atropinium bromide; 8-(*p*-phenylbenzyl)atropinium bromide; xenytropon; FX-501; N-399).
Xenytropon* *see* Xenytropium bromide.
'Xerac' *see* Benzoyl peroxide.
'Xerene' *see* Mephenoxalone.
'Xeroform' *see* Bismuth tribromophenate.
XIBENOLOL*** ((±)-1-(*tert*-butylamino)-3-(2,3-xylyloxy)-2-propanol; (±)-1-(*tert*-butylamino)-3-(2,3-dimethylphenoxy)-2-propanol; xibenolol hydrochloride; D-32).

XIBORNOL*** (4,5-dimethyl-2-(1,7,7-trimethyl-bicyclo[2.1.1]hept-2-yl)phenol; 6-isobornyl-3,4-xylenol; 2-(1,7,7-trimethylbicyclo[2.2.1]hept-2-yl)-3,4-xylenol; CP3H; IBX; IHP; 'nanbacin').

Xilamide *see* Proglumide.

'Xilina' *see* Lidocaine.

XILOBAM** (1-(1-methylpyrrolidin-2-ylidene)-3-(2,6-xylyl)urea; McN-3113).

XIMOPROFEN*** (2-[*p*-[3-(hydroxyimino)cyclohexyl]phenyl]propionic acid; *p*-(3-oxocyclohexyl)hydratropic acid oxime).

XINIDAMINE** (1-(2,4-dimethylbenzyl)-1*H*-indazole-3-carboxylic acid).

XINOMILINE*** (2-amino-4,4-dimethyl-2-oxazoline).

XIPAMIDE*** (5-(aminosulfonyl)-4-chloro-*N*-(2,6-dimethylphenyl)-2-hydroxybenzamide; 4-chloro-2′,6′-dimethyl-5-sulfamoylsalicylanilide; 4-chloro-5-sulfamoyl-2′,6′-salicyloxylidide; Bei-1293; MJF-10938; 'aquaphor'; 'diurexan'). *See also under* Reserpine.

XIPRANOLOL*** (1-[bis(2,6-dimethylphenyl)-methoxy]-3-(isopropylamino)-2-propanol; 1-[di(2,6-xylyl)methoxy]-3-(isopropylamino)-2-propanol; BS-7977D).

XL-7 *see* Bithionol.

XL-90 *see* Guaifenesin.

XLG *see* Polyglactin(s).

'Xobaline' *see* Cobamamide.

XORPHANOL*** (17-(cyclobutylmethyl)-8β-methyl-6-methylenemorphinan-3-ol).

XORPHANOL MESILATE (xorphanol mesylate; xorphanol methanesulfonate; TR-5379M).

'Xtro' *see* Atropine oxide.

XXI/07 *see* Chloraniformethan.

Xycaine (tr) *see* Lidocaine.

'Xyde' *see* Proglumide.

'Xyduril' *see* Clofibrate.

XYLAMIDE (*ar,ar*-dimethylbenzamide).

'Xylamide' *see* Proglumide.

XYLAMIDINE* (*N*-[2-(*m*-methoxyphenoxy)propyl]-*m*-tolylacetamidine).

XYLAMIDINE TOSILATE*** (xylamidine *p*-toluenesulfonate hemihydrate; xylamidine tosylate; BW-545C64).

Xylamidine tosylate* *see* Xylamidine tosilate.

XYLAMINE (*N*-(2-chloroethyl)-*N*-ethyl-2-methylbenzylamine; *N*-(2-chloroethyl)-*N*-ethyl-*o*-toluidine).

XYLAZINE** (5,6-dihydro-2-(2,6-xylidino)-4*H*-1,3-thiazine; 2-(2,6-dimethylanilino)-5,6-dihydro-4*H*-1,3-thiazine; xylazine hydrochloride; BAY-1470; Bayer-1470; BAY Va-1470; 'rompun').

XYLENE (dimethylbenzene).

XYLIDINE (*ar,ar*-dimethylaniline).

2-(2,3-Xylidino)nicotinic acid *see* Nixylic acid.

2-(2,6-Xylidino)nicotinic acid *see* Metanixin.

Xyloascorbic acid *see* Ascorbic acid.

'Xylocaine' *see* Lidocaine.

XYLOCHOLINE (choline 2,6-xylyl ether bromide; [2-(2,6-dimethylphenoxy)ethyl]trimethyl-ammonium bromide; TM-10).

'Xylocitin' *see* Lidocaine.

XYLOCOUMAROL*** (4-hydroxy-3-(3,5-xylyl)-coumarin; BS-7173-D).

XYLOMETAZOLINE*** (2-(4-*tert*-butyl-2,6-di-methylbenzyl)-2-imidazoline; Ba-11391).

'Xylonest' *see* Prilocaine.

XYLOPROPAMINE (3,4-dimethylamphetamine; α-3,4-trimethylphenethylamine).

p-(D-Xylosylamino)benzoic acid *see* Benaxibine.

'Xylotocan' *see* Tocainide.

XYLOXEMINE** (2-[2-[[bis(2,6-dimethylphenyl)-methoxy]ethoxy]-*N*,*N*-dimethylethylamine; 2-[2-(di-2,6-xylylmethoxy)ethoxy]-*N*,*N*-dimethyl-ethylamine; BS-6748).

N-(2,3-Xylyl)anthranilic acid *see* Mefenamic acid.

[[(2,6-Xylylcarbamoyl)methyl]imino]diacetic acid *see* Lidofenin.

o-Xylylcyclopentanecarboxylic acid diethylamino-ethyl ester *see* Metcarphen.

3,4-XYLYL METHYLCARBAMATE (3,4-di-methylphenyl methylcarbamate; 'meobal').

3,5-XYLYL METHYLCARBAMATE (3,5-di-methylphenyl methylcarbamate; 'cosban').

2,4-Xylylmethyl 2,2-dimethyl-3-(2-methylpropenyl)-cyclopropanecarboxylate *see* Dimethrin.

1-(3,5-Xylyloxymethyl)oxazolidin-2-one *see* Metaxalone.

N-(2,6-Xylyl)phthalamic acid *see* Ftaxilide.

Y

Y-3642 *see* Tinoridine.
Y-4153 *see* Clocapramine.
Y-6047 *see* Clotiazepam.
Y-6124 *see* Bufetolol.
Y-9213 *see* Miroprofen.
'Yadalan' *see* Chlorothiazide.
Yageine *see* Harmine.
'Yal' *see under* Docusate sodium.
'Yambolap' *see* Ipriflavone.
'Yatren' *see* Chiniofon.
YB-2 *see* Indenolol.
YC-93 *see* Nicardipine.
'Yermonil' *see under* Ethinylestradiol.
YM-08054-1 *see* Indeloxazine.
YM-09330 *see* Cefotetan.
YM-09583 *see* Amosulalol.
YM-11170 *see* Famotidine.
'Yobin' *see* Yohimban.
'Yobinol' *see* Yohimbine.

'Yodanodia' *see* Prolonium iodide.
YOHIMBAN (dodecahydrobenz[*g*]indolo[2,3-*a*]-quinolizine).
YOHIMBIC ACID*** (17α-hydroxyyohimban-16α-carboxylic acid; yohimboaic acid; yohimboic acid).
YOHIMBINE (methyl yohimbate; aphrodine; corynine; quebrachine).
α-Yohimbine *see* Rauwolscine.
δ-Yohimbine *see* Ajmalicine.
Yohimboaic acid *see* Yohimbic acid.
Yohimboic acid *see* Yohimbic acid.
'Yomesan' *see* Niclosamide.
'Yonit' *see* Bitoscanate.
Yoshi 864 *see* Improsulfan.
Yperite *see* Mustard gas.
'Yugocillin' *see* Penicillin G.
'Yutopan' *see* Ritodrine.
'Yxin' *see* Tetracycline.

Z

Z-10-TR *see* Oxazepam.
Z-100 *see* Propoxur.
Z-203 *see* Strychnine *N*-oxide.
Z-326 *see* Fentonium bromide.
Z-424 *see* Viminol.
Z-867 *see* Dextropropoxyphene theobromin-1-yl-acetate.
Z-905 *see* Pinazepam.
Z-1141C *see under* Dexamethasone pivalate.
Z-3011 *see* Monoxerutin.
Z-4828 *see* Trofosfamide.
Z-4942 *see* Ifosfamide.
Z-6000 *see* Troxerutin.
Z-12001 *see* Troxerutin.
Z-12007 *see* Monoxerutin.
Z-15042 *see* Cloperastine.
Z-28200 *see* Gliflumide.
'Zactane' *see* Ethoheptazine.
'Zaditen' *see* Ketotifen fumarate.
'Zanchol' *see* Florantyrone.
'Zanil' *see* Oxyclozanide.
'Zanosar' *see* Streptozocin.
'Zantac' *see* Ranitidine.
'Zantic' *see* Ranitidine.
ZAPIZOLAM* (8-chloro-6-(*o*-chlorophenyl)-4*H*-pyrido[2,3-*f*]-*s*-triazolo[4,3-*a*][1,4]diazepine).
ZAPRINAST* (3,6-dihydro-5-(*o*-propoxyphenyl)-7*H*-*v*-triazolo[4,5-*d*]pyrimidin-7-one; M&B-22948).
'Zariviz' *see* Cefotaxime.
'Zarontin' *see* Ethosuximide.
'Zaroxolyn' *see* Metolazone.
Zearalanol *see* Zeranol.
ZEARALENONE (6-(10-hydroxy-6-oxo-*trans*-1-undecenyl)-β-resorcylic acid lactone; F-2).
'Zeazint' *see* Atrazine.
'Zectran' *see* Mexacarbate.
ZEDALAN (*trans*-3-glyoxylamidoacrylamide oxime; NSC-85680).
See also under Streptozocin.
'Zeisin' *see* Chlordiazepoxide.
'Zelio' *see* Thallium sulfate.
'Zelmid' *see* Zimeldine.
'Zelmidine' *see* Zimeldine.
'Zenadrid' *see* Prednisone.
'Zenalosyn' *see* Oxymetholone.
'Zentel' *see* Albendazole.
Zeolith A *see* Sodium aluminium silicate.
'Zeozon' *see* Esculetin.
ZEPASTINE* (6,11-dihydro-6-methyl-11-(1α*H*,5α*H*-tropan-3α-yloxy)dibenzo[*c,f*]-[1,2]thiazepine 5,5-dioxide).
'Zepelin' *see* Feprazone.
'Zeph' *see* Phenylephrine.
'Zephiran' *see* Benzalkonium chloride.
'Zephirol' *see* Benzalkonium chloride.
ZERANOL* ((3*S*,7*R*)-3,4,5,6,7,8,9,10,11,12-decahydro-7,14,16-trihydroxy-3-methyl-1*H*-2-benzoxacyclotetradecin-1-one; 6-(6,10-dihydr-oxyundecyl)-β-resorcylic acid lactone; zearal-anol; THFES(HM); MK-188; P-1496; 'frideron'; 'ralabol'; 'ralgro').
'Zerlate' *see* Ziram.
ZETIDOLINE* (1-(*m*-chlorophenyl)-3-[2-(3,3-dimethyl-1-azetidinyl)ethyl]-2-imidazolidinone; zetidoline hydrochloride; DL-308-IT; L-9308; MDL-308).
ZIDAPAMIDE (4-chloro-*N*-(1-methylisoindol-in-2-yl)-3-sulfamoylbenzamide; 2-(4-chloro-3-sulfamoylbenzamido)-1-methylisoindoline; isodapamide; isoindapamide).
ZIDOMETACIN* (1-(*p*-azidobenzoyl)-5-meth-oxy-2-methylindole-3-acetic acid).
Ziksorin (tr) *see* Flumecinol.
ZILANTEL* (1,2-ethanediylbis(phenylmethyl)-bis[(diethoxyphosphinyl)carbonimidodithioate]; phosphonodithioimidocarbonic acid ethylene di-benzyl *P,P,P′,P′*-tetraethyl ester; CL-64976).
'Zimate' *see* Ziram.
ZIMELDINE ((*Z*)-3-[1-(*p*-bromophenyl)-3-(di-methylamino)propenyl]pyridine; (4-bromo-γ-pyrid-3-ylcinnamyl)dimethylamine; 3-(4-bromo-phenyl)-*N,N*-dimethyl-3-pyrid-3-ylallylamine; zi-melidine; zimelidine hydrochloride; H-102/09; 'normud'; 'zelmid'; 'zelmidine').
Zimelidine *see* Zimeldine.
'Zinacef' *see* Cefuroxime.
'Zinamide' *see* Pyrazinamide.
'Zinate' *see* Zineb.
ZINC ACETATE BASIC (hexakis(μ-acetato)-μ-4-oxotetrazinc).
Zinc bis(pyridine-2-thiol 1-oxide) *see* Pyrithione zinc.
Zinc dimethylcarbamodithioate *see* Ziram.
Zinc dimethyldithiocarbamate *see* Ziram.
Zinc ethylenebis(carbamodithioate) *see* Zineb.
Zinc ethylenebis(dithiocarbamate) *see* Zineb.
'Zincfrin' *see under* Phenylephrine.
'Zinc omadine' *see* Pyrithione zinc.
Zinc pyridinethione *see* Pyrithione zinc.
Zinc pyrithione *see* Pyrithione zinc.
ZINC RICINOLEATE ('grillocin').

ZINC SULFANILATE ('nizin').

ZINC SULFATE ('solvezink'; 'verazinc').
See also under Phenylephrine.

Zinc tetracosactide *see* Tetracosactide zinc phosphate complex.

ZINEB* (zinc ethylenebis(carbamodithioate); zinc ethylenebis(dithiocarbamate); 'cynkotox'; 'dithane Z 78'; 'lonacol'; 'parzate'; 'zinate').
See also Mancozeb; Propineb.

ZINGERONE (4-(4-hydroxy-3-methoxyphenyl)-2-butanone; 2-(4-hydroxy-3-methoxyphenyl)ethyl methyl ketone; vanillylacetone; zingiberone).

Zingiberone *see* Zingerone.

ZINOCONAZOLE* (5-chloro-2-thienyl imidazol-1-ylmethyl ketone (*E*)-(2,6-dichlorophenyl)-hydrazone).

'Zinophos' *see* Thionazin.

ZINOSTATIN* (polypeptide from *Str. carcinostaticus*; neocarzinostatin; NSC-69856).

ZINTEROL* (5'-[2-[(α,α-dimethylphenethyl)-amino]-1-hydroxyethyl]-2'-hydroxymethanesulfonanilide; zinterol hydrochloride; MJ-9184-1).

ZINVIROXIME* ((*Z*)-2-amino-6-benzoyl-1-(isopropylsulfonyl)benzimidazole oxime; 2-amino-1-(isopropylsulfonyl)-6-benzimidazole phenyl ketone oxime).

ZIPEPROL* (1-(2-hydroxy-3-methoxy-3-phenylpropyl)-4-(2-methoxy-2-phenylethyl)piperazine; 1-methoxy-3-[4-(2-methoxy-2-phenylethyl)piperazin-1-yl]-1-phenyl-2-propanol; α-(α-methoxybenzyl)-4-(β-methoxyphenethyl)-1-piperazineethanol; CERM-3024; 'respilene').

ZIRAM* (*S,S*'-bis(dimethylcarbamodithioato)-zinc; zinc dimethylcarbamodithioate; zinc dimethyldithiocarbamate; 'corozate'; 'fuclasin'; 'fuklasin'; 'karbam white'; 'metasan'; 'milbam'; 'rhodiacid'; 'zerlate'; 'zimate'; 'zirberk').

ZIRAM plus 2-BENZOTHIAZOLETHIOL ZINC ('vancide Z').

'Zirberk' *see* Ziram.

'Zitofenton' *see* Mannomustine heparinate.

'Zitostop' *see* Mannosulfan.

'Zixoryn' *see* Flumecinol.

ZK-25095 *see* Moxnidazole.

ZK-57671 *see* Sulprostone.

ZK-62711 *see* Rolipram.

ZK-71630 *see* Iotetric acid.

ZK-76004 *see* Pirazolac.

ZN-6 *see* Fusidic acid.

'Zoalene' *see* Dinitolmide.

'Zoamix' *see* Dinitolmide.

ZOCAINONE* ((*E*)-3-[*o*-[2-(diethylamino)ethoxy]phenoxy]-4-phenyl-3-buten-2-one).

ZOFENOPRIL* ((4*S*)-*N*-[(*S*)-3-mercapto-2-methylpropionyl]-4-(phenylthio)-L-proline benzoate (ester)).

ZOFICONAZOLE* (1-[2,4-dichloro-β-[3-(*p*-chlorophenoxy)propoxy]phenethyl]imidazole).

ZOLAMINE* (2-[[2-(dimethylamino)ethyl](*p*-methoxybenzyl)amino]thiazole; *N*-(*p*-methoxybenzyl)-*N'*,*N'*-dimethyl-*N*-thiazol-2-ylethylenediamine; zolamine hydrochloride; B-194; WL-291).

ZOLAZEPAM* (4-(*o*-fluorophenyl)-6,8-dihydro-1,3,8-trimethylpyrazolo[3,4-*e*][1,4]diazepin-7(1*H*)-one; CI-716).
See also under Tiletamine.

ZOLENZEPINE* (4,9-dihydro-1,3-dimethyl-4-[(4-methylpiperazin-1-yl)acetyl]pyrazolo[4,3-*b*]-[1,5]benzodiazepin-10(1*H*)-one).

ZOLERTINE* (1-phenyl-1-(2-tetrazol-5-yl-ethyl)piperazine; phenpiperazole; zolertine hydrochloride; MA-1277).

'Zolicef' *see* Cefazolin.

ZOLIMIDINE* (2-[*p*-(methylsulfonyl)phenyl]-imidazole[1,2-*a*]pyridine; zoliridine; 'gastronilo'; 'solimidine').
See also under Indometacin.

Zoliridine* *see* Zolimidine.

'Zolone' *see* Phosalone.

ZOLOPERONE* (4-(*p*-fluorophenyl)-5-[2-[4-(*o*-methoxyphenyl)piperazin-1-yl]ethyl]-4-oxazolin-2-one; LR-511).

'Zolyse' *see* Chymotrypsin.

'Zomac' *see* Zomepirac.

'Zomax' *see* Zomepirac.

ZOMEBAZAM* (4,8-dihydro-1,3,8-trimethyl-4-phenylpyrazolo[3,4-*b*][1,4]diazepine-5,7(1*H*,6*H*)-dione).

ZOMEPIRAC* (5-(*p*-chlorobenzoyl)-1,4-dimethylpyrrole-2-acetic acid; zomepirac sodium; McN-2783-21-98; 'zomac'; 'zomax').

ZOMETAPINE* (4-(3-chlorophenyl)-1,6,7,8-tetrahydro-1,3-dimethylpyrazolo[3,4-*e*][1,4]diazepine; CI-781).

'Zonol' *see* Benzyl benzoate.

'Zonulysin' *see* Chymotrypsin.

Zookumarin (tr) *see* Warfarin.

ZOPICLONE* (4-methyl-1-piperazinecarboxylic acid ester with 6-(5-chloropyrid-2-yl)-6,7-dihydro-7-hydroxy-5*H*-pyrrolo[3,4-*b*]pyrazin-5-one; RP-27267).

'Zoralin' *see under* DDT.

ZORBAMYCIN* (antibiotic from *Str. bikiniensis*; laramycin; U-30604).

ZORUBICIN* (benzoic acid hydrazide 3-hydrazone with daunorubicin; benzohydrazide daunorubicin hydrazone; daunorubicin benzoylhydrazone; zorubicin hydrochloride; NSC-164011; RP-22050; 'rubidazone').

'Zostrum' *see* Idoxuridine.

ZOTEPINE* (8-chloro-10-[2-(dimethylamino)-ethoxy]dibenzo[*b,f*]thiepin; 2-[(8-chlorodibenzo-[*b,f*]thiepin-10-yl)oxy]-*N*,*N*-dimethylethylamine).

'Zothelone' *see* Quinuronium sulfate.

'Zovirax' *see* Aciclovir.

ZOXAZOLAMINE* (2-amino-5-chlorobenzoxazole; McN-485).

'Zoxine' *see* Zoxazolamine.

ZR-515 *see* Methoprene.

ZUCLOMIFENE* ((*Z*)-2-[*p*-(2-chloro-1,2-diphenylvinyl)phenoxy]triethylamine; 2-[*p*-(2-chloro-*cis*-1,2-diphenylvinyl)phenoxy]triethylamine; transclomifene; transclomiphene; RMI-16312).
See also Clomifene; Enclomifene.

ZUCLOPENTHIXOL** ((*Z*)-4-[3-(2-chlorothio-xanthen-9-ylidene)propyl]-1-piperazineethanol; *cis*-clopenthixol; *Z*-clopenthixol; zuclopenthixol decanoate; zuclopenthixol hydrochloride; 'clo-pixol').

'Zwitsalax' *see* Dantron.

'Zyklolat' *see* Cyclopentolate.

Zykzorin (tr) *see* Flumecinol.

ZYLOFURAMINE*** (D-*threo*-α-benzyl-*N*-eth-yltetrahydrofurylamine).

'Zyloprim' *see* Allopurinol.

'Zyloric' *see* Allopurinol.

'Zymarocan' *see* Hexacamphamine.

'Zymofren' *see* Aprotinin.

'Zytostatika' *see* Inproquone.

'Zytostop' *see* Mannosulfan.